BOOKMAN'S
PRICE INDEX

BOOKMAN'S PRICE INDEX

A Guide to the Values of
Rare and Other Out-of-Print Books

VOLUME 17

DANIEL F. McGRATH

GALE RESEARCH COMPANY • BOOK TOWER • DETROIT, MICHIGAN

Library of Congress Catalog Card Number 64-8723
ISBN 0-8103-0617-4
Copyright © 1979 by Gale Research Company
Printed in the United States of America

Contents

How to Use This Book

All listings in this volume of *Bookman's Price Index* are based on descriptions of books offered for sale by leading dealers primarily in their 1978 catalogs.

Dealer's descriptions have been followed closely, although extensive details not essential to establishing condition or determining price have been condensed or omitted. In any case, however, there has been no addition to or revision of the content of the dealer's description, even in the few cases where a description might have been in error.

Every effort has been made to report prices and other details accurately; the user should keep in mind, however, that the possibility of typographical error—for which the publisher assumes no responsibility—does exist, and, furthermore, that an individual dealer's evaluation of a book may not represent a professional consensus.

Arrangement

Listings are alphabetical according to name of author, or, if no author is mentioned, according to the first word not an article in the title.

Names under which entries appear in *BPI* have been standardized as much as possible, and therefore are not always given in the exact form in which they appear on some title pages, or in the catalogs of some dealers. Familiar and common forms of names have been preferred. Various editions of a single work have been brought together, even though alphabetical order is in some cases violated thereby. (See the discussion of the handling of such editions in the introduction to Volume 4.)

Order of Information

Within each entry, the following information is given in this order:

1. Author's name
2. Title
3. Place and date of publication
4. Description of the book, including its condition when offered by the dealer
5. Name of dealer publishing catalog
6. Number of catalog in which offered, and item number within . catalog
7. Year date (or year of receipt) of catalog in which book is offered
8. Price at which offered

Dealers Represented
in This Volume

WILLIAM H. ALLEN
2031 Walnut Street
Philadelphia, Pennsylvania 19103

THE AMERICANIST
1525 Shenkel Road
Pottstown, Pennsylvania 19464

ARGOSY BOOK STORES, INC.
116 East 59th Street
New York, New York 10022

AUSTIN BOOK SHOP
Post Office Box 36
Kew Gardens, New York 11415

BALDWIN'S BOOK BARN
865 Lenape Road
Westchester, Pennsylvania 19380

BALLINGERS BOOK SERVICE
147 West King Street
Hillsborough, North Carolina 27278

BATTERY PARK BOOK COMPANY
Box 710
Forest Hills, New York 11375

BELL BOOKS
80 Long Acre
London WC2, England

BENNETT & MARSHALL
8214 Melrose Avenue
Los Angeles, California 90046

STEPHEN C. BERNARD
10017 Penfold Court
Potomac, Maryland 20854

BIBLO & TANNEN
63 Fourth Avenue
New York, New York 10003

THE BOOK CHEST
19-A Oxford Place
Rockville Center, New York 11570

VAN ALLEN BRADLEY
Box 4130 Hopi Station
Scottsdale, Arizona 85258

BROADFOOT'S BOOKMARK
Route 2, Box 28A
Wendell, North Carolina 27591

ROGER BUTTERFIELD, INCORPORATED
Whitehouse Route 205
Hartwick, New York 13348

CURRENT COMPANY
Box 46
Bristol, Rhode Island 02809

DAWSON'S BOOK SHOP
535 North Larchmont Boulevard
Los Angeles, California 90004

DEIGHTON BELL & COMPANY
13 Trinity Street
Cambridge CB2 1TD, England

REBECCA B. DESMARAIS
Post Office Box 2286
Nixon Road
Framingham, Massachusetts 01701

PHILIP B. DUSCHNES
699 Madison Avenue
New York, New York 10021

JEFF DYKES
Box 38
College Park, Maryland 20740

PETER EATON, LIMITED
80 Hollan Park Avenue
London W11 3RE, England

FRANCIS EDWARDS
83 Marylebone High Street
London W1M 4AL, England

JAMES O'D. FENNING II
12 Glenview, Rochestown
Dun Laoghaire
County Dublin, Ireland

W. FORSTER
83A Stamford Hill
London N16 5TP, England

GEORGE'S
89 Park Street
Bristol BS1 5PW, England

GILHOFER & RANSCHBURG
Haldenstrasse 9
Luzern, Switzerland

MICHAEL GINSBERG BOOKS, INC.
Box 402
Sharon, Massachusetts 02067

LUCIEN GOLDSCHMIDT
1117 Madison Avenue
New York, New York 10028

PAULETTE GREENE
140 Princeton Road
Rockville Centre, New York 11570

R.D. GURNEY INC.
23 Campden Street
Kensington Church Street
London W8, England

T & L HANNAS
33 Farnaby Road
Bromley Kent, BR1 4BL, England

ROBERT G. HAYMAN
Box 188
Carey, Ohio 43316

PETER MURRAY HILL
35 North Hill
Highgate, London N6, England

DORA HOOD'S BOOK ROOM LIMITED
34 Ross Street
Toronto M5T 129, Canada

GEORGE J. HOULE
8064 Melrose Avenue
Los Angeles, California 90046

JOHN HOWELL
434 Post Street
San Francisco, California 94102

HOWES BOOKSHOP
Trinity Hall Braybrooke Terrace
Hastings, East Sussex, TN34 1HQ, England

C.P. HYLAND
Old Rectory Wallstown
Castletown Roche
County Cork, Ireland

JARNDYCE
68 Neal Street
Covent Garden
London WC2, England

JENKINS COMPANY
Post Office Box 2085
Austin, Texas 78768

K BOOKS
Waplington Hall
Allerthorpe, York YO4 4RS, England

CLIFFORD KING
2 St. John Lodge
Harley Road
London NW3 3BY, England

H. P. KRAUS
16 East 46th Street
New York, New York 10017

J. STEPHEN LAWRENCE, RARE BOOKS
230 North Michigan Avenue, Suite 205
Chicago, Illinois 60601

LIMESTONE HILLS BOOKSHOP
Post Office Box 1125
Glen Rose, Texas 76043

GEORGE S. MACMANUS COMPANY
1317 Irving Street
Philadelphia, Pennsylvania 19107

EDWARD MORRILL & SONS, INC.
25 Kingston Street
Boston, Massachusetts 02111

HAROLD R. NESTLER
13 Pennington Avenue
Waldwick, New Jersey 07463

JEREMY NORMAN & COMPANY, INC.
442 Post Street
San Francisco, California 94102

EMIL OFFENBACHER
84-50 Austin Street
Kew Gardens, New York 11415

ALFRED W. PAINE
Wolfpits Road
Bethel, Connecticut 06801

R. PETRILLA
Post Office Box 65
Doylestown, Pennsylvania 18901

BERNARD QUARITCH, LIMITED
5-8 Lower John Street
Golden Square
London W1R 4AU, England

RITTENHOUSE
1706 Rittenhouse Square
Philadelphia, Pennsylvania 19103

BERTRAM ROTA
30 & 31 Long Acre
London WC2E 9LT, England

WILLIAM SALLOCH
Pines Bridge Road
Ossining, New York   10562

CHARLES J. SAWYER
No. 1 Grafton Street
New Bond Street
London W1X 3LB, England

JORG SCHAFER
Alfred-Escher-Strasse 76
CH 8002 Zurich, Switzerland

HELLMUT SCHUMANN AG
25 Raemistrasse
CH 8024 Zurich, Switzerland

G. SEXTON
53 Ship Street
Brighton, Sussex BN1 1AF, England

ALAN G. THOMAS
c/o Westminster Bank
300 Kings Road
London SW3, England

TOTTERIDGE BOOK SHOP
Rd. 1 247A North Road
Amenia, New York   12501

CHARLES TRAYLEN
49-50 Quarry Street
Guildford, Surrey, England

UPCROFT BOOKS
66 St. Cross Road
Winchester, Hants S0239PS, England

C ? J VAN DER PEET
33-35 North Spiegel Straat
Amsterdam, Holland

VICTORIA BOOK SHOP
307 Fifth Avenue
New York, New York   10016

WILLIAM P. WOLFE
222 Rue De L'Hopital
Montreal, Canada

XIMENES RARE BOOKS
120 East 85th Street
New York, New York   10028

ZEITLIN & VERBRUGGE
815 North La Cienega Boulevard
Los Angeles, California   90069

A

THE ABC of the NRA. Washington, 1934. 8vo., d.w., 1st ed., orig. cloth. Morrill 241-643 1978 $10

A. E. PSEUD.
Please turn to
RUSSELL, GEORGE WILLIAM

AALUND, H.   Soil Survey Report of Southeastern New Brunswick. Fredericton, 1950. Card cover, maps. Hood 117-954 1978 $10

ABANO, PIETRO D'   De Venenis. Rome, 1484. Sm. 4to., blind-stamped calf, 15th Century style, fine copy, 3rd ed. Norman 5-1 1978 $1,850

ABBATT, WILLIAM   The Attack on Young's House February 3, 1780. Tarrytown, 1926. Illus., map, ex-lib., fine, ltd. to 250 copies. MacManus 239-541 1978 $25

ABBATT, WILLIAM   The Battle of Pell's Point Oct. 18, 1776. New York, 1901. Tall thin 4to., illus., fold. map, ltd. to 500 copies. MacManus 239-542 1978 $20

ABBONDANTI, ANTONIO   Viaggio di Colonia Capitoli Piacevoli D'Antonio Abbondanti da Imola. Venezia, 1627. Tall 12mo., calf, first ed. King 7-1 1978 £25

ABBOT, A.   Letters Written in the Interior of Cuba... Boston, 1829. Orig. bds., rebacked, 8vo, stain in margin of few pgs., cover soiled. Edwards 1012-706 1978 £30

ABBOTT, CHARLES C.   Bird-Land Echoes. Philadelphia, 1896. 1st ed., illus., orig. dec. cloth. MacManus 239-1227 1978 $25

ABBOTT, CHARLES C.   The Freedom of the Fields. Philadelphia, 1898. Illus., fine. MacManus 239-1228 1978 $25

ABBOTT, CHARLES C.   Travels in a Tree-Top. Philadelphia, 1894. 1st ed., orig. cloth, scarce. MacManus 239-1229 1978 $25

ABBOTT, CHARLES C.   Upland and Meadow. New York, 1886. 1st ed., orig. pic. cloth. MacManus 239-1230 1978 $30

ABBOTT, CHARLES C.   Waste-Land Wanderings. New York, 1887. 1st ed. MacManus 239-1231 1978 $25

ABBOTT, CHARLES D.   A Chronicle. New York, 1925. Illus. by Pyle, very fine. Victoria 34-664 1978 $50

ABBOTT, E. C.   We Pointed Them North: Recollections of a Cowpuncher. New York, 1939. 1st ed., illus. Jenkins 116-1 1978 $60

ABBOTT, EDITH   Historical Aspects of the Immigration Problem. 1926. Austin 79-1 1978 $17.50

ABBOTT, EDITH   Immigration. 1924. Ex-lib. Austin 79-2 1978 $17.50

ABBOTT, GEORGE   A Brief Description of the Whole World. London, 1620. 5th ed., 4to., 3/4 calf, few pages dampstained, otherwise very good copy. Salloch 345-1 1978 $300

ABBOTT, H. H.   Black & White. London, 1922. 1st ed., laid paper, orig. bds., signed by author, very good or better. Limestone 9-3 1978 $8.50

ABBOTT, HENRY L.   United States Military Academy. Boston, n.d. (ca. 1904). 8vo., orig. wrs. Morrill 239-281 1978 $7.50

ABBOTT, JACOB   Marco Paul's Travels and Adventures in the Pursuit of Knowledge. Boston, 1845. 5th ed., illus., very good. Victoria 34-2 1978 $10

ABBOTT, JACOB   Marco Paul's Voyages and Travels on the Erie Canal. (New York, 1852). 16mo., red cloth, slightly rubbed, woodcut frontis. map, vignette illus. signed by William Roberts. Butterfield 21-89 1978 $65

ABBOTT, JACOB   Marco Paul's Voyages & Travels. New York, (1852). Illus., very good. Victoria 34-3 1978 $8.50

ABBOTT, JACOB   The Rollo Philosophy. Philadelphia, (1842). 4 vols., marbled boards, leather spines, illus., all 1st ed., spines worn, hinges cracked, texts very good. Victoria 34-4 1978 $25

ABBOTT, JACOB   The Studio; or, Illustrations of the Theory and Practice of Drawing, for Young Artists at Home. New York, (1855). Clean, orig. binding, illus., inconspicuous blindstamp on title-pg. Hayman 71-379 1978 $10

ABBOTT, JOHN S. C.   The Child at Home. New York, (1833). 12mo., engraved t.p. & f.p., very good. Victoria 34-6 1978 $15

ABBOTT, JOHN S. C.   Miles Standish, Captain of the Pilgrims. New York, 1898. Cloth. Hayman 73-1 1978 $8.50

ABBOTT, JOHNSTON   The Seigneurs of La Saulaye, Gentlemen Adventurers of New France. Toronto, 1928. Some wear. Hood 116-449 1978 $12.50

ABBOTT, KATHERINE M.   Old Paths and Legends of New England. New York, 1903. Over 170 illus. Baldwins' 51-389 1978 $7.50

ABBOTT, LAWRENCE F.   Twelve Great Modernists. 1927. First ed. Austin 82-1 1978 $12.50

ABBOTT, MAUDE E.   Atlas of Congenital Cardiac Disease. New York, 1936. Folio, illus., orig. binding. Wolfe 39-359 1978 $50

ABBOTT, MAUDE E.   History of Medicine in the Province of Quebec. Montreal, 1931. Autograph pres. inscription by author, orig. binding. Wolfe 39-346 1978 $60

ABBOTT, WILBUR C.   New York in the American Revolution. New York, 1929. Illus. MacManus 239-543 1978 $17.50

ABBOTT, WILLIS, J.   Panama and The Canal in Picture and Prose. New York, 1913. Ci. illus., color plts., orig. binding. Hayman 71-2 1978 $10

A'BECKETT, ARTHUR WILLIAM   The a'Becketts of 'Punch': Memories of Father and Sons. 1903. Frontis., orig. cloth gilt, scarce, 8vo. Howes 194-584 1978 £6

A'BECKETT, GILBERT ABBOTT   The Comic Blackstone. 1857. New ed., illus. by George Cruikshank, 12mo., orig. wrs. Morrill 239-282 1978 $15

A'BECKETT, GILBERT ABBOTT   The Comic History of Rome. London, (1851-2). 1st ed., 8vo., illus., hand-colored plts., fine set, full straight grained green mor. slipcase, rare. Current Misc. 8-1 1978 $235

A'BECKETT, GILBERT ABBOTT   The Quizzology of the British Drama. 1846. Engraved frontis., illus., orig. cloth, good. Jarndyce 16-286 1978 £15

ABEEL, J. A.   A Discourse, Delivered April 6th, 1801, in the Middle Dutch Church, Before the New-York Missionary Society... New York, 1801. Wrappers, title-browned, spotting in text, 8vo. Edwards 1012-462 1978 £20

ABEL, ANNIE HELOISE   A Side-Light on Anglo-American Relations... 1927. 1st ed., orig. cloth, very good. MacManus 239-1 1978 $25

ABEL, PARKER   Uncle Tom in England: or a Proof that Black's White. New York, 1852. Bell Wiley's copy, wrs. chipped, bent & soiled. Broadfoot's 44-1 1978 $25

ABEL, O.   Palaobiologie und Stammesgeschichte. Germany, 1929. Text in German, 8vo, orig. cloth. Book Chest 17-1 1978 $25

ABERCROMBIE, JOHN   Inquiries Concerning the Intellectual Powers and the Investigation of the Truth. London, 1838. Ninth ed., hinge weak, some wear. Rittenhouse 49-1 1976 $20

ABERCROMBIE, LASCELLES   The Epic. London, n.d. Orig. cloth, d.j., 1st ed., mint. MacManus 238-601 1978 $20

ABERCROMBIE, LASCELLES   Interludes and Poems. London, 1908. 8vo, light green cloth, gilt lettering on spine, small stain on front cover, some browning of flyleaves, 1st ed., collector's cond. Desmarais 1-1 1978 $35

ABERCROMBIE, LASCELLES   Romanticism. London, 1926. 8vo, half yellow cloth, buff paper boards, uncut, spine lightly browned, 1st ed., collector's cond. Desmarais 1-2 1978 $15

ABERCROMBIE, LASCELLES   The Sale of Saint Thomas. Gloucestershire, 1911. Blue wrappers. Eaton 45-2 1978 £5

ABERCROMBIE, LASCELLES   Towards a Theory of Art. London, 1922. 1st. ed., orig. cloth, octavo, nice copy. Rota 216-1 1979 £5

ABERCROMBY, DAVID   A Discourse of Wit. London, 1686. 2nd. ed., 12mo, contemp. calf, gilt spine, leather label. Traylen 88-92 1978 £155

ABERDEEN, ISHBEL   Edward Marjoribanks, Lord Tweedmouth, K.T., 1849-1909, Notes and Recollections. 1909. Roy. 8vo, orig. cloth, gilt, faded, plts., pres. copy to Winston Churchill. Sawyer 298-58 1978 £32

ABERG, N.   Vorgeschichtliche Kulturkreise in Europa. 1936. Oblong 4to., plt. Allen 234-4 1978 $25

ABLAING VAN GIESSENBURG, W. J.   Nederlands Adelsboek of Verzameling van Adels-erkenningen, Inlijvingen, Verheffingen en Verleeningen van Titel in het Koninkrijk der Nederlanden Sedert 1814. 's-Gravenhage, 1887. 8vo., orig. covers. Van der Peet H-64-237 1978 Dfl 45

ABLETT, WILLIAM H.   English Trees and Tree-Planting. London, 1880. Illus., back cover lightly stained, 1st ed., 8vo, orig. cloth. Morrill 241-1 1978 $10

ABOUT, EDMOND   Les Mariages de Province. Paris, 1868. Cloth. Eaton 45-3 1978 £5

ABRAMOVITZ, MOSES   Inventories and Business Cycles. 1950. Ex-lib. Austin 80-394 1978 $12.50

ABRAMS, ERNEST R.   Power in Transition. 1940. Austin 80-395 1978 $12.50

ABREGE de L'Embryologie Sacree, ou Traite des Devoirs de Pretes, des Medecins, des Chirurgiens & des Sages-Femmes envers les Enfants qui sont dans le sein de leurs meres. Paris, 1774. Thick 12mo., 2nd French ed., engr. plts., contemp. mottled calf, light browning & foxing, very good copy, early library stamp, bkplt. of Dr. Alfred M. Hellman. Zeitlin 245-36 1978 $150

ABREGE Methodique Des Principes Heraldiques... 1681. Illus., orig. full calf, 12mo. Baldwins' 51-255 1978 $50

ABSTRACT Of Infantry Tactics.... Boston, 1830. 30 plts., orig. full calf, worn, hinge cracked. Baldwins' 51-298 1978 $27.50

ABSTRACT of the Accounts of the Several Commissaries upon Foreign Stations. 1823. Folio, wrappers. F. Edwards 1013-230 1978 £12

AN ABSTRACT Of The Evidence Delivered Before a Select Committee of the House of Commons in 1790 and 1791 on the Part of the Petitioners for the Abolition of the Slave-Trade. London, 1791. 2nd. ed., folding plts., 12mo, modern bds. K Books 239-447 1978 £15

ABSTRACTS of Presentments Granted at the Spring Assizes, 1894. Wr. (worn), text good, reprint. Hyland 128-912 1978 £9.50

ACADEMIE ROYALE DES SCIENCES, PARIS   Liste de Messieurs de l'Academie Royale des Sciences Depuis l'etablissement de cette Compagnie en 1666, Jusqu'en 1733. Amsterdam, 1737. 12mo., contemp. vellum, blind-stamped centerpiece on sides, fine copy. Offenbacher 30-1 1978 $150

ACCADEMIA DEL CIMENTO   Lettre Scientifiche, ed Erudite del conte.... Florence, (1721). 1st ed., quarto, half-title, frontis., full contemp. vellum, gilt lettered spine, fine. Bennett 20-133 1978 $450

ACCADEMIA Della Crusca. Florence, 1739. 5 vols., 4to., contemp. calf, labels missing, few hinges cracked. Howes 194-239 1978 £25

ACCENT. Urbana, 1940-43. 16mo, red cloth, 1st 3 bound vols, ex-lib. small bookplate, small ink stamp on bound-in covers, 1st ed., collector's cond. Desmarais 1-3 1978 $60

ACCIOLI DE CERQUEIRA E SILVA, EGNACIO   Memoria on Dissertacao Historica Ethnographica.... Bahia, 1848. Later limp green roan, 8vo. K Books 244-334 1978 £40

AN ACCOUNT of Chang and Eng, the World Renowned Siamese Twins. New York, 1853. Illus., new cloth. Broadfoot 50-32 1978 $35

AN ACCOUNT of the Celebration Commemorative of the Opening of Railroad Communication Between Boston and Canada. Boston, 1852. Large fold. map, orig. binding. Wolfe 39-467 1978 $30

AN ACCOUNT Of The Celebration of the Jubilee, on the 25th October, 1809; Being the Forty-Ninth Anniversary of the Reign of George the Third. (1809). 1st. ed., lg. 4to, portrait, orig. paper bds., newer cloth spine, new end-papers, uncut. Hannas 54-138 1978 £17.50

AN ACCOUNT of the Dedication of the West Window of St. John's Church, Beverly Farms...1925. (Boston), 1925. Quarto, full red mor., gilt, gilt and hand rubricated throughout, 1 of 130 copies, fine. Duschnes 220-207 1978 $75

AN ACCOUNT of the Free-School Society of New-York. New York, 1814. Uncut, orig. plain bds. Butterfield 21-497 1978 $25

ACCOUNT of the Terrific and Fatal Riot at the New-York Astor Place Opera House...Night of May 10th, 1849. New York, 1849. Frontis. by Dunnel, mod. buckram, orig. front wr. bound in. Butterfield 21-480 1978 $17.50

ACCUM, FRIEDRICH   Description of the Process of Manufacturing Coal Gas for the Lighting of Streets, Houses, and Public Buildings. London, 1819. 8vo., very fine handcolored plts., handcolored vignette on title, half mor., gilt, fine copy, 1st ed. Norman 5-3 1978 $375

ACCUM, FRIEDRICH   A Practical Treatise on Gas-light .... R. Ackermann, 1815. 2nd. ed., coloured aquatint plts., roy. 8vo, orig. bds., uncut, printed paper label, fine copy. Fenning 32-1 1978 £85

ACCUM, FRIEDRICH   A Practical Treatise on Gas-Light. London, 1815. 8vo., handcolored plts., half antique calf, gilt, fine copy, 2nd ed., illus. Norman 5-2 1978 $200

ACCUM, FRIEDRICH   A Treatise on Adulteration of Foods. London, 1820. Orig. bds., very good copy, 2nd ed. Norman 5-4 1978 $150

ACHESON, FRANK O. V.   Plume of the Arawas. 1930. First ed., d.j. Austin 82-3 1978 $27.50

ACHILLINI, ALESSANDRO   Anotom cae Annotationes Magni Alexandri Achillini Bonon. 1520. Sm. 4to., laid in an antique style blind-stamped calf binder, "Achillinus" and "1520" stamped on covers, fine lg. paper copy, very rare 1st ed. Zeitlin 245-1 1978 $4,500

ACKERLEY, J. R.   Hindoo Holiday: an Indian Journal. 1932. Covers little soiled, good, T.L.s. by author laid in. Bell Book 17-001 1978 £10

ACKERMANN, RUDOLPH   Forget Me Not: A Christmas and New Year's Present for 1826. 1826. Engraved plates by Pugin, pict. decor. boards, spine cracked, inscribed by publisher to Prof. Hartmann. Victoria 34-7 1978 $30

ACKERMANN, RUDOLPH   The History of the Abbey Church of St. Peter's Westminister, Its Antiquities and Monuments. London, 1812. 2 vols., illus., 1st ed., quarto, contemp. mor., marb. bds., gilt spines, gilt tops damaged, lib. withdrawal stamp on sev. pages, scarce, 1st issue. Totteridge 29-2 1978 $550

ACKERMANN, RUDOLPH   A History of the University of Oxford, its Colleges Halls and Public Buildings. 1814. Portrait, coloured plts., 2 vols., lg. 4to., half calf, rebacked, very good. Howes 194-1362 1978 £850

ACKERMANN, RUDOLPH   Microcosm of London. 1808-10. 3 vols., roy. 4to., coloured aquatine plts. by Pugin and Rowlandson, red mor. gilt, gilt edges. Quaritch 983-282 1978 $5,750

ACKERMANN, RUDOLPH   The Microcosm of London, or, London in Miniature. London, 1904. Reprint of lst ed., 3 vols., 4to, 104 coloured aquatint plts., half parchment bds., chipped, contain duplicate labels, tipped-in to each vol. Deighton 5-108 1978 £55

ACOSTA, CHRISTOVAL   Tractado de las drogas, y medicinas de las Indias Orientales. Burgos, 1578. 4to., woodcuts, 18th century vellum with gilt Borghese crest on spine, Salva-Heredia-Arents copy, first ed., attractive copy, rare. Quaritch 977-1 1978 $3,000

ACOSTA, JOSEPH DE   Historia Naturale e Morale Delle Indie. Venice, 1596. 4to., contemp. vellum, very nice. Quaritch 977-2 1978 $300

ACOSTA, JOSEPH DE   Historia Natural y Moral de Las Indias. Madrid, 1792. Full old calf, 2 vols. in 1. Biblo 247-75 1978 $52.50

ACRELIUS, ISRAEL   A History of New Sweden. Philadelphia, 1874. 1st ed. in English, fine. MacManus 239-2 1978 $40

ACRES, W. MARSTON   The Bonk of England from Within 1694-1900. 1931. Illus., 2 vols., roy. 8vo. George's 635-267 1978 £18

ACROSS Patagonia. London, 1880. Engr., illus., orig. cloth, 8vo., ex-lib., lst ed. Morrill 241-117 1978 $8.50

ACTON, HAROLD   Aquarium; poems. London, 1923. First ed., orig. bindings, head and foot of spine torn, good. Rota 211-1 1978 £5

ACTON, HAROLD   Five Saints and an Appendix. London, 1927. Batik bds., spine slightly darkened, nice, first ed. Rota 211-2 1978 £5

ACTON, HAROLD   Humdrum. London, 1928. First ed., orig. binding, spine and covers somewhat soiled, otherwise nice, A.L.s. from author loosely inserted. Rota 211-3 1978 £25

ACTON, HAROLD   Memoirs of an Aesthete. London, 1949. 8vo, green cloth, ex-lib, near fine, tight, lst ed., collector's cond. Desmarais 1-4 1978 $35

ACTON, HAROLD   This Chaos. Paris, Hours Press, 1930. One of 150 copies, signed by the author, unnumbered and marked "Review", 4to., qtr. mor., patterned bds., nice. Rota 211-4 1978 £35

ACTON, JOHN EMERICH EDWARD DALBERG, IST BARON   History of Freedom and Other Essays. 1922. Portr., 8vo. George's 635-521 1978 £5.25

ACTON, JOHN EMERICH EDWARD DALBERG, IST BARON   Letters to Mary, Daughter of W. E. Gladstone. 1913. Portr., 8vo. George's 635-1229 1978 £5.25

ADAIR, A. GARLAND   Austin: Its Place Under Texas Skies. Austin, 1946. lst ed., pict. wr. Jenkins 116-1366 1978 $15

ADAIR, A. GARLAND   Under Texas Skys, Featuring What's What About Texas. Austin, 1947. lst ed., printed wr. Jenkins 116-1516 1978 $12.50

ADAM OF SAINT-VICTOR   The Liturgical Poetry of Adam of St. Victor. 1881. 3 vols., parallel Latin/English text, 8vo. Upcroft 12-2 1978 £15

ADAM, ALEXANDER   Roman Antiquities.... Edinburgh, 1792. 8vo., contemp. calf, nice copy. Fenning 32-3 1978 £6.50

ADAM, ALEXANDER   Antiquites Romaines, ou Tableau des Moeurs, Usages et Institutions des Romains. Paris, 1818. 2 vols., half calf, 8vo. Van der Peet H-64-238 1978 Dfl 75

ADAM, ROBERT   Decorative Work. 1901. Plts., folio, half parchment, rubbed. George's 635-73 1978 £40

ADAM, VICTOR   Entrennes Lyriques Recueil de Romances et Nocturns. Paris, 1830. lst ed., oblong octavo, lithographs, papered boards, very good. Victoria 34-9 1978 $37.50

ADAM, WILLIAM   The Law & Custom of Slavery in British India... Boston, 1840. lst ed., early orig. ?, patterned brown cloth, brown leather label, inscription on leading freen endpaper, v.g. Jarndyce 16-1053 1978 £35

ADAMI, ANNIBALE   Elogii Storici de' Due Marchesi Capizucchi Fratelli Camillo, e Biagio.... Roma, 1685. Folio, limp vellum, portraits. King 7-2 1978 £20

ADAMIC, LOUIS   Cradle of Life. 1936. Austin 79-3 1978 $8.50

ADAMIC, LOUIS   Dinner at the White House. 1946. Austin 80-34a 1978 $8.50

ADAMIC, LOUIS   Dynamite. 1934. Rebound. Austin 79-4 1978 $10

ADAMIC, LOUIS   From Many Lands. 1940. Austin 79-5 1978 $7.50

ADAMIC, LOUIS   Laughing in the Jungle. 1932. Orig. ed. Austin 79-6 1978 $8.50

ADAMIC, LOUIS   A Nation of Nations. 1945. Illus. Austin 79-7 1978 $7.50

ADAMIC, LOUIS   The Native's Return. 1934. Austin 79-8 1978 $7.50

ADAMIC, LOUIS   Robinson Jeffers, A Portrait. Seattle, 1929. lst ed., mint, uncut, unopened. Ballinger 11-102 1978 $30.00

ADAMIC, LOUIS   What's Your Name. 1942. Austin 79-10 1978 $8.50

ADAMS, ANDY   The Log of a Cowboy. Boston & New York, 1903. Pic. cloth, illus., lst ed., very good copy, slipcase. Dykes 34-14 1978 $50

ADAMS, ANDY   The Log of a Cowboy: A Narrative of the Old Trail Days. Boston, 1903. Illus., original cloth, lst ed. Ginsberg 14-1 1978 $50

ADAMS, ANDY   Log of a Cowboy. Boston, (1903). lst ed., illus., full page owner inscription, waterstain in top margin of text, cover w/moderate staining, very good. Victoria 34-10 1978 $20

ADAMS, BROOKS   The Law of Civilization and Decay. New York, 1896. 8vo., orig. cloth. Morrill 241-3 1978 $7.50

ADAMS, CHARLES FRANCIS 1807-1886   Texas and the Massachusetts Resolutions. Boston, 1844. Orig. yellow prtd. wr. Jenkins 116-5 1978 $85

ADAMS, CHARLES FRANCIS 1835-1915   An Autobiography. Boston, 1916. lst ed. Baldwins' 51-169 1978 $15

ADAMS, CHARLES FRANCIS 1835-1915   Trans-Atlantic Historical Solidarity. Oxford, 1918. Bell Wiley's copy. Broadfoot 44-2 1978 $12

ADAMS, E. C. L.   Congaree Sketches. Chapel Hill, 1927. Broadfoot 50-1a 1978 $15

ADAMS, E. C. L.   Congaree Sketches. Chapel Hill, 1927. Ltd. and signed, cover slightly stained. Broadfoot 50-1b 1978 $30

ADAMS, EPHRAIM D.　　　　Great Britain and the American Civil War.
New York, n.d. 2 vols. in I, illus. Biblo 251-24 1978 $15

ADAMS, FRANKLIN P.　　　　Among Us Mortals. 1917. Austin 82-4 1978
$11

ADAMS, FRANKLIN P.　　　　Christopher Columbus and Other Patriotic Verses.
Viking, 1931. First ed. Austin 82-5 1978 $12.50

ADAMS, FRANKLIN P.　　　　The Conning Tower Book. 1926. Ltd. to 100
numbered copies, signed by author, very good, d.j. Austin 82-6 1978 $20

ADAMS, FRANKLIN P.　　　　In Cupid's Court. Evanston, 1902. 1st ed.,
sm. 8vo, orig. bds., some spine wear, signed by Adams. Americanist 103-1
1978 $20

ADAMS, FRANKLIN P.　　　　In Other Words. New York, 1912. 1st ed.,
spine faded, name in ink on flyleaf & title page, good copy. Biblo 251-389 1978
$15

ADAMS, FRANKLIN P.　　　　Nods and Becks. 1944. First ed. Austin 82-10
1978 $11

ADAMS, FRANKLIN P.　　　　Overset. 1922. First ed. Austin 82-11 1978
$11

ADAMS, FRANKLIN P.　　　　The Second Conning Tower Book. 1927. Austin
82-7 1978 $20

ADAMS, FRANKLIN P.　　　　The Second Conning Tower Book. 1927. Austin
82-8 1978 $10

ADAMS, FRANKLIN P.　　　　So Much Velvet. 1924. Austin 82-12 1978
$8.50

ADAMS, FRANKLIN P.　　　　Something Else Again. New York, 1920.
1st ed., edges rubbed. Biblo 251-390 1978 $9.50

ADAMS, FRANKLIN P.　　　　Tobogganing on Parnassus. 1912. Austin 82-13
1978 $10

ADAMS, FREDERICK UPHAM　　The Story of Edward Hines Who is Falsely Accused
of Having Secured by Bribery the Election of William Lorimer to the Senate of the
United States. N.P., n.d. (1912). Prtd. wrs. Hayman 73-276 1978 $10

ADAMS, GEORGE　　　　An Essay on Electricity. London, 1792. 8vo.,
frontis., fldg. plts., old half mor., light foxing of plts., very good copy, old
inscription on title, 4th ed. Norman 5-*1 1978 $150

ADAMS, GEORGE　　　　The Lawrence Directory, Containing the City
Record, the Names of the Citizens, a Business Director. Lawrence, 1857. 12mo.,
one corner worn, orig. cloth. Morrill 241-313 1978 $15

ADAMS, H. G.　　　　Favorite Song Birds. London, 1856. 2nd ed.,
hand-coloured plts., fcap. 8vo., gilt cloth. K Books 244-2 1978 £16

ADAMS, H. G.　　　　Favourite Song Birds. London, 1889. 8vo,
orig. cloth, plts., very good. Book Chest 17-4 1978 $65

ADAMS, H. I.　　　　Wild Flowers of the British Isles. 1910. Colored
plts. by author, text foxed, 2 vols., 4to., ex-library. George's 635-949 1978
£15

ADAMS, HENRY　　　　A Catalogue of the Books of John Quincy Adams
Deposited in the Boston Atheneum... Boston, 1938. Orig. cloth, 1st ed., 1 of
300 copies printed by the Merrymount Press, very fine. MacManus 238-847 1978
$40

ADAMS, HENRY　　　　The Degradation of the Democratic Dogma. New
York, 1919. 1st ed., orig. cloth, d.j., chipped, very good copy. MacManus
239-4 1978 $12.50

ADAMS, HENRY　　　　The Degradation of the Democratic Dogmas.
1919. First ed. Austin 82-14 1978 $17.50

ADAMS, HENRY　　　　The Formative Years. Boston, 1947. Maps,
2 vols., orig. cloth, d.js., orig. box, fine set. MacManus 239-5 1978 $30

ADAMS, HENRY　　　　History of the United States...During the Administration of Thomas Jefferson, 1801-17. New York, 1921. 9 vols., scarce,
orig. cloth, spines faded. MacManus 239-6 1978 $150

ADAMS, HENRY　　　　History of the United States of America during the
First Administration of Thomas Jefferson... New York, 1962. Ltd. to 750 sets,
9 vols. Biblo 247-1 1978 $95

ADAMS, HENRY　　　　Letters of Henry Adams 1858-1891. 1930. First
ed. Austin 82-17 1978 $27.50

ADAMS, HENRY　　　　Letters of Henry Adams 1858-1891. 1930. Austin
82-18 1978 $17.50

ADAMS, HENRY　　　　Letters of Henry Adams 1892-1918. 1938. Austin
82-15 1978 $17.50

ADAMS, HENRY　　　　Letters to a Niece. 1920. First ed. Austin 82-
16 1978 $17.50

ADAMS, HENRY　　　　Letters to a Niece and Prayer to the Virgin of
Chartres. Boston, 1920. Fine with bkplt. Desmarais B-3 1978 $7.50

ADAMS, HERBERT B.　　　　Maryland, Virginia and Washington. Baltimore,
1885. Vol. 3, Bell Wiley's copy. Broadfoot 46-469 1978 $16

ADAMS, ISABEL　　　　Wild Flowers of the British Isles. London,
1907-10. 8vo, orig. cloth, 2 vols. Book Chest 17-2 1978 $45

ADAMS, J. DONALD　　　　The Shape of Books to Come. New York, 1944.
First ed., second printing, blue bds. Millburn 1-1 1979 $10

ADAMS, JAMES TRUSLOW　　Album of American History. New York, 1944-
48. 4 vols., Bell Wiley's copy. Broadfoot 46-470 1978 $35

ADAMS, JAMES TRUSLOW　　Album of American History. New York, 1944-49.
5 vols., 4to., illus., first eds., d.w.'s. Biblo 247-2 1978 $72.50

ADAMS, JAMES TRUSLOW　　Big Business in a Democracy. 1945. Austin 80-
396 1978 $7.50

ADAMS, JAMES TRUSLOW　　The Founding of New England. Boston, (1921).
Illus. MacManus 239-7 1978 $8.50

ADAMS, JAMES TRUSLOW　　New England in the Republic, 1776-1850. Boston, 1927. Illus., fine. MacManus 239-8 1978 $10

ADAMS, JAMES TRUSLOW　　Our Business Civilization. 1929. Austin 80-397
1978 $8.50

ADAMS, JOHN　　　　The House of Kitcat, a Story of Bookbinding,
1798-1948. 1948. Illus., 4to. George's 635-1209 1978 £10.50

ADAMS, JOHN QUINCY　　The Diary, 1794-1845. New York, 1928. Fine.
MacManus 239-11 1978 $12.50

ADAMS, JOHN QUINCY　　Oration on the Life and Character of Gilbert
Motier De Lafayette.... Washington, 1835. Orig. printed wr., with signature "Thomas Hale 1835" on cover, 1st ed., very good or better. Limestone
9-4 1978 $20

ADAMS, JOHN QUINCY　　Oration on the Life and Character of Gilbert
Motier de Lafayette. Washington, 1835. Disbound. Hayman 71-4 1978 $7.50

ADAMS, JOHN QUINCY　　Report Upon Weights and Measures. Washington,
1821. Fldg. tables, 8vo, orig. bds., edges untrimmed, rebacked, text lightly
dampstained, 1st ed. Morrill 239-283 1978 $37.50

ADAMS, JOHN QUINCY　　Speech...Relating to the Annexation of Texas.
Washington, 1838. Handsome half morocco, gilt, 1st ed. Jenkins 116-6 1978
$125

ADAMS, JOHN S.   Town & Country; or, Life at Home & Abroad,
Without & Within US. Boston, 1855. lst ed., publisher's full mor., decor. in
gold with floral, mid-century binding, 8vo., very good. Americanist 103-2
1978 $35

ADAMS, JOSEPH T.   Lecture on the Subject of Re-Annexing Texas
to the United States. New Bedford, 1845. Sewn. Jenkins 116-8 1978 $45

ADAMS, L. S.   Recueil De Sculptures Antiques Greques et Romaines. Nancy, 1754. lst. ed., engraved title-pg., engraved plts., contemporary
calf, morocco label gilt, back worn, joints weak. Deighton 5-109 1978 £30

ADAMS, NEHEMIAH   A South-side View of Slavery. Boston, 1854.
Scarce. MacManus 239-833 1978 $32.50

ADAMS, RAMON F.   Western Words. Norman, 1944. lst ed., cloth,
fine copy in d.w., reinforced, scarce. Dykes 34-79 1978 $20

ADAMS, RANDOLPH G.   British Headquarters. Ann Arbor, 1928. Bookplt., frontis., scarce. MacManus 239-544 1978 $27.50

ADAMS, RANDOLPH G.   The Passports Printed by Benj. Franklin at His
Passy Press. Ann Harbor, Harvard University Press, 1925. lst ed., ltd. to 505
copies, folio, orig. cloth-backed marbled bds., illus., 8vo., very good. Americanist 103-35 1978 $35

ADAMS, ROBERT   The Narrative of Robert Adams, a Sailor, Who
Was Wrecked on the Western Coast of Africa, in the Year 1810... London, 1816.
lst. ed., folding map, 4to, half calf. K Books 239-3 1978 £90

ADAMS, RUSSELL B.   Voices of the Stones. London, 1925. Spine
lightly rubbed, near fine. Desmarais B-6 1978 $10

ADAMS, SAMUEL HOPKINS   Average Jones. Indianapolis. 1911. Illus., first
ed. Austin 82-23 1978 $17.50

ADAMS, SAMUEL HOPKINS   Safe Money. Auburn, (1949). Illus., wr.
Butterfield 21-3 1978 $10

ADAMS, SAMUEL HOPKINS   Success. 1921. First ed. Austin 82-24 1978
$12.50

ADAMS, SAMUEL HOPKINS   Whispers. 1940. 313 pages. Austin 82-25 1978
$11

ADAMS, THOMAS   Outline of Town and City Planning. New York,
1936. 8vo, orig. cloth, many illus. Sexton 7-1 1978 £12

ADAMS, THOMAS   Poetical Works. 1811. First ed., wood engra.
vignettes by Bewick, sm. 8vo., contemp. half mor., good. Howes 194-1371
1978 £25

ADAMS, W. D.   By-Ways in Book-Land. Battery Park 1-255 1978
$22.50

ADAMS, W. D.   With Poet and Player. Battery Park 1-256 1978
$25.00

ADAMSON, J. W.   The Illiterate Anglo-Saxon and other essays on
education, medieval and modern. Cambridge, 1946. Plts., 8vo. Upcroft 12-
4 1978 £5

ADAMSON, JOHN   The Muses Welcome to the High and Mighty
Prince James by the Grace of God King of Great Britaine, France and Ireland...
Edinburgh, 1618. lst. ed., woodcut portrait, folio, 19th century polished calf,
gilt. Traylen 88-93 1978 £110

ADAMSON, WILLIAM AGAR   Salmon-fishing in Canada. London, 1860. Orig.
binding, covers worn, hinges cracked. Wolfe 39-2 1978 $55

ADDAMS, JANE   Twenty Years at Hull-House. 1930 (1910).
Illus. Austin 79-11 1978 $10

ADDEY, MARKINFIELD   "Stonewall Jackson." New York, 1863.
Minor wear at corners, title page coming loose from binding at top. Hayman 73-
2 1978 $12.50

ADDISON, JOSEPH   The Evidences of the Christian Religion. Dublin, 1758. 12mo, wrapper, dusty & mounted, very good copy. Fenning 32-4
1978 £6.50

ADDISON, JOSEPH   The Free-Holder. 1716. Fine, contemp. calf,
lettering piece, 8vo., first ed. in book form. Howes 194-118 1978 £32

ADDISON, JOSEPH   The Freeholder or Political Essays. 1732. 5th.
ed., half title, orig. calf, gilt border, hinges weak, good. Jarndyce 16-28
1978 £8

ADDISON, JOSEPH   The Guardian. 1747. Vignette on titles, 2
vols., thk. 8vo., contemp. calf, joints cracked, labels missing. Howes 194-119
1978 £15

ADDISON, JOSEPH   Remarks on Several Parts of Italy...In the Years
1701, 1702, 1703. 1705. First ed., contemp. panelled calf, very good, 8vo.
Howes 194-120 1978 £48

ADDISON, JOSEPH   Remarks On Several Parts of Italy... 1718.
2nd. ed., sm. 8vo, engraved head & tailpieces, sl. worming of lst. 32 pgs., neatly
rebacked, polished calf. Deighton 5-195 1978 £30

ADDISON, JOSEPH   Remarks on Several Parts of Italy, etc., in the
Years 1701, 1702, 1703. 1726. 3rd ed., 12mo., contemp. panelled calf, lacks
lettering-piece, some contemp. ink annotation. George's 635-1164 1978 £5.25

ADDISON, JOSEPH   Remarks on Several Parts of Italy. 1726. 5th.
ed., orig. mottled calf, leading hinge split, o/w good. Jarndyce 16-27 1978
£7.50

ADDISON, JOSEPH   The Spectator. 1747. Lg. title-page vignettes,
8 vols., demy 8vo., contemp. calf, labels missing. Howes 194-470 1978 £35

ADDISON, JOSEPH   Works. Birmingham, Baskerville Press, 1761. 4
vols., roy. 4to., portr. frontis., plts., contemp. dark green mor., elab. gilt
backs, bkplt., light foxing, fine copy, binding exceptionally well-preserved
state. Quaritch 979-17 1978 $1,250

ADDISON, R.   Dialogues upon the Usefulness of Ancient Medals.
1726. Vol. 3 only of a collected ed. of the Works, without general title-page,
woodcut illus., 12mo., new qtr. cloth, marbled bd. sides, neat. George's 635-
442 1978 £7.50

ADDISON, THOMAS   Dissertatio Medica Inauguralis Quaedam de Syphi-
lide et Hydrargyro. Edinburgi, 1815. 8vo., disbound, marginal foxing, good
copy, pres. inscr. from author. Zeitlin 245-2 1978 $325

ADDRESS of the Friends of Domestic Industry, Assembled in Convention, at New-
York, October 26, 1831, to the People of the United States. Baltimore, 1831.
Disbound. Hayman 73-3 1978 $15

ADDRESS of the Grand Council of the Tammany Society...Upon...the Political
Use of Tammany Hall. New York, 1853. Butterfield 21-550a 1978 $7.50

ADDRESS of the Republican General Committee of the Young Men of the City and
County of New-York, Friendly to the Election of Gen. Andrew Jackson to the Pre-
sidency, to the Republican Electors of the State of New-York. New-York, 1828.
Disbound. Hayman 72-626 1978 $40

ADDRESS to the Roman Catholic of Ireland on the Conduct They Should Pursue
at the Present Crisis on the Subject of an Union. Dublin, 1799. Plain wrs.,
reprint. Hyland 128-272 1978 £10

THE ADDRESSES and Other Papers Connected with the Dedication of the Parsons
Memorials...and the Pioneers Who Settled Kingsborough. Gloversville, 1932.
Illus., wr. Butterfield 21-190 1978 $15

ADDRESSES on the Presentation of the Sword of Andrew Jackson to the Congress
of the United States... Washington, 1855. Wrs., moderate wear. Hayman 71-
359 1978 $8.50

ADE, GEORGE   Forty Modern Fables. 1901. Illus., first ed.
Austin 82-26 1978 $27.50

ADE, GEORGE   In Babel. Stories of Chicago. 1903. Austin 82-
27 1978 $10

ADE, GEORGE
82-28 1978 $12.50
In Pastures New. 1906. Illus., first ed. Austin

ADE, GEORGE
82-30 1978 $20
More Fables in Slang. 1900. First ed. Austin

ADE, GEORGE
1978 $10
The Old Time Saloon. 1931. Austin 82-31

ADE, GEORGE
strip faded, else good. Austin 82-33 1978 $12.50
People You Know. 1903. Illus., first ed., back-

ADE, GEORGE
1978 $8.50
People You Know. 1903. Illus. Austin 82-34

ADER, GUILLAUME
Tolosae, 1623. Sm. 8vo., browned, some foxing, bkplts, good copy, very rare
ed. Zeitlin 245-3 1978 $175
Enarrationes, de Aegrotis, et Morbis in Euangelio.

ADIRONDACK and Green Mountain Tourist Guide. Lake George, 1917. Tall
& narrow 8vo., maps, photo. illus., ads, orig. stiff wr., minor tears. Butterfield 21-5 1978 $20

ADLARD, G.
1870. Plts., pres. copy, octavo, good. Upcroft 10-198 1978 £14
Amye Robsart and the Earl of Leycester...

ADLER, CYRUS
the Diplomatic Correspondence of the U. S., 1840-1938. New York, 1943.
Biblo 251-683 1978 $15
American Intercession on Behalf of Jews in

ADLER, CYRUS
Austin 79-12 1978 $27.50
The Voice of America on Kishineff. 1904.

ADLER, ELMER
Papers Wherein Each of a Select Group of Authors Tells of the Difficulties of Author-
ship and How Such Trials are Met. New York, 1937. Orig. cloth, 1st ed.
MacManus 238-876 1978 $25
Breaking Into Print. Being a Compilation of

ADLER, OTTO
Ber in, 1924. 8vo., maroon cloth, stamps, some browning, good copy, 4th ed.
Zeitlin 245-4 1978 $50
Die Mangelhafte Geschlechtsempfindung des Weibes.

ADLERFELT, GUSTAF
English ed., 3 vols., 8vo, portrait, folding battle plans, contemp. calf, worn,
joints cracked. Hannas 54-114 1978 £42
The Military History of Charles XII. 1740. 1st.

ADLUM, JOHN
America, and the Best Mode of Making Wine. Washington, 1823. 8vo., orig.
bds., rebacked, 1st ed., few leaves foxed, else fine, uncut, stamp on flyleaf.
Howell 5-1 1978 $200
A Memoir on the Cultivation of the Vine in

ADOLPHUS, JOHN
George III to 1783. 1802. Engraved portrait, 3 vols., half calf rubbed, 8vo.
George's 635-525 1978 $12.50
The History of England from the Accession of

ADOLPHUS, JOHN
London, 1802-03. 2 vols., rebinding set. Biblo 247-649 1978 $20
The History of France, from the Year 1790 to 1802.

THE ADVENTURES and Feelings of a Griffin. Edinburgh, 1830. First ed., 2 vols.,
orig. cloth, entirely untrimmed, printed labels rubbed, pres. copy inscribed by
author. Howes 194-591 1978 £24

THE ADVENTURES and Feelings of a Griffin. Edinburgh, 1830. 2 vols., 8vo.,
1st ed., orig. cloth paper labels, bkplt. of Dunbar of Westfield, rare. Quaritch
979-1 1978 $75

ADVENTURES in Americana. 1492-1897. The Romance of Voyage and Discovery
from Spain to the Indies, the Spanish Main, and North America; Inland to the Ohio
Country; on Toward the Mississippi... New York, 1928. 2 vols., folio, illus.,
orig. cloth, pub. box, 1st ed., 1 of 200 copies. MacManus 238-962 1978 $175

THE ADVENTURES of Congo in Search of His Master. London, 1828. 12mo.,
3rd ed., orig. roan-backed bds., crease in upper bd., very good. Victoria 34-
11 1978 $27.50

THE ADVENTURES of George Maitland, Esq. 1786. First ed., 3 vols., 12mo.,
contemp. sheep, joints weak, rare. Howes 194-139 1978 £38

THE ADVENTURES of the Guildford Jack-Daw. (c. 1794). 12mo., woodcuts,
orig. decor. paper-wr., sewn as issued, good clean state. Quaritch 979-84
1978 $115

ADVICE to the Officers of the British Army. Dublin, 1783. Sm. 8vo., sixth ed.,
contemp. bds., new calf back. F. Edwards 1013-232 1978 £30

THE AERO Manual. London, 1909. First ed., illus., limp bds., 8vo. K Books
244-3 1978 £16

AEROPAGITICA: A Speech by John Milton for the Liberty of Unlicensed Printing.
De Vinne Press, 1890. 12mo., 1 of 325 copies prtd. on Holland paper, new cloth
spine. Battery Park 1-140 1978 $75

AESCHYLUS
8vo, green stamped cloth, gilt lettering on spine, 1st ed, fine. Desmarais 1-56
1978 $35
The Agamemon of Aeschylus. London, 1877.

AESCHYLUS
title, orig. green cloth, good. Jarndyce 16-324 1978 £6.50
The Agamemnon of ... 1877. 1st. ed., half

AESCHYLUS
4to, half calf, marbled bds., hinges weakening, some brown -spotting, o/w good.
Jarndyce 16-166 1978 £18
The Tragedies of ... Norwich, 1777. 1st ed.,

AESCHYLUS
4 vols., full calf, a little rubbed, lacks lettering pieces. George's 635-443 1978
£8.50
Tragoediae quae supersunt.... Londini, 1823.

AESOPUS
illustratae, & latinius quam antehac interpretatae. Antwerp, Christopher
Plantin, 1565. 16 mo., woodcut illus., fine copy, pocket ed., 17th century
vellum. Schafer 19-1 1978 sFr. 900
Aesopi Phrygis et aliorum fabulae, iconibus

AESOPUS
1692-99. Portrait, plt., 2 parts in 1 vol., folio, panelled calf, rebacked.
Howes 194-2 1978 £95
Fables of Aesop and Other Eminent Mythologists.

AESOPUS
1st Exeter ed., 12mo., calf, foxed, very good. Victoria 34-12 1978 $32.50
Fabulae Aesopi Selectae:.... Boxton, 1799.

AESOPUS
foxed, minor cover defects. Victoria 34-13 1978 $15
Aesopi Fabulae. Boston, 1812. 12mo, calf,

AESOPUS
don, 1812. New ed., frontis. and vignettes, 12mo, contemp. tree calf, rebacked,
rubbed. Totteridge 29-4 1978 $50
Select Fables of Esop and Other Fabulists. Lon-

AESOPUS
ed., designs on wood by Thomas Bewick, orig. bds. George's 635-95 1978 £45
The Fables of Aesop. Newcastle, 1823. Second

AESOPUS
books. 1824. 12mo., contemp. sheep, back repaired, woodcuts. P. M. Hill
142-15 1978 £18
Select Fables of Esop and other Fabulists. In three

AESOPUS
man Nature. (1857). 4to., plts. in colour, contemp. half leather. Quaritch
983-293 1978 $140
Fables of Aesop and Others Translated into Hu-

AESOPUS
1st ed., sq. octavo, bound in black half mor., gilt lettering and blind stamping
on spine. Totteridge 29-3 1978 $125
The Fables of Aesop and Others. London, (1857).

AESOPUS
1669, (c. 1860). 3rd ed., folio, half calf, rubbed. George's 635-1165 1978
£12.50
Fables of Aesop and other eminent Mythologists.

AESOPUS
1882. Sm. cr. 8vo, orig. cloth, good. Sexton 7-2 1978 £7
Aesop's Fables: A New Version... London,

AESOPUS
b/w drawings crudely colored. Victoria 34-669 1978 $10
Aesop's Fables. London, (1933). Color plts.,

AESOPUS   The Subtyl Historyes and Fables of Esope. San Francisco, 1930. Full brown mor., near mint, I of 200 numbered copies. Dawson's 447-51 1978 $200

AFLALO, F. G.   Sunset Playgrounds. London, 1909. Illus., orig. binding. Wolfe 39-3 1978 $15

AGARD, WALTER R.   The Greek Tradition in Sculpture. Baltimore, 1930. Illus. Biblo BL781-311 1978 $12.50

AGASSIZ, ELIZABETH CARY   Louis Agassiz. Boston, 1885. 8vo, orig. cloth, 2 vols. Book Chest 17-5 1978 $75

AGASSIZ, ELIZABETH CARY   Louis Agassiz. His Life and Correspondence. Boston, 1885. 1st ed., 2 vols., illus., orig. cloth, spines faded and worn, but good set. MacManus 239-718 1978 $37.50

AGASSIZ, ELIZABETH CAREY   Louis Agassiz: His Life and Correspondence. Boston, 1886. 2 vols., illus. Baldwins' 51-170 1978 $15

AGASSIZ, JEAN LOUIS RODOLPHE   Methods of Study in Natural History. Boston, 1863. 1st ed., very nice copy, orig. cloth. MacManus 239-12 1978 $30

AGATHA, SISTER M.   Texas Prose Writings, A Reader's Digest. Dallas, 1936. 1st ed. Jenkins 116-12 1978 $45

AGEE, JAMES   Permit Me Voyage. New Haven, 1934. 8vo., orig. blue cloth, 1st ed., spine faded, else fine. Howell 5-2 1978 $150

AGGINUNTI, NICCOLO   Oratio de Mathematica Laudibus Habita in Florentissima Pisarum Academia cum Ibidem Publicam Illius Scientiae Explicationem Agressurus Foret. Rome, 1627. 4to., half-vellum, 1st ed. Gilhofer 74-105 1978 sFr 900

AGGREGATE Meeting of Dublin Dusts. Dublin, 1821. 8vo, disbound, "Second edition", bit soiled, very scarce. Ximenes 47-154 1978 $15

AGNESI, DONNA MARIA GAETANA   Instituzioni Analitiche ad uso della Gioventu italiana. Milano, 1748. 4to., old cloth, lettering pieces gilt, 2 vols., plts. King 7-121 1978 £90

AGNEW, DANIEL   A History of the Region of Pennsylvania North of the Ohio and West of the Allegheny River... Philadelphia, 1887. Very scarce, rebound. MacManus 239-1349 1978 $50

AGNEW, GEORGETTE   Let's Pretend. New York & London, 1927. 1st Amer. ed., illus. by Ernest H. Shepard, very fine, pict. dj. Victoria 34-14 1978 $30

AGOSTINI, LEONARDO, OF SIENA   Gemmae et Sculpturae Anitquae Depictae ab Leonardo Augustino Senensi. Franeker, 1694. Small quarto, in two parts; part I with engravings, cameo portraits, part two with contemporary calf, rubbed, gilt-tooled paneled spine with red leather label. Bennett 20-1 1978 $550

AGREEMENT Between the Delaware & Hudson Company and the Locomotive Engineers...Employment, Rates of Pay...April 1st, 1910. N. P. Stiff wr. Butterfield 21-152F 1978 $7.50

AGRESTI, OLIVIA ROSSETTI   David Lubin. 1922. 1st ed. Austin 79-14 1978 $15

AGRIPPA, CAMILLO   Modo da Comporre il Moto Nella Sfera. Rome, 1575. 4to., lg. fold. plt., wrs. Gilhofer 74-1 1978 sFr 700

AGRIPPA VON NETTESHEIM, HEINRICH CORNELIUS   De Occulta Philosophia Libri Tres. (Cologne, 1533). Folio, cont. blind tooled calf, woodcut, rebacked and edges restored, dampstaining, fine, first complete ed. Norman 5-5 1978 $1,500

AGRIPPA VON NETTESHEIM, HEINRICH CORNELIUS   De Incertitudine & Vanitate Scientiarum Declamatio Invectiva. N.P. (Cologne), 1539. Woodcut portr., sm. 8vo., full red mor., gilt edges, early ed. Salloch 345-3 1978 $200

AGRIPPA VON NETTESHEIM, HEINRICH CORNELIUS   Operum Pars Posterior. Lyon, n.d. (c. 1630). 8vo., contemp. vellum. Salloch 345-4 1978 $225

AGUILAR, GRACE   Essays and Miscellanies. Philadelphia, 1853. Austin 79-15 1978 $27.50

AGUILAR, GRACE   Home Influence. 1897. Austin 79-16 1978 $12.50

AGUILAR, GRACE   The Vale of Cedars. 1870. Frontis., Amer. ed. Austin 79-17 1978 $17.50

AGUILAR, GRACE   The Vale of Cedars and Other Tales. London, 1902. First ed., illus. Biblo 247-353 1978 $15

AGUILLON, FRANCOIS D'   Opticorum Libri Sex. Antwerp, 1613. Folio, frontis., engr. vignettes, text illus., full antique calf, skillfully washed, repairs to margins, but fine copy, 1st ed. Norman 5-6 1978 $1,850

AGUSTIN, ANTONIO   De Legibus et Senatusconsultis Liber:.... Paris, 1584. Small folio, woodcut initials and decor., three signatures on t.p., original calf rubbed, one signature of Andrew Fletcher of Saltoun, one signature of Adrian Beverland, Beverland's armorial bookplate on verso of t.p. Bennett 20-2 1978 $250

AHLERS, FRANCISCO HENRIQUE   Instruccas Sobre os Corpos Celestes Principalmente sobre os Cometas. Lisbon, 1758. Sm. 4to., plts., leather, good. Paine 78-2 1978 $47.50

AHUMANDA MORENO, PASCUAL   Guerra del Pacifico. Valparaiso, 1884-1891. Orig. cloth, 8 vol. in 4, folio, 1/2 leath., spines worn. Paine 78-1 1978 $200.00

AIKEN, CONRAD   Bring! Bring! And Other Stories. New York, 1925. Inscriptions fr. & back endpapers, near mint in lightly chipped d.w. Desmarais B-7 1978 $40

AIKEN, CONRAD   Senlin: a Biography. 1925. Orig. patterned bds., covers little browned, very good, partly unopened, first Eng. ed. Bell Book 17-005 1978 £25

AIKEN, PETER F.   A Comparative View of the Constitutions of Great Britain and the United States of America, in Six Lectures. Longman & Co., 1842. 1st. & only collected ed., sm. 8vo, orig. cloth, lightly faded, fine copy. Fenning 32-5 1978 £7.50

AIKEN, W. A.   The Conduct of the Earl of Nottingham... New Haven, 1941. Imp. 8vo, portrait, good. Upcroft 10-1 1978 £15

AIKIN, ANNA LETITA
Please turn to
BARBAULD, ANNA LETITA (AIKIN)

AIKIN, C. R.   A Concise View of all the Most Important Facts Which Have Hitherto Appeared Concerning the Cow Pox. Boston, 1801. Third ed., 12mo., orig. bds., joints split. Quaritch 977-3 1978 $175

AIKIN, JOHN   Essays on Song-Writing. (1772). Cr. 8vo., first ed., full 19th cent. turquoise diced calf. Howes 194-134 1978 £28

AIKIN, JOHN   Letters from a Father to His Son, on Various Topics,.... Philadelphia, 1796. Contemp. calf, 8vo. Americanist 101-2 1978 $40

AIKIN, LUCY   Robinson Crusoe in Words of One Syllable. New York, (1870). Color plates in pristine condition, light rubbing of cover cloth, Victoria 34-15 1978 $15

AIKMAN, J.   Annals of the Persecution in Scotland From the Restoration to the Revolution. 1842. Octavo, good. Upcroft 10-201 1978 £15

AIMARD, GUSTAVE   The Prairie Flower. New York, (1891). Pict. wrs., slightly worn. Hayman 73-4 1978 $7.50

AIME-MARTIN, L.   Moralistes Anciens. Paris, 1840. 8vo., contemp. 1/2 calf with label. Salloch 348-79 1978 $20

AINSWORTH, WILLIAM FRANCIS   Travels and Researches In Asia Minor, Mesopotamia, Chaldea, and Armenia. London, 1842. 1st. ed., 2 vols. in 1, 8vo, woodcut frontispieces, folding maps, illus., plts., orig. cloth, stained, gilt back, little loose in binding. Deighton 5-196 1978 £42

AINSWORTH, WILLIAM HARRISON   Auriol or The Elixir of Life.   Routledge, n.d. (1865). Illus. by Phiz, lower margins stained, orig. red cloth blocked in black.   Easton 45-7 1978 £5

AINSWORTH, WILLIAM HARRISON   Auriol or The Elixir of Life.   Routledge, n.d. Illus. by Phiz, orig. green cloth.   Eaton 45-8 1978 £6

AINSWORTH, WILLIAM HARRISON   Ballads, Romantic, Fantastical and Humorous.   1855. 1st ed., 8vo., illus. by John Gilbert, engraved by Dalziel, half green mor. gilt, bookplates.   Eaton 45-4 1978 £30

AINSWORTH, WILLIAM HARRISON   Beau Nash or Bath in the Eighteenth Century.   1880. Illus. by Frederick Gilbert, 8vo, orig. cloth, A.L.S. by author to Henry Wood.   Sawyer 299-109 1978 £75

AINSWORTH, WILLIAM HARRISON   Collected Works.   Routledge, c. 1890. Orig. illus. ed., orig. illus. by Cruikshank, 16 vols., in 17, orig. red cloth, 8vo.   Howes 194-586 1978 £35

AINSWORTH, WILLIAM HARRISON   The Constable of the Tower: An Historical Romance.   1861. Illus. by John Gilbert, 1st ed, 3 vols., orig. red cloth, spines dulled a little unevenly.   Jarndyce 16-249 1978 £36

AINSWORTH, WILLIAM HARRISON   Crichton.   1837. 1st ed., 3 vols., orig. half calf, marbled bds., gilt spines, red & brown labels, fine.   Jarndyce 16-241 1978 £65

AINSWORTH, WILLIAM HARRISON   Crichton.   1853. 4th ed. revised, illus. by H. K. Browne, orig. blue cloth, v.g.   Jarndyce 16-246 1978 £12

AINSWORTH, WILLIAM HARRISON   Historical Romances.   Philadelphia, (1900) 8vo., 20 vols., red cloth, paper labels, uncut, fine 1st state, lib. ed., ltd. to 1000 sets, pr. on Japan vellum, 1st ed., collector's cond.   Desmarais 1-5 1978 $125

AINSWORTH, WILLIAM HARRISON   Jack Sheppard.   1839. 1st ed., 3 vols., 27 illus. by George Cruikshank, half calf, rebacked retaining orig. black labels, v.g.   Jarndyce 16-242 1978 £45

AINSWORTH, WILLIAM HARRISON   Jack Sheppard. A Romance.   London, 1839. Illus. by George Cruikshank, 3 vols., orig. cloth, 1st ed., inner hinges cracked in vol. II, but very fine, half mor. case.   MacManus 238-154 1978 $250

AINSWORTH, WILLIAM HARRISON   The Lancashire Witches. A Romance of Pendle Forest.   London, 1849. 3 vols., orig. dec. cloth, 1st ed., hinges split on vol. I, otherwise very good, half mor. slipcase.   MacManus 238-156 1978 $150

AINSWORTH, WILLIAM HARRISON   Merry England: or, Nobles and Serfs.   London, 1874. 3 vols., orig. cloth, 1st ed., 2nd bind., very good.   MacManus 238-157 1978 $150

AINSWORTH, WILLIAM HARRISON   Mervyn Clitheroe.   Routledge, n.d. Orig. cloth, illus. by Hablot K. Browne.   Eaton 45-6 1978 £6

AINSWORTH, WILLIAM HARRISON   The Miser's Daughter: A Tale.   1855. Illus. by George Cruikshank, orig. blue cloth, v.g.   Jarndyce 16-247 1978 £8.50

AINSWORTH, WILLIAM HARRISON   Old Saint Paul's.   1841. 1st ed., 3 vols., 20 eng. plts. by John Franklin, contemp. half calf, gilt spine, blind stamp on titles.   Easton 45-9 1978 £20

AINSWORTH, WILLIAM HARRISON   Old Saint Paul's.   1841. 3 vols., sm. 8vo., 1st ed., illus., orig. cloth, good copy.   Quaritch 979-338 1978 $120

AINSWORTH, WILLIAM HARRISON   Ovingdean Grange.   1860. 1st ed., wood-eng. frontis & 7 illus. after Hablot K. Brown, contemp. half green calf, lightly worn.   Eaton 45-11 1978 £10

AINSWORTH, WILLIAM HARRISON   Rockwood.   Routledge, n.d. Illus. by George Cruikshank & Sir John Gilbert, orig. green cloth, Armorial bookplt.   Eaton 45-12 1978 £5

AINSWORTH, WILLIAM HARRISON   Sir John Chiverton: A Romance.   1826. 1st ed., orig. blue calf, patterned in blind & gilt, hinges slightly rubbed, otherwise v.g.   Jarndyce 16-240 1978 £38

AINSWORTH, WILLIAM HARRISON   The Spanish Match or Charles Stuart at Madrid.   1865. 2nd ed., 2 vols., orig. blue cloth, v.g.   Jarndyce 16-250 1978 £20

AINSWORTH, WILLIAM HARRISON   The Spendthrift.   Routledge, n.d. Illus. by Hablot K. Browne, orig. blue cloth.   Eaton 45-5 1978 £6

AINSWORTH, WILLIAM HARRISON   The Tower of London.   New York, 1903. New ed., woodcuts by Cruikshank, plt.   Biblo 251-217 1978 $12.50

AINSWORTH, WILLIAM HARRISON   Windsor Castle.   1843. 1st ed., 3 vols., frontis. etchings by G. Cruikshank, browned, vol. 3 with half-title, 1/4 calf, gilt spines.   Eaton 45-10 1978 £20

AINSWORTH, WILLIAM HARRISON   Windsor Castle.   1843. 1st illus. ed., frontis., engraved title & plts. by Cruikshank & Johannot, orig. half calf, black label, spine rubbed otherwise rubbed.   Jarndyce 16-244 1978 £10.50

AINSWORTH, WILLIAM HARRISON   Windsor Castle. An Historical Romance.   London, 1843. Frontis. by George Cruikshank, 3 vols., orig. half cloth bds., bind. wear, good set, half mor. slipcase.   MacManus 238-155 1978 $250

AINSWORTH, WILLIAM HARRISON   Windsor Castle.   1844. Illus. by George Cruikshank & Tony Johannot, half green calf, maroon labels, hinges little rubbed, v.g.   Jarndyce 16-245 1978 £8.50

THE AIRCRAFT Year Book for 1945.   New York, (1945). Illus., 8vo., d.w.   Morrill 241-647 1978 $15

AIRY, OSMUND   Charles II.   London, 1901. Quarto, hand-colored frontis., orig. pr. wr. bound in, quarter straight-grained red mor., salmon cloth boards, fine, one of 1250 numbered copies, engravings.   Bennett 7-2 1978 $150

AITON, JOHN   The Lands of the Messiah, Mahomet, and The Pope; As Visited in 1851.   London, 1852. 1st. ed., 8vo, vignette title-pg., engraved frontispiece, engraved plts., coloured folding engraved map, neatly repaired, last leaf neatly repaired, modern quarter calf, gilt back.   Deighton 5-172 1978 £42

AKELEY, C. E.   In Brightest Africa.   1923. 8vo, orig. cloth, illus., pres. inscription from Akeley.   Edwards 1012-274 1978 £25

AKEN, DAVID   Pioneers of the Black Hills; or, Gordon's Stockade Party of 1874.   Milwaukee, [ca. 1920]. Illus, original wr.   Ginsberg 14-302 1978 $50

AKENSIDE, MARK   Odes on Several Subjects.   1745. 4to., unbound, first ed.   P. M. Hill 142-239 1978 £35

AKENSIDE, MARK   The Pleasures of Imagination.   Glasgow, Foulis Press, 1777. 12mo., contemp. sheep, crimson label, joints little cracked.   Howes 194-268 1978 £5

AKENSIDE, MARK   Poems.   London, 1772. 1st. collected ed., portrait frontis, 4to, contemp. calf, joints weak.   Traylen 88-94 1978 £40

AKERLY, SAMUEL   An Essay on the Geology of the Hudson River, and the Adjacent Regions....   New York, 1820. Folding plate, discolor on boards, good copy.   Nestler Rare 78-93 1978 $165

AKINS, THOMAS B.   Selections from the Public Documents of the Province of Nova Scotia.   Halifax, 1869.   Hood 117-228 1978 $150

AKIYAMA, KENZO   The History of Nippon.   Tokyo, 1941. Illus., decorated boards.   Dawson's 449-101 1978 $15

ALAIN, D'   Ingres.   Paris, 1949. 4to., orig. covers, plts., some in colour, ltd. & numbered ed.   Van der Peet H-64-1 1978 Dfl 65

ALARCON, PEDRO ANTONIO DE   The Three-Cornered Hat.   New York, Wells College Press, 1944. Woodcuts, cloth in d.w., mostly unopened, fine, 500 copies prtd. by hand.   Dawson's 447-59 1978 $65

ALATORRE, A. F.   Voto Particular Presentado por un Individuo de la Comision Especial de la Camara de Diputados,.... Mexico, 1845. Half vellum. Jenkins 116-14 1978 $275

THE ALBANY Directory, for...1857. Albany. Illus. ads., prtd. bds. Butterfield 21-22C 1978 $25

THE ALBANY Directory, for...1860. Part of backstrip gone, sound. Butterfield 21-22D 1978 $20

THE ALBANY Directory, for...1862. Front cover gone. Butterfield 21-22F 1978 $12.50

ALBEE, FRED H.   Injuries and Diseases of the Hip. New York, 1937. Rittenhouse 49-4 1976 $15

ALBERDI, JUAN B.   The Life and Industrial Labours of William Wheelwright in South America. Boston, 1877. 8vo, recent calf-backed marbled bds., gilt ruled spine, fine copy. Fenning 32-6 1978 £34

ALBERT, GEORGE D.   History of the County of Westmoreland, Pennsylvania, With Biographical Sketches of Many of its Pioneers and Prominent Men. Philadelphia, 1882. Rebound, clean, scarce. Hayman 71-633 1978 $75

ALBERTI, GIUSEPPE ANTONIO   Trattato della Misura delle Fabbriche. Venice, 1757. 8vo., frontis., errata leaf, contemp. bds., fine, uncut copy, 1st ed. Gilhofer 74-22 1978 sFr 600

ALBERTI, LEON BATTISTA   Dialogo...de republica, de vita civile, de vita rusticana, de fortuna. Venice, 1543. 8vo., old card boards, extremely rare 16th century ed.. Schafer 19-4 1978 sFr. 1,100

ALBERTI DI VILLANOVA, FRANCESCO D'   Grand Dictionnaire Francois-Italien Compose... London, 1840. 2 vols., 4to., full calf, gilt panelled spines, hinges cracked, else good. Sexton 7-71 1978 £45

ALBERTI DI VILLANOVA, FRANCESCO D'   Nuovo Dizionario Italiano-Francese ... Geneva, 1811. 2 vols., 4to., 1/4 mor., sm. gilt lib. crest at foot of spines. Eaton 45-132 1978 £10

ALBERTIS, GIOVANNI DE   Bibliotheca Universalis Magno Jam Studio Collecta a Joanne De Albertis Juris-consulto et Serenissimi Venetiarum Dominij Advocato Fiscali. Venetis, 1792. 4to., wrappers, wanting spine, very good, woodcut vignette, uncut and mainly unopened, first ed. King 7-122 1978 £60

ALBERTSON, CATHERINE   In Ancient Albemarle. Historical Sketches of the Albemarle Region. Raleigh, 1914. Illus. Broadfoot 50-2 1978 $18

ALBERTUS MAGNUS   De Celo et Mundo. Venice, 1495. Folio, woodcut diagrams, annotations and diagrams in later hand, quarter vellum over boards, leather label on spine, bookplate of Harrison D. Horblit on front pastedown endpaper, very nice copy, 2nd ed. Bennett 20-3 1978 $2500

ALBERTUS MAGNUS   De Duabus Sapientiis et de Recapitulatione Omnium Librorum Astronomiae. (Nuremberg, c. 1493-1496). 4to., half mor., 1st & only 15th Cent. ed., fine copy. Offenbacher 30-2 1978 $2,200

ALBION, G.   Charles I and the Court of Rome; A Study in Seventeenth Century Diplomacy. 1935. Illus., octavo, good. Upcroft 10-203 1978 £12.50

ALBION, ROBERT GREENHALGH   The Rise of New York Port 1815-1860. New York, 1939. 1st ed., pict. dust jacket, out of print. Butterfield 21-477 1978 $25

ALBOHAZEN, HALY   Deiudiciis Astrorum. Basle, 1551. Folio, 1/2 mor., fine copy. Salloch 345-5 1978 $225

ALBRAND, MARTHA   Endure No Longer. Boston, 1944. 1st ed., Kenneth Roberts' signature on flyleaf. Biblo BL781-895 1978 $15

ALBRIGHT, S. C.   The Story of the Moravian Congregation at York, Pa. (York, 1927). Illus. MacManus 239-1350 1978 $17.50

ALBRO, LEWIS C.   Domestic Architecture. New York, 1912. 4to., plts., edges rubbed, bind. poor. Biblo BL781-535 1978 $34.50

ALCIATI, ANDREA   Emblematum Flumen Abundans. 1871. Sm. 4to., orig. cloth. Howes 194-587 1978 £14

ALCIATI, ANDREA   Emblematum Fontes Quatuor. 1870. Sm. 4to., orig. cloth. Howes 194-588 1978 £16

ALCOCK, T.   An Essay on the use of Chlorurets of Oxide of Sodium and of Lime.... 1827. Engraved frontis., half calf rubbed, 8vo. George's 635-990 1978 £25

ALCOTT, LOUISA M.   Hospital Sketches. Boston, 1863. 12mo., orig. bds., 1st ed., 1st print., very nice. MacManus 238-417 1978 $60

ALCOTT, WILLIAM A.   The Young Mother. Boston, 1836. 12mo., lacks backstrip, 1st ed. Morrill 239-6 1978 $12.50

ALDEN, HENRY MILLS   Magazine Writing and the New Literature. 1908. Frontis., first ed. Austin 82-36 1978 $20

ALDEN, ISABELLA M.   Miss Dee Dunmore Bryant... Toronto, 1890. Cover loose. Hood 116-450 1978 $7.50

ALDEN, JOHN ELIOT   Rhode Island Imprints. 1727-1800. New York, 1949. 8vo., orig. cloth. MacManus 238-1030 1978 $30

ALDERFER, E. B.   Economics of American Industry. 1942. Illus., 1st ed. Austin 80-399 1978 $12.50

ALDINGTON, RICHARD   D.H. Lawrence: An Indiscretion. Seattle, 1927. 8vo., wrs., 1st ed. J.S. Lawrence 38-L122 1978 $25

ALDINGTON, RICHARD   D.H. Lawrence. London, 1930. Sm. 8vo., linen-backed printed bds., 1st ed., ltd. to 260 copies, no. and signed by Aldington. J.S. Lawrence 38-L121 1978 $65

ALDINGTON, RICHARD   Death of a Hero. London, 1929. 8vo, black cloth, gilt lettering on spine, foredge foxed, d. w. rubbed, near mint, 1st ed., collector's cond. Desmarais 1-7 1978 $25

ALDINGTON, RICHARD   Death of a Hero. 1929. Fine, d.w., first Eng. ed. Bell Book 17-006 1978 £12

ALDINGTON, RICHARD   A Dream in the Luxembourg. London, 1930. Near mint in d.w. Desmarais B-12 1978 $15

ALDINGTON, RICHARD   The Eaten Heart. Chapelle-Reanville, 1929. 4to, decor. paper boards, cloth back, extremities rubbed, uncut, 1 of only 200 copies signed by Aldington, 1st ed., collector's cond. Desmarais 1-8 1978 $60

ALDINGTON, RICHARD   Last Straws. Paris, Hours Press, 1930. Thin quarto, green suede cloth, rubbed, 1 of 200 copies signed by author, 1st ed., fine. Duschnes 22 0-147 1978 $40

ALDINGTON, RICHARD   Life of a Lady. New York, 1936. Ownership inscr., fine in tattered d.w. Desmarais B-15 1978 $12.50

ALDINGTON, RICHARD   The Romance of Casanova. London, 1946. 16mo, green cloth, 1 inch tear in d.w., fine, 1st ed. Desmarais 1-10 1978 $15

ALDINGTON, RICHARD   Soft Answers. London, 1932. 8vo, red cloth, gilt lettering on spine, d.w. chipped at bottom, mint, 1st ed. Desmarais 1-9 1978 $10

ALDINGTON, RICHARD   The Strange Life of Charles Waterton 1782-1865. New York, (1949). 8vo., orig. cloth, plts. Book Chest 17-7 1978 $27

ALDINGTON, RICHARD   Two Stories. 1930. 1st. ed., no. 231 of 530 copies signed by author, v.g. in d.w. Jarndyce 16-1191 1978 £14.50

ALDINGTON, RICHARD   Wellington. 1946. Maps, plts., near fine, d.w., English first ed. Bell Book 16-004 1978 £6.50

ALDINI, GIOVANNI   Essai Theorique et Experimental Sur le Galvanisme, Avec une Serie d'Experiences. Paris, 1804. 8vo., 2 vols. in 1, fold. plts., half-calf, 1st ed. Gilhofer 74-106 1978 sFr 800

ALDRICH, ARMISTEAD A.   The History of Houston County, Texas, Together with Biographical Sketches... San Antonio, 1943. 1st ed., signed by author, illus. Jenkins 116-673a. 1978 $65

ALDRICH, LEWIS CASS   History of Yates County. Thick tall 8vo., plts., half lea., fine cond., all edges gilt, illus. & biographical sketches. Butterfield 21-476 1978 $85

ALDRICH, LORENZO D.   A Journal of the Overland Route to California & the Gold Mines. Los Angeles, 1950. Fldg. map, bds., some soiling to spine. Dawson's 447-123 1978 $25

ALDRICH, THOMAS BAILEY   The Story of a Bad Boy. Boston, 1870. 1st ed., 1st issue, illus., very scarce, very good. Victoria 34-16 1978 $135

ALEMAN, MATEO   Primera y Segunda Parte de Guzman de Alfarache. Madrid, 1641. 1st Madrid ed., octavo, full contemporary vellum, ties, title in contemporary hand on spine, MS notations in contemporary hand at end of Part I and on last leaf, rare in this ed. Bennett 20-4 1978 $200

ALEMBERT, JEAN LEROND D'   Eloges lus dans les Seances Publiques de l'Academie Francoise. Paris, 1779. Sm. 8vo., contemp. polished calf, fine, first ed. Howes 194-535 1978 £35

ALEMBERT, JEAN LEROND D'   Melanges de Litterature, d'Histoire, et de Philosophie. Amsterdam, 1773. 5 vols., 12mo., contemp. calf, spines lightly rubbed. Howes 194-536 1978 £35

ALEMBERT, JEAN LE ROND D'   Opuscules Mathematiques. Paris, 1761, Briasson, 1764-73, Jombert, 1780. 8 vols., 4to., fldg. plts., contemp. mottled calf, richly gilt spines, rubbed but fine set, sm. stamp on titles, & bklabel, 1st ed. Norman 5-**2 1978 $950

ALEMBERT, JEAN LE ROND D'   Recherches sur Differens Points du Systeme du Monde. Paris, 1754-56. 4to., fldg. plts., table of contents of vol. 2 misbound, contemp. mottled calf, richly gilt spines, rubbed but fine set, sm. stamp on titles & bklabel, 1st ed. Norman 5-**1 1978 $600

ALESSIO PIEMONTESE PSEUD.
Please turn to
RUSCELLI, GIROLAMO

ALESSIO ROBLES, VITO   La Primera Imprenta en Las Provincias Internas De Oriente: Texas, Tamaulipas, Nuevo Leon, Y Coahuila. Mexico, 1939. Illus., scarce. Jenkins 116-1188 1978 $30

ALEX, ANGEL   Mother's Night Light and Plato's Descendants. Lowell, 1929. In Greek. Austin 79-20 1978 $37.50

ALEXANDER, BERNHARD   Spinoza. Munich, 1923. Port., 8vo., cloth. Salloch 348-260 1978 $15

ALEXANDER, DE ALVA STANWOOD   History and Procedure of the House of Representatives. Boston, 1916. 1st ed. Biblo BL781-189 1978 $9

ALEXANDER, DEALVA STANWOOD   A Political History of the State of New York...1774-1782. New York, 1906-1909. 3 vols. Butterfield 21-49 1978 $20

ALEXANDER, DONALD CRICHTON   The Arkansas Plantation 1920-1942. New Haven, 1943. Bell Wiley's copy. Broadfoot's 44-841 1978 $14.00

ALEXANDER, EDWARD P.   Military Memoirs of a Confederate. New York, 1907. 1st ed., cloth, maps. MacManus 239-862 1978 $25

ALEXANDER, EDWARD P.   Military Memoirs of a Confederate. New York, 1907. Sketch-maps by author, scarce 1st ed., cloth. Hayman 73-102 1978 $37.50

ALEXANDER, EDWARD P.   Military Memoirs of a Confederate. New York, 1912. Bell Wiley's copy. Broadfoot 46-2 1978 $45

ALEXANDER, JAMES EDWARD   Sketches in Portugal. 1835. Vignette, 8vo., orig. cloth backed bds., coloured aquatint frontis. F. Edwards 1013-233 1978 £25

ALEXANDER, JAMES W.   Princeton--Old and New. New York, 1898. Illus., sm. 8vo., ex-lib., 1st ed. Morrill 239-541 1978 $8.50

ALEXANDER, JESSIE   Jessie Alexander's Platform Sketches, Original and Adapted. Toronto, 1916. Hood 117-457 1978 $7.50

ALEXANDER, JOHN BREVARD   Reminiscences of the Past Sixty Years. Charlotte, 1908. Scarce, new cloth. Broadfoot 50-4 1978 $50

ALEXANDER, KIRKLAND B.   The Log of the North Shore Club. New York, 1911. Cloth. Hayman 73-7 1978 $17.50

ALEXANDER, THOMAS
Please turn to
BROWNE, THOMAS ALEXANDER

ALEXANDER, THOMAS B.   Political Reconstruction in Tennessee. Nashville, 1950. Pres. copy from author to Bell Wiley. Broadfoot's 44-622 1978 $20

ALEXANDER, W.   Picturesque Representations of the Dress and Manners of the English. 1814. Sm. 4to., coloured plts., some minor spotting, half calf. Quaritch 983-Addenda a 1978 $550

ALEXANDER, WILLIAM HARDY   These Twenty-Five Years. Toronto, 1933. Hood's 115-374 1978 $25

ALEXANDER, WILLIAM JOHN   The University of Toronto and Its Colleges, 1827-1906. Toronto, 1906. Illus. Hood's 116-359 1978 $25

THE ALEXANDER Biddle Papers. New York, 1943. Facsimiles, 2 vols., 8vo., orig. wrs. Morrill 241-19 1978 $8.50

ALEXIS OF PIEDMONT PSEUD.
Please turn to
RUSCELLI, GIROLAMO

ALFIERI, VITTORIO   Memoirs of the Life and Writings... 1810. 2 vols., some foxing, contemp. 1/2 russia, joints rubbed, gilt spines. Eaton 45-13 1978 £20

ALFIERI, VITTORIO   Panegirico di Plinio a Trajano, nuovamente trovato, e tradotto. Paris, 1789. Roy. 8vo., uncut, contemp. half calf. Howes 194-539 1978 £22

ALFIERI, VITTORIO   Tragedie. Firenze, 1855. 2 vols., cr. 8vo, 1/2 red morocc, 1 joint cracked, ex-lib., bdg. Eaton 45-15 1978 £5.50

ALFIERI, VITTORIO   Vita Di Vittorio Alfieri Da Asti Scritta De Esso. Roma 1811-1810. 2 vols. in 1, 1/4 leather, signature in ink of H. C. Robinson, signt. of A. E. Street. Eaton 45-14 1978 £10

ALFONSO X, KING OF CASTILE   Libros Del Saber De Astronomia. Madrid, 1863-1867. 5 vols., color plts., facsimiles, tables, text illus., tall folio, modern Spanish tree calf with labels, only modern ed. Salloch 345-6 1978 $500

ALFONSO DE LIGUORI   Operetti spirituali. Napoli, 1763. Engraved frontis., worn, 12mo. George's 635-1020 1978 £5

ALFRAGANUS   Elementa Astronomica. Amsterdam, 1669. 4to., 3 parts in 1 vol., contemp. marbled calf, gilt paneled back, worn, some light marginal waterstains, 1st ed. Gilhofer 74-2 1978 sFr 1,200

ALFRIEND, FRANK H.   The Life of Jefferson Davis. Cincinnati, 1868. Orig. binding, cover faded with some spotting, inner hinges cracking, clean. Hayman 71-116 1978 $10

ALGAROTTI, FRANCESO   Il Congreso di Citera Accresciute del alcune Lettere e del Giudizio d'Amore. Londra, 1774. 12mo., calf, woodcut, very good. King 7-125 1978 £15

ALGAROTTI, FRANCESO   Il Congresso di Citera. Parigi, 1787. 12mo., calf, rubbed, joints weak, marbled endpapers. King 7-126 1978 £15

ALGAROTTI, FRANCESCO   Lettere di Polianzo ad Ermogene intorno alla Traduzione dell'Eneide del Caro. Venezia, 1745. 8vo., calf, somewhat worn, vignette. King 7-123 1978 £20

ALGAROTTI, FRANCESCO   Lettere Filologiche. 1826. Sm. 8vo., marbled bds., calf spine, portrait frontispiece, very good. King 7-127 1978 £15

ALGAROTTI, FRANCESCO   Il Newtonianismo per le Dame ovvero Dialoghi sopra La Luce e i Colori. Napoli, 1737. 4to., contemp. vellum, frontispiece, very fine, tall, unpressed, first ed. P. M. Hill 142-16 1978 £185

ALGAROTTI, FRANCESCO   Saggio Sopra la Pittura. Livorno, 1763. Sm. 8vo., contemp. bds., rare ed. Gilhofer 74-23 1978 sFr 200

ALGAROTTI, FRANCESCO   Saggio sopra la Vita di Orazio. Venezia, 1760. 8vo., patterned paper wrappers, backstrip missing, good. King 7-124 1978 £15

ALGEMEENE Literatuur Geschiedenis... Utrecht-Antw.-Brussel-Gent-Leuven, n.d. (ab. 1950). 5 vols., lg. 8vo., half cloth, plts. in color. Van der Peet H-64-366 1978 Dfl 85

ALGER, HORATIO   Luke Walton or The Chicago Newsboy. Philadelphia, n.d. Color plates, plate on cover with decorations, very good. Victoria 34-18 1978 $15

ALGER, HORATIO   The Telegraph Boy. Philadelphia, n.d. Illus., very good, firm. Victoria 34-17 1978 $15

ALGER, R. A.   Ship Canal at Sabine Pass, Texas. Washington, 1898. Folding maps, some in color, boards, leather label. Jenkins 116-723 1978 $65

ALGRANATI, GINA   Basilicata e Calabria. 1929. Illus., in Italian. Austin 79-21 1978 $27.50

ALKEN, H.   The Art and Practise of Etching; with Directions for Other Methods of Light and Entertaining Engraving. 1849. Sm. 4to., plts., some minor spotting, orig. cloth. Quaritch 983-148 1978 $200

ALLAIN, E.   Pliny le Jeune et ses Heritiers. 1902. Vol. 3 only, buckram. Allen 234-760 1978 $7.50

ALLAN, GEORGE   Life With Critical Notices of Sir Walter Scott's Writings. Edinburgh, 1834. 1st. ed., frontis portrait, 2 other plts., orig. half calf, black label, leading hinge little weak, otherwise good. Jarndyce 16-1019 1978 £28

ALLAN, J. T.   Nebraska and Its Settlers:... Omaha, 1883. Orig. printed pictorial wr., 1st ed. Ginsberg 14-704 1978 $125

ALLAN, P. B. M.   The Book Hunter at Home. London, 1922. One of 500, 2nd ed. Battery Park 1-233 1978 $35

ALLAN, P. B. M.   The Book-Hunter at Home. London, (1922). Orig. cloth-backed bds., 2nd ed., rev'd., 1 of 500 copies. MacManus 238-851 1978 $25

ALLAN, ROBERT   Evening Hours: Poems and Songs. Glasgow, 1836. 12mo, orig. purple cloth (faded), pr. paper labels (bit soiled), 1st ed. Ximenes 47-1 1978 $40

ALLARD, CHRISTOPHE   Promenade au Canada et aux Etats-Unis. Paris, 1878. Original printed wr., 1st ed. Ginsberg 14-3 1978 $50

ALLARDYCE, ALEXANDER   The City of Sunshine: A Novel. 1877. 1st. ed., 3 vols., half titles, orig. half calf, red & black labels, v.g. Jarndyce 16-251 1978 £55

ALLASON, THOMAS   Picturesque Views on the Antiquities of Pola in Istria. London, 1819. Lg. folio, bds., cloth spine, rubbed, plts., nice, first ed. King 7-333 1978 £175

ALLDRIDGE, LIZZIE   The Queen's House. A Narrative. London, 1886. 3 vols., orig. cloth, 1st ed., bookplts., otherwise very good. MacManus 238-332 1978 $85

ALLEMAGNE, HENRY RENE D'   Les Accessoires du Costume et du Mobilier Depuis le Treizieme Jusqu'au Milieu au Dixneuvieme Siecle. Paris, 1928. 3 vols., 4to., plts., orig. bds., cloth backs, recased, ltd. to 1,000 copies. Quaritch 983-62 1978 $550

ALLEMAN, TILLIE   At Gettysburg or What a Girl Saw and Heard of the Battle. New York, 1889. Map taped at seams. Bell Wiley's copy. Broadfoot 46-3 1978 $40

ALLEN, ALBERT H.   Arkansas Imprints 1821-1876. New York, 1947. 8vo., orig. cloth, 1st ed. MacManus 238-852 1978 $17.50

ALLEN, ALBERT H.   Dakota Imprints 1858-1889. New York, 1947. 8vo., orig. cloth, 1st ed. MacManus 238-853 1978 $17.50

ALLEN, ALEXANDER VIETS GRISWOLD   Life and Letters of Phillips Brooks. New York, 1901. Illus., 3 vols. in 5, 8vo., orig. bds., buckram backs, bindings dust-soiled, 1 of 250 lg. paper copies signed by author. Morrill 241-5 1978 $12.50

ALLEN, C.   Cabbage, Cauliflower & Allied Vegetables. 1901. 12mo, orig. cloth. Book Chest 17-451 1978 $10

ALLEN, C. D.   American Book-Plates. London, 1895. Newly rebound in cloth, t.e.g., illus. Battery Park 1-285 1978 $35

ALLEN, E. C.   The Out-of-Doors. Toronto, 1932. Etchings by R. Horsfall. Hood 117-605 1978 $7.50

ALLEN, FREDERICK LEWIS   The Lords of Creation. New York, 1935. Illus., 1st ed. Biblo BL781-79 1978 $9.50

ALLEN, FREDERICK LEWIS   Since Yesterday. New York, 1940. Illus., 1st ed. Biblo 251-18 1978 $15

ALLEN, GEORGE   The Complaint of Mexico, and Conspiracy Against Liberty. Boston, 1843. Sewn, 1st ed., rare. Jenkins 116-18 1978 $225

ALLEN, GEORGE HOWARD   Individual Initiative in Business. 1950. Austin 80=400 1978 $12.50

ALLEN, GRANT   Dumaresq's Daughter. A Novel. London, 1891. 3 vols., orig. cloth, 1st ed., lib. labels on 2 covers, but very good, scarce. MacManus 238-158 1978 $90

ALLEN, H. T.   Tunis' Illustrated Guide to Niagara. Niagara Falls, 1877. Revised, card cover, illus., folding map. Hood's 115-782 1978 $35

ALLEN, HARRISON   Studies in the Facial Region. (Philadelphia), 1875. Woodcuts, 8vo. Morrill 239-7 1978 $7.50

ALLEN, HERVEY   Action at Aquila. New York, 1938. Fine in chipped d.w. Desmarais B-19 1978 $7.50

ALLEN, HERVEY   Anthony Adverse. Mount Vernon: The Limited Editions Club, 1937. Lg. 8vo., 3 vols., illus., orig. cloth, pub. box, 1 of 1500 sets, signed by illus., fine. MacManus 238-813 1978 $25

ALLEN, HERVEY   Christmas Epithalamium. New York, Christmas, 1925. 295 copies, handmade paper, uncut, bds., d.j., fine. Limestone 9-5 1978 $15

ALLEN, HERVEY   Israfel: The Life and Times of Edgar Allan Poe. New York, 1926. Tall 8vo, 2 vols., red cloth, t.e.g., d.w. with minor chips and tears, boxed, fine, 1st issue, 1st ed. Desmarais 1-14 1978 $50

ALLEN, IVAN   Atlanta From the Ashes. Atlanta, 1928. Illus. from drwgs., 8vo., nice, #17 of a ltd. ed. Morrill 239-399 1978 $12.50

ALLEN, J. A.   The American Museum Congo Expedition Collection of Insectivora. New York, 1922. 8vo, orig. cloth, orig. wr., plates. Book Chest 17-9 1978 $18.50

ALLEN, J. A.   A List of the Birds of Massachusetts with Annotations. Salem, 1878. 8vo, orig. cloth, 1st ed. Book Chest 17-11 1978 $22

ALLEN, J. A.   Primates Collected By The American Museum
Congo Expedition. New York, 1925. Chipped wr., 8vo, orig. cloth, plts.,
excellent. Book Chest 17-10 1978 $32

ALLEN, JAMES LANE   Aftermath. 1896. 135 pages. Austin 82-37
1978 $12.50

ALLEN, JAMES LANE   The Bride of the Mistletoe. 1909. First ed.
Austin 82-38 1978 $12.50

ALLEN, JAMES LANE   A Cathedral Singer. 1916. Colored frontis., first
ed. Austin 82-40 1978 $17.50

ALLEN, JAMES LANE   The Choir Invisible. 1897. First ed. Austin 82-
42 1978 $12.50

ALLEN, JAMES LANE   The Choir Invisible. (1897). 1898. Austin 82-
41 1978 $8.50

ALLEN, JAMES LANE   The Choir Invisible. 1900. Illus. Austin 82-43
1978 $11

ALLEN, JAMES LANE   Flute and Violin and Other Kentucky Tales and
Romances. 1891. First ed., bookplate, inscription of former owner. Austin 82-44
1978 $27.50

ALLEN, JAMES LANE   The Heroine in Bronze. 1912. First ed., inscribed by Allen. Austin 82-45 1978 $47.50

ALLEN, JAMES LANE   A Kentucky Cardinal. 1895. Illus., third printing. Austin 82-46 1978 $12.50

ALLEN, JAMES LANE   The Landmark. 1925. First edition. Austin 82-
48 1978 $12.50

ALLEN, JAMES LANE   The Mettle of the Pasture. 1903. Austin 82-
49 1978 $7.50

ALLEN, JAMES LANE   The Reign of Law. 1900. 385 pages. Austin 82-
50 1978 $7.50

ALLEN, JOSEPH   Battles of the British Navy. London, 1853.
2 vols., illus., nice set. MacManus 239-1733 1978 $17.50

ALLEN, JOSEPH HENRY   The Statesman and The Man. Washington, 1848.
Front wrapper soiled, lacks back wrapper. Hayman 71-7 1978 $7.50

ALLEN, LEWIS F.   The American Herd Book Containing Pedigrees of
Short-Horn Cattle... Buffalo, 1875. Vols. 7 & 8, 2 vols. in 1 as issued, clean,
minor dampstain, orig. binding. Hayman 71-105 1978 $10

ALLEN, LEWIS F.   The American Herd Book Containing Pedigrees of
Short-Horn Cattle... Buffao, 1877. Vol. 2, 2nd. ed., revised & corrected, cl.,
orig. binding. Hayman 71-104 1978 $10

ALLEN, PAUL   Journal of the Times. (Baltimore, 1818-1819).
Orig. bds., cloth. MacManus 239-389 1978 $35

ALLEN, RICHARD L.   The American Farm Book. New York, 1850.
Orig. cloth, fine, illus. MacManus 239-13 1978 $35

ALLEN, RICHARD L.   Last Letters of Richard L. Allen. New York,
1871. Cover little worn, faded & inner hinges cracking. Hayman 73-9 1978
$8.50

ALLEN, SAMUEL ADAMS   My Own Home and Fireside;.... Philadelphia,
1846. Lacks spine, front cover detached, 12mo. Greene 78-320 1978 $155

ALLEN, THOMAS   The History and Antiquities of the Parish of Lambeth. 1826. 1st. ed., frontis, 2 folding maps & numerous plts., many hand-
coloured, rebound in half green morocco, marbled bds., a.e.g., sm. repair to
1 map, some browning otherwise good copy. Jarndyce 16-819 1978 £35

ALLEN, THOMAS   Memorial of the President and Directors of the
Pacific Railroad. Jefferson City, 1852. Sewn, uncut. Ginsberg 14-859 1978
$125

ALLEN, WILLIAM   A Narrative of the Expedition Sent by Her
Majesty's Government to the River Niger, in 1841 Under the Command of Capt.
H. D. Trotter. London, 1848. Illus. with wood-engr., fldg. map, 2 vols.,
orig. embossed cloth, 1st ed. Argosy Special-3 1978 $175

ALLEN, WINNIE   Pioneering in Texas: True Stories of the Early
Days. Dallas, 1935. 1st ed., illus. Jenkins 116-20 1978 $7.50

ALLEN, ZACHARIAH   Bi-Centenary of the Burning of Providence in
1676. Providence, 1876. 8vo., fine, 1st ed., orig. cloth. Morrill 241-488
1978 $7.50

ALLEN'S Illustrated Guide to Niagara. Buffalo, 1880. Lg. fldg. map, fine
cond., pict. wr., 1st (?) ed. Butterfield 21-302 1978 $25

ALLEN-OLNEY, M.   The Private Life of Galileo. London, 1870.
8vo., ads, illus., orig. cloth, gilt, uncut, very good copy. Norman 5-121 1978
$50

ALLENDE, INES L. C. DE   Cytology of the Human Vagina. New York,
1950. D.j. Rittenhouse 49-7 1976 $15

ALLENDY, RENE   Les Reves et Leur Interpretation Psychanalytique.
Paris, 1926. Sm. 8vo., orig. prtd. wrs., backstrip chipped, somewhat browned,
good uncut copy, pres. inscr. from author. Zeitlin 245-5 1978 $75

ALLERS, W.   Rund um die Erde. Stuttgart-Berlin, n.d.
(c.1920). Folio, half cloth, plts., illus., orig. covers. Van der Peet 127-271
1978 Dfl 195

ALLESTREE, RICHARD   The Art of Contentment. Oxford, 1675. 1st
ed., engraved f.p., t.p. vignette, 8vo., contemp. tree calf, joints tender, very
good, scarce. Victoria 34-19 1978 $75

ALLESTREE, RICHARD   The Causes of the Decay of Christian Piety.
London, 1669-70. 8vo, contemp. calf, spine worn. Traylen 88-95 1978 £21

ALLESTREE, RICHARD   The Gentleman's Calling. 1696. Orig. engraved
title-pg., orig. blank leaf, contemp. panelled calf, gilt spine, nice copy.
Fenning 32-7 1978 £28.50

ALLEY, FELIX E.   Random Thoughts and the Musings of a Moun-
taineer. Salisbury, 1941. Pres. copy from author, cover faded. Broadfoot 50-
5 1978 $30

ALLHANDS, J. L.   Gringo Builders. N.P., 1931. 1st ed., signed
by author. MacManus 239-1895 1978 $25

ALLIBONE, SAMUEL AUSTIN Critical Dictionary of English Literature and
British & American Authors. 1885. 3 vols., imp. 8vo., half mor., rubbed.
Eaton 45-16 1978 £30

ALLINGHAM, HELEN   Happy England. London, 1903. Plts. in color.
Biblo BL781-610 1978 $12.50

ALLINGHAM, MARGERY   More work for the Undertaker. 1948. Very good,
d.w., first English ed. Bell Book 16-224 1978 £7.50

ALLINGHAM, MARGERY   Traitor's Purse. 1941. Very good, worn d.w.,
first English ed. Bell Book 16-225 1978 £17.50

ALLINGHAM, WILLIAM   Day and Night Songs. 1860. Sm. 8vo., 1st ed.,
woodcuts, orig. green cloth, uncut. Quaritch 979-2 1978 $220

ALLINSON, E. P.   Philadelphia, 1681-1887... Philadelphia,
1887. MacManus 239-1353 1978 $17.50

ALLISON, ROBERT   Lectures and Addresses. 1913. Cloth. Eaton 45-17 1978 £5

ALLOM, THOMAS   China, In A Series of Views... (1843). Engraved vignette title, engraved plts., 4 vols. in 2, 4to, contemp. green morocco, sides tooled in gold, spines gilt, g.e., slight foxing in few plts.   Edwards 1012-180 1978 £180

ALLOM, THOMAS   Forty-Six Views of Tyrolese Scenery. London, n.d. 4to, coloured engraved vignette title-pg., coloured engraved view, folding engraved map, newly rebound in green half morocco, marbled bds., gilt, new endpapers.   Deighton 5-110 1978 £280

ALLOM, THOMAS   Views in the Tyrol. With Letterpress Descriptions, by a Companion of Hofer. (1836). 4to., map, plts., some foxing, marginal spotting of plts., contemp. half calf.   Quaritch 983-283 1978 $300

ALLORI, ANGELO CALLED IL BRONZINO
Please turn to
BRONZINO, ANGELO

ALLOTT, ROBERT   Englands Parnassus. N.P., 1600. Sm. 8 vo., old russia, gilt, 1st ed.   Quaritch Summer, 1978-40 1978 $8,000

ALLSTON, WASHINGTON   Monaldi: A Tale. Boston, 1841. Orig. cloth, 1st ed., bind. B, covers slightly faded, else very fine.   MacManus 238-418 1978 $50

ALLSTROM, OLIVER   Poet and Priest: The Story of the Flag Incident at Houston, Texas, U.S.A.   Houston, 1921. Printed wr.   Jenkins 116-569 1978 $35

ALLUSIONS to Shakespeare, A. D. 1592-1693. London, 1886. 2 vols. in 1, lg. 8vo., hinges partly cracked, pres.   Morrill 241-528 1978 $15

ALLWOERDEN, HENRICUS AB   Historia Michaelis Serveti. Helmstadt, (1727-1728). 4to., port., old bds., 1st ed.   Gilhofer 74-77 1978 sFr 1,300

ALMANACH de la Noblesse du Royaumde de France Pour l'Annee 1848.   Paris, 1848. 8vo., cloth.   Van der Peet H-64-262 1978 Dfl 55

ALMANACH Voor het Verstand en Hart voor het jaar 1802.   Amsterdam, 1802. Engraved plates, 16mo., orig. bds.   George's 635-528 1978 £7.50

AN ALMANACK, Calculated for the Island of Dominica, 1811. Roseau, (1811). 12mo, contemp. wrapper, worn, preserved in modern cloth folder.   Edwards 1012-710 1978 £45

AN Almanack For the Year 1801. (?St. John's, 1801). 12mo, front portion of contemp. wrapper only, worn, preserved in modern cloth folder.   Edwards 1012-702 1978 £60

ALMONTE, JUAN N   Amparo Promovido por la Senora Dolores Quesada de Almonte,....   Mexico, 1879.   Jenkins 116-21 1978 $45

ALONSO y de los Ruizes de Fontecha, Juan   Diez Previlegios Para Mugeres Prenadas.   1606. 8vo., armorial device of the Duchess of Gandia, orig. limp vellum, some browning, foxing & dampstains, 1st & apparently the only ed. Zeitlin 245-6 1978 $1,650

ALOTTI, W.   Thesaurus bibliorum omnern vitae utriusque antidotum secundum veteris et novi instrumenti veritaten et historiam succinete complectens.   1612. Title in red, some staining, headlines shaved, calf, blind tooled, 8vo.   George's 635-1022 1978 £6.50

ALPHABETISCHES Sachregister von den in den Jahrgangen des Kalenders fur den Sachsischen Berg-und Hutten-Mann und Zugehorigen Jahrbuches von 1827 bis 1840 ... Dresden, (ca. 1840). 8vo., old cloth, copy belonged to Raphael Pumpelly. Morrill 239-286 1978 $15

ALSBERG, HENRY G.   The American Guide. New York, (1949). Maps, 4 vols.   Biblo 247-6 1978 $15

ALSBERG, HENRY G.   The American Guide. New York, (1949). Cl., fine copy in d.j., d.j. shows negligible signs of wear.   Hayman 71-21 1978 $10

ALSTON, J. W.   Hints to Young Practitioners in the Study of Landscape Painting...to Which are Added Instructions in the Art of Painting on Velvet. (London, 1805). 2nd ed., 8vo., coloured and plain plts., some staining, bds., rebacked, uncut.   Quaritch 983-149 1978 $65

ALTER, J. CECIL   James Bridger: Trapper, Frontiersman, Scout and Guide. Salt Lake City, 1925. Illus., original cloth, 1st ed., limited to 1000 copies signed by author.   Ginsberg 14-58 1978 $85

ALTER, J. CECIL   James Bridger, Trapper, Frontiersman, Scout and Guide. Salt Lake City, (1925). Ltd. to 1000 copies, signed.   Biblo 247-183 1978 $87.50

ALTFIELD, E. MILTON   The Jew's Struggle For Religious and Civil Liberty in Maryland. Baltimore, 1924. Illus.   Baldwins' 51-273 1978 $10

ALTON, H.   The King's Customs, an Account of Maritime Revue and Contraband Traffic in England, Scotland and Ireland to 1800. 1908. Illus., 8vo.   George's 635-276 1978 £6.50

ALTSHUL, FRANK   Let No Wave Engulf. 1941.   Austin 80-401 1978 $8.50

ALVARA, By Which King Joao VI Confers on His First-Born Son Dom Pedro, the title Royal Prince of the United Kingdom of Portugal, Brasil and Algarves.   Rio de Janeiro, 1817. Sm. folio, orig. cloth.   Edwards 1012-614 1978 £35

ALVAREZ, WALTER CLEMENT   The Mechanics of the Digestive Tract.   New York, 1939. Second ed., signed by author.   Rittenhouse 49-8 1976 $20

ALVORD, C. W.   Invitation Serieuse aux Habitants des Illinois... Providence, 1908. Repr. from orig. ed...Philadelphia, 1772, ltd. to 100 copies. Biblo BL781-38 1978 $34.50

ALZOG, JOHN   Manual of Universal Church History. Cincinnati, 1874-1878. 3 vols., 8vo., orig. cloth, ex-lib., 1st Amer. ed.   Morrill 241-7 1978 $35

AMBASSADES Memorables de la Compagnie de Indes Orientales des Provinces Unies... Amsterdam, 1680. Folding map, engraved plts., folio, calf, rebacked, one leaf missing, 8vo.   Edwards 1012-201 1978 £270

AMBERG, HANS CHRISTIAN   Fuldstaendig Tydsk og Dansk Ordbog.   Copenhagen, 1787-97. 1st. ed., 2 vols., 8vo, contemp. calf, worn, 2 leaves loose, one with slight loss of text.   Hannas 54-182 1978 £10

AMBLER, CHARLES HENRY   A History of Transportation in the Ohio Valley... Glendale, 1932. Illus., very fine.   MacManus 239-24 1978 $37.50

AMBLER, HENRY LOVEJOY   Facts, Fads and Fancies About Teeth.   Cleveland, 1900.   Rittenhouse 49-9 1976 $15

AMBLER, I. W.   Truth is Stranger than Fiction. Boston, (1873). 8vo., orig. cloth.   Morrill 241-8 1978 $10

AMBROSE, ISAAC   Prima & Ultima. 1640. 1st. ed., engraved title-pg., 4to, old calf-backed bds., worn at corners, sound, light foxing throughout, very good copy of scarce volume.   Fenning 32-9 1978 £85

AMERICAN ACADEMY IN ROME   Supplementary Papers. 1905. Vol. I only, folio, plt.   Allen 234-25 1978 $10

AMERICAN ACADEMY OF POLITICAL AND SOCIAL SCIENCE   Farm Relief. (1929).   Austin 80-577 1978 $12.50

AMERICAN Agriculturist, for the Farm, Garden & Household. New York, 1879. Illus., 4to., orig. wrs.   Morrill 241-9 1978 $10

AMERICAN ASSOC. FOR A DEMOCRATIC GERMANY   Der Neue Kampf Um Freiheit. New York City, n.d. Paper, in German.   Austin 79-276 1978 $20

AMERICAN BOOKPLATE SOCIETY   First Year Book. Kansas City, 1915. 8vo., bds., edges rubbed, one of 210 copies, illus. Battery Park 1-286 1978 $35

AMERICAN COUNCIL OF LEARNED SOCIETIES   Studies in the History of Culture. 1942. Allen 234-26 1978 $7.50

AMERICAN ECONOMIC ASSOC.   Readings in the Social Control of Industry. 1942. Ex-lib. Austin 80-402 1978 $17.50

AMERICAN ECONOMIC ASSOC.   Readings in the Theory of Income Distribution. Philadelphia, 1946. Illus. Austin 80-403 1978 $27.50

AMERICAN FRUIT DRIER MANUFACTURING CO.   Dr. Ryder's American Fruit Drier or Pneumatic Evaporator. (Chambersburg, 1881). Wrappers, slightly soiled. Hayman 71-89 1978 $12.50

AMERICAN Historical Association, Annual Report 1903, Vol. I. Washington, 1904. Bell Wiley's copy. Broadfoot 46-472 1978 $10

AMERICAN Historical Association, Annual Report 1904. Washington, 1905. Bell Wiley's copy. Broadfoot 46-472a 1978 $10

AMERICAN IRISH HISTORICAL SOCIETY   The Journal of the American Irish Historical Society. 1928. Vol. XXVII for year 1928. Austin 79-24 1978 $20

AMERICAN IRISH HISTORICAL SOCIETY   The Journal of the American Irish Historical Society. 1932. Vol. XXX. Austin 79-25 1978 $20

THE AMERICAN Joe Miller. Philadelphia, 1841. Illus., 16mo., orig. stamped cloth, engrav. frontis. Wolfe 39-23 1978 $55

AMERICAN Journal of Conchology. Philadelphia, 1871-2. 8vo., orig. cloth, orig. issue in wr., plates (some loose), 4 vols. Book Chest 17-13 1978 $50

THE AMERICAN Merchant: Or, the History of Jacky and Molly. London, n.d. (c. 1792). 3 x 3-1/2 in., orig. pict. wrs., woodcuts. Americanist 102-7 1978 $50

AMERICAN Petroleum, Supply and Demand. New York, 1925. 8vo., 1st ed., orig. cloth. Morrill 241-11 1978 $7.50

THE AMERICAN Phrenological Journal and Miscellany. Philadelphia, Oct. 1838-March 1839. Vol. I, Nos. 1-6, 8vo., old calf-backed bds., covers loose, ex-lib. Morrill 239-8 1978 $10

AMERICAN Primer, or an Easy Introduction to Spelling & Reading. Philadelphia, 1813. 4th improved ed., sm. oval woodcuts, sm. 12mo., orig. pic. wrs. Argosy Special-4 1978 $75

AMERICAN Slavery As It Is. New York, 1839. 8vo., unbound, 1st ed. Morrill 241-616 1978 $10

AMERICAN TYPE FOUNDERS CO.   Illustrated Catalogue & Price List of Printing Machinery & Supplies, Wood Goods & Wood Type, Fine Printing Inks. Everything for the Printer. N.P. (New York), 1897. 8vo., illus., orig. cloth, very good. Americanist 103-7 1978 $85

AMERICAN TYPE FOUNDERS CO.   Specimen Book and Catalogue. Jersey City, 1923. Illus., thick 4to., orig. cloth. Morrill 241-548 1978 $25

AMERICANA and Canadiana. New York, 1925. 8vo., orig. wrs., library of the late W. W. C. Wilson. Morrill 241-20 1978 $8.50

AMERICANS in Paris. 1920-30. Pict. wrs., illus., very fine. Battery Park 1-312 1978 $35

AMERVAL, E. d'   La Grande Diablerie. Paris, 1884. Sm. 8vo., cloth portfolio, ltd. ed. of 1000 numbered copies, signed. Van der Peet H-64-413 1978 Dfl 100

AMES, FISHER   A Sketch of the Character of Alexander Hamilton. (Boston, 1804). Disbound, sm. lib. label, rare. Hayman 72-24 1978 $20

AMES, J. H.   Lincoln, The Capital of Nebraska:.... Lincoln, 1870. Orig. we., 1st ed. Ginsberg 14-703 1978 $125

AMES, NATHANIEL   An Astronomical Diary: Or Almanack, for 1770. Boston, (1769). Sewed, sm. piece torn from corner of 1st. leaf, affecting few letters. Hayman 71-8 1978 $20

AMES, NATHANIEL   An Astronomical Diary; or Almanack for the Year of Our Lord Christ 1771. Boston, (1770). Sm. 12mo., unpaginated, some page browning, fine copy, delicate. Current 24-65 1978 $210

AMES, O.   Orchidaceae, Illustrations and Studies of... Fascicle VII, Pogonia and its allies in northeastern U.S. and other papers. Boston, 1922. Plates by Blanche Ames, 8vo., orig. cloth. Book Chest 17-14 1978 $35

AMES, O.   Schedulae Orchidianae. Boston, 1922. Wr., orig. cloth, 8vo. Book Chest 17-15 1978 $13.50

AMHERST, ALICIA MARGARET TYSSEN - , HON. MRS. EVELYN CECIL
Please turn to
ROCKLEY, ALICIA MARGARET (TYSSEN-AMHERST) CECIL, BARONESS

AMHERST OF HACKNEY, LORD   The Amherst Tablets, Being an Account of the Babylonian Inscriptions in the Collection of the Right Hon. Lord Amherst of Hackney, at Didlington Hall... 1908. Roy. 4to., plts., illus., bds., cloth back. Quaritch 983-1 1978 $50

AMHERST College. A Record of the Class of 1831. Hartford, 1866. 12mo., orig. cloth wrs., ex-lib. Morrill 239-505 1978 $7.50

AMI De La Jeunesse. Paris, 1825-35. 11 vols., sm. woodcuts, 24mo., contemp. gray 1/2 calf. Argosy Special-5 1978 $350

AMIS, KINGSLEY   Bright November: Poems. Fortune Press, (1947). Near fine, unopened, scarce, first English ed. Bell Book 17-008 1978 £22.50

AMMEN, DANIEL   The Atlantic Coast. New York, 1883. Bell Wiley's copy. Broadfoot 46-5 1978 $10

AMMIANUS, MARCELLINUS c. 330-391   Rerum Gestarum. Paris, 1681. Map, folio, contemp. calf, good. Howes 194-523 1978 £45

AMONG the Silver Seams. Georgetown, 1886. Plates, original printed wr., 1st ed. Ginsberg 14-249 1978 $75

AMORON, CALVIN   The French Canadians in New England. Springfield, 1892. Austin 79-26 1978 $27.50

AMORY, THOMAS   The Life of John Buncle, Esq... 1766. 2 vols., 8vo, 1st. complete ed., contemp. calf rebacked. Hannas 54-1 1978 £65

AMORY, THOMAS   The Life of John Buncle, Esq. London, 1825. 3 vols., sm. 8vo., contemp. bds., calf backs & corners, fr. hinge of Vol. 3 cracked, signature of Curtis in each vol. Morrill 239-359 1978 $27.50

AMOSS, HARRY   Sunday-Monday, Selected Poems. Toronto, 1947. Ex-lib. Hood 117-777 1978 $7.50

LES AMOURS de Mr. Vieux Bois. (c. 1825). Title worn, mounted, drawings, oblong 8vo., half calf, worn. George's 635-1167 1978 £7.50

AMPERE, ANDRE-MARIE   Description d'un Appareil Electro-Dynamique, Construit Par M. Ampere. Paris, 1824. Disbound, 8vo., cloth fldr., 1st ed. Offenbacher 30-3 1978 $300

AMPERE, ANDRE MARIE   Essai sur la Philosophie des Sciences. Paris, 1834. Part I, 8vo., fldg. tables, orig. prtd. wrs., uncut, soiled & spine repaired, occas. light foxing, dampstaining, but very good copy, 1st ed. Norman 5-*2 1978 $150

AMSDICK, P.   Tunbridge Wells, and Its Neighbourhood, Illustrated by a Series of Etchings, and Historical Descriptions... 1810. Roy. 4to., lg. paper, frontis., plts., some plts. slightly spotted, half calf. Quaritch 983-284 1978 $250

AMUNDSEN, ROALD   "The North West Passage"... London, 1908. 1st. English ed., 2 vols., lg. 8vo, plts., illus., orig. green cloth, gilt, trifle shaken in binding. Deighton 5-154 1978 £60

THE AMUSING Instructer. 1727. 12mo., contemp. calf, joints and spine cracked, with half-title. Howes 194-137 1978 £21

ANACREON   Anacreon done into English out of the Original Greek. Oxford, 1683. 1st ed. 8 vo., fine, orig. calf. Quaritch Summer, 1978-2 1978 $500

ANACREON   Anacreon, Done Into English Out of the Original Greek. Oxford, 1683. Thin 8vo, contemp. calf, gilt spine. Traylen 88-214 1978 £120

ANACREON   Odes. 1800. 4to., new buckram. Allen 234-1508 1978 $12.50

THE ANALYSIS of the Ballance of Power: Wherein Its Necessity, Origin and History is Examin'd, and Deduc'd From the Common Principles of Justice and Society. 1720. 1st. ed., 8vo, disbound. Hannas 54-2 1978 £12.50

ANALYTICUS   Jews are Like That! 1928. Illus. Austin 79-28 1978 $12.50

ANAND, MULK RAJ   The Lost Child and other Stories. 1934. Ltd. to 200 copies, signed by author, wood-engraved frontis. by Gill, 12mo., orig. wrappers, slightly faded. George's 635-171 1978 £5

ANANIA, GIOVANNI LORENZO D'   La Universale Fabrica del Mondo,.... Naples, 1573. 4to, vellum, t.p. has marginal repairs, light spots, marginal annotations by old hand, extremely rare 1st ed. Gilhofer 75-4 1978 SFr 1,500

ANBUREY, THOMAS   Travels Through the Interior Parts of America, in a Series of Letters. London, 1789. 2 vols., 1st ed., octavo, bound in dark blue half levant, map and all plts. Totteridge 29-5 1978 $575

ANBUREY, THOMAS   Travels Through the Interior Parts of America in a Series of Letters. London, 1789. 1st ed., 2 vols., illus., plts., cloth. MacManus 239-26 1978 $100

ANCIENT Spanish Ballads; Historical and Romantic. London, 1841. 4to., contemp. mor., corners rubbed, a.e.g., fine. MacManus 238-318 1978 $60

ANDERSEN, HANS CHRISTIAN   Fairy Tales. London, 1873. 1st English ed., 4to., a.e.g., orig. green cloth, elaborate gilt & black decor's, colored frontis, chromo-litho. plts., spine faded, interior generally fine, previous owner's inscrip., very good copy. Current 24-1 1978 $100

ANDERSEN, HANS CHRISTIAN   The Improvisatore: or, Life in Italy. 1845. 2 vols., 8vo., 1st ed., contemp. half calf, gilt backs. Quaritch 979-3 1978 $110

ANDERSEN, HANS CHRISTIAN   The Nightingale. New York, 1898. Thin sq. 8vo., illus. by Mary J. Newill, binding worn. Battery Park 1-205 1978 $25

ANDERSEN, HANS CHRISTIAN   Only a Fiddler! 1847. 1st. ed., 3 vols., half calf, good. Jarndyce 16-253 1978 £40

ANDERSEN, HANS CHRISTIAN   Only A Fiddler! and O. T. or Life in Denmark. London, 1847. 3 vols., 1st ed. in English, spine labels chipped, text clean and fresh, very good, rare. Victoria 34-21 1978 $150

ANDERSEN, HANS CHRISTIAN   The Poet's Bazaar. 1846. 1st. ed., 3 vols., frontis portrait, half calf, red & green labels, slight rubbing of heads of spines, otherwise v.g. Jarndyce 16-252 1978 £30

ANDERSEN, HANS CHRISTIAN   Stories and Fairy Tales. 1893. Lg. paper ed., hand made paper, ltd. to 300 copies, illus., 2 vols., roy. 8vo., orig. cream buckram, soiled. George's 635-151 1978 £25

ANDERSEN, HANS CHRISTIAN   Stories from Hans Andersen. London, (1911). Illus. by Edmund Dulac, 1 of 750 copies signed by Dulac, folio, full brown mor., gilt fillets, silk endpapers, edges extra gilt, cloth slipcase, color plts., fine. Houle 10-96 1978 $695

ANDERSEN, HANS CHRISTIAN   Hans Andersen's Story Book. New York, 1849. 1st Amer. ed., memoir by Mary Howitt, 12mo, binding quite worn, text very good. Victoria 34-22 1978 $25

ANDERSEN, HANS CHRISTIAN   Wonderful Stories for Children. London, 1846. 1st ed., color plates, excellent, almost fine. Victoria 34-23 1978 $250

ANDERSON, A. J.   The Romance of a Friar and a Nun. New York, 1909. Illus. Biblo 247-367 1978 $17.50

ANDERSON, ALEXANDER   A Brief Catalogue of Books Illustrated with Engravings by Dr. Alexander Anderson with a Biographical Sketch. New York, 1885. One of 100 copies, orig. binding. Americanist 102-8 1978 $75

ANDERSON, C. L. G.   Arizona as a Health Resort. Hagerstown, 1890. Original printed wr., 1st ed. Ginsberg 14-5 1978 $35

ANDERSON, CHARLES   An Address Delivered Before the Society of Alumni of Miami University, at Their Anniversary, August 13th, 1840. Oxford, 1840. Disbound. Hayman 73-489 1978 $17.50

ANDERSON, DAVID   Notes of the Flood at the Red River, 1852 by the Bishop of Rupert's Land. London, (1853). Fine copy in orig. binding. Hood 117-874 1978 $200

ANDERSON, EVELYN   Hammer or Anvil. London, 1945. Pulp paper. Biblo 251-308 1978 $15

ANDERSON, EPHRAIM MC D.   Memoirs; Historical and Personal; Including the Campaigns of the First Missouri Confederate Brigade. Saint Louis, 1868. Cloth, faded with some spotting and some wear, rare. Hayman 72-118 1978 $125

ANDERSON, G. K.   The Literature of the Anglo-Saxons. Princeton, 1949. Maps, 8vo. Upcroft 12-7 1978 £7.50

ANDERSON, GEORGE BAKER   Landmarks of Rensselaer County. Syracuse, 1897. Tall thick 8vo., portrs., near-fine cond., all edges gilt. Butterfield 21-363 1978 $45

ANDERSON, J. P.   The Book of British Topography. London, 1881. Med. 8vo., orig. cloth. Forster 130-180 1978 £15

ANDERSON, J.W.   From the Plains to the Pulpit. Goose Creek, 1907. Illus., presentation copy signed by Mrs. J. W. Anderson, some outer wear. Jenkins 116-22 1978 $35

ANDERSON, JAMES   A Practical Treatise on Draining Bogs and Swampy Grounds... 1797. Woodcut illus., folding engraved plt., half title, 8vo, orig. bds., uncut, nice copy. Fenning 32-10 1978 £32.50

ANDERSON, JOHN   A History of Edinburgh from the Earliest Period to the Completion of the Half Century 1850. Edinburgh, 1856. 8vo., orig. cloth, cover very faded. K Books 244-4 1978 £10

ANDERSON, JOHN REDWOOD   English Fantasies. 1935. Very good, pres. copy inscribed by author, A.L.s. by author laid in, English first ed. Bell Book 16-007 1978 £8.50

ANDERSON, JOHN REDWOOD   Paris Symphony. London, 1947. 1st ed., d.j., very good or better. Limestone 9-7 1978 $13.50

ANDERSON, JOSEPH   History of the Soldiers' Monument in Waterbury, Conn. N.P., 1886. Illus., Bell Wiley's copy. Broadfoot 46-317 1978 $8

ANDERSON, M. D.   Animal Carvings in British Churches. Cambridge, 1938. Plts., 8vo. Upcroft 12-8 1978 £5

ANDERSON, MAXWELL   Valley Forge. Washington, 1934. Gray cloth, 1st ed., very good in mended d.j. Bradley 49-5 1978 $10

ANDERSON, ROBERT   An Artillery Officer in the Mexican War 1846-1847. New York, 1911. Illus., original cloth, 1st ed. Ginsberg 14-530 1978 $30

ANDERSON, RUFUS   The Close Communion of the Baptists, in Principle and Practice, Proved to be Unscriptural, and of a Bad Tendency. Salem, 1805. 8vo., orig. wr., 1st ed. Morrill 241-12 1978 $10

ANDERSON, SHERWOOD   The American County Fair. New York, 1930. Ltd. to 875 copies, v.g. Austin 82-1148 1978 $22.50

ANDERSON, SHERWOOD   Beyond Desire. New York, (1932). Orig. cloth, 1st ed., 1 of 165 copies signed by author, very good. MacManus 238-606 1978 $100

ANDERSON, SHERWOOD   Dark Laughter. New York, 1925. Orig. parchment-backed bds., 1st ed., 1 of 350 copies signed by author, parchment darkened, but nice. MacManus 238-604 1978 $75

ANDERSON, SHERWOOD   Hello Towns! New York, 1929. First U.S. ed., plts., half-inch tear at foot of upper joint, very good. Bell Book 16-008 1978 £12

ANDERSON, SHERWOOD   Hello Towns. 1929. first ed., brown cloth. Austin 82-1149 1978 $35

ANDERSON, SHERWOOD   Horses and Men. 1923. First ed., very good, d.j. Austin 82-54 1978 $27.50

ANDERSON, SHERWOOD   The Modern Writer. San Francisco, Lantern Press, 1925. Bds., bkplts., 1 of 1000 numbered copies. Dawson's 447-48 1978 $25

ANDERSON, SHERWOOD   Sherwood Anderson's Notebook. Containing Articles Written During the Author's Life as a Story Teller, and Notes of His Impressions from Life, Etc. New York, 1926. Orig. cloth-backed bds., pub. box, 1st ed., 1 of 225 signed copies, very good. MacManus 238-605 1978 $75

ANDERSON, SHERWOOD   Sherwood Anderson's Notebook. 1926. First ed., v.g., frayed d.j. Austin 82-1150 1978 $27.50

ANDERSON, SHERWOOD   A Story Teller's Story. New York, 1924. Orig. cloth, 1st ed., edges a little stained, else fine, d.j. MacManus 238-603 1978 $32.50

ANDERSON, SHERWOOD   Tar. 1926. First ed. Austin 82-1151 1978 $12.50

ANDERSON, SHERWOOD   The Triumph of the Egg. 1921. Illus., first ed. Austin 82-1152 1978 $17.50

ANDERSON, T.   Observations on the Employment, Education, and Habits of the Blind. London, 1837. 8vo., plt., pres. copy from author, orig. pr. bds. Quaritch 977-4 1978 $75

ANDERSON, V.   World Currents and Canada's Course. Toronto, 1937. Hood's 115-571 1978 $15

ANDERSON, WILLIAM   Descriptive and Historical Catalogue of a Collection of Japonese and Chinese Paintings in the British Museum. London, 1886. Cloth, some wear, hinges a little weak, endpapers browned. Dawson's 449-102 1978 $75

ANDERSON-MORSHEAD, A. F. M.   The History of the Universities' Mission to Central Africa 1859-1909. London, 1909. New & revised ed., 105 illus., folding map, 8vo. K Books 239-6 1978 £6

ANDERSSON, CHARLES JOHN   Lake Ngami... London, 1856. 1st. ed., roy. 8vo, tinted lithograph plts., woodcut illus., modern half calf. Deighton 5-1 1978 £85

ANDERSSON, CHARLES JOHN   Lake Ngami;.... New York, 1856. 12mo, original green cloth, spine evenly faded, 1st Amer. ed., illus., very nice copy. Ximenes 47-4 1978 $60

ANDERSSON, CHARLES JAMES   Notes of Travel in South-Western Africa. New York, 1882. 2nd ed., cr. 8vo., orig. cloth, good ex-lib. K Books 239-7 1978 £25

ANDERSSON, J. G.   Researches into the Prehistory of the Chinese. (Stockholm, 1943). Rebound, plts., cloth, ex library copy. Dawson's 449-1 1978 $50

ANDERTON, B.   Bookman's Toys, Gleanings and Shorts. Oxford, Shakespeare Head Press, (c. 1926). Fcap. 8vo., orig. bds. George's 635-924 1978 £5

ANDRAE, W.   Coloured Ceramics from Ashur, and Earlier Ancient Assyrian Wall-Paintings... 1925. Folio, coloured and plain plts., cloth. Quaritch 983-2 1978 $190

ANDRE, E.   A Naturalist in The Guianas. 1904. Folding map, illus., 2 coloured, orig. cloth, 8vo. Edwards 1012-615 1978 £25

ANDRE, E.   A Naturalist in the Guianas. London, n.d. Maps, plates, illus., front inner hinge cracked, 16mo, orig. cloth. Book Chest 17-17 1978 $13.50

ANDRE, JOHN   The Cow Chace. Albany, 1866. Lg. fold. map, orig. bds., worn, very good copy, ltd. to 100 copies. MacManus 239-546 1978 $30

ANDRE, JOHN   The Cow Chace. Albany, 1866. Tall 8vo., fldg. map on tissue, 3/4 lea. & marbled bds., nice copy on lg. paper. Butterfield 21-51 1978 $125

ANDREADES, A.   History of the Bank of England. 1909. 2 vols. in 1, 8vo. George's 635-268 1978 £5.50

ANDREAE, JOHANNES   Super Arboribus Consanguinitatis. Nuremberg, 1477. Sm. folio, coloured by hand woodcuts, mod. parchment gilt, bookplate, rare. Quaritch 978-2 1978 $1,350

ANDREWS, ALFRED   Genealogy and Ecclesiastical History of New Britain, Conn. Chicago, 1867. Illus. MacManus 239-951 1978 $27.50

ANDREWS, BESSIE A.   Colonial and Old Houses of Greenwich, New Jersey. Vineland, 1907. 1st ed., illus., orig. cloth, fine. MacManus 239-1233 1978 $50

ANDREWS, BESSIE A.   Historical Sketches of Greenwich in Old Cohansey. Vineland, 1905. Orig. cloth, very good, very scarce. MacManus 239-1234 1978 $50

ANDREWS, C.C.   Hints to Company Officers On Their Military Duties. New York, 1863. Baldwins' 51-299 1978 $25

ANDREWS, E. BENJAMIN   History of the Last Quarter-Century in the U.S. 1870-1895. New York, 1896. 2 vols., illus., uncut. MacManus 239-28 1978 $17.50

ANDREWS, EDWARD D.   The Community Industries of the Shakers. Albany, 1933. Plts., wr. Butterfield 21-414 1978 $12.50

ANDREWS, EDMUND   A Comparative Dictionary of the Tahitian Language. Chicago, 1944. Wrs., little soiled. Dawson's 127-243 1978 $12.50

ANDREWS, EDWIN A.   Reminiscent Musings. Spring Arbor, (1926). Cloth. Hayman 73-23 1978 $8.50

ANDREWS, ELIZA FRANCES   The War-Time Journal of a Georgia Girl. NY, 1908. Bell Wiley's Copy. Broadfoot's 44-8 1978 $25.00

ANDREWS, EVANGELINE W.   Journal of a Lady of Quality... New Haven, 1922. Illus., maps. MacManus 239-29 1978 $12.50

ANDREWS, EVANGELINE W.   Journal of a Lady of Quality... New Haven, 1921. Shelf worn. Broadfoot 50-6 1978 $17

ANDREWS, HENRY C.   The Botanists Repository Comprising Coloured Engravings of New and Rare Plants only.... (London), 1797-1814. Complete set, engraved title-pages, hand coloured engraved plts., 10 vols. in 5, thick 4to, olive green half morocco, some joints repaired. Traylen 88-643 1978 £2800

ANDREWS, HENRY C.   Coloured Engravings of Heath. London, 1802-1809. 3 vols., coloured plts., folio, contemp. half russia leather. Traylen 88-530 1978 £2800

ANDREWS, HENRY C.   Geraniums... London, 1805-(10). 2 vols. in 1, hand coloured plts., thick 4to, modern half calf, edges uncut. Traylen 88-531 1978 £3600

ANDREWS, HENRY NATHANIEL   Ancient Plants. New York, 1947. 8vo., orig. cloth. Book Chest 17-449 1978 $12.50

ANDREWS, HENRY PORTER   The Descendants of John Porter of Windsor, Conn. Saratoga Springs, 1893. 2 vols., full index, cloth bindings rubbed. Butterfield 21-194 1978 $35

ANDREWS, J.   The Parterre: or, Beauties of Flora. 1842. Folio, hand-coloured plts., orig. dec. cloth gilt, slightly worn, matching mor., very clean. Quaritch 983-285 1978 $1,200

ANDREWS, JAMES PETTIT   Anecdotes. 1789. 8vo., new half calf, frontispiece, drawn by the author. P. M. Hill 142-18 1978 £16

ANDREWS, JAMES PETTIT   Anecdotes, &c., Antient and Modern. 1790. New ed., 2 parts in 1 vol., engrav. frontis., contemp. tree calf, nice, 8vo. Howes 194-138 1978 £18

ANDREWS, JOHN   History of the War with America, France, Spain, and Holland. London, 1785/86. Full lea. with new lea. spines, black title patches and new endpapers. Hood 117-113 1978 $400

ANDREWS, JOHN B.   Administrative Labor Legislation. New York, 1936. Biblo BL781-799 1978 $10

ANDREWS, MATTHEW PAGE   The Dixie Book of Days. 1912. Frontis., 1st ed. Austin 82-55 1978 $12.50

ANDREWS, MATHEW PAGE   History of Maryland... New York, 1929. Ltd. signed, one of 275 copies, illus., maps. Baldwin's 51-274 1978 $35

ANDREWS, MATTHEW PAGE   Virginia the Old Dominion. Garden City, 1937. Very fine in dw. Bernard 5-278 1978 $10

ANDREWS, PHILLIP   Air News Yearbook: 1942. 1942. Many illus. Austin 80-2 1978 $27.50

ANDREWS, PHILLIP   Navy Year Book. 1944. Many illus. Austin 80-4 1978 $27.50

ANDREWS, ROY CHAPMAN   On the Trail of Ancient Man; a Narrative of the Field Work of the Central Asiatic Expeditions. New York, 1927. Illus. Hood 116-398 1978 $15

ANDREWS, W. S.   Illustrations of the West Indies. 1860. Plts., tinted litho. plts., oblong sm. folio, 2 vols., rebacked, old spines laid down, sm. stain in corner of most litho. plts., some browning. Edwards 1012-701 1978 £500

ANDREWS, WILLIAM LORING   Gossip About Book Collecting. New York, 1900. Plts., some in color, 2 vols., sm. 8vo., full brown levant, moire satin endleaves, 1 of only 32 copies prtd. on Japan vellum, orig. wrs. bound in, bkplt. of M. C. D. Borden. Argosy Special-6 1978 $600

ANDRONICUS RHODIUS   Ethicorum Nicomacheorum Paraphrasis. Cambridge, 1679. Greek and Latin text, 8vo., bds. Salloch 348-2 1978 $135

ANECDOTES of the American Indians. New York, 1844. 1st ed., 12mo, woodcuts, very good. Victoria 34-24 1978 $20

ANETHAN, ELEANORA MARY (HAGGARD) BARONNE D'   Fourteen Years of Diplomatic Life in Japan. London, (c. 1912). Illus., cloth, foxed, ex-lib., worn. Dawson's 449-104 1978 $25

ANGAS, W. MACK   Rivalry on the Atlantic. New York, (1939). Illus., ex-lib., good used copy. Biblo 247-717 1978 $15

ANGEL, ROSA EVANGELINE   The Subtile Flame of "Unto These My Brethren." Cincinnati, 1892. Orig. binding. Hayman 71-23 1978 $12.50

ANGELO, H.   Angelo's Pic Nic. 1905. Plts., some coloured, imp. 8vo. George's 635-1487 1978 £20

ANGELO, H.   Reminscences. 1904. Plts., some coloured, 2 vols., imp. 8vo. George's 635-1488 1978 £37.50

ANGER, BENJAMIN   Traite Iconographique des Maladies Chirurgicales. Paris, 1865. 4to., plts. in color, half-mor., fine copy, some lib. stamps., 1st ed. Gilhofer 74-78 1978 sFr 900

ANGER, W. H.   Digest of the Mercantile Law of Canada and Newfoundland... Toronto, 1929. 13th. ed., rev. to date. Hood's 115-624 1978 $10

ANGERS, A. R.   Le Coup d'etat ou le Renvoi du Cabinet de Boucherville... Quebec, 1878. Hood 116-502 1978 $40

ANGERSTEIN, JOHN JULIUS   A Catalogue of the Celebrated Collection of Pictures of the late John Julius Angerstein. London, 1829. Plts., 4to., orig. cloth, rather faded and backstrip laid down. K Books 244-336 1978 £16

ANGLE, PAUL M.   One Hundred Years of Law. Springfield, 1928. Illus., 8vo., 1st ed., orig. cloth. Morrill 241-680 1978 $10

ANGLE, PAUL M.   A Shelf of Lincoln Books. 1946. Fine, d.j. MacManus 239-893 1978 $20

THE ANGLERS Pocket Book. London, 1805. Contemp. marbled bds., half calf, badly rubbed, front cover loose, internally very good, frontis. Wolfe 39-4 1978 $45

ANGLICUS, BARTHOLOMAEUS
Please turn to
BARTHOLOMAEUS ANGLICUS

ANGLO-Saxon Chronicle, according to the several Original Authorities. 1861. Folding plates, 2 vols., roy. 8vo., half calf. George's 635-530 1978 £35

ANGO, PIERRE   L'Optique divisee en Trois Livres ou l'on demontre d'une maniere aisee tout ce qui regarde.... Paris, 1682. 12mo., contemp. calf, plt., woodcut diagrams, first ed. Gurney 75-2 1978 £210

ANGOULEME, MARGUERITE D'
Please turn to
MARGUERITE D'ANGOULEME

ANGOVE, JOHN   In The Early Days: The Reminiscences of Pioneer Life on the South African Diamond Fields. Kimberley & Johannesburg, 1910. 25 plts., cr. 8vo., orig. cloth. K Books 239-8 1978 £24

ANGUS, ALEXANDER D.   Old Quebec, in the Days Before Our Day. Montreal, 1949. Ltd., numbered, ed. Hood 117-167 1978 $40

ANGUS, WILLIAM   English Grammer. Glasgow, 1817. 3rd ed., 12mo., sheep. K Books 244-337 1978 £6

ANGUS, WILLIAM   The Seats of the Nobility and Gentry in Great Britain and Wales in a Collection of Select Views. 1787. Engrav., oblong 4to., contemp. crimson straight-grained mor., gilt edges. Howes 194-1363 1978 £135

THE ANIMAL Parasites of Man. (Tokyo, 1889). 8vo., fldg. litho. plts., illus., orig. brown cloth, gilt lettering on spine in English & Japanese, worn, bkplt. of Charles A. Kofoid, rare. Zeitlin 245-134 1978 $50

ANKETELL, JOHN   Poems on Several Subjects. Dublin, 1793. 1st. ed., uncut, rebound in half calf, cloth bds., good. Jarndyce 16-29 1978 £48

ANNA Thomas, or The Good Girl. Cincinnati, late 1830's. Illus. wrappers, fine. Victoria 34-25 1978 $20

ANNABEL, RUSSELL   Tales of a Big Game Guide. New York, Derrydale Press, (1938). 1 of 95 copies inscribed and signed by author, 4to., orig.
cloth, plts. Houle 10-84 1978 $125

ANNALES Archeologiques. 1863-65. Vols. 23-25, 4to., plts., new buckram,
blind stamp. Allen 234-1088 1978 $12.50

ANNALS OF FOUR MASTERS   Annals of the Kingdom of Ireland by the Four
Masters. 1856. 2nd (& best) ed., 7 vols., superb uncut copy, original green
cloth, bookplt. of Earl of Arran, mint. Hyland 128-250 1978 £325

ANNALS OF FOUR MASTERS   Annals of the Kingdom of Ireland by the Four
Masters. Rebind, very good, octavo bound in cloth. Hyland 128-251 1978
£250

THE ANNALS Of Horticulture... 1846. Hand-coloured frontispiece& numerous
woodcut illus., maroon pebble-grained cloth, good. Jarnydce 16-673 1978 £6.50

ANNALS of the General Society of Mechanics & Tradesmen of City of NY. New
York, 1882. Illus., good. Nestler Rare 78-113 1978 $35

ANNALS of the Propagation of the Faith. 1840/2. Vols. III, IV & V, bound
in 1 vols., 1/2 leather, good, reprint. Hyland 128-380 1978 £15

ANNALS of Wyoming. Laramie, 1925-1968. Vols. 3 through 46, orig. pr. wr.
Ginsberg 14-1070 1978 $475

ANNIXTER, P.   Wilderness Ways. Philadelphia, (1930). 8vo,
orig. cloth, plates, illus. by Charles Livingston Bull, pict. cover. Book Chest
17-18 1978 $27

ANNUAL Announcement of the University of the State of Missouri.... Columbia,
1868. Wrps. Hayman 71-476 1978 $7.50

ANNUAL Circular of Massachusetts Medical College, with a History of the Medical Department of Harvard University... Boston, 1846. Lithos, 8vo., orig. wrs.
Morrill 239-172 1978 $20

ANNUAL Journal of the State Eclectic Medical Association of Michigan. Grand
Rapids, 1874. 8vo., orig. wrs. Morrill 239-177 1978 $10

THE ANNUAL of Bookmaking. (New York), 1933. 4to., orig. decor. cloth,
very good. Americanist 103-118 1978 $50

THE ANNUAL of Bookmaking. New York, 1938. Cloth, very good, unpaged.
Dawson's 447-31 1978 $40

ANNUAL Report on British New Guinea from 1st July, 1900 to 30th June, 1901;....
(Brisbane, c. 1902). Plts., illus., maps, disbound, lacking title, covers detached
and missing pieces. Dawson's 127-279 1978 $50

ANNUNZIO, GABRIELE D'   Francesca da Rimini. Milan, 1902. Sq. 8vo.,
publisher's cloth with gold lettering, uncut, 1st ed., illus. by Adolfo de Carolis,
very clean. Goldschmidt 110-9 1978 $175

ANNUNZIO, GABRIELE D'   Le Vergini Delle Rocco. Milan, 1919. Wrappers. Eaton 45-134 1978 £5

ANOUILH, JEAN   L'Invitation au Chateau. 1948. First ed., cr.
8vo. George's 635-1306 1978 £5

ANSALDI, CASTO INNOCENZO   P. Casti Innocentis Ansaldi O.P. de Princi-
piorum Legis Naturalis Traditione. 1742. 4to., polished calf, spine gilt, upper
joint weak, wide margins, very good. King 7-130 1978 £35

ANSIDEI PERUGINO, G.   Trattato Cavalleresco Contra l'Abuso del Mante-
nimento delle Private Inimicitic, etc. Perugia, 1691. 12mo.; old vellum, frontis. Van der Peet H-64-587 1978 Dfl 95

ANSON, CLODAGH   Book. (London), 1931. Cloth, illus., 1st ed.,
rare, very good copy, inscr. by author, slipcase. Dykes 34-130 1978 $75

ANSON, GEORGE   A Voyage Round the World, 1740-44.   1748.
1st. ed., copper plts., 4to, calf, rebacked. Edwards 1012-1 1978 £120

ANSON, GEORGE   A Voyage Round The World, In the Years 1740,
1, 2, 3, 4, by George Anson.... Edinburgh, 1804. 2 vols. in 1, sm. 8vo, rebound
in cloth, gilt back. Deighton 5-173 1978 £58

ANSPACH, FREDERICK R.   The Sons of the Sires... Philadelphia, 1855.
1st ed. MacManus 239-238 1978 $35

ANSPACHER, LOUIS K.   Slow Harvest. New York, (1943). 1st ed.
Biblo 251-392 1978 $15

ANSTEY, CHRISTOPHER   The New Bath Guide. Cambridge, 1766. Second
ed., 8vo., contemp. calf, upper hinge cracked. P. M. Hill 142-241 1978 £15

ANSTEY, CHRISTOPHER   The New Bath Guide. Cambridge, 1766. Second ed., contemp. qtr. sheep, 8vo. Howes 194-140 1978 £18

ANSTEY, CHRISTOPHER   The New Bath Guide. 1766. 3rd. ed., orig.
calf, dark green label, v.g. Jarndyce 16-34 1978 £16

ANSTEY, CHRISTOPHER   The New Bath Guide. 1773. 9th. ed., frontispiece, rebound in half calf, hand marbled bds., black label, good. Jarndyce 16-
35 1978 £10.50

ANSTEY, CHRISTOPHER   The New Bath Guide. 1791. 14th. ed., engraved
frontis, orig. calf, red labels, hinges weak, v.g. Jarndyce 16-36 1978 £7

ANSTEY, CHRISTOPHER   The Poetical Works. 1808. First ed., plts.,
4to., full contemp. polished buff mor., raised bands, sole collected ed. Howes
194-141 1978 £45

ANSTEY, CHRISTOPHER   Poetical Works... 1808. 4to, portraits, bookplt. of United University Club Lib., 1/2 green morocco, worn. Eaton 45-20 1978
£35

ANSTEY, F. PSEUD.
Please turn to
GUTHRIE, THOMAS ANSTEY

ANSTIE, FRANCIS EDMUND   Stimulants and Narcotics, Their Mutual Relations. Philadelphia, 1865. 8vo., blind-stamped cloth, gilt, library stamps,
but good copy, 1st Amer. ed. Zeitlin 245-8 1978 $125

ANTHING, J. F.   Collection de cent Silhouettes des Personnes Illustres et celebres. Dessinees D'apres les Originaux. Weimer, 1913. 8vo., plts.,
fine, red mor., gilt panelled back, gilt top. Quaritch 983-150 1978 $115

ANTHOLOGIA Graeca. Florence, 1494. 272 leaves (of 280, lacks last leaf of
text and dedication to Piero de'Medici, these except for blank leaf, have been
supplied from a later ed.), good margins, sm. 4to., 19th cent. russia, rebacked.
Thomas 37-51 1978 £1250

ANTHOLOGIA Graeca. Tauchnitz, 1893. 16mo., stiff wrs., 3 vols. Allen
234-30 1978 $7.50

ANTHONY, A. V. S.   Three Essays. Gillis Press, 1916. Illus. with
woodcuts, 8vo., 1 of 260 copies, newly rebound in cloth. Battery Park 1-146
1978 $50

ANTHONY, JOSEPH   Casanova Jones. New York, (1930). Illus., 1st
ed., covers faded, lightly rubbed. Biblo BL781-896 1978 $9

ANTHONY, JOSEPH   The Lost Shirt. New York, 1929. 1st ed.,
d.j., good. Limestone 7-8 1978 $12.50

ANTHONY, N.   The Book of Ballyhoo. New York, (1931).
4to., illus. Biblo 251-154 1978 $15

THE ANTIDOTE for the Poison. San Francisco, 1860. Half morocco, 1st ed.
Ginsberg 14-70 1978 $150

ANTIN, MARY   They Who Knock at Our Gates. 1914. Austin 79-32 1978 $10

ANTONIDES VAN DER GOES, JOHANNES   De Ystroom. Amsterdam, 1671. First ed., sm. 4to., frontis., plts., fine, cont. vellum. Quaritch Summer 1978-3 1978 $1,800

ANTONINUS PIUS   Iter Britanniarum. Cambridge, 1799. Maps, 4to., contemp. calf. Howes 194-143 1978 £40

ANTONIUS DE VERCELLIS   Sermones Quadragesimales de. Venice, 1492. 1st ed., quarto, contemp. vellum binding, notations in contemp. script, bookplate, very good copy. Bennett 20-6 1978 $1500

ANTWERP, W. C. VAN   The Stock Exchange from Within. 1913. Illus. from photos. Austin 80-405 1978 $11

APAFI, MICHAEL   The Declaration of the Hungarian War.... London, 1682. Folio, disbound, 1st ed., with parallel Latin and English texts. Ximenes 47-5 1978 $80

APIANUS, PETRUS   Cosmographia Petri Apiani, per Gemmam Frisivm apud Louanienses Medicum & Mathematicum insignem,.... Antwerp, 1550. Sm. 4to Roman letter, map and woodcut diagrams, modern red mor. gilt. Quaritch 978-4 1978 $1,475

APIANUS, PETRUS   Cosmographiae Introductio. Venice, 1551. Woodcuts, maps, sm. 8vo., bds. with label. Salloch 345-8 1978 $250

APIANUS, PETRUS   Cosmographia. Antwerp, 1574. Woodcut, illus., 4to., calf. Salloch 345-7 1978 $750

APIANUS, PETRUS   Quadrans Apani Astronomicus et iam Recens Inventus et nunc primum editus. Ingoldstadt, 1532. Folio, roman letter throughout, woodcuts, rebound in mor., first ed. Quaritch 977-173 1978 $3,000

APICIUS COELIUS   De Opsoniis et Condimentis, sive Arte Coquinaria, Libri Decem. Amsterdam, 1709. Sm. 8vo., contemp. vellum, some staining of leaves at beginning and end. Howes 194-524 1978 £28

APOLLONIUS OF TYRE   Ein Hubsche Hystori Von dem Kunig Appolonius. Augsburg, 1552. Sm. 4to., woodcut illus., modern vellum, very good copy. Schafer 19-3 1978 sFr 4,800

THE APPEAL of the Religious Society of Friends in Penna., New Jersey, Delaware, &C.... Philadelphia, 1858. 1st ed., orig. printed wrs., nice copy, 8vo. Americanist 101-21 1978 $30

APPEL, BENJAMIN   Brain Guy. New York, 1934. First ed., grey cloth stamped in red, fresh, fine. Houle 10-4 1978 $25

APPEL, THEO   Recollections of College Life, at Marshal College, Mercersburg, Pa., from 1839 to 1845: A Narrative with Reflections. Reading, 1886. 1st ed., spine faded, worn, 8vo., orig. binding. Americanist 101-4 1978 $17.50

APPENDIX Containing Sundry Resolutions for Carrying on a Secret Expedition.. Passed Sept. 16, 1777. Boston, 1777. Good. Nestler Rare 78-170 1978 $135

APPERLEY, CHARLES JAMES   Memoirs of the Life of the Late John Mytton Esq. of Halston, Shropshire.... London, n.d. Reprinted, illus. of H. Aiken and T. J. Rawlins in color, roy. 8vo. Baldwins' 51-538 1978 $25

APPERLEY, CHARLES JAMES   Remarks on the Condition of Hunters, the Choice of Horses and their Management. 1831. Some scoring and foxing, half calf, worn, 8vo. George's 635-1502 1978 £12.50

APPLEGATE, JOHN S.   Early Courts and Lawyers of Monmouth County. N.P., 1911. MacManus 239-1235 1978 $35

APPLEMAN, ROY E.   Okinawa: The Last Battle. 1948. Fldg. maps. Austin 80-5 1978 $75

APPLETON, NATHAN   Speech of Mr..., of Massachusetts, in Reply to Mr. McDuffie, of South Carolina, on the Tariff. Delivered in the House...30th of May, 1932. Washington, 1832. Sewed, a little worn. Hayman 72-27 1978 $10

APPLETONS' Illustrated Almanac, for 1869. New York, (1868). Ads, pict. wrs., slight wear. Hayman 73-23 1978 $7.50

APTHEKER, HERBERT   The Negro in the Civil War. NY, 1938. Wraps, Bell Wiley's Copy. Broadfoot's 44-12 1978 $10.00

APULEIUS, LUCIUS   Apulejo, Dell'asino D'Oro, Traslatato da Messer Agnolo Firenzuola, di Latino in Lingua Toscana. Parigi, 1781. 8vo., bds., fine, uncut, unopened copy. King 7-131 1978 £15

APULEIUS, LUCIUS   De Cupidinis et Psyches Amoribus. Vale Press. Imp. 8vo., one of 310 copies, paper over bds., cloth spine, illus., fine copy. Battery Park 1-230 1978 $350

APULEIUS, LUCIUS   The Excellent Narration of the Marriage of Cupide and Psyches. Vale Press. Illus., trans. into English, one of only 210 copies, cloth binding, soiled. Battery Park 1-229 1978 $250

APULEIUS, LUCIUS   The Golden Asse. 1913. Orig. qtr. buckram, edges untrimmed, 8vo., ltd. to 1,150 copies. Howes 194-592 1978 £4.50

APULEIUS, LUCIUS   The XI. Bookes of the Golden Asse. (Waltham Saint Lawrence): The Golden Cockerel Press, 1923. 4to., cloth-backed bds., paper label, 1 of 450 copies, uncut, a bit rubbed, fine. MacManus 238-790 1978 $60

APULEIUS, LUCIUS   The Golden Ass. 1930. Ltd. to 900 copies, bookplate. Biblo 247-459 1978 $14.50

APULEIUS, LUCIUS   The Metamorphosis or Golden Ass, and Philosophical Works. London, 1822. 1st. ed., 8vo, old half morocco, edges uncut. Traylen 88-96 1978 £40

APULEIUS, LUCIUS   Psyche Et Cupido. London, 1913. 1 of 525 numbered copies on Riccardi hand-made paper, thin 4to., orig. linen-backed bds., orig. printed d.w. Americanist 102-99 1978 $35

ARABIAN NIGHTS   The Arabian Nights Entertainments. 1811. 6 vols., cr. 8vo., full contemp. calf, first ed. Howes 194-144 1978 £50

ARABIAN NIGHTS   Arabian Nights Entertainment. Calcutta, 1814. 1 vol., tree calf, rebacked, preserved orig. spine, orig. Arabic. Eaton 45-22 1978 £40

ARABIAN NIGHTS   The Arabian Nights. London, 1838. 4 vols., cr. 8vo., 2 vols. rather shaken, covers faded. K Books 244-6 1978 £10

ARABIAN NIGHTS   The Arabian Nights Entertainment. 1898. First English ed., illus., orig. pict. cloth gilt, a.e.g., very good. Bell Book 17-541 1978 £8.50

ARABIAN NIGHTS   The Seven Voyages of Sinbad The Sailor From the Ababian Nights Entertainment. Park Ridge, 1939. Bds., ltd. to 1500 copies, color illus. Hayman 71-694 1978 $7.50

ARABIAN NIGHTS   Stories from the Arabian Nights. 1907. Coloured plts. by Edmund Dulac, roy. 8vo. George's 635-140 1978 £27.50

ARABIAN NIGHTS   The Thousand and One Nights. London, (1906). 4 vols., red levant and cloth, 1st print., fine bind. Petrilla 13-131 1978 $37.50

ARAGO, F.   Astronomie Populaire...Oeuvre Posthume. Paris, 1854-57. 4 vols., 8vo., engrav. plts., woodcuts, contemp. quarter calf. Quaritch 977-174 1978 $125

ARAGO, JACQUES ETIENNE VICTOR   Promenade autour du Monde Pendant les Annees 1817, 1818, 1819 et 1820... Paris, 1822. 2 vols., 8vo., plts., map, contemp. half-calf, lightly rubbed, 1st ed. Gilhofer 74-52 1978 sFr 2,000

ARAI, HAKUSEKI   The Sword and Same. Plts., roy. 8vo. Traylen 88-498 1978 £10

ARBER, EDWARD   The Story of the Pilgrim Fathers, 1606-1623.... London, 1897. Frontis, port. Baldwins' 51-390 1978 $12.50

ARBLAY, FRANCES BURNEY D'   Camilla: or, A Picture of Youth. London, 1796. 5 vols., full contemp. speckled calf, black mor. labels, 1st ed., bookplts., front outer hinge of vol. I strained, but fine set, half mor. slipcase. MacManus 238-106 1978 $250

ARBLAY, FRANCES BURNEY D'   Camilla: or A Picture of Youth. 1796. 1st ed., 5 vols., sm. blind-stamp on t-p's., cloth, leather labels, spines faded. Eaton 45-72 1978 £35

ARBLAY, FRANCES BURNEY D'   Camilla: or A Picture of Youth. 1796. 5 vols., 1st ed., orig. calf, old rebacks, brown labels, good. Jarndyce 16-48 1978 £32

ARBLAY, FRANCES BURNEY D'   Diary and Letters of Madame D'Arblay... 1843-46. 7 vols., sm. 8vo., frontis., half olive green calf, gilt, gilt tops, stamp in each vol., very good state. Quaritch 979-64 1978 $160

ARBLAY, FRANCES BURNEY D'   Fanny Burney Diary and Letters. London, n.d. c. 1890. 8vo., 8vols., illus., plts., full pressed red levant mor., sumptuous copy, gilt tops. Traylen 88-219 1978 £300

ARBLAY, FRANCES BURNEY D'   Evelina, or The History of a Young Lady's Entrance into The World. 1805. 2 vols., new ed., title vignettes, vol. I lacking frontis., some foxing, 1/4 modern calf, marbled bds. Eaton 45-74 1978 £10

ARBLAY, FRANCES BURNEY D'   Evelina or the History of a Young Lady's Entrance Into the world. London, 1805. 2 vols., new ed., leather. Hayman 71-72 1978 $15

ARBLAY, FRANCES BURNEY D'   The Wanderer; or, Female Difficulties. London, 1814. 5 vols., orig. bds., paper labels, worn and illegible, 1st ed., extremities worn, but very good set, uncut, fold. cloth box. MacManus 238-107 1978 $450

ARBLAY, FRANCES BURNEY D'   The Wanderer. 1814. First ed., 5 vols., sm. 8vo., contemp. half roan. Howes 194-191 1978 £55

ARBUCKLE, JOHN   Civil War Experiences of a Foot-Soldier Who Marched with Sherman. Columbus, 1930. Cover speckled, Bell Wiley's copy. Broadfoot's 44-489 1978 $18

ARBUTHNOT, C.   Tales of Ancient Coins, Weights and Measures. 1727. 4to., new binders buckram. George's 635-261 1978 £35

ARBUTHNOT, HARRIET   Journal, 1820-32. 1950. Plts., 2 vols., 8vo. George's 635-534 1978 £8.50

ARCHAEOLOGIA. 1907-1920 & 1949. 4to., plts., illus., Vols. 60-69 & 93. Allen 234-B 1978 $10

ARCHAEOLOGICAL Journal. 1846-48. 2nd ed., Vols. 1-5, illus. vol. I rebound, margins worm-eaten, Vols. 2-5 slightly worn. Allen 234-C 1978 $37.50

ARCHAEOLOGIST, & Journal of Antiquarian Science. 1842. Nos. 1-10 in I vol., plt., new buckram, blind stamp. Allen 234-1089 1978 $10

ARCHER, GEOFFREY   The Birds of British Somaliland and The Gulf of Aden. London, 1931-1964. Coloured plts., photo plts., maps, 4 vols., orig. buckram. Traylen 88-532 1978 £420

ARCHER, THOMAS   Charles Dickens: A Gossip about his Life, Works and Characters. c. 1890. sketches by Frederick Barnard reproduced in photogravure and other illus., folio, orig. half mor., 8vo. Howes 194-786 1978 £14

ARCHER, THOMAS   Our Sovereign Lady Queen Victoria, her Life and Jubilee. 1887. Etchings, 4 vols., roy. 8vo. George's 635-788 1978 £5.25

ARCHER, THOMAS   W. E. Gladstone, and his Contemporaries, 50 years of Social and Political Progress. 1883. Portraits, 4 vols. in 2, roy. 8vo., half calf. George's 635-660 1978 £5

ARCHER, WILLIAM   Report...On The Subject Of The Annexation Of Texas. Washington, 1845. Jenkins 116-30 1978 $25

LES ARCHIVES de Folklore. I. Montreal, 1946. Wrs., pgs. unopened. Hood 116-3 1978 $15

ARCHIVO dos Acures, publicacao periodica destinada a Vulgarisacao dos elementos indispensaveis para todos os ramos da historia Acoriana. 1884. Half calf, rubbed. George's 635-535 1978 £5

ARCTIC Travels. Dublin, 1830. Illus. with engrs., lea. binding, fr. cover loose. Hood 117-91 1978 $55

THE ARCTIC World: Its Plants, Animals, and Natural Phenomena... 1876. 4to., orig. cloth, cover spotted. Edwards 1012-558 1978 £12

ARCULARIUS, HENRY   School of the Gunner, or Field Piece; Being an Extract From a French Work on the Service of Field Artillery. New York, 1838. 16mo, spine much worn. Baldwins' 51-300 1978 $50

ARDENE, JEAN PAUL DE ROME D'   Traite sur la Connoissance et la Culture de Jacintes... Avignon, 1759. Plts., 8vo., cont. mottled calf, gilt spine. Traylen 88-563 1978 £12

ARENDTZ, HERMANN F.   The Way Out of Depression. 1931. Austin 80-406 1978 $11

ARETINO, PIETRO   Il Genesi Di M. Pietro Aretino Con La Visione Di Noe Ne La Quale Vede I Misterii Del Testamento Vecchio E Del Nuovo, Diviso in Tre Libri. [Venice], 1539. Small 8vo, italic letter, 18th century French red mor., gilt triple line border on sides, flat spine gilt with floral ornaments, gilt edges, rare. Quaritch 978-5 1978 $475

ARETINO, PIETRO   Le Lettre Di M. Pietro Aretino. Venice, 1538. 8vo, Italic letter. 17th century mottled calf, gilt back. Quaritch 978-6 1978 $475

ARETINO, PIETRO   Del Primo (-Sesto) Libro de le Lettere di M. Pietro Aretino. Parigi, 1609. 6 vols. in 3, 8vo., limp vellum, worn at edges, portrait, woodcut initials, italic letter, first collected ed. King 7-7 1978 £135

ARETINO, PIETRO   Quattro Comedie Del Divino Pietro Aretino. London, 1588. 8vo, woodcut medallion portrait, French 18th century red mor., backstrip panelled in gilt, marbled endpapers, gilt inner borders, excellent. Quaritch 978-7 1978 $550

ARGENS, JEAN BAPTISTE DE BOYER   Chinese Letters. 1741. 12mo., contemp. calf, hinges worn, lacking label, first English translation, scarce. P.M. Hill 142-20 1978 £75

ARETINO, PIETRO   Les Ragionamenti. 1950. Ltd. ed., coloured plts. by P. E. Becat, roy. 8vo., qtr. mor., wrappers bound in at end. George's 635-876 1978 £8.50

ARGENS, JEAN BAPTISTE DE BOYER, MARQUIS D'   Lettres Juives ou Corresponance Philosphique Historique et Critique. La Haye, 1738. 6 vols., gilt-panelled calf spines over mottled bds., hinges weakening, each vol. contains engr. title page by J. V. Schley. Bennett 20-233 1978 $225

ARGENSOLA, LUPERCIO   Rimas de Lupercio i del Dotor Bartolome Leonardo de Argensola. En Zaragoza, 1634. 1st ed., small 4to, full stiff vellum, partial binding, ties present, newer end papers, fine crisp copy. Bennett 20-7 1978 $300

ARGOLI, ANDREA   De Diebus Criticis et de Aegrorum Decubitu. Patavii, 1639. 4to., contemp. limp vellum, 1st ed., 2 parts in 1 vol. Offenbacher 30-63 1978 $250

ARGUMENT of Plaintiff's Counsel in the Case of Willard Peele and Others Versus the Merchants' Insurance Company. Boston, 1826. 8vo., orig. wrs. Morrill 239-442 1978 $7.50

ARGYLE, ARCHIE   Cupid's Album.   New York, 1866.   Original cloth, 1st ed.   Ginsberg 14-4 1978 $65

ARGYLL, JOHN GEORGE CAMPBELL, 9TH DUKE OF   Memories of Canada and Scotland.   Montreal, 1884.   Cover loose.   Hood's 116-700 1978 $7.50

ARGYLL, JOHN GEORGE CAMPBELL, 9TH DUKE OF   A Trip to the Tropics and Home Through America.   1867.   Frontis., orig. cloth, 8vo.   Edwards 1012-400 1978 £12

ARIAS MONTANO, BENNEDICTO   In XXXI Davidis Psalmos Priores Commentaria.   Antverpiae, 1605.   Quarto, Plantin device on t.p. and last leaf, woodcut initials throughout, full contemporary calf, rehinged, title gilt-stamped on spine, boards warped and foxed, complete and sound copy.   Bennett 20-8 1978 $195

ARIOSTO, LODIVICO   Orlando Furioso.   Venice, 1603.   Octavo, engraved t.p., full-page woodcuts, full modern calf, in imitation of medieval binding, clasps and floral endpapers, some light foxing, very closely trimmed at top, fine copy.   Bennett 20-9 1978 $250

ARIOSTO, LODOVICO   Orlando Furioso.   Baskerville, Birmingham, 1773.   4 vols., octavo, full brown calf, rebacked with old spine over new, front cover of 4th vol. detached, gilt spines, bookplates, foxing, plts.   Totteridge 29-7 1978 $250

ARIOSTO LODOVICO   Orlando Furioso..Con Note.   Londra, 1801.   3 vols., 12mo, 1/2 russia, gilt, bookplts.   Eaton 45-23 1978 £10

ARIOSTO, LODOVICO   Orlando Furioso.   1803-4.   4 vols., 4to, lg. paper, plts., contemp. red half morocco, uncut, largely unopened.   Hannas 54-3 1978 £50

ARISTARCHUS   De Magnitudinibus, et Distantiis solis, et Lunae Liber cum Pappi Alexandrini Explicationibus Quibusdam.   Pisauri (Pesaro), 1572.   Sm. 4to., full antique calf, little rubbed, some foxing, few leaves dampstained at edges, but fine copy, 1st separate ed.   Norman 5-*3 1978 $750

ARISTEAS' EPISTLE   The History of the Seventy-Two Interpreters.   1715.   12mo., new calf antique, nice.   P.M. Hill 142-21 1978 £42

ARISTOPHANES   Comoediae Novem...   Florence, 1515.   1st. ed., 2 vols. in 1, text in Greek, 8vo, new calf antique style, leather label, sm. natural hole in one leaf.   Traylen 88-425 1978 £195

ARISTOPHANES   Comedies, Literally & Completely.   1931.   2 vols., plt.   Allen 234-43 1978 $7.50

ARISTOPHANES   The Frogs.   New York, Limited Editions Club, 1937.   Folio, wood engrs., canvas in orig. folder, damaged, slipcase.   Quaritch 979-222 1978 $45

ARISTOPHANES   Lysistrata.   New York, Limited Editions Club, 1934.   4to., orig. pict. bds., uncut, slipcover, ltd. ed. prtd. in two colors on Rives paper, illus. by Pablo Picasso, light foxing in text, well preserved.   Goldschmidt 110-51 1978 $1,100

ARISTOPHANES   Lysistrata.   New York, Limited Editions Club, 1934.   Illus., sm. folio, decor. beige bds., 1 of 1500 signed by Picasso, fine in slipcase.   Bradley 49-6 1978 $1,250

ARISTOTLES   The Basic Works of...   New York, 1941.   4to., cloth.   Salloch 348-5 1978 $15

ARISTOTLES   Compleat Masterpiece.   Booksellers, 1749.   23rd. ed., woodcut frontis, woodcuts, 8vo, orig. sheep.   Traylen 88-97 1978 £21

ARISTOTLES   History of Animals.   London, 1887.   8vo., cloth.   Salloch 345-12 1978 $12

ARISTOTLES   Physica.   8vo., cloth.   Salloch 345-13 1978 $10

ARISTOTLES   Von Der Seele Und Von Ser Welt.   Leipzig, 1829.   8vo., 3/4 calf.   Salloch 348-6 1978 $40

ARISTOTLES   The Works.   Oxford, 1947.   8vo., cloth, translated into English.   Salloch 345-14 1978 $10

ARIZONA   Inventory of the County Archives of Arizona No. 7 Maricopa County (Phoenix).   Phoenix, 1940.   Illus., original wr.   Ginsberg 14-15 1978 $30

ARIZONA   Inventory of the County Archives of Arizona No. 12 Santa Cruz County (Nogales).   Phoenix, 1941.   Original wr.   Ginsberg 14-16 1978 $30

THE ARKANSAS Grant, A Brief History.   N.P., 1901.   Original cloth.   Jenkins 116-82 1978 $185

ARKELL, REGINALD   Richard Jefferies.   1933.   Very good, first English ed.   Bell Book 16-509 1978 £6

ARLEN, MICHAEL   May Fair.   1925.   Good, first English ed., covers slightly marked, 1-inch tear at foot of upper joint.   Bell Book 16-022 1978 £4

ARLES, HENRI D'
Please turn to
BEAUDE, HENRI 1870-

ARLINGTON, HENRY BENNETT   Letters.   1701.   Frontispieces, 2 vols., cr. 8vo., nice, contemp. calf, first ed.   Howes 194-145 1978 £38

ARLOTT, JOHN   Of Period and Place; poems.   London, 1944.   First ed., orig. binding, nice, inscribed by author.   Rota 211-27 1978 £6.50

ARMAND DE BOURBON, PRINCE DE CONTI   The Works of...   1711.   1st. English ed., 8vo, portrait, contemp. calf, lacks label.   Hannas 54-321 1978 £35

ARMBREST, D.   The Beech Woods.   Toronto, 1916.   Illus.   Hood 117-605 1978 $7.50

ARMBRUSTER, EUGENE L.   The Eastern District of Brooklyn.   New York, 1912.   Illus., maps.   MacManus 239-339 1978 $32.50

ARMENIAN HISTORICAL SOCIETY   The Armenians in Massachusetts.   Boston, 1937.   Illus., 1st ed., in dust jacket.   Austin 79-34 1978 $27.50

ARMENINI, GIOVANNI BATTISTA   De Veri Precetti Della Pittura....   Ravenna, 1587.   Sm. 4to., Italic letter, woodcut device on title, old sheep, gilt spine, red edges, 1st ed., very rare.   Quaritch 978-8 1978 $950

ARMENINI, GIOVANNI BATTISTA   De' veri Precetti della Pittura Libri Tre.   Ravenna, 1587.   4to., vellum, 1st ed., 2nd issue.   Gilhofer 74-25 1978 sFr 2,200

ARMES, ETHEL   Stratford Hall the Great House of the Lees.   Richmond, 1936.   1st ed., lg. thick 4to., illus., very fine, d.j., scarce.   MacManus 239-636 1978 $50

ARMISTEAD, J.J.   An Angler's Paradise and How to Obtain It.   Scarborough, 1898.   Third ed., orig. binding.   Wolfe 39-5 1978 $12.50

ARMISTICE Ceremonial.   Toronto, (1928).   Canadian Anniversary Edition, suede cover, illus.   Hood 117-114 1978 $15

ARMITAGE, JOHN   The History of Brazil...   London, 1836.   1st ed., lg. 8vo., 2 vols., frontis's, orig. bds. with uncut leaf edges, fine cond.   Current 24-69 1978 $475

ARMITAGE, MERLE   Accent on America.   New York, 1944.   One of 1675 copies, inscribed by author, first ed., d.j., fine, illus., 8vo., good.   Houle 10-5 1978 $65

ARMITAGE, MERLE   The Aristocracy of Art.   Los Angeles, 1929.   1 of 500 cooies, 4 to., stiff wrappers, d.j., scarce.   Houle 10-7 1978 $50

ARMITAGE, MERLE   Books and Typography Designed By Merle Armitage.   N.Y., 1938.   1st ed., sm. 4 to., stiff printed wrappers, fine.   Houle 10-8 1978 $35

ARMITAGE, MERLE   Notes on Modern Printing. New York, (1945).
1 of 2000 copies, stiff printed wrs., inscribed. Houle 10-9 1978 $45

ARMITAGE, MERLE   Notes on Modern Printing. N.Y., (1945).
1 of 2,000, stiff paper wrappers. Houle 10-10 1978 $25

ARMOR, WILLIAM C.   Lives of the Governors of Pennsylvania, with a
History of the State from 1609-1872. Philadelphia, 1872. Illus. MacManus
239-1356 1978 $20

ARMORY, THOMAS   The Life of John Buncle, Esq. 1825. New ed.,
8vo., 3 vols., 19th-century half calf, gilt backs, nice. P. M. Hill 142-182
1978 £50

ARMOUR, J. OGDEN   The Packers, The Private Car Lines, and The
People. Philadelphia, 1906. Illus., original pictorial cloth, 1st ed. Ginsberg
14-34 1978 $50

ARMOUR, RICHARD   Leading with My Left. New York, (1945).
1st ed. Biblo 251-394 1978 $12.50

ARMS, J.   Design in Flower Arrangement. New York, 1949.
8vo, orig. cloth. Book Chest 17-456 1978 $8

ARMSTRONG, CAPTAIN   Turkish Lovers; or, A Pasha's Revenge. Bath,
1845. 8vo, contents rather soiled, orig. cloth, worn, author's pres. copy. Eaton
45-24 1978 £5

ARMSTRONG, A. J.   Intimate Glimpses from Browning's Letter File,
Selected from Letters in the Baylor University Browning Collection. Waco, 1934.
Jenkins 116-34 1978 $25

ARMSTRONG, G. H.   The Origin and Meaning of Place-Names in
Canada. Toronto, 1930. 1st. ed., cover loose. Hood's 115-1 1978 $25

ARMSTRONG, HAMILTON F.   Chronology of Failure. 1940. Austin 80-6
1978 $10

ARMSTRONG, J.S.   A Report of the Proceedings on an Indictment for
a Conspiracy in the Case of the Queen V Daniel O'Connell..(& others)..in
Michaeimas Term, 1843 & Hilary 1844. Dublin, 1844. Needs recasing, text
good, octavo bound in cloth, reprint. Hyland 128-216 1978 £30

ARMSTRONG, JOHN 1709-1779   The Art of Preserving Health. 1744. 4to.,
unbound, first ed. P. M. Hill 142-242 1978 £42

ARMSTRONG, JOHN 1709-1779   The Art of Preserving Health.... 1796.
Sm. cr. 8vo., frontis. portrait, 4 eng. by T. Stothard, tree calf, rebacked. Eaton
45-25 1978 £8

ARMSTRONG, JOHN 1784-1829   Practical Illustrations of Typhus and Other
Fevers. Boston, 1829. Lea., little worn at top of spine, lacks fr. flyleaf.
Hayman 73-30 1978 $12.50

ARMSTRONG, LOUISE V.   We Too Are People. 1938. Austin 79-36
1978 $10

ARMSTRONG, MARTIN   The Fiery Dive and Other Stories. London, 1929.
8vo, cloth, vellum spine, 1 of 150 copies signed by author, 1st ed., fine. Duschnes
220-4 1978 $15

ARMSTRONG, MARTIN   Portrait of the Misses Harlow. 1928. 1st. ed.,
no. 513 of 530 copies, signed by author, unopened, near fine in slight torn d.w.
Jarndyce 16-1192 1978 £10.50

ARMSTRONG, MARTIN   The Sleeping Fury. London, 1929. 8vo, cloth,
vellum spine, 1 of 125 copies signed by author, 1st ed., fine. Duschnes 220-5
1978 $15

ARMSTRONG, MOSES K.   Centennial Address on Dakota Territory, Giving
Its History, Growth, Population and Resources.... Philadelphia, 1876. Original
printed wr., half morocco slipcase, 1st ed. Ginsberg 14-303 1978 $175

ARMSTRONG, MOSES K.   The Early Empire Builders of the Great West. St.
Paul, 1901. Illus. MacManus 239-1898 1978 $10

ARMSTRONG, ORLAND K.   Old Massa's People, the Old Slaves Tell
Their Story. Indianapolis, (1931). 1st prtg., ptc. d.w., signed inscr. by Armstrong, 8vo., very good. Americanist 103-19 1978 $25

ARMSTRONG, R. B.   The Irish & Highland Harps. (1904). Reprint,
octavo bound in cloth. Hyland 128-929 1978 £12

ARMSTRONG, S. C.   Report of a Trip Made in Behalf of the Indian
Rights Association to Some Indian Reservations of the Southwest. Philadelphia,
1884. Original printed wr., 1st ed. Ginsberg 14-35 1978 $75

ARMSTRONG, WARREN   Battle of the Oceans. 1944. Austin 80-7 1978
$10

ARMSTRONG, WILLIAM C.   The Battles in the Jerseys and the Significance of each. New Jersey, May 16, 1916. 1st ed., plts., very good or
better. Limestone 9-327 1978 $20

ARMY of the Valley, Forsberg's Brigade-Resolutions of Forsberg's Brigade, Wharton's Division. N.P., 1865. Wrs., Bell Wiley's copy. Broadfoot 46-420 1978
$60

ARNETT, L. D.   Elements of Library Methods. New York, 1925.
8vo., cloth. Battery Park 1-237 1978 $25

ARNO, PETER   Peter Arno's Circus. New York, (1931). 4to.,
1st ed. Biblo 251-155 1978 $13.50

ARNO, PETER   For Members Only. 1935. Illus., first ed.
Austin 82-57 1978 $12.50

ARNO, PETER   Peter Arno's Parade. New York, (1929). 4to.,
pres. ed., ltd. to 1000 copies. Biblo 251-156 1978 $20

ARNO, PETER   Peter Arno's Sizzling Platter. 1949. Illus.
Austin 82-58 1978 $12.50

ARNOLD, A. S.   The Story of Thomas Carlyle. 1888. Half title,
orig. dull brown cloth, little marked, good. Jarndyce 16-376 1978 £6.50

ARNOLD, EDWIN   The Light of the World. 1893. Plts., 4to.,
orig. cloth, nice, first English ed. Bell Book 16-1009 1978 £15

ARNOLD, EDWIN   Poems Narrative and Lyrical. Oxford, 1853.
8vo., binder's cloth, uncut, first ed. P. M. Hill 142-243 1978 £18

ARNOLD, ELLIOTT   Blood Brother. 1947. Autographed by Arnold.
Austin 82-59 1978 $12.50

ARNOLD, ELLIOTT   The Commandos. 1942. Austin 82-60 1978
$8.50

ARNOLD, ELLIOTT   Walk With the Devil. 1950. First ed., d.j.
Austin 82-61 1978 $12.50

ARNOLD, FRIEDRICH   Anatomische und Physiologische Untersuchungen
uber das Auge des Menschen. Heidelberg und Leipzig, 1832. Copperplts., lg.
4to., contemp. bds., rebacked, uncut, 1st ed., library stamp, some foxing.
Offenbacher 30-113 1978 $150

ARNOLD, FRIEDRICH   Icones Nervorum Capitis. Turici, n.d. (1834).
Plts., each accompanied by plt. in outline, folio, orig. bds., rebacked, uncut,
fine copy. Offenbacher 30-5 1978 $350

ARNOLD, H. H.   Global Mission. New York, (1949). First ed.
Illus. Biblo 247-776 1978 $15

ARNOLD, HOWARD PAYSON   Memoir of Jonathan Mason Warren, M. D.
Boston, 1886. Portr., 8vo., 1st ed. Morrill 239-9 1978 $15

ARNOLD, ISAAC   The Life of Benedict Arnold; His Patriotism and
His Treason. 1880. Binding faded. Nestler Rare 78-154 1978 $45

ARNOLD, MATTHEW   Cromwell: A Prize Poem, Recited in the Theatre,
Oxford; June 28, 1843. Oxford, 1843. Sm. 8vo, disbound, 1st ed. Ximenes
47-6 1978 $125

ARNOLD, MATTHEW   Irish Essays & Others. 1882. 1st. ed., orig. dark blue cloth, half title, little rubbed. Jarndyce 16-270 1978 £9.50

ARNOLD, MATTHEW   Merope. 1857. 1st. ed., 8vo, orig. blind-stamped cloth with binder's ticket, pres. inscription from author, sm. defect in top edge of upper cover, o/w fine copy. Sawyer 299-110 1978 £125

ARNOLD, MATTHEW   Merope. A Tragedy. London, 1858. Orig. cloth, 1st ed., signature on t.p., very good. MacManus 238-162 1978 $85

ARNOLD, MATTHEW   Merope, A Tragedy. 1858. 1st. ed., half title, orig. green cloth, v.g. Jarndyce 16-269 1978 £28

ARNOLD, MATTHEW   Merope. 1858. 1st. ed., blind stamp on title-pg., hinges weak, orig. cloth, spine worn, bookplt. Eaton 45-28 1978 £20

ARNOLD, MATTHEW   New Poems. 1867. Orig. green cloth, good, first English ed. Bell Book 16-023 1978 £8.50

ARNOLD, MATTHEW   New Poems. London, 1867. 8vo, lib. stamp on several leaves, 1/2 green calf. Eaton 45-27 1978 £10

ARNOLD, MATTHEW   On Translating Homer. Oxford, 1861. 1st. ed., sm. blind stamp on title-pg., orig. cloth, spine defective. Eaton 45-26 1978 £30

ARNOLD, MATTHEW   On Translating Homer. 1861. 8vo., 19th-century half green roan, rubbed, first ed., pres. copy inscribed by author. P. M. Hill 142-22 1978 £42

ARNOLD, MATTHEW   Poems. 1853. New ed., fcap. 8vo., orig. embossed drab green cloth, first ed. Howes 194-596 1978 £50

ARNOLD, MATTHEW   Poems, 2nd. Series. 1855. 1st. ed., orig. green patterned cloth, v.g. Jarndyce 16-267 1978 £32

ARNOLD, MATTHEW   Poems. 1857. 3rd. ed., half title, orig. green cloth, v.g. Jarndyce 16-268 1978 £12.50

ARNOLD, MATTHEW   Poetical Works. 1908. Portrait, half crimson mor., gilt top, 8vo. Howes 194-595 1978 £7.50

ARNOLD, MATTHEW   The Strayed Reveller and Other Poems. London, 1849. 12mo., orig. cloth, 1st ed., very nice, signature. MacManus 238-161 1978 $300

ARNOLD, OREN   Hot Irons: Heraldry of the Range. New York, 1940. Original cloth, 1st ed. Ginsberg 14-36 1978 $30

ARNOLD, OREN   Sun in Your Eyes. Albuquerque, 1947. 1st ed., ills. Jenkins 116-35 1978 $15

ARNOLD, RICHARD   The Customs of London, Otherwise Called Arnold's Chronicle:.... London, 1811. Quarto, 3/4 19th-century calf over marbled boards, hinges scuffed, some browning, good. Bennett 7-3 $150

ARNOLD, SAMUEL G.   History of the State of Rhode Island and the Providence Plantations 1636-1790. New York, 1894. 2 vols., orig. cloth, nice. MacManus 239-418 1978 $32.50

ARNOLD, SETH S.   A Sermon Preached at Alstead, on the First Sabboth in January, 1826. Alstead, 1826. 8vo, disbound, 1st ed. Ximenes 47-7 1978 $40

ARNOLD, THURMAN W.   The Folklore of Capitalism. Yale University Press, 1937. Austin 80-408 1978 $10

ARNOLD, THURMAN W.   The Folklore of Capitalism. 1941. Austin 80-407 1978 $10

ARNOLD, WILLIAM HARRIS   Ventures in Book Collecting. New York, 1923. 8vo, orig. cloth-backed bds., 1st ed. MacManus 238-856 1978 $15

ARNOLD, WILLIAM HARRIS   Ventures in Book Collecting. New York, 1923. 8vo., orig. bds., cloth back, illus. Morrill 239-290 1978 $10

ARNOLD, WILLIAM HARRIS   Ventures in Book Collecting. 1923. Frontis., illus. Battery Park 1-239 1978 $15

ARNOT, FRED S.   Garenganze. London, c. 1890. 2nd ed., map, illus., decor. cloth, good, 8vo. K Books 244-338 1978 £15

ARNOT, HUGO   An Essay on Nothing. Edinburgh, 1776. 1st. ed., 19th. century half calf, some pencil marking, good. Jarndyce 16-37 1978 £18

ARNOTT, J.   On Neuralgic, Rheumatic, and Other Painfull Affections. London, 1851. 8vo., unbound. Quaritch 977-5 1978 $50

ARNOTT, J. A.   The Petit Trianon. 1908. Plts., loose in portfolio as issued, folio. George's 635-75 1978 £18

ARNOTT, N.   On Warming and Ventilating. 1838. 8vo., woodcuts, good, orig. limp cloth. Quaritch 977-200 1978 $100

ARNOUL, BISHOP OF LISIEUX   The Letters of... 1939. 8vo., Upcroft 12-12 1978 £5

ARNULF
Please turn to
ARNOUL, BISHOP OF LISIEUX

ARNUP, J. H.   A New Church Faces a New World. Toronto, 1937. Inscribed and signed. Hood 116-276 1978 $7.50

ARONSON, J.   The Book of Furniture and Decoration. New York, 1936. Lg. 8vo., cloth, plts. Van der Peet H-64-95 1978 Dfl 50

AROUND the Horn in '49. [Wethersfield?], 1898. Illus., original cloth, signed by publisher. Ginsberg 14-221 1978 $100

ARRAGOIZ, FRANCISCO   Mejico Desde 1808 Hasta 1867. Madrid, 1871-1872. 4 vols., rare. Jenkins 116-36 1978 $175

ARRHENIUS, SVANTE   La Dissociation Electrolytique des Solutions. Paris, 1900. 8vo., orig. wrappers, pres. copy, inscribed by author. Gurney 75-3 1978 $50

ARRIANUS, FLAVIUS   Ars Tactica, Acies contra Alanos. 1683. Sm. 8vo., plt., text in Greek and Latin, contemp. calf. F. Edwards 1013-243 1978 £100

ARRIANUS, FLAVIUS   Texnh Takitikh...Arstactica, Acies Contra Alanos. Periplus ponti Euxini Periplus Maris Erythraei... Amsterdam, 1683. Fold. maps, old vellum, rare. Biblo BL781-317 1978 $87.50

ARRIGHI DA VICENZA, LODOVICO DEGLI   Regola da Imparare Scrivere varii Caratteri de Littere con li suoi Compassi et Misure. Venice, 1533. Sm. 4to., 19th cent. full dark green mor., blind panelled with corner ornaments, woodcuts. Schumann 511-1 1978 sFr 12,000

ARRIGO DA SETTIMELLO   Arrighetto ovvero Trattato contro all Avversita della Fortuna di Arrigo da Settimello. Firenze, 1730. Sm. 4to., marbled bds., lettering piece gilt, very clean, crisp, tall copy, first ed. King 7-132 1978 £50

ARROWSMITH, H. W.   The House Decorator and Painter's Guide... 1840. 4to., plain and coloured plts., occasional sl. foxing, bds., calf back. Quaritch 983-78 1978 $550

ARSCHOT-SCHOONHAVEN, PHILIPPE PAUL ALEXIS GUILLAUME, COMTE   Histoire d'une Famille. Bruxelles, n.d. (ab. 1940). 4to., orig. covers, colored frontis., plts., out of text, lg. genealogical fldg. table, scarce. Van der Peet H-64-241 1978 Dfl 95

ARSEVEN, CELAL ESAD   Les Arts Decoratifs Turcs. Istanbul, n.d. Sm. folio, fine copy. Baldwins' 51-25 1978 $42.50

ART GALLERY OF TORONTO   Lawren Harris Paintings, 1910-1948. Toronto, 1948. Card cover, plts. Hood 117-174 1978 $30

ART GALLERY OF TORONTO   Ontario Society of Artists, Fifty-sixth Annual Exhibition; and, Morris, Edmund: Memorial Exhibition, Mar. 3-Apr. 8, 1928. Wrs., plts. Hood 116-162 1978 $7.50

ART Hand-Book...Official Handbook...and Art Catalogue of the Pan-American Exposition. Buffalo, 1901. Lg. fldg. map tipped in, prtd. wr., very good, illus. Butterfield 21-79 1978 $15

THE ART Journal. London, 1893. Etchings, tinted plts., 8vo., orig. cloth. K Books 244-7 1978 £15

THE ART Journal. London, 1897. Etchings, tinted plts., half calf, 8vo. K Books 244-9 1978 £15

ART News Annual, XVIII. New York, (1948). 4to., plts., 50 in color. Biblo 251-150 1978 $17.50

THE ART Work of Louis C. Tiffany. Garden City, 1914. 1st ed., 1 of 492 copies on Japan vellum, sm. folio, t.e.g., plts., color, photogravures, orig. gilt decor. bds., tissue guards, interior very fine, unusual. Current Misc. 8-59 1978 $985

ARTAGNAN, D'   Memoires de Monsieur d'Artagnan, Capitaine-Lieutenant de la Premiere Compagnie des Mouquetaires de Roy. Paris, 1947. 4to., bds., slipcase, woodcut portr. & plts., ltd. ed. of 365 copies. Van der Peet H-64-588 1978 Dfl 85

ARTAUD, ANTONIN   Galapagos. Paris, 1955. 8vo., in sheets, uncut, etched wr. prtd. in color, slipcover & case, 1st ed., prtd. in 135 numbered copies, copy on velin de Rives paper, signed by artist, orig. etchings by Max Ernst, pristine cond. Goldschmidt 110-22 1978 $3,000

ARTAUD, CHEV   Italie and Sicile. (Paris, 1835). 8vo., bds., mor. back, rubbed, plts. King 7-334 1978 £75

ARTEMIDORUS   De Somniorum Interpretationem. Basle, 1544. 8vo., vellum. Salloch 345-15 1978 $200

ARTHUR, ARCHIBALD   Discourses on Theological and Literary Subjects. Glasgow, 1803. 1st. ed., orig. calf, black label, good. Jarndyce 16-271 1978 £18

ARTHUR, CHESTER A.   Message from...Submitting a Draft of a Bill "To Accept and Ratify an Agreement with the Confederate Tribes of the Flathead,.... Washington, 1883. Folding maps, cloth with leather label. Ginsberg 14-612 1978 $35

ARTHUR, CHESTER A.   Message from...Transmitting Communication of the Secretary of the Interior in Relation to the Condition of the Cheyenne and Arapaho Indians. Washington, 1885. Disbound, 1st ed. Ginsberg 14-238 1978 $12.50

ARTHUR, GEORGE   Life of Lord Kitchener. 1920. Illus., 3 vols. George's 635-833 1978 £5

ARTHUR, GEORGE   The Story of the Household Cavalry. 1909-26. Coloured plts., maps, 3 vols., thick imp. 8vo., orig. cloth. F. Edwards 1013-462 1978 £100

ARTHUR, JOHN W.   The Seventeenth Highland Light Infantry, Record of War Service, 1914-1918. Glasgow, 1920. Plts., 8vo., orig. cloth. K Books 244-10 1978 £6

ARTHUR, TIMOTHY SHAY   The Last Penny, and Other Stories. Philadelphia, 1872. Clean, orig. binding. Hayman 71-380 1978 $7.50

ARTHUR, TIMOTHY SHAY   The Mill & The Tavern. New York, (1878). Orig. pict. wrs., worn, 8vo. Americanist 101-10 1978 $20

ARTHUR, TIMOTHY SHAY   Ten Nights in a Bar-Room, And What I Saw There. Glasgow, 1855. 16mo, orig. cloth, gilt, very good, 1st. U.K. ed. Fenning 32-12 1978 £24.50

ARTHUR, TIMOTHY SHAY   Ten Nights in a Bar-Room and What I Saw There. 1873. Frontis, orig. brown cloth, v.g. Jarndyce 16-272 1978 £7

ARTHUR, TIMOTHY SHAY   Three Years in a Man-Trap. Philadelphia, 1872. 1st ed., illus., 8vo., orig. binding. Americanist 101-11 1978 $20

ARTIFICIAL Legs for Ankle and Partial Foot Amputations Made of Aluminum with Rubber Feet Attached... (New York, n.d., 1892?). Wrs., soiled. Hayman 72-100 1978 $8.50

ARTIGO Separado da Convencao Assignada Em Londres Aos 28 de Julho de 1817. Rio de Janeiro, 1818. Sm. folio, unbound. Edwards 1012-676 1978 £50

ARTISTIC Alphabets for Marking and Engrossing. New York, 1897. 8vo., orig. linen wrs., fine. Morrill 241-14 1978 $10

THE ARTISTIC Guide to Chicago and the World's Columbian Exposition. Chicago, 1892. Fold. frontis., cloth. Hayman 72-317 1978 $10

ARTMAN, WILLIAM   Beauties and Achievements of the Blind. Auburn, 1858. Clean, orig. binding. Hayman 71-25 1978 $8.50

ARTS AND CRAFTS EXHIBITION SOCIETY   Arts and Crafts Essays by Members of the... London, 1899. Thick 12mo., blue bds., linen backstrip, fine. Duschnes 220-215 1978 $50

ARTZYBASHEFF, BORIS   Poor Shaydullah. New York, 1931. Illus. by author, 1st ed., d.w. badly torn. Biblo 251-519 1978 $17.50

ARTZYBASHEFF, BORIS   Poor Shaydullah. New York, 1931. 1st ed., plates, very fine, excellent dj. Victoria 34-28 1978 $22.50

ARUNDALE, F.   Illustrations of Jerusalem and Mount Sinai... 1837. Map, tinted litho plts., 4to, orig. cloth, spine repaired. Edwards 1012-63 1978 £150

ASBURY, FRANCIS   The Journal of...Bishop of the Methodist Episcopal Church From August 7, 1771 to December 7, 1815. New York, 1821. 6 vols., 1/2 leather, marbled bds., slightly worn. Broadfoot 50-8 1978 $600

ASCH, SHOLEM   One Destiny. 1945. Austin 79-27a 1978 $7.50

ASCHAM, ANTONY   Of the Confusions and Revolutions of Governments. London, 1649. 1st. ed., 8vo, contemp. calf. Traylen 88-99 1978 £55

ASCHAM, ROGER   The English Works of Roger Ascham, Preceptor to Queen Elizabeth. (1762). First ed., second issue, contemp. calf, 4to. Howes 194-146 1978 £80

ASHBEE, JANE E.   The Courtyer of Count Baldessar Castillio. London, 1900. Thick 8vo, bound in full vellum with ties, fine. Duschnes 220-92 1978 $100

ASHBRIDGE, W. T.   Ashbridge Book Relating to Past and Present Ashbridge Families in America. Toronto, 1912. 4to, spine much worn & chipped, bottom of text waterstained. Baldwins' 51-240 1978 $37.50

ASHBY, J. F.   The Story of the Banks. 1934. Illus., roy. 8vo. George's 635-269 1978 £5

ASHDOWN, CHARLES H.   Armour and Weapons in the Middle Ages. Illus., cr. 8vo. Traylen 88-483 1978 £5

ASHE, ROBERT P.   Two Kings of Uganda; or, Life by the Shores of Victoria Nyanza. London, (1890). Cr. 8vo, folding map, 3 plts., orig. cloth. K Books 239-9 1978 £10

ASHE, SAMUEL A'COURT   History of North Carolina. Greensboro, 1908. Vol. 1, rebound. Broadfoot 50-9c 1978 $40

ASHE, SAMUEL A'COURT   History of North Carolina. Greensboro, 1908.
Vol. I, cloth. Broadfoot 50-9b 1978 $50

ASHE, SAMUEL A'COURT   History of North Carolina. Greensboro, 1908.
Vol. I, 3/4 leather. Broadfoot 50-9a 1978 $60

ASHE, SIMEON   Living Loves Betwixt Christ and Dying Christians.
London, 1654. Sm. 4to, old half calf, rubbed, few top margins closely trimmed.
Traylen 88-100 1978 £15

ASHER, CASH   He Was "Just Folks." The Life and Character of
Warren Gamaliel Harding as Mirrored in the Tributes of the American Press. Chicago, (1923). Cloth, scarce. Hayman 72-30 1978 $10

ASHLEY, C. B.   Gilbert The Trapper or the Heir in Buckskin.
New York, n.d. (1880's?). Clean, orig. binding, one signature pulled, little
rubbed. Hayman 71-27 1978 $7.50

ASHLEY, CLIFFORD W.   The Yankee Whaler. Boston, 1926. Scarce
1st ed., ltd. to 1625 copies, 4to., orig. cloth-backed bds., illus., very good.
Americanist 103-106 1978 $95

ASHLEY, J. M.   Speech of Hon..., of Ohio, Delivered in the
House...January 6, 1865, on the Constitutional Amendment for the Abolition of
Slavery. New York, 1865. Wrs. Hayman 72-708 1978 $15

ASHLEY, M. P.   Financial and Commercial Policy under the Cromwellian Protectorate. 1934. 8vo. George's 635-270 1978 £6.50

ASHLEY, W.   The Bread of our Forefathers, an Inquiry in Economic History. Oxford, 1928. Illus., 8vo. George's 635-271 1978 £7.50

ASHMEAD, HENRY GRAHAM   Historical Sketch of Chester, Pa., on Delaware.
Chester, 1883. Illus., very scarce, fine. MacManus 239-1357 1978 $65

ASHMEAD, HENRY GRAHAM   History of Delaware Co., Pa. Philadelphia,
1884. Illus., lg. thick 4to., rebound, fine. MacManus 239-1358 1978 $100

ASHTON, JAMES M.   Ice-Bound. New York, 1928. Map, illus., 8vo.,
light cover stains, autographed, orig. cloth. Morrill 241-16 1978 $12.50

ASTON, FRANCIS WILLIAM   Isotopes. London, 1922. 8vo., plts., orig.
cloth, fine, first ed. Norman 5-13 1978 $150

ASHTON, JOHN   History of Gambling in England. 1898. 8vo.,
covers stained. George's 635-1500 1978 £6

ASHTON, L.   An Introduction to the Study of Chinese Sculpture.
1924. 4to., map, coloured frontis., plts., orig. pigskin, gilt top, special ed. of
75 copies, signed by author. Quaritch 983-134 1978 $360

ASHTON, T. S.   The Coal Industry of the 18th Century. Manchester, 1929. 8vo. George's 635-275 1978 £8

ASHTON, T. S.   Economic and Social Investigations in Manchester,
1833-1933. 1934. Portraits, 8vo. George's 635-272 1978 £5.25

ASHTON, T. S.   Iron and Steel in the Industrial Revolution. Manchester, 1924. Illus., 8vo. George's 635-274 1978 £7.50

ASHTON-WOLFE, ASHTON   The Thrill of Evil. Boston, 1930. Illus., 1st
ed., spine faded. Biblo 251-280 1978 $15

ASHWORTH, JOHN HENRY   Rathlynn. A Novel. London, 1864. 3 vols.,
orig. cloth, 1st ed., few inner hinges cracked, slightly worn, scarce. MacManus
238-335 1978 $75

ASIATIC SOCIETY OF BENGAL   Asiatic Researches; or, Transactions of the
Society Instituted in Bengal... London, 1799-1812. 1st. ed., printed in England,
II vols. of 20, 4to, engraved maps, coloured plts., bound in full tree calf, gilt
rules, joints cracked, some foxing. Deighton 5-62 1978 £485

ASIMOV, ISAAC   Pebble in the Sky. New York, 1950. First U.S.
ed., fine, repaired d.w. Bell Book 17-322 1978 £25

ASKEW, JOHN   An Exact History of the Battle of Floddon in Verse.
Newcastle, 1809. Orig. tree calf, v.g. Jarndyce 16-273 1978 £15.50

ASPLUND, KARL   Anders Zorn, His Life and Work. London, 1921.
64 plts. Baldwins' 51-26 1978 $37.50

ASQUITH, CYNTHIA   Queen Elizabeth, Her Intimate and Authentic
Life Story. London, (1937). Illus., first ed. Biblo 247-681 1978 $15

ASSEMBLEE Des Notables.... Paris, 1776-1789. 4 vols., 8vo., half calf, gilt
back. Gilhofer 74-53 1978 sFr 1,200

ASSENSIO Y MEJORADA, FRANCISCO   Geometria de la Letra Romana Mayus-
cula y Minuscula. Madrid, 1780. 8vo., marbled bds., engravings, first ed.
Schumann 511-2 1978 sFr 1,200

ASSISI, FRANCIS OF
Please turn to
FRANCESCO D'ASSISI, SAINT

ASTARLOA, PABLO PEDRO DE   Apologia de la Lengua Bascongada, o Ensayo
Critico Filosofico de Su Perfeccion .... Madrid, 1803. 1st ed., quarto, full
contemporary calf, leather label on spine, marbled end-papers, all edges red,
very good copy. Bennett 20-11 1978 $225

ASTIER, F. J.   Graphodromie, ou Ecriture Cursive... Paris,
1816. Eng. plts., 8vo., cont. half red mor., fine, first ed. Schumann 511-3
1978 sFr 500

ASTLEY, THOMAS   A New General Collection of Voyages and
Travels:.... London, 1745-7. 4 vols., 1st ed., small quarto, contemp. tree
calf, 1st vol. rebacked with old spine over new, some browning. Totteridge
29-6 1978 $500

ASTLEY, THOMAS   A New General Collection of Voyages and
Travels... 1745-47. Maps, plts., 4 vols., thick 4to, calf, rebacked, uncut.
Edwards 1012-2 1978 £300

ASTON, FRANCIS WILLIAM   Isotopes. London, 1922. 1st ed., 8vo., orig.
blue cloth, trifle wrinkled on back, very good copy, plts. Current 24-113 1978
$485

ASTON, FRANCIS WILLIAM   Isotopes. London, 1922. 8vo., plts., illus.,
orig. blue cloth, 1st ed. Gilhofer 74-108 1978 sFr 500

ASTON, JOHN   The History of the 12th Battalion East Surrey Regiment. 1936. Plts., imp. 8vo., orig. cloth. F. Edwards 1013-506 1978 £10

AN ASTRONOMICAL Diary: or Almanack, for...1806. Boston, (1805). Hayman
73-11 1978 $10

ASTRUC, JOHANNE JEAN   De Morbis Venereis. Paris, 1738. Six books
in one. Rittenhouse 49-42 1976 $75

ASTRUP, E.   With Peary Near The Pole. 1898. Map, portraits, plts., illus., orig. cloth, 8vo. Edwards 1012-559 1978 £15

AT THE COUNCIL-Chamber in Whitehall. London, 1688. Sm. folio, unbound.
Gurney 75-4 1978 £20

ATCHESON, N.   Report of a Case Recently Argued and Determined
on the Validity of a Sentence of Condemnation by an Enemy's Consul in a Neutral
Port.... 1800. 8vo., wrappers. F. Edwards 1013-7 1978 £10

ATHEARN, WALTER S.   Measurements and Standards in Religious Education. 1924. Illus. Austin 79-37 1978 $27.50

ATHENAEUS   Dipnosophistarum Sive Coenae Sapientium
Libri XV. Venice, 1556. Tall folio, vellum, 1st Latin ed. Salloch 348-7 1978
$225

THE ATHENIAN Oracle. 1706-08. 3rd ed & 2nd ed., 3 vols., 8vo., contemp.
panelled calf. Quaritch 979-129 1978 $250

ATHERTON, GERTRUDE   Adventures of a Novelist. 1932. Illus. Austin 82-63 1978 $10

ATHERTON, GERTRUDE   Adventures of a Novelist. 1932. Illus., first ed. Austin 82-62 1978 $12.50

ATHERTON, GERTRUDE   American Wives and English Husbands. 1901. Austin 82-64 1978 $8.50

ATHERTON, GERTRUDE   Ancestors. New York, 1907. Orig. binding, clean, spine faded, private bookplt., 1st. ed. Hayman 71-215 1978 $8.50

ATHERTON, GERTRUDE   Ancestors. 1907. First ed. Austin 82-65 1978 $12.50

ATHERTON, GERTRUDE   The Aristocrats. 1902. Austin 82-6o 1978 $7.50

ATHERTON, GERTRUDE   The Avalanche. 1919. 229 pages. Austin 82-68 1978 $8.50

ATHERTON, GERTRUDE   The Avalanche. 1919. First edition. Austin 82-67 1978 $11

ATHERTON, GERTRUDE   Before the Gringo Came. N.Y., (1894). 1st ed., pictorial red cloth, portion of A.L.s from author laid in. Houle 10-15 1978 $55

ATHERTON, GERTRUDE   California. An Intimate History. 1914. Biblo BL781-262 1978 $10

ATHERTON, GERTRUDE   Can Women be Gentlemen? 1938. First ed., d.j., signed by Atherton. Austin 82-69 1978 $27.50

ATHERTON, GERTRUDE   The Conqueror. 1902. First ed., first issue. Austin 82-71 1978 $17.50

ATHERTON, GERTRUDE   The Conqueror. London, 1902. First English ed., some cover spots but good. Austin 82-73 1978 $27.50

ATHERTON, GERTRUDE   The Conqueror. 1902. Maroon cloth, first ed., white lettering on backstrip flaking off, front cover bright and clear. Austin 82-73 1978 $15

ATHERTON, GERTRUDE   The Conqueror. 1902. First ed., maroon cloth, with typewritten note signed by author. Austin 82-70 1978 $47.50

ATHERTON, GERTRUDE   The Conqueror. 1916. Austin 82-74 1978 $8.50

ATHERTON, GERTRUDE   A Daughter of the Vine. 1899. First ed. Austin 82-75 1978 $22.50

ATHERTON, GERTRUDE   The Gorgeous Isle. 1908. First ed., cover rubbed. Austin 82-77 1978 $12.50

ATHERTON, GERTRUDE   The Goregeous Isle. 1908. Illus., first ed., inscribed by Atherton. Austin 82-76 1978 $37.50

ATHERTON, GERTRUDE   House of Lee. New York, 1940. 1st ed., d.j., good, inscribed by author. Houle 10-16 1978 $15

ATHERTON, GERTRUDE   The Living Present. 1917. First ed., signed by Atherton. Austin 82-78 1978 $20

ATHERTON, GERTRUDE   Mrs. Balfame. 1916. Austin 82-79 1978 $8.50

ATHERTON, GERTRUDE   My San Francisco. 1946. Austin 82-80 1978 $10

ATHERTON, GERTRUDE   Perch of the Devil. 1914. First ed., signed by author. Austin 82-81 1978 $20

ATHERTON, GERTRUDE   Rezanov. 1906. Signed. Austin 82-82 1978 $22.50

ATHERTON, GERTRUDE   Rulers of Kings. 1904. Brown dec. cloth, first ed., note on flyleaf signed by author. Austin 82-83 1978 $47.50

ATHERTON, GERTRUDE   Rulers of Kings. 1904. First ed. Austin 82-84 1978 $17.50

ATHERTON, GERTRUDE   Senator North. 1900. Austin 82-85 1978 $8.50

ATHERTON, GERTRUDE   The Sophisticates. 1931. First ed., signed by author. Austin 82-86 1978 $20

ATHERTON, GERTRUDE   The Splendid Idle Forties. 1902. Illus., first ed. Austin 82-87 1978 $17.50

ATHERTON, GERTRUDE   Tower of Ivory. 1910. Austin 82-89 1978 $8.50

ATHERTON, GERTRUDE   What Dreams May Come True. A Romance. Chicago, (1888). 12mo., orig. cloth, 1st ed., covers very slightly soiled, but near-fine. MacManus 238-419 1978 $150

ATHERTON, GERTRUDE   The White Morning. 1918. First ed., signed by Atherton. Austin 82-91 1978 $20

ATHERTON, GERTRUDE   The White Morning. 1918. Ex-lib. Austin 82-92 1978 $8.50

ATHERTON, WILLIAM   Narrative of the Suffering and Defeat of the North-Western Army... Frankfort, 1842. 12mo, orig. marbled bds., printed label on front cover, new leather spine. Edwards 1012-465 1978 £65

ATIYA, A. S.   The Crusade in the later Middle Ages. 1938. Plts. in colour, maps, 8vo. Upcroft 12-14 1978 £15

ATKINS, J. B.   Further Memorials of the Royal Yacht Squadron 1901-38. 1939. Illus., roy. 8vo. George's 635-800 1978 £12.50

ATKINS, J. W. H.   English Literary Criticism – the Medieval Phase. Cambridge, 1943. 8vo. Upcroft 12-16 1978 £8.50

ATKINS, JOHN BLACK   The Relief of Ladysmith. 1900. 2nd. & best ed., plts., map, 8vo, orig. pictorial cloth gilt, faded, o/w very good copy. Sawyer 298-60 1978 £46

ATKINSON, BROOKS   The Greenwood Hat. New York, 1938. Nice in d.w. Desmarais B-58 1978 $10

ATKINSON, C. T.   The Dorsetshire Regiment. Oxford, 1947. 2 vols., 8vo., orig. cloth. F. Edwards 1013-511 1978 £35

ATKINSON, C. T.   The History of the South Wales Borderers 1914-1918. 1931. Roy. 8vo., orig. cloth, maps. F. Edwards 1013-498 1978 £18

ATKINSON, C. T.   Marlborough and the Rise of the British Army. 1930. Plts., maps, sm. 8vo., orig. cloth. F. Edwards 1013-357 1978 £4

ATKINSON, CHRISTOPHER WILLIAM   A Historical and Statistical Account of New Brunswick.... Edinburgh, 1844. 3rd ed., folding map, plt., woodcuts, sm. 8vo., orig. leather rebacked, old spine laid down. Edwards 1012-414 1978 £35

ATKINSON, CHRISTOPHER WILLIAM   A Historical and Statistical Account of New Brunswick, B.N.A., With Advice to Emigrants. Edinburgh, 1844. 3rd ed. rebound, leather spine, gilt edged pages, folding map. Hood's 115-198 1978 $85

ATKINSON, FRANK H.   Atkinson Sign Painting Up to Now.   Chicago, (1909). Illus., oblong 4to., binding stained, orig. cloth. Morrill.241-17 1978 $25

ATKINSON, HENRY GEORGE   Letters On The Laws of Man's Nature & Development. 1851. 1st ed., half title, orig. green cloth, block in blind, spine faded, otherwise very good. Jarndyce 16-275 1978 £56

ATKINSON, JOHN   Memorials of Methodism in New Jersey... Philadelphia, 1860. 1st ed., frontis., covers worn, foxing, otherwise good copy. MacManus 239-1236 1978 $35

ATKINSON, JOSEPH   The History of Newark, N.J.   Newark, 1878. Illus., 4to. MacManus 239-1237 1978 $30

ATKINSON, WILLIAM B.   A Biographical Dictionary of Contemporary American Physicians and Surgeons. Philadelphia, 1880. Second ed., enlarged and revised, very slight wear on edges of bds. Rittenhouse 49-43 1976 $75

ATKINSON, WILLIAM CHRISTOPHER Historical & Statistical Account... Please turn to
ATKINSON, CHRISTOPHER WILLIAM

ATKINSON, WILLIAM WALKER   Suggestion and Auto-Suggestion. Chicago, 1909. 8vo., orig. cloth, 1st ed. Morrill 241-18 1978 $10

ATLAS of Montgomery and Fulton Counties from Actual Surveys by...B. Nichols. New York, 1868. Tall, square folio, fine maps, plans, prtd. in color, orig. cloth covers, lea. backstrip, good cond., maps near fine. Butterfield 21-283 1978 $85

ATLAS of Otsego County from Actual Surveys by...F. W. Beers. New York, 1869. Colored maps, & plans, orig. cloth, worn but holding, maps fine & bright. Butterfield 21-339 1978 $85

ATLAS of Susquehanna Co., Pennsylvania... New York, 1872. Folio, orig. cloth, rebacked. MacManus 239-1691 1978 $100

ATLEE, EDWIN A.   Essays at Poetry, or a Collection of Fugitive Pieces;.... Philadelphia, 1828. 1st ed., orig. boards, uncut, spine worn, 8vo. Americanist 101-14 1978 $35

ATTAR, FERID-EDIN   Pend-Nameh. Ou Le Livre de Conseils... Paris, 1819. 8vo., calf rebacked with label. Salloch 348-8 1978 $145

ATTILA, A Tragedy. 1832. 12mo., half calf, frontispiece. P. M. Hill 142-244 1978 £10

ATWATER, EDWARD E.   History of the City of New Haven to the Present Time. New York, 1887. 1st ed., thick 4to., illus., cloth, very good. MacManus 239-953 1978 $55

ATWATER, FRANCIS   Atwater: History and Genealogy. Meriden, 1901. Illus., front inner hinge split. Biblo BL781-54 1978 $12.50

ATWATER, I.   History of the City of Minneapolis. New York, 1893. 2 vols., lg. thick 4tos., rebound, illus., fine. MacManus 239-1059 1978 $65

ATWATER, RICHARD   Mr. Popper's Penguins. Boston, 1938. 1st ed., color plates, B&W drawings, fine copy. Victoria 34-488 1978 $25

ATWOOD, A.   Glimpses in Pioneer Life on Puget Sound... Seattle, 1903. Illus., original cloth, 1st ed. Ginsberg 14-38 1978 $30

ATWOOD, ANNE   Being Made of Earth. Pasadena, 1940. 1st ed., sm. 4to., illus. with orig. sofe focus photographs by author, orig. half cloth over simulated wood bds., inscribed poem by author. Houle 10-17 1978 $35

AUBER, PETER   China. 1834. 1st. ed., folding coloured map, 8vo, inscription erased from title, some light foxing, very good copy, recent quarter blue morocco, gilt, gilt spine, label. Fenning 32-13 1978 £26

AUBERT, LOUIS   Americains et Japonais. Paris, 1908. Fldg. map, in French, paper. Austin 79-38 1978 $47.50

AUBERT DE GASPE, PHILLIPPE Les Anciens Canadiens. Quebec, 1864. Deuxieme ed., broche, couv. orig. imprimes. Wolfe 39-28 1978 $100

AUBREY, JOHN   Lives of Eminent Men. 1813. 2 vols. in 3, 8vo., 19th-century half calf, gilt backs, marbled sides, first ed. P. M. Hill 142-25 1978 £52

AUCASSIN and Nicolette. New York, (n.d.). Sq. 8vo, vellum over boards, gilt, t.e.g., decor. endpapers, color plts., music and illus., 1 of 125 copies signed by Evelyn Paul. Duschnes 220-7 1978 $110

AUCHAMPAUGH, PHILIP GERALD   James Buchanan and His Cabinet on the Eve of Secession. (Lancaster), 1926. 1st ed., illus., inscribed by author, scarce. MacManus 239-33 1978 $37.50

AUCHAMPAUGH, PHILIP GERALD   James Buchanan and His Cabinet on the Eve of Secession. Lancaster, 1926. Wrs., Bell Wiley's copy. Broadfoot's 44-13 1978 $8

AUCLAIR, L'ABBE ELIE-J.   Histoire de la Paroisse de Sant-Joseph-de-Soulanges ou Les Cedres (1702-1927). Montreal, (1927). Illus. Wolfe 39-29 1978 $20

AUDEN, WYSTAN HUGH   Another Time. 1940. First English ed., very good. Bell Book 16-025 1978 £15

AUDEN, WYSTAN HUGH   Another Time. 1940. Very good, first English ed. Bell Book 17-029 1978 £17.50

AUDEN, WYSTAN HUGH   The Ascent of F6; a tragedy. London, 1936. First ed., orig. binding, spine and covers somewhat darkened and worn, nice. Rota 211-29 1978 £18

AUDEN, WYSTAN HUGH   City Without Walls, and Other Poems. Mint in d.w. Desmarais B-39 1978 $7.50

AUDEN, WYSTAN HUGH   The Collected Poetry of W. H. Auden. New York, (1945). 1st ed., 1st issue, 8vo., 1st binding with spine panel in brown, top edges stained dark green & orig. dark blue-green cloth, near mint. Current 24-3 1978 $85

AUDEN, WYSTAN HUGH   The Collected Poetry of W. H. Auden. New York, 1945. First U.S. ed., near fine. Bell Book 16-026 1978 £15

AUDEN, WYSTAN HUGH   Collected Shorter Poems, 1930-44. 1950. Very good, slightly worn d.w., first English ed. Bell Book 16-027 1978 £15

AUDEN, WYSTAN HUGH   The Dog Beneath the Skin. London, 1935. Ownership inscription, covers soiled, nice. Desmarais B-40 1978 $35

AUDEN, WYSTAN HUGH   The Dog Beneath the Skin. 1935. Spine slightly dull, lower joint little split, else good, first English ed. Bell Book 17-038 1978 £12.50

AUDEN, WYSTAN HUGH   Education: today - and tomorrow. Hogarth Press, 1939. Very good, wraps, first English ed. Bell Book 16-033 1978 £25

AUDEN, WYSTAN HUGH   In Letters of Red. 1938. Frontis. by Low, cr. 8vo., cover trifle faded and stained. Howes 194-598 1978 £7.50

AUDEN, WYSTAN HUGH   On The Frontier. 1938. Very good, first English ed. Bell Book 16-032 1978 £15

AUDEN, WYSTAN HUGH   On this Island. New York, (1937). Brown cloth, 1st Amer. ed., fine in worn dust jacket. Bradley 49-10 1978 $50

AUDEN, WYSTAN HUGH   The Orators. 1932. First ed., orig. black cloth, 8vo. Howes 194-597 1978 £30

AUDEN, WYSTAN HUGH   Our Hunting Fathers. (Cambridge), 1935. 1st ed., decor. paper wrs. with silver label, slightly tarnished, ltd. to 22 copies, #D of 5 copies. Quaritch 979-255 1978 $330

AUDEN, WYSTAN HUGH   Poem. 1933. 12mo., 1st ed., decor. wrs. with grey label, 1 of 22 copies, #2 of 5 on Kelmscott. Quaritch 979-256 1978 $315

AUDEN, WYSTAN HUGH   Poems. London, 1930. 8vo, stiff white card with light-blue wr., fine, drop-back cloth box with printed spine label, 1st ed. Desmarais 1-19 1978 $325

AUDEN, WYSTAN HUGH   The Poet's Tongue. 1935. 2 vols., spine faded, good, first English ed. Bell Book 16-030 1978 £17.50

AUDEN, WYSTAN HUGH   The Poet's Tongue: an Anthology. 1935. Very good, slightly worn d.w., first English ed. Bell Book 17-039 1978 £16.50

AUDEN, WYSTAN HUGH   Sir, No Man's Enemy. New Haven, 1932. 12mo., handwritten & illuminated in gold & colours, orig. watercolour frontis., decor. paper wrs., Prokosch bkplt., #1 of 5 copies, duplicate of frontis. in colours laid in. Quaritch 979-257 1978 $275

AUDEN, WYSTAN HUGH   Some Poems. London, (1940). Bds., slight smudging & browning to spine. Dawson's 447-203 1978 $20

AUDEN, WYSTAN HUGH   Sonnet. (Cambridge), 1935. 1st ed., decor. paper wrs., ltd. to 22 copies, #III of 5 on Brussels vellum. Quaritch 979-258 1978 $300

AUDEN, WYSTAN HUGH   Spain. 1937. Very good, slightly faded wraps, first English ed. Bell Book 17-037 1978 £18.50

AUDEN, WYSTAN HUGH   This Lunar Beauty. New Haven, 1932. 12mo., handwritten & illuminated in gold & colours, orig. watercolour frontis., decor. paper wrs., Prokosch bkplt., #4 of 5 copies, "colour model" for frontis. laid in. Quaritch 979-259 1978 $330

AUDEN, WYSTAN HUGH   Two Poems. 1934. 12mo., 1st ed., gold decor. wrs., ltd. to 22 copies, #a of 5 on Curfew. Quaritch 979-260 1978 $330

AUDET, F. J.   Canadian Historical Dates and Events, 1492-1915. Ottawa, 1917. Hood 116-5 1978 $45

AUDIFFREDI, GIOVANNI BATTISTA   Specimen Historico-Criticum Editionum Italicarum Saeculi XV. Romae, 1794. 1st ed., quarto, orig. marbled bds., later calf spine, gilt title, fine. Bennett 20-12 1978 $275

AUDIGUIER, VITAL D'   A Tragi-Comicall History of Our Times Under The Borrowed Names of Lisander, And Calista. 1627. 1st. English ed., folio, contemp. calf rebacked, some waterstains and traces of use. Hannas 54-4 1978 £125

AUDIN, MARIUS   L'Epopee du Papier. Paris, 1945. Copy #554, illus. Battery Park 1-438 1978 $50

AUDSLEY, G. A.   Ceramic Art of Japan. 1881. Roy. 8vo., tinted plts., orig. red. cloth gilt. Quaritch 983-135 1978 $160

AUDSLEY, W.   Polychromatic Decoration as applied to Buildings in the Mediaeval Styles. London, 1882. Coloured plts., folio, orig. cloth. K Books 244-11 1978 £60

AUDUBON, JOHN JAMES   The Birds of America, From Drawings Made in the United States and Their Territories. New York, 1870. 8 vols., bound as issued in 1/2 mor., marbled boards, gilt lettering on spines, 500 lithograph plts., plts. by J. T. Bowen with color backgrounds, fine, tight set, minimal wear, 1st ed. Desmarais 1-Cover 1978 $4,000

AUDUBON, JOHN JAMES   Delineations of American Scenery and Character. New York, 1926. Frontis. MacManus 239-34 1978 $20

AUDUBON, JOHN JAMES   Journal of John James Audubon made While Obtaining Subscriptions to his "Birds of America" 1840-1843. Cambridge, 1929. Presentation bookplate, uncut, untrimmed, mint, 8vo, orig. cloth. Book Chest. 17-23 1978 $125

AUDUBON, JOHN JAMES   Ornithological Biography, or an Account of the Habits of the Birds of the U.S.A.:.... Edinburgh, 1831. 3/4 leather, very scuffed and worn at hinges and corners, slight scattered foxing, tall 8vo, orig. cloth, Vol. I only including rare Prospectus for Vol. I plus plt. list. Book Chest 17-22 1978 $155

AUDUBON, JOHN JAMES   Ornithological Biography or an Account of the Habits of the Birds of the United States of America.... Philadelphia, 1832. Newly rebound in 3/4 brown morocco, autographed to Miss Fanney Kemble. Baldwins' 51-173 1978 $2000

AUERBACH, FELIX   The Zeiss Works & the Carl Zeiss Foundation in Jena, their Scientific, Technical & Sociological Developments & Importance. London, n.d. (ca. 1927). Illus., 8vo., orig. cloth, very good. Americanist 103-64 1978 $25

AUGE, M.   Lives of the Eminent Dead and Biographical Notices of Prominent Living Citizens of Montgomery County, Pa. Norristown, 1879. MacManus 239-1359 1978 $17.50

AUGUSTIN, BRUNO   De Medicis Quos Halberstadiensis, Quedlinburgensis, Wernigerodensi Ditio Vel Genuit Vel Aliut. Halberstadii, 1840. 8vo., contemp. red lea.-backed bds., only ed. Offenbacher 30-7 1978 $135

AUGUSTIN, GEORGE   History of Yellow Fever. New Orleans, 1909. Frontispiece, very thick 8vo., cloth, first ed. Rittenhouse 49-44 1976 $60

AUGUSTINO DA SIENA, PADRE   Opera... Venice, 1570. Sm. 4to., mod. vellum, calligraphic samples cut in wood, fine, rare. Schumann 511-4 1978 sFr 8,750

AUGUSTINUS, AURELIUS   Les Confessions, Abregees, ou l'on n'a Mis Que est le Plus Touchant. 1738. Old Calf. Allen 234-64 1978 $10

AUGUSTINUS, AURELIUS   Confessions. 1900. Ltd. to 400 copies, printed on Arnold and Foster's unbleached handmade paper, illus., parchment. George's 635-1024 1978 £6.50

AUGUSTINUS, AURELIUS   The Meditations, Soliloquia and Manual. 1686. Title mounted, soiled, 12mo., diced calf, rubbed. George's 635-1025 1978 £7.50

AUGUSTINUS, AURELIUS   Les Soliloques, Les Meditations et le Manual. 1706. Old calf, spine rather worn. Allen 234-66 1978 $10

AULAIRE, INGRI (MORTENSON) D'   Don't Count Your Chicks. New York, 1943. First ed., plts., d.j. Victoria 34-219 1978 $15

AULAIRE, INGRI (MORTENSON) D'   The Star Spangled Banner. New York, 1942. First ed., quarto, color plts., v.g. Victoria 34-218 1978 $12.50

AULNOY, MARIE CATHERINE JUMELLE DE BERNEVILLE, COMTESSE D'   Memoirs of the Court of England in 1675. 1913, 1927. Plts., octavo, good. Upcroft 10-5 1978 £6

AULT, N.   Seventeenth Century Lyrics From the Original Texts. 1928, 1950. Octavo, good. Upcroft 10-6 1978 £7.50

AULTMAN, MILLER & CO.   Buckeye Mower & Table Rake Reaper. New York, (1881?). Wrps. Hayman 71-517 1978 $12.50

AUMONT, ANTOINE DE   Lettre du Marechal d'Aumont au Roy Ou il lui Rend Conte de ce Qu'il a Fait aves son Armee Depuis le Commancement de la Campagne iusques au 6. Septembre. (N.P.), 1651. Sm. folio. Gilhofer 74-65a 1978 sFr 100

AUNGERVILLE, RICHARD   Philobiblon, a Treatise on the Love of Books. Albany, 1861. 1st Amer. ed., 1 of 200 copies on small paper, cloth covers bubbled & worn. Butterfield 21-285 1978 $17.50

AUNGERVILLE, RICHARD   The Philobiblon of.... New York, 1945. Ltd. to 600 copies, orig. cloth, pub. slipcase, fine. MacManus 238-902 1978 $25

AUNGERVILLE, RICHARD   The Philobibion. California, 1948. 1st print., fine, d.j., leather bookplate. Ballinger 11-27 1978 $17.50

AUNGERVILLE, RICHARD   Philobiblon. Berkeley, 1948. D.w. Battery Park 1-354 1978 $15

AUNT Louisa's Railway A. B. C. London, c.1875. Quarto, color plts., spine edge chipped, sewn, almost fine. Victoria 34-34 1978 $25

AURELIUS ANTONINUS, MARCUS   The Commentaries of the Emperor.... London, 1747. 8vo., 1/2 calf over marbled bds., red leather label. Salloch 348-135 1978 $85

AURELIUS ANTONINUS, MARCUS   The Emperor Marcus Antoninus his Conversation with himself. 1702. Portrait, very good, contemp. panelled calf, second ed., 8vo. Howes 194-147 1978 £25

AURELIUS ANTONINUS, MARCUS   Meditations Concerning Himself. 1673. Fourth ed., sm. 8vo., contemp. calf, joints cracked. Howes 194-71 1978 £30

AURELIUS ANTONINUS, MARCUS   Marcus Aurelius Antoninus, the Roman Emperour, His Meditations, Concerning Himself... London, 1673. 4th ed., 8vo., cont. calf. Salloch 348-134 1978 $75

AURELIUS ANTONINUS, MARCUS   The Meditations of ... Glasgow, 1742. 12mo, contemp. calf worn. Hannas 54-5 1978 £24

AURELIUS VICTOR, SEXTUS   Historia Romana, cum Notis Integris D. Machanei.... Amsterdam & Utrecht, 1733. Plt., frontispiece, 4to., contemp. blind-stamped vellum. Howes 194-525 1978 £35

AUSONIUS, DECIMUS MAGNUS   Patchwork Quilt. Fanfrolico Press. Full bound blue buckram, patchwork design blind stamped on covers, Charles I paper, 1 of 400 numbered copies, signed by Jack Lindsay. Battery Park 1-98 1978 $75

AUSTELLUNG Der Werke Von William Blake. Zurich, 1947. Color plt., plts., very good or better. Limestone 9-27 1978 $16.50

AUSTEN, JANE   The Complete Novels. London, 1928. One vol. ed., 8vo., orig. cloth. K Books 244-13 1978 £5

AUSTEN, JANE   Mansfield Park. 1853. Engraved frontis, half title, green calf, red label, fine. Jarndyce 16-277 1978 £18

AUSTEN, JANE   Northanger Abbey: and Persuasion. 1818. 4 vols., sm. 8vo., 1st ed., contemp. half mor., tall copy. Quaritch 979-13 1978 $950

AUSTEN, JANE   Pride and Prejudice. London, 1908. 2 vols., 12mo., illus. in color. Biblo 247-346 1978 $15

AUSTEN, JANE   Sense & Sensibility. 1813. 2nd. ed., 3 vols., half brown calf, mottled bds., bookplt. removed from vol. 1, leading hinge vol. 1 slightly weak, otherwise fine. Jarndyce 16-276 1978 £120

AUSTEN, JANE   Sense and Sensibility: A Novel. 1813. 3 vols., 2nd. ed., 12mo, red half morocco. Hannas 54-6 1978 £95

AUSTEN, JANE   Sense and Sensibility, Emma, Lady Susan, Memoir, Pride and Prejudice, Mansfield Park, Persuasion, and Northanger Abbey. London, 1886-1901. 6 vols., octavo, bound uniformly in 3/4 blue mor. and cloth, gilt rules, raised spine bands. Bennett 7-4 1978 $250

AUSTEN-LEIGH, JAMES EDWARD   Memoir of Jane Austen. Oxford, 1926. 8vo, plts., orig. paper bds., cloth spine, uncut. Hannas 54-7 1978 £5

AUSTIN, ALFRED   My Satire and Its Censors. London, 1861. 1st ed., orig. cloth, scarce, covers a bit darkened and stained. MacManus 238-163 1978 $50

AUSTIN, EMILY M.   Mormonism; or, Life Among the Mormons. Madison, 1882. Orig. cloth, 1st ed. Ginsberg 14-638 1978 $75

AUSTIN, HORACE   Minnesota: Its Resources and Progress:.... St. Paul, 1870. Large folding map, original printed wr., 1st ed., inscribed by author. Ginsberg 14-543 1978 $95

AUSTIN, J. G.   Outpost. Boston, 1867. Cloth, 1st ed. Hayman 73-160 1978 $10

AUSTIN, J. P.   The Blue and The Gray. Atlanta, 1899. Cover soiled, Bell Wiley's copy. Broadfoot's 44-497 1978 $40

AUSTIN, JOHN   A Plea for the Constitution. 1859. 8vo., unbound, inscribed by author, title dust-soiled. P. M. Hill 142-26 1978 £12

AUSTIN, MARY   The Land of Little Rain. Boston, 1903. 1st ed., original pictorial cloth, t.e.g., illus. Jenkins 116-38 1978 $60

AUSTIN, MARY   The Lovely Lady. 1913. First ed., frontis. Austin 82-93 1978 $20

AUSTIN, MOSES   A Sumary Description of the Lead Mines in Upper Louisiana .... Washington, 1804. Sewn, exceedingly rare. Jenkins 116-40 1978 $450

AUSTIN, SAM C.   Comp. Records, Statistics and Best Performances. New York, 1908. Portrs., 24mo., unbound. Morrill 241-31 1978 $7.50

AUSTIN, SARAH   Characteristics of Goethe. 1833. First ed., 3 vols., portrait, orig. cloth-backed bds., printed labels, entirely uncut, nice, in orig. state. Howes 194-891 1978 £40

AUSTIN, STELLA   Mother Bunch. London, 1885. 2nd ed., illus., gilt pictorial binding, bright, very fine. Victoria 34-37 1978 $20

AUSTIN, STELLA.   Our Next Door Neighbor. London, 1882. 3rd ed., illus., fine copy in handsome gilt & black pictorial cloth. Victoria 34-36 1978 $15

AUSTIN, STEPHEN F.   Address of the Honorable S. F. Austin, One of the Commissioners of Texas, Delivered in Louisville, Kentucky, on the 7th of March 1836. New York, 1836. Full calf, gilt. Jenkins 116-1577 1978 $650

AUSTIN, WALTER   William Austin, the Creator of Peter Rugg. Boston, 1925. 8vo., illus., d.w., first ed. Morrill 239-293 1978 $12.50

AUSTIN, WILLIAM   Literary Papers of William Austin. Boston, 1890. Portr., 8vo., ex-lib., ed. ltd. to 250 copies. Morrill 239-292 1978 $10

THE AUSTIN Papers, 1789-1827. Washington, 1924. 2 vols., lacks 2 vols. Jenkins 116-1518 1978 $25

AUSTIN, Texas: "The City of the Violet Crown". Austin, 1917. Printed wr., illus. Jenkins 116-1369 1978 $40

AUSUBEL, NATHAN   Superman: The Life of Frederick the Great. New York, 1931. Covers faded, author's signed pres. Biblo 247-686 1978 $20

AN AUTHENTIC Account of the Late Unfortunate Dr. William Dodd. N.P., 1777. 1st ed.?, 8vo., disbound, corner of title torn, removing 4 letters. Hannas 54-87 1978 £6

AUTOBIOGRAPHY of Charles Biddle, Vice President of the Supreme Executive Council of Penna. Philadelphia, 1883. MacManus 239-1375 1978 $40

THE AUTOMOTOR and Horseless Vehicle Pocket Book of Automotive Formulae and Commercial Intelligence for 1898. London, 1898. Sm. 8vo., ads, illus. & tables, orig. limp mor., gilt, rubbed & fr. cover creased, but very good copy. Norman 5-15 1978 $85

AVARY, MYRTA LOCKETT   A Virginia Girl in the Civil War 1861-1865. NY, 1903. Soiled, worn cover, Bell Wiley's Copy. Broadfoot's 44-16 1978 $16.00

AVERA, HOMER   Dr. Roger's Ordeal. 1938. Austin 82-95 1978 $17.50

AVERA CRUCE, ALFONSO   Dialectica. Madrid, 1945. Facs. ed., ltd. no. ed., 4to., wrs. Salloch 348-276 1978 $60

AVERILL, ESTHER   Daniel Boone. Paris, (1931). Folio, 1st ed., 1st work of Fedor. Rojankovsky, 1st Domino Press book, color throughout and on board covers, mint copy. Victoria 34-704 1978 $50

AVERILL, M.   Japanese Flower Arrangement. New York, 1913. 8vo., orig. cloth. Book Chest 17-450 1978 $9

AVERY, A. C.   Memorial Address on Life and Character of Lieutenant General D. H. Hill, May 10th, 1893. Raleigh, N. C., 1893. Wrs., front wr. chipped. Bell Wiley's copy. Broadfoot 46-6 1978 $25

AVERY, CLARA A.   Averell-Averill-Avery Family. 1914. Nicely bound in half lea., fine condition. Baldwins' 51-241 1978 $37.50

AVERY, S. P.   Collection of Prints & Art Books in the N. Y.
Public Library. 1901. Battery Park 1-313 1978 $25

AVILA, COMTESSE DE   Pour La Femme. Paris, 1912. 8vo, full blue
calf, pres. inscription on half title. Traylen 88-426 1978 £8

AVIS, F. C.   Edward Philip Prince. London, 1939.
1st ed., 1 of 1,000 ed. copies made & printed for author, plts., d.j., fine.
Limestone 9-234 1978 $35

AVISON, CHARLES   An Essay on Musical Expression. London, 1753.
Second ed., contemp. calf, 8vo. K Books 244-15 1978 £20

AVITI Epistola Ad Perillam, Virginem Scotam; Editoris Ecphrasi et Annotationibus
Illustrata. Londini, 1760. 1st. ed., 4to, disbound, some marginal water-stains.
Hannas 54-8 1978 £12.50

AWDE, ROBERT   Jubilee, Patriotic and Other Poems. Toronto,
1887. Some slight staining. Hood 116-794 1978 $12.50

AXE, JOHN WORTLEY   The Horse, Its Treatment in Health and Diseases.
1906 (1908). Plts., some in colour, illus., 9 vols., roy. 8vo, orig. cloth, gilt,
tear in 1 leaf without loss, an earlier owner indented initials on upper cover,
however, nice set. Fenning 32-17 1978 £45

AXELSON, ERIC   South-East Africa 1488-1530. London, (1940).
12 plts. & maps, 8vo, orig. cloth. K Books 239-10 1978 £7

AYER, MARY FARWELL   Boston Common in Colonial and Provincial Days.
Boston, 1903. Illus. Biblo 247-100 1978 $15

AYERS, NATHANIEL M.   Building a New Empire. New York, 1910. Illus.,
orig. cloth, 1st ed. Ginsberg 14-705 1978 $35

AYLIFFE, JOHN   The Antient and Present State of the University
of Oxford. 1714. 1st. ed., 2 vols., 8vo, contemp. calf rebacked. Hannas
54-9 1978 £55

AYLWARD, ALFRED   The Transvaal of Today. Edinburgh, 1878. 8vo,
full blue crushed morocco gilt, heavy foxing. K Books 239-11 1978 £30

AYMAR, GORDON C.   A Treasury of Sea Stories. New York, (1948).
Illus., 1st ed., name on flyleaf. Biblo BL781-627 1978 $9.50

AYMONIER, E.   Dictionnaire khmer-francais. Saigon, 1878.
Folio, half calf, ltd. publication. Van der Peet 127-9 1978 Dfl 290

AYRES, ALFRED   The Verbalist. Toronto, 1884. Green cloth,
loosely bound, front endpapers missing, stain on cover. Hood 117-458 1978
$12.50

AYRES, ANNE   The Life and Work of William Augustus Muhlenberg. New York, 1881. Clean, sl. wear at top of spine, orig. binding. Hayman
71-31 1978 $10

AYRES, C. E.   The Divine Right of Capital. Boston, 1946.
Austin 80-409 1978 $11

AYRES, C. E.   The Theory of Economic Progress. Chapel Hill,
1944. 1st ed. Jenkins 116-49 1978 $15

AYRTON, M.   Wrought Iron and Its Decorative Use. 1929.
Folio, frontis., buckram. Quaritch 983-122 1978 $95

AYSCOUGH, FLORENCE   The Autobiography of a Chinese Dog. Boston,
1926. Sketches by L. Douglass, 8vo, orig. cloth. Book Chest 17-26 1978
$12.50

AYSCOUGH, FLORENCE   A Chinese Mirror. Boston, (1925). Author's
signed pres., illus., frontis has artist's signed pres., edges rubbed. Biblo 247-915
1978 $15

AYSCOUGH, FLORENCE   Firecracker Land. Boston, 1932. Illus., first
ed., author's signed pres. Biblo 247-916 1978 $12.50

AYSCOUGH, SAMUEL   An Index to the Remarkable Passages and Words
made use of by Shakespeare. 1790. Half calf, roy. 8vo., first ed. Howes 194-
456 1978 $22.50

AYSCOUGH, SAMUEL   An Index to the Remarkable Passages and Words
Made Use of by Shakespeare. 1790. Roy. 8vo, rebound in grey bds., paper
spine & label. Eaton 45-29 1978 £6

AYSCU, EDWARD   A Historie Contayning the Warres, Treaties,
Marriages and Other Occurents betweene England and Scotland,.... London,
1607. Quarto, half-calf over marbled boards, gilt-ruled spine with floral devices,
gilt, woodcut devices, floral initials, wide-margined text, exceedingly scarce.
Bennett 20-13 1978 $300

AYTOUN, WILLIAM EDMONDSTOUNE   Firmilian: or the Student of Badajoz.
Edinburgh, 1854. 8vo, original red cloth (a little dark), 1st ed., very scarce.
Ximenes 47-11 1978 $90

AZUNI, DOMENICO ALBERTO   Dissertation sur L'Origine de la Boussole.
Paris, (1805). 8vo, contemp. bds., calf back. F. Edwards 1013-9 1978 £21

AZUNI, DOMENICO ALBERTO   Dissertation sur l'Origine de la Boussole.
Paris, 1809. Second ed., 8vo., half calf. F. Edwards 1013-10 1978 £30

B

B., A.   Gloria Britannica. 1689. Sm. 4to., modern calf. F. Edwards 1013-11 1978 £500

B. H. NEWDIGATE Scholar-Printer 1869-1944. Oxford, 1950. Sm. 4to. Battery Park 1-477 1978 $75

BAALBEK, PALMYRA   Photographs by Hoyningen-Huene. 1946. 4to., plt. Allen 234-807 1978 $8.50

BABBAGE, CHARLES   On the Economy of Machinery and Manufactures. 1832. Post 8vo., engrav. title soiled and mounted, text woodcut, orig. cloth, spine faded, first ed. Quaritch 977-201 1978 $130

BABBAGE, CHARLES   On the Economy of Machinery and Manufactures. 1832. Fcap. 8vo., covers faded. George's 635-277 1978 £5.25

BABBAGE, CHARLES   Passages from the Life of a Philosopher. London, 1864. 8vo., frontis., orig. cloth, uncut, hinges repaired, occas. foxing & lib. stamp on title, good copy, 1st ed. Norman 5-16 1978 $175

BABBITT, IRVING   Democracy and Leadership. Boston, (1925). Biblo BL781-802 1978 $8.50

BABBSON, JOHN J.   History of the Town of Gloucester, Cape Ann, Including the Town of Rockport. Gloucester, 1860. 1st ed., fold. map, orig., very good, inscribed by author. MacManus 239-1027 1978 $45

BABCOCK, LOUIS L.   The War of 1812 on the Niagara Frontier. Buffalo, 1927. 1st ed., illus., fold. maps, orig. cloth, cover stained, otherwise good copy. MacManus 239-479 1978 $20

BABCOCK, WILLOUGHBY M., JR.   Selections from the Letters and Diaries of Brevet-Brigadier General Willoughby Babcock of the Seventy-Fifth New York Volunteers. New York, 1922. Illus., wrs., Bell Wiley's copy. Broadfoot's 44-558 1978 $10

BABINGTON, JOHN   Pyrotechnia. London, 1635. Sm. folio, plts., woodcuts, some light marginal waterstains, fine, contemp. calf, very neatly re-backed, only ed. Quaritch 977-202 1978 $1,000

BABSON, ROGER W.   Business Fundamentals. 1923. Austin 80-411 1978 $7.50

BABSON, ROGER W.   Fundamentals of Prosperity. 1920. Austin 80-412 1978 $8.50

BABSON, ROGER W.   Looking Ahead Fifty Years. 1948. Austin 80-413 1978 $8.50

BABSON, ROGER W.   The Sea Made Men. 1937. Illus. Austin 80-414 1978 $10

BABST, EARL D.   Occasions in Sugar. Ltd. to 500 copies. Austin 80-415 1978 $17.50

BACA, MANUEL C. D.   Vincente Silva and His 40 Bandits. Washington, 1947. Original cloth, 1 of 300 copies signed by translator and illustrator. Ginsberg 14-39 1978 $65

BACCARIA, GIAMBATISTA   Dell'Elettricismo Artificiale, e Naturale Libri Due. Torino, 1753. 4to, full contemporary vellum, very good copy, 1st ed. Bennett 20-20 1978 $600

BACCHYLIDES   The Poems of...From a Papyrus in the British Museum. London, 1897. Ex-lib., Biblo 247-460 1978 $20

BACCIUS, ANDREAS   De Thermis Andreae Baccii el Pidiani,.... Romae, 1622. 1st Roman ed., folio, full contemporary calf, gilt spine panels, some discoloration of endpapers, hinges slightly tender, very nice. Bennett 20-17 1978 $200

BACHE, WILLIAM   Historical Sketches of Bristol Borough in the County of Bucks... Bristol, 1853. Very scarce. MacManus 239-1360 1978 $45

BACHELDER, JOHN B.   Gettysburg Battlefield Directory, with Index.... Hyde Park, n.d. Wrps. Hayman 71-118 1978 $10

BACHELLER, IRVING   D'ri and I. Boston, (1901). Illus., first edition. Biblo 247-496 1978 $15

BACHELLER, IRVING   The Turning of Griggsby. New York, 1913. Orig. cloth, 1st ed., fine, rare pict. d.j., somewhat torn. MacManus 238-420 1978 $20

BACK, GEORGE   Narrative of an Expedition in H.M.S. Terror.... 1838. Folding map, litho. plts., some spotting, spine faded, orig. cloth, 8vo. Edwards 1012-560 1978 £135

BACKHOUSE, JANET   John Skottowe's Alphabet Books. London, 1974. Plts. in facsimile, lg. 4to, quarter red morocco, 50 copies printed for members of Roxburghe Club. Traylen 88-324 1978 £125

BACKMAN, A. P.   Fundamenta Ornithologia. Upsalia, 1765. Rare orig. pr., 8vo, orig. cloth. Book Chest 17-27 1978 $110

BACKMAN, GEORGE W.   The Issue of Compulsory Health Insurance. 1948. Ex-lib. Austin 80-416 1978 $10

BACKUS, CHARLES   The High Importance of Love to Jesus Christ in the Ministers of the Gospel. Amherst, 1799. 8vo., unbound, 1st ed. Morrill 241-386 1978 $12.50

BACKUS, M.   Siam and Laos; A seen by our American Missionaries. Philadelphia, 1884. Cloth, map, plts., ports., rare, illus., 8vo. Van der Peet 127-218 1978 Dfl 65

BACON, EDGAR MAYHEW   Chronicles of Tarrytown and Sleepy Hollow. New York, 1897. 1st. ed., illus., front hinge starting, otherwise very good copy, bookplates. Baldwins' 51-409 1978 $15

BACON, EDGAR MAYHEW   The Hudson River from Ocean to Source. New York, 1910. Illus., map, 8vo., bkplt. removed, orig. cloth. Morrill 241-402 1978 $15

BACON, EDWIN M.   Narragansett Bay, Its Historic and Romantic Associations with Picturesque Setting. New York, 1904. Royal 8vo, illus., map, orig. pic. cloth. MacManus 239-36 1978 $20

BACON, FRANCIS   The Essayes or Covnsels, Civill and Morall... London, 1625. 8vo., full contemp. calf, blind tooled, 1st complete ed., 2nd issue. MacManus 238-92 1978 $750

BACON, FRANCIS   The Essayes or Counsels, Civill and Morall... London, 1639. Sm. 4to, contemp. calf, title mounted & inner margins of 1st. 2 leaves repaired. Traylen 88-101 1978 $50

BACON, FRANCIS   The Essayes. 1639. Newly enlarged, sm. 4to., woodcut initials, newly rebound in half calf gilt antique style. Howes 194-5 1978 £50

BACON, FRANCIS   Essays, Moral, Economical, and Political. Edinburgh, 1817. Lg. 8vo., orig. bds., uncut. P. M. Hill 142-28 1978 £28

BACON, FRANCIS   Essays and Colours of Good and Evil. 1877. Fscp. 8vo., full brown levant mor., gilt edges. Howes 194-599 1978 £10

BACON, FRANCIS   Essays, Colours of Good and Evil and Advancement of Learning. 1900. 8vo., blue calf, gilt panelled back, gilt edges. Quaritch 979-14 1978 $35

BACON, FRANCIS   The History of the Reigne of King Henry the Seventh. London, 1629. Folio, full new calf in 17th-century style, gilt paneled spine, leather labels, blind-ruled paneled covers, new endpapers, title and few leaves lightly stained, fine copy, 3rd ed. Bennett 20-14 1978 $195

BACON, FRANCIS   Letters, Speeches, Charges, Advices.... 1702. First ed., contemp. calf, mor. label, 8vo. Howes 194-148 1978 £25

BACON, FRANCIS   Letters, Speeches, Charges, Advices,... London, 1763. Full contemp. calf, front cover detached, 1st ed., worn. MacManus 238-93 1978 $25

BACON, FRANCIS   The Naturall and Experimentall History of Winds. 1653. Thick 12mo., contemp. sheep, untrimmed, first Eng. ed., lacks portrait, has cat. at end. Howes 194-6 1978 £65

BACON, FRANCIS   Novum Organum. London, 1844. 16mo, 3/4 leather, gilt, marbled edges, 1st Pickering ed., joints weak, owners stamp on preface page, fine. Duschnes 220-8 1978 $35

BACON, FRANCIS   Of Gardens, an Essay. Eragny Press, 1902. Ltd. to 226 copies, this copy inscribed 'From Esther & L', woodcut frontis., sm. slim 8vo., orig. patterned bds., spine slightly darkened, edges uncut. George's 635-883 1978 £120

BACON, FRANCIS   Of Gardens, an Essay. London, Eragny Press, 1902. Narrow 12mo., orig. bds., uncut, ltd. ed. issued in 226 copies. Goldschmidt 110-53 1978 $130

BACON, FRANCIS   Of Gardens. Chelsea on Thames: The Swan Press, 1928. 4to., orig. cloth-backed bds., ltd. to 100 copies, fine. MacManus 238-845 1978 $20

BACON, FRANCIS   Of the Advancement and Proficience of Learning or the Partitions of Sciences. Oxford, 1640. Folio, collated and perfect, full old calf, very good. Bennett 7-5 1978 $750

BACON, FRANCIS   Opera Omnia, quae extant: Philosophica, Moralia, Politica, Historica. Frankfurt, 1665. Portrait, vignette, folio, contemp. vellum, with unsigned leaf "Bibliopola ad Lectorem". Howes 194-4 1978 £80

BACON, FRANCIS   The Philosophical Works. 1905. Roy. 8vo., orig. buckram. Howes 194-600 1978 £9.50

BACON, FRANCIS   The Two Books...of the Proficience and Advancement of Learning, Divine and Human. 1825. Sm. 8vo., contemp. diced calf. Howes 194-1096 1978 £10

BACON, FRANCIS   The Wisedome of the Ancients, Written in Latine.... London, 1619. 12mo, full maroon crushed levant, ruled in blind, half morocco slipcase, 1st ed. in English, bookplate, fine copy. Ximenes 47-13 1978 $900

BACON, FRANCIS   The Wisedome of the Ancients... London, 1619. 1st. ed. in English, sm. woodcut on title-pg., very slight water-staining, 12mo, old calf neatly rebacked, spine gilt, leather label. Traylen 88-102 1978 £350

BACON, G. W.   Abraham Lincoln Geschetst in Ziji Leven En Daden. Amsterdam, 1865. Wrps., some wear, light stain on front wrapper. Hayman 71-419 1978 $35

BACON, LEONARD   The Genesis of the New England Churches. New York, 1874. First ed., illus. Baldwin's 51-391 1978 $7.50

BACON, LEONARD   The Goose on the Capitol. New York, 1936. 1st ed., d.w. frayed. Biblo 251-396 1978 $15

BACON, LEONARD WOOLSEY   A History of American Christianity. 1897. Austin 79-39 1978 $11

BACON, ROGER   Opus Majus. Venetiis, 1750. Copperplts., folio, old half calf, very rare. Offenbacher 30-8 1978 $400

BACON, THOMAS   The Orientalist: Containing a Series of Tales, Legends, and Historical Romances. 1843. First ed., vignette, plts., lg. 8vo., orig. cloth, gilt edges. Howes 194-1384 1978 £20

BADDELEY, ST. CLAIR   Rome & Its Story. 1904. 4to., colored plt., top of spine frayed, one cover dented. Allen 234-823 1978 $7.50

BADEAU, ADAM   Military History of Ulysess S. Grant From April, 1861 to April, 1865. New York, 1881. 3 vols., port., maps, fine, scarce. MacManus 239-863 1978 $55

BADEN-POWELL, R. S. S.   The Matabele Campaign 1896. London, 1897. 2nd. ed., 8vo, 100 illus., orig. gilt-dec. cloth, slightly shaken & backstrip chafed at head & tail. K Books 239-12 1978 £24

BADER, CL.   La Femme Grecque. Paris, 1872. 2 vols., 8vo., orig. covers. Van der Peet H-64-242 1978 Dfl 50

BADER, LOUIS   World Developments in the Cotton Industry. New York University Press, 1925. Ex-lib. Austin 80-417 1978 $12.50

BADHAM, C. D.   Prose Halieutics. 1854. Post 8vo. George's 635-1490 1978 £6.25

BADLEY, J. F.   Bookplates. London, 1927. Sm. 4to., bds., cloth spine, illus. Battery Park 1-237 1978 $35

BAEDEKER, KARL   The Eastern Alps Including the Bavarian Highlands, Tyrol, Salzburg, Upper and Lower Austria, Styria, Carinthia and Carniola. London, 1907. Maps, 12mo, orig. cloth, 11th. ed., good. Sexton 7-120 1978 £8.50

BAEDEKER, KARL   South Eastern France From the Loire to the Riviera and the Italian Frontier Including Corsica. London, 1895. 12mo, orig. cloth, maps, 2nd. ed., good. Sexton 7-122 1978 £6.50

BAEDEKER, KARL   The United States with an Excursion into Mexico. Leipzig, 1893. Maps, plans, 12mo., 1st ed., orig. cloth. Morrill 241-36 1978 $20

BAER, KARL ERNST VON   Reden Gehalten in Wissenschaftlichen Versammlungen und Kleinere Aufsatze Vermischten Inhalts. St. Petersburg, 1864, 1876 and 1873. 3 vols. in 1, lg. 8vo., first ed., cont. half cloth. Schafer 19-44 1978 sFr 1,200

BAGBY, GEORGE W.   The Old Virginia Gentleman and Other Sketches. 1910. First ed. Austin 82-96 1978 $27.50

BAGBY, GEORGE W.   The Old Virginia Gentleman and Other Sketches. 1948. Illus. Austin 82-97 1978 $11

BAGDANOFF, A.   A Short Course of Economic Science. 1925. Paper. Austin 80-438 1978 $15

BAGEHOT, WALTER   Literary Studies. 1895. Portrait, 3 vols., cr. 8vo., orig. cloth. Howes 194-601 1978 £6

BAGEHOT, WALTER   Shakespeare, the man. New York, 1901. 1st ed., orig. pr. wr., very good or better. Limestone 9-261 1978 $8.50

BAGG, M. M.   The Pioneers of Utica. Utica, 1877. Plts., orig. cloth. Butterfield 21-311 1978 $25

BAGLIVI, GIORGIO   De Fibra Motrice et Morbosa; nec non de Experimentis, ac Morbo Salivae, Bilis and Sanguinis... Perugia, 1700. Woodcuts, half-mor., fine copy, light marginal waterstain at last leaves, rare, 1st ed. Gilhofer 74-79 1978 sFr 1,500

BAGNOLD, ENID   "National Velvet" London, (1935). 1st ed., fine in dj. Victoria 34-37 1978 $25

BAGNOLD, ENID   National Velvet. London, (1935). 8vo, cloth, d.j., chipped, drawings by Laurian Jones, 1st ed., fine. Duschness 220-9 1978 $15

BAHRENS, JOHANN CHRISTOPH FRIEDRICH   Der Animalische Magnetismus und Die Durch ihn Bewirkten Kuren. Elberfeld und Leipzig, 1816. 8vo., contemp. calf, 1st ed., fine copy. Offenbacher 30-98 1978 $115

BAIF, LAZARE DE   Annotations in Legem II De Captiuis & Postliminio Reuersis.... Basileae, 1541. Quarto, woodcuts, pictorial initials, ruled margins, half-vellum over marbled boards, spine label, gilt, expert restoration of title-leaf, fine copy. Bennett 20-15 1978 $300

BAIKIE, JAMES   A History of Egypt From the Earliest Times to the End of the XVIIIth Dynasty. London, 1929. 8vo, 2 vols., 2 maps, 48 plts., orig. cloth, spines faded. K Books 239-14 1978 £10

BAILEY, ALFRED G.   The Conflict of European and Eastern Algonkian Cultures, 1504-1700, a Study in Canadian Civilization. Saint John, 1937. 1st ed., card covers. Hood 116-399 1978 $35

BAILEY, ALFRED G.   Railways and the Confederation Issue in New Brunswick, 1863-1865. 1940. Hood's 115-951 1978 $7.50

BAILEY, C. T. P.   Knives and Forks. 1927. Coloured plts., roy. 8vo. George's 635-252 1978 £15

BAILEY, F. M.   Birds of New Mexico. 1928. Plates, 8vo, orig. cloth. Book Chest 17-28 1978 $125

BAILEY, H. C.   Clunk's Claimant. 1937. Very good, faded d.w., first English ed. Bell Book 17-216 1978 £18.50

BAILEY, HENRY TURNER   Yankee Notions. 1929. First ed. Austin 82-99 1978 $12.50

BAILEY, JAMES MONTGOMERY   Life in Danbury. 1873. Illus. Austin 82-100 1978 $20

BAILEY, JOHN   Walt Whitman. London, 1926. 1st ed., laid paper, uncut, orig. cloth, very good or better. Limestone 9-321 1978 $25

BAILEY, L. H.   Country Life in America. 1901-2. Vol. 1, folio, 8vo, orig. cloth. Book Chest 17-488 1978 $15

BAILEY, L. H.   Cultivated Evergreens. New York, 1923. Plates, 8vo, orig. cloth. Book Chest 17-29 1978 $25

BAILEY, L. H.   The Standard Cyclopedia of Horticulture. New York, 1947. Coloured plts., text illus., 3 vols., imp. 8vo. George's 635-950 1978 £27.50

BAILEY, NATHAN   Divers Proverbs. New Haven, 1917. Bkplt., very fine. Desmarais B-44 1978 $7.50

BAILEY, NATHANIEL   An Universal Etymological English Dictionary. 1735. 7th. ed., 8vo, hinges strained, contemp. calf, later rebacked, edges rubbed. Eaton 45-31 1978 £10

BAILEY, OLGA   Mollie Bailey: The Circus Queen of the Southwest. Dallas, 1943. Illus., fine in d.j. Jenkins 116-50 1978 $15

BAILEY, PERCIVAL   Intracranial Tumors. Baltimore, 1933. Ex-library worn, underlinings. Rittenhouse 49-47 1976 $15

BAILEY, PERCIVAL   Intracranial Tumors of Infancy and Childhood. Chicago, 1939. Library markings, torn top of spine affecting title. Rittenhouse 49-46 1976 $12.50

BAILEY, RALPH E.   An American Colossus, The Singular Career of Alexander Hamilton. Boston, (1933). Clean, orig. binding. Hayman 71-34 1978 $7.50

BAILEY, ROSALIE FELLOWS   Pre-Revolutionary Dutch Houses and Families in Northern New Jersey and Southern New York. New York, 1936. Illus., thick 4to., orig. cloth, boxed, box broken, ltd. to 666 copies. Morrill 241-37 1978 $87.50

BAILEY, SAMUEL   Essays on the Formation and Publication of Opinions and On Other Subjects. 1837. 3rd. ed., revised & enlarged, 1/4 morocco, worn. Eaton 45-32 1978 £5

BAILEY, T. MELVILLE   The History of Dundurn Castle and Sir Allan MacNab. Hamilton, 1943. Card cover, photo plts. Hood 117-719 1978 $12.50

BAILEY, TEMPLE   The Holly Hedge and Other Christmas Stories. Phila., 1925. Pres. bookplate signed and dated by author, 1st ed., 8 vo., orig. gilt stamped red cloth, color frontispiece, very good. Houle 10-20 1978 $25

BAILEY, WILLIAM THEODORE   Richfield Springs and Vicinity. New York & Chicago, 1874. Plt., illus. Butterfield 21-340 1978 $15

BAILLET, ADRIEN   La Vie De Mr. Descartes. Paris, 1692. 8vo., contemp. marbled calf. Salloch 348-47 1978 $60

BAILLIE, JOHANNA   A Collection of Poems. 1823. Contemp. half calf, 8vo. Howes 194-603 1978 £14

BAILLOU, GUILLAUME DE   Epidemiorum et Ephemeridum Libri Duo.... Paris, 1640. 4to., contemp. armorial ex libris of Chevallier Sanlaville, Seigneur de Bellan en Bugey, hand painted in colour, contemp. calf, first ed. Quaritch 977-7 1978 $500

BAILLOU, GUILLAUME DE   Opuscula Medica, de Arthritide, de Calculo et de Urinarum Hypostasi. Paris, 1643. 4to., contemp. armorial ex libris of Chevalier Sanlaville, Seigneur de Bellan en Bugey, hand painted in colour, contemp. calf, first ed. Quaritch 977-6 1978 $1,000

BAILLY, JEAN-SYLVAIN   Lettres sur l'Origine des Sciences.... London and Paris, 1777. 1st ed., octavo, full contemporary calf, gilt spines, title on red morocco label, gilt, very good copy, very scarce work. Bennett 20-16 1978 $200

BAIN, GEORGE   The River Findhorn from Source to Sea. Nairn, 1911. Frontis., plts., orig. cloth, 8vo. K Books 244-17 1978 £6

BAIN, J. A.   Fridtjof Nansen, His Life and Explorations. London, 1897. Illus., 2nd. ed. Hood's 115-239 1978 $10

BAIN, J. A.   Life and Adventures of Nansen. London, 1897. Full red calf, 8vo., frontis., illus., map, spine faded. Van der Peet H-64-243 1978 Dfl 65

BAINBRIDGE, GEORGE COLE   The Fly Fisher's Guide. London, 1840. Coloured plts., fourth ed., fcap. 8vo., neatly recased in orig. cloth. K Books 244-18 1978 £22

BAINBRIDGE, HENRY CHARLES   Peter Carl Faberge, Goldsmith and Jeweller to the Russian Imperial Court and the Principal Crowned Heads of Europe. London, (1949). Illus., plts., some in color, 4to., d.w., orig. cloth, 1st ed. Morrill 241-38 1978 $50

BAINES, EDWARD   History of the Cotton Manufacture in Great Britain. London, 1835. 8vo., portrait, engravings, woodcuts, orig. cloth, shaken, first ed. Quaritch 977-203 1978 $125

BAINES, EDWARD   History of the Wars of the French Revolution, 1792-1815, comprehending the Civil History of Great Britain and France during that period. 1817. Maps, plans, portraits, 2 vols. in 1, 4to., half calf, neatly rebacked. George's 635-536 1978 £21

BAINES, THOMAS   Explorations in South-West Africa. London, 1864. 1st. ed., 8vo, coloured lithograph frontispiece, maps coloured in outline, plts., newly rebound in polished half calf, marbled bds., panelled back. Deighton 5-3 1978 £225

BAIRD, CHARLES W.   History of Rye Westchester Co., New York... New York, 1871. Illus., nice, cloth. MacManus 239-1097 1978 $50

BAIRD, G. H.   A Brief History of Upshur County. Gilmer, 1946. Fine copy, scarce. Jenkins 116-1408 1978 $20

BAIRD, ROBERT　　　　　Impressions and Experiences of the West Indies and North America in 1849. Philadelphia, 1850. 1st. American ed., sm. 8vo, orig. brown embossed cloth, gilt, corners worn, 1 joint trifle split, sl. worming. Deighton 5-28 1978 £78

BAIRD, SAMUEL J.　　　　　Southern Rights and Northern Duties in the Present Crisis. Philadelphia, 1861. 8vo., unbound, 1st ed. Morrill 241-39 1978 $7.50

BAIRNSFATHER, BRUCE　　　　　The Bystanders Fragments from France, Nos. 1-7. (1915-19). 7 nos. in 1 vol., imp. 8vo., binders cloth, 3 parts orig. wrappers. George's 635-105 1978 £7.50

BAIRNSFATHER, BRUCE　　　　　The Collected Drawings of. New York, 1931. 4to., 1st Amer. ed., signed. Biblo 251-157 1978 $32.50

BAITAL-PACHIST　　　　　Vikram and the Vampire. London, 1870. Illus. by Ernest Griset, 1st ed., orig. red cloth stamped in black and gilt, bookplate, very good. Houle 10-54 1978 $135

BAITAL-PACHIST　　　　　Vikram and the Vampire or Tales of Hindu Devilry. London, 1870. 1st ed., illus., text very good, inner hinges taped, spine and tips worn. Victoria 34-357 1978 $25

BAITAL-PACHIST　　　　　Vikram and The Vampire or Tales of Hindu Devilry. 1870. 1st. ed., illus. by Ernest Griset, orig. dec. cloth, shaken, bookplt. Eaton 45-77 1978 £20

BAITER, A. Z.　　　　　Moving Picture Glue Book,.... New York, (1912). 1st ed., cut up, flaps placed properly, colored pictorial boards, slight cover penciling, very good. Victoria 34-558 1978 $35

BAKELESS, JOHN　　　　　Lewis and Clark, Partners in Discovery. New York, 1947. Illus.; d.j. MacManus 239-37 1978 $12.50

BAKER, A. T.　　　　　St. Modwenna. 1947. 8vo. Upcroft 12-385 1978 £7.50

BAKER, ARTHUR　　　　　The House is Sitting. 1958. 1st. ed., 8vo., illus., orig. cloth, pres. copy to Winston Churchill, very good copy. Sawyer 298-62 1978 £150

BAKER, BENJAMIN M.　　　　　Fifth Biennial Report of the Superintendent of Republic Instruction for the Scholastic Years Ending August 31, 1885, and August 31, 1886.... Austin, 1886. Back wr. missing. Jenkins 116-52 1978 $9.50

BAKER, BLANCH M.　　　　　Dramatic Bibliography. New York, 1933. Name in ink, very good. Ballinger 11-9 1978 $14.75

BAKER, C. H. COLLINS　　　　　Catalogue of the Principal Pictures in the Royal Collection at Windsor Castle. 1937. Plts., ltd. to 750 copies, 4to., orig. qtr. mor. George's 635-2 1978 £20

BAKER, C.L.　　　　　Geology and Underground Waters of the Northern Llano Estacado. Austin, 1915. Folding maps. Jenkins 116-53 1978 $8.50

BAKER, DAVID ERSKINE　　　　　Biographia Dramatica. 1782. 2 vols., 8vo., contemp. calf, rebacked, portrait. P. M. Hill 142-223 1978 £65

BAKER, DAVID ERSKINE　　　　　The Companion to the Play-House. 1764. 2 vols., sm. 8vo., 1st ed., early wrs., rebacked, uncut, almost entirely unopened. Quaritch 979-15 1978 $160

BAKER, DENYS VAL　　　　　Little Reviews Anthology 1945 & 1946. 1945/6. Very good, d.w., first English ed. Bell Book 16-969 1978 £4

BAKER, DE WITT CLINTON　　　　　A Texas Scrapbook, Made Up on the History, Biography, and Miscellany of Texas and Its People. New York, 1875. 1st ed. Jenkins 116-54 1978 $110

BAKER, EDWARD CHARLES STUART　　　　　The Game Birds of India, Burma and Ceylon. 1919-1925. Complete set of 13 parts in 16, coloured plts., roy. 8vo., binders' cloth. Traylen 88-534 1978 £20

BAKER, EDWARD CHARLES STUART　　　　　The Game Birds of India, Burma and Ceylon. London, 1921-1930. Pictorial titles, maps, coloured & plain plts., 3 vols, roy. 8vo., vols. 1 & 2 in half green mor., vol. 3 half green cloth. Traylen 88-533 1978 £90

BAKER, GEORGE　　　　　The Sad Sack. N.P., 1944. Austin 80-13 1978 $7.50

BAKER, GEORGE E.　　　　　The Life of William H. Seward with Selections from His Works. New York, 1855. Cloth, worn at corners, some chipping along spine edges, 1st ed. under this title. Hayman 72-32 1978 $10

BAKER, GEORGE H.　　　　　Anne Boleyn. Philadelphia, 1850. First ed. Austin 82-214 1978 $27.50

BAKER, HENRY　　　　　The Microscope Made Easy. 1742. First ed., table, plts., contemp. calf, 8vo. Howes 194-149 1978 £75

BAKER, HENRY　　　　　The Microscope Made Easy. London, 1743. 8vo., engr. plts., many fldg., contemp. marbled calf, Ex-lib., very good copy, illus. Zeitlin 245-9 1978 $225

BAKER, JACOB　　　　　Cooperative Enterprise. Vanguard Press, 1937. Ex-lib. Austin 80-419 1978 $10

BAKER, JAMES L.　　　　　Slavery. Philadelphia, 1860. 8vo., unbound, orig. cloth, 1st ed. Morrill 241-40 1978 $8.50

BAKER, MARCUS　　　　　The Northwest Boundary of Texas. Washington, 1902. Printed wr., folding map. Jenkins 116-55 1978 $45

BAKER, R. P.　　　　　Croynan Hall, the Maid of the Mask; a Tale of Rothenburg. Toronto, 1908. Unopened. Hood 116-795 1978 $12.50

BAKER, SIR RICHARD　　　　　A Chronicle of the Kings of England. London, 1674. Folio, 19th-century mor. over cloth, edges rubbed, else very good, bookplate, 6th ed. Bennett 7-7 1978 $150

BAKER, RICHARD ST. BARBE　　　　　Africa Drums. London, 1942. 8vo, orig. cloth, 48 illus. K Books 239-15 1978 £5

BAKER, RICHARD ST. BARBE　　　　　Among the Trees. 1935. Photographs, cr. 4to., half parchment. George's 635-977 1978 £5

BAKER, SAMUEL WHITE　　　　　The Albert N'Yanza, Great Basin of the Nile, and Explorations of the Nile Sources. London, 1867. 2 vols., maps, plts., text-illus., cr. 8vo, one map repaired, little thumbed, recased in orig. gilt-dec. cloth. K Books 239-17 1978 £16

BAKER, SAMUEL WHITE　　　　　The Albert N'Yanza, Great Basin of the Nile, and Explorations of the Nile Sources. London, 1874. New ed., map, plts., text-illus., cr. 8vo, 2 lib. stamps, modern quarter calf. K Books 239-18 1978 £12

BAKER, SAMUEL WHITE　　　　　Ismailia; A Narrative of the Expedition to Central Africa for the Suppression of the Slave Trade... 1874. Coloured maps, plts., 2 vols., orig. cloth, rebacked, worn, some plts. loose, 8vo. Edwards 1012-276 1978 £50

BAKER, SAMUEL WHITE　　　　　Ismailia: A Narrative of the Expedition to Central Africa for the Suppression of the Slave Trade, Organized by Ismail, Khedive of Egypt. New York, 1875. 1st Amer. ed., woodcut illus., maps, portrs., tall 8vo., pic. cloth. Argosy Special-7 1978 $85

BAKER, SAMUEL WHITE　　　　　The Nile Tributaries of Abyssinia, and The Sword Hunters of the Hamran Arabs. London, 1867. 1st. ed., 2 maps, 24 plts., roy. 8vo, orig. gilt-dec. cloth, neatly recased, corners & head & tail of spine slightly chafed, covers slightly marked. K Books 239-19 1978 £60

BAKER, SAMUEL WHITE　　　　　The Nile Tributaries of Abyssinia and the Sword Hunters of the Hamran Arabs. Philadelphia, 1869. 5th ed., 3/4 calf, 8vo, illus., folding color map, newly rebound. Book Chest 17-30 1978 $58

BAKER, SAMUEL WHITE　　　　　The Nile Tributaries of Abyssinia, and the Sword Hunters of the Hamran Arabs. London, 1874. New ed., 2 maps, 24 illus., cr. 8 vo, slight foxing, nice copy, recent half morocco. K Books 239-20 1978 £20

BAKER, SAMUEL WHITE　　　　　The Nile Tributaries of Abyssinia, and The Sword Hunters of the Hamran Arabs. London, 1880. New ed., 2 maps, 24 plts., cr. 8vo, orig. cloth, slight age-marking, corners bumped. K Books 239-21 1978 £16

BAKER, THEODORE   A Biographical Dictionary of Musicians. New York, 1900. Portrs. from drwgs. in pen & ink by Alex Gribavedoff, 8vo., half mor., 1st ed. Morrill 239-297 1978 $15

BAKER, THEODORE   A Pronouncing Pocket-Manual of Musical Terms. London, 1905. Pr. wr., sm. pocket book pr. in U.S.A., thumbnail biogs., nice. Limestone 9-216 1978 $10

BAKER, WILLIAM SPOHN   Character Portraits of Washington, as Delineated by Historians, Orators and Divines. Philadelphia, 1887. Orig. cloth. MacManus 239-490 1978 $30

BAKER, WILLIAM SPOHN   Itinerary of General Washington from June 15, 1775, to Dec. 23, 1783. Philadelphia, 1892. Port. MacManus 239-38 1978 $35

BAKER, WILLIAM SPOHN   William Sharp Engraver. Philadelphia, 1875. 1st ed., frontis., port., cloth, very scarce, fine. MacManus 239-637 1978 $35

BAL Olympique Vrai Bal Sportif Costume. Paris, 1924. 4to., illus. by Picasso and others, unbound as issued. Quaritch 978-128 1978 $130

BALCH, DAVID ARNOLD   Elbert Hubbard...Genius of Roycroft. New York, 1940. 1st ed., illus., author's signed pres. Biblo 251-508 1978 $22.50

BALCH, EMILY GREENE   Our Slavic Fellow Citizens. 1910. Illus., 1st ed. Austin 79-41 1978 $17.50

BALCH, THOMAS   The French in America. During the War of Independence of the United States... Philadelphia, 1891-95. 1st ed., 2 vols., illus., orig. cloth, hinges cracking, otherwise good, A.L.s. MacManus 239-1362 1978 $75

BALDI, BERNARDINO   Memorie Concernenti la Citta Di Urbino.... Rome, Gio, 1724. Title printed in red & black, engraved frontis, vignette map, plts., 2 folding, folio, half russia, joints rubbed & weak. Traylen 88-427 1978 £300

BALDINUCCI, FILIPPO   Vocabolario Toscano dell'Arte del Disegno, nel quale si Esplicano i Propri Termini e Voci, non solo della Pittura, Scultura and Architettura, ma ancora di altre Arti a quelle subordinate, e Che Abbiano per Fondamento... Firenze, 1681. Contemp. vellum, 1st ed., some light browning. sFr 1,200

BALDRY, A.   Burne-Jones, Illustrated With Eight Reproductions in Colour. London & New York, (1909). 1st ed., frontispiece, d.j., pictorial bds., very good or better. Limestone 9-44 1978 $18

BALDUCCI, ALESSANDRO, DURANTINO   La Vita di S. Sigismondo re di Borgogna. Bologna, 1618. Sm. 4to., limp vellum soiled, portrait, first ed. King 7-13 1978 £25

BALDWIN, CHARLES N.   A Universal Biographical Dictionary, Containing The Lives of the Most Celebrated Characters of Every Age and Nation. Richmond, 1826. Leather. Hayman 71-749 1978 $15

BALDWIN, DONALD C.   Capital Control in N.Y. 1920. Austin 80-420 1978 $27.50

BALDWIN, EBENEZER   Annals of Yale College, from Its Foundation to the Year 1831. New Haven, 1838. Second ed., old calf, rubbed, front bd. loose, backstrip worn, internally somewhat marked by damp. Wolfe 39-30 1978 $35

BALDWIN, EUGENE F.   Doctor Cavallo. Peoria, 1895. Sm. 8vo., fr. cover & sm. part of text dampstained, 1st ed. Morrill 239-10 1978 $15

BALDWIN, GEORGE   La Prima Musa Clio. N.P., n.d. (Prehaps 1802). 1st ed., 4to, contemp. straight-grained blue morocco, pres. copy inscribed by author to Lord Northwick, with a letter of pres. loosely inserted. Hannas 54-10 1978 £55

BALDWIN, HANSON W.   What the Citizen Should Know About the Navy. 1942. Rev. ed., illus. Austin 80-14 1978 $10

BALDWIN, HENRY   The Orchids of New England. New York, 1884. Plates, 8vo., orig. cloth. Book Chest 17-31 1978 $60

BALDWIN, JAMES   James Baldwin-Autobiographical Notes. New York, 1935. 1st ed., rare, typescript in reproduc. Bradley 49-11 1978 $25

BALDWIN, LELAND D.   Pittsburgh the Story of a City. Pittsburgh, 1937. Illus. MacManus 239-1363 1978 $10

BALDWIN, MARTIN   Aspects of Contemporary Painting in Canada. Andover, 1942. Biographies, illus. Hood 117-168 1978 $40

BALDWIN, THOMAS   Narrative of the Massacre, by the Savages, of the Wife and Children of Thomas Baldwin...In the Extreme Western Part of the State of Kentucky... New York, 1835. Large foldout plate, original plain wr. bound in half morocco, 1st ed. Ginsberg 14-40 1978 $150

BALDWIN, WILLIAM CHARLES   African Hunting and Adventure From Natal to the Zambesi, Including Lake Ngami, the Kalahari Desert, Etc. From 1852 to 1860. London, 1894. 8vo., orig. cloth, frontis, folding map, wood-engraved illus. by James Wolf & J.B. Zwecker, good ex-lib. K Books 239-22 1978 £40

BALEN, W.J. VAN   Nederlands Voorhoede. Amsterdam, 1941. 8vo., cloth, plts., illus. Van der Peet H-64-244 1978 Dfl 30

BALFOUR, GRANT   Canada, My Home and Other Poems. Toronto, 1910. Unopened. Hood 116-796 1978 $7.50

BALFOUR, JAMES   Historical Works: Annales of Scotland, Edinburgh, 1824-25. Edinburgh, 1824-25. 4 vols., octavo, 3/4 grey calf, spines gilt, bookplates. Bennett 7-8 1978 $165

BALFOUR, JOHN HUTTON   Opinions and Argument from Speeches and Addresses of the Earl of Balfour, 1910-1927. 1928. 1st ed. Austin 79-42 1978 $17.50

BALGARNIE, R.   Sir Titus Salt, Baronet: his Life and Lessons. London, 1877. Mounted woodbury types, cr. 8vo., orig. cloth. K Books 244-19 1978 £15

BALIANI, GIOVANNI BATTISTA   De Motu Naturali Gravium Solidorum et Liquidorum. Genuae, 1646. 4to., contemp. limp vellum. Offenbacher 30-45 1978 $750

BALL, JOHN   Contributions to the Geography of Egypt. Cairo, 1939. Roy. 8vo, cloth-backed printed bds., short tear in backstrip. K Books 239-23 1978 £6

BALL, JOHN   The Distribution of Plants on So. Side of Alps. (1895). 4to, wr. minus covers. Book Chest 17-458 1978 $13

BALL, MAX W.   This Fascinating Oil Business. 1940. Austin 80-421 1978 $8.50

BALL, NICHOLAS   Voyages of...from 1838 to 1853, in Tabulated Form with Notes... Boston, 1895. Illus., orig. cloth, 1st ed. Ginsberg 14-1086 1978 $125

BALL, ROBERT STAWELL   The Story of the Heavens. London, 1888. Plts. some coloured, text illus., roy. 8vo., half red mor., fine. K Books 244-20 1978 £8

BALLADS of the B.E.F. New York, 1932. 1st ed., worn pic. d.w., illus., 8vo., very good. Americanist 103-22 1978 $25

BALLANTINE, E.   Address Delivered in the Chapel of the Ohio University, on Christmas Day, 1839. Athens, 1840. Orig. blank wrps. Hayman 71-511 1978 $15

BALLANTINE, SERJEANT   Some Experience of a Barrister's Life. 1882. 1st. ed., 2 vols., woodbury type photo frontis, half titles, half red roan, little rubbed. Jarndyce 16-279 1978 £7.50

BALLANTYNE, ROBERT MICHAEL   The Coral Island: A Tale of the Pacific Ocean. London, 1858. 1st ed., 1st issue, colored lith. plates, very bright, spine and cover gilt very fresh, very faint small faded spots on rear cover, partial splitting of upper inner hinge, text fine, very scarce. Victoria 34-40 1978 $400

BALLANTYNE, ROBERT MICHAEL   Gascoyne, the Sandalwood Trader.   New York, (1908). Wrs., minor wear. Hayman 72-214 1978 $7.50

BALLANTYNE, ROBERT MICHAEL   Hudson's Bay.... Edinburgh and London, 1848. 2nd ed., illus., orig. cloth, rebacked with orig. spine laid down. Mac-Manus 239-39 1978 $37.50

BALLANTYNE, ROBERT MICHAEL   Hudson's Bay.... Edinburgh and London, 1948. Illus., 2nd ed., spine worn. Hood 116-62 1978 $40

BALLANTYNE, ROBERT MICHAEL   The Kitten Pilgrims. (1882). 1st ed., color plts., glazed pict. bds. in color, tips rubbed, minor cover scratches, scarce, very good. Victoria 34-39 1978 $75

BALLANTYNE, ROBERT MICHAEL   Martin Rattler.   London, 1881. Decor. cover. Hood 117-503 1978 $12.50

BALLANTYNE, ROBERT MICHAEL   Ungava: a Tale of Esquimau Land. 1897. New ed., colored title & frontis., sm. 8vo., orig. cloth. Edwards 1012-415 1978 £10

BALLARD, G. A.   Rulers of the Indian Ocean. London, 1927. 8vo, orig. cloth, illus., map, good. Sexton 7-164 1978 £5

BALLMER, DANIEL   Sammlung Von Neuen Recepten und Bewaehrten Kuren Fuer Menschen und Vieh. Cincinnati, 1849. Orig. blank wrs. Hayman 73-34 1978 $25

BALLOU, ADIN   History of Milford. 1882. Map. MacManus 239-1039 1978 $35

BALMIS, FRANCISCO XAVIER DE   Demostracion De La Eficaces Virtudes Neuvamente Descubiertas En Las Raices De Dos Plantas De Nueva-Espana... Madrid, 1794. 8vo., colored fldg. plts., old bds. backed in red cloth, browning & staining, wormholes & trails, 1st ed., rare. Zeitlin 245-297 1978 $150

BALSAMO, GUISEPPE   Memorial or Brief, For the Comte de Cagliostro, Defendant... 1786. 1st. English ed., 8vo, disbound. Hannas 54-11 1978 £6

BALZAC, HONORE DE   Oeuvres choisies. 1950. 10 vols., orig. leatherette, 8vo. George's 635-1181 1978 £5.25

BALZAC, HONORE DE   Le Peche Veniel. Paris, 1901. Royal 8vo., full jansenist tobacco brown mor., inner gilt dentelle, uncut, bound by Riviere, only 400 copies, numbered, 1 of 35 on Whatman paper, illus. in three states, very clean copy. Goldschmidt 110-2 1978 $115

BALZAC, JEAN LOUIS GEUZ DE   New Epistles of Monsieur de Balzac. London, 1638. 8vo, contemp. vellum, 2nd & 3rd. vols., good copy. Sexton 7-129 1978 £115

BAMFORD, JOHN   Illustrations of the Field Movements of Cavalry. 1824. Plts., folio, unbound, in cloth slipcase. F. Edwards 1013-247 1978 £40

BANCK, LAURENTIUS   Bizzarrie Politiche Ouer, Raccolta Delle piu notabili prattiche di Stato.... 1658. Vellum, 12mo., first ed., rare. King 7-14 1978 £60

BANCROFT, EDWARD   An Essay on the Natural History of Guiana... 1769. Frontis, modern half calf, name on title & verso of frontis, 8vo. Edwards 1012-616 1978 £150

BANCROFT, GEORGE   History of the Battle of Lake Erie, and Miscellaneous Papers. New York, 1891. Ads, 1st ed. Butterfield 21-458 1978 $12.50

BANCROFT, GEORGE   History of the United States, from the Discovery of the American Continent. Boston, 1848. 10 vols., orig. cloth, nice set, illus. MacManus 239-40 1978 $50

BANCROFT, HUBERT HOWE   History of the North Mexican States and Texas. San Francisco, 1886. 2 vols. Jenkins 116-58 1978 $175

BANCROFT, HUBERT HOWE   The New Pacific. New York, 1913. Rev. ed., pages gilt topped. Hood 117-876 1978 $25

BANCROFT, SQUIRE   Mr. & Mrs. Bancroft on and off the Stage. 1888. First ed., frontis., half cerise calf gilt, 2 vols., 8vo. Howes 194-1259 1978 £18

BANDELIER, A. F.   Contributions to the History of the Southwestern Portions of the United States. Cambridge, 1890. Folding map, 1st ed. Jenkins 116-59 1978 $150

BANDESSON, COMAN   Au Pays des Superstitions et des Rites. Paris, 1932. Drawings, photos., 8vo, orig. covers. Van der Peet 127-10 1978 Dfl 40

BANGS, JOHN KENDRICK   The Bicycles and Three Other Farces. 1896. Illus, first ed. Austin 82-101 1978 $27.50

BANGS, JOHN KENDRICK   From Pillar to Post. 1917. Illus., inscribed by author. Austin 82-102 1978 $17.50

BANGS, JOHN KENDRICK   A House-Boat on the Styx. New York, 1895. Ownership inscription, spine slightly darkened, fine bright copy. Desmarais B-49 1978 $15

BANGS, JOHN KENDRICK   A House Boat on the Styx. N.P., 1895. Illus. Austin 82-104 1978 $8.50

BANGS, JOHN KENDRICK   A House Boat on the Sytx. 1896. Illus., first ed. Austin 82-103 1978 $12.50

BANGS, JOHN KENDRICK   The Inventions of the Idiot. 1904. First ed., green cloth, illuminated front cover. Austin 82-105 1978 $20

BANGS, JOHN KENDRICK   The Lorgnette 1886. 1886. Illus., inscribed by Bangs to G. H. Bangs, pages brittle and loose in binding, but complete, back cover waterstained. Austin 82-106 1978 $250

BANGS, JOHN KENDRICK   Mr. Bonaparte of Corsica.. 1895. Yellow cloth, illus. cover, first ed., second state. Austin 82-107 1978 $20

BANGS, JOHN KENDRICK   Over the Plum Pudding. 1901. Illus., first ed., some cover wear, else good. Austin 82-108 1978 $15

BANGS, JOHN KENDRICK   Peeps at People. 1899. Illus., first ed. Austin 82-109 1978 $12.50

BANGS, JOHN KENDRICK   Peeps at People. New York, 1899. Nice. Desmarais B-50 1978 $7.50

BANGS, JOHN KENDRICK   The Pursuit of the House Boat. 1897. Illus., tan cloth, first ed., first state. Austin 82-110 1978 $27.50

BANGS, JOHN KENDRICK   Pursuit of the Houseboat. 1897. Illus., very good. Austin 82-111 1978 $12.50

BANGS, JOHN KENDRICK   Pursuit of the Houseboat. 1899. Illus. Austin 82-112 1978 $10

BANISTER, T. ROGER   The Coastwise Lights of China:..... (Shanghai, 1932). Cloth, leather spine, worn and repaired. Dawson's 449-6 1978 $30

BANKES, JOHN   The Destruction of Troy, a Tragedy, Acted at His Royal Highness the Duke's Theatre. London, 1679. 1st ed., sm. 4to., sm. worm hole, text otherwise better than fine, rebound in modern marbled bds. backed in calf, golt lettering on spine, binding otherwise mint, rare. Current 24-5 1978 $315

BANKES, WILLIAM JOHN   Narrative of the Life and Adventures of Giovanni Finati. 1830. First ed., map, 2 vols. in 1, contemp. half calf, binding rubbed, 8vo. Howes 194-608 1978 £21

BANKS, C. STANLEY   Laurel Heights Methodist Church, 1909-1949. San Antonio, 1949. 1st ed., illus., t.p. design by Carl Hertzog. Jenkins 116-99 1978 $15

BANKS, C. STANLEY   Laurel Heights Methodist Church, 1909-1949. San Antonio, 1949. Cloth, illus., 1st ed., edges a little worn else very good, scarce. Dykes 35-258 1978 $75

BANKS, CHARLES EDWARD   The Planters of the Commonwealth.   Boston, 1930. Illus., uncut, ltd. to 750 copies, scarce. MacManus 239-295 1978 $35

BANKS, CHARLES EDWARD   The Planters of the Commonwealth.   Boston, 1930. Illus., 8vo., orig. bds., cloth back, boxed, few light dust spots on covers, very nice, ltd. to 787 copies. Morrill 241-314 1978 $35

BANKS, CHARLES EDWARD   A True Relation Concerning the Estate of New England as it was Presented to His Matie. (Boxton, 1886). Cloth, ex-lib. MacManus 239-42 1978 $15

BANKS, CHARLES EDWARD   The Winthrop Fleet of 1630.   Boston, 1930. Illus., ltd. to 550 copies. MacManus 239-41 1978 $32.50

BANKS, CHARLES EDWARD   The Winthrop Fleet of 1630.   Boston, 1930. Illus., ltd. 530. Baldwins' 51-244 1978 $37.50

BANKS, ELEANOR   Wandersong. 1950. Cloth, map end sheets, map, illus., 1st ed., very good copy in d.w., reinforced, scarce. Dykes 34-265 1978 $15

BANKS, J.   A Sermon Preached Before the Incorporated Society for the Propagation of the Gospel in Foreign Parts... 1828. Cloth, leather spine, title slightly browned, 8vo. Edwards 1012-416 1978 £45

BANKS, JOHN 1709-51   A New History of the Life and Reign of the Czar Peter the Great. 1755. Third ed., portrait, sm. 8vo., contemp. calf, joints cracked. Howes 194-413 1978 £14

BANKS, REV. LOUIS ALBERT   Immortal Songs of Camp and Field.   Cleveland, 1898. Bell Wiley's copy, illus. Broadfoot's 44-19 1978 $14

BANKS, DR. WILLIAM MITCHELL   A Narrative of the Voyage of the Argonauts in 1880. 1881. Illus., 8vo., orig. cloth, pres. copy from author, A.L.s. from author inserted. F. Edwards 1013-12 1978 £50

BANNATYNE, NEIL   History of the Thirtieth Regiment.... Liverpool, 1923. Coloured plts., maps, thick roy. 8vo., orig. buckram, pres. copy inscribed by author. F. Edwards 1013-505 1978 £80

BANNERMAN, DAVID ARMITAGE   The Birds of Tropical West Africa.... Edinburgh, 1930-1951. Maps, coloured plts., 8 vols., roy. 8vo., orig. buckram, scarce. Traylen 88-535 1978 £360

BANNERMAN, HELEN.   The Story of Little Black Sambo.   New York-Philadelphia, n.d. 1st Amer. Ed., colored illus., laid-down cover plate, library stamps, hinge cracked, rear cover heavily marked, excessively rare. Victoria 34-40 1978 $200

BANNING, KENDALL   Bypaths in Arcady, a Book of Love Songs. Chicago, 1915. Illus. in photogravure, 1st ed., 1 of 77 copies on Japan vellum, folio, orig. full vellum, light stain on cover, bkplt. of Merle Johnson, signed quote from Banning, 2 typed letters signed by Banning laid in, scarce, very good. Americanist 103-73 1978 $125

BANNING, KENDALL   Songs of the Love Unending, a Sonnet Sequence. Chicago, Village Press, 1912. 1st ed., ltd. to 375 copies, fronts, sm. thin 4to., orig. linen-backed light bds., signed inscr. by Banning, very good. Americanist 103-129 1978 $45

BANNING, KENDALL   Songs of the Love Unending, a Sonnet Sequence. Uninscribed. Americanist 103-130 1978 $37.50

BANNING, THOMAS HAINES   Disputatio Medica Inauguralis de Angina Pectoris. Edinburgi, 1809. 8vo., disbound, very good copy. Zeitlin 245-11 1978 $75

BANTA, D. D.   A Historical Sketch of Johnson County, Indiana. Chicago, 1881. Wrps., facsimile reprint. Hayman 71-347 1978 $10

BANVARD, JOSEPH   The American Statesman; or Illustrations of the Life Character of Daniel Webster. Boston, 1854. A.e.g., cloth. Hayman 72-35 1978 $10

BAQUET, CAMILLE   History of the First Brigade, New Jersey Volunteers, 1861 to 1865. Tranton, 1910. Illus., orig. cloth, scarce. MacManus 239-864 1978 $47.50

BARBARO, HERMOLAO   Compendium Scientiae Naturalis Ex Aristotele. Paris, 1547. Thin 8vo., marbled bds. Salloch 345-10 1978 $145

BARBAROUX, CHARLES O.   Voyage du General Lafayette aux Etats-Unis d-Amerique en 1824. Burxelles, 1825. Portr., 3 vols. in 1, 16mo., contemp. bds., lea. back, nice, 2nd ed. Morrill 239-470 1978 $35

BARBAULD, ANNA LETITA (AIKIN)   Evenings at Home of the Juvenile Budget Opened. Philadelphia, c. 1815-20. 3 vols., 4th Amer. ed., hand colored plts., roan backed marbled bds., foxed, v.g., upper hinge partly cracked. Victoria 34-42 1978 $225

BARBAULD, ANNA LETITA (AIKIN)   Hymns in Prose, for the Use of Children. New York, 1816. 24mo., woodcuts, 4 signed by Anderson, illus. wrs., v.g. Victoria 34-42 1978 $55

BARBAULD, ANNA LETITA (AIKIN)   Little Marian. Boston, c. 1835. 16mo., pict. stiff wrs., plts., bottom wr. gone, text foxed. Victoria 34-44 1978 $7.50

BARBAULD, ANNA LETITA (AIKIN)   Poems. 1773. 4to., cont. calf gilt, first ed., fine. P.M. Hill 142-238 1978 £45

BARBAULD, ANNA LETITIA (AIKIN)   The Works. 1825. First ed., portrait, 2 vols., cont. half calf. Howes 194-609 1978 £21

BARBE-MARBOIS, FRANCOIS, MARQUIS DE   Historie De La Louisiane Et De La Cession De Cette Colonie Par La France Aux Etats-Unis. Paris, 1829. Large colored folding map, half calf, 1st ed. Jenkins 116-1569 1978 $300

BARBEAU, ALFRED   Life and Letters at Bath in the XVIII Century. London, 1904. 1 of 100 numbered copies, plates, sm. 4to., full gilt stamped white vellum, t.e.g., uncut, good. Houle 10-21 1978 $85

BARBEAU, MARIUS   Alaska Beckons. Caldwell, 1947. Illus. by Arthur Price, decor. endpapers. Hood 117-664 1978 $60

BARBEAU, MARIUS   L'arbre des Reves. Montreal, 1947. Card cover, illus. Hood 117-504 1978 $25

BARBEAU, MARIUS   Cornelius Krieghoff, Pioneer Painter of North America. Toronto, 1934. 14 Coloured plts. Hood's 115-160 1978 $225

BARBEAU, MARIUS   Folk-songs of Old Quebec. Ottawa, n.d. Illud., card cover. Hood 116-504 1978 $17.50

BARBEAU, MARIUS   Henri Julien. Toronto, 1941. Card cover, plts. Hood 117-193 1978 $22.50

BARBEAU, MARIUS   Quebec, Where Ancient France Lingers. Toronto, 1936. Illus. by Marjorie Borden, colored card cover. Hood 117-199 1978 $35

BARBEE, DAVID RANKIN   The Capture of Jefferson Davis. Bell Wiley's copy. Broadfoot 46-7A 1978 $10

BARBER, EDWIN ATLEE   American Glassware, Old and New. Philadelphia, 1900. Illus., scarce. MacManus 239-638 1978 $35

BARBER, EDWIN ATLEE   Tulip Ware of the Pennsylvania German Potters. Philadelphia, 1903. 1st ed., 4to., illus., some in color, uncut, fine, ltd. to 300 copies. MacManus 239-639 1978 $75

BARBER, EDWIN ATLEE   Tulip Ware of the Pennsylvania-German Potters. Philadelphia, 1903. Illus., tall 8vo., 1 of 300 signed lg. paper copies. Morrill 241-649 1978 $75

BARBER, JOHN WARNER   City Guide to New Haven... New Haven, 1860. 1st ed., 12mo, colored frontis. map, orig. cloth, fine. MacManus 239-92 1978 $22.50

BARBER, JOHN WARNER   Historical Collections. Worcester, 1839. Engrs., map, 8vo., contemp. calf, front hinge cracked, 1st ed., clean copy. Morrill 241-693 1978 $45

BARBER, JOHN WARNER   Historical Collections of the State of New York. New York, 1842. Illus., cloth. MacManus 239-343 1978 $45

BARBER, JOHN WARNER   Historical Collections of the State of New Jersey... New York, 1844. 1st ed., illus., cloth, very good. MacManus 239-1238 1978 $50

BARBER, JOHN WARNER   History and Antiquities of New Haven, Conn.... New Haven, 1856. Colored frontis. map, illus., orig. cloth, rebacked, bookplts. MacManus 239-96 1978 $25

BARBER, MARY   Poems on Several Occasions. 1734. 1st. ed., 4to, contemp. half calf, very worn, paper stripped from bds., 1st gathering misbound, good shape internally. Hannas 54-12 1978 £65

BARBER, THOMAS   Barber's Picturesque Guide to the Isle of Wight..., Completed to the End of 1850. 1850. New ed., 8vo., maps, plts., some slight foxing, orig. green cloth, gilt edges. Quaritch 983-286 1978 $135

BARBETTE, PAUL   The Practice of the Most Successful Physician Paul Barbette. London, 1675. 8vo., early 18th century signature on letterpress titlepage, contemp. sheep. Quaritch 977-8 1978 $575

BARBON, NICHOLAS   A Discourse of Trade 1690. Lord Baltimore Press, 1905. Paper. Austin 80-422 1978 $12.50

BARBOT, JOHN   The Tryal of .... London, 1753. Folio, calf, worn. Edwards 1012-739 1978 £100

BARBOUR, J. S.   A History of Wm. Patterson and the Darien Company. 1907. Illus., cr. 8vo. George's 635-279 1978 £5

BARBOUR, R. W.   Pensees, Poems and Letters. Glasgow, 1894. 8vo., half vellum, gilt tooled spine, slipcase, frontis. Van der Peet H-64-391 1978 Dfl 85

BARCENA, MANUEL DE LA   Manifiesto Al Mundo, La Justicia Y La Necesidad De La Indedencia De La Nueva Espana. Puebla, 1821. Laid in half mor. slipcase, rare and valuable. Jenkins 11-65 1978 $575

BARCLAY, HUGH   A Digest of the Law of Scotland. Edinburgh, 1865. Roy. 8vo., 3rd ed., orig. cloth. K Books 244-341 1978 £10

BARCLAY, JAMES   A Complete and Universal Dictionary of the English Language. (c. 1851). New ed., portraits, maps coloured in outline, 4to., half calf, rubbed, 8vo. George's 635-1462 1978 £22.50

BARCLAY, JOHN   Barclay His Argenis. 1636. 2nd ed., new buckram, plts., illus. Allen 234-1100a 1978 $75

BARCLAY, JOHN   Argenis. 1659. 16mo., vellum. Allen 234-1099 1978 $30

BARCLAY, JOHN   Argenis. Leyden, 1659. Octavo, full contemporary limp vellum, fine engraved frontispiece, portrait of author, fine crisp copy, Sir Alexander MacDonald's copy with his armorial bookplate. Bennett 20-18 1978 $125

BARCLAY, JOHN   Argenis. Leiden & Rotterdam, 1664. Contemp. panelled calf, portrait, neatly rebacked, 8vo. Howes 194-7 1978 £25

BARCLAY, JOHN   L'Argenide di Gio: Barclaio Tradotta da Francesco Pona. Venetia, 1669. 12mo., sheepskin. King 7-15 1978 £15

BARCLAY, JOHN   Argenis. Amsterdam, 1671. 24mo., lacks front cover & spine. Allen 234-1100 1978 $15

BARCLAY, ROBERT   An Apology for the True Christian Divinity. 1736. Sixth ed., thk. cr. 8vo., contemp. calf, title soiled. Howes 194-150 1978 £15

BARCLAY, ROBERT   An Apology for the True Christian Divinity. Providence, 1840. Lea., stain on cover. Hayman 73-35 1978 $10

BARCLAY, ROBERT   An Apology For the True Christian Divinity.... 1886. 14th. ed., octavo, good. Upcroft 10-9 1978 £5

BARD, SAMUEL A.
Please turn to
SQUIER, EPHRAIM GEORGE

BARDSLEY, CHARLES   Curiosities of Puritan Nomeclature. New York, 1880. Good. Nestler Rare 78-238 1978 $15

BARDSLEY, CHARLES W.   John Lexley's Troubles. 1877. 1st. ed., half titles, orig. brown cloth, mint. Jarndyce 16-280 1978 £90

BAREA, ARTURO   The Broken Root. London, 1950. First English ed., fine, frayed d.w., orig. binding, inscribed by Ilsa Barea. Rota 211-30 1978 £10

BARETTI, GIUSEPPE   A Dictionary of the English and Italian Languages. 1760. 2 vols., 4to., contemp. calf, rebacked, first ed. Howes 194-240 1978 £40

BARETTI, GIUSEPPE   Dizionario Italiano Ed Inglese. Bologna, 1830 and Florence, 1832. 2 vols., 4to, 1/2 green morocco, ex-lib. bdg., rubbed, head of spines slightly defective. Eaton 45-33 1978 £15

BARETTI, JOSEPH   An Account of the Manners and Customs of Italy... 1768. 1st. ed., 2 vols., 8vo., plts., contemp. half calf, joints broken. Hannas 54-13 1978 £55

BARGAW, JOHN G.   Random Shots. Raleigh, 1945. Pres. copy, d.j. Broadfoot 50-18 1978 $20

BARGY, HENRY   La Religion Dans La Societe Aux Etats-Unis. Paris, 1902. Bds., cloth sp., 1st ed. Ginsberg 16-823 1978 $25.00

BARHAM, R. A. DALTON   The Life & Remains of Theodore Edward Hook. 1848. 1st. ed., 2 vols., frontis portraits, half calf, spine gilt, v.g. Jarndyce 16-740 1978 £28.50

BARHAM, R. H.   The Ingoldsby Legends. London, 1867. Plts. by Leech and Cruikshank, full calf gilt, g.e., 8vo. K Books 244-21 1978 £21

BARING, MAURICE   Robert Peckham. N.P. (London), 1934. 8vo, orig. tan pr. self-wr., ltd. to 100 copies, numbered and signed by author, presentation copy, inscribed on fly-leaf, nice copy. Ximenes 47-12 1978 $60

BARING, MAURICE   Robert Peckham. (London), 1934. Orig. wrs., 1st ed., 1 of 100 copies signed by author, front cover marked, spine worn. MacManus 238-607 1978 $40

BARING-GOULD, SABINE   Further Reminiscences 1864-1894. London, 1925. Illus., first ed., orig. binding, very nice, d.w. Rota 211-688 1978 £15

BARING-GOULD, SABINE   A History of Sarawak Under Its Two White Rajahs. London, 1909. Illus. Baldwins' 51-326 1978 $12.50

BARING-GOULD, SABINE   A History of Sarawak under its Two White Rajahs, 1839-1908. London, 1909. Illus., folding map, cloth (dull, hinges weakening). Dawson's 127-245 1978 $35

BARING-GOULD, SABINE   Life of Napoleon Bonaparte. 1897. Photogravure plts., illus., sm. folio, orig. buckram, gilt, a little rubbed and stained. George's 635-724 1978 £8.50

BARING-GOULD, SABINE   Old Country Life. London, 1890. 1st ed., 8vo., orig. gilt stamped decorative blue cloth, bevelled edges, t.e.g., uncut, illus. Houle 10-22 1978 $20

BARINGER, WILLIAM E.   A House Dividing. Springfield, 1945. Illus., small nick at tope of front cover. Biblo 248-58 1978 $18.50

BARKER, LADY   Station Life in New Zealand. London, 1871. New ed., frontis., 12mo., ex-lib., orig. cloth. Morrill 241-42 1978 $7.50

BARKER, BENJAMIN   Corilia, or, The Indian Enchantress. Boston, 1847. 8vo, recent cloth-backed boards, 1st ed. Quaritch 978-116 1978 $150

BARKER, EUGENE C.   The Life of Stephen F. Austin, Founder of Texas.
Dallas, 1926. Special ed., limited to 250 numbered, autographed copies, rare
desirable. Jenkins 116-44 1978 $150

BARKER, EUGENE C.   Life of Stephen F. Austin, Founder of Texas,
1793-1836. Austin, 1949. Illus. Baldwins' 51-174 1978 $17.50

BARKER, EUGENE C.   A School History of Texas. Chicago, 1912.
1st ed., illus. Jenkins 116-66 1978 $10

BARKER, F. D.   An Angler's Paradise. 1929. 8vo., d.w., cloth.
Quaritch 979-330 1978 $45

BARKER, GEORGE   Calamiterror. 1937. Very good, d.w., first
English ed. Bell Book 17-042 1978 £12.50

BARKER, GEORGE   The View from a Blind I. Very good, d.w., first
English ed. Bell Book 17-968 1978 £6.50

BARKER, LEWELLYS F.   The Nervous System and Its Contituent Neurones.
New York, 1901. Ex-library, worn. Rittenhouse 49-52 1976 $25

BARKER, REN   Military History (Michigan Boys), Company "D"
66th Illinois, Birge's Western Sharpshooters in the Civil War. Reed City, 1905.
Illus., Bell Wiley's copy. Broadfoot's 44-468 1978 $25

BARLEE, WILLIAM   A Concordance of All Written Lawes Concerning
Lords of Mannors, Theire Free Tenantes, and Copieholders. 1911. Octavo, good.
Upcroft 10-10 1978 £5

BARLER, MILES   Early Days in Llano, N.P., c.1949. Cloth.
Jenkins 116-831 1978 $7.50

BARLOW, FRANK   Durham Jurisdictional Peculiars. Oxford, 1950.
Maps, 8vo. Upcroft 12-24 1978 £8.50

BARLOW, FREDERIC   The Complete English Peerage. 1772. First ed.,
plts., 2 vols., contemp. calf, crimson labels, 8vo. Howes 194-151 1978 £18

BARLOW, JANE   The End of Elfintown. London, 1894. Illus. by
Laurence Housman, 12mo., orig. dec. cloth, 1st ed., covers a bit worn. Mac-
Manus 238-282 1978 $85

BARLOW, JOEL   The Vision of Columbus. A Poem in Nine Books.
Hartford, 1787. Contemp. calf, upper hinge cracked, slightly worn, 1st ed. Mac-
Manus 238-421 1978 $75

BARLOW, R.   An Account of the Various Properties Obtained
from the Carbonization of Coal and Wood. London, 1814. 8vo., unbound, edges
frayed, in cloth folder. Quaritch 977-205 1978 $50

BARLOW, W.   Considerations on the Employment of the Press
as a Means of Diffusing the Principles of the Church. New York, 1826. Prtd.
wr., near-mint. Butterfield 21-463 1978 $10

BARLOW, W. M.   The McLean Silver Mining Company of Montana.
Philadelphia, 1865. Cloth. Ginsberg 14-613 1978 $125

BARLOW, WILLIAM   Magneticall Advertisements. London, 1616.
4to., errata slip tipped in, text woodcuts, old vellum, gilt-stamped signature of
Latimer Clark, his stamp & signature, fine copy, 1st ed. Norman 5-18 1978
$4,000

BARMAN, CHRISTIAN   The Bridge. A Chapter in the History of Building.
London, (1926). Illus., some in color, sm. 4to., 1st ed. Biblo BL781-612 1978
$17.50

BARN Plans and Outbuildings. New York, 1898. Clean, orig. binding, illus.
Hayman 71-36 1978 $7.50

BARNABE, STEPHEN   Unterweisung de Spanishen Sprach. Wien in
Oesterreich, 1657. 16mo., comtemporary vellum boards, slight wormholing, fine,
crisp copy. Victoria 34-45 1978 $185

BARNARD, CHESTER I.   Organization and Management. Harvard University Press, 1949. One chapter underlined in ink, otherwise clean. Austin 80-
423 1978 $17.50

BARNARD, DANIEL D.   An Address Delivered Before the Philoclean and
Peithessophian Societies of Rutgers College...July 18th, 1837. Albany, 1837.
8vo., orig. wrs., 1st ed. Morrill 241-396 1978 $7.50

BARNARD, EVAN G.   A Rider of the Cherokee Strip. Boston, 1936.
Cloth, map end sheets, illus., 1st ed., fine copy, d.w., reinforced, scarce.
Dykes 34-80 1978 $35

BARNARD, JONATHAN G.   The Dangers and Defences of New York. New
York, 1859. 8vo., orig. wrs., top margin lightly dampstained, 1st ed. Morrill
239-546 1978 $12.50

BARNARD, JONATHAN G.   The Peninsular Campaign and Its Antecedents,
as Developed by the Report of Maj. Gen. Geo. B. McClellan, and Other Published Documents. New York, 1864. Fldg. map, 1st ed., orig. cloth. Morrill
241-650 1978 $12.50

BARNARD, THOMAS   An Historical Character Relating to the Holy and
Exemplary Life of the Right Honorable the Lady Elisabeth Hastings. Leeds, 1742.
Large 21mo, contemporary calf, gilt, a trifle worn, 1st ed., very good copy.
Ximenes 47-15 1978 $70

BARNER, JAKOB B.   Wohlgemeinte Nachricht...der Hermetischen
Kunst. Danzig, (1683). 12mo., 18th Century vellum, gilt, foxed, but very good
copy, lib. stamp, 18th Cent. bkplt. of Ernst Graf zu Stolberg, 1st ed. Norman
5-19 1978 $200

BARNES, ALBERT   The Church and Slavery. Philadelphia, 1857.
Cloth. Hayman 72-709 1978 $15

BARNES, B. H.   Johnson of Nyasaland. London, 1933. 8vo.,
orig. cloth, maps & illus., covers faded. K Books 239-26 1978 £5

BARNES, CHARLES MERRITT   Combats and Conquests of Immortal Heroes
Sung in Song and Told in Story. San Antonio, 1910. 1st ed., illus., orig.
red cloth, few pages at end browned, else very good or better. Limestone
Y-13 1978 $65

BARNES, DJUNA   A Book. New York, (1923). Illus. by author,
orig. bds., paper label, 1st ed., spine faded and slightly worn, otherwise very
good. MacManus 238-608 1978 $175

BARNES, DJUNA   Nightwood. 1936. Good, first English ed.
Bell Book 16-041 1978 £15

BARNES, DJUNA   Nightwood. New York, 1937. First U.S. ed.,
spine faded, good. Bell Book 16-971 1978 £12.50

BARNES, HARRY E.   The Evolution of Penology in Pennsylvania...
Indianapolis, (1927). Illus., inscribed. MacManus 239-1364 1978 $25

BARNES, JOHN S.   The Logs of the Serapis - Alliance - Ariel, Under
the Command of John Paul Jones. New York, 1911. Orig. bds., vellum back,
ltd. to 300 copies, scarce. MacManus 239-1734 1978 $35

BARNES, LEMUEL CALL   Two Thousand Years of Missions Before Carey.
Chicago, 1900. Map, illus., 8vo., 1st ed. Morrill 239-299 1978 $7.50

BARNES, MARY CLARK   Neighboring New Americans. 1920. Austin
79-44 1978 $10

BARNES, MARY CLARK   The New America. 1913. Illus. Austin 79-
45 1978 $12.50

BARNES, THURLOW WEED   Souvenir of the Albany Bi-Centennial. Albany,
1886. Folio, illus. ads, chromolitho. plts., wr. Butterfield 21-20 1978 $15

BARNES, WILL C.   Arizona Place Names. Tuscon, 1935.
1st ed., orig. printed wr., worn, rebacked, interior very good. Limestone
9-9 1978 $20

BARNES, WILL C.   Western Grazing Grounds and Forest Ranges.
Chicago, 1913. Cloth, illus., scarce, 1st ed., minor wear, very good copy, slipcase. Dykes 34-15 1978 $50

BARNES, WILLIAM H.   The Fortieth Congress of the U.S.: Historical
and Biographical. New York, 1869. 2 vols., illus., scarce. MacManus 239-
44 1978 $40

BARNETT, LIONEL D.　　　El Libro De Los Acuerdos.　Oxford University Press, 1931.　Illus.　Austin 79-46　1978　$27.50

BARNEY, JOSHUA　　　A Biographical Memoir: from Autobiographical Notes and Journals.　Boston, 1832.　Port., 1st ed., bind. worn, some foxing.　Biblo BL781-234　1978　$17.50

BARNS, T. ALEXANDER　　　An African Eldorado.　London, (1926).　8vo, 4 maps, 32 illus., orig. cloth, spine faded.　K Books 239-27　1978　£10

BARNS, T. ALEXANDER　　　Angolan Sketches.　London, (1928).　8vo, orig. cloth, 3 maps, 20 illus.　K Books 239-28　1978　£9

BARNUM, H. L.　　　The Spy Unmasked.　New York, 1828.　Plts., map, ads, early bds., worn, crudely rebacked, light damp-staining, good copy, 1st ed.　Butterfield 21-371　1978　$65

BARNUM, H. L.　　　The Spy Unmasked; or Memoirs of Enoch Crosby... 1829.　1st. ed., 2 vols., uncut, half black calf, rubbed, Dover Lib. labels.　Jarndyce 16-281　1978　£52

BARNUM, H. L.　　　The Spy Unmasked, or Memoirs of Enoch Crosby, Alias Harvey Birch.　Cincinnati, 1831.　2nd ed., cut signature of Crosby, binding worn.　Nestler Rare 78-155　1978　$55

BARNWELL, ROBERT GIBBES　A Sketch of the Life and Times of John De Witt to Which is Added His Treatise on Life Annuities.　New York, 1856.　Backstrip detached, else good.　Austin 82-113　1978　$27.50

BARO, C. M.　　　Eventails Anciens.　Lausanne, (1937).　Wrs., 12mo., illus. in color.　Biblo 247-332　1978　$7.50

BARÔ, PETER 1534-99　　　In Jonam Prophetam Praelectiones 39.　London, 1579-78.　2 parts in 1 vol., 4to., tables, contemp. limp vellum with thongs, ties missing.　Howes 194-8　1978　$175

BARON, SALO WITTMAYER　　　Modern Nationalism and Religion.　1947.　1st ed. in dust jacket.　Austin 79-47　1978　$20

BARONI, CLEMENTE　　　L'Impotenza del Demonio Di Trasportare a talento per l'aria da un luogo all'altro i Corpi Umani.　Rovereto, 1753.　8vo., paper bds., uncut, unopened, fine.　King 7-133　1978　£50

BARONIUS, CESARE 1538-1607　　　Annales Ecclesiastici ex XII Tomis Caesaris Baronii, opera Henrici Spondani.　Mainz, 1618.　Portrait frontis., thk. folio, contemp. calf, rebacked.　Howes 194-526　1978　£70

BARR, AMELIA E.　　　The Preacher's Daughter.　A Domestic Romance.　Boston, (1892).　Cloth.　Hayman 72-215　1978　$7.50

BARR, E. OSMUN　　　Flying Men and Medicine.　The Effects of Flying Upon the Human Body.　New York, 1943.　Rittenhouse 49-54　1976　$10

BARR, ROBERT　　　Cardillac.　New York, 1909.　Hood 116-451　1978　$10

BARRASS, E.　　　Smiles and Tears; or, Sketches from Real Life.　Toronto, 1879.　1st series, gold tipped pgs.　Hood 116-673　1978　$12.50

BARRASS, E.　　　A Gallery of Distinguished Men.　Napanee, 1870.　3/4 leather.　Hood 116-6　1978　$17.50

BARRATT, N. S.　　　Outline of the History of Old St. Paul's Church Philadelphia, Pa. 1760-1898.　(Lancaster), 1917.　4to., illus., uncut.　MacManus 239-1638　1978　$17.50

BARREIRO, ANTONIO　　　Ojeada Sobre Nuevo Mexico, Que da Una Idea de sus Producciones Naturales,.....　Puebla, 1832.　Tables, half mottled calf.　Ginsberg 14-748　1978　$600

BARRELIER, JACQUES　　　Plantae Per Gallium, Hispaniam et Italiam Observatae.　Paris, 1714.　Engraved titles, engraved plts., thick folio, contemp. French red morocco, spine gilt, gilt edges, fine copy.　Traylen 88-536　1978　£1200

BARRETT, C. R. B.　　　The 85th King's Light Infantry.　1913.　Thick imp. 8vo., publisher's half mor., plts. coloured.　F. Edwards 1013-537　1978　£50

BARRETT, EATON STANNARD　　　Woman, A Poem, and Occasional Poems.　1818.　Frontis eng. & wood engs., full leather, gilt, rubbed, Roger Senhouse's book label, with pencil notes by him.　Eaton 45-34　1978　£10

BARRETT, H. J.　　　Modern Methods in the Office.　1918.　Austin 80-424　1978　$11

BARRETT, H. M.　　　Boethius; some aspects of his times and work.　Cambridge, 1940.　8vo.　Upcroft 12-29　1978　£5.50

BARRETT, JAY A.　　　The History and Government of Nebraska.　Lincoln, 1892.　Cloth.　Hayman 72-36　1978　$8.50

BARRETT, NORRIS STANLEY　Outline of the History of Old St. Paul's Church, Philadelphia, Pa.　Pennsylvania, 1917.　Illus. with photos, portraits.　Baldwins' 51-422　1978　$14.50

BARRETT, S. M.　　　Geronimo's Story of His Life.　New York, 1906.　Illus., original cloth, 1st ed., advance review copy with slip pasted in.　Ginsberg 14-362　1978　$25

BARRETT, WALTER　　　The Old Merchants of New York City.　New York, 1866.　4th series, clean, orig. binding.　Hayman 71-37　1978　$7.50

BARRIE, JAMES MATTHEW　　　The Admirable Crichton.　London, (1914).　Tall quarto, full vellum with pict. stamping in gilt, t.e.g., others uncut, tipped-in color illus. and drawings in black and white by Hugh Thomson, 1 of 500 copies signed by artist.　Duschnes 220-305　1978　$165

BARRIE, JAMES MATTHEW　　　Auld Licht Idylls.　London, 1888.　8vo, blue buckram and black end papers, ownership inscription, rear hinge beginning to loosen, 1st ed., collector's cond.　Desmarais 1-20　1978　$25

BARRIE, JAMES MATTHEW　　　Courage.　London, (1922).　4to, white cloth, gilt stamped, large paper ed., 1st ed., collector's cond.　Desmarais 1-21　1978　$30

BARRIE, JAMES MATTHEW　　　Echoes of the War.　New York, 1918.　1st Amer. ed.　Biblo 251-397　1978　$8.50

BARRIE, JAMES MATTHEW　　　An Edinburgh Eleven.　London, 1889.　1st ed., first issue, cream wrappers, very good, boxed.　Greene 78-2　1978　$45

BARRIE, JAMES MATTHEW　　　An Edinburgh Eleven.　New York, n.d. (1889).　Pirated Am. ed., blue cloth, very good.　Greene 78-3　1978　$45

BARRIE, JAMES MATTHEW　　　The Entrancing Life.　London, 1930.　4to., tan cloth, near mint, d.w., first ed.　Desmarais 1-22　1978　$10

BARRIE, JAMES MATTHEW　　　The Little Minister.　London, 1891.　3 vols., sm. 8vo., orig. brown cloth, 1st ed., light cover wear, occasional light foxing, else fine, uncut, rare, box.　Howell 5-5　1978　$250

BARRIE, JAMES MATTHEW　　　The Little Minister.　London, 1891.　3 vols., orig. cloth, slightly soiled, 1st ed., very good.　MacManus 238-165　1978　$225

BARRIE, JAMES MATTHEW　　　The Little Minister.　New York, 1891.　8vo, blue cloth, gilt lettering on spine, small bookplt., hinges weakening, 1st Amer. ed., nice.　Desmarais 1-23　1978　$40

BARRIE, JAMES MATTHEW　　　The Little Minister.　New York, (1898).　Drawings.　Biblo 247-799　1978　$17.50

BARRIE, JAMES MATTHEW　　　The Little White Bird.　London, 1902.　8vo, cloth, frontispiece, 1st ed., top of spine chipped, fine.　Duschness 220-12　1978　$20

BARRIE, JAMES MATTHEW　　　The Little White Bird.　1902.　First ed., frontispiece, orig. buckram, gilt top, 8vo.　Howes 194-612　1978　£4

BARRIE, JAMES MATTHEW　　　Peter and Wendy.　New York, 1911.　Bkplt., ownership inscription, fr. hinge started, near fine.　Desmarais B-57　1978　$10

BARRIE, JAMES MATTHEW   Quality Street. London, (1913). 1st ed., tipped-in color plates, gilt-decorated pictorial covers in cloth, fine. Victoria 34-794 1978 $75

BARRIE, JAMES MATTHEW   Quality Street. London, n.d. (1913). 1st. ed., 4to, picture cloth gilt, little faded, inscription on title-pg., coloured plts. & other illus. by Hugh Thomson. Traylen 88-418 1978 £18

BARRIE, JAMES MATTHEW   Quality Street. London, n.d. Large quarto, the signed, limited ed., tipped-in color plates, mounted on Japan vellum with colored boarders, printed and decor. tissue guards, bound in full vellum, stunning over-all gilt decorated designs, large pictorial vignette, fine copy, limited to 1,000 copies. Victoria 34-802 1978 $200

BARRIE, JAMES MATTHEW   Sentimental Tommy, The Story of His Boyhood. London, 1896. Blue cloth, 1st ed., 1st issue, bevelled edges, t.e.g., very good. Greene 78-140 1978 $25

BARRIE, JAMES MATTHEW   Tommy and Grizel. London, 1900. 1st ed., blue cloth, bevelled edges, t.e.g., spine dark, lettering faded. Greene 78-142 1978 $15

BARRIE, JAMES MATTHEW   Tommy and Grizel. New York, 1900. Illus., first American ed. Biblo 247-497 1978 $17.50

BARRIE, JAMES MATTHEW   Two of Them. New York, (1893). 1st ed., cloth, gilt vignette on cover, very good condition. Greene 78-143 1978 $50

BARRIE, JAMES MATTHEW   Works. London, 1913. Kirriemuir ed., 10 vols., roy. 8vo, orig. bds., cloth spines, gilt tops. Traylen 88-103 1978 £35

BARRIE, JAMES MATTHEW   Works. 1913. Kirriemuir ed., 10 vols., roy. 8vo., orig. cloth-backed bds., gilt tops, ltd. to 1,000 numbered sets only. Howes 194-610 1978 £40

BARRIE, ROBERT   Cruises, Mainly in the Bay of the Chesapeake. Bryn Mawr, 1909. 8vo., illus., orig. cloth, binding partly faded, slightly spotted, autographed by George Barrie. Morrill 241-44 1978 $15

BARRINGTON, ARCHIBALD   A Familiar Introduction to Heraldry. London, 1848. Hand-coloured plts., fcap. 8vo., neatly rebacked. K Books 244-22 1978 £12

BARRINGTON, DAINES   Miscellanies. 1781. 2 maps, engraved plts., 4to., half morocco. Edwards 1012-4 1978 £250

BARRINGTON, DAINES   The Possibility of Approaching the North Pole Asserted. 1818. 2nd. ed., vignette on title, folding map, browned, orig. cloth, rebacked, old spine laid down, 8vo. Edwards 1012-561 1978 £75

BARROSO, GUSTAVO   Maripunga. London, 1924. Small 4to, boards, vellum spine, d.w. chipped and darkened, 1st ed., collector's cond. Desmarais 1-194 1978 $25

BARROW, ISAAC   Of Industry, in Five Discourses... London, 1693. Portrait frontis, inner border closely bound & little frayed, sm. 8vo, old calf, new spine, gilt, leather label. Traylen 88-104 1978 £80

BARROW, JOHN   An Account of Travels into the Interior of Southern Africa in the Years 1797 and 1798. London, 1801-04. First ed., 2 vols., lg. fold. map foxed and repaired, other maps, 2 coloured in outline, 4to, cont. diced calf, good, rebacked. K Books 239-29 1978 £210

BARROW, JOHN   An Auto-Biographical Memoir of ... 1847. 8vo, engraved portrait, orig. cloth. Edwards 1012-5 1978 £25

BARROW, JOHN   A Chronological History of Voyages into the Artic Regions... 1818. Folding map, half-title, woodcuts, orig. bds., rebacked cloth, edges uncut, slight repair to marings of 4 pgs., 8vo. Edwards 1012-562 1978 £75

BARROW, JOHN   The Life of Richard Earl Howe, K.G., Admiral of the Fleet, and General of Marines. 1838. 8vo, contemp. calf, spine rubbed, portrait frontis. F. Edwards 1013-101 1978 £30

BARROW, JOHN   Navigatio Britannica. 1750. Plts., sm. 4to., contemp. calf, rebacked. F. Edwards 1013-17 1978 £160

BARROW, JOHN   Travels in China.... London, 1806. 2nd ed., 4to, coloured aquatint plts., engraved plts., polished blue half calf, marbled bds., gilt lines, blind & gilt tooled panelled back, marbled endpapers & edges. Deighton 5-63 1978 £120

BARROW, JOHN   Travels Into the Interior of Southern Africa. London, 1806. 2nd. ed., 2 vols., 4to, 8 coloured aquatint plts., 9 coloured & other maps, polished blue calf, marbled bds., gilt tooled panelled backs. Deighton 5-4 1978 £395

BARROW, JOHN   Voyage Dans La Partie Meridionale de L'Afrique, 1797-98... Paris, 1801. Lg. folding map, plt., 2 vols., calf, repaired. Edwards 1012-293 1978 £90

BARROW, JOHN   A Voyage to Cochincina, in the Years 1792 and 1793. London, 1806. 1st. ed., 20 hand coloured aquatints, 4to, plts., one slightly waterstained, very good copy, contemp. half calf, upper joint cracked at top. K Books 239-30 1978 £220

BARROW, JOHN   A Voyage to Cochinchina in The Years 1792 and 1793... London, 1806. 1st. ed., 4to, engraved coloured map, coloured aquatint plts., contemporary polished blue half calf, gilt, marbled endpapers & edges. Deighton 5-174 1978 £325

BARROW, JOHN   Voyages of Discovery and Research Within the Arctic Regions from the Year 1818 to the Present Time. London, 1846. Port., maps. Hood 116-63 1978 $155

BARROWS, EDWARD M.   The Great Commodore, the Exploits of Matthew Calbraith Perry. Indianapolis, (1935). Illus., 1st ed., d.j. MacManus 239-802 1978 $10

BARROWS, JOHN R.   Ubet. Caldwell, 1934. Pict. cloth, illus., 1st ed., top and bottom of spine worn, lettering on spine dull else very good, signed by author. Dykes 35-136 1978 $35

BARROWS, MARJORIE   Who's Who in the Zoo. Chicago, (1932). Large quarto, colored plates, slight cover fading, fine. Victoria 34-875 1978 $15

BARROWS, SAMUEL J.   The Isles and Shrines of Greece. Boston, 1898. Illus. Biblo BL781-321 1978 $9

BARROWS, SAMUEL J.   The Shaybacks in Camp. Boston, 1892. Orig. binding. Wolfe 39-141 1978 $25

BARROWS, WILLIAM   The General; or, Twelve Nights in the Hunters' Camp... Boston, 1869. 1st. ed., plts. by G. White, sm. 8vo, spine faded, orig. cloth. Edwards 1012-466 1978 £25

BARRUCAND, VICTOR   Le Chariot de Terre Cuite. Paris, 1921. 4to., uncut, orig. pict. wr., slipcover, deluxe publication issued in 910 copies, illus. with color compositions by Leon Carre, 1 of 25 numbered copies on Imperial Japan paper, includes orig. watercolor, clean copy. Goldschmidt 110-10 1978 $300

BARRUS, CLARA   The Heart of Burrough's Journals. Boston, 1928. Limited ed. (300), 8vo, orig. cloth. Book Chest 17-33 1978 $22

BARRUS, CLARA   The Life and Letters of John Burroughs. Boston, 1925. 2 vols., tall 8vo, orig. cloth. Book Chest 17-32 1978 $45

BARRUS, CLARA   Whitman and Burroughs Comrades. Boston, 1931. 1 of 250 copies, large paper, uncut, 1st ed., cloth, fine. Houle 10-367 1978 $45

BARRUS, HIRAM   History of the Town of Goshen, Hampshire Co., Mass., From Its First Settlement in 1761 to 1881. Boston, 1881. Illus., ports., plts., orig. cloth, lib. marks, very good. MacManus 239-1028 1978 $40

BARRY, GEORGE   The History of the Orkney Islands. Edinburgh, 1805. Map, plts., foxed, modern half calf, 4to. K Books 244-23 1978 £85

BARRY, J. S.   History of Boston. Boston, 1855-57. 3 vols. MacManus 239-290 1978 $27.50

BARRY, WILLIAM   The New Antigone. London, 1888. New ed.,
3 vols. in one, orig. cloth. Greene 78-5 1978 $20

BARRY, WILLIAM FRANCIS   Newman. 1904. 1st ed., spine faded, very
good, octavo bound in cloth. Hyland 128-178 1978 £4

BARSTOW, J. WHITNEY   In Memoriam. N.P. (Concord, N.H.?), 1877.
8vo., orig. wrs. Morrill 239-14 1978 $10

BARTER, CHARLES   The Dorp and The Veld; Or Six Months in Natal.
London, 1852. Sm. 8vo, half calf. Deighton 5-5 1978 £56

BARTER, CHARLOTTE   Alone Among the Zulus. London, c.1888. Cr.
8vo, orig. cloth, few illus., shabby & shaken, reading copy only. K Books 239-
31 1978 £10

BARTH, HEINRICH   Travels and Discoveries in North and Central
Africa. London, 1890. Orig. cloth, map, plts., text-illus., cr. 8vo, slight
foxing. K Books 239-32 1978 £9

BARTH, HEINRICH   Travels and Discoveries in Central Africa. London, 1890. Orig. cloth, cr. 8vo, illus., shabby copy. K Books 239-33 1978 £7

BARTHE, ULRIC   Wilfrid Laurier on the Platform 1871-1890....
Quebec, 1890. Illus. Hood's 115-574 1978 $50

BARTHELEMY, JEAN JACQUES Nouvel abrege du voyage du jeune Anacharsis en
Grece. (c. 1840). Map, engravings, 2 vols., fcap. 8vo., full green calf, rubbed
spines faded. George's 635-445 1978 £7.50

BARTHELMY, JEAN JACQUES Travels of Anacharsis the Younger in Greece,
During the Middle of the Fourth Century Before the Christian Era. London, 1793-
1794. Maps, plans, plts., 7 vols., 8vo., contemp. calf, ex-lib., atlas, 2nd ed.
Morrill 239-300 1978 $50

BARTHEZ, PAUL JOSEPH   Nouveaux Elements de la Science de l'Homme...
Montpellier, 1778. 8vo., contemp. half-calf, gilt back, lightly rubbed, fine,
rare, 1st ed. Gilhofer 74-80 1978 sFr 1,800

BARTHEZ, PAUL JOSEPH   Nouveaux Elements de la Science de L'Homme.
Montpellier, 1778. 8vo., fine contemp. red mor. & gilt binding, gilt-decor.
spine & gilt inner dentelles, blue silk endpapers, silk marker, fine copy, rare 1st
ed. Zeitlin 245-12 1978 $1,250

BARTHEZ, PAUL JOSEPH   Nouvelle Mechanique des Mouvements de l'Homme
et des Animaux. Carcassonne, (1790). 4to., contemp. half calf, rubbed, 1st ed.
Gilhofer 74-81 1978 sFr 500

BARTHOLDT, RICHARD   From Steerage to Congress. 1930. Frontis.,
pres. copy signed by author, very good copy, 1st ed. Austin 79-48 1978 $20

BARTHOLIN, THOMAS   Anatomia, ex Caspari Bartholini. 1651. 8vo.,
engr. portr., fldg. plts., contemp. vellum, overlapping edges, light foxing &
browning, library stamp, but very good copy, 3rd ed. Zeitlin 245-13 1978 $275

BARTHOLIN, THOMAS   Casp. Bartholini...Institvtiones Anatomicae, Novis
Recentiorum opinionibus & observationibus...Secundo auctae ab Auctoris Filio
Thoma Bartholino. 1645. 8vo., engr. portrs., fldg. plts., contemp. vellum
with overlapping edges, light foxing, library stamp, but very good copy, 2nd ed.
Zeitlin 245-14 1978 $250

BARTHOLIN, THOMAS   Responsio de Experimentis Anatomicis Bilsianis
et Difficili Hepatis resurrectione, ad clarissimum Virum Nicolaum Zas. Copenhagen, 1661. 8vo., bds., dampstains. Gurney 75-5 1978 £50

BARTHOLOMAEUS ANGLICUS Medieval Lore; an epitome of the science, geography, animal and plant folk-lore and myth of the Middle Ages. 1893. Orig.
buckram, rebacked, 8vo. Upcroft 12-30 1978 £8.50

BARTHOLOW, ROBERTS   Manual of Hypodermic Medication. Philadelphia, 1869. Frontis., sm. 8vo., 1st ed., pres. from author. Morrill 239-15
1978 $37.50

BARTHOLOW, ROBERTS   Medical Electricity. Applications of Electricity
to Medicine and Surgery. Philadelphia, 1882. Rittenhouse 49-55 1976 $15

BARTLET, J.   Pharmacopoeia Bartleiana. Eton, 1773. Sm.
8vo., plts., contemp. sheep, worn, joint cracked. George's 635-1503 1978
£7.50

BARTLET, S. C.   Historical Sketch of the Missions of the American
Board Among North American Indians. Boston, 1880. Orig. wrps., 1st ed.
Ginsberg 16-824 1978 $75.00

BARTLETT, ALBERT LEROY Some Memories of Old Haverhill. Haverhill,
1915. Sm. 8vo., portr., orig. cloth, ltd. to 500 copies, pres. copy. Morrill
241-315 1978 $10

BARTLETT, D. W.   The Life of Gen. Franklin Pierce, of New-
Hampshire, the Democratic Candidate for President of the United States. Auburn,
1852. Cloth, some wear at ends of spine & corners, library blindstamp on title-
page, library stamps on endpapers. Hayman 73-37 1978 $8.50

BARTLETT, EDWARD O,   The "Dutchess County Regiment" in the Civil
War. Danbury, 1907. Orig. cloth. Butterfield 21-118 1978 $27.50

BARTLETT, HENRIETTA C.   Mr. William Shakespeare; Original and Early
Editions of His Quartos and Folios... New Haven, 1922. Octavo, good. Upcroft
10-216 1978 £8.50

BARTLETT, JOHN RUSSELL   The Barbarities of the Rebels, As Shown In Their
Cruelty To The Federally Wounded and Prisoners,.... Providence, 1863. Original
printed wr., lightly chipped. Jenkins 116-72 1978 $80

BARTLETT, JOHN RUSSELL   Dictionary of Americanisms: a Glossary of Works
and Phrases, colloquially used in the United States. New York and London, 1849.
Roy. 8vo., orig. cloth, printed label, faded, inner hinges weak. Howes 194-792
1978 £12.50

BARTLETT, S. C.   Historical Sketch of the Missions of the American
Board Among the North American Indians. Boston, 1880. Illus., map, original
printed wr., 1st ed. Ginsberg 14-41 1978 $75

BARTLETT, W. C.   An Idyl of War-Times. New York, 1890.
Cloth. Hayman 73-170 1978 $10

BARTLETT, WILLIAM HENRY   American Scenery. 1840. Portrait, 2 vols.,
plts., 4to., full contemp. calf, first ed. Howes 194-1364 1978 £350

BARTLETT, WILLIAM HENRY   The Christian in Palestine; or, Scenes of Sacred
History, Historical and Descriptive... (1847). 4to., engravings, maps, some
foxing of plts., full green mor. gilt, a little rubbed, gilt edges. Quaritch 983-
289 1978 $165

BARTLETT, WILLIAM HENRY   The Christian in Palestine; or, Scenes of Sacred
History, Historical and Descriptive... (c. 1855). 5th ed., roy. 8vo., frontis.,
map, plts., illus., fine, orig. orange cloth gilt. Quaritch 983-287 1978 $120

BARTLETT, WILLIAM HENRY   Forty Days in the Desert. London, c. 1870.
Engravings, text-illus., map, recased in orig. distinctive tortoiseshell binding,
8vo. K Books 244-24 1978 £35

BARTLETT, WILLIAM HENRY   The History of the United States of America...
New York, n.d.(1856). 3 vols., cloth, illus., plts., portraits, minor wear, but
nice, sm. 4tos. MacManus 239-45 1978 $50

BARTLETT, WILLIAM HENRY   The Nile Boat; or, Glimpses of the Land of Egypt.
London, 1852. 3rd. ed., roy. 8vo., engraved title, frontispiece, map, slightly
shaken, minor foxing, good, orig. gilt-dec. cloth. K Books 239-34 1978 £25

BARTLETT, WILLIAM HENRY   Pictures from Sicily... 1853. Roy. 8vo., 1st
ed., plts., illus., some plts. a little spotted, front fly-leaf removed, orig. red
cloth, joints a little worn. Quaritch 983-288 1978 $125

BARTLEY, NEHEMIAH   Opals and Agates... Brisbane, 1892. 1st. ed.,
8vo, frontispiece portrait, plts., title-page & 1st. few leaves stained in inner margin, sl. tears with loss to inside margin of title-pg., orig. cloth. Deighton 5-197
1978 £38

BARTLEY, THOMAS W.   Speech of...on the Subject of the Law to Or-
ganize the Territories of Kansas and Nebraska... Mansfield, 1854. Original
printed wr., 1st ed. Ginsberg 14-42 1978 $75

BARTON, ALBERT O.   La Follette's Winning of Wisconsin (1894-1904).
Madison, 1924. Illus., 2nd ed. Biblo 251-84 1978 $15

BARTON, ALBERT O.   La Follette's Winning of Wisconsin, (1894-1904).
Madison, 1922. Illus., 1st ed., good. Biblo BL781-211 1978 $12

BARTON, BERNARD   A New Year's Eve, and Other Poems. 1828.
First ed., contemp. half grey calf, 8vo. Howes 194-613 1978 £21

BARTON, BERNARD   Selections from the Poems and Letters of Bernard
Barton. 1849. Plts., cr. 8vo., orig. cloth, first ed. Howes 194-856 1978
£30

BARTON, BERNARD   Selections From the Poems and Letters. 1849.
1st. ed., frontis portrait, plt., orig. light blue cloth, block in blind & gilt, spine
faded, otherwise v.g. Jarndyce 16-282 1978 £26

BARTON, BERNARD   Selections from the Poems and Letters of Bernard
Barton. 1849. 8vo., portr., orig. blue cloth, spine faded, very good copy,
uncut, 1st ed. Quaritch 979-144 1978 $110

BARTON, CLARA   The Story of my Childhood. New York, 1907.
16mo., frontis. photo. portr., plts., red mor. rebacked with red cloth, gilt
lettering, upper hinge cracked, good copy, 1st ed. Zeitlin 245-15 1978 $45

BARTON, W. M.   The Road to Washington. Boston, (1919). 1st
ed., illus., d.j. MacManus 239-477 1978 $12.50

BARTON, WILLIAM E.   Abraham Lincoln and His Books... Chicago,
1920. Port., orig. parchment-backed bds. MacManus 239-865 1978 $20

BARTON, WILLIAM E.   Abraham Lincoln and the Hooker Letter, an
Address Delivered Before the Pennell Club of Philadelphia. New York, 1928.
750 copies on handmade paper, lg. fldg. facsimile. Bell Wiley's copy. Broadfoot 46-9 1978 $14

BARTON, WILLIAM E.   A Beautiful Blunder, The True Story of Lincoln's
Letter to Mrs. Lydia A. Bixby. Indianapolis, 1926. Worn spine, Bell Wiley's
copy, ltd. to 500 numbered autographed copies. Broadfoot's 44-24 1978 $20

BARTSCH, P.   New and Old Land Shells from the Island of
Luzon, Philippines. 1939. Wr., uncut, 8vo, orig. cloth. Book Chest 17-35
1978 $12.50

BARUCH, BERNARD M.   Report on War and Post-War Adjustment Policies.
February 15, 1944. Austin 80-17 1978 $12.50

BARZEVI, A. H.   Migrants of the Stars Being an Account of the
Discovery of the Marvelous Land of Niames... 1931. First ed. Austin 82-115
1978 $27.50

BARZINI, LUIGI   The Little-Match Man. Philadelphia, 1917. 1st
ed., illus. by Hattie Longstreet, color plates, almost fine. Victoria 34-46 1978
$25

BARZONI, VITTORIO   I Romani in Grecia. Londra, 1798. Sm. 8vo.,
wrappers. King 7-134 1978 £30

BASANOFF, ANNE   Itinerario Della Carta Dall' Oriente All' Occidente a sua Diffusions in Europe. Milan, 1965. Sm. folio, 1 of 200, plts. in
monochrome & color, 1/2 gray cloth, cloth of green & white design on both covers,
edges uncut, illus. Battery Park 1-439 1978 $250

BASCOM, JOHN   Aesthetics or the Science of Beauty. 1862. First
ed. Austin 82-116 1978 $17.50

BASHKIRTSEFF, MARIE   The Journal. 1890. First English ed., frontis.,
2 vols., half dark green levant mor. gilt, gilt tops, 8vo. Howes 194-1260 1978
£18

BASIL, ARCHBISHOP OF SELEVCIA   Basilii Selveciae in Isavria Episcopi De
Vitae ac Miracvlis D. Theclae Virginis Martyris Iconiensis Libri Dvo. Antwerp,
1608. 4to., plate, cont. Dutch calf with elaborate gilt centre and cornerpieces,
ties lacking, first ed. Quaritch 978-12 1978 $300

BASILE, GIAMBATTISTA   The Pentamerone. 1893. Vol. 1 only (ex 2),
covers slightly rubbed, 8vo. George's 635-1184 1978 £5

BASILE, GIAMBATTISTA   The Pentamerone. 1932. Portrait, illus., 2
vols, roy. 8vo. George's 635-1183 1978 £18

BASKIN, O. L.   History of the Arkansas Valley, Colorado. Chicago, 1881. Illus., original half leather, 1st ed. Ginsberg 14-250 1978 $150

BASSET, JOSHUA   An Essay towards Proposal for Catholick Communion. 1704. Sm. 8vo., new half mor., first ed. P. M. Hill 142-30 1978 £25

BASSETT, ANCEL H.   A Concise History of the Methodist Protestant
Church from Its Origin; with Biographical Sketches of Several Leading Ministers...
Pittsburgh, 1882. 2nd ed., rev'd. and enlarged, faded, cloth, mod. wear. Hay-
man 72-37 1978 $10

BASSETT, JOHN SPENCER   The Constitutional Beginnings of North Carolina.
Baltimore, 1894. Disbound, Bell Wiley's copy. Broadfoot 46-477 1978 $8

BASSETT, JOHN SPENCER   Running the Blockade from Confederate
Ports. 1898. Wrs. Bell Wiley's copy. Broadfoot 46-10 1978 $12

BASSETT, JOHN Y.   The Medical Reports of John Y. Bassett, M.D.,
the Alabama Student. Springfield, 1941. Rittenhouse 49-58 1976 $10

BASSO, HAMILTON   Beauregard, the Great Creole. New York,
1933. Bell Wiley's copy. Broadfoot 46-11 1978 $22

BASSO, HAMILTON   Beauregard, the Great Creole. Bell Wiley's
copy. Broadfoot 46-11A 1978 $16

BASTABLE, C. F.   Commerce of Nations. 1892. Austin 80-425
1978 $10

BASTER, JOB   Opuscula Subseciva, Observationes Miscellaneas
de Animalculis et Plantis Quibusdam Marinis, Eorumque Ovariis et Seminibus Con-
tinentia. Harlem, 1762/65. Orig. ed. in 2 parts in 1 vol., 4to., fldg. colored
plts., excellent cond., bound in contemp. calf, very minor browning of paper,
occas. very light foxing, plts. mint. Current 24-114 1978 $685

BASTIDE, FILIPPO   De Ordinis S. Benedicti Gallicana Propagatione
Liber Unicus.... 1683. 4to., vellum, broad side margins. King 7-265 1978
£25

BASYE, A. H.   The Lords Commissioners of Trade and Plantations
Commonly known as the Board of Trade, 1748-82. New Haven, 1925. 8vo.
George's 635-280 1978 £6

BATCHELDER, GEORGE ALEXANDER   A Sketch of the History and Resources of
Dakota Territory. Yankton, 1870. Wrs. Hayman 73-39 1978 $8.50

BATCHELDER, GEORGE ALEXANDER   A Sketch of the History and Resources of
Dakota Territory. Yankton, 1928. Original wr., reprint of 1870 ed. Ginsberg
14-304 1978 $10

BATCHELOR, JOHN   Ainu Life and Lore: Echoes of a departing race.
Tokyo, n.d. (c. 1927). Cloth, illus., front cover stained. Dawson's 449-104
1978 $40

BATE, HENRY   The Vauxhall Affray... 1773. 3rd. ed.,
folding frontis, portrait, 8vo, recent bds., light foxing, very good copy. Fenning
32-18 1978 £24.50

BATE, P.   English Table Glass. (1913). 8vo., plts., cloth,
a little spotted. Quaritch 983-97 1978 $35

BATEMAN, HENRY MAYO   A Book of Drawings. 1921. Drawings, 4to.
George's 635-107 1978 £6.50

BATEMAN, HENRY MAYO   A Book of Drawings. 1921. Signed by artist,
drawings, 4to., top of spine defective. George's 635-108 1978 £7.50

BATEMAN, HENRY MAYO   Brought Forward. 1931. Drawings, 4to.
George's 635-109 1978 £5

BATEMAN, HENRY MAYO   Burlesques. 1916. Drawings, roy. 8vo., orig.
pict. bds. George's 635-110 1978 £5

BATEMAN, HENRY MAYO   Cartoons. 1937. Drawings, cr. 4to. George's
635-106 1978 £5

BATEMAN, HENRY MAYO   Considered Trifles. (1932). Drawings, 4to.
George's 635-111 1978 £5

BATEMAN, HENRY MAYO   A Mixture. 1924. Drawings, 4to. George's
635-112 1978 £5

BATEMAN, HENRY MAYO   A Mixture. 1924. Drawings, 4to., signed by
artist. George's 635-113 1978 £6.50

BATEMAN, HENRY MAYO   More Drawings. 1922. Drawings, 4to.
George's 635-114 1978 £5

BATEMAN, HENRY MAYO   Rebound a Book of Drawings. 1927. Drawings,
4to., signed by artist. George's 635-116 1978 £6.50

BATEMAN, HENRY MAYO   Rebound a Book of Drawings. 1927. Drawings,
4to. George's 635-115 1978 £5

BATEMAN, HENRY MAYO   Suburbia, Caricatured. 1922. Drawings, 4to.,
signed by artist. George's 635-118 1978 £6.50

BATEMAN, HENRY MAYO   Suburbia, Caricatured. 1922. Drawings, 4to.
George's 635-117 1978 £5

BATEMAN, JAMES   The Orchidaceae of Mexico and Guatemala.
London, (1837)-1843. Hand-coloured litho. plts. by M. Gauci, engraved vignettes 2 by George Cruikshank, few plts. little foxed, elephant folio, old half
russia leather, little worn, gilt edges, orig. subscriber's copy, only 125 published.
Traylen 88-644 1978 £6000

BATEMAN, THOMAS   A Practical Synopsis of Cutaneous Diseases.
Philadelphia, 1824. 8vo., color engr. frontis plt., contemp. sheep, gilt on
spine, browned, some foxing, 2nd Amer. ed. Zeitlin 245-16 1978 $75

BATES, D. B.   Incidents on Land and Water; or, Four Years on
the Pacific Coast· Being a Narrative of the Burning of the Ships Nonantum, Huma-
yoon and Fanchon... Boston, 1857. Illus., original cloth, 1st ed. Ginsberg
14-43 1978 $30

BATES, E. C.   The History of Westborough, Mass. Westborough, 1891. Rebound, illus. MacManus 239-1055 1978 $30

BATES, ERNEST SUTHERLAND The Story of Congress, 1789-1935. New York,
1936. Spine faded. Biblo 248-15 1978 $15

BATES, FINIS L.   Escape and Suicide of John Wilkes Booth, Assasin
of President Lincoln. Memphis, 1907. Illus., sm. 8vo., ex-lib., orig. cloth.
Morrill 241-45 1978 $17.50

BATES, FREDERICK   The Life and Papers of Frederick Bates. St.
Louis, 1926. 2 vols, illus., original cloth, 1st ed. Ginsberg 14-580 1978 $30

BATES, H. W.   The Naturalist on the River Amazons... 1892.
8vo, orig. cloth, portrait, map, 2 coloured plts., illus. Edwards 1012-617 1978
£25

BATES, HERBERT ERNEST   Catherine Foster. London, 1928. 8vo, green
cloth, gilt lettering on spine, 4 line inscription by Bates, fine, 1st ed. Desmarais
1-24 1978 $15

BATES, HERBERT ERNEST   Charlotte's Row. 1931. Fine, d.w., first Eng.
ed. Bell Book 17-045 1978 £21

BATES, HERBERT ERNEST   Charlotte's Row. 1931. One of 107 copies
signed by author, unnumbered, marked "Presentation", quarter mor., marbled bds.,
t.e.g., nice, first English ed. Bell Book 17-046 1978 £65

BATES, HERBERT ERNEST   Charlotte's Row. London, (1931). 1st ed., d.w.
torn. Biblo 251-398 1978 $27.50

BATES, HERBERT ERNEST   Country Tales. 1938. Bds., good, first English
ed. Bell Book 17-047 1978 £6

BATES, HERBERT ERNEST   Dear Life. 1950. Pict. cloth, very good, torn
d.w., first English ed. Bell Book 16-047 1978 £6.50

BATES, HERBERT ERNEST   Down the River. London, 1937. 8vo, blue
cloth, top and bottom of spine bumped, near fine, 1st ed. Desmarais 1-25 1978
$7.50

BATES, HERBERT ERNEST   The Flying Goat. 1939. Fine, first English ed.
Bell Book 16-049 1978 £15

BATES, HERBERT ERNEST   The Hessian Prisoner. London, 1930. 8vo, red
cloth, uncut, partially unopened, near Mint in light glassine wr., 1st ed., line
drawing by John Austin, no. 467 of 550 copies. Desmarais 1-26 1978 $12.50

BATES, HERBERT ERNEST   The Hessian Prisoner. London, 1930. 8vo,
buckram, gilt, t.e.g., frontispiece line drawing by John Austen, 1 of 550 copies
signed by author, 1st ed., inscrip. by Bates, fine. Duschness 220-13 1978
$27.50

BATES, HERBERT ERNEST   Holly and Sallow. 1931. One of 100 copies
signed by author, this copy unnumbered, good, rare, first English ed. Bell Book
17-055 1978 £32.50

BATES, HERBERT ERNEST   The Last Bread: A Play in One Act. London,
1926. 8vo, buff wr. printed in blue, Mint in orig. protective wr., 1st ed. Desmarais 1-27 1978 $12.50

BATES, HERBERT ERNEST   Mrs. Esmond's Life. London, 1931. 8vo, yellow
buckram, gilt lettering on front cover and spine, t.e.g., near Mint, limited to
300 signed copies, 1st ed. Desmarais 1-28 1978 $20

BATES, HERBERT ERNEST   Sally Go Round the Moon. White Owl Press,
1932. No. 105 of 150 copies, signed by author, fine, first English ed. Bell Book
17-064 1978 £45

BATES, HERBERT ERNEST   Spella Ho. 1938. Good, first English ed.
Bell Book 16-054 1978 £8.50

BATES, HERBERT ERNEST   The Story Without an End & The Country Doctor.
White Owl Press, 1932. Cloth-backed bds., fine, d.w., first English ed. Bell
Book 16-055 1978 £22.50

BATES, HERBERT ERNEST   The Story Without an End & The Country Doctor.
White Owl Press, 1932. No. 117 of 130 copies numbered & signed by author,
frontis., buckram, t.e.g., fine, first English ed. Bell Book 17-067 1978 £45

BATES, HERBERT ERNEST   A Threshing Day. 1931. No. 281 of 300 copies
signed by author, buckram, near fine, first English ed. Bell Book 16-972 1978
£22.50

BATES, HERBERT ERNEST   Through the Woods. London, 1936. Engravings
on wood by Agnes Miller Parker, 1st ed., quarto, orig. brown cloth. Totteridge
29-8 1978 $25

BATES, HERBERT ERNEST   Through the Woods, the English Woodland-April
to April. 1936. Wood engravings by Agnes Miller, first ed., roy. 8vo. George's
635-1307 1978 £5

BATES, HERBERT ERNEST   The Tree. (1930). Fine, wraps, first English ed.
Bell Book 17-070 1978 £15

BATES, J.   A Sermon, Preached at Boston, Jan. 4, 1816...
Dedham, 1816. Wrappers, some spotting, 8vo. Edwards 1012-467 1978 £15

BATES, W. H.   The Cure of Imperfect Sight by Treatment Without Glasses. New York, 1920. Rittenhouse 49-59 1976 $10

BATES, WALTER   Henry More Smith; Being an Authentic Account of the Numerous Arrests, Remarkable Doings and Wonderful Excapes of the Most Noted Road Agent Who Ever Pestered the Authorities of New Brunswick. St. John, 1910. Wrappers. Hood's 115-200 1978 $35

BATES, WILLIAM   Maclise Portrait Gallery, of "Illustrious Literary Characters" with Memoirs. 1883. 8vo, half title, 85 plts., orig. red cloth, spine faded. Jarndyce 16-843 1978 £16

BATESON, F. W.   Cambridge Bibliography of English Literature. New York, 1941. 4 vols., orig. cloth, fine. MacManus 238-882 1978 $100

BATESON, WILLIAM   Materials for the Study of Variation Treated with Especial Regard to Discontinuity in the Origin of Species. London, 1894. 8vo., illus., orig. cloth. K Books 244-25 1978 £16

BATH, WILLIAM PULTENEY, EARL OF   The Case of the Revival of the Salt Duty Full Stated and Considered with Some Remarks on the Present State of Affairs. 1732. Stain on title, fcap. 8vo., wrs. George's 635-385 1978 £40

BATH, WILLIAM PULTENEY, EARL OF   A State of the National Debt, as it Stood December the 24th, 1716. 1727. 1st ed., 4to., thick paper, half title. Hannas 54-246 1978 £20

BATHURST, CHARLES   Letters to a Niece. 1850. 1st. ed., half title, orig. maroon/brown cloth, faded, inscribed pres. copy from author. Jarndyce 16-283 1978 £6

BATIFFOL, L.   La Duchesse de Chevreuse. Paris, 1913. 8vo., full brown mor., gilt tooling on both sides, gilt tooled spine, a.e.g., frontis., plts., illus., fine binding. Van der Peet H-64-246 1978 Dfl 95

BATTELY, JOHN 1647-1708   Opera Posthuma. Oxford, 1745. 2 parts in 1 vol., plts., vignettes, 4to., newly bound in half calf antique with lettering pieces, very good. Howes 194-156 1978 £40

BATTEN, JOHN M.   Reminiscences of Two Years in the United States Navy. Lancaster, Pa., 1881. Bell Wiley's copy. Broadfoot 46-12 1978 $45

BATTEN, JOHN M.   Reminiscences of Two Years in the United States Navy. Cvr. speckled. Bell Wiley's copy. Broadfoot 46-12A 1978 $30

BATTEY, THOMAS C.   The Life and Adventures of a Quaker Amont the Indians. Boston, 1875. 1st ed., illus. MacManus 239-1143 1978 $30

BATTINE, CECIL   The Crisis of the Confederacy a History of Gettysburg and the Wilderness. London, 1905. Illus., frontis., 1st ed., scarce, bookplt., hinges weak, else nice. MacManus 239-866 1978 $45

BATTLE, J. H.   History of Bucks County, Pa. Philadelphia, 1887. Illus., rebound, very scarce. MacManus 239-1366 1978 $85

BATTLE, KEMP PLUMMER   History of the University of North Carolina 1868-1912. Raleigh, 1912. 2 vols. Broadfoot 50-10 1978 $100

BATTLE, KEMP PLUMMER   Memories of an Old Time Tar Heel. Chapel Hill, 1945. Illus. Broadfoot 50-11 1978 $12

THE BATTLE of the Aleutians: a Graphic History, 1942-1943. (San Francisco, 1944). Illus., maps, oblong blue wrs., 1st ed., extremely scarce. Bradley 49-366 1978 $150

BATTLE-FIELDS of the South from Bull Run to Fredericksburg, by an English Combatant. NY, 1864. Maps, Bell Wiley's Copy. Broadfoot's 44-25 1978 $50.00

BATTLES of Atlanta. Atlanta, 1895. Chipped, taped wraps, maps, Bell Wiley's copy. Broadfoot's 44-26 1978 $10

BATTY, ROBERT   Welsh Scenery from Drawings by... 1823. 8vo., plts., orig. grey bds. Quaritch 983-290 1978 $150

BAUD-BOVY, DANIEL   Peasant Art in Switzerland. London, 1924. 431 illus. some in colour, sm. folio. Traylen 88-402 1978 £18

BAUDELAIRE, CHARLES   Les Fleurs du Mal. Paris, Limited Editions Club, 1940. Sq. 8vo., orig. wr., uncut, ltd. ed., numbered copy on Rives paper, illus. Goldschmidt 110-61 1978 $50

BAUDELAIRE, CHARLES   Intimate Journals. Blackamore Press, 1930. One of 400 numbered copies, very nice. Rota 212-2 1978 £40

BAUDELAIRE, CHARLES   Intimate Journals. Hollywood, 1947. Near fine, drawings, d.w. Bernard 5-26 1978 $30

BAUDELOCQUE, JEAN LOUIS   An Abridgment of Mr. Heath's Translation of Baudelocque's Midwifery. Philadelphia, 1811. Engr. plts., 8vo., contemp. calf, foxing, bottom of fr. cover lightly dampstained, 2nd Amer. ed. Morrill 239-16 1978 $20

BAUDELOCQUE, JEAN LOUIS   Principes sur l'Art des Accouchements, par Demandes et Reponses, en Faveur des Sages-Femmes. Paris, 1812. 4th ed., engr. fldg. plts., sm. 8vo., full contemp. mottled calf. Argosy Special-8 1978 $200

BAUDOIN, D. -F.   Traite Theorique de l'Art du Savonnier, deduit des Procedes pratiques de la Fabrication de Marseille. Marseille, 1808. 8vo., orig. wrappers, uncut, plts., first ed. Gurney 75-6 1978 £65

BAUGHAN, ROSA   Character indicated by Handwritings. London, c. 1912. Second ed., cr. 8vo., orig. cloth, extremities chafed. K Books 244-26 1978 £7

BAUGHMAN, THEODORE   The Oklahoma Scout. Chicago, n.d. (1890's?). Cloth, inner hinges cracking. Hayman 72-38 1978 $10

BAUHINUS, JOHANNES   De Plantis a Divis Sanctis've Nomen Habitus. Basileae, 1591. 8vo., old limp bds., 1st ed., fine copy. Offenbacher 30-9 1978 $300

BAUM, LYMAN FRANK   The Magic of Oz. Chicago, (1919). 1st ed., 1st issue, color plates by Neill, remarkably fine, except for heavy mottling, text and covers almost like new. Victoria 34-49 1978 $110

BAUM, LYMAN FRANK   The Master Key. An Electrical Fairy Tale. Indianapolis, (1901). Illus. by F. Y. Cory, orig. cloth, some rubbing, color pict. paste-label, 1st ed., very good. MacManus 238-423 1978 $35

BAUM, LYMAN FRANK   Rinkitink in Oz. Chicago, c.1930. Color plates, upper spine chipped, inner hinges cracked. Victoria 34-51 1978 $15

BAUM, LYMAN FRANK   The Songs of Father Goose. Chicago,1900. 1st ed., illus. by W. W. Denslow, quarto, colored pict. boards, very good copy. Victoria 34-52 1978 $75

BAUM, LYMAN FRANK   The Songs of Father Goose. For the Kindergarten, the Nursery, and the Home. Chicago, (1900). 4to., orig. pict. bds., linen back, 1st ed., minor wear along edges, nice. MacManus 238-422 1978 $75

BAUM, LYMAN FRANK   Tik-Tok of Oz. Chicago, (1914). 1st ed.,1st issue, illus. by John R. Neill, full-color plates, text is fine and solid, crackling of paper of inner hinge, cover color plate and tips rubbed, very good. Victoria 34-50 1978 $125

BAUM, LYMAN FRANK   The Wonderful Wizard of Oz. Chicago, 1900. 1st ed., 1st issue, verso of t.p. with rubber-stamped copyright notice, first state of binding, variant 3, recased with original pictorial cloth laid-down, text & endpapers in marvelous cond, plates bright and fresh. Victoria 34-54 1978 $625

BAUMER, LEWIS   Bright Young Things. 1928. Coloured plts., 4to. George's 635-119 1978 £6

THE BAUSCH & Lomb Lens Souvenir. Rochester, 1903. Tall 4to., plts. Butterfield 21-353 1978 $35

BAX, B. W.   The Eastern Seas: Being a Narrative of the Voyage of H.M.S. "Dwarf" in China, Japan, and Formosa.... London, 1875. Illus., folding map, cloth (moderate use, hinges weak, some leaves carelessly opened). Dawson's 127-246 1978 $35

BAX, C.   Shaw & Yeats Letters to Florence Farr. 1946. D.w., very good, octavo bound in cloth. Hyland 128-882 1978 £6

BAX, E. BELFORT   Rise and Fall of the Anabaptists. 1903. 8vo. George's 635-1026 1978 £6

BAXTER, ALBERT   History of the City of Grand Rapids, Michigan. New York, 1891. 1st ed., thick 4to., illus., ports., orig. 3/4 calf, very good. MacManus 239-1057 1978 $50

BAXTER, BEVERLEY   The Parts Men Play. Toronto, 1920. Spine worn. Hood 117-459 1973 $12.50

BAXTER, GEORGE   Philadelphia, (ca. 1925). Illus., many in color, tall thick 8vo., pic. cloth. Argosy Special-9 1978 $125

BAXTER, J. H.   Statistics, Medical and Anthropological, of the Provost-Marshal-General's Bureau... Washington, 1875. Vol. II only, signed by Wiley, Bell Wiley's copy. Broadfoot 46-293 1978 $25

BAXTER, JAMES PHINNEY   The Pioneers of New France in New England... Albany, 1894. Illus., untrimmed, very nice copy, cloth. MacManus 239-46 1978 $40

BAXTER, KATHARINE SCHUYLER   A Godchild of Washington. New York, (1897). Illus., 4to. MacManus 239-499 1978 $30

BAXTER, RICHARD   A Call to the Unconverted. New York, n.d. (c.1840). Sm. 2 1/4 x 3", dated February 18, 1844 laid in, orig. binding. Hayman 71-38 1978 $7.50

BAXTER, RICHARD   The Saints Everlasting Rest. 1651. Second ed., portrait, 4 parts in 1 vol., thk. sm.4to., contemp. binding of olive mor., orig. clasps missing, good. Howes 194 1978 £50

BAXTER, RICHARD   The Saints Everlasting Rest. (1771). Lacks title, some pages stained, sq. 8vo., contemp. calf, rubbed. George's 635-1027 1978 £7.50

BAXTER, WILLIAM   Pea Ridge and Prairie Grove, or- Scenes and Incidents of the War in Arkansas. Cincinnati, 1864. Bell Wiley's copy. Broadfoot's 44-429 1978 $50.00

BAXTER, WILLIAM 1650-1723   Glossarium Antiquitatum Britannicarum. 1733. Second ed., portrait, contemp. calf, neatly rebacked, 8vo. Howes 194-157 1978 £28

BAY, J. CHRISTIAN   Denmark in English and American Literature. Chicago, 1915. Austin 79-50 1978 $20

BAY, J. CHRISTIAN   A Handful of Western Books. Cedar Rapids, Torch Press, 1935. One of 350., frontis. Battery Park 1-243a 1978 $55

BAY, J. CHRISTIAN   In the House of Memories. Torch Press, 1946. One of 400, frontis. Battery Park 1-246 1978 $25

BAY, J. CHRISTIAN   Rare and Beautiful. 1922. 8vo., thin. Battery Park 1-243 1978 $35

BAY, J. CHRISTIAN   A Second Handful of Western Books. Torch Press, 1936. Frontis., one of 400 copies. Battery Park 1-244 1978 $50

BAY, J. CHRISTIAN   A Third Handful of Western Books. Torch Press, 1937. One of 400 copies, frontis. Battery Park 1-245 1978 $50

BAYARD, RALPH   Lone Star Vanguard: The Catholic Re-Occupation of Texas, 1838-1848. St. Louis, 1945. Fine copy, partly uncut. Jenkins 116-79 1978 $25

BAYER, HENRY G.   The Belgians First Settlers in New York and in the Middle States. New York, 1925. Fine copy in dust jacket, out of print. Butterfield 21-66 1978 $20

BAYER, HENRY G.   The Belgians, First Settlers in New York and in the Middle States... New York, 1925. Illus., fine. MacManus 239-48 1978 $17.50

BAYER, JOHANN   Uranometria Omnium Asterismorum Continens Schemata, Nova Methodo Delineata, Aereis Laminis Expressa. Augsburg, 1603. Folio, maps, contemp. blindstamped vellum, first ed., round wormhole in inner margin ofpre lims & first two plts., faint waterstain in corner of about 12 plts., otherwise very crisp, bright copy. Quaritch 977-175 1978 $4,000

BAYEUX Tapestry. (c. 1900). Text in French and English, photographs, oblong folio, orig. wrappers, loose in cloth cover. George's 635-538 1978 £6.50

BAYLES, RICHARD M.   History of Providence County, Rhode Island. New York, 1891. 2 vols., illus., contemp. 3/4 calf, fine. MacManus 239-1119 1978 $95

BAYLEY, ADA ELLEN   A Hardy Norseman. London, 1890. 3 vols., orig. 3/4 cloth, 1st ed., ex-lib., covers a bit worn, but good. MacManus 238-347 1978 $70

BAYLEY, J. R.   A Brief Sketch of the Early History of the Catholic Church on the Island of New York. New York, 1870. 2nd ed., illus., orig. cloth, bookplt., good copy. MacManus 239-333 1978 $20

BAYLEY, THOMAS HAYNES   Songs, Ballads And Other Poems. 1844. 1st. collected ed., portrait frontis, 2 vols., 8vo, half green morocco gilt, spines gilt, t.e.g., fine copy, A.L.S. by author inserted. Sawyer 299-111 1978 £21

BAYLEY, W. S.   Catalogue of the Main Geological Collection, with a Brief Outline History of the Two Surveys of the State. Waterville, 1890. Wrs. Hayman 72-39 1978 $7.50

BAYLIE, THOMAS   Certamen Religiosum: Or A Conference Between His Late Majestie Charles King of England, and Henry Late Marquis and Earl of Worcester, Concerning Religion... 1649. 1st. ed., orig. calf, front hinge split, very good. Jarndyce 16-1 1978 £40

BAYLIS, S. M.   Camp and Lamp. Montreal, 1897. Signed, numbered & ltd. ed. Hood 117-460 1973 $10

BAYLOR, GEORGE   Bull Run to Bull Run, or Four Years in the Army of Northern Virginia. Richmond, 1900. Spine discolored, Bell Wiley's copy. Broadfoot's 44-649 1978 $36

BAYLY, ADA ELLEN   The Autobiography of a Slander. Lond., 1892. Fir. Ed., orig. cloth binding, top edge gilt, mint cond. Greene 78-252 1978 $30.00

BAYNE, S. G.   On an Irish Jaunting-Car. N.Y., (1902). 1st ed., 1st printing,8 vo., illus. with half-tone photographs, fine green pictorial cloth, t.e.g., uncut, inscribed by author. Houle 10-23 1978 $25

BAYRE-POWELL, R.   English Country Life in the 18th Century. 1937. Illus., 8vo. George's 635-539 1978 £5

BE Kind to the Loved Ones at Home. Boston, (1847). Sheet music, wrs., little soiled, removed from bound vol., inscr'd. Hayman 73-463 1978 $7.50

BEACH, REX   The Barrier. New York, 1908. First play ed. with illus. Austin 82-117 1978 $27.50

BEACH, REX   Going Some. 1910. Illus., first ed. Austin 82-118 1978 $12.50

BEACH, REX   The Goose Woman and Other Stories. 1925. First ed., ex-lib. Austin 82-119 1978 $11

BEACH, REX   Jungle Gold. 1935. First ed. Austin 82-120 1978 $10

BEACH, REX   Men of the Outer Islands. (1929). 1932. Illus., first ed., ex-lib. Austin 82-121 1978 $12.50

BEACH, REX   Padlocked: A Novel. 1926. Austin 82-122 1978 $8.50

BEACH, REX   Rainbow's End. New York, 1916. Blue cloth, first ed. Austin 82-123 1978 $20

BEACH, REX   The Winds of Chance. 1918. Illus., first ed.,
some cover water stains, else good. Austin 82-124 1978 $10

BEACH, WILLIAM H.   The First New York Cavalry. New York, 1902.
1st ed., illus., orig. cloth, very good, scarce. MacManus 239-867 1978 $35

BEADNELL, C. M.   An Encyclopedic Dictionary of Science and War.
London, 1943. Ex-lib. Austin 80-18 1978 $27.50

BEALE, ANNIE   The Miller's Daughter. New York, n.d. (c.1892).
1st Amer. ed., illus. by Marcella Walker, cloth, good. Greene 78-145 1978
$15

BEALE, THOMAS   The Natural History of the Sperm Whale...
1839. Engraved plts., sm. thick 8vo, orig. cloth, spine repaired. Edwards
1012-355 1978 £120

BEALS, ALLEN E.   History of the First Presbyterian Church at Plainfield, N.J. N.P., (1925). Illus. MacManus 239-1239 1978 $10

BEALS, CARLETON   Porfirio Diaz,...Dictator of Mexico. (1932).
Illus. Biblo BL781-108 1978 $9.50

BEAMISH, NORTH LUDLOW   The Discovery of American by the Northmen, in
the Tenth Century... London, 1841. Full leather with marbled end-papers & page
edges, gilt tooling, raised bands, 2 folding maps, 1 folding plt. Hood's 115-201
1978 $150

BEAMISH, RICHARD   Memoirs of the Life of Sir Marc Isambard Brunel.
London, 1862. 8vo, original green cloth (bit rubbed and shaken), cloth slightly
bubbled on front cover, 1st ed. Ximenes 47-16 1978 $20

BEAMISH, RICHARD J.   The Boy's Story of Lindbergh, the Lone Eagle.
Philadelphia, 1928. Frontis., plts., text illus., pict. cover, 8vo. K Books 244-
27 1978 £5

BEAN, C. E. W.   The Official History of Australia in the War of
1914-1918. Sydney, 1936-42. 12 vols., thick 8vo, orig. cloth, plts. some
coloured, maps, illus. F. Edwards 1013-249 1978 £75

BEAN, ELLIS P.   Memoir of Col. Ellis P. Bean, Written by Himself,.... Dallas, 1930. 1st ed in this format, limited ed to 200 numbered copies.
Jenkins 116-134 1978 $125

BEAN, JAMES   On Family Religion. (Boston, n.d.c.1815).
Disbound. Hayman 71-39 1978 $8.50

BEAN, THEODORE W.   History of Montgomery County, Pa. Philadelphia, 1884. Illus., 4to., rebound. MacManus 239-1572 1978 $100

BEAN, WILLIAM JACKSON   Trees and Shrubs hardy in the British Isles. 1936.
Illus., 3 vols., 8vo. George's 635-951 1978 £18

BEARD, AUGUSTUS FIELD   A Story of John Frederick Oberlin. 1909.
Illus. Austin 79-51 1978 $12.50

BEARD, CHARLES A.   Basis of Politics. 1923. Austin 80-427 1978
$7.50

BEARD, GEORGE MILLER   A Plea for Scientific Reform. New York, 1872.
12mo., sewn, good copy, 1st ed. Zeitlin 245-17 1978 $45

BEARD, PATTEN   What Happened After Stories. 1929. Illus.
Austin 82-125 1978 $20

BEARDSLEE, C. S.   A Popular Guide to the Public Buildings and Museum of Amherst College. Amherst, 1875. 12mo., orig. wrs., 1st ed. Morrill
241-316 1978 $12.50

BEARDSLEY, AUBREY   Letters from Aubrey Beardsley to Leonard Smithers.
London, 1937. Sq. 8vo, decor. cloth, gilt, pict. endpapers, 1st ed., fine.
Duschness 220-14 1978 $50

BEASLEY, NORMAN   Freighters of Fortune. New York, 1930. 1st
ed., illus., 8vo., orig. cloth. Morrill 241-651 1978 $15

BEASLEY, NORMAN   Main Street Merchant. 1948. Austin 80-428
1978 $10

BEASLEY, ROBERT E.   A Plan to Stop the Present and Prevent Future
Wars:.... Rio Vista, 1864. Original printed wr., 1st ed., with very rare imprint.
Ginsberg 14-73 1978 $150

BEATSON, ROBERT   A Political Index to the Histories of Great
Britain and Ireland. N.P., 1786. 3 parts in 1 vol., full contemp. calf,
normal wear, very good or better. Limestone 9-15 1978 $100

BEATTIE, GEORGE WILLIAM   Heritage of the Valley, San Bernardino's First
Century. Pasadena, 1939. Cloth, fold. map, illus., 1st ed., fine, very scarce.
Dykes 35-36 1978 $75

BEATTIE, GEORGE WILLIAM   Heritage of the Valley. Pasadena, 1939.
Cloth, fldg. map, illus., 1st ed., fine copy, very scarce. Dykes 34-244 1978
$75

BEATTIE, JAMES   Elements of Moral Science. Edinburgh, 1790-93.
First ed., 2 vols., contemp. tree calf, very good, 8vo. Howes 194-1426 1978
£65

BEATTIE, JAMES   The Minstrel. 1797. Plts., 12mo., contemp.
half calf. Howes 194-158 1978 £5

BEATTIE, WALTER FREDERIC   General Index to B. F. Hubbard's "Forests and
Clearings." Stanstead, 1939. Autograph inscription by Beattie, applies only to
p 1 to 113, plain wrappers. Wolfe 39-150 1978 $15

BEATTIE, WILLIAM   Scotland Illustrated. 1838. First ed., 2 vols.,
4to., contemp. half calf, labels missing, plts. Howes 194-1368 1978 £75

BEATTIE, WILLIAM   Switzerland. London, 1836. First ed., 2 vols.,
in 1, map, plts., 4to., good, half blue calf. K Books 244-28 1978 £225

BEATTIE, WILLIAM   Switzerland... 1836. 2 vols., 4to., illus. by
W. H. Bartlett, map, half mor. gilt, a little rubbed, very little foxing. Quaritch
983-291 1978 $735

BEATTIE, WILLIAM   Switzerland. London, n.d. Illus. by W. H.
Bartlett, 2 vols., map, plts., 4to., orig. cloth. K Books 244-342 1978 £225

BEATTIE, WILLIAM   The Waldenses or Protestant Valleys of Piedmont,
Dauphiny, and the Ban de la Roche. 1838. First ed., portrait, map, 4to., contemp. full coarse-grained mor. Howes 194-1369 1978 £105

BEATTIE, WILLIAM   The Waldenses Or Protestant Valleys of Piedmont,
Dauphiny, And The Ban De La Roche. London, 1838. 4to, coloured engraved
portrait, coloured vignette title-pg., folding engraved map, newly rebound in
green half morocco, marbled bds., gilt, fine copy. Deighton 5-111 1978 £250

BEATTY, EDWARD   Transportation and the Public Pocket; An Address.
N.P., 1938. Hood's 115-953 1978 $7.50

BEATTY, JOHN   The Citizen-Soldier: or, Memoirs of a Volunteer.
New York, 1946. Bell Wiley's copy. Broadfoot's 44-581 1978 $10

BEATTY, JOHN   Uncle Peter Sked. Columbus, 1907. Cloth.
Hayman 73-171 1978 $3.50

BEATTY, RICHARD C.   William Byrd of Westover. Boston, 1932. Illus.
MacManus 239-733 1978 $15

BEAUCHAMP, WILLIAM MARTIN   A History of the New York Iroquois, Now
Commonly Called the Six Nations. Albany, 1905. Illus. MacManus 239-1144
1978 $37.50

BEAUCHAMP, WILLIAM MARTIN   Iroquois Folk Lore Gathered from the Six
Nations of New York. Syracuse, 1922. Half lea. & red silk cloth, handsomely
bound copy inscr'd by Beauchamp to Alvin H. Dewey, dated Dec. 12, 1922.
Butterfield 21-212 1978 $25

BEAUCHAMP, WILLIAM MARTIN   Revolutionary Soldiers Resident or Dying in
Onondaga County, with a Supplementary List of Possible Veterans. Syracuse,
1903. Wr., fine, uncut. Butterfield 21-321 1978 $10

BEAUCLERK, G.   A Journey to Marocco, In 1826. London, 1828.
lst. ed., 8vo, lithograph frontispiece on india paper, 8 other lithograph plts.,
diced calf, gilt, neatly rebacked, all edges gilt. Deighton 5-8 1978 £105

BEAUDE, HENRI 1870-   Eaux-fortes et Tailles-douches. Quebec, 1913.
Hood 116-683 1978 $50

BEAUDE, HENRI 1870-   Louis Frechette. Toronto, n.d. (c.1924). Hood
116-684 1978 $7.50

BEAUFOY, S.   Butterfly Lives. London, 1947. Large wide 8vo,
orig. cloth. Book Chest 17-36 1978 $12

BEAUMAN, BENTLEY   The Airmen Speak. 1943. British. Austin 80-
19 1978 $8.50

BEAUMARCHAIS, PIERRE AUGUSTIN CARON DE   Le Mariage de Figaro ou la
Folle Journee. Seville, 1785. Folding plated, red mor., exceedingly rare illus.
ed., plts., fine, uncut. Gilhofer 75-5 1978 SFr 2,800

BEAUMONT, CYRIL W.   The First Score. Beaumont Press, 1927. 8vo.,
frontis., plts. in color, bds., vellum back, ltd. to only 80 copies signed by
author. Quaritch 979-19 1978 $140

BEAUMONT, CYRIL W.   The Romantic Ballet in Lithographs of the Time.
1938. Roy. 8vo., plts., orig. silver cloth, fine copy with dust wrs. Quaritch
979-18 1978 $250

BEAUMONT, CYRIL W.   The Strange Adventures of a Toy Soldier. Decor.
in color, illus. covers in color, paper over bds., vellum spine. Battery Park 1-
7 1978 $75

BEAUMONT, EDOUARD DE   Fleur des Belles Epees. Paris, 1885. Folio,
orig. parchment portfolio, cloth back, ltd. ed. on Holland paper. F. Edwards
1013-250 1978 £30

BEAUMONT, FRANCIS   Fifty Comedies and Tragedies. 1679. Folio,
2nd. collected ed., eng. frontis, portraits, damaged & laid down, title laid down,
old calf, rebacked & corners repaired, raised bands, leather label. Eaton 45-36
1978 £90

BEAUMONT, FRANCIS   The Knight of the Burning Pestle. N.P.,1635.
Sm. 4 to., fine, 3/4 mor., genuine 2nd ed. Quaritch Summer,1978-4 1978
$1,100

BEAUMONT, FRANCIS   The Maides Tragedy. New York, 1932. 4to.,
wood engrs. by Freda Bone, ltd. ed., fine in slightly worn slipcase. Biblo 251-
427 1978 $28.50

BEAUMONT, FRANCIS   The Wild-Goose Chase. London, 1652. lst.
ed., thin folio, brown levant morocco, gilt edges. Traylen 88-105 1978 £390

BEAUMONT, FRANCIS   Works. 1711. Plts., portraits, 7 vols., contemp. polished calf gilt, first Octavo ed. Howes 194-159 1978 £110

BEAUMONT, FRANCIS   Works. 1750. Portraits, 10 vols., contemp.
calf, nice, 8vo. Howes 194-160 1978 £55

BEAUMONT, FRANCIS   The Works of. 1839. 2 vols., illus., frontis,
portraits & titles, 1/2 red morocco. Eaton 45-37 1978 £12

BEAUMONT, WILLIAM   Experiments and Observations on the Gastric
Juice and the Physiology of Digestion. Plattsburgh, 1833. 8vo., woodcut illus.,
washed copy, modern bds., uncut, first ed. Quaritch 977-9 1978 $900

BEAUMONT, WILLIAM   Experiments and Observations on the Gastric
Juice and the Physiology of Digestion. New York, 1941. Portr., 8vo. Morrill
239-17 1978 $10

BEAUREGARD, OLLIVER   Les Divinites Egyptiennes. Leur Origine, Leur
Culte et son Expansion dans le Monde. Paris, 1866. 1/2 leather, rubbed.
Biblo BL781-322 1978 $14.50

BEAUTIES of the New-England Primer. New York, 1820. First and last leaves
pasted to wrappers, profusely illus., hexagonal shape. Victoria 34-55 1978
$37.50

BEAUTIFUL St. Paul. Buffalo, 1906. Wrs., photo. views. Hayman 73-450
1978 $7.50

BEAUTIFUL San Antonio: The Story of the Sunny Alamo City to Date in Pictorial
Eloquence. San Antonio, c.1914. Jenkins 116-100 1978 $12.50

BEAVAN, A. H.   Tube, Train, Tram and Car; or, Up to Date
Locomotion. London, 1903. Illus., 8vo, orig. cloth, good. Sexton 7-193 1978
£6

BEAVERBROOK, LORD   Politicians and The War, 1914-1916. London,
1928. Hood's 115-89 1978 $10

BEAZIANO, AGOSTINO   Lachrymae in funere Petri Bembi. Venice, 1548.
8 vo., modern half vellum, good copy. Schafer 19-6 1978 sFr. 550

BEBHARD, ELIZABETH L.   The Parsonage Between Two Manors. Hudson.
4to. Butterfield 21-141 1978 $7.50

BECCATTINI, FRANCESCO   Istoria della Citta di Gibiltrra in Spagna con la
descrizione della medesima.... Firenze, 1782. 8vo., contemp. wrs., portrait,
wide margins, uncut. King 7-135 1978 £70

BECH, B.   Five Years in a Sailor's Life. Toronto, 1886.
Hood 116-237 1978 $10

BECHDOLT, FREDERICK R.   When the West was Young. New York, (1922).
Good. Biblo BL781-263 1978 $8.50

BECHER, JOHANN JOACHIM   Institutiones Chimicae Prodromae i.e....Oedi-
pus Chimicus. Frankfurt, 1664. 12mo., frontis., plt., half mor., browned
throughout due to poor quality paper, but very good copy, lst ed. Norman 5-20
1978 $500

BECHSTEIN, J. M.   Cage and Chamber-Birds. London, 1872. Illus.
in black & white, 12mo., ex-lib., library binding, embossed library stamp.
Morrill 239-301 1978 $12.50

BECHTOLD, FRITZ   Deutsche am Nanga Parbat, der Ungriff 1934.
Munchen, 1935. Map, photographs, orig. linen, 8vo. George's 635-1511 1978
£5

BECK, HENRY C.   Fare to Midlands. Forgotten Towns of Central
New Jersey. New York, 1939. 1st ed., fine, d.j. MacManus 239-1240
1978 $35

BECK, HENRY C.   Fare to Midlands. New York, 1939. Illus., first
ed., d.w. Biblo 247-111 1978 $30

BECK, JOHN B.   An Introductory Lecture, Delivered at the College of Physicians and Surgeons of the City of New York, November 6, 1829.
New York, 1829. Disbound. Hayman 73-40 1978 $15

BECK, S. W.   Gloves, their Annals and Associations. 1883.
Text illus., cr. 8vo. George's 635-239 1978 £5

BECKE, LOUIS   The Naval Pioneers of Australia. London, 1899.
lst ed., illus., 8vo., ex-lib., rebacked with library tape, orig. cloth. Morrill
241-46 1978 $12.50

BECKER, EDNA   Hugh and Denis, Twelve Tales of Two Boys of
the Middle Ages. 1934. Mor. pic. end sheets, gilt top, illus., 1st ed., 1 of 10
no. copies signed by author, fine, plastic d.w., slipcase. Dykes 35-137 1978
$25

BECKER, ETHEL A.   Klondike '98. Portland, (1949). First ed., fine,
d.w., sm. 4to., illus. Biblo 247-4 1978 $10

BECKER, MAY L.   Golden Tales of Canada. New York, 1938.
Hood 117-505 1978 $15

BECKET, ANDREW   Prose Miscellanies. n.d. and 1838. 2 vols. in 1,
half title to vol. 2, orig. half calf, marbled bds., good. Jarndyce 16-285 1978
£12.50

BECKETT, SAMUEL   Echo's Bones, and other Precipitates. Paris, Europa Press, 1935. One of 327 copies, orig. wraps, covers little dusty & browned,
nice. Bell Book 17-079 1978 £145

BECKETT, SAMUEL How It Is. 1964. No. 87 of 100 copies on hand-made paper, signed by author, printed in advance of first ed., full mor., t.e.g., fine, unopened, slightly worn slip-case. Bell Book 17-082 1978 £95

BECKETT, SAMUEL How It Is. London, 1964. 1 of 100 numbered and signed copies on handmade paper, 1st ed., full white vellum, t.e.g., uncut, unopened, fine. Houle 10-25 1978 $275

BECKETT, SAMUEL More Pricks than Kicks. 1970. No. 28 of 100 copies numbered & signed by the author, qtr. calf, a.e.g., fine, linen slipcase, first English ed. Bell Book 16-059 1978 £90

BECKETT, SAMUEL No's Knife. 1967. No. A91 of 100 copies numbered & signed by author, full calf, a.e.g., fine, cloth slip-case, first English ed. Bell Book 16-060 1978 £90

BECKETT, SAMUEL Proust & Three Dialogues. 1965. No. 50 of 100 copies numbered & signed by the author, qtr. calf, a.e.g., near fine, cloth slipcase, first English ed. Bell Book 16-061 1978 £90

BECKFORD, GREGORY W. The Beckford Family. London, 1898. 2nd. ed., ltd. to 250 copies, crimson cloth, a.e.g., very good. Greene 78-146 1978 $55

BECKFORD, PETER Thoughts on Hunting. 1802. 4th. ed., sm. 4to, half title, engraved frontis, 2 plts., orig. blue bds., expertly respines, uncut & partially unopened, fine. Jarndyce 16-287 1978 £35

BECKFORD, PETER Thoughts Upon Hare and Fox Hunting in a Series of Letters to a Friend... London, 1796. 8vo., a.e.g., engrs., fine 19th Cent. full black French mor. binding, fine. Current 24-205 1978 $155

BECKFORD, WILLIAM An Arabian Tale, From an Unpublished Manuscript: with Notes Critical and Explanatory. London, 1786. 8vo, full mid-19th century green morocco, gilt, spine and inner dentelles gilt, a.e.g., 1st ed. Ximenes 47-17 1978 $350

BECKFORD, WILLIAM Italy; With Sketches of Spain and Portugal. London, 1834. 2 vols., octavo, orig. boards, pr. title labels on spines chipped, some pages lightly foxed, spine chipped, hinges cracking, bookplates of William Brodie, two-wing cloth wr., green cloth slipcase with leather label. Totteridge 29-11 1978 $250

BECKFORD, WILLIAM A Catalogue of a Portion of the Library of William Beckford,.... London, n.d. (1817). 8vo, sewn, as issued, very fine condition. Ximenes 47-18 1978 $175

BECKFORD, WILLIAM Recollections of an Excursion to the Monastery of Alcobaca and Batalba. 1835. 8vo., 1st ed., portr., contemp. bds. uncut, bookseller's catalogue dated 1835 bound in. Quaritch 979-23 1978 $175

BECKFORD, WILLIAM Recollections of an Excursion to the Monasteries of Alcobaca and Batalha. London, 1835. Octavo, half calf, rubbed, bookplates, some light foxing, 1st ed. Bennett 7-11 1978 $150

BECKFORD, WILLIAM The Valuable Library of Books in Fonthill Abbey. (London: 1823). 8vo, contemporary half red morocco, rebacked, original spine laid down (bit rubbed), bookplate within. Ximenes 47-19 1978 $150

BECKFORD, WILLIAM Vathek. 1816. 3rd. ed. revised & corrected, frontis, foxed, orig. calf, gilt borders, rebacked, retaining orig. endpapers. Jarndyce 16-288 1978 £32

BECKFORD, WILLIAM Vathek. 1823. Fourth ed., 8vo., half calf, marbled sides, frontispiece. P. M. Hill 142-183 1978 £12

BECKLEY, HOSEA The History of Vermont. Brattleboro, 1846. 1st ed., rebound, nice copy. MacManus 239-467 1978 $25

BECQUEREL, HENRI Memoire sur l'etude des Radiations Infra-Rouges au moyen des Phenomenes de Phosphorescence. Paris, 1883. 8vo., old wrs., plt. Gurney 75-7 1978 £30

BECQUEREL, HENRI Recherches sur une Propriete Nouvelle de la Matiere Activite Radiante Spontanee ou Radio-Activite de la Matiere. Paris, 1903. 4to., plts., orig. wrs., enclosed in cloth case. Quaritch 977-85 1978 $275

BEDDARD, FRANK F. Animal Coloration. London, 1892. Coloured plts., text illus., 8vo., orig. cloth. K Books 244-29 1978 £18

BEDDOES, THOMAS 1760-1808 The History of Isaac Jenkins, and of the Sickness of Sarah His Wife,.... London, n.d. (ca. 1815). 12mo, original pale blue printed wrappers, fine copy. Ximenes 47-20 1978 $25

BEDDOES, THOMAS LOVELL 1803-49 Complete Works. Fanfrolico Press, 1928. Portrait, illus., 2 vols., roy. 8vo., decor. batik bds., linen backs, uncut. Howes 194-851 1978 £42

BEDDOME, R. H. The Flora Sylvatica From Southern India... Madras, 1869-1873. Plts., plt. 110 bound upside down, 3 vols. in 4, half calf, leather labels, 4to, new cloth sides. Traylen 88-537 1978 £350

BEDE Ecclesiasticae Historiae Gentis Anglorum Libri Qvinqve Diligenti studio a mendis.... Antwerp, 1550. Title soiled and frayed at edges, some other stains, folio, contemp. vellum, somewhat worn and soiled, body of book quite clean, marginal notes in an early hand. Thomas 37-65 1978 £100

BEDE Miscellaneous Works, in Original Latin. 1843. 6 vols., half calf, rubbed, spines lack labels. Allen 234-1107 1978 $50

BEDE, CUTHBERT PSEUD.
Please turn to
BRADLEY, EDWARD

BEDFORD, AERBRAND RUSSELL Science and Fruit Growing. 1919. Plts., illus., 8vo., orig. cloth, nice copy. Fenning 32-19 1978 £8

BEDFORD, HILORY G. Texas Indian Troubles. Dallas, 1905. Pic. cloth, illus., 1st ed., recased, margins fraying but text very good, scarce, slipcase. Dykes 35-235 1978 $100

BEDIER, J. Histoire de la Litterature Francaise Illustree. Paris, 1923. 2 vols., 4to., half calf, plts., illus. Van der Peet H-64-414 1978 Dfl 85

BEDOS DE CELLE, DOM FRANCOIS L'Art du Facteur d'Orgues. Paris, 1766-1778. Folio, 4 parts in one vol., engraved full-page plates, contemp. calf, rubbed, rebacked, 1st ed. Gilhofer 75-6 1978 SFr 5,500

BEEBE, LUCIUS Legends of the Comstock Lode. Oakland, 1950. Illus., first ed., d.w. Biblo 247-173 1978 $17.50

BEEBE, LUCIUS The Saga of Wells Fargo. New York, 1949. Sm 4to, 1st ed., d.w. Biblo 248-224 1978 $22.50

BEEBE, LUCIUS U.S. West. The Saga of Wells Fargo. New York, 1949. Sm. 4to., illus., signed by Beebe. Biblo BL781-264 1978 $14.50

BEEBE, WILLIAM A Monograph of the Pheasants. London, 1918-1922. Plates by Thorburn and others, smooth and "egg-shell" paper, only 600 sets, 4 vols., folio, orig. maroon cloth, some foxing, marginal spotting, 8vo. Book Chest 17-37 1978 $2,550

BEEBE, WILLIAM A Monograph of the Pheasants. London, 1918-1922. Coloured plts. by Thorburn, Lodge & Gronvold & others, photo plts., maps, 4 vols., folio, modern half brown morocco, cloth sides, gilt tops. Traylen 88-538 1978 £1100

BEECHER, EDWARD Narrative of the Riots at Alton: in Connection with the Death of Rev. Elijah P. Lovejoy. Alton, 1838. Cloth, faded, minor spotting and wear. Hayman 72-318 1978 $35

BEECHER, EDWARD Narrative of the Riots at Alton: in Connection with the Death of Rev. Elijah P. Lovejoy. Alton, 1838. 1st ed., cloth. MacManus 239-23 1978 $30

BEECHER, GEORGE A. A Bishop of the Great Plains. Philadelphia, 1950. Cloth. Hayman 73-41 1978 $7.50

BEECHER, HARRIS H. Record of the 114th Regiment, N.Y.S.V. Norwich, 1866. Plts., spine lightly faded, tight crisp copy. Butterfield 21-117 1978 $35

BEECHER, HENRY WARD The Beecher Trial. New York, 1875. Wr. Butterfield 21-482c 1978 $7.50

BEECHER, HENRY WARD   Memorial of Henry Ward Beecher. New York, 1887. Cloth. Hayman 73-42 1978 $10

BEECHER, HENRY WARD   Norwood; or, Village Life in New England. New York, 1868. Cloth., covers dull. Hayman 72-216 1978 $7.50

BEECHER, HENRY WARD   Star Papers. New York, 1855. First ed., cr. 8vo., orig. cloth, cover chafed. Howes 194-617 1978 £10

BEECHER, HENRY WARD   Star Papers. New York, 1855. Cloth, minor repair to one edge of spine. Hayman 73-43 1978 $8.50

BEECHEY, FREDERICK WILLIAM   Narrative of a Voyage to the Pacific and Beering's Strait, to Co-operate with the Polar Expeditions:.... London, 1831. New (octavo) ed., 2 vols., plates, double-page and folding maps, illus., original boards, original printed paper labels on spines, signatures on t.p., superb copy. Bennett 20-21 1978 $650

BEECHEY, FREDERICK WILLIAM   Narrative of a Voyage to the Pacific and Beering's Strait to Co-Operate With the Polar Expeditions.... 1831. 2 vols., plts., half mor., 8vo., slight foxing & covers repaired. Edwards 1012-356 1978 £250

BEEDING, FRANCIS   The Six Proud Walkers. Boston, 1928. Cloth, 1st Amer. ed., d.j. worn. Hayman 72-180 1978 $7.50

BEEDOME, THOMAS   Select Poems Divine and Humane. Bloomsbury, 1928. Orig. limp vellum, uncut, 1 of 1250 copies. Americanist 102-14 1978 $35

BEER, GEORGE L.   British Colonial Policy, 1754-1765. New York, 1922. Hood 116-603 1978 $55

BEER, GEORGE L.   The Old Colonial System, 1660-1754. New York, 1912. 2 vols., octavo, good. Upcroft 10-221 1978 £12.50

BEER, GEORGE L.   The Old Colonial System, 1660-1754. New York, 1912. 2 vols., 8vo. George's 635-282 1978 £8.50

BEER, GEORGE L.   The Origins of the British Colonial System, 1578-1600. New York, 1908, 1922. Octavo, good. Upcroft 10-220 1978 £8.50

BEER, M.   A History of British Socialism. 1929. 2 vols., spines faded. George's 635-283 1978 £10.50

BEERBOHM, MAX   And Even Now. London, 1920. Orig. cloth, paper label, d.j., 1st ed., fine. MacManus 238-611 1978 $40

BEERBOHM, MAX   And Even Now. London, 1920. 1st ed., uncut, partly unopened, cloth, very good or better. Limestone 9-16 1978 $30

BEERBOHM, MAX   And Even Now. London, 1920. 8vo, yellow cloth, paper label, spine and covers soiled and label chipped, very good, 1st ed. Desmarais 1-33 1978 $12.50

BEERBOHM, MAX   Catalogue of an Exhibition Entitled "Ghosts".... London, 1928. 16mo, Mint, covers slightly sunned around edges, 1st ed. Desmarais 1-35 1978 $15

BEERBOHM, MAX   The Happy Hypocrite. London, 1918. 4to, pict. cloth, illus. by George Sheringham, colored plates, collector's cond., 1st ed. Desmarais 1-34 1978 $25

BEERBOHM, MAX   Mainly on the Air. London, 1946. 1st ed., very good or better. Limestone 9-17 1978 $13

BEERBOHM, MAX   Observations. London, (1925). 4to., illus., colored frontis. and plts., orig. cloth, 1st ed., bookplt. removed, but very good. MacManus 238-613 1978 $60

BEERBOHM, MAX   Seven Men. 1919. Blue cloth, spine worn. Eaton 45-43 1978 £5

BEERBOHM, MAX   Seven Men. -London, 1919. 1st. ed., sm. 4to, inscription on fly-leaf. Traylen 88-106 1978 £8

BEERBOHM, MAX   A Survey. London, 1921. Illus. with colored plts., orig. cloth, 1st ed., faded, otherwise very good. MacManus 238-612 1978 $45

BEERBOHM, MAX   Things New and Old. 1923. First ed., 4to., orig. cloth. Howes 194-618 1978 £30

BEERBOHM, MAX   Yet Again. 1909. Fourth ed., orig. blue cloth, pres. copy with holograph inscription by author, 8vo. Howes 194-619 1978 £25

BEERBOHM, MAX   Zuleika Dobson, or an Oxford Love Story. London, 1911. Orig. cloth, 1st ed., rough cloth bind., nice. MacManus 238-609 1978 $150

BEERBOHM, MAX   Zuleika Dobson. New York, 1924. 4th American Ed., embossed pictorial cover, very good or better. Limestone 9-18 1978 $9

BEERS, F. W.   Atlas of Greene County. New York, 1867. Tall folio, colored maps, prtd. on thin paper folded & tipped in, cloth covers loose, backstrip chipped away, maps, very good. Butterfield 21-199 1978 $65

BEERS, F. W.   County Atlas of Sullivan New York from Recent and Actual Surveys. New York, 1875. Sq. folio, orig. cloth, lea. back, worn but sound, rare. Butterfield 21-425 1978 $100

BEERS, FANNIE A.   Memories: A Record of Personnel Experience and Adventure During Four Years of War. Philadelphia, 1888. Cover worn, Bell Wiley's copy. Broadfoot's 44-28 1978 $15

BEERS, HENRY A.   Initial Studies in American Letters. New York, 1891. Clean, little rubbed, orig. binding. Hayman 71-42 1978 $7.50

BEESON, MARVIN F.   Die Organization Der Negererziehung in Den Dereinigten Staaten Von America Seit 1860. Leipzig, Germany, 1915. Wrs. Wrs. chipped. Bell Wiley's copy. Broadfoot 46-16 1978 $10

BEET, GOTTFRIED ZUR   Die Geheimnisse Der Weisen Von Zion. Minich, 1939. Paper, in German. Austin 79-53 1978 $47.50

BEETHOVEN, L. VON   Fidelio. New York, 1839. Portrait, orig. printed wrappers. Wolfe 39-35 1978 $25

BEETLE, DAVID H.   Up Old Forge Way. Utica, (1948). Plts., out of print, scarce. Butterfield 21-67 1978 $10

BEETLE, DAVID H.   West Canada Creek. Utica, (1946). Plts., out of print. Butterfield 21-68 1978 $12.50

BEETON, SAMUEL O.   The Siliad... (1873). 1st. ed., folding coloured plts., other illus., printed wrappers, leaves bound in, 4to, roan-backed bds., spine worn but sound, fine internally. Fenning 32-20 1978 £8.50

BEETS, N.   Dichtwerken, 1830-1884. Roeselare, n.d. (ab. 1930). 4 vols. in 2, lg. thick 8vo., full calf, shaved, a.e.g. Van der Peet H-64-367 1978 Dfl 150

BEETS, N.   Nederlandsche Prentkunst uit de 15e, 16e en 17e eeuw, Voornamelijk uit de Collectie Van's Rijks Prentenkabinet te Amsterdam. Amsterdam, n.d. 8vo., cloth, plts. Van der Peet H-64-4 1978 Dfl 40

BEGG, ALEX   History of British Columbia from Its Earliest Discovery to the Present Time. Toronto, 1894. Illus., 1st ed., leather bind. restored. Hood 116-844 1978 $50

BEHAINE, RENE   The Survivors. London, 1938. First English ed., nice, orig. binding. Rota 211-116 1978 £5

BEHARRELL, T. G.   Odd Fellows Monitor and Guide Containing History of the Degree of Rebekah...and Teachings of Ritual... Indianapolis and Canton, 1884. Rev'd., illus., cloth. Hayman 72-40 1978 $7.50

BEHIND the Mirrors. The Psychology of Disintegration at Washington. New York, 1922. Cloth. Hayman 72-41 1978 $8.50

BEHN, APHRA   The City-Heiress; or, Sir Timothy Treat -All. London, 1682. 1st. ed., 4to, new quarter dark red morocco, marbled bds., gilt lettered spine, slight staining, one corner repaired. Traylen 88-107 1978 £95

BEHN, APHRA   The City-Heiress: Or, Sir Timothy Treat-All.
1698. 2nd. ed., 4to, lacks half-title, half cloth, paper heavily browned & waterstained, some head-lines cut into. Hannas 54-14 1978 £20

BEHN, APHRA   Love-Letters Between a Nobleman and His Sister...
London, 1718. 3 parts, 5th. ed., cr. 8vo, slightly wormed on lower margins, text
unaffected, contemp. calf, rebacked with orig. spine, corners bumped. Eaton
45-44 1978 £50

BEHN, APHRA   Plays Written by the Late Ingenious ... 1724.
3rd. ed., 4 vols., 12mo, modern red morocco, gilt, a.e.g. Hannas 54-15 1978
£85

BEHNKE, ARNO   The Sailing of a Refugee Ship. New York, 1914.
Sm. 8vo., 1st ed. Morrill 239-302 1978 $15

BEIDELMAN, WILLIAM   The Story of the Pennsylvania Germans...
Easton, 1898. Hinges weak otherwise fine. MacManus 239-1368 1978 $17.50

BEIGEL, HERMANN   On the Inhalation of Atomized Fluids. Boston,
(1866). Illus., 8vo., orig. wrs. Morrill 239-18 1978 $17.50

BEIGEL, HERMANN   Pathologische Anatomie der Weiblichen Unfrucht-
barkeit (Sterilitat), deren mechanik und behandlung. Braunschweig, 1878.
8vo., illus., many in color, 3/4 calf, gilt on spine, 1st ed., good copy, from the
library of Dr. Alfred M. Hellman. Zeitlin 245-18 1978 $45

BEILSTEIN, FRIEDRICH   Handbuch der Organischen Chemie. Hamburg
& Leipzig, 1881-83. 3 vols., 8vo., half mor., gilt, good set, 1st ed. Norman
5-21 1978 $125

BEIRNE, FRANCIS F.   The War of 1812. New York, 1949. Maps by
Dorothy De Fontaine. Baldwins' 51-302 1978 $7.50

BELCHER, EDWARD   The Last of the Arctic Voyages... 1855. Thick
roy. 8vo, orig. cloth gilt, stain on back cover, coloured litho. plts., other plts.,
woodcuts, 2 vols. in 1. Edwards 1012-563 1978 £150

BELCHER, EDWARD   Narrative of a Voyage Round the World,....
London, 1843. 1st ed., octavo, 2 vols., engravings, vignettes, maps, original
publisher's blindstamped cloth lettered in gold on spine, bookplate owner's inscription on front pastdown, very good copy. Bennett 20-22 1978 $650

BELCHER, EDWARD   Narrative of a Voyage Round The World...
1843. 1st. ed., 2 vols., 8vo, engraved plts., folding maps, illus., modern half
calf, gilt backs. Deighton 5-176 1978 £140

BELCHER, GEORGE   Potted Char and other Delicacies. 1933. 4to.,
drawings. George's 635-120 1978 £6

BELCHER, HENRY   The First American Civil War. First Period 1775-
1778. London, 1911. 2 vols., cloth, light dampstain at bottom of some leaves,
but good solid set. Hayman 73-44 1978 $20

BELCHER, JOHN   Later Renaissance Architecture in England. 1901.
Plts., text illus., loose in lg. folio portfolios as issued, half linen. George's 635-
76 1978 £30

BELCOURT, G. E.   Mission de la Riviere Rouge. Quebec, 1842.
Original printed wr., 1st ed. Ginsberg 14-44 1978 $125

BELDING, PAUL AND CO.   The Self Instructor in Silk Knitting, Crocheting,
and Embroidery. Montrel, 1891. Rev. ed., back wr. taped on, fr. wr. missing.
Hood 117-610 1978 $12.50

BELFOUR, JOHN   Fables on Subjects Connected with Literature.
1804. Fcap. 8vo., nice, contemp. tree calf, first ed. Howes 194-161 1978 £24

BELFRAGE, CEDRIC   Abide With Me. 1948. Austin 82-126 1978
$12.50

THE BELGIAN Congo. 1944. Maps, 2 lg. folding, illus., orig. cloth, 8vo.
Edwards 1012-243 1978 £20

BELIN, ELIESER BEN JAKOB ASCHKENASI   Sepher Ivranot. Frankfurt, 1691.
4to., illus., bds. Gilhofer 74-3 1978 sFr 1,300

BELISLE, ORVILLA S.   The Prophets; or, Mormonism Unveiled. Philadelphia, 1855. Illus., orig. cloth, 1st ed. Ginsberg 14-639 1978 $75

BELKNAP, HENRY WYCKOFF   Trades & Tradesmen of Essex County (Mass.)
Chiefly of the 17th Century. 1929. Excellent. Nestler Rare 78-218 1978 $25

BELKNAP, JEREMY   A Discourse, Intended to Commemorate the Discovery of America by Christopher Columbus. Boston, 1792. Thin 8vo., 3/4 mor.
Salloch 345-17 1978 $150

BELL, A.   Letter From...Transmitting...Certain Papers
Relating To The Private Land Claim In The Territory Of Arizona Known As El Soport.
Washington, 1884. Cloth with leather label. Ginsberg 14-6 1978 $40

BELL, A. E.   Christian Huygens and the Development of Science
in the XVII Century. 1947. Illus., 8vo. George's 635-936 1978 £5

BELL, ALEXANDER GRAHAM   Upon the Production of Sound by Radiant Energy.
Washington, D. C., 1881. 8vo., plts., orig. prtd. wrs., faded at edges, spine
repaired but fine copy, 1st ed. Norman 5-*4 1978 $125

BELL, ANDREW   British-Canadian Centennium; 1759-1859. Montreal, 1859. Printed wrappers. Wolfe 39-36 1978 $100

BELL, ANDREW   History of Canada, From the Time of Its Discovery
Till the Union Year 1840-41... Toronto, 1876. Spine faded, 2 vols., 3rd. ed.,
rev., cover on vol. 1 mended. Hood's 115-575 1978 $50

BELL, C. N.   The Old Forts of Winniped(1738-1927). Winnipeg, 1927. New series, card cover, maps & illus. Hood's 115-991 1978 $20

BELL, CHARLES   Injuries of the Spine and of the Thigh Bone.
London, 1824. Spine cloth missing, hinges separated. Rittenhouse 49-62 1976
$25

BELL, CHARLES   Tibet Past & Present. 1924. 1st. ed., folding
maps, frontispiece & illus., cover slightly dampstained, 8vo, orig. cloth. Edwards
1012-134 1978 £15

BELL, CHARLES H.   History of the Town of Exeter, N.H. Exeter,
1888. 1st ed., 4to., frontis., orig. cloth, lib. marks, fine. MacManus 239-
1069 1978 $40

BELL, CHARLES H.   John Taylor Gilman, M. D., Portland, Maine.
(Exeter, N.H.), 1885. Portr., 8vo., 1st ed., pres. copy. Morrill 239-19 1978
$7.50

BELL, CHARLES W.   Who Said Murder? Toronto, 1935. Hood 117
333 1978 $25

BELL, CLIVE   An Account of French Painting. 1931. Plts.,
orig. linen, very good, first English ed. Bell Book 16-069 1978 £7.50

BELL, G. H.   Guide to Correct Language, a Book of Ready Reference in Three Parts. Battle Creek, 1895. Rev'd. and enlarged. Hood 116-
361 1978 $10

BELL, G. K. A.   Randall Davidson, Archbishop of Canterbury.
1935. Illus., 2 vols., 8vo. George's 635-1048 1978 £5

BELL, GEORGE   Rough Notes of an Old Soldier, During Fifty
Years' Service.... 1867. 1st. ed., portrait, 2 vols., 8vo, recent half calf,
gilt, some very light signs of use, very good copy. Fenning 32-21 1978 £28.50

BELL, GEORGE HAMILTON   A Short Exposition of the Circulation and Nervous System. Edinburgh & London, 1854. 8vo., orig. cloth, gilt lettering,
backstrip faded, lightly browned, good copy, pres. inscr. from the author, bkplt.
of Brougham and Faux, the Lord Chancellor, & later bkplts. of physicians, 1st ed.,
very rare. Zeitlin 245-19 1978 $95

BELL, GERTRUDE   The Arab War. 1940. 4to., fine prtd. in Perpetua type on mould-made paper, linen, mor. back, t.e.g., back slightly faded,
ltd. to 500 copies. Quaritch 979-349 1978 $200

BELL, GERTRUDE   The Letters of Gertrude Bell. London, 1927.
2 vols., nice in damaged d.w.'s. Desmarais B-75 1978 $20

BELL, GERTRUDE   The Letters of Gertrude Bell of Arabia. N.Y.,
1927. 1st American ed., 8 vo., d.j., illus., 2 vols., very good-fine. Houle
10-27 1978 $35

BELL, GERTRUDE   The Letters of Gertrude Bell of Arabia.
London, 1927. 2 vols., 1st ed., cloth. Houle 10-28 1978 $75

BELL, H. I.   The Development of Welsh Poetry. 1936. Cr.
8vo., frontis., orig. cloth. Howes 194-621 1978 £4

BELL, HORACE   Reminiscences of a Ranger; or, Early Times in
Southern California. Los Angeles, 1881. Original pictorial cloth, 1st ed. Ginsberg 14-74 1978 $75

BELL, JOHN   The Anatomy and Physiology of the Human Body.
New York, 1822. Three vols., binding orig., usual browning. Rittenhouse 49-
61 1976 $35

BELL, JOHN 1691-1780   Travels From St. Petersburg in Russia, To Diverse
Parts of Asia. Glasgow, 1763. 1st. ed., 2 vols., 4to, folding engraved map,
contemporary speckled calf, panelled backs, morocco labels, gilt, joints weak,
bookplt. of Frances Mary Richardson Currer. Deighton 5-112 1978 £155

BELL, LANGDON   The Old Free State. A Contribution to the History of Lunenburg County and Southside Virginia. Richmond, (1927). 2 vols.,
illus., maps. MacManus 239-1129 1978 $65

BELL, MALCOLM   Sir Edward Burne-Jones. London, 1901. Revised,
illus., plates, very good. Victoria 34-57 1978 $25

BELL, N. D'ANVERS   The Companion Volume to Heroes of Discovery
in South Africa. London, c.1899. Head & tail of spine slightly frayed, 8vo,
illus., dec. cloth. K Books 239-37 1978 £5

BELL, N. D'ANVERS   Heroes of Discovery in South Africa. London,
c.1899. Portrait frontispiece, illus., dec. cloth, 8vo, g.e., covers slightly chafed.
K Books 239-36 1978 £7

BELL, R. W.   Canada in War-Paint. London and Toronto, 1917.
Dedicated to men of 1st. Can. Infantry Batt., Ont. Reg. Hood's 115-90 1978
$12.50

BELL, T.   Kalogynomia. Walpole Press, 1899. Plts., no.
956 of 100 copies, half mor., very good, first English ed. Bell Book 16-319 1978
£35

BELL, THOMAS fl. 1573-1610 The Anatomie of Popish Tyrannie.... London,
1603. 1st. ed., sm. 4to, old half calf, rebacked, slight staining, black letter,
title-pg. with ornament & printer's device. Traylen 88-108 1978 £90

BELL, THOMAS fl. 1573-1610 The Tryall of the New Religion. London, 1608.
Sm. 4to, old paper wrappers, some staining. Traylen 88-109 1978 £50

BELL, THOMAS 1792-1880 A History of British Quadrupeds. London, 1837.
Woodcut illus., orig. cloth dull, 8vo. K Books 244-31 1978 £14

BELL, THOMAS EVANS   The Bengal Reversion, Another "Exceptional
Case". 1872. 1st. ed., 8vo, orig. cloth, gilt, nice copy. Fenning 32-16 1978
£8.50

BELL, WILLIAM E.   Carpentry Made Easy. Philadelphia, 1889.
Lg. 8vo., lithos, 2nd ed., orig. cloth, very good. Americanist 103-10 1978
$75

BELLAMY, EDWARD   Equality. Toronto, 1897. Buckram, calf back,
covers worn. Wolfe 39-37 1978 $15

BELLAMY, EDWARD   Looking Backward 2000-1887. Boston, 1888.
Orig. cloth, 1st ed., 1st state, cover faintly soiled, but fine. MacManus 238-
424 1978 $125

BELLAMY, EDWARD   Looking Backward. Los Angeles, Limited Editions
Club, 1941. Ltd. ed., mint, signed by Elise, protective cellphane cover torn.
Biblo 247-582 1978 $37.50

BELLAMY, EDWARD   Looking Backward. (Hollywood, 1941). Illus.
by Elise, 1 of 1,500 signed by illus., red stamped yellow cloth, orig. acetate
slipcase, fine. Houle 10-13 1978 $55

BELLASIS, GEORGE HUTCHINS   Views of Saint Helena. 1815. Oblong folio,
hand-coloured aquatint plts., orig. wrs., calf backed cloth portfolio. Quaritch
983-292 1978 $725

BELLAY, J. DUE   Les Regrets. Paris, 1925. Sewn, port., ltd.
ed. of 380 copies only, 8vo., orig. covers. Van der Peet H-64-593 1978 Dfl 65

BELLAY, J. DUE   Les Regrets. Fine half calf, 8vo. Van der Peet
H-64-593a 1978 Dfl 125

BELLENGHI, D. ALBERTINO   Fossili del Catria e Monti Adiacenti Scoperte ed
osservazioni. Roma, 1819. 8vo., half calf, joints rubbed, very good. King 7-
136 1978 £15

BELLEW, CLARA   The Merry Circle. London, n.d.(c.1872). Illus.,
orig. illus. cloth binding, good. Greene 78-321 1978 $65

BELLINCINI   Guinte All'Opera. Modenon, 1711. 8vo., full
vellum. Van der Peet H-64-594 1978 Dfl 50

BELLINGSHAUSEN, CAPTAIN   The Voyage of Captain...to the Antarctic Seas
1819-1821. London, 1945. 2 vols., map, fine, orig. cloth. Paine 78-6 1978
$100.00

BELLOC, HILAIRE   The Battle of Blenheim. 1911. Illus. with 2
coloured & 8 uncoloured maps, sm. 8vo, orig. cloth. Sawyer 298-63 1978 £30

BELLOC, HILAIRE   The Battleground. Philadelphia, 1936. Illus.,
maps, 1st Amer. ed. Biblo 251-1 1978 $17.50

BELLOC, HILAIRE   But Soft – We Are Observed! 1928. Drawings
by G. K. Chesterton, very good, first English ed. Bell Book 16-973 1978 £7.50

BELLOC, HILAIRE   Cromwell. 1934. First ed., frontis., maps,
8vo., orig. cloth. Howes 194-623 1978 £5.50

BELLOC, HILAIRE   The Eye-Witness. 1908. Very good, first English
ed. Bell Book 17-969 1978 £8.50

BELLOC, HILLAIRE   The Four Men: A Farrago. London, n.d.
8vo, brown stamped cloth, gilt lettering on spine, illus., very fine, 1st ed.
Desmarais 1-37 1978 $10

BELLOC, HILAIRE   A General Sketch of the European War; the 2nd
Phase. 1916. Very good, first English ed. Bell Book 16-070 1978 £4

BELLOC, HILAIRE   The Girondin. 1911. First ed., coloured frontispiece, cr. 8vo., orig. green cloth. Howes 194-624 1978 £6

BELLOC, HILAIRE   A History of England, Vol. IV, the Transformation
of England. 1931. First ed., signed pres. copy from the author, 8vo. George's
635-1309 1978 £8.50

BELLOC, HILAIRE   Lambkin's Remains. Oxford, 1900. First ed.,
orig. blue cloth, fine, fscp. 8vo. Howes 194-625 1978 £18

BELLOC, HILAIRE   The Missing Masterpiece: a novel. 1929.
First ed., illus. by G. K. Chesterton, cr. 8vo., orig. cloth. Howes 194-626
1978 £7.50

BELLOC, HILAIRE   Mrs. Markham's New History of England, Being:
an Introduction for Young People to the Current History and Institutions of Our
Time. Kensington, Cayme Press, 1926. 8vo., bds., frontis. Van der Peet H-64-
392 1978 Dfl 45

BELLOC, HILAIRE   The Mercy of Allah. 1922. Very good, worn
d.w., first English ed. Bell Book 17-970 1978 £7.50

BELLOC, HILAIRE   The Modern Traveller. 1898. 1st. ed., b/w
illus., pictorial bds., linen back. Eaton 45-46 1978 £10

BELLOC, HILLAIRE   The Modern Traveller. London, 1923. 8vo,
pictorial boards, cloth back, covers soiled, illus. by B.T.B., 1st ed., collector's
cond. Desmarais 1-38 1978 $10

BELLOC, HILAIRE   New Cautionary Tales. 1930. Sm. 4to., cloth-
backed pict. bds., covers somewhat soiled, else very good, first English ed. Bell
Book 17-092 1978 £12.50

BELLOC, HILAIRE. Nine Nines or Novenas from a Chinese Litany of Odd Numbers. Oxford, 1931. 1st ed., plates by Thomas Derrick, pictorial boards, light cover soiling, spine edge rubbing, fine. Victoria 34-58 1978 $35

BELLOC, HILAIRE The Party System. London, 1911. 1st ed., 8 vo., orig. black stamped red cloth, gilt stamped spine, cloth slipcase, fine. Houle 10-29 1978 $55

BELLOC, HILAIRE The Path to Rome. London, 1902. Illus., cloth pict. upper cover. Eaton 45-45 1978 £10

BELLOC, HILLAIRE Places. London, 1942. Near mint in chipped d.w., review copy. Desmarais B-78 1978 $12.50

BELLOC, HILAIRE The Praise of Wine. 1931. Roy. 8vo., 1st ed., rebound in half cloth, pres. copy from author, signed inscr., bkplt. Quaritch 979-26 1978 $140

BELLOC, HILAIRE Richelieu. 1930. First ed., plts., maps, lg. 8vo., fine, d.w. Howes 194-627 1978 £7.50

BELLOC, HILAIRE The Road. 1923. Maps, illus., qtr. buckram, leather label, fine, first English ed. Bell Book 16-071 1978 £8.50

BELLOC, HILAIRE Robespierre: a Study. 1901. Portrait, buckram, t.e.g., good, first Eng. ed. Bell Book 17-093 1978 £8.50

BELLOC, HILLAIRE The Stane Street. London, 1913. 8vo., brown stamped cloth, gilt lettering on cover and spine bright, foxing, tight, 1st ed., collector's cond. Desmarais 1-39 1978 $10

BELLOC, HILAIRE Verses and Sonnets. London, 1896. 1st ed., 1st issue, 16mo., paper unusual, bkplt. of former owner & ink mark on half title, light foxing of preliminaries & terminals, interior very fine, orig. green cloth covers, very light rubbing, very rare. Current 24-6 1978 $195

BELLOC, HILAIRE Wolsey. 1930. Plt., one leaf repaired. Allen 234-1497 1978 $7.50

BELLOCQ, E. J. Storyville Portraits. New York. Photos from circa 1912, illus., 4to., wrs., fine. Biblo 251-235 1978 $17.50

BELLORI, GIOVANNI PIETRO Descrizione delle Immagini dipinte da Raffaelle d'Urbino nel Palazzo Vaticano e nella Farnesina alla Lungara.... Roma, 1751. Sm. 8vo., contemp. half calf, woodcut initials, fine. King 7-138 1978 £40

BELLORI, GIOVANNI PIETRO Picturae Antiquae Cryptarum Romanorum et Sepulcri Nasonum Delineatae.... 1738. Lg. folio, vellum bds., vignettes. King 7-137 1978 £135

BELLOW, SAUL Humboldt's Gift. New York, n.d. Orig. wrs., uncorrected proof copy, covers lightly soiled, but very good. MacManus 238-614 1978 $75

BELLOW, SAUL The Victim. 1947. First ed., v.g., d.j. Austin 82-1154 1978 $97.50

BELLOW, SAUL The Victim. New York, (1947). Orig. cloth, d.j., a bit worn, 1st ed., top of spine slightly worn, but fine. MacManus 238-615 1978 $100

BELLOW, SAUL The Victim. 1948. Very good, d.w., first Eng. ed. Bell Book 17-096 1978 £25

BELMONT, PERRY Executive Officers in Congress. A Paper Read Before the American Social Science Association, at Cincinnati, May 22, 1878. New York, 1878. Wrs., minor marginal chipping of back wr. Hayman 72-42 1978 $7.50

BELON, PIERRE Les Observations Des Plusieurs Singularitez Et Choses Memorables. Paris, 1553. Woodcuts, 4to., calf, rebacked, some light foxing & stains, otherwise good. Salloch 345-18 1978 $700

BELOT, JEAN Les Oevvres. Lyons, 1654. Woodcut portr., 3 vols. in 1, 8vo., old mor., back gilt. Salloch 345-19 1978 $225

BELSER, MR. Remarks of..., of Alabama, on the Bill Making Appropriations for Certain Rivers and Harbors. Delivered in the House...April 18, 1844. N.P., n.d. Disbound. Hayman 72-665 1978 $7.50

BELSHAM, WILLIAM 1752-1827 Memoirs of the Reign of George III to the Session of Parliament ending A.D. 1793. 1796. 4 vols., contemp. calf, 8vo. Howes 194-162 1978 £25

BELT, T. The Naturalist in Nicaragua... 1874. 1st. ed., map, illus., orig. cloth, 8vo, spine slightly creased. Edwards 1012-686 1978 £30

BELTRAMI, J. C. La Decouverte Des Sources du Mississippi et de la Riviere Sanglante. Nouvelle-Orleans, 1824. Leather spine rubbed, mottled bds., private lib. identification, errata sheet tipped in. Hood's 115-576 1978 $350

BELTRAMI, J. C. A Pilgrimage in Europe and America, Leading to the Discovery of the Sources of the Mississippi and Bloody River... London, 1828. 2 vols., 1 fldg. map, fldg. plan, orig. binding carefully restored, private lib. perforated identification on title page, errata sheet tipped in. Hood's 115-577 1978 $300

BELTRAMI, LUCA Novissima Lezione Vinciana in due Parti con Intermezzo. Milan, 1919. 8vo., orig. prtd. wrs. Norman 5-L20 1978 $15

BELZONI, GIOVANNI BATTISTA Narrative of the Operations and Recent Discoveries within the Pyramids, Temples, Tombs and Excavations in Egypt and Nubia.... London, 1821. 2nd ed., 4to., lithograph frontis. portrait, lithograph map, full calf, raised bands, gilt, brown mor. label, marbled edges, some foxing, heavy on a few leaves. Deighton 5-6 1978 £75

BELZONI, GIOVANNI BATTISTA Narrative of the Operations and Recent Discoveries within the Pyramids, Temples, Toombs, and Excavations, in Egypt and Nubia.... London, 1821. 3rd ed., 2 vols., 8vo., contemp. calf, rebacked, retaining the orig. backstrips, double mor. labels, corners repaired. Deighton 5-6A 1978 £40

BEMBO, PIETRO Historiae Venetae Libri XII. Venice, 1551. 1st. ed., woodcut device on title-page, few marginal notes, folio, 18th. century calf, fine copy. Traylen 88-428 1978 £85

BEMBO, PIETRO Historiae Venetae Libri XII. Venice, 1551. Folio, woodcut, old bds., 1st ed., good, rare. Gilhofer 74-54 1978 sFr 1,100

BEMBO, PIETRO Prose, nelle quali si ragione della volgar lingua. Sm. folio, rare 1st ed., old vellum over boards, good copy. Schafer 19-5 1978 sFr. 1,100

BEMELMANS, LUDWIG The Castle Number Nine. New York, 1937. 1st ed., illus. in color, very fine, dust jacket. Victoria 34-60 1978 $45

BEMELMANS, LUDWIG The Golden Basket. New York, 1936. 1st ed., color, very fine, dj. Victoria 34-59 1978 $35

BEMELMANS, LUDWIG I love You. I Love You. I Love You. N.Y., (c.1944). Illus. by author, 1st Armed Services ed., No. S-3, oblong 16 mo., pictorial wrappers, very good. Houle 10-31 1978 $15

BEMELMANS, LUDWIG Madeline. New York, 1930. 1st ed., very good, colored pictorial dust jacket. Victoria 34-61 1978 $50

BEMENT, C. N. The American Poulterer's Companion. New York, 1856. Illus. on wood & stone, 8vo., orig. cloth, faded, new ed. Morrill 241-48 1978 $12.50

BEMIS, EDWARD W. Local Government in the South and the Southwest. Baltimore, 1893. Jenkins 116-90 1978 $45

BENAVENTE Y BENAVIDES, DON CRISTOVAL DE Advertencias para Reyes, Principes y Embaxadores. Madrid, 1643. 1st ed., octavo, original limp vellum, ties present, engraved pictorial t.p., full-page engraved portrait. Bennett 20-23 1978 $210

BENCHLEY, ROBERT After 1903 - What? New York, 1938. First U.S. ed., drawings, pict. cloth, very good. Bell Book 16-072 1978 £7.50

BENCHLEY, ROBERT   No Poems or Around the World Backwards and Sideways. 1932. Illus., first ed. Austin 82-127 1978 $12.50

BENEDICT, GEORGE GRENVILLE   Army Life in Virginia. Burlington, 1895. 1st ed., illus., orig. cloth, pres. copy from author, bookplt., very good. MacManus 239-868 1978 $30

BENEDICT, H. Y.   The Book of Texas. Garden City, 1916. 1st ed., frontispiece, illus., very good or better. Limestone 9-22 1978 $30

BENEDICT, H. Y.   A Source Book Relating to the History of the University of Texas: Legislative, Legal, Bibliographical, and Statistical. Austin, 1917. Later cloth. Jenkins 116-1371 1978 $35

BENEDICTUS, EDOUARD   Relais 1930. 1930. Folio, plts. in coloured pochoir, excellent condition, cloth box. Quaritch 978-11 1978 $675

BENET, STEPHEN VINCENT   The Ballad of William Sycamore 1790-1880. New York, (1923). 1st ed., thin 8vo, orig. bds., ltd. to 400 copies, very good. Americanist 103-114 1978 $22.50

BENET, STEPHEN VINCENT   The Beginning of Wisdom. New York, 1921. 1st ed., name in ink on flyleaf. Biblo 251-404 1978 $15

BENET, STEPHEN VINCENT   Burning City: New Poems. New York, 1936. Ownership inscription, fine in torn d.w. Desmarais B-80 1978 $10

BENET, STEPHEN VINCENT   Five Men and Pompey. Boston, 1915. 12mo., orig. paper-covered bds., 1st ed., 2nd state, fine. MacManus 238-616 1978 $45

BENET, STEPHEN VINCENT   James Shore's Daughter. New York, 1934. Orig. bds., upper joint cracked, 1st ed., 1 of 307 copies numbered and signed by author, very good. MacManus 238-617 1978 $37.50

BENET, STEPHEN VINCENT   John Brown's Body. (Garden City, 1928). Black cloth, 1st trade ed., fine in chipped dust jacket. Bradley 49-18 1978 $10

BENET, STEPHEN VINCENT   Johnny Pye & the Fool-Killer. Weston, The Countryman Press, (1938). Blue cloth with prtd. tan wraparound band, 1st ed., 1 of 750 signed by author & artist, rare review copy, unnumbered, publisher's date announcement slip laid in, spine sunfaded, very good in orig. acetate box. Bradley 49-19 1978 $65

BENET, STEPHEN VINCENT   Thirteen O'Clock: Stories of Several Worlds. New York, (1937). Light blue cloth, 1st ed., 1st issue, fine in worn dust jacket. Bradley 49-20 1978 $12.50

BENET, STEPHEN VINCENT   Western Star. New York, 1943. Fine in chipped d.w. Desmarais B-81 1978 $7.50

BENET, WILLIAM ROSE   Man Possessed. New York, (1927). 8vo., 1st ed., autographed. Morrill 239-303 1978 $10

BENET, WILLIAM ROSE   Merchants from Cathay. New York, 1913. Orig. cloth, 1st ed., signed inscription from author, note in Benet's hand tipped in, spine slightly soiled, otherwise very good. MacManus 238-618 1978 $85

BENEZET, ANTHONY   A Caution to Great Britain and Her Colonies... 1796. 8vo, wrappers. Edwards 1012-244 1978 £75

BENEZET, ANTHONY   A Caution to Great Britain and Her Colonies,.... Philadelphia, 1784. 8vo, disbound, 2nd London ed. Ximenes 47-21 1978 $27.50

BENEZIT, EMMANUEL   Dictionnaire Critique et Documentaire des Peintres, Sculpteurs, Dessinateurs et Graveurs de tous les Temps et de tous les Pays par un Groupe d'Ecrivains Specialistes Francais et Etrangers. Paris, 1976. Nouvelle ed., 10 vols., roy. 8vo., port., buckram. Quaritch 983-151 1978 $360

BENGOUGH, M. A.   So Near Akin. 1891. 1st. ed., 3 vols., orig. green cloth, W.H. Smith labels inside front covers, slightly rubbed. Jarndyce 16-289 1978 £32

BENHAM, GEORGE C.   A Year of Wreck. NY, 1880. Bell Wiley's copy. Broadfoot's 44-704 1978 $16.00

BENICIA: Its Resources and Advantages for Manufacture. Oakland, c. 1881. Original wr., map, 1st ed. Ginsberg 14-75 1978 $75

BENJAMIN, ASHER   The American Builders Companion or, A New System of Architecture .... Boston, 1806. Plates, 1st ed., scarce, binding worn, front cover detached. Nestler Rare 78-244 1978 $125

BENJAMIN, B. E.   Texas' Children: The Report of the Texas Child Welfare Survey. Austin, 1938. Illus., maps, charts, exhaustive. Jenkins 116-91 1978 $15

BENJAMIN, MARY A.   Autographs: a Key to Collecting. New York, 1946. Plts., cloth, 1st ed., ltd. to 3000 copies. Hayman 73-45 1978 $10

BENJAMIN, ROBERT SPIERS   I Am An American. 1941. Austin 79-58 1978 $12.50

BENJAMIN Sherwood Hedrick. Chapel Hill, 1910. New cloth. Broadfoot 50-89 1978 $8

BENNET, JAMES HENRY   Practical Treatise on Inflammation of the Uterus, Its Cervix and Appendages, and on Its Connection with Uterine Disease. Philadelphia, 1856. 4th Amer. ed., tall 8vo., orig. brown stamped cloth, gilt on backstrip, chipped and worn, signature of early owner & bkplt. of Dr. Alfred M. Hellman, light foxing, good copy. Zeitlin 245-20 1978 $65

BENNETT, AGNES MARIA   Anna. 1785. 4 vols., 12mo., contemp. tree calf, gilt backs, first ed., scarce. P. M. Hill 142-184 1978 £235

BENNETT, ARNOLD   Don Juan de Marana. A Play in Four Acts. London, 1923. Frontis. port., orig. parchment-backed bds., paper label, d.j., spine slightly worn, 1st ed., ltd. to 1,000 copies signed by author. MacManus 238-620 1978 $50

BENNETT, ARNOLD   Don Juan de Marana: A Play in Four Acts. London, 1923. 8vo, two toned boards, covers and d.w. slightly soiled, uncut, ed. limited to 1,000 signed copies, 1st ed., collector's cond. Desmarais 1-40 1978 $25

BENNETT, ARNOLD   Don Juan de Marana; a play. London, 1923. One of 1,000 numbered copies, signed by the author, half parchment, very nice, first ed. Rota 211-38 1978 £15

BENNETT, ARNOLD   Elsie and the Child. 1924. First ed., cr. 8vo., orig. cloth. Howes 194-628 1978 £6

BENNETT, ARNOLD   Hilda Lessways. 1911. First English ed., very good. Bell Book 16-073 1978 £5.50

BENNETT, ARNOLD   The Human Machine. New York, n.d. Author's ed., covers soiled, nice. Desmarais B-83 1978 $10

BENNETT, ARNOLD   The Journals of Arnold Bennett, 1896-1928. 1932-33. Plts., 3 vols., buckram, split at hinge in Vol. I, very good, slightly worn d.w., first English ed. Bell Book 17-098 1978 £17.50

BENNETT, ARNOLD   Lilian. 1922. Very good, first English ed. Bell Book 16-074 1978 £4

BENNETT, ARNOLD   The Old Wives' Tale. A Novel. London, 1908. Orig. cloth, spine edges slightly worn, covers somewhat faded, 1st ed. MacManus 238-619 1978 $150

BENNETT, ARNOLD   The Old Wives' Tale. London, 1927. Quarto, cloth, vellum backs, t.e.g., author's note especially for this ed., signed by Bennett, 1 of 500 copies, 2 vols., fine. Duschness 220-15 1978 $75

BENNETT, ARNOLD   The Old Wives' Tale. 1927. One of 500 copies, signed by author, 2 vols., 4to., quarter vellum, gilt tops, nice, first English ed. Bell Book 17-099 1978 £70

BENNETT, ARNOLD   Paris Nights. New York, 1913. First U.S. ed., plts., roy. 8vo., cloth-backed bds., very good. Bell Book 16-075 1978 £12.50

BENNETT, ARNOLD   The Reasonable Life: hints for men & women. 1907. Cloth-backed bds., t.e.g., some foxing, else very good, first English ed. Bell Book 16-076 1978 £4.50

BENNETT, ARNOLD   Riceyman Steps. 1923. Fine, first English ed. Bell Book 16-077 1978 £7.50

BENNETT, ARNOLD   Sacred and Profane Love: a play. 1919. Very good, first English ed. Bell Book 16-078 1978 £4

BENNETT, ARNOLD   Things That Interested Me. Burslem, 1906-08. Three vols., cloth, each one of 100 numbered copies, rare, covers soiled, labels worn, nice. Rota 212-3 1978 £200

BENNETT, ARNOLD   What the Public Wants: a play. 1910. Cloth gilt, t.e.g., very good, first English ed. Bell Book 16-079 1978 £4

BENNETT, CHARLES H.   Fun and Earnest: or, Rhymes with Reason. London, 1865. 1st ed., hand-colored plates, gilt covers rubbed and soiled. Victoria 34-62 1978 $15

BENNETT, CHARLES H.   Shadow and Substance. 1860. 8vo., colour plts. by Charles Bennett, orig. cloth, gilt back and edges. Quaritch 983-294 1978 $180

BENNETT, CHARLES H.   Shadow and Substance. 1860. Coloured engravings, orig. cloth, gilt, stain on front cover, 8vo. George's 635-1185 1978 £18

BENNETT, E.   Shots and Snapshots in British East Africa. London, 1914. Orig. cloth, 8vo, 2 maps in pocket, 51 plts. K Books 239-40 1978 £18

BENNETT, EDWARD TURNER The Gardens and Menagerie of the Zoological Society Delineated. Chiswick, 1830-31. 1st ed., 2 vols., 8vo., a.e.g., engrs., perforated library stamps, occas. spot or two, nicely bound in 1/2 red mor. over marbled bds. & endpapers, nearly very fine. Current 24-115 1978 $165

BENNETT, EDWARD TURNER The Gardens and Menagerie of the Zoological Society Delineated. London, 1835. Wood engrs., drwgs. by William Harvey, 2 vols., 8vo., orig. cloth, fine set. Salloch 345-20 1978 $175

BENNETT, G. W.   An Illustrated History of British Guiana... Georgetown, 1866. 1st. ed., orig. photos, some light spotting, roy. 8vo, orig. cloth. Edwards 1012-618 1978 £85

BENNETT, G. W.   An Illustrated History of British Guiana... Georgetown, 1875. 2nd. ed., 3 photos, orig. cloth, 8vo, lightly spotted in margin. Edwards 1012-619 1978 £40

BENNETT, GEOFFREY D. S. Famous Harness Horses. London, 1932. Illus. by W.A. Rouch, vol. 2, 4to. Baldwins' 51-539 1978 $22.50

BENNETT, GEORGE   Wanderings in New South Wales, Batavia, Pedir Coast, Singapore, and China. London, 1834. 2 vols., 1st ed., royal 8vo, frontis. lithographs, illus., foxed throughout, contemp. paper bds. Current 24-172 1978 $125

BENNETT, GEORGE FLETCHER Early Architecture of Delaware. Wilmington, (1932). 1st ed., 4to., illus., plts., colored frontis., orig. embossed cloth, very fine, ltd. to 1,200 copies. MacManus 239-640 1978 $100

BENNETT, GEORGE FLETCHER Early Architecture of Delaware. Wilmington, 1932. 1st. ed., sm. folio. Baldwins' 51-212 1978 $75

BENNETT, GRACE   Memoirs of ... Macclesfield, 1803. Half title, grey bds., cloth spine, good. Jarndyce 16-290 1978 £17.50

BENNETT, H. S.   English Books and Readers 1475-1640. Cambridge. n.d. 3 vol., vol. 2 2nd ed., vol. 1 and 2 ink name, d.j., fine. Ballinger 11-11 $35.00

BENNETT, J. H.   Winter and Spring on the Shores of the Mediterranean... 1875. 5th. ed., maps, illus., thick sm. 8vo, cover slightly worn, orig. cloth. Edwards 1012-43 1978 £20

BENNETT, JOHN   Master Skylark. New York, 1897. 1st ed., illus., finest copy, contents virtually mint. Victoria 34-63 1978 $85

BENNETT, JOHN C.   The History of the Saints;.... Boston, 1842. Illus., orig. gold stamped cloth, 1st ed. Ginsberg 14-640 1978 $125

BENNETT, LEONORA   Historical Sketch and Guide to the Alamo. San Antonio, 1904. New stiff wr., illus., maps. Jenkins 116-94 1978 $20

BENNETT, R. E.   Nigerian Studies or the Religious and Political System of the Yoruba. London, 1910. 8vo, orig. cloth, map, illus. K Books 239-114 1978 £12

BENNETT, SANFORD FILLMORE The Pioneer; an Idyl of the Middle-West. Chicago, Lakeside Press, 1898. Cloth. Hayman 73-277 1978 $12.50

BENNETT, WHITMAN   A Practical Guide to American 19th Century Color Plate Books. 1949. Good. Nestler Rare 78-194 1978 $38

BENN'S Sixpenny Library. London, 1927-1930. 125 vols. of 150, 8vo, orig. wrappers. Traylen 88-110 1978 £30

BENOIS, A.   Tresors d'Art en Russia. Khud. Sokrovishiha Rossii. St. Petersburgh, 1901-07. 7 vols., 4to., text mostly in Russian, plts., several in colour, some leaves of text missing, some stains in vols. 3 and 7, half calf, orig. wrs. to vols. 2 and 6 bound in, rare. Quaritch 983-152 1978 $2,150

BENSLEY, EDWARD R.   A New Dictionary of the Spanish and English Languages. Paris, 1895-96. 2 vols., roy. 8vo., binder's cloth. Howes 194-804 1978 £5

BENSON, ADOLPH B.   America of the Fifties. New York, 1924. Bell Wiley's copy. Broadfoot 46-480 1978 $12

BENSON, ADOLPH B.   Sweden and the American Revolution. New Haven, 1926. Cloth, illus. MacManus 239-548 1978 $17.50

BENSON, ADOLPH B.   Swedes in America, 1638-1938. New Haven, 1938. Illus. MacManus 239-49 1978 $25

BENSON, ARTHUR CHRISTOPHER The Book of the Queen's Doll's House. London, 1924. Ltd. ed., 2 vols., illus., very nice. Baldwins' 51-28 1978 $275

BENSON, ARTHUR CHRISTOPHER Cambridge Essays on Education. Cambridge, 1918. 8vo. George's 635-1294 1978 £5.25

BENSON, ARTHUR CHRISTOPHER The Professor. Eton, 1895. 4to, original grey-green printed wrappers (a bit worn), 1st ed., privately printed in ed. of 100 copies, presentation copy, inscribed on front wrappers, rare. Ximenes 47-22 1978 $125

BENSON, ARTHUR CHRISTOPHER Ruskin. London, 1911. 1st ed., orig. green cloth, very good or better. Limestone 9-251 1978 $13.50

BENSON, B. K.   Bayard's Courier. New York, 1902. Maps, illus., 8vo., 1st ed. Morrill 239-304 1978 $10

BENSON, E. F.   As We Were. New York, 1930. Illus., first American ed. Biblo 247-658 1978 $15

BENSON, E. F.   Bensoniana. 1912. Vignettes, 12mo., stiff wraps, very good, worn slipcase, first English ed. Bell Book 16-080 1978 £4

BENSON, E. F.   Charlotte Bronte. 1932. Plts., very good, first English ed. Bell Book 16-116 1978 £4.50

BENSON, LOUIS F.   The English Hymn. Philadelphia, 1915. Baldwins' 51-327 1978 $12.50

BENSON, MARTIN   Sermons on Various Subjects, Moral and Theological. 1794. Tree calf, rubbed, 8vo. George's 635-1028 1978 £5

BENSON, NATHANIEL A.   Dollard, a Tale in Verse. Toronto, 1933. Illus. by Walter J. Phillips, owner's name clipped from bland fly-leaf. Hood's 115-860 1978 $35

BENSON, NATHANIEL A.   Modern Canadian Poetry. Ottawa, 1930. Orig. binding. Wolfe 39-34 1978 $10

BENSON, ROBERT HUGH   Poems. London, 1915. 2nd Imp., pencil notes on rear free end sheet, very good or better. Limestone 9-23 1978 $7.50

BENSON, SALLY   Emily. 1938. First ed., frayed d.j. Austin 82-129 1978 $12.50

BENSON, STELLA   Christmas Formula, and other stories. 1932. One of 550 copies numbered & signed by author, roy. 8vo., buckram, t.e.g., near fine, orig. cellophane wrapper, torn, first English ed. Bell Book 16-081 1978 £8.50

BENSON, THOMAS W.   Fundamentals of Television. New York, (1930). 8vo., illus., orig. cloth, very good copy. Norman 5-270 1978 $75

BENSUSAN, S. L.   Morocco. London, 1904. 8vo, 74 coloured plts., dec. cloth, g. t., Black's Colour Book. K Books 239-42 1978 £5

BENT, ARTHUR C.   Life Histories of North American Gulls and Terns. 1921. Orig. wr., spine crudely taped, 8vo., plts., some colored. Book Chest 17-38 1978 $26.50

BENT, ARTHUR C.   Life Histories of North American Jays, Crows and Titmice. 1946. Plts., wrs., uncut, 8vo. Book Chest 17-40 1978 $18.50

BENT, ARTHUR C.   Life Histories of North American Marsh Birds. 1926. Orig. issue, plates, wr., orig. cloth, 8vo. Book Chest 17-39 1978 $27

BENT, CHARLES   History of Whiteside County, Illinois... Morrison, 1877. Illus., contemp. calf. MacManus 239-971 1978 $55

BENT, J. THEODORE   The Ruined Cities of Mashonaland, Being a Record of Excavation and Exploration in 1891. London, 1895. Cr. 8vo, new ed., illus., orig. cloth, bit shabby. K Books 239-43 1978 £10

BENTHEM, HENRICH LUDOLFF   Engelanddischer Kirchund Schulen-Staat. Luneburg, 1694. 1st. ed., 8vo, frontispiece, plts., half cloth, paper on lst. gathering slightly defective & repaired, slight marginal worming, unused good copy. Hannas 54-183 1978 £25

BENTIVOGLIO, CARDINAL GUIDO   Della Gverra di Fiandra. Venetia, 1637. 2 vols. in 1, 4to., calf, spine gilt, portrait plt. King 7-16 1978 £20

BENTIVOGLIO, ERCOLE   Les Fantomes et Le Jalous Comedies Italiennes Traduites en Francois(par Jean Fabre). Oxford, 1731. Bds., parchment back, no paper on bds., Italian & French text. Eaton 45-47 1978 £10

BENTLEY, EDMUND CLERIHEW   Biography for Beginners. (1905). Drwgs. by G. K. Chesterton, sm. 4to., orig. pict. wrs., covers somewhat dampstained & creased at corners, some foxing, else good, scarce, lst Eng. ed. Bell Book 17-100 1978 £25

BENTLEY, EDMUND CLERIHEW   Elephant's Work. New York, 1950. First Amer. ed., d.w. Biblo BL781-925 1978 $9.50

BENTLEY, EDMUND CLERIHEW   More Biography. London, (1929). Sm. 4to., first ed., covers and edges rubbed, illus. Biblo 251-405 1978 $22.50

BENTLEY, EDMUND CLERIHEW   Those Days. 1940. First ed., portraits, 8vo., orig. cloth. Howes 194-629 1978 £5

BENTLEY, EDWARD CLERIHEW   Trent's Last Case. (1913). Coloured frontis., hinges sprung, very good, first English ed. Bell Book 17-217 1978 £15

BENTLEY, H. L.   A Report Upon the Grasses and Forage Plants of Central Texas. Washington, D. C., 1898. Wrs., illus., lst ed., very good copy from the Allred Collection, rare. Dykes 34-245 1978 $25

BENTLEY, W. HOLMAN   Life on the Congo. London, 1887. Cr. 8vo, illus., dec. cloth, little thumbed, lacks lst. free endpaper. K Books 239-44 1978 £8

BENTLEY, W. HOLMAN   Pioneering On the Congo. 1900. lst. ed., 2 vols., 8vo, coloured map, plts. & illus., orig. blue cloth, gilt, t.e.g, lib. labels removed from spines, indelible lib. stamp in margins, trifle shaken in binding. Deighton 5-7 1978 £32

BENTON Collection of the Book of Common Prayer & Books Connected with Its Origin & Growth. Boston, 1914. 2nd ed., t.e.g, pres. copy inscr'd in red crayon, bds., cloth spine, binding rubbed. Battery Park 1-315 1978 $75

BENTON, C.   A Statistical View of the Number of Sheep in the Northeast. Cambridge, 1837. Sheep & marbled bds., lst ed., outer hinges briken, new end sheets, very good, 4-point slipcase, rare. Dykes 34-266 1978 $40

BENTON, CHARLES E.   Four Days on the Webutuck River. Amenia, 1925. Limited to 200 copies, introduction by Sinclair Lewis, wr. Nestler Rare 78-97 1978 $24

BENTON, J. A   California as She Was, As She Is, As She Is To Be. Sacramento, 1850. Original printed wr. Ginsberg 14-76 1978 $2,250

BENTON, JESSE JAMES   Cow By The Tail. Boston, 1943. Illus., original cloth, lst ed. Ginsberg 14-47 1978 $25

BENTON, JOEL   Life of Hon. Phineas T. Barnum. N.P., (1891). Elegantly illus., clean, orig. binding. Hayman 71-43 1978 $7.50

BENTON, JOSIAH HENRY   Warning Out in New England, 1656-1817. Boston, 1911. 8vo., orig. bds., cloth back, fine, lst ed. Morrill 241-49 1978 $10

BENTON, NATHANIEL S.   A History of Herkimer County. Albany, 1856. Maps, plts., good, slight wear on cloth binding. Butterfield 21-204 1978 $35

BENTON, THOMAS HART   Speech of Hon...., of Missouri, on the Loan Bill. Delivered in the Senate...July 19, 1841. N.P., n.d. Disbound. Hayman 72-43 1978 $7.50

BENTON, THOMAS HART   Texas Annexation Bill. Washington, 1844. Wr. Jenkins 116-95 1978 $25

BENTON, THOMAS HART   Thirty Years View; or, a History of the Working of the American Government...from 1820 to 1850. New York, 1854. 2 vols., rebound. MacManus 239-50 1978 $25

BENZONI, GIROLAMO   Novae Novi Orbis Historiae... (Geneva), 1857. lst. Latin ed., old calf, light waterstain affecting text, name on title, 8vo. Edwards 1012-620 1978 £175

BERARD, VICTOR   Les Pheniciens et l'Odyssee. 1902-03. 2 vols., 4to., illus., half bds., corner of one spine torn. Allen 234-446 1978 $75

BERCOVICI, KONRAD   Around the World in New York. 1924. Illus. Austin 79-60 1978 $12.50

BERCOVICI, KONRAD   It's the Gypsy in me. 1941. Austin 79-61 1978 $10

BERCOVICI, KONRAD   On New Shores. 1925. Illus., good. Austin 79-62 1978 $10

BERCOVICI, KONRAD   The Story of the Gypsies. 1928. Illus. in color. Austin 79-59 1978 $12.50

BERDMORE, THOMAS   A Treatise on the Disorders and Deformities of the Teeth and Gums...the Whole Illustrated with Cases and Experiments. London, 1768. 8vo., mod. full-calf, gilt back, fine copy, lib. stamps on t.p., rare lst ed. Gilhofer 74-82 1978 sFr 3,900

BERDNIKOV, A.   Elements of Political Education. Chicago, 1926. Austin 80-431 1978 $12.50

BERENBERG, DAVID P.   The Kid. New York, 1931. lst ed. Biblo 251-406 1978 $8.50

BERENGER, RICHARD   The History and Art of Horsemanship. London, 1771. Copperplts., 2 vols., sq. 4to., full polished calf, lst ed. Argosy Special-11 1978 $350

BERENS, E.   Village Sermons. 1821. Bds., roughly rebacked, fcap. 8vo. George's 635-1029 1978 £6

BERENSON, BERNARD   The Drawings of the Florentine Painters. Chicago, 1938. Amplified ed., illus., 3 vols., folio, orig. qtr. parchment. George's 635-3 1978 £55

BERENSON, BERNARD   The Study and Criticism of Italian Art.   1901-16.
Illus., 3 vols., spine of vol. 2 faded, 8vo.   George's 635-6 1978 £15

BERENSON, BERNHARD   The Study and Criticism of Italian Art.   London,
1931. Illus.   Biblo 251-152 1978 $27.50

BERENSON, BERNARD   Venetian Painting in America.   1916. Illus.,
8vo. George's 635-7 1978 £8.50

BERESFORD, CHARLES WILLIAM DE LA POER   Nelson and His Times.   London,
n.d. c. 1910. 4to., orig. cloth, illus., good. Sexton 7-165 1978 £11

BERESFORD, CHARLES WILLIAM DE LA POER   Refutation of Col. Napier's
Justification of His 3rd Volume.   1834. Engr. map, orig. bds. George's 635-
846 1978 £6.50

BERESFORD, JOHN DAVYS   The Early History of Jacob Stahl.   1911. Spine
little faded & rubbed at joints, else good, first English ed. Bell Book 17-101 1978
£5

BERESFORD, WILLIAM CARR   Colleccao Das Ordens do Dia do...   Goimbra,
1810. Sm. 4to, orig. cloth. Edwards 1012-621 1978 £30

BERESFORD, WILLIAM CARR   Further Strictures on those Parts of Col. Napier's
History of the Peninsular War....   1832. 1st ed., lg. folding map, 8vo., wrapper, nice. Fenning 32-22 1978 £16

BERESFORD, WILLIAM CARR   Regulamento Para a Disciplina e Exercico dos
Regimentos de Cavallaria do Exercito de S.A.R. O Principe Regente do Reino
Unido de Portugal...Lisboa, 1816. Sm. 8vo, orig. cloth, tables. Edwards 1012-
622 1978 £40

BERESFORD, WILLIAM CARR   Strictures on Certain Passages of Lieut.-Col.
Napier's History of the Peninsular War....   1831. 1st ed., 8vo., wrapper, nice.
Fenning 32-23 1978 £15

BERESTEYN, E. H. VAN   Genealogisch Repertorium.   's-Gravenhage,
1948. 8vo., cloth. Van der Peet H-64-249 1978 Dfl 45

BERGAMO, JACOBO FILIPPO
Please turn to
FORESTI DA BERGAMO, JACOBO FILIPPO

BERGEN, TEUNIS G.   Register...of the Early Settlers of Kings County,
Long Island, N.Y....   New York, 1881. MacManus 239-1092 1978 $40

BERGENROTH, A. VON   Wanderings in Venice.   Zurich, 1900. Ed. de
luxe, illus., folio, orig. pict. bds. George's 635-1186 1978 £5.25

BERGER, OSCAR   A La Carte. The Gourmet's Phantasmagoria in
Fifty Cartoons.   New York, (1948). 1st ed., d.w. frayed. Biblo 251-158 1978
$9.50

BERGES, MAX L.   Cold Pogrom.   1939. Austin 79-63 1978
$10

BERGEY, DAVID H.   Genealogy of the Bergey Family....   New York,
1925. lg. thick 8vo, illus., orig. binding. Americanist 101-57 1978 $25

BERGMAN, STEN   In Korean Wilds and Villages.   London, (1938).
Boards, illus., folding map, cloth back, covers worn and stained. Dawson's
449-208 1978 $35

BERGMAN, TORBERN   Outlines of Mineralogy.   Birmingham, 1783.
8vo., half antique calf, some foxing, but fine copy, inscr'd by Withering, 1st
ed. in English with additional notes. Norman 5-22 1978 $450

BERGMANN, T.   Twee Rijnlandsche Novellen.   Amsterdam, n.d.
(1935). Fine green calf, sm. gilt tooled borders on both sides, very attractive
binding. Van der Peet H-64-368 1978 Dfl 125

BERGOMENSIS, JACOBUS PHILIPPUS
Please turn to
FORESTI DA BERGAMO, JACOBO FILIPPO

BERGSON, HENRI   Duree et Simultaneite a Propos de la Theorie
d'Einstein.   Paris, 1922. 8vo., orig. printed wrs., 1st ed. Gilhofer 74-109
1978 sFr 250

BERINGTON, JOSEPH   A Literary History of the Middle Ages...   1814.
4to, errata slip, lst. few leaves foxed, orig. bds., joints worn. Eaton 45-48
1978 £30

BERJEAU, J. PH.   The Book-Worm.   London, 1866-69. Illus.,
roy. 8vo., orig. wrappers, rather soiled and frayed, scarce. K Books 244-43
1978 £20

BERKELBACH VAN DER SPRENKEL, J. W.   Regesten Van Oorkonden Betreffende
de Bisschoppen Van Utrecht uit de Jaren, 1301-1340.   1937. Sewn. Allen 234-
1111 1978 $7.50

BERKELEY, ANTHONY   The Second Shot.   Garden City, (1931). Cloth,
1st Amer. ed., slightly worn d.j. Hayman 72-181 1978 $7.50

BERKELEY, AUGUST   A Modern Quixote, or My Wife's Fool of a
Husband. Cleveland, 1885. Cloth. Hayman 73-172 1978 $7.50

BERKELEY, CARA   Some Roman Monuments in the Light of History.
1927. 2 vols. Allen 234-824 1978 $12.50

BERKELEY, G. F. -H.   Italy in the Making, 1815-48.   Cambridge, 1932-
40. Frontis. maps, 3 vols., 8vo. George's 635-540 1978 £12.50

BERKELEY, GEORGE   Historical Applications and Occasional Meditations upon Several Subjects.   1670. Sm. 8vo., contemp. red mor. gilt, fine.
P.M. Hill 142-1 1978 £60

BERKELEY, GEORGE   A Miscellany, Containing Several Tracts on
Various Subjects.   1752. 1st. ed., 8vo, contemp. mottled calf. Hannas 54-16
1978 £85

BERKELEY, GEORGE   Siris; A Chain of Philosophical Reflexions and
Inquiries concerning Tar Water.   Dublin, London, 1744. Second ed., 8vo., 19th-
century half calf. P. M. Hill 142-31 1978 £36

BERKELEY, GEORGE   A Treatise Concerning the Principles of Human
Knowledge.   1734. 1st. collected ed., 8vo, modern calf, old style, one pg.
stained, margins browned. Hannas 54-17 1978 £45

BERKELEY, GRANTLEY F.   My Life and Recollections.   1865. Portraits,
foxed, 4 vols., half calf, spines gilt, rubbed, 8vo. George's 635-1231 1978
£17.50

BERKELEY. ORDINANCES   The Ordinances of the Town of Berkeley, Ala-
meda County, California.   Berkeley, 1882. Original printed wr., 1st ed.
Ginsberg 14-162 1978 $90

BERKENHOUT, JOHN   First Lines of the Theory and Practice of Philosophical Chemistry.   London, 1788. Copperplts., 8vo., contemp. calf, only ed.,
fine copy. Offenbacher 30-11 1978 $250

BERKS COUNTY HISTORICAL SOCIETY   Transactions of the...   1904. Vol. 1,
illus. MacManus 239-1372 1978 $27.50

BERKS COUNTY HISTORICAL SOCIETY   Transactions.   Reading, 1910. Vol.
2, illus. MacManus 239-1373 1978 $22.50

BERKS COUNTY HISTORICAL SOCIETY   Transactions of the...   Reading, 1923.
Vol. 3, illus. MacManus 239-1374 1978 $15

BERLANDIER, JEAN LUIS   Diario De Viage De La Comision De Limites Que
Puso El Govierno De La Republica,....   Mexico, 1850. Original morocco.
Jenkins 116-96 1978 $325

BERLE, ADOLPH A.   Christianity and the Social Rage.   1914.
Austin 79-64 1978 $12.50

BERLYN, MRS. ALFRED   Sunrise-Land.   London, 1894. Illus. in b/w
by Arthur Rackham, sm. 8vo, picture cloth, usually nice copy. Traylen 88-406
1978 £40

BERNANOSE, M.   Les Arts decoratifs au Tonkin. Paris, 1922.
Large 8vo, illus. on plts, orig. covers. Van der Peet 127-11 1978 Dfl 35

BERNARD DE CLAIRVAUX, SAINT   Select Treatises. Cambridge, 1926. 8vo.
Upcroft 12-35 1978 £8.50

BERNARD, AUGUSTE   Geogroy Troy. 1909. Quarto, boards stamped
with design after Troy, gilt, 1 of 370 copies designed by Bruce Rogers, fine.
Duschnes 220-269 1978 $275

BERNARD, CLAUDE   Lecons de Pathologic Experimentale. Paris,
1857. Rittenhouse 49-67 1976 $165

BERNARD, CLAUDE   Lecons de Physiologie Experimentale applique a
la Medecine. Paris, 1855-56. 2 vols., top of spine cloth on vol. 1 missing, not
affecting title. Rittenhouse 49-69 1976 $150

BERNARD, CLAUDE   Lecons sur la Physiologie et la Pathologie du
Systeme nerveux. Paris, 1858. 2 vols., 8 vo., wood engraved illus., 1st ed.,
fine copy, contemp. black half-leather, gilt back. Schafer 19-45 1978
sFr. 1,200

BERNARD, CLAUDE   Lecons sur la Physiologie et la Pathologie du
Systeme Nerveux. Paris, 1858. 8vo., 2 vols., illus., half-calf, 1st ed. Gilhofer 74-83 1978 sFr 900

BERNARD, CLAUDE   Lecons sur les Effets des Substances Toxiques et
Medicamenteuses. Paris, 1857. First ed. Rittenhouse 49-68 1976 $125

BERNARD, CLAUDE   Nouvelles Recherches Experimentales sur les Phenomenes Glycogeniques du Foie. Paris, 1858. 8vo., complete vol., plts., bound
in contemp. half brown mor., gilt on spine, marbled bds., very good copy, 1st ed.,
rare. Zeitlin 245-21 1978 $350

BERNARD, CLAUDE   La Science Experimentale. Paris, 1890. Third
ed. Rittenhouse 49-70 1976 $15

BERNARD, DAVID   Light on Masonry. Utica, 1829. Plts., 12mo.,
contemp. calf, 1st ed. Morrill 239-305 1978 $30

BERNARD, DAVID   Light on Masonry: a Collection of all the Most
Important Documents. Utica, 1829. 2 engr. frontis's by Vistus Balch, superior
copy, old lea., rubbed but sound. Butterfield 21-55 1978 $100

BERNARD, JOHN   Retrospections of America 1797-1811. New
York, 1887. Illus., orig. cloth. MacManus 239-51 1978 $25

BERNARD, M.   The Praise of Hell. (c. 1750). Engraved frontis,
foxed, title soiled, 12mo., half calf, spine defective. George's 635-1030 1978
£8.50

BERNARD, M.   The Praise of Hell. (1765). One page of contents defective, one torn, sm. 8vo., new half calf. George's 635-1187 1978
£10.50

BERNARDONI, GIOVANNI
Please turn to
FRANCESCO D'ASSISI, SAINT

BERNARDUS DE GORDONIO   De Conservatione Vitae Humanae. Leipzig,
1570. Sm. 8vo., 1/2 vellum. Salloch 345-21 1978 $30

BERNATZIK, H. A.   Gari-Gari. London, 1936. 8vo, orig. cloth,
folding map, frontis, 116 illus. from photos. K Books 239-45 1978 £6

BERNATZIK, H. A.   De geesten van de gele bladeren. (Burma),
1942. Halfcloth, plts, maps, 8vo. Van der Peet 127-13 1978 Dfl 25

BERNAYS, ALBERT J.   Household Chemistry... 1853. Sm. 8vo,
wrapper, nice copy. Fenning 32-24 1978 £10.50

BERNDORFF, H. R.   Espionage! New York, 1930. Biblo 251-283
1978 $9.50

BERNERI, GIUSEPPE   Il Meo Patacca overo Roma in Feste nei trionfi
di Vienna. Roma, 1695. 8vo., diced calf, gilt, first ed., printed in roman
throughout. King 7-17 1978 £85

BERNERS, GERALD HUGH, BARON   Far from the Madding War. 1941. Plts.
by author, very good, worn d.w., first English ed. Bell Book 17-102 1978
£7.50

BERNERS, GERALD HUGH, BARON   The Romance of a Nose. 1941. Frontis.
by author, very good, first English ed. Bell Book 17-103 1978 £6

BERNERS, JULIANA   The Boke of Saint Albans. London, 1901. Large
octavo, cream paper boards foxed, parchment spine, ink lettering on spine faded,
spine chipped, pages uncut, endpapers foxed. Totteridge 29-12 1978 $75

BERNHARDT, F. A.   Questions relating to Fires in General, the
Draught of Smoke, and the Saving of Fuel. London, 1835. 8vo, disbound, 1st
ed., scarce. Ximenes 47-25 1978 $35

BERNHEIM, H.   Suggestive Therapeutics. A Treatise on the Nature and Uses of Hypnotism. New York, 1889. Translated from the second and
revised French ed. Rittenhouse 49-71 1976 $17.50

BERNHEIMER, CHARLES S.   Half a Century in Community Service. Association Press, 1948. Austin 79-65 1978 $20

BERNIER, FRANCOIS   Abrege de la Philosophie de Gassendi. Lyon,
1678. 12mo., contemp. calf, 1st complete ed. Offenbacher 30-55 1978 $350

BERNIER, FRANCOIS   Voyages. Amsterdam, 1724. Illus., engr.
frontis., fldg. engr. maps, fldg. plts., 2 vols., 12mo., contemp. vellum.
Argosy Special-12 1978 $250

BERNOULLI, DANIEL   Hydrodynamica, Sive De Viribus et Motibus
Fluidorum Commentarii. Argentorati, 1738. Copperplts., 1st ed., very good
copy. Offenbacher 30-12 1978 $500

BERNOULLI, JAKOB   Ars Conjectandi, Opus Posthumum. Basel,
1713. 4to., fldg. tables, fldg. plt., contemp. mottled calf, gilt, head & foot of
spine repaired, fine copy in half mor. dropbox, 1st ed. Norman 5-23 1978
$2,500

BERNSTEIN, ABRAHAM   Fifteen and Five. 1932. Austin 79-66 1978
$10

BERNSTEIN, ALINE   An Actor's Daughter. New York, 1941. 1st
ed., d.w. frayed. Biblo 251-408 1978 $22.50

BERNSTEIN, ALINE   An Actor's Daughter. 1941. First ed., d.j.,
very good. Austin 82-1127 1978 $17.50

BERNSTEIN, ALINE   Three Blue Suits. New York, 1933. 8vo, linen,
paper labels, frontis. by John P. Heins, 1 of 600 copies signed by author, 1st and
only ed., fine. Duschness 220-16 1978 $75

BERNSTEIN, HERMAN   The History of a Lie. New York, (1921).
Author's signed pres. Biblo 251-684 1978 $20

BEROALDO, FILIPPO   Symbola Pythagorae... Paris, 1510. Woodcut,
4to., wrs. Salloch 348-12 1978 $125

BERQUIN, ARNAUD   The Children's Friend. Boston, (1793?). 12mo,
calf, rebacked with original leather spine laid-down, very good. Victoria 34-65
1978 $115

BERQUIN, ARNAUD   The Children's Friend and Youth's Monitor.
Philadelphia, New York, 1796. 12mo, calf, very good. Victoria 34-64 1978
$110

BERQUIN, ARNAUD   The Looking-Glass for the Mind;.... London,
1796. Cuts by John Bewick, 19th century full leather, decor. in gilt, raised bands,
gilt dentelles, marbled endpapers, superior binding, fine. Victoria 34-576 1978
$200

BERQUIN, ARNAUD   The Looking-Glass for the Mind; or, Intellectual
Mirror. London, 1806. 10th ed., 12mo, contemp. calf, corners worn, rebacked,
bookplt., cuts by John Bewick. Totteridge 29-13 1978 $60

BERQUIN, ARNAUD   Select Stories for the Instruction and Entertainment
of Children. London, 1791. 2nd ed., sm. 8vo, copperplates by M. Brown, expertly rebacked, fine. Victoria 34-66 1978 $40

BERRIMAN, M. W.   The Militiaman's Manual. New York, 1864.
Fourth ed., sm. 8vo., orig. cloth, plts. F. Edwards 1013-589 1978 £35

BERRUYER, I. J.   Histoire du Peuple de Dieu, Depuis Son Origine Jusqu'a la Naissance du Messie. Paris, 1742. 10 vols., sm. 8vo., full calf, gilt tooled spines, fldg. engr. maps, genealogical tables, bindings shaved, spines occas. damaged. Van der Peet H-64-253 1978 Dfl 450

BERRY, MARY   Extracts of the Journals and Correspondence of Miss Berry from the year 1783 to 1852. London, 1865. 3 vols., contemp. half calf, marbled boards, spines gilt, hinges weak, illus., 1st ed. Bennett 7-68 1978 $75

BERRY, MARY   Extracts of the Journals and Correspondence of Miss Berry from the Year 1783 to 1852. 1865. First ed., frontispieces, 3 vols., rebound in buckram, 8vo. Howes 194-631 1978 £18

BERRY, MARY   Some Account of the Life of Rachel Wriothesley Lady Russell. 1820. Contemp. half calf, some foxing, 8vo. Howes 194-445 1978 £12.50

BERRY, ROSE V. S.   The Dream City. Its Art in Story and Symbolism. (San Francisco, 1915). Cloth, fine. Hayman 72-44 1978 $10

BERRY, W.   Genealogica Antiqua. 1816. Sm. folio, bds., worn. George's 635-541 1978 £6

BERTELIUS, JOANNES   Respublica Lytzenbyrgensis, Hannoniae, et Namvrcensis. Amstelodami, 1635. 16mo., canvas cloth. King 7-266 1978 £20

BERTEREAU, MARTINE DE   La Restitution de Pluton. Paris, 1640. 8vo., contemp. calf, 1st ed., very rare, fine. Offenbacher 30-13 1978 $400

BERTHELOT, A.   l'Asie Ancienne. Paris, 1930. Maps, 8vo, orig. covers. Van der Peet 127-277 1978 Dfl 45

BERTHELOT, PIERRE EUGENE MARCELLIN   Chimie Organique fondee sur la Synthese. Paris, 1860. 8vo., 2 vols., old half sheep, rubbed, first ed. Gurney 75-9 1978 £75

BERTHELOT, PIERRE EUGENE MARCELLIN   Essai de Mecanique Chimique Fondee Sur la Thermochimie. Pairs, 1879. 2 vols., 8vo., port., contemp. half calf, 1st ed. Gilhofer 74-110 1978 sFr 500

BERTHOLD, VICTOR M.   The Pioneer Steamer California, 1848-1849. Boston, 1932. Illus., original cloth, slipcase, 1st ed, limited to 550 copies. Ginsberg 14-77 1978 $60

BERTHOLD, VICTOR M.   The Pioneer Steamer California 1848-1849. Boston, 1932. Illus., 1st ed., ltd. to 550 copies, very fine untrimmed copy, box. MacManus 239-1735 1978 $35

BERTOLDO Bertoldino e Cacaseno. Venezia, 1802. 2 vols. in 1, sm. 8vo., marbled bds., calf spine, very good. King 7-139 1978 £20

BERTHOLLET, CLAUDE LOUIS   Elements de l'art de la Teinture. Paris, 1791. 2 vols., 8vo., contemp. tree calf, gilt red lea. labels, fine set in handsome binding, 1st ed. Norman 5-24 1978 $375

BERTHOLLET, CLAUDE LOUIS   Elements of the Art of Dying. Edinburgh, 1792. 8vo., modern marbled bds., some foxing & soiling, very good copy, 2nd ed. in English. Norman 5-25 1978 $125

BERTHOLLET, CLAUDE LOUIS   Researches into the Laws of Chemical Affinity. Baltimore, 1809. 12mo., contemp. calf, gilt, rubbed, browning, poor quality paper, but good copy, 2nd Amer. ed. Norman 5-26 1978 $85

BERTRAM, C.   Artic and Antarctic: The Technique of Polar Travel. 1939. 1st. ed., end-paper maps, illus., orig. cloth, 8vo. Edwards 1012-564 1978 £10

BERTRAM, JAMES M.   First Act in China: The Story of the Sian Mutiny. New York, 1938. Cloth, some staining and soiling. Dawson's 449-8 1978 $15

BERTRAND, ALEXANDRE   Archeologie Celtique et Gauloise. Paris, 1889. 2nd ed., rev'd., illus., 3/4 leather, rubbed. Biblo BL781-325 1978 $32.50

BERTRAND, L. A.   Memoires D'Un Mormon. Paris, 1862. Orig. wrps., 1st ed. Ginsberg 16-919 1978 $100.00

BERTUCH, F. J.   Tafelin Der Allgemeinen Naturgeschichte Nach Ihren Drey Reichen. Weimar 1801-1807. Handcolored plts., orig. prtd. wrs. Salloch 345-22 1978 $450

BERZELIUS, JONS JACOB   Autobiographical Notes. Baltimore, 1934. 8vo., portr., cloth, fine copy, 1st ed. in English. Norman 5-29 1978 $30

BERZELIUS, JONS JACOB   Forelasningar i Djurkemien. Stockholm, 1806-08. 2 vols. in 1, 8vo., old half mor., gilt, one corner chipped, some foxing, very good copy, 1st ed. Norman 5-27 1978 $375

BERZELIUS, JONS JACOB   The Use of the Blowpipe in Chemical Analysis, and in the Examination of Minerals. London, 1822. Trans. from French, notes & additions by translator, 8vo., plts., lg. fldg. chart, contemp. cloth-backed bds., uncut, contemp. signature, fine copy, 1st ed. in English. Norman 5-28 1978 $375

BESANT, WALTER   Fifty Years Ago. London, 1888. 8vo, orig. cloth, plts., woodcuts, good. Sexton 7-132 1978 £6

BESCHRYVINGE van 't Staduis van Amsterdam. Amsterdam, 1770. Sm. 8vo., orig. bds., fldg. engr. plts., rare, binding shaved, joints shaved but firm. Van der Peet H-64-254 1978 Dfl 150

BESENVAL, PIERRE J. D. DE, BARON   Memoires de.... Paris, 1805-06. 1st. ed., portrait, 8vo, contemp. half red calf, gilt, nice set. Fenning 32-25 1978 £24.50

BESOLDUS, CHRISTOPHERUS   Tractatvs Posthvmvs Jvris Pvbblici. 1659. 12mo., cloth. King 7-267 1978 £25

BESSE, S. B.   U.S. Ironclad Monitor. Newport News, Va., 1936. Illus., charts., Bell Wiley's Copy. Broadfoot's 44-31 1978 $7.00

BESSON, MAURICE   The Scourge of the Indies. 1929. Coloured reproduction plts., illus., 4to., orig. cloth. F. Edwards 1013-19 1978 £40

BEST, R. D.   Brass Chandelier, a Biography of R. H. Best by his Son. 1940. Illus., 8vo. George's 635-284 1978 £5

THE BEST from Yank the Army Weekly. 1945. 255p. Austin 90-385 1978 $12.50

BEST Ghost Stories. London, 1945. First ed., orig. binding, very nice, d.w. Rota 211-6 1978 £5

THE BEST Terrible Tales From The German. London, n.d. Uncut, t.e.g., faded, stained orig. cloth, interior very good, scarce. Limestone 9-24 1978 $20

BETANCES, L. M.   La Granulation Azurophile. Paris, 1918. Tall 8vo., plts., illus., half cloth, orig. prtd. wrs. bound in, author's pres. inscr., very good copy. Zeitlin 245-22 1978 $75

BETHE, E.   Die Griechische Dichtung. Potsdam, 1929. 4to., cloth, plts., some in color, text illus. Van der Peet H-64-463 1978 Dfl 65

BETHLEN, JEAN DE   Rerum Transylvanicarum. (Amsterdam?), 1664. Sm. 12mo., cloth, good, first ed. King 7-268 1978 £30

BETHUNE, GEORGE W.   Memoirs of Mrs. Joanna Bethune. New York, 1863. Clean, sl. wear at top of spine, orig. binding. Hayman 71-44 1978 $10

BETHUNE, JOHN   Essays and Dissertations on Various Subjects, Relating to Human Life and Happiness. Edinburgh, 1771. 1st. Edinburgh ed., 2 vols., 12mo, probably lacking half-titles, contemp. calf. Hannas 54-18 1978 £20

BETHUNE, MAXIMILIEN DE, DUC DE SULLY
Please turn to
SULLY, MAXIMILIEN DE BETHUNE, DUC DE

BETHUNE, N.   Memoir of the Rt. Rev. John Strachan, first Bishop of Toronto. Toronto, 1879. Hood's 115-240 1978 $35

BETJEMAN, JOHN   Continual Dew. 1937. 1st. ed., illus. by Osbert Lancaster, sm. 8vo, orig. gilt-embossed cloth, d.w., signed by author. Sawyer 299-112 1978 £57

BETJEMAN, JOHN   Ghastly Good Taste. London, 1933. Fldg. illus., 1st ed. Biblo 251-410 1978 $32.50

BETJEMAN, JOHN   Ghastly Good Taste. 1933. First ed., illus., orig. printed bds., cloth-backed, sm. 8vo., very good. Howes 194-632 1978 £48

BETJEMAN, JOHN   Ghastly Good Taste. 1933. Plt., cloth-backed bds., bds. faded & little rubbed, very good, first English ed. Bell Book 17-105 1978 £12.50

BETJEMAN, JOHN   Metro-Land. 1977. Coloured lithographs, no. 29 of 220 copies signed by author, sm. oblong 4to., new in slip case, first English ed. Bell Book 16-086 1978 £60

BETJEMAN, JOHN   Mount Zion. The James Press, (1931). Very good, first English ed. Bell Book 16-087 1978 £110

BETJEMAN, JOHN   Murray's Buckinghamshire: Architectural Guide. 1948. Map, first ed., roy. 8vo., d.w., orig. cloth. Howes 194-633 1978 £6

BETJEMAN, JOHN   Old Lights for new Chancels. 1940. Sm. 8vo., 1st ed., frontis., orig. wrs., slightly faded. Quaritch 979-27 1978 £40

BETTI, GIOVANNI BATTISTA   A' Dilettanti delle Bell'Arti. Florence, 1785. Oblong folio, half vellum, second ed. Schumann 511-5 1978 sFr 1,750

BETTS, E.   Thomas Jefferson's Garden Book 1766-1824,.... Pennsylvania, 1944. Plates, 8vo, orig. cloth. Book Chest 17-42 1978 $30

BEUGHEM, CORNELIUS   Bibliographia Mathematica et Artificiosa Novissima. Amsterdam, 1688. Thick 12mo., full dark brown calf with red label, fine copy. Salloch 345-23 1978 $400

BEURLING, G. F.   Malta Spitfire; the Story of a Fighter Pilot. Toronto, 1943. Hood 116-108 1978 $20

BEVEN, THOMAS   Principles of the Law of Negligence. London, 1889. 1st ed., thick lg. 8vo., orig. cloth. Morrill 241-51 1978 $10

BEVER, JOSEPH   The Christian Songster: A Collection of Hymns and Spiritual Songs.... Dayton, 1858. Leather, light marginal dampstain on 1st. few leaves. Hayman 71-513 1978 $12.50

BEVER, SAMUEL   The Cadet. A Military Treatise. By an Officer. London, 1756. 8vo, contemporary calf, gilt, spine gilt, 1st ed., folding plate, fine copy. Ximenes 47-26 1978 $175

BEVERIDGE, ALBERT JEREMIAH   Abraham Lincoln, 1809-1858. Boston, 1928. 1st ed., 2 vols., illus. Biblo 248-59 1978 $32.50

BEVERIDGE, ALBERT JEREMIAH   Abraham Lincoln...1809-1858. Boston, 1928. First ed., 2 vols., illus. Biblo 247-81 1978 $22.50

BEVERIDGE, ALBERT JEREMIAH   Abraham Lincoln. Cambridge, 1928. 2 vols., Bell Wiley's copy. Broadfoot's 44-34 1978 $15

BEVERIDGE, ALBERT JEREMIAH   The Life of John Marshall. Boston, (1916). 4 vols., illus. MacManus 239-792 1978 $25

BEVERIDGE, ALBERT JEREMIAH   The Life of John Marshall. Boston, (1919). Cloth, 4 vols., standard library ed., tiny waterspot on 1 vol., but good solid set. Hayman 73-47 1978 $15

BEVERIDGE, ALBERT JEREMIAH   The Life of John Marshall. Boston, 1929. 4 vols. in 2. Biblo BL781-846 1978 $16.50

BEVERIDGE, WILLIAM HENRY BEVERIDGE, BARON - 1879   Voluntary Action. A Report on Methods of Social Advance. London, (1949). Biblo BL781-803 1978 $9

BEVEROVICIUS, JOHANNES   Epistolica Quaestio De Vitae Termino, Fatali An Mobili. Leyden, 1636. 4to., calf, rebacked, 2nd ed. of the 1st part & 1st ed. of the 2nd part. Salloch 345-24 1978 $125

BEWICK, THOMAS   Emblems of Mortality (The Dance of Death). London, 1789. 1st ed., cuts by both Bewicks, full contemporary tree calf, one signature a bit pulled, covers minimally rubbed, almost fine. Victoria 34-70 1978 $350

BEWICK, THOMAS   A General History of Quadrupeds. Newcastle, 1820. Seventh ed., old style half calf, 8vo. K Books 244-32 1978 £60

BEWICK, THOMAS   A General History of Quadrupeds. Newcastle, 1824. Eighth ed., pleasant copy, calf gilt, 8vo. K Books 244-33 1978 £60

BEWICK, THOMAS   A History of British Birds. Newcastle, 1821. 2 vols., 8vo., contemp. diced calf gilt, joints repaired, royal ed. Quaritch 983-153 1978 $420

BEWICK, THOMAS   A History of British Birds. Newcastle, 1832. 2 vols., 8vo., hundreds of fine wood engrs., nicely bound in 1/2 calf, full gilt decor. spines, marbled bds., endpapers, spines slightly faded, interior fine & better. Current 24-249 1978 $215

BEWICK, THOMAS   A Natural History of British Quadrupeds... Alnwick, 1809. Sm. 8vo., frontis., orig. green printed wrs. Quaritch 983-154 1978 $130

BEWICK, THOMAS   A Natural History of Fishes. Alnwick, 1809. Sm. 8vo., engravings on wood, orig. printed wrs. Quaritch 983-155 1978 $130

BEWICK, THOMAS   A New Lottery Book of Birds and Beasts for Children to learn their Letters by. Newcastle, 1771. 12mo., engrs., new floral gilt Dutch paper bds., very scarce. Quaritch 979-28 1978 $750

BEWICK, THOMAS   Works. Newcastle, 1822. Woodcuts by Bewick, 5 vols., tall 8vo., full contemp. russia, all edges gilt, fine, first collected ed. Howes 194-1370 1978 £250

BEYEN, H. G.   Ueber Stilleben Aus Pompeii und Herculaneum. 1928. 4to., plts., buckram, Mary H. Swindler's copy. Allen 234-102 1978 $25

BEYER, JOHANNE-HARTMANNO   Stereo-metriae Inanium Nova et Facilis Ratio,.... Francofurti, 1603. 1st and only ed., quarto, full period limp vellum, Earl of Hopetoun's bookplate, title vignette is device of Jonas Rhodius. Bennett 20-25 1978 $300

BEYLE, MARIE-HENRI   La Chartreuse De Parme. New York, 1895. Illus., 3 vols., 1 of 750 numbered sets, uncut, 1st ed. in English, 8vo., orig. cloth, very good. Americanist 103-16 1978 $35

BEYLE, MARIE-HENRI   Rome, Naples, and Florence, in 1817. 1818. 8vo., orig. bds., uncut, very good, first London ed. P. M. Hill 142-32 1978 £105

BEZOUT, ETIENNE   Trattato Di Navigazione. Naples, 1801. 8vo., ·plts., contemp. half calf, rubbed. F. Edwards 1013-20 1978 £35

BHAVSINJI, H. H.   Forty Years of the Rajkunmar College 1870-1910. (1910). Map, plans, plts., 7 vols., roy. 4to. George's 635-1293 1978 £25

BIALIK, CHAIM NACHMAN   Selected Poems. New York, 1926. First ed. Biblo 247-500 1978 $7.50

BIANCHINI, FRANCESCO   Hesperi et Phosphiri Nova Phaenomena Sive Observationes Circa Planetam Veneris. Rome, 1728. Folio, frontis., plts., text illus., orig. bds., rubbed, uncut, very fine, only ed. Norman 5-30 1978 $1,500

BIANCONI, GIAN-LODOVICO   Due Lettere di Fisica al Signor Marchese Scipione Maffei. Venezia, 1746. Copperplt., contemp. limp bds., 4to., 1st ed., fine copy. Offenbacher 30-14 1978 $125

BIART, L.   Adventures of a Young Naturalist. New York, (c. 19th century). Illus., 8vo., orig. cloth. Book Chest 17-43 1978 $12.50

BIBESCO, LE PRINCE   Le Duel. Paris, 1900. 8vo., cloth, orig. cover wrapped up. Van der Peet H-64-597 1978 Dfl 30

BIBLE - CREE

BIBLE   The New Testament Translated into Cree Language. London, 1876. Leather. Hood 117-679 1978 $175

BIBLE - ENGLISH

BIBLE   New Testament. Coverdale's Version. Antwerp, 1538. Very rare, black letter, woodcuts, remarkably good condition, sm. 8vo., 18th cent. dark blue mor., raised bands, gilt-tooled panels, bookplt. of Andrew Gifford, booklabel of Bristol Bapt. College. Thomas 37-17 1978 £5500

BIBLE   The Nevv Testament of Iesvs Christ,.... Rhemes, 1582. Small 4to, orig. calf, joints skillfully repaired, 1st ed. of Roman Catholic version of New Testament in English. Quaritch 978-13 1978 $800

BIBLE   The Holy Bible...Faithfully Translated into English out of the Authenticall Latin. 1609-10. 1st. ed. of Roman Catholic old testament, 2 vols., sm. 4to, newly bound in full blind stamped sprinkled calf, gilt border, raised bands on spine, red morocco labels. Traylen 88-112 1978 £460

BIBLE   The Holy Bible. London, 1633. Folio, full 17th cent. gilt tooled black calf, ruled in red, once belonged to Henry Hyde, superb copy. Bennett 7-12 1978 $950

BIBLE   The Holy Bible. Oxford, 1753. 4to., full calf, first page loose and frayed. K Books 244-34 1978 £14

BIBLE.   The Holy Bible Abridged:.... Windsor, 1811. Marbled paper over oak, minor stains. Victoria 34-414 1978 $65

BIBLE   The Holy Bible..With the Apocrypha. Philadelphia, 1813. Maps, binding very worn, front cover detached. Nestler Rare 78-33 1978 $10

BIBLE   The Holy Bible containing the Old Testament and the New. 1814. 12mo., contemp. red mor. panelled in gilt and blind, gilt edges, binders stamp partially erased. Quaritch 979-33 1978 $85

BIBLE   The English Bible, containing the Old Testament and the New.... Hammersmith, 1902-1905. Reprinted, folio, full limp vellum as issued, 1 of 500 sets printed in black and red, 5 vols., foxing in vols. I and II, fine. Duschnes 220-87a 1978 $2,100

BIBLE   The Holy Bible. London, Nonesuch Press, 1924-27. 5 vols., sm. folio, orig. parchment bds., gilt spines faded, orig. slipcase, on Jap. vellum, copperplts., engravings by Stephen Gooden. Totteridge 29-76 1978 $200

BIBLE   The New Testament of Our Lord and Saviour Jesus Christ. New York, n.d. Inscr'd, black cloth, 12mo. Hood 117-693 1978 $30

BIBLE - FIJIAN

BIBLE   Koe Tohi of Fuakava Foou... Vavau, 1849. Contemp. cloth, rebacked, 8vo, Fijian New Testament. Edwards 1012-370 1978 £60

BIBLE - GERMAN

BIBLE   Das Neue Testament...Nach Der Deutschen Uebersetzung D. Martin Luthers...Erste Auflage. Lancaster, 1812. Orig. full leather w/line stamping in blind, clasps, rubbed, 8vo. Americanist 101-16 1978 $20

BIBLE   Das Neue Testament... Libanon, 1840. Leather, foxed. Hayman 72-602 1978 $10

BIBLE   Biblia, Das Ist: Die Helige Schrift Altes Und Neues Testaments, Nach Der Teutschen Uebersetzung D. Martin Luthers.... Germantown, 1763. 4to, orig. full leather, clasps gone, good comp. copy of the 2nd Saur Bible. Americanist 101-127 1978 $500

BIBLE - GREEK

BIBLE   Biblia graeca. Venice, Aldus, 1518. Folio, Greek letter, fine, Dutch 17th century calf gilt, 1st published Greek Bible. Quaritch Summer, 1978-5 1978 $19,000

BIBLE - HEIROGLYPHIC

BIBLE   Hieroglyphick Bible. London, 1789. 7th ed., engraved by John Bewick, 16mo, recased with original pictorial paper covers laid-down, endpapers retained, cover papers rubbed, fine copy. Victoria 34-402 1978 $125

BIBLE   A Curious Hieroglyphick Bible;.... London, 1796. 12mo, woodcuts by John Bewick, orig. illus. papered boards, lightly rubbed, paper spine intact, very good copy. Victoria 34-67 1978 $110

BIBLE - ITALIAN

BIBLE   La Sacra Bibbia, tradotta in lingua Italiana da Giovanni Diodati.... Geneva, 1641. John Evelyn's Italian Bible, Seconda ed., four parts in 1 vol., folio, 332 by 220 mm., contemp. Parisian mottled calf, armorial stamp. Thomas 37-21 1978 £600

BIBLE - KIBONDEI

BIBLE   Angili Kwa Mattayo. London, 1890. 12mo, orig. cloth, backstrip slightly frayed, good ex-lib. K Books 239-46 1978 £10

BIBLE - LATIN

BIBLE   Biblia. Paris, Robertus Stephanus, 1528-27. First critical ed. of Vulgate, generally in clean sound quite crisp condition, folio, contemp. blind-stamped calf by Nicholas Spierinck, rebacked, margins wide. Thomas 37-16 1978 £250

BIBLE   Jesu Christi D. N. Novum Testamentum. London, 1580. 16mo., old calf, joints cracked, portion of spine missing, wormholes, stained throughout, margins cut down, unique. Allen 234-104 1978 $125

BIBLE   Testamenti Veteris Biblia Sacra sive Libri Canonici Prisca Judaeorum Ecclesiae a Deo Traditi.... London, 1581. 6 parts in 1 vol., woodcut initials, neatly ruled in red throughout, thk. sm. 4to., well bound in full dark calf, orig. gilt edges, second ed. of the complete Latin Bible to be printed. Howes 194-11 1978 £280

BIBLE   Biblia Sacra, Sive Libri Canonici. London, 159(2)-3. Title within woodcut border, folio, 18th Century calf rebacked. Traylen 88-429 1978 £88

BIBLE   Novum Testamentum. Glasgow, 1759. Sm. 4to., 19th cent. full olive mor., gilt top, other edges entirely untrimmed, greek letter. Howes 194-270 1978 £25

BIBLE   Bible in Latin. Leipzig, 1913-14. Facs. of Gutenberg bible, 2 vols., folio, full brown pigskin, blind-stamped, ltd. to 297 copies. Howell 5-7 1978 $4,500

BIBLE - POLYGLOT

BIBLE   Quincuplex Psalterium. Gallicum. Romanum. Hebraicum. Vetus. Concilliatu. Paris, 1509. First ed. of the five-fold psalter, woodcut border, some worming, apart from this book in excellent clean sound condition, sm. folio, 18th cent. panelled calf, rebacked, rather worn, the Foulis copy. Thomas 37-15 1978 £600

BIBLE   Bible in Hebrew and Greek. Antwerp, Christopher Platin, 1584. Folio, 18th cent. red mor., gilt, panelled sides, handsome. Thomas 37-19 1978 £250

BIBLE - WELSH

BIBLE   Y Bibl Cyssegr-Lam Sef Yr Hen Destament A'r Newydd. London, 1620. Second ed. of the bible in Welsh, black letter, O.T. in excellent condition, N.T. somewhat worn, folio, 19th cent. diced calf, rebacked. Thomas 37-20 1978 £350

BIBIENA, FERDINANDO GALLI DA
Please turn to
GALLI DA BIBIENA, FERDINANDO

BIBLIOGRAPHIES of Modern Authors No. 1: Robert Bridges. London, 1921. Sm. 8vo., orig. wrs., autographed by Bridges. Morrill 239-317 1978 $17.50

A BIBLIOGRAPHY of Oliver Cromwell. A List of Printed Materials Relating to Oliver Cromwell, Together with a List of Portraits and Caricatures. Cambridge, 1929. Orig. cloth, pres. copy, A.L.s. from author laid in. MacManus 238-897 1978 $37.50

A BIBLIOGRAPHY of Oliver Wendell Holmes. New York, 1907. 8vo., orig. cloth, 1st ed., 1 of 530 no. copies. MacManus 238-946 1978 $35

A BIBLIOGRAPHY of the King's Book or Eikon Basilike. London, 1896. 4to., contemp. half-mor. gilt. MacManus 238-913 1978 $40

BIBLIOPHILE SOCIETY BOSTON First Year Book. Boston, 1902. Bds., one of 500 copies, frontis. Battery Park 1-251 1978 $75

BIBLIOTHECA Americana Nova:.... New York, n.d. 2 vols., revised ed., two new supplements. Jenkins 116-115 1978 $40

BIBLIOTHECA Askeviana Sive Catalogus Librorum Rarissimorum Antonii Askew, M. D., Quorum Auctio Fiet Apud S. Baker & G. Leigh in Vico Dicto York Street, Covent Garden, Londoni, Die Lunae 13 Februarii MDCCLXXV, & in Undeviginti Sequentes Dies. London, (1775). 8vo., contemp. calf, rebacked. Offenbacher 30-6 1978 $160

BIBLIOTHECA Geographica & Historica, or a Catalogue of a Nine Days Sale of Rare & Valuable Ancient and Modern Books, Maps, Charts, Manuscripts... London, 1872. 8vo., orig. wrs. Morrill 241-21 1978 $17.50

BIBLIOTHECA Washingtonian. A Descriptive List of the Biographies and Biographical Sketches of George Washington. Philadelphia, 1889. 4to., port., ltd. to 400 copies. MacManus 239-488 1978 $35

BIBLIOTHEQUES Des Anciens Philosophes. Paris, 1771. 9 vols., 8vo., marbled calf, fine set, contemp. binds. Salloch 348-13 1978 $90

BI-CENTENNIAL Of Old Kennett Meeting House, 1710-1910. Philadelphia. Map, illus., fine copy. Baldwins' 51-470 1978 $20

BICHAT, MARIE FRANCOIS XAVIER Anatomie Generale,..... Paris, 1801. 8vo, 2 parts in 4 vols., contemp. half calf, gilt back, red and green mor. labels, 1st ed., very fine. Gilhofer 75-7 1978 SFr 1,100

BICHAT, MARIE FRANCOIS XAVIER Pathological Anatomy: The Last Course. Philadelphia, 1827. Rittenhouse 49-74 1976 $35

BICHAT, MARIE FRANCOIS XAVIER Traite d'Anatomie Descriptive. Paris, 1801-03. Cont. half calf, 8vo., 5 vols., first ed. Gilhofer 75-8 1978 sFr 800

BICKLEY, F. J.M. Synge & The Irish Dramatic Movement. 1912. 1st ed., port., good, octavo bound in cloth. Hyland 128-631 1978 £5

BICKERDYKE, J. The Curiosities of Ale and Beer. Leadenhall Press, (c. 1890). Illus., roy. 8vo., orig. parchment, edges uncut. George's 635-1345 1978 £18

BICKERSTAFFE, ISAAC d. 1812? Love in a Village; A Comic Opera. 1814. 8vo, cloth, uncut. Hannas 54-20 1978 £7.50

BICKERSTETH, J. B. The Land of Open Doors, Being Letters from Western Canada. London, 1914. Illus., pages gilt topped. Hood 117-877 1978 $30

BICKHAM, WILLIAM D. From Ohio to the Rocky Mountains. Editorial Correspondence of the Dayton Ohio Journal. Dayton, 1879. 1st ed., orig. cloth, fine, pres. copy from author. MacManus 239-1899 1978 $27.50

BICKNELL, E. A Review of the Summer Birds of a Part of the Catskill Mts. New York, 1882. Signature of C. H. Townsend, 8vo, orig. cloth. Book Chest 17-44 1978 $20

BICKNELL, THOMAS WILLIAMS A History of Barrington, Rhode Island. Providence, 1898. Illus., 8vo., inner hinges cracked, 1st ed. Morrill 239-589 1978 $25

BIDDER, F. H. Zur Lehre von dem Verhaltniss der Ganglienkorper zu den Nervenfasern, Nebst einem Anhange von Dr. A. W. Volkmann. Leipzig, 1847. 4to., orig. wrappers, rebacked, first ed., plts. Gurney 75-10 1978 £30

BIDDLE, ANTHONY J. DREXEL The Madeira Islands. London, 1900. 2 vols., illus., nice signed inscript. by Biddle, orig. binding, 8vo. Americanist 101-18 1978 $25

BIDDLE, EDWARD The Life and Works of Thomas Sully. Philadelphia, 1921. 1st ed., 4to., illus., orig. 3/4 cloth and bds., 1 of 50 lg. paper copies, signed by authors. MacManus 239-709 1978 $100

BIDDLE, HARRY D. Extracts From the Journal of Elizabeth Drinker, 1759 to 1807. Philadelphia, 1888. Baldwins' 51-424 1978 $40

BIDDLE, NICHOLAS Correspondence of...Dealing with National Affairs 1807-1844. Boston, 1919. 1st ed., illus., scarce. MacManus 239-52 1978 $30

BIDDLE, NICHOLAS Oration Delivered Before the Pa. State Society of Cincinnati, on the Fourth of July, MDCCCXI. Philadelphia, 1811. 1st ed., mod. quarter cloth with marbled boards, uncut copy, soiled margins, signature of Job Roberts, 8vo. Americanist 101-19 1978 $30

BIDDLE, S. A Moose Hunt in New Brunswick. 1926. Illus., orig. wrs., fine. MacManus 239-53 1978 $12.50

BIDDLECOMBE, GEORGE The Art of Rigging. Salem, Southworth Press, 1925. Orig. buckram, illus., 8vo., very good. Americanist 103-81 1978 $30

BIDDULPH, JOHN The Nineteenth and Their Times. 1899. 8vo., orig. cloth, port. frontis., coloured plts. F. Edwards 1013-473 1978 £25

BIDWELL, DANIEL D. As Far As the East is from the West. Tales of a Traveler who Toured the World Toward the Rising Sun. Hartford, 1910. Cloth, t.p. foxed. Hayman 72-55 1978 $7.50

BIEDL, ARTUR Innere Sekretion. 1922. 8vo., color plts., illus., modern red buckram, gilt lettered, very good copy from the library of Dr. Alfred M. Hellman, 4th ed. Zeitlin 245-23 1978 $27.50

BIENVENU, CHARLES LEON Grande Mythologie Tintararesque. Paris, 1881. 8vo., half calf, color frontis., handcolored plts., rare, some foxing. Van der Peet H64-288 1978 Dfl 95

BIERBAUM, OTTO JULIUS Der Bunte Vogel von 1897 and 1899. Berlin und Leipzig, 1896-1898. 2 vols., 8vo., uncut, orig. pict. wr., 1st ed., illus. Goldschmidt 110-71 1978 $210

BIERCE, AMBROSE Battle Sketches. Oxford: The Shakespeare Head Press, 1930. 4to., illus., full limp vellum, gilt, 1 of 350 copies, uncut, covers somewhat rubbed, but fine. MacManus 238-843 1978 $85

BIERCE, AMBROSE Can Such Things Be. 1926. Very good, first English ed. Bell Book 16-090 1978 £4

BIERCE, AMBROSE Collected Works. N.Y., 1909-1912. Autograph ed., signed by author, fine 3/4 brown crushed levant mor., t.e.g., bookplates, 12 vols., scarce set. Houle 10-32 1978 $795

BIERCE, AMBROSE Fantastic Fables. New York, 1899. 12mo., orig. pict. cloth, 1st ed., 1st print., covers a bit soiled, but nice, scarce. MacManus 238-426 1978 $85

BIERCE, AMBROSE The Monk and the Hangman's Daughter. 1927. Very good, first English ed. Bell Book 16-091 1978 £4

BIERCE, AMBROSE Shadow on the Dial. S.F., 1909. 1st ed., 4to., orig. cloth, very good. Houle 10-33 1978 $15

BIERCE, AMBROSE The Shadow on the Dial and Other Stories. San Francisco, 1909. Orig. cloth, d.j., 1st ed., fine. MacManus 238-427 1978 $60

BIERCE, AMBROSE The Shadow on the Dial and Other Essays. San Francisco, 1909. Cloth, spine slightly faded, light scratches on back. Dawson's 447-204 1978 $40

BIERCE, AMBROSE Tales of Soldiers and Civilians. San Francisco, 1891. Orig. cloth, somewhat soiled, 1st ed., bind. B, scarce. MacManus 238-425 1978 $110

BIERMAN, WILLIAM   The Medical Applications of the Short Wave Current. Baltimore, 1939. Library marks. Rittenhouse 49-75 1976 $15

BIERMAN, WILLIAM   Physical Medicine in General Practice. New York, 1944. Rittenhouse 49-76 1976 $10

BIERSTADT, O. E.   The Library of Robert Hoe. New York, De Vinne Press, 1895. One of 350 copies, prtd. on Japan paper, illus., cloth. Battery Park 1-253 1978 $75

BIESELE, RUDOLPH L.   The History of the German Settlements in Texas, 1831-1861. Austin, 1930. 1st ed., illus., folding maps. Jenkins 116-1522 1978 $85

BIG Trees of California. San Francisco, (1912). Illus., original printed pictorial wr. Ginsberg 14-78 1978 $25

BIGELOW, FRANCIS HILL   Historic Silver of the Colonies and Its Makers. New York. 1st. ed., fully illus. Baldwins' 51-29 1978 $30

BIGELOW, HORATIO   Flying Feathers. Richmond, (1937). Illus. Baldwins' 51-540 1978 $17.50

BIGELOW, HORATIO R.   Hydrophobia. Philadelphia, 1881. 8vo., 1st ed. Morrill 239-20 1978 $25

BIGELOW, JACOB   Elements of Technology, Taken Chiefly from a Course of Lectures Delivered at Cambridge, on the Application of the Sciences to the Useful Arts. Boston, 1829. Plts., 8vo., edges untrimmed, partly unopened, spine faded, nice copy, 1st ed. Morrill 239-307 1978 $85

BIGELOW, JACOB   Florula Bostoniensus. Boston, 1840. 3rd ed., enlarged, contemp. 3/4 calf, marbled bds. MacManus 239-286 1978 $20

BIGELOW, JACOB   Nature in Disease .... Boston, 1854. Fine copy. Baldwins' 51-328 1978 $42.50

BIGELOW, JACOB   A Treatise on the Materia Medica, Intended as a Sequel to the Pharmacopoeia of the United States. Boston, 1822. Usual wear on covers. Rittenhouse 49-78 1976 $75

BIGELOW, JOHN   The Campaign of Chancellorsville. New Haven, 1910. Ltd. to 1000 copies, folding wrs., fine copy, with letters from Wiley laid in, Bell Wiley's copy. Broadfoot's 44-36 1978 $100

BIGELOW, JOHN   The Life of Benjamin Franklin. Philadelphia, 1875. 3 vols., portr. MacManus 239-146 1978 $35

BIGELOW, JOHN   The Life of Samuel J. Tilden. New York, 1895. 2 vols., illus. MacManus 239-822 1978 $27.50

BIGELOW, JOHN   Memoir of the Life and Public Services of John Charles Fremont... New York, 1856. Cloth. Hayman 73-52 1978 $10

BIGELOW, JOHN   The Mystery of Sleep. New York, 1897. 8vo., orig. bds., white cloth back, lightly dust soiled, 1st ed. Morrill 239-21 1978 $10

BIGEON, LOUIS FRANCOIS   Medecine Physiologique. Paris, 1845. 8vo., disbound, lightly browned, foxed, marginal dampstains, but good copy, 1st collected ed. Zeitlin 245-24 1978 $65

BIGG-WITHER, T. P.   Pioneering in South Brazil: Three Years of Forest and Prairie Life in the Province of Parana. 1878. Map, woodcut illus., 2 vols., sm. 8vo, modern half green leather, some lib. stamps. Edwards 1012-623 1978 £40

BIGGAR, E. B.   Hydro-electric Development in Ontario. Toronto, 1920. Illus., fold. map. Hood 116-721 1978 $17.50

BIGGERS, DON H.   From Cattle Range to Cotton Patch:.... Bandera, 1944. Wr. Jenkins 116-116 1978 $25

BIGGERS, DON H.   From Cattle Range to Cotton Patch. Bandera, 1944. Wrs., reprint, very rare, wrs. fading, fine copy, scarce. Dykes 34-44 1978 $20

BIGGS, WILLIAM   The Military History of Europe. 1755. Contemp. calf, lettering-piece, joints cracked, first English ed., 8vo. Howes 194-165 1978 £30

BIGHAM, MADGE A.   Stories of Mother Goose Village. Chicago, New York, (1903). 1st ed., 8vo, color plates, colored text illus., very good. Victoria 34-72 1978 $12.50

BIGLAND, RALPH   Observations on Marriages, Baptisms, and Burials. 1764. 4to., 19th-century half calf, title slightly soiled, tall copy, most fore-edges uncut. P. M. Hill 142-35 1978 £24

BIGLER, JOHN   Governor's Message in Answer to a Resolution of the Assembly Requesting Information in Relation to Water Lots in the City of San Francisco Sold in 1850. Sacramento, 1853. Cloth, 1st ed. Ginsberg 14-79 1978 $175

BIGSBY, JOHN J.   The Shoe and Canoe; or, Pictures of Travel in the Canada... London, 1850. Illus., plts., maps, 2 vols., some foxing. Hood 116-604 1978 $200

BILANCIONI, GUGLIELMO   l'Orecchio e il Naso Nel Sistema Antropometrico di Leonardo. Rome, 1920. 8vo., illus., orig. prtd. wrs., uncut. Norman 5-L22 1978 $30

BILBY, T.   The Nursery Book,.... London, c.1840. New ed. with additions, sq. 12mo, lithographed plates, Orbis Pictus format, marbled boards, 3/4 leather, moderate rubbing, very good. Victoria 34-73 1978 $45

BILL, ALFRED HOYT   The Beleaguered City, Richmond 1861-1865. New York, 1946. Illus., handwritten pgs. of Wiley's notes, Bell Wiley's copy. Broadfoot's 44-37 1978 $14

BILL, ALFRED HOYT   The Campaign of Princeton 1776-1777. Princeton, 1948. Maps. MacManus 239-549 1978 $10

BILLET, ANNE LOUISE FRANCOISE   Memoires Historiques de Stephanie-Louise de Bourbon-Conti, Ecrits Par Elle-Meme. Paris, (1798). 1st. ed., 2 vols., 8vo, no half-titles, contemp. half calf. Hannas 54-22 1978 £25

BILLINGS, JOHN D.   Hardtack and Coffee. Boston, 1888. Cover worn, Bell Wiley's copy. Broadfoot's 44-522 1978 $35

BILLINGS, JOHN D.   The History of the Tenth Massachusetts Battery of Light Artillery in the War of the Rebellion. Boston, 1909. Lower spine torn and crudely repaired, Bell Wiley's copy. Broadfoot's 44-523 1978 $16

BILLINGS, ROBERT WILLIAM   The Baronial and Ecclesiastical Antiquities of Scotland. Edinburgh, 1845-52. First ed., 4 vols., plts., wood-engravings in text, 4to., half hard grain mor. gilt, nice. K Books 244-36 1978 £70

BILLINGS, WILLIAM R.   Some Details of Water-Works Construction. New York, 1888. Illus. from Sketches by author, 8vo., ex-lib., 1st ed. Morrill 239-303 1978 $7.50

BILLINGTON, C.   Shrubs of Michigan. Michigan, 1949. Illus., 8vo, orig. cloth, 2nd ed., colored front. Book Chest 17-45 1978 $12

BILLINGTON, RAY ALLEN   Westward Expansion. New York, 1949. First ed., fine, d.w., maps. Biblo 247-178 1978 $15

BILLON, FREDERIC L.   Annals of St. Louis in Its Territorial Days from 1804-1821 Being a Cont. of the...Annals of the French and Spanish Period. St. Louis, 1888. Illus., orig. cloth, slightly worn. MacManus 239-1938 1978 $32.50

BILLOTEY, P.   L'Indochine en zigzags. Paris, 1929. 5th ed., 8vo, orig. covers. Van der Peet 127-16 1978 Dfl 25

BILLROTH, CHRISTIAN ALBERT THEODOR   Chirurgische Klinik. Zurich 1860-1867. Wien 1868-1876. Berlin, 1869-1879. 8vo., 4 vols. in 2, fold. plts., illus., half-calf, some lib. stamps, 1st ed. Gilhofer 74-84 1978 sFr 1,100

BILLROTH, THEODOR   Clinical Surgery. London, 1881. 8vo., litho. plts., woodcuts, orig. brown blind-stamped cloth, gilt, library stamps, some foxing, but good copy, 1st English ed. Zeitlin 245-25 1978 $85

BILLROTH, THEODOR   Lectures on Surgical Pathology and Therapeutics. London, 1877-78. 2 vols., ends of spine chipped. Rittenhouse 49-80 1976 $50

BILSON, THOMAS 1547-1616   The Effect of Certaine Sermons Touching the Full Redemption of Mankind by the Death and Blood of Christ Jesus. 1599. Sm. 4to., 19th cent. panelled sheep, joints cracked, sole ed. Howes 194-12 1978 £75

BINGAY, MALCOLM W.   Of Me I Sing. Indianapolis, (1949). Illus. Biblo BL781-765 1978 $9

BINGER, WALTER D.   What the Citizen Should Know About Civilian Defense. Norton, 1942. Illus. by Arthur Smith. Austin 80-21 1978 $8.50

BINGHAM, HIRAM   Elihu Yale,...the American Nabob of Queen Square. New York, 1939. Illus., 1st ed. Biblo BL781-37 1978 $10

BINGHAM, HIRAM   A Residence of Twenty-One Years in the Sandwich Islands. Hartford, 1847. 1st ed., thick royal 8vo., plts., fldg. map, re-backed with orig. spine laid down, mild cover spotting, else fine, name of Solomon Bingham Collin on front endpaper. Current 24-71 1978 $145

BINGHAM, J.   The French Churches Apology for the Church of England. 1706. Panelled calf, rubbed, 8vo. George's 635-1032 1978 £6

BINGHAM, JOHN A.   Speech of Hon...., of Ohio, on the Reconstruction of the Union; Delivered in the House...January 16, 1867. Washington, 1867. Unbound as issued. Hayman 72-57 1978 $7.50

BINGHAM, JOSEPH   A Scholastical History of the Practice of the Church. 1712, 1714. 2 parts in 1 vol., 8vo., contemp. panelled calf. P. M. Hill 142-36 1978 £15

BINGHAM, PEREGRINE   The Pains of Memory. 1811. First ed., 12mo., contemp. crimson mor. gilt. Howes 194-166 1978 £7.50

BINGLEY, BARBARA   Tales of the Turquoise. Boar's Head Press, 1933. One of 150 numbered copies, wood-engravings by Lettice Sandford, roy.8vo., orig. pict. bds. George's 635-878 1978 £12.50

BINGLEY, WILLIAM   Useful Knowledge... 1818. 2nd. ed., engraved plts., 3 vols., lg. 12mo., orig. bds., uncut, printed paper labels, fine copy. Fenning 32-26 1978 £21.50

BINGLEY, WILLIAM   Useful Knowledge... 1821. 3rd. ed., 3 vols., plts., uncut, orig. brown bds., paper labels rubbed. Jarndyce 16-292 1978 £36

BINING, ARTHUR CECIL   Pennsylvania Iron Manufacture in the Eighteenth Century. Harrisburg, 1938. Illus. MacManus 239-1376 1978 $20

BINING, ARTHUR CECIL   Penna. Iron Manufacture In the Eighteenth Century. Harrisburg, 1938. Illus. Baldwins' 51-425 1978 $20

BINKLEY, W. C.   The Expansionist Movement in Texas, 1836-1850. Berkeley, 1925. 1st ed., uncut and untripped. Jenkins 116-119 1978 $75

BINNEY, A.   The Terrestrial Air-Breathing Mollusks of the U.S. & Adjacent Territories of N. Amer. Boston, 1851. 2 vols., 4to, orig. 1/2 leather, worn. Book Chest 17-46 1978 $90

BINNS, ARCHIE   The Land is Bright. New York, 1939. Near mint in faded d.w. Desmarais B-89 1978 $10

BINNS, R. W.   Catalogue of a Collection of Worcester Porcelain, and Notes on Japanese Specimens, in the Museum at the Royal Porcelain Works. Worcester, 1884. Illus., 8vo., orig. stiff wrs. Morrill 239-309 1978 $10

BINNS, W. M.   The First Century of English Porcelain. 1906. Plts., many coloured, 4to., a little loose in case, covers a little soiled. George's 635-226 1978 £30

BINYON, LAURENCE   The Art of Botticelli, An Essay in Pictorial Criticism. London, 1913. Etched frontis by Muirhead Bone, 23 fine plts. in colour, folio, orig. half vellum cloth sides, ltd. ed. of 275 copies. Traylen 88-365 1978 £80

BINYON, LAURENCE   Brief Candles. 1938. 6 engravings by Helen Binyon, 5 1/2 x 4 1/4", purple cloth. Eaton 45-207 1978 £20

BINYON, LAURENCE   Chinese Paintings in English Collections. Paris, Brussels, 1927. Cloth, bds. bit warped, plts. Dawson's 449-9 1978 $135

BINYON, LAURENCE   The Drawings and Engravings of William Blake. 1922. Plts., some in colour, 4to., orig. qtr. parchment. George's 635-98 1978 £30

BINYON, LAURENCE   The Madness of Merlin. London, 1947. Fine in chipped and soiled d.w. Desmarais B-90 1978 $20

BINYON, LAURENCE   The Sirens: An Ode. London, 1925. Rev. ed., fine in d.w. Desmarais B-91 1978 $12.50

BINYON, LAURENCE   The Spirit of Man in Asian Art. Cambridge, 1936. D.j., illus. Baldwins' 51-30 1978 $15

BIOGRAPHIA Britannica: Or, The Lives of the Most Eminent Persons, Who Have Flourished in Great Britain and Ireland... 1747-48-50-57-60-63-66. 6 vols. in 7, tall folio, half-titles, orig. speckled calf brown & black labels, fine handsome set. Jarndyce 16-38 1978 £160

BIOGRAPHIA Britannica. 1747-66. First ed., 6 vols. in 7, folio, contemp. half calf, labels missing, very good, entirely uncut and unpressed. Howes 194-167 1978 £125

BIOGRAPHICAL Annals of Lancaster County, Pa., Containing Biographical and Genealogical Sketches of Prominent and Representative Citizens and Many of the Early Settlers. N.P., 1903. Illus., lg. thick 4to., cloth, very scarce. MacManus 239-1530 1978 $110

BIOGRAPHICAL Review...Sketches of the Leading Citizens of Columbia County. Boston, 1894. 4to., illus., lea., rubbed, good tight copy. Butterfield 21-139 1978 $45

BIOGRAPHY of Lieut. Col. Julius P. Garesche, Assistant Adjutant-General, U. S. Army. Philadelphia, 1887. Illus., 8vo., orig. cloth, 1st ed., A.L.s. from author tipped in. Morrill 241-150 1978 $50

BION, NICOLAS   Consturction and Principal Uses of Mathematical Instruments ... 30 full-page plts., folio, buckram, gilt, ltd. ed. of 500 copies. Traylen 88-486 1978 £17.50

BIRAGO AVOGADRI, GIO. BATTISTA   Historia della Divisione del Regno di Portogalio Dalla Corona di Castiglia. Amsterdam, 1647. Sm. 8vo., cloth, second ed. King 7-20 1978 £25

BIRCH, T. W.   Maps Topographical and Statistical. Oxford, 1949. Biblo 247-446 1978 $18.50

BIRCH, THOMAS   The Heads of Illustrious Persons of Great Britain.... London, 1743, 1751. 2 vols. in 1, 1st ed., folio, contemp. red straight-grained mor. with elaborate gilt border, gilt edges, silk endpapers, bookplt., plts. Totteridge 29-14 1978 $250

BIRCH, W. DE GRAY   An Ancient Manuscript of the Eighth or Ninth Century, formerly belonging to St. Mary's Abbey. 1889. Map, 8vo. Upcroft 12-38 1978 £8.50

BIRCH, W. DE GRAY   Catalogue of a Collection of Original Manuscripts formerly Belonging to the Holy Office of the Inquisition in the Canary Islands. Edinburgh, 1903. 2 vols., roy. 8vo., orig. cloth. Forster 130-183 1978 £21

BIRCH, W. DE GRAY   Seals. 1907. Plts., imp. 8vo. George's 635-8 1978 £25

BIRKENHEAD, FREDERICK EDWIN SMITH   More Famous Trials. New York, 1929. Illus., 1st Amer. ed. Biblo 251-284 1978 $15

BIRD, ISABELLA L.   The Hawaiian Archipelago. 1875. Folding map, plts., half morocco, 8vo, short tear in one map. Edwards 1012-357 1978 $20

BIRD, ISABELLA L.   Korea & Her Neighbors:.... London, 1898. 2 vols., illus., folding maps, cloth, bindings a bit worn, leaves a little frayed or browned. Dawson's 127-209 1978 $50

BIRD, ISABELLA L.   A Lady's Life in the Rocky Mountains. 1879.
Ist. London ed., plts., sm. 8vo, modern cloth. Edwards 1012-469 1978 £20

BIRD, ISABELLA L.   A Lady's Life in the Rocky Mountains. New
York, 1879-80. Cloth, little worn at corners and bottom of spine, cover rather
heavily waterspotted. Hayman 72-58 1978 $7.50

BIRD, ROBERT MONTGOMERY   The Infidel; or the Fall of Mexico, A Romance.
Philadelphia, 1835. 2 vols., Ist ed., orig. cloth, edges of spines worn, 8vo.
Americanist 101-20 1978 $45

BIRD, WILL R.   Here Stays Good Yorkshire. Toronto, 1945. 1st
ed. Hood 116-452 1978 $12.50

BIRD, WILL R.   The Passionate Pilgrim. Toronto, 1949.
Hood 117-506 1978 $15

BIRD, WILLIAM   A Treatise of the Nobilitie of the Realme.
London, 1642. Woodcut border round title, 12mo, contemp. calf, spine worn.
Traylen 88-463 1978 £40

BIRD'S Eye View of the Panama Canal and Map of Panama. Panama, n.d. (c.1914).
Wrapper, photos, large map. Hayman 71-613 1978 $8.50

THE BIRDS of Berkshire and Buckinghamshire. Eton & London, 1868. Ist ed.,
8vo., hand-colored mounted photos bound in, very good copy, scarce, orig. green
cloth , gilt decor. on front bd. & spine, hinges repaired. Current Misc. 8-34
1978 $440

BIRINGUCCIO, VANNOCCIO   De La Pirotechnia. Venice, 1540. Sm. 4to.,
text woodcuts, 18th Cent. French calf, gilt, upper hinge repaired, fine copy,
signature of Denis Bouthillier, bkplt., Ist ed. Norman 5-33 1978 $3,750

BIRINGUCCIO, VANOCCIO   Pirotechnia. Venice, 1558. 4to., old limp
vellum, woodcuts. Gurney 75-11 1978 £250

BIRKBECK, M.   Notes on a Journey in America, From the Coast
of Virginia to the Territory of Illinois. 1818. Ist. London ed., modern half calf,
8vo. Edwards 1012-470 1978 £45

BIRKET, JAMES   Some Cursory Remarks Made by...in His Voyage
to North America 1750-51. New Haven, 1916. Cloth bds., ltd. to 300 copies.
MacManus 239-54 1978 $25

BIRKS, W. M.   The Chancel, Before and After. Toronto, 1947.
Illus., bound. Hood 116-170 1978 $12.50

BIRMINGHAM, GEORGE A. PSEUD.
Please turn to
HANNAY, JAMES OWEN

BIRNEY, JAMES GILLESPIE   Letters...1831-1857. New York, (1938). 2 vols.
Biblo 247-88 1978 $22.50

BIRRELL, AUGUSTINE   Collected Essays. 1899. First ed., 2 vols.,
cr. 8vo., orig. cloth. Howes 194-635 1978 £5.50

BIRRELL, AUGUSTINE   Things Past Redress. London, 1937. 1st ed.,
portraits, illus., very good or better. Limestone 9-25 1978 $17.50

BIRRELL, AUGUSTINE   Three Essays. New York, The Grolier Club,
1924. 4to., bds., fr. cover creased, cloth spine, 1 of an ed. of 300 copies on
Grolier handmade paper. Battery Park 1-125 1978 $75

BIRT, H. N.   The Elizabethan Religious Settlement... 1907.
Plts., head of spine rubbed, octavo, good. Upcroft 10-227 1978 £6.50

BIRT, R.   XXII Dragoons 1760-1945. The Story of a Regiment. 1950. Coloured frontis., plts., maps, 8vo., cloth. F. Edwards 1013-474
1978 £6

THE BIRTH And Growth of Canada. Montreal, 1927. Card cover, illus. Hood's
115-578 1978 $7.50

BISCHOFF, HERMAN   Deadwood to the Big Horns, 1877. [Bismarck,
1931]. Mimeo, oblong 8vo, plain mimeo wr., one of 50 copies. Ginsberg
14-306 1978 $150

BISHOP, ABRAHAM   Connecticut Republicanism. An Oration on the
Extent and Power of Political Delusion. Delivered in New-Haven, on the Evening
Preceding the Public Commencement, September, 1800. (New Haven?), 1800.
Sewed. Hayman 72-625 1978 $75

BISHOP, DANIEL   The Constitution of Society as Designed by God.
London, 1835. 8vo., contemp. half-cloth, 1st ed. Gilhofer 74-10 1978
sFr 250

BISHOP, HARRIET E.   Minnesota; Then and Now. Saint Paul, 1869.
Wrs., some of paper worn from spine. Hayman 73-451 1978 $20

BISHOP, JOSEPH B.   Theodore Roosevelt and His Time. New York,
1920. 2 vols., illus., orig. cloth. MacManus 239-809 1978 $10

BISHOP, JOSEPH B.   Uncle Sam's Panama Canal and World History....
1913. Illus. Baldwins' 51-3 1978 $12.50

BISHOP, MARIA C.   A Memoir of Mr. Augustus Craven. 1895. 2
vols., portraits, cr. 8vo., orig. cloth. Howes 194-762 1978 £7.50

BISHOP, MORRIS   Champlain, the Life of Fortitude. London, 1949.
Illus., maps. Hood 116-238 1978 $17.50

BISHOP, MORRIS   Champlain, The Life of Fortitude. London,
(1949). Clean, folding map, orig. binding. Hayman 71-50 1978 $7.50

BISHOP, N. H.   The Pampas and Andes. Boston, 1869. Sm. 8
vo, orig. cloth. Edwards 1012-624 1978 £15

BISHOP, N. H.   Voyage of the Paper Canoe... Boston, 1878.
Orig. cloth, 8vo, maps, illus. Edwards 1012-382 1978 £20

BISHOP, R. H.   An Address, Delivered to the Graduates of
Miami University, August 13th, 1840. Oxford, 1840. Disbound. Hayman 73-
492 1978 $15

BISHOP, W. A.   The Flying Squad. London, 1928. Hood's
115-954 1978 $15

BISHOP, WILLIAM WARNER   A Checklist of American Copies of "Short-Title
Catalogue" Books. Ann Arbor, 1944. 8vo., orig. wrs., 1st ed. MacManus
238-862 1978 $20

BISHOP Onderdonk's Statement...of Facts and Circumstances. New York and
Philadelphia, 1845. Orig. prtd. wr., fine. Butterfield 21-529a 1978 $10

BISSET, P.   The Book of Water Gardening. New York, 1924.
4to, orig. cloth. Book Chest 17-465 1978 $16.50

BITLINGER, J. B.   Nebraska: A Plea for Humanity. Cleveland, 1854.
Orig. wr., Ist ed., rare. Ginsberg 14-706 1978 $75

BITTELMAN, ALEXANDER   Jewish Unity for Victory. 1943. Austin
79-73 1978 $20

BITTINGER, B. F.   Historic Sketch of the Monument Erected in
Washington City Under the Auspices of the American Institute of Homoeopathy to
the Honor of Samuel Hahnemann. (New York), 1900. Illus., 8vo. Morrill
239-107 1978 $15

BITTINGER, LUCY F.   German Religious Life in Colonial Times. Philadelphia, 1906. Clean, orig. binding. Hayman 71-51 1978 $10

BITTNER, H.   Rome. 1950. 4to., illus. Allen 234-825 1978
$10

BIVINS, PERCY A.   The Ratio Chart in Business. 1926. Illus. Austin 80-434 1978 $10

BJORK, KENNETH O.   Saga in Steel and Concrete. 1947. Illus.
Austin 79-74 1978 $17.50

BJORNSON, BJORNSTJERNE   Ovind: A Story of Country Life in Norway.
1869. Occasional foxing, orig. cloth. Eaton 45-51 1978 £5

BLACK, A. P.   The End of the Long Horn Trail. Selfridge, n.d. (1936?). Wrs., illus., 1st ed., scarce, very good. Dykes 35-194 1978 $22.50

BLACK, MRS. GEORGE   My Seventy Years. London, (1939). Illus., library markings, good, orig. binding. Wolfe 39-38 1978 $35

BLACK, JEREMIAH S.   Essays and Speeches. New York, 1885. 8vo., 1st few leaves lightly dampstained, 1st ed. Morrill 239-310 1978 $10

BLACK, JOHN JANVIER   Forty Years in the Medical Profession, 1858-1898. Philadelphia, 1900. 8vo., 1st ed. Morrill 239-22 1978 $10

BLACK, JOSEPH   De Humore Acido a Cibis Orto, et Magnesia Alba. Edinburgi, 1754. 8vo., fldg. engr. plts., contemp. calf, browning, good copy. Zeitlin 245-26 1978 $750

BLACK, JOSEPH   Lectures on the Elements of Chemistry. Edinburgh, 1803. 2 vols., 4to., frontis. portr. & plts., contemp. calf, rubbed, rebacked, occas. foxing, very good set, 1st ed. Norman 5-35 1978 $850

BLACK, M. L.   Yukon Wild Flowers. Vancouver, n.d. Illus., card cover. Hood's 115-50 1978 $25

BLACK, ROBERT   The Art of Jacob Epstein. Cleveland, (1942). 4to., plts. Biblo 247-421 1978 $32.50

BLACK, ROBERT L.   The Little Miami Railroad. (1940). Illus., map, excellent. Nestler Rare 78-58 1978 $25

BLACK, W.   Narrative of Cruises in the Mediterranean in H.M.S. Euryalus and Chanticleer During the Greek War of Independence, 1822-26. Edinburgh, 1900. Plts. 2 coloured, 8vo, orig. cloth. Edwards 1012-44 1978 £35

BLACK, WILLIAM   White Wings: a Yachting Romance. 1880. 3 vols., 8vo., 1st ed., orig. blue cloth, tight set, pres. copy inscr. by Black. Quaritch 979-34 1978 $190

BLACK and White Budget, Vols. 1-3. 1899-1900. Illus., Vol. 1 lacks title, 3 vols., imp. 8vo., half roan, worn, one spine defective. George's 635-801 1978 £6.50

BLACK And White Budget. Vols. 1 to 4. London, 1899-1901. Bound in 3 vols., illus., imperial 8vo, little thumbed, good, orig. cloth. 1st. vol. bit shaken, short tear in one joint. K Books 239-51 1978 £20

BLACK'S Picturesque Tourist of Scotland. Edinburgh, 1873. 20th. ed., new preface, steel engravings, vignettes, folding maps, separate lg. map, orig. green cloth, gilt, good. Jarndyce 16-997 1978 £15.50

THE BLACKBIRD'S Nest. Philadelphia, 1812. Pictorial wrappers, copperplate engravings, fine copy. Victoria 34-75 1978 $60

BLACKBURN, HENRY   Breton Folk. London, 1880. Quarto, 1st large paper ed., illus. by Caldecott, fine copy, spine edges worn. Victoria 34-126 1978 $35

BLACKBURN, HENRY   Randolph Caldecott. 1887. Fifth ed., illus., 8vo. George's 635-102 1978 £7.50

BLACKBURN, HENRY   Travelling in Spain in the Present Day. London, 1866. Plts., 8vo., 1st ed., orig. cloth. Morrill 241-53 1978 $7.50

BLACKBURN, I. W.   Illustrations of the Gross Morbid Anatomy of the Brain in the Insane. Washington, 1908. Shaken, worn, ex-library. Rittenhouse 49-87 1976 $15

BLACKER, J. F.   The ABC of English Salt-Glaze Stoneware. London, 1922. Over 200 illus. in line & half-tone, thick 8vo. Traylen 88-364 1978 £15

BLACKETT, BASIL P.   Planned Money. 1933. Illus. with chart. Austin 80-435 1978 $12.50

BLACKFOOT Catechism and Prayers. N.P., 1920. Bound. Hood 116-400 1978 $175

BLACKFORD, CHARLES M.   Campaign and Battle of Lynchburg, Va. Lynchburg, Va., 1901 Wraps, Marginal stains, Stained & chipped cover, Bell Wiley's Copy. Broadfoot's Copy. 44-39 1978 $25.00

BLACKIE, JOHN STUART   Lyrical Poems. Edinburgh, 1860. First ed., prize calf gilt, inscribed by author, 8vo. K Books 244-37 1978 £12

BLACKLOCK, AMBROSE   A Treatise on Sheep. New York, 1841. 1st Amer. ed., pic. cloth, plts., very good, rare. Dykes 34-267 1978 $50

BLACKMAN, EMILY C.   History of Susquehanna County, Pa. Philadelphia, 1873. Illus., fold. maps, rebound. MacManus 239-1377 1978 $45

BLACKMAN, WINIFRED S.   The Fellahin of Upper Egypt. London, 1927. 8vo, orig. cloth, 180 illus. K Books 239-49 1978 £7

BLACKMAR, FRANK W.   Spanish Institutions of the Southwest. Baltimore, 1891. Illus., plates, maps, original cloth, 1st ed. Ginsberg 14-48 1978 $35

BLACKMORE, RICHARD d. 1729   Essays Upon Several Subjects. 1716. 1st ed., rebound in full calf, maroon label, very good copy. Jarndyce 16-39 1978 £54

BLACKMORE, RICHARD d. 1729   A Paraphrase on the Book of Job. 1700. 1st ed., folio, orig. calf, fine. Jarndyce 16-2 1978 £58

BLACKMORE, RICHARD d. 1729   Prince Arthur: An Heroick Poem. 1695. Second ed., folio, contemp. panelled calf, good. Howes 194-13 1978 £35

BLACKMORE, RICHARD DODDRIDGE   Dariel. A Romance of Surrey. London, 1897. Illus. by Chris Hammond, 8vo., orig. cloth, 1st ed., nice. MacManus 238-168 1978 $35

BLACKMORE, RICHARD DODDRIDGE   Lorna Doone. 1910. Coloured plts., roy. 4to., full green mor., gilt, top edges gilt, nice copy, no. 85 of ltd. ed. of 250 numbered copies. Fenning 32-27 1978 £38.50

BLACKMORE, RICHARD DODDRIDGE   Perlycross. New York, 1894. 1st Amer. ed., cloth, very good, 3 vols. in 1. Greene 78-148 1978 $15

BLACKMORE, RICHARD DODDRIDGE   Springhaven. A Tale of the Great War. London, 1887. 3 vols., orig. pict. cloth, 3rd ed., spines faded & worn, but good, sm. stamp. MacManus 238-167 1978 $50

BLACKMORE, RICHARD DODDRIDGE   Tales from the Telling-House. 1896. Sm. 8vo., 1st ed., orig. decor. buff cloth. Quaritch 979-35 1978 $25

BLACKWELL, ANTHONY   An Introduction to the Classics... 1828. 4th. ed., half calf, lib. no. on spine, good. Jarndyce 16-294 1978 £15

BLACKWELL, ELIZABETH   Pioneer Work in Opening the Medical Profession to Women: Autobiographical Sketches. London, 1895. 1st ed. Argosy Special-14 1978 $75

BLACKWELL, GEORGE   Large Examination Taken at Lambeth, According to His Majesties Direction, of M. George Blackwell, Made Archpriest of England, by Pope Clement 8. 1607. Limp vellum, text stained, corners bent. Allen 234-1115 1978 $75

BLACKWELL, I. A.   Rudolf of Varosnay: A Tragedy. 1841. First ed., contemp. half calf, 8vo. Howes 194-636 1978 £12.50

BLACKWELL, THOMAS   An Enquiry into the Life and Writings of Homer. 1735. Lg. 8vo., contemp. calf gilt, large and thick paper, fine, portrait, map. P. M. Hill 142-37 1978 £38

BLACKWELL, THOMAS   An Enquiry into the Life and Writings of Homer. 1736. Second ed., 8vo., contemp. panelled calf, hinges slightly worn. P. M. Hill 142-38 1978 £18

BLACKWOOD, ALGERNON   The Fruit Stoners; being the adventure of Maria among the fruit stoners. 1934. Very good, first English ed. Bell Book 16-321 1978 £5

BLACKWOOD, ALGERNON   The Fruit Stoners. New York, 1935. 1st Amer. ed. Biblo BL781-957 1978 $10

BLACKWOOD, ALGERNON   Full Circle. 1929. No. 358 of 530 copies no. & signed by author, bds., some fading of covers, very good, first English ed. Bell Book 17-108 1978 £18.50

BLACKWOOD, ALGERNON   Jimbo; a fantasy. 1909. Orig. patterned cloth, very fine, first English ed. Bell Book 16-322 1978 £10

BLACKWOOD, ALGERNON   A Prisoner in Fairyland... New York, 1913. 1st Amer. ed., inner hinges split. Biblo BL781-958 1978 $12

BLACKWOOD, ALGERNON   A Prisoner in Fairyland. London, 1925. Biblo BL781-959 1978 $10

BLADES, WILLIAM   The Enemies of Books. 1880. Second ed., 8vo., half mor., t.e.g., others uncut, frontispiece, plts., wrappers preserved, very good. P. M. Hill 142-39 1978 £18

BLADES, WILLIAM   The Enemies of Books. Battery Park 1-253 1978 $25

BLAEU, JOAN   Le Grand Atlas; ou Cosmographie Blaviane. (Amsterdami, 1662). Facs. ed., 12 vols., double-page maps, replica of orig. vellum binding. Van der Peet 127-278 1978 Dfl 3750

BLAGDON, F. W.   An Historical Memento, Representing the Different Scenes of Public Rejoicing, Which Took Place the First of August, in St. James's and Hyde Parks, London, in Celebration of the Glorious Peace of 1814... 1814. 4to., hand-coloured plts., a little foxed, old half mor. Quaritch 983-295 1978 $540

BLAIKIE, WILLIAM GARDEN   The Personal Life of David Livingstone. London, 1880. 8vo, orig. cloth, folding map, portrait, slightly shaken, covers dull. K-Books 239-50 1978 £8

BLAINE, DELABERE   Canine Pathology... 1832. Frontis, 8vo, little spotting, very good copy, contemp. half calf. Fenning 32-28 1978 £21.50

BLAINE, JAMES GILLESPIE   Twenty Years of Congress. Norwich, 1884. First ed., 2 vols. Biblo 248-90 1978 $37.50

BLAINE, JAMES GILLESPIE   Twenty Years of Congress From Lincoln to Garfield. Norwich, 1884. 2 vols., illus. Baldwins' 51-4 1978 $12.50

BLAINE, JAMES GILLESPIE   Twenty Years of Congress: From Lincoln to Garfield. Norwich, 1884-6. Portrs., 2 vols., 8vo., very nice, orig. cloth. Morrill 241-54 1978 $12.50

BLAINE, JAMES GILLESPIE   Twenty Years of Congress: From Lincoln to Garfield. Norwich, Conn., 1886. Full leather, Hinges starting, Bell Wiley's Copy. Broadfoot's 44-41 1978 $20.00

BLAIR, EDWARD TYLER   Lloyd Lee. N.P., n.d. (New Haven, 1878). Orig. binding, clean, worn at ends of spine & corners. Hayman 71-216 1978 $17.50

BLAIR, HUGH   Essays on Rhetorick: Abridged Chief From... Lectures on that Science. Boston, 1793. Contemp. calf, 8vo, very good. Americanist 103-21 1978 $25

BLAIR, HUGH   Lectures on Rhetoric and Belles Lettres. 1793. Engrav. portrait, 3 vols., half calf, little rubbed, 8vo. George's 635-1374 1978 £18

BLAIR, HUGH   Lectures on Rhetoric and Belles Lettres. London, 1796. Sixth ed., 3 vols., portrait, contemp. calf, endpapers very discoloured, new labels, 8vo. K Books 244-38 1978 £14

BLAIR, J. M.   Seeds of Destruction: Study in the Functional Weaknesses of Capitalism. 1938. Austin 80-436 1978 $10

BLAIR, JAMES   Our Saviour's Divine Sermon on the Mount. London, 1740. Second ed., 4 vols., 19th cent. calf, new labels, 8vo. K Books 244-39 1978 £80

BLAIR, JOHN   The Chronology and History of the World from the Creation to 1753 illustrated in 56 Tables. 1754. Vignette on title, tables, folio, contemp. calf a little rubbed. George's 635-544 1978 £20

BLAIR, JOHN   The Chronology and History of the World, from the Creation to 1753. 1756. Folio, contemp. calf, neatly rebacked, first ed. Howes 194-168 1978 £68

BLAIR, ROBERT   The Grave. 1743. 4to., 1st ed., disbound, fastened into grey wrs., age staining, good copy. Quaritch 979-36 1978 $150

BLAIR, ROBERT   The Grave. London, 1808. Illus. by etchings by Louis Schiavonetti, tall quarto, 3/4 red mor., cloth sides, port. of Blake by Schiavonetti from painting by T. Philip, 1st ed., fine. Duschnes 220-25 1978 $650

BLAKE, EUPHEMA VALE   Arctic Experiences: Containing Capt. George E. Tyson's Wonderful Drift on the Ice-Floe, a History of the Polaris Expedition.... New York, 1874. Mod. cloth, rebound. Hayman 72-60 1978 $10

BLAKE, FRANCIS 1738-1818   Political Tracts. 1795. New ed., newly bound in half calf antique, lettering-piece, entirely untrimmed, second collected ed, 8vo. Howes 194-169 1978 £35

BLAKE, FRANK   Memoir of George Smith Blake, Commodore, U. S. N., by his Nephew. (Cambridge), 1871. Sm. 8vo., 1st ed., pres. copy, orig. cloth. Morrill 241-55 1978 $10

BLAKE, GEORGE   The Coasts of Normandy. London, 1929. 32mo, blue paper covers, stitching loose, covers lightly sunned, 1st ed., collector's cond. Desmarais 1-110 1978 $10

BLAKE, HENRY T.   Chronicles of New Haven Green. New Haven, 1898. Illus. MacManus 239-952 1978 $25

BLAKE, JAMES   Annals of the Town of Dorchester, 1750. Boston, 1846. Facsimile, sm. 8vo., orig. bds., cloth back. Morrill 241-318 1978 $12.50

BLAKE, W. H.   A Fisherman's Creed. Toronto, 1923. Hood 117-451 1978 $10

BLAKE, W. O.   The History of Slavery and The Slave Trade, Ancient and Modern... Columbus, 1858. Rebound copy, clean, some foxing on title-pg., lt. dampstains at bottom corner of last few leaves. Hayman 71-52 1978 $20

BLAKE, WILLIAM   Auguries of Innocence. Pear Tree Press, 1904. 8vo., engr., vellum, 1 of only 25 signed by printer. Quaritch 979-253 1978 $580

BLAKE, WILLIAM   The Book of Thel. 1920. 4to., orig. wrs., ltd. to only 50 copies. Quaritch 979-37 1978 $320

BLAKE, WILLIAM   The Book of Thel. London, 1928. Quarto, cloth, gilt, repro. in color, 1 of 850 copies, fine. Duschnes 220-31 1978 $50

BLAKE, WILLIAM   Illustrations of the Book of Job. 1902. Folio, plts., wrs., bkplt., signature. Quaritch 979-38 1978 $100

BLAKE, WILLIAM   Illustrations to the Divine Comedy of Dante. 1922. Ltd. to 250 sets, plts., title stained, folio portfolio, stained and worn. George's 635-97 1978 £100

BLAKE, WILLIAM   Illustrations to the Divine Comedy of Dante. 1922. Folio, plts., bds., portfolio linen back, soiled. Quaritch 979-39 1978 $230

BLAKE, WILLIAM   Jerusalem the Emanation of the Giant Albion. 1804 (1877). Folio, half mor., decor. upper wr. bound in, 100 numbered copies. Quaritch 979-40 1978 $300

BLAKE, WILLIAM   The Life of George Romney, Esq. Chichester, 1809. 4to., frontis., plts., contemp. straight-grained green mor., back faded and a little rubbed. Quaritch 983-299 1978 $375

BLAKE, WILLIAM   The Marriage of Heaven and Hell. 1927. 4to., plts., cloth, neat signature. Quaritch 979-41 1978 $40

BLAKE, WILLIAM　　　　　The Poems of William Blake. London, 1874.
12mo, full niger mor. by Bayntun, gilt, t.e.g., marbled endpapers, joints starting,
fine. Duschnes 220-26 1978 $37.50

BLAKE, WILLIAM　　　　　Poetical Sketches by W. B. 1926. 8vo., paper
bds., wormed at lower bd. and inner margins, reproduction. Quaritch 979-42
1978 $30

BLAKE, WILLIAM　　　　　The Poetical Works of ... Oxford, 1905.
8vo, bound in full polished light brown calf, gilt panelled spine in compartment,
good. Sexton 7-133 1978 £30

BLAKE, WILLIAM　　　　　Poetical Works. 1913. Plts., cr. 8vo., orig.
maroon cloth, all edges gilt, India Paper issue of the Oxford ed. Howes 194-638
1978 $8.50

BLAKE, WILLIAM　　　　　Poetry and Prose. Nonesuch Press, 1927. Cr.
8vo., centenary ed., orig. buckram. Howes 194-639 1978 £7.50

BLAKE, WILLIAM　　　　　Songs of Experience. 1927. Sm. 4to., coloured
reproductions, cloth, inscr. Quaritch 979-43 1978 $50

BLAKE, WILLIAM　　　　　Songs of Innocence. 1926. Sm. 4to., coloured
reproductions, cloth gilt with signature. Quaritch 979-44 1978 $50

BLAKE, WILLIAM　　　　　The Works of William Blake, Poetic, Symbolic,
and Critical. London, 1893. Large 8vo, 3 vols., brown imitation leather
covers, leather spine and corners, scarce large paper ed., memoir and inter. by
Ellis, shelf wear, vols. II & III shaken, very Nice, ed. ltd. to 150 copies, 1st ed.
Desmarais 1-435 1978 $600

BLAKE, WILLIAM　　　　　The Writings of William Blake. London, Nonesuch Press, 1925. Quarto, full crushed niger mor., t.e.g., others uncut, repro.
illus. by Blake, 1 of 75 copies on India paper, 3 vols. issued in 1 vol., bookplt.,
fine. Duschnes 220-30 1978 $325

BLAKE, WILLIAM P.　　　　The Discovery of Tin Ore in the Black Hills,
Dakota. New York, 1883. Half mor. Ginsberg 14-307 1978 $75

BLAKEMORE, T.　　　　　The Art of Herbert Schmalz... 1911. Folio,
plain and coloured plts., parchment, bind. a little soiled but contents clean, uncut, ltd. to 150 copies, signed by artist. Quaritch 983-254 1978 $150

BLAKENEY, EDWARD HENRY　　Alpine Poems. Winchester, 1929. 1st ed.,
1 of 60 numbered copies, ed. 2, #4, sq. 8vo., orig. stiff wrs. Americanist 102-
20 1978 $35

BLAKENSHIP, GEORGIANA M.　Lights and Shades of Pioneer Life on Puget
Sound. Olympia, 1923. Orig. pr. wr., 1st ed. Ginsberg 14-1025 1978 $45

BLAKEY, D.　　　　　The Minerva Press 1790-1820. 1939. Plts.,
text illus., 8vo. George's 635-1190 1978 £40

BLAKEY, R.　　　　　Lives of the Primitive Fathers. 1842. Lg. 8vo.,
orig. cloth, uncut, plts. P. M. Hill 142-40 1978 £18

BLAKSTON, W. A.　　　　The Illustrated Book of Canaries and Cage Birds,
British and Foreign. (c. 1880). Coloured plts., woodcuts in text, pp. 57-64
misbound after p. 88, 4to., binders cloth. George's 635-1003 1978 £45

BLANC, CH.　　　　　Grammaire des Arts du Dessin. Paris, 1870.
2nd ed., lg. thick 8vo., half calf, plts. Van der Peet H-64-101 1978 Dfl 85

BLANCHAN, N.　　　　　Bird Neighbors. New York, 1900. Hinges
repaired, 4to., orig. cloth, colored plts. Book Chest 17-49 1978 $14

BLANCHAN, N.　　　　　Game-Birds - Birds that Hunt and are Hunted.
New York, 1908. Plts. and half-tones, sm. 4to, plts. in color, orig. cloth. Book
Chest 17-48 1978 $20

BLANCHARD, LAMAN　　　　The Poetical Works... 1876. 1st. ed., photographic vignette on title, half title, orig. green cloth, fine copy. Jarndyce 16-
295 1978 £12.50

BLANCHARD, MARY MILES　　The Basketry Book. New York, 1914. Fully
illus. Baldwins' 51-31 1978 $12.50

BLANCHARD, PIERRE　　　　Les Jeunes Enfans Contes. Paris, n.d. c.1845.
7th ed., 12mo, engraved plates, board rubbing, pencilling, very good. Victoria
34-76 1978 $15

BLANCHARD, RUFUS　　　　The Discovery and Conquests of the Northwest
Including the Early History of Chicago, Detroit, Vincennes, St. Louis, Ft. Wayne,
Prairie Du Chien, Marietta, Cincinnati, Cleveland... Chicago, 1880. 1st ed.,
illus., maps, orig. cloth, fine. MacManus 239-1900 1978 $40

BLANCHARD, SYDNEY　　　　Mr. Puchn: His Origin and Career. (1870). 1st.
ed., 12mo, half maroon morocco, slightly rubbed, bookplt. of Edmund Yates.
Jarndyce 16-296 1978 £12.50

BLANCHET, FRANCIS NORBERT　　Farewell Pastoral of Archbishop Blanchet.
N.P., ca. 1881. Disbound. Ginsberg 14-49 1978 $25

BLANCHET, FRANCOIS NORBET　　Memoire Presente a la S. Congregation de la
Propagande sur le Territoire de L'Oregon. Quebec, 1847. Original printed wr.,
1st ed. Ginsberg 14-50 1978 $125

BLANCHET, FRANCOIS XAVIER　　Dix Ans sur la Cote du Pacifique par un
Missionaire Canadien. Quebec, 1873. Orig. wr., 1st ed. Ginsberg 14-806
1978 $100

BLANCOURT, JEAN HAUDICQUER DE
Please turn to
HAUDICQUER DE BLANCOURT, JEAN

BLAND, DAVID　　　　　A History of Book Illustration. Berkeley & Los
Angeles. 8vo., thick, frontis., illus., d.w. Battery Park 1-252 1978 $32.50

BLAND, HUMPHREY　　　　A Treatise of Military Discipline. 1743. Fifth
ed., contemp. calf, inner hinges cracked, 8vo. Howes 194-170 1978 £32

BLAND, HUMPHREY　　　　A Treatise of Military Discipline. 1759. 8vo.,
eighth ed., contemp. calf, rebacked. F. Edwards 1013-252 1978 £45

BLAND, J. O. P.　　　　Recent Events and Present Policies in China.
London, 1912. Cloth, some wear and foxing, hinges weak. Dawson's 449-10
1978 $35

BLAQUIERE, LT. COL. DE　　A Short View of the Actual State of the Volunteers. 1804. 8vo., wrappers. F. Edwards 1013-253 1978 £10

BLATCHFORD, ROBERT　　　Merrie England. Girard, 1903. Wrs., moderately worn. Hayman 73-53 1978 $7.50

BLATZ, W. E.　　　　　The Five Sisters; A Study of Child Psychology.
Toronto, 1938. Hood's 115-378 1978 $15

BLAU, JOSEPH L.　　　　American Philosophic Addresses: 1700-1900.
1946. Austin 82-212 1978 $12.50

BLAZE DE BURY, BARONESS MARIE PAULINE ROSE　　Germania: Is Court, Camps
& People. London, 1850. 1st ed. in 2 vols., orig. blue cloth, very fine condition.
Greene 78-7 1978 $135

BLEDSOE, ALBERT TAYLOR　　An Essay on Liberty and Slavery. Philadelphia,
1856. 1st ed. MacManus 239-834 1978 $30

BLEDSOE, ALBERT TAYLOR　　Is Davis a Traitor; or, Was Secession a
Constitutional Right Previous to the War of 1861? Baltimore, 1866. Rebound
by hand. Bell Wiley's copy. Broadfoot 46-20 1978 $20

BLEDSOE, ALBERT TAYLOR　　The War Between the States. Lynchburg, Va.,
1915. Illus., Cover spotted, Bell Wiley's Copy. Broadfoot's 44-44 1978 $10.00

BLEECKER, ANN ELIZA　　The Posthumous Works of...in Prose and Verse...
New York, 1793. Orig. roan, rubbed, upper cover detached, 1st ed., some
staining throughout. MacManus 238-428 1978 $50

BLEEKER, P.　　　　　Recherches sur les Crustaces de L'Inde Archipe-
lagique. Botavia, 1856. French text, bound in black cloth, ex-lib with stamps,
water stained, scarce, 8vo. Book Chest 17-50 1978 $22.50

BLEGEN, THEODORE C. Civil War Letters of Colonel Han Christian Heg. 1936. Frontis. Austin 79-80 1978 $20

BLEGEN, THEODORE C. The Civil War Letters of Colonel Hans Christian H Heg. Northfield, 1936. Illus., Bell Wiley's copy. Broadfoot's 44-681 1978 $20

BLEGEN, THEODORE C. Norwegian Migration to America. 1940. Illus., lst ed. Austin 79-79 1978 $15

BLEGNY, ETIENNE DE Les Elemens ou Premieres Instructions de la Jeunesse. Paris, 1605. (i.e. 1705). 8vo., cont. mottled calf, plts., early ed. Schumann 511-6 1978 sFr 875

BLENNERHASSET, LADY Madame De Stael, Her Friends & Her Influences in Politics & Literature. London, 1889. lst ed., orig. cloth, spine ends damaged, 3 vols., good set. Greene 78-149 1978 $65

BLESSING, WILLIAM LESTER The Semitic Race. 1946. Austin 79-81 1978 $27.50

BLESSINGTON, JOSEPH P. The Campaigns of Walker's Texas Division... New York, 1875. Original cloth, wear to covers, lst ed. Jenkins 116-122 1978 $100

BLESSINGTON, MARGUERITE POWER FARMER GARDINER, COUNTESS OF The Victims of Society. London, 1837. 3 vols., 12mo., original grey bds., pr. paper labels, inner hinges a bit brittle, lst ed., fine copy, orig. cond. Ximenes 47-27 1978 $175

BLETTERIE, JEAN DE LA 1696-1722 Histoire de l'Emperur Jovien. Paris, 1776. Sm. 8vo., contemp. calf, spine gilt. Howes 194-557 1978 £18

BLEWETT, JEAN The Cornflower and Other Poems. Toronto, 1907. Hood 117-781 1978 $10

BLEWETT, JEAN Poems. Toronto, 1922. Inscribed and signed. Hood 116-799 1978 $12.50

BLIGH, WILLIAM Narrative of the Mutiny on Boards H.M.S. Bounty... 1790. lst. ed., 4to, half calf, slight foxing on l chart, few other leaves, light offsetting. Edwards 1012-358 1978 £1200

BLIGH, WILLIAM Vogage in the Resource... Golden Cockerel Press, 1937. Folio, engravings on wood, ltd. ed. of 350 numbered copies. Edwards 1012-359 1978 £320

THE BLIND Man's Friend and Other Tales. Hudson, 1855. Sq. 16mo, rare chapbook, woodcuts, large wrapper but, signed by W.T. Norman and H. Rooers, almost fine. Victoria 34-78 1978 $20

BLISH, J. K. Genealogy of the Blish Family in America. Kewanee, 1905. Ltd. to 315 copies, illus., orig. cloth, some staining. MacManus 239-915 1978 $35

BLISS, CARMAN Far Horizons. Toronto, 1925. Hood's 115-863 1978 $12.50

BLISS, DOUGLAS PERCY A History of Wood-Engraving. London, 1928. 1st ed., 4to, illus., orig. cloth, very good. MacManus 239-641 1978 $45

BLISS, WILLIAM ROOT Colonial Times on Buzzard's Bay. Boston, 1888. lst. ed. Baldwins' 51-392 1978 $17.50

BLIXEN, KAREN Out of Africa. London, (1937), reprint 1946. 8vo, orig. cloth, covers sunned. K Books 239-52 1978 £5

BLOCH, CHAJIM Das Judische Amerika. Vienna, 1926. Illus. with photos, in German, binding needs repair. Austin 79-82 1978 $20

BLOCH, IWAN Marquis De Sade: His Life and Works. (N.Y., Brittany Press, 1948). 8 vo., d.j., very good. Houle 10-36 1978 $20

BLOCKADE of Quebec in 1775-76 by the American Revolutionists. Quebec, 1906. Printed wrappers. Wolfe 39-461 1978 $25

BLOMFIELD, EZEKIEL Lectures on the Philosophy of History. London, 1819. 4to., old bds. re-papered in black, uncut, coloured maps. P. M. Hill 142-43 1978 £18

BLOMFIELD, R. A History of Renaissance Architecture in England, 1500-1800. 1897. Drawings by author, 2 vols., 4to., covers a little soiled. George's 635-77 1978 £21

BLONDEL, JACQUES-FRANCOIS De la Distribution des Maisons de Plaisance, et de la Decoration des Edifices en General. Paris, 1737-38. Engr. copperplts., 2 vols., 4to., contemp. tooled vellum, lst ed. Argosy Special-15 1978 $750

BLOOD, GRACE H. Manchester on the Merrimack. Manchester, (1948). Illus., lst ed. Biblo BL781-139 1978 $10

BLOOM, SOL History of the Formation of the Union Under the Constitution... Washington, 1935. Illus., 4to. Biblo BL781-193 1978 $12

BLOOMFIELD, J. K. The Oneidas. New York, 1909. Illus., orig. cloth, some wear, scarce. MacManus 239-1145 1978 $37.50

BLOOMFIELD, ROBERT The Banks of the Wye; a Poem. 1811. 1st. ed., frontis, 3 plts., uncut in orig. grey bds., paper label, spine defective at head & tail, otherwise v.g., orig. condition. Jarndyce 16-297 1978 £28

BLOOMFIELD, ROBERT The Farmer's Boy. 1800. 4to., lst quarto ed., wood engrs., half blue mor., bkplt. of Clement K. Shorter. Quaritch 979-53 1978 $300

BLOOMFIELD, ROBERT The Farmer's Boy; a Rural Poem. 1800. 4to., 1st quarto ed., wood engravings by Thomas Bewick, half blue mor. Quaritch 983-301 1978 $375

BLOOMFIELD, ROBERT Rural Tales, Ballads, and Songs. London, 1802. 2nd ed., plates by Thomas Bewick, staining of first and last few leaves, contemporary calf, upper cover held by stitching, text very good. Victoria 34-79 1978 $35

BLOSIUS, ABBOT Meditations on the Life and Death of the Holy Jesus, and two Discourses by the Archbishop of Cambray. Edinburgh, 1730. 12mo. old calf, worn. George's 635-1033 1978 £5

BLOUET, LEON P. John Bull and His Island. (1884). Cr. 8vo, orig. cloth, worn but sound, very good. Fenning 32-29 1978 £10.50

BLOUNT, CHARLES The Miscellaneous Works. N.P., 1695. Sole ed., small octavo, 3/4 calf over marbled boards, raised spine bands, gilt spine rules, foxed lightly throughout, scarce, else fine. Bennett 7-13 1978 $175

BLOUNT, CHARLES The Two First Books, of Philostratus, Concerning the Life of Apollonius Tyaneus:.... London, 1680. Tall quarto, early half calf over marbled boards, bookplate of Lovell Edgeworth and his signature, lst ed. Bennett 7-14 1978 $95

BLOUNT, HENRY A Voyage into the Levant:.... London, 1671. 12mo, wormhole in lower blank margins, contemp. calf, last ed. Quaritch 978-15 1978 $180

BLOUNT, THOMAS Fragmenta Antiquitatis. 1679. Sm. 8vo., well bound in full 19th cent. polished calf gilt, fine, first ed., with license leaf signed by Francis North. Howes 194-14 1978 £55

BLOXAM, MATTHEW HOLBECHE The Principles of Gothic Ecclesiastical Architecture. London, 1843. Fifth ed., plts., wood-engravings, 12mo., backstrip snagged, 8vo. K Books 244-40 1978 £7

BLUM, ANDRE Les Origines Du Papier De L'Imprimerie et de la Gravure. Paris, 1935. Newly bound in cloth, frontis. Battery Park 1-442 1978 $75

BLUM'S Farmer's and Planter's Almanac. Salem. Wrs., some covers chipped, 1853, 1871, 1872, 1875, 1876, 1877, 1879, 1880, 1881, 1882, 1884, 1885, 1886, 1892, 1894, 1895, 1896, 1897, 1898, 1913, 1918, and 1924. Broadfoot 50-14 1978 $150

BLUME, KARL LUDWIG   Flora Javae Nec Non Insularum Adjacentium.
Brussels, 1828–62. Frontis, plts. mostly hand coloured, 3 vols., lg. folio, modern
green morocco gilt, edges uncut, brilliant & complete copy. Traylen 88–645
1978 £2400

BLUMENBACH, JOHANN FRIEDRICH   Handbuch der Vergleichenden Anatomie. Gottingen, 1805. 8vo., plts., contemp. bds., very fine copy, 1st ed.
Gilhofer 74–85 1978 sFr 2,200

BLUMHARDT, J. F.   Catalogues of the Hindi, Panjabi, Sindhi, and
Pushtu Printed Books. London, 1893. Demy 4to., orig. cloth. Forster 130–185
1978 £10

BLUMHARDT, J. F.   Catalogue of Hindustani Printed Books. London,
1889. Demy 4to., orig. cloth, lacks half of spine. Forster 130–184 1978 £7.50

BLUNDELL, WILLIAM   Cavalier; Letters of William Blundell to His
Friends. 1938. Good, octavo. Upcroft 10–14 1978 £7.50

BLUNDEN, EDMUND   In Summer. 1931. First ed., orig. bds., ltd.
to 250 copies only, signed by author, 8vo. Howes 194–646 1978 £10

BLUNDEN, EDMUND   Masks of Time. (Westminster, Beaumont Press,
1925). Decor. bds., vellum spine, fine, 1 of 80 copies on Japanese vellum,
signed by author. Dawson's 447–205 1978 $50

BLUNDEN, EDMUND   Masks of Time: a new collection of poems.
Beaumont Press, 1925. No. 177 of 310 copies signed by author, cloth-backed bds.,
very good, first English ed. Bell Book 16–096 1978 £30

BLUNDEN, EDMUND   Nature in English Literature. London, Hogarth
Press, 1929. 8vo, cloth, 1st ed., fine. Duschnes 220–142 1978 $15

BLUNDEN, EDMUND   Near and Far. London, 1929. 8vo, green cloth,
spine faded, handmade paper, uncut, no. 118 of ltd. ed. of 160, 1st ed, collector's
condition, signed by Blunden. Desmarais 1–46 1978 $35

BLUNDEN, EDMUND   Near and Far. New Poems. London, 1929.
Unopened, near mint in darkened d.w. Desmarais B–93 1978 $15

BLUNDEN, EDMUND   Near and Far. London, 1929. Cloth, unopened,
near fine, browned & torn d.w. Dawson's 447–206 1978 $20

BLUNDEN, EDMUND   Near and Far. New York, Golden Hind Press,
1930. Paste-paper bds., in d.w., very fine, publisher's box, repaired with tape,
1 of 105 copies signed by author, hand-colored frontis, 1st Amer. ed. Dawson's
447–207 1978 $75

BLUNDEN, EDMUND   On Several Occasions; poems. London, Corvinus
Press, 1938. One of 60 numbered copies on Arnold and Foster handmade paper,
signed by author, printed in 18pt. Corvinus light italic, roy. 8vo., cloth over bds.,
upper cover slightly damp-stained, nice. Rota 212–5 1978 £135

BLUNDEN, EDMUND   Poems, 1930–1940. 1940. Cloth, edges soiled.
Eaton 45–52 1978 £5

BLUNDEN, EDMUND   Retreat. 1928. Very good, d.w., signed by
the author, first English ed. Bell Book 16–097 1978 £25

BLUNDEN, EDMUND   Retreat. Thavies Inn, (1928). Cloth, bit foxed,
Dawson's 447–208 1978 £20

BLUNDEN, EDMUND   Shelley: A Life Story. London, 1946. 8vo,
red cloth, 1st ed., mint in d.w. Desmarais 1–47 1978 $12.50

BLUNDEN, EDMUND   A Summer's Fancy. London, 1930. Orig. vellum-backed bds., 1st ed., 1 of 80 copies of an ed. of 405 on parchment vellum
signed by author, fine. MacManus 238–621 1978 $65

BLUNDEN, EDMUND   To Nature: New Poems by Edmund Blunden.
London, 1923. 8vo patterned boards, cloth back, near mint, 1st ed., ed. ltd. to
390 copies, 380 for sale and this is no. 240. Desmarais 1–48 1978 $25

BLUNDEN, EDMUND   To Themis. Poems on Famous Trials. With Other
Pieces. London, 1931. Orig. vellum-backed bds., 1st ed., 1 of 80 copies of a
total ed of 405 on parchment vellum signed by author, fine. MacManus 238–622
1978 $60

BLUNDEN, EDMUND   To Themis: Poems on Famous Trials, with other
pieces. Beaumont Press, 1931. One of 325 numbered copies on handmade paper,
frontis, cloth-backed bds., fine, unopened, first English ed. Bell Book 17–113
1978 £20

BLUNDEN, EDMUND   Undertones of War. 1928. Good, inscribed by
author, 3rd imp., covers somewhat dull, first English ed. Bell Book 16–098 1978
£35

BLUNDEN, EDMUND   The Waggoner and other poems. London, 1920.
Second issue, green cloth, fine, scarce. Rota 211–44 1978 £17

BLUNDEN, EDMUND   The Waggoner and Other Poems. London, 1920.
Near mint in chipped d.w., author's 1st published book. Desmarais B–94 1978
$50

BLUNT, E. M.   American Coast Pilot... New York, 1847.
15th ed., 1st issue, orig. leather rubbed, charts, 8vo, good. Paine 78–8 1978
$45.00

BLUNT, E. M.   The American Coast Pilot...Eighteenth Edition.
New York, 1857. Spine defective, orig. sheep, 8vo. Paine 78–9 1978 $35.00

BLUNT, R.   The Cheyne Book of Chelsea China and Pottery.
(1924). One of 100 numbered copies, signed by author, colour plts., cr. 4to.,
orig. qtr. vellum, cloth sides. George's 635–227 1978 £50

BLUNT, WILFRID SCAWEN   Love Lyrics. Kelmscott Press, 1892. 8vo., prtd.
in black & red, woodcut borders, vellum with ties. Quaritch 979–213 1978 $350

BLUNT, WILFRID SCAWEN   The Love Sonnets of Proteus. 1881. Frontispiece
by author, orig. cloth, soiled. Eaton 45–53 1978 £10

BLUNTSCHLI, J. C.   Allgemeine Geschichte Des Staats Rechts Und
Der Politik... Munich, 1864. Tall 8vo., contemp. marbled bds. with label, top
of spine chipped. Salloch 348–14 1978 $25

THE BOA Constrictor and Other Stories. Boston, 1852. Clean, orig. binding,
minor internal dampstains. Hayman 71–381 1978 $7.50

BOARDMAN, ANNE COWLEY   Such Love is Seldom. 1950. Austin 79–
83 1978 $8.50

BOARDMAN, J. A.   Vocabulary in the English, Latin, German,
French, Italian, Spanish and Portuguese Languages. n.d. Bds., paper spine.
Eaton 45–54 1978 £10

BOARDMAN, JAMES   America and the Americans. London, 1833.
New cloth, 1st ed. MacManus 239–55 1978 $37.50

BOARDMAN, WILLIAM H.   The Lovers of the Woods. 1901. Very good.
Nestler Rare 78–98 1978 $20

BOAS, F. S.   The Year's Work in English Studies. Oxford &
London, 1940–64. 18 vols., 8vo, orig. bds. Traylen 88–236 1978 £40

BOAS, FRANZ   Handbook of American Indian Languages.
Washington, D.C., 1911–1922. 2 vols., nice, rebound. MacManus 239–1146
1978 $60

BOAS, FRANZ   The Mind of Primitive Man. (1911) 1921.
Austin 79–84 1978 $11

BOAS, GEORGE   The Adventures of Human Thought... New
York, 1929. 8vo., cloth. Salloch 348–15 1978 $12.50

BOAS, I.   Diseases of the Stomach. Philadelphia, 1908.
Shaken, ex-library. Rittenhouse 49–90 1976 $10

BOATENG, OTTO AMPOFO   Songs for Infant Schools. London, (1949). 2nd
impression, 12mo, pictorial wrappers, fine. Victoria 34–81 1978 $10

BOATFIELD, ROSAMOND   The King's Fairy Air Force. (Bombay, 1915). 1st ed., limited to 1,000 copies, quarto, color plates, colored pictorial boards, rubbed and tiny scratches, very decent. Victoria 34-214 1978 $50

BOBRINSKY, COUNT A. A.   Russian Peasant Art. New York, n.d. Plates, very large quarto, photos, all plates laid-in loose as issued, within cloth folder, minor chipping of heavy plate paper, very scarce. Victoria 34-82 1978 $75

BOCCACCIO, GIOVANNI   Amorous Flammetta. 1926. Orig. cloth, gilt top, uncut, 8vo. Howes 194-648 1978 £7.50

BOCCACCIO, GIOVANNI   De Claris Mulieribus. Berne, 1539. Folio, illus., red mor., gilt, fine copy, 1st ed. Gilhofer 74-128 1978 sFr 3,500

BOCCACCIO, GIOVANNI   Contes De Boccacce Illustrations de Jacques Wagrez Traduction et Notes de Francisque Reynard. Paris, n.d. 3 vols., lg. 8vo., cloth, very good. King 7-335 1978 £25

BOCCACCIO, GIOVANNI   Il Decamerone di M. Giovan Boccaccio, alla sva intera perfettione ridotto,..... Venice, 1554. 4to, Italic letter, woodcut illus., one or two marginal defects, some occasional light staining, contemp. mottled calf, gilt spine repaired at top and base. Quaritch 978-17 1978 $225

BOCCACCIO, GIOVANNI   Decamerone. 1762. Engrav. frontispiece, 4to., contemp. calf, joints cracked. Howes 194-171 1978 £35

BOCCACCIO, GIOVANNI   The Decameron. 1887. Sm. 4to., large paper, contemp. vellum gilt, uncut, nice. P. M. Hill 142-44 1978 £24

BOCCACCIO, GIOVANNI   Decameron of Giovanni Boccaccio. London, n.d. (c. 1920). Thick 8 vo., printed on laid paper special made for Navarre Society, t.e.g., uncut, partly unopened, 2 vols., fine set. Houle 10-61 1978 $35

BOCCACCIO, GIOVANNI   Boccacio's Decameron. Oxford, Shakespeare Head Press, 1934-5. 2 vols., quarto, bound in orig. full blue mor., gilt lettering on spine, minor rubbing, gilt top, 1 of 325 pr., woodcuts, very good. Totteridge 29-94 1978 $400

BOCCACCIO, GIOVANNI   Ioannis Boccatii De Certaldo Insigne opus de Claris Mulieribus.... Berne, 1539. Small folio, roman letter, woodcuts by Jacob Kallenberg, old limp boards, blue edges. Quaritch 978-16 1978 $1,550

BOCCACCIO, GIOVANNI   A Translation of Giovanni Boccaccio's Life of Dante. Devinne Press, 1900. One of 300 copies prtd. on Italian handmade paper, illus., decor. binding. Battery Park 1-64 1978 $125

BOCCACCIO, GIOVANNI   Novelle Ventotto di Messer Giovanni Boccacci. Padova, 1739. 8vo., marbled bds., calf spine, very good. King 7-140 1978 £20

BOCCACCIO, GIOVANNI   The Story of Griselda...from the Decameron. (London, 1909). 1 of 500 copies on hand-made paper, thin 4to., orig. dec. wrs., uncut. Americanist 102-100 1978 $50

BOCCACCIO, GIOVANNI   The Story of Griselda. 1909. One of 500 copies on Batchelor hand-made paper, linen backed bds., ink inscription on f.e.p. Eaton 45-336 1978 £5

BOCCACCIO, GIOVANNI   Thirteene most pleasant and delectable Questions. 1927. Ed. ltd. to 520 copies, recent leatherette. George's 635-879 1978 £12.50

BOCCALINI, TRAJANO 1556-1613   Ragguagli di Parnasso. 1656. First ed. in English, folio, lacks portrait, contemp. calf, sometime rebacked, corners defective, new endpapers. Howes 194-15 1978 £22

BOCCALINI, TRAJANO 1556-1613   Ragguagli di Parnasso. 1674. Engraved portrait, folio, newly bound in qtr. calf, first and last leaves slightly stained, third ed. Howes 194-16 1978 £45

BOCHART, SAMUEL   Opera Omnia. Leyden, 1692. Engr. title, engr. maps, tall folio, vellum, few water stains, generally very good cond. Salloch 345-26 1978 $85

BOCKLER, G. A.   Theatrum Machinarum Novum, Exhibens Aquarias, Alatas lumentarias, Manuarias,.... Cologne, 1662. Folio, plts., 6 plts. remargined and mounted, 18th century blind panelled calf, neatly rebacked and restored. Quaritch 977-206 1978 $2,250

BOCKWITZ, HANS H.   The Feldmuehle Chronicles. 1935. Sm. folio, cloth, illus. Battery Park 1-458 1978 $275

BOCTHOR, ELLIOUS   Dictionnaire Francaise-Arabe... Paris, 1828. 2 vols., lg. 8vo, little foxed, rebound in cloth. Eaton 45-55 1978 £15

BODDAM-WHETHAM, JOHN W.   Roraima and British Guiana. London, 1879. Frontis., map, 8vo., dampstains, spine worn, orig. cloth. Morrill 241-56 1978 $25

BODDY, ALEXANDER A.   To Kairwan the Holy. London, 1885. Cr. 8vo, map, 8 plts., lib. stamp on title, back of map soiled, binders buckram. K Books 239-55 1978 £8

BODE, C. A.   Travels in Luristan and Arabistan. London, 1845. 1st ed., royal 8vo., plts., fldg. maps, fldg. plt. of inscrip's, orig. maroon cloth bindings, spines faded, some foxing. Current 24-173 1978 $195

BODE, WILHELM   Florentine Sculptors of the Renaissance. 1908. 4to., plts., foxed. Allen 234-1117 1978 $30

BODILLY, R. B.   The Voyage of Captain Thomas James for the Discovery of the North-West Passage, 1631. London, 1928. Hood 116-64 1978 $45

BODIN, JEAN   Methodus as facilem historiarum cognitionem. Paris, 1566. 1st ed., rare, sm. 4 to., French contemp. blind-stamped calf. Quaritch Summer,1978-6 1978 $1,800

BOECKH, AUGUSTUS   Public Economy of Athens. 1842. 2nd rev. ed. Austin 80-437 1978 $27.50

BOEDO, EMILIO CASTRO   Estudios Sobre la Navegacion del Bermejo y Colonizaciondel Chaco. Buenos Ayres, 1873. 1/2 leath., worn, 8vo. Paine 78-10 1978 $12.50

BOEHME, JACOB   Aurora das ist: Morgen Roete Um Aufgangg Und Mutter Der Philosophiae. N.P., 1634. 12mo., calf, spine gilt with label, 1st ed., fine. Salloch 348-16 1978 $1,100

BOEHN, M. VON   Der Tanz. Berlin, 1925. Sm. 8vo., half calf, illus. Van der Peet H-64-103 1978 Dfl 40

BOELSCHE, WILHELM   Haeckel, His Life and Work. Philadelphia, n.d. Illus. Salloch 345-88 1978 $30

BOEMUS, JOANNES   The Fardle of facions conteining the aunciente maners, customes, and Lawes,.... London, 1555. Small 8vo, black letter, some sidenotes, headlines on last three leaves cut into, wormholes, contemp. limp vellum, 1st English ed. Quaritch 978-18 1978 $4,250

THE BOER War, 1899-1900. London, 1900. Roy. 8vo, 10 plts., age-browned throughout due to poor paper, dec. cloth, covers little dull. K Books 239-56 1978 £12

BOERHAAVE, HERMANN   Elements of Chemistry. London, 1735. 2 vols., 4to., fldg. plts., antique speckled calf, gilt, fine copy, 1st unabridged ed. in English. Norman 5-39 1978 $750

BOERHAAVE, HERMANN   Institutiones et Experimenta Chemiae. Paris (Leiden?), 1724. 2 vols., 8vo., fldg. plt., old calf, gilt, fine set, 1st ed. Norman 5-37 1978 $450

BOERSCHMANN, ERNST   Baukunst und Lanschaft in China. Berlin, (1926). Cloth, faded, warped, rear hinge tender, plts. Dawson's 449-11 1978 $40

BOFARULL Y SANS, DON FRANCISCO DE A   Los Animales en las Marcas Del Papel. Oliva, 1910. 4to., 3/4 lea., watermarks. Battery Park 1-441 1978 $250

BOGAN, ZACHARY   Meditations of the Mirth of a Christian Life. Oxford, 1653. 1st. ed., sm. 8vo, contemp. calf rebacked, slight water-stains. Hannas 54-23 1978 £28

BOGATZKY, C.H. v.   A Golden Treasury for the Children of God. New York, 1811. Sq. 12mo., calf covers rubbed, text browned, very good and solid. Victoria 34-83 1978 $12.50

BOGUET, HENRY   An Examen of Witches drawn from various trials of many of this Sect in the district of Saint Oyan de Joux.... 1929. Ed. ltd. to 1275 numbered copies, cr. 8vo., orig. qtr. green parchment, spine discoloured. George's 635-1421 1978 £21

BOHER, PIERRE   The Art of Knowing Ones Self.... London, 1696. 2 parts in one vol., sm. 8vo, contemp. calf. Traylen 88-118 1978 £75

BOHM-BAWERK, EUGEN V.   The Positive Theory of Capital. 1891. 1st English Ed.   Austin 80-439 1978 $37.50

BOHN, HENRY G.   A Dictionary of Quotations from the English Poets. London, 1881. Orig. cloth, 8vo.   K Books 244-41 1978 £5

BOHR, NIELS HENDRIK DAVID   On the Quantum Theory of Line-Spectra. Copenhagen, 1918-1922. 1st ed., orig. pr. wr., uncut copy. Gilhofer 75-12 1978 SFr 1,800

BOHR, NIELS HENDRIK DAVID   Uber die Quanteentheorie der Linienspektren. Braunschweig, 1923. 8 vo., 1st German ed., half cloth.   Schafer 19-46 1978 sFr. 200

BOILEAU, DANIEL   The Nature and Genius of the German Language. 1820. First ed., table, contemp. half calf, joints cracked, 8vo.   Howes 194-294 1978 £10

BOILEAU-DESPREAUX, NICOLAS   Oeuvres Diverses du Sieur D***. Paris, 1685. Nouvelle ed., engravings, lacks one, sm. cr. 8vo, bookplt. & signature of Robert Lord Raymond, old calf, gilt, joints tender. Eaton 45-56 1978 £20

BOILEAU-DESPREAUX, NICOLAS   Les Oeuvres. Paris, 1740. 2 vols., 4to., contemp. calf, gilt backs, labels missing. Howes 194-530 1978 £22

BOISGELIN DE KERDU, LOUIS DE   Ancient and Modern Malta. London, 1805. 3 parts in 2 vols., 4to., contemp. bds., cloth spine, plts., mainly unopened. King 7-338 1978 £330

BOISSEAU, F. G.   A Treatise on Cholera Morbus. New York, 1832. 8vo., orig. bds., cloth back, foxed, 1st Amer. ed. Morrill 239-23 1978 $30

BOISSONADE, P.   Life and Work in Medieval Europe, 5th to 15th Centuries. 1927. Illus., roy. 8vo. George's 635-561 1978 £6

BOISSONADE, P.   Le Socialisme d'etat, l'industrie et les classes industrielles en France pendant les deux premiers siecles de l'ere moderne (1453-1661). 1927. Roy. 8vo. George's 635-286 1978 £6.25

BOIVIN, MARIE ANNE VICTOIRE   Traite Pratique Des Maladies De L'Uterus Et De Ses Annexes, fonde sur un grand nombre d'observations cliniques. Paris, 1833. 2 vols., 8vo., folio atlas, plts. bound in separate folio, contemp. mottled bds., calf backs very worn, folio vol. of explanation in mottled bds., backed in green library cloth, lightly browned & foxed, bkplts., library stamps, good copy, 1st ed., scarce. Zeitlin 245-298 1978 $575

BOJER, JOHAN   The Emigrants. 1925. Austin 79-85 1978 $7.50

BOK, EDWARD W.   America's Taj Mahal. The Singing Tower of Florida. Tate, n.d. 4to., plts. Biblo BL781-731 1978 $12

BOKER, GEORGE HENRY   The Legend of the Hounds. New York, 1929. One of 200 deluxe copies, pictures by Gordon Ross, prints hand colored, frontis signed by Ross, in slip box. Baldwins' 51-541 1978 $27.50

BOLAS, THOMAS   Glass Blowing and Working for Amateurs, Experimentalists, and Technicians. London, n.d.(1898?). Orig. binding, colored frontispiece, numerous illus., clean. Hayman 71-53 1978 $8.50

THE BOLD Soldier Boy's Song Book. Richmond, 1863. Wrs., Bell Wiley's copy. Broadfoot 46-460 1978 $150

BOLDUC, J. B. Z.   Mission de la Colombie. Quebec, 1845. Half morocco, 1st ed. Ginsberg 14-51 1978 $100

BOLINGBROKE, HENRY ST. JOHN 1678-1751   A Collection of Political Tracts. 1848. First ed., contemp. calf, spine rubbed, label missing, slight foxing, 8vo. Howes 194-172 1978 £28

BOLINGBROKE, HENRY ST. JOHN 1678-1751   Bolingbroke's Defence of the Treaty of Utrecht.... Cambridge, 1932. Octavo, good. Upcroft 10-151 1978 £5

BOLINGBROKE, HENRY ST. JOHN 1678-1751   A Letter to Sir William Windham. 1753. Portrait, first ed., contemp. calf, 8vo., spine rubbed, label missing. Howes 194-174 1978 £30

BOLINGBROKE, HENRY ST. JOHN 1678-1751   A Letter to Sir William Windham.... London, 1753. Full contemp. calf, 1st ed., fine copy. MacManus 238-96 1978 $75

BOLINGBROKE, HENRY ST. JOHN 1678-1751   Letters and Correspondence, Public and Private, during the time he was Secretary of State to Queen Anne. 1798. 4vols., contemp. tree calf, 2 joints cracked, 8vo. Howes 194-175 1978 £42

BOLINGBROKE, HENRY ST. JOHN 1678-1751   Letters on the Spirit of Patriotism.... London, 1749. 8vo., orig. grey wrs., uncut, 1st authorized ed., spine defective, corners worn, but very good. MacManus 238-95 1978 $100

BOLINGBROKE, HENRY ST. JOHN 1678-1751   Letters on the Study and Use of History. 1752. First published ed., 2 vols. in 1, contemp. calf, spine rubbed, 8vo. Howes 194-177 1978 £30

BOLINGBROKE, HENRY ST. JOHN 1678-1751   Philosophical Works. 1754. 5 vols., contemp. calf, some joints cracked, first octavo ed. Howes 194-178 1978 £35

BOLINGBROKE, HENRY ST. JOHN 1678-1751   Remarks on the History of England. 1747. Second ed., contemp. calf, label missing, 8vo. Howes 194-179 1978 £25

BOLINGBROKE, HENRY ST. JOHN 1678-1751   A Voyage to the Demerary... London, 1809. Disbound, 2nd ed., 8vo. Paine 78-12 1978 $25

BOLITHO, HECTOR   Twelve Jews. London, 1934. Illus., first ed., orig. binding, spine faded, very good, torn d.w. Rota 211-24 1978 £6

BOLLAND, WILLIAM   Miracles; A Seatonian Prize Poem. Cambridge, 1797. 1st ed., 4to, contemp. tree calf. Traylen 88-119 1978 £52

BOLLER, HENRY A.   Among the Indians: Eight Years in the Far West, 1858-1866, Embracing Sketches of Montana and Salt Lake. Philadelphia, 1868. Folding map, original cloth, 1st ed. Ginsberg 14-52 1978 $475

BOLLES, ALBERT S.   The Financial History of the United States from 1861-1865. NY, 1894 Hinges cracked, Worn upper spine, Bell Wiley's Copy. Broadfoot's 44-45 1978 $16.00

BOLLES, ALBERT S.   Industrial History of the United States, from the Earliest Settlements to the Present Time. Norwich, 1879. Illus., engrav., orig. binding. Wolfe 39-39 1978 $37.50

BOLLES, ALBERT S.   Pennsylvania, Province and State... Philadelphia, 1899. 2 vols., ports. MacManus 239-1378 1978 $30

BOLLMAN, ERICK   Plan of an Improved System of the Money-Concerns of the Union. Philadelphia, 1816. 1st ed., sewn, some wear. Americanist 102-22 1978 $40

BOLSTER, E.   A History of the Diocese of Cork from Times to the Reformation. Reprint, octavo bound in cloth. Hyland 128-931 1978 £5

BOLT, ROBERT   Brother and Sister. n.d. 4to., very good, slightly creased wraps, first English ed. Bell Book 16-102 1978 £5

BOLTON, ARTHUR T.   The Architecture of Robert & James Adam. London, 1922. 2 vols., folio, illus. Argosy Special-17 1978 $250

BOLTON, ETHEL S.   Wax Portraits and Silhouettes. Boston, 1915. Orig. bds., illus., uncut, worn. MacManus 239-642 1978 $20

BOLTON, HERBERT E.   Athanase De Mezieres and the Louisiana-Texas Frontier. Cleveland, 1914. 2 vols., near mint, 1st ed., loosely inserted two leaves from orig. manuscript, numerous corrections in Bolton's hand. Jenkins 116-126 1978 $385

BOLTON, HERBERT E. The Beginnings of Mission Nuestra Sonora Del Refugio. Austin, 1916. Off-print in printed wr. Jenkins 116-127 1978 $9.50

BOLTON, HERBERT E. The Padre on Horseback:...Eusebio Francisco Kino... San Francisco, 1932. Orig. cl., d. j., 1st ed. Ginsberg 16-888 1978 $20.00

BOLTON, HERBERT E. Spanish Activities on the Lower Trinity River, 1746-1771. Austin, 1918. Orig. printed wr., uncut. Jenkins 116-128 1978 $15

BOLTON, HERBERT E. Texas in the Middle Eighteenth Century. Berkeley, 1915. Folding maps. Jenkins 116-129 1978 $85

BOLTON, HERBERT E. With the Makers of Texas: A Source Reader in Texas History. New York, 1904. 1st ed., illus. Jenkins 116-31 1978 $20

BOLTON, REGINALD PELHAM An Expensive Experiment, the Hydro-Electric Commission of Ontario, New York, 1913. Ex-lib. Hood's 115-785 1978 $15

BOLTON, REGINALD PELHAM Indian Paths in the Great Metropolis, N.Y.C. New York, 1922. Illus. MacManus 239-1147 1978 $22.50

BOLTON, ROBERT A History of the County of Westchester, from Its First Settlement. New York, 1848. 2 vols., 1st ed., maps, plts., family charts, orig. red cloth, neatly rebacked, orig. backstrip laid down, hinges reinforced, excellent set. Butterfield 21-464 1978 $75

BOLTON, ROBERT The History of the Several Towns, Manors, and Patents of the County of Westchester... New York, 1905. 2 vols., thick 8vos., orig. cloth, some wear, spines repaired, illus., very scarce, ltd. to 240 sets. MacManus 239-1104 1978 $150

BOLTON, THEODORE Early American Portrait Draughtsmen in Crayons. New York, 1923. Illus., ltd. to 325 copies, fine. MacManus 239-643 1978 $40

BOLYAI, WOLFGANG Geometrische Untersuchungen mit Unterstutzung der Ungarischen Akademie der Wissenschaften.... Leipzig and Berlin, 1913. 8 vol., 2 vols. in 1, qtr. mor., wrappers, frontis., first German ed. Gurney 75-12 1978 £40

BOLZONI, GIAMBATISTA Memoria sopra due Statue Egizie mandate in dono alla Sua Patria dal Dignor Giambatista Bolzoni Cittadino Padovano. 1819. 8vo., stiff wrs., engrav. frontis., very good, uncut. King 7-141 1978 £20

BONANNI, FILIPPO
Please turn to
BUONANNI, FILIPPO

BONAPARTE, NAPOLEON Memoirs of the Life and Campaigns... n.d. 1st. ed., 2 vols., frontis, engraved titles, portraits, folding maps, orig. half calf, rebacked. Jarndyce 16-326 1978 £23

BONAR, JOHN Considerations on the Proposed Application to His Majesty and to Parliament, for the Establishment of a Licensed Theatre in Edinburgh. N.P., (Edinburgh), 1767. 1st. ed., 12mo, disbound. Hannas 54-322 1978 £45

BONARELLI, PROSPERO Il Solimano Tragedia.... Florence, 1620. 4to, etched title and 5 folding etchings by Jacques Callot, contemp. signature partially erased, one plate trimmed, another bound somewhat askew, calf antique, 1st Illus. ed. Quaritch 978-19 1978 $1,250

BONATUS, GUIDO The Astrologers Guide. London, 1886. 8vo, orig. cloth, little worn, good. Sexton 7-61 1978 £8

BONAVENTURA, SAINT Dieta Salutis a Beato Bonaventure Nouiter Impressus ac Emendatus. Venice, 1497/(8). 1st ed., octavo, marginal MS notations in early hand, full early style calf, blind-tooled panelled and floral stamped in blind. Bennett 20-231 1978 $900

BONAVENTURA, SAINT Vita del Serafico S. Francesco. Venice, 1598. 4to, engraved plates, one plate signed by Giacomo Franco, text in Roman letter, old quarter calf, re-issue of 1593 ed. Quaritch 978-20 1978 $400

BOND, A. L. Three Gems in One Setting. London, c. 1860. 1st ed., chromolithographed plts., binding is illus., handsome colored inset, deeply embossed cover panels blocked in gold and blind, unusually fine Victorian binding. Victoria 34-84 1978 $50

BOND, BEVERLY W. The Civilization of the Old Northwest. New York, 1934. Clean, 1st. ed., nice copy in d.j., orig. binding. Hayman 71-45 1978 $15

BOND, EARL D. Dr. Kirkbride and His Mental Hospital. Philadelphia, (1947). Illus. MacManus 239-1379 1978 $12.50

BOND, FRANK S. The Texas and Pacific Railway. Washington, 1878. Printed wr. Jenkins 116-132 1978 $35

BOND, FREDERIC DREW Stock Movements and Speculation. 1930. Austin 80-440 1978 $12.50

BOND, HENRY Genealogies of the Families and Descendants of the Early Settlers of Watertown, Mass... Boston, 1855. 2 vols., illus., fold. map, contemp. 3/4 calf, very good. MacManus 239-1054 1978 $45

BOND, HENRY A Plaine and Easie Rule to Rigge any Ship by the Length of his Masts, and Yards. 1664. Sm. 4to., full mor. F. Edwards 1013-25 1978 £700

BOND, J. Field Guide of Birds of the West Indies. New York, 1947. Test figs. by E. Poole, 8vo, orig. cloth. Book Chest 17-52 1978 $18.50

BOND, J. WESLEY Minnesota and Its Resources; to Which are Appended...Notes of a Trip from St. Paul to Pembina and Selkirk Settlement on the Red River of the North. New York, 1853. Black fabric. Hood 116-845 1978 $55

BOND, J. WESLEY Minnesota and Its Resources. Chicago, 1856. 1st of this ed., frontis., orig. cloth, library marks. MacManus 239-315 1978 $40

BOND, JOHN Oriens Ab Occidente: Or a Dawning in the West. 1645. Good. Jarndyce 16-8 1978 £8.50

BOND, W. R. Sometime Officer Brigade Staff Army Northern Virginia Pickett of Pettigrew? Weldon, 1888. Bound in half red leather. Baldwins' 51-200 1978 $20

BONE, GERTRUDE Children's Children. 1908. Ltd. ed. of 215 copies, signed by illus., illus. by Muirhead Bone, printed on Japanese vellum, 4to, blue morocco, gilt, t.e.g., pres. inscription from author. Sawyer 299-113 1978 £75

BONE, JAMES Edinburgh Revisited. London, 1911. Drawings by Hanslip Fletcher, illus., 4to., gilt-dec. cover, 8vo. K Books 244-42 1978 £14

BONE, MUIRHEAD Glasgow. Glasgow, 1911. Special ed. of 100 copies with an orig. etching, lg. 4to., orig. cloth. K Books 244-343 1978 £20

BONENFANT, J. C. Cultural and Political Implications of French-Canadian Nationalism. 1946. Hood 116-505 1978 $10

BONFINI, ANTONIO 1427-1502 Rerum Ungaricum Decades Quatuor cum Dimidia. Frankfurt, 1581. Thk. folio, 2 parts in 1 vol., contemp. calf over oak bds., brass clasps, catches gone, head of spine worn, good copy. Howes 194-531 1978 £135

BONHAM, JOHN M. Industrial Liberty. New York, 1888. Orig. binding, clean. Hayman 71-54 1978 $10

BONHOTE, ELIZABETH The Rambles of Mr. Frankly. 1772. 2 vols., 8vo., contemp. sheep gilt, first ed., rare. P. M. Hill 142-185 1978 £200

BONI, MAURO Leterre Sui Primi Libri a Stampa d'alcune citta e Terre dell' Italia Superiore. Venice, 1794. Large quarto, fine unopened copy, we., scarce, 1st ed. Bennett 20-26 1978 $185

BONN, M. J. The Crisis of Capitalism in America. 1932. Austin 80-441 1978 $7.50

BONNARD, C. Costumes Historiques des XIII, XIV et XV, Siecles, Extrait des Monumens les Plus Authentiques de Peinture et de Sculpture,... Paris, 1845. 2 vols., 4to., hand-coloured plts., some leaves foxed, dampstain in vol. 2. Quaritch 983-60 1978 $500

BONNETAIN, P.   L'Extreme-Orient. Paris, n.d. (c. 1888). 4to, cloth, gilt, num. plts., illus., maps. Van der Peet 127-24 1978 Dfl 85

BONNEY, EDWARD   The Banditti of the Prairies. Chicago, n.d. (circa 1890?). Wrs., fr. wr. mounted, lacks back wr., scarce, not a very good copy. Hayman 73-56 1978 $7.50

BONNEY, SHERMAN GRANT   Calvin Fairbanks Bonney. (Concord, N.H., 1930). Illus., 8vo, ltd. ed., 2 T.L.s.'s inserted from author. Morrill 239-24 1978 $30

BONNYCASTLE, RICHARD HENRY   Canada and the Canadians, in 1846. London, 1846. 2 vols., 12mo, orig. rose cloth, 1st ed., inner hinge tender, very fine bright copy. Ximenes 47-28 1978 $175

BONNYCASTLE, RICHARD HENRY   The Canadas in 1841. London, 1841. 2 vols., orig. binding, illus. & vignettes. Hood 117-553 1978 $300

BONNYCASTLE, RICHARD HENRY   The Canadas in 1841. London, 1842. 2 vols., sm. 8vo, 2 vignette title pgs., lithograph frontispieces, engraved map, neatly repaired, illus., half calf, gilt backs. Deighton 5-29 1978 £68

BONNYCASTLE, RICHARD HENRY   Spanish America. Philadelphia, 1819. Maps, extensive index, calf & bds. Jenkins 116-133 1978 $150

BONONCINI, EUGENE   Autobiography of Re. Eugene Bononcini, D. D. Early Kansas Missionary. St. Paul, 1942. Illus., original wr., 1st ed. Ginsberg 14-439 1978 $15

BONSELS, WALDEMAR   An Indian Journey. New York, 1928. Bds. Hayman 72-62 1978 $7.50

BONSOR, GEORGE EDWARD   An Archaeological Sketch-book of the Roman Necropolis at Carmona. New York, (1931). 4to, plts., some in color. Biblo BL781-327 1978 $42.50

BONSTETTEN, CHARLES VICTOR DE   L'homme du Midi et l'Homme du Nord ou l'Influence du Climat. Geneve and Paris, 1834. 8vo, orig. pink wrs., fine uncut copy, 1st ed. Gilhofer 74-86 1978 sFr 300

BOOK of Biographies. Biographical Sketches of Leading Citizens of Berks County, Pa. Buffalo, 1898. 4to., illus., rebound. MacManus 239-1370 1978 $65

A BOOK of Cape May, New Jersey. Cape May, 1937. 1st ed., orig. cloth, very good. MacManus 239-1247 1978 $40

BOOK OF COMMON PRAYER
Please turn to
CHURCH OF ENGLAND

BOOK of Cuts Designed for the Amusement & Instruction of Young People. New York, 1834. 16mo, f.p. and large cut on every page, lightly foxed, almost fine. Victoria 34-85 1978 $20

BOOK of Favourite Modern Ballads. (c. 1860). Engravings from drawings, orig. cloth, gilt, oval coloured illus. inlaid on upper cover, corners rubbed, new endpapers. George's 635-99 1978 £8.50

BOOK of Games. London, 1810. Engraved plates, roan-backed boards, contents foxed, several stains. Victoria 34-86 1978 $55

BOOK OF HOURS
Please turn to
CATHOLIC CHURCH, LITURGY & RITUALS. HOURS

THE BOOK of Oz Cooper: an Appreciation. Chicago, 1949. Cloth, very fine. Dawson's 447-32 1978 $25

THE BOOK of Oz Cooper. An Appreciation of Oswald Bruce Cooper. With Characteristic Examples of His Art in Lettering, Type Designing and Such of His Writings as Reveal the Cooperian Typographic Gospel. Chicago, 1949. 4to., illus., orig. cloth, 1st ed., pres. copy, fine. MacManus 238-1070 1978 $35

THE BOOK of Peace. Boston, 1845. 8vo., 1st ed., orig. cloth. Morrill 241-652 1978 $15

THE BOOK of Piscatorial Society, 1831-1936. 1936. Coloured frontis., photographs, roy. 8vo. George's 635-1491 1978 £6.50

A BOOK of Princeton Verse 1916. Princeton University Press, 1916. 1st ed., orig. d.w., 8vo., very good. Americanist 103-23 1978 $20

A BOOK of Princeton Verse II 1919. Princeton University Press, (1919). 1st ed., orig. d.w., 8vo., very good. Americanist 103-24 1978 $65

A BOOK of Princeton Verse II. Princeton, 1919. 8vo., cloth, 1st ed., cloth sunned, partially unopened. J. S. Lawrence 38-F21 1978 $100

THE BOOK of Prominent Pennsylvanians. Pittsburgh, 1913. Portrs., 4to., orig. full lea. Morrill 241-455 1978 $10

BOOK OF ST. ALBANS
Please turn to
BERNERS, JULIANA

THE BOOK Of Shells... 1837. Frontis, illus., orig. cloth, 12mo, very good copy. Fenning 32-30 1978 £8.50

BOOK of Sports. New York, c.1845. Hand-colored plate, t.p. vignette and text cuts, impressed cloth, very good. Victoria 34-87 1978 $30

BOOK of the Bear. Nonesuch Press, 1926. Coloured illus. by R. garnett, 12mo., orig. buckram backed bds., printed on japon. Howes 194-1070 1978 £5

THE BOOK of Trades or Library of the Useful Arts. Whitehall, 1807. 1st Amer. ed., very good, orig. papered bds., plts., great rarity, 3 vols. Victoria 34-88 1978 $450

THE BOOK of Trades. Glasgow, 1835. 1st ed., thick 16mo, engraved plates, original cloth, very good. Victoria 34-89 1978 $160

THE BOOK of Trinity College Dublin, 1591 - 1891. 1892. 1st ed., cloth with parchment spine, demi 4to, illus., very good. Hyland 128-698 1978 £10

A BOOKE of Christmas Carols. Illuminated from Ancient Manuscripts in the British Museum. London, 1846. Old full leather bind., spine rubbed. Americanist 102-62 1978 $85

A BOOKLET Devoted to the Book Plate of Elisha Brown Bird Being a Collection Printed in Photogravure. Village Press, 1907. Frontis., ex-lib., #4 of 110 copies on Van Gelder handmade paper, spine worn, t.e.g. Battery Park 1-120 1978 $100

THE BOOK-Plates of Ludvig Standoe Ipsen. Boston, The Troutsdale Press, 1901. Illus. Battery Park 1-292 1978 $50

BOOKPLATES. Portland, The Anthoensen Press. 1 of 300 numbered copies, illus., 8vo., cloth, boxed, as new. Battery Park 1-4 1978 $35

BOOK-PRICES Current: a record of the Prices at Which Books have been Sold at Auction from Dec. 1891 to Aug. 1956. Vols. 6, 8-15, 17-64, Indexes to first 30 years, 3 vols. London, 1893-(1957). 60 vols. in all, demy 8vo., orig. buckram and cloth. Forster 130-115 1978 £160

BOOK-PRICES Current: a Record of the Prices at Which Books have been sold at Auction from Dec. 1886 to Aug. 1956. London, 1888 -(1957). Vols. 1-64, Indexes to the first 30 years, 3 vols., 67 vols. in all, demy 8vo., orig. buckram and cloth, nice set. Forster 130-114 1978 £200

BOOK-PRICES Current: a Record of the Prices at Which Books have been Sold at Auction from Dec. 1894 to Aug. 1946. Vols. 9-10, Index to first 10 vols. (1887-96), 19-20, Index to second decade 1897-1906, 21, 24, 32, 36, 38-64. London, 1896-1957. 37 vols., demy 8vo., orig. cloth. Forster 130-116 1978 £85

BOOKMAKING on the Distaff Side. (N. P.), 1937. Paste-paper bds., cloth spine, very fine in slipcase, 1 of 100 numbered copies. Dawson's 447-17 1978 $150

THE BOOKMAN Christmas Double Number, 1913. 1913. Plts., some in colour, illus. in text, 4to., orig. limp linen. George's 635-1195 1978 £5

BOOKS, Manuscripts and Heirlooms of Thomas Hutchinson. New York, 1918. 8vo., orig. wrs., facsimiles. Morrill 241-22 1978 $9.50

BOOKWALTER, J.   A Condensed Description of Counties in Minnesota Traversed by the St. Paul,.... [St. Paul, 1884?]. Disbound. Ginsberg 14-544 1978 $35

BOOKWALTER, J.   Minnesota as It Is. [St. Paul, 1887]. Illus., orig. pr. wr. Ginsberg 14-1101 1978 $50

BOOKWALTER, JOHN W.   Siberia and Central Asia. Springfield, 1899. Orig. binding, clean, very elusive 1st. ed., private circulation only. Hayman 71-56 1978 $32.50

THE BOOKWORM, An Illustrated Treasury of Old-time Literature. Vols. 1 and 7. London, 1888-94. 2 vols., illus., med. 8vo., orig. cloth. Forster 130-121 1978 £6

BOOLE, G.   A Treatise on the Calculus of Finite Differences. London, 1880. 8vo., orig. cloth, third ed. Quaritch 977-138 1978 $55

BOOSEY, THOMAS   Piscatorial Reminiscences and Gleanings. London, 1835. Orig. binding. Wolfe 39-6 1978 $50

BOOTH, ANDREW B.   Recors of Louisiana Confederate Soldiers and Louisiana Confederate Commands. New Orleans, 1920. 3 vols., vol. 3 in 2 parts, Bell Wiley's copy. Broadfoot's 44-505 1978 $400

BOOTH, C.   The Aged Poor in England and Wales. 1894. 8vo. George's 635-287 1978 £6

BOOTH, E. R.   History of Osteopathy and Twentieth Century Medical Practice. Cincinnati, 1905. Fresh, clean, tight. Rittenhouse 49-92 1976 $35

BOOTH, JOHN   In Memoriam:.... Austin, 1884. Pink pr. wr. Ginsberg 14-727 1978 $150

BOOTH, MARY L.   History of the City of New York, From Its Earliest Settlement to the Present. New York, 1859. 1st ed., illus., fine copy, cloth. MacManus 239-365 1978 $37.50

BOOTH, NEWTON   His Speeches and Addresses. New York, 1894. Illus., original cloth, 1st ed. Ginsberg 14-80 1978 $12.50

BOOTH Memorials. New York, 1866. Portr., sm. 8vo., 1st ed., orig. cloth. Morrill 241-57 1978 $22.50

BOOTHBY, BROOKE   Sorrows. 1796. 1st. ed., folio, frontispiece, 2 plts., lg. vignettes in text, later half calf, worn, some foxing. Hannas 54-25 1978 £28

BOOTHBY, BROOKE   Sorrows, Sacred to the Memory of Penelope. 1796. 1st. ed., folio, frontispiece, rebound in half calf, hand marbled bds. Jarndyce 16-40 1978 £45

BOOTHBY, GUY   The Beautiful White Devil. 1896. Illus. by Stanley L. Wood, orig. pict. cloth, very good, first English ed. Bell Book 16-105 1978 £8.50

BOOTHBY, GUY   A Bid for Fortune. New York, 1895. 1st Amer. ed., quarter calf, marbled boards. Greene 78-152 1978 $20

BOOTHBY, GUY   The Fascination of the King. London, 1897. Signed Boothby inscrip., 1st ed., orig. cloth. Greene 78-153 1978 $55

BOOTHBY, GUY   The Marriage of Esther. New York, 1895. 1st Amer. ed., quarter calf, marbled boards, lacks half-inch top of spine, good. Greene 78-154 1978 $10

BOOTHBY, MISS HILL   An Account of the Life of Dr. Samuel Johnson. 1805. Sm. 8vo., orig. bds., uncut, later buckram back. P. M. Hill 142-153 1978 £75

BORAH, W. E.   The Closing Argument of W. E. Borah for the Prosecution, in the Great Coeur D'Alene Riot-Murder Trial, Delivered July 27, 1899. Wallace, 1899. Sewn, 1st ed. Ginsberg 14-400 1978 $30

BORASTON, J. H.   Sir Douglas Haig's Despatches. 1919. Plts., orig. cloth, roy. 8vo. F. Edwards 1013-324 1978 £15

BORCKE, HEROS VON   Memoirs of the Confederate War for Independence. Edinburgh, 1866. 2 vols. Bell Wiley's copy. Broadfoot 46-21 1978 $125

BORCKE, HEROS VON   Memoirs of the Confederate War for Independence. New York, 1938. 2 vols. Bell Wiley's copy. Broadfoot 46-22 1978 $40

BORDE, ANDREW   The Breuiary of Healthe, for all Maner of Syckenesses and Diseases. Anno, 1556. Sm. 4to., woodcut, old polished calf, lightly browned, good copy, bkplts. of Wm. Edw. Bools & Robert George Windsor-Clive, Earl of Plymouth, rare, 3rd ed. Zeitlin 245-27 1978 $2,375

BORDEAUX, H.   Au Pays des Amours de Lamartine. Grenoble, n.d. (ab. 1921). Sm. 8vo., green calf, sm. gilt tooled border, t.e.g., illus., uncut, attractive binding, orig. wr. bound up, slightly faded. Van der Peet H-64-257 1978 Dfl 75

BORDEN, W. C.   The Use of the Roentgen Ray by the Medical Department of the United States Army in the War with Spain, 1898. Washington, 1900. Ticket on spine, some wear. Rittenhouse 49-93 1976 $35

BORDET, JULES   Studies in Immunity. New York, 1909. Library marks. Rittenhouse 49-94 1976 $10

BORDILLON, F. W.   Ailes D'Alovette. Oxford: H. Daniel, 1890. Orig. paper wrs., ltd. to 100 copies, wrs. a little worn, but very good. MacManus 238-787 1978 $100

BORDINI, FRANCESCO   Quaesitorum, et Responsorum Mathematicae Disiplinae ad Totius Universi Cognitiunem Spectantium Chilias... Bologna, 1573. 4to., red half-mor., 1st ed. Gilhofer 74-56 1978 sFr 1,250

BORDON, R. L.   Canada and The Peace, A Speech on the Treaty of Peace. Ottawa, 1919. Hood's 115-92 1978 $7.50

BORELIUS, H.   Die Nordischen Literaturen. Potsdam, 1931. 4to., cloth, plts., some in color, text illus. Van der Peet H-64-464 1978 Dfl 55

BOREUX, CHARLES   L'Art Egyptien. Paris, 1926. Sm. 4to., plts., wrs. Biblo BL781-328 1978 $17.50

BORGHESE, S. E. D. PAOLO   Cat. de la Bibliotheque. Rome, 1892-3. 2 vols., plt., illus., med. 8vo., marbled bds., calf backs. Forster 130-125 1978 £35

BORGHINI, RAFFAELLO   Il Riposo in cui della Pittura, e della Scultura si Favella, de' piu Illustri Pittori... Florence, 1584. 8vo., woodcut, contemp. vellum, rare 1st ed. Gilhofer 74-29 1978 sFr 1,500

BORLASE, WILLIAM   Observations on the Antiquities, Historical and Monumental, of the County of Cornwall. Oxford, 1754. Folio, 1st ed., maps, plts., contemp. calf. Quaritch 983-5 1978 $540

BORNEMAN, HENRY S.   Early Freemasonry in Pennsylvania. Philadelphia, 1931. Nice copy, orig. bds., illus. MacManus 239-1380 1978 $17.50

BORNEMAN, HENRY S.   Pennsylvania German Illuminated Manuscripts,.... Norristown, 1937. 1st ed., oblong folio, plates, 8vo., orig. binding. Americanist 101-22 1978 $150

BOROCHOV, BER   Nationalism and the Class Struggle. 1937. 1st ed. in English. Austin 79-86 1978 $17.50

BORRA, LUIGI   L'Amorose Rime Di Luigi Borra.... Milan, 1542. 1st ed., sm. 4to, printed in Castiglione's distinctive upright italic, few contemp. annotations and underlinings, recent vellum boards. Quaritch 978-21 1978 $625

BORRETT, W. C.   Historic Halifax. Toronto, 1943. Illus. by R. Chambers. Hood 117-231 1978 $17.50

BORROW, GEORGE   The Bible in Spain;.... London, 1843. 2nd ed., 3 vols., large duodecimo, orig. green publisher's cloth, paper spine labels, very good. Bennett 7-15 1978 $45

BORROW, GEORGE   Lavengro; The Scholar-The Gypsy-The Priest. London, 1851. 3 vols., octavo, half dark calf over marbled boards, 1st ed. Bennett 7-16 1978 $95

BORROW, GEORGE   Lavengro: The Scholar- The Gypsie- The Priest. London, 1851. 1st ed. in 3 vols., blue cloth, good set. Greene 78-8 1978 $70

BORROW, GEORGE   Lavengro; the Scholar – the Gypsy – the Priest. London, 1851. 3 vols., orig. blue cloth, spines faded, some rubbing, 1st ed., frontis. port., good. MacManus 238-169 1978 $55

BORROW, GEORGE   Lavengro. London, 1900. New ed., unaltered text, orig. ed., cloth. Greene 78-9 1978 $20

BORROW, GEORGE   Romano Lavo-Lil: Word-Book of the Romany... 1874. 1st. ed., half title, orig. cloth, paper label, v.g. Jarndyce 16-298 1978 £52

BORROW, GEORGE   The Romany Rye. 1875. 2 vols., 4to., 1st ed., orig. dark blue cloth, sound set. Quaritch 979-54 1978 $125

BORSENVEREINS der Deutschen Buchhandler Halbjahrverzeichnis der im deutschen Buchhandel erschienenen Bucher, Zeitschriften und Landkarten.... Leipzig, 1929-33. 9 vols., roy. 8vo., cloth. Forster 130-126 1978 £20

BORY, PAUL   Les Pays Nouveaux. London, 1884. Illus., cr. 8vo, gilt stamp on upper cover, orig. cloth. K Books 239-59 1978 £7

THE BORZOI: Being a Sort of Record of Ten Years of Publishing. New York, (1925). Tall 8vo., batik bds., cloth, pres. copy signed by Knopf, Blanche, Alfred and Samuel, first ed., fine. Duschnes 220-53 1978 $60

THE BORZOI 1925. New York. One of 500 copies printed on Borzoi all rag paper, half tone plts., prtd. on ivory cameo paper, Batik paper over bds., cloth spine. Battery Park 1-194 1978 $100

BOSANQUET, BERNARD   Logic of the Morphology of Knowledge. Oxford, 1888. 1st ed., 8vo, 2 vols., orig. publisher's cloth. Gilhofer 75-13 1978 SFr 180

BOSCOVIC, RUDJER JOSIP   A Theory of Natural Philosophy. Chicago and London, 1922. Latin-English ed., imperial 4to., diagrams, orig. cloth, a little soiled. Quaritch 977-86 1978 $250

BOSCOVICH, RUGGIERO GIUSEPPE
Please turn to
BOSKOVIC, RUDJER JOSIP

BOSCOWITZ, ARNOLD   Les Volcans et les Tremblements de Terre. Paris, (1866). Publisher's 1/2 hardgrain mor., illus. with color lithos. & woodcuts. Goldschmidt 110-13 1978 $95

BOSE, JAGADIS CHUNDER   Plants Autographs. New York, 1927. 8vo, orig. cloth. Book Chest 17-467 1978 $12

BOSMAN, WILLIAM   A New and Accurate Description of the Coast of Guinea... London, 1721. 2nd. ed., folding map, torn & backed, 7 engraved plts., title-leaf backed, age-browned throughout, good, modern half morocco gilt, 8vo. K Books 239-60 1978 £200

BOSSCHE, GULIELMUS VAN DEN   Historia Medica, in qua libris IV. Brussels, 1639. 4to., contemp. mottled calf, gilt spine, first ed. Quaritch 977-11 1978 $1,500

BOSSCHERE, JEAN DE   The City Curious. New York & London, 1920. 1st ed., tissue-guarded color plts., b & w text drawings, pict. cloth, fine. Victoria 34-224 1978 $45

BOSSCHERE, JEAN DE   The City Curious. 1920. Coloured plts., illus. by author, orig. pict. cloth, 8vo. George's 635-100 1978 £12.50

BOSSE, ABRAHAM   Traicte des Manieres de Graver en Taille Douce Sur l'airin. Paris, 1645. 8vo., engr. titles, copperplts., engr. vignette, drawn & engr. by author, contemp. mottled calf, rebacked, dampstaining, but fine copy, 1st ed. Norman 5-41 1978 $1,000

BOSSERT, HELMUTH THOMAS   Altkreta. Hunst und Handwerk in Griechenland, Kreta and auf den Kykladen Waehrend der Bronzezeit. Berlin, 1923. Sm. 4to., illus., some margin notations. Biblo BL781-329 1978 $22.50

BOSSI, GIUSEPPE   Del Cenacolo di Leonardo da Vinci. 1810. Lg. 4to., bds., calf spine gilt, plts., very good, first ed. King 7-143 1978 £60

BOSSUIT, FRANCIS VAN   Cabinet de Sculpture par le Fameux Sculpteur Francis van Bossuit gravees d'apres les Dessins de Barent Graat par Mattys Pool. 1727. Sm. folio, plts., contemp. calf, back richly gilt. Gilhofer 74-30 1978 sFr 1,400

BOSSUT, J. C.   A General History of Mathematics from the Earliest Times to the Middle of the Eighteenth Century. 1803. 8vo., new bds., uncut, first English ed. Quaritch 977-139 1978 $95

BOSTICK, D. F.   Carmel – at Work and Play. Carmel, 1925. Illus., 1st ed. Biblo BL781-266 1978 $9.50

BOSTON Directory for the Year 1856, Embracing the City Record, a General Directory for the Citizens, and a Business Directory. Boston, 1856. 8vo., orig. bds., cloth back, spine torn, loose front cover held with scotch tape. Morrill 241-319 1978 $7.50

BOSTON Handel and Haydn Society Collection of Church Music. Boston, 1829. 7th ed., oblong 8vo., orig. bds., calf back. Morrill 241-58 1978 $12.50

BOSTON Merchantile Library Catalogue. Boston, 1854. Orig. binding, worn. Battery Park 1-316 1978 $75

BOSTWICK, HOMER   Nature and Treatment of Seminal Diseases. New York, 1848. Second ed. Rittenhouse 49-96 1976 $20

BOSWELL, GEORGE   A Treatise on Watering Meadows. 1779. First ed., plts., contemp. calf, neatly rebacked, 8vo. Howes 194-121 1978 £35

BOSWELL, IRA M.   Recollections of a Red-Headed Man. Cincinnati, (1915). Orig. binding, clean. Hayman 71-398 1978 $8.50

BOSWELL, JAMES   An Account of Corsica, the Journal of a Tour to that Island; and Memoirs of Pascal Paoli. Glasgow, 1768. Illus., 8vo., lg. fold. map, full contemp. calf, red mor. label, 1st ed. MacManus 238-97 1978 $175

BOSWELL, JAMES   An Account of Corsica, The Journal of a Tour to That Island;.... London, 1768. 1st ed., octavo, contemp. calf, newly rebacked, gilt spine, leather title label, corners repaired, bookplates. Totteridge 29-15 1978 $275

BOSWELL, JAMES   An Account of Corsica, the Journal of a Tour to that Island, and Memoirs of Pascal Paoli. 1768. Newly bound in half calf, very good, 8vo. Howes 194-182 1978 £42

BOSWELL, JAMES   The Journal of a Tour to the Hebrides with Samuel Johnson, LLD... London, 1785. 2nd. ed., revised & corrected, neatly rebacked, orig. calf binding with half title, lacks map. Baldwins' 51-330 1978 $87.50

BOSWELL, JAMES   The Life of Samuel Johnson, LL.D. London, 1791. 1st ed., 1st issue, 4to., 2 vols., lacks portr., two facsimiles, old marbled bds. faded & backed in calf, hinges cracked & weak, nearly very fine, penciled notes, rare. Current 24-7 1978 $425

BOSWELL, JAMES   The Life of Samuel Johnson, LL.D.,..... London, 1791. 2 vols., quarto, frontis. portrait of Dr. Johnson, half old calf, marbled boards and endpapers, bookplates, 1st ed., 1st issue, fine lg. copy. Bennett 7-17 1978 $1,500

BOSWELL, JAMES   The Life of Samuel Johnson. 1791. 2 vols., 4to., 1st ed., frontis. portr., fine copy, early marbled bds., rebacked with sprinkled calf, uncut, buckram box. Quaritch 979-55 1978 $2,250

BOSWELL, JAMES   Life of Johnson. Oxford, 1887. Portraits, 6 vols., orig. publisher's roan gitl, gilt tops, 8vo. Howes 194-967 1978 £35

BOSWELL, JAMES   The Life of Samuel Johnson. 1900. 3 vols., 8vo., blue calf, gilt panelled backs, gilt edges. Quaritch 979-56 1978 $80

BOSWELL, JAMES   The Life of Samuel Johnson. London, 1934-1926. Drawings in pen & ink by H. Railton, portraits, 3 vols., 8vo, well bound in half dark blue morocco, cloth sides to match, gilt tops. Traylen 88-121A 1978 £30

BOTERO, GIOVANNI   De La Ragion De Stato... Venice, 1640.
4to., old mor. Salloch 348-17 1978 $110

BOTERO, GIOVANNI   Le relationi universali. Venice, 1622.
8 parts in 1 vol., 8 vo., fine, contemp. calf, complete with the rare
"Aggiunta", woodcuts. Quaritch Summer, 1978-7 1978 $6,000

BOTERO, GIOVANNI   Relations of the Most Famous Kingdomes and
Commonwealths Thorowout the World. 1630. Map, sm. 4to, contemp. calf.
Edwards 1012-8 1978 £200

BOTHMER, COUNTESS VON   From London to Lahore. 1868. 1st. ed., folding
frontis, map, orig. red cloth, gilt, spine little rubbed. Jarndyce 16-300 1978
£10.50

BOTTA, CARLO   Storia D'Italia dal 1789 al 1814. Florence,
1825. 3 vols., 12mo., half calf, very good. King 7-144 1978 £20

BOTTA, CHARLES   History of the War of the Independence of the
U.S.A. Buffalo, 1854. 2 vols. in 1, fine copy, orig. cloth, illus., lg. thick
8vo. MacManus 239-551 1978 $30

BOTTICELLI, S.   Zeichnungen von Sandro Botticelli zu Dante's
Goettlicher Homoedie. (Berlin, 1884-86). 2 vols., lg. folio, plts., some slight
foxing, orig. half vellum. Quaritch 983-156 1978 $375

BOTTOMLEY, GORDON   King Lear's Wife. 1920. 4to., decor. bds.,
good, first English ed. Bell Book 16-106 1978 £6.50

BOTTOMLEY, GORDON   Laodice and Danae. N.P., 1909. 8vo, orig.
blue printed wrappers, cloth folder, 1st ed., presentation copy, inscribed by
author. Ximenes 47-32 1978 $45

BOTTOMLEY, GORDON   Lyric Plays. 1932. Very good, orig. patterned
wraps, first English ed. Bell Book 16-107 1978 £4

BOTTOMLEY, GORDON   Midsummer Eve. (Harting, 1905). Drawings by
James Guthrie, 1 of 120 copies, orig. linen-backed bds. Americanist 102-82
1978 $135

BOTTOMLEY, GORDON   Poems of Thirty Years. London, 1925. 8vo,
green stamped cloth, gilt lettering on spine, t.e.g., uncut, partially unopened,
some foxing and sun fading of spine, fine, 1st ed. Desmarais 1-49 1978 $25

BOTTOMLEY, GORDON   A Vision of Giorgione. London, 1922.
8vo, green stamped cloth, gilt lettering on spine, foxing, ownership inscription
on flyleaf, 1st collected English ed., collector's cond. Desmarais 1-50 1978
$40

BOTTS, JOHN M.   Union or Disunion. N. P., n.d. 8vo., unbound. Morrill 241-597 1978 $12.50

BOTUME, ELIZABETH HYDE   First Days Amongst the Contrabands. Boston,
1893. Bell Wiley's Copy. Broadfoot's 44-49 1978 $20.00

BOUCHET, JEAN   Epistres Morales and Familieres du Traverseur...
Poitiers, 1545. First and only ed., folio, Roman letter, cont. calf, excellent
clean copy. Quaritch 978-23 1978 $950

BOUCHET, JEAN   Sensuyt le labyrinth de fortune & seiour des troys
nobles Dames Compose par lacteur des Regners traversans et loups rauisans. Paris,
c. 1525. Sm. 4to., large woodcut, occasional foxing, French 18th century red mor.
gilt, gilt edges. Quaritch 978-22 1978 $1,700

BOUCHETTE, JOSEPH   A Topographical Description of the Province of
Lower Canada with Remarks Upon Upper Canada and on the Relative Connexion
of Both Provinces with the United States of America. London, 1815. 1st ed.,
thick 8vo., engr. tables, maps, scarce, good cond., light water marks on some
plts., rebound in 3/4 dark brown mor., marbled bds. Current 24-174 1978 $435

BOUCHETTE, JOSEPH   A Topographical Description of the Province of
Lower Canada, with Remarks Upon Upper Canada, and on the Relative Connexion
of Both Provinces with the United States of America. London, 1815. 3/4 leather,
marbled bds., plts., maps. Hood 116-506 1978 $250

BOUCHETTE, JOSEPH   A Topographical Description of the Province of
Lower Canada. London, 1815. Contemp. grey bds., leather back, portrait, maps,
plts., tables. Wolfe 39-40 1978 $200

BOUCHETTE, JOSEPH   A Topographical Dictionary of the Province of
Lower Canada. London, 1832. Folio, contemp. cloth, front cover loose, backstrip chipped, uncut. Wolfe 39-42 1978 $150

BOUCHETTE, JOSEPH   A Topographical Dictionary of the Province of
Lower Canada. London, 1832. Re-spined and cornered. Hood 116-507 1978
$175

BOUCHOT, HENRI   Expositions des Primitifs Francais au Palais du
Louvre.... Paris, 1904. Plts., med. 8vo., marbled bds., mor. back. Forster
130-134 1978 £6

BOUCHOT, HENRI   Le Livre, L'Illustration, La Reliure. Paris,
(1886). Illus., post 8vo., orig. cloth. Forster 130-132 1978 £5

BOUCHOT, HENRI   Le Luxe Francais, l'Empire. Paris, n.d. (ab.
1920). Lg. 8vo., half green mor., richly gilt tooled spine, raised bands, t.e.g.,
frontis., fine plts., some in color, text illus. Van der Peet H-64-258 1978 Dfl
165

BOUCHOT, HENRI   La Miniature Francaise 1750-1825. Paris, 1910.
Demy 8vo., half mor., t.e.g. Forster 130-133 1978 £6

BOUCHOT, HENRI   The Printed Book. London, 1887. 8vo., cloth,
gilt decor. & lettered cover & spine, t.e.g. Battery Park 1-298 1978 $50

BOUCHOT, HENRI   La Restauration. Paris, 1893. 4to., half calf,
frontis., plts. in color, text illus., frontis & title foxed. Van der Peet H-64-259
1978 Dfl 125

BOUCKE, O. FRED   Laissez Faire and After. 1932. Austin 80-442
1978 $12.50

BOUDINOT, E.   Documents in Relation to the Validity of the Cherokee Treaty of 1835.... Washington, 1838. Disbound. Ginsberg 14-233 1978
$25

BOUGAINVILLE, LOUIS DE   Voyage Autour Du Monde, Par Le Fregate Du
Roi La Boudeuse, Et La Flute L'Etoile... Paris, 1771. 1st. ed., 4to, folding
engraved map, engraved plts., one leaf of text repaired, contemporary calf,
morocco label gilt, panelled back, worn & joints weak. Deighton 5-177 1978
£475

BOUGARD, R.   The Little Sea Torch... London, 1801. 1st.
English ed., folio, rare half-title "Appearances", coloured aquatint panorams,
maps, sl. spotting & light browning, title-pg. neatly repaired, newly bound in
quarter dark blue morocco, marbled sides, gilt back, raised bands, new endpapers.
Deighton 5-178 1978 £850

BOUGHTON, RUTLAND   Music Drama of the Future, Ulter and Igraine
choral drama. 1911. Frontis., covers faded, 8vo. George's 635-1398 1978
£5.25

BOUGUER, PIERRE   De La Methode D'Observer en Mer La Declinaison
De la Boussole. Paris, 1731. Plts., 4to., modern wrappers. F. Edwards 1013-
28 1978 £60

BOUGUER, PIERRE   Traite d'optique sur la gradation de la lumiere
(ed. La Caille). Paris, 1860. Rare 1st ed., 4to., engraved folding plates, contemp.
calf, gilt back, red edges, fine. Gilhofer 75-14 1978 SFr 1,900

BOUHOURS, DOMINIQUE   The Life of St. Ignatius, Founder of the Society of
Jesus. 1686. Sm. 8vo., contemp. calf, neatly rebacked, sole English ed. Howes
194-63 1978 £45

BOUILLAUD, JEAN BAPTISTE Traite Clinique des Maladies du Coeur, precede
de Recherches Nouvelles sur l'Anatomie et la Physiologie de cet Organe. Paris,
1835. 2 vols., 8vo., fldg. engr. plts., bound in contemp. bds. backed in brown
lea., gilt ornamented spines, foxing, good copy, bkplts. of Drs. Emmet Field
Horine & Carleton B. Chapman, 1st ed. Zeitlin 245-28 1978 $450

BOUILLAUD, JEAN BAPTISTE Traite Clinique du Rhumatisme Articulaire, et
de la Loi de Coincidence des Inflammations du Coeur avec cette Maladie. Paris,
1840. 8vo., contemp. mottled bds., backed in mor., gilt ornamented spine,
light foxing & browning, very good copy from the libraries of Drs. Emmet Field
Horine & Carleton B. Chapman, rare 1st ed. Zeitlin 245-29 1978 $385

BOULANGER, NICOLAS ANTOINE The Origin and Progress of Despotism in
the Oriental, and Other Empires, of Africa, Europe, and America.... London,
1764. Foolscap octavo, 3/4 mottled calf, marbled boards, title page somewhat soiled, some marginal stains, 1st ed. in English. Bennett 7-18 1978 $195

BOULANGIER, E.   Un hiver au Cambodge. Tours, 1888. 2nd ed.,
4to, cloth, numerous plts., illus. Van der Peet 127-25 1978 Dfl 80

BOULENGER, E. G.   Wonders of the Sea. New York, (1945). Folio,
cloth, color plts., painted by Paul A. Robert. Biblo 251-153 1978 $20

BOULTON, W. H.   The Romance of the British Museum. London,
n.d. (ab. 1935). 8vo., cloth, colored frontis., illus. on plts. Van der Peet
H-64-105 1978 Dfl 35

BOULTON, W. H.   The Romance of the British Museum. London,
(193-). Colored plts., demy 8vo., orig. cloth. Forster 130-135 1978 £4

BOULTON, WILLIAM B.   The Amusements of Old London. London, 1901.
2 vols., octavo, 12 hand-colored plates, contemp. blue cloth, gilt top covers,
t.e.g., spines chipped. Bennett 7-19 1978 $95

BOUQUET, DOM M.   Rerum Gallicarum et Francicarum Scriptores...
Paris, 1738-1904. 24 vols., royal folio, complete set, fold. tinted maps, engraved plts., vols. 1-23 in contemp. French cat's paw calf, final vol. in half calf to
pattern, grained cloth sides, uniformly rebacked in calf. Quaritch 983-6 1978
$3,750

BOUQUET for BR: a Birthday Garland Gathered by the Typophiles. 1950. Decor. bds., cloth back, near mint, 1 of 600 copies. Dawson's 447-178 1978 $25

BOURASSA, HENRI   Le Canada Apostolique; Revue des Oeuvres de
Missions des Communautes Franco-Canadiennes. N.P., 1919. Card cover. Hood
116-282 1978 $12.50

BOURASSE, JEAN JACQUES   Residences Royales et Imperiales de France.
Tours, 1864. Plts., 4to, orig. lea.-backed cloth, ex-lib., embossed stamp on
plts., 1st ed. Morrill 241-59 1978 $25

BOURDEAU, L.   Theorie Des Sciences. Paris, 1882. Tall thick
8vo., 2 vols., orig. prtd. wrs., uncut & unopened, some waterstains. Salloch
345-27 1978 $25

BOURDIGNE, CHARLES   La Legende de Maistre Pierre Faifeu... Paris,
1723. Sm. cr. 8vo, eng. vingette ornaments & initials, one end-paper torn, 1/2
red calf, gilt spine, bookplts. Eaton 45-59 1978 £8

BOURDON, JEAN-BAPTISTE-ISIDORE   Recherches sur le Mechanisme de la
Respiration et sur la Circulation du Sang. Paris, 1820. 8vo., contemp. marbled
bds., backed on roan, gilt on spine, fine copy, pres. inscr., 1st ed., bkplts. of
Drs. Emmet Field Horine & Carleton B. Chapman. Zeitlin 245-30 1978 $67.50

BOURGELAT   Elemens D'Hippiatrique, Ou Nouveaux Principes sur le Connoissance et sur la medecine des Chevaux. 1750-51. 2 vols.
of 3, contemp. calf, spines taped crudely, French text, 1st ed., 12mo. Book
Chest 17-54 1978 $90

BOURGEOIS, M.   J.M. Synge & The Irish Theatre. 1913. Good,
octavo bound in cloth, reprint. Hyland 128-632 1978 £7

BOURGUET, EMILE   Les Ruines de Delphes. Paris, 1914. Sm. 4to.,
illus., full leather, slightly rubbed. Biblo BL781-331 1978 $32.50

BOURIENNE, LOUIS ANTOINE FAUVELET DE   Memoirs of Napoleon Bonaparte.
1836. 4 vols., 8vo, maps, plts., little foxed, contemp. half morocco, spines
blind-tooled & gilt. Hannas 54-122 1978 £24

BOURINOT, A. S.   Collected Poems. Toronto, 1947. Pres. copy.
Hood 117-783 1978 $35

BOURINOT, A. S.   Discovery... Toronto, 1940. Card cover,
unopened. Hood 116-800 1978 $10

BOURINOT, A. S.   Pattering Feet, a Book of Childhood Verses. Ottawa, 1925. Some illus. coloured. Hood 116-801 1978 $15

BOURINOT, J. G.   The Story of Canada. London, Toronto, 1896.
Illus., fldg. map & plt. Hood's 115-580 1978 $15

BOURKE, JOHN G.   The Urine Dance of the Zuni Indians of New
Mexico.... Privately printed, 1920. Cloth, 100 copies printed. Ginsberg
14-749 1978 $100

BOURKE, U. J.   The Life & Times of John McHale, Archbishop
of Tuam. 1882. 1st ed., wr., very good. Hyland 128-911 1978 £7.50

BOURKE-WHITE, MARGARET   Portrait of Myself. Illus., 8vo., orig. bds.,
cloth back, advance copy of 1st ed., inserted is orig. signed photo. by Alfred
Eisenstaedt. Morrill 239-312 1978 $30

BOURNE, GEORGE   The Picture of Quebec. Quebec, 1829. 16mo.,
full contemp. calf, gilt, plts., pencil signature of Mary Bourne. Wolfe 39-44
1978 $100

BOURNE, H. R. FOX   English Merchants, Memoirs in illustration of the
Progress of British Commerce. 1866. Illus., 2 vols., post 8vo. George's 635-
288 1978 £12.50

BOURNE, H. R. FOX   Famous London Merchants. New York, 1869.
Orig. binding, clean, nice copy. Hayman 71-382 1978 $7.50

BOURNE, HENRY   Antiquitates Vulgares. New castle, 1725. 8vo.,
19th-century half calf, first ed., woodcuts. P. M. Hill 142-47 1978 £75

BOURNE, RANDOLPH   History of a Literary Radical and Other Essays.
1920. First ed., v.g., frayed d.j. Austin 82-1156 1978 $37.50

BOURNE, VINCENT   Miscellaneous Poems: Consisting of Originals
and Translations. 1772. 1st. collected ed., 4to, modern half morocco, top edge
trimmed, others uncut. Hannas 54-26 1978 £42

BOURRET, R.   La Faune de l'Indochine: vertebres. Hanoi, 1927.
4to, numerous plts, illus., orig. covers. Van der Peet 127-26 1978 Dfl 145

BOURRIN, CL.   Le vieux Tonkin; Le Theatre-Lesport-La vie
mondaine, de 1890 a 1894. Hanoi, 1941. Large 8vo, plts, maps, scarce, orig.
covers. Van der Peet 127-27 1978 Dfl 90

BOUTCHER, WILLIAM   A Treatise on Forest Trees, The Best Methods of
their Cultivation.... Edinburgh, 1775. Full calf, newer spine, 1st ed., 8vo,
orig. cloth. Book Chest 17-55 1978 $215

BOUTELL, H. S.   First Editions of To-day and How to Tell Them
U. S. & England. Philadelphia, 1937. 2nd rev. ed., enlarged, d.w. Battery
Park 1-299 1978 $15

BOUTELL, LEWIS H.   The Life of Roger Sherman. Chicago, 1896.
1st ed., illus., orig. cloth, fine. MacManus 239-815 1978 $25

BOUTELLE, A.   Sermon Occasioned by the Death of Newell
Marsh, at Shasta City, California, Nov. 1852:.... Concord, (1853). Original
printed wr., 1st ed. Ginsberg 14-82 1978 $50

BOUTET DE MONVEL, LOUIS MAURICE   Joan of Arc. Philadelphia, 1918.
Amer. ed., color plts., several taped areas, cover color plate. Victoria 34-
234 1978 $12.50

BOUTON, NATHAN   Festal Gathering of the Early Settlers and Present
Inhabitants of the Town of Virgil. Dryden, 1878. Frontis., prtd. wr., enlarged
2nd ed. Butterfield 21-147 1978 $25

BOUTRUCHE, R.   Une Societe Provinciale en lutte contre le Regime ieodal, l'alleu en Bordelais et en Bazadais du XIe au XVIIIe siecle. Rodez,
1947. Maps, 8vo. George's 635-566 1978 £5

BOUVET, MARGUERITE   A Child of Tuscany. Chicago, 1895. 1st ed.,
profusely illus. by Will Phillips Hooper, fine. Victoria 34-91 1978 $12.50

BOVALLIUS, CARL   Resa i Central-Amerika, 1881-1883. Upsula,
1886-7. 1st ed., 8vo., 1st issue, fldg. maps, plts., woodcuts, pic. blue wrs.,
scarce in orig. wrs. Current Misc. 8-51 1978 $335

BOVEY, M.   Whistling Wings. New York, 1947. Drawings
by F. L. Jaques, 8vo, orig. cloth. Book Chest 17-56 1978 $32

BOVEY, WILFRID   Canadien. London, 1934. Illus. Austin
79-87 1978 $12.50

BOVSHOVER, JOSEPH   To the Toilers & Other Verses. Berkeley
Heights, Oriole Press, 1928. 1 of 450 copies, portr., 8vo., orig. cloth, very
good. Americanist 103-65 1978 $55

BOWDEN, JAMES   The History of the Society of Friends in America. London, 1850-54. 2 vols., maps, nice set, orig. calf. MacManus 239-57 1978 $42.50

BOWDEN, JOHN   Norway; Its People, Products, and Institutions. London, 1867. 8vo, original green cloth, 1st ed., fine copy. Ximenes 47-33 1978 $30

BOWDEN, ROBERT D.   Boise Penrose Symbol of an Era. New York, (1937). Illus. MacManus 239-801 1978 $12.50

BOWDICH, THOMAS EDWARD   Mission From Cape Coast Castle to Ashantee... 1819. Maps, plts., 7 coloured, 4to, half calf, covers worn, some offsetting. Edwards 1012-246 1978 £150

BOWDITCH, HENRY I.   Memoir of Amos Twitchell, M.D. Boston, 1851. Sm. 8vo., binding faded, back cover bit warped, 1st ed. Morrill 239-26 1978 $15

BOWDITCH, JAMES H.   "The City by the Sea". Newport. Providence, 1884. Orig. printed wrs., some wear, but nice, illus., lg. fold. map. MacManus 239-415 1978 $25

BOWDITCH, NATHANIEL 1773-1838   The New American Practical Navigator. New York, 1811. 3rd ed., 8vo., ads, plts., map, bound in orig. brown calf, red label, bds. & spine rubbed & chipped, binding firm, text foxed throughout, good copy, scarce. Current 24-72 1978 $385

BOWDITCH, NATHANIEL INGERSOLL   A History of the Massachusetts General Hospital. Boston, 1872. 2nd ed., thick 8vo., illus., pres. copy from George E. Ellis. Morrill 239-27 1978 $60

BOWDITCH, NATHANIEL INGERSOLL   Memoir of Nathaniel Bowditch. Boston, 1840. Portrs., 4to., orig. cloth, fine copy of 2nd ed. Morrill 239-313 1978 $30

BOWDLER, JANE   Poems and Essays. Bath, 1786. 2 vols., cr. 8vo., contemp. calf, joints cracked, labels missing, second ed. Howes 194-183 1978 £20

BOWDLER, JANE   Poems and Essays. 1798. 10th. ed., 4to, fine frontispiece, portraits, orig. calf, marbled bds., spine slight rubbed, very good. Jarndyce 16-41 1978 £10

BOWDOIN, WILLIAM GOODRICH   Jack and Jill According to the Modern School of Fiction. Brooklyn, 1906. 1 of 200 numbered copies, orig. printed wrs., uncut. Americanist 102-54 1978 $25

BOWDOIN College, 1794-1894. Brunswick, 1894. 8vo., orig. cloth. Morrill 241-690 1978 $12.50

BOWEN, CATHERINE DRINKER   John Adams...and the American Revolution. Boston, 1950. Illus. Biblo 251-99 1978 $9.50

BOWEN, CLARENCE WINTHROP   The Boundary Disputes of Connecticut. Boston, 1882. Maps, 4to., 1st ed., pres. copy. Morrill 239-348 1978 $47.50

BOWEN, ELIZABETH   The Hotel. 1927. Covers little soiled, good, scarce, first English ed. Bell Book 17-118 1978 £15

BOWEN, ELIZABETH   The Hotel. New York, 1928. First US ed., partly split at hinge, good   Bell Book 17-119 1978 £8.50

BOWEN, ELIZABETH   The House in Paris. New York, 1936. First Amer. ed., spine faded, covers dust-marked, very good, orig. binding. Rota 211-45 1978 £6

BOWEN, ELIZABETH   The House in Paris. New York, 1936. First US ed., nick at head of spine, very good, worn d.w. Bell Book 17-120 1978 £10

BOWEN, FRANK C.   Conquest of the Seas. New York, 1940. Plts., illus., thick imp. 8vo., orig. cloth, first ed. F. Edwards 1013-29 1978 £20

BOWEN, FRANK C.   From Carrack to Clipper. 1948. Coloured plts., illus., imp. 8vo., orig. cloth. F. Edwards 1013-30 1978 £18

BOWEN, FRANK C.   The Sea Its History and Romance. New York, 1927. 1st ed., 4to., 4 vols., colored frontis., illus., plts., ports., orig. cloth, spine tops slightly frayed, hinges repaired, fine set, bookplt. MacManus 239-1736 1978 $75

BOWEN, MARJORIE   A Knight of Spain. 1913. Cloth gilt, some foxing, very good, first English ed. Bell Book 16-974 1978 £4

BOWEN, MARJORIE   Sophie Dawes,...the Scandal. New York, 1935. 1st ed. Biblo BL781-781 1978 $9

BOWEN'S Picture of Boston or the Citizen's and Stranger's Guide to the Metropolis of Massachusetts... Boston, 1838. 12mo, illus., cloth. MacManus 239-283 1978 $42.50

BOWER, ARCHIBALD   The History of the Popes From the Foundation of the See of Rome to the Present Time. 1750-66. 7 vols., 4to, vols. 1 & 2 - 3rd. ed., vols. 3-7 - 1st. ed., orig. calf, red & green labels, fine set. Jarndyce 16-42 1978 £50

BOWER, B. M.   Chip, of the Flying U. New York, 1906. Illus. by Charles M. Russell, red illus., cloth binding excellent. Nestler Rare 78-59 1978 $18

BOWER, F. O.   The Origin of a Land Flora. London, 1908. Illus., 8vo. Traylen 88-540 1978 £6

BOWERS, CLAUDE G.   Beveridge and the Progressive Era. Cambridge, 1932. Illus., 1st ed. Biblo BL781-190 1978 $9

BOWERS, CLAUDE G.   Jefferson and Hamilton; Jefferson in Power; The Young Jefferson. Boston, (1936-45). 3 vols., illus., fine, d.w. Biblo 247-68 1978 $30

BOWERS, CLAUDE G.   The Party Battles of the Jackson Period. Boston, 1928. Illus. Biblo 247-14 1978 $12.50

BOWERS, CLAUDE G.   Thomas Jefferson in Power. Boston, 1936. 1st ed., illus. Biblo BL781-208 1978 $9.50

BOWERS, DAVID F.   Foreign Influences in American Life. Princeton University Press, 1944. Illus., hard covers. Austin 79-88 1978 $17.50

BOWERS, F.   Japan, Islands of the Rising Sun. New York, 1945. Photographs by E. Fieger, in colour, oblong folio. George's 635-1270 1978 £8.50

BOWERS, HENRY   Thinking for Yourself. Toronto, 1947. Hood 117-462 1978 $10

BOWLE, JOHN   Western Political Thought... London, 1949. Salloch 348-18 1978 $20

BOWLES, CAROLINE   Mornings With Mama... Edinburgh and London, 1830. 8vo, orig. blind stamped cloth. Traylen 88-137 1978 £15

BOWLES, E. A.   My Garden in Autumn and Winter; Spring and Summer. London, 1914-1915. 3 vols., coloured & black & white plts., roy. 8vo, covers little worn, scarce. Traylen 88-542 1978 £30

BOWLES, PAUL   A Little Stone: stories. 1950. Very good, d.w., first English ed. Bell Book 16-111 1978 £16.50

BOWLES, PAUL   The Sheltering Sky. New York, 1949. First US ed., near fine, slightly worn d.w. Bell Book 17-122 1978 £21

BOWLES, S.   Our New West... Hartford, 1869. Map, portraits, frontis, plts., 8vo, orig. cloth, spine slightly worn. Edwards 1012-474 1978 £30

BOWLES, SAMUEL   Across the Continent: A Summer's Journey to the Rocky Mountains, the Mormons, and the Pacific States, with Speaker Colfax. Springfield, 1865. Folding map, original cloth, 1st ed. Ginsberg 14-57 1978 $50

BOWLES, SAMUEL   Across the Continent: A Summer's Journey to the Rocky Mountains, the Mormons, and the Pacific States. Springfield, Mass., 1865. Orig. cloth, 1st ed., scarce. Ginsberg 16-827 1978 $50.00

BOWLIN, JAMES B.   Speech of Mr..., of Missouri, on the Bill for Making Appropriations for Certain Rivers and Harbors. In the House... April 5, 1844. N.P., n.d. Disbound. Hayman 72-667 1978 $7.50

BOWLIN, JAMES B.   Speech of Mr..., of Missouri, on the Removal of Obstructions in the Mississippi River and Its Tributaries. Delivered in the House... January 16, 1844. Washington, 1844. Disbound. Hayman 72-666 1978 $8.50

BOWMAN, ANNE   Esperzanza; or, the Home of the Wanderers. London, (c.1860). New ed., illus., orig. blue cloth, good condition. Greene 78-10 1978 $30

BOWMAN, BOB   Dieppe. Ottawa, (1942). Wrs. Hood 117-115 1978 $10

BOWMAN, HEATH   Death is Incidental. 1937. Illus., block print signed by both authors. Austin 82-215 1978 $17.50

BOWMAN, JOHN   A Practical Handbook of Medical Chemistry. Philadelphia, 1866. 12mo., illus., orig. cloth, gilt, very good copy, 4th American ed. Norman 5-42 1978 $25

BOWMAN, SAMUEL MILLARD   Sherman and His Campaigns. New York, 1865. Bds., spine repaired but complete. Hayman 71-117 1978 $10

BOWMAN TECHNICAL SCHOOL   Your Future & Our School. Lancaster, 1914. Illus., 12mo., orig. wrs. Morrill 241-60 1978 $10

BOWRING, JOHN   The Kingdom and People of Siam... 1857. Folding map, 8 coloured and 10 other plts., 2 vols., binders' cloth, some lib. stamps, 8vo. Edwards 1012-146 1978 £50

BOWYER, WILLIAM   Biographical and Literary Anecdotes of ... 1782. 1st. ed., fine frontispiece, portrait, orig. calf, old reback, v.g., bookplt. of A.N.L. Munby. Jarndyce 16-43 1978 £120

BOX, MICHAEL JAMES   Capt. James Box's Adventures and Explorations in New and Old Mexico,.... New York, 1861-69. Orig. cloth. Jenkins 116-141 1978 $450

BOY SCOUTS OF AMERICA   Handbook For Scout Masters Boy Scouts of America. (1914). Orig. cloth, very good, sound copy. Baldwins' 51-332 1978 $100

BOY SCOUTS OF AMERICA   Handbook for Scout Masters. New York, (1914). 1st ed., illus., some underlining, pict. cloth worn, text very good. Victoria 34-95 1978 $10

BOY SCOUTS OF AMERICA   The Official Handbook for Boys. New York, 1911. 2nd ed., illus., pict. cloth, very good. Victoria 34-93 1978 $25

BOY SCOUTS OF AMERICA   The Official Handbook for Boys. Garden City, 1913. 4th ed., good copy. Baldwins' 51-331 1978 $50

BOYCE, W. SCOTT   Economic and Social History of Chowan County, North Carolina 1880-1915. New York, 1917. New cloth. Broadfoot 50-16 1978 $20

BOYD, A. K. HUTCHINSON   The Recreations of a Country Parson. 1881/76/78. 1st., 2nd., 3rd. series, 3 vols., half titles, orig. green cloth, v.g. Jarndyce 16-303 1978 £14.50

BOYD, CHARLES RUFUS   Resources of South-West Virginia Showing the Mineral Deposits of Iron, Coal, Zinc, Copper and Lead... New York, 1881. Illus., lacks map, scarce. MacManus 239-1878 1978 $35

BOYD, CHARLES RUFUS   Resources of South-West Virginia Showing the Mineral Deposits of Iron, Coal, Zinc, Copper and Lead. New York, 1881. Lg. fldg. map, cloth, pres. inscr. from author, minor tear in free endpaper in fr., slight fading of spine, very nice copy in orig. binding. Hayman 73-713 1978 $32.50

BOYD, E. S.   Many Coloured Mountains and Some Seas Between. London, 1911. Illus. Hood's 115-242 1978 $10

BOYD, ERNEST   H. L. Mencken. 1925. Austin 82-216 1978 $7.50

BOYD, ERNEST   Literary Blasphemies. 1927. First ed., very good, d.j. Austin 82-217 1978 $17.50

BOYD, ERNEST   Portraits Real and Imaginary. 1924. First ed., good copy. Austin 82-218 1978 $12.50

BOYD, J. L. R.   John Angus Campbell, Pfc., CSA, 1840-1933. Atlanta, Ga., n.d. Letter from Boyd to Wiley laid in. Bell Wiley's copy. Broadfoot 46-23 1978 $16

BOYD, JAMES   Long Hunt. New York, 1930. 1st ed., ltd. to 260, pres. copy, very fine, slipcase. Ballinger 11-107 1978 $70.00

BOYD, JAMES P.   Men and Issues of '92... N.P., 1892. Illus., very nice copy, orig. pic. cloth. MacManus 239-58 1978 $22.50

BOYD, JAMES P.   Military and Civil Life of Ulysses S. Grant. Philadelphia, 1885. 1/2 leather. Hayman 71-58 1978 $10

BOYD, JAMES P.   The Political History of the United States...Presidents and Administrations...Rise and Fall of Parties... Chicago, 1889. Leather. Hayman 72-65 1978 $15

BOYD, LOUISE A.   The Fiord Region of East Greenland. New York, 1935. Map, illus., 2 vols., orig. cloth, 8vo. Edwards 1012-565 1978 £30

BOYD, LUCINDA   The Sorrows of Nancy. Cynthiana, 1943. Spine poor. Broadfoot 50-17 1978 $15

BOYD, MARTIN   Lucinda Brayford. 1946. Very good, first English ed. Bell Book 17-973 1978 £5

BOYD, THOMAS   Light-horse Harry Lee. New York, 1931. 1st ed. MacManus 239-552 1978 $12.50

BOYD, THOMAS   Mad Anthony Wayne. New York, 1929. 1st ed., cloth bds., illus., ltd. to 500 copies, signed. MacManus 239-553 1978 $22.50

BOYD, THOMAS   Simon Girty, the White Savage. New York, 1928. Illus., 1st ed. MacManus 239-1148 1978 $15

BOYD, WILLIAM H.   Boyd's Philadelphia City Business Directory... Philadelphia, 1880. Orig. cloth, worn. MacManus 239-1604 1978 $25

BOYD, WILLIAM H.   Boyd's Philadelphia City Business Directory... Philadelphia, 1881. Orig. cloth, good copy. MacManus 239-1605 1978 $25

BOYD, ZACHARY   Biographical Sketch... Glasgow, 1832. Frontis portrait, half calf, bds., paper label, 2 missing pgs. Jarndyce 16-304 1978 £7.50

BOYD'S Auburn Directory and Business Directory of Cayuga Co. 1859-60. New York, 1859. Pict. ads., disbound, fldg. map laid in. Butterfield 21-104 1978 $20

BOYDEN, ANNA L.   Echoes from Hospital and White House. Boston, (1884). Frontis., plts., sm. 8vo., 1st ed. Morrill 241-654 1978 $12.50

BOYER, ABEL   The Compleat French-Master... 1733. 8vo, contemp. unlettered sheep, spine rubbed, but sound, nice copy. Fenning 32-32 1978 £21.50

BOYER, CHARLES C.   American Boyers. Allentown, 1940. Lg. 8vo, scarce, orig. binding, best ed. Americanist 101-58 1978 $50

BOYER, CHARLES S.   Early Forges and Furnaces of New Jersey. Philadelphia, 1931. 1st ed., fine, d.j., illus., very scarce. MacManus 239-1244 1978 $55

BOYER'S Dictionary Abridged in 2 Parts. 1797. Orig. tree calf, red label, fine, 19th. ed. Jarndyce 16-44 1978 £18

BOYESEN, HJALMOR HJORTH   Literary and Social Silhouettes. 1894. Austin 79-89 1978 $12.50

BOYKIN, E. M.   The Falling Flag. New York, 1874. Cover spotted, Bell Wiley's copy. Broadfoot's 44-52 1978 $65

BOYKIN, RICHARD MANNING   Captain Alexander Hamilton Boykin, One of South Carolina's Distinguished Citizens. New York, 1942. Illus., privately printed ltd. edition, Bell Wiley's copy. Broadfoot's 44-598 1978 $36

BOYLE, LADY E. V.   Child's Play. London, 1881. 1st ed., small 8vo, plates and text illus. all in red, soiled. Victoria 34-97 1978 $20

BOYLE, LADY E. V.   A New Child's-Play. London, 1877. 1st ed., plts., minor cover edge rubbing, fine. Victoria 34-96 1978 $75

BOYLE, F.   Canon Sheehan; A Sketch of His Life & Works. 1927. 1st ed., good, octavo bound in cloth. Hyland 128-517 1978 £5

BOYLE, FREDERICK   The Savage Life. London, 1876. 1st. ed., 8vo, orig. brown cloth, neatly recased, corners repaired, sl. worming of cover, very good copy. Deighton 5-198 1978 £48

BOYLE, JAMES E.   Speculation and the Chicago Board to Trade. (1920) 1929. Austin 80-444 1978 $12.50

BOYLE, JOHN   Letters from Italy. 1773. Sm. 8vo., contemp. calf, short splits in hinges, first ed. P. M. Hill 142-48 1978 £24

BOYLE, KAY   His Human Majesty. 1949. Austin 82-220 1978 $10

BOYLE, KAY   My Next Bride. New York, (1934). First ed., binding faded, d.w. frayed. Biblo 247-501 1978 $15

BOYLE, KAY   Primer for Combat. 1942. Austin 82-222 1978 $8.50

BOYLE, KAY   Short Stories. Paris, Black Sun Press, 1929. 8vo., flexible wrs., one of 150 copies, first ed., fine. Duschnes 220-54 1978 $137.50

BOYLE, KAY   Wedding Day and Other Stories. New York, 1930. 1st ed., very good. Ballinger 11-108 1978 $32.50

BOYLE, KAY   Year Before Last. New York, (1932). 2nd issue of 1st ed., mended d.j., very good or better. Limestone 9-29 1978 $10

BOYLE, MARY LOUISA   The State Prisoner... 1837. 1st. & apparently only ed., 2 vols., lg. 12mo, contemp. half calf, sm. lib. stamp in 2 places, nice copy. Fenning 32-33 1978 £36

BOYLE, CAPT. ROBERT   The Voyages & Adventures of
Please turn to
CHETWOOD, WILLIAM RUFUS

BOYLE, ROBERT   Certain Physiological Essays. London, 1661. Sm. 4to., contemp. calf, rebacked, endpapers renewed, fine copy, 1st ed. Norman 5-**6 1978 $3,750

BOYLE, ROBERT   The Excellancy of Theology, compar'd with Natural Philosophy,.... London, 1674. Octavo, 1st ed., full contemporary sprinkled calf, hinges weakened. Bennett 20-28 1978 $1100

BOYLE, ROBERT   New Experiments and Observations Touching Cold. 1683. Sm. 4to., old calf, rebacked, lettering piece, cheap copy of 2nd ed., lacking 2 plts. Howes 194-18 1978 £60

BOYLE, ROBERT   Opera Varia. Geneva, 1714. Frontis. portr., plts., contemp. calf, rubbed, light dampstaining, some foxing, but very good set, 4 vols., 4to., 2 1st eds. in Latin. Norman 5-43 1978 $1,000

BOYLE, ROBERT   Some Considerations About the Reconcileableness of Reason and Religion. London, 1675. 1st ed., octavo, slightly later calf, rebacked, preserving original spine, bookplate, some soiling. Bennett 20-29 1978 $650

BOYLE, ROBERT   The Works. London, 1772. New ed., 4to., 6 vols., contemp. calf, rebacked, corners renewed, fine portrait, plts. Gurney 75-14 1978 £320

BOYLE, VIRGINIA FRAZER   Brokenburne. New York, 1897. Illus. by William Henry Walker, 8vo., 1st ed. Morrill 239-314 1978 $8.50

BOYLEN, J. C.   Toronto Normal School, 1847-1947. Toronto, 1947. Coloured card cover, illus. Hood's 115-379 1978 $12.50

BOYNTON, EDWARD C.   History of West Point, and Its Military Importance During the Revolution... New York, 1871. 2nd ed., illus., maps, some in color, orig. cloth, fine. MacManus 239-59 1978 $35

BRABNER, H. H. F.   Comprehensive Gazetteer of England and Wales. (1893). Plts., 6 vols., roy. 8vo. George's 635-1463 1978 £12.50

BRACE, CHARLES LORING   The Dangerous Classes. New York, 1872. Illus., nice copy, orig. cloth. MacManus 239-362 1978 $40

BRACE, CHARLES LORING   The Dangerous Classes of New York, and Twenty Years' Work Among Them. New York, 1872. Plts., shaken, 1st ed., inscr'd by author. Butterfield 21-483 1978 $7.50

BRACE, CHARLES LORING   Homelife in Germany. New York, 1853. 8vo., slightly rubbed & faded, 1st ed. Morrill 239-315 1978 $12.50

BRACE, CHARLES LORING   The New West: or, Califronia in 1867-1868. New York, 1869. 1st ed., rebound, fine. MacManus 239-1904 1978 $35

BRACEBRIDGE, C. H.   Authentic Details of the Valdenses in Piemont and other Countries. London, 1827. 8vo., half calf, new spine, first ed. King 7-336 1978 £75

BRACHET, JEAN LOUIS   De L'Emploi De L'Opium Dans Les Phlegmasies Des Membranes Muqueuses, Sereuses et Fibreuses. Paris, Montpellier, Bruxelles, 1828. 8vo., contemp. half mor., gilt on spine, browning & foxing, good copy, rare 1st ed. Zeitlin 245-299 1978 $125

BRACHET, JEAN LOUIS   Recherches sur la Nature et le Siege de L'Hysterie et de L'Hypocondrie et sur L'Analogie et les Differences de ces Deux Maladies. Paris, 1832. 8vo., modern red cloth, gilt lettering on spine, foxing, early owner's stamp, very good copy, 1st ed. Zeitlin 245-31 1978 $67.50

BRACHT, VIKTOR   Texas in 1848. San Antonio, 1931. 1st ed. in English. Jenkins 116-142 1978 $65

BRACKEN, HENRY   Farriery Improv'd. 1749. Sixth ed., 2 vols., sm. 8vo., contemp. sheep, bindings rather rubbed, joints weak, labels missing, contents good. Howes 194-184 1978 £15

BRACKENRIDGE, HENRY MARIE   History of the Late War Between the United States and Great Britain.... Philadelphia, 1844. Illus., plts. MacManus 239-473 1978 $25

BRACKETT, CYRUS F.   Electricity in Daily Life. New York, 1890. 8vo., ex-lib., library binding, 1st ed. Morrill 241-61 1978 $10

BRACKETT, JEFFREY R.   The Negro in Maryland. Baltimore, 1889. 1st ed., orig. cloth, hinges weak, nice, scarce. MacManus 239-845 1978 $35

BRADALBANE, MARCHIONESS OF   The High Tops of Black Mount. Edinburgh, 1907. Plts., decor. cloth, 8vo. K Books 244-45 1978 £7

BRADBROOK, M. C.   Andrew Marvell. Cambridge, 1940. 2 plts., octavo, good. Upcroft 10-234 1978 £5

BRADBROOK, M. C.   Elizabethan Stage Conditions; A Study of Their Place in the Interpretation of Shakespeare's Plays. Cambridge, 1932. Octavo, good. Upcroft 10-233 1978 £5

BRADBURY, RAY   Dark Carnival. Sauk City, 1947. Signed by Bradbury, fine in acetate dw, orig. dw cover front inserted loosely underneath, scarce. Bernard 5-360 1978 $200

BRADBURY, RAY   The Martian Chronicles. Garden City, 1950. Signed by Bradbury, very good in d.w. Bernard 5-361 1978 $125

BRADBURY, RAY   Old Ahab's Friend, and Friend to Noah, Speaks His Piece. (Glendale, 1971). 1st ed., limited to 485 copies, 1 of 40 numbered, signed by author, large 8 vo., wrappers, cover printed in dark green, d.j., mint with acetate jacket. Houle 10-39 1978 $150

BRADDON, MARY ELIZABETH
Please turn to
MAXWELL, MARY ELIZABETH (BRADDON)

BRADEN, JAMES A.   Little Brother of the Hudson. A Tale of the Last Eries. New York, 1928. Illus., 1st ed., d.w. Biblo BL781-1018 1978 $9.50

BRADFOR, SARAH H.   Scenes in the Life of Harriet Tubman. Auburn, 1869. Frontis. portr., orig. cloth, ends of spine rubbed, sound copy, 1st ed. Butterfield 21-73 1978 $65

BRADFORD, ALDEN   History of Massachusetts fron July 1764, to July, 1775... Boston, 1832. 1st ed., orig. calf, nice copy. MacManus 239-291 1978 $22.50

BRADFORD, ALDEN   History of the Federal Government, for Fifty Years... Boston, 1840. 1st ed., orig. cloth, foxed, extremities worn, else good copy. MacManus 239-60 1978 $22.50

BRADFORD, E. D. S.   Contemporary Jewellry and Silver Design. London, (1950). 4to., illus., some in color, 1st ed. Biblo BL781-642 1978 $13.50

BRADFORD, WILLIAM   History of Plymouth Plantation 1620-1647. 1912. 4to, 2 vols., illus., ports., orig. cloth-backed bds., fine set. MacManus 239-292 1978 $65

BRADLEE, FRANCIS B. C.   Marblehead's Foreign Commerce... Salem, 1929. 1st ed., illus., orig. cloth, fine copy. MacManus 239-1737 1978 $20

BRADLEY, A. G.   The Fight with France for North America. Westminster, 1900. Fold. maps, 1st ed. Hood 116-112 1978 $30

BRADLEY, A. G.   Highways and Byways in North Wales. London, 1901. Illus. Biblo BL781-632 1978 $13.50

BRADLEY, A. G.   Wolfe. London, 1895. Frontis. portrait, orig. binding. Wolfe 39-567 1978 $7.50

BRADLEY, C.   Fox-Hunting from Shire to Shire with many noted packs. 1912. Colour plts., text illus., roy. 8vo. George's 635-1504 1978 £10.50

BRADLEY, EDWARD   The Adventures of Mr. Verdant Green. The Further Adventures of Mr. Verdant Green... London, 1853-57. 4 vols., 12mo., orig. printed wrs., 1st eds. MacManus 238-166 1978 $350

BRADLEY, HENRY   Collected papers. Oxford, 1928. Plts., 8vo. Upcroft 12-47 1978 £12

BRADLEY, ISAAC S.   A Bibliography of Wisconsin's Participation in the War between the States Based Upon Material Contained in the Wisconsin Historical Library. (Madison), 1911. Cloth, 1500 copies prtd. Hayman 73-58 1978 $8.50

BRADLEY, J. W.   A Dictionary of Miniaturists Illuminators, Calligraphers, and Copyists...From the Establishment of Christianity to the 18th Century. London, 1889. Vol. 3 only (O-Z), demy 8vo., orig. rosburghe. Forster 130-151 1978 £5

BRADLEY, J. W.   A Manual of Illumination. (c. 1865). 11th ed., wood engravings, cr. 8vo. George's 635-9 1978 £5.25

BRADLEY, WILL   The American Chap-Book. September 1904-August 1905. Decor. bds., fine cond., cloth-covered slipcase, slightly soiled, inscr. & signed by Bradley. Dawson's 447-18 1978 $700

BRADLEY, WILL   The Delectable Art of Printing. (New York), 1905. Pic. wrs., fine. Dawson's 447-19 1978 $350

BRADSBY, H. C.   History of Bradford Co., Penna. Chicago, 1891. Lg. thick 4to., cloth, illus., a.e.g. MacManus 239-1383 1978 $150

BRADSBY, H. C.   History of Luzerne County, Pa... Chicago, 1893. 4to., illus. MacManus 239-1384 1978 $75

BRADSHAW, H.   Collected Papers. Cambridge, 1889. Demy 8vo., orig. cloth, plts. Forster 130-153 1978 £12

BRADSHAW, P. V.   The Art of the Illustrator. London, n.d. Orig. portfolios, semi-stiff wrappers, folio, tipped-in portrait of artist, plts. some colored, orig. cloth box, soiled and defective, contents fine. Forster 130-154 1978 £45

BRADSHAW'S Railway Companion. Manchester, 1842. Diagram, coloured maps, sm. 12mo., orig. cloth, fine. K Books 244-44 1978 £40

BRADY, CYRUS TOWNSEND   Border Fights and Fighters. 1916. Illus. Austin 82-227 1978 $11

BRADY, CYRUS TOWNSEND   Colonial Fights and Fighters. 1909. Illus. Austin 82-228 1978 $20

BRADY, CYRUS TOWNSEND   Hohenzollern. 1902. Illus., first ed. Austin 82-229 1978 $12.50

BRADY, CYRUS TOWNSEND   Indian Fights and Fighters. (1904). 1909. Illus. Austin 82-230 1978 $20

BRADY, CYRUS TOWNSEND   A Little Book for Christmas. 1917. Illus., first ed. Austin 82-231 1978 $12.50

BRADY, CYRUS TOWNSEND   Most Politely, Being the Strange and Exhiliarating Experiences of a Certain Young Friend of Mine. Kansas City, (1910). 1st ed., fine colored t.p. with signed portrait of author, limited ed., fine. Victoria 34-99 1978 $15

BRADY, CYRUS TOWNSEND   Northwestern Fights and Fighters. 1910. Illus., maps. Austin 82-232 1978 $20

BRADY, CYRUS TOWNSEND   Reuben James. 1900. First ed., illus. Austin 82-233 1978 $12.50

BRADY, CYRUS TOWNSEND   Revolutionary Fights and Fighters. 1909. Illus. Austin 82-234 1978 $12.50

BRADY, CYRUS TOWNSEND   South American Fights and Fighters and Other Tales of Adventure. 1910. First ed., illus. Austin 82-235 1978 $12.50

BRADY, CYRUS TOWNSEND   When the Sun Stood Still. 1917. Austin 82-236 1978 $12.50

BRADY, JAMES T.   Oration...Before the Independence Guard... July 4th, 1844. New York, 1844. Wr., sewn, back cover & some pages stained. Butterfield 21-233 1978 $10

BRAGDON, CLAUDE   Yoga for You. 1945. Illus. Austin 82-237 1978 $12.50

BRAGG, JEFFERSON DAVIS   Louisiana in the Confederacy. Baton Rouge, 1941. Bell Wiley's copy. Broadfoot's 44-506 1978 $16.00

BRAGG, WILLIAM HENRY   X-rays and Crystal Structure. London, 1915. 8vo., ads, plts., diagrs., orig. cloth, fine copy, 1st ed. Norman 5-44 1978 $150

BRAHE, TYCHO   Astronomiae instauratae Mechanica. Nuremburg, 1602. Folio, portrait, woodcuts, engravings, contemp. vellum, green edges, 1st Public ed., very fine. Gilhofer 75-15 1978 SFr 18,000

BRAHE, TYCHO   Epistolarum Astronomicarum. Uraniborg, 1596. 4to., 1/2 calf, paper foxed. Salloch 345-28 1978 $1,500

BRAHE, TYCHO   De Mundi Aetherei Recentioribus Phaenomenis Liber Secundus. Uraniborg & Prague, 1603.

BRAHE, TYCHO   Opera Omnia Sive Astronomiae Instauratae Progymnasmata. Frankfurt, 1648. 2 vols. in 1, woodcuts, tables, 4to., vellum, paper browned. Salloch 345-30 1978 $1,000

BRAIM, THOMAS HENRY   A History of New South Wales, From Its Settlement to the Close of the Year 1844. London, 1846. 1st. ed., 2 vols., half-title, tinted lithograph frontispieces, wood-cut illus., orig. blind stamped cloth, neatly rebacked, pres. copy, lib. stamps, & label. Deighton 5-97 1978 £165

BRAINERD, THOMAS   The Life of John Brainerd... Philadelphia, (1865). 1st ed., frontis., orig. cloth, recased. MacManus 239-726 1978 $17.50

BRAITHWAITE, RICHARD   Barnabae Itinerarium. 1818. Seventh ed., 12 mo., orig. bds., backstrip repaired, uncut, frontispiece, plts. P. M. Hill 142-245 1978 £12

BRAITHWAITE, WILLIAM C.   The Beginnings of Quakerism.   London, 1912.
MacManus 239-61 1978 $15

BRAITHWAITE, WILLIAM C.   The Second Period of Quakerism.   London, 1919.
MacManus 239-62 1978 $15

BRAMAH, ERNEST PSEUD.
Please turn to
SMITH, ERNEST BRAMAH

BRAMAN, DWIGHT   San Diego: Southern California.   (Boston, 1892).
Illus., folding map, orig. front wr. only. Ginsberg 14-83 1978 $75

BRAMSTON, JAMES   The Man of Taste.   London, 1733. Frontis., 1st
ed., small folio, recently bound in green quarter mor., gilt lettering, bookplate.
Totteridge 29-16 1978 $175

BRAMSTON, JOHN   The Autobiography of ...   1845. Octavo , good.
Upcroft 10-17 1978 £7.50

BRANAGAN, THOMAS   The Excellency of Virtue, Contrasted with the
Deformity of Vice....   Philadelphia, 1808. 1st ed., contemp. calf, rubbed, fronts,
8vo. Americanist 101-23 1978 $30

BRANAGAN, THOMAS   The Penitential Tyrant; or,....   New York, 1807.
12mo, contemporary calf, rubbed but sound, 2nd ed., "enlarge", very scarce,
engraved frontispiece. Ximenes 47-34 1978 $125

BRANCA, FIOVANNI   Le Machine, volume nuovo et di molto artificio
da fare effeti maravigliosi tanto spiritali quanto di animale operatione. Rome,
1629. Very rare 1st ed., woodcuts, contemp. vellum over boards, lightly rubbed.
Gilhofer 75-16 1978 SFr 6,500

BRANCH, EDWARD DOUGLAS   The Hunting of the Buffalo.   New York, 1929.
Illus., first ed., d.w. Biblo 247-182 1978 $30

BRANCH, EDWARD DOUGLAS   The Hunting of the Buffalo.   New York/London,
1929. Ex-library, good, orig. binding. Wolfe 39-45 1978 $25

BRAND, ADAM   Relation Du Voyage De Mr. Evert Isbrand Envoye
De Sa Majeste Czarienne a l'Empereur de la Chine en 1692, 1693, et 1694. Amsterdam, 1699. Engr. frontis, fldg. map, 8vo., vellum. Salloch 345-31 1978
$300

BRAND, CHARLES   Journal of a Voyage to Peru....   London, 1828.
1st. ed., 8vo, half-title, aquatint plts., orig. publisher's blind stamped purple
cloth, gilt back, neatly rebacked retaining the orig. gilt back. Deighton 5-30
1978 £105

BRAND, JOHN   Observations on the Popular Antiquities of Great
Britain.   1849-53. Cr. 8vo., orig. cloth, frontispieces, 3 vols., some hinges
sprung. George's 635-546 1978 £8.50

BRANDAT, P.   Mers de l'Inde (1860-1864).   Paris, 1870. 8vo,
orig. covers. Van der Peet 127-28 1978 Dfl 35

BRANDES, GEORG   Impressions of Russia.   London, c. 1890. Portrait, cr. 8vo., orig. cloth. K Books 244-344 1978 £6

BRANDES, GEORGE   Main Currents in 19th Century Literature.   1906.
Illus., 6 vols., 8vo. George's 635-1375 1978 £21

BRANDOLESE, PIETRO   Pitture, Sculture, Architteture ed altre Cose Notabili di Padova, nuovamente descritte da Pietro Brandolese, con Alcune Brevi Notizie Intorno gli Artefici Mantovani. Padua, 1795. 8vo., errata leaf, 1st ed.
Gilhofer 74-31 1978 SFr 600

BRANDON, EDGAR E.   A Pilgrimage of Liberty.   Athens, 1941. Fldg.
map, cloth, fine copy. Hayman 73-59 1978 $10

BRANDOW, JOHN HENRY   The Story of Old Saratoga.   Albany, 1919. Illus.,
fine copy, maps. MacManus 239-554 1978 $22.50

BRANDT, ELLIS   Emma Cheyne.   1875. 1st. ed., 8vo, recent
bds., nice copy. Fenning 32-15 1978 £8.50

BRANDT, FRANCIS B.   The Majestic Delaware, the Nation's Foremost
Historic River. Philadelphia, (1929). 4to., illus. MacManus 239-1385 1978
$12.50

BRANDT, P.   Sehen und Erkennen.   Leipzig, 1929. 8vo.,
cloth, colored mounted frontis, colored plts., text illus. Van der Peet H-64-106
1978 Dfl 55

BRANGWYN, FRANK   Book-plates by... R.A.   Philadelphia, London,
(1920). Sm. 4to., illus., orig. dec. cloth, slightly worn and soiled, good. Mac-
Manus 238-875 1978 $35

BRANGWYN, FRANK   Historical Paintings in the Great Hall in London
of the Worshipful Company of Skinners aforetime of the Craft and Mystery of the
Guild of the Body of Christ. Caradoc Press, 1909. Plts., folio. George's 635-
101 1978 £35

BRANGWYN, FRANK   Windmills.   1923. 4to., ltd. ed., plts. in colour,
bds., parchment back, gilt top, uncut, ltd. to 75 copies. Quaritch 979-58
1978 $180

BRANNON, GEORGE   Vectis Scenery.   1832. Map, hand coloured in
outline, orig. roan-backed bds., oblong 4to., very good. Howes 194-1428 1978
£65

BRANT, SEBASTIAN   Stultifera navis...olim a Sebastiano Brant...
conscriptus, & per Iacobum Locher....   Basel, March, 1572. 8 vo., woodcuts,
very fine copy, very scarce ed., orig. contemp. limp binding. Schafer 19-7
1978 sFr. 2,900

BRANTLEY, RABUN LEE   Georgia Journalism of the Civil War Period.
Nashville, 1929. Wrs., letter from author to Wiley laid in, Bell Wiley's copy.
Broadfoot 46-322 1978 $14

BRANTOME, PIERRE DE BOURDEILLE   The Lives of Gallant Ladies.   Golden
Cockerel Press, 1924. 2 vols., 4to., woodcut illus., bds., cloth backs, little
worn, 625 copies prtd. Quaritch 979-162 1978 $65

BRASSEY, THOMAS   Life and Labours of Mr. Brassey.   1872. 3rd.
ed., frontis portrait, plts., orig. half calf, label, one corner rubbed otherwise v.g.
Jarndyce 16-306 1978 £15.50

BRATHWAITE, RICHARD   The Arcadian Princesse:....   London, 1635.
8vo, 19th-century full red morocco, gilt, spine gilt, a.e.g., 1st ed., fine copy,
engraved frontispiece by Marshall, bookplate. Ximenes 47-35 1978 $750

BRATT, JOHN   Trails of Yesterday.   Lincoln, 1921. Pic. cloth,
illus., 1st ed., fine copy, slipcase, very scarce. Dykes 34-16 1978 $85

BRAUNGART, RICHARD   Das Moderne Deutsche Gebrauchs.   Munchen,
1922. Ex-libris, illus. Battery Park 1-288 1978 $35

BRAY, S. ALICE   The Baby's Journal.   New York, 1882. Illus.,
oblong 8vo., orig. pict. bds., fine in orig. box. Morrill 239-316 1978 $12.50

BRAY, THOMAS   The Acts of Dr. Bray's Visitation, Held at Anno-
polis in Mary-Land, May 23, 24, 25, Anno 1700. London, 1700. Probably, the
2nd prtg. Kraus 152-52 1978 $1,200

BRAY, THOMAS   The Layman's Library.   (London, c. 1700). Folio,
550 copies. Kraus 152-54 1978 $4,200

BRAY, THOMAS   A Letter from Dr. Bray to Such as Have Contributed Towards the Propagating Christian Knowledge in the Plantations. (London,
1701). 1st ed., contemp. inscr., not in Bray's hand. Kraus 152-55 1978 $1,450

BRAY, THOMAS   A Memorial Representing the Present Case of the
Church in Mary-Land, with Relation to Its Establishment by Law. (London, 1700).
Folio, cloth case, this Memorial known only from this copy, unique. Kraus 152-
53 1978 $5,000

BRAY, THOMAS   A Memorial Representing the Present State of
Religion on the Continent of North-America. London, 1701. Folio, 2nd ed.
Kraus 152-56 1978 $1,500

BRAY, THOMAS   Proposals for the Encouragement and Promoting
of Religion and Learning in the Foreign Plantations. (London, 1697). Pamphlet,
9th ed. Kraus 152-51 1978 $1,750

BRAY, WILLIAM L.   The Vegetation of Texas.   Austin, 1906. Illus.
Jenkins 116-148 1978 $15

BRAY, WILLIAM L.   Vegetation of the Sotol Country in Texas.   Austin,
1905. Illus. Jenkins 116-147 1978 $8.50

BRAYLEY, EDWARD WEDLAKE   Topographical History of Surrey... (1841-48). 5 vols., 4to., 1st ed., woodcuts, green mor., gilt edges, some marginal foxing, fine. Quaritch 983-302 1978 $625

BREA, MANUEL ANTONIO DE   Principios Universales y Reglas Generales de La Verdadera Destreza del Espadin. Madrid, 1805. Sm. 4to., contemp. Spanish tree calf, plts. F. Edwards 1013-256 1978 £50

BREASTED, CHARLES   Pioneer to the Past, the Story of James Henry Breasted. New York, 1943. First ed. Biblo 247-281 1978 $13.50

BREASTER, J. H.   Geschichte Aegyptens. Sweite Auflage. Vienna, (1936). 4to., illus., plts. in color. Biblo BL781-332 1978 $25

BREBNER, J. B.   New England's Outpost; Acadia Before the Conquest of Canada. New York, 1927. 1st ed. Hood 116-209 1978 $55

BREBNER, J. B.   North Atlantic Triangle. New Haven, 1945. Maps, diagrs., pencilled annotations by author. Hood 117-554 1978 $50

BREBNER, J. B.   Scholarship for Canada, The Function of Graduate Studies. Ottawa, 1945. Paper cover. Hood's 115-380 1978 $7.50

BRECHT, BERTOLT   A Penny for the Poor. 1937. Spine faded, some foxing, good, very scarce, first English ed. Bell Book 17-126 1978 £45

BREEN, MATTHEW P.   Thirty Years of New York Politics. New York, 1899. Illus. MacManus 239-373 1978 $17.50

BREEN, PARTICK   Diary of...One of the Donner Party. Berkeley, 1910. Wrs. Biblo BL781-265 1978 $18.50

BREES, S. C.   Pictorial Illustrations of New Zealand. London, 1849. Folio, engraved vignette title-pg., engraved mezzotint plts. by Henry Melville, folding engraved map, orig. red cloth, blind & gilt, all edges gilt. Deighton 5-98 1978 £245

BREGER, DAVE   Private Breger in Britain. London, The Pilot Press, 1944. Cartoons by Dave Breger. Austin 80-27 1978 $8.50

BREIDENBACH, BERNHARDO   Peregrinatio Ad Terram Sanctam.... Wittenberg, 1536. Sm. 8vo, sl. staining in margin, last leaf neatly repaired, modern half calf, gilt back. Deighton 5-64 1978 £185

BREITHAUPT, T.   Chronicle of the Breithaupt Family. 1903. Inscr. by Breithaupt family member. Austin 79-91 1978 $47.50

BREMER, FREDRIKA   America of the Fifties. 1924. Austin 79-92 1978 $15

BREMER, FREDERIKA   The Home: or Family Cares and Family Joys. New York, 1842. Rittenhouse 49-100 1976 $10

BREMER, FREDERIKA   The Home. 1843. 2nd. ed., 2 vols., half titles, orig. brown cloth, v.g. Jarndyce 16-308 1978 £10.50

BREMER, FREDERIKA   The Homes of the New World; Impressions of America. New York, 1854. 2 vols., orig. cloth, fine set, signature clipped from title-page. MacManus 239-63 1978 $40

BREMER, FREDERIKA   The Neighbours. 1843. 3rd. ed., 2 vols., half titles, orig. dark brown cloth, v.g., except for wear to head of spines. Jarndyce 16-307 1978 £10.50

BREMER, FREDERIKA   The President's Daughters. A Narrative of a Governess. Boston, 1843. Rittenhouse 49-101 1976 $10

BREMNER, M. D. K.   The Story of Dentistry. Brooklyn, 1946. Illus., 8vo., 2nd ed. Morrill 239-28 1978 $20

BRENAN, G.   A History of the House of Percy From the Earliest Times Down to the Present Century. London, 1902. 2 vols., plts. & genealogies, 8vo. Traylen 88-457 1978 £15

BRENCHLEY, JULIUS LUCIUS   Jottings During the Cruise of H.M.S. Curacoa Among the South Sea Islands in 1865. London, 1873. 1st ed., royal thick 8vo., illus., fldg. color-plt. frontis., fldg. map, green gilt-decor. cloth, no foxing, plts. in fine cond. Current 24-175 1978 $385

BRENIER, FLACOURT   Les principaux Oleagineux de l'Indo-Chine. Hanoi, 1906. 4to, illus., plts., orig. covers. Van der Peet 127-29 1978 Dfl 45

BRENNAN, J. FLETCHER   A General History of Free-Masonry in Europe... Cincinnati, 1867. Mod. wear at extremities. Hayman 72-66 1978 $10

BRENTANO, L.   On the History and Development of Gilds and the Origin of Trade Unions. (1870). 8vo. George's 635-289 1978 £6

BRENTON, E. P.   The Naval History of Gt. Britain, 1783-1836. 1837. Portraits, plans, 2 vols., half calf. George's 635-803 1978 £10.50

BRERETON, LEWIS H.   The Brereton Diaries. New York, 1946. Biblo 247-779 1978 $13.50

BRERETON, WILLIAM   Letter Sent to the Honoble William Lenthal... 1645. 1st. ed., 4to, disbound, dust-soiled. Hannas 54-27 1978 £15

BRESCHET, GILBERT   Memoire sur un Vice de Conformation Congeniale des Enveloppes du Coeur. (Paris, 1826). Orig. 4to., brown prtd. wr., engr. plt., illus., 8vo. text of Memoire tipped in, uncut, foxed, good copy. Zeitlin 245-32 1978 $37.50

BRESSANY, R. P. F.-J.   Relation Abregee, de Queiques Missions des Peres de la Compagnie de Jesus dans la Nouvelle France. Montreal, 1852. Illus., orig. binding. Wolfe 39-46 1978 $80

BRET, ANT. DE.   Theatre. Paris, 1778. 2 vols. in I, vol. I with eng. title, contemp. mottled calf, later rebacked, a.e.g. gilt crest on upper cover, ex-libris Holland House. Eaton 45-63 1978 £40

BRETON, M.   China: Its Costume, Arts, Manufactures, Etc. 1813. 5th. ed., 4 vols., 85 colour plts., half titles, foxing to text only, plts. fine, straight-grained red morocco, borders in blind & gilt, gilt spines, a.e.g., fine. Jarndyce 16-385 1978 £180

BRETON, NICHOLAS   Melancholike Humours, In Verses of Diverse Natures. 1929. Octavo, good. Upcroft 10-18 1978 £5

BRETON, P. N.   Breton's Illustrated Canadian Coin Collector. Montreal, (1890). Printed wrappers. Wolfe 39-398 1978 $17.50

BRETON, P. N.   Popular Illustrated Guide to Canadian Coins, Medals.... Montreal, (1912). Printed wrappers. Wolfe 39-397 1978 $15

BRETT, W. H.   The Indian Tribes of Guiana... 1868. 8vo, orig. cloth, map, coloured lithos, illus. Edwards 1012-628 1978 £57

BRETT, W. H.   Legends and Myths of the Aboriginal Indians of British Guiana. (1851). Illus., sm. 8vo, orig. cloth, headband repaired. Edwards 1012-627 1978 £18

BREVE Description de las Festivas Demonstraciones. Barcelona, 1701. 8vo., orig. covers, rare. Van der Peet H-64-263 1978 Dfl 75

BREWER, GEORGE   The Juvenile Lavater. London, c.1812. 1st ed., plates, heavily worn. Victoria 34-100 1978 $12.50

BREWER, JAMES NORRIS   A Descriptive and Historical Account of Various Palaces and Public Buildings, English and Foreign. 1821. Frontispiece, 4to., contemp. diced calf, head of spine cracked. Howes 194-1429 1978 £35

BREWER, LUTHER A.   Around the Library Table. Cedar Rapids, Torch Press, 1920. 12mo., bds., vellum spine, 1 of 225 copies. Battery Park 1-302 1978 $50

BREWER, LUTHER A.   The Fascination of Prints Another of Our Hobbies. Torch Press, 1915. One of 170 copies, frontis., 12mo., bds., vellum spine. Battery Park 1-301 1978 $50

BREWER, LUTHER A.   Marginalia. Cedar Rapids, 1926. Portraits, parchment backed bds. Eaton 45-64 1978 £6

BREWER, REGINALD   The Delightful Diversion. The Whys and Where-fores of Book-Collecting. New York, 1935. Orig. cloth. MacManus 238-877 1978 $12.50

BREWER, THOMAS   Devil of Edmonton, The Life and Death of the Merry. 1631. Sm. 8vo, woodcut, lower half of right margin chewed, mod. boards. Victoria 34-101 1978 $175

THE BREWER. 1867. Orig. purple/brown cloth, new ed., v.g. Jarndyce 16-309 1978 £14.50

BREWSTER, DAVID   The Life of Sir Isaac Newton. London, 1831. Sm. 8vo., frontis. portr., text illus., contemp. calf, gilt, little rubbed, but fine copy, 1st ed. Norman 5-*40 1978 $100

BREWSTER, DAVID   The Life of Sir Isaac Newton. London, 1831 (1838). Sm. 8vo., engraved portrait, vignette, contemp. cloth, first ed. Quaritch 977-122 1978 $50

BREWSTER, WILLIAM   History of the Certified Township of Kingston, Pa., 1769-1929. (Wilkes-Barre, 1930). Illus., fold. map, very fine. Mac-Manus 239-1386 1978 $20

BRIDENBAUGH, CARL   Peter Harrison, First American Architect. Chapel Hill, 1949. Illus., 4to. Baldwins' 51-33 1978 $15

BRIDENBAUGH, CARL   Peter Harrison, The First American Architect. Chapel Hill, 1949. Illus., d.j. Baldwins' 51-88 1978 $15

BRIDENBAUGH, CARL   Rebels and Gentlemen. Philadelphia in the Age of Franklin. New York, (1942). 1st ed., ltd. to 1,000 signed copies, illus. MacManus 239-1647 1978 $22.50

BRIDGE, HORATIO   Journal of an African Cruiser... London, 1846. 8vo, orig. cloth, rather shabby working copy, 1st. English ed. K Books 239-62 1978 £35

BRIDGES, ROBERT   Edin: An Oratoria. London, 1891. 8vo, blue paper wr., 1st reg. ed. limited to 1015 copies, covers are loose, collector's cond. Desmarais 1-52 1978 $20

BRIDGES, ROBERT   The Feast of Bacchus. Oxford, Daniel Press, 1889. One of 105 numbered copies, vellum-backed bds., good, first English ed. Bell Book 16-114 1978 £25

BRIDGES, ROBERT   Milton's Prosody. Oxford, 1893. 4to, purple cloth, gilt lettering, t.e.g., uncut, bookplt. of Walter Raleigh, Large Paper ed., ltd. to 250 copies and this is no. 160, flyleaves darkened, covers sunfaded. Desmarais 1-53 1978 $30

BRIDGES, ROBERT   Milton's Prosody. London, 1901. New ed., special issue, bound in full limp vellum, signed by author, nice, silk ties frayed. Rota 212-6 1978 £35

BRIDGES, ROBERT   Poems Written in the Year MCMXIII. Ashendene Press, 1914. Ltd. ed. of 85 copies, sm. 4to, holland backed blue paper bds., uncut, cloth box, fine copy, author's note tipped in. Sawyer 299-139 1978 £450

BRIDGES, ROBERT   The Shorter Poems. 1890. First ed., fcap. 8vo., orig. cloth. Howes 194-655 1978 £8.50

BRIDGES, ROBERT   The Spirit of Man: An Anthology in English and French from the Philosophers and Poets. 1916. First ed., sm. 8vo., orig. parchment backed bds. Howes 194-656 1978 £5

BRIDGES, ROBERT   The Testament of Beauty. Oxford, 1929. 8vo, white stamped boards, uncut, unopened, light foxing on flyleaves, mint copy in d.w., 1st ed. Desmarais 1-54 1978 $30

BRIDGEWATER, FRANCIS HENRY   Description du Plan Incline Souterrain execute par Francis Egerton.... Paris, 912. 8vo., orig. wrappers, uncut, plt. Gurney 75-15 1978 £20

BRIDGMAN, FREDERICK ARTHUR   Winters in Algeria. New York, 1890. 8vo, cloth, illus., rather shabby ex-lib. copy. K Books 239-63A 1978 £6

BRIDGMAN, FREDERICK ARTHUR   Winters in Algeria. New York, 1890. Illus., 8vo, cloth, bright copy. K Books 239-63 1978 £9

BRIDIE, JAMES   The Perilous Adventure of Sir Bingo Walker of Alpaca Square. 1931. Drawings, pict. cloth, good, first English ed. Bell Book 16-115 1978 £4.50

A BRIEF Account of the Coronation of His Majesty, George IV. July 19, 1821. 1821. 8vo., port., hand-coloured plts., orig. bds., new calf back. Quaritch 983-330 1978 $100

A BRIEF Description and a Few Testimonials Concerning the Corn Belt of South Dakota, one of the Most Protective and Healthful Countries in the U.S. Yankton, 1893. Illus., original printed wr., 1st ed. Ginsberg 14-308 1978 $75

BRIEF in Re Canon De Chama Grant. Washington, 1884. Orig. pr. wr., 1st ed. Ginsberg 14-750 1978 $60

BRIEF Observations on Mr. Zea's Columbia Loan. London, (1823). 8vo, postmarked on verso of last leaf. Quaritch 978-38 1978 $175

BRIEF Record of the Advance of the Egyptian Expeditionary Force under Gen. Sir. E. H. H. Allenby, July 1917-Oct. 1918. 1919. Portrait, maps, 4to., orig. bds. George's 635-804 1078 £7.50

BRIEF Record of the Advance of the Egyptian Expeditionary Force under Gen. Sir E. H. H. Allenby, July 1917-Oct. 1918. 1919. Orig. wrappers, 8vo. George's 635-805 1978 £5.25

A BRIEF Record of the Egyptian Expeditionary Force--July 1917 to October 1918. Cairo, 1919. 1st. ed., coloured maps, plans, 4to, slightly dusty, nice copy, orig. printed wrappers. K Books 239-257 1978 £50

A BRIEF Review of the Action, Labour, Production, Commerce and Consumption, Under Their Existing Forms and Practice; with Proposed Expedients for Improvement. (Philadelphia, 1849). Disbound, some foxing. Hayman 72-67 1978 $7.50

A BRIEF Statement of the Efforts of Philadelphia Yearly Meeting...to Promote the Civilization and Improvement of the Indians. Philadelphia, 1866. Self-wr., tape backstrip. Butterfield 21-218 1978 $15

A BRIEF Statement of the Romulus and Remus Silver Mine, in the Reese River Mining District, Lander County.... New York, 1864. Orig. pr. front wr., 1st ed. Ginsberg 14-728 1978 $85

BRIEGER, L.   Ein Jahrhundert deutscher Erstausgaben die wichtigsten Erst-und Originalausgaben von etwa 1750 bis etwa 1880. Stuttgart, (1925). Orig. cloth. Forster 130-169 1978 £7.50

BRIERLY, BENJAMIN   "Ab-O'th'-Yate" Sketches and Other Short Stories. Oldham, 1896. 3 vols., illus., orig. cloth, 1st ed., covers a bit worn, but very good. MacManus 238-171 1978 $75

BRIERLY, BENJAMIN   Thoughts for the Crisis:... San Francisco, 1856. Original printed wr., 1st ed. Ginsberg 14-84 1978 $75

BRIEUX   Voyage aux Indes et en Indo-Chine. Paris, 1910. 8vo, orig. covers. Van der Peet 127-30 1978 Dfl 40

BRIGGS, E. C.   Address to the Saints in Utah and California. Plano, 1869. Orig. pr. wr., 1st ed. Ginsberg 14-642 1978 $125

BRIGGS, ERASMUS   History of the Original Town of Concord... Rochester, 1883. 1st ed., illus., ports., orig. calf, very scarce, rubbed, but good. MacManus 239-1084 1978 $90

BRIGGS, L. VERNON   California and the West, 1881 and Later. [Boston], 1931. Illus., plates, original cloth, 1st ed., inscribed presentation copy from Briggs. Ginsberg 14-85 1978 $50

BRIGGS, L. VERNON   Experiences of a Medical Student on Honolulu, and on the Island of Oahu, 1881. Boston, 1926. Rittenhouse 49-102 1976 $60

BRIGGS, L. VERNON   History and Genealogy of the Briggs Family. Boston, 1938. 1st ed., 3 vols., illus., orig. cloth, mint set. MacManus 239-916 1978 $30

BRIGGS, L. VERNON   Smoke Abatement. Boston, 1941. Plts., 8vo., ex-lib., 1st ed. Morrill 239-29 1978 $15

BRIGGS, SAM   The Essays, Humor, and Poems of Nathaniel
Ames, Father and Son of Dedham, Mass. Cleveland, 1891. Tall 8vo, uncut.
Baldwins' 51-393 1978 $35

BRIGGS, WILLIAM HARLOWE   Dakota in the Morning. New York, 1942.
1st ed., author's initialed pres., very good, d.w. Biblo 251-414 1978 $10

BRIGHAM, ALBERT PERRY   Cape Cod and the Old Colony. New York, 1920.
8vo., orig. cloth, illus., 1st ed. Morrill 241-320 1978 $10

BRIGHAM, CLARENCE S.   History and Bibliography of American Newspapers
1690-1820. Worcester, 1947. 2 vols., 4to., orig. cloth. MacManus 238-879
1978 $100

BRIGHAM, CLARENCE S.   Journals and Journeymen. Philadelphia, 1950.
D.w. Battery Park 1-306 1978 $15

BRIGHMAN, S. J.   Under Blue Skies. New York, (1886). Colored
lithographed plates, colored pictorial boards chipped at edges. Victoria 34-104
1978 $20

BRIGHT, GEORGE L.   Brief for the Rio Grande Railroad Company,
Plaintiffs in Error, Versus A. J. Gomila & Co. N.P., 1889. Printed wr., sewn,
stamped with name of James B. Wells. Jenkins 116-155 1978 $25

BRIGHT, P. M.   A Monograph of the British Aberrations of the
Chalk-Hill Blue Butterfly. Bournemouth, 1938-1941. Plts. some coloured, extra
pages 139-144 loosely inserted at the end, 4to. Traylen 88-543 1978 £18

BRIGHTFIELD, MYRON F.   Victorian England in its Novels (1840-1870).
Los Angeles, 1968. 4 vols., only 50 copies printed, very scarce set, all vols.
in fine condition. Ballinger 11-22 1978 $300

BRILL, A. A.   Psychanalysis. Its Theories and Practical Application. Philadelphia, 1918. Second ed. Rittenhouse 49-104 1976 $10

BRIMBLE, L.   Flowers in Britain. London, 1945. 8vo, orig.
cloth. Book Chest 17-469 1978 $12.50

BRINCKMANN, A. E.   Die Baukunst des 17 und 18. Potsdam, n.d.
4to., cloth, plts., illus. Van der Peet H-64-107 1978 Dfl 45

BRINCKMANN, A. E.   Kunst des Barocks und Rokokos. Berlin, 1924.
Sm. 4to., cloth, illus., colored plts. Van der Peet H-64-10 1978 Dfl 30

BRINDLEY, W.   Ancient Sepulchral Monuments. 1887. Plts.,
damp stained, folio, binding badly stained. George's 635-78 1978 £9

BRINGAS DE MANZANEDA Y ENCINAS, DIEGO MIGUEL   Indice Apologetico
de las Razones que Recomiendan la Obra... Valencia, 1834. Paper wr., uncut
& unopened. Ginsberg 14-751 1978 $600

BRININSTOOL, E. A.   Trail Dust of a Maverick. New York, 1914.
1st ed., illus., very good or better. Limestone 9-33 1978 $35

BRINKLEY, F.   Japan, Its History, Arts and Literature. Boston
and Tokyo, 1901-02. 12 vols., plts., many coloured, 8vo, orig. cloth, ltd. to
1000 copies. Edwards 1012-203 1978 £120

BRINLEY, G.   Away to Cape Breton. New York, 1936. Illus.
by P. Brinley, colored frontis. Hood 117-232 1978 $20

BRINLEY, GEORGE   Catalogue of the American Library of the Late
Mr. George Brinley of Hartford, Conn. Hartford, 1878. Parts 1 and 2 in one vol.,
half mor., printed wrappers preserved at back. Wolfe 39-47 1978 $40

BRINTON, DANIEL G.   Essays of an Americanist. Philadelphia, 1890.
1st ed., fine. MacManus 239-1149 1978 $35

BRINTON, DANIEL G.   The Laws of Health in Relation to the Human Form.
Springfield, 1870. Engr. plts., 8vo., spine faded, 1st ed. Morrill 239-30 1978
$15

BRINTON, DANIEL G.   A Lenape-English Dictionary. Philadelphia,
1888. Port., rebound. MacManus 239-1150. 1978 $40

BRINTON, DANIEL G.   Personal Beauty: How to Cultivate and Preserve
It in Accordance with the Laws of Health. Springfield, 1870. Cloth, spine faded.
Hayman 72-69 1978 $10

BRINTON, WILLARD C.   Graphic Methods for Presenting Facts. 1914.
Illus., 1st ed., inscr'd by author. Austin 80-446 1978 $27.50

BRINTON, WILLARD C.   Graphic Methods for Presenting Facts. 1914.
Illus., orig. ed. Austin 80-447 1978 $20

BRIQUET, P.   Traite Therapeutique du Quinquina et de ses Preparations. Paris, 1853. Half leather marbled bds. and end papers. Rittenhouse
49-105 1976 $95

BRISCO, NORRIS A.   Economics of Efficiency. 1914 (1917). Austin
80-448 1978 $8.50

BRISCOE, JOHN   An Explanatory Dialogue of a Late Treatise, Intit-
uled, A Discourse on the Late Funds of the Million-Act, Lottery-Act, and Bank of
England. London, 1694. Sm. 4to, marbled wrappers, 1st. ed. Traylen 88-70
1978 £95

BRISCOE, T.   Orchids for Amateurs. London, (1948). 8vo,
orig. cloth. Book Chest 17-59 1978 $12

BRISSEAU, MICHEL   Traite de la Cataracte et du Glaucoma. Paris,
1709. Fldg. copperplts., 12mo., contemp. calf, back gilt, 1st ed., foxed, stamps.
Offenbacher 30-114 1978 $600

BRISSON, MATHURIN-JACQUES   Principes Elementaires de l'Histoire Naturelle
et Chymique des Substances Minerales; Ouvrage Utile Aux Ecoles Centrales.
Paris, (1797). 8vo., contemp. blue wrs., uncut, rare, partly damps tained.
Offenbacher 30-16 1978 $200

BRISSON, PIERRE RAYMOND DE   Histoire Du Naufrage Et De La Captivite.
Geneva, 1789. Sm. 8vo., contemp. calf. Edwards 1012-235 1978 £110

BRISSOT DE WARVILLE, JACQUES PIERRE   The Commerce of America with
Europe.... New York, 1795. 1st American ed., 12mo., frontis., port., cloth,
nice copy. MacManus 239-66 1978 $50

BRISSOT DE WARVILLE, JACQUES PIERRE   New Travels in the United States of
America.... Dublin, 1792. 1st Irish ed., cloth, foxing, but good, scarce.
MacManus 239-67 1978 $75

BRISSOT DE WARVILLE, JACQUES PIERRE   Nouveau Voyage Dan Les Etats-Unis
de L'Amerique Septentrionale, Fait en 1788. Paris, 1791. 3 vols., leather spines,
mottled bds., fldg. chart, private lib. identification, orig. binding. Hood's
115-582 1978 $300

BRISSOT DE WARVILLE, JACQUES PIERRE   Nouveau Voyage Dans Les Etats-Unis
de l'Amerique Septentrionale.... Paris, 1791. 1st ed., 3 vols., contemp. calf,
natural defect in corner of 6 ll, corner of title vol. 2 restored, 8vo. Edwards
1012-475 1978 £200

BRISTED, CHARLES ASTOR   The Interference Theory of Government. 1867.
Austin 80-449 1978 $20

BRISTOL, FRANK MILTON   The Life of Chaplain McCabe, Bishop of the
Methodist Episcopal Church. New York, 1908. Bell Wiley's copy. Broadfoot
46-26 1978 $20

BRISTOL, WILLIAM M.   Californiana: and Sketches of the Southwest...
Los Angeles, (1901). Illus., bds., oblong, mod. edge wear. Hayman 72-70
1978 $15

BRISTOW, ARCH   Old Time Tales of Warren County, Pa. N.P.,
1932. Illus., scarce. MacManus 239-1387 1978 $27.50

BRITANNIA PRINTING WORKS   Type-Founders Catalogue. Sheffield, n.d.
(1887?). Roy. 8vo., binders cloth. K Books 244-315 1978 $30

BRITISH AND FOREIGN BIBLE SOCIETY   20th Report of.... 1824. 8vo.,
orig. printed wrapper, uncut, nice copy. Fenning 32-35 1978 £6.50

THE BRITISH Annual of Literature. 1938/9. 2 vols., very good, octavo bound in
cloth. Hyland 128-278 1978 £10

THE BRITISH Gallery of Contemporary Portraits being a Series of Engravings of the Most Eminent Persons Now Living or Lately Deceased, in Great Britain and Ireland. 1822. 2 vols., 4to., plts., half dark red mor. Quaritch 983-157 1978 $100

BRITISH Liberties. 1766. 8vo., contemp. calf, nice, first ed. P. M. Hill 142-49 1978 £48

BRITISH Marine Painting. 1919. Plts., some in colour, imp. 8vo., covers stained and worn. George's 635-10 1978 £8.50

BRITISH North America: Comprising Canada, British Central North America, British Columbia, Vancouver's Island, Nova Scotia and Cape Breton, New Brunswick, Prince Edward's Island, Newfoundland and Labrador. London, (1866). Maps. Hood 116-606 1978 $50

THE BRITISH Plutarch. (1762). Copperplts., portraits, 9 vols. (ex 12) in 3, 18mo., contemp. calf, lacks one lettering piece. George's 635-1233 1978 £8.50

THE BRITISH Poets. 1875-88 and n.d. 52 vols. in 26, 12mo., Aldine ed., half brown mor., double gilt rule, gilt tops, good sound set, bkplt. Quaritch 979-59 1978 $210

BRITISH Volunteers. (c. 1860). Lg. wood-engrav. illus., coloured, lg. 8vo., orig. pict. bds., cloth back. F. Edwards 1013-258 1978 £50

BRITISH Workman and Friends of the Sons of Toil 1855-1859. Bound, half lea., illus. & engrs., very good. Austin 80-450 1978 $47.50

BRITISH Workman 1861-1867. Bound, half lea., illus. & engrs., very good. Austin 80-451 1978 $67.50

BRITTAIN, F.   Arthur Quiller-Couch. Cambridge, 1947. 1st ed., color portrait, illus., d.j., very good or better. Limestone 9-238 1978 $17.50

BRITTEN, JAMES   European Ferns. London, c. 1880. Coloured plts., wood-engravings, 4to., half roan, gilt spine. K Books 244-47 1978 £25

BRITTON, JOHN   The Fine Arts of the English School; Illustrated by a Series of Engravings from Paintings, Sculpture and Architecture of Eminent English Artists... 1812. Folio, plts., contemp. blue straight-grained mor., gilt spine, slightly rubbed. Quaritch 983-159 1978 $125

BRITTON, JOHN 1771-1857   Devonshire and Cornwall Illustrated, from Original Drawings... 1832. 2 vols. in 1, 4to., maps, plts., contemp. red mor., slightly rubbed, gilt edges. Quaritch 983-303 1978 $575

BRITTON, WILEY   The Aftermath of the Civil War. Kansas City, (1924). 8vo., 1st ed., orig. cloth. Morrill 241-657 1978 $15

BROADLEY, A. M.   Chats on Autographs. London, 1910. Illus., orig. cloth. Forster 130-242 1978 £4

BROADUS, E. K.   Saturday and Sunday. Toronto, 1935. Hood 117-453 1978 $10

BROCH, HERMANN   James Joyce und die Gegenwart. Zurich, Vienna, Leipzig, 1936. First ed., roy. 8vo., orig. wrappers, printed label. Howes 194-972 1978 £5.50

BROCHNER, JESSIE   Danish Life in Town and Country. 1903. Illus. Austin 79-95 1978 $12.50

BROCK, SALLIE A.   Richmond During the War, NY, 1867. New binding, Bell Wiley's copy. Broadfoot's 44-661 1978 $25.00

BROCKDORF, C. V.   Descartes Und Die Fortbildung Der Kartesian-ischn Lehre. Munich, 1923. Salloch 348-48 1978 $12.50

BROCKETT, LINUS PIERPONT   Handbook of the United States of America and Guide to Emigration. 1883. Frontis. Austin 79-96 1978 $20

BROCKETT, LINUS PIERPONT   Woman's Work in the Civil War... Philadelphia, 1867. 8vo, vignette title, engraved portraits, half calf, gilt spine, some spotting. Edwards 1012-542 1978 £15

BROCKHAUS' Konversations-Lexikon. Leipzig, 1908-1910. 17 vols., lg. thick 8vo., half calfbindings, plts., illus., colored maps, nice set. Van der Peet H-64-264 1978 Dfl 250

BRODHEAD, JOHN ROMEYN   The Final Report of...Agent of the State of New York, to Procure and Transcribe Documents in Europe Relative to the Colonial History of Said State. Albany, 1845. Well-preserved copy. Butterfield 21-74 1978 $20

BRODHEAD, JOHN ROMEYN   Oration on the Conquest of New Netherland, Delivered Before the New York Historical Society...Oct. 12, 1864. New York, 1864. 4to., ports., fold. map, 3/4 mor., edges rubbed, orig. wrs. bound in. Biblo BL781-155 1978 $24.50

BRODIE, BERNARD   A Layman's Guide to Naval Strategy. Princeton University Press, 1942. Austin 80-29 1978 $8.50

BROGLIE, LOUIS DE   An Introduction to the Study of Wave Mechanics. London, (1930). 8vo., ads, orig. cloth, gilt, uncut, fine copy, probably 1st ed. in English. Norman 5-**8 1978 $75

BROGLIE, LOUIS DE   Ondes et Mouvements. Paris, 1926. Orig. prtd. wrs., 8vo., uncut, spine faded, but fine copy in cloth case, 1st ed. Norman 5-*5 1978 $450

BROGLIE, MAURICE DE   Introduction a la Physique des Rayons X et Gamma. Paris, 1928. 8vo., ads, illus., orig. prtd. wrs., uncut, little faded, sm. tear in fr. wr., but very good copy, 1st ed. Norman 5-45 1978 $75

BROMFIELD, LOUIS   Early Autumn. 1926. Austin 82-239 1978 $8.50

BROMFIELD, LOUIS   The Farm. 1933. First ed. Austin 82-241 1978 $10

BROMFIELD, LOUIS   The Farm. 1933. 346 pages. Austin 82-242 1978 $7.50

BROMFIELD, LOUIS   A Few Brass Tacks. 1946. First ed., d.j. Austin 82-243 1978 $11

BROMFIELD, LOUIS   A Good Woman. 1927. 432 pages. Austin 82-244 1978 $7.50

BROMFIELD, LOUIS   The Green Bay Tree. 1924. Austin 82-245 1978 $7.50

BROMFIELD, LOUIS   Here Today and Gone Tomorrow. 1934. Austin 82-246 1978 $10

BROMFIELD, LOUIS   It Takes All Kinds. 1938. Austin 82-247 1978 $8.50

BROMFIELD, LOUIS   Kenny. 1947. First ed. Austin 82-248 1978 $10

BROMFIELD, LOUIS   Malabar Farm. 1948. First ed., illus. Austin 82-249 1978 $10

BROMFIELD, LOUIS   The Man Who Had Everything. 1935. First ed. Austin 82-250 1978 $10

BROMFIELD, LOUIS   The Man Who Had Everything. 1935. Austin 82-251 1978 $7.50

BROMFIELD, LOUIS   Mrs. Parkington. 1943. 330 pages. Austin 82-253 1978 $7.50

BROMFIELD, LOUIS   Night in Bombay. 1940. Austin 82-255 1978 $8.50

BROMFIELD, LOUIS   Out of the Earth. 1950. Photos, first ed., frayed d.j. Austin 82-257 1978 $12.50

BROMFIELD, LOUIS   Pleasant Valley. 1945. Illus. Austin 82-258 1978 $10

BROMFIELD, LOUIS   Pleasant Valley. London, 1946. First English
ed., drawings, good, frayed d.j. Limestone 9-35 1978 $10

BROMFIELD, LOUIS   Possession. 1925. 493 pages. Austin 82-259
1978 $7.50

BROMFIELD, LOUIS   The Rains Came. 1937. Austin 82-260 1978
$8.50

BROMFIELD, LOUIS   The Strange Case of Miss Annie Spragg. 1928.
Austin 82-262 1978 $7.50

BROMFIELD, LOUIS   Tabloid News. 1930. Printed yellow wrs., first
ed. Austin 82-263 1978 $20

BROMFIELD, LOUIS   Twenty Four Hours. 1930. Austin 82-264 1978
$8.50

BROMFIELD, LOUIS   Until the Day Break. 1942. Austin 82-265 1978
$7.50

BROMFIELD, LOUIS   What Became of Anna Bolton. 1944. First ed.,
frayed d.j., signed by author. Austin 82-266 1978 $15

BROMFIELD, LOUIS   What Became of Anna Bolton. First ed., slightly
frayed d.j. Austin 82-267 1978 $11

BROMFIELD, LOUIS   The Wild Country. 1948. First ed. Austin 82-
268 1978 $10

BROMFIELD, LOUIS   Wild is the River. 1941. Austin 82-269 1978
$8.50

BROMFIELD, LOUIS   The World We Live In. 1944. Austin 82-271
1978 $8.50

BROMFIELD, W. A.   Letters From Egypt and Syria. 1856. Engraved
title, joints repaired, lib. stamp on title, orig. cloth, 8vo. Edwards 1012-216
1978 $20

BRONGNIART, ALEX   Coloring and Decoration of Ceramic Ware. Chicago, 1898. 8vo., orig. cloth, 1st Amer. ed. Morrill 241-62 1978 $25

BRONIKOWSKI, ALEXANDER AUGUST FERDINAND VON OPPELN   Archao-
logische Entdeckungen im 20 Jahrhundert. Berlin, 1931. Illus. Biblo 251-135
1978 $20

BRONSON, EDGAR BEECHER   Reminiscenses of a Ranchman. Chicago, 1910.
Pict. front cover, revised ed., illus. Jenkins 116-157 1978 $45

BRONSON, H.   History of Waterbury... 1858. Map., ports.,
rebound. MacManus 239-959 1978 $40

BRONSON, J.   The Domestic Manufacturers Assistant, and Family
Directory, in the Arts of Weaving and Dyeing:.... Utica, 1817. Light wear on
binding. Nestler Rare 78-250 1978 $145

BRONSON, WILLIAM WHITE   The Inscriptions in St. Peter's Church Yard,
Philadelphia. Camden, 1879. Baldwins' 51-483 1978 $12.50

BRONTE, CHARLOTTE   Life and Works of Charlotte Bronte and her Sisters.
1899-1900. Portraits, 7 vols., thick cr. 8vo., half green calf, gilt tops, spines
faded. Howes 194-659 1978 $75

BRONTE, CHARLOTTE   Novels of the Sisters Bronte. London,
1898-99. 1905. Thornton ed., gilt stamped green cloth, frontispiece, t.e.g.,
uncut 12 vols., bookplates. Houle 10-50 1978 $225

BRONTE, CHARLOTTE   Villette. New York, 1853. 1st Amer. ed.,
quarter morocco & marbled boards, spine damaged, boards rubbed, damp-stains,
contents good. Greene 78-155 1978 $85

BRONTE, CHARLOTTE   Works. Edinburgh, 1924. Thornton ed., 12
vols., plts., orig. green cloth, 8vo. Howes 194-660 1978 $65

BRONTE, EMILY   Wuthering Heights. London, 1947.
D.j., very good or better. Limestone 9-36 1978 $9

BRONZINO, ANGELO   Sonetti...ed altre rime inedite di piu Insigni
Poeti. Firenze, 1823. 4to., bds., lg. paper copy, uncut, partly unopened, fine.
King 7-129 1978 £20

BROOK, STEPHEN   A Bibliography of the Gehenna Press, 1942-1975.
Northampton, Gehenna Press, 1976. 8vo., cloth, 1 of 400 numbered copies,
engr. frontis. portr., new. Battery Park 1-107 1978 $40

BROOKE, CHARLES   Ten Years in Sarawak.... London, 1866. 1st.
ed., 2 vols., cr. 8vo, folding lithograph map, tipped-in on linen & coloured in
outline, plts., rebound in buckram, gilt, 1st. page of vol. I repaired. Deighton
5-65 1978 £30

BROOKE, CHARLOTTE   Reliques of Irish Poetry. Dublin, 1789. 4to.,
new half calf, first ed. P. M. Hill 142-246 1978 £30

BROOKE, HENRY   The Fool of Quality... 1767-70. Vols. 1 & 2-
2nd. ed., vols. 3-5- 1st. ed., orig. calf, red labels, gilt bands, good. Jarndyce
16-45 1978 £110

BROOKE, HENRY   The Fool of Quality. 1767-70. 5 vols., sm.
8vo., contemp. speckled calf, occasional age-browning, fine. Howes 194-185
1978 £55

BROOKE, JAMES   Narrative of Events in Borneo and Celebes, down
to the Occupation of Labuan:.... London, 1848. 2 vols., illus., folding maps,
stamped cloth, some wear, two hinges weakening. Dawson's 127-248 1978 $125

BROOKE, JAMES   Rajah Brooke & Baroness Burdett Coutts:....
London, (1935). Illus., soiled cloth, hinges weak. Dawson's 127-249 1978 $15

BROOKE, RICHARD   On the Life and Character of Margaret of Anjou,
the Queen of King Henry IV. Liverpool, 1859. 8vo., orig. printed wrappers,
inscribed by author. P. M. Hill 142-50 1978 £8

BROOKE, RUPERT   Complete Poems. 1932. Portrait, buckram, very
good, first English ed. Bell Book 16-117 1978 £8.50

BROOKE, RUPERT   Democracy and the Arts. 1946. Very good,
first English ed. Bell Book 16-118 1978 £5

BROOKE, RUPERT   John Webster and the Elizabethan Drama. London, 1916. Corners bumped, fine in d.w. Desmarais B-101 1978 $40

BROOKE, RUPERT   Lithuania. Chicago, 1915. 1st ed., 8 vo.,
stiff pictorial wrappers, color-art nouveau design, bookplate, 1/2 blue mor.
slipcase, fine. Houle 10-51 1978 $185

BROOKE, RUPERT   "1914": Five Sonnets. London, 1915. Prtd. wrs.,
1st ed., very good, without orig. prtd. envelope. Bradley 49-41 1978 $25

BROOKE, RUPERT   Poems. London, 1911. 12mo., orig. cloth,
paper label, 1st ed., spine label slightly discolored, but fine, 500 copies printed.
MacManus 238-623 1978 $150

BROOKE, RUPERT   Poems. 1911. Very good, first English ed.,
Noel Compton Burnett's copy with his signature. Bell Book 17-129 1978 £55

BROOKE, Z. N.   The English church and the Papacy from the
Conquest to the reign of John. Cambridge, 1931. 8vo. Upcroft 12-51 1978
£10

BROOKE-RAWLE, WILLIAM   Gregg's Cavalry Fight at Gettysburg. Philadelphia, 1884. Wrs., Bell Wiley's copy. Broadfoot 46-360 1978 $8

BROOKER, B.   The Robber, A Tale of the Time of the Herods.
Toronto, 1949. 1st. ed. Hood's 115-416 1978 $10

BROOKFIELD, CHARLES   Mrs. Brookfield and Her Circle. 1905. Portraits, 2 vols., roy. 8vo., orig. buckram. Howes 194-663 1978 £12.50

BROOKINGS, ROBERT S.   Economic Democracy, America's Answer to Socialism and Communism. 1929. 1st ed. Austin 80-452 1978 $12.50

BROOKS, ANNE S.　　　　I Met Some Little People.　Toronto, 1941. Illus. Hood 116-804 1978 $15

BROOKS, CHARLES　　　History of the Town of Medford, Middlesex Co., Mass. From Its First Settlement, in 1630, to the Present Time, 1855. Boston, 1855. Illus., ports., 3/4 calf, lib. marks, very good.　MacManus 239-1037 1978 $25

BROOKE, CHARLES　　　Ten Years in Sarawak.　London, 1866. 2 vols., cloth, (worn, part of joint split, library label on rear cover of one vol., other vol. re-backed with original spine laid down).　Dawson's 127-247 1978 $50

BROOKS, CHARLES M.　　　Texas Missions: Their Romance and Architecture. Dallas, 1936. Limited ed. of 200 copies, signed by author, illus, d.j.　Jenkins 116-158 1978 $35

BROOKS, CHARLES T.　　　The Tall Student.　Boston, 1873. 1st ed., Busch illustrations, imaginative cover gilt vignette, very good.　Victoria 34-103 1978 $30

BROOKS, CHARLES W. S.　　　Aspen Court: A Story of Our Own Time.　1857. 2nd., 1st. one-vol. edition, 8vo, recent bds.　Fenning 32-36 1978 £8.50

BROOKS, CLEANTH　　　Modern Poetry and the Traditions.　1948.　Very good, worn d.w., first English ed.　Bell Book 16-574 1978 £4

BROOKS, ELBRIDGE S.　　　In Blue and White.　Boston, 1899. First ed., illus. Biblo 247-502 1978 $10

BROOKS, ELISHA　　　A Pioneer Mother of California.　San Francisco, 1922. Illus., signed by author.　Ginsberg 14-86 1978 $45

BROOKS, J. TYRWHITT　　　Four Months Among the Gold-Finders in Alta California...　London, 1849. 1st. ed., 8vo, engraved map, some spotting, orig. red blind stamped cloth, gilt back.　Deighton 5-59 1978 £58

BROOKS, JUANITA　　　The Mountain Meadows Massacre.　Stanford, (1950). First ed., fine, d.w. Biblo 247-184 1978 $17.50

BROOKS, JUANITA　　　The Mountain Meadows Massacre.　Standord, 1950. Orig. cloth, d.j., 1st ed.　Ginsberg 14-643 1978 $30

BROOKS, SARAH MERRIAM　　　Across the Isthmus to California in '52.　San Francisco, 1894. Orig. wrs.　Ginsberg 14-87 1978 $45

BROOKS, SHIRLEY　　　Sooner or Later.　1868. 1st. ed., 2 vols., illus., orig. half calf, marbled bds., good.　Jarndyce 16-312 1978 £28

BROOKS, U. R.　　　Butler & His Cavalry in the War of Secession 1861-1865. Columbia, S. C., 1909.　Bell Wiley's copy.　Broadfoot 46-29 1978 $60

BROOKS, VAN WYCK　　　New England: Indian Summer, 1865-1915. (New York), 1940. 1st ed., 1 of 997 numbered lg. paper copies, signed by Brooks, lg. thick 8vo., orig. linen-backed marbled bds.　Americanist 102-24 1978 $37.50

BROOKS, WILLIAM E.　　　Lee of Virginia: A Biography.　Indianapolis, 1932. Illus., letter from author laid in.　Bell Wiley's copy.　Broadfoot 46-30 1978 $20

BROOKS, WILLIAM KEITH　　　The Foundations of Zoology.　New York, 1899. Spotted binding, 8vo, orig. cloth.　Book Chest 17-61 1978 $27.50

BROOKSHAW, GEORGE　　　Groups of Flowers, Drawn and Accurately Coloured after Nature.　London, 1819. 2nd. ed., plts. some in colour, thin folio, orig. pink bds., paper label on upper cover, very fine copy.　Traylen 88-544 1978 £280

BROOKSHAW, GEORGE　　　The Horticultural Repository....　London, 1823. Hand-coloured plts., 2 vols. in 1, roy. 8vo, modern half calf, edges uncut, orig. paper label bound in, fine copy from Arpad Plesch lib.　Traylen 88-646 1978 £600

BROOKSHAW, GEORGE　　　Six Birds, Accurately Drawn And Coloured After Nature...　London, 1819. 2nd. ed., 11 of 12 plts. 5 in colour, thin folio, orig. pink bds., paper label on upper cover.　Traylen 88-545 1978 £150

BROPHY, TRUMAN W.　　　Cleft Lip and Palate.　Philadelphia, 1923. Cover detached, bookplts., library marks, should be rebound.　Rittenhouse 49-109 1976 $15

BROUGHAM AND VAUX, HENRY PETER BROUGHAM, BARON　　　History of England & France Under the House of Lancaster.　1855. New buckram.　Allen 234-1129 1978 $10

BROUGHTON, RHODA　　　Doctor Cupid, a Novel.　1886. 1st. ed., 3 vols., Smith's labels on leading free endpaper, orig. black cloth, yellow lettering, gilt lettering on spines, v.g.　Jarndyce 16-313 1978 £52

BROUGHTON, RHODA　　　Scylla or Chardis.　New York, 1892. 1st Amer. ed., quarter calf, marbled boards, spine worn, good.　Greene 78-156 1978 $20

BROUGHTON, RHODA　　　Second Thoughts.　Chicago, 1881. Orig. binding, clean.　Hayman 71-217 1978 $8.50

BROUGHTON, T. D.　　　Letters Written in a Mahratta Camp During the Year 1809.　1813. 4to., coloured plts., old half green mor., marbled sides. Quaritch 983-304 1978 $300

BROUGHTON, THOMAS 1704-74　　　A Prospect of Futurity.　1768. First ed., fine, contemp. calf, 8vo.　Howes 194-186 1978 £20

BROUN, HEYWOOD　　　Christians Only.　1931.　Austin 79-97 1978 $10

BROUN, M.　　　Index to North American Ferns.　1938. Presentation copy, signed and inscribed to Frank Cunningham, 8vo, orig. cloth. Book Chest 17-62 1978 $22.50

BROUWER, E. H.　　　De Veldtogt van het Jaar 1866 in Duitsland... Utrecht, 1869. 2 vols., 8vo, half calf, illus., fldg. maps, bindings shaved. Van der Peet H-64-265 1978 Dfl 45

BROWER, D. H. B.　　　Danville, Montour County, Pa. A Collection of Historical and Biographical Sketches.　Harrisburg, 1881. Frontis.　MacManus 239-1388 1978 $30

BROWN, A. A.　　　A Dryad in Nanimo.　Toronto, 1931.　Hood 117-785 1978 $15

BROWN, A. A.　　　The Tree of Resurrection, and Other Poems.　Toronto, 1937.　Hood 116-805 1978 $20

BROWN, A. J.　　　History of Newton County, Mississippi.　Jackson, 1894. 1st ed., errata, very scarce.　MacManus 239-1061 1978 $65

BROWN, ALEXANDER　　　English Politics in Early Virginia History.　Boston, 1901.　MacManus 239-1869 1978 $15

BROWN, ALICE　　　Louise Imogen Guiney.　New York, 1921. Frontispiece by Timothy Cole, signed in pencil by Cole, light wear on binding.　Nestler Rare 78-4 1978 $18

BROWN, ALICE　　　The Prisoner.　1916. 471 pages.　Austin 82-272 1978 $8.50

BROWN, ALICE　　　Rose Macleod.　1908.　Austin 82-273 1978 $10

BROWN, ALICE　　　Tiverton Tales.　1899. First ed., owner's rubber stamp.　Austin 82-274 1978 $12.50

BROWN, BERNARD J.　　　From Pharaoh to Hitler.　Chicago, 1933. Frontis.　Austin 79-98 1978 $20

BROWN, BOB　　　Bob Brown: 1450-1950.　Paris, The Black Sun Press, (1929). 1st ed., ltd. to 150 copies, tall 8vo., d.j., orig. glassine d.j., worming, black cloth slipcase, Ernest Hemingway's copy.　Current Misc. 8-4 1978 $825

BROWN, BOLTON　　　Lithography.　New York. 8vo., bds., cloth spine, #387 of 500 numbered copies.　Battery Park 1-206 1978 $25

BROWN, BRIAN　　　The Wisdom of the Hindus.　New York, (1921). Edges rubbed.　Biblo 251-2 1978 $10

BROWN, C.   A Register of Middle English Religious & Didactic Verse. Part II. Oxford, 1920. Vol. 2 only, f'scap. 4to., orig. bds., holland back. Forster 130-255 1978 £10

BROWN, C. BARRINGTON   Fifteen Thousand Miles on the Amazon and its Tributaries. London, 1878. Frontis. map, text-illus., signed inscription from both authors, covers a little shabby, 8vo. K Books 244-48 1978 £14

BROWN, C. F.   The Turf Expositor... 1829. 1st. & only ed., half title, lg. 12mo, orig. cloth-backed bds., printed paper label, nice copy. Fenning 32-37 1978 £32

BROWN, CHARLES BROCKDEN   Arthur Mervyn; or, Memoirs of the Year, 1793. Philadelphia, 1857. 2 vols., revised ed., bound in half-calf, marbled boards. Greene 78-13 1978 $35

BROWN, CHARLES BROCKDEN   Edgar Huntley; or, Memoirs of a Sleep-Walker. Philadelphia, 1857. Revised ed., half-calf, 3 vols. in 1, marbled boards. Greene 78-14 1978 $35

BROWN, CURTIS   Contacts. Intimate Memories. New York, 1935. 8vo., cloth, d.j., 1st ed., fine. J.S. Lawrence 38-L125 1978 $20

BROWN, DAVID PAUL   The Forum; or, Forty Years Practice at the Philadelphia Bar. Philadelphia, 1856. 2 vols., fine set, cloth, scarce. MacManus 239-1611 1978 $45

BROWN, EDWARD   Cochin-China, and My Experience of It. London, 1861. 8vo, 2 lib. stamps, red half calf, raised bands, morocco label, gilt, worn. Deighton 5-66 1978 £38

BROWN, EDWARD   Wadsworth Memorial: Containing an Account of the Proceedings of the Celebration of the Sixtieth Anniversary of the First Settlement of the Township of Wadsworth, Ohio... Wadsworth, 1875. Cloth, dampstained. Hayman 72-559 1978 $50

BROWN, ELI F.   Alcohol: Its Effects on Body and Mind. Indianapolis, 1890. Clean, some wear, orig. binding. Hayman 71-65 1978 $7.50

BROWN, ELIZABETH STOWE   The History of Nutley, Essex Co., New Jersey. Nutley, 1907. 1st ed., 12mo., illus., orig. wrs., very good. MacManus 239-1245 1978 $20

BROWN, EVERIT   A Dictionary of American Politics: Comprising Accounts of Political Parties, Measures and Men. New York, 1892. Cloth, minor flecking, pres. bookplt. Hayman 72-68 1978 $7.50

BROWN, FRANCES J.   One America. 1945. Austin 79-99 1978 $17.50

BROWN, G. B.   Saxon art and industry in the Pagan period, Part 1, The Arts of Early England III. 1915. Plts., illus., ex-lib., cloth dull, 8vo. Upcroft 12-53 1978 £6

BROWN, G. W.   Canada... Berkeley and Los Angeles, 1950. Hood 116-607 1978 $20

BROWN, GEORGE S.   Yarmouth, Nova Scotia: A Sequel to Campbell's History. Boston, 1888. 8vo., binding & text dampstained, 1st ed., orig. cloth. Morrill 241-63 1978 $25

BROWN, GEORGE W.   Historical Sketches, Chiefly Relating to the Early Settlement of Friends at Falls, in Bucks County, Pa. Philadelphia, 1882. Orig. cloth. MacManus 239-1389 1978 $25

BROWN, HARRY   The Violent; new poems. Norfolk, Conn., 1943. Wrappers, nice, first ed., A.L.s. and T.L.s. from author inserted. Rota 211-50 1978 £5

BROWN, HENRY   A Narrative of the Anti-Masonick Excitement in the Western Part of the State of New York. Batavia, 1829. Plain bds. with hand-lettered title, sm. marginal tear, near new. Butterfield 21-56 1978 $75

BROWN, HENRY COLLINS   Old New York Yesterday & Today. New York, 1922. Illus., 4to., 1st ed., orig. cloth. Morrill 241-406 1978 $12.50

BROWN, HENRY J.   A Voice from the Pious Dead of the Medical Profession. Philadelphia, 1855. 8vo., binding stained, foxed, 1st ed. Morrill 239-31 1978 $12.50

BROWN, HORATIO ROBERT FORBES   The Venetian Printing Press. London, 1891. Ltd. to 265 copies for England, post 4to., orig. buckram. Forster 130-256 1978 £25

BROWN, IVOR   Years of Plenty. n.d. Reprinted, good, worn d.w., 2 autograph postcards and 2 A.L.s.s from author laid in. Bell Book 17-131 1978 £5

BROWN, JAMES   The History of Sanquhar. Dumfries, 1891. 2nd ed., 8vo., orig. cloth. K Books 244-345 1978 £12

BROWN, JAMES B.   Views of Canada and the Colonists, Embracing the Experience of an Eight Years' Residence. Edinburgh, 1851. Fldg. map, orig. binding, some wear, 2nd ed., corrected throughout & greatly enlarged. Hood 117-555 1978 $125

BROWN, JAMES S.   Life of a Pioneer, Being the Autobiography of... Salt Lake City, 1900. Illus., original cloth, 1st ed. Ginsberg 14-60 1978 $125

BROWN, JOHN 1715-1766   The Cure of Saul. London, 1763. 4to, stitched (later sewing), 1st oratorio ed., very good copy. Ximenes 47-36 1978 $125

BROWN, JOHN 1810-1882   Health. Five lay Sermons to Lay People. New York, 1862. Rittenhouse 49-111 1976 $7.50

BROWN, JOHN 1810-1882   Health. Five Lay Sermons to Working People. New York, 1862. 1st Amer. ed., flex. cloth, some wear. Greene 78-157 1978 $35

BROWN, JOHN 1810-1882   Spare Hours. Boston, 1862. 1st Amer. ed., brown cloth, t.e.g. Greene 78-158 1978 $25

BROWN, JOHN C.   Argument...Before the Judiciary Committee of the House... Washington, 1878. Printed wr. Jenkins 116-162 1978 $40

BROWN, JOHN C.   Reply...to Mr. Campbell, Before the Judiciary Committee of the House.... Washington, 1878. Pr. wr. Jenkins 116-163 1978 $45

BROWN, JOHN HENRY   The Encyclopedia of the New West,... Marshall, 1881. 1st ed., full embossed brown calf, massive quarto. Jenkins 116-1523 1978 $375

BROWN, JOHN MASON   To All Hands. 1943. Illus. with photos. Austin 80-32 1978 $8.50

BROWN, JOSEPH E.   Special Message to the Legislature of Georgia, on Our Federal Relations, Retaliatory State Legislation, the Right of Secession, November 7, 1860. Milledgeville, 1860. Orig. cloth, 8vo., unbound, 1st ed. Morrill 241-155 1978 $17.50

BROWN, JOSEPH MACKEY   The Mountain Campaigns in Georgia or War Scenes on the W & A. New York, 1889. Illus., pres copy, soiled and detached cover. Broadfoot's 44-57 1978 $20

BROWN, L. Q. C.   Kenneth Cameron. Philadelphia, (1888). Clean, orig. binding. Hayman 71-218 1978 $17.50

BROWN, LLOYD A.   Notes on the Care & Catalogueing of Old Maps. Windham, 1941. 16mo., cloth, frontis., illus. Battery Park 1-166 1978 $35

BROWN, LLOYD A.   The Story of Maps. Boston, 1949. First ed., d.w., 4to., illus. Biblo 247-447 1978 $47.50

BROWN, MARCIA   Henry-Fisherman. New York, 1949. 1st ed., color plates, very fine, dust jacket. Victoria 34-105 1978 $20

BROWN, MAUD MORROW   The University Greys, Company A, Eleventh Mississippi Regiment Army of Northern Virginia 1861-1865. Richmond, 1940. Bell Wiley's copy. Broadfoot's 44-538 1978 $25

BROWN, NELSON COURTLANDT   The American Lumber Industry. 1923. Illus., ex-lib. Austin 80-453 1978 $20

BROWN, P. A.   Development of the Legend of Thomas Becket. 1930. Inscribed. Allen 234-1476 1978 $7.50

BROWN, P. HUME   Life of Goethe. 1920. Orig. ed., plts., 2 vols., orig. cloth, 8vo. Howes 194-892 1978 £7.50

BROWN, R.   Observations on the Organs and Mode of Fecundation in Orchidae and Asclepiadeae. London, 1833. Plates, bound in worn marbled boards, spine perishing, 4to, orig. cloth. Book Chest 17-65 1978 $65

BROWN, RALPH H.   Historical Geography of the United States. New York, (1948). Illus., maps. Biblo 247-15 1978 $10

BROWN, RALPH H.   Mirror For Americans Likeness of the Eastern Seaboard. New York, 1943. Illus., maps, 4to. Baldwins' 51-5 1978 $15

BROWN, ROBERT   Our Earth and its Story. Cassell, 1887. 2 vols., coloured plts., maps, woodcuts, roy. 8vo., half roan, gilt spines. K Books 244-347 1978 £6

BROWN, ROLLO W.   Harvard Yard in the Golden Age. New York, 1948. Biblo BL781-23 1978 $9

BROWN, S.   Alpine Flora of the Canadian Rocky Mountains. New York, (1907). Plates after water-color drawings and photos by Mrs. C. Schaffer, sm. 8vo., orig. cloth. Book Chest 17-66 1978 $25

BROWN, SAMUEL   Lectures on the Atomic Theory and Essays Scientific and Literary. Edinburgh, 1858. 2 vols., 8vo., orig. cloth. Quaritch 977-88 1978 $55

BROWN, STEPHEN   An Index of Catholic Biographies. Dublin, 1930. Paper. Austin 79-100 1978 $27.50

BROWN, THERON   Battle of the Frogs. Windham, 1934. 8vo., pattern paper over bds., cloth, 1 of 260 copies. Battery Park 1-164 1978 $50

BROWN, THOMAS   Inquiry into the Relation of Cause and Effect. Andover, 1822. Bds., short crack in upper joints. Hayman 71-66 1978 $10

BROWN, THOMAS   The Reasons of Mr. Bays Changing His Religion. 1688. 1st. ed., 4to, early 20th century half calf, a.e.g. Hannas 54-96 1978 £45

BROWN, VARINA DAVIS   A Colonel at Gettysburg and Spotsylvania. Columbia, 1931. Illus., folding maps, Bell Wiley's copy. Broadfoot's 44-603 1978 $35

BROWN, VARINA DAVIS   A Colonel at Gettysburg and Spotsylvania. Columbia, S. C., 1931. Illus., fldg. maps, good in dust jacket. Bell Wiley's copy. Broadfoot 46-372 1978 $30

BROWN, W.   New Zealand and Its Aborigines... 1851. 2nd. ed., cover slightly worn, orig. cloth, 8vo. Edwards 1012-346 1978 £20

BROWN, W. J.   The Gods had Wings. 1936. Wood engravings by J. Farleigh, cr. 8vo. George's 635-141 1978 £5

BROWN, WALTER   Fables. 1884. Plts. and illus. by Bewick, cr. 4to., orig. cloth backed bds., rubbed. Howes 194-1372 1978 £8

BROWN, WELDON A.   Empire or Independence. 1941. 1st ed. Biblo 248-200 1978 $16.50

BROWN, WILLIAM G.   The Lower South in American History. New York, 1930. MacManus 239-1798 1978 $8.50

BROWN, WILLIAM M.   Biographical, Genealogical and Descriptive History of the State of New Jersey. N.P., 1900. Illus., orig. full leather, scuffed. MacManus 239-1246 1978 $40

BROWN, WILLIS M.   Life and Conversion of a Kentucky Infidel in His Own Words. Autobiography of... Anderson, (1904). Cloth. Hayman 72-394 1978 $12.50

BROWN, WILLIS M.   Life and Conversion of a Kentucky Infidel in his Own Words. Autobiography of Willis M. Brown. Anderson, (1904). Cloth. Hayman 73-359 1978 $12.50

BROWNE, CHARLES FARRAR   Artemus Ward's Lecture. Lond., 1869. Illus., green cloth bind., stamped in gilt, w/brown end papers, all edges gilt, very good copy, unique book. Greene 78-312 1978 $165.00

BROWNE, CHARLES FARRAR   His Works, Complete. New York, 1875. 4 vols. in 1, illus., 1st ed., edges rubbed. Biblo 251-416 1978 $17.50

BROWNE, DANIEL JAY   The American Bird Fancier...Breeding, Rearing, Feeding, Management, & Peculiarities of Cage & House Birds. New York, 1850. 1st ed., orig. pic. cloth stamped in gold & blind, fronts, illus., 8vo., very good. Americanist 103-17 1978 $25

BROWNE, DANIEL JAY   The American Bird Fancier Considered with References to Breeding, Rearing, Feeding, Management & Peculiarities. New York, 1860. 12mo, illus., orig. cloth. Book Chest 17-64 1978 $30

BROWNE, DANIEL JAY   The American Poultry Yard... New York, 1850. 1st ed., illus., orig. pic. cloth, fine. MacManus 239-398 1978 $30

BROWNE, DANIEL JAY   The Sylva Americana. Boston, 1832. Wood engrs., litho. frontis., 8vo., marbled bds., 1st ed. Salloch 345-32 1978 $110

BROWNE, G. F.   Alcuin of York. 1908. Plts., 8vo. Upcroft 12-54 1978 £5

BROWNE, G. ST. J.   The Vanishing Tribes of Kenya. London, 1925. 8vo., orig. cloth, maps, plts. K Books 239-65 1978 £14

BROWNE, GEORGE WALDO   Japan: The Place and the People. Boston, (1904). Colored plts., half-tones, illus., decor. cloth, spine somewhat faded. Dawson's 449-109 1978 $55

BROWNE, GEORGE WALDO   The St. Lawrence River.... New York, (1905). Illus., fine copy, orig. cloth. MacManus 239-68 1978 $25

BROWNE, IRVING   Ballads of a Book-Worm. East Aurora, 1899. 8vo., newly rebound retaining the orig. bds., cloth spine, prtd. on fine paper. Battery Park 1-305 1978 $75

BROWNE, IRVING   The Judicial Interpretation of Common Words and Phrases. San Francisco, 1883. 12mo., lightly dampstained, 1st ed. Morrill 239-318 1978 $7.50

BROWNE, ISAAC HAWKINS   Essays Religious and Moral. 1815. First ed., contemp. half calf, 8vo. Howes 194-1430 1978 £18

BROWNE, ISAAC HAWKINS   Poems Upon Various Subjects, Latin and English. 1768. 1st. ed., 8vo, portrait, contemp. calf, spine worn. Hannas 54-28 1978 £25

BROWNE, JAMES   The History of Scotland Its Highlands, Regiments and Clans. London, 1909. 8 vols., Sterling ed. ltd. to 100 sets, t.e.g., copy #17, colored frontis, matching photogravure, map, colored plts. & b & w plts., bound in 3/4 blue levant bordered in gilt, marbled bds. & endpapers, spines faded to green, no shelf wear, near mint. Current 24-239 1978 $135

BROWNE, J. ROSS   Relacion de Los Debates de la Convencion de California Sobre la Formacion de la Constitucion de Estado...1849. New York, 1851. Full calf, worn, scarce. Biblo 247-186 1978 $62.50

BROWNE, J. ROSS   Report of the Debates in the Convention of California, on the Formation of the State Constitution, in Sept. and Oct. 1849. Washington, 1850. 1st ed., calf rubbed, foxed. Biblo BL781-267 1978 $38.50

BROWNE, NINA E.   A Bibliography of Nathaniel Hawthorne. Boston, 1905. Frontis. port., orig. cloth, paper label, 1st ed., ltd. to 550 copies, spine label slightly worn, but very good. MacManus 238-940 1978 $40

BROWNE, R. W.   A History of Roman Classical Literature. London, n.d. (ab. 1870). 8vo., full calf, gilt tooling on front cover with gilt lettering, prize-binding. Van der Peet H-64-266 1978 Dfl 55

BROWNE, ROBERT H.   Abraham Lincoln and the Men of His Time. Chicago, 1907. Rev. 2nd ed., illus., 2 vols., nice set, fairly scarce. Hayman 73-383 1978 $15

BROWNE, S. H.   The Manual of Commerce. Springfield, 1871. Austin 80-454 1978 $11

BROWNE, T. H.   History of the English Turf, 1904-30. 1931. Illus., 2 vols., imp. 8vo., covers of Vol. 2 stained. George's 635-1505 1978 £21

BROWNE, THOMAS 1605-1682   Pseudodoxia Epidemica. London, 1646. Sm. folio, contemp. calf, worn, very good copy, 1st ed., signature of former owner "T. Kerrich". Zeitlin 245-33 1978 $450

BROWNE, THOMAS 1605-1682   Pseudodoxia Epidemica; Or Enquiries Into Very Many Received Tenets, and Commonly Presumed Truths. London, 1646. 1st ed., sm. folio, contemp. calf, rebacked, excellent copy. Traylen 88-124 1978 £180

BROWNE, THOMAS 1605-1682   Pseudodoxia Epidemica. London, 1658. 4th ed., 4to., engr. plts., illus., contemp. blind-ruled sprinkled calf, worn, worm-trails, upper cover detached, browned, pencil marks, signatures of former owners, good copy. Zeitlin 245-34 1978 $125

BROWNE, THOMAS 1605-1682   Pseudodoxia Epidemica:.... London, 1672. Quarto, full early calf, worn. Bennett 7-20 1978 $175

BROWNE, THOMAS 1605-1682   La Religion du Medecin, c'est a dire. 1668. 12mo., contemp. calf, spine gilt with lettering piece, 18th cent. inscription on title, crisp, first French ed. Howes 194-21 1978 £75

BROWNE, THOMAS 1605-1682   The Works. 1686. Engraved portrait, folio, finely bound in full crimson crushed levant mor., all edges gilt, first collected ed. Howes 194-19 1978 £240

BROWNE, THOMAS 1605-1682   Works. 1686. Folio, fine frontispiece, portrait title in red & black, orig. calf rebacked, alphabetical index misbound, very good. Jarndyce 16-3 1978 £150

BROWNE, THOMAS 1605-1682   Works. London, 1686. 1st collected ed., portrait, title printed in red & black, engravings, folio, contemp. calf, gilt spine. Traylen 88-122 1978 £200

BROWNE, THOMAS 1605-1682   The Works of the Learned Sir Thomas Brown, KT., Doctor of Physick, Late of Norwich. London, Basset, Chiswell, &c., 1686. Engr. portr., folio, old suede, rebacked with calf, 1st collected ed., few water-stains. Salloch 345-33 1978 $175

BROWNE, THOMAS 1605-1682   Works. Edinburgh, 1912. Plts., 3 vols., orig. buckram-backed bds., leather labels, gilt tops, bindings trifle soiled, 8vo. Howes 194-664 1978 £16

BROWNE, THOMAS 1654?-1741   The Story of the Ordination of Our First Bishop's in Queen Elizabeth's Reign. 1731. 8vo., contemp. panelled calf. P. M. Hill 142-51 1978 £15

BROWNE, WILLIAM   The Works. 1772. 3 vols. in one, sm. 8vo., 19th-century red mor. gilt, first collected ed. P. M. Hill 142-52 1978 £75

BROWNELL, H.   North and South America Illustrated, From Its First Discovery to the Present Administration... Baltimore, 1859. 2 vols., cloth gilt, one spine faded, front end-papers missing, engraved plts., 17 of these por-traits. Edwards 1012-383 1978 £30

BROWNELL, HENRY HOWARD   Lines of Battle and Other Poems. Boston, 1912. 1st ed., ltd. to 330 numbered copies, orig. bds., uncut, boxed, box slightly worn, A.L.s. from Bruce Rogers laid in. Americanist 102-102 1978 $225

BROWNING, CHARLES H.   Welsh Settlement of Pennsylvania. Philadelphia, 1912. Illus. MacManus 239-1390 1978 $35

BROWNING, ELIZABETH BARRETT   Casa Guidi Windows, a Poem. 1851. 1st. ed., half title, orig. blue cloth, blocked in blind, bookplt., v.g. Jarndyce 16-314 1978 £35

BROWNING, ELIZABETH BARRETT   Poems. 1844. 2 vols., fscp. 8vo., contemp. half green calf, upper joint split at extrems. in Vol. II, very good, internal-ly crips & clean, first English ed. Bell Book 17-132 1978 £150

BROWNING, ELIZABETH BARRETT   Poems. London, 1850. 8vo, 2 vols., full green calf, raised bands, marbled edges and endpapers, 2nd ed, collector's cond. Desmarais 1-55 1978 $230

BROWNING, ELIZABETH BARRETT   Poems Before Congress. 1860. 1st. ed., 8vo, orig. red cloth, gilt, binding lightly stained, sound & very good copy. Fenning 32-38 1978 £28.50

BROWNING, ELIZABETH BARRETT   Twenty Two Unpublished Letters of Eliza-beth Barrett Browning and Robert Browning Addressed to Henrietta and Arabella Moulton Barrett. New York, Watch Hill Press, 1935. Frontis., gray-green bds., white pigskin spine, gilt, 1st ed., 1 of 1188 copies prtd., fine in slipcase. Brad-ley 49-42 1978 $60

BROWNING, ROBERT   Asolando: Fancies and Facts. 1890. 1st. ed., orig. cloth. Eaton 45-67 1978 £8

BROWNING, ROBERT   Balaustion's Adventure. 1871. 1st. ed., orig. brown cloth, good. Jarndyce 16-318 1978 £7

BROWNING, ROBERT   Christman Eve and Easter Day. 1850. 1st. ed., orig. cloth. Eaton 45-69 1978 £20

BROWNING, ROBERT   Christmas Eve & Easter Day, a Poem. 1850. 1st. ed., half title, orig. green cloth, gilt imprint, v.g. Jarndyce 16-315 1978 £14.50

BROWNING, ROBERT   Dramatis Personae. 1864. First ed., orig. mor. cloth, spine little faded, 8vo. Howes 194-667 1978 £30

BROWNING, ROBERT   Dramatis Personae. 1864. 1st. ed., half title, orig. cloth, little wear to top of spine, otherwise v.g. Jarndyce 16-316 1978 £25

BROWNING, ROBERT   Dramatis Personae. 1864. 1st. ed., half title, orig. cloth, slightly worn, inner hinge broken. Jarndyce 16-317 1978 £18

BROWNING, ROBERT   Ferthisha's Fancies. London, 1884. 8vo, green olive cloth, bevelled edges, covers stamped in black, bookplate of Sir Sidney Colvin, 1st ed., collector's cond. Desmarais 1-57 1978 $30

BROWNING, ROBERT   Fifine at the Fair. 1872. 1st. ed., half title, orig. brown cloth, good. Jarndyce 16-320 1978 £7.50

BROWNING, ROBERT   Fifine at the Fair. 1872. First ed., sm. 8vo., orig. puce bevelled cloth, nice. Howes 194-668 1978 £10

BROWNING, ROBERT   The Inn Album. 1875. 1st. ed., half title, orig. green cloth, good. Jarndyce 16-323 1978 £7.50

BROWNING, ROBERT   Jocoseria. 1883. First ed., sm. 8vo., orig. maroon bevelled cloth, spine slightly faded. Howes 194-669 1978 £7.50

BROWNING, ROBERT   Men and Women. London, 1855. 1st ed., fools-cap 8vo., 2 vols., 1st issue, orig. green blind-stamped cloth with gilt lettering on spines, spines & extremities badly faded, interior clean, binding tight, very good copy. Current 24-8 1978 $215

BROWNING, ROBERT   Pacchiarotto and How He Worked in Distemper... 1876. 1st. ed., orig. cloth. Eaton 45-68 1978 £8

BROWNING, ROBERT   Pacchiarotto and how he worked in Distemper, with other Poems. 1876. First ed., sm. 8vo., orig. grey bevelled cloth, nice. Howes 194-670 1978 £10

BROWNING, ROBERT   The Pied Piper of Hamelin. London, (1939). Illus. by Arthur Rackham, full color frontispiece, drawings, early ed., 8 vo., acetate d.j., illus. stiff wrappers, very good. Houle 10-272 1978 $35

BROWNING, ROBERT   The Poetical Works. 1901. India paper ed., portraits, 2 vols., cr. 8vo., full crushed navy levant mor., watered silk doublures, all edges gilt. Howes 194-665 1978 £75

BROWNING, ROBERT   Poetical Works. 1908. Portraits, 2 vols., con-temp. half red crushed mor., 8vo. Howes 194-666 1978 £24

BROWNING, ROBERT   Prince Hohenstiel-Schwangau, Savior of Society. 1871. 1st. ed., orig. blue cloth, good. Jarndyce 16-319 1978 £6.50

BROWNING, ROBERT   Prince Hohenstiel-Schwangau, Saviour of Society. 1871. First ed., sm. 8vo., orig. prussian blue bevelled cloth. Howes 194-671 1978 £10

BROWNING, ROBERT   Rabbi Ben Ezra. (Concord: Will Bradley, n.d.). 12mo., illus. with woodcut title by Bradley, orig. bds., very fine unopened copy. MacManus 238-779 1978 $50

BROWNING, ROBERT   Red Cotton Night-Cap Country or Turf and Towers. 1873. 1st. ed., orig. green cloth, good. Jarndyce 16-322 1978 £8

BROWNING, ROBERT   Red Cotton Night-Cap Country. 1873. First ed., sm. 8vo., orig. dark green bevelled cloth, spine slightly darkened. Howes 194-672 1978 £10

BROWNING, ROBERT   Red Cotton Night-Cap Country, or Turf and Towers. London, 1873. 8vo, green cloth stamped in black with gilt lettering on spine, hinges somewhat loose back and front, owners name in ink on flyleaf, 1st ed., collector's cond. Desmarais 1-58 1978 $20

BROWNING, ROBERT   The Ring and the Book. London, 1868. 4 vols., orig. cloth, 1st ed., 1st issue, two inner hinges partly cracked, but fine. MacManus 238-173 1978 $125

BROWNING, ROBERT   The Ring and the Book. 1872. 2nd. ed., 4 vols., orig. brown cloth, good. Jarndyce 16-321 1978 £12

BROWNING, ROBERT   La Saisiaz: The Two Poets of Croisic. 1878. First ed., sm. 8vo., orig. turquoise bevelled cloth, nice. Howes 194-673 1978 £8.50

BROWNING, ROBERT   La Saiaiaz: The Two Poets of Croisic. 1878. 1st. ed., orig. blue cloth, good. Jarndyce 16-325 1978 £6.50

BROWNING, ROBERT   Some Poems. Eragny Press, 1904. One of 215 copies on paper, pr. in red and black, coloured woodcut frontis., orig. patterned bds., edges uncut. George's 635-884 1978 £105

BROWNING, ROBERT   Strafford. 1837. 8vo., 1st ed., full mor., gilt top, Esher copy with bkplt. Quaritch 979-61 1978 $150

BROWNLEE, CHARLES   Reminiscences of Kaffir Life and History, and Other Papers. Lovedale, 1896. 8vo, orig. cloth, covers little beetle-marked. K Books 239-66 1978 £40

BROWNLOW, F. -M. CHARLES H.   Stray Notes on Military Training and Khaki Warfare. (c. 1910). Portraits, plts., 8vo., orig. red cloth. F. Edwards 1013-260 1978 £12

BROWNSON, O. A.   The Two Brothers; or, Why Are You a Protestant? Detroit, 1888. Orig. binding, clean, fine copy. Hayman 71-462 1978 $12.50

BROWNSON, O. A.   Uncle Jack and His Nephew... Detroit, 1888. Orig. binding, clean, fine copy. Hayman 71-463 1978 $12.50

BROWNSVILLE Affray Reports. Washington, 1907-1911. Ten large thick vols. Jenkins 116-1578 1978 $657

BRUCE, JAMES   Travels To Discover The Source of the Nile, 1768-73. Edinburgh, 1790. 1st. ed., maps, plts., 5 vols., thick 4to, calf, rebacked, slight staining. Edwards 1012-278 1978 £300

BRUCE, JAMES   Travels to Discover the Source of the Nile, in the Years 1769-1773. Edinburgh, 1813. 3rd. ed., corrected & enlarged, 8 vols., plts., maps, 8vo, contemp. polished calf, fully gilt spines, gilt labels, cracks in the joints of Atlas Vol. K Books 239-67 1978 £110

BRUCE, JAMES DOUGLAS   The Evolution of Arthurian Romance, from the Beginnings to the Year 1300. 1928. Second ed., 2 vols., cloth, 8vo. Howes 194-677 1978 £12.50

BRUCE, JOHN M.   Utilities & Universal Prosperity. 1929. Austin 80-455 1978 $10

BRUCE, PETER HENRY   Memoirs of Peter Henry Bruce, Esq. A Military Officer, In the Services of Prussia, Russia, and Great Britain. 1782. First ed., 4to., contemp. calf, fine. F. Edwards 1013-261 1978 £180

BRUCE, PETER HENRY   Memoirs. Dublin, 1783. Second ed., 8vo., contemp. calf-backed bds., label detached, ex-lib. F. Edwards 1013-262 1978 £120

BRUCE, PHILIP ALEXANDER   Brave Deeds of Confederate Soldiers. Philadelphia, (1916). 8vo., 1st ed., orig. cloth. Morrill 241-64 1978 $12.50

BRUCE, PHILIP ALEXANDER   Institutional History of Virginia in the 17th Century... New York, 1910. 1st ed., 2 vols., fine set, orig. cloth. MacManus 239-1873 1978 $37.50

BRUCE, PHILIP ALEXANDER   The Virginia Plutarch. Chapel Hill, 1929. 1st ed., 2 vols., illus., uncut. MacManus 239-1884 1978 $35

BRUCE, ROBERT   50 Years Among the Shorthorrns. London, 1907. Cloth, illus., 1st ed., very good copy, scarce. Dykes 34-106 1978 $35

BRUCE, WILLIAM CABELL   Benjamin Franklin, Self-Revealed. New York, 1923. 2 vols., uncut, scarce. MacManus 239-156 1978 $30

BRUCKE, ERNST WILHELM VON   Grundzuge der Physiologie und Systematik der Sprachlaute fur Linguisten und Taubstummenlehrer. Wien, 1856. 8vo., cloth-backed bds., plt., 1st ed. in book form. Offenbacher 30-17 1978 $185

BRUEGEL, PETER   Die Gemaelde. 1941. Oblong 4to., colored plts. Allen 234-1130 1978 $25

BRUGIS, THOMAS   The Marrow of Physic. London, 1648. Small 4to., folding table, woodcut, contemp. calf, second issue of orig. 1640 ed., worm hole through first 4 signatures affecting a few words. Quaritch 977-12 1978 $400

BRUGSCH, HEINRICH   Die Aegyptologie. Leipzig, 1891. Edged rubbed, contents very good. Biblo BL781-337 1978 $18.50

BRUMBAUGH, MARTIN G.   A History of the German Baptist Brethren in England and America. Mount Morris, 1899. Illus., 1st ed. MacManus 239-1391 1978 $27.50

BRUMMITT, STELLA W.   Looking Backward, Thinking Forward. Cincinnati, 1930. Orig. binding, clean. Hayman 71-67 1978 $7.50

BRUMUND, J. F. G.   Indiana. Amsterdam, 1853. Folding maps, illus., 2 vols., orig. bds., cloth back, lib. stamp on title, 8vo. Edwards 1012-159 1978 £30

BRUN, ROBERT   Le Livre Illustre on France au XVIe Siecle. Paris, 1930. Ltd. to 100 copies, plts., cr. 4to., orig. wrappers. Forster 130-265 1978 £50

BRUNEAU, ALFRED   Musiques de Russie et Musiciens de France. Paris, 1903. Sm. 8vo., bds., mor. back, orig. wrs. bound in, ex-lib. Morrill 239-319 1978 $10

BRUNEL   The Culturing of Algae - A Symposium. Ohio, 1950. 1 page written on, 8vo, orig. cloth. Book Chest 17-68 1978 $17.50

BRUNELL, BRUNO C. ADOLFO   Callegari Ville Del Brenta E Degli Euganei. Milano, n.d. Sm. folio, rubber stamps on half title & title pgs., illus. Baldwins' 51-34 1978 $35

BRUNET, G.   La Reliure Ancienne et Moderne.... Paris, 1884. Ltd. to 800 copies on "papier Verge", post 4to., half mor., t.e.g. Forster 130-266 1978 £60

BRUNET, JACQUES CHARLES   Manuel du Libraire et de l'Amateur de Livres. Berlin, 1921. Reprint of 5th and best ed., vols. 3-5 H-Z, 3 vols., demy 8vo., orig. half vellum. Forster 130-267 1978 £15

BRUNHOFF, JEAN DE   Babar and his Children. New York, (1938). 1st Amer. ed., very fine copy, dust jacket. Victoria 34-111 1978 $125

BRUNHOFF, JEAN DE   Zephir's Holidays. New York, (1937). 1st Amer. ed., fine, dust jacket with rip. Victoria 34-112 1978 $110

BRUNHOUSE, ROBERT L.   The Counter-Revolution in Pennsylvania, 1776-1790. Harrisburg, 1942. Maps. MacManus 239-1392 1978 $15

BRUNN, HEINRICH   Geschichte der Griechischen Kunstler. Zweite Auflage. Stuttgart, 1889. 2 vols. in 1, spine torn, contents very good. Biblo BL781-338 1978 $14.50

BRUNNER, DAVID B.   The Indians of Berks County, Pa. Reading, 1897. 2nd and rev'd ed., illus., scarce. MacManus 239-1393 1978 $50

BRUNNER, DAVID B.   The Indians of Berks County, Pa.... Reading, 1897. Tall 8vo., text-illus. & many plates, orig. binding. Americanist 101-24 1978 $35

BRUNNER, DAVID B.   The Indians of Berks County, Pa.   Reading,1881.
New red lib. buckram, illus. Baldwins' 51-426 1978 $25

BRUNO, GIORDANO   De Triplici Minimo Et Mensura.... Frankfurt,
1591. Sm. 8vo., old limp vellum, woodcuts, 1st ed. Salloch 348-19 1978
$4,500

BRUNORI, CAMILLO   Il Medico Poeta, Ovvero la Medicina Esposta in
Versi, e Prose Italiane. Fabriano, 1726. Folio, half vellum, 1st ed., rare.
Offenbacher 30-19 1978 $250

BRUNNER, JOHANN CONRAD   Foetum Monstrosum et Bicipitem, Dissertatione
hac Inaugurali. Argentorati, 1672. Copperplt., 4to., stitched, 1st ed., very
rare. Offenbacher 30-18 1978 $225

BRUNS, VICTOR VON   Dissertatio Inauguralis Medica sistens Disquistiones
Anatomico-Physiologicas de Nervis Cetaceorum Cerebralibus. Tubingen, 1836.
8vo., wrappers. Gurney 75-16 1978 £20

BRUNTON, WINIFRED   Great Ones of Ancient Egypt. London, (1929).
4to, dec. cloth, 17 tipped-in plts., mostly coloured, text illus. K Books 239-
68 1978 £7

BRUNTON, WINIFRED   Kings and Queens of Ancient Egypt. London,
n.d. 4to, dec. cloth, 18 tipped-in illus., mostly coloured. K Books 239-69
1978 £6

BRUSENDORFF, AAGE   The Chaucer Tradition. 1925. Orig. ed., plts.,
8vo., orig. cloth. Howes 194-722 1978 £7.50

BRUSH, DANIEL H.   Growing Up with Southern Illinois 1320 to 1861
from the Memoirs of... Chicago, 1944. Hayman 73-280 1978 $10

BRUSHFIELD, T. N.   The Life and Bibliography of Andrew Brice, author
and journalist. London, 1888. Plts., demy 4to., cloth, mor. back, t.e.g.
Forster 130-167 1978 £10

BRUSONI, GIROLAMO   Della Historia D'Italia Libri XLVI. Turin, 1680.
Folio, full contemporary calf, gilt-stamped spine panels and borders, woodcut
printer's devices, Andrew Fletcher copy with signature on rear endpaper. Bennett
20-30 1978 $250

BRUSSE, M. J.   Vijf en Twintig Jaar Onder de Menschen. Rotterdam, 1920. 2 vols., full calf, spines gilt tooled, gilt tooled front covers, drwgs.
by E. B. Van Dullemen Krumpelman, binding of S. H. de Roos, 1 of 100 copies
calf bound, shaved. Van der Peet H-64-369 1978 Dfl 110

BRUTCHER, CHARLES   Joshua: A Man of the Finger Lake Country.
N.P., 1927. Orig. cloth, good, with appendix. Butterfield 21-105 1978 $150

BRUTCHER, CHARLES   Joshua: A Man of the Finger Lake Country.
Virtually new, bright lettering, but lacking appendix. Butterfield 21-106 1978
$75

BRUTON, E.   Le Climat de L'Indochine, et les typhons de la
Mer de Chine. Hanoi, 1929. Large 8vo., plts., tables, folding maps, orig.
covers. Van der Peet 127-32 1978 Dfl 95

BRUTUS, STEPHANUS JUNIUS   Vindiciae Contra Tyrannos. Frankfurt, 1622.
12mo., full calf, leather label, few pgs. slightly foxed. Salloch 348-112 1978
$225

BRUYS, FRANCOIS   The Art of Knowing Women. 1730. Cr. 8vo.,
contemp. calf, neatly rebacked, orig. label mounted, first English ed. Howes
194-187 1978 £75

BRYAN, DANIEL   The Mountain Muse: Comprising the Adventures
of Daniel Boone; and the Power of Virtuous and Refined Beauty. Harrisonburg,
1813. 12mo., contemp. calf, 1st ed., somewhat worn, foxed, stained, very good.
MacManus 238-429 1978 $85

BRYAN, DANIEL   Poetic Biographical Sketches of Earl Beaconsfield. (1882). 2nd. ed., orig. red cloth, blocked in black & gilt, mint. Jarndyce 16-619 1978 £9.50

BRYAN, JULIAN   Siege. New York, 1940. Illus., 4to., photos
by author, 1st ed., author's signed pres. Biblo 251-237 1978 $27.50

BRYAN, MICHAEL   Dictionary of Painters and Engravers. 1903-05.
New ed., illus., 5 vols., imp. 8vo. George's 635-13 1978 £50

BRYAN, WILHELMUS B.   A History of the National Capital from Its
Foundation Through the Period of the Adoption of the Organic Act. New York,
1914-1916. 2 vols., cloth, fine bright set. Hayman 73-58 1978 $35

BRYAN, WILLIAM JENNINGS   Letters to a Chinese Official. New York, 1906.
Bds., with label, little rubbed. Hayman 71-68 1978 $7.50

BRYANT, JACOB   A New System. 1807. Portrait, plts., 6 vols.,
full calf gilt, spines worn, covers detached. George's 635-1422 1978 £18

BRYANT, JOHN FREDERICK   Verses, Together With His Life. 1787. 2nd. ed.,
8vo, portrait, lacking half title, wrappers. Hannas 54-31 1978 £28

BRYANT, THOMAS   A Manual for the Practice of Surgery. Philadelphia, 1881. Illus., ads, lea., little scuffed. Hayman 73-69 1978 $10

BRYANT, WILLIAM CULLEN   A Discourse on the Life, Character and Genius of
Washington Irving... New York, 1860. Cloth, 1st ed., sm. paper ed., nice.
Hayman 72-75 1978 $15

BRYANT, WILLIAM CULLEN   A Discourse on the Life, Character and Genius of
Washington Irving... New York, 1860. 1st trade ed., orig. bind. Americanist
102-63 1978 $27.50

BRYANT, WILLIAM CULLEN   The Fountain and Other Poems. New York, 1842.
12mo., orig. cloth, 1st ed., state B, bind. F, bind. and spine label a bit rubbed,
somewhat foxed. MacManus 238-430 1978 $40

BRYANT, WILLIAM CULLEN   The Poems of... New York: The Limited Editions
Club, 1947. Illus., orig. full leatherette, pub. box, 1 of 1,500 copies, signed
by illustrator, fine. MacManus 238-815 1978 $20

BRYANT, WILLIAM CULLEN   Thirty Poems. New York, 1864. 12mo, brown
blind-stamped cloth, gift inscription on flyleaf, rubbed top and bottom of spine,
1st ed., collector's cond. Desmarais 1-59 1978 $40

BRYANT AND MAY LTD.   The Bryant and May Museum of Fire-Making Appliances. Catalogue of the Exhibits... 1926-28. 2 vols., 8vo., illus., fine,
orig. bds., cloth back, limp bds. Quaritch 983-Addenda b 1978 $100

BRYCE, GEORGE   Everyman's Geology of the Three Prairie Provinces of the Canadian West. Winnipeg, 1907. Maps & diagrs. Hood 117-879
1978 $30

BRYCE, GEORGE   The Remarkable History of the Hudson's Bay Company, Including that of the French Traders of North-Western Canada, and of the
North-west... London, 1900. Ex-lib. Hood 116-569 1978 $45

BRYCE, JAMES 1784? -1866   A Sketch of the State of British India. Edinburgh, 1810. Contemp. russia, 8vo. Edwards 1012-93 1978 £16

BRYCE, JAMES 1806-1877   The Geology of Arran and the other Clyde Islands. Glasgow, 1872. 4th ed., coloured frontis., text-illus., cr. 8vo., rather
foxed, orig. cloth. K Books 244-49 1978 £12

BRYCE, JAMES BRYCE, VISCOUNT 1838-1922   The American Commonwealth.
London, 1888. 1st ed., 3 vols., 8vo. Traylen 88-125 1978 £15

BRYCE, JAMES BRYCE, VISCOUNT 1838-1922   The American Commonwealth.
London, 1888. 3 vols., tall 8vo., cloth, 1st ed., fine set. Argosy Special-18
1978 $125

BRYCE, JAMES BRYCE, VISCOUNT 1838-1922   The American Commonwealth.
New York, 1891. 2 vols. MacManus 239-70 1978 $12.50

BRYCE, JAMES BRYCE, VISCOUNT 1838-1922   The American Commonwealth.
New York, 1901. 2 vols., cloth, 3rd ed., rev'd. Hayman 72-76 1978 $15

BRYCE, JAMES BRYCE, VISCOUNT 1838-1922   The American Commonwealth.
New York, 1907. 3rd ed., 2 vols., thick 8vo., t.e.g., T. S. Eliot's copy, bkplts., red cloth slipcase, unique. Current Misc. 8-5 1978 $985

BRYCE, JAMES BRYCE, VISCOUNT 1838-1922   The Holy Roman Empire. New
York, n.d. Biblo 251-261 1978 $8.50

BRYCE, JAMES BRYCE, VISCOUNT 1838-1922   Studies in History and Jurisprudence. Oxford, 1901. 2 vols., thick 8vo., one cover little stained. Traylen
88-126 1978 £15

BRYCE, PETER   Annual Message. Montgomery, 1878. 8vo.,
orig. wrs., lst separate ed. Morrill 239-32 1978 $10

BRYDGES, SAMUEL E.   The Topographer. 1789. Vol. 1, plts., contemp. calf, spine gilt, 8vo. Howes 194-498 1978 £9

BRYDONE, PATRICK   A Tour Through Sicily and Malta. London, 1776.
New ed., 2 vols., 8vo, half-titles, folding engraved map, polished half calf, gilt,
neatly rebacked, morocco labels. Deighton 5-199 1978 £35

BRYDSON, THOMAS   A Summary View of Heraldry in Reference to the
Usages of Chivalry and the General Economy of the Feudal System. 1795. Orig.
cloth-backed bds., uncut, 8vo. Howes 194-188 1978 £10

BRYNER, EDNA   Dressmaking and Millinery. 1916. Austin 80-
838 1978 $8.50

BRYNER, EDNA   The Garment Trades. 1916. Austin 80-839 1978
$8.50

BUBER, MARTIN   Die Geschichten des Rabbi Nachman. Frankfurt, 1916. Biblo 251-687 1978 $15

BUCCI, ANTONI   De Instituenda Regendaque Mente libri tres.
Rome, 1772. Portr., 8vo., contemp. vellum-backed bds. Argosy Special-19
1978 $75

BUCHAN, ALEXANDER   Description of St. Kilda Giving an Account of Its
Situation. N.P., 1752. 16mo. Baldwins' 51-333 1978 $17.50

BUCHAN, JOHN   The Battle of the Somme, First Phase. London,
n.d. Maps, photos, card cover. Hood's 115-93 1978 $7.50

BUCHAN, JOHN   The Blanket of the Dark. London, 1931.
lst ed., very good or better. Limestone 9-38 1978 $20

BUCHAN, JOHN   The Dancing Floor. Boston, 1926. lst Amer.
ed., spine creased, dull. Biblo 251-417 1978 $10

BUCHAN, JOHN   The Fifteenth (Scottish) Division 1914-1919.
Edinburgh, 1926. Plts., maps, 4to., orig. cloth. K Books 244-52 1978 £9

BUCHAN, JOHN   The Free Fishers. London, 1934. 1st ed.,
very good or better. Limestone 9-39 1978 $21

BUCHAN, JOHN   The Gap in the Curtain. 1932. Very good, first
English ed. Bell Book 17-974 1978 £7.50

BUCHAN, JOHN   Greenmantle. London, 1935. Hood 116-454
1978 $7.50

BUCHAN, JOHN   A History of the Great War. London, 1922.
4 vols., maps, 8vo., orig. cloth. K Books 244-50 1978 £15

BUCHAN, JOHN   The History of the Royal Scots Fusiliers. 1925.
Orig. cloth, 8vo., coloured plts., maps, spine faded. F. Edwards 1013-496
1978 £40

BUCHAN, JOHN   The King's Grace, 1910-1935. London,
1935. 1st ed., portrait, illus., d.j., very good. Limestone 9-40 1978
$15

BUCHAN, JOHN   A Lost Lady of Old Years. 1899. lst. ed.,
lacks f.e.p. & inscription on half title, top & tail of hinges split, good copy of
rare & fragile item. Jarndyce 16-1195 1978 £20

BUCHAN, JOHN   The Magic Walking Stick. 1932. Drawings,
very good, d.w., first English ed. Bell Book 16-121 1978 £12.50

BUCHAN, JOHN   Montrose. London, (1928). First ed., maps,
plts., 8vo., orig. cloth. K Books 244-51 1978 £7

BUCHAN, JOHN   Mountain Meadow. New York, 1941. Hood
117-507 1978 $7.50

BUCHAN, JOHN   The Path of the King. (1921). Spine faded,
good, first English ed. Bell Book 16-122 1978 £8.50

BUCHAN, JOHN   Poems Scots and English. London & Edinburgh, 1917. 1st ed., uncut, blue cloth, very good or better. Limestone
9-41 1978 $25

BUCHAN, JOHN   Prester John. 1910. Frontis. map, covers
somewhat dull, good, first English ed. Bell Book 16-123 1978 £8.50

BUCHAN, JOHN   Some Eighteenth Century Byways. 1908. Very
good, first English ed. Bell Book 17-975 1978 £15

BUCHAN, JOHN   The Thirty-Nine Steps. 1915. Good, first
English ed. Bell Book 16-124 1978 £8.50

BUCHAN, JOHN   Sir Walter Scott. New York, 1932. 8vo,
light blue cloth with fading at edges, spine faded, front edge uncut, ownership
signature on front free endpaper, 1st ed., collector's cond. Desmarais 1-60
1978 $15

BUCHAN, SUSAN   Funeral March of a Marionette. London,
Hogarth Press, 1935. Hood 117-503 1978 $12

BUCHAN, WILLIAM   Domestic Medicine. Norwich, 1778. 3rd
Amer. ed., additions by author, sm. 8vo., contemp. calf. Morrill 239-33 1978
$35

BUCHAN, WILLIAM   Domestic Medicine. Philadelphia, 1784. Orig.
leather, title strip, ribbed spine. Rittenhouse 49-113 1976 $40

BUCHAN, WILLIAM   Domestic Medicine... 1784. 8vo, contemp.
calf, worn but sound, light signs of use & corner of one leaf defective. Fenning
3 2-39 1978 £24

BUCHAN, WILLIAM   Domestic Medicine. Boston, 1809. 8vo.,
contemp. calf. Morrill 239-34 1978 $25

BUCHAN, WILLIAM   Domestic Medicine. Exeter, 1828. Binding
frayed, much worn on spine, some foxing. Rittenhouse 49-112 1976 $20

BUCHANAN, ANGUS   Three Years of War in East Africa. London,
1920. 8vo, dec. cloth, 3 maps, 8 plts. K Books 239-71 1978 £10

BUCHANAN, DONALD W.   Canadian Painters from Paul Kane to the Group
of Seven. London, 1945. Phaidon ed., plts., 4 in color. Hood 117-201 1978
$110

BUCHANAN, DONALD W.   James Wilson Morrice. Toronto, 1947. Hood
116-173 1978 $10

BUCHANAN, FRANCIS   A Journey From Madras Through the Countries of
Mysore, Canara and Malabar... 1807. lst. ed., portraits, plts., folding coloured
map, 3 vols., 4to, calf, rebacked, some foxing. Edwards 1012-92 1978 £180

BUCHANAN, GEORGE 1506-81   Opera Omnia.... Edinburgh, 1715. 2
vols., folio, contemp. calf, sm. cracks in upper joints, first collected ed. Howes
194-189 1978 £55

BUCHANAN, JAMES   Mr. Buchanan's Adminstration on the Eve of the
Rebellion. New York, 1866. Cloth. MacManus 239-71 1978 $17.50

BUCHANAN, JAMES   The Works of... New York, 1960. Ltd. to 550
sets, fine, 12 vols. Biblo 247-16 1978 $250

BUCHANAN, ROBERT   The Fleshly School of Poetry. 1872. 12mo., lst
ed., orig. pink prtd. wrs., very minor browning, orig. cond. Quaritch 979-62
1978 $170

BUCHANAN, ROBERT   London Poems. London and New York, 1866.
8vo, original green decorated cloth, 1st ed., very good copy. Ximenes 47-37
1978 $30

BUCHANAN, ROBERTSON   Practical and Descriptive Essays on the Economy of Fuel, and Management of Heat. Glasgow, 1810. 8vo., plts., contemp. half calf, rebacked with orig. spine laid down. Quaritch 977-208 1978 $150

BUCHANAN, ROBERTSON   A Practical Treatise on Propelling Vessels by Steam, &c. Glasgow, 1816. 8vo., plts., orig. bds., new paper spine, uncut, first ed. Quaritch 977-207 1978 $375

BUCK, J. H.   Old Plate. Its Makers and Marks. New York, 1903. New and enlarged ed., illus., bind. poor, contents very good, scarce. Biblo BL781-529 1978 $30

BUCK, JAMES S.   Pioneer History of Milwaukee, From the First American Settlement in 1833, to 1841. Milwaukee, 1876. Illus., errata leaf, rebound, lib. marks, very good. MacManus 239-1140 1978 $27.50

BUCK, M. S.   Book Repair & Restoration. Philadelphia. One of 1000 copies, illus. Battery Park 1-273 1978 $35

BUCK, PEARL S.   The Chinese Novel. 1939. Cloth-backed bds. Eaton 45-70 1978 £5

BUCK, PEARL S.   Is There a Case for Foreign Missions? New York, 1932. 1st ed., orig. wrs., 8vo. Americanist 101-25 1978 $30

BUCK, TIM   The Yankee Occupation of Canada. Toronto, 1950. Hood 116-608 1978 $7.50

BUCK, WILLIAM J.   History of Montgomery County Within the Schuylkill Valley... Norristown, 1859. MacManus 239-1394 1978 $45

BUCK, WILLIAM J.   William Penn in America. Philadelphia, 1888. Ltd. to 300 copies, scarce. MacManus 239-1395 1978 $15

BUCKBEE, EDNA BRYAN   The Saga of Old Tuolumne. New York, 1935. Illus., ltd. to 200 copies, signed by author. Biblo 247-187 1978 $50

BUCKE, CHARLES   Amusements in Retirement. 1816. 8vo., half calf. P. M. Hill 142-53 1978 £10

BUCKHOLTZ, L. V.   Tactics for Officers of Infantry, Cavalry and Artillery. Richmond, 1861. Orig. bds., Bell Wiley's copy. Broadfoot 46-454 1978 $80

BUCKINGHAM, MR.   Report for the Relief of D.G. and D.A. Sanford. Washington, 1874. Jenkins 116-1221 1978 $10

BUCKINGHAM, CHARLES E.   Circumstances Affecting Individual and Public Health. Boston, 1848. 8vo., orig. wrs., 1st ed. Morrill 239-35 1978 $10

BUCKINGHAM, CHARLES E.   Correspondence Concerning a Fatal Case of Placenta Proevia. Boston, 1870. 8vo., orig. wrs., 1st ed. Morrill 239-36 1978 $7.50

BUCKINGHAM, GEORGE VILLIERS, 2ND DUKE OF   The Rehearsal. 1914. Ltd. to 510 copies, lacks spine label, octavo, good. Upcroft 10-177 1978 £7

BUCKINGHAM, JAMES SILK   America, Historical, Statistical, & Descriptive. London, 1841. 3 vols., port., map, illus., bindings dull, good. Nestler Rare 78-229 1978 $65

BUCKINGHAM, JAMES SILK   America, Historical, Statistic, and Descriptive. London, (1841). 1st ed., 3 vols., 8vo., illus., ports., orig. cloth, front inner hinge of Vol. I weak, else very good set. MacManus 239-72 1978 $60

BUCKINGHAM, JAMES SILK   Autobiography. 1855. First ed., portrait, 2 vols., cr. 8vo., contemp. half calf. Howes 194-678 1978 £20

BUCKINGHAM, JAMES SILK   Canada, Nova Scotia, New Brunswick, and Other British Provinces in North America, with a Plan of National Colonization. London, (1843). Plts., foxed. Hood 117-557 1978 $100

BUCKINGHAM, JOHN SHEFFIELD, DUKE OF   The Works. 1740. 3rd ed., 2 vols., vignettes, cont. calf, rebacked, frontis., 8vo. Howes 194-461 1978 £35

BUCKLAND, FRANCIS T.   Curiosities of Natural History. London, 1865-63. 2 vols., frontispieces, cr. 8vo., orig. cloth. K Books 244-53 1978 £8

BUCKLAND, WILLIAM   Geology and Mineralogy. Philadelphia, 1837. 2 vols., litho. plts., partly colored, 8vo., 1st Amer. ed., cloth covers faded. Salloch 345-34 1978 $150

BUCKLER, WILLIAM   The Larvae of the British Butterflies and Moths. London, 1886-1901. Coloured illus., 9 vols., 8vo. Traylen 88-546 1978 £180

BUCKLEY, ARABELLA B.   The Fairy-land of Science. London, 1890. 8vo., orig. cloth. Book Chest 17-69 1978 $14.50

BUCKLEY, WILFRED   The Art of Glass... 1939. 4to., plts., illus., cloth. Quaritch 983-98 1978 $210

BUCKLEY, WILFRED   The Art of Glass. 1939. Illus., plts., sm. folio. George's 635-244 1978 £30

BUCKMAN, GEORGE REX   Colorado Springs, Colorado. Colorado Springs, 1892. Illus., original wr., 1st ed. Ginsberg 14-251 1978 $35

BUCKS COUNTY HISTORICAL SOCIETY   Papers. 1909. Vol. 2, illus. MacManus 239-1396 1978 $25

BUCKS COUNTY HISTORICAL SOCIETY   Papers. 1932. Vol. 6, illus., maps. MacManus 239-1397 1978 $20

BUCKS COUNTY HISTORICAL SOCIETY   Papers. 1937. Vol. 7, illus., maps. MacManus 239-1398 1978 $20

BUDD, THOMAS   Good Order Established in Pennsylvania & New Jersey. Cleveland, 1901. Reprtd. from orig. ed., 1 of 250 numbered copies, illus., orig. bds., uncut, 8vo., very good. Americanist 103-25 1978 $30

BUDD, THOMAS   Good Order Established in Pennsylvania and New Jersey. Cleveland, 1902. Very fine untrimmed copy, orig. bds., ltd. to 250 copies, reprinted from 1685 ed. MacManus 239-1403 1978 $37.50

BUDGE, ERNEST ALFRED THOMPSON WALLIS   Cook's Handbook for the Egypt and the Egyptian Sudan. London, 1911. 3rd ed., 12mo., orig. cloth, maps. Sexton 7-123 1978 £8.50

BUDGE, ERNEST ALFRED THOMPSON WALLIS   Facsimiles of Egyptian Hieratic Papyri in the British Museum With Descriptions, Summaries of Contents Etc. British Museum, 1923. Plts., lg. folio, quarter leather, spine worn. Traylen 88-39 1978 £25

BUDGE, ERNEST ALFRED THOMPSON WALLIS   The Nile. London, 1897. 5th ed., map, illus., cr. 8vo., orig. cloth, few margins & covers ink-marked. K Books 239-73 1978 £6

BUDGE, ERNEST ALFRED THOMPSON WALLIS   The Nile. London, 1912. Maps, illus., 12th ed., thick cr. 8vo., orig. limp cloth, good. Sexton 7-84 1978 £7

BUDGE, ERNEST ALFRED THOMPSON WALLIS   Osiris and the Egyptian Resurrection. London, 1911. Illus., 2 vols., demy 8vo., orig. cloth, lg. folding coloured frontis., plts., good. Sexton 7-82 1978 £38

BUDGE, ERNEST ALFRED THOMPSON WALLIS   The Rosetta Stone in the British Museum. London, 1929. Plts., 8vo., orig. cloth, good. Sexton 7-85 1978 £12

BUDGE, ERNEST ALFRED THOMPSON WALLIS   Some Account of the Collection of Egyptian Antiquities in the Possession of Lady Meux of Theobolds Park, Waltham Cross. London, 1893. 4to., orig. cloth, folding frontis., piece cut from top of half title, 200 copies for Private Circulation only. Sexton 7-83 1978 £18

BUDGEN, L. M.   Life Coals. (c. 1895). Coloured plts., roy. 4to., orig. cloth, neatly recased. George's 635-1531 1978 £30

BUEK, G. K.   Wildflowers of America - Botanical Fine Art Weekly. New York, (1894). Worn binding, bound issue, oblong folio, 8vo., orig. cloth, colored plts. Book Chest 17-70 1978 $35

BUELL, AUGUSTUS C.   History of Andrew Jackson Pioneer, Patriot, Soldier, Politician, President. New York, 1904. 2 vols., illus. MacManus 239-773 1978 $20

BUELL, AUGUSTUS C.   Paul Jones, Founder of the American Navy... New York, 1900. 2 vols., cloth. Hayman 72-77 1978 $10

BUENA Vista and Tributary Mining Camps. Buena Vista, 1882. Original printed wr., 1st ed. Ginsberg 14-252 1978 $125

BUER, M.C.   Health, Wealth, and Population in the early days of the Industrial Revolution. 1926. 8vo. George's 635-294 1978 £7.50

BUFFON, GEORGE LOUIS LECLERC, COMTE DE   Histoire Naturelle. Paris, 1942. Lg. 4to. in sheets, uncut, in orig. wr., slipcover, box partly renewed, 225 copies only, illus. by Pablo Picasso. Goldschmidt 110-52 1978 $8,500

BUFFON, GEORGE LOUIS LECLERC, COMTE DE   Natural History, General and Particular, by the County De Buffon. London, 1791. Trans. into English, 3rd ed., 8vo., 9 vols., portr., plts., half calf with marbled bds. & endpapers, better than fine set, little or no foxing, bindings firm, ribbon bkmarks intact, very nice collector's set. Current 24-119 1978 $385

BUFFON, GEORGE LOUIS LECLERC, COMTE DE   The Natural History of Birds. London, 1793. 8vo., 8 out of 9 vols., missing Vol. II, plts., bound in half calf with marbled bds. & endpapers, interiors very fine, plts. nice. Current 24-117 1978 $235

BUGEIA, JULIA H.S.   In Old Missisquoi. Montreal, 1910. Half calf, backstrip bare. Wolfe 39-138 1978 $30

BUGGE, GUNTHER   Das Buch der Grossen Chemiker. Berlin, 1929-30. 2 vols., 8vo., orig. cloth, plts., very good set. Norman 5-32 1978 $75

BUGNICOURT, FR.   Les Fusarium et cylindracarpon de l'Indochine. Paris, 1939. Plts., 4 in color, 8vo, orig. covers. Van der Peet 127-33 1978 Dfl 45

BUHLER, G.   The Laws of Manu translated with extracts from seven commentaries. Oxford, 1886. Demy 8vo., orig. cloth, inner hinges cracked. Forster 130-280 1978 £4

BUILDER'S Practical Director. (1856). Plts., some partially coloured, 4to., half roan, worn. George's 635-79 1978 £65

BUIST, ROBERT   The American Flower Garden Directory. Philadelphia, 1841. New ed., with numerous additions, bds. Hayman 73-70 1978 $20

BUIST, ROBERT   The Family Kitchen Gardener... New York, 1847. Spine worn. Baldwins' 51-334 1978 $25

BUKHARIN, N.   Historical Materialism, a System of Sociology. New York, 1933. Covers dull, 8vo. George's 635-1484 1978 £5

BULEY, R. CARLYLE   The Old Northwest. 1950. First ed., fine set, boxed, 2 vols., illus. Biblo 247-191 1978 $47.50

BULFINCH, THOMAS   The Age of Fable; or, Stories of Gods and Heroes. Boston, 1855. 8vo., orig. blind-stamped mauve cloth, 1st ed., 1st state, bookplt. Howell 5-14 1978 $160

BULL, EDWARD   The Life of Mrs. Jordan. 1831. 2nd. ed., 2 vols., frontis portrait, half title, orig. grey bds., paper labels, good. Jarndyce 16-789 1978 £38

BULL, LUCY CATLIN   A Child's Poems from October to October, 1870-1871. Hartford, 1872. 1st ed., fine. Victoria 34-114 1978 $30

BULL, MARCUS   Experiments to Determine the Comparative Value of the Principal Varieties of Fuel Used in the United States, and Also in Europe. Philadelphia, 1827. 8vo., orig. bds., rebacked with brown paper, foxing. Morrill 239-320 1978 $40

BULLAR, J.   A Winter in the Azores and A Summer at the Baths of the Furnas. 1841. Coloured frontispieces, plain text illus., 2 vols., 8vo, orig. cloth, fine set. Edwards 1012-311 1978 £50

BULLARD, S.C.   Princeton, 1872. Guide to Wachusett Mountain, with Accompanying Map. Fldg. map, 16mo., orig. cloth. Morrill 241-322 1978 $15

BULLEN, A.H.   Musa Proterva; Love Poems of the Restoration. 1889. Half vellum, octavo, leather label, t.e.g., ltd. to 750 copies, good. Upcroft 10-21 1978 £7.50

BULLEN, A.H.   Musa Proterva: Love-Poems of the Restoration. 1889. Sq. 8vo., orig. qtr. calf, gilt top, uncut, ltd. to 780 copies. Howes 194-680 1978 £7.50

BULLEN, FRANK THOMAS   The Cruise of the "Cachalot" Round the World after Sperm Whales. London, 1898. 1st ed., octavo, newly bound in blue full mor., emblematic gilt spine, illus. Totteridge 29-18 1978 $175

BULLEN, FRANK THOMAS   The Cruise of the "Cachalot" round the world after sperm whales. 1898. First ed., map, plts., 8vo., orig. cloth. F. Edwards 1013-33 1978 £60

BULLEN, FRANK THOMAS   The Cruise of the "Cachalot" Round the World After Sperm Whales. London, 1898. Illus., orig. cloth, 1st ed., good copy, some cover soiling. MacManus 238-174 1978 $75

BULLEN, G.   Catalogue of Books in the Library of the British Museum printed in England, Scotland and Ireland, and of Books in English Printed Abroad to the Year 1640. London, 1884. 3 vols., demy 8vo., orig. cloth. Forster 130-189 1978 £55

BULLETIN Bibliographique & Critique d'Histoire de Normandie. 1925-27. 8 nos., sewn. Allen 234-1135 1978 $10

BULLETT, GERALD   Dreaming. New York, 1929. 1st ed., portrait, uncut, cloth-backed bds., d.j., very good or better. Limestone 9-42 1978 $15

BULLIALDO, ISMAELE   Theonis Smyrnaei Platonici, Eorum, Quae in Mathematicis ad Platonis Lectionem Utilia Sunt, Expositio. Paris, 1644. 4to., parallel Greek and Latin texts, woodcut diagrams, contemp. vellum, somewhat warped, first ed. Quaritch 977-172 1978 $250

BULLIARD, PIERRE   Herbier de la France.... Paris, 1780-93, 1797. Engraved plts. mostly coloured, engraved title, 2nd. ed., folio, quarter red straight-grained morocco, uncut, scuffed. many plts. partially waterstained in margin, 12 vols. Traylen 88-647 1978 £1200

BULLINGER'S Postal and Shippers Guide for the United States and Canada. New York, 1914. Biblo 247-17 1978 $20

BULLOCK, ALEXANDER H.   Abraham Lincoln: the Just Magistrate, the Representative Statesman, the Practical Philanthropist... Worcester, (1865). Wrs., slight wear. Hayman 72-423 1978 $20

BULLOCK, CHARLES   The Queen's Resolve and Her Doubly Royal Reign. London, n.d. (c. 1901). Illus. Biblo 247-731 1978 $15

BULLOCK, JOHN   The Rudiments of the Art of Building. New York, 1853. 1st ed., profusely illus., tiny spine chips, very rare, only 3 library copies recorded, very good. Victoria 34-115 1978 $125

BULLOCK, MOTIER A.   Congregational Nebraska. Lincoln, 1905. Illus., orig. cloth, 1st ed. Ginsberg 14-707 1978 $25

BULWER-LYTTON, EDWARD GEORGE EARLE OF LYTTON, 1ST BARON LYTTON 1803-1873
Please turn to
LYTTON, EDWARD GEORGE EARLE LYTTON BULWER-LYTTON, 1ST BARON 1803-1873

THE BUMMER Boy, A "Spoony" Biography. Washington, 1868. Wrs., illus., Bell Wiley's copy. Broadfoot's 44-687 1978 $10

BUNBURY, HENRY WILLIAM   An Academy for Grown Horsemen,.... W. Dickinson, 1787. 1st ed., quarto, bound in imitation brown half mor., very good tall copy. Totteridge 29-19 1978 $150

BUNBURY, SELINA　　　Russia After The War. London, 1857. 1st. ed., 2 vols., cr. 8vo, orig. yellow ribbed cloth, neatly recased, lib. label removed, covers somewhat soiled. Deighton 5-200 1978 £33

BUNCE, L.　　　Nature's Aid to Design. New York, 1907. 4to, orig. cloth. Book Chest 17-470 1978 $12

BUNGE, GUSTAV VON　　　Lehrbuch der Physiologischen und Pathologischen Chemie. Leipzig, 1887. 8vo., contemp. half mor., little rubbed but fine copy, bklabel of Herbert McLean Evans, 1st ed. Norman 5-46 1978 $150

BUNKLEY, J. W.　　　Military and Naval Recognition Book. 1941. Austin 80-35 1978 $12.50

BUNKLEY, J. W.　　　Military and Naval Recognition Book. 1943. Plts., colored, illus., 4th ed. Austin 80-36 1978 $12.50

BUNN, ALFRED　　　Old England and New England... 1853. 1st. ed., coloured frontis, 2 vols., sm. 8vo, cloth gilt. Edwards 1012-477 1978 £40

BUNN, ALFRED　　　Old England and New England, a Series of Views. London, 1853. Colored frontis., 2 vols. MacManus 239-73 1978 $25

BUNNELL, STERLING　　　Surgery of the Hand. Philadelphia, 1944. Rittenhouse 49-116 1976 $12

BUNNER, H. C.　　　The Poems of.... New York, 1896. 1st ed., portrait, uncut, green cloth, t.e.g., very good or better. Limestone 9-43 1978 $20

BUNNER, H. C.　　　Short Sixes: Stories to be Read While the Candle Burns. New York, 1891. 8vo, 1st ed., light green boards with green cloth spine, some fading of edges of boards, letter from author written on Puck stationary tipped into front free endpaper, and inscribed by C. Jay Taylor, collector's cond. Desmarais 1-61 1978 $30

BUNSEN, FRANCES　　　A Memoir of Baron Bunsen. 1868. Portrait, 2 vols., lithographs, woodcuts, full diced calf gilt, rubbed, spines faded. George's 635-1234 1978 £10.50

BUNTEN, A. C.　　　Life of Alice Barnham (1592-1650), Wife of Sir Francis Bacon. 1919. Tables, portraits, octavo, good. Upcroft 10-241 1978 £5

BUNYAN, JOHN　　　The Holy War Made By Shaddai Upon Diabolus For the Regaining of the Metropolis of the World.... Philadelphia, 1794. Orig. full calf, fine copy, "James M. Climtock copy". Baldwins' 51-427 1978 $22.50

BUNYAN, JOHN　　　The Pilgrim's Progress from this World to that which is to come. 1895. 8vo., plts., blue mor., gilt panelled back, gilt edges, from the Cortlandt F. Bishop library. Quaritch 979-63 1978 $315

BUNYAN, JOHN　　　Select Works. 1865. Portrait, wood-engrav., orig. full crimson mor., thick 4to. Howes 194-683 1978 £12.50

BUNYAN, JOHN　　　The Works of. 1692. Portrait, map, has special leaf with space for subscriber's name, badly foxed, acceptable copy, folio, 19th cent. half roan. Thomas 37-37 1978 £500

BUNYAN, JOHN　　　Works. 1859. 3 vols., thick roy. 8vo., plts., full contemp. mor. over thick bds., all edges gilt. Howes 194-682 1978 £35

BUONAFEDE, APPIANO　　　Della Malignita Istorica Discorsi Tre di Agatopisto Cromaziano Contro Pier Francesco Le Courayer.... Napoli, 1787. 8vo., vellum. King 7-145 1978 £15

BUONAIUTI, B. S.　　　Italian Scenery; Representing the Manners, Customs, and Amusements of the Different States of Italy... 1806. Folio, plt., contemp. maroon mor. gilt, a little rubbed. Quaritch 983-305 1978 $1,000

BUONAMICI, CASTRUCCIO, COUNT　　　Commentariorum De Bello Italico. Lugduni Batavaorum, (Genoa), 1750-51. 1st. ed., 3 vols. in 4, complete, bound in 2 vols., 4to, contemp. vellum, 6 leaves misbound, fine copy otherwise. Fenning 32-40 1978 £14.50

BUONANNI, FILIPPO　　　Ricreatione Del'Occhio E Della Mente Nell Osservation Delle Chiccide. (Rome, 1681). Frontis., plts., illus., rare 1st ed. Salloch 345-34a 1978 $300

BUONARROTI, MICHEL ANGELO　　　Mappe des Kunstwarts, Die Hauptbilder der Sixtinadecke. Muchen, (c. 1900). Plts., text sewn as issued, folio, in paper portfolio. George's 635-193 1978 £5

BUONARROTI, MICHEL ANGELO　　　Rime Di Michelangelo Buonarroti. Florence, 1623. Sm. 4to., old (possibly cont.) bds., edges entirely uncut, first ed., v.f. Quaritch 978-108 1978 $1100

BUONARROTI, MICHEL ANGELO　　　Le Rime...Testo di Lingua Italiana. 1817. 4to., vellum, fine, uncut. King 7-146 1978 £30

BUONINSEGNI, DOMENICO DI LEONARDO　　　Storie della Citta di Firenze Dall'Anno 1410 al 1460. Florence, 1637. 1st ed., quarto, woodcut t.p. and initials, roman face with Italic marginal gloss, full contemporary backed vellum. Bennett 20-31 1978 $275

BURBANK, LUTHER　　　His Methods and Discoveries - Their Practical Application. 1914-15. 12 vols., plates tipped in, 8vo, orig. cloth. Book Chest 17-71 1978 $245

BURBANK, LUTHER　　　The Training of the Human Plant. New York, 1907. Portr., 12mo., 1st ed., orig. cloth. Morrill 241-65 1978 $15

BURBRIDGE, FREDERICK W.　　　The Gardens of the Sun... 1880. 1st. & only ed., plts., other illus., 8vo, orig. cloth, gilt, binding little dull, joints weak, very good copy. Fenning 32-41 1978 £24.50

BURCH, EDWIN W.　　　A Burch Book. Council Bluffs, n.d. (1925). Cloth. Hayman 73-226 1978 $20

BURCH, JOHN P.　　　Charles W. Quantrell: A True Story of His Guerrilla Warfare on the Missouri and Kansas Border...As Told by Captain Harrison Trow. Vega, 1923. 1st ed., d.j. Jenkins 116-1118 1978 $12.50

BURCH, L. D.　　　Kansas as It Is:.... Chicago, 1878. Folding map, original printed front wr., 1st ed. Ginsberg 14-440 1978 $75

BURCHARD, CHARLES　　　A Statement of Facts in Relation to the Case of Rev. Jacob Knapp. New York, 1846. Prtd. wr., dusty. Butterfield 21-266 1978 $15

BURCHETT, WILFRED G.　　　Pacific Treasure Island. Melbourne, 1942. 2nd ed., illus. Biblo 247-662 1978 $10

BURCKHARDT, JAKOB　　　Civilization of the Renaissance. 1944. 4to., illus. Allen 234-1136 1978 $12.50

BURDER, GEORGE　　　Early Piety or Memoirs of Children. Baltimore, 1821. Pictorial wrs. Victoria 34-116 1978 $10

BURDETT, OSBERT　　　A Little Book of Cheese. London, 1935. First ed., orig. binding, covers slightly marked, otherwise nice copy. Rota 211-57 1978 £5

BURDETTE, ROBERT J.　　　The Rise and Fall of the Mustache and Other "Hawk-Eyetems". Burlington, 1877. Cloth, 1st ed., spine state A. Hayman 73-71 1978 $10

BURDICK, USHER L.　　　Marquis de Mores at War in the Bad Lands. Fargo, 1929. Wrs., frontis., 1st ed., fine. Dykes 35-195 1978 $15

BURDICK, USHER L.　　　Marquis de Mores at War in the Bad Lands. Fargo, 1929. 2nd ed., very good. Dykes 35-196 1978 $7.50

BUREAU, P.　　　Catalogue des Tableaux Anciens, Tableaux Modernes...Oeuvres Importantes de Daumier. Paris, 1927. 4to., plts., wrs. Quaritch 983-160 1978 $50

BURGEFF, H.　　　Saprophytismus und Symbiose. Jena, 1932. Illus., 8vo, orig. cloth. Book Chest 17-72 1978 $25

BURGER, CARL GOTTLIEB　　　Handbuch der Chirurgischen Verbandlehre zum Gebrauche fur Angehende und Ausubende Wundarzte. Stuttgart, 1849. Illus., 8vo., contemp. cloth-backed bds., 1st ed. Offenbacher 30-20 1978 $75

BURGER, K.　　　The Printers and Publishers of the XV Century with Lists of their works. London, 1902. Demy 8vo., bds., holland back. Forster 130-282 1978 £45

BURGESS, FRED W.   Antique Jewelry & Trinkets. 1937. Allen 234-133 1978 $10

BURGESS, FRED W.   Chats on Old Coins. London, 1937. Sm. thick 8vo., cloth, illus. Van der Peet H64-108 1978 Dfl 45

BURGESS, GELETT   Look Eleven Years Younger. New York, 1937. Very nice. Desmarais B-110 1978 $7.50

BURGESS, GEORGE H.   The Centennial History of the Pennsylvania Railroad Co. Philadelphia, 1949. Illus., fine. MacManus 239-409 1978 $30

BURGESS, GEORGE H.   Centennial History of the Pennsylvania Railroad Co. 1846-1946. Philadelphia, 1949. 1st ed., thick 8vo., signed inscript. by Clement, orig. binding. Americanist 101-28 1978 $27.50

BURGESS, JAMES   Flora of Moray. Elgin, 1935. Frontis., inscribed by author, 8vo., orig. cloth. K Books 244-54 1978 £5

BURGESS, JOHN W.   The Administration of President Hayes. The Larwill Lectures, 1915, Delivered at Kenyon College. New York, 1916. Cloth. Hayman 72-78 1978 $7.50

BURGESS, T.   The Burgess Animal Book for Children. Boston, 1920. 1st ed., worn, slightly shaken binding, orig. cloth, 8vo. Book Chest 17-73 1978 $20

BURGESS, THOMAS   Foreign-Born Americans and Their Children. n.d. ca. 1920. Photos, orig. bds., rebacked. Austin 79-103 1978 $12.50

BURGESS, W. RANDOLPH   The Reserve Banks and the Money Market. 1927. Illus. Austin 80-458 1978 $11

BURGH, JAMES   The Art of Speaking. Baltimore, 1804. Leather, 1st. Baltimore ed. Hayman 71-69 1978 $20

BURGHCLERE, WINIFRED   The Life of James, First Duke of Ormonde, 1610-1688. 1912. 2 vols., plts., octavo, good. Upcroft 10-242 1978 £15

BURGHLEY, WILLIAM CECIL, 1ST BARON   A Description of Maps and Architectural Drawings in the Collection Made by...Now at Hatfield House. 1971. Frontis, plts., buckram, mor. back. Quaritch 983-39 1978 $240

BURGON, JOHN W.   The Portrait of a Christian Gentleman. 1859. 8vo., orig. cloth uncut, nice. P. M. Hill 142-54 1978 £10

BURGOYNE, ARTHUR G.   Homestead. Pittsburgh, 1893. Clean, orig. binding. Hayman 71-71 1978 $17.50

BURGOYNE, JOHN   The Lord of the Manor. Dublin, 1794. Cr. 8vo., frontis., portrait, browned, 4 plays bound in 1 vol., cloth, bottom of all leaves and corners charred, not affecting text. Eaton 45-71 1978 £10

BURGOYNE, JOHN   The Maid of Oaks: A New Dramatic Entertainment. London, 1774. Sm. 8vo., disbound, 1st ed., contemp. signature and author's name on t.p. MacManus 238-104 1978 $50

BURGOYNE, JOHN   A State of the Expedition from Canada, as Laid Before the House of Commons. London, 1780. Second ed., later cloth, fold. maps, 2 of which are mounted on linen and handcoloured in part, dampstains and light discolouration throughout. Wolfe 39-53 1978 $175

BURGOYNE, R. H.   Historical Records of the 93rd Sutherland Highlanders. 1883. 8vo., coloured plts., orig. cloth. F. Edwards 1013-544 1978 £40

BURGSDORF, F.   Abbildung der Hundert Deutschen Wilden Holz-Arten Nach dem numern-verzeichnis im Forst-Handbuch. Stuttgart, 1790-94. German text, orig. paper covered bds., staining to margins, foxing, marginal spotting, sm. 4to., plts. Book Chest 17-74 1978 $220

BURIGNY, J. L. DE   The Life of Hugo Grotius...Together with a Critical Account of His Works. London, 1754. 8vo., calf with label. Salloch 348-21 1978 $90

BURKBECK, M.   Letters From Illinois. 1818. 2nd. London ed., modern half calf, 8vo. Edwards 1012-471 1978 £28

BURKE, C. E.   Science Teaching and Research in the Canadian Democracy. Hamilton, 1948. Card cover, illus. Hood 116-363 1978 $7.50

BURKE, EDMUND   An Account of the European Settlements in America. Vol. II. In six parts. London, 1760. Map, old calf, covers loose, area torn away from "Contents" leaf affecting text on both sides, third ed. Wolfe 39-54 1978 $35

BURKE, EDMUND   A Letter From Edmund Burke, Esq. London, 1777. 2nd ed., 3/4 leather binding rubbed. Nestler Rare 78-157 1978 $75

BURKE, EDMUND   A Letter to a Noble Lord, on the Attacks made upon him and his Pension in the House of Lords by the Duke of Bedford and the Earl of Lauderdale. 1796. Soiled, disbound. George's 635-567 1978 £5

BURKE, EDMUND   A Philosophical Inquiry into the Origin of our Ideas of the Sublime and Beautiful. 1801. Engrav. portrait, fcap. 8vo., half calf, worn, crudely repaired. George's 635-1453 1978 £7.50

BURKE, EDMUND   Reflections on the Revolution in France. Dublin, 1790. 1st. Dublin ed., tree calf, rebacked, maroon label, some spotting on title, v.g. Jarndyce 16-46 1978 £32

BURKE, EDMUND   Reflections on the Revolution in France. Dodsley, 1790. 8vo., 1/2 calf, rebacked. Salloch 348-22 1978 $125

BURKE, EDMUND   Speeches. Dublin, 1865. Sm. 8vo., orig. cloth. Morrill 241-66 1978 $7.50

BURKE, EDMUND   Substance of the Speeches Made in the House of Commons, on Wednesday, the 15th of December, 1779. London, 1779. 1st ed. MacManus 238-105 1978 $60

BURKE, EDMUND   The Works. 1808-12-13. 12 vols., new ed., 1st. & last 2 leaves in vols. 6 & 12 affected by damp, orig. morocco, blank labels, generally strong & handsome set. Jarndyce 16-327 1978 £68

BURKE, JACKSON   Prelum to Albion: a History of the Development of the Hand Press from Gutenberg to Morris. San Francisco, 1940. Bds., cloth back, near mint, 1 of 250 copies printed by hand, signed pres. by Burke. Dawson's 447-22 1978 $50

BURKE, PETER   The Romance of the Forum... 1852. 1st. ed., 2 vols., half titles, orig. purple cloth, v.g. Jarndyce 16-328 1978 £30

BURKE, THOMAS   Nights in Town: a London autobiography. 1915. Orig. cloth, some foxing, nice, scarce, first English ed. Bell Book 16-130 1978 £25

BURKE, THOMAS TRAVERS   The Royal Visit: A Poem, On The Arrival In Ireland of His Most Gracious Majesty, George the Fourth,.... Dublin, 1821. 8vo, disbound, 1st ed., scarce partiotic poem. Ximenes 47-38 1978 $20

BURKET, WALTER C.   Bibliography of William Henry Welch. New York, 1934. Rittenhouse 49-117 1976 $35

BURKETT, C.   Cotton. New York, 1908. 8vo, orig. cloth. Book Chest 17-471 1978 $10

BURKHALTER, F. E.   A World-Visioned Church: Story of First Baptist Church, Waco, Texas. Nashville, 1946. Autographed. Jenkins 116-866 1978 $12.50

BURKS, ARTHUR J.   Here are My People. New York, 1934. 1st ed. Biblo BL781-303 1978 $10

BURLAGE, JOHN   Abstract of Valid Land Claims, Compiled from the Records of the General Land Office and Court of Claims of the State of Texas. Austin, 1859. Original calf, boards, 1st ed. Jenkins 116-168 1978 $475

BURLEIGH, BENNET   Sirdar and Khalifa, or the Re-Conquest of the Soudan, 1898. 1898. 1st. ed., portrait, folding map, illus., half title, 8vo, very light signs of use, very good copy, recent half calf, gilt. Fenning 32-42 1978 £24

BURLEY, WALTER   De Vita Philosophorum Et Poetarum... Strasbourg, 1516. 4to., marbled wrs., some margins torn, some light stains, leaf mounted. Salloch 348-23 1978 $110

BURLINGAME, ROGER   Of Making Many Books. New York, 1946. Orig. bind., very good, pub. pres. bookplt., 1st ed. Petrilla 13-6 1978 $10

BURLINGHAME, ROGER   Of Making Many Books. New York, 1946. Very good, first U.S. ed. Bell Book 16-103 1978 £10.50

BURLINGTON FINE ARTS CLUB   Catalogue of a Collection of Italian Sculpture and Other Plastic Art of the Renaissance. 1913. Roy. 4to., plts., buckram, gilt top. Quaritch 983-204 1978 $125

BURLINGTON FINE ARTS CLUB   Catalogue of an Exhibition of Ancient Egyptian Art. 1922. 4to., plts., buckram. Quaritch 983-180 1978 $125

BURLINGTON FINE ARTS CLUB   Catalogue of an Exhibition of Florentine Painting Before 1500. 1920. 4to., plts., buckram, rather faded. Quaritch 983-184 1978 $65

BURLINGTON FINE ARTS CLUB   Catalogue of Objects of Greek Ceramic Art, Exhibited in 1888. 1888. Roy. 4to., plts., brown mor., one of 25 copies on Jap. paper. Quaritch 983-105 1978 $375

BURLINGTON FINE ARTS CLUB   Exhibition of English Mezzotint Portraits from c. 1750 to about 1830. London, 1902. 8vo., folio, cloth, fine plts. Van der Peet H64-29 1978 Dfl 65

BURLINGTON FINE ARTS CLUB   Exhibition of Portrait Miniatures. 1899. Roy. 4to, orig. cloth, gilt, binding little dull, sm. tear in headband, plts., nice copy. Fenning 32-43 1978 £38.50

BURLINGTON FINE ARTS CLUB   Exhibition of the Faience of Persia and the Nearer East. 1908. Folio, plts., some in color, buckram. Quaritch 983-136 1978 $300

BURLINGTON FINE ARTS CLUB   Porcelain. Short Description of the English and Continental Porcelain, Exhibited June, 1873. 1873. Roy. 4to., plts., bds., roan back, a little rubbed, plt. margins slightly foxed, rare. Quaritch 983-Addenda c 1978 $80

BURN, JAMES DAWSON   Three Years Among the Working-Classes in the United States During the War. London, 1865. Rebound by hand. Bell Wiley's copy. Broadfoot 46-31 1978 $40

BURN, ROBERT S.   The Steam-Engine, Its History and Mechanism... 1854. 1st. ed., illus., 8vo, wrapper, very good copy. Fenning 32-44 1978 £16.50

BURN-MURDOCH, WILLIAM GORDON   From Edinburgh to India and Burmah. London, n.d. (c. 1901). Plts. in color, 8vo., orig. covers. Van der Peet 127-164 1978 Dfl 65

BURNAND, F. C.   The "A.D.C." Being Personal Reminiscences of the University Amateur Dramatic Club. Cambridge, 1880. 1st. ed., half title, orig. green cloth, v.g. Jarndyce 16-329 1978 £10.50

BURNAY, J.   Chrestomathie Siamoise. Paris, 1938. 4to, orig. covers. Van der Peet 127-38 1978 Dfl 35

BURNES, ALEXANDER   Travels Into Bokhara.... London, 1835. 2nd. ed., 3 vols., 12mo, lithograph frontispiece portrait, map, engraved plts., half calf, gilt. Deighton 5-67 1978 £65

BURNET, GILBERT   An Enquiry Into The Reasons For Abrogating the Test Imposed on All Members of Parliament. N.P., n.d. (London, 1688). 1st. ed., 4to, disbound, uncut. Hannas 54-33 1978 £6

BURNET, GILBERT   An Essay on the Memory of the Late Queen, Mary. 1695. 1st. ed., frontispiece, portrait, orig. panelled calf, rebacked, good. Jarndyce 16-4 1978 £25

BURNET, GILBERT   History of his own Time, from the Restoration of Charles II to the Treaty of Utrect in the Reign of Queen Anne. 1753. Engraved portrait, 4 vols., old calf, worn, 2 covers detached. George's 635-568 1978 £5

BURNET, GILBERT   History of His Own Time. 1809. 4 vols., thk. roy. 8vo., contemp. full straight-grained mor., gilt edges. Howes 194-190 1978 £80

BURNET, GILBERT   The Life and Death of Sir Mathew Hale, Kt.... 1682. 2nd. ed., 8vo, portrait, 19th. century roan, joint split. Hannas 54-34 1978 £15

BURNET, GILBERT   Reflections on a Book by Francis Atterbury, Entitled, 'The Rights, Powers and Privileges of an English Convocation, Stated and Vindicated'. 1700. 1st. ed., 4to, half-title, disbound, loose. Hannas 54-35 1978 £6

BURNET, GILBERT   Reflections on Mr. Varillas's History of the Revolutions That Have Happened in Europe in Matters of Religion. Amsterdam, 1686. 1st. ed., 12mo, contemp. calf, lacks label. Hannas 54-36 1978 £28

BURNET, GILBERT   A Sermon Preached at the Funeral of the Honourable Robert Boyle... 1692. 1st. ed., Fulton's issue "A", 4to, half-title, wrappers. Hannas 54-37 1978 £15

BURNET, GILBERT   Some Passages of the Life and Death of the Right Honourable John Earl of Rochester. 1680. 1st. ed., 1st. issue, 8vo, portrait, modern quarter calf, name & finger mark s on title. Hannas 54-38 1978 £38

BURNET, GILBERT   Some Passages in the Life and Death of John Earl of Rochester. 1805. Portrait, old calf, joints cracked, octavo, good. Upcroft 10-22 1978 £5

BURNET, GILBERT   Three Letters Concerning the Present State of Italy. 1688. 12mo., contemp. sheep, covers scratched. P.M. Hill 142-2 1978 £30

BURNET, JACOB   Notes on the Early Settlement of the North-Western Territory. Cincinnati, 1847. 1st ed., cloth, very fine, clean copy. MacManus 239-74 1978 $45

BURNET, JOHN   Pracitcal Hints on Composition in Painting... 1828. 3rd ed., 4to., plts., plts. spotted, orig. bds., rebacked. Quaritch 983-162 1978 $65

BURNET, JOHN   Practical Hints on Light and Shade in Painting. 1829. 3rd ed., 4to., plts. rather spotted, orig. cloth backed bds., repaired. Quaritch 983-163 1978 $65

BURNET, JOHN   Practical Hints on Light and Shade in Painting. 1838. Illus., plts., sm. folio, orig. bds. George's 635-14 1978 £5

BURNET, JOHN   Practical Hints on Light and Shade in Painting. 1849. 6th ed., 4to., plts., occasional slight foxing, orig. cloth backed bds. Quaritch 983-164 1978 $55

BURNET, JOHN   A Practical Treatise on Painting, in Three Parts. 1830. New ed., 4to., half red calf gilt, fine, coloured plts., orig. water colours. P. M. Hill 142-23 1978 £48

BURNET, JOHN   A Treatise on Painting in Four Parts. Consisting of an Essay on the Education of the Eye with Reference to Painting, and Practical Hints on Composition, Chiaroscuro, and Colour. 1837. 4to., plts., some coloured by hand, some foxing of plts. Quaritch 983-165 1978 $145

BURNET, JOHN R.   Tales of the Deaf and Dumb, with Miscellaneous Poems. Newark, 1835. 12mo., orig. bds., cloth back, 1st ed. Morrill 239-38 1978 $20

BURNET, THOMAS 1635-1715   Archaeologiae Philosophicae. 1692. Sm. 4to., contemp. calf, joints cracked, neat contemp. annotations on a few pages, first ed. Howes 194-23 1978 £36

BURNETT, BISHOP   The Sacred Theory of the Earth. 1816. Engraved plts., a little foxing, 4to., contemp. calf. George's 635-1039 1978 £15

BURNETT, CHARLES H.   A Textbook on Diseases of the Ear, Nose and Throat. Philadelphia, 1901. Library binding. Rittenhouse 49-119 1976 $10

BURNETT, EDMUND CODY   Letters of Barnett Hardeman Cody, William Henderson Cody, James Newell Lightfoot, Thomas Reese Lightfoot, and William Edwin Lightfoot 1861-1864. Georgia, 1942. Bound in cloth, Bell Wiley's copy. Broadfoot's 44-413 1978 $15

BURNETT, FRANCES HODGSON   Giovanni and the Other. New York, 1892. 1st ed., illus. by Birch, very good. Victoria 34-117 1978 $17.50

BURNETT, FRANCES HODGSON   In Connection With the DeWilloughby Claim. New York, (1899). Orig. binding, clean, very minor flecking on cover. Hayman 71-219 1978 $7.50

BURNETT, FRANCES HODGSON   Little Lord Fauntleroy. New York, 1886. Drawings, first ed. Biblo 247-559 1978 $27.50

BURNETT, FRANCES HODGSON   That Lass O'Lowrie's. New York, 1877. Illus., orig. cloth, 1st ed., 1st state, very good. MacManus 238-431 1978 $75

BURNETT, FRANCES HODGSON   Two Little Pilgrims' Progress. New York, 1895. 1st ed., illus, some cover soiling, very good. Victoria 34-118 1978 $10

BURNETT, W. R.   The Asphalt Jungle. 1949. First ed., d.j. Austin 82-279 1978 $20

BURNETT, W. R.   High Sierra. 1940. 292 pages. Austin 82-280 1978 $8.50

BURNETT, W. R.   Iron Man. 1930. 312 pages. Austin 82-281 1978 $8.50

BURNETT, W. R.   King Cole. 1936. First ed. Austin 82-282 1978 $11

BURNETT, W. R.   Nobody Lives Forever. New York, 1943. Vg in dw. Bernard 5-37 1978 $7.50

BURNEY, FANNY
Please turn to
ARBLAY, FRANCES BURNEY D'

BURNHAM, CLARA LOUISE   Doctor Latimer. Boston, 1893. 12mo., orig. wrs., autographed. Morrill 239-499 1978 $8.50

THE BURNING Village and Other Indian Stories. New York, c.1850. Sq. 12 mo, plates, light foxing, very good. Victoria 34-119 1978 $7.50

BURNLEY, W. H.   Observations on the Present Condition of the Island of Trinidad... 1842. 8vo, orig. cloth, rebacked, with inscription from author. Edwards 1012-744 1978 £100

BURNS, FRANKLIN L.   The Ornithology of Chester County, Pa. Boston, (1919). Illus. MacManus 239-1404 1978 $20

BURNS, J. A.   Catholic Education. 1917. Ex-lib. Austin 79-106 1978 $12.50

BURNS, JOHN   Principles of Midwifery. 1820, 1821. Fifth Amer. ed., two vols., orig. leather. Rittenhouse 49-120 1976 $35

BURNS, ROBERT   The Correspondence Between Burns & Clarinda. Edinburgh, 1843. 1st. ed., frontis, engraved title, orig. red cloth, gilt spine. Jarndyce 16-332 1978 £14.50

BURNS, ROBERT   The Cotter's Saturday Night. New York, 1867. 1st ed., plates & engravings by F. A. Chapman, fine quality thick paper, gilt edges, impressed full leather finding in black and gilt, gilt dentelles, fine copy. Victoria 34-120 1978 $50

BURNS, ROBERT   The Merry Muses of Caledonia. 1911. 8vo., qtr. mor., uncut, fine. P. M. Hill 142-247 1978 £30

BURNS, ROBERT   The Merry Muses of Caledonia. N. P., n.d. (ca. 1911). 8vo., orig. bds., cloth back & corners, ltd. to 750 copies. Morrill 241-67 1978 $22.50

BURNS, ROBERT   Poems, Chiefly in the Scottish Dialect. Edinburgh, 1787. 8vo, full green crushed levant, gilt, spine and inner dentelles gilt, a.e.g., by Riviere, 1st Edinburgh ed., fine and attractive copy. Ximenes 47-39 1978 $275

BURNS, ROBERT   Poems, Chiefly in the Scottish Dialect. London, 1787. 3rd ed., frontis., tall octavo, bound in dark blue levant, gilt spine, gilt top, other edges uncut. Totteridge 29-20 1978 $250

BURNS, ROBERT   The Poems, Letters and Land of Robert Burns. (1840). Plts., 2 vols., 4to., full contemp. green mor., orig. tissue guards in place. Howes 194-1365 1978 $75

BURNS, ROBERT   Poetical Works. New York, c. 1900. Frontis., full tree calf, 8vo. K Books 244-55 1978 £6

BURNS, ROBERT   Songs from Robert Burns. Golden Cockerel Press. Wood engrs., #176 of 450 numbered copies, fine. Battery Park 1-113 1978 $75

BURNS, ROBERT   Tam O'Shanter. London, 1855. Illus. by John Faed, engravings, folio, bds. K Books 244-56 1978 £6

BURNS, ROBERT   Works. 1801. 2nd. ed., 4 vols., frontis, half titles, orig. calf, spines worn. Jarndyce 16-330 1978 £15

BURNS, ROBERT   The Works. Edinburgh, 1877. New Library ed., 6 vols., roy. 8vo., lg. paper 7 x 10 1/4 inches, plts., full dark green crushed levant mor., gilt tops, other edges untrimmed, extra illus. set. Howes 194-684 1978 £175

BURNS, THOMAS W.   Initial Ithacans...Sketches and Portraits of the Forty-Four Presidents of the Village...(1821-1888) and the First Eight Mayors of the City (1888-1903). Ithaca, 1904. Green cloth, very good. Butterfield 21-432 1978 $20

BURPEE, LAWRENCE J.   The Discovery of Canada. Toronto, 1944. Hood's 115-583 1978 $12.50

BURPEE, LAWRENCE J.   Modern Public Libraries and Their Methods. 1902. Card cover. Hood 116-7 1978 $12

BURPEE, LAWRENCE J.   The Search for the Western Sea. New York, 1936. New and revised ed., two vols., orig. d.j., orig. binding. Wolfe 39-55 1978 $65

BURR, ANNA ROBESON   The Portrait of a Banker, James Stillman. 1850-1918. 1927. Illus. Austin 80-460 1978 $12.50

BURR, E. F.   Dio the Athenian. New York, 1880. Cloth. Hayman 73-173 1978 $15

BURR, JOHN G.   The Framework of Battle. 1943. 1st ed., inscr'd by author. Austin 80-37 1978 $17.50

BURR, MALCOLM   A Fossicker in Angola. London, (1933). Map, 8 plts. corners bumped, 8vo, orig. cloth. K Books 239-76 1978 £8

BURRAGE, HENRY S.   History of the Thirty-Sixth Regiment Massachusetts Volunteers. Boston, 1884. Bell Wiley's copy. Broadfoot 46-340 1978 $25

BURRAGE, HENRY S.   Thomas Hamlin Hubbard, Bvt. Brigadier General U. S. Vols. (Augusta), 1923. Portr., 8vo., orig. cloth, 1st ed. Morrill 241-302 1978 $12.50

BURRITT, ELIHU   Chips from Many Blocks. Toronto, 1878. Hood 116-674 1978 $15

BURROUGHS, ALAN   Art Criticism From a Laboratory. Boston, 1938. 1st ed., 4 to., illus., d.j., very good. Houle 10-52 1978 $20

BURROUGHS, EDGAR RICE   The Beasts of Tarzan. 1918. Very good, first English ed. Bell Book 16-326 1978 £15

BURROUGHS, EDGAR RICE   The Gods of Mars. London, 1920. Green cloth. Eaton 45-75 1978 £5

BURROUGHS, EDGAR RICE   The Monster Men. Chicago, 1929. 8vo., occas. cover stains, 1st ed., orig. cloth. Morrill 241-68 1978 $15

BURROUGHS, EDGAR RICE   Tarzan and the Ant-Men. 1925. Very good, first English ed. Bell Book 16-327 1978 £8.50

BURROUGHS, EDGAR RICE   Tarzan and the Foreign Legion. Tarzana, 1947. First U.S. ed., mint, d.w., plts. Bell Book 17-325 1978 £15

BURROUGHS, EDGAR RICE   Tarzan of the Apes. New York, 1914. Orig. green cloth, frontis, was lettered in white but white worn away leaving blind impression. Eaton 45-74 1978 £10

BURROUGHS, JOHN   Bird and Bough. Boston, 1906. 12mo., orig.
cloth, 1st ed., 1 of 150 lg. paper copies, fine. MacManus 238-432 1978 $35

BURROUGHS, JOHN   The Breath of Life. Boston and New York, 1915.
Frontis, orig. cloth, gilt, Bessie Sullivan bookplt., signatures of author & Bessie
Sullivan. Eaton 45-76 1978 $5

BURROUGHS, JOHN   In The Catskills. Boston, 1910. Illus. by photos
by Clifton Johnson, 8vo, orig. cloth. Book Chest 17-75 1978 $22

BURROUGHS, JOHN   John James Audubon. Boston, 1902. Portr.,
illus., 8vo., uncut, unopened, fine, 1 of 350 lg. paper copies, 1st ed., autographed. Morrill 241-659 1978 $47.50

BURROUGHS, JOHN   Locusts and Wild Honey. Boston, 1879. 1st ed.,
presentation copy, spine scuffed, 8vo, orig. cloth. Book Chest 17-76 1978
$23.50

BURROUGHS, JOHN   Writings of... 1904. Ltd. to 750 copies, 23
vols., some spines faded, signed by Burroughs. Austin 82-283 1978 $195

BURROUGHS, JOSEPH B.   Titan, Son of Saturn. Oberlin, 1907. Orig.
binding, clean. Hayman 71-220 1978 $7.50

BURROUGHS, STEPHEN   Memoirs of the Notorious Stephen Burroughs of
New Hampshire. N.P., 1924. Preface by Robert Frost. Nestler Rare 78-5 1978
$15

BURROUGHS WELLCOME AND CO.   The Romance of Exploration and Emergency
First-aid from Stanley to Byrd. London, (c.1934). Illus. Hood 116-609 1978
$25

BURROWES, T. H.   State-Book of Pennsylvania... Philadelphia,
1846. Frontis map, other maps, sm. 8vo, orig. printed bds., leather spine.
Edwards 1012-478 1978 £18

BURROWS, G.   The Land of the Pigmies. New York, (1898).
Illus., bookplt. of T.D. Carter, 8vo, orig. cloth. Book Chest 17-78 1978 $55

BURROWS, G. M.   An Inquiry into Certain Errors Relative to Insanity;
and Their Consequences; Physical, moral, and civil. London, 1820. 8vo., fold.
plt., rebound in cloth, uncut. Quaritch 977-13 1978 $325

BURROWS, M.   The Dead Sea Scrolls of St. Mark's Monastery.
Vol. I. New Haven, 1950. Ltd. to 2000 copies, portrait, plts., demy 4to.,
orig. cloth. Forster 130-291 1978 £7.50

BURROWS, RONALD M.   The Discoveries in Crete and Their Bearing on the
History of Ancient Civilization. London, 1907. Illus. Biblo BL781-339 1978
$17.50

BURROWS, RONALD M.   Discoveries in Crete & Their Bearing on the History of Ancient Civilization. 1907. Spot on cover, maps. Allen 234-248 1978
$7.50

BURSTEIN, ABRAHAM   The Boy of Wilna. 1941. Illus. Austin
79-108 1978 $10

BURT, A. L.   The United States, Great Britain, and British
North America from the Revolution to the War of 1812. New Haven, 1940. Orig.
ed., maps. Hood 117-558 1978 $50

BURT, EDWARD   Letters From a Gentleman in the North of Scotland to His Friend in London. 1818. 5th. ed., 2 vols., 8vo, probably lacking
half-titles, contemp. half russia, joints weak, uncut. Hannas 54-292 1978 £20

BURT, STRUTHERS   Holy Experiment. New York, 1945. First ed.,
fine, d.w., illus. Biblo 247-118 1978 $15

BURTON, MRS. CHARLES HENRY   Abbots Thorpe; or, the Two Wills. London,
1864. 2 vols., orig. cloth, 1st ed., slightly worn and soiled, but very good.
MacManus 238-336 1978 $65

BURTON, E. MILBY   South Carolina Silversmiths 1690-1860.
Charleston, 1942. Illus. MacManus 239-645 1978 $35

BURTON, EARL   By Sea and By Land. 1944. Illus. Austin 80-
34 1978 $10

BURTON, GIDEON   Reminiscences. Cincinnati, 1895. MacManus
239-1405 1978 $20

BURTON, HARLEY TRUE   A History of the Ja Ranch. Austin, 1928.
1st ed., portrait, illus., orig. red cloth, very good or better. Limestone
9-46 1978 $100

BURTON, ISABEL   A Narrative of Travel, Arabia, Egypt, India.
1879. 1st. ed., 8vo, half-title, coloured engraved map, lib. stamps on half-title,
orig. cloth, worn, silver & gilt back, a little loose in binding. Deighton 5-201
1978 £65

BURTON, J.   Lectures on Female Education and Manners.
Dublin, 1802. 4th. ed., 12mo, contemp. sheep, joints cracked, paper little
browned. Hannas 54-40 1978 £15

BURTON, JOHN   Sacerdos Paroecialis Rusticis. 1757. 8vo., unbound, first ed. P. M. Hill 142-248 1978 £8

BURTON, JOHN HILL   The Book-Hunter, Etc. New York, 1883. Half-
leather, rubbed. MacManus 238-880 1978 $7.50

BURTON, JOHN HILL   The Book-Hunter. Thick sm. 4to., prtd. on
fine paper, frontis., illus., binding reinforced, rubbed, t.e.g., signature by
Dembrose Derby. Battery Park 1-307 1978 $75

BURTON, JOHN HILL   The History of Scotland, from the Revolution to the
Extinction of the Last Jacobite Insurrection, 1689-1748. 1853. 2 vols., 8vo.
George's 635-570 1978 £5.25

BURTON, JOHN HILL   The History of Scotland, from Agricola's Invasion
to the Extinction of the Last Jacobite Insurrection. Edinburgh, 1873. 8 vols.,
cr. 8vo. George's 635-569 1978 £10.50

BURTON, JOHN HILL   The History of Scotland From Agricola's Invasion
to the Extinction of the Last Jacobite Insurrection. 1905. 8 vols., octavo, good.
Upcroft 10-244 1978 £20

BURTON, RICHARD FRANCIS   The City of Saints, and Across the Rocky Mountains to California. New York, 1862. Illus., orig. cloth, 1st Amer. ed. Ginsberg 14-1087 1978 $150

BURTON, RICHARD FRANCIS   Etruscan Bologna: a Study. London, 1876. 8vo,
original grey-blue decorated cloth, 1st ed., very fine copy. Ximenes 47-40
1978 $100

BURTON, RICHARD FRANCIS   A Mission to Gelele... 1864. 2 vols., vol. I
1st. ed., vol. 2- 2nd. ed., plts., orig. cloth, rebacked, old spines laid down,
8vo, slight foxing on few leaves. Edwards 1012-247 1978 £70

BURTON, RICHARD FRANCIS   Il Pentamerone; or, The Tale of Tales. London,
1893. 2 vols., large-paer limited ed. of 165 copies, bound in modern buckram
and morocco spines, mint copy, very scarce. Victoria 34-121 1978 $150

BURTON, RICHARD FRANCIS   Selected Papers on Anthropology, Travel and
Exploration. London, 1924. 8vo, original tan buckram cloth, 1st ed., one of
only 100 numbered copies, very good copy. Ximenes 47-41 1978 $150

BURTON, RICHARD FRANCIS   Sind Revisited: With Notices of the Anglo-
Indian Army; Railroads; Past, Present and Future. London, Bentley, 1877.
1st ed., orig. grey-mauve cloth, 2 vols., scarce, good. Houle 10-53 1978
$225

BURTON, RICHARD FRANCIS   Tales From the Gulistan. 1928. Illus. by John
Kettelwell, cloth, worn d/w. Eaton 45-78 1978 £10

BURTON, RICHARD FRANCIS   Vikram and the Vampire
Please turn to
BAITAL-PACHIST   Vikram and the Vampire

BURTON, ROBERT   The Anatomy of Melancholy. London, 1806.
2 vols., frontispieces, contemp. reversed calf, 8vo. K Books 244-57 1978 £20

BURTON, ROBERT   The Anatomy of Melancholy. London, 1925.
2 vols., folio, illus. in color, bds., vellum back, ltd. ed. Biblo 251-587 1978
$175

BURTON, ROBERT   The Anatomy of Melancholy.   London, The
Nonesuch Press, 1925. 2 vols., small folio, decor. boards, quarter vellum spine,
gilt lettering, one of 750 numbered copies on Dutch paper.   Totteridge 29-75
1978 $150

BURTON, ROBERT   Melancholy.   1801. 8vo., old half roan, frontispiece, first ed.   P. M. Hill 142-58 1978 £16

BURTON, T. F.   The African Slave Trade.   1839. Orig. cloth,
8vo, rebacked.   Edwards 1012-248 1978 £90

BURTON, THEODORE E.   Financial Crises.   1902. Ex-lib.   Austin 80-461
1978 $11

BURTON, WARREN   The District School As It Was, By One Who Went
To It.   Boston, 1850. Frontis., orig. cloth, 12mo.   Morrill 241-69 1978 $8.50

BURTY, PHILIPPE   Chefs-D'Oeuvre of the Industrial Arts: Pottery
and Porcelain, Glass, Enamel, Metal, Goldsmiths' Work, Jewellery, and Tapestry.
New York, 1869. 1st U.S. ed., 1/2 mor., marbled bds., illus.   Americanist
102-25 1978 $30

BURWASH, N.   Inductive Studies in Theology Including the Doctrines of Sin and the Atonement.   Toronto, 1896.   Hood 116-285 1978 $12.50

BURWASH, N.   Memorials of the Life of Edward & Lydia Ann
Jackson.   Toronto, 1876.   Hood 117-340 1978 $15

BURWELL, WILLIAM M.   Memoir Explanatory of the Transunion and Teh-
uantepec Route Between Europe and Asia.   Washington, D.C., 1851. Wrs.,
stained at upper margins, scarce.   Biblo BL781-105 1978 $42.50

BURY, LADY CHARLOTTE   The Exclusives.   New York, 1830. 1st Am. ed.,
half cloth, boards, some edges rubbed, internal foxing.   Greene 78-18 1978 $65

BURY, J. B.   Cambridge Ancient History.   1923-32. Vols. 1-
9, 3 vols. not uniform in binding.   Allen 234-F 1978 $150

BURY, J. B.   Cambridge Ancient History.   1928-29. 12 vols.,
bindings not uniform, 5 vols. of plts.   Allen 234-E 1978 $250

BURY, RICHARD DE
Please turn to
AUNGERVILLE, RICHARD

BURY, T. T.   Coloured Views on the Liverpool and Manchester
Railway, with Plates of the Coaches, Machines...   1833. 4to., hand-coloured
plts., text in French, half blue levant mor.   Quaritch 983-306 1978 $1,200

BUSBECQ, OGIER GHISLAIN DE   ....Legationis Turcicae Epistolae Quatuor....
Hanover, 1605. 2nd ed. of complete work, small octavo, woodcut initials, full
calf, paneled spine with red leather label, endpapers stained, signature at top of
t.p., internally fine, very little foxing.   Bennett 20-33 1978 $350

BUSBEY, T. ADDISON   The Biographical Directory of the Railway Offi-
cials of America.   Chicago, (1901). 8vo., orig. cloth.   Morrill 241-70 1978
$12.50

BUSBY, F.   Three Men of the Tudor Time.   1911. Portraits,
octavo, good.   Upcroft 10-247 1978 £7.50

BUSCH, MORITZ   Geshichte de Mormonen Nebst Einer Darstellung
Ibres Glaubens und Ihrer Gegenwartigen Socialen und Politischen Berhaltnisse.
Leipzig, [1869]. Orig. decor. cloth, 1st ed.   Ginsberg 14-644 1978 $150

BUSCH, NIVEN   They Dream of Home.   New York, (1944). First
ed., d.w.   Biblo 247-504 1978 $12.50

BUSCHBECK, E. H.   Meisterwerke aus Oesterreich. Gemalde und
Bildteppiche. Herausgegeben von Alfred Stix.   Zurich-Wien, (1949). 4to., plts.,
some in color.   Biblo BL781-560 1978 $17.50

BUSCHOR, ERNST   Fruehgriechische Juenglinge.   Munich, (1950).
Sm. 4to.   Biblo BL781-340 1978 $12.50

BUSCHOR, ERNST   Griechische Vasenmalerei. Zweite Auflage.
Munich, 1914. Illus.   Biblo BL781-341 1978 $27.50

BUSEY, SAMUEL C.   Pictures of the City of Washington in the Past.
Washington, 1898. 1st ed., scarce.   MacManus 239-124 1978 $30

BUSH, IRVING T.   Working with the World.   1928.   Austin 80-462
1978 $10

BUSHNELL, HORACE   Thirteenth Annual Report to the Ladies' City
Missionary Association.   Cincinnati, 1856. Disbound.   Hayman 71-520 1978
$7.50

BUSK, HANS   The Vestriad, a Poem.   1819. 1st. ed., 8vo,
one plt. of 3?, half morocco, rubbed.   Hannas 54-323 1978 £12.50

BUSSY, DOROTHY   Olivia by Olivia.   Hogarth Press, 1949. Very
good, d.w., first English ed.   Bell Book 16-441 1978 £5.50

BUSTAMENTO, CARLOS MARIA DE   Cuadro Historico de la Revolucion de la
America Mexicana...   Mexico, 1823. Sm. 4to., 3/4 leath.   Paine 78-27
1978 $65.00

BUTLER, A. P.   Speech of Hon..., of South Carolina, on the Dif-
ficulty of Messrs. Brooks and Sumner, and the Causes Thereof. Delivered in the
Senate...June 12-13, 1856.   Washington, 1856. Unbound as issued, scarce.
Hayman 72-82 1978 $15

BUTLER, ARTHUR GARDINER   Birds Eggs of the British Isles.   London, 1907.
Coloured plts., 4to.   Traylen 88-548 1978 £9

BUTLER, ARTHUR GARDINER   British Birds.   1896-98. Illus. by F. W. Frohawk,
coloured plts., 6 vols., roy. 4to., orig. cloth, soiled.   George's 635-1005 1978
£25

BUTLER, BENJAMIN F.   Trade and Intercourse with Indian Tribes:....
Washington, 1837. Tables, disbound.   Ginsberg 14-67 1978 $25

BUTLER, C. M.   A Farewell Sermon, Preached in Zion Church,
Palmyra, N.Y. on Sunday Evening, August 23, 1840.   Washington, 1840. Disbound.   Hayman 71-490 1978 $7.50

BUTLER, CHARLES   The English Grammar; or The Institution of Letters,
Syllables and Words in the English Tongue.   Oxford, 1633. 1st. ed., sm. 4to.,
vellum, uncut & partly unopened.   Traylen 88-127 1978 £480

BUTLER, CHARLES   Life of Erasmus, with Historical Remarks on State
of Literature Between 10th & 16th Centuries.   1825. Bds., amateurishly rebacked.
Allen 234-1224 1978 $7.50

BUTLER, CHARLES   Reminiscences.   1824. Fourth ed., frontis.,
contemp. half calf, 8vo.   Howes 194-686 1978 £6.50

BUTLER, D.   Lives of the Fathers, Martyrs and other Principal
Saints.   1949. Coloured plts., 5 vols., roy. 8vo., covers dull.   George's 635-
1040 1978 $8.50

BUTLER, D. P.   Butler's System of Health-Exercise.   Boston, 1868.
8vo., orig. wrs., 1st ed.   Morrill 239-39 1978 $7.50

BUTLER, E.   For Good Consideration.   Battery Park 1-260
1978 $22.50

BUTLER, ELLIS PARKER   The Water Goats and Other Troubles.   New
York, 1910. Clean, 1st. ed., orig. binding.   Hayman 71-74 1978 $7.50

BUTLER, FRANCES ANNE KEMBLE
Please turn to
KEMBLE, FRANCES ANNE

BUTLER, H. E.   Post-Augustan Poetry from Seneca to Juvenal.
1909.   Allen 234-139 1978 $8.50

BUTLER, J.   An Eulogy Upon the Character of George Swan.
Oxford, 1840. Disbound.   Hayman 73-496 1978 $10

BUTLER, JAMES D.   Nebraska: Its Characteristics and Prospects.
[N.P., 1873]. Disbound.   Ginsberg 14-708 1978 $40

BUTLER, JOSEPH   The Analogy of Religion Natural and Revealed.
1765. 5th. ed., orig. calf, red label, v.g.   Jarndyce 16-49 1978 £7.50

BUTLER, NATHANIEL   Six Dialogues About Sea-Services. 1685. Very good, 8vo., contemp. calf. F. Edwards 1013-34 1978 £750

BUTLER, NICHOLAS MURRAY   Across the Busy Years. Recollections and Reflections. New York, 1939-40. 2 vols., cloth, 1st ed., very good, d.js. Hayman 72-83 1978 $10

BUTLER, PIERCE   A Check List of 15th Century Books in the Newberry Library and in other Libraries of Chicago. Chicago, 1933. Ltd. to 850 copies, med. 8vo., orig. buckram. Forster 130-302 1978 £7.50

BUTLER, PIERCE   The Newberry Library. Check List of Books Printed during the 15th Century. Chicago, 1924. Roy. 8vo., orig. wrappers. Forster 130-301 1978 £6

BUTLER, PIERCE   The Origin of Printing in Europe. Chicago, (1940). Frontis. Battery Park 1-300 1978 $22.50

BUTLER, SAMUEL 1612-1680   Characters and Passages from Note Books. 1908. Orig. cloth, 8vo. Howes 194-687 1978 £6.50

BUTLER, SAMUEL 1612-1680   The Genuine Remains in Prose and Verse. 1759. First ed., 2 vols., contemp. calf, joints slightly cracked, 8vo. Howes 194-192 1978 £22

BUTLER, SAMUEL 1612-1680   Hudibras, in Three Parts... Cambridge, 1744. Vol. I only, 8vo, contemp. full calf, portrait, plts., some folding, good. Sexton 7-135 1978 £22

BUTLER, SAMUEL 1612-1680   Hudibras. 1770. 3 vols., 12mo., full contemp. mor. Howes 194-193 1978 £18

BUTLER, SAMUEL 1612-1680   Hudibras, In Three Parts; Written in the Time of the Late Wars... 1764. 2nd. ed., engraved portrait, engraved plts., 2 vols., 8vo, contemp. calf, gilt, gilt spines, contrasting labels, nice copy. Fenning 32-46 1978 £35

BUTLER, SAMUEL 1612-1680   Hudibras. 1793. Portraits, 3 vols., 4to., full contemp. russia, fine, lg. paper copy. Howes 194-1373 1978 £90

BUTLER, SAMUEL 1612-1680 Hudibras. London, 1822. New ed., engrs., 2 vols., orig. bds., internally good, plts., full brown mor. slipcase with fldg. cloth liners. Dawson's 447-209 1978 $175

BUTLER, SAMUEL 1612-1680   Poetical Works. 1866. 2 vols., grey paper bds. Eaton 45-79 1978 £8

BUTLER, SAMUEL 1612-1680   The Postuhumous Works of... 1730. 3rd. ed., 9 engravings & frontis portrait, marginal tear in pg. 3, affecting 2 letters of a word, calf, worn. Eaton 45-80 1978 £20

BUTLER, SAMUEL 1774-1840   Atlas of Ancient Geography. Philadelphia, 1839. Maps, in color, 8vo., 3/4 red calf. Salloch 345-35 1978 $45

BUTLER, SAMUEL 1774-1840   An Atlas of Antient Geography. 1851. New ed., re-engraved, coloured engraved maps, 8vo, wrapper, some light signs of use, very good copy. Fenning 32-45 1978 £7.50

BUTLER, SAMUEL 1835-1902   The Way of All Flesh. London, 1903. Orig. cloth, 1st ed., inner hinges cracked, covers a bit worn, but good. MacManus 238-177 1978 $185

BUTLER, SAMUEL 1835-1902   Erewhon. New York, 1931. Illus. by H. Charles Tomlinson, ltd. ed., fine, boxed. Biblo 251-428 1978 $37.50

BUTLER, SAMUEL 1835-1902   The Humor of Homer. A Lecture Delivered at the Working Men's College...London, January 30, 1892. Cambridge, 1892. Orig. printed wrs., 1st ed., very nice, cloth fold. case. MacManus 238-176 1978 $125

BUTLER, W.   Arithmetical Questions, on a New Plan. London, 1832. 12mo., contemp. sheep, slightly defective. Quaritch 977-140 1978 $30

BUTLER, WILLIAM FRANCIS   The Great Lone Land: A Narrative of Travel and Adventure in the North-west of America. London, 1875. Illus., map, 7th ed., orig. bind. Hood 116-65 1978 $30

BUTLER, WILLIAM FRANCIS   Red Cloud, The Solitary Sioux... London, 1887. New & cheaper ed., illus. by H. Petherick, decorated cover. Hood's 115-739 1978 $25

BUTLER, WILLIAM FRANCIS   Red Cloud. London, (1911). Illus. by George Lambert. Hood 117-669 1978 $20

BUTLER, WILLIAM FRANCIS   The Wild North Land: Being the Story of a Winter Journey, with Dogs, Across Northern North America. London, 1878. Illus., 7th ed., full leather, marbled-edged pgs., map. Hood 116-66 1978 $45

BUTLER, WILLIAM FRANCIS   The Wild Northland... New York, 1903. 12mo., map, 1st ed. Biblo BL781-2 1978 $25

BUTT, BEATRICE MAY   Ingelheim. Edinburgh, 1842. 1st ed., 3 vols., blue cloth, public complimentary copy, good condition. Greene 78-19 1978 $55

BUTT, BEATRICE MAY   Ingelheim. Edinburgh, 1892. 3 vols., orig. cloth, 1st ed., covers stained, labels removed, inner hinges cracked. MacManus 238-337 1978 $75

BUTT, G. E.   My Travels in North West Rhodesia. London, c.1910. Cr. 8vo, 48 illus., orig. cloth, occasional foxing, covers little chafed. K Books 239-77 1978 £12

BUTTERFIELD, ROGER   The American Past.... New York, (1947). 4to. Biblo 248-17 1978 $17.50

THE BUTTERFLY'S Ball, or the Grasshopper's Feast. London, c.1850. 12mo, hand-colored engraving, sewn, wrappers worn, very nice. Victoria 34-122 1978 $15

BUTTS, MARY   The Crystal Cabinet; my childhood at Salterns. 1937. Very good, first English ed. Bell Book 16-131 1978 £8.50

BUTTS, MARY   The Crystal Cabinet. London, (1937). 1st ed., frontispiece sketch, 8 vo., d.j., very good. Houle 10-56 1978 $55

BUTTS, MARY   Death of Felicity Taverner. 1932. Covers little rubbed, bookplt., else good, first English ed. Bell Book 17-976 1978 £8.50

BUTTS, R. FREEMAN   The American Tradition in Religion and Education. 1950. Austin 79-110 1978 $11

BUXTON, B. H.   Sceptre and Ring. A Novel. London, 1881. 3 vols., orig. cloth, 1st ed., covers worn, lib. labels. MacManus 238-338 1978 $45

BUXTON, EDWARD NORTH   Short Stalks: or, Hunting Camps North, South, East, and West. New York, 1892. Illus., orig. cloth, 8vo., binding dust-soiled. Morrill 241-71 1978 $15

BUXTON, GEORGE   The Political Quixote ... 1820. 1st. ed., half title, vignette t.p., orig. grey bds., uncut, paper label, fine. Jarndyce 16-334 1978 £25

BUXTON, THOMAS FOWELL   The African Slave Trade and Its Remedy... London, (1840). 1st. ed., 8vo., date being erased from title-pg., folding engraved map, orig. straight-grained cloth, gilt back, little faded. Deighton 5-9 1978 £110

BUXTORFIO, JO. LUDOVICO   Cura Valetudinis Reigiosorum. Basileae, 1770. Second ed. Rittenhouse 49-121 1976 $17.50

BUZTORF, JOHANNES   Grammaticae Chaldaicae et Syriacae Libri III... 1650. 8vo, contemp. calf, worn but sound, very good. Fenning 32-47 1978 £18.50

BY Land & Water. New York, (1889). Large quarto, color plates by R. Andre, all plates very good, wrappers chipped, spine neatly taped. Victoria 34-123 1978 $12.50

BYAM, GEORGE   Wild Life in the Interior of Central America. London, 1849. 1st. ed., 12mo, tinted lithograph frontispiece, some staining & soiling, half calf, gilt. Deighton 5-31 1978 £35

BYERLEY, THOMAS   Relics of Literature. 1823. 8vo., contemp. watered cloth, plt. P. M. Hill 142-59 1978 £15

BYERS, SAMUEL HAWKINS MARSHALL   Iowa in War Times.   Des Moines, 1888. Illus., original cloth, 1st ed.   Ginsberg 14-407 1978 $35

BYERS, SAMUEL HAWKINS MARSHALL   What I Saw in Dixie; or Sixteen Months in Rebel Prisons.   Dansville, 1868. Bound in 3/4 lea., Bell Wiley's copy.   Broadfoot 46-331 1978 $35

BYNNER, WITTER   An Ode to Harvard and other Poems.   Boston, 1907. 8vo, red cloth, ownership inscription on flyleaf, fine, unopened copy, 1st ed., collector's cond.   Desmarais 1-64 1978 $40

BYNNER, WITTER   An Ode to Harvard and Other Poems.   Boston, 1907. Ownership inscription, unopened, fine.   Desmarais B-111 1978 $40

BYRD, RICHARD EVELYN   Alone.   New York, 1933. 8vo, d.w., pres. from Byrd.   Morrill 239-321 1978 $10

BYRD, RICHARD EVELYN   Skyward.   New York, 1928. Illus., 8vo, orig. cloth, photogravure portr.   Morrill 241-72 1978 $10

BYRD, WILLIAM   Another Secrey Diary...1739-1741....   Richmond, 1942. Fine, d.j.   MacManus 239-1799 1978 $17.50

BYRNE, DONN   An Alley of Flashing Spears and Other Stories. 1934. First American ed., ex-lib.   Austin 82-285 1978 $12.50

BYRNE, DONN   Blind Raftery.   1924. First ed.   Austin 82-286 1978 $12.50

BYRNE, DONN   Blind Raftery and His Wife, Hilaria.   New York, (1924). Illus., brown-orange cloth, 1st ed., lightly worn.   Bradley 49-43 1978 $8.50

BYRNE, DONN   Blind Raftery.   New York, 1924. Ownership inscription, fine.   Desmarais B-114 1978 $15

BYRNE, DONN   Destiny Bay.   Boston, 1928. First ed., ex-lib.   Austin 82-287 1978 $11

BYRNE, DONN   Field of Honor.   New York, (1929). Decor. bds., parchment spine, 1st ltd. ed., 1 of 500 lg. paper copies signed by Dorothea Donn-Byrne, very good.   Bradley 49-44 1978 $10

BYRNE, DONN   Field of Honor.   1929.   Austin 82-288 1978 $8.50

BYRNE, DONN   The Foolish Matrons.   1920. First ed., frayed d.j.   Austin 82-289 1978 $12.50

BYRNE, DONN   Hangman's House.   New York, (1926). Illus., tan bds., vellum spine, 1st Amer. ed., 1st prtg., 1 of 350 signed by author, very good.   Bradley 49-45 1978 $15

BYRNE, DONN   Hangman's House.   1926. First ed., lg. paper ed., signed, ltd. to 350 copies.   Austin 82-290 1978 $47.50

BYRNE, DONN   Messer Marco Polo.   New York, 1921. Frontis., plts., brown-orange cloth, 1st ed., fine in rare dust jacket.   Bradley 49-47 1978 $50

BYRNE, DONN   O'Malley of Shanganagh.   1925. Illus., first ed., some cover stains.   Austin 82-292 1978 $10

BYRNE, DONN   O'Malley of Shanganagh.   1925. Illus., very good.   Austin 82-291 1978 $15

BYRNE, DONN   The Wind Bloweth.   New York, 1922. 2nd state, near fine.   Desmarais B-113 1978 $7.50

BYRNES, ROBERT F.   Anti-Semitism in Modern France.   New Brunswick, (1950). Vol. 1.   Biblo 251-688 1978 $15

BYROM, JOHN   Miscellaneous Poems.   Manchester, 1773. 2 vols., 8vo, 19th-century cloth.   P. M. Hill 142-249 1978 £45

BYRON, GEORGE GORDON   The Age of Bronze.   1823. 2nd. ed., modern 1/4 calf, marbled bds.   Eaton 45-82 1978 £9

BYRON, GEORGE GORDON   Beppo, a Venetian Story.   1818. 3rd. ed., rebound in grey bds., v.g.   Jarndyce 16-342 1978 £10.50

BYRON, GEORGE GORDON   Childe Harold's Pilgrimmage to the Dead Sea: Death on the Pale Horse: and Other Poems.   New York, 1818. Wrs., v.g.   Victoria 34-152 1978 $12.50

BYRON, GEORGE GORDON   Childe Harold's Pilgrimage.   A Romaunt by... New York: Harrison of Paris, (1931). 4to, illus., orig. pict. cloth, 1 of 660 copies, fine.   MacManus 238-805 1978 $40

BYRON, GEORGE GORDON   The Corsair, A Tale.   London, 1814. 8vo, orig. blue wrappers (neatly rebacked), cloth folding case, 1st ed., contemp. signature on the t.p., fine copy.   Ximenes 47-42 1978 $275

BYRON, GEORGE GORDON   The Deformed Transformed; a Drama.   1824. 2nd. ed., half title, half brown cloth, marbled bds., good.   Jarndyce 16-346 1978 £10.50

BYRON, GEORGE GORDON   Don Juan.   London, 1906. Titles printed in red & black, 2 vols., 4to, half brown levant morocco, cloth sides to match, gilt tops.   Traylen 88-128 1978 £36

BYRON, GEORGE GORDON   English Bards and Scotch Reviewers; A Satire. 1810, (1818?). 3rd. ed., 8vo, orig. bds., uncut, printed paper label on upper cover, slight wear to foot of spine, nice almost fine copy.   Fenning 32-48 1978 £12.50

BYRON, GEORGE GORDON   English Bards & Scotch Reviewers; a Satire. (1811). 4th. ed., half title, rebound in half calf, v.g.   Jarndyce 16-335 1978 £8.50

BYRON, GEORGE GORDON   English Bards, and Scotch Reviews; A Satire. 1811. 4th. ed., half-title, l.p., rebound in 1/4 calf.   Eaton 45-83 1978 £10

BYRON, GEORGE GORDON   Hebrew Melodies.   1815. 1st ed., 8vo, little spotting, wrapper, very good copy.   Fenning 32-49 1978 £28.50

BYRON, GEORGE GORDON   The Lament of Tasso.   1817. 3rd. ed., rebound in grey bds., v.g.   Jarndyce 16-340 1978 £10.50

BYRON, GEORGE GORDON   Lara, a Tale.   1814. Sm. 8vo, 1st ed., contemp. calf, gilt panelled back, gilt top, bkplt., nice copy.   Quaritch 979-70 1978 $105

BYRON, GEORGE GORDON   Lara, a Tale.   1814. Sm. 8vo, 1st ed., orig. drab bds., uncut, fine copy, signature dated September 1814.   Quaritch 979-71 1978 $160

BYRON, GEORGE GORDON   Lara, a Tale.   1814. 4th. ed., rebound in brown bds., good.   Jarndyce 16-336 1978 £12.50

BYRON, GEORGE GORDON   Letters and Journals of Lord Byron:.....   London, 1830. 2 vols., quarto, orig. dark green cloth, expertly rebacked preserving orig. spines and pr. paper labels, edges uncut, light spotting and rubbing of bindings, orig. spines faded, light foxing.   Bennett 7-22 1978 $250

BYRON, GEORGE GORDON   Manfred, A Dramatic Poem.   London, 1817. Demy octavo, full early calf, paneled in blind, ruled in gilt, marbled endpapers, bookplate of Oliver Britt, 1st ed., 2nd issue, fine, scarce.   Bennett 7-23 1978 $195

BYRON, GEORGE GORDON   Manfred, a Dramatic Tale.   1817. 1st. ed., rebound in half calf, handmarbled bds., v.g.   Jarndyce 16-341 1978 £22

BYRON, GEORGE GORDON   Manfred.   Fanfrolico Press, 1929. 4to, cloth, vellum spine, illus., t.e.g, paper is arches mould-made, watered blue silk.   Battery Park 1-99 1978 $100

BYRON, GEORGE GORDON   Marino Faliero, Doge of Venice.   1821. 1st ed., 1st issue, 8vo, wrapper, little light spotting, but very good copy.   Fenning 32-50 1978 £24

BYRON, GEORGE GORDON   Marino Faliero, Doge of Venice.   An Historical Tragedy, in Five Acts...   London, 1821. Orig. bds., hinges broken, spine rubbed, 1st ed., 1st issue.   MacManus 238-181 1978 $100

BYRON, GEORGE GORDON   Marino Faliero, Doge of Venice. An Historical Tragedy, in Five Acts. London, 1821. Orig. bds., lst ed., 2nd issue, bds. worn and soiled, hinges cracked, otherwise nice. MacManus 238-180 1978 $40

BYRON, GEORGE GORDON   Marino Faliero. 1821. 2nd. issue or 2nd. ed., lacking half-title, orig. bds., later rebacked, retaining orig. paper label. Eaton 45-85 1978 £10

BYRON, GEORGE GORDON   Mazeppa, a Poem. 1819. lst ed., lst issue, 8vo., wrapper, light spotting, very good copy. Fenning 32-51 1978 £14.50

BYRON, GEORGE GORDON   Mazeppa, a Poem. 1819. lst. ed., slight foxing, orig. diced calf, gilt borders, rebacked, v.g. Jarndyce 16-343 1978 £24

BYRON, GEORGE GORDON   Monody on the Death of the Rt. Hon. R. B. Sheridan. 1816. lst. ed., rebound in half calf, v.g. Jarndyce 16-337 1978 £25

BYRON, GEORGE GORDON   Ode to Napoleon Buonaparte. London, 1814. 8vo., disbound, 3rd ed. Ximenes 47-43 1978 $40

BYRON, GEORGE GORDON   Poems on Various Occasions. Newark, 1807. Full contemp. mottled calf, floral borders, gilt, inner dentelles gilt, marbled endpapers, lst ed., rare, only 100 copies prtd., fr. outer hinge cracked, fine, protective red cloth fldr., red half mor. slipcase. Bradley 49-50 1978 $1,650

BYRON, GEORGE GORDON   Poems. 1816. 8vo., lst ed., later wrs., internally dust soiled. Quaritch 979-69 1978 $55

BYRON, GEORGE GORDON   Poems. 1816. lst. ed., half title, rebound in half calf, marbled bds., good. Jarndyce 16-338 1978 £20

BYRON, GEORGE GORDON   Poems. 1816. 2nd. ed., rebound in grey bds., v.g. Jarndyce 16-339 1978 £12.50

BYRON, GEORGE GORDON   Poems. 1923. Orig. half vellum, gilt top, special ed., hand made paper, ltd. to 260 numbered copies, 8vo. Howes 194-693 1978 £12.50

BYRON, GEORGE GORDON   Poems of Lord Byron Selected and Arranged in Chronological Order. 1923. Eaton 45-186 1978 £5

BYRON, GEORGE GORDON   Poetical Works. 1855. Portrait, 6 vols., demy 8vo., full contemp. mor. Howes 194-692 1978 £55

BYRON, GEORGE GORDON   The Prisoner of Chillon. 1816. 8vo., lst ed., lst issue, orig. drab wrs., spine worn, good uncut copy, cloth case. Quaritch 979-72 1978 $315

BYRON, GEORGE GORDON   The Prisoner of Chillon and Other Poems. London, 1816. Wrs., lst issue, fine. MacManus 238-178 1978 $150

BYRON, GEORGE GORDON   The Prisoner of Chillon. (London), 1865. lst ed., chromolithographed by W.R. Tymms, large quarto, color plates, heavily decor. impressed gilt designs, some foxing, binding fine. Victoria 34-29 1978 $95

BYRON, GEORGE GORDON   Sardanapalus. 1821. 8vo., lst ed., orig. bds. uncut, worn & little foxed, bkplt. Quaritch 979-73 1978 $65

BYRON, GEORGE GORDON   Sardanapalus... 1821. lst. ed., half title, sm. tear repaired, uncut, fairly recent grey/green bds., paper label, good. Jarndyce 16-345 1978 £28

BYRON, GEORGE GORDON   Sardanapalus, The Two Foscari, Cain. 1821. lst. ed., half title, uncut, orig. grey bds., paper label, fine copy in orig. condition, Palmerston's copy, signed by him. Jarndyce 16-344 1978 £58

BYRON, GEORGE GORDON   Sardanapalus, a Tragedy... London, 1821. Orig. bds., lst ed., spine worn, covers detached, but internally fine. Mac-Manus 238-182 1978 $75

BYRON, GEORGE GORDON   The Siege of Corinth. A Poem. Parisina. A Poem. London, 1816. Orig. drap paper wrs., bottom of spine worn, uncut, lst ed., fine, fold. cloth case. MacManus 238-179 1978 $200

BYRON, GEORGE GORDON   The Works. 1830. 4 vols., sm. 8vo, frontis., some dampstaining, 1/4 leather. Eaton 45-86 1978 £15

BYRON, GEORGE GORDON   Works complete in one volume. London, 1837. Roy. 8vo., half red calf, frontis., spine sunned. K Books 244-58 1978 £9

BYRON, ROBERT   First Russia, Then Tibet. 1933. Coloured frontis., plts., 4to., t.e.g., near fine, first English ed. Bell Book 16-133 1978 £15

BYRON, ROBERT   The Road to Oxiana. 1950. Advance Proof copy, plts., publisher's drab wraps, very good. Bell Book 16-134 1978 £4

BYSSHE, EDWARD   The Art of English Poetry. 1737. Eighth ed., 2 vols. in 1, 12mo., contemp. rebacked. P. M. Hill 142-250 1978 £22

BYWATER, iNGRAM   Elenchus Librorum Vetustiorum apud xx Hospitantium. Oxford, 1911. Demy 8vo., half vellum, orig. wrappers bound in, uncut. Forster 130-312 1978 £15

BYWATER, RECTOR C.   The Great Pacific War. Boston, 1932. 8vo., d.w., orig. cloth. Morrill 241-73 1978 $7.50

C

C., C.   Mercy. (Liverpool, 1809). lst. ed., 8vo, disbound. Hannas 54-309 1978 £8.50

C., J.   The Coin Act. London, 1777. 8vo, disbound, lst ed., scarce. Ximenes 47-44 1978 $35

CABANIS, PIERRE JEAN GEORGES   Rapports du Physique et du Moral de l'Homme. Paris, 1802. lst ed., 8vo, 2 vols., contemp. boards. Gilhofer 75-17 1978 SFr 1,500

CABATON, A.   L'Indochine; Choix de textes prededes d'une etude. Paris, 1932. Illus., map, 8vo, orig. covers. Van der Peet 127-40 1978 Dfl 45

CABELL, JAMES BRANCH   The Certain Hour. London, 1917. 1st English ed., scarce in d.j., very good, Zane Grey's copy. Houle 10-57 1978 $35

CABELL, JAMES BRANCH   The Devil's Own Dear Son. New York, 1949. Ownership inscription, very fine in damaged d.w. Desmarais B-115 1978 $17.50

CABELL, JAMES BRANCH   The Eagle's Shadow. New York, 1904. Orig. cloth, some minor staining to back cover, a little rubbed, 1st issue, very good. MacManus 238-624 1978 $40

CABELL, JAMES BRANCH   Figures of Earth: a comedy of appearances. 1921. D.w., illus., fine, first English ed. Bell Book 17-138 1978 £5

CABELL, JAMES BRANCH   The First Gentleman of America. New York, 1942. Very fine in torn d.w. Desmarais B-116 1978 $27.50

CABELL, JAMES BRANCH   Gallantry, an 18th Century Dizain... New York, 1907. Illus. in color by Howard Pyle, 1st ed., 1st bind., lg. 8vo, nice. Americanist 102-96 1978 $45

CABELL, JAMES BRANCH   Gallantry. New York and London, 1907. 8vo, half calf with raised bands, tan cloth boards, color plates by Howard Pyle, uncut, t.e.g., lst ed., collector's cond. Desmarais 1-65 1978 $35

CABELL, JAMES BRANCH   The High Place: a Comedy of Disenchantment. 1923. D.w., illus., fine, first English ed. Bell Book 17-139 1978 £5

CABELL, JAMES BRANCH   Ladies and Gentlemen, A Parcel of Reconsiderations. New York, 1934. lst ed., fine, d.j. Ballinger 11-109 1978 $20.00

CABELL, JAMES BRANCH   The Line of Love. New York, 1905. Illus in color by Howard Pyle, orig. dec. cloth, 1st ed., fine. MacManus 238-625 1978 $35

CABELL, JAMES BRANCH   The Music from Behind the Moon. New York, 1926. Tall 4to, black boards, limited to 3,000 copies, wood engravings by Leon Underwood, in glassine wr., broken black box, lst ed., collector's cond. Desmarais 1-66 1978 $30

CABELL, JAMES BRANCH   The Music From Behind the Moon. New York, 1926. Ltd. ed., lst ed., wood engrav., fine, slipcase. Ballinger 11-110 1978 $30.00

CABELL, JAMES BRANCH   Preface to the Past. New York, 1936. lst ed., fine, d.j. Ballinger 11-112 1978 $20.00

CABELL, JAMES BRANCH   Smirt. New York, 1934. lst ed., fine, d.j. Ballinger 11-113 1978 $12.50

CABELL, JAMES BRANCH   Smirt. New York, 1935. lst ed., fine, d.j. Ballinger 11-114 1978 $15.00

CABELL, JAMES BRANCH   Some of Us. New York, 1930. 1 of 1295, fine, cracked slipcase, orig. glassine wraps. Ballinger 11-115 1978 $35.00

CABELL, JAMES BRANCH   Some of Us; an essay in epitaphs. New York, 1930. First U.S. ed., no. 93 of 1295 copies signed by author, linen-backed bds., very good. Bell Book 16-135 1978 £25

CABELL, JAMES BRANCH   Something About Eve. New York, 1927. lst ed. fine, d.j. Ballinger 11-116 1978 $15.00

CABELL, JAMES BRANCH   Something About Eve. New York, 1927. Blue bds. & linen, lst ed., 1 of 850 signed. Bradley 49-52 1978 $25

CABELL, JAMES BRANCH   Something About Eve: a Comedy of Fig-leaves. 1927. Cloth, fine, slightly worn d.w., first English ed. Bell Book 17-140 1978 £10

CABELL, JAMES BRANCH   Something About Eve. New York, 1929. Illus., 4 to., orig. gilt stamped black cloth, uncut, fine. Houle 10-252 1978 $45

CABELL, JAMES BRANCH   Special Delivery. New York, 1933. lst ed., fine, d.j. Ballinger 11-118 1978 $10.00

CABELL, JAMES BRANCH   The Way of Ecben. New York, 1929. 1st imp., fine, glassine wrap, slipcase. Ballinger 11-119 1978 $10.00

CABELL, JAMES BRANCH   The Way of Ecben. New York, 1929. Lg. paper ed., signed, vellum back, boxed. Biblo 251-418 1978 $47.50

CABELL, JAMES BRANCH   The White Robe. New York, 1928. Tall 4to, cover is modern adaptation of Medieval leather and oaken-board binding, fore and bottom edges uncut, vol. designed by William Dana Orcutt, mint, box, lst ed. Desmarais 1-67 1978 $25

CABELL, JAMES BRANCH   The White Robe. New York, (1928). 4to., illus. by Robert E. Locher, ltd. ed., spine scuffed. Biblo 251-419 1978 $16.50

CABELL, SEARS WILSON   The "Bulldog" Longstreet at Gettysburg and Chickamauga. Atlanta, 1938. Wrs., Bell Wiley's copy. Broadfoot's 44-63 1978 $7

CABEO, NICCOLO   Philosophia Magnetica. Ferrara, 1629. Contemp. vellum, upper cover buckled, head of spine little wormed & light damp-staining, but fine copy, lst ed. Norman 5-47 1978 $1,500

THE CABINET Album. 1830. 8vo., blue calf, gilt. P. M. Hill 142-61 1978 £12

LE CABINET du Naturaliste. Paris, (c. 1790-1815). 6 vols. in 3, marbled boards, vellum, soiled and time-darkened, occasional foxing, 8vo, orig. cloth. Book Chest 17-20 1978 $70

THE CABINET of Genius.... London, 1787. Quarto, period-style tree calf, newer leather spine, raised spine bands, gilt, very good. Bennett 7-25 1978 $150

CABLE, GEORGE WASHINGTON   The Amateur Garden. 1914. Illus., lst ed. Austin 82-1158 1978 $97.50

CABLE, GEORGE WASHINGTON   The Creoles of Louisiana. New York, 1884. 1st ed., pict. cloth, illus. MacManus 239-1818 1978 $35

CABLE, GEORGE WASHINGTON   The Grandissimes. New York, 1880. 8vo., lst ed. Morrill 239-483 1978 $25

CABLE, GEORGE WASHINGTON   Kincaid's Battery. New York, 1908. Cloth, lst ed., illus. by Alonzo Kimball. Hayman 73-174 1978 $8.50

CABLE, GEORGE WASHINGTON   Old Creole Days. New York, 1879. 12mo, pict. orig. dark peacock blue cloth, lst ed., inscription on flyleaf, fine. Duschnes 220-58 1978 $50

CABLE, GEORGE WASHINGTON   "Posson Jone" and Pere Raphael. New York, 1909. Illus. in color, Bell Wiley's copy. Broadfoot's 44-883 1978 $25

CABLE, GEORGE WASHINGTON   Strange True Stories of Louisiana.   New York, 1889. Illus., orig. cloth, 1st ed., covers slightly soiled. MacManus 238-433 1978 $30

CABLE, GEORGE WASHINGTON   Strong Hearts. New York, 1899. Spine faded, near fine. Desmarais B-117 1978 $15

CABLE, JOHN RAY   Bank of the State of Missouri. 1923. Paper, 1st ed. Austin 80-463 1978 $12.50

CABLE, MAURICE L.   William Gudger. Revolutionary War Soldier and Pioneer. N.P., n.d. New Cloth. Broadfoot 50-26 1978 $12

CABOT, A.   Attaque et Defense sur le Terrain. Paris, 1888. 8vo., half cloth, frontis., orig. cover wrapped up. Van der Peet H-64-601 1978 Dfl 35

CABOT, RICHARD C.   Case Teaching in Medicine. Boston, 1907. Rittenhouse 49-123 1976 $10

CABRERA DE CORDOBA, LUIS   Filipe secundo Rey de Espana. Madrid, 1619. Folio, contemp. limp vellum, 1st ed. Gilhofer 74-58 1978 sFr 1,500

CACCIA, ANTONIO   Europa ed America Scene Della Vita Dal 1848 al 1850. Monaco, 1850. Original cloth, 1st ed., very scarce. Ginsberg 14-88 1978 $125

CADBURY, W. A.   Labour in Portuguese West Africa. London, 1909. Folding map, cr. 8vo, orig. cloth. K Books 239-78 1978 £10

CADDEO, R.   La Tipografia Elvetica di Capolago, Uomini-Vicende, Tempi. Milan, 1931. Ltd. to 1000 copies, plts., demy 4to., half parchment. Forster 130-313 1978 £30

CADMAN, S. PARKES   Christianity and the State. 1924. Austin 79-112 1978 $8.50

CADY, ANNIE COLE   History of Pennsylvania in Words of One Syllable. Chicago, 1889. 1st ed., orig. cloth-backed color pict. boards, map & illus., 8vo. Americanist 101-30 1978 $15

CAESAR, GAIUS JULIUS   De Bellis Gallico et Civili Pompejano, nec non A. Hirtii.... 1737. 4to., vellum, illus., very good, plts. King 7-339 1978 £50

CAESAR, GAIUS JULIUS   Commentaria.... Venice, 1517. Small folio, Roman letter, maps, woodcuts, old French red mor. extra back richly gilt, gilt edges, by Derome, Musgrave arms in gold on sides. Quaritch 978-25 1978 $1,250

CAESAR, GAIUS JULIUS   I Commentari, Nuovamente Trad. da M. Francesco Baldelli in Linqua Thoscana. Venice, 1558. Vellum, maps, illus., hole in center of spine, lightly stained. Allen 234-147 1978 $25

CAESAR GAIUS, JULIUS   C. Julii Caesaris Commentarii... Venetis, 1576. Octavo, 19th cent.calf over bds., woodcuts, maps. Bennett 20-34 1978 $150

CAESAR, GAIUS JULIUS   I Commentari, con le Figure in Rame de gli Alloggiamenti. 1618. Engr. plt., half calf, lower portion badly stained. Allen 234-1511 1978 $25

CAESAR, GAIUS JULIUS   The Commentaries of C. Julius Caesar.... 1677. Plts., sm. folio, contemp. mottled calf, fine, John Evelyn's copy. F. Edwards 1013-289 1978 £200

CAESAR, GAIUS JULIUS   Commentaries of His Wars in Gallia... 1677. Trans. into English, old calf, joints cracked. Allen 234-143 1978 $75

CAESAR, GAIUS JULIUS   Commentaries of His Wars in Gallia... 1695. Old calf, one cover detached, one broken, marginal wormholes. Allen 234-144 1978 $50

CAESAR, GAIUS JULIUS   Opera, quae extant cum notis et animadversionbus D. Vossi.... Amstelodami, 1677. Engraved title, contemp. panelled calf, spine worn, 8vo. George's 635-450 1978 £7.50

CAESAR, GAIUS JULIUS   Opera, accuratissime cum libris editis et Mss. optimis collata, recognita et correcta accesserunt annotations S. Clarke. 1720. Engraved portrait, contemp. panelled calf, 8vo. George's 635-452 1978 £5.25

CAESAR, GAIUS JULIUS   Quae Extant. Philadelphia, 1804. Editio prima Americana, old calf, maps, lacks front flyleaves, fore-edge slightly stained. Allen 234-140 1978 $7.50

CAESARIUS OF HEISTERBACH   The Dialogue on Miracles. 1929. Illus., 2 vols., 8vo. George's 635-1041 1978 £10.50

IL CAFFE, ossia brevi e varij discorsi distribuiti in foglij periodici. Brescia, 1765-1766. Very rare 1st ed., 4to, 2 vols., contemp. boards, uncut, fine. Gilhofer 75-18 1978 SFr 1,600

CAHN, HERMAN   Capital To-Day. 1918. 3rd ed. Austin 80-464 1978 $10

CAIN, GEORGES   Anciens Theatres de Paris. Paris, 1906. Illus., 8vo., orig. wrs., binding broken along backstrip, otherwise nice, 1st ed. Morrill 239-322 1978 $15

CAIN, JAMES M.   The Butterfly. New York, 1947. Vg in sl. creased dw. Bernard 5-40 1978 $10

CAIN, JAMES M.   Love's Lovely Counterfeit. New York, 1942. Cloth, nice, 1st ed. Hayman 72-182 1978 $8.50

CAIN, JAMES M.   Love's Lovely Counterfeit. New York, 1942. Vg in worn dw. Bernard 5-43 1978 $12.50

CAIN, JAMES M.   Mildred Pierce. 1943. Very good, d.w., first English ed. Bell Book 16-136 1978 £12

CAIN, JAMES M.   Mildred Pierce. London, (1943). Good in chipped dw. Bernard 5-46 1978 $15

CAIN, JAMES M.   The Moth. New York, 1948. Fine in dw. Bernard 5-47 1978 $12.50

CAIN, JAMES M.   Our Government. 1930. Austin 82-293 1978 $20

CAIN, JAMES M.   Past All Dishonor. New York, 1946. Signed by author, bookplt, good. Bernard 5-48 1978 $20

CAIN, JAMES M.   The Postman Always Rings Twice. NY, ND. Vg in dw. Bernard 5-49 1978 $8.50

CAIN, JAMES M.   Serenade. NY, 1937. Signed by Cain, spine cocked; fair to good. Bernard 5-51 1978 $15.00

CAIN, JAMES M.   Three of a Kind. n.d. Very good, worn & repaired d.w., first English ed. Bell Book 16-229 1978 £12.50

CAIN, JAMES M.   Three of a Kind. New York, 1943. Name, vg in chipped dw. Bernard 5-52 1978 $12.50

CAINE, HALL   The Bondsman. London, 1890. 1st ed., orig. cloth, fine 2 page letter, signed by Caine, 1st issue, 3 vols. Greene 78-21 1978 $70

CAINE, HALL   The Deemster. London, 1913. New Impression, very good or better. Limestone 9-47 1978 $7.50

CAINE, HALL   The Prime Minister. 1918. Pres. copy to Winston Churchill, 8vo, orig. paper wrappers, spine worn & defective. Sawyer 298-65 1978 £95

CAIRNES, JOHN ELLIOTT   Political Essays. 1873. 1st. ed., 8vo, orig. cloth, fine copy. Fenning 32-52 1978 £16.50

CAIRNES, JOHN ELLIOT   The Slave Power: Its Character, Career and Probable Designs... New York, 1862. 2nd. ed. Baldwins' 51-378 1978 $17.50

CAIRNES, JOHN ELLIOTT   Some Leading Principles of Political Economy. London, 1874. 1st Eng. ed., rubbed around edges, otherwise good. Austin 80-465 1978 $37.50

CAIRNS, H.   Masterpieces of Painting from the National Gallery of Art. Washington, 1945. Coloured plts., folio. George's 635-36 1978 £5.25

CAIRNS, MARY LYONS   Grand Lake: The Pioneers. Denver, 1946.
Cloth, map, illus., 1st ed., fine, autographed by author, d.w. Dykes 35-101
1978 $12.50

CAIUS, JOHN   The Annals of Gonville and Caius College.
1904. 8vo, wrappers, good. Upcroft 10-24 1978 £8

CALAMANDREI, PIERO   Eulogy of Judges. Princeton, 1942. Biblo
BL781-804 1978 $7.50

CALAMY, EDWARD   The Godly Mans Ark. 1657. First ed., sm. 8vo.
contemp. sheep, rebacked, remains of orig. backstrip preserved, some age-staining,
recent printed label. Howes 194-24 1978 £30

CALCUTTA: A Poem. 1811. First ed., frontispiece, half mor., cr. 8vo., gilt
top, other edges untrimmed. Howes 194-194 1978 £15

THE CALCUTTA Stable Directory:.... Calcutta, 1805. Sm. 8vo, very worn
leather, lacking 1st blank, endpaper torn and detached, orig. cloth. Book Chest
17-19 1978 $48

CALDCEUGH, ALEXANDER   Travels in South America, During the Years 1819-
20-21. London, 1825. 2 vols., 1st ed., 8vo., handcolored frontis, plts., foxed,
some with sm. library stamp, fldg. map, newly bound in 3/4 tan calf, marbled bds.
Current 24-176 1978 $190

CALDECOTT, RANDOLPH   Collection of Pictures and Songs. London, (1881).
1st collected ed., plates and illus. in color, colored pictorial cloth, very good.
Victoria 34-127 1978 $42.50

CALDECOTT, RANDOLPH   R. Caldecott's Collection of Pictures & Songs.
n.d. 2 vols., coloured plts., 4to., orig. pict. cloth, very good, first English ed.
Bell Book 16-480 1978 £45

CALDECOTT, RANDOLPH   Gleanings from the Graphic. London, 1889.
1st ed., plates, fine copy, board edges rubbed and spine ends taped. Victoria
34-130 1978 $35

CALDECOTT, RANDOLPH   "Graphic" Pictures, Complete Edition. London,
1891. Ltd. to 1250 copies, oblong 4to, orig. cloth, worn, spine damaged, front
free end-paper missing, some leaves of text loose. Sexton 7-10 1978 £35

CALDECOTT, RANDOLPH   "Graphic" Pictures. London, 1891. Oblong
large quarto, sepia illus., contents fine, cracked inner hinges, cloth covers dulled
and rubbed. Victoria 34-128 1978 $95

CALDECOTT, RANDOLPH   Randolph Caldecott's Picture Books. London,
1878-84. 7 vols., thin small quarto, oblong quarto, pict. wr. Totteridge 29-21
1978 $125

CALDERON DE LA BARCA, PEDRO   Life's a Dream: The Great Theatre of the
World. 1856. 8vo., orig. orange cloth, fair. P. M. Hill 142-251 1978 £16

CALDERON DE LA BARCA, PEDRO   Love the Greatest Enchantment... 1861.
4to, orig. violet cloth, gilt, fine copy. Fenning 32-53 1978 £14.50

CALDERON DE LA BARCA, PEDRO   Mysteries of Corpus Christi. Dublin, 1867.
Sm. sq. 8vo, orig. blue cloth, gilt, edges gilt, signed "J.L." on spine, fine copy.
Fenning 32-54 1978 £14.50

CALDWELL, ERSKINE   The Bastard. New York, (1929). Illus., orig.
cloth, 1st ed., 1 of 1,100 no. copies, signed by Caldwell, spine slightly faded.
MacManus 238-626 1978 $75

CALDWELL, ERSKINE   A House in the Uplands. New York, (1946).
Vg in chipped dw. Bernard 5-54 1978 $10

CALDWELL, ERSKINE   Journeyman. New York, 1935. First U.S. ed.,
one of 1475 numbered copies, very good, worn slipcase. Bell Book 16-138 1978
£10

CALDWELL, ERSKINE   Journeyman. New York, 1935. Red cloth, 1st
ed., 1 of 1475 copies, slipcase. Bradley 49-53 1978 $25

CALDWELL, ERSKINE   This Very Earth. New York, 1948. Near mint
in torn d.w. Desmarais B-118 1978 $12.50

CALDWELL, ERSKINE   Tobacco Road. New York, 1932. First U.S.
ed., good, upper cover somewhat stained. Bell Book 16-139 1978 $12.50

CALDWELL, J. E.   Songs of the Pines. Toronto, 1895. Inscr'd &
signed by author. Hood 117-786 1978 $22.50

CALDWELL, WILLIAM B.   Address Delivered Before the Graduates of the
Erodelphian Society, of the Miami University, at Its Fourteenth Anniversary,
August 7th, A. D. 1839. Oxford, 1839. Disbound. Hayman 73-497 1978
$12.50

CALEF, ROBERT   More Wonders of the Invisible World:... London,
1700. Rebound in 1880's with leather backstrip and gold lettering, front flyleaf
loose. Nestler Rare 78-6 1978 $850

CALENDAR of the Howard Collection of Texana. Austin, 1944. Autographed by
Dr. William E. Howard. Jenkins 116-182 1978 $10

CALENDAR of Twelve Travelers Through The Pass of the North. El Paso, 1947.
Pictorial wr., portraits by Tom Lea. Jenkins 116-614 1978 $12.50

A CALENDAR of Verse. 1912. Engrav. frontispiece, orig. vellum gilt, watered-
silk doublures, slip case, only 20 copies printed, 8vo. Howes 194-699 1978 £15

CALEY, PERCY B.   Child Life in Colonial Western Pennsylvania.
N.P., n.d. (circa 1926). Wrs. Hayman 73-602 1978 $7.50

CALHOUN, JOHN C.   The Works of.... New York, 1854. 6 vols.,
one-half simulated leather, 3 spines badly chipped, some hinges cracked, some
hinges repaired, Bell Wiley's copy. Broadfoot's 44-920 1978 $60

CALHOUN, JOHN C.   Works. New York, 1874-1870. 6 vols., 8vo.,
ex-lib., orig. cloth. Morrill 241-76 1978 $30

CALHOUN, S. F.   Fifteen Years in the Church of Rome. Lowell,
1886. Austin 79-114 1978 $17.50

CALHOUN, W. L.   History of the 42nd Regiment, Georgia Volunteers,
Confederate States Army, Infantry. Atlanta, 1900. Original wrs. bound in,
Bell Wiley's copy. Broadfoot's 44-450 1978 $65

CALI, F.   l'Art des Conquistadors. Paris, 1950. 8vo.,
cloth, plts., illus. Van der Peet H-64-109 1978 Dfl 35

CALIFF, JOSEPH M.   Record of the Services of the Seventh Regiment,
U.S. Colored Troops, From Sept. 1863 to Nov. 1866. Providence, 1878. Wrs.
soiled & frayed, interior good, Bell Wiley's copy. Broadfoot's 44-685 1978 $40

CALIFORNIA. CONSTITUTION of the State of California. Sacramento, 1879.
8vo, sewn, very good unopened copy. Ximenes 47-45 1978 $100

CALIFORNIA. LAWS   An Act Empowering the Governor to Appoint
Commissioners of Deeds and Defining the Duties of Such Officers. San Jose, 1850.
Signed in type by Bigler, Burnett, and W. Van Voorhies, also A.l.s. from Van
Voorhies to Samuel Ward. Ginsberg 14-69 1978 $600

CALIFORNIA and the Expositions. (Chicago, 1915?). Wrs. Hayman 73-154
1978 $7.50

CALIFORNIA Indian Nights Entertainments. Glendale, 1930. Illus., map, 1st
ed. Biblo BL781-73 1978 $12.50

CALIFORNIEN, en Skildring af Landet, dess Klimat och Guldminor Jemte Rad for
Utvandrare om de Fordelaktigaste Satten att Nedsatta Sig Derstades... Stockholm,
1859. Map and plate, original printed wr., rare. Ginsberg 14-89 1978 $200

CALISCH, EDWARD N.   The Jew in English Literature. 1909. Austin 79-115 1978 $8.50

CALKINS, CLINCH   Some Folks Won't Work. New York, (1930).
1st ed. Biblo 251-318 1978 $10

CALKINS, EARNEST ELMO   Business the Civilizer. 1928. Austin 80-466
1978 $8.50

CALKINS, EARNEST ELMO   A Sentimental Pilgrimage. New York, Marchbanks Press, 1922. 1 of 200 numbered copies, tall thin 8vo., orig. bds., uncut,
very good. Americanist 103-117 1978 $20

CALL, F. O.   Sonnets for Youth. Toronto, 1944. Card cover.
Hood 117-787 1978 $10

CALL, HUGHIE   Golden Fleece. Cambridge, 1942. Pic. cloth, map end sheets, 1st ed., fine copy inscr. by author, d.w., very scarce. Dykes 34-271 1978 $25

CALLAGHAN, MORLEY   The Varsity Story. Toronto, 1948. Illus., ex-lib. Hood 116-455 1978 $15

CALLAGHAN, MORLEY   The Varsity Story. Toronto, 1948. Fine, d.j., orig. binding. Wolfe 39-58 1978 $15

CALLAHAN, JAMES M.   History of the Making of Morgantown, West Virginia. 1926. Illus., maps. MacManus 239-1136 1978 $25

CALLANDER, JOHN   Two Ancient Scottish Poems; The Gaberlunzie Man, and Christ's Kirk on the Green. Edinburgh, 1782. Rebound in bds., buckram spine and paper label. Eaton 45-87 1978 £20

CALLAWAY, J. S.   Sybaris. 1950. Pencilled notes. Allen 234-1512 1978 $7.50

CALLENDER, L.   The Windmill. London, 1923. 1st ed., frontis., illus., cloth over bds., very good or better. Limestone 9-324 1978 $25

CALLENDER, L.   The Windmill. 1923. Illus., colour plts. by Rackham & Lovat Fraser, 4to., cloth-backed bds., very good, first English ed. Bell Book 16-020 1978 £4.50

CALLOW, EDWARD   The Phynodderree and Other Legends of the Isle of Man. London, (1882). 1st ed., plates and woodcuts by W. J. Watson, handsome gilt and black impressed designs, very good, scarce. Victoria 34-131 1978 $30

CALMETTE, JOSEPH   Louis XI, Jean II et la Revolution Catalane, 1461-73. 1902. Half calf, top of one joint cracked. Allen 234-1144 1978 $15

CALOT, F.   Guide Pratique de Bibliographie. Paris, 1950. 12mo., back wrapper loose, 2nd ed. Forster 130-316 1978 £4

CALTHROP, D. C.   English Costume Painted & Described. London, 1926. Thick 8vo, orig. cloth, plts., illus. in colour. Sexton 7-11 1978 £6

CALTHROP, HENRY   The Liberties, Usages and Customes of the City of London.... London, 1642. Sm. 4to, marble wrappers. Traylen 88-71 1978 £34

CALVERLEY, C. S.   Complete Works. 1910. Portrait, half crimson mor., gilt top, 8vo. Howes 194-700 1978 £7.50

CALVERT, F.   The Isle of Wight Illustrated, in a Series of Coloured Views, Engraved...by Mr. Percy Roberts... 1846. 4to., sepia lithograph frontis., plts., half green mor., gilt edges. Quaritch 983-307 1978 $960

CALVI, IGNAZIO   l'Architettura Militare di Leonardo. Milan, 1943. 8vo., illus., orig. prtd. wrs., very good copy. Norman 5-L32 1978 $45

CALVIN, JEAN   Institutione della Religion Christiana di Messer Giovanni Calvino. Geneva, 1557. Sm. 4to., olf half calf, spine defective, very rare first Italian ed., rather good copy. Schafer 19-9 1978 sFr 3300

CALVIN, JEAN   Institutio Christiana Religionis, ... Genevae, 1618. Octavo, half early-style calf over marbled boards, spine gilt ruled, title gilt. Bennett 20-35 1978 $75

CALVIN, ROSS   Sky Determines. 1948. First ed., d.j. Austin 82-295 1978 $17.50

CALY, CHARLES P.   The Settlement of the Jews in North America. New York, 1893. Austin 79-187 1978 $27.50

CAM, H. M.   Liberties and Communities in Medieval England. Cambridge, 1944. Maps, rebound ex-lib. copy, 8vo. Upcroft 12-61 1978 £4

CAMBELL, JOHN   Memoirs of David Nasmith. 1841. Portrait, post 8vo., stain on front cover. George's 635-1100 1978 £10.50

CAMBELL, M. F.   Merry-Go-Round. Toronto, 1946. Card cover. Hood 117-789 1978 $12.50

CAMBRIDGE, ADA   Fidelis. New York, 1895. 1st Amer. ed., quarter calf, marbled boards, edges rubbed. Greene 78-160 1978 $10

CAMBRIDGE, RICHARD OWEN   The Scribleriad: An Heroic Poem in Six Books. 1751. 1st. ed., 4to, engraved frontispiece, wide margined copy, lower margins very slightly discoloured by damp, half calf, paper-marbled bds. Jarndyce 16-50 1978 £48

CAMBRIDGE, RICHARD OWEN   The Scribleriad. 1751. 4to., contemp. half calf, neatly rebacked, marbled sides, frontispiece, plts. P. M. Hill 142-252 1978 £70

CAMBRIDGE, RICHARD OWEN   The Works. 1803. 4to., early 19th-century blue mor., gilt, very fair, plts. P. M. Hill 142-253 1978 £60

CAMBRIDGE, RICHARD OWEN   The Works...Including Several Pieces Never Before Published... London, 1803. 4to., illus., plts., full contemp. calf, spine defective, 1st ed., pres. copy, internally fine copy. MacManus 238-108 1978 $40

CAMBRIDGE Essays. 1855. 8vo., contemp. calf. P. M. Hill 142-64 1978 £18

CAMBRIDGE History of American Literature. 1819-1921. 4 vols., buckram, 2 spines darkened, bookplates, few lib. stamps. Eaton 45-89 1978 £20

CAMBRIDGE Medieval History, Vol. 8, Close of the Middle Ages. Cambridge, 1936. Maps. George's 635-572 1978 £8.25

CAMBRIDGE Modern History. Cambridge, 1905-25. Complete set with Atlas, 14 vols., qtr. green mor., spines faded, cloth sides of 2 vols. stained. George's 635-573 1978 £45

CAMBRIDGE Modern History. Cambridge, 1934. Cheap reissue, no atlas done, 13 vols. George's 635-574 1978 £25

CAMDEN, WILLIAM   Annales Rerum Anglicarum et Hibernicarum, Regnante Elizabetha. Amsterdam, 1677. Engr. portr., blind-stamped calf with gold stamped heraldic device, joints broken. Allen 234-1147 1978 $75

CAMDEN, WILLIAM   Camden's Britannia. London, 1695. Trans. into English, folio, unnumbered leaves, maps, plts., old orig. binding scuffed & worn, near perfect copy, contents nearly pristine, scarce. Current 24-209 1978 $2250

CAMDEN, WILLIAM   Camden's Britannia, Newly Translated into English: With Large Additions and Improvements. London, 1695. 1st. ed. of Gibson's translation, folio, hand coloured engraved frontispiece portrait, engraved plts., folding maps, contemporary speckled calf, neatly rebacked, morocco label gilt, bookplt. of Duke of Norfolk. Deighton 5-114 1978 £1,550

CAMDEN, WILLIAM   Remaines of a Greater Worke, Concerning Britaine... London, 1605. 1st. ed., 4to, old half calf, rebacked, some water-stains, gutter of last 2 leaves repaired. Hannas 54-42 1978 £65

CAMERARIUS, IOANNES RUDOLPHUS   Horarum Natalium Centuriae I & II, Sive Narratio Historica Variorum in Vita Casuum, Mirabilium Naturae. Frankfurt, 1610. 4to., 1/2 calf, over marbled bds. Salloch 345-36 1978 $175

CAMERON, CHARLES A.   A Manual of Hygiene, Public and Private and Compendium of Sanitary Laws... Dublin & London, 1874. 1st. & only ed., illus., 8vo, recent bds., nice copy. Fenning 32-55 1978 £9.50

CAMERON, G. POULETT   Personal Adventures and Excursions in Georgia, Circassia, and Russia. London, 1845. 1st. ed., 2 vols., half calf, gilt backs. Deighton 5-115 1978 £50

CAMERON, J.   Our Tropical Posessions in Malayan India... 1865. Double pg. coloured frontis, tinted plts., orig. green cloth, gilt, 8vo, recased, slight foxing, pres. copy. Edwards 1012-160 1978 £45

CAMERON, LUCY LYTTELTON (BUTT)   Memoirs of Emma and Her Nurse... London, n.d. 11th ed., engr. frontis. & title page, marbled bds., lea. spine with light edge cracks, endpaper gone, very good. Victoria 34-132 1978 $15

CAMERON, LUCY LYTTELTON (BUTT)   The Three Flower-Pots. London, 1847. New ed., chapbook, illus., very good. Victoria 34-133 1978 $7.50

CAMERON, LUCY LYTTELTON (BUTT)   The Use of Talents. 1837. 1st ed., half calf, little rubbed, spine gilt, label, good. Jarndyce 16-350 1978 £18.50

CAMERON, NORMAN   Forgive Me, Sire. 1950. Covers somewhat soiled, good, wraps, signed by the author, first English ed. Bell Book 16-140 1978 £4.50

CAMERON, VERNEY LOVETT   Across Africa. New York, 1877. Map in pocket, 33 plts. & illus., orig. gilt cloth, recased & backstrip laid down, 8vo. K Books 239-80 1978 £33

CAMERON, W. A.   Rainbows Through the Rain; Yorkminster Sermons. Toronto, 1938. Hood 116-286 1978 $7.50

CAMERON, WILLIAM   Poems on Various Occasions. Edinburgh, 1780. Sm. 8vo., new full panelled calf antique, only ed., scarce. P. M. Hill 142-254 1978 £45

CAMERON, WILLIAM J.   The Voice of a Business. Philadelphia, Ayer Press, 1935. Austin 80-468 1978 $10

CAMILLI, CAMILLO   Imprese illustri di diversi, coi discorsi. Venice, 1586. 1st ed., 4to, 3 parts in one vol., old vellum. Gilhofer 75-19 1978 SFr 1,100

CAMM, F. U.   Newnes Television and Short-Wave Handbook. (1934). 8vo., plts., numerous text illus., orig. cloth. Quaritch 977-210 1978 $40

CAMO, P.   Maillol mon Ami. Lausanne, 1950. 8vo., orig. covers, illus., some in color. Van der Peet H-64-14 1978 Dfl 40

CAMOENS, LUIS DE   The Lusiad. Oxford, 1776. Lg. 4to., contemp. calf, rebacked, fine, first ed. P. M. Hill 142-257 1978 £55

CAMOENS, LUIS DE   The Lusiad. 1798. 3rd ed., 2 vols., half cloth, faded, 8vo. George's 635-1272 1978 £5

CAMOENS, LUIS DE   Poems, from the Portuguese. 1803. Sm. 8vo., contemp. calf, portrait. P. M. Hill 142-255 1978 £15

CAMOENS, LUIS DE   Poems from the Portuguese. 1805. Fourth ed., sm. 8vo., contemp. blue mor., gilt, g.e., portrait. P. M. Hill 142-256 1978 £18

CAMP, CHARLES L.   Kit Carson in California: With Extracts from His Own Story. Cleveland, 1922. Illus., original wr., one of 150 copies. Ginsberg 14-229 1978 $15

CAMP, PHINEAS   Poems of the Mohawk Valley, and on Scenes in Palestine. Utica, 1859. 12mo., 1st ed. Morrill 239-547 1978 $7.50

THE CAMPAIGN of One Day: A Poem, in Two Cantos. London, 1816. 8vo, disbound, 1st ed., scarce. Ximenes 47-247 1978 $30

THE CAMPAIGN of 1760 in Canada. Quebec, 1887. Orig. printed wrappers. Wolfe 39-460 1978 $15

CAMPAN, MME. JEANNE LOUISE HENRIETTE (GENEST)   Memoirs of the Private Life of Marie Antoinette. New York, (1917). 2 vols., illus., covers dull & rubbed, contents fine. Biblo 247-712 1978 $20

CAMPAN, MME. JEANNE LOUISE HENRIETTE (GENEST)   The Private Journal of. 1825. 8vo., contemp. calf, hinges cracked. P.M. Hill 142-65 1978 £12

CAMPANA, GIOVANNI PIETRO   Antiche opere in plastica. Rome, 1842-1852. Very rare orig. ed., contemp. half-calf, lightly rubbed, orig. pr. wr. bound-in. Gilhofer 75-20 1978 SFr 1,200

CAMPANELLA, THOMAS   De Sensu Rerum Et Magia, Libri Quatuor. Paris, 1637. 4to., vellum, dedicated to Richelieu. Salloch 345-37 1978 $450

CAMPBELL, MAJOR-GENERAL   Standing Orders, As Given Out and Enforced by the Late Major-General Robert Craufurd.... 1861. 16mo., orig. printed wrs., slightly worn. F. Edwards 1013-263 1978 £30

CAMPELL, ALEXANDER   Speech of Sir Alex. Campell on the Second Reading of a Bill to Incorporate the Pacific Railway Company. Ottawa, (1881). Prtd. wrs., frayed. Wolfe 39-471 1978 $40

CAMPBELL, ARCHIBALD   Lexiphanes, a Dialogue. 1783. Contemp. sheep, joints weak, third ed., sm. 8vo. Howes 194-336 1978 £25

CAMPBELL, ARCHIBALD J.   Nests and Eggs of Australian Birds Including the Geographical Distribution of the Species and Popular Observations Thereon. Sheffield, 1900. Map, coloured plts., photo illus., thick roy. 8vo., fine copy. Traylen 88-550 1978 £120

CAMPBELL, AUSTIN   They Shall Build Anew. Toronto, 1944. Card cover. Hood 117-788 1978 $7.50

CAMPBELL, D.   Sacramental Meditations on the Sufferings and Death of Christ. Glasgow, 1769. 12mo., calf, rubbed, unlettered. George's 635-1042 1978 £5

CAMPBELL, D. H.   The Structure and Development of Mosses and Ferns. New York, 1918. 3rd. ed., numerous illus., 8vo. Traylen 88-551 1978 £6

CAMPBELL, DOUGLAS   The Puritan in Holland, England, and America. New York, 1892. 2 vols., cloth, 1st ed., name on t.p. Hayman 72-90 1978 $15

CAMPBELL, DOUGLAS   The Title of the Texas and Pacific Railroad Co. to the Property of the Memphis, El Paso, and Pacific Railroad Co. Washington, 1878. Printed wr. Jenkins 116-1126 1978 $37.50

CAMPBELL, DUDLEY M.   A History of Oneonta. Oneonta, 1906. Plts., 1st prtg. Butterfield 21-341 1978 $7.50

CAMPBELL, DUGALD   Wanderings in Wildest Africa. London, 1931. 8vo, orig. cloth, 2 maps, 28 illus. K Books 239-83 1978 £6

CAMPBELL, DUNCAN   Nova Scotia, in its Historical, Mercantile, and Industrial Relations... Montreal, 1873. 1st ed., orig. cloth, recased, scarce, nice copy. MacManus 239-78 1978 $55

CAMPBELL, DUNCAN   Nova Scotia in its Historical, Mercantile and Industrial Relations. Montreal, 1873. Orig. cloth binding. Hood's 115-203 1978 $60

CAMPBELL, GEORGE   A Dissertation on Miracles. Edinburgh, 1766. 12mo., contemp. sheep, gilt back. P. M. Hill 142-143 1978 £45

CAMPBELL, GEORGE   A Dissertation on Miracles. Edinburgh, 1797. Third ed., 2 vols., 8vo., orig. bds., uncut, backstrips and hinges rather worn, good. P. M. Hill 142-144 1978 £30

CAMPBELL, GEORGE   Log Letters From "The Challenger". London, 1876. 1st. ed., 8vo, folding, coloured, engraved map, occasional lib. stamp, half calf, gilt back. Deighton 5-179 1978 £45

CAMPBELL, HUGH   The White League Conspiracy Against Free Government. New Orleans, 1875. Original printed wr. bound in boards, 1st ed. Ginsberg 14-494 1978 $150

CAMPBELL, J. F.   A Short American Tramp in the Fall of 1864. 1865. Vignette on title, map, frontis, orig. cloth, 8vo, cover faded & slightly soiled. Edwards 1012-385 1978 £20

CAMPBELL, JANE C.   The Money-Maker, and Other Tales. New York, 1854. Cloth, little rubbed, lacks front flyleaf. Hayman 72-219 1978 $12.50

CAMPBELL, JOHN 1708-1775   Lives of the Admirals, and Other Eminent British Seamen. 1742. 2 vols., contemp. calf, labels missing, first ed., 8vo. Howes 194-195 1978 £15

CAMPBELL, JOHN 1708-1775   Lives of the Admirals and other Eminent British Seamen. 1750. 4 vols., second ed., 8vo., contemp. calf, rebacked. F. Edwards 1013-36 1978 £65

CAMPBELL, JOHN 1708-1775   Lives of the British Admirals. 1812-17. 8 vols., 8vo., contemp. tree calf, rebacked. F. Edwards 1013-37 1978 £80

CAMPBELL, JOHN 1766-1840   Travels in South Africa.... 1815. Portrait, folding map, plts., modern bds., uncut, some foxing, 8vo. Edwards 1012-294 1978 £85

CAMPBELL, JOHN 1766-1840   Travels in South Africa.... London, 1822. 2 vols., folding coloured map, 12 hand-coloured aquatint plts., some foxing, age-browning, good, old diced calf, neatly rebacked, 8vo. K Books 239-81 1978 £200

CAMPBELL, JOHN 1766-1840   Travels in South Africa.... London, 1822. 8vo., 2 vols., folding coloured map, 12 hand-coloured aquatint plts., half calf, little rubbed, short split in one joint, few blind-embossed lib. stamps. K Books 239-82 1978 £200

CAMPBELL, JOHN 1766-1840   Voyages to and from the Cape of Good Hope, in the years 1812 and 1814: for the Entertainment of Young People. London, 1819. 1st ed., engraved f.p., contemporary linen (stained) over boards, orig. spine lacking?, minor margin stains, some text darkening. Victoria 34-134 1978 $15

CAMPBELL, JOHN 1794-1867   The Martyr of Erromanger... London, 1842. 2nd ed., 1/2 calf, frontis in color, 8vo. Paine 78-28 1978 $15.00

CAMPBELL, JOHN 1840-1904   The Origin of the Haidahs of the Queen Charlotte Islands. 1897. Hood 116-402 1978 $12.50

CAMPBELL, JOHN C.   Worlds Displayed: for the Benefit of Young People, by a Familiar History of Some of their inhabitants. Boston, 1815. Homemade cloth spine, minor fraying and tears. Victoria 34-135 1978 $50

CAMPBELL, JOSEPH   A Skeleton Key to Finnegans Wake. 1947. First English ed., spine faded, very good. Bell Book 17-520 1978 £5.50

CAMPBELL, L. B.   Shakespeare's 'Histories"; Mirrors of Elizabethan Policy. San Marion, 1947. 2 plts., octavo, good. Upcroft 10-248 1978 £5

CAMPBELL, LEWIS   Religion in Greek Literature. 1898. Top of spine slightly torn. Allen 234-161 1978 $10

CAMPBELL, LEWIS D.   Alleged Assault Upon Senator Sumner...Mr. L.D. Campbell, from the Select Committee, Made the Following Report... (Washington, 1856). Stitched as issued, 1st and last leaves little soiled. Hayman 72-91 1978 $8.50

CAMPBELL, LEWIS D.   Speech of .... On The Gardiner and Galphin Claims... (Washington, 1852). Disbound. Hayman 71-644 1978 $8.50

CAMPBELL, M.   The English Yeoman Under Elizabeth and the Early Stuarts. New Haven, 1945. Octavo, good. Upcroft 10-249 1978 £6.50

CAMPBELL, M. W.   The Saskatchewan. New York, 1950. Illus. by I. H. Kerr. Hood 117-881 1978 $22.50

CAMPBELL, R.   A History of the Scotch Presbyterian Church, St. Gabriel Street, Montreal. Montreal, 1887. Orig. binding. Wolfe 39-59 1978 $35

CAMPBELL, RICHARD L.   Historical Sketches of Colonial Florida. Cleveland, 1892. 1st ed., illus., cloth, nice copy, scarce. MacManus 239-1804 1978 $35

CAMPBELL, ROY   Choosing a Mast. (1931). Coloured frontis., no. 80 of 300 copies on large paper, numbered & signed by author, bds., good, first English ed. Bell Book 17-141 1978 £25

CAMPBELL, ROY   Collected Poems. 1949. No. 93 of 175 copies of De Luxe ed., full mor. gilt, t.e.g., nice, first English ed. Bell Book 17-142 1978 £35

CAMPBELL, ROY   Collected Poems. 1949. Very good, first English ed. Bell Book 16-141 1978 £5.50

CAMPBELL, ROY   The Flaming Terrapin. New York, 1924. Decor. bds. & cloth, 1st Amer. ed., fine on torn & mended dust jacket, Bradley 49-54 1978 $8.50

CAMPBELL, ROY   The Flaming Terrapin. 1924. Cloth-backed bds., bookplt., else near fine, largely unopened, slightly worn d.w., first English ed. Bell Book 17-143 1978 £35

CAMPBELL, ROY   The Georgiad... London, (1931). Orig. cloth-backed bds., glassine d.j., 1st ed., 1 of 170 copies signed by poet, almost mint. MacManus 238-627 1978 $100

CAMPBELL, ROY   The Georgiad. 1931. One of 170 copies, numbered & signed by author, quarter buckram, t.e.g., fine, first English ed. Bell Book 17-144 1978 £45

CAMPBELL, ROY   The Gum Trees. 1930. No. 352 of 400 copies signed by the author, drawings, bds., very good, first English ed. Bell Book 16-142 1978 £25

CAMPBELL, ROY   Poems. Paris, Hours Press, 1930. Quarto, pict. boards, leather backstrip, 1 of 200 copies signed by author, handset and printed on handpress, 1st ed., binding worn, fine. Duschnes 220-146 1978 $55

CAMPBELL, ROY   Poems. Paris, 1930. No. 53 of 200 copies numbered & signed by author, sm. folio, quarter calf, vermillion bds., two drawings by author, very good, first English ed. Bell Book 17-145 1978 £120

CAMPBELL, ROY   Pomegranates; a poem. 1932. No. 57 of 99 copies on handmade paper signed by author, fine, first English ed. Bell Book 16-144 1978 £55

CAMPBELL, T. J.   Pioneer Priests of North America, 1642-1710. New York, 1908-10-11. 3 vols., illus., orig. cloth, hinges weak, good set. MacManus 239-76 1978 $45

CAMPBELL, THOMAS 1733-1795   A Philosophical Survey of the South of Ireland,.... Dublin, 1778. 8vo., contemp. calf, gilt (trifle rubbed, but sound), 1st ed., very good copy. Ximenes 47-46 1978 $125

CAMPBELL, THOMAS 1777-1844   Gertrude of Wyoming.... 1809. 1st ed., 4to., orig. bds., uncut, printed paper label, very nice copy, signature of Arthur Brooke Cooper on title. Fenning 32-56 1978 £21.50

CAMPBELL, THOMAS 1777-1844   Gertrude of Wyoming; a Pennsylvanian Tale. 1809. 1st ed., 4to., contemp. half calf, joint cracked, some slight foxing. Hannas 54-43 1978 £12.50

CAMPBELL, THOMAS 1777-1844   Gertrude of Wyoming: A Pennsylvanian Tale. 1809. 4to., contemp. diced russia gilt, title a little spotted, nice, first ed. P. M. Hill 142-258 1978 £35

CAMPBELL, THOMAS 1777-1844   Gertrude of Wyoming: A Pennsylvanian Tale, and Other Poems. 1809. 4to., half calf, scarce blank leaf. Edwards 1012-550 1978 £20

CAMPBELL, THOMAS 1777-1844   Gertrude of Wyoming, and Other Poems. 1810. 3rd ed., 12mo., orig. sprinkled calf, gilt borders & spine, black label, v.g. Jarndyce 16-351 1978 £11.50

CAMPBELL, THOMAS 1777-1844   Life of Mrs. Siddons. 1839. Sm. 8vo., contemp. half blue calf gilt, slightly worn, portrait. P. M. Hill 142-224 1978 £16

CAMPBELL, THOMAS 1777-1844   Life of Petrarch. 1841. First ed., plts., 2 vols., full polished calf, 8vo. Howes 194-1092 1978 £18

CAMPBELL, THOMAS 1777-1844   The Pleasures of Hope and other Poems. Edinburgh, 1806. Ninth ed., plts., fcap. 8vo., contemp. calf. Howes 194-196 1978 £7.50

CAMPBELL, THOMAS 1777-1844   The Pleasures of Hope, With Other Poems. Edinburgh, 1808. 12mo., 4 engravings, browned, 1/4 calf, joints cracked. Eaton 45-88 1978 £5

CAMPBELL, THOMAS 1777-1844   The Poetical Works of....Including Several Poems From the Original Manuscript Never Before Published in This Country..a Biog.... Albany, 1810. 2 vols., rebound, very good. Nestler Rare 78-34 1978 $35

CAMPBELL, THOMAS 1777-1844   Poetical Works. London, 1837. Portrait frontis., illus., full red calf, upper margins water stained, quite scarce, 8vo. K Books 244-61 1978 £10

CAMPBELL, THOMAS 1777-1844   Specimens of the British Poets. 1819. 1st ed., 7 vols., cr. 8vo., contemp. half russia. Howes 194-197 1978 £50

CAMPBELL, THOMAS 1777-1844   Specimens of the British Poets... 1819. 1st. ed., 7 vols., 8vo, contemp. diced calf, gilt, red & black labels, little foxing, very good set. Hannas 54-44 1978 £75

CAMPBELL, TOM W.   Two Fighters and Two Fines. Little Rock, 1941. 2nd ed., book very good, but dust jacket little worn. Hayman 73-81 1978 $7.50

CAMPBELL, WILFRED   The Beauty, History, Romance and Mystery of the Canadian Lake Region. Toronto, 1910. Illus., some colour. Hood 116-725 1978 $40

CAMPBELL, WILFRED   Poetical Tragedies. Toronto, 1908. Hood 117 790 1978 $45

CAMPBELL, WILFRED   The Scotsman in Canada. Toronto, 1911. 2 vols. Hood 116-8 1978 $60

CAMPBELL, WILLIAM J.   The Collection of Franklin Imprints in the Museum of the Curtis Publishing Company... Philadelphia, 1918. Tall 8vo., orig. cloth, 1st ed., ltd. to 475 no. copies, pres. copy. MacManus 238-923 1978 $75

CAMPBELL, WILLIAM W.   Annals of Tryon County. New York, 1831. Orig. cloth-covered bds., fine copy, 1st ed., fldg. map, facsimile letter from Joseph Brant, dated, marginal tear. Butterfield 21-86 1978 $75

CAMPBELL, WILLIAM W.   Annals of Tryon County. New York, 1849. Enlarged 2nd ed., orig. cloth, new endpapers, frontis. map not present. Butterfield 21-87 1978 $15

CAMPBELL, WILLIAM W.   Annals of Tryon County. Cherry Valley, 1880. 3rd ed., orig. cloth. Butterfield 21-88 1978 $20

CAMPBELL-PRAED, MRS.   Mrs. Tregaskiss, A Novel of Anglo-Australian Life. New York, 1895. 1st Amer. ed., quarter calf, marbled boards. Greene 78-161 1978 $15

CAMPE, JOACHIM HEINRICH VON   The New Robinson Crusoe: Designed for Youth. New Haven, 1819. Pictorial wrappers, woodcuts, sewn, dark stain through most leaves. Victoria 34-136 1978 $65

CAMPER, PIETER   Dissertation Physique Sur les Differences Reelles que Presentent les Traits du Visage Chez les Hommes de Differents Pays et de Differents Ages... Utrecht, 1791. 4to., plts., contemp. calf, gilt back, rubbed, 1st French ed. Gilhofer 74-87 1978 sFr 600

CAMPION, THOMAS   The Maske. Kensington, Cayme Press, 1924. 8vo., half cloth, frontis., plt., ltd. ed. of 500 numbered copies only, uncut, bkplt., spine shaved. Van der Peet H-64-393 1978 Dfl 65

CAMPOS, HIERONYMOS   Sylva De Varias Questiones Naturales Y Morales. Valencia, 1587. 8vo., vellum, 2nd ed. Salloch 348-24 1978 $350

CAMUS, C. E. L.   De La Mature Des Vaisseaux. Paris, 1728. Plts., 4to., modern half calf, t.e.g. F. Edwards 1013-38 1978 £60

CANADA. COMMISSION OF CONSERVATION   Sea Fisheries of Eastern Canada, Being the Proceedings of a Meeting of the Committee on Fisheries, Game and Fur-Bearing Animals. Ottawa, 1912. Bound, maps, diagrs. Hood 117-931 1978 $15

CANADA. DEPT. OF AGRICULTURE   Agricultural Assistance, War and Post-War. Ottawa, 1949. Card cover. Hood 117-933 1978 $10

CANADA. DEPT. OF MINES   Molybdenum Metallurgy and Uses, and the Occurence, Mining and Concertration of its Ores. Photos, drawings, 3 folding maps in pocket. Hood's 115-537 1978 £15

CANADA. DEPT. OF MINES   Some Myths and Tales of the Ojibwa of Southeastern Ontario. Ottawa, 1914. Card cover. Hood 117-670 1978 $20

CANADA. DEPT. OF TRANSPORTATION   List of Lights, Fog Signals and Radio Aids to Navigation on the Atlantic Coast. Ottawa, 1941. Card cover. Hood's 115-958 1978 $12.50

CANADA'S Missionary Congress...Addresses with Reports of Committees. Toronto, (1909). Cover stained. Hood 117-341 1978 $15

CANADIAN BROADCASTING CORPORATION   We Have Been There. Toronto, 1942. Wrs. Hood 117-118 1978 $10

CANADIAN HISTORICAL ASSOCIATION   Reports of Annual Meetings with Historical Papers from...Up to and Including... 1939-1965. Lacking 1 year, 1945, 17 vols. Hood 116-917 1978 $170

CANADIAN KODAK CO., LIMITED   How To Make Good Pictures. Toronto, n.d.(Evidently about 1910). Illus., card cover. Hood's 115-166 1978 $20

CANADIAN MILITARY INSTITUTE   The Golden Book. Toronto, 1927. Hood 116-115 1978 $35

CANADIAN PACIFIC RAILWAY COMPANY   Quebec; La Doulce Province. Montreal, n.d. (About 1925). Card cover, illus. with woodcuts. Hood's 115-961 1978 $15

CANADIAN PACIFIC RAILWAY COMPANY   Quebec Summer and Winter. Montreal, 1902. Card cover, illus., folding map. Hood's 115-959 1978 $10

CANADIAN NATIONAL RAILWAYS   Hunting in Canada. (Montreal, ca. 1926). Card cover, illus. Hood 117-615 1978 $10

THE CANADIAN Dental Directory. Toronto, 1909. Tall 12mo., cloth. Wolfe 39-122 1978 $30

CANADIAN Group of Painters, 1947-1948 Exhibition. Toronto, Montreal, 1947-48. Illus., card cover. Hood's 115-143 1978 $10

THE CANADIAN Hymnal; a Collection of Hymns and Music, Revised and Enlarged. Toronto, 1900. Heavy card cover. Hood 116-287 1978 $10

THE CANADIAN Naturalist and Geologist. Ottawa, (1857-1863). Vol. II through Vol. VIII, orig. bds., new spines, gold stamped. Hood 116-919 1978 $210

THE CANADIAN Patriot, a Monthly Magazine of Literature and Social Science. Montreal, 1864. 4to., orig. printed wrappers, separated at spine. Wolfe 39-80 1978 $50

THE CANADIAN Sunday-School Organ. Toronto, n.d. Blank fly leaf and t.p. missing, heavy card cover. Hood 116-288 1978 $20

CANDEE, HELEN CHURCHILL   Decorative Styles and Periods in the Home. New York, (1906). Illus. Hayman 72-94 1978 $12.50

CANDEE, HELEN CHURCHILL   New Journeys in Old Asia; Indo-China, Siam, Java and Bali. New York, 1927. Cloth, plts., illus., 8vo. Van der Peet 127-52 1978 Dfl 45

CANDEE, HELEN CHURCHILL   The Tapestry Book. New York, 1935. 103 illus., 4 in color, d.j., box. Baldwins' 51-38 1978 $12.50

CANDEZE, ERNEST   The Adventures of Grillo or the Cricket Who Would be King. Boston-New York, (1912). Profusely illus., scarce. Victoria 34-136 1978 $65

CANDOLLE, AUGUSTIN PYRAMUS DE   Plantes Rares Du Jardin De Geneve. Geneva, 1825. Color plts., tall folio, uncut, orig. cloth-backed prtd. bds., spine renewed. Salloch 345-38 1978 $800

CANDOLLE, AUGUSTIN PYRAMUS DE   Plantes Rares du Jardin de Geneve. Geneve, (1825-1829). Plts. prtd. in colors & partly finished by hand, folio, half green mor., orig. prtd. wrs. bound in, only ed., fine copy. Offenbacher 30-21 1978 $850

CANE, MELVILLE   A Wider Arc. New York, 1947. 1st ed., advance copy review slip pasted in, d.w. slightly frayed. Biblo 251-421 1978 $10

CANER, H.   A Candid Examination of Dr. Mayhews Observations on the Charter and Conduct of the Society for Propagation of the Gospel in Foreign Parts. Boston, 1763. Good. Nestler Rare 78-7 1978 $50

CANFIELD, WILLIAM W.   The Legends of the Iroquois. New York, 1902 (1904). Colored frontis., illus., orig. cloth, fine. MacManus 239-1151 1978 $17.50

CANIFF, MILTON   April Kane and the Dragon Lady. 1942. Illus., paper. Austin 82-297 1978 $12.50

THE CANINE Race. New Haven, c.1835. 12mo, woodcut plates, text cuts, pictorial wrappers, very good. Victoria 34-138 1978 $20

CANISIUS, PETRUS, SAINT   Catholischer Catechismus Worin die Catholische Lehre nach den funf Hapstucken V. P. Petri Canisii. Philadelphia, 1810. Marbled boards, almost fine. Victoria 34-139 1978 $15

CANISIUS, PETRUS, SAINT   Summa Doctrinae Christianae, ex Postrema Recognitione. Antverpiae, 1589. Sm. 8vo., full red mor., gilt crest, richly gilt tooled, engrs., excellent cond., very attractive binding. Van der Peet H-64-270 1978 Dfl 950

CANIVELL Y VILA, FRANCISCO   Tratado de Vendages y Apositos, para el uso de los Reales Colegios de Cirugia. Madrid, 1785. 4to., folding plts., contemp. calf, head of spine chipped. Quaritch 977-14 1978 $100

CANNIFF, WILLIAM   History of the Province of Ontario, (Upper Canada). Toronto, 1872. Cover scuffed, inside clean. Hood 117-722 1978 $110

CANNIFF, WILLIAM   History of the Settlement of Upper Canada (Ontario) with Special Reference to the Bay Quinte. Toronto, 1869. Restored. Hood 117-723 1978 $115

CANNING, GEORGE   Speeches Delivered on Publich Occasions in Liverpool. Liverpool, 1825. 1st ed., frontis portrait, orig. half calf, good. Jarndyce 16-353 1978 £12.50

CANNON, CARL L.   American Book Collectors and Collecting from Colonial Times to the Present. New York, 1941. 8vo., orig. cloth, 1st ed. MacManus 238-885 1978 $30

CANNON, FRANK J.   Under the Prophet in Utah. 1911. Austin 79-118 1978 $10

CANNON, GEORGE QUAYLE   Writings from the "Western Standard" Published in San Francisco. Liverpool, 1864. Half calf, privately printed. Ginsberg 14-998 1978 $125

CANNON, J. P.   Inside of Rebeldom: The Daily Life of a Private in the Confederate Army. Washington, 1900. Wrs. worn, Bell Wiley's copy. Broadfoot's 44-688 1978 $25

CANNON, RICHARD   Historical Record of the First, or Royal Regiment of Foot. 1847. Coloured plts., 8vo., orig. cloth. F. Edwards 1013-479 1978 £30

CANNON, RICHARD   Historical Record of the Seventh Regiment. 1847. Coloured plts., 8vo., orig. cloth, spine faded. F. Edwards 1013-484 1978 £30

CANNON, RICHARD   Historical Record of the Eighth. 1844. Coloured plt., 8vo., orig. cloth. F. Edwards 1013-486 1978 £18

CANNON, RICHARD   Historical Record of the Eleventh. 1845. 8vo., orig. cloth, varnished, coloured plt. F. Edwards 1013-488 1978 £18

CANNON, RICHARD   Historical Record of the Ninety-Second Regiment. 1851. Coloured plts., orig. cloth, 8vo. F. Edwards 1013-543 1978 £35

CANOVA, ANTONIO   The Works of..., in Sculpture and Modelling. London, 1849. 3 vols., 4tos., nice set, cloth. MacManus 239-647 1978 $50

CANOVA, ANTONIO   Works in Sculpture and Modeling. 1876. Plts. engraved in outline by W. Moses, 4to., loose in case due to gutta-percha binding. George's 635-263 1978 £10.50

CANOVAI, STANISLAS   Elogio D'Amerigo Vespucci...1788. (Florence), 1790. 4to., contemp. decor. bds. Salloch 345-39 1978 $80

CANSON and Montgolfier Sample Book. New York, 1925. Lg. 4to., orig. cloth-backed bds., ltd. to 500 copies, bookplt., slightly soiled. MacManus 238-1024 1978 $50

CANSON et Montgolfier. Paris-Vidalon-New York. 4to., bds., cloth spine, #84 of 500 numbered copies. Battery Park 1-445 1978 $250

CANTOR, ALFRED J.   Ambulatory Proctology. New York, 1946. Rittenhouse 49-125 1976 $10

CANU, FERDINAND   North American Later Tertiary & Quaternary Bryozoa. Washington, 1923. Wr. worn, 8vo., orig. cloth. Book Chest 17-81 1978 $45

CANVANE, PETER   A Dissertation on the Oieum Palmae Christi, sive Oleum Ricini. Bath, n.d. (c. 1765). 8vo., bds., plt., first ed. Gurney 75-17 1978 £40

CAOURSIN, GUILLAUME   Fondement de l'ordre de la chevalerie des hospitaliers de saint jehan baptiste de iherusalem. Paris, 1493. Small folio, Gothic letter, orig. Paris binding of blind stamped calf over wooden boards, slight wear to lower cover, fine fresh copy in orig. state, apparently 1st ed. Quaritch 978-28 1978 $15,000

CAPA, ROBERT   Slightly Out of Focus. 1947. Illus., first ed., v.g., frayed d.j. Austin 82-1159 1978 $27.50

CAPEK, THOMAS   The Czechs in America. 1920. Illus., 1st ed., some wear to backstrip. Austin 79-119 1978 $12.50

CAPEK, THOMAS   The Slovaks of Hungry. 1906. Illus., 1st ed., some cover fade. Austin 79-120 1978 $20

CAPEL, ARTHUR   Daily Observations or Meditations, Divine, Morall. (London), 1654. 1st. ed., lg. 8vo in fours, engraved portrait, old half calf. Traylen 88-130 1978 £80

CAPEL, ARTHUR   Letters written by Arthur Capel, Lord Lieutenant of Ireland, in the Year 1675. 1770. First ed., 4to., contemp. calf, rebacked, portrait. Howes 194-198 1978 £35

CAPELLONI, LORENZO   Varii Ragionamenti Historici, e Politici di Lorenzo Capelloni.... Milano, 1623. Scarce ed., octavo, full contemporary vellum, backed, ex-Fletcher with signature on back paste-down. Bennett 20-36 1978 $85

CAPGRAVE, J.   The Book of the Illustrious Henries. 1858. Roy. 8vo., orig. qtr. roan. George's 635-588 1978 £20

THE CAPITALS of the World. 1892. Illus., 4 vols., folio. George's 635-1273 1978 £10.50

CAPITOLI, et Privilegii Concessi.... Florence, 1571. Vignette, sm. 4to., wrappers. F. Edwards 1013-264 1978 £25

CAPOTE, TRUMAN   Other Voices, Other Rooms. New York, (1948). Orig. cloth, d.j., chipped, 1st ed. MacManus 238-628 1978 $45

CAPOTE, TRUMAN   Other Voices, Other Rooms. New York, (1948). Very good in chipped dw. Bernard 5-56 1978 $45

CAPOTE, TRUMAN   A Tree of Night and Other Stories. New York, (1949). 1st ed., d.w. Biblo BL781-901 1978 $12

CAPOTE, TRUMAN   A Tree of Night and Other Stories. New York, 1949. Nice in damaged d.w. Desmarais B-125 1978 $27.50

CAPPER, JAMES   Observations on the Passage to India, Through Egypt and Across the Great Desert... London, 1784. 2nd. ed., additions, 4to, folding maps, some spotting on 1st. few leaves, edges uncut, bds., printed paper label. Deighton 5-180 1978 £75

CAPPER, JOHN   The Duke of Edinburgh in Ceylon... 1871. 8 chromo-litho. plts., slight foxing, roy. 8vo, half morocco. Edwards 1012-123 1978 £20

CAPPURI, ANTONIO   De Peculiari Cataracta in Anteriorum Oculi Cameram Prolapsa Commentarius. Bononiae, 1794. 4to., bds., 1st ed., very scarce. Offenbacher 30-115 1978 $65

CAPRA, BALTHASAR   Consideratione Astronomica Circa la Nova, and Portentosa Stella che Nell'anno 1604 a di 10 Ottobre Apparse, Con un Breve Judicio Delli Suoi Significanti. Padova, 1605. 8vo., fold. plt., half-vellum, 1st ed. Gilhofer 74-4 1978 sFr 1,200

CAPRA, BALTHASAR   Tyrocinia Astronomica, in Quibus non Solum Calculis Eclipsis Solaris, ab Astronomo Magno Tychone Brahe Restitutus Clarissime Explicatur... Patavii, 1606. 4to., half mor., 1st ed., very scarce. Offenbacher 30-46 1978 $350

CAPRETZ, G.   La Vergogna del Duello. Padova, 1926. 8vo., orig. covers. Van der Peet H-64-602 1978 Dfl 30

CAPTAIN Midnight and the Secret Squadron. Racine, (1941). Very good. Bernard 5-334 1978 $10

CARCO, FRANCIS   Rien Qu'une Femme. Paris, 1923. Royal 8vo., contemp. 3/4 red hard grain mor., panelled gilt back, uncut, ltd. ed., 1 of 1100 numbered copies prtd. on velin du Marais paper, orig. etchings by Maurice Asselin. Goldschmidt 110-1 1978 $50

CARD, HENRY   The Reign of Charlemagne... 1807. 1st. ed., orig. calf, rebacked, v.g. Jarndyce 16-354 1978 £14

CARDANO, GIROLAMO   De Subtilitate. Lyons, 1554. Woodcuts, thick 8vo., contemp. calf gilt-tooled. Salloch 345-41 1978 $125

CARDANO, GIROLAMO   De Utilitate Ex Adversis Capienda. Franeker, 1648. Engr. frontis., thick 8vo., 1/2 calf. Salloch 345-40 1978 $185

CARDEN, ROBERT W.   The City of Genoa. London, 1908. Illus. in color. Biblo 247-664 1978 $15

CARDINALL, A. W.   The Natives of the Northern Territories of the Gold Coast. London, c. 1930. 8vo., orig. cloth, map, illus. K Books 239-85 1978 £12

CARDONNE, M.   Histoire de L'Afrique Et De L'Espagne...
Paris, 1765. 3 vols., sm. 8vo, contemp. calf, covers slightly worn.   Edwards
1012-236 1978 £60

CARDWELL, J. H.   Men and Women of Soho, Famous & Infamous.
(1903). 1st. ed., numerous portraits, orig. red cloth, v.g.   Jarndyce 16-834
1978 £10.50

CARE, HENRY   The Weekly Pacquet of Advice From Rome: or,
The History of Popery. 1678-82. 1st. ed., 4 vols. in 2, 4to, contemp. calf,
worn rebacked, sm. stamp on titles, some water-stains.   Hannas 54-45 1978 £55

CARE, HENRY   The Weekly Pacquet of Advice From Rome: or,
The History of Popery. 1678-82. 3rd. vol. only, bound from orig. parts, contemp.
calf, worn, worming in inner margins.   Hannas 54-46 1978 £8.50

CAREW, BAMPFYLDE MOORE   Life and Adventures, commonly called King of
the Gypsies, an impartial Account of his Life.   1835. Engraved portrait, fcap.
8vo., qtr. roan.   George's 635-1274 1978 £7.50

CAREW, GEORGE   A Retrospect Into the Kings Certain Revenue
Annexed to the Crown... London, 1661. Title & text ruled in red, thin folio,
contemp. panelled calf, rubbed, slight worming in lower margin.   Traylen 88-72
1978 £300

CAREW, THOMAS   The Poems. 1949. Portrait, 8vo., orig. cloth.
Howes 194-704 1978 £5

CAREW, THOMAS   A Rapture.   Golden Cockerel, 1927. 12mo.,
d.w., #186 of 375 copies, engrs.   Battery Park 1-115 1978 $45

CAREW, THOMAS   A Selection from the Poetical Works of.   1810.
8vo., old calf, hinges cracked.   P. M. Hill 142-259 1978 £12

CAREY, MATHEW   Brief View of the System of Internal Improvement
of...Pennsylvania... Philadelphia, 1831. Orig. printed wrs., a little worn,
2,000 copies printed.   Americanist 102-26 1978 $25

CAREY, MATHEW   The Olive Branch.   Philadelphia, 1815. 6th
ed., enlarged, lea.   Hayman 73-86 1978 $15

CAREY, MATTHEW   The Olive Branch.   Philadelphia, 1815. 7th
ed., cloth.   MacManus 239-80 1978 $27.50

CAREY, MATHEW   A Short Account of the Malignant Fever, Lately
Prevalent in Philadelphia...   Philadelphia, 1793. 3rd ed., improved, untrimmed,
orig. wrs., former owner's signature on t.p., bit frayed.   MacManus 239-1406
1978 $75

CAREY, MATHEW   Short Account of the Malignant Fever Lately
Prevalent in Philadelphia.   Philadelphia, 1794. Fourth ed., improved, leather,
slightly worn on spine.   Rittenhouse 49-126 1976 $90

CAREY, ROBERT   Memoirs of.   1759. 8vo., contemp. calf gilt,
very nice, frontispiece.   P. M. Hill 142-67 1978 £32

CAREY, ROSA NOCHETTE   Only The Governess.   1888. 1st. ed., 3 vols.,
bound in half moroon roan, chip from tail of spine vol. I, generally rubbed.
Jarndyce 16-355 1978 £12.50

CARLES, P.   Album d'Ecritures en tous Genres.   Paris, 1855.
(1856). Lg. 4to., cont. half red mor., triple gilt fillets, dedication copy,
extremely rare.   Schumann 511-7 1978 sFr 3,300

CARLETON, GEORGE   A Thankful Remembrance of Gods Mercy.   1627.
Third ed., engrav. frontispiece, sm. 4to., contemp. calf, neatly rebacked, some
leaves soiled.   Howes 194-25 1978 £80

CARLETON, HENRY GUY   The Thompson Street Poker Club, from "Life".
NY, 1888. Fir. Ed., illus. by E. W. Kemble, quarter calf, marbled boards,
lacking spine, int. good condition.   Greene 78-322 1978 $85.00

CARLETON, WILL   City Ballads.   New York, 1886. Illus.   Hood
117-793 1978 $12.50

CARLETON, WILL   Farm Festivals.   New York, 1881. Illus.   Hood
116-808 1978 $25

CARLETON, WILLIAM   The Squanders of Castle Squander.   1852. 2 vols.,
sm. 8vo., 1st ed., plts., orig. red cloth, worn.   Quaritch 979-77 1978 $85

CARLETON, WILLIAM   The Works of... New York, 1882. 3 vols.,
uniform cloth, lg. 8vo.   Greene 78-22 1978 $45

CARLETTI, NICCOLO   Istruzioni d'Architettura Civile.   Naples, 1772.
4to., 2 vols., fold. plts., half-mor., some very light spots, 1st ed.   Gilhofer 74-
32 1978 sFr 500

CARLIN, WILLIAM   Old Doctor Carlin's Recipes Being a Complete
Collection of Recipes on Every Known Subject...   Toledo & Boston, 1881. Clean,
worn, orig. binding.   Hayman 71-84 1978 $7.50

CARLISLE, FREDERICK HOWARD, 5TH EARL OF   Poems, Consisting of the
Following Pieces...   London, 1773. 4to., disbound, first ed.   Ximenes 47-140
1978 $45

CARLISLE, FREDERICK HOWARD, 5TH EARL OF   Poems.   1807. New ed.,
cr. 8vo., engr. frontis., full diced calf, gilt, bkplts.   Eaton 45-90 1978 £10

CARLISLE, FREDERICK HOWARD, 5TH EARL OF   Tragedies and Poems.   1801.
8vo., contemp. straight grained red mor., from the library of A.N.L. Munby.
Quaritch 979-78 1978 $85

CARLISLE, GEORGE WILLIAM FREDERICK HOWARD, 7TH EARL OF   Diary
in Turkish and Greek Waters.   1854. 2nd ed., sm. 8vo., orig. cloth, cover
slightly worn.   Edwards 1012-45 1978 £18

CARLISLE, Pa. Old and New.   Harrisburg, 1907. Illus.   MacManus 239-1407
1978 $12.50

CARLTON, CAPT. W.   Hyde Marston; or, A Sportsman's Life.   1844.
1st. ed., 3 vols., polished half blue morocco, raised bands gilt, fine.   Jarndyce
16-378 1978 £75

CARLTON, WILLIAM J.   Charles Dickens, Shorthand Writer.   London,
1926. 1st ed., frontispiece, illus., very good or better.   Limestone 9-83
1978 $13.50

CARLTON, WILLIAM J.   Timothe Bright, Doctor of Phisicke.   1911.
8vo., plts., illus., scarce, orig. cloth.   Howes 194-657 1978 £8.50

CARLYLE, R. W.   A History of Mediaeval Political Theory in the
West, Vols. I-V.   1950. Five vols. (ex 6), ex-lib., 8vo.   Upcroft 12-64 1978
£6.50

CARLYLE, THOMAS   Chartism.   1840. 1st. ed., orig. green cloth,
v.g.   Jarndyce 16-360 1978 £40

CARLYLE, THOMAS   Collectanea 1821-1855.   Canton, Kirgate
Press, 1902. 1st ed., 1 of 500 copies on Old Stratford paper, uncut, 8vo.,
orig. cloth, very good.   Americanist 103-26 1978 $20

CARLYLE, THOMAS   Collected Works.   1869-73. Library ed., full
polished tree calf, 34 vols., frontispieces, very good, 8vo.   Howes 194-705 1978
£125

CARLYLE, THOMAS   Critical & Miscellaneous Essays...   1847. 3rd.
ed., 4 vols., half titles, calf, maroon & green labels, some rubbing.   Jarndyce
16-363 1978 £18.50

CARLYLE, THOMAS   Critical & Miscellaneous Essays...   1857. 4th.
ed., 4 vols., some water staining to vol. 4, orig. brown cloth, good sound set.
Jarndyce 16-364 1978 £18.50

CARLYLE, THOMAS   Critical and Miscellaneous Essays.   Boston, 1860.
4 vols., 3/4 leather and bds., covers worn.   Biblo 247-809 1978 $27.50

CARLYLE, THOMAS   The Early Kings of Norway...   1875. 1st. ed.,
orig. brown cloth, little rubbed.   Jarndyce 16-371 1978 £6.50

CARLYLE, THOMAS   Early Letters (1814-1826).   1886. 1st. ed., 2
vols., half titles, frontis, orig. dark olive cloth, v.g.   Jarndyce 16-375 1978
£12.50

CARLYLE, THOMAS   Early Letters, 1814-1826.   1886. Frontispieces,
2 vols., orig. cloth, first ed., 8vo.   Howes 194-706 1978 £7.50

CARLYLE, THOMAS   The French Revolution.   1837. 1st. ed., 3 vols.,
half titles, orig. half calf, labels rubbed, otherwise v.g.   Jarndyce 16-359 1978
£52

CARLYLE, THOMAS   German Romance... Edinburgh, 1827. lst. ed., 4 vols., vignette half titles in all vols., orig. calf, spines gilt, black labels, trifle worn. Jarndyce 16-357 1978 £38

CARLYLE, THOMAS   German Romance. Edinburgh, 1827. lst. ed., 4 vols., engraved title & half title, half dark blue roan, rubbed, spine defective vol. I, pres. copy from publishers to John Wilson. Jarndyce 16-358 1978 £12.50

CARLYLE, THOMAS   Jocelin of Brakelond, From Past and Present. New York: William Edwin Rudge, 1923. 12mo., orig. cloth, 1 of 500 copies printed by Bruce Rogers, good. MacManus 238-782 1978 $25

CARLYLE, THOMAS   Latter-Day Pamphlets. 1850. Orig. half calf, spine rubbed, green label. Jarndyce 16-365 1978 £20

CARLYLE, THOMAS   Latter-Day Pamphlets. 1855. Calf, gilt borders, labels, slight rubbing at head of spine. Jarndyce 16-366 1978 £7.50

CARLYLE, THOMAS   Letters... 1899. lst. ed., orig. dark green cloth, portraits, illus., v.g. Jarndyce 16-377 1978 £6

CARLYLE, THOMAS   The Life of Frederick Schiller. 1825. lst. ed., frontis portrait, half title, orig. grey bds., uncut, slight wear to hinges, otherwise v.g. in orig. condition. Jarndyce 16-356 1978 £45

CARLYLE, THOMAS   The Life of John Sterling. London, 1851. Orig. cloth, 1st ed., inner hinges cracked and repaired, top of spine worn, otherwise good. MacManus 238-185 1978 $35

CARLYLE, THOMAS   On Heroes, Hero-Worship and the Heroic in History. 1841. lst. ed., orig. brown cloth, inner hinges weak, spine slightly defective. Jarndyce 16-361 1978 £10.50

CARLYLE, THOMAS   On Heroes, Hero-Worship, & The Heroic in History. London, 1841. 12mo, full contemp. blind-stamped publisher's cloth, lst ed. Bennett 7-26 1978 $95

CARLYLE, THOMAS   On the Choice of Books. 1866. lst. ed., 2 portraits, orig. green cloth, v.g. Jarndyce 16-370 1978 £15

CARLYLE, THOMAS   Past and Present. London, 1843. Orig. cloth, spine faded and chipped, 1st ed., light spotting throughout. MacManus 238-184 1978 $35

CARLYLE, THOMAS   Past & Present. 1843. lst. ed., half title, some pencil marginalia, parchment-covered bds., v.g. Jarndyce 16-362 1978 £20

CARLYLE, THOMAS   Reminiscences. 1881. lst. ed., 2 vols., frontis, half title, orig. green cloth, v.g. Jarndyce 16-373 1978 £6.50

CARLYLE, THOMAS   Reminiscences. New York, 1881. lst. American ('authorized) ed., half title, orig. brown cloth, bit worn. Jarndyce 16-374 1978 £5

CARLYLE, THOMAS   Carlyle's Unpublished Lectures. 1892. Lg. 8vo., orig. cloth. P. M. Hill 142-68 1978 £15

CARLYLE, THOMAS   Works. London, 1885-88. Ashburton edition, 17 vols., illus., 3/4 leather, edges rubbed. Biblo 247-665 1978 $95

CARMAN, BLISS   Earth Dieties and Other Rhythmic Masques. New York, 1914. lst ed. Biblo 251-423 1978 $15

CARMAN, BLISS   The Kinship of Nature. Toronto, 1904. Decor. cover. Hood 117-950 1978 $30

CARMAN, BLISS   Low Tide on Grand Pre: A Book of Lyrics. New York, 1893. Orig. lavender cloth, spine faded. Wolfe 39-82 1978 $35

CARMAN, BLISS   Pipes of Pan, Containing "From the Book of Myths", "From the Green Book of the Bards".... Boston, 1929. Definitive ed. Hood 116-807 1978 $30

CARMAN, EZRA A.   Special Report on the History and Present Condition of the Sheep Industry of the United States. Washington, D.C., 1892. Cloth, plts., lst ed., from the Allred Collection, scarce, slipcase. Dykes 34-272 1978 $50

CARMER, CARL   For the Right of Men. New York, (1947). Illus., lst ed. Biblo BL781-1019 1978 $9

CARMER, CARL   French Town. New Orleans, 1928. Wr. over boards, very good, wr. complete but very worn. Nestler Rare 78-35 1978 $85

CARMER, CARL   The Hudson. New York, (1938). Illus., 1st ed., d.w. Biblo BL781-157 1978 $10

CARMER, CARL   Listen for a Lonesome Drum. New York, 1936. Biblo 247-113 1978 $12.50

CARMICHAEL-SMITH, JAMES   Precis of the Wars in Canada, from 1755 to the Treat of Ghent in 1814. London, 1826. Orig., inscribed & signed. Hood's 115-95 1978 $325

CARNCROSS, HORACE   The Escape from the Primitive. 1926. Austin 80-876 1978 $10

CARNEY, T. J.   What I Must Try To Be. Boston, 1852. lst ed., chapbook, printed wrappers, very good. Victoria 34-140 1978 $7.50

CARNOCHAN, F. G.   The Empire of the Snakes. London, (1935). 8vo, orig. cloth, plts., little shaken, covers faded. K Books 239-86 1978 £5

CARO, ANNIBALE   Apologia de gli Accademici di Banchi di Roma, contra M. Lodovico Castelvetro da Modena. Parma, 1558. Extremely rare lst ed., 4to., old half calf, inner margins of lst leaves repaired, very light stains. Gilhofer 75-21 1978 SFr 500

CARO, E.   La Fin du Dix-Huitieme Siecle: Etudes et Portraits. Paris, 1880. Half sage green mor., gilt edges, 2 vols., cr. 8vo. Howes 194-708 1978 £12

CARO-DELVAILLE, HENRY   Phidias ou le Genie Grec. Paris, 1922. Illus., wrs. Biblo BL781-342 1978 $7.50

CARON, FRANCIS   A true Description Of The Mighty Kingdoms Of Japan and Siam. London, 1663. Sm. 8vo, folding map, plates, light browning, polished calf gilt, gilt edges, by Riviere, rare. Quaritch 978-82 1978 $1,250

CARPENTER, CHARLES E.   Dollars and Sense. 1928. Austin 80-470 1978 $10

CARPENTER, EDWARD   The Drama of Love and Death. 1912. Good, covers somewhat soiled, first English ed. Bell Book 16-146 1978 $5

CARPENTER, EDWARD   Samuel Carpenter and His Descendants. Philadelphia, 1912. Orig. cloth, stained, illus., 4to., very scarce. MacManus 239-917 1978 $60

CARPENTER, HELEN K.   The Cinderella Man. London, n.d. Signed by both authors, dated Mar. 1, 1920, pulp paper. Biblo 251-424 1978 $17.50

CARPENTER, M.   Last Days in England of the Rajah Rammohun Roy. 1866. Lithograph portrait frontis., 2 plts., covers marked, 8vo. George's 635-1257 1978 £15

CARPENTER, MATTHEW H.   The Powers of Congress. The Constitutionality of Its Acts on Reconstruction. Alarming Tendency of the Seymour Democracy. Speech of Hon..., at Chicago, Ill., August 12th, 1868. (Washington, 1868?). Unbound as issued. Hayman 72-635 1978 $10

CARPENTER, WESLEY M.   Proceedings at the Dinner Given by the Medical Profession of...N. Y....To Oliver Wendell Holmes. New York, 1883. lst ed., illus., tall 8vo., slight wear, orig. cloth, very good. Americanist 103-44 1978 $22.50

CARPENTER, WILLIAM   The Israelites Found in the Anglo-Saxons. London, 1874. 12mo., lst ed. Morrill 239-323 1978 $7.50

CARPENTIER, DOM PIERRE   Alphabetum Tironianum...cum Pluribus Ludovici Pii Chartis. Paris, 1747. plts., folio, cont. bds., uncut. Schumann 511-8 1978 sFr 640

CARPI, UGO DA   Thesauro de Scrittori. N.P.; (Rome), 1530 (i.e. 1545). Sm. 4to., full brown mor., by Lortic, very rare, gilt coat of arms of the Prince d'Essling on sides, woodcuts. Schumann 511-9 1978 sFr 12,000

CARR, BENJAMIN   The Spanish Hymn Arranged & Composed For The Concerts Of The Musical Fund Society Of Philadelphia.... Philadelphia, 1826. Folio, engraved sheet-music, disbound, 8vo. Americanist 101-103 1978 $75

CARR, EMILY   Klee Wyck. Toronto, 1950. Hood 117-202 1978 $30

CARR, HARRY   Los Angeles, City of Dreams. 1935. Illus., first ed., very good. Austin 82-924 1978 $20

CARR, HARRY   The West is Still Wild. Romance of the Present and the Past. Boston, 1932. Cloth, little rubbed, 1st ed. Hayman 72-95 1978 $7.50

CARR, J. A.   The Life and Times of Archbishop Usher, Archbishop of Armagh. 1895. Portraits, maps, octavo, good. Upcroft 10-253 1978 £7.50

CARR, JOHN D.   The Life of Sir Arthur Conan Doyle. 1949. Plts., orig. cloth, 8vo. Howes 194-817 1978 £4.50

CARR, JOHN FOSTER   Guida Degli Stati Uniti Per L'Immigrante Italiano. 1910. Illus. with photos, fldg. map, paper covers, ex-lib., good cond. Austin 79-123 1978 $27.50

CARRACCI, ANNIBALE   Le Arti di Bologna. (Roma), (1966). Folio, loose in folder and slipcase as issued, portrait, plts., fine hand printed ed. on handmade paper, very good, no. 28 of ed. ltd. to 100 copies. King 7-148 1978 £50

CARRICK, ALICE VAN LEER   Collector's Luck in Spain. Boston, 1930. 1st ed., frontispiece, illus. d.j., photos, very good or better. Limestone 9-51 1978 $30

CARRINGTON, HENRY B.   Battles of the American Revolution 1775-1781... New York, (1876). 4to., old 1/2 calf, rubbed, illus. MacManus 239-559 1978 $35

CARRIERES, M. DES   Petit Parnasse Francois ou Recueil de Morceaux Choisis...À l'Usage de la Jeunesse. Londres, 1797. Sq. 12mo, original marbled boards, leather spine, very good. Victoria 34-141 1978 $20

CARRINGTON, J. B.   The Plate of the Worshipful Company of Goldsmiths. Oxford, 1926. 85 plts., 4to, buckram, gilt top. Traylen 88-366 1978 £30

CARRINGTON, MARGARET I.   Absaraka. Chicago, 1950. 12mo., orig. cloth. Morrill 241-251 1978 $7.50

CARRINGTON, RICHARD CHRISTOPHER   Observations on the Spots on the Sun from November 9, 1853 to March 24, 1861, made at Redhill. Edinburgh, 1863. Lg. 4to., plts., orig. blindstamped cloth, partly unopened, stains on upper cover, but fine copy, 1st ed. Norman 5-48 1978 $300

CARROLL, ANNA E.   The Great American Battle... New York, 1856. 1st ed., illus., cloth, old libr. stamp, scarce. MacManus 239-239 1978 $27.50

CARROLL, E. MALCOM   Origins of the Whig Parts. Durham, 1925. 1st ed., maps, fine. MacManus 239-81 1978 $20

CARROLL, GEORGE D.   Art Stationery and Usages of Polite Society. New York, 1879. 16mo., cloth, illus., t.e.g. Battery Park 1-356 1978 $75

CARROLL, GLADYS HASTY   As the Earth Turns. 1933. First ed., signed by author. Austin 82-300 1978 $22.50

CARROLL, GORDON   History in the Writing. 1945. Austin 80-42 1978 $8.50

CARROLL, J.   A History of Texas Baptists. Dallas, 1923. Jenkins 116-63 1978 $45

CARROLL, LEWIS PSEUD.
Please turn to
DODGSON, CHARLES LUTWIDGE

CARROLL, WALLACE   We're in This With Russia. 1942. Ex-lib. Austin 30-43 1978 $7.50

CARRUTHERS, J.   Retrospect of Thirty-six Years' Residence in Canada West. Hamilton, 1861. Orig. cloth, joint tender. Wolfe 39-84 1978 $50

CARSKADON, THOMAS R.   U.S.A. 1949. Paper, ex-lib. Austin 80-477 1978 $10

CARSON, HAMPTON L.   A History of the Historical Society of Pennsylvania. Philadelphia, 1940. 2 vols., illus. MacManus 239-1408 1978 $15

CARSON, JAMES PETIGRU   Life, Letters and Speeches of James Louis Petigru. Washington, 1920. Bell Wiley's copy. Broadfoot's 44-921 1978 $25.00

CARSON, JULIA M. H.   Home Away from Home. 1940. Illus. with photos. Austin 80-44 1978 $11

CARSON, THOMAS   Ranching, Sport and Travel. New York, London, (1912). Pic. cloth, gilt top, illus., 1st Amer. ed., fine copy, slipcase. Dykes 34-202 1978 $65

CARSTARPHEN, JAMES E.   My Trip to California in '49. [Louisiana,] 1914. Illus., original printed wr., 1st ed. Ginsberg 14-90 1978 $37.50

CARSWELL, CATHERINE   The Savage Pilgrimage: A Narrative of D.H. Lawrence. New York, (1932). 8vo., cloth, d.j., 1st Amer. ed., mint. J.S. Lawrence 38-L128 1978 $25

CARSWELL, CATHERINE   The Savage Pilgrimage: a narrative of D. H. Lawrence. 1932. Portrait, very good, soiled & worn d.w., new ed. Bell Book 17-549 1978 £6.50

CARTER, CLARENCE EDWIN   Great Britain and the Illinois Country 1763-1774. Washington, 1910. 1st ed., fine. MacManus 239-82 1978 $22.50

CARTER, CLARENCE EDWIN   The Territory Northwest of the River Ohio 1787-1803. Washington, 1934. 2 vols. Bell Wiley's copy. Broadfoot 46-489 1978 $25

CARTER, CLARENCE EDWIN   The Territory South of the River Ohio 1790-1796. Washington, 1936. Vol. IV, Bell Wiley's copy. Broadfoot 46-488 1978 $20

CARTER, ELIZABETH   Memoirs of .... 1807. 1st. ed., 4to, frontis portrait, little brown spotting & browning, fully rebound in half calf, marbled bds., red label, good. Jarndyce 16-380 1978 £45

CARTER, FREDERICK   D.H. Lawrence and the Body Mystical. London, (1932). Tall 8vo., vellum-backed gilt-stamped pict. parchment, 1st ed., ltd. to 250 no. copies, very fine. J.S. Lawrence 38-L129 1978 $100

CARTER, FREDERICK,   D. H. Lawrence and the Body Mystical. London, 1932. 8vo, red vellum with black pr. on cover, uncut, evidence of water-staining at bottom, signed artist's proof of eng. portrait of Lawrence, no. 15 of 75 copies, 1st ed., collector's cond. Desmarais 1-271 1978 $20

CARTER, HOWARD   The Tomb of Tutankhamen... 1923-33. 3 vols., 1st. ed., frontis, plts., orig. cloth, 8vo. Edwards 1012-217 1978 £90

CARTER, HUNTLEY   The New Spirit in the Cinema. London, (1930). Illus., tall 8vo. Argosy Special-21 1978 $50

CARTER, JOHN   The Firm of Charles Ottley, Landon and Co. Footnote to an Enquiry. London, 1948. Orig. wrs., 1st ed., very good. MacManus 238-887 1978 $35

CARTER, JOHN   Specimens of the Ancient Sculpture and Painting now remaining in England from the earliest period to the Reign of King Henry VIII. London, 1887. New ed., lg. folio, bds., half calf, frontis., coloured plts., good. King 7-340 1978 £50

CARTER, JOHN   Taste and Technique in Book-Collecting... New York, 1948. Orig. cloth, 1st Amer. ed., very good. MacManus 238-886 1978 $17.50

CARTER, RICHARD   Valuable Medical Prescriptions, for the Cure of All Nervous and Putrid Disorders. Cincinnati, 1830. Leather, joints cracked, very rare. Hayman 72-111 1978 $250

CARTER, RUSSELL GORDON   The White Plume of Navarre. Joliet, n.d. 4th ed., color plates, text illus. in color by Beatrice Stevens, fine. Victoria 34-146 1978 $15

CARTER, THOMAS FRANCIS   The Invention of Printing in China and Its Spread Westward. New York, 1925. 8vo., orig. cloth, 1st ed., plts. MacManus 238-888 1978 $30

CARTER, W. C.   History of York Co., Pa. Harrisburg, 1930. New ed., frontis., ltd. to 1,000 copies. MacManus 239-1410 1978 $45

CARTER'S Newburgh City Directory...for the Year Ending June 1st, 1874. Newburgh, 1873. Ads, prtd. bds., dusty. Butterfield 21-330 1978 $17.50

CARTERET, JOHN DUNLOE   A Fortune Hunter: or, the Old Stone Corral. Cincinnati, 1888. Original cloth, 1st ed. Ginsberg 14-230 1978 $25

CARTIER-BRESSON, HENRI   The Decisive Moment. New York, (1952). Folio, photos, pict. bds., d.w. designed by Matisse. Biblo 247-395 1978 $250

CARTON DE WIART, H.   Les Vertus Bourgeioises. Bruxelles, 1912. Thick 4to, slipcase, colored text illus., 1 of 500 copies on "Hollande a la cuve van Gelder". Van der Peet H-64-418 1978 Dfl 150

CARTWRIGHT, EDMUND   Armine and Elvira, a Legendary Tale. 1771. 4to., unbound, fine, first ed. P. M. Hill 142-260 1978 £25

CARTWRIGHT, GEORGE   A Journal of Transactions and Events, During a Residence of Nearly Sixteen Years on the Coast of Labrador... Newark, 1792. 1st. ed., 3 vols., 4to, engraved frontispiece, folding engraved map, half calf, morocco labels, gilt. Deighton 5-202 1978 £995

CARTWRIGHT, JULIA   Isabella d'Este, Marchioness of Mantua, 1474-1539. 1914. 2 vols., plts. Allen 234-1317 1978 $12.50

CARTWRIGHT, JULIA   Isabella D'Este, Marchioness of Mantua 1474-1539, a Study of the Renaissance. New York, (1926). 2 vols., illus. Baldwins' 51-57 1978 $12.50

CARVALHO, DAVID N.   Forty Centuries of Ink. New York, 1904. 1st ed. Battery Park 1-464 1978 $100

CARVER, JONATHAN   Three Years Travels Through the Interior Parts of North America. Edinburgh, 1798. Lacks map, cloth. MacManus 239-83 1978 $35

CARVER, JONATHAN   Travels Through the Interior Parts of North America, in the Years 1766, 1767 and 1768. Dublin, 1779. Engr. plts., fldg. map, 8vo., calf, 2nd ed. & 1st Dublin ed. Salloch 345-42 1978 $300

CARVER, JONATHAN   A Treatise on the Culture of the Tobacco Plant... London, 1779. 1st. ed., sm. 8vo, coloured engraved plts., rebound in late 18th century style half calf, matching bds., gilt. Deighton 5-32 1978 £425

CARVER, ROBIN   Stories of Poland. Boston, 1833. 1st ed., plts., sq. 12mo., orig. cloth, very good. Americanist 103-45 1978 $35

CARVER, THOMAS NIXON   The Essential Factors of Social Evolution. Cambridge, 1935. 8vo. George's 635-1485 1978 £7.50

CARVER, THOMAS NIXON   Human Relations. Boston, 1923. Austin 80-475 1978 $12.50

CARVER, THOMAS NIXON   Principles of National Economy. 1921. 1st ed. Austin 80-473 1978 $20

CARVER, THOMAS NIXON   Principles of Political Economy. 1919. Austin 80-472 1978 $12.50

CARVER, THOMAS NIXON   Principles of Rural Economics. 1911. 1st ed. Austin 80-474 1978 $12.50

CARY, A. D. L.   Regimental Records of the Royal Welch Fusiliers (23rd Foot), 1689-1918. 1921-29. Illus. by G. Hudson, 4 vols., roy. 8vo. George's 635-806 1978 £35

CARY, ALICE   Clovernock; or, Recollections of Our Neighborhood in the West. (1853). 1st. U.K. ed., engraved title-pg., frontis, lg. 12mo, contemp. half calf, very good copy. Fenning 32-58 1978 £9.50

CARY, ALICE   Snow-Berries. Boston, 1867. 1st ed., illus., almost fine. Victoria 34-147 1978 $20

CARY, ELIZABETH LUTHER   William Morris. New York, (1903). Illus., 8vo., orig. cloth. Morrill 241-660 1978 $15

CARY, G. T.   The Lower St. Lawrence, or Quebec to Halifax via Gaspe and Pictou... Quebec, 1862. Hood 116-510 1978 $50

CARY, HENRY FRANCIS   Lives of English Poets From Johnson to Kirke White. London, 1846. Sole ed., orig. blue cloth, a. e.g., very good or better. Limestone 9-54 1978 $40

CARY, JOYCE   The African Witch. 1936. Covers slightly rubbed, some foxing, else very good, first English ed. Bell Book 17-150 1978 £6.50

CARY, JOYCE   An American Visitor. 1933. Very good, slightly worn d.w., first English ed. Bell Book 17-151 1978 £15

CARY, JOYCE   The Drunken Sailor. 1947. Sm. 8vo., 1st ed., illus., cloth, d.w. Quaritch 979-79 1978 $15

CARY, JOYCE   The Drunken Sailor. London, 1947. Very fine in chipped d.w. Desmara's B-131 1978 $20

CARY, JOYCE   Marching Soldier. 1945. Fine, d.w., first English ed. Bell Book 16-151 1978 £18.50

CARY, JOYCE   The Old Strife at Plants. 1956. Ltd. ed. of 100 copies, signed by author & printer, 6 plts., duplicates in colour initialled "J.C.", 8vo, orig. grey bds., fine copy, pres. copy by author. Sawyer 299-114 1978 £375

CARY, JOYCE   To Be a Pilgrim. New York, 1942. First U.S. ed., covers dull, good. Bell Book 16-152 1978 £5

CARY, K.   Arranging Flowers Throughout the Year. 1934. 8vo, orig. cloth. Book Chest 17-473 1978 $10

CARY, M. B.   A Bibliography of the Village Press. Press of the Wooly Whale. Set by hand, 1 of 260 numbered copies, illus., addenda laid in, very fine. Battery Park 1-119 1978 $150

CARY, S. F.   The National Temperance Offering and Sons and Daughters of Temperance Gift. 1850. Lacks backstrip. Austin 82-968 1978 $27.50

CARYL, JOSEPH   Joy Out-Joyed or, Joy in Overcoming Evil Spirits and Evil Men... 1646. Good. Jarndyce 16-9 1978 £9.50

CASA, GIOVANNI DELLA 1503-56   Galateo. 1774. Fcap. 8vo., fine, contemp. calf, first ed. Howes 194-225 1978 £35

CASANOVA DE SEINGALT, GIACOMO GIROLAMO   Memoirs. 1922. Ltd. to 1,000 sets, frontispieces, 12 vols., roy. 8vo., orig. qtr. parchment, spines soiled, some lettering-panels rubbed. George's 635-880 1978 £15

CASAREGI, GIUSEPPE MARIA   Il Consolato del Mare colla Spiegazione di Giuseppe Maria Casaregi.... Venezia, 1737. Finely pr. Italian ed., quarto, full contemp stiff vellum, fine, uncut copy. Bennett 20-37 1978 $200

CASAS, BARTOLOME DE LAS   La Liberta. Ventia, 1636. Mottled bds., cloth back. Biblo 247-77 1978 $57.50

CASAS, BARTOLOME DE LAS   La Liberta. Ventia, 1640. Bds., cloth back. Biblo 247-76 1978 $48.50

CASAS, BARTOLOME DE LAS   Narratio Regionum Indicarum Per Hispanos Quosdam Devastatarum Verissima. Frankfurt, 1598. Engraved title, copperplts., 4to, old vellum, soiled, outer margin of title skilfully restores, few ink stains in text. Edwards 1012-631 1978 £300

CASAS, BARTOLOME DE LAS   Tryannies et Cruautez Des Espagnols... Rouen, 1630. Sm. 4to, calf, rebacked, sides rubbed, some slight browning to text, few passages underlined in ink. Edwards 1012-632 1978 £150

CASE, JOHN   Sphaera Civitatis, Authore Magistro Johanne Caso Oxeniensi, Olim Collegii Divi.... Oxoniae, 1588. 1st ed., octavo, full early vellum, marginalia in contemporary hand and notations on fly-leaves, rare. Bennett 20-38 1978 $360

CASE, THOMAS   A Model of True Spiritual Thanksgiving. 1646. Good. Jarndyce 16-10 1978 £7.50

CASE, THOMAS   A Sermon..Before the.. House of Commons Aug. 22, 1645..for Their Solemn Thanksgiving..to the Forces of Parliament..in Gaining Bath, Bridgewater, Scarborough Castle, Sherborn Castle, for the Dispersing of the Clubmen and the Goode Success in Pembroke-shire. 1645. Good. Jarndyce 16-7 1978 £12.50

CASE as to the Legality of the Arrest & Imprisonment of William Smith O'Brien.... 1846. 1st ed., disbound, t.p. dusty & marked, good, octavo bound in cloth. Hyland 128-202 1978 £15

THE CASE of the Importation of Bar-Iron,.... London, 1756. 8vo, disbound, 1st ed., very uncommon. Ximenes 47-14 1978 $200

CASEY, DANIEL E.   Slash Those Taxes. 1948. Austin 80-476 1978 $8.50

CASEY, JOHN K.   Reliques of .... Dublin, 1878. 1st. collected ed., cr. 8vo, orig. green cloth, gilt, nice copy. Fenning 32-59 1978 £16

CASEY, ROBERT J.   Battle Below. 1945. Illus., 1st ed. in slightly frayed dust jacket. Austin 80-45 1978 $12.50

CASEY, ROBERT J.   The Black Hills and Their Incredible Characters. (1949). Illus. Biblo 247-194 1978 $15

CASEY, ROBERT J.   Four faces of Siva: the detective story of vanished race. London-Sydney, 1929. Cloth, maps, plans, plts., illus., 8vo. Van der Peet 127-41 1978 Dfl 55

CASEY, ROBERT J.   Torpedo Junction. 1942. Illus. Austin 80-46 1978 $8.50

CASEY, SILAS   U. S. Infantry Tactics for the Instruction, Exercise, and Maneuvres of the United States Infantry... Philadelphia & New York, 1862. 3 vols., fldg. plts. Bell Wiley's copy. Broadfoot 46-34 1978 $60

CASGRAIN, L'ABBE H. R.   Extraits des Archives des Ministeres de la Marine et de la Guerre a Paris. Quebec, 1890. 4to., broche. Wolfe 39-85 1978 $15

CASGRAIN, P. B.   L'habitation de Samos. 1906. Illus. Hood 116-511 1978 $10

CASGRAIN, P. B.   The Monument to Wolfe on the Plains of Abraham, and the Old Statue at "Wolfe's Corner." 1904. Hood 116-512 1978 $7.50

CASKEY, WILLIE MALVIN   Secession and Restoration of Louisiana. University, 1938. Bell Wiley's copy. Broadfoot's 44-508 1978 $25

CASPARY, VERA   Bedelia. 1945. Slight fading of covers, else very good, d.w., first English ed. Bell Book 17-218 1978 £5.50

CASPER, LEOPOLD   A Textbook of Genito-Urinary Diseases Including Sexual Disorders in Man. Philadelphia, 1909. Second ed. Rittenhouse 49-127 1976 $15

CASS, LEWIS   Substance of a Speech Delivered by Hon. Lewis Cass of Michigan, in Secret Session of the Senate of the United States, on the Ratification of the Oregon Treaty with Additions.... Detroit, (c. 1846). Sewn as issued, 1st ed. Ginsberg 14-808 1978 $75

CASSA, LUIGI   An Introduction to the Study of Political Economy. London, 1893. 1st English ed. Austin 80-524 1978 $27.50

CASSAU, THEODOR   The Consumers Co-operative Movement in Germany. New York, (1925). Biblo BL781-805 1978 $9

CASSEL, DANIEL K.   History of the Mennonites Historically and Biographically Arranged From the Time of the Reformation. Philadelphia, 1888. Illus. Baldwins' 51-428 1978 $27.50

CASSERLY, LIEUT.-COL.   Algeria Today. London, c.1922. 8vo, orig. cloth, 24 plts. K Books 239-88 1978 £5

CASSIDY, P. J.   The Catholic Home Library. Ca. 1915. 2 vol., illus. Austin 79-124 1978 $17.50

CASSINI DE THURY, C. F.   La Meridienne de l'Observatoire Royal de Paris. Paris, 1744. 4to., old calf, repaired, vignettes, first ed., plts. Gurney 75-18 1978 £75

CASSIRER, ERNST   The Myth of the State. New Haven, 1946. Tall 8vo., cloth, 1st ed. Salloch 348-26 1978 $15

CASSIUS, ANDREAS   De extremo illo et perfactissimo naturae opificio ac principe terraenorum sidere auro. Hamburg, 1685. Very rare 1st ed., contemp. vellum, 8vo, foxing. Gilhofer 75-22 1978 SFr 1,200

CASSIUS DIO COCCEIANUS   Dionis Nicaei Rerum Romanorum a Pompeio Magno ad Alexandrum Mamaeae, Epitome authore Ioanne Xiphilino. Paris, 1551. 4to., old calf, rebacked. Gilhofer 74-62 1978 sFr 900

CASSON, JEAN   Picasso. New York, (1940). 1st American ed., plts., some color, folio, d.j., very good. Houle 10-259 1978 $40

CASTANEDA, CARLOS E.   The Mexican Side of the Texas Revolution. Dallas, 1928. 1st ed., illus., endpaper maps, nice. Limestone 9-55 1978 $65

CASTANEDA, CARLOS E.   The Mexican Side of the Texas Revolution, by the Chief Mexican Participants. Dallas, 1928. 1st ed. Jenkins 116-1579 1978 $75

CASTANEDA, CARLOS E.   Our Catholic Heritage in Texas, 1519-1936. Austin, 1936-1958. 7 vols., large quarto, plates, folding maps, extremely fine, bright set, 1st ed. of each vol. Jenkins 116-204 1978 $875

CASTEEL, D. GERARDUS   Controversiae Ecclesiastico-Historicae utiliter curiosae, non Compositae.... Cologne, 1734. Fine engrav. frontispiece, sm. 4to., contemp. calf. Howes 194- 532 1978 £15

CASTELLI, BARTOLOMEO   Amaltheum Castello-Brunonianum: sive Lexicon Medicum. Nuremberg, 1688. 4to., contemp. calf, repaired and rebacked, portrait, first ed. Gurney 75-19 1978 £30

CASTELLI, BARTOLOMEO   Amaltheum Castello-Brunonianum. Norimbergae, 1688. 3 vols., frontis., 4to., old calf, backs richly gilt. Offenbacher 30-22 1978 $300

CASTELLO, GABRIELE L.   Le Antiche Iscrizioni di Palermo, Raccolte, e Spiegate. Palermo, 1762. Plts., folio, strong 19th cent. half calf. Howes 194-563 1978 £45

CASTER, M.   Etudes sur Alexandre ou Le Faux Prophete de Lucien. 1938. Browned. Allen 234-561 1978 $7.50

CASTERLEIN, A. S. J.   The Congo State. London, 1907. Cr. 8vo, wrappers slightly frayed. K Books 239-89 1978 £10

CASTI, GIOVANNI BATTISTA   Poesie Liriche di Gio. Adrianopoli, 1795. 12mo., marbled bds., calf spine, very good. King 7-149 1978 £20

CASTIGLIONE, BALDASSARE   Il Libro del Cortegiano. Venice, 1528. 1st ed., small folio, contemp. dark brown calf, gilt lettering on spine and panels. Gilhofer 75-23 1978 SFr 15,000

CASTIGLIONE, BALDASSARE   Il Libro Del Cortegiano... Venice, 1571. Port., 4to., bds. Salloch 348-29 1978 $75

CASTIGLIONE, BALDASSARE   Opere Volgari, e Latine. Padova, 1733. 4to., vellum, very good, portrait plt. King 7-150 1978 £50

CASTILLO, BERNAL DIAZ DEL
Please turn to
DIAZ DEL CASTILLO, BERNAL

CASTLE, W. E.   Genetics and Eugenics. London, 1925. Third ed. Rittenhouse 49-128 1976 $10

CASTLEMAN, JOHN B.   Active Service. Louisville, 1917. Cover slightly worn, Bell Wiley's copy. Broadfoot's 44-496 1978 $100

CASTOR, HENRY   The Spanglers. Garden City, 1948. Signed by Castor, very good in dw. Bernard 5-510 1978 $7.50

CASTRO, J. PAUL DE   The Gordon Riots. 1926. Illus., 8vo. George's 635-591 1978 £10.50

CASTRONE, BENEDETTO MARIA DEL   Il Vero Nuovo Geodeta Siciliano.... Roma, 1733. 4to., cloth backed bds., diagrams, plt., first ed. King 7-151 1978 £30

CASWALL, H.   The Western World Revisited. Oxford, 1854. Sm. 8vo., orig. cloth. Edwards 1012-386 1978 £10

CATALANI, GIUSEPPE   Prefazioni...agli Annali D'Italia Compilati da Lodovico Antonio Muratori. Milano, 1756. 8vo., calf, new spine, gilt. King 7-152 1978 £15

CATANEO, PIETRO DI GIACOMO   Le Pratiche Delle due Prime Mathematiche.... Venice, 1546. Sm. 4to., woodcut diagrams, large, clean copy, recent vellum, earliest recorded ed. Quaritch 977-141 1978 $700

CATE, WIRT ARMISTEAD   Lucius Q. C. Lamar- Secession and Reunion. Chapel Hill, 1935. Pres. copy from author to Bell Wiley. Broadfoot's 44-894 1978 $14

CATHER, WILLA   December Night. New York, 1933. 8vo, printed boards, 1st ed. in this format, near Mint, repaired d.w. Desmarais 1-75 1978 $15

CATHER, WILLA   Lucy Gayheart. New York, 1935. Orig. cloth, pub. slipcase, 1st ed., ltd. to 750 signed copies, fine. MacManus 238-629 1978 $90

CATHER, WILLA   Lucy Gayheart. New York, 1935. Blue buckram, 1st ed., 1 of 749 signed by author, fine in dust jacket & slipcase. Bradley 49-63 1978 $100

CATHER, WILLA   Lucy Grayheart. New York, 1935. 8vo, blue cloth, bevelled edges, Croxley rag paper, uncut, t.e.g., spine sun-faded, Mint, orig. box and acetate wr., no. 642 of ed. limited to 749 copies, 1st ed. Desmarais 1-77 1978 $80

CATHER, WILLA   Lucy Grayheart. New York, 1935. 8vo, green cloth, pr. labels, stated 1st ed., d.w. somewhat rubbed and chipped, collector's cond. Desmarais 1-76 1978 $12.50

CATHER, WILLA   My Mortal Enemy. 1928. First English ed., vignettes, orig. cloth backed bds., fine, d.w., 8vo. Howes 194-713 1978 £6.50

CATHER, WILLA   Obscure Destinities. New York, 1932. 8vo, green cloth, paper labels, stated 1st ed., spine sun-faded, collector's cond. Desmarais 1-78 1978 $10

CATHER, WILLA   The Old Beauty and Others. New York, 1948. 8vo, red stamped cloth, stated 1st ed., d.w. slightly chipped, mint. Desmarais 1-79 1978 $10

CATHER, WILLA   One of Ours. New York, 1922. 8vo, gray-green cloth 1st trade ed., uncut, collector's cond. Desmarais 1-80 1978 $25

CATHER, WILLA   Sapphira and the Slave Girl. New York, 1940. Green bds. & cloth, gilt, 1st ed., 1 of 520 signed by author, fine in dust jacket & slipcase. Bradley 49-64 1978 $85

CATHER, WILLA   Sapphira and the Slave Girl. New York, 1940. 1st ed., d.w., bookplt. Biblo BL781-902 1978 $9.50

CATHER, WILLA   Sapphria and the Slave Girl. New York, 1940. Hood 116-456 1978 $10

CATHER, WILLA   Sapphira and the Slave Girl. New York, 1940. Ownership inscription, nice in chipped d.w. Desmarais B-135 1978 $10

CATHER, WILLA   Shadows on the Rock. New York, 1931. 8vo., red decor. vellum binding, uncut, 1st ed., 1 of only 199 copies on Japan vellum, signed by Willa Cather, d.w., t.e.g. Battery Park 1-195 1978 $200

CATHERINE DE MEDICIS   Lettres, publiees par M. le Cte. H. de la Ferriere, tome 4me., 1570-74. 1891. 4to., half calf, rubbed. George's 635-593 1978 £8.50

CATHOLIC CHURCH. LITURGY & RITUAL. HOURS   A La Louenge de Dieu... Furent Commencees ces Presentes Heures pour Anthoine Verard Libraire Demourant sur le Pont Nostredame a Lymaige Saint Jehan Levangeliste... Paris, 1498. 4to., printed on vellum, illus. uncolored, initials in gold, fine, old quarter mor. Quaritch 978-79 1978 $16,500

CATHOLIC CHURCH. LITURGY & RITUAL. HOURS   Horae in Laudem Dei, ac Beatissimae Virginis Mariae... Paris, 1555. Sm. 8vo., Roman letter, woodcuts in the style of Geoffrey Tory, cont. parisian binding of calf, stamped in gold. Quaritch 978-80 1978 $4,250

CATHOLIC CHURCH. LITURGY & RITUAL. HOURS.   A Book of Hours. New York, 1937. First ed., ltd. to 550 copies, signed by artist, plts. by Donald Culross Peattie, v.f., uncut, orig. slipcase. Victoria 34-841 1978 $50

CATHOLIC CHURCH. LITURGY & RITUAL. MISSAL   Canon Sacratissime Misse une cum Expositione eiusdem... Nuremburg, 1503. Sm. 4to., Gothic letter, old blind stamped mor., woodcut. Quaritch 978-110 1978 $750

CATHOLIC CHURCH. LITURGY & RITUAL. MISSAL.   Missale ad Veru et Integru Insignis Ecclesie Parisien Ritu. Paris, 1504. Woodcuts, 5 painted in colours and heightened with gold, folio, 18th cent. mor., raised bands, handsome book, bookplt. of John Sterne. Thomas 37-58 1978 £850

CATHOLIC CHURCH. LITURGY & RITUAL. MISSAL.   Missal Gothica Seu Mozarabica... Los Angeles, 1770. First Mexican ed., sm. folio, plts., engr. orig. binding of chestnut calf, gilt. Quaritch 978-106 1978 $1,500

CATHOLIC CLUB OF N. Y.   Columbus Memorial Volume. 1893. Illus., ex-lib. Austin 79-126 1978 $27.50

CATLIN, GEORGE   The Breath of Life or Mal-Respiration... New York, 1872. Illus., orig. cloth, good. MacManus 239-1152 1978 $30

CATLIN, GEORGE   Illustrations of the Manners, Customs, and Condition of the North American Indians... London, 1848. 2 vols., 7th ed., 350 engravings from author's orig. paintings, rebound in red cloth with gold stamping on spine, little light foxing. Hood's 115-744 1978 $100

CATLIN, GEORGE   Illustrations of the Manners, Customs, and Condition of the North American Indians. London, 1843. Engrs. from author's orig. paintings, 2 vols., 7th ed., rebound in red cloth with gold stamping on spine, little light foxing. Hood 117-671 1978 $125

CATLIN, GEORGE   Letters and Notes on the Manners, Customs and Condition of the North American Indians. New York, 1844. 2 vols., third ed., illus., bindings rubbed, contents fine. Biblo 247-58 1978 $250

CATTON, BRUCE   The War Lords of Washington. 1948. Austin 80-47 1978 $8.50

CATULLUS, GAIUS VALERIUS   Opera. Birminghamiae, Baskerville Press, 1772. 1st Baskerville ed., 4to., 1st state, internally clean & unfoxed, bound in later 1/2 brown mor. over green cloth bds., nice copy. Current 245-248 1978 $225

CATULLUS, GAIUS VALERIUS   The Poems of... New York, 1950. Biblo 251-262 1978 $15

CAUCHY, AUGUSTIN LOUIS   Quelques Mots aux Hommes de Bon Sens et de Bonne Fois. Prague, 1833. 2nd ed., 8vo., orig. printed wrs., light marginal waterstain, very rare 1st ed. Gilhofer 74-11 1978 sFr 300

CAUGHEY, JOHN WALTON   History of the Pacific Coast of North America. New York, 1938. Illus., maps, excellent. Hood 117-882 1978 $35

CAULFIELD, JAMES   Portraits, Memoirs, and Characters of Remarkable Persons, 1688 to the end of the Reign of George II. 1819. Engraved plts., 4 vols., roy. 8vo., parchment, rubbed and soiled. George's 635-592 1978 £35

CAULO, A.   Nouvelle Collection de Lettres de Differentes Genres a l'Usage de M. M. les Peintres, Graveurs... Paris, n.d. (1845). 4to., orig. pr. wrs., half cloth. Schumann 511-10 1978 sFr640

CAUSTIC, CHRISTOPHER   Terrible Tractoration. New York, 1804. First Amer. ed., needs binding, title page present but loose, broken. Rittenhouse 49-130 1976 $20

CAUTHEN, CHARLES EDWARD   South Carolina Goes to War 1860-1865. Chapel Hill, 1950. New cloth, Bell Wiley's copy. Broadfoot's 44-607 1978 $16

CAUTLEY, G. S.   The Fairy Fountains: A Faery Epic of Euboea... 1869. 1st. ed., green half title, orig. purple cloth, v.g. Jarndyce 16-382 1978 £8.50

CAUTLEY, H. MUNRO   Suffold Churches and Their Treasures. London, 1938. 2nd. ed., sm. 4to, orig. cloth, 3 colour & other photos. Sexton 7-101 1978 £12

CAVALCANTI, BARTOLOMEO   Trattati Overo Discorsi Sopra Gli Ottimi Regimenti Delle Republiche Antiche Et Moderne. Venice, 1571. 4to., vellum, loose in bind., sone pgs. slightly foxed. Salloch 348-30 1978 $135

CAVALIERI, BONAVENTURA   Lo Specchio Ustorio Overo Trattato Delle Settione Coniche, et Alcuni Loro Mirabili Effecti Intorno al Lume, Caldo, Freddo, Suono, e Moto Ancora. Bologna, 1632. Plts., 4to., old limp vellum, 1st ed., very rare, fine copy. Offenbacher 30-24 1978 $400

CAVALIERI, BONAVENTURA   Trattato della Ruota Planetaria Perpetua e Dell'uso di Quella.... Bologna, 1646. 1st ed., quarto, numerous tables, quarter calf over modern boards, original endpapers with contemporary MS notes retained, lightly foxed. Bennett 20-39 1978 $600

CAVALIERI, BONAVENTURA   Trigonometria Plana, et Sphaerica, Linearis, & Logarithmica. Bologna, 1643. Sm. 4to., engrav. frontispiece, engrav. plt., old vellum. Quaritch 977-142 1978 $225

CAVALIERI, P. F. DE   Specimina Codicum Graecorum Vaticanorum.
1910. 4to., plts. Allen 234-174 1978 $15

CAVALLO, TIBERIUS   A Complete Treatise on Electricity in Theory and
Practice. London, 1777. 8vo., plts., contemp. calf, rebacked, first ed.
Quaritch 977-89 1978 $225

CAVALLO, TIBERIUS   A Complete Treatise of Electricity. London,
1777. 8vo., ads, fldg. plts., contemp. calf, gilt, little rubbed & staining, but
very good copy, 1st ed. Norman 5-49 1978 $300

CAVALLO, TIBERIUS   A Complete Treatise on Electricity. London,
1786. 2 vols., 8vo., fldg. plts., old half calf, gilt, some foxing, but very good
set, 3rd ed. with additions. Norman 5-49a 1978 $200

CAVALLO, TIBERIUS   The Elements of Natural or Esperimental Philosophy. London, 1803. 1st ed, octavo, four vols., plates, 3/4 calf, marbled
boards and edges, owner's signature neatly inscribed on versos of t.p. Bennett
20-40 1978 $550

CAVALLOTTO, GIANDOMENICO   Saggio Di Osservazioni Particolari Sopra lo
stato in cui attrovasi presentemente la Naval Costruzione in Venezia. Venice,
1766. 8vo., contemp. calf, plts. F. Edwards 1013-39 1978 £50

CAVANAUGH, MICHAEL   Memoirs of Gen. Thomas Francis Meagher.
Worcester, 1892. Pictorial cover, hinges cracked, spine rubbed, Bell Wiley's copy.
Broadfoot's 44-563 1978 $20

CAVANAGH, WILLIAM HENRY   The Word Protestant. Philadelphia, 1899.
Austin 79-129 1978 $20

CAVE, WILLIAM   Apostolici: or, The History of the Lives, Acts,
Death and Martyrdom of those Who Were Contemporary With, or Immediately
Succeeded the Apostles. 1716. 4th ed., engraved frontis, engraved title-pg.,
folio, contemp. calf, neatly & recently rebacked, nice copy. Fenning 32-
61 1978 £15

CAVE, WILLIAM   Primitive Christianity. 1675. 2nd ed., old
calf, worn, spine defective. George's 635-1043 1978 £7.50

CAVE, WILLIAM   Primitive Christianity. 1676. 3 parts in 1 vol.,
thk. cr. 8vo., contemp. calf, sometime rebacked. Howes 194-26 1978 £25

CAVE-BROWNE-CAVE, GENILLE   From Cowby to Pulpit. London, 1926.
Cloth, illus., 1st ed., little worn, very good copy, slipcase, scarce. Dykes
34-131 1978 $50

CAVENDISH, GEORGE   The Life of Cardinal Wolsey. 1827. 2nd. ed.,
plts., cloth-backed bds., label rubbed, stain on bottom margin of prelims., good,
octavo. Upcroft 10-26 1978 £8.50

CAVENDISH, HENRY   Government of Canada. Debates of the House of
Commons in the Year 1774, on the Bill for Making More Effectual Provision for the
Government of the Province of Quebec... London, 1839. Map, inscribed. Hood
116-513 1978 $135

CAVENDISH, HENRY   Observations on Mr. Hutchin's Experiments for
Determining the Degree of Cold at Which Quicksilver Freezes. London, 1784.
Lg. 4to., stitched as issued, unopened, very fine. Offenbacher 30-25 1978
$225

CAVVADIAS, P.   Les Musees d'Athenes. Pt. I: - Fouilles de Acro-
pole. Athens, 1886. In Greek, German, French and English, lg. 4to., plts.,
stiff wrs. Biblo BL781-347 1978 $12.50

CAWEIN, MADISON   The Poet and Nature and the Morning Road. Louisville, (1914). Orig. binding. Wolfe 39-87 1978 $15

CAWSE, JOHN   Introduction to the Art of Painting in Oil
Colours. London, 1822. 8vo., original quarter roan and drab boards, red printed
paper side-label (binding soiled, but sound), 1st ed. Ximenes 47-49 1978 $125

CAXTON, WILLIAM   The History of Reynard the Foxe. (Hammersmith:
The Kelmscott Press, 1892). Lg. 4to., full vellum, gilt-lettered spine, ltd. to 300
copies, very light browning to a few leaves, else fine, almost unopened. Howell
5-38 1978 $500

CAXTON Club Exhibition of Whistleriana from the Collection of Walter S. Brewster. Chicago, 1917. 12mo., wr., illus. Battery Park 1-318 1978 $35

CAXTON'S Game and Playe of the Chesse, 1474. 1883. Lg. 8vo., qtr. roan,
uncut, woodcuts. P. M. Hill 142-69 1978 £24

CAYLEY, GEORGE   Aeronautical and Miscellaneous Note-Book
(ca. 1799-1826). Cambridge, 1933. 4to., 2 facsimile MS. leaves, orig. prtd.
wrs., fine copy, 1st ed. Norman 5-53a 1978 $50

CEBA, ANSALDO   Il Cittadino di Repubblica. Milano, 1830.
2 vols. in 1, 16mo., marbled bds., roan spine gilt, very good. King 7-153
1978 £15

CECIL, ALICIA MARGARET (TYSSEN-AMHERST) - HON. MRS. EVELYN CECIL
Please turn to
ROCKLEY, ALICIA MARGARET (TYSSEN-AMHERST) CECIL, BARONESS

CELERIER, P.   Menaces sur le Viet-Nam. Saigon, 1950.
Illus., 8vo., orig. covers. Van der Peet 127-43 1978 Dfl 35

CELESIA, DOROTHEA   Almida, A Tragedy..By a Lady. Dublin, 1771.
1st. Irish ed., 12mo, wrapper, nice copy. Fenning 32-62 1978 £18

CELINE, LOUIS-FERDINAND   Death on the Instalment Plan. 1938. Very good,
somewhat worn d.w., first English ed. Bell Book 17-153 1978 £18.50

CELLARIUS, ANDREAS   Regni Poloniae, Magnique Ducatus Lituaniae.
Amstelodami, 1659. Sm. 12mo., cloth, very good, upper hinge broken. King
7-271 1978 £100

CELLARIUS, CHRISTOPHORUS   Geographia Antiqua, Luxta et Nova. Jena,
1731. 2 vols. in 1, frontis., very thick 12mo., vellum. Salloch 345-44 1978
$90

CELLARIUS, CHRISTOPHORUS   Geographia Antiqua. London, 1745. 5th ed.,
8vo., cont. calf, maps. Salloch 345-43 1978 $135

CELLARIUS, CHRISTOPHORUS   Historia Antiqua Multis Accessionibus aucta
et emenda,.... Cizae,1685. 1st ed., 12mo, contemporary calf with gilt back.
Bennett 20-41 1978 $300

CELLINI, BENVENUTO   Due Trattati. Florence, 1568. 4to., contemp.
limp vellum, some foxing, but fine copy, 1st ed. Norman 5-54 1978 $1,750

CELLINI, BENVENUTO   The Life of Benvenuto Celini: a Florentine
Artist. London, 1771. 2 vols., 8vo, contemporary calf, spines gilt, contrasting
morocco labels, 1st ed., frontispiece portrait, very fine and pretty copy. Ximenes
47-50 1978 $250

CELLINI, BENVENUTO   The Life of Benvenuto Cellini. Vale Press, 1900.
2 vols., folio, half red mor., raised bands, fine, only 310 copies were printed.
Howes 194-1299 1978 £45

CELLINI, BENVENUTO   Life of, Written by Himself. New York, 1906.
Portrait, plts., 2 vols., 8vo, half red morocco, mottled cloth sides, gilt top.
Traylen 88-133 1978 £20

CELLINI, BENVENUTO   The Life of... New York, (1906). 2 vols., illus., 1st of this ed., 3/4 leather, rubbed, name on t.pgs. Biblo BL781-903 1978
$18.50

CELLINI, BENVENUTO   The Life of... Written by Himself. Verona for
the Limited Editions Club, 1937. Folio, illus. by Fritz Kredel, orig. patterned
cloth, mor. label, pub. box, 1 of 1,500 copies, signed by illustrator, some foxing,
otherwise fine, d.j. MacManus 238-816 1978 $35

CELLINI, BENVENUTO   Due Trattati uno intorno alle otto principali arti
dell'oreficeria,.... Florence, 1568. Rare 1st ed., XVIIIth century vellum, gilt
back, light marginal waterstain, very fine, 4to. Gilhofer 75-24 1978 SFr 5,200

CELLINI, BENVENUTO   Vita di Benvenuto Cellini...Nella Quale Molte
Curiose Particolarita si Toccano Appartenenti alle Arti ed all l Istoria del suo Tempo,
tratto da un l ottimo Manoscritto... (Florence, 1792). 4to., half calf antique, a
counterfeit of the 1st ed. of 1728. Quaritch 983-166 1978 $100

CELSUS, AURELIUS CORNELIUS   De Re Medica, libri octo eruditissimi.
1528. 4to., contemp. vellum, rebacked, sm. stains, very good & complete
copy from library of Dr. Alfred M. Hellman, laid in brown cloth slipcase, scarce,
rare 1st ed., prtd. in italics. Zeitlin 245-38 1978 $750

CELSUS, ARELIUS CORNELIUS   De Re Medica Libri Octo. 1542. Sm. 8vo.,
old bds., backed in calf, faint dampstain, good copy, rare. Zeitlin 245-39
1978 $175

CELSUS, AURELIUS CORNELIUS   Medicinae Libri. 1528. 8vo., old vellum
over bds., dampstain, very good copy laid in a half red mor. slipcase, gilt with
ties. Zeitlin 245-37 1978 $850

CELSUS, AURELIUS CORNELIUS   Ueber Die Arzneiwissenschaft. Braunschweig, 1906. German trans., thick 8vo., half cloth.   Salloch 345-46 1978 $55

CENDRARS, BLAISE   La Fin du Monde Filmee par l'Ange Notre-Dame. Paris, 1919. 4to., orig. pict. wrs., lst ed., illus. by Fernand Leger, numbered copy on velin Lafuma paper. Goldschmidt 110-44A 1978 $475

CENDRARS, BLAISE   Kodak. Paris, 1924. 12mo., orig. wr., uncut, lst ed., issued in ltd. number, l of 77 numbered copies on Holland Van Gelder paper. Goldschmidt 110-47 1978 $250

CENDRARS, BLAISE   Panama: or, The Adventures of My Seven Uncles. New York, 1931. Illus., pic. wrs., partly unopened, numbered slipcase, defective, l of 300 numbered copies signed by Cendrars & Dos Passos. Dawson's 447-210 1978 $50

CENDRARS, BLAISE   Petits Contes Negres pour les Enfants des Blancs. Argenteuil, 1929. 4to., illus. by Pierre Pinsard, uncut, orig. dec. wrs., one of 500 copies, fine, orig. drawing. Quaritch 978-30 1978 $680

CENNI, GIACOMO MARIA   Della Vita di Gaio Cilnio Mecenate Cavaliere Romano. Roma, 1684. Sm. 8vo., vellum. King 7-29 1978 £20

CENTENARY Celebration of the Battle of Lundy's Land, July 25, 1914. Niagara Falls, 1919. Card cover, illus., signed by R.W. Geary. Hood 116-738 1978 $20

THE CENTENNIAL Celebration of General Sullivan's Campaign Against the Iroquois in 1779. (Waterloo, 1880). 8vo., illus., fine, lst ed., orig. cloth. Morrill 241-406 1978 $15

CENTRAL TYPE FOUNDRY   Specimens of Brass Type for Bookbinders, Also of Copper Alloy Type... (St. Louis?), 1893. Tall thin 8vo., orig. flexible cloth. Americanist 102-27 1978 $50

A CENTURY of Service to Dentistry 1844-1944. Philadelphia, 1944. Illus. Austin 80-540 1978 $12.50

A CENTURY of the National Bank of Germantown 1814-1914. N.P., n.d. Illus., orig. cloth. MacManus 239-1606 1978 $10

CEREMONIAL de l'Empire Francais. Paris, 1805. 8vo., half calf, handcolored frontis., handcolored costume plts. Van der Peet H-64-486 1978 Dfl 125

CEREMONIAL des Religieuses Hospitalieres de la Misericorde de Jesus, Ordre de St. Augustin. Quebec, 1882. 3/4 lea., nouvelle ed., rev. & corrected. Hood 17-343 1978 $200

CEREMONIAL Des Religieuses Hospitalieres de la Misericorde de Jesue, Ordre de St. Augustin. Quebec, 1882. Nouvelle ed., rev. ed.corr., 3/4 leather. Hood's 115-921 1978 £17.50

CERILLO, EDOARDO   Dipinti Murali Di Pompei Medaglie Istituto d' Incoraggiamento di Napoli.... (1888). Elephant folio, green levant mor., joints cracking, a.e.g., fine plts. King 7-155 1978 £50

CERTIFIED Copies of Ancient Field Notes & Maps, Totten and Crossfield's Purchase, 1772, Macomb's Purchase, 1796, Old Military Tract, 1787-1797. 1905. Lg. fldg. maps, fine cond, stiff wr. Butterfield 21-248 1978 $25

CERVANTES SAAVEDRA, MIGUEL DE   The History of Valorous and Witty Knight Errant Don Quixote of the Mancha. London, 1675. Quarto, fine early Spanish-style half calf over brown marbled bds., former owner's signature. Bennett 7-27 1978 $250

CERVANTES SAAVEDRA, MIGUEL DE   The History of the renowned Don Quixote de la Mancha. 1743. Engraved plts., 3 vols., contemp. mottled calf, recently rebacked modern mor. George's 635-1275 1978 £10.50

CERVANTES SAAVEDRA, MIGUEL DE   The History and Adventures of the Renowned Don Quixote. 1755. Plts., 2 vols., 4to., contemp. calf, orig. labels preserved, first ed. Howes 194-468 1978 £65

CERVANTES SAAVEDRA, MIGUEL DE   The Life and Exploits of the Ingenious Gentleman Don Quixote de la Mancha. London, 1809. 4 vols., 16mo., contemp. mottled calf fully gilt, neat. K Books 244-63 1978 £18

CERVANTES SAAVEDRA, MIGUEL DE   The History and Adventures of the renowned Don Quixote. 1818. Frontispiece, 2 vols., 12mo., full navy calf. Howes 194-201 1978 £12.50

CERVANTES SAAVEDRA, MIGUEL DE   Don Quixote de la Mancha.... 1818. 4 vols., 8vo., plts., half green mor. Quaritch 983-308 1978 $225

CERVANTES SAAVEDRA, MIGUEL DE   The History of the renowned Don Quixote de la Mancha. 1819. Fine coloured engr. plts., 4 vols., full straight grained mor. gilt, gilt inside borders, fine. George's 635-1276 1978 £150

CERVANTES SAAVEDRA, MIGUEL DE   L'ingenieux Hidalgo Don Quichotte de la Manche. Paris, 1863. 2 vols., lg. folio, publisher's binding, orig. red cloth stamped in gilt, uncut, 1st issue. Goldschmidt 110-17 1978 $325

CERVANTES SAAVEDRA, MIGUEL DE   The History of the renowned Don Quixote de la Mancha. 1885. Map, 4 vols., 8vo. George's 635-1277 1978 £10.50

CERVANTES SAAVEDRA, MIGUEL DE   Don Quixote. London, 1888. l of 250 on Dutch handmade paper, 5 vol., very good. Ballinger 11-120 1978 $75.00

CERVANTES SAAVEDRA, MIGUEL DE   Don Quixote de la Mancha. New York, 1941. Illus. Biblo BL781-616 1978 $10

CERVANTES SAAVEDRA, MIGUEL DE   Don Quixote. New York, 1949. 2 vols. Biblo BL781-904 1978 $17.50

CERVANTES SAAVEDRA, MIGUEL DE   Don Quixote. The Ingenious Gentleman of La Mancha. (Imprenta Nuevo Mundo, Mexico City): The Limited Editions Club, 1950. 2 vols., 4to., orig. cloth-backed marbled bds., mor. labels, pub. box, ltd. to 1500 sets, fine. MacManus 238-817 1978 $60

CERVANTES SAAVEDRA, MIGUEL DE   La Galatea, Romanzo Pastorale.... Ginerva, 1788. 1/4 calf. Eaton 45-92 1978 £5

CESALPINO, ANDREA   De Plantis Libri XVI. Florentiae, 1583. 4to., woodcut, contemp. vellum painted pink & brown, gilt lettering on spine, lightly browned & foxed, sm. hole, fine copy, lst ed., rare. Zeitlin 245-40 1978 $4,500

CESARI, ANTONIO   Fioeretti di S. Francesco. Verona, 1822. lst ed., large quarto, quarter-vellum over marbled boards, engraved pictorial t.p., laid paper, scarce work. Bennett 20-42 1978 $185

CESARI, ANTONIO   Vita del Cavalier Clementino Vannetti di Roverto. Verona, 1795. 8vo., soft bds., uncut, portrait, first ed. King 7-156 1978 £20

CESCINSKY, HERBERT   Early English Furniture and Woodwork. London, 1922. 2 coloured frontis', textual illus., 2 vols., folio, half morocco, gilt tops, best ed. Traylen 88-367 1978 £60

CESCINSKY, HERBERT   English and American Furniture. New York, Garden City, (ca. 1929). Illus., 4to., d.w. Morrill 239-323a 1978 $20

CESCINSKY, HERBERT   English Domestic Clocks... (1914). Illus. by authors, 4to., coloured frontis., half mor. Quaritch 983-80 1978 $240

CESCINSKY, HERBERT   English Furniture from Gothic to Sheraton. Grand Rapids, 1929. Illus., 4to. MacManus 239-648 1978 $40

CESCINSKY, HERBERT   English Furniture from Gothic to Sheraton. New York, 1937. Illus., sm. folio. George's 635-245 1978 £35

CESIO, CARLO   Cognitione dei muscoli del corpo humano per il disegno. Rome, 1679. Folio, engraved title, plates, contemp. half-calf, lightly worn, light stains, extensively rare lst ed. Gilhofer 75-25 1978 SFr 1,800

CESSAS, CON BARTHOLOMEW DE LAS   An Account of the First Voyages and Discoveries Made by the Spaniards in America... London, 1699. Illus., full brown calf, very scarce. Baldwins' 51-7 1978 $275

CEYLON Almanac and Compendium of Useful Information for the Year 1837. Colombo, (1836). Half calf, foxed, edges somewhat worn, marginal worm damage. Dawson's 127-250 1978 $60

CHABAS, F.   Etudes sur l'Antiquite Historique d'apres les Sources Egyptiennes et les Monuments Reputes Prehistoriques. Paris, 1879. 2nd ed., illus., 1/2 leather, rubbed. Biblo BL781-348 1978 $27.50

CHABAS, F.   Le Papyrus Magique Harris... Chalon-Sur-Saone, 1860. 4to, half calf, some foxing, plts., facsimiles. Edwards 1012-218 1978 £40

CHABOT, CHARLES   The Handwriting of Junius Professionally Investigated. 1871. 4to, sm. blind-stamp on t.p., many facsimile plts., 1/2 calf, rebacked, lib. crest on upper cover. Eaton 45-93 1978 £30

CHABOT, FREDERICK C.   San Antonio and Its Beginnings, 1691-1731. San Antonio, 1931. 1st ed., printed wr., illus. Jenkins 116-102 1978 $25

CHABOT, FREDERICK C.   With the Makers of San Antonio. San Antonio, 1937. 1st ed., embossed cloth, illus. Jenkins 116-103 1978 $45

CHADWICK, D.   Social Life in the Days of Piers Plowman. Cambridge, 1922. 8vo. Upcroft 12-66 1978 £6

CHADWICK, EDWARD MARION   The People of the Longhouse. Toronto, 1897. Illus. Hood 116-405 1978 $40

CHADWICK, FRENCH ENSOR   Causes of the Civil War. New York, 1906. Front f/l clipped out, Bell Wiley's copy. Broadfoot's 44-72 1978 $8

CHADWICK, HECTOR MUNRO   The Growth of Literature. 1932-40. 3 vols., lg. 8vo., orig. cloth, nice, orig. ed., pres. copy inscribed from author. Howes 194-715 1978 £32

CHADWICK, NORA KERSHAW   Russian Heroic Poetry. 1932. Orig. ed., plts., binding soiled, 8vo. Howes 194-716 1978 £5

CHAFFERS, WILLIAM   Hall Marks on Gold and Silver Plate. 1905. 9th ed., frontis., roy. 8vo., covers spotted. George's 635-253 1978 £10.50

CHAFFERS, WILLIAM   Marks and Monograms on European and Oriental Pottery and Porcelain. London, 1908. 12th. ed., illus., orig. cloth, gilt, t.e.g., other edges uncut, fine copy. Baldwins' 51-39 1978 £22.50

CHAFFIN, WILLIAM L.   History of the Town of Easton, Mass. Cambridge, 1886. Illus., ports., plts., orig. cloth. MacManus 239-1026 1978 $40

CHAILLE, S. E.   Intimidation and the Number of White and of Colored Voters in Louisiana in 1876,.... New Orleans, 1877. Original printed wr., 1st ed. Ginsberg 14-495 1978 $125

CHAILLEY-BERT, J.   La colonisation de l'Indo-chine; l'Experience anglaise. Paris, 1892. 8vo, orig. covers. Van der Peet 127-44 1978 Dfl 45

CHALFANT, HARRY M.   Father Penn and John Barleycorn. Harrisburg, (1920). Biblo BL781-806 1978 $9

CHALLAMEL, AUGUSTIN   Les Plus Jolis Tableaux. Paris, c.1845. Quarto, lithographed plates by Leon Noel and others, navy glazed paper over boards, ornately framed gilt title, chipped at spine, cover edges chipped, sev. plates heavily foxed. Victoria 34-150 1978 $35

CHALLONER, RICHARD 1691-1781   Britannia Sancta. 1745. 2 parts in 1 vol., 4to., contemp. mottled calf, first ed. Howes 194-202 1978 £30

CHALMERS, GEORGE   An Estimate of the Comparative Strength of Great-Britain, During the Present and Four Preceding Reigns... 1794. 8vo, contemp. calf, rebacked, folding table. Edwards 1012-479 1978 £50

CHALMERS, HARVEY   West to the Setting Sun. Toronto, 1946. Signed by author, cover faded. Hood 116-457 1978 $20

CHALMERS, JAMES   Work and Adventure in New Guinea 1877 to 1885. London, 1885. Pictorial cloth (worn, new endpapers). Dawson's 127-251 1978 $50

CHALMERS, THOMAS   A Saga of Scotland. (1930). 8vo., dark red calf, spine faded, plts., illus. F. Edwards 1013-528 1978 £15

CHALMERS, THOMAS   A Series of Discourses on the Christian Revelation, Viewed in Connexion with the Modern Astronomy. New York, 1817. 8vo., orig. prtd. bds., edges uncut, fr. hinge partly broken, 1st Amer. ed. Morrill 239-324 1978 $10

CHAM, AMEDEE-CHARLES-HENRY   Paris a Bruzelles. Paris, n.d. (c.1875). Litho. title page, litho. plts., 4to, orig. printed bds., spine repaired, loose in case. Traylen 88-368 1978 £15

CHAMBAUD, LOUIS   A Grammar of the French Tongue. 1769. Fifth ed., table, cr. 8vo., contemp. sheep. Howes 194-241 1978 £15

CHAMBAUD, LOUIS   Nouveau Dictionnaire Francois-Anglois & Anglois-Francois. 1805. 2 vols., thk. 4to., contemp. calf, joints cracked, spines chipped at head. Howes 194-242 1978 £15

CHAMBERLAIN, C. J.   Methods in Plant Histology. Chicago, 1916. 3rd. ed., illus., 8vo. Traylen 88-552 1978 £5

CHAMBERLAIN, HENRY   Vistas e Costumes da Cidade e Arredores do Rio de Janeiro em 1819-1820. Rio de Janeior, (1943). Color plts., oblong 4to, half red calf, 1st ed., light cover wear, edges rubbed, else fine. Howell 5-15 1978 $150

CHAMBERLAIN, HOPE SUMMERELL   History of Wake County, N.C. Raleigh, 1922. Good copy, uncut. Broadfoot 50-31 1978 $50

CHAMBERLAIN, HOPE SOMMERELL   Old Days in Chapel Hill. Being the Life and Letters of Cornelia Phillips Spencer. Chapel Hill, 1926. Illus. Broadfoot 50-30 1978 $10

CHAMBERLAIN, HOUSTON STEWART   Richard Wagner. 1897. First English ed., portraits, illus., 4to., orig. cloth gilt, gilt top, edges untrimmed, binding dull and trifle soiled. Howes 194-1308 1978 £14

CHAMBERLAIN, JACOB CHESTER   A Bibliography of the First Editions in Book Form of the Writings of Henry Wadsworth Longfellow. New York, 1908. Orig. bds., 1st ed., ltd. to 500 no. copies. MacManus 238-971 1978 $35

CHAMBERLAIN, M.   A Documentary History of Chelsea. Boston, 1908. 2 vols., illus. MacManus 239-1021 1978 $37.50

CHAMBERLAIN, SAMUEL   Cape Cod in the Sun. New York, (1937). Photos, 1st ed. Biblo BL781-674 1978 $9

CHAMBERLAIN, SAMUEL   Ever New England. New York, (1945). Photos. Biblo 247-101 1978 $10

CHAMBERLAIN, SAMUEL   Fair is Our Land. New York, (1942). Sm. 4to., illus., 1st ed. Biblo BL781-675 1978 $10

CHAMBERLAND, CHARLES   Le Charbon et la Vaccination Charbonneuse d' apres les Travaux recents de M. Pasteur. Paris, 1883. 8vo., orig. cloth, illus., first ed. Gurney 75-84 1978 £35

CHAMBERLIN, WILLIAM HENRY   Japan Over Asia. 1942. Illus., revised, enlarged ed. Austin 80-48 1978 $8.50

CHAMBERS, ANDREW JACKSON   Recollections by... N.P., [ca. 1947]. 12mo, half morocco, small ed. Ginsberg 14-231 1978 $100

CHAMBERS, E. H.   Shakespearean Gleanings. Oxford, 1944. Octavo, good. Upcroft 10-258 1978 £5.50

CHAMBERS, E. K.   Essays and Studies by Members of the English Association. London, 1924-66. 22 vols., 8vo., orig. cloth. Traylen 88-237 1978 £40

CHAMBERS, E. K.   Samuel Taylor Coleridge. Oxford, 1938. Blind-stamp on t.p., buckram, slightly faded. Eaton 45-107 1978 £5

CHAMBERS, ERNEST J.   The Book of Canada. Montreal and Toronto, 1905. Quarto, many illus. & adverts. Hood's 115-6 1978 $30

CHAMBERS, ERNEST J.   The Origin and Services of the 3rd Montreal Field Battery of Artillery. Montreal, 1898. 4to., rebound in buckram. Wolfe 39-86 1978 $35

CHAMBERS, GEORGE F.   Descriptive Astronomy. Oxford, 1867. 8vo., plts., illus., orig. cloth, repaired, first ed. Quaritch 977-176 1978 $85

CHAMBERS, RAYMOND WILSON   The Place of St. Thomas More in English Literature and History. 1937. Illus., octavo, good. Upcroft 10-260 1978 £5

CHAMBERS, REUBEN   The Thomsonian Practice of Medicine. Bethania, 1842. Scuffing, 1st fly much browned. Rittenhouse 49-131 1976 $25

CHAMBERS, ROBERT   Chamber's Cyclopaedia of English Literature. London, 1876. 3rd ed., 2 vols., thick, large octavos, very good. Victoria 34-151 1978 $22.50

CHAMBERS, ROBERT   History of the Rebellion in Scotland in 1745, 1746. Philadelphia, 1833. 1st Amer. ed., 2 vols. in 1, orig. cloth with spine mis-labeled, scuffing. Greene 78-162 1978 $55

CHAMBERS, ROBERT   The Scottish Songs Collected and Illustrated by.... Edinburgh, 1829. 1st ed in 2 vols., orig. cloth, scratched, hinges weak, foxed. Greene 78-163 1978 $65

CHAMBERS, ROBERT   Traditions of Edinburgh. 1825. 1st. ed., 2 vols., orig. purple cloth, paper labels, fine. Jarndyce 16-383 1978 £22

CHAMBERS, ROBERT W.   Outdoorland, a Story for Children. New York, 1902. Illus. in color, 1st ed., lg. 8vo, pic. covers in color, color plts., very good. Americanist 103-27 1978 $20

CHAMBERS, WILLIAM   A Treatise on Civil Architecture. 1759. First ed., plts., lg. folio, calf, firmly rebacked. Thomas 37-10 1978 £125

CHAMBON DE MONTAUX, NICOLAS   Des Maladies des Femmes. Paris, 1784. 2 vols., 12mo., contemp. half calf, plain bds., ownership inscr. of Dr. J. Oppenheimer & bkplt. of Dr. Alfred M. Hellman, light browning good copy, rare 1st ed. Zeitlin 245-42 1978 $350

CHAMEROVZOW, L. A.   Philip of Lutetia or, The Revolution of 1789. 1848. First ed., half mor., v.g., plts. by Robert Cruikshank. Jarndyce 16-448 1978 £12.50

CHAMPLAIN, SAMUEL DE   Voyages and Explorations of. New York, 1922. 2 vols., illus., maps. MacManus 239-85 1978 $17.50

CHAMPNEY, A. C.   Irish Ecclesiatical Architecture. (1910). Reprint, octavo bound in cloth. Hyland 128-934 1978 £12.60

CHAMPNEY, ELIZABETH W.   Romance of Old Belgium. New York, 1915. Illus. Biblo 247-666 1978 $15

CHAMPNEY, LIZZIE W.   Three Vassar Girls Abroad. Boston, 1883. 1st ed., illus., orig. pict. bds., very good. MacManus 238-434 1978 $50

CHANAL, FRANCOIS VICTOR ADOLPHE DE   L'Armee Americaine. Paris, 1872. Marginal stains, fldg. plts., full lea., Bell Wiley's copy. Broadfoot's 44-75 1978 $16

CHANCELLOR, E. B.   Old Rowley. New York, 1926. Cloth, good set, 6 vols., illus. Biblo 247-667 1978 $40

CHANDLER, MARY   The Description of Bath. 1738. 4th ed., 8vo., uncut, rebound in cloth. Quaritch 979-80 1978 $105

CHANDLER, RAYMOND   Farewell My Lovely. New York, 1940. First U.S. ed., very good. Bell Book 17-219 1978 £70

CHANDLER, RAYMOND   Finger Man and Other Stories. New York, (1950). Wrs., minor wear, 2nd ed., scarce. Hayman 72-183 1978 $7.50

CHANDLER, RAYMOND   The Little Sister. Boston, 1949. First U.S. ed., fine. Bell Book 17-220 1978 £35

CHANDLER, RAYMOND   The Little Sister. 1949. Very good, first English ed. Bell Book 16-156 1978 £18.50

CHANDLER, RAYMOND   Red Wind. Cleveland, 1946. 1st ed., very good, d.j. Ballinger 11-121 1978 $15.00

CHANDLER, RAYMOND   Spanish Blood. Cleveland, (1946). Cloth, covers little dull, 1st ed. Hayman 73-97 1978 $7.50

CHANDLER, RAYMOND   Spanish Blood. New York and Cleveland, (1946). Pages browned, chipped dw. Bernard 5-511 1978 $30

CHANDLER, SAMUEL   A Review of the History of the Man After God's Own Heart. 1762. 8vo., contemp. calf, fine. P. M. Hill 142-70 1978 £30

CHANDLER, THOMAS BRADBURY   The Appeal Defended: or, the Proposed American Episcopate Vindicated, in Answer to the Objections and Misrepresentations of Dr. Chauncy and Others. New York, 1769. 1st ed., sewn as issued, uncut, front blank soiled, some wear. Americanist 102-51 1978 $55

CHANDLER, W.   Decidous Orchards. Philadelphia, 1942. 8vo, orig. cloth. Book Chest 17-474 1978 $12.50

CHANDLER'S Visitor's Guide In and Around Boston. Boston, 1870. Illus., 12mo, orig. wrs. Morrill 241-323 1978 $10

CHANGLER, Z. M.   A Class Book of English Grammar and Analysis. Zanesville, (1862). Printed bds. Hayman 71-605 1978 $7.50

CHANNING, WILLIAM ELLERY   A Letter to the Hon. Henry Clay, on the Annexation of Texas. Boston, 1837. Self-wr., 1st ed. Jenkins 116-210 1978 $65

CHANT, C. A.   Our Wonderful Universe, an Easy Introduction to the Study of the Heavens. London, 1923. Illus., inscr'd by author, lea. Hood 117-465 1973 $10

CHANTELOUP, JEAN ANTOINE CLAUDE, COMTE DE
Please turn to
CHAPTAL DE CHANTELOUP, JEAN ANTOINE CLAUDE

CHANTER, CHARLOTTE   Over the Cliffs. Boston, 1861. 1st Am. ed., "Author's Edition", orig. binding. Greene 78-23 1978 $25

CHANUTE, OCTAVE   Progress in Flying Machines. New York, (1894?). 8vo., illus., photos, orig. cloth, gilt, worn, but very good copy, signature on endpaper, 1st ed. in book form. Norman 5-55 1978 $250

CHAPAIS, THOMAS   Cours D'histoire du Canada. Quebec, 1919. 4 vols., marbled bds. Hood 116-515 1978 $60

CHAPELLE, HOWARD IRVING   The Baltimore Clipper. Its Origin and Development. Salem, 1930. 1st ed., 4to., illus., fine copy, orig. mor. grain cloth. MacManus 239-1738 1978 $75

CHAPELLE, HOWARD IRVING   The History of American Sailing Ships. New York, 1935. Drwgs. by author & others, 4to., 1st ed. Morrill 239-328 1978 $25

CHAPELLE, HOWARD IRVING   The History of the American Sailing Navy. New York, (1949). Illus., some fldg., 4to., 1st ed. Morrill 239-329 1978 $25

CHAPIN, CALVIN   A Sermon, Delivered in Hartford, May 18, 1814... Hartford, 1814. Sewed. Hayman 71-106 1978 $10

CHAPIN, HOWARD M.   Gazette Francoise. New York, 1926. Folio, orig. cloth-backed bds., very good, ltd. to 300 copies. MacManus 239-86 1978 $35

CHAPMAN, ARTHUR   The Pony Express, the Record of a Romantic Adventure in Business. New York, 1932. 1st ed., illus. MacManus 239-1907 1978 $20

CHAPMAN, BERLIN BASIL   The Founding of Stillwater. (Oklahoma City, 1948). Cloth, illus., 1st ed., scarce, fine copy in d.w., reinforced. Dykes 34-246 1978 $35

CHAPMAN, E. N.   Antagonism of Alcohol and Diptheria. Brooklyn, 1878. 12mo., 1st ed. Morrill 239-41 1978 $7.50

CHAPMAN, F. SPENCER   Lhasa, The Holy City. 1938. Maps, coloured plts., illus., 8vo, orig. cloth, fine copy in d.w. Edwards 1012-135 1978 £30

CHAPMAN, F. SPENCER   Northern Lights: The Official Account of the British Arctic Air-Route Expedition, 1930-31. 1932. Maps, illus., roy. 8vo, orig. cloth. Edwards 1012-566 1978 £10

CHAPMAN, F. SPENCER   Watkins' Last Expedition. 1934. 8vo, orig. cloth, maps, illus. Edwards 1012-567 1978 £15

CHAPMAN, JAMES   Travels in the Interior of South Africa, Comprising Fifteen Years' Hunting and Trading... London, 1868. 2 vols., 2 folding maps, foxed, one linen-backed, frontispieces, 6 plts., wood-engravings, occasional foxing throughout, nice copy, modern half green calf, 8vo, fully gilt spines, morocco labels. K Books 239-90 1978 £180

CHAPMAN, JOHN A.   History of Edgefield County from the Earliest Settlements to 1897. Newberry, 1897. Old. lib. stamp, fine, orig. cloth. MacManus 239-1120 1978 $65

CHAPMAN, NATHANIEL   An Essay on the Canine State of Fever. Philadelphia, 1801. Good. Nestler Rare 78-216 1978 $45

CHAPMAN, S. J.   The Lancashire Cotton Industry, a Study in Economic Development. Manchester, 1904. 8vo. George's 635-298 1978 £10

CHAPMAN, WILLIAM Observations on the Various Systems of Canal Navigation. London, 1797. 4to., map, plts., contemp. half calf, rebacked, first ed. Quaritch 977-211 1978 $600

CHAPPE D'AUTEROCHE, JEAN A Voyage to California to Observe the Transit of Venus, with an Historical Description of the Author's Route through Mexico, and the Natural History of the Province. London, 1778. Folding plan, full contemp. calf, recased. Ginsberg 14-232 1978 $600

CHAPPELL, E. Narrative of a Voyage to Hudson's Bay in H.M.'s Ship "Rosamond"... 1817. Map, plts., slightly browned, lib. stamped, illus., modern half calf, 8vo. Edwards 1012-419 1978 £100

CHAPPELL, E. Voyage of H.M.'S Ship "Rosamond" to Newfoundland and the Southern Coast of Labrador... 1818. Map, plts., slightly browned, lib. stamped, illus., modern half calf, 8vo. Edwards 1012-420 1978 £120

CHAPTAL, J. A.
Please turn to
CHAPTAL DE CHANTELOUP, JEAN ANTOINE CLAUDE

CHAPTAL DE CHANTELOUP, JEAN ANTOINE CLAUDE L'Art Faire, Gouverner. Paris, 1801. 8vo., orig. wrs., uncut, v.g., first ed. Norman 5-56 1978 $450

CHARBONNEAUX, JEAN L'Art Egeen. 1929. 4to., sewn, spine slightly chipped, plts. Allen 234-179 1978 $10

CHARCOT, JEAN MARTIN Lecons sur les Maladies des Vieillards et les Maladies Chroniques. Paris, 1868. Illus., colored plts., 8vo., orig. cloth, 2nd ed. Argosy Special-22 1978 $100

CHARITABLE MECHANIC ASSOCIATION Publisher's Circular of the Eleventh Exhibition of American Manufactures, New Inventions and Works of Art, to be Held in Boston, September and October, 1869. Boston, 1869. Illus., 4to., orig. wrs. Morrill 241-358 1978 $15

CHARLES I, KING OF ENGLAND An Exact Collection of all Remonstrances, Declarations, Votes, Orders, Ordinances...and other Remarkable Passages between the Kings most Excellent Majesty, and his High Court.... 1642. Thk. sm. 4to., contemp. calf, very good, first ed. Howes 194-27 1978 £90

CHARLES I, KING OF ENGLAND The Letters, Speeches and Proclamations of ... 1935. Octavo, good. Upcroft 10-30 1978 £5

CHARLES, ELIZABETH (RUNDLE) Diary of Mrs. Kitty Trevylyan. New York, 1864. First Amer. ed., orig. cloth. Greene 78-24 1978 $35

CHARLES, ROLAND WILBUR Troopships of World War II. 1947. Many illus. Austin 80-50 1978 $27.50

CHARLES Dickens As I Knew Him The Story of The Reading Tours in Great Britain and America (1866-1870). 1887. Orig. red cloth, v.g. Jarndyce 16-588 1978 £6.50

THE CHARLES Dickens Birthday Book. London, 1882. Illus., edges gilt, decorated cloth, unused, very good. Greene 78-178 1978 $150

CHARLESWORTH, HECTOR A Cyclopaedia of Canadian Biography. Toronto, 1919. Illus., ex-lib. Hood 116-17 1978 $60

CHARLEVOIX, PIERRE FRANCOIS XAVIER DE Journal of a Voyage to North America. London, 1761. 2 vols., modern cloth, complete with half titles, fold. map, light discolouring throughout. Wolfe 39-88 1978 $300

CHARLTON, JOHN Speeches and Addresses; Political, Literary and Religious. Toronto, 1905. Hood 116-675 1978 $10

CHARNOCK, STEPHEN A Discourse of Divine Providence. 1685. 8vo, contemp. calf, badly worn, some foxing throughout, marginal worming, signature of Isaac Hawkins Browne on past-down. Hannas 54-29 1978 £18.50

CHARPENTIER, JOHAN FRIEDRICH WILHELM VON Essai sur les Glaciers et sur le Terrain Erratique du Bassin du Rhone. Lausanne, 1841. 1st ed., octavo, text illus., lithographs by Spengler, folding map, half cloth, rebacked. Bennett 20-43 1978 $250

CHARRIERE, ISABELLA AGNETA (VAN TUYLL) DE Four Tales by Zelide. New York, 1926. Plts., orig. binding, 1st U.S. ed. Petrilla 13-9 1978 $10

CHARRON, PIERRE De La Sagesse. Leyde, 1646. Thick 12mo., fine green straight-grained mor., gilt ornament spine, gilt inner dentelles, red silk paste-downs & endpapers, lightly browned, very good copy, ex-libris of Alexander Robert Goldie & Lytton Strachey, Elzevir ed. Zeitlin 245-44 1978 $185

CHARRON, PIERRE De La Sagnesse. En Trois Livres. Paris, 1657. Frontis., thick 12mo., red mor., gilt edges, fine French mor. bind., slipcase. Salloch 348-31 1978 $185

CHARRON, PIERRE De La Sagesse. Paris, 1797. Frontis., port., 2 vols., 12mo., contemp. marbled paper bds. with labels, fine, orig. paper bind. Salloch 348-32 1978 $65

The Chartered Surveyor, His Training and His Work. (1932). 1st. ed., 8vo, blue-cloth-backed bds., as issued. Sawyer 298-34 1978 £12.50

CHARTERIS, EVAN The Life and Letters of Sir Edmund Gosse. 1931. First ed., plts., roy. 8vo., orig. cloth. Howes 194-901 1978 £6.50

CHARTERIS, LESLIE The Ace of Knaves. 1937. Pres. copy inscribed by author, covers soiled & rubbed, good, first English ed. Bell Book 16-230 1978 £8.50

CHASE, ALLAN Falange. New York, (1943). Author's signed pres. to Robert Anderson. Biblo 251-286 1978 $15

CHASE, FREDERICK A History of Dartmouth College and the Town of Hanover, New Hampshire. Cambridge, 1891. 1st eds., 2 vols., illus., orig. cloth, very fine set. MacManus 239-109 1978 $45

CHASE, FREDERICK A History of Dartmouth College and the Town of Hanover, New Hampshire. Brattleboro, 1928. Frontis., illus., 2nd ed., fine, uncut. MacManus 239-1066 1978 $20

CHASE, JOSEPH CUMMINGS The Romance of an Art Career. New York, (1928). 1st ed., author's signed pres. Biblo 251-193 1978 $32.50

CHASE, MARY ELLEN Jonathan Fisher,...1768-1847. New York, 1948. Illus., 1st ed., d.w. Biblo BL781-134 1978 $8

CHASE, MARY K. Negociations de la Republique du Texas en Europe, 1837-1845. Wr., uncut, scarce. Jenkins 116-212 1978 $65

CHASE, S. An Examination of Roman Catholic Indulgences. New York, 1841. 16mo., prtd. bds., very good. Butterfield 21-53 1978 $25

CHASE, S. P. Reclamation of Fugitives from Service. Cincinnati, 1847. Disbound. Biblo 247-89 1978 $27.50

CHASE, SALMON P. Speech of Hon..., Delivered at the Republican Mass Meeting in Cincinnati, August 21, 1855; Together with Extracts from His Speeches in the Senate on Kindred Subjects... Columbus, 1855. Sewed. Hayman 72-523 1978 $15

CHASE, STUART The Economy of Abundance. 1934. 1st ed. Austin 80-495 1978 $11

CHASE, STUART The Economy of Abundance. 1934. Ex-lib. Austin 80-496 1978 $7.50

CHASE, STUART Men and Machines. 1929. Illus. by W. T. Murch, 1st ed. Austin 80-497 1978 $11

CHASE, STUART Men and Machines. 1929. Austin 80-498 1978 $7.50

CHASE, STUART The Nemesis of American Business. 1931. 1st ed. Austin 80-499 1978 $12.50

CHASE, STUART The Proper Study of Mankind. 1948. 1st ed. in dust jacket. Austin 80-888 1978 $12.50

CHASE, STUART The Road We are Traveling. 1914-1942. 1942. Austin 80-501 1978 $7.50

CHASE, STUART The Tragedy of Waste. 1925. Austin 80-503 1978 $7.50

CHASE, STUART Your Money's Worth. 1927. 1st ed. Austin 80-505 1978 $10

CHASSENEUX, BARTHELEMY DE   Catalogus Gloriae Mundi.... Lyons, 1546.
Generally clean and sound, heavily scored through in ink, folio, 18th cent. vellum.
Thomas 37-52 1978 £1250

CHASTEL, G.   Un siecle d'Epopee francaise en Indochine
(1774-1874). Paris, n.d. (c. 1930). Illus., plts., map, 8vo, orig. covers.
Van der Peet 127-45 1978 Dfl 40

CHASTELLUX, FRANCOIS JEAN   Voyages dans L'Amerique Septentrionate,
dans les Annees 1780, 1781 & 1782. Paris, 1788-1791. 2nd ed.   Wolfe 39-89
1978 $125

CHATAUVILLARD, COMTE DE   Essai sur le Duel.   Paris, 1836. 8vo., half
calf, spine damaged, corners broken.   Van der Peet H-64-604 1978 Dfl 40

CHATEAUBRIAND, FRANCOIS AUGUSTE RENE DE   Atala, Avec les Dessins de
Gustave Dore. Paris, 1863. Lg. folio, publisher's red cloth stamped in gilt,
uncut, 1st ed. with illus. by Gustave Dore, slight foxmarks, lib. stamp on title.
Goldschmidt 110-18 1978 $325

CHATEAUBRIAND, FRANCOIS AUGUSTE RENE DE   A Collection of Works.
Brussels, 1826-28. 24 vols., 8vo., 8 x 5 inches, contemp. qtr. sheep.   Howes
194-717 1978 £60

CHATEAUBRIAND, FRANCOIS AUGUSTE RENE DE   The Monarchy According
to the Charter. 1816. 1st Eng. ed., 8vo., half calf, very good ex-lib. copy.
Hannas 54-54 1978 £15

CHATEAUBRIAND, FRANCOIS AUGUSTE RENE DE   Travels in America and
Italy. 1828. 1st ed. of this title, 2 vols., 8vo., contemp. blue calf, gilt, red
labels, pretty set. Hannas 54-55 1978 £68

CHATEAUBRIAND, FRANCOIS AUGUSTE RENE DE   Travels in America and
Italy. London, 1828. Two vols., marbled bds., calf back, rehinged with holland
tape. Wolfe 39-90 1978 $100

CHATEAUBRIAND, FRANCOIS AUGUSTE RENE DE   Travels in America and
Italy. London, 1828. 1st ed. in English, roy. 8vo., ads, orig. bds., rebacked,
fine. Current 24-74 1978 $135

CHATEAUBRIANT, ALPHONSE DE   Monsieur des Lourdines. Paris, 1929.
Quarto, bound in dark brown mor. with broad band of lighter brown and two thin
strips of green mor. inlaid onto both covers, gilt lettering on spine, gilt top, orig.
paper covers bound in. Totteridge 29-22 1978 $225

CHATELET, GABRIELLE-EMILIE, MARQUISE DU   Dissertation Sur la Nature
du Feu. Paris, 1744. 8vo., modern bds., 1st separate ed. Offenbacher 30-26
1978 $175

CHATTANOOGA, Illustrated.   New York, 1890. Oblong 12mo., orig. cloth.
Morrill 241-568 1978 $12.50

CHATTERTON, EDWARD KEBLE   Danger Zone. Boston, 1934. Plts., illus.,
thick 8vo., orig. cloth.   F. Edwards 1013-40 1978 £10

CHATTERTON, EDWARD KEBLE   Old Sea Paintings. 1928. 4to., colored plts.,
orig. cloth, 1st ed., illus.   F. Edwards 1013-41 1978 £55

CHATTERTON, EDWARD KEBLE   Old Sea Paintings. London, (1928). 15
illus. in color, 95 others, 4to.   Baldwins' 51-503 1978 $50

CHATTERTON, EDWARD KEBLE   Old Ship Prints. London & New York, (1927).
15 illus. in color, 95 others, fine copy.   Baldwins' 51-504 1978 $50

CHATTERTON, EDWARD KEBLE   Sailing Models, Ancient and Modern. 1934.
Colored plts., illus., plans, 4to., covers faded and stained.   George's 635-807
1978 £45

CHATTERTON, EDWARD KEBLE   Ship Models. London, 1923. Ltd. to 1,000
copies, illus., 4to., some in color, scarce. MacManus 239-1739 1978 $65

CHATTERTON, EDWARD KEBLE   Ship-Models. London, 1923. Ltd. 1000
copies, 4to., 142 plts., some in color.   Baldwins' 51-505 1978 $75

CHATTERTON, EDWARD KEBLE   Steamship Models. 1924. Color plts., 4to.,
orig. buckram, spine faded, ltd. ed., signed by author.   F. Edward's 1013-42
1978 £60

CHATTERTON, EDWARD KEBLE   Steamship Models. London, 1924. 1st ed.,
4to., illus., plts., orig. cloth, very good, ltd. to 1,000 copies.   MacManus
239-1740 1978 $65

CHATTERTON, EDWARD KEBLE   Windjammers and Shellbacks. 1926. Colored
plts., 8vo., orig. cloth, illus.   F. Edwards 1013-43 1978 £10

CHATTERTON, FENIMORE   The State of Wyoming:... Laramie, 1904.
Illus., orig. pr. pict. wr., 1st ed.   Ginsberg 14-1072 1978 $25

CHATTERTON, RUTH   Homeward Borne. 1950. Austin 79-132 1978
$7.50

CHATTERTON, THOMAS   Poems Supposed to Have Been Written at Bristol,
by Thomas Rowley, and Others in the Fifteenth Century. 1777. 8vo., 1st ed.,
contemp. calf, joints a little cracked, bkplt. of A. N. L. Munby.   Quaritch
979-82 1978 $115

CHATTERTON, THOMAS   Poems, Supposed to Have Been Written at Bristol,
by Thomas Rowley and Others.   London, 1777. 1st ed., modern marbled boards,
calf spine, very good copy.   Victoria 34-153 1978 $110

CHATTO, CLARENCE I.   The Story of the Springfield Plan. 1945.
Illus. with photos.   Austin 79-133 1978 $11

CHATTO, WILLIAM ANDREW   A Treatise on Wood Engraving Historical and
Practical. New York, (1861). Full tree calf, spine dry, hinges weak, illus. by
John Jackson. Baldwins' 51-40 1978 $65

CHAUCER, GEOFFREY   The Canterbury Tales of Chaucer. London, 1775-
8. 5 vols., 8vo, contemporary calf, spine gilt, 1st ed., very good and handsome
set. Ximenes 47-320 1978 $175

CHAUCER, GEOFFREY   The Canterbury Tales. Oxford, 1795. 3 vols.,
8vo., recent full buckram. P. M. Hill 142-261 1978 £21

CHAUCER, GEOFFREY   Canterbury Tales. Oxford, 1798. 2nd. ed.,
2 vols., 4to, frontis, portrait, new red buckram, paper labels. Eaton 45-95 1978
£40

CHAUCER, GEOFFREY   The Canterbury Tales. Oxford, clarendon Press,
1798. Second ed., portrait, 2 vols., 4to., contemp. half mor. Howes 194-205
1978 £50

CHAUCER, GEOFFREY   The Canterbury Tales. Waltham St. Lawrence,
Golden Cockerel Press, 1929-31. 4 vols., sm. folio, paper bds., backed in gilt
lettered niger mor., ltd. to 485 copies, few worn corners, else fine, uncut, wood
engravings by Eric Gill. Howell 5-27 1978 $1,150

CHAUCER, GEOFFREY   Canterbury Tales. N.Y., 1930. 1 of 924
numbered copies, folio, blue cloth, t.e.g., uncut, 2 vols., illus. & signed by
Rockwell Kent, bookplates, fine. Houle 10-180 1978 $225

CHAUCER, GEOFFREY   The Canterbury Tales. London: The Limited Editions Club, 1934. Sm. folio, orig. cloth-backed bds., 2 vols., frontis., pub.
box, 1 of 1,500 copies, bookplt., fine. MacManus 238-818 1978 $37.50

CHAUCER, GEOFFREY   The Flower and the Leaf. Essex House Press, 1902.
Sm. 8vo., prtd. on vellum, hand-coloured frontis., slightly soiled, 165 copies
prtd. Quaritch 979-136 1978 $180

CHAUCER, GEOFFREY   Troilus and Criseyde. 1927. Folio, finely prtd.
in black, red & blue on handmade paper, woodcut decor., illus., bds., mor.
back, back very slightly faded, fine copy, 225 copies prtd. Quaritch 979-348
1978 $2,000

CHAUCER, GEOFFREY   The Workes...With Dyvers Workes Whiche Were
Never in Print Before. (c. 1545). Third collected ed., some stains, underlining
and signs of use, sound, reasonable copy, folio, contemp. calf, rebacked and repaired, rubbed but sound. Thomas 37-38 1978 £1050

CHAUCER, GEOFFREY   The Works of Geoffrey Chaucer Compared with the Former Editions.... London, 1721. Folio, brown full calf, blind stamped, gilt spine, large paper copy, 1 of 250 copies. Totteridge 29-23 1978 $350

CHAUCER, GEOFFREY   The Complete Works. Oxford, 1894-97. 7 vols., frontis, plts., orig. cloth, 2 vols., rebacked to match. Eaton 45-94 1978 £60

CHAUCER, GEOFFREY   The Complete Works of Geoffrey Chaucer. (Hammersmith, 1896). Folio, superb binding by Birdsall, t.e.g., others uncut, illus. designed by Sir Edward Burne Jones, engraved on wood by Hooper, 1 of 426 copies, fine, bound in crimson levant mor., green levant mor. doublures, tan watered silk free endpapers, verso and facing fly-leaves lined in red satin, matching crimson half mor. folding case with drop front lined in green silk. Duschnes 220-170 1978 $15,000

CHAUCER, GEOFFREY   Works. Oxford, 1928-29. Ltd. ed. of 375 copies, 8 vols., printed in red, blue & black, hand-coloured woodcuts by Hugh Chesterman & Lynton Lamb, sm. folio, orig. bds., some slightly marked, holland backs, uncut. Traylen 88-135 1978 £260

CHAUCER, GEOFFREY   The Works of. London, (1905). Ltd. to 1000 copies, this copy not numbered, imp. 4to., blind-stamped mor., t.e.g. Forster 130-194 1978 £90

CHAUCHETIERE, CLAUDE   The Life of B. Catherine Tegakwitha, Now Called the Holy Savage. Manhattan, Cramoisy Press, 1887. English trans., carbon typescript, bound in stiff card, index. Hood 117-673 1978 $75

CHAULIEU, GUILLAUME AMFRYE DE   Oeuvres de l'Abbe de Chaulieu. Amsterdam, 1757. 2 vols., 12mo, frontispiece, half-titles, 2 blank leaves, contemp. mottled calf, gilt spines. Hannas 54-56 1978 £15

CHAUMETON, FRANCOIS PIERRE   Flore Medicale. Paris, 1814-20. 7 vols. in 8, 8vo., colour printed plts. by P.J.F. Turpin and Mme Panckoucke, folding tables, contemp. quarter calf, trifle worn, rare first ed. Quaritch 977-15 1978 $1,150

CHAUNDY, L.   Bibliographies of Modern Authors No. 1. London, 1921. Signed by Robert Bridges, very good or better. Limestone 9-32 1978 $12.50

CHAUVELOT, R.   En Indochine. Grenoble, 1931. 4to, plts., illus., colored plts. after watercolours, 8vo, orig. covers. Van der Peet 127-46 1978 Dfl 75

CHAUVELOT, R.   Visions de l'Extreme-Orient. Paris, 1928. Large 8vo, frontisp, ornaments, photos, orig. covers. Van der Peet 127-47 1978 Dfl 45

CHEAP, JOHN   John Cheap the Chapman's Library: The Scottish Chap Literature of Last Century Classified. Glasgow, 1877. 1st ed., illus., upper spine tip frayed, very good. Victoria 34-154 1978 $40

CHEAP Homes in the Sauk Valley. Sauk Centre, 1879. Original printed wr., 1st ed. Ginsberg 14-547 1978 $75

CHEATHAM, KITTY   A Nursery Garland. New York, (1917). 4to., pictures in color. Biblo BL781-1024 1978 $10

CHEESMAN, D. W.   The National Currency, and on the Repeal of the Specific Contract Act of the State of California. Washington, 1869. Original printed wr. Ginsberg 14-92 1978 $15

CHEETHAM, JEAN DICK   The Farmers' Centennial History of Ohio 1803-1903. Springfield, 1904. Wrps. Hayman 71-519 1978 $7.50

CHEEVER, DAVID W.   A History of the Boston City Hospital from Its Foundation Until 1904. Boston, 1905. Illus., 8vo., 1st ed. Morrill 239-42 1978 $20

CHEEVER, GEORGE B.   God Against Slavery. Cincinnagi, n.d. (c. 1857). Fine copy. MacManus 239-835 1978 $27.50

CHEEVER, GEORGE B.   God Against Slavery: and the Freedom and Duty of the Pulpit to Rebuke It, as a sin Against God. Cincinnati, n.d.(c.1860). Cl., lacks free endpaper in front, orig. binding. Hayman 71-110 1978 $12.50

CHEEVER, GEORGE S.   The American Common-Place Book of Poetry. Boston, 1831. 12mo., contemp. calf, frontispiece. P. M. Hill 142-240 1978 £10

CHEIRO'S Language of the Hand. London, (1900). Illus., lg. 8vo, very good. Bernard 5-206 1978 $20

CHEKE, JOHN   The Hurt of Sedition, How Grieuuous It is to a Common Welth. London, 1569. 2nd. ed., black letter, title within woodcut border, sm. 8vo, 18th. century vellum-backed marbled bds. Traylen 88-136 1978 £130

THE CHEMICAL Gazette or Journal of Practical Chemistry. Volumes I-VI. London, 1842-48. 6 vols., 8vo., cloth, uncut. Quaritch 977-90 1978 $200

CHENEY, JOHN V.   Memoriable American Speeches. Chicago, 1909. Orig. binding, cl., very scarce. Hayman 71-111 1978 $20

CHENIER, M. -J. DE   Tableau historique de l'etat et des progres de la literature francaise depuis 1789. 1816. Contemp. calf, spine gilt, 8vo. George's 635-1377 1978 £7.50

CHENU, DR.   Encyclopedie d'Histoire Naturelle ou Traite Complet de Cette Science d'Apres les Travaux des Naturalistes les Plus Eminants de tous les Pays de Toutes les Epoques. Paris, n.d. (ab. 1860). 2 vols., lg. 8vo., half calf, frontis., plts., bindings shaved. Van der Peet H-64-294 1978 Dfl 95

CHERNE, LEO   The Rest of Your Life. 1944. Austin 80-506 1978 $7.50

CHERRY, PETER PETERSON   The Western Reserve and Early Ohio. Akron, 1921. 1st ed., illus., fine, scarce. MacManus 239-382 1978 $35

CHERRY, PETER PETERSON   The Western Reserve and Early Ohio. Akron, 1921. Cloth. Hayman 73-502 1978 $12.50

CHERRY-GARRARD, APSLEY
Please turn to
GARRARD, APSLEY CHERRY

THE CHERRY Valley Turnpike. Waterville, (1927). Sq. 8vo., maps, pict. wr., red slip pasted in. Butterfield 21-115 1978 $7.50

THE CHERRY Valley Turnpike. Signed by William C. Waldron. Butterfield 21-116 1978 $10

CHERTABLON, P. DE   La Maniere de se Bein Preparer a la Mort par des Considerations sur la Cene, la Passion, and la mort de Jesus-Christ... Antwerp, 1700. Lg. 4to., illus., contemp. vellum, gilt back, 1st French ed. Gilhofer 74-129 1978 sFr 1,100

CHESHIRE, JOSEPH B.   The Church in the Confederate States. New York, 1912. Bell Wiley's copy. Broadfoot 46-37 1978 $25

CHESNIER-DUCHESNE, C.   Les Hieroglyphes Francais, ou Methode Figurative Appliquee a l'Insturction Primaire. Paris, 1843. 8vo., orig. pr. wrs., plts., first ed. Schumann 511-11 1978 sFr 275

CHESNUT, MARY BOYKIN   A Diary from Dixie.... New York, 1905. 1st ed., 1st print., cracked hinges, worn spine, Bell Wiley's copy. Broadfoot's 44-77 1978 $20

CHESNUT, MARY BOYKIN   A Diary from Dixie. Boston, 1949. First of this ed., fine., d.w. Biblo 247-155 1978 $17.50

CHESNUTT, CHARLES W.   The Colonel's Dream. New York, 1905. Orig. cloth, 1st ed., covers worn. MacManus 238-437 1978 $45

CHESNUTT, CHARLES W.   The Conjure Woman. Boston, 1899. 12mo., orig. pict. cloth, 1st ed., fine, scarce. MacManus 238-435 1978 $135

CHESNUTT, CHARLES W.   The Marrow of Tradition. Boston, 1901. Orig. cloth, 1st ed., covers soiled, scarce. MacManus 238-436 1978 $65

CHESTER, GEORGE RANDOLPH   Get-Rich-Quick Wallingford. Philadelphia, (1908). 1st ed., 8vo., very fine throughout, pict. red cloth, boxed in red cloth slipcase, exceedingly scarce. Current 24-9 1978 $100

CHESTERFIELD, PHILIP DORMER STANHOPE   Letters to Several Celebrated Individuals of the Time of Charles II, James II, William III, and Queen Anne.... 1829. First ed., portrait, contemp. half calf, red mor. label, 8vo. Howes 194-724 1978 £15

CHESTERFIELD, PHILIP DORMER STANHOPE   Letters Written by the Late Right Honourable...Earl of Chesterfield, to His Son, Philip Stanhope, Esq... London, 1774. 2 vols., 4to., frontis. portr., contemp. calf, rebacked in matching calf, mor. label, 1st ed. MacManus 238-109 1978 $300

CHESTERFIELD, PHILIP DORMER STANHOPE   Letters Written...to his Son. 1774. 4 vols., portrait, contemp. calf, fifth ed., 8vo. Howes 194-207 1978 £32

CHESTERFIELD, PHILIP DORMER STANHOPE   Letters Written by. 1817. 12mo., half calf, marbled sides, first ed., scarce. P. M. Hill 142-72 1978 £65

CHESTERFIELD, PHILIP DORMER STANHOPE   Supplement to the Letters...to his Son. 1787. 8vo., unbound, fine. P. M. Hill 142-73 1978 £12

CHESNUT, MARY BOYKIN   A Dairy from Dixie. Boston, 1949. Bell Wiley's copy. Broadfoot 46-38 1978 $10

CHESTERTON, GILBERT KEITH   Autobiography. London, 1936. 8vo., black cloth, gilt lettering on spine, front cover bumped, fine, 1st ed. Desmarais 1-81 1978 $12.50

CHESTERTON, GILBERT KEITH   Autobiography. 1936. No. 45 of 250 copies, plts., quarter calf, spine faded, v.g., first Eng. ed. Bell Book 16-161 1978 £22.50

CHESTERTON, GILBERT KEITH   The Collected Poems. 1927. Spine a little marked, else very good, first English ed. Bell Book 17-157 1978 £7.50

CHESTERTON, GILBERT KEITH   Five Types: A Book of Essays. London, 1910. 8vo., stiff white card, pr. buff wr., uncut, near mint, in original box, 1st ed. Desmarais 1-82 1978 $15

CHESTERTON, GILBERT KEITH   Five Types; a book of essays. 1910. 12mo., stiff wraps, very good, worn slipcase, first English ed. Bell Book 16-162 1978 £8.50

CHESTERTON, GILBERT KEITH   G. F. Watts. 1904. Illus., 12mo., red cloth gilt, t.e.g., very good, first English ed. Bell Book 17-158 1978 £6

CHESTERTON, GILBERT KEITH   George Bernard Shaw. 1910. T.e.g., very good, first English ed. Bell Book 16-163 1978 £8.50

CHESTERTON, GILBERT KEITH   George Bernard Shaw. New York, 1910. 8vo., red cloth, 1st Amer. ed., near fine. Desmarais 1-83 1978 $10

CHESTERTON, GILBERT KEITH   George Bernard Shaw. 1910. 1st ed., good, octavo bound in cloth. Hyland 128-506 1978 £9

CHESTERTON, GILBERT KEITH   The Incredulity of Father Brown. 1926. Very good, first English ed. Bell Book 16-231 1978 £32.50

CHESTERTON, GILBERT KEITH   The Incredulity of Father Brown. New York, 1926. First U.S. ed., very good. Bell Book 17-159 1978 $15

CHESTERTON, GILBERT KEITH   The Innocence of Father Brown. 1911. Plts. by Sydney Seymour Lucas, joints & extrems. of spine split, else good, first English ed. Bell Book 17-160 1978 £38.50

CHESTERTON, GILBERT KEITH   Manalive. 1912. First ed., coloured frontis., cr. 8vo., orig. royal blue cloth, nice. Howes 194-726 1978 £10

CHESTERTON, GILBERT KEITH   Manalive. 1912. Coloured frontis., very good, first English ed. Bell Book 16-164 1978 £7.50

CHESTERTON, GILBERT KEITH   The Paradoxes of Mr. Pond. (1937). Good, 1st Eng. ed. Bell Book 16-978 1978 £4.50

CHESTERTON, GILBERT KEITH   Poems. Cheswick Press, 1915. Portrait, very good, 12mo., buckram gilt, t.e.g., first English ed. Bell Book 16-165 1978 £10

CHESTERTON, GILBERT KEITH   The Resurrection of Rome. (1930). 1st ed., orig. cloth, 8vo. Howes 194-727 1978 £5.50

CHESTERTON, GILBERT KEITH   Robert Louis Stevenson. London, (1927). 1st ed., 8vo., dust jacket, very good-fine. Houle 10-63 1978 $35

CHESTERTON, GILBERT KEITH   Superstition of Divorce. London, 1920. First ed., black cloth stamped in red, good. Houle 10-64 1978 $30

CHESTERTON, GILBERT KEITH   Thackeray. 1909. Portrait, cloth gilt, t.e.g., very good, first English ed. Bell Book 17-162 1978 £6.50

CHESTERTON, GILBERT KEITH   The Turkey and the Turk. Ditchling, S. Dominic's Press, 1930. Illus. by Thomas Derrick, no. 64 of 100 numbered copies, signed by author & artist, 4to., 3/4 black mor., fine, 1st ed. Rota 212-8 1978 £175

CHESTERTON, GILBERT KEITH   The Way of the Cross. London, (1935). One of 250 numbered copies, signed by Brangwyn & Chesterton, folio, vellum, fine, slipcase, 1st ed. Rota 211-62 1978 £110

CHESWICKE, LOUIS   The Life of Joseph Chamberlain. (1904). 4 vols., roy. 8vo., portraits, illus. George's 635-1236 1978 £5.50

CHETWOOD, WILLIAM RUFUS   Captain Robert Boyle's Voyages, Including the History of Mistress Villars and Several Other Marvelous Characters. Sagadahock, 1854. Cloth. Hayman 72-114 1978 $10

CHETWOOD, WILLIAM RUFUS   Voyages and Adventures of Captain Robert Boyle, in Several Parts of the World. London, 1768. Frontis., 12mo., contemp. calf. Argosy Special-23 1978 $100

CHETWOOD, WILLIAM RUFUS   The Voyages, Dangerous Adventures, and Imminent Escapes of Capt. Richard Falconer.... 1764. 5th ed., engraved frontis., 12mo., tear repaired, marginal repair to title & few pages of text, some browning, contemp. bds., rubbed, new calf spine. Edwards 1012-387 1978 $50

CHEVALLIER, GABRIEL   Clochmerle. 1936. Fine, d.w., first English ed. Bell Book 16-166 1978 £8.50

CHEVES, LANGDON   Letter of the Honorable Langdon Cheves, to the Editors of the Charleston Mercury. Charleston, 1844. Sewn, very rare. Jenkins 116-1585 1978 $250

CHEVREUL, MICHEL EUGENE   The Principles of Harmony and Contract of Colours, and Their Applications to the Arts. London, 1854. Trans. from French, 8vo., ads, plts., fldg. tables, orig. cloth, uncut, gilt, worn, hinges weak, but very good copy, 1st ed. in English. Norman 5-59 1978 $200

CHEVREUL, MICHEL EUGENE   Theorie des Effets Optiques que Presentent les Etoffes de Soie. Paris, 1846. 8vo., fldg. chromolitho. plts., contemp. half mor., foxing, but very good copy, 1st ed. Norman 5-58 1978 $150

CHEVY-CHASE, with a Preface Endeavouring to Prove that the Author Intended the Earl of Douglass for his Hero. Aberdeen, MDCCLIV. Sm. 8vo., early calf backed bds. Quaritch 979-83 1978 $60

CHEYNE, JOHN   An Essay on Cynanche Trachealis, or Croup. Philadelphia, 1813. Sm. 8vo., orig. wrs., part of covers & text dampstained, heavily in spots, 1st Amer. ed. Morrill 239-43 1978 $17.50

CHEYNE, JOHN   An Essay on Cynanche Trachealis or Croup. Philadelphia, 1813. Rittenhouse 49-138 1976 $47

CHEYNE, JOHN   An Essay on the Bowel Complaints of Children, More Immediately Connected with the Biliary Secretion, and Particularly of Strophia Ablactatorum, or Weaning Brash. Philadelphia, 1813. Sm. 8vo., orig. wrs., part of covers & text dampstained, 1st Amer. ed. Morrill 239-44 1978 $17.50

CHEZAL, G.   De, Prachute en Indochine (a travers l'Indochine en Feu). Paris, 1947. 8vo, orig. covers. Van der Peet 127-49 1978 Dfl 25

THE CHICAGO Record's Book for Gold Seekers. Toronto, (1897). Illus., pict. cover badly faded, binding firm, internally good. Wolfe 39-91 1978 $25

CHICKERING, J.   A Sermon, Preached in Boston, Before the American Society for Educating Pious Youth For the Gospel Ministry... Dedham, 1817. 8vo, wrappers. Edwards 1012-481 1978 $20

CHIDSEY, A. D.   A Frontier Village. Pre-Revolutionary Easton. Easton, 1940. 2nd ed., illus., orig. cloth, bookplt., very good. MacManus 239-1416 1978 $25

CHIDSEY, A. D.   The Penn Patents in the Forks of the Delaware. Easton, 1937. Ports., maps, 4to., ltd. to 200 copies, very scarce. MacManus 239-1417 1978 $42.50

CHIDSEY, DONALD BARR   The Gentleman from New York...Life of Roscoe Conkling. Yale University Press, 1935. Ex-lib. Butterfield 21-144 1978 $8.50

CHIDSEY, DONALD BARR   Sir Walter Raleigh, that Damned Upstart. New York, 1931. Broadfoot 50-33 1978 $12

CHILD, FRANCIS JAMES   A Scholar's Letters to a Young Lady.... Boston, (1920). Illus., ltd. to 585 copies, bds., corners dented. Biblo BL781-905 1978 $10

CHILD, HAMILTON   Gazetteer and Business Directory of Cattaraugus County for 1874-5. Syracuse, 1874. Map tipped in, illus. ads, orig. cloth, very good. Butterfield 21-102 1978 $35

CHILD, HAMILTON   Gazetteer and Business Directory of Chenango County for 1869-70. Syracuse, 1869. Illus. ads, fldg. map, fine cond., orig. cloth. Butterfield 21-112 1978 $35

CHILD, HAMILTON   Gazetteer and Business Directory of Montgomery and Fulton Counties...for 1869-70. Syracuse, 1870. Fldg. map, orig. cloth, worn. Butterfield 21-284 1978 $25

CHILD, HAMILTON   Gazetteer and Business Directory of Saratoga County and Queensbury, Warren County. Syracuse, 1871. Folded map tipped in, inserted table of census for 1870, 1865 & 1860, illus. ads, covers lightly worn, but very good. Butterfield 21-398 1978 $45

CHILD, JOSIAH 1630-99   A New Discourse of Trade. Glasgow, Foulis Press, 1751. Fifth ed., fcap. 8vo., contemp. calf, joints cracked, label missing. Howes 194-269 1978 £20

CHILD, L. MARIA   Philothea: A Grecian Romance. New York, 1845. New & corrected ed., clean, moderate wear, front flyleaf lacking, orig. binding. Hayman 71-221 1978 $8.50

CHILD, L. MARIA   Rainbows for Children. Boston, 1857. Cloth, worn at extremities, illus. Hayman 72-379 1978 $8.50

CHILD, WILLIAM   A History of the Fifth Regiment New Hampshire Volunteers in the American Civil War, 1861-1865. Bristol, 1893. Illus., 8vo., orig. cloth, 1st ed. Morrill 241-388 1978 $25

CHILD RESEARCH CLINIC OF THE WOODS SCHOOLS   The Challenge of the Progressive Education. 1938. Paper. Austin 80-807 1978 $10

CHILD RESEARCH CLINIC OF THE WOODS SCHOOLS   The Contribution of the Sciences. 1935. Paper. Austin 80-803 1978 $10

CHILD RESEARCH CLINIC OF THE WOODS SCHOOLS   Meeting the Challenge of the Exceptional Child. 1936. Paper. Austin 80-804 1978 $10

CHILD RESEARCH CLINIC OF THE WOODS SCHOOLS   Modern Science and the Exceptional Child. 1938. Paper. Austin 80-806 1978 $10

CHILD RESEARCH CLINIC OF THE WOODS SCHOOLS   Twenty Five Years of Progress in Education. 1939. Paper. Austin 80-808 1978 $10

CHILD RESEARCH CLINIC OF THE WOODS SCHOOLS   What Science Offers the Emotionally Unstable Child. 1936. Paper. Austin 80-805 1978 $10

THE CHILD'S Coloured Juvenile Picture and Reading Book. London, n.d. Hand-colored woodcut, very good. Victoria 34-161 1978 $20

CHILD'S Month of Mary,... Tulalip, 1885. 12 mo half mor. Ginsberg 14-1027 1978 $175

CHILD'S Scripture Question-Book... Philadelphia, 1853. Engravings. Hood 116-289 1978 $20

CHILDE, ISABELLA   The Child's Picture Testament. New York, c. c.1845. Thick 3" miniature, woodcut plates, lacks front fly-leaf, light rubbing & foxing, spine bright, very good. Victoria 34-543 1978 $25

CHILDERS, JAMES S.   From Siam to Suez. New York, 1932. Illus. Biblo 251-3 1978 $17.50

CHILDREN'S Chapbooks. York, (c. 1810). 13 vols. in 1, 12mo., woodcut illus., early calf, orig. wrs. bound in, some unopened, fine state. Quaritch 979-85 1978 $240

CHILDREN'S Chapbooks. Glasgow & Stirling, (c. 1850)-1852. 22 vols. in 1, woodcuts, half straight-grained mor. gilt top, edges uncut. Quaritch 979-86 1978 $350

CHILDS, GOERGE W.   Recollections of General Grant. Philadelphia, 1890. 16mo., orig. cloth wrs., 1st ed. Morrill 241-79 1978 $15

CHILDS, HARWOOD A.   Reference Guide to the Study of Public Opinion. Princeton, 1934. 1st ed. Austin 80-812 1978 $17.50

CHILICOTHE, Ohio's First Capital. (Chillicothe, 1941). Wrs., scarce. Hayman 72-568 1978 $8.50

CHILLINGWORTH, WILLIAM   The Religion of Protestants a Safe Way to Salvation. 1638. 2nd. ed., folio, recent quarter calf, gilt, over marbled bds., outer margin of 1 leaf defective, otherwise nice copy. Fenning 32-64 1978 £45

CHILVERS, HEDLEY A.   Out of the Crucible. London, (1929). 8vo, orig. cloth, reprint, 16 illus. from drawings by W.M. Timlin. K Books 239-91 1978 £5

CHILVERS, HEDLEY A.   The Yellow Man Looks On. London, (1933). 2nd. ed., slight foxing, orig. cloth, 8vo. K Books 239-92 1978 £5

CHIN, ROBERT   An Analysis of Conformity Behavior. 1943. Paper. Austin 80-813 1978 $10

CHINARD, GILBERT   The Correspondence of Jefferson and Du Pont De Nemours... Baltimore, 1931. Port., uncut. MacManus 239-222 1978 $27.50

CHINARD, GILBERT   George Washington as the French Knew Him. Princeton, 1940. Illus., fine. MacManus 239-493 1978 $17.50

CHINARD, GILBERT   Thomas Jefferson: The Apostle of Americanism. Boston, 1929. Ilus., first ed., binding faded, edges rubbed. Biblo 248-49 1978 $16.50

CHINARD, GILBERT   Thomas Jefferson. Boston, 1929. First ed., illus. Biblo 247-69 1978 $30

CHINIQUY, CHARLES   Fifty Years in the Church of Rome. 1886. Illus., orig. ed. Austin 79-135 1978 $12.50

CHINIQUY, CHARLES   Forty Years in the Church of Christ. Chicago, New York, Toronto, 1900. Hood's 115-923 1978 $30

CHINIQUY, CHARLES   Manual of the Temperance Society, Dedicated to the Youth of Canada. Montreal, 1847. 1st English ed., prtd. wr. Hood 117-344 1978 $30

CHINIQUY, CHARLES   Manuel des Societes de Temperance Dedie a la Jeunesse du Canada. Montreal, 1849. 3rd ed. Hood 116-290 1978 $20

CHINIQUY, CHARLES   The Priest, the Woman and the Confessional. n.d. Illus., paper. Austin 79-137 1978 $11

CHIROL, VALENTINE   The Egyptian Problem. London, 1920. 8vo, orig. cloth, shaken, few pencil notes. K Books 239-93 1978 £8

CHISHOLM, HUGH J, JR.   White Horses Verses. The Ashlar Press, 1932. 75 copies prtd., cloth illus. binding in red & white, August Heckscher's bkplt., very fine, boxed, worn. Battery Park 1-5 1978 $75

CHISHOLME, DAVID   The Lower Canada Watchman. Pro Patria. Kingston, 1829. 18mo., orig. bind. Hood 116-516 1978 $200

CHITTENDEN, HIRAM MARTIN   The Yellowstone National Park. Cincinnati, 1903. Orig. binding, cl., folding map. Hayman 71-112 1978 $7.50

CHITTENDEN, J.   Greek Art. London, (1947). Illus. Biblo BL781-350 1978 $12

CHITTENDEN, LUCIUS E.   The Capture of Ticonderoga. Rutland, 1872. Near fine. Butterfield 21-372 1978 $20

CHITTENDEN, WILLIAM LAWRENCE   Ranch Verses. New York, London, 1893. Pic. cloth, illus., lst ed., minor wear, fine copy, slipcase. Dykes 34-17 1978 $50

CHITTICK, V. L. O.   Ring-Tailed Roarers. 1941. Cloth, 1st ed., inscription, pic. bookplt. else very good, rather scarce. Dykes 35-138 1978 $12.50

CHIVAS-BARON, CL.   Contes et Legendes de l"annam. Paris, 1917. 2nd ed., half calf, fine binding, illus. on spine. Van der Peet 127-50 1978 Dfl 65

CHOATE, REFUS   A Discourse Delivered at Dartmouth College, July 27, 1853. Boston and Cambridge, 1853. lst. ed., 8vo, half roan, orig. printed wrappers bound in. Hannas 54-184 1978 £6

CHOCHOD, L.   Le Faune Indochine. Paris, 1950. Illus., 8vo, orig. covers. Van der Peet 127-286 1978 Dfl 30

CHOISY, FRANCOIS TIMOLEON   Journal ou Suite du Voyage de Siam. Amsterdam, 1687. Sm. 8vo., calf, rubbed. King 7-272 1978

CHOISY, FRANCOIS TIMOLEON   Journal du Voyage de Scain, fait en 1685 et 1686. Paris, 1930. Reprinted ed., plts., ltd. ed., 8vo., orig. covers. Van der Peet 127-51 1978 Dfl 70

CHOLMONDELEY, MARY   Diana Tempest. London, 1893. 3 vols., 8vo, original quarter grey-blue cloth, flowered boards (a bit worn, spines dull), lst ed., decent copy. Ximenes 47-51 1979 $75

CHOLMONDELEY, MARY   Red Pottage. 1899. 1/2 green calf, bookplt. Eaton 45-96 1978 £5

CHRIST, JOHANN FRIEDRICH   Dictionnaire des Monogrammes, Chiffres... Paris, 1750. First French ed., eng. plts., 8vo., calf. Schumann 511-12 1978 sFr 875

CHRIST, W. VON   Geschichte der Griech. 1924. Allen 234-186 1978 $20

CHRISTENSEN, C. B.   FRA Amerikas Kultur et aandslivs historie Lunds. Minneapolis, 1898. Illus., paper. Austin 79-139 1978 $27.50

CHRISTENSEN, L.   Such is the Antarctic. 1935. 8vo, orig. cloth, end-paper map, illus. Edwards 1012-569 1978 £25

CHRISTIAN V OF DENMARK   Rigis (Gloriosiss Memoriae) Christiani Quinti Leges Danicae Quas Augustiss Atz;.... Hauniae, 1710. lst Latin ed., quarto, full contemp. calf, Andrew Fletcher of Saltoun's copy with signature. Bennett 20-232 1978 $650

CHRISTIAN, ARTHUR   Debuts de L'Imprimerie en France. Paris, 1905. 4to., newly bound, 3/4 cloth, marbled paper over bds., orig. wr. bound in. Battery Park 1-465 1978 $125

CHRISTIAN, F. A.   Homes and Gardens in Old Virginia. Richmond, (1931). Illus. MacManus 239-1871 1978 $7.50

CHRISTIAN, W. ASBURY   Richmond. Her Past and Present. Richmond, 1912. 1st ed., thick 8vo., colored frontis., illus., orig. cloth, fine copy. MacManus 239-1880 1978 $30

THE CHRISTIAN Almanack, for...1827... Boston, (1826). Sewed. Hayman 72-12 1978 $7.50

THE CHRISTIAN Diadem and Family Keepsake. New York, 1852-53. Vols. II & III, 1/2 lea. Hayman 73-99 1978 $12.50

THE CHRISTIAN Movement in Japan. Tokyo, 1906. Orig. wrps. Ginsberg 16-881 1978 $10.00

THE CHRISTIAN Year. Oxford, 1853. Sm. 8vo., maroon mor., gilt tooled on both sides & spines, a.e.g., with fore-edge painting. Van der Peet H-64-333 1978 Dfl 450

CHRISTIE, AGATHA   The Body in the Library. 1942. Spine faded, good, first English ed. Bell Book 16-232 1978 $8.50

CHRISTIE, AGATHA   Cards on the Table. 1936. Very good, first English ed. Bell Book 16-233 1978 £28.50

CHRISTIE, AGATHA   Death in the Clouds. 1935. Good, first English ed. Bell Book 17-223 1978 £28.50

CHRISTIE, AGATHA   The Murder at the Vicarge. N.Y., 1930. 1st American ed., green cloth, fresh copy. Houle 10-66 1978 $25

CHRISTIE, AGATHA   The Mysterious Mr. Quin. New York, 1930. lst Amer. ed. Biblo 251-440 1978 $12.50

CHRISTIE, AGATHA   The Secret of Chimneys. London, (1925). 1st ed., orig. blue cloth, stamped in black, top edge stained blue, good-very good, clean copy. Houle 10-67 1978 $60

CHRISTIE, AGATHA   The Sittaford Mystery. 1931. Good, first English ed. Bell Book 17-979 1978 £24

CHRISTIE, AGATHA   Towards Zero. London, (1944). Very good in chipped & soiled dw. Bernard 5-62 1978 $15

CHRISTIE, AGATHA   The Under Dog. (1929). Rare, 12mo., gilt bds., good, first English ed. Bell Book 16-236 1978 £40

CHRISTIE, ROBERT   A Brief Review of the Political State of Lower Canada, Since the Conquest of the Colony, to the Present Day. New York, 1818. Grey front bd. only remains, backstrip bare, uncut. Wolfe 39-92 1978 $200

CHRISTIE, ROBERT   A History of the Late Province of Lower Canada, Parliamentary and Political. Quebec, 1848. Vols. I & II only, orig. binding. Wolfe 39-93 1978 $45

CHRISTLICHE Kinder-Lehr oder das heilige Vatter unser der Englische Gruss. Prag, 1721. 12mo, engraved double-folded f.p., plates signed by Samuel Hawel, orig. yellow Dutch flowered papered boards, very fine condition. Victoria 34-159 1978 $550

CHRISTMAN, ENOS   One Man's Gold. New York, 1930. First ed., illus., editor's signed pres. Biblo 247-195 1978 $50

CHRISTMAS Eve, and Other Stories. Boston, 1852. Cloth. Hayman 72-380 1978 $7.50

CHRISTMAS with the Poets. A Collection of Songs, Carols and Descriptive Verses. London, 1862. Illus. by Birket Foster, 4th ed., leather, edges rubbed. Biblo BL781-619 1978 $18.50

CHRISTOPHLE, ALBERT   La Rupture. Paris, 1904. 4to., orig. wr., uncut, ltd. ed., in 300 numbered copies, 1 of 25 preferred copies on Imperial Japan paper, illus. by A. Robida, excellent. Goldschmidt 110-59 1978 $140

CHRISTOWE, STOYAN   The Lion of Yanina. 1941. Austin 79-141 1978 $20

CHRISTOWE, STOYAN   This is My Country. 1938. Illus. Austin 79-142 1978 $10

CHRYSOLITE SILVER MINING COMPANY. Prospectus. New York, 1880. Large folding map, orig. pr. quarto wr., lst ed. Ginsberg 14-253 1978 $100

CHRYSOSTOM
Please turn to
CHRYSOSTOMUS, JOANNES

CHRYSOSTOMUS, JOANNES   Homelies, Ou, Sermons, sur l'Epistre de S. Paul Aux Romains. 1675. Old calf, spine worn, one cover detached. Allen 234-187 1978 $15

CHUBB, PERCIVAL   On the Religious Frontier. 1931. Austin 79-143 1978 $12.50

CHUBB, RALPH   Woodcuts. 1928. One of 200 copies, plts., sm. 4to., orig. marbled wraps, covers faded & somewhat worn, good, first English ed. Bell Book 17-483 1978 $22.50

CHUDLEIGH, ELIZABETH   An Authentic Detail of Particulars Relative to the late Duchess of Kingston. 1788. New ed., 8vo., claf, gilt, cracks in one hinge. P. M. Hill 142-79 1978 £20

CHUDLEY, MARY   Essays Upon Several Subjects in Prose and Verse. 1710. lst. ed., 8vo, modern bds., cloth spine. Hannas 54-57 1978 £35

CHUNG HENRY   The Case of Korea. New York, (1921). Illus., cloth, very good. Dawson's 127-210 1978 $15

CHURCH, ALBERT E.   Elements of Descriptive Geometry, with Its Applications to Spherical Projections. New York, (1864). Cloth, spine repaired along one edge. Hayman 73-100 1978 $7.50

CHURCH, ARTHUR H.   Japanese Sword Guards. Some Tsuba in the Collection of Sir... 1914. 4to., plts., orig. cloth, ltd. to 100 copies. Quaritch 983-Addenda d 1978 $475

CHURCH, D. W.   The Records of a Journey. A Prologue. Greenfield, (1888). Cloth. Hayman 72-115 1978 $10

CHURCH, JERRY   Journal of Travels, Adventures, and Remarks of... Harrisburg, 1933. Clean, orig. binding, reprint, very minor spotting on cover. Hayman 71-113 1978 $20

CHURCH, JOHN   A Cabinet of Quadrupeds with Historical and Scientific Descriptions. London, 1805. Engr. plts. by J. Tookey, 2 vols., folio, 1/2 cloth. Salloch 345-47 1978 $150

CHURCH, RICHARD   British Authors; a twentieth century gallery. London, 1943. Illus., fine, d.w., first ed., orig. binding. Rota 211-64 1978 £5

CHURCH, RICHARD   Plato's Mistake. London, 1941. Stiff wrappers, very nice, inscribed by author's sister, first ed. Rota 211-63 1978 £6

CHURCH, RICHARD   The Solitary Man. London, 1941. 8vo, red cloth, uncut, unopened, light foxing, d.w., near mint, ed. limited to 900 copies, 1st ed. Desmarais 1-85 1978 $20

CHURCH, RICHARD   Twentieth-Century Psalter. London, 1941. 8vo, gray cloth, ownership inscription, fine, d.w., 1st ed., collector's cond. Desmarais 1-86 1978 $20

CHURCH, RICHARD   Twentieth Century Psalter. London, 1943. First ed., orig. binding, fine, author's autograph signature. Rota 211-65 1978 £8

CHURCH, RICHARD   Twentieth-Century Psalter. London, 1943. Fine in chipped d.w. Desmarais B-142 1978 $15

CHURCH, THOMAS   History of Philip's War, Commonly Called the Great Indian War, of 1675 and 1676. Exeter, 1829. 2nd ed., plts., 12mo., contemp. calf. Morrill 237-331 1978 $25

CHURCH, W. A.   Patterns of Inlaid Tiles from Churches in the Diocese of Oxford. Wallingford, 1845. 4to., old cloth, lea. back, colored plts. drawn & engr. by Church, ex-lib., rubber stamp on verso of each plt. Morrill 339-332 1978 $12.50

CHURCH, W. F.   Constitutional Thought in 16th Century France, a Study in the Evolution of Ideas. Cambridge, 1941. 8vo. George's 635-596 1978 £6

CHURCH OF ENGLAND   The Book of Common Prayer and Administration of the Sacraments... 1669. Folio, cont. reversed calf. Howes 194-17 1978 £35

CHURCH OF ENGLAND   Book of Common Prayer, with the Psalter or Psalms of David. 1671. Sm. 8vo., contemp. calf, spine worn, unlettered. George's 635-1034 1978 £7.50

CHURCH OF ENGLAND   Book of Common Prayer, with the Psalter or Psalms of David. Oxford, 1726. Piece cut from title and first leaf, 12mo., contemp. calf, gilt, spine and corners worn. George's 635-1036 1978 £5.50

CHURCH OF ENGLAND   Book of Common Prayer, with the Psalter or Psalms of David. Oxford, 1726. Title scored and soiled, cr. 4to., old calf, unlettered. George's 635-1035 1978 £7.50

CHURCH OF ENGLAND   The Book of Common Prayer...Protestant Episcopal Church. Wilmington, 1800. New full brown calf. Baldwins' 51-219 1978 $37.50

CHURCH OF ENGLAND   The Book of Common Prayer.. 1849/50. 2 vols, v.g., reprint, octavo bound in cloth. Hyland 128-566 1978 $12.50

CHURCH Music and Musical Life In Pennsylvania in the 18th Century. Philadelphia, 1938-1947. Vol. 3, parts 1 & 2, fully illus., photos, 2 vols. Baldwins' 51-429 1978 $35

CHURCHILL, CHARLES   The Apology. 1761. 4to., unbound, first ed., fine. P. M. Hill 142-262 1978 £38

CHURCHILL, CHARLES   The Duellist. 1764. 4to., 1st ed., modern calf-backed bds. Quaritch 979-95 1978 $65

CHURCHILL, CHARLES   Poems. 1763. 1st. collected ed., 4to, orig. calf, old reback, brown label, fine. Jarndyce 16-55 1978 £25

CHURCHILL, CHARLES   Poems. 1766. Third ed., 2 vols., 8vo., contemp. calf, hinges wearing. P. M. Hill 142-263 1978 £18

CHURCHILL, CHARLES   The Rosciad and the Apology. London, 1891. 1 of 400 numbered copies, folio, frontispiece etching, etchings, t.e.g., uncut, half red mor., good , edited by Robert W. Lowe. Houle 10-68 1978 $60

CHURCHILL, FLEETWOOD   Essays on the Puerperal Fever and Other Diseases Peculiar to Women. London, 1849. Rittenhouse 49-137 1976 $20

CHURCHILL, FLEETWOOD   On the Diseases of Infants and Children. Philadelphia, 1850. 8vo., orig. stamped cloth, gilt lettering on spine, some foxing, ex-lib., good copy, 1st Amer. ed. Zeitlin 245-45 1978 $75

CHURCHILL, WILLIAM   Beach-La-Mar. 1911. Ex-lib. Austin 80-816 1978 $17.50

CHURCHILL, WILLIAM   Club Types of Nuclear Polynesia. 1917. Plts., ex-lib., top & bottom of backstrip frayed. Austin 80-817 1978 $27.50

CHURCHILL, WILLIAM   Easter Island. 1912. Ex-lib., backstrip worn, inscr'd by author on title page. Austin 80-818 1978 $60

CHURCHILL, WILLIAM   The Polynesian Wanderings. 1911. Tables, fldg. maps, ex-lib., library binding. Austin 80-819 1978 $47.50

CHURCHILL, WILLIAM   Sissano. 1916. Fldg. maps, ex-lib., top & bottom of backstrip frayed. Austin 80-820 1978 $37.50

CHURCHILL, WILLIAM   The Subanu. 1913. Fldg. maps, ex-lib., top & bottom backstrip frayed, inscr'd by author on title page. Austin 80-822 1978 $47.50

CHURCHILL, WILLIAM   Weather Words of Polynesia. n.d. Ex-lib., library binding. Austin 90-821 1978 $20

CHURCHILL, RANDOLPH HENRY SPENCER   Men, Mines and Animals in South Africa. London, 1892. 2nd ed., 8vo., fldg. map, plts., text-illus., decor. cloth. K Books 239-95 1978 £20

CHURCHILL, WINSTON LEONARD SPENCER   Arms and The Covenant. 1938. 1st. ed., frontis, 8vo, orig. blue cloth, signed by Churchill, spine little faded, very good copy, pres. copy, rare. Sawyer 298-7 1978 £275

CHURCHILL, WINSTON LEONARD SPENCER   Arms and The Covenant. 1938. 1st. ed., frontis, 8vo, blue cloth, variant d.w., yellow with red print, good copy. Sawyer 298-8 1978 £70

CHURCHILL, WINSTON LEONARD SPENCER   Blood, Sweat and Tears. 1941. Austin 80-51 1978 $7.50

CHURCHILL, WINSTON LEONARD SPENCER   Charles, IXth Duke of Marlborough. London, 1934. Wrappers, fine, first ed. Rota 211-68 1978 £15

CHURCHILL, WINSTON LEONARD SPENCER   Charles IXth Duke of Marlborough, K.G. 1934. 1st. ed., 8vo, orig. wrappers, in choice state, very scarce. Sawyer 298-33 1978 £21

CHURCHILL, WINSTON LEONARD SPENCER   Charles, IXth Duke of Marlborough K.G. 1934. Fine, wraps, first English ed. Bell Book 17-164 1978 £15

CHURCHILL, WINSTON LEONARD SPENCER   Charles IXth Duke of Marlborough, K. G. 1934. Sm. 4to., orig. wrs. Quaritch 979-96 1978 $40

CHURCHILL, WINSTON LEONARD SPENCER   The Dawn of Liberation. Boston, 1945. Covers lightly soiled, fine. Desmarais B-143 1978 $15

CHURCHILL, WINSTON LEONARD SPENCER   Great Contemporaries. 1937. 1st. ed., plts., 8vo, orig. blue cloth, d. w., very good set. Sawyer 298-128 1978 £65

CHURCHILL, WINSTON LEONARD SPENCER   Great Contemporaries. 1937. Proof copy of 1st. ed., illus., 8vo, orig. paper wrapper, slightly soiled, good copy. Sawyer 298-9 1978 £55

CHURCHILL, WINSTON LEONARD SPENCER   The Great War. 1933. Maps, drwgs., 3 vols., photos, roy. 8vo.   George's 635-597 1978 £10.50

CHURCHILL, WINSTON LEONARD SPENCER   Ian Hamilton's March. 1900. 1st. ed., portrait, maps, 8vo, orig. cloth, mark on upper cover, good copy. Sawyer 298-10 1978 £82

CHURCHILL, WINSTON LEONARD SPENCER   Ian Hamilton's March. Toronto, (1900). Portrait, maps, plans, beige cloth.   Wolfe 39-94 1978 $75

CHURCHILL, WINSTON LEONARD SPENCER   India. 1931. 1st. ed., 8vo, orig. orange printed wrappers, fine copy, rare.   Sawyer 298-11 1978 £120

CHURCHILL, WINSTON LEONARD SPENCER   India. 1931. Orig. wrs., nice, first ed.   Rota 211-67 1978 £135

CHURCHILL, WINSTON LEONARD SPENCER   Into Battle: Speeches. 1941. 1st ed., portr., d.w., 8vo, orig. cloth.   Howes 194-728 1978 £6

CHURCHILL, WINSTON LEONARD SPENCER   Liberalism and the Social Problem. 1909. 1st. ed., 8vo, orig. red cloth, spine slightly rubbed, good copy, rare. Sawyer 298-13 1978 £145

CHURCHILL, WINSTON LEONARD SPENCER   London to Ladysmith via Pretoria. 1900. 1st. ed., maps, 3 folding, 8vo, orig. pictorial cloth, slight foxing on pre-lim. leaves.   Sawyer 298-14 1978 £47.50

CHURCHILL, WINSTON LEONARD SPENCER   Lord Randolph Churchill. 1906. 1st ed., plts., some in color, 2 vols., lg. 8vo, orig. cloth, very good.   Howes 194-729 1978 £32

CHURCHILL, WINSTON LEONARD SPENCER   Marlborough, His Life and Times. 1933-38. 1st. ed., portraits, maps, facsimiles, 4 vols., lg. 8vo, buckram, vol. 3 lacks d.j., spine slightly faded, good set, scarce.   Sawyer 298-17 1978 £95

CHURCHILL, WINSTON LEONARD SPENCER   My African Journey. 1908. 1st. ed., maps, illus., 8vo, orig. pictorial cloth, slight mark on front cover, fine copy, scarce.   Sawyer 298-18 1978 £120

CHURCHILL, WINSTON LEONARD SPENCER   My Early Life. 1930. 1st. ed., maps, illus., 8vo, orig. cloth, d.w., very good copy.   Sawyer 298-19 1978 £95

CHURCHILL, WINSTON LEONARD SPENCER   My Early Life. Oldhams, 1949. Illus., plts., maps, 8vo, orig. cloth, d.w., pres. inscription from author on f/l, part of d.w. torn, otherwise good copy.   Sawyer 298-20 1978 £55

CHURCHILL, WINSTON LEONARD SPENCER   Painting as a Pastime. 1948. 1st. ed., portrait, coloured reproductions of paintings, 8vo, orig. cloth, d.w., pres. incription on f/l, very good copy.   Sawyer 298-21 1978 £45

CHURCHILL, WINSTON LEONARD SPENCER   Painting as a Pastime. 1948. 1st. ed., portrait, coloured reproductions of paintings, 8vo, orig. cloth, d.w., d.w. frayed & fading at foot of covers, good copy.   Sawyer 298-129 1978 £5.50

CHURCHILL, WINSTON LEONARD SPENCER   The People's Rights. 1910. 1st. ed., 2nd. issue, 8vo, orig. yellow paper covers, portrait & turquois lettering, sm. corner of wrappers torn off & slightly frayed, internally brown, otherwise good. Sawyer 298-22 1978 £140

CHURCHILL, WINSTON LEONARD SPENCER   The People's Rights. 1910. 1st. ed., 8vo, orig. yellow paper covers, portrait & green lettering, covers rather frayed & internal spotting, variant binding, words "Yorkshite Observer Edition" inserted above price, good copy.   Sawyer 298-23 1978 £185

CHURCHILL, WINSTON LEONARD SPENCER   Public Expenditure and Revenue. 1926. 8vo, orig. paper cover, soiled & creased. Sawyer 298-24 1978 £45

CHURCHILL, WINSTON LEONARD SPENCER   The River War. 1899. 1st. ed., maps, illus., 2 vols., 8vo, orig. pictorial cloth, ex-lib. copy, labels & stamps removed, slight foxing, otherwise good copy.   Sawyer 298-25 1978 £285

CHURCHILL, WINSTON LEONARD SPENCER   The Second World War. Boston, 1948-1953. 1st. American ed., plts., maps, 6 vols., 8vo, orig. cloth, d.w. Sawyer 298-26 1978 £15

CHURCHILL, WINSTON LEONARD SPENCER   Set The People Free. 1948. 8vo, orig. paper cover, portrait on front.   Sawyer 298-27 1978 £35

CHURCHILL, WINSTON LEONARD SPENCER   The Story of the Malakand Field Force. 1898. 1st. ed., 1st. issue, portrait frontis, maps, 8vo, orig. green cloth, mostly unopened, good copy, inscribed by Jack Churchill.   Sawyer 298-28 1978 £385

CHURCHILL, WINSTON LEONARD SPENCER   The Story of the Malakand Field Force. 1898. 1st. issue of 1st. ed., portrait, 8vo, orig. cloth, spine slightly darkened, bookplt. on free end-paper, slight foxing on prelims., good copy, very scarce.   Sawyer 298-29 1978 £285

CHURCHILL, WINSTON LEONARD SPENCER   Thoughts and Adventures. Old-hams, 1948. 8vo, orig. cloth, d.w., pres. incription on f/l, good copy. Sawyer 298-30 1978 £35

CHURCHILL, WINSTON LEONARD SPENCER   War Speeches and Post-War Speeches. 1941-61. 1st. ed., 12 vols., 8vo, orig. cloth, d.w., very good set. Sawyer 298-31 1978 £95

CHURCHILL, WINSTON LEONARD SPENCER   War Speeches. 1945-46. Portrs., 6 vols., 8vo.   George's 635-601 1978 £12.50

CHURCHILL, WINSTON LEONARD SPENCER   Collected Works. Library of Imperial History, 1976. 8vo, 34 vols., publisher's full calf gilt, ltd. ed. of 2000 sets.   Sawyer 298-132 1978 £1250

CHURCHILL, WINSTON LEONARD SPENCER   The World Crisis, 1911-18. 1923-27. Vols. 2, 3, 4 1st eds., 4 vols., 8vo.   George's 635-603 1978 £12.50

CHURCHILL, WINSTON LEONARD SPENCER   The World Crisis 1911-1918. 1923-31. Complete set of 1st. eds., maps, illus., 6 vols., 8vo, orig. cloth, vols. 5 & 6 with d.w., spine of vol. 2 little bubbled, corner of vol. 6 little rubbed, good set. Sawyer 298-32 1978 £120

CHURCHILL, WINSTON LEONARD SPENCER   The World Crisis, 1911-18. Portr., 2 vols., 8vo.   George's 635-602 1978 £5.25

CHURCHILL'S Collection of Voyages and Travels... 1704-32. Numerous engraved maps & plts., 6 vols., thick folio, calf, rebacked.   Edwards 1012-9 1978 £900

CHURCHMAN, JOHN   An Account od the Gospel Labours, and Christian Experiences of...John Churchman. 1780. First English ed., contemp. calf, red mor. label.   Howes 194-209 1978 £20

CHURCHYARD, THOMAS 1530-1604   The Worthines of Wales, a Poem. 1776. Sm. 8vo., orig. calf-backed bds., spine worn, joints cracked.   Howes 194-210 1978 £12.50

CIAMPINI, GIOVANNI   De Sacris Aedificiis a Constantino Magno Construc-tis. Rome, 1693. Folio, plts., contemp. half-vellum, fine, 1st ed.   Gilhofer 74-33 1978 sFr 1,900

CIANO, GALEAZZO   The Ciano Diaries, 1939-43. New York, 1946. Biblo 247-668 1978 $10

CIBBER, COLLEY   An Apology For the Life of Mr. Colley Cibber, Comedian. 1740. 1st. ed., portrait frontispiece, 4to, contemp. mottled calf gilt, green morocco label, top of upper hinge weak, o/w fine copy, pres. copy from author.   Sawyer 299-115 1978 £350

CIBBER, COLLEY   An Apology for the Life of Mr. Colley Cibber... 1740. 2nd. ed., orig. calf, old reback, v.g.   Jarndyce 16-56 1978 £48

CIBBER, COLLEY   An Apology for the Life of Colley Cibber, Comed-ian. 1740. Second ed., contemp. calf, rebacked, 8vo.   Howes 194-211 1978 £35

CIBBER, COLLEY   An Apology for the Life of, With an Historical View of the Stage During His Own Time. London, 1740. 2nd. ed., title in red & black, 8vo, contemp. calf rebacked. Traylen 88-209 1978 £20

CIBBER, COLLEY   An Apology for the Life of..., Comedian, and Late Patentee of the Theatre-Royal. (Waltham St. Lawrence): The Golden Cockerel Press, 1925. 2 vols., sm. 4to., orig. cloth-backed bds., 1 of 450 copies, slightly soiled, but very good. MacManus 238-792 1978 $75

CIBBER, COLLEY   The Life of Edwin Forrest, with Reminiscences and Personal Recollections. Philadelphia, (1874). 1st ed., frontis., orig. cloth. MacManus 239-752 1978 $10

CIBBER, COLLEY   Plays. 1721. 1st. collected ed., 2 vols., 4to, half-title in vol. 2, contemp. panelled rough calf, worn, tear in 1 leaf, removing 8 or 10 words, occasional slight stains. Hannas 54-60 1978 £145

CIBBER, COLLEY   She Wou'd, and She Wou'd Not, or the Kind Impostor. 1703. 1st. ed., 4to, disbound, working copy, title-laid down, sm. tear in most leaves "repaired" by sellotape. Hannas 54-59 1978 £7.50

CICCOLINA, SOPHIA MARQUISE A.   Deep Breathing, as a Means of Promoting the Art of Song, and of Curing Weaknesses and Affections of the Throat and Lungs, Especially Consumption. New York, (1883). Illus., sm. 8vo., Amer. ed. Morrill 239-334 1978 $8.50

CICERO, MARCUS TULLIUS   Cato. 1773. Contemp. calf, joints cracked, vignette on title, first ed. of this translation, 8vo. Howes 194-386 1978 £25

CICERO, MARCUS TULLIUS   Correspondence... 1901. Vol. 78, Index, only. Allen 234-196 1978 $7.50

CICERO, MARCUS TULLIUS   Les Deux Livres de la divination. Paris, 1710. 12mo., contemp. calf. George's 635-457 1978 £7.50

CICERO, MARCUS TULLIUS   Epistles to Atticus. 1806. New ed., 3 vols., new buckram, blind stamp on title. Allen 234-201 1978 $20

CICERO, MARCUS TULLIUS   Epistolae ad Atticum, ad M. Brutum, ad Q. Fratrem. Florence, Giunta Press, 1571. Woodcut initials, printed in italic, full mor., gilt top, other edges uncut, very good, exceptionally lg. copy, 6.9 x 4.8 inches. Howes 194-551 1978 £115

CICERO, MARCUS TULLIUS   Epistolarum ad Familiares Libri XVI. Amsterdam, 1659. 12mo., contemp. half calf, crimson label. Howes 194-533 1978 £12.50

CICERO, MARCUS TULLIUS   Epistolarum Libri XVI ad Familiares ut Vilgo Vocantur. Roterodami, 1704. Sm. thick 8vo., full vellum. Van der Peet H-64-295 1978 Dfl 45

CICERO, MARCUS TULLIUS   The Letters of Marcus Tullius Cicero to Several of his Friends. 1753. First ed., 3 vols., contemp. polished calf, lettering pieces, nice, 8vo. Howes 194-387 1978 £40

CICERO, MARCUS TULLIUS   Letters to Several of his Friends. 1804. 3 vols., contemp. mottled calf, rebacked, orig. labels preserved, nice, sixth ed., 8vo. Howes 194-213 1978 £25

CICERO, MARCUS TULLIUS   Les Libres de la veillesse et l'amitie.... Paris, 1708. 12mo., contemp. calf. George's 635-458 1978 £7.50

CICERO, MARCUS TULLIUS   Tully's Offices in English. 1714. 3rd ed., orig. panelled calf, v.g. Jarndyce 16-59 1978 £7.50

CICERO, MARCUS TULLIUS   De Officics, trad. en Francois sur l'edition latine et graevius avec les notes et de sommaires des chapitres. Paris, 1714. 12mo., contemp. calf. George's 635-455 1978 £7.50

CICERO, MARCUS TULLIUS   Les Offices De.... Paris, 1768. 2nd ed., 8vo., contemp. marbled calf, back gilt, with label, marbled endpapers, Latin and French text. Salloch 348-35 1978 $30

CICERO, MARCUS TULLIUS   De Officics, libri tres, ad solam priscorum exemplarium fidem recensuit.... Brunsuigae, 1783. Contemp. calf, 8vo. George's 635-454 1978 £5

CICERO, MARCUS TULLIUS   Opera. Paris, 1768. Frontis., 14 vols., 8vo., marbled calf, spines gilt with labels, gilt edges, orig. bind., 1st vol. some light waterstains, Latin text. Salloch 348-34 1978 $150

CICERO, MARCUS TULLIUS   Opera. Cum Indicibus et Variis Lectionibus. Oxford, 1783. 10 vols., 4to., contemp. polished calf, joints cracked. Howes 194-212 1978 £85

CICERO, MARCUS TULLIUS   Orationes quaedam selectae, cum interpretatione & Notis...quibus praefigitur Vita Ciceronis. 1729. Contemp. calf, front joint broken, 8vo. Howes 194-214 1978 £7.50

CICERO, MARCUS TULLIUS   De oratore ad Q. Fratrem. Oxon, 1696. Engraved frontis., vignette on title, contemp. calf, unlettered, spine a little rubbed, 8vo. George's 635-456 1978 £10.50

CICERO, MARCUS TULLIUS   Oraisons choislès, en latin, et en francois.... Paris, 1723. 12mo., contemp. calf. George's 635-459 1978 £7.50

CICERO, MARCUS TULLIUS   The Orations, The Offices, The Cato and Laelius. London, 1833. 3 vols., sm. 8vo., 3/4 calf, labels missing. Salloch 348-36 1978 $20

CICERO, MARCUS TULLIUS   Select Orations. 1799. New ed., contemp. half russia, joints weak, 8vo. Howes 194-215 1978 £10

CICERO, MARCUS TULLIUS   M. T. C. Tusculanarum Quaestionum Aphorismi Hoc Est,.... Basileae, 1580. 1st ed., octavo, full contemporary vellum, Andrew Fletcher copy with signature on recto of back cover. Bennett 20-45 1978 $300

CICERO, MARCUS TULLIUS   Select Orations. 1777. 2 vols., calf, worn. Allen 234-1514 1978 $15

CICERO, MARCUS TULLIUS   Traite des Loix. Paris, 1719. 12mo., contemp. calf. George's 635-460 1978 £7.50

CICOGNARA, LEOPOLDO   Storia della Scultura dal Suo Risorgimento in Italia.... Venezia, 1813, 1816, 1818. Lg. folio, shell patterned bds., half calf, plts., vignettes, very good, first ed. King 7-158 1978 £150

CINCINNATI Young Men's Merchantile Library Association. 1855. New cloth. Battery Park 1-319 1978 $75

CINDERELLA and the Glass Slipper. New York, c.1860. Colored illus., pictorial wrappers, sewn. Victoria 34-160 1978 $8.50

CINDERELLA or, the Little Glass Slipper. Albany, 1816. Woodcuts, wrappers, fine copy. Victoria 34-162 1978 $75

CIOCCHI, GIOVANNI MARIA   La Pittura in Parnaso. Florence, 1725. 4to., contemp. bds., 1st ed. Gilhofer 74-34 1978 sFr 250

THE CIRCULATOR Of Useful Knowledge, Amusement, Literature, Science and General Information... 1825. Wood engravings, orig. half title, red label. Jarndyce 16-386 1978 £18.50

CIST, CHARLES   Sketches and Statistics of Cincinnati in 1851. Cincinnati, 1851. Orig. cloth, nice copy, illus. MacManus 239-380 1978 $45

CIST, HENRY M.   The Army of the Cumberland. New York, 1882. Bell Wiley's copy. Broadfoot 46-40 1978 $10

THE CITY of Stockton:.... Stockton, 1883. Illus., folding view, original printed wr. Ginsberg 14-163 1978 $75

THE CITY of Watertown. Watertown, 1900. Side-opening 4to., photo. illus., pict. ads, wr., good. Butterfield 21-225 1978 $12.50

CITY Scenes or a Peep into London for Children. Darton, 1818. 12mo., engrs. on copper, orig. bds., red lea. back, illus., rare. Quaritch 979-92 1978 £230

CIVIALE, JEAN   Traite Pratique sur les Maladies des Organes Genito-Urinaires. Paris, 1837. Lithographed plts., 2 vols., 8vo., all edges gilt, first ed., margins dampstained, some foxing, covers detached. Rittenhouse 49-140 1976 $35

CIVIC CLUB OF CARLISLE, PA. Carlisle Old & New. Harrisburg, 1907. Orig. pict. cloth, illus., 8vo. Americanist 101-32 1978 $12.50

CIVIL And Criminal Justice: First (and second) report of the Commissioner of Inquiry into the Administration of Civil and Criminal Justice in the West Indies. 1826-1827. Folio, contemp. half calf, fine. Fenning 32-65 1978 £125

CLACK, LOUISE   Our Refugee Household. New York, 1866. Loose in binding, extensive damage to margins, bds. poor, Bell Wiley's copy. Broadfoot's 44-79 1978 $12

CLAGETT, NICHOLAS   A Perswasive to an Ingenuous Tryal of Opinions in Religion. 1685. 1st. ed., 4to, disbound. Hannas 54-61 1978 £6

CLAIBORNE, JOHN FRANCIS HAMTRAMCK   Life and Times of Gen. Sam Dale, the Mississippi Partisan. New York, 1860. Illus., lst ed., orig. cloth, recased, lib. bkplt., very scarce. MacManus 239-742 1978 $25

CLAIBORNE, JOHN FRANCIS HAMTRAMCK   Life and Times of Gen. Sam Dale, the Mississippi Partisan. New York, 1860. Illus. by John M'Lenan. Baldwins' 51-520 1978 $50

CLAIBORNE, JOHN FRANCIS HAMTRAMCK   Life and Correspondence of John A. Quitman. New York, 1860. 2 vols., orig. cloth. Jenkins 116-1119 1978 $125

CLAIBORNE, JOHN FRANCIS HAMTRAMCK   Life and Correspondence of John A. Quitman. New York, 1869. 2 vols. Jenkins 116-917 1978 $150

CLAIBORNE, JOHN HERBERT   Cataract Extraction. New York, 1908. Rittenhouse 49-141 1978 $10

CLAIBORNE, JOHN HERBERT   William Claiborne of Virginia. With Some Account of His Pedigree. New York, 1917. Illus., map, sm. stain on fr. cover, scarce, fine copy. MacManus 239-1887 1978 $20

CLAPHAM, A. W.   Lesnes Abbey in the Parish of Erith, Kent. 1915. 4to., plts., some in colour, illus. Upcroft 12-75 1978 £20

CLAPHAM, JOHN   The Bank of England, a History, 1694-1914. Cambridge, 1944. Portraits, 2 vols., 8vo. George's 635-299 1978 £15

CLAPHAM, JOHN   An Economic History of Modern Britain, The Early Railway Age, 1820-50. Cambridge, 1926. Roy. 8vo. George's 635-300 1978 £5

CLAPP, EBENEZER   Clapp Family in America. Boston, 1876. Baldwins' 51-247 1978 $30

CLAPP, EBENEZER   History of the Town of Dorchester. Boston, 1859. MacManus 239-1025 1978 $35

CLAPP, EDWIN J.   The Port of Boston. New Haven, 1916. Maps, plans, 8vo., ex-lib., lst ed. Morrill 239-506 1978 $8.50

CLAPP, FRANK L.   Introduction to Education. 1929. Austin 80-824 1978 $8.50

CLAPP, GEORGE WOOD   The Life and Work of James Leon Williams, Doctor of Dental Surgery. New York, 1925. Illus., 8vo., orig. bds., cloth back, lst ed. Morrill 239-46 1978 $10

CLAPP, WILLIAM W.   A Record of the Boston Stage. Boston, 1853. Sm. 8vo., orig. cloth, ex-lib., lst ed. Morrill 241-324 1978 $17.50

CLAPPERTON, H.   Journal of a Second Expedition Into the Interior of Africa... 1829. Portrait, folding map, 4to, calf, rebacked & repaired, sm. stamp on verso of title. Edwards 1012-249 1978 £120

CLAPPERTON, H.   Journal of a Second Expedition Into the Interior of Africa From the Bight of Benim to Soccatoo. Philadelphia, 1829. Map, frontis torn, orig. bds., covers loose. Baldwins' 51-336 1978 $17.50

CLARE, ISRAEL S.   A Brief History of Lancaster County, Pa. Lancaster, 1892. Illus. MacManus 239-1419 1978 $17.50

CLARENDON, EDWARD HYDE, EARL OF   A Collection of Tracts. 1727. lst ed., folio, orig. calf, old reback, v.g. Jarndyce 16-58 1978 £32

CLARENDON, EDWARD HYDE, EARL OF   The History of the Rebellion & Civil Wars in England.... 1703. Half-titles, orig. panelled calf; rebacked, lst ed. of abridgement, v.g. Jarndyce 16-57 1978 £24

CLARENDON, EDWARD HYDE, EARL OF   The History of the Rebellion and Civil Wars in England, begun in 1641. Oxford, 1731-32. Engraved portraits, 3 vols. in 1, half calf, lacks spines, covers detached, crudely repaired. George's 635-605 1978 £5

CLARETIE, JULES   Bouddha. Paris, 1888. 12mo, full leather binding by Chambolle-Duru, brown mor. with tan inlays and gilt, a.e.g., orig. wrs. bound in, frontis. and vignettes by Robaudi, engraved by A. Nargeot, 1 of 150 copies, printed on Japon et verge du Marais, numbered and initialled. Duschnes 220-20 1978 $350

CLARETIE, JULES   Le Drapeau... Paris, 1879. 4to, 1/2 red morocco, marbled bds., map plts., illus. Eaton 45-98 1978 £9

CLARETIE, JULES   Shakespere and Moliere. New York, April 3, 1900. lst ed., orig. pr. decorative wr., very good or better. Limestone 9-262 1978 $ 8.50

CLARK, ALICE   Working Life of Women in the 17th Century. 1919. 8vo. George's 635-301 1978 £6.50

CLARK, ALLEN C.   Life and Letters of Dolly Madison. Washington, D.C., 1914. Illus. MacManus 239-788 1978 $20

CLARK, ARTHUR HAMILTON   The Clipper Ship Era... New York, (1910). Illus. MacManus 239-1741 1978 $20

CLARK, ARTHUR HENRY   A Bibliography of the Publications of the Rowfant Club. Cleveland, 1925. Orig. cloth-backed bds., boxed, 1 of 140 copies on Venetia hand-made paper, fine. MacManus 238-1048 1978 $75

CLARK, BARRETT H.   The British and American Drama of To-Day. New York, 1915. Biblo 247-896 1978 $8

CLARK, BENNETT CHAMP   "Old Man Eloquent". Boston, 1932. lst ed., signed, illus. Biblo 248-3 1978 $20

CLARK, C. M.   The Picturesque Ohio. Cincinnati, (1887). Cloth. Hayman 73-510 1978 $8.50

CLARK, CHARLES E.   Catalogue of the Dr. Charles E. Clark Collection of American Portraiture, Including a Remarkably Fine Collection of Washington Portraits.... Boston, 1901. Illus., 8vo., bds., buckram back, orig. wrs. bound in. Morrill 241-23 1978 $12.50

CLARK, DELBER W.   The World of Justus Falckner. Philadelphia, (1946). Biblo BL781-39 1978 $9

CLARK, EDNA M.   Ohio Art and Artists. Richmond, (1932). Cloth, covers little rubbed but good tight copy. Hayman 73-509 1978 $50

CLARK, EDWARD L.   Daleth or the Homestead of the Nations. Boston, 1864. Illus., plts. in color, tint, & b & w, 8vo., fr. cover partly waterstained, text lightly dampstained, lst ed. Morrill 239-335 1978 $15

CLARK, EMMONS   History of the Seventh Regiment of New York 1806-1889. New York, 1890. 2 vols., illus., nice set, orig. cloth. MacManus 239-347 1978 $35

CLARK, EVANS   The Internal Debts of the United States. 1933. Austin 80-509 1978 $22.50

CLARK, EWAN   Miscellaneous Poems. Whitehaven, 1779. First ed., half calf, entirely uncut, 8vo. Howes 194-216 1978 £24

CLARK, FRANCIS E.   The Continent of Opportunity. New York, (1907). Cloth. Hayman 73-123 1978 $7.50

CLARK, G. N.   The Dutch Alliance, and the War against French Trade, 1688-97. Manchester, 1923. 8vo. George's 635-302 1978 £6

CLARK, H.   A Short and Easy Introduction to Heraldry in Two Parts. London, 1788. 6th. ed., copperplts., 12mo, orig. bds., back strip missing. Sexton 7-137 1978 £10

CLARK, HAROLD F.   Economic Theory and Correct Occupational Distribution. 1931. Austin 80-510 1978 $27.50

CLARK, J.   Trails of the Hunted. Boston, 1928. Signed inscription to T. D. Carter, Carter bookplate, 8vo, orig. cloth. Book Chest 17-85 1978 $22

CLARK, J. HENRY   Sight and Hearing, How Preserved and How Lost. New York, 1856. 8vo., lst ed. Morrill 239-47 1978 $15

CLARK, JOHN A.   The Christian Keepsake and Missionary Annual. Philadelphia, 1839. Engraved plts., orig. handsome red leather, plts. with usual foxing, fine. Victoria 34-158 1978 $17.50

CLARK, JOHN BATES   The Distribution of Wealth. 1899. Austin 80-511 1978 $12.50

CLARK, JOHN W.   The Care of Books. Cambridge, 1901. Illus. Battery Park 1-346 1978 $100

CLARK, JOSEPH B.   Leavening the Nation. The Story of American... Home Missions. New York, (1903). Cloth. Hayman 72-139 1978 $8.50

CLARK, JOSEPH G.   Lights and Shadows of Sailor Life,..... Boston, 1848. Original cloth. Ginsberg 14-240 1978 $50

CLARK, KENNETH   Landscape into Art. London, (1949). 1st ed., plts., d.w., orig. cloth, 8vo. K Books 244-349 1978 £5

CLARK, LEWIS   Narratives of the Sufferings of Lewis and Milton Clarke,.... Boston, 1846. 12mo, original brown printed wrappers (bit worn), 1st ed., two portraits, light waterstains throughout, sound copy, scarce in wrappers. Ximenes 47-53 1978 $50

CLARK, MAMIE PHIPPS   Changes in Primary Mental Abilities with Age. 1944. Paper. Austin 80-826 1978 $10

CLARK, MARY AUGUSTA   Recording and Reporting for Child Guidance Clinic. 1930. Austin 80-827 1978 $10

CLARK, R.   Sir William Trumbull in Paris, 1685-1686. Cambridge, 1938. Plts., octavo, good. Upcroft 10-266 1978 £10

CLARK, R. N.   New York and San Juan Mining and Smelting Company. New York, 1880. Colored frontis, map, original wr., 1st ed. Ginsberg 14-254 1978 $75

CLARK, R. T.   R. T. Clark's New System of Training the Horse and Other Animals. Richmond, 1877. Wrps. Hayman 71-340 1978 $12.50

CLARK, RICHARD   An Account of the National Anthem entitled God Save the King. 1822. First ed., plts., portraits, contemp. blind-stamped calf, gilt edges, rebacked, 8vo. Howes 194-733 1978 £20

CLARK, SAMUEL   The Laws of Chance. London, 1758. 8vo., first ed., contemp. unlettered calf, joints weak, rare. Quaritch 977-146 1978 $220

CLARK, SAMUEL   The Lives of sundry Eminent Persons in this Later Age. London, 1683. Tall folio, half sheep over marbled boards, leather spine label, frontis. portrait of Clark, sheep worn, lightly foxed. Bennett 7-28 1978 $135

CLARK, STERLING B. F.   How Many Miles from St. Jo? San Francisco, 1929. Illus., original boards, cloth backstrip, 1st ed. Ginsberg 14-241 1978 $12.50

CLARK, THOMAS   Discipline and the Derelict. 1921. Austin 80-828 1978 $10

CLARK, THOMAS M.   Reminiscences. New York, 1895. Orig. cl., 1st ed. Ginsberg 16-851 1978 $10.00

CLARK, WALTER 1846-1924   Histories of the Several Regiments and Battalions from North Carolina. Goldsboro, 1901. 5 vols., pict. covers bright, Bell Wiley's copy. Broadfoot's 44-571 1978 $450

CLARK, WALTER VAN TILBURG   Christmas Comes to Hjalsen. (Reno, 1930). 8vo., pict. wrs., 1st ed., fine, orig. mailing envelope, rare. Howell 5-16 1978 $20

CLARK, WALTER VAN TILBURG   The City of Trembling Leaves. 1946. Austin 82-305 1978 $8.50

CLARK, WALTER VAN TILBURG   The Ox-Bow Incident. 1940. Austin 82-306 1978 $8.50

CLARK, WALTER VAN TILBURG   The Track of the Cat. 1949. First ed., d.j. Austin 82-307 1978 $20

CLARK, WILLIAM GEORGE   Peloponnesus: Notes of Study and Travel. London, 1858. 1st ed., 8vo, engraved maps, full calf, spine panelled, ruled & lettered in gilt, marbled edges, armorial book-plt. Deighton 5-203 1978 £55

CLARK, WILLIAM SMITH   Chief Patterns of World Drama. Boston, (1946). Biblo 247-897 1978 $12.50

CLARK, WILLIS G.   An Address on the Character of Lafayette and Washington... Philadelphia, 1840. Disbound, some foxing, former owner's name on title-pg. Hayman 71-627 1978 $8.50

CLARK-KENNEDY, A. E.   Stephen Hales, D.D., F.R.S. An Eighteenth Century Biography. Cambridge, 1929. Rittenhouse 49-145A 1976 $35

CLARKE, CHARLES MANSFIELD   Observations of Those Diseases of Females Which are Attended by Discharges. Boston, 1826. Second Amer. ed., good. Rittenhouse 49-143 1976 $10

CLARKE, D.   Public School Explorers in Newfoundland. London, n.d. Hood's 115-206 1978 $25

CLARKE, DONALD HENDERSON   In the Reign of Rothstein. 1930. Austin 79-147 1978 $7.50

CLARKE, E. D.   Travels in Various Countries of Europe, Asia and Africa. 1810-23. Engraved maps, plts. & plans, 4to, contemp. calf gilt, rebacked, offsets from plts. & some slight foxing. Edwards 1012-10 1978 $200

CLARKE, EDWARD H.   A Century of American Medicine, 1776-1876. Philadelphia, 1876. 12mo., later buckram, first ed. Rittenhouse 49-144 1976 $65

CLARKE, EDWARD H.   Visions. Boston, 1878. Portr., sm. 8vo., covers dampstained, 1st ed. Morrill 239-49 1978 $12.50

CLARKE, F.   Quebec and South Africa; a Study in Cultural Adjustment. London, 1934. Card cover. Hood 116-517 1978 $10

CLARKE, F. Y.   Atlanta Illustrated. Containing Glances at its Population, Business, Manufactures, Industries, Institutions, Society... Atlanta, 1881. Illus., cloth. MacManus 239-1807 1978 $25

CLARKE, GEORGE KUHN   History of Needham, Mass. 1711-1911. Illus. MacManus 239-1041 1978 $35

CLARKE, H. F.   Jeremiah Dummer. Colonial Craftsman and Merchant. Boston, 1935. 4to., illus., frontis., t.e.g., untrimmed, very fine, ltd. to 225 copies, slipcase. MacManus 239-649 1978 $125

CLARKE, JOHN M.   L'Ile Percee. 1923. 1st ed., illus., maps, orig. cloth, good copy. MacManus 239-77 1978 $15

CLARKE, JOSEPH I. C.   My Life and Memories. New York, 1926. Illus., 8vo., orig. cloth. Morrill 241-81 1978 $10

CLARKE, K.   One Hundred Details from Pictures in the National Gallery... 1938-41. 2 vols., folio, buckram, a little faded. Quaritch 983-167 1978 $55

CLARKE, M. A.   Directions for the Management of Children, from the Time of their Birth to the Age of Seven Years. London, 1773. 8vo., qtr. calf, cloth sides, orig. and apparently only ed. Gurney 75-20 1978 £70

CLARKE, M. V.   The Medieval City State, an Essay on Tyrrany and Federation in the Later Middle Ages. 1926. Cr. 8vo. George's 635-606 1978 £5

CLARKE, M. V.   Medieval Representation and Consent; a study of early parliaments in England and Ireland. 1936. 8vo. Upcroft 12-77 1978 £12.50

CLARKE, MARY ANNE   The Rival Princes. 1810. Portrait, 2 vols., sm. 8vo., half calf, worn. F. Edwards 1013-265 1978 £15

CLARKE, PETER D.   Origin and Traditional History of the Wyandotts... Toronto, 1870. Orig. binding, clean, scarce. Hayman 71-142 1978 $50

CLARKE, R.   Sierra Leone. London, (1846). 8vo., map, plts., orig. cloth, repaired, pres. copy from author. Quaritch 977-16 1978 $200

CLARKE, SAMUEL 1675-1729   Three Practical Essays, on Baptism, Confirmation, and Repentence. 1730. Fifth ed., 12mo., contemp. calf, little age-staining. Howes 194-217 1978 £10

CLARKE, SEYMOUR   Cameron Highlanders, Officers Present at the Various Campaigns.... 1913. Imp. 8vo., orig. cloth, partly unopened. F. Edwards 1013-532 1978 £12

CLARKE, T. WOOD   Emigres in the Wilderness. 1941. Illus. Austin 79-148 1978 $17.50

CLARKE, THOMAS   History of Intolerance... 1819. 1st. ed., 8vo, orig. bds., uncut, spine worn, cords holding, fine internally. Fenning 32-66 1978 £24

CLARKE, THOMAS CURTIS   The American Railway, Its Construction, Development, Management and Appliances. New York, 1889. 200 illus., rebacked in blue lib. buckram. Baldwins' 51-8 1978 $22.50

CLARKE, WILLIAM   The Natural History of Nitre. London, 1670. Sm. 8vo., contemp. calf, upper cover detached, backstrip chipped, marginal browning, some foxing, very good copy, scarce 1st ed. Zeitlin 245-46 1978 $400

CLARKE, WILLIAM   Three Courses and a Desert. 1836. 51 illus. by George Cruikshank, 3rd. ed., orig. half morocco, marbled bds., good. Jarndyce 16-387 1978 £18

CLARKESSE, CHARLES   The Act of Tonnage & Poundage, and Book of Rates... 1675. Lg. 12mo, contemp. unlettered calf, 4 leaves misbound, fine copy. Fenning 32-57 1978 £35

CLARKSON, L.   Buttercups Visit to Little Stay at Home. New York, 1881. 1st printing of enlarged ed., color illus., text foxed, board edges and spine rubbed, very good. Victoria 34-167 1978 $20

CLARKSON, ROBERT H.   Church Work in Nebraska and Dakota. New York, 1867. Disbound, 1st ed. Ginsberg 14-243 1978 $50

CLARKSON, THOMAS   Histoire des Quakers. Geneve-Paris, 1820. 8vo., half calf, rare. Van der Peet H-64-296 1978 Dfl 75

CLARKSON, THOMAS   The History of the Rise, Progress, and Accomplishment of the Abolition of the African Slave-Trade by.... London, 1808. 2 vols., 1st ed., octavo, newly bound in brown half mor., marbled boards, leather title labels, occasional foxing. Totteridge 29-24 1978 $325

CLARKSON, THOMAS   The History of the Rise, Progress and Accomplishment of the Abolition of the African Slave-Trade, by the British Parliament. Wilmington, 1816. Leather, slight wear of spine at bottom. Hayman 71-143 1978 $25

CLARKSON, THOMAS   Memoirs of the Private and Public Life of William Penn. London, 1813. 1st ed., 2 vols., orig. bds., cloth, very good untrimmed set. MacManus 239-1420 1978 $55

CLARKSON, THOMAS   Memoirs of the Public and Private Life of William Penn. 1849. Engraved frontis., map, fcap. 8vo. George's 635-1253 1978 £5

CLARKSON, THOMAS   A Portraiture of Quakerism... Indianapolis, 1870. Leather, stain on cover. Hayman 72-140 1978 $10

CLARKSON, THOMAS STREATFEILD   A Biographical History of Clermont, or Livingston Manor...with a Sketch of the First Steam Navigation by Fulton and Livingston. Clermont, 1869. "150 copies prtd.", illus., good & sound, scarce. Butterfield 21-140 1978 $20

CLASON'S Texas Road Map and Railway Guide. Denver, ca. 1918. Large folding map. Jenkins 116-217 1978 $45

CLASSIFICATION of Operating Expenses as Prescribed by the Railroad Commission of the State of Texas. Austin, 1899. Revised issue, original printed wr. Jenkins 116-1127 1978 $20

CLAUDEL, PAUL   Les Choephores D'Eschyle... Paris, 1920. Lg. 8vo., orig. paper covers, ltd. ed. Eaton 45-99 1978 £10

CLAUDEL, PAUL   Les Enumenides D'Eschyle. Paris, 1920. Ltd. ed., wrps., no. 61 of 100 copies reserved for la Nouvelle Revue Francaise. Eaton 45-100 1978 £10

CLAUDIN, ANATOLE   Histoire de L'Imprimerie en France au XVe et au XVI Siecle. Paris, 1900-1904. Special ed. printed on Japan paper, coloured plts., illus., 3 vols., lg. & thick folio, half brown levant morocco gilt, gilt top, choice copy. Traylen 88-43 1978 £800

CLAUSIUS, R.   Ueber den zweiten Hauptsatz der Mechanischen Warmetheorie. Brunswick, 1867. 8vo., orig. wrappers, first ed. Gurney 75-21 1978 £50

CLAVIGERO, F. S.   History of Mexico... 1807. 2nd. ed. in English, map, plts., 2 vols., 4to, contemp. diced calf, rebacked. Edwards 1012-687 1978 £150

CLAY, ALBERT T.   Miscellaneous Inscriptions in the Yale Babylonian Collection. 1915. Plts., autographed texts, ex-lib., lacks backstrip, covers worn. Austin 80-830 1978 $27.50

CLAY, ALBERT T.   Neo-Babylonian Letters from Erech. 1919. Plts., ex-lib., lacks backstrip, autographed texts. Austin 80-829 1978 $37.50

CLAY, ALBERT T.   Personal Names from Cuneiform Inscriptions of the Cassite Period. 1912. Ex-lib., backstrip frayed top & bottom of backstrip. Austin 80-831 1978 $37.50

CLAY, CHARLES   Muskrat Man. Toronto, 1946. 1st ed. Hood 116-458 1978 $12.50

CLAY, HENRY   Letters of Messrs. Clay, Benton, and Barrow, ... Washington, 1844. Jenkins 116-220 1978 $150

CLAY, HENRY   The Private Correspondence. New York, 1856. Ex-library, cloth, mor. back, plts. Wolfe 39-95 1978 $25

CLAY, JEHU C.   Annals of the Swedes on the Delaware. Chicago, 1938. 4th ed., illus., maps. MacManus 239-116 1978 $25

CLAY, JOHN   My Life on the Range. Chicago, [1924]. Illus., original cloth, 1st ed. Ginsberg 14-244 1978 $125

CLAY, JOHN   My Life on the Range. Chicago, (1924). Illus., first ed., scarce. Biblo 247-192 1978 $125

CLAY, LUCIUS D.   Decision in Germany. 1950. Illus. Austin 80-59 1978 $8.50

CLAY, R. S.   The History of the Microscope. 164 Illus., Traylen 88-489 1978 £12.50

CLAYBAUGH, JOSEPH   Introductory Address, to the Students of the Theological Seminary, of the Second A. R. Synod of the West. Oxford, 1839. Disbound. Hayman 73-511 1978 $12.50

CLAYTON, JOSHUA E.   Prospectus and Statement of the Rescue Mining Company. New York, 1877. Orig. pr. wr., 1st ed. Ginsberg 14-729 1978 $75

CLAYTON, ROBERT   A Journal from Grand Cairo to Mount Sinai and back again. 1753. 4to., old marbled sides, rubbed, parchment back, plts. P.M. Hill 142-80 1978 £18

CLAYTON, W. W.   History of Steuben County, New York... Philadelphia, 1879. 1st ed., thick 4to., illus., cloth, good. MacManus 239-1100 1978 $100

CLEATON, IRENE   Books and Battles: American Literature, 1920-1930. Boston, 1937. 8vo., cloth, d.j., 1st ed., illus. J. S. Lawrence 38-F132 1978 $20

CLEATON, IRENE   Books and Battles: American Literature 1920-1930. 1937. Illus., first ed. Austin 82-308 1978 $15

CLEATOR, P. E.   Rockets Through Space, the Dawn of Interplanetary Travel. New York, 1936. 1st U. S. ed., illus., publisher's file copy, 8vo., orig. cloth, very good. Americanist 103-78 1978 $20

CLEAVELAND, AGNES MORLEY   No Life For A Lady. Boston, 1941. Illus., original cloth. Ginsberg 14-245 1978 $15

CLEAVELAND, ELISHA L.   A Thanksgiving Discourse, for Recent Military Successes, Delivered in the Third Congregational Church, New Haven,..... New Haven, (1864). Unbound. Hayman 72-141 1978 $7.50

CLEAVELAND, PARKER   An Elementary Treatise on Mineralogy and Geology, Being an Introduction to the Study of These Sciences, and Designed for the Use of Pupils. Boston, 1816. Fldg. plts., colored map, 8vo., half lea., marbled sides, nice, lst ed., very scarce. Morrill 239-336 1978 $200

CLEAVES, FREEMAN   Rock of Chickamauga: Life of Gen. George H. Thomas. Norman, 1948. Illus., Bell Wiley's copy. Broadfoot's 44-80 1978 $20

CLEBURNE. CHARTERS   Charter for the City of Cleburne, Texas, Recommened by the Citizens' Committee of Thirty. Cleburne, 1914. Jenkins 116-747 1978 $12.50

CLEETON, GLEN U.   Making Work Human. 1949. Ex-lib. Austin 80-837 1978 $10

CLEIRIGH, A. UA   History of Ireland to the Coming of Henry II. n.d. Vol I, very good, octavo bound in cloth, reprint. Hyland 128-710 1978 £7

CLEIS, G.   Essais Fantaisies Decoratives. Paris, c.1900. Folio, plts., contemp. mor. backed cloth, soiled. Quaritch 983-169 1978 $50

CLELAND, JOHN   The Way to Things by Words, and to Words by Things;.... London, 1766. 8vo, half calf, lst ed. Ximenes 47-52 1978 $125

CLELAND, THOMAS MAITLAND   The Decorative Work of.... New York, 1929. Portr. litho. by Rockwell Kent, cloth, fine, used & soiled d.w., 1 of 1200 numbered copies, plt. Dawson's 447-29 1978 $75

CLEMEN, RUDOLPH A.   The American Livestock and Meat Industry. New York, 1923. Illus., original cloth, lst ed. Ginsberg 14-246 1978 $37.50

CLEMENCEAU, GEORGES   Au Pied du Sinai. Paris, (1898). Orig. litho. illus., tall 8vo., pic. wrs., 1 of 354 numbered copies on velin d'Arches. Argosy Special-89 1978 $4,500

CLEMENS, SAMUEL LANGHORNE   The Adventures of Huckleberry Finn. London, 1884. lst ed., 8vo., lst issue, illus., orig. red cloth, gilt lettering, black decor. on front bd. & spine, white endpapers prtd. in ochre, bkplt. of Cleveland Museum of Art, near fine copy, scarce. Current Misc. 8-6 1978 $850

CLEMENS, SAMUEL LANGHORNE   Adventures of Huckleberry Finn. New York, 1885. Illus., orig. cloth, lst ed., later issue, good. MacManus 238-438 1978 $85

CLEMENS, SAMUEL LANGHORNE   The Adventures of Huckleberry Finn... New York, 1885. lst ed., bright, rebacked, orig. cloth laid on spine, repair unnoticeable, extremely nice. Ballinger 11-180 1978 $425

CLEMENS, SAMUEL LANGHORNE   Adventures of Huckleberry Finn. New York, 1885. 8vo, green stamped cloth, port. frontis. inserted, covers worn, spine rubbed, shaken, lst ed., collector's cond. Desmarais 1-88 1978 $175

CLEMENS, SAMUEL LANGHORNE   The Adventures of Huckleberry Finn. New York: The Limited Editions Club, 1933. 8vo., illus. by E. W. Kemble, orig. pict. cloth, pub. box, 1 of 1,500 copies, fine. MacManus 238-819 1978 $45

CLEMENS, SAMUEL LANGHORNE   The Adventures of Tom Sawyer. Hartford, 1876. Frontis., 8vo., orig. 1/2 mor., a.e.g., lst Amer. ed., lst print., very scarce, light cover wear, only 200 copies. Howell 5-17 1978 $1,250

CLEMENS, SAMUEL LANGHORNE   The Adventures of Tom Sawyer. Hartford, 1876. Illus., orig. pict. cloth, lst Amer. ed., 2nd printing, recased, spine restored, covers worn. MacManus 238-439 1978 $100

CLEMENS, SAMUEL LANGHORNE   The Adventures of Tom Sawyer. (1875). 1892. Illus., orig. ed., illus. Austin 82-1003 1978 $11

CLEMENS, SAMUEL LANGHORNE   The Adventures of Tom Sawyer. Hartford, 1876. lst ed., lst issue, 8vo., prtd. on wove paper, orig. blue cloth, recased with orig. spine laid down over new buckram back, binding bit soiled, good copy, very scarce. Current Misc. 8-7 1978 $535

CLEMENS, SAMUEL LANGHORNE   The Adventures of Tom Sawyer. 1937. No box, good, illus. Austin 82-1005 1978 $10

CLEMENS, SAMUEL LANGHORNE   American Claimant. 1892. Illus., first ed., good. Austin 82-1006 1978 $27.50

CLEMENS, SAMUEL LANGHORNE   American Claimant. 1892. Illus., first ed., cover rubbed around edges. Austin 82-1007 1978 $17.50

CLEMENS, SAMUEL LANGHORNE   A Connecticut Yankee in King Arthur's Court. New York, 1889. 8vo, green stamped cloth, lst ed., near mint. Desmarais 1-90 1978 $185

CLEMENS, SAMUEL LANGHORNE   The Curious Republic of Gondour and Other Whimsical Sketches. New York, 1919. Orig. cloth-backed bds., lst ed., very good. MacManus 238-444 1978 $50

CLEMENS, SAMUEL LANGHORNE   Extracts from Adam's Diary. 1904. Illus. Austin 82-1008 1978 $22.50

CLEMENS, SAMUEL LANGHORNE   Following the Equator. Hartford, 1897. Cloth, previous owner's name & address & dated, near fine. Dawson's 447-211 1978 $75

CLEMENS, SAMUEL LANGHORNE   Following the Equator. 1897. First ed. Austin 82-1009 1978 $37.50

CLEMENS, SAMUEL LANGHORNE   Following the Equator. A Journey Around the World... Hartford, 1897. Cloth, lst ed., lst issue, inner hinges little weak. Hayman 72-142 1978 $35

CLEMENS, SAMUEL LANGHORNE   Mark Twain's Good-Bye. Hannibal, 1935. lst ed., scarce. Morrill 239-341 1978 $17.50

CLEMENS, SAMUEL LANGHORNE   The Letters of Quintus Curtius Snodgrass. Dallas, 1946. lst ed., lst prtg., never acknowledged by Twain, foreward by E. E. Leisy, with considerable support. evid., almost fine, dust jacket, scarce. Ballinger 11-182 1978 $15

CLEMENS, SAMUEL LANGHORNE   Mark Twain's Library of Humor. New York, 1888. Leather, good, tight copy, second state. Austin 82-1011 1978 $37.50

CLEMENS, SAMUEL LANGHORNE   Life on the Mississippi... Boston, 1883. Illus., orig. gilt pict. cloth, lst ed., lst state, fine. MacManus 238-441 1978 $150

CLEMENS, SAMUEL LANGHORNE   Life on the Mississippi. Boston, 1883. 8vo., publisher's orig. half calf, marbled sides, lst ed., lst state. Morrill 239-339 1978 $37.50

CLEMENS, SAMUEL LANGHORNE   Life on the Mississippi. Boston, 1883. Illus., orig. cloth, lst ed., lst state, near-fine. MacManus 238-442 1978 $175

CLEMENS, SAMUEL LANGHORNE   Life on the Mississippi by Mark Twain. 1883. Sm. 8vo., lst ed., illus., red cloth decor. with pic. design, slightly faded, bright, sound copy. Quaritch 979-97 1978 $70

CLEMENS, SAMUEL LANGHORNE   Life on the Mississippi. 1923. Austin 82-1010 1978 $10

CLEMENS, SAMUEL LANGHORNE   The Man that Corrupted Hadleyburg. 1900. Orig. pict. cloth, covers somewhat soiled, spine dull, good, first English ed. Bell Book 17-875 1978 £10

CLEMENS, SAMUEL LANGHORNE   Merry Tales by Mark Twain. New York, 1892. Cloth, lg. bkplt. Dawson's 447-213 1978 $25

CLEMENS, SAMUEL LANGHORNE   Merry Tales. New York, 1892. 8vo, green stamped cloth, binding in state A with pr. endpapers, lst ed., collector's cond. Desmarais 1-89 1978 $35

CLEMENS, SAMUEL LANGHORNE   The Movie Story of Tom Sawyer. Racine, (1931). Colored illus., pict. bds. Petrilla 13-139 1978 $8

CLEMENS, SAMUEL LANGHORNE   The 1,000,000 Bank-Note and Other New Stories. 1893. First ed., stamping bright. Austin 82-1013 1978 $37.50

CLEMENS, SAMUEL LANGHORNE   The 1,000,000 Bank-Note and Other New Stories. 1893. Frontis., backstrip darkened. Austin 82-1014 1978 $27.50

CLEMENS, SAMUEL LANGHORNE   The Prince and the Pauper. Montreal, 1881. 8vo., contemp. maroon cloth, first Canadian ed. Wolfe 39-96 1978 $250

CLEMENS, SAMUEL LANGHORNE   The Prince and the Pauper. Boston, 1882. Ist Amer. ed., 8vo., Ist issue, second state of bindings, interior fine, green cloth bds. stamped in gold & black, very good copy boxed in green cloth slipcase. Current 24-10 1978 $125

CLEMENS, SAMUEL LANGHORNE   Rambling Notes of an Idle Excursion. Toronto, 1878. Ist ed., scarce, clean, little rubbed, good tight copy. Hayman 71-144 1978 $50

CLEMENS, SAMUEL LANGHORNE   Mark Twain's Sketches. New York, (1874). Ist ed., orig. paper wrs., lacks back wrapper, illus., very good. Greene 78-339 1978 $55

CLEMENS, SAMUEL LANGHORNE   The Stolen White Elephant, etc. London, 1900. Pict. glazed boards, "yellow-back" format. Greene 78-127 1978 $35

CLEMENS, SAMUEL LANGHORNE   The $30,000 Bequest and Other Stories. New York, 1906. First ed., 2nd issue, illus., bookplate of Will M. Clemens. Biblo 247-632 1978 $20

CLEMENS, SAMUEL LANGHORNE   Three Aces. Jim Todd's Episode in Social Euchre. A Poem and a Denial. (Westport, 1929, New York, c.1930). Orig. printed wrs., Ist ed., 1 of about 50 copies printed, sm. portion of front wr. torn, else fine. MacManus 238-445 1978 $100

CLEMENS, SAMUEL LANGHORNE   Three Sketches by Mark Twain. Stamford, 1946. Wrs., very fine. Dawson's 447-115 1978 $25

CLEMENS, SAMUEL LANGHORNE   Tom Sawyer Abroad. 1894. Ist. English ed., illus. by Dan Beard, half title, orig. red cloth blocked in black & gilt, spine slightly faded, o/w v.g. Jarndyce 16-1153 1978 £14.50

CLEMENS, SAMUEL LANGHORNE   A Tramp Abroad. Hartford, 1880. 8vo., Ist ed., thinner issue. Morrill 239-333 1978 $17.50

CLEMENS, SAMUEL LANGHORNE   A Tramp Abroad. Hartford, 1880. Orig. pict. cloth, illus., Ist ed., state "B", port. frontis., slightly faded and worn, but nice. MacManus 238-440 1978 $100

CLEMENS, SAMUEL LANGHORNE   A Tramp Abroad. Hartford, 1880. 8vo., illus., Ist ed., thick paper issue. Morrill 239-337 1978 $20

CLEMENS, VENCESLAUS A LYBEO-MONTE   Trinobantiados Augustae sive Londini Libri VI... (Leyden, 1636). First ed., quarto, cont. pressed vellum London binding, spotted, sound, pres. inscription from author to Archbishop William Laud. Bennett 20-46 1978 $285

CLEMENS, WILL M.   Mark Twain His Life and Work. Chicago & New York, 1894. Bds. Hayman 71-145 1978 $10

CLEMENT XIV, POPE   Interesting Letters of Pope Clement XIV (Ganganelli). 1777. Third ed., portrait vignettes, 2 vols., sm. 8vo., contemp. calf, rebacked. Howes 194-218 1978 £18.50

CLEMENT, ARTHUR W.   Our Pioneer Potters. 1947. Ltd. to only 500 copies, plts., autographed. Nestler Rare 78-89 1978 $35

CLEMENT, JEAN-MARIE-BERNARD   Revolution des Welches Predite dans les Jours Anciens. Paris. Sm. sq. 12mo., marbled bds., calf spine, fine, uncut, first and only ed. King 7-341 1978 £50

CLEMENT, NICOLAS   Austrasiae Reges et Duces Epigrammatis. Cologne, 1591. Sm. 4to., illus., contemp. vellum, excellent cond., Ist ed. Gilhofer 74-130 1978 sFr 1,200

CLEMENTS, BENNET A.   Memoir of Jonathan Letterman, M. D., Surgeon United States Army and Medical Director of the Army of the Potomac. Washington, D.C., 1909. Wrs. Bell Wiley's copy. Broadfoot 46-46 1978 $10

CLEMO, JACK   Wilding Graft; a novel. 1948. Covers faded, good, first English ed. Bell Book 16-168 1978 £4.50

CLEMSON, THOMAS G.   Observations on the La Motte Mines and Domain in the State of Missouri,.... Washington, 1838. Disbound, Ist ed. Ginsberg 14-581 1978 $85

CLEPHAN, R. COLTMAN   The Tournament. Its Periods and Phases. 1919. Coloured frontis. and plts., 4to., orig. red cloth, spine faded. F. Edwards 1013-266 1978 £85

CLERCO, R. DE   Gedichten. Amsterdam, 1907. Sm. 8vo., half cloth, colored illus. by J. B. Heukelom. Van der Peet H-64-370 1978 Dfl 45

CLERK-MAXWELL, JAMES
Please turn to
MAXWELL, JAMES CLERK

CLERY, JEAN BAPTISTE   A Journal of Occurrences at the Temple, During The Confinement of Louis XVI, King of France. London, 1798. Ist. English ed., 8vo, 3 plts., modern paper bds., uncut, edges dust-soiled. Hannas 54-123 1978 £8.50

CLEVELAND, GROVER   Letters of... , 1850-1908. Boston, 1933. Ist. ed. Baldwins' 51-175 1978 $12.50

CLEVELAND, ROSE E.   You and I, or Moral, Intellectual and Social Culture. Detroit, 1886. Cloth. Hayman 72-144 1978 $15

THE CLEVELAND STORE FIXTURE COMPANY   High-Grade Show Cases. Cigar Store Fixture Catalog.... (Akron, n.d., c.1895). Wrs. Hayman 72-101 1978 $8.50

CLEVELAND Illustrated. N.P., n.d. (1900?). Wrps. Hayman 71-524 1978 $8.50

CLEVER, CHARLES P.   New Mexico:.... Washington, 1868. Orig. pr. wr., Ist ed. Ginsberg 14-752 1978 $150

CLEVERDON, CATHERINE L.   The Woman Suffrage Movement in Canada. Toronto, 1950. As new in d.j., orig. binding. Wolfe 39-97 1978 $25

CLIFFORD, C. R.   The Junk Snupper, the Adventures of an Antique Collector. New York, (1927). Cloth. Hayman 73-127 1978 $8.50

CLIFFORD, H.   Further India; Being the Story of Exploration from the earliest times in Burma, Malaya, Siam and Indo-China. London, 1905. Cloth, illus., plts., maps, 8vo. Van der Peet 127-53 1978 Dfl 65

CLIFFORD, MRS. W.K.   Love Letters of a Wordly Woman. New York, 1892. Ist Amer. ed., cloth, t.e.g., bookplate Margaret Armstrong. Greene 78-164 1978 $15

CLIFFORD, WILLIAM KINGDON   I, the Unseen Universe: II. 1886. Paper, worn. Austin 80-832 1978 $10

CLINTON, DEWITT   Letters on the Natural History & Internal Resources of State of New York by Hibernicus. 1822. Rebound copy. Nestler Rare 78-103 1978 $38

CLINTON, ISAAC   Household Baptism. Lowville, 1838. Pasted-in errata, orig. bds., worn & chipped but sound. Butterfield 21-250 1978 $35

CLINTON-BAKER, HENRY   Illustrations of Conifers. Hertford, 1909. 3 vols., plts., 4to., mod. 1/2 mor., t.e.g., Ist ed., light foxing to backs of some plts., else fine. Howell 5-18 1978 $450

THE CLINTON Monument M DCCC XL VIII. New York, 1848. Litho. frontis., wr., loose. Butterfield 21-127 1978 $10

CLODD, EDWARD   The Childhood of the World. 1873. Austin 80-833 1978 $12.50

CLODD, EDWARD   I Pionieri Dell'Evoluzione Da Talete Ad Huxley. Torino, 1910. 2nd ed., 3/4 mor. Salloch 345-48 1978 $15

CLOETE, HENRY   The History of The Great Boer Trek and The Origin of the South African Republics. 1900. 3rd. ed., pres. copy to Winston Churchill, 8vo, orig. red cloth, spine faded & little worn, covers slightly affected by damp, Ist. section becoming loose. Sawyer 298-66 1978 £65

CLOKIE H. MC D.   Canadian Government and Politics. Toronto, (1946). Biblo 251-22 1978 $15

CLOPPER, E. N.   An American Family: Its Ups and Downs.... Cincinnati, 1950. Jenkins 116-221 1978 $15

CLOPTON, A. G.　　An Eulogy on the Life and Character of Dr.
Ashbel Smith.　Jefferson, 1886.　Orig. pr. wr.　Ginsberg 14-949　1978　$225

CLOPTON, A. G.　　An Eulogy on the Life and Character of Dr. Ashbel
Smith.　Jefferson, 1886.　Original printed wr., extremely rare and unrecorded.
Jenkins 116-1249　1978　$225

CLOUGH, ARTHUR HUGH　　The Bothe of Toper-Na-Fuosich. A Long-Vacation
Pastoral.　Oxford, 1848.　Orig. limp blue cloth, 1st ed., very good.　MacManus
238-186　1978　$135

CLOUGH, ARTHUR HUGH　　Poems.　London, 1862.　1st collected ed., 12mo.,
near fine copy, orig. green cloth, gilt & black fillets, some blemishes here and
there.　Current 24-11　1978　$135

CLOUGH, ARTHUR HUGH　　The Poems and Prose Remains of...　London, 1869.
2 vols., first ed., stained and foxed on first few leaves.　Biblo 247-813　1978
$18.50

CLOUSTON, K. WARREN　　The Chippendale Period in English Furniture.　London, 1897.　Illus. by author, 4to., ex-lib., crudely rebacked with white tape,
embossed stamp on plts., orig. cloth.　Morrill 241-82　1978　$15

CLOUSTON, W. A.　　The Book of Noodles.　Battery Park 1-259　1978
$25

CLUB and Professional Life of Rhode Island.　N. P., n.d. (ca. 1900).　Portrs.,
4to., inner hinges cracked, orig. cloth.　Morrill 241-489　1978　$10

CLUNE, G.　　The Medieval Gild System.　1942.　8vo.　Upcroft 12-79　1978　£6

CLUSIUS, CAROLUS
Please turn to
L'ECLUSE, CHARLES DE

CLUTE, EUGENE　　The Practical Requirements of Modern Buildings.
New York, 1928.　Illus., 4to., covers rubbed.　Biblo BL781-538　1978　$17.50

CLUTTON-BROCK, A.　　More Essays on Books.　London, 1921.
1st ed., very good or better.　Limestone 9-57　1978　$8.50

CLUVERIUS, JOANNES　　Historiarum Totius Mundi Epitome....　Leiden,
1657.　Engrav. title, sm. 4to., contemp. calf.　Howes 194-534　1978　£28

COADY, M. M.　　Masters of Their Own Destiny.　Nova Scotia,
1939.　Austin 80-513　1978　$20

COALE, GRIFFITH BARLEY　　North Atlantic Patrol; The Log of a Seagoing
Artist.　New York, Toronto, 1942.　B/W reproductions of paintings.　Hood's 115-
207　1978　$25

COALE, GRIFFITH BARLEY　　The North Atlantic Patrol.　1942.　Illus.　Austin
80-61　1978　$12.50

COAN, TITUS　　Life in Hawaii: An Autobiographic Sketch of mission life and labors (1835-1881).　New York, (1882).　Cloth, bit worn.　Dawson's
127-318　1978　$20

COARSE Fodder (Bran, Chips and Sawdust Mostly) Raked Up By An Old Settler,
Being Facts, Figures and Things Relating to Fergus Falls, Minnesota.　Minneapolis,
1881.　Folding map, original printed wr., 1st ed.　Ginsberg 14-548　1978　$85

COATS, R. H.　　Features of Present-Day Canada.　Philadelphia,
1947.　Hood's 115-585　1978　$15

COATSWORTH, ELIZABETH　　Night and the Cat.　New York, 1950.　Illus.
by Foujita, 1st ed., d.w. slightly frayed.　Biblo 251-522　1978　$15

COBB, HUMPHREY　　Paths of Glory.　New York, 1935.　Blue & red
cloth, 1st ed., signed by author, very good, mended jacket.　Bradley 49-67
1978　$25

COBB, HUMPHREY　　Paths of Glory.　1935.　First ed., d.j.　Austin
82-309　1978　$12.50

COBB, IRVIN S.　　Exit Laughing.　Indianapolis, (1941).　1st ed.
Biblo BL781-907　1978　$9

COBB, IRVIN S.　　Roughing It De Luxe.　New York, (1914).
Illus. by John T. McCutcheon, 1st ed.　Biblo 251-431　1978　$12.50

COBB, LYNMAN　　New Juvenile Reader No. III.　1845.　Frontis,
bds., leather spine.　Eaton 45-101　1978　£5

COBB, SYLVANUS, JR.　　The Gunmaker of Moscow; or Vladmir the Monk.
New York, 1888.　1st book ed., 1st issue, dated on t.p., "New York Ledger Library"
at spine foot, very good.　Victoria 34-168　1978　$65

COBB, THOMAS　　The Little Clown.　London, 1901.　1st ed., inscr.,
striped binding, thick 16mo, light dust-soiling and rubbing, very good.　Victoria
34-169　1978　$20

COBB, W. P.　　Spiritual Healing.　1914.　Austin 80-834　1978
$12.50

COBBAN, J. MACLAREN　　The King of Andaman, A Savoir of Society.
New York, 1895.　1st Amer. ed., quarter calf, marbled boards.　Greene 78-165
1978　$15

COBBETT, WILLIAM　　The American Gardener.　London, 1821.　Bds.,
moderate wear.　Hayman 73-128　1978　$50

COBBETT, WILLIAM　　A French Grammar...　London, 1824.　Sm. cr.
8vo, 1/2 calf.　Eaton 45-103　1978　£15

COBBETT, WILLIAM　　A Grammar of the English Language.　1819.
3rd. ed., frontis, number of blanks bound in, portraits, 2 pgs. missing, orig. bds.,
spine defective.　Eaton 45-102　1978　£8

COBBETT, WILLIAM　　A Grammar of the English Language.　London,
1823.　12mo., contemp. calf, first ed.　K Books 244-68　1978　£9

COBBETT, WILLIAM　　A Grammar of the English Language, In a
Series of Letters.　1823.　Lg. 12mo, wrapper, very good.　Fenning 32-68　1978
£18.50

COBBETT, WILLIAM　　A History of the Protestant "Reformation" in
England and Ireland.　London, 1824.　First ed., foxed and thembed throughout,
12mo., half roan.　K Books 244-69　1978　£12

COBBETT, WILLIAM　　Life and Adventures of Peter Porcupine with
Other Records of His Early Career...　London, 1927.　Ltd. ed., illus., bds.,
uncut, bookplt.　MacManus 239-89　1978　$25

COBBETT, WILLIAM　　Life of Andrew Jackson.　London, 1834.　Engrav.
frontis, orig. binding.　Wolfe 39-252　1978　$35

COBBETT, WILLIAM　　Porcupine's Works.　London, 1801.　12 vols.,
contemp. calf, rubbed, some covers loose.　Wolfe 39-99　1978　$200

COBBETT, WILLIAM　　A Years Residence in the U.S.A.　London,
1819.　Rebound, ex-lib., lacks map, good.　Nestler Rare 78-104　1978　$45

COBBOLD, RALPH R.　　Innermost Asia, Travel & Sport in the Pamirs.
London, 1900.　Maps, plts., illus., covers faded and marked, inscribed from the
author, 8vo.　K Books 244-70　1978　$20

COBBOLD, RICHARD　　The Character of Woman....　(1848).　Orig.
cloth, spine worn, lacks free endpaper, good.　Jarndyce 16-389　1978　£14.50

COBDEN-SANDERSON, THOMAS JAMES　　Amantium Irae.　1914.　Ltd. ed. of
150 copies on paper, sm. 4to., orig. limp vellum, gilt title on spine, uncut, preserved in buckram, slip-in case, fine copy, inscribed by author.　Sawyer 299-
117　1978　£325

COBDEN-SANDERSON, THOMAS JAMES　　Credo: Pleni Sunt Coeli Et Terra
Gloria Sua. (Hammersmith, Doves Press, 1908).　12mo., orig. tan crushed levant
mor., one of 12 copies on vellum, gilt.　Houle 10-70　1978　$1,500

COBDEN-SANDERSON, THOMAS JAMES　　Ecce Mundus Industrial Ideals and
the Book Beautiful.　Cheswick Press.　Battery Park 1-36　1978　$75

COBDEN-SANDERSON, THOMAS JAMES　　The Ideal Book or Book Beautiful,
a Tract on Calligraphy, Printing and Illustration and on the Book Beautiful as a
Whole.　N.P., n.d.　Sq. 8vo., orig. calf-backed bds., very slightly rubbed,
uncut, unopened.　Americanist 102-29　1978　$40

COBERN, CAMDEN M.   The New Archeological Discoveries. And Their Bearing Upon the New Testament... New York, (1920). 4th ed., illus. Biblo BL781-353 1978 $17.50

COBLENTZ, STANTON A.   The Decline of Man. New York, 1925. 1st ed. Biblo 251-129 1978 $12.50

COCA, ARTHUR F.   Asthma and Hay Fever in Theory and Practice. London, 1931. Ex-library, three parts. Rittenhouse 49-148 1976 $15

COCCEI, JOHANNES   Lexicon et Commentarius Sermonis Hebraici et Chaldaici Veteris Testament. Amstelodami, 1669. 1st ed., tall quarto, full contemporary blind-stamped vellum, engraved portrait of author, two-color pictorial t.p. Bennett 20-47 1978 $275

COCHIN, AUGUSTIN   The Results of Emancipation. Boston, 1863. Spine incomplete, Bell Wiley's copy. Broadfoot's 44-706 1978 $10.00

COCHIN, AUGUSTIN   The Results of Slavery. Boston, 1863. Stained & worn, Bell Wiley's copy. Broadfoot's 44-707 1978 $8.00

COCHRAN, DORIS M.   Poisonous Reptiles of the World: A Wartime Handbook. 1943. Illus., paper. Austin 80-62 1978 $10

COCHRAN, DORIS M.   Poisonous Reptiles of the World: A Wartime Handbook. Washington, 1943. 8vo, orig. cloth. Book Chest 17-87 1978 $14

COCHRANE, C. N.   Christianity & Classical Culture. 1944. Allen 234-225 1978 $7.50

COCHRANE, C. N.   David Thompson, The Explorer. Toronto, 1928. Hood's 115-244 1978 $15

COCHRANE, JOHN DUNDAS   Narrative of a Pedestrian Journey Through Russia and Siberian Tartary... 1824. 2nd. ed., folding maps, 2 coloured frontispieces, 4 plts., 2 vols., contemp. calf gilt, 8vo. Edwards 1012-11 1978 £120

COCHRANE, THOMAS 10TH EARL OF DONDONALD
Please turn to
DUNDONALD, THOMAS COCHRANE, 10TH EARL OF

COCHRANE, WARREN ROBERT   History of Francestown, N.H. From Its Earliest Settlement April, 1758 to January 1, 1891... Nashua, 1895. Thick 8vo., illus., cloth, very good. MacManus 239-1070 1978 $50

COCK, MICAJAH R.   The American Poultry Book... New York, 1843. 1st ed., 12mo, orig. cloth, very good. MacManus 239-397 1978 $35

COCK ROBIN & Jenny Wren, The Courtship, Merry Marriage, and Pic-nic Dinner, of. London, c.1830?. Hand-colored woodcut on each leaf, fine copy. Victoria 34-170 1978 $125

COCKALORUM: a Sequel to Chanticleer and Pertelote. (London, 1950). Illus., cloth, very fine, slightly frayed d.w., trade ed. Dawson's 447-47 1978 $20

COCKBURN, GEORGE   A Voyage to Cadiz and Gibraltar, up the Mediterranean to Sicily and Malta, in 1810 & 11. London, Dublin, 1815. 2 vols., 8vo., half calf, marbled bds., plts. coloured by hand, vignettes, first ed. King 7-342 1978 £200

COCKBURN, GEORGE   A Voyage to Cadiz and Gibraltar, Up the Mediterranean to Sicily and Malta, in 1810, and 11... 1815. 2 vols., 8vo., plts., mostly coloured, t.p. to vol. I foxed and a little foxing of text, good copy, uncut, orig. bds., cloth backs. Quaritch 983-310 1978 $375

COCKBURN, HENRY   Memorials of His time. Edinburgh, 1856. Half calf, portrait, 8vo. K Books 244-71 1978 £9

COCKBURN, WILLIAM   Virulentae Gonorrhae Symptomata, Natura, Causa & Curationes.... 1717. 8vo., vellum, vignette, first part discoloured and with some water stains. King 7-343 1978 £40

COCKERELL, DOUGLAS   Some Notes on Bookbinding. London, 1929. Illus., 12mo. Battery Park 1-274 1978 $25

COCKTON, HENRY   Stanley Thorn. London, 1841. 3 vols., 12mo, half brown morocco, gilt, spines gilt, t.e.g., 1st ed., very rare, illus. frontispiece, plates, some by George Cruikshank, Leech and Crowquill. Ximenes 47-54 1978 $225

COCOANUT Grove by Bay Biscayne. (Harrisburg, n.d. 1909?). Wrs. Hayman 73-215 1978 $7.50

COCTEAU, JEAN   Round the World Again in 80 Days. 1937. First English ed., covers faded, good. Bell Book 16-169 1978 £7.50

COCTEAU, JEAN   La Voix Humaine. Paris, 1957. Narrow folio, in sheets, uncut, orig. wr., slipcover & case, deluxe ed. ltd. to 150 numbered copies, signed by Cocteau & illus'r, Bernard Buffet, prtd. on handmade Auvergne Richard de Bas paper, perfect state of preservation. Goldschmidt 110-8 1978 $700

CODDINGTON, J. W.   A Course of Instruction in the Laboratory and Repository Exercises. (c.1822). Sm. 4to., water-colour illus., half-mor. gilt, a little worn. Quaritch 977-228 1978 $630

CODIGO Civil Del Estado De Coahuila De Zaragoza. Saltillo, 1898. Jenkins 116-222 1978 $22.50

CODIGO De Precedimientos Penales...De Coahuila De Zaragoza. Saltillo, 1884. 1/2 calf. Jenkins 116-223 1978 $25

CODRINGTON, GEORGE W.   Rudolph Diesel and Alexander Winton. 1946. Pamphlet. Austin 80-514 1978 $10

CODY, H. A.   Fighting Stars. Toronto, 1937. Hood 117-509 1978 $10

CODY, WILLIAM F.   Story of the Wild West and Camp-Fire Chats. Philadelphia, (1888). Binding worn, frontis. in color, illus. Biblo 247-188 1978 $25

CODY, WILLIAM F.   A Peep at Buffalo Bill's Wild West. New York, 1887. Chromo-litho. illus., tinted illus., 4to, wrapper slightly chipped at bottom, orig. cloth. Edwards 1012-482 1978 £35

COE, CHARLES FRANCIS   Hooch! 1929. First U.S. ed., very good, worn d.w. Bell Book 17-227 1978 £15

COE, GEORGE ALBERT   Education in Religion and Morals. 1904. Austin 80-845 1978 $10

COE, GEORGE ALBERT   The Motives of Men. (1928) 1930. Austin 80-846 1978 $8.50

COE, GEORGE ALBERT   The Psychology of Religion. University of Chicago Press, 1916. Austin 80-847 1978 $8.50

COE, GEORGE ALBERT   A Social Theory of Religious Education. 1918. Austin 80-848 1978 $10

COFFIN, A. I.   A Treatise on the Diseases of the Generative Organs with the Means of Cure by Botanical Remedies. London, n.d. (1860-65?). Eighth ed., spine cloth gone, covers present but detached. Rittenhouse 49-149 1976 $12.50

COFFIN, CHARLES C.   The Life of Elijah Coffin; with a Reminiscence. [Cincinnati], 1863. Protrait, original cloth, 1st ed. Ginsberg 14-247 1978 $150

COFFIN, CHARLES G.   My Days and Nights on the Battle-Field. Boston, (1887). Orig. binding, minor soiling on cover, clean. Hayman 71-119 1978 $7.50

COFFIN, GEORGE   A Pioneer Voyage to California and Round the World. 1848 to 1852. (Chicago, 1908). Orig. cloth, 8vo., fine. Paine 78-30 1978 $27.50

COFFIN, J. HERSCHEL   Visual Outline of the Psychology of Personality. 1940. Paper. Austin 80-849 1978 $7.50

COFFIN, JOHN G.   Domestic Medicine. Boston, 1825. Worn orig. covers, broken at page 425. Rittenhouse 49-150 1976 $20

COFFIN, LEVI   Reminiscences of Levi Coffin, the Reputed President of the Underground Railroad. London, 1876. 1st English ed., engraved portraits, very good, several prelims loose, heavy stippled cloth. Limestone 9-272 1978 $30

COFFIN, R. P. T.   Kennebec. New York, (1937). Illus. Biblo 251-102 1978 $14

COFFIN, SELDEN J.   The Men of Lafayette, 1826-1893. Easton, 1891. Tall 8vo., portrs., spine partly torn. Morrill 239-575 1978 $7.50

COFFIN, W. F.   1812; The War, and Its Moral; A Canadian Chronicle. Montreal, 1864. Orig.binding, cover scuffed. Hood's 115-96 1978 $35

COGGESHALL, WILLIAM T.   Ohio's Prosperity, Social and Material; an Argument Against Rebellion, Applied to the Duty of Citizens. N.P., n.d. (1863?). Unbound as issued. Hayman 72-529 1978 $12.50

COGHLAN, TIMOTHY A.   The Wealth and Progress of New South Wales, 1886-87. 1887. 1st. ed., lg. folding map, 8vo, orig. pale pink printed paper bds., little wear at corners, but sound nice copy. Fenning 32-69 1978 £28.50

COGNIAT, R.   Danses d'Indo-chine (texte - et Album des Planches). Paris, 1932. 4to, plts., orig. covers. Van der Peet 127-57 1978 Dfl 85

COHEN, CHARLES J.   Rittenhouse Square Past & Present. N.P., 1922. 1st ed., tall 8vo., index, many illus., orig. binding. Americanist 101-35 1978 $30

COHEN, CHARLES J.   Rittenhouse Square. Past and Present. 1922. Illus., very scarce, inscribed by Cohen. MacManus 239-1648 1978 $35

COHEN, HERMANN   Ethik Des Reinen Willens. Berlin, 1907. 4to., 1/2 calf. Salloch 348-38 1978 $30

COHEN, HYMAN   The Tents of Jacob. 1926. Austin 79-151 1978 $10

COHEN, I. DAVID   Principles and Practices of Vocational Guidance. 1929. Austin 80-850 1978 $8.50

COHEN, J. X.   Jewish Life in South America. New York, 1941. Illus. Biblo 251-689 1978 $15

COHEN, MORRIS R.   A Preface to Logic. 1944. Austin 80-851 1978 $12.50

COHEN, MORRIS R.   Reflections of a Wondering Jew. Boston, 1950. Biblo 251-691 1978 $13.50

COHEN, OCTAVUS ROY   Black to Nature. 1935. First ed., backstrip faded, else good. Austin 82-310 1978 $15

COHEN, OCTAVUS ROY   Highly Colored. 1921. Frontis., ex-lib. Austin 82-311 1978 $12.50

COHN, DAVID L.   God Shakes Creation. New York, 1935. Bell Wiley's copy. Broadfoot 46-492 1978 $12

COHN, DAVID L.   The Good Old Days. New York, 1940. Cloth, Illus. Hayman 73-129 1978 $10

COHN, DAVID L.   This is the Story. 1947. Illus. Austin 80-63 1978 $10

COHN, GUSTAV   A History of Political Economy. 1894. 1st Amer. ed., some water stains on bottom of pages & cover, otherwise good. Austin 80-515 1978 $17.50

COIGNARD, JOHN   The Spectacle of a Man. 1939. Austin 82-313 1978 $11

COINDET, JEAN FRANCOIS   Memoire Sur L'Hydrencephale Ou Cephalite Interne Hydrencephalique. Paris, Geneve, 1817. 8vo., old half sprinkled calf, label & gilt on spine, light foxing, few ms. notes, very good copy with author's pres. inscr., 1st ed., rare. Zeitlin 245-301 1978 $175

COKAYNE, G. E.   The Complete Peerage of England, Scotland, Ireland, Great Britain and the United Kingdom, Extinct or Dormant. London, 1910. Complete set of 14 vols., sm. folio, orig. buckram. Traylen 88-448 1978 £650

COKE, E. T.   A Subaltern's Furlough. London, 1833. Illus., orig. bds., some foxing on plts., 4 missing. Hood 117-560 1978 $125

COKE, EDWARD   Les Reports de...L'attorney generall le Roigne,... [Together with]: Le Second Part des Reportes...Le Tierce Part...Le Quart Part.... London, 1619, 1618, 1619, 1618. Quarto, four parts in one vol., 17th-century calf, staining on front cover, end leaves soiled and creased, sign. of "Dan: Fleming", other inscriptions and notations. Bennett 20-48 1978 $500

COKE, THOMAS   A Journal of the Rev. Dr. Coke's Third Tour through the West-Indies;.... London, 1791. 12mo, disbound, uncut, 1st ed., very scarce. Quaritch 978-152 1978 $135

COKER, FRANCIS W.   Readings in Political Philosophy. New York, 1929. Biblo 251-325 1978 $12

COLAS, R.   Le Style Roman en France. Paris, 1927. Lg. 8vo., half calf, plts., illus. Van der Peet H-64-117 1978 Dfl 75

COLBURN, ZERAH   The Permanent Way & Coal-Burning Locomotive Boilers of European Railways,.... New York, 1858. Front hinge separated, lacks plate of Paddington Railroad station. Nestler Rare 78-205 1978 $65

COLBY, CHARLES W.   Canadian Types of the Old Regime 1608-1698. New York, 1908. Orig. binding. Wolfe 39-103 1978 $30

COLBY, CHARLES W.   Canadian Types of the Old Regime 1608-1698. New York, 1908. Autograph pres. inscription by author, orig. binding. Wolfe 39-102 1978 $40

COLBY, LOU ELEANOR   Drawings, Painting, Making, Decorating for Primary Teachers. 1909. Austin 80-836 1978 $12.50

COLDEN, CADWALLADER   The History of the Five Indian Nations of Canada which are the Barrier Between the English and the French in that part of the World ... London, 1750. 2nd ed., 8vo., bound in 19th Cent. calf with raised bands on spine, simple gilt ruled borders, marbled endpapers, ribbon bookmark, fine, fldg. map. Current 24-76 1978 $415

COLDEN, CADWALLADER   The History of the Five Indian Nations of Canada. New York, 1902. 2 vols., frontis. port., orig. cloth, fine. MacManus 239-1153 1978 $22.50

COLDEN, CADWALLADER   The Life of Robert Fulton. New York, 1817. 8vo., frontis., old half mor., gilt, uncut, t.e.g., rubbed, some foxing, very good, first ed. Norman 5-*20 1978 $85

COLDEN, CADWALLADER   The Life of Robert Fulton. New York, 1817. Cloth, foxed. MacManus 239-754 1978 $40

COLE, A. P.   Timothy Cole. New York, 1935. Illus., limited to 750 copies, good. Nestler Rare 78-105 1978 $28

COLE, ALPHAEUS   Wood-Engravers. New York, 1935. Ltd. signed edition. Baldwins' 51-45 1978 $25

COLE, ARTHUR CHARLES   The Era of the Civil War 1848-1870 Centennial History of Illinois. Springfield, 1919. Bell Wiley's copy. Broadfoot's 44-475 1978 $16.00

COLE, CORNELIUS   Memoirs of...Ex-Senator of the U.S. from California. New York, 1908. Port., 1st ed., unopened. Biblo BL781-269 1978 $18.50

COLE, FAY-COOPER   The Long Road: From Savagery to Civilization. (Baltimore), 1933. Austin 80-852 1978 $8.50

COLE, G. D. H.   The British People, 1746-1946. New York, 1947. Maps, second ed. Biblo 247-670 1978 $12.50

COLE, G. D. H.   British Working Class Politics, 1832-1914. 1941. 8vo. George's 635-304 1978 £5

COLE, G. D. H.   Fabian Socialism. 1943. 8vo. George's 635-305 1978 £5.25

COLE, G. D. H.   A Guide Through World Chaos. 1932. Austin 80-516 1978 $10

COLE, G. D. H.   An Introduction to Trade Unionism, a Short Study of the Present Position of Trade Unionism in Great Britain. 1918. Folding frontis., covers faded, 8vo. George's 635-306 1978 £5

COLE, G. E.   Early Oregon, 1850 to 1860. (Spokane, 1905). 1st ed. Biblo BL781-270 1978 $9.50

COLE, HUGH M.   The Lorraine Campaign. 1950. Maps. Austin 80-65 1978 $75

COLE, J.   Herveiana. Scarborough, 1822-23. Plts., woodcuts, 2 vols. in 1, 12mo., new buckram. George's 635-1247 1978 £12.50

COLE, LAWRENCE   Factors of Human Psychology. 1930. Austin
80-853 1978 $10

COLE, LUELLA   Psychology of Adolescence. 1942. Illus., rev.
ed. Austin 80-854 1978 $10

COLE, LUELLA   Psychology of the Elementary School Subjects.
1934. Austin 80-855 1978 $10

COLE, MAUD WYNNE   Songs From South Africa. Wynberg, Cape,
c.1925. 8vo., orig. cloth, covers slightly soiled. K Books 239-97 1978 $5

COLE, OWEN B.   The Legend of Naworth. Dublin, 1846.
1st. ed., engraved vignettes, illus., 8vo, orig. glazed printed paper wrapper,
lettered "Decidua No.1", edges gilt, fine. Fenning 32-70 1978 £18

COLE, WILLIAM   A Physico-Medical Essay Concerning the Late
Frequency of Apoplexies. Oxford, 1689. Sm. 8vo., antique style calf, first ed.
Quaritch 977-17 1978 $500

COLECCION De Canciones Patrioticas, Hechas En Demonstracion De La Lealtad
Espanola,.... Cadiz, (1809). Quarto, full 19th-century mottled calf, gilt-ruled
borders and dentelles, gilt-stamped floral designs on spine, exceptionally fine copy,
bookplate of Lord Aldenham. Bennett 20-49 1978 $125

COLEMAN, A. P.   Elementary Geology. Toronto, 1930. Rev. ed.
Hood's 115-699 1978 $25

COLEMAN, A. P.   The Nickel Industry: With Special Reference to
the Sudbury Region, Ontario. Ottawa, 1913. Many plts., drawings, maps.
Hood's 115-698 1978 $40

COLEMAN, MRS. GEORGE P.   Virginia Silhouettes. Contemporary Letters
Concerning Negro Slavery in the State of Virginia... Richmond, 1934. 1st ed.,
frontis., orig. cloth, very good. MacManus 239-1885 1978 $12.50

COLEMAN, HANNAH HEMPHILL   Stories & Of't Told Tales of the
Confederacy. N.P., n.d. Spiral bound, limp cvrs. Bell Wiley's copy.
Broadfoot 46-48 1978 $14

COLEMAN, HARRY J.   Give Us a Little Smile, Baby. New York, 1943.
Illus., 1st ed., d.w. Biblo BL781-767 1978 $9

COLEMAN, J. WINSTON, JR.   A Bibliography of Kentucky History. Lexington, 1949. 8vo., orig. cloth, 1st ed., pres. copy from author, bookplt. Mac-
Manus 238-964 1978 $32.50

COLEMAN, R. V.   The First Frontier. New York, 1948. First ed.,
fine, d.w., maps, illus. Biblo 247-26 1978 $18.50

COLEMAN, SATIS N.   Creative Music for Children. 1922. Illus. with
plts. Austin 80-857 1978 $12.50

COLEMAN, WILLIAM   A Collection of the Facts and Documents Relative
to the Death of Major-General Alexander Hamilton. New York, 1804. 1st ed.,
8vo., slight & occas. spotting, bound in full brown inlaid calf, gilt decor. spine,
nice. Current Misc. 8-8 1978 $95

COLEMAN, WILLIAM   A Collection of the Facts and Documents, Relative to the Death of Major General Alexander Hamilton... New York, 1904.
Reprint of 1804 ed., ltd. to 430 copies, fully untrimmed. MacManus 239-191
1978 $27.50

COLENSO, FRANCES   History of the Zulu War and Its Origin. London,
1880. 8vo, orig. cloth, lacks map, little dusty & shaken. K Books 239-98 1978
£18

COLENSO, JOHN WILLIAM   The Pentateuch and Book of Joshua Critically
Examined. Longmans, Green, 1862. 1st. ed., 8vo, orig. cloth, printed paper
label, nice copy. Fenning 32-71 1978 £8.50

COLENSO, JOHN WILLIAM   Ten Weeks in Natal. 1855. Fldg. map, sm.
8vo., engr. plts., half mor., lib. stamp on title. Edwards 1012-295 1978 £25

COLER, BIRD S.   Two and Two Make Four. 1912. Austin 80-858
1978 $8.50

COLERIDGE, E. H.   The Life of Thomas Coutts, Banker. 1920. 2
vols., illus., 8vo. George's 635-308 1978 £6.50

COLERIDGE, H. M.   Six Months in the West Indies, in 1825. 1832.
3rd. ed., 12mo, modern half leather. Edwards 1012-705 1978 £20

COLERIDGE, HARTLEY   Letters. 1941. Portrait, 8vo., orig. cloth.
Howes 194-737 1978 £6.50

COLERIDGE, MRS. SAMUEL TAYLOR   Minnow Among Tritons. 1934. 8vo.,
portr., facsimile, buckram, d.w. Quaritch 979-240 1978 $40

COLERIDGE, SAMUEL TAYLOR   Aids to Reflection. 1825. 1st. ed., uncut,
rebound in bds., v.g., errata corrections in contemp. hand, signatures on t.p.
Jarndyce 16-393 1978 £48

COLERIDGE, SAMUEL TAYLOR   Biographia Literaria. New York, 1847. 2
vols., Victorian half calf, raised band, brown labels, v.g. Jarndyce 16-391
1978 £34

COLERIDGE, SAMUEL TAYLOR   Christabel and the Lyrical & Imaginative Poems
of .... 1869. 1st. ed., half title, limp blue cloth, good. Jarndyce 16-1088
1978 £7.50

COLERIDGE, SAMUEL TAYLOR   Christabel, Kubla Khan, Fancy in Nubibus,
and Song from Zapolya. Eragny Press, 1904. One of 226 copies on paper, inscribed pres. copy from Lucien and Esther Pissaro, woodcut frontis., orig. patterned bds., edges uncut. George's 635-885 1978 £120

COLERIDGE, SAMUEL TAYLOR   Letters. 1895. First Collected ed., 2 vols.,
plts., orig. cloth, scarce, 8vo. Howes 194-740 1978 £21

COLERIDGE, SAMUEL TAYLOR   Letters of .... 1895. 2 vols., portraits,
illus., orig. cloth, gilt, spines slightly defective at head. Eaton 45-106 1978
£17

COLERIDGE, SAMUEL TAYLOR   The Literary Remains. London, 1836. 2 vols.,
octavo, half dark mor., red marbled boards, raised spine bands, gilt, 1st ed., very
good. Bennett 7-29 1978 $100

COLERIDGE, SAMUEL TAYLOR   Poems. 1921. Sm. 8vo., portr. frontis.,
calf gilt panelled back. Quaritch 979-98 1978 $20

COLERIDGE, SAMUEL TAYLOR   Poems Chosen out of the Work of... Hammersmith, Kelmscott Press, 1896. 8vo., one of 300 copies, full limp vellum, green
silk ties, v.f. Current Misc 8-27 1978 $450

COLERIDGE, SAMUEL TAYLOR   The Poetical and Dramatic Works of... 1880.
4 vols., sm. 8vo, blind stamp on titles, lib. bookplts., orig. cloth, head of spines
chipped. Eaton 45-105 1978 £12

COLERIDGE, SAMUEL TAYLOR   The Rime of the Ancient Mariner. San
Francisco, 1926. Folio, fine, large t.p. cut, woven cloth stained, very good.
Victoria 34-698 1978 $15

COLERIDGE, SAMUEL TAYLOR   The Rime of the Ancient Mariner. New York,
1931. Folio, illus. in color by H. Charles Tomlinson, ltd. ed., spine faded, boxed.
Biblo 251-429 1978 $27.50

COLERIDGE, SAMUEL TAYLOR   Sibylline Leaves. London, 1817. 1st ed.,
8vo., uncut, fine copy, orig. bds., blue mor. backed case, rare. Current Misc.
8-9 1978 $635

COLERIDGE, SARA   Phantasmion: Prince of Palmland. New York,
1839. 2 vols., 12mo, early half calf, gilt, spines gilt, 1st Amer. ed. Ximenes
47-55 1978 $100

COLES, ELISHA   Dictionary, English-Latin & Latin-English. 1749.
15th ed., buckram, flyleaf scribbled on. Allen 234-228 1978 $15

COLES, ELISHA   Le Parthenon. 1914. 4to., illus., plts. Allen
234-233 1978 $10

COLES, WILLIAM   Adam in Eden. London, 1657. Folio, contemp.
calf, repaired, edges of last gatherings worn, first ed., very good. Quaritch 977-
18 1978 $1,200

COLETTE, SIDONIE GABRIELLE   Dialogue de Betes. Paris, n. d. Yellow paper
covers, editions Baudiniere. Eaton 45-108 1978 £5

COLEY, H.   Clavis Astrologiae Elimata. London, 1676,1675.
8vo., portraits, woodcuts, rather soiled, rebound in half calf, second ed. Quaritch 977-117 1978 $650

COLGAN, JOHN C.   Poems of. Toronto, 1873. Autograph pres. inscription, full mor. binding, paneled, goldstamped, a.e.g. Wolfe 39-104 1978
$30

COLGATE, WILLIAM   Canadian Art, Its Origin and Development. Toronto, 1943. 1st ed., illus. Hood 116-176 1978 $125

A COLLECTION In English of the Statues Nowe in Force, Continued From the Beginning of Magna Charta Made in the 9 Yeere of the Reigne Of King Henry III... London, n.d. (1583). Black letter, thick folio, old calf, little worn. Traylen 88-480 1978 £150

A COLLECTION Of Eleven Ledger Books Kept by The Dana Family, a Pioneer Washington County Family... Belpre, 1814-1887. Handwritten in ink, unique. Hayman 71-601 1978 $400

COLLECTION of English Literature Including the Works of the Chief Elizabethan, Jacobean and Restoration Authors. Bangs, 1902. Cloth, fine copy. Battery Park 1-328 1978 $100

A COLLECTION of Papers Read Before the Bucks County Historical Society. (Easton, n.d.). Vol. I, illus., orig. cloth, hinges cracking. MacManus 239-1399 1978 $30

A COLLECTION Of Poems. London, 1870. Litho. & printed title pg., sm. 8vo, cloth, gilt edges. Traylen 88-210 1978 £5

A COLLECTION of Poems in Six Volumes by Several Hands. London, 1766. 9th ed., 6 vols., sm. 8vo., bound in full tan calf, raised bands, gold tooled decor., very nice set. Current 24-2 1978 $125

A COLLECTION Of Psalms and Hymns Suited to the Various Occasions of Public Worship and Private Devotion. Elkhart, 1893. Orig. binding, clean. Hayman 71-455 1978 $8.50

COLLECTION of 16 Acts between 1743-1832, relating to the Poor Laws. 1743-1832. Sewn, 8vo. George's 635-522 1978 £30

THE COLLECTION of the Late Alfred H. Mulliken, Chicago and New Canaan, Conn. New York, 1933. Illus., 4to., orig. wrs. Morrill 241-25 1978 $7.50

A COLLECTION of the Letters of Atticus, Lucius, and Junius, and Others. 1769. New ed., orig. wrappers, frayed and worn, 8vo. George's 635-1278 1978 £16

COLLECTION of 25 Acts between 1722-1834, mainly mid 18th Century on various subjects. 1722-1834. All sewn, sm. folio. George's 635-523 1978 £30

COLLECTIONS of Cayuga County Historical Society. Auburn, 1878-1889. Nos. 1-8, bound in 3 vols., 3/4 lea. & marbled endpapers, bkstps. on 2 vols. worn, ltd. to 250. Butterfield 21-107 1978 $45

COLLECTIONS on the History of Albany...with Biographical Sketches of Citizens Deceased. Albany, 1870. Unbound, unopened signatures, prtd. self-wr., vol. 3 only, sm. 4to., plts., dusty, some chipping. Butterfield 21-21 1978 $7.50

COLLEGE of Industrial Arts, Denton, Texas, 1915-1916. Denton, 1915. Wr. Jenkins 116-316 1978 $7.50

COLLEGIUM Divi Johannis Evangelistae 1511-1911. Cambridge, 1911. Sm. 4to., cloth, frontis., plts., portrs., facs.-plts., lg. paper copy, pencil annotations in margins. Van der Peet H-64-297 1978 Dfl 45

COLLES, A.   The Works of Abraham Colles. London, 1881. Rittenhouse 49-152 1976 $25

COLLES, JULIA KEESE   Authors and Writers Associated with Morristown. Morristown, 1893. Illus., binding rubbed, sm. tear on frontis. Biblo 251-68 1978 $38.50

COLLIER, EDWARD A.   A History of Old Kinderhook from Aboriginal Days to the Present Time. New York, 1914. Illus., fine, t.e.g. MacManus 239-1090 1978 $40

COLLIER, J. PAYNE   The History of English Dramatic Poetry to the Time of Shakespeare and Annals of the Stage to the Restoration. 1879. 3 vols., new ed., sm. 4to, 1/2 maroon morocco, rubbed, lib. stamp on liner, crest on spines. Eaton 45-109 1978 £35

COLLIER, J. PAYNE   Notes and Emendations to the Text of Shakespeare's Plays from early Manuscript Corrections in a Copy of the Folio, 1632. 1853. 8vo., polished calf, gilt panelled back with marbled edges, bkplt., some foxing. Quaritch 979-293 1978 $30

COLLIER, JEREMY   A Defence of the Short View of the Profaneness and Immorality of the English Stage. 1699. 1st. ed., 8vo, modern sheep, one gathering including title heavily foxed, stamp on verso of title. Hannas 54-324 1978 £40

COLLIER, JOHN   His Monkey Wife. 1930. Covers soiled, good, first English ed. Bell Book 17-168 1978 £16

COLLIER'S America's Foremost Illustrated Weekly. New York, (1901). Tall 8vo., orig. cloth-backed dec. bds., very slight wear, illus., scarce. Americanist 102-30 1978 $20

COLLIN, JOHN F.   A History of Hillsdale, Columbia Co., New York. Philmont, 1883. Orig. cloth, hinges repaired, nice, scarce. MacManus 239-1088 1978 $60

COLLIN, VICTOR   Des Diverses Methodes D'Exploration De La Poitrine, et de leur application du Diagnostic de ses Maladies. Paris, 1824. 8vo., orig. blue prtd. wrs., faint dampstains, lightly browned, very good, uncut, signature of early owner, bkplt. of Dr. Alfred M. Hellman, laid in brown cloth box, 1st complete ed., rare. Zeitlin 245-47 1978 $225

COLLIN, W. E.   The White Savannahs. Toronto, 1936. 1st. ed. Hood's 115-333 1978 $50

COLLINA, ABONDIO   Considerazioni Istoriche. Faenza, 1748. Sm. 4to., orig. vellum. F. Edwards 1013-45 1978 £30

COLLING, JAMES K.   Details of Gothic Architecture. London, 1856. 192 plts., 2 vols., 4to, unusually nice copy. Traylen 88-370 1978 £32

COLLING, JAMES K.   Gothic Ornaments. London, (ca. 1848). Vol. I only, plts., many in color, 4to., half mor., ex-lib. Morrill 239-344 1978 $30

COLLINGWOOD, R. G.   Roman Britain. Oxford, 1932. 12mo., illus. Biblo BL781-354 1978 $9

COLLINGWOOD, STUART DODGSON   The Life and Letters of Lewis Carroll. London, 1899. 2nd ed., illus., cr. 8vo., orig. cloth, faded, little worn, sm. snag at head of spine. Sexton 7-76 1978 £12

COLLINS, ARTHUR   The Peerage of England. 1756. Third ed., 5 vols. in 6, contemp. calf, spines gilt, 8vo. Howes 194-219 1978 £45

COLLINS, D.   An Account of the English Colony in New South Wales... 1798-1802. Copperplts., 3 are coloured, engravings some coloured, 2 vols., with the rare 2nd. vol., 4to., contemp. sprinkled calf gilt, repairs to joints. Edwards 1012-326 1978 £1850

COLLINS, DENNIS   The Indian's Last Fight; or, The Dull Knife Raid. [Girard, 1915]. Illus., orig. cloth, 1st ed. Ginsberg 14-1091 1978 $150

COLLINS, F. HOWARD   An Epitome of the Synthetic Philosophy. 1889. Austin 80-859 1978 $12.50

COLLINS, HUBERT E.   Warpath and Cattle Trail. New York, 1928. 1st ed., illus., untrimmed, fine. MacManus 239-1908 1978 $25

COLLINS, J.   Life in Old Dublin. Reprint, octavo bound in cloth. Hyland 128-921 1978 £5.45

COLLINS, J. B.   Christian Mysticism in the Elizabethan Age... Baltimore, 1940. Wrps., octavo, good. Upcroft 10-623 1978 £5

COLLINS, J. CHURTON   Voltaire, Montesquieu and Rousseau in England. 1908. Plts., orig. cloth, 8vo. Howes 194-744 1978 £5

COLLINS, LOREN WARREN   The Story of a Minnesotan. N.P., n.d. Bell Wiley's copy. Broadfoot 46-342 1978 $15

COLLINS, MARY   Colour Blindness. 1925. Illus., 1st ed. Austin 80-860 1978 $27.50

COLLINS, MARY   Experimental Psychology. 1926. 2nd ed., diags. Austin 90-861 1978 $10

COLLINS, VARNUM LANSING   The Continental Congress at Princeton. Princeton, 1908. Illus., fine. MacManus 239-1250 1978 $27.50

COLLINS, VARNUM LANSING   Princeton. New York, 1914. Illus., 1st ed. Biblo BL781-31 1978 $9.50

COLLINS, W. W.   Cathedral Cities of Italy. New York, 1913. Illus. in color. Biblo 247-347 1978 $12.50

COLLINS, WILLIAM   The Poetical Works. 1781. New ed., sm. 8vo., half calf, gilt back. P. M. Hill 142-264 1978 £21

COLLINS, WILLIAM   The Poetical Works. London, 1798. Octavo, full early tree calf. Bennett 7-30 1978 $60

COLLINS, WILLIAM T.   A Christian Views New York Jewry. 1933. Illus., paper. Austin 79-154 1978 $20

COLLINS, WILLIAM WILKIE   The Evil Genius. Leipzig, 1886. 2 vols., copy-right ed., sm. 8vo, cont. half calf, very good. Fenning 32-72 1978 £12

COLLINS, WILLIAM WILKIE   The Guilty River. New York, 1884. Paper covers, 1st ed., spine flaking, good, scarce. Greene 78-166 1978 $175

COLLINS, WILLIAM WILKIE   Mr. Wray's Cash-Box. 1852. Fscp. 8vo., orig. cloth, good, first English ed. Bell Book 16-171 1978 £65

COLLINS, WILLIAM WILKIE   The Moonstone. New York, 1868. 1st. Ameri-can ed., numerous illus., rebound in half dark blue calf, hand-marbled bds., v.g. Jarndyce 16-401 1978 £25

COLLINS, WILLIAM WILKIE   The Moonstone. 1871. New ed. revised, orig. dark green cloth, half title, fine. Jarndyce 16-402 1978 £14.50

COLLINS, WILLIAM WILKIE   No Name. Boston, 1863. Vol. 2 complete in itself, illus., first Amer. ed., covers faded, some stains. Biblo 247-506 1978 $20

COLLINS, WILLIAM WILKIE   No Name. 1866. Half red morocco, marbled bds., good. Jarndyce 16-400 1978 £10

COLLINS, WILLIAM WILKIE   A Plot in Private Life and Other Tales. Leipzig, 1859. Half title, half red morocco, good. Jarndyce 16-397 1978 £17.50

COLLINS, WILLIAM WILKIE   The Queen of Hearts. New York, (1874). Illus., 1st Amer. ed. Biblo 251-432 1978 $17.50

COLLINS, WILLIAM WILKIE   The Woman in White. 1860. 2nd. ed., 3 vols., blue binders' cloth, bottom of spine vol. 1 defective, otherwise sound copy. Jarn-dyce 16-398 1978 £28

COLLINS, WILLIAM WILKIE   The Woman in White. 1861. Frontis portrait, orig. half calf, marbled bds., new preface. Jarndyce 16-399 1978 £15

COLLINSON, J.   The Life of Thuanus. 1807. First ed., contemp. half calf, upper joint cracked, some foxing of text, 8vo. Howes 194- 493 1978 £18

COLLIS, EDGAR L.   The Health of the Industrial Worker. (Philadel-phia), 1921. 1st Amer. ed. Austin 80-519 1978 $47.50

COLLIS, M.   Siamese White. London, 1936. Cloth, map, 8vo. Van der Peet 127-58 1978 Dfl 25

COLLMANN, H.   Britwell Handlist. Buckinghamshire, 1933. 2 vols., 400 copies printed, 2 portraits, plts., cr. 4to., orig. cloth. Forster 130-241 1978 £30

COLLODI, CARLO, PSEUD.
Please turn to
LORENZINI, CARLO

COLLUM, RICHARD S.   History of the United States Marine Corps. Philadelphia, 1890. 1st ed., illus. MacManus 239-90 1978 $37.50

COLLUM, RICHARD S.   History of the United States Marine Corps. New York, 1903. Portrs., 8vo., 1st ed., scarce, orig. cloth. Morrill 241-661 1978 $50

COLLYER, ROBERT   Nature and Life: Sermons... Boston, 1867. Orig. cl., 1st ed. Ginsberg 16-852 1978 $7.50

COLMAN, ELIZABETH   Chinatown U. S. A. 1946. Almost all photos, ex-lib., good. Austin 79-155 1978 $12.50

COLMAN, GEORGE   Broad Grins, My Nightgown & Slippers, and Other Humorous Works. London, 1898. Frontis., 8vo., ex-lib., orig. cloth. Morrill 241-84 1978 $15

COLMAN, GEORGE   The Days of Old. Boston, (1796). 12mo., un-bound, 2nd Amer. ed. Morrill 239-345 1978 $22.50

COLMAN, GEORGE   The Poor Gentleman. Boston, 1802. 3rd ed., 12mo., unbound, 1st Amer. ed. Morrill 239-346 1978 $15

COLMAN, GEORGE   Prose on Several Occasions. 1787. First ed., portrait frontispiece, 3 vols., contemp. calf, rebacked. Howes 194-220 1978 £32.50

COLNETT, JAMES   A Voyage To The South Atlantic and Round Cape Horn Into The Pacific Ocean, For The Purpose of Extending The Spermaceti Whale Fisheries.... London, 1798. 1st. ed., 4to, engraved portrait frontispiece, half calf, gilt back, folding engraved maps, folding engraved plt. Deighton 5-204 1978 £1,650

COLOMBIA. CONSTITUTION   Coleccion de las leyes Dadas por el Congresso Constitucional de la Republica de Colombia...1823 y 1824. Bogota, 1826. Sm. 4to., buckram, good. Paine 78-31 1978 $125

COLOMBO, REALDO   De Re Anatomica libri XV. Frankfurt, 1593. 8vo., old calf, fifth ed.? Gurney 75-23 1978 £150

THE COLOPHON: A Book Collectors Quarterly. New York, 1930-35. 20 vols., 4to., fine cond., orig. glassine d.j.'s. Current Misc. 8-11 1978 $350

THE COLOPHON, Parts 1-4. 1930. 4 vols., with plts., illus., facsimiles, dec. bds., all very good, except for 1 or 2 corners bumped. Eaton 45-110 1978 £40

COLQUHOUN, A. R.   Across Chryse... 1883. 3 coloured maps, plts., text illus., 2 vols., slight foxing, orig. cloth, 8vo. Edwards 1012-186 1978 £50

COLQUHOUN, A. R.   Autone du Tonkin; La chine meridionale, de Canton a Mandalay. Paris-Poitiers, 1884. 2 vols., cloth, plts., illus., port., 8vo. Van der Peet 127-59 1978 Dfl 145

COLQUHOUN, JAMES   Adventures in Red Russia, From the Black Sea to The White Sea. 1926. Pres. copy to Winston Churchill, plts., 8vo, orig. morocco backed buckram, t.e.g., other uncut, spine weak at top, mark on lower cover. Sawyer 298-67 1978 £105

COLQUHOUN, PATRICK   A Treatise on the Police of the Metropolis... 1797. 4th. ed., folding table, orig. bds., uncut, 8vo. Edwards 1012-327 1978 £40

COLQUHOUN, PATRICK   A Treatise on the Police of the Metropolis. 1800. Very good, contemp. tree calf, 8vo. Howes 194-221 1978 £34

COLTON, C. C.   Lacon. New York, 1849. Cloth, minor wear top of spine, light to moderate foxing, rev. ed. with index. Hayman 73-131 1978 $10

COLTON, CALVIN   The Life and Times of Henry Clay. New York, 1846. 2nd ed., 2 vols., frontis. port., orig. cloth. MacManus 239-738 1978 $20

COLTON, CALVIN   Tour of the American Lakes, and Among the Indians of the North-West Territory in 1830... London, 1833. 2 vols., rebound, clean, leather labels on spine. Hayman 71-153 1978 $125

COLTON, CHARLES CALEB   Napoleon: A Poem,.... London, n.d. (1812). 8vo, disbound, 1st ed., very scarce. Ximenes 47-56 1978 $40

COLTON, JOSEPH H.   The Emigrant's Handbook.... New York, 1848. Large folding map, original cloth, 1st ed. Ginsberg 14-280 1978 $125

COLTON, WALTER   Deck and Port... New York, 1850. 1st. ed., 2nd. issue, map, portrait, tinted litho. plts., sm. 8vo, half morocco. Edwards 1012-388 1978 £45

COLTON, WALTER   Three Years in California. Stanford, (1949). Fine, d.w. Biblo 247-195 1978 $17.50

COLUM, PADRAIC   Creatures. New York, 1927. Ltd. to 300 copies, signed by artist and author, plates, silver boards, spine sunned, very fine, orig. labelled and hand-numbered slipcase. Victoria 34-27 1978 $75

COLUM, PADRAIC   Dramatic Legends and Other Poems. New York, 1922. Ownership inscription, fine. Desmarais B-148 1978 $10

COLUM, PADRAIC   The White Sparrow. New York, 1933. 1st ed., plates, endpapers and text illus. all in color, very fine, d.j. Victoria 34-844 1978 $20

COLUMBIA ASSOC. IN PHILOSOPHY   An Introduction to Reflective Thinking. 1923. Austin 80-863 1978 $10

THE COLUMBIAN World's Fair Atlas Containing Complete Illustrations of the world's fair grounds and buildings.... Tiffin, n.d. (1892). Illus., maps, clean, moderate wear, orig. binding. Hayman 71-204 1978 $15

COLVIN, FRED H. American Compound Locomotives. New York, 1903. 1st ed., illus., 3/4 mor., cloth, fine. MacManus 239-408 1978 $35

COLVIN, I. D. The Germans in England, 1066-1598. 1915. Map of Hanseatic League, 8vo. George's 635-608 1978 £5

COLVIN, IAN The Life of Jameson. London, 1922. 8vo, orig. cloth, 2 vols., 2 maps, 4 portraits. K Books 239-100 1978 £12

COLVIN, STEPHEN Human Behavior. 1913. Austin 80-865 1978 $8.50

COLVIN, VERPLANCK First Annual Report of the Commissioners of State Parks. Albany, 1873. Wr., little dusty & stained, very scarce, signed in type by Governor Seymour. Butterfield 21-6 1978 $50

COLVIN, VERPLANCK Report of the Topographical Survey of the Adirondack Wilderness...for...1873. Albany, 1874. Orig. cloth, very good, maps, plts., errata slips, excellent cond. Butterfield 21-7 1978 $35

COLVIN, VERPLANCK Report of the Topographical Survey of the Adirondack Wilderness...for...1873. Binding very good, few pages & plts. loose, minor tears, complete reading copy. Butterfield 21-8 1978 $25

COLVIN, VERPLANCK Seventh Annual Report on the...Topographical Survey of the Adirondack Region...to the Year 1879. Binding little worn, marginal tears in some maps, excellent working copy. Butterfield 21-10 1978 $35

COLVIN, VERPLANCK Seventh Annual Report on the...Topographical Survey of the Adirondack Region...to the Year 1879. Albany, 1880. Maps, engrs. & chromo-lithos., orig. cloth, fine cond. Butterfield 21-9 1978 $45

COLYAR, A. S. Life and Times of Andrew Jackson, Soldier-Statesman-President. Nashville, 1904. Cloth, 2 vols. Hayman 73-132 1973 $25

COMAN, KATHARINE Economic Beginnings of the Far West. New York, 1912. 2 vols., cloth, minor wear, scarce 1st ed., tiny puncture in fr. cover, good solid set. Hayman 73-133 1973 $25

COMBE, GEORGE Phrenology Applied to Painting and Sculpture. 1855. 8vo., contemp. half calf, marbled sides. P. M. Hill 142-81 1978 £38

COMBE, WILLIAM The Dance of Life. London, 1817. Frontis., color plts. by Thomas Rowlandson, 8vo., full red crushed mor., gilt, first ed., fine. Howell 5-52 1978 $260

COMBE, WILLIAM The Justification: A Poem. 1777. 4to., unbound, fine. P. M. Hill 142-265 1978 £45

COMBE, WILLIAM The Tour of Doctor Syntax in Search of the Picturesque. 1813. 3rd ed., lg. 8vo., frontis, coloured plts., contemp. red straight grained mor., gilt panelled sides, gauffred edges, tall copy. Quaritch 979-100 1978 $325

COMBE, WILLIAM The Tour of Doctor Syntax through London, or the Pleasures and Miseries of the Metropolis. 1820. 8vo., 1st ed., coloured plts., orig. tissue guards, rebound in full calf, bkplt. Quaritch 979-101 1978 $470

COMBE, WILLIAM The Tour of Doctor Syntax Through London, or the Pleasures and Miseries of the Metropolis... 1820. 8vo., 1st ed., coloured plts., full calf, bookplt. Quaritch 983-311 1978 $595

COMBE, WILLIAM The Tour of Doctor Syntax Through London. 1820. Aquatint plts. coloured by hand, roy. 8vo., 9.75 x 6.5 inches, orig. bds., entirely uncut, good, first ed. Howes 194-1374 1978 £125

COMBE, WILLIAM The Tour of Dr. Syntax. London, 1844. Illus. by Alfred Crowquill, wood-engravings, recased in gilt-decor. cover, 8vo. K Books 244-72 1978 £12

COMBINAZIONE Colori Della Cadillac. (c. 1925). Oblong folio, plts., very slightly soiled, orig. bds., worn. Quaritch 977-209 1978 $850

COMBINED Atlas of the County of Suffolk. Philadelphia, 1873. Colored maps, folio, orig. cloth. Morrill 241-357 1978 $50

COMBLES, DE d. 1770? A Treatise Upon the Culture of Peach Trees. 1768. 8vo., new cloth, 1st ed. in English. P.M. Hill 142-89 1978 £38

COME Not, Lucifer!: a romantic anthology. 1945. Plts., very good, worn d.w., first English ed. Bell Book 16-320 1978 £8.50

COMEAU, NAPOLEON A. Life and Sport on the North Shore of the Lower St. Lawrence and Gulf. Quebec, 1923. Illus., 2nd ed. Biblo 247-18 1978 $15

COMEAU, NAPOLEON A. Life and Sport on the Lower St. Lawrence and Gulf. London, (n.d.). Slightly frayed d.j., orig. decor. cloth. Wolfe 39-8 1978 $45

COMEGYS, JOSEPH P. Memoir of John M. Clayton. Wilmington, 1882. Frontis, top of title pg. memoir "To Barney Reybold" by author. Baldwins' 51-215 1978 $32.50

COMENIUS, JOHANN AMOS Orbis Sensualium Pictus...Visible World. 1777. Woodcuts, fcap. 8vo., cont. calf, rebacked, 12th ed. Howes 194-346 1978 £75

COMETTANT, OSCAR Les Civilisations Inconnues. Paris, 1863. Half mor., 1st ed. Ginsberg 14-1102 1978 $85

COMFORT, ALEX Letters from an Outpost. London, 1947. Nice in torn d.w. Desmarais B-149 1978 $12.50

COMFORT, ALEX The Novel and Our Time. 1948. Very good, bds., d.w., first English ed. Bell Book 16-577 1978 £4

COMINES, PHILIP DE The History of Comines. 1897. Orig. ed., 2 vols., orig. buckram-backed bds., 8vo. Howes 194-1296 1978 £10

COMINES, PHILIP DE The Memoirs. 1723. 2 vols., contemp. calf, rebacked, lettering-pieces, 8vo. Howes 194-222 1978 £25

COMLY, JAMES M. Representation of Minorities. Columbus, 1873. Pamphlet binder. Hayman 71-528 1978 $7.50

COMMANDERY of the State of Massachusetts. Boston, 1900. 2 vols., new cloth, Bell Wiley's copy. Broadfoot 46-43 1978 $33

COMMEMORATIVE Biographical Encyclopedia of the Juniata Valley, Comprising the Counties of Huntingdon, Mifflin, Juniata and Perry, Pa. Chambersburg, 1897. Illus., 2 vols., 4to. MacManus 239-1517 1978 $85

COMMEMORATIVE Biographical Record of Northeastern Pennsylvania.... Chicago, 1900. Large, thick 4to, rebound in library cloth, a.e.g., illus., 8vo. Americanist 101-36 1978 $70

COMMEMORATIVE Biographical Record of Northeastern Pa. Including the Counties of Susquehanna, Wayne, Pike, and Monroe... Chicago, 1900. Rebound, illus., fine. MacManus 239-1593 1978 $75

COMMEMORATIVE Biographical Record of the Counties of Harrison and Carroll, Ohio. Chicago, 1891. 1st ed., thick 4to., illus., orig. dec. mor., rubbed, good. MacManus 239-1110 1978 $47.50

COMMEMORATIVE Biographical Record of the County of York Ontario... Toronto, 1907. Illus., black fab. Hood 116-20 1978 $110

COMMONS, JOHN R. The Distribution of Wealth. New York, 1893. 1st ed. Biblo BL781-807 1978 $10

COMMONS, JOHN R. Trade Unionism and Labor Problems. New York, (1905). Biblo BL781-808 1978 $9

COMMUNICATION of the Mayor, on the Fiscal Concerns of the City, in Common Council, January 19, 1824. New York, 1824. Sewn, orig. plain orange wr., very good. Butterfield 21-486 1978 $15

COMPAYRE, GABRIEL The Elements of Psychology. 1890. Austin 80-866 1978 $10

COMPAYRE, GABRIEL Horace Mann and the Public School in the U. S. 1907. Austin 80-867 1978 $10

COMPENDIUM of Abstracts of Papers on the Therapeutic Use of Radium. Pittsburgh, 1920, 1925. Sturdy looseleaf binder. Wolfe 39-365 1978 $25

COMPILATION of Facts Relative to the Mining Property Known as the San Pedro and Canon Del Agua Grants Situate in the Counties of Bernalillo and Santa Fe,.... Washington, 1867. Folding map, orig. pr. wr., 1st ed. Ginsberg 14-753 1978 $150

COMPLETE Business Directory of Boston, for 1857. (Boston, 1857). Commercial ed., orig. printed bds., cloth spine, 8vo. Edwards 1012-472 1978 £25

A COMPLETE Collection of State Trials & Proceedings for High-Treason & Other Crimes & Misdemeanours from the Reign of George I. 1730. 6 vols., 2nd ed., folio, 1/4 sheep, lacks spine on 2 vols., text very good except vol. 8, lower inside margin show worm traces. Hyland 128-566 1978 £75

COMPOSITE Book-Plates 1897-1893. London, (1893). 8vo., pict. cover, bds., cloth spine. Battery Park 1-289 1978 $50

COMPTON-BURNETT, IVY   Pastors and Masters: a study. 1925. Very good, first English ed. Bell Book 17-169 1978 £38.50

COMPTON-BURNETT, IVY   Two Worlds and Their Ways. 1949. Bookplt., else very good, first English ed. Bell Book 17-171 1978 £6.50

COMSTOCK, J.   The Young Botanist. New York, 1836. Age stained, front hinge chipped, 16mo, orig. cloth. Book Chest 17-91 1978 $25

COMSTOCK, JOHN H.   The Spider Book. New York, 1912. Illus., 4to. Traylen 88-555 1978 £15

COMTE, MME. ACHILLE   Nouveaux Contes du Jour de l'An. Paris, 1858. 1st ed., leather binding soiled and rubbed. Victoria 34-174 1978 $22.50

COMTE, AUGUSTE   Cours de Philosophie Positive. Paris, 1830-1842. 1st ed., 8vo, 6 vols., contemp. half-calf, red and green mor. labels, marbled edges. Gilhofer 75-26 1978 SFr 2,500

COMTE, AUGUSTE   The Positive Philosophy. London, 1896. 3 vols. Salloch 348-39 1978 $25

CONANT, THOMAS   Upper Canada Sketches... Toronto, 1898. Illus., ports., maps, coloured illus. by E. S. Shrapnel. Hood 116-728 1978 $200

CONARD, HENRY SHOEMAKER   Water-Lilies. New York, 1909. 8vo., orig. cloth. Book Chest 17-483 1978 $10

CONARD, HOWARD LOUIS   "Uncle Dick" Wootton...The Pioneer Frontiersman of the Rocky Mountain Region. Columbus, 1950. Illus., reprint of 1890 Ed., Ltd. to 500 copies, fine, d.w. Biblo 248-300 1978 $30

CONCEICAO, JOSE MANOEL DA   As Exequias Abrahao Lincoln President dos Estados-Unidos America... Rio De Janeiro, n.d. (1865). Wrs. Hayman 72-424 1978 $25

CONCILII Plenarii Baltimorensis II... Baltimore, 1877. Orig. cl., 1st ed. Ginsberg 16-845 1978 $22.50

CONDER, CLAUDE R.   Syrian Stone-Lore... London, 1886. Edged Rubbed, top spine chipped. Biblo BL781-356 1978 $14.50

CONDER, CLAUDE R.   Syrian Stone-Lore; or, the Monumental History of Palestine. London, 1886. Illus., very good. Biblo BL781-355 1978 $17.50

CONDER, JAMES   The Modern Traveller. London, 1825. 2 vol., 12mo., old 1/2 morocco. Paine 78-32 1978 $22.50

CONDER, JOSIAH   Africa. London, 1830. 3 vols., folding map, 11 plts., sm. 8vo, slight foxing, half calf gilt. K Books 239-102 1978 £25

CONDER, JOSIAH   Egypt, Nubia & Abyssinia. London, 1830. 2 vols., sm. 8vo, 2 maps, 6 plts., orig. cloth, dirty & shaken. K Books 239-104 1978 £12

CONDER, JOSIAH   Egypt, Nubia & Abyssinia. London, 1830. 2 vols., 2 folding maps, 6 plts., little foxed, sm. 8vo, half calf gilt. K Books 239-103 1978 £15

CONDER, JOSIAH   The Flowers of Japan and the Art of Floral Arrangement. Tokyo, 1891. Folio, plain and hand-colored plts., mod. half calf, orig. cloral wrs., 1st ed. Quaritch 983-137 1978 $300

CONDIE, FRANCIS   Practical Treatise on the Diseases of Children. Philadelphia, 1858. Fifth ed., very good. Rittenhouse 49-156 1976 $15

CONDIT, UZAL W.   The History of Easton, Penna. From the Earliest Times to the Present 1779-1885. N.P., (1885). Lg. 4to., illus., orig. cloth, scarce. MacManus 239-1424 1978 $85

CONDORCET, MARIE JEAN ANTOINE NICOLAS CARITAT MARQUIS DE   Esquisse d'un Tableau Historique des Progres de l'Esprit Humain. Paris, (1795). 1st ed., 8vo, contemp. half-calf, light marginal waterstain. Gilhofer 75-27 1978 SFr 800

CONDORCET, MARIE JEAN ANTOINE NICOLAS CARITAT, MARQUIS DE Esquisse D'Un Tableau Historique Des Progres De L'Esprit Humain. Paris, (1795-6). 2nd ed., octavo, quarter vellum over marbled bds., pencil notations in contemp. French hand. Bennett 20-50 1978 $250

CONDORCET, MARIE JEAN ANTOINE NICOLAS CARITAT, MARQUIS DE Outlines of an Historical View of the Progress of the Human Mind. London, 1795. 8vo., half calf, cloth sides, uncut, first English ed. Gurney 75-25 1978 £120

CONE, JONATHAN   The Salvation of Sinners, The Result of God's Gracious Purpose. Norwich, 1830. Sewed. Hayman 71-155 1978 $12.50

CONE, SPENCER W.   The Fairies of America. New York, 1859. Cloth, plts., handcolored. Hayman 73-350 1973 $12.50

CONESTAGGIO, GERONIMO FRANCHI DE   Dell'Unione del Regno di Portogallo alla Corona di Castiglia. Genova, 1589. 4to., 18th century calf, gilt back, 2nd ed. Gilhofer 74-60 1978 sFr 750

CONFESSION OF Faith, Covenant, and Articles of Practice, Adopted by the First Church in New-Haven. N.P., n.d. (New Haven?,1810?). Sewed, age stains. Hayman 71-158 1978 $8.50

CONFUCIUS   The Analects of Confucius. 1938. Covers somewhat soiled, good, first English ed. Bell Book 16-866 1978 £6.50

CONGDON, HERBERT WHEATON   Old Vermont Houses. Battleboro, 1940. Illus. by author. Baldwins' 51-394 1978 $12.50

CONGRESS FOR EDUCATION FOR DEMOCRACY   Education for Democracy. 1939. Austin 80-868 1978 $17.50

CONGRESS FOR EDUCATION FOR DEMOCRACY   Education for Democracy. 1939. Austin 80-868 1978 $17.50

CONGREVE, WILLIAM   The Double-Dealer, A Comedy. London, 1694. 4to, full dark blue morocco, gilt, spine gilt, t.e.g., 1st ed, small surface tear, fine copy, good margins. Ximenes 47-57 1978 $750

CONGREVE, WILLIAM   The Dramatick Works. 1733. Frontis., orig. panelled calf, old reback retaining label, v. g. Jarndyce 16-60 1978 £16.50

CONGREVE, WILLIAM   Love For Love: A Comedy. 1695. 4to., paper bds., title dust-soiled, little frayed, final leaf torn, neatly stitched together again. Hannas 54-63 1978 £85

CONGREVE, WILLIAM   A Pindarique Ode, Humbly Offer'd to the King on His Taking Namure. 1695. 1st. ed., folio, disbound, somewhat foxed. Hannas 54-64 1978 £43

CONGREVE, WILLIAM   The Tears of Amaryllis for Amyntas. London, 1703. Folio, half citron morocco, gilt, by Roger de Coverly (a trifle rubbed), 1st ed., fine copy. Ximenes 47-58 1978 $700

CONGREVE, WILLIAM   The Way of the World. London, The Haymarket Press, 1928. Signed etching by A. R. Middleton Todd, sm. 4to., ltd. to 975 numbered copies on Japan vellum, bound in crushed marbled velveteen cover. Battery Park 1-163 1978 $75

CONGREVE, WILLIAM   The Works of... 1730. 3 vols., 5th. ed., 12mo, contemp. panelled calf, corners bumped, rebacked, gilt crests on upper covers. Eaton 45-112 1978 £25

CONGREVE, WILLIAM   Works. Birmingham, Baskerville Press, 1761. 3 vols., plts., contemp. calf, good, 8vo. Howes 194-152 1978 £90

CONGREVE, WILLIAM   The Works of ... In Three Volumes. Birmingham, 1761. 3 vols., 8vo, portrait, 5 plts., contemp. calf, gilt, headbands worn, joints tender. Hannas 54-65 1978 £75

CONKLIN, EDMUND S.   Principles of Abnormal Psychology. 1927. Austin 80-869 1978 $10

CONKLIN, EDMUND S.   The Psychology of Religious Adjustment. 1929. Austin 80-870 1978 $10

CONKLIN, EDWIN GRANT   The Direction of Human Evolution. 1921. 1st ed. in dust jacket. Austin 80-871 1978 $17.50

CONKLIN, EDWIN GRANT   Heredity and Environment. Princeton University Press, 1919. 3rd rev. ed. Austin 80-872 1978 $10

CONKLING, GRACE HAZARD   Ship's Log and Other Poems. New York, 1924. 1st ed., edges rubbed, spine chipped at extremities. Biblo BL781-909 1978 $10

CONKLING, HOWARD   Le Chevalier de la Luzerne. New York, 1908. Orig. binding, clean, little worn, short vertical crease on front cover. Hayman 71-157 1978 $7.50

CONKLING, ROSCOE   The Issue of 1880. N.P., n.d. (1880). Disbound. Hayman 71-650 1978 $7.50

CONN, WILLIAM   Cowboys and Colonels. London, 1887. Pic. cloth, brown end sheets, illus., 1st ed. in English, very good copy, slipcase. Dykes 34-18 1978 $150

CONNANT, M.   Urim an Thummin; or, The Clergies Dignity and Duty Recommended in a Visitation Sermon Preached at Lewes, April 27, 1669. London, 1669. Sm. 4to, later calf, rubbed, dedicated to Henry King. Traylen 88-211 1978 £20

CONNECTICUT   Annual Report of the Adjutant-General of the State of Connecticut...1864. Hartford, 1864. New cloth, Bell Wiley's copy. Broadfoot 46-318 1978 $16

CONNECTICUT ACADEMY OF ARTS AND SCIENCES   Memoirs. New Haven, 1810. Vol.I, part I, 8vo., fldg. plts., orig. bds., uncut, rebacked, stamp of Surgeon General's Office Library, but fine copy. Norman 5-61 1978 $150

CONNECTICUT VALLEY HISTORICAL SOCIETY   Papers and Proceedings of the .... Springfield, 1881-1912. 3 vols., 8vo. Morrill 239-512 1978 $50

CONNELL, FRANCIS J.   Morals in Politics and Professions. 1946. Exlib. Austin 79-158 1978 $12.50

CONNELLEY, WILLIAM E.   History of Kansas Newspapers: A History...1854-1916... Topeka, 1916. Illus., original wr., 1st ed. Ginsberg 14-441 1978 $15

CONNELLEY, WILLIAM E.   Quantrill and the Border Wars. Cedar Rapids, 1910. Cloth, free endpaper, removed in fr., leaving fr. inner hinges little ragged, uncut, partly unopened. Hayman 73-135 1978 $30

CONNELLEY, WILLIAM E.   Wild Bill and His Era. The Life and Adventures of James Butler Hickok. New York, 1933. Illus., uncut, fine copy. MacManus 239-1909 1978 $30

CONNELLY, HENRY   The First Annual Message of Governor Connelly, Delivered Before the Legislative Assembly of the Territory of New Mexico,.... Santa Fe, 1861. Half mottled calf. Ginsberg 14-754 1978 $600

CONNETT, EUGENE V.   A Decade of American Sporting Books & Prints. New York, Derrydale Press, 1927. 1 of 950 copies, illus. Battery Park 1-61 1978 $100

CONNETT, EUGENE V.   Duck Shooting Along the Atlantic Tidewater... New York, 1947. 1st ed., lg. 4to., orig. bind. Americanist 102-109 1978 $50

CONNEY, MRS.   A Line of Her Own. London, 1891. 3 vols., orig. cloth, 1st ed., covers a bit worn and stained. MacManus 238-339 1978 $85

CONNINGHAM, F. A.   An Alphabetical List of 5735 Titles of N. Currier and Currier & Ives Prints. New York, 1930. 8vo., 1000 copies prtd., orig. cloth. Morrill 241-91 1978 $20

THE CONNOISSEUR. Oxford, 1774. 6th ed., 4 vols., sm. 8vo., contemp. calf. Quaritch 979-99 1978 $55

THE CONNOISSEUR. A Series from the Commencement in September 1901 to 1929. 1901-29. 80 vols., 4to., coloured illus., 1 vols. sewed as issued, remainder cloth, 2 vols. not uniform, vols. 1 to 73, 75 to 78 and 81 to 83. Quaritch 983-171 1978 $315

CONNOLLY, C. P.   The Truth About the Frank Case. New York, 1915. Paper. Austin 79-159 1978 $20

CONNOLLY, CYRIL   The Condemned Playground; essays, 1927-1944. London, 1945. Very nice, inscribed by the author, first ed., orig. binding. Rota 211-72 1978 £60

CONNOLLY, CYRIL   The Condemned Playground: essays, 1927-44. 1945. Portrait, very good, first English ed. Bell Book 17-977 1978 £14

CONNOLLY, CYRIL   Enemies of Promise. 1938. First ed., very good, d.w., orig. cloth, 8vo. Howes 194-752 1978 £18

CONNOLLY, CYRIL   Enemies of Promise. London, 1938. Fine, first ed., orig. binding, d.w. Rota 212-9 1978 £50

CONNOLLY, CYRIL   Horizon. Nos. 1-121. London, 1940-1950. Wrappers, good, first ed. Rota 211-74 1978 £200

CONNOLLY, CYRIL   The Rock Pool. Paris, Obelisk Press, 1936. First ed., wrappers, good. Rota 211-70 1978 £60

CONNOLLY, CYRIL   The Unquiet Grave. Horizon, 1944. One of 1,000 numbered copies on handmade paper, orig. cloth, very nice, d.w., scarce, inscribed by author, first ed. Rota 211-71 1978 £85

CONNOLLY, JAMES B.   Fisherman of the Banks. London, (1928). Illus., orig. cloth, 1st Eng. ed., spine slightly faded, but very good. MacManus 238-637 1978 $20

CONNOLLY, T. W. J.   The History of the Corps of Royal Sappers and Miners. 1855. Coloured plts., 2 vols., half calf, 8vo. Edwards 1012-328 1978 £65

CONNOR, BOYD   History of North Carolina. Chicago, 1919. 6 vols., covers stained. Broadfoot 50-36b 1978 $80

CONNOR, BOYD   History of North Carolina. Chicago, 1919. 6 vols., fine set. Broadfoot 50-36a 1978 $120

CONNOR, R. D. W.   North Carolina, Rebuilding an Ancient Commonwealth. Chicago, 1929. 4 vols., covers spotted. Broadfoot 50-38 1978 $80

CONNOR, RALPH   The Arm of Gold. Toronto, 1932. 1st. ed. Hood's 115-420 1978 $10

CONNOR, RALPH   Beyond the Marshes. Toronto, 1898. Card cover, marginal decors. Hood 117-453 1978 $15

CONNOR, RALPH   The Man From Glengarry; A Tale of the Ottawa. Toronto, 1901. Hood's 115-421 1978 $10

CONNOR, RALPH   The Major. Toronto, 1929. Hood 116-460 1978 $10

CONNOR, RALPH   The Sky Pilot in No Man's Land. Toronto, 1919. 1st. ed. Hood's 115-422 1978 $7.50

CONOVER, G. S.   The Birth-Places of Sa-Go-Ye- Wat-Ha, or the Indian Red Jacket... Waterloo, 1884. 8vo, orig. printed wrapper, orig. cloth, inscription by author. Edwards 1012-551 1978 £18

CONRAD C. M.   Report of...Communicating...a Report of the Tulare Valley, Made by Lieutenant Derby. Washington, 1852. Folding map, disbound, 1st ed. Ginsberg 14-93 1978 $15

CONRAD, HENRY C.   History of the State of Delaware From the Earliest Settlements to 1907. Wilmington, 1908. Illus., maps, vol. 1 only. Baldwins' 51-217 1978 $25

CONRAD, HENRY C.   History of the State of Delaware from the Earliest Settlements to 1907. Wilmington, 1908. Illus., maps, 3 vols. Baldwins' 51-216 1978 $85

CONRAD, HERBERT S.   Characteristics and Uses of Item - Analysis Data. 1948. Paper. Austin 80-874 1978 $8.50

CONRAD, JESSIE   Joseph Conrad as I Knew Him. New York, 1927. Very fine in torn d.w. Desmarais B-152 1978 $12.50

CONRAD, JOSEPH   Almayer's Folly. London, 1896. 2nd ed., red cloth, t.e.g., very good or better. Limestone 9-60 1978 $35

CONRAD, JOSEPH   The Arrow Of Gold. Garden City, 1919. 1st. ed., 2nd. issue, orig. binding, clean. Hayman 71-164 1978 $7.50

CONRAD, JOSEPH   The Arrow of Gold. New York, 1919. 8vo, blue cloth, gilt stamped cover and spine, light foxing, 1st ed., collector's cond. Desmarais 1-92 1978 $60

CONRAD, JOSEPH   Falk, Amy Foster, To-Morrow. New York, 1903. First U.S. ed., good. Bell Book 17-978 1978 $22.50

CONRAD, JOSEPH   Geography and Some Explorers. London, 1924.
1 of 30 numbered copies signed by author, 1st ed., 8 vo., orig. printed grey
wr., uncut, glassine jacket, fine, enclosed in green half mor. slipcase, rare.
Houle 10-383 1978 $1,250

CONRAD, JOSEPH   Last Essays. London & Toronto, 1926. 1st
ed., frontispiece, green cloth, d.j., very good or better. Limestone 9-61
1978 $40

CONRAD, JOSEPH   Laughing Anne: a play. 1923. No. 122 of
200 copies numbered & signed by author, printed in two colours on Kelmscott handmade paper, full vellum, t.e.g., very fine, somewhat worn slipcase, first English
ed. Bell Book 17-174 1978 £115

CONRAD, JOSEPH   Laughing Anne and One Day More. London,
1924. 8vo, green cloth, ownership inscription, edges foxed, near Fine, darkened
d.w., 1st ed. Desmarais 1-93 1978 $15

CONRAD, JOSEPH   Laughing Anne and One Day More. London,
1924. Ownership inscription, near fine in torn & darkened d.w. Desmarais B-150
1978 $15

CONRAD, JOSEPH   Letters from Conrad 1892 to 1924. Nonesuch
Press, 1928. Portraits, orig. red buckram, other edges untrimmed, top edge rough
gilt, ltd. to 925 numbered copies, 8vo. Howes 194-1071 1978 £18

CONRAD, JOSEPH   Letters from Conrad, 1895 to 1924. London,
Nonesuch Press, 1928. 8vo, red cloth, uncut, unopened, Francis Meynell's copy
with bookplt., ed. ltd. to 925 copies, 1st ed., collector's cond. Desmarais
1-94 1978 $90

CONRAD, JOSEPH   Letters from Conrad: 1895-1924. (London),
Nonesuch Press, (1928). 1 of 925 numbered copies, cloth (spine sunned), t.e.g.,
uncut, very good. Houle 10-71 1978 $45

CONRAD, JOSEPH   Lord Jim: a tale. 1900. Covers dull & little
soiled, good, scarce, first English ed. Bell Book 16-177 1978 £20

CONRAD, JOSEPH   Conrad's Manifesto. 1966. 1 of 100 copies,
portr. prtd. on Shizuoka vellum & signed by artist, cloth slipcase, very fine.
Battery Park 1-109 1978 $175

CONRAD, JOSEPH   Nigger of the Narcissus. London, 1898. 1st
state with ads dated 1897, 1st ed., orig. slate-grey cloth, uncut (inner joints
cracked, bookplate), else very good, enclosed in half mor. slipcase. Houle
10-72 1978 $225

CONRAD, JOSEPH   Nostromo. A Tale of the Seaboard. London,
1904. Orig. cloth, 1st ed., good, cracked inner hinges, slightly soiled covers,
bookplt. removed. MacManus 238-631 1978 $75

CONRAD, JOSEPH   Nostromo, A Tale of the Seaboard. London,
New York, 1904. 8vo, blue cloth, gilt lettering on spine, very fine, 1st ed.
Desmarais 1-95 1978 $75

CONRAD, JOSEPH   Notes on Life and Letters. 1921. 1st. ed., nice
clean copy, orig. cloth, ink sig. of f.e.p. Eaton 45-115 1978 £9

CONRAD, JOSEPH   The Rescue: a Romance of the Shallows. 1920.
Near fine, first English ed. Bell Book 17-177 1978 £5

CONRAD, JOSEPH   The Rover. 1923. 1st. ed., d.w., soiled &
slightly torn. Eaton 45-113 1978 £15

CONRAD, JOSEPH   The Rover. 1923. Very good, slightly defective
d.w., first English ed. Bell Book 17-178 1978 £17.50

CONRAD, JOSEPH   The Rover. Garden City, 1923. 8vo, jap vellum, gilt, t.e.g., d.j., port. frontis., 1 of 377 copies signed by author, 1st ed.,
fine. Duschnes 220-68 1978 $200

CONRAD, JOSEPH   The Rover. Garden City, 1923. Blue cloth, 1st
trade ed., bookshop stamp, lightly worn. Bradley 49-69 1978 $12.50

CONRAD, JOSEPH   The Rover. London, (1923). Signed by author
and dated 1923, 1st ed., d.j., bookplate, nice copy. Houle 10-73 1978 $250

CONRAD, JOSEPH   The Rover. 1923. Fine, d.w., first English ed.
Bell Book 16-178 1978 £15

CONRAD, JOSEPH   The Rover. London, 1925. Medallion
Ed., portrait, very good or better. Limestone 9-62 1978 $8

CONRAD, JOSEPH   The Secret Agent. London, 1907. 8vo, ruby-
red cloth, fine, 1st ed. Desmarais 1-96 1978 $65

CONRAD, JOSEPH   The Secret Agent: a Simple Tale. 1907. Good,
first English ed. Bell Book 17-179 1978 £28.50

CONRAD, JOSEPH   The Shadow-Line: a confession. 1917. Edges
of text somewhat foxed, else very good, first English ed. Bell Book 17-180 1978
£15

CONRAD, JOSEPH   Suspense. London, 1925. 1st English ed.,
d.j., very good. Limestone 9-63 1978 $40

CONRAD, JOSEPH   Suspense. London, 1925. Red cloth, 1st English
ed., fine in dust jacket. Bradley 49-70 1978 $60

CONRAD, JOSEPH   Tales of Hearsay. London, 1925. Nice in torn
d.w. Desmarais B-151 1978 $35

CONRAD, JOSEPH   Tales of Hearsay. London, 1925. 1st ed.,
spine fading, sm. spine indentation, very good or better. Limestone 9-65
1978 $25

CONRAD, JOSEPH   Tales of Hearsay. (1925). 1st. ed., orig.
green cloth, contents good, binding damp-spotted. Eaton 45-114 1978 £8

CONRAD, JOSEPH   Tales of Hearsay. London, 1925. 1st ed.,
green cloth, d.j., very good or better. Limestone 9-64 1978 $42.50

CONRAD, JOSEPH   Tales of Hearsay. 1925. Very good, d.w.,
first English ed. Bell Book 16-179 1978 £15

CONRAD, JOSEPH   Tales of Hearsay. London, 1925. 8vo, green
cloth, ownership inscription, somewhat worn and chipped d.w., 1st ed., collector's
cond. Desmarais 1-97 1978 $35

CONRAD, JOSEPH   The Tremolino. New York, A. Colish Press,
1942. One of 1000 copies, boxed, illus., t.e.g. Battery Park 1-25 1978 $35

CONRAD, JOSEPH   Twenty Letters to Joseph Conrad. London,
Limited Ed. Club, 1926. Decor. paper wr., 1st ed., collector's cond. Desmarais
1-98 1978 $35

CONRAD, JOSEPH   Typhoon and Other Stories. London, 1903.
Orig. cloth, 1st Eng. ed., fine. MacManus 238-630 1978 $50

CONRAD, JOSEPH   Victory. G.C., 1915. 1st ed., issued 6
months prior to English ed., blue cloth, map, nice copy. Houle 10-74 1978
$85

CONRAD, JOSEPH   Victory. 1915. First English ed., cr. 8vo.,
orig. cloth, good. Howes 194-754 1978 £15

CONRAD, JOSEPH   Within the Tides. London & Toronto, 1915.
1st issue of 1st ed., spine sunned, very good or better. Limestone 9-66
1978 $35

CONRAD, JOSEPH   The Works. 1921. 18 vols., printed on rag paper
specially made for this ed., orig. buckram-backed bds., signed by author, ltd to
780 sets, 8vo. Howes 194-753 1978 £90

CONRAD, JOSEPH   Works. 1921-27. 20 vols., 8vo., uniform standard ed., prtd. on rag paper, bds., cloth backs, good set with d.ws., some worn,
ltd. to 780 sets, 1st vol. signed by author. Quaritch 979-367 1978 $600

CONRAD, JOSEPH   Youth: a Narrative and Two Other Stories.
1902. First ed., cr. 8vo., orig. pale green cloth. Howes 194-755 1978 £28

CONRAD, JOSEPH   Youth: a narrative, and two other stories. 1902.
Very good, first English ed. Bell Book 17-181 1978 £42.50

CONRAD, STEPHEN   The Second Mrs. Jim. Boston, 1904. Cloth,
nice copy of 1st ed. Hayman 73-175 1978 $7.50

CONROY, WILLIAM   Personality Development. 1937. Paper. Austin
80-875 1978 $10

CONSEQUENCES. Golden Cockerel Press, 1932. Wood-engrav. frontispiece,
orig. cloth, d.w., ltd. to 1,000 copies signed by printer, Robert Gibbings, 8vo.
Howes 194-895 1978 £15

CONSETT, MATTHEW   A Tour Through Sweden, Swedish-Lapland, Finland, and Denmark. Stockton, 1789. 1st. ed., 4to, engraved frontispiece by Thomas Bewick, engraved & other plts., half calf, gilt back. Deighton 5-116 1978 £265

CONSIDERATIONS Occasioned by a Proposal for Reducing Interest to Three Per Cent. London, 1737. 8vo, disbound, 1st ed. Ximenes 47-89 1978 $40

CONSIDERATIONS on the Subject of the New-York and Erie Railroad. (New York, 1833). Sewn, never bound, supporting letter from Benjamin Wright dated April 19, 1833, addressed to Eleazar Lord. Butterfield 21-360 1978 $35

CONSTABLE, JOHN   The Conversation of Gentlemen Considered in Most of the Ways,.... London, 1738. 12mo, contemporary calf, gilt, spine gilt (bit rubbed), 1st ed., very good copy. Ximenes 47-60 1978 $150

CONSTABLE'S Miscellany, Vols. XXVII-XXVIII: Memorials of the Late War. Edinburgh, 1828. 2 vols., 12mo, bound in 1, contemp. half calf, very good. Fenning 32-74 1978 £8.50

CONSTANT, BENJAMIN   Adolphe and the Red Note-book. 1948. 12mo., cloth-backed bds., very good, slightly worn d.w., first English ed. Bell Book 17-685 1978 £6.50

CONSTANT, BENJAMIN   Adolphe: Anecdote Trouvee Dans les Papiers D'Un Inconnu...Gravures Au Burin de Pierre Gandon. Paris, 1930. 8vo., pr. wrs., boxed, fine, 1 of only 50 copies. Argosy Special-26 1978 $150

CONSTANT, G. L. M. J.   Reformation in England. 1942. Ex-lib., Vol. 2 only. Allen 234-1182 1978 $7.50

CONSTANTIA. 1770. Sm. 8vo., 1st ed., half mor., scarce. Quaritch 979-248 1978 $130

CONSTANTINI, ANGELO   The Birth Life and Death of Scaramouch. 1924. 8vo., finely prtd., plts., decor. bds., vellum back, ltd. to 80 copies prtd. on handmade parchment vellum signed by translators. Quaritch 979-20 1978 $100

CONSTANTINOPLE And The Scenery of the Seven Churches of Asia Minor Illustrated... (1840). 1st. & 2nd. series, maps, engraved titles, engraved plts., 2 vols. in 1, 4to, binders cloth, some marginal staining throughout. Edwards 1012-46 1978 £120

THE CONSTITUTIONALITY of Slavery. Boston, 1848. Disbound, 48 pages. Biblo 247-87 1978 $20

CONTACT Collection of Contemporary Writers. (Paris, Three Mountains Press, 1925). Gray wrs., 1st ed., 300 copies issued, former owner's name, fldg. box. Bradley 49-71 1978 $135

CONTARENUS, GASPARO   De Elementis Eorumque Mixtionibus. Leyden, 1633. 12mo., vellum. Salloch 345-49 1978 $75

CONTARENUS, NICOLAUS   De Perfectione Rerum. Lyon, 1587. 8vo., vellum, rare ed. Salloch 345-50 1978 $110

CONTENAU, G.   Le Deluge Bablonien suivi de Ishtar aux Enfers La Tour de Babel. Paris, 1941. Illus., 3/4 leather, lightly rubbed. Biblo BL781-357 1978 $17.50

CONTI, GIOVANIBALISTA   Scelta dei Poesie Castigliane Tradolte in Verso Toscano. Madrid, 1782. 3 vols., contemp. 1/2 calf, marbled bds., Italian & Spanish text. Eaton 45-116 1978 £20

CONTRACT of Agreement, for Building an Exchange, in the City of Edinburgh, Between the Magistrates and Town Council, and the Tradesmen. Edinburgh, 1754. 8vo., frontis., fine, uncut copy, stitched, orig. blue wrs. Quaritch 983-35 1978 $225

CONVENTION Between Her Majesty and the United States of America, Relative to the Establishment of a Communication by Ship-Canal Between the Atlantic and Pacific Oceans... 1859. Sm. folio, modern cloth. Edwards 1012-694 1978 £25

CONVERSATION d'une mere avec sa fille, en francais et en anglais.... Paris, (1804). 8vo., calf, slightly rubbed, text in two columns: French and English, very good. King 7-344 1978 £15

CONVERSATIONS At Cambridge. 1836. 12mo, cloth. Eaton 45-117 1978 £5

CONWAY, HENRY S.   False Appearances; A Comedy. Dublin, 1789. 1st. Irish ed., 12mo, wrapper, nice copy. Fenning 32-75 1978 £8.50

CONWAY, M. F.   Shall the War Be For Union and Freedom, or Union and Slavery? Washington, 1861. Unbound as issued, foxing on final blank leaf. Hayman 71-120 1978 $7.50

CONWAY, MONCURE D.   The Life of Thomas Paine. New York, 1892. 2 vols., ports., nice. MacManus 239-798 1978 $35

CONWAY, WILLIAM MARTIN   The Alps From End To End. Westminster, 1895. 3rd. ed., roy.8vo, plts. by A.D. M'Cormick, orig. quarter brown cloth, green cloth sides, lettered in gilt, very sl. foxing on some leaves. Deighton 5-205 1978 £35

CONWAY, WILLIAM MARTIN   The Alps. London, 1904. Color plates, t.e.g., bookplt., else very good. Bernard 5-67 1978 $40

CONWAY, WILLIAM MARTIN   Climbing and Exploration in the Karakoram-Himalayas. London, 1894. 1st. ed., roy. 8vo, folding map, repaired, plts., illus. by A.D. McCormick, orig. brown cloth, neatly recased, t.e.g., lib. stamp & label removed. Deighton 5-206 1978 £65

CONWAY, WILLIAM MARTIN   Climbing and Exploration in the Karakoram-Himalayas. London, 1894. Illus., fldg. map, tall thick 8vo., pic. cloth, 1st ed. Argosy Special-25 1978 $60

CONWELL, RUSSELL H.   History of the Great Fire in Boston, November 9 and 10, 1872. Boston, 1873. Illus., sm. 8vo., orig. cloth, 1st ed. Morrill 241-325 1978 $10

COOCH, EDWARD W.   Delaware Historic Events. (1946). Map. Baldwins' 51-218 1978 $10

COOK, CHARLES   Among the Pimas or the Mission to the Pima and Maricopa Indians. New York, 1893. Illus., orig. cloth, 1st ed. Ginsberg 14-281 1978 $45

COOK, DESMOND   Confessions of An Incurable Collector. London, 1928. Illus. Baldwins' 51-41 1978 $10

COOK, MRS. E. T.   Highways and Byways in London. London, 1902. Illus., 1st ed., inner hinges split. Biblo BL781-637 1978 $22.50

COOK, FREDERICK   Journals of the Military Expedition of Major General John Sullivan Against the Six Nations of Indians in 1779. Auburn, 1887. Maps, plts. Butterfield 21-385 1978 $35

COOK, JAMES   Captain Cook's Three Voyages to the Pacific Ocean. New York, 1814. 2 vols., 12mo, abridged, calf, chip in upper spine, fine set. Victoria 34-175 1978 $50

COOK, JAMES   Journal of Captain Cook's Last Voyage to the Pacific Ocean. Dublin, 1781. Frontispiece, plts., old style half calf, 8vo. K Books 244-75 1978 £40

COOK, JAMES   Voyage dans l'hemisphere australe et autour du monde.... (Paris, 1778.) Old calf, worn and rebacked, plts., atlas only. Dawson's 127-252 1978 $200

COOK, JAMES   A Voyage Towards the South Pole, and Round the World...Years 1772...1775. Dublin, 1784. contem. calf, 2 vol., 8vo. Paine 78-33 1978 $145.00

COOK, JAMES H.   Fifty Years on the Old Frontier. New Haven, 1923. Cloth, illus., 1st ed., very good copy. Dykes 34-52 1978 $27.50

COOK, JAMES H.   Fifty Years on the Old Frontier as Cowboy, Hunter, Guide, Scout, and Ranchman. New Haven, 1923. Illus., original cloth, 1st ed. Ginsberg 14-282 1978 $25

COOK, JANE E.   The Sculptor Caught Napping. England, 1874. Folio, 1st ed., plates, orig. 3/4 leather, rubbed at edges, plates very fine, foxing, excellent copy, rare. Victoria 34-176 1978 $100

COOK, JIM LANE   Lane of the Llano. Boston, 1936. Illus., d.j., very fine. Jenkins 116-246 1978 $25

COOK, N. F.   Satan in Society. Cincinnati & New York, 1871. 8vo., 1st ed. Morrill 239-51 1978 $15

COOK, PARSONS   The Baptismal Question. Hints to an Enquirer... Boston, 1842. Orig. wrps., 1st ed. Ginsberg 16-854 1978 $15.00

COOK, REGINALD L.   Passage to Walden. Boston, 1949. First ed., d.j.
Austin 82-314 1978 $12.50

COOK, SHERWIN L.   Torchlight Parade. Our Presidential Pageant.
New York, 1929. Cloth, tiny piece torn from d.j., otherwise fine. Hayman 72-
153 1978 $8.50

COOK, T.   Carnations & Pinks. New York, c. 1910. 8vo,
orig. cloth. Book Chest 17-484 1978 $9

COOK, THOMAS   India, Burma and Ceylon. London, 1894. Sm.
8vo, cloth, folding maps in color. Van der Peet 127-60 1978 Dfl 25

COOKE, ALISTAIR   Garbo and the Night Watchmen. 1937. Good,
covers soiled & rubbed, first English ed. Bell Book 16-403 1978 £6.50

COOKE, EDWARD WILLIAM   Views of the Old and New London Bridges...
1833. Lg. folio, plts., orig. cloth, rebacked, pres. inscription from Cooke.
Quaritch 983-172 1978 $540

COOKE, GEORGE P.   Moolelo O Molokai. Honolulu, 1949. Fabricoid,
map end sheets, frontis. in color, illus., 1st ed., fine copy autographed by
author, d.w., reinforced, very scarce, slipcase. Dykes 34-53 1978 $75

COOKE, GEORGE WILLIS   A Bibliography of Ralph Waldo Emerson. Boston
and New York, 1908. 8vo., orig. cloth, paper label, 1st ed., 1 of 350 copies.
MacManus 238-915 1978 $35

COOKE, GEORGE WILLIS   Unitarianism in America. Boston, 1902. Illus.
MacManus 239-106 1978 $17.50

COOKE, H. C.   Geology of Matachewan District, Northern Ontario. Coloured fold. map. Wolfe 39-107 1978 $25

COOKE, JOHN ESTEN   Henry St. John, Gentleman, of "Flower of Hundreds" in the County of Prince, Virginia. A Tale of 1774. New York, 1859.
Orig. cloth, 1st ed., bind. A, spine faded, otherwise very good. MacManus
238-447 1978 $45

COOKE, JOHN ESTEN   Leather Stocking and Silk; or, Hunter John Myers
and His Times. A Story of the Valley of Virginia. New York, 1854. Orig. cloth,
1st ed., bind. A, rare, covers faded and rubbed. MacManus 238-446 1978 $100

COOKE, JOHN ESTEN   A Life of General Robert E. Lee. New
York, 1871. Illus. Bell Wiley's copy. Broadfoot 46-50 1978 $40

COOKE, JOHN ESTEN   Mohun, or The Last Days of Lee and His
Paladins. Charlottesville, Va., 1936. Bell Wiley's copy. Broadfoot 46-52
1978 $25

COOKE, JOHN ESTEN   Stonewall Jackson: A Military Biography. New
York, 1866. Illus., maps, orig. cloth, nice. MacManus 239-869 1978 $37.50

COOKE, JOHN ESTEN   Stonewall Jackson: A Military Biography.
New York, 1876. Portr., full lea. Bell Wiley's copy. Broadfoot 46-51 1978
$35

COOKE, M. C.   A Plain and Easy Account of British Fungi with
Especial Reference to the Eculent and Economic Species. Edinburgh, 1904. Cr.
8vo., coloured plts., third ed., orig. cloth. K Books 244-76 1978 £15

COOKE, PHILIP ST. GEORGE   The Conquest of New Mexico and California;
An Historical and Personal Narrative. New York, 1878. Folding map, orig. cloth,
1st ed. Ginsberg 14-1092 1978 $130

COOKE, ROSE TERRY   Somebody's Neighbors. Boston, 1881. Cloth,
second state, covers dull, some dampstains on back cover, fr. flyleaf lacking.
Hayman 73-176 1978 $7.50

COOKE, THOMAS   A Hymn to Liberty. 1746. 1st. ed., folio,
disbound, uncut. Hannas 54-66 1978 £100

COOKE, THOMAS   Mr. Cooke's Original Poems, With Imitations
and Translations. 1742. 1st. collected ed., 12mo, old half calf, slightly waterstained. Hannas 54-67 1978 £55

COOKE, WILLIAM BERNARD   Rome and its surrounding scenary. London, 1845.
4to., red bds., plts., very good. King 7-345 1978 £140

COOKE, WILLIAM BERNARD   The Thames. 1811. First ed., plts., 2 vols.,
contemp. cloth backed marbled bds., entirely uncut, roy. 8vo. Howes 194-1375
1978 £130

COOLEY, CHARLES H.   Sociological Theory and Social Research. 1930.
1st ed. Austin 80-878 1978 $27.50

COOLEY, ELI F.   Genealogy of Early Settlers in Trenton and Ewig,
"Old Hunterdon County", N.J. Trenton, 1883. Orig. cloth, some wear but
nice, very scarce. MarManus 239-1251 1978 $60

COOLIDGE, AUSTIN J.   A History and Description of New England, General and Local. Boston, 1859. Vol. 1, 1st ed., illus., maps, near fine copy,
orig. cloth, scarce. MacManus 239-107 1978 $75

COOLIDGE, BERTHA   Some Unrecorded Letters of Caroline Norton in
the Altschul Collection of the Yale University Library. 1914. Sm. 4to., pattern
paper over bds., cloth spine, thin, only 75 copies. Battery Park 1-207 1978
$100

COOLIDGE, CALVIN   Foundations of the Republic. New York, 1926.
8vo., 1st ed. Morrill 239-350 1978 $7.50

COOLIDGE, CALVIN   The Price of Freedom. New York, 1924. 8vo.,
1st ed. Morrill 239-351 1978 $7.50

COOLIDGE, GEORGE A.   Brochure of Bunker Hill. Boston, 1875. Plts.,
facsimiles, text cuts, oblong 12mo., orig. wrs., chipped. Morrill 241-326 1978
$15

COOLIDGE, SUSAN   Cross Patch and Other Stories. Boston, 1881.
1st ed., illus., very good. Victoria 34-178 1978 $15

COOLIDGE, SUSAN   What Katy Did. A Story. Boston, 1873. Illus.,
most wanted and scarcest, bright copy, light rubbing at edges, 2 signatures pulled,
very good. Victoria 34-179 1978 $75

COOMARASWAMY, ANANDA KENTISH   Buddha and the Gospel of Buddhism.
New York, 1916. Illus., cloth. Dawson's 127-296 1978 $35

COOMARASWAMY, ANANDA KENTISH   Rajput Painting: Being an Account
of the Hindu Paintings of Rajasthan and the Panjab Himalayas from the Sixteenth
to the Nineteenth Century... 1916. 2 vols., folio, plain & colored plts., marginal pencil annotations, buckram, ltd. to 525 copies. Quaritch 983-138 1978
$540

COON, CHARLES L.   The Beginnings of Public Education in North
Carolina. Raleigh, 1908. 2 vols., spine of vol. 2 spotted. Broadfoot 50-40
1978 $30

COONEY, ROBERT   A Compendious History of the Northern Part of
the Province of New Brunswick, and the District of Gaspe, in Lower Canada. Halifax, 1832. Orig. bds., cloth back, joints tender. Wolfe 39-108 1978 $250

COONLEY, LYDIA AVERY   Under the Pines & Other Verses. Chicago,
Lakeside Press, 1895. 1st ed., orig. decor. cloth, uncut, 8vo., very good.
Americanist 103-142 1978 $35

COOPER, REV. MR.   A New History of England: from the Earliest
Period,.... London, 1801. 11th ed., board covers worn, , text solid. Victoria
34-575 1978 $45

COOPER, ALFRED M.   Supervision of Governmental Employees. 1943.
Austin 80-879 1978 $10

COOPER, ASTLEY   The Anatomy and Surgical Treatment of Abdominal
Hernia. Philadelphia, 1844. Litho. plts., tall 8vo., rebound in later buckram,
fr. cover & text dampstained. Morrill 239-52 1978 $20

COOPER, ASTLEY   Illustrations of the Diseases of the Breast. In Two
Parts, Part I. London, 1829. Lg. 4to., orig. bds., uncut, coloured plts., first
ed. Gurney 75-26 1978 £185

COOPER, ASTLEY   Principles and Practice of Surgery. Philadelphia,
1839. Clean tight. Rittenhouse 49-157 1976 $15

COOPER, C. H.   Memoir of Margaret, Countess of Richmond and
Derby. Cambridge, 1874. Orig. cloth, recased, octavo, good. Upcroft 10-271
1978 £10

COOPER, COURTNEY RYLEY   Action in Diamonds. 1942. First ed. Austin 82-
315 1978 $12.50

COOPER, COURTNEY RYLEY   Circus Day. 1931. Illus., first ed. Austin 82-
316 1978 $11

COOPER, COURNEY RYLEY   Here's to Crime. Boston, 1937. Biblo 251-289
1978 $10

COOPER, D.   Haig. 1935-36. Maps, photographs, 2 vols., with the slipcase. George's 635-821 1978 £7.50

COOPER, FRANCIS HODGES   Some Colonial History of Beaufort County, N.C. Chapel Hill, 1916. New cloth. Broadfoot 50-41 1978 $10

COOPER, HOWARD M.   Historical Sketch of Camden, N. J. Camden, 1909. Illus. MacManus 239-1252 1978 $17.50

COOPER, JAMES FENIMORE   Autobiography of a Pocket Handkerchief. Evanston, 1897. Some soil on binding. Nestler Rare 78-108 1978 $15

COOPER, JAMES FENIMORE   The Bravo. Philadelphia, 1839. New ed., 2 vols., 8vo., orig. bds., untrimmed. Morrill 241-92 1978 $15

COOPER, JAMES FENIMORE   The Deerslayer: or, the First War-Path. A Tale. Philadelphia, 1841. 2 vols., orig. cloth, paper labels, a bit rubbed, 1st ed., covers worn, somewhat foxed throughout, but very good, cloth fold. box. Mac-Manus 238-453 1978 $225

COOPER, JAMES FENIMORE   The Deerslayer: A Tale. 1841. 2nd. ed., 3 vols., half calf, dark brown labels, v.g. Jarndyce 16-405 1978 £20

COOPER, JAMES FENIMORE   The Deerslayer. New York, 1929. Full-page color plates by N.C. Wyeth, near mint, acetate dw. Bernard 5-68 1978 $30

COOPER, JAMES FENIMORE   A Descriptive Bibliography of the Writings of... New York, 1934. Orig. cloth, 1st ed., 1 of 500 copies. MacManus 238-894 1978 $50

COOPER, JAMES FENIMORE   Gleanings in Europe. New York, 1928. 1st of this ed. Biblo 251-433 1978 $15

COOPER, JAMES FENIMORE   The Heidenmauer; or, the Benedictines. A Legend of the Rhine. Philadelphia, 1832. 2 vols., orig. bds., printed paper labels, 1st ed., foxing throughout, cover worn, very good. MacManus 238-450 1978 $100

COOPER, JAMES FENIMORE   The History of the Navy of the United States of America. London, 1839. 2 vols., rebound, ports., 1st Eng. ed., fine. Mac-Manus 239-1742 1978 $50

COOPER, JAMES FENIMORE   Homeward Bound: or, the Chase. A Tale of the Sea. Philadelphia, 1838. 2 vols., orig. cloth, paper labels, 1st Amer. ed., covers a little worn, foxed, but good, fold. cloth box. MacManus 238-452 1978 $90

COOPER, JAMES FENIMORE   Jack O'Lantern, or The Privateer. 1845. 2nd. ed., frontis, contemp. 1/2 calf, gilt spine, lightly rubbed. Eaton 45-118 1978 £5

COOPER, JAMES FENIMORE   The Lake Gun. New York, 1932. Limited to 450 copies, good. Nestler Rare 78-109 1978 $15

COOPER, JAMES FENIMORE   The Last of the Mohicans; a Narrative of 1757. 1826. 1st. ed., 3 vols., half calf, marbled bds., corners little rubbed, good. Jarndyce 16-404 1978 £58

COOPER, JAMES FENIMORE   The Last of the Mohicans. Avon, n.d. Color illus. by Ed. A. Wilson, mint in slipcase. Bernard 5-69 1978 $15

COOPER, JAMES FENIMORE   Lionel Lincoln; or, the Leaguer of Boston. New York, 1825. 2 vols., orig. bds., 1st ed., inner hinges repaired, very clean. MacManus 238-449 1978 $85

COOPER, JAMES FENIMORE   Lionel Lincoln; or, the Leager of Boston. Paris, 1825. 1st. Continental ed., 3 vols., 12mo, orig. printed wrappers, uncut. Hannas 54-68 1978 £32

COOPER, JAMES FENIMORE   Lionel Lincoln. Philadelphia, 1827. Two vols., contemp. marbled bds., half calf, second ed. Wolfe 39-109 1978 $45

COOPER, JAMES FENIMORE   Mercedes of Castile: or, The Voyage to Cathay. Philadelphia, 1840. 2 vols., 1st ed., 1st state of cover labels, latter foxed, frayed, inked library number, cloth covers lightly faded and spotted, very good and firm. Victoria 34-180 1978 $40

COOPER, JAMES FENIMORE   New York, Being an Intro. to an Unpublished Manuscript...Entitled "The Towns of Manhattan." New York, 1930. 1st separate ed., 1 of 750 numbered copies, boxed, illus. Americanist 102-34 1978 $30

COOPER, JAMES FENIMORE   The Pathfinder; or, the Inland Sea... New York, 1854. 1 vol., rev'd., cloth, slight wear at bottom of spine. Hayman 72-155 1978 $8.50

COOPER, JAMES FENIMORE   The Pilot. New York, 1823. 2 vols., old lea., red label, sound & good, minimal foxing. Butterfield 21-145 1978 $150

COOPER, JAMES FENIMORE   The Pioneers, or the Sources of the Susquehanna; a Descriptive Tale. New York, 1823. 2 vols., old calf, rubbed, 1st ed., 1st state of 1st vol., 2nd state of vol. 2, good, foxing throughout. MacManus 238-448 1978 $100

COOPER, JAMES FENIMORE   The Prairie. Menasha: The Limited Editions Club, 1940. Sm. 4to., illus. by John Steuart Curry, orig. half-leather and pict. cloth, pub. bd. box, 1 of 1,500 copies, signed by illustrator, fine. MacManus 238-820 1978 $22.50

COOPER, JAMES FENIMORE   Sketches of Switzerland. Philadelphia, 1836. 2 vols., orig. cloth, paper labels, 1st ed., covers a bit faded and worn, but very good, bookplt. MacManus 238-451 1978 $75

COOPER, JAMES FENIMORE   The Two Admirals. Philadelphia, 1843. 12mo., 2 vols., 1st ed., rare, slight foxing, very fine to mint cond., scarce, prtd. terra cotta wr. Current Misc. 8-12 1978 $300

COOPER, JAMES FENIMORE   The Water Witch or the Skimmer of the Seas. Dresden, 1930. 3 vols., first ed., marbled paper bds., leather backstrips. Austin 82-317 1978 $3,950

COOPER, SUSAN FENIMORE   Rural Hours by a Lady. New York, 1851. Gold stamped green leather, 8vo., orig. cloth, colored plts. Book Chest 17-95 1978 $180

COOPER, M.   Grass. New York, 1925. 8vo, orig. cloth. Book Chest 17-487 1978 $8.50

COOPER, SAMUEL   A Dictionary of Practical Surgery. Philadelphia, 1816. Two vols. Rittenhouse 49-158 1976 $30

COOPER, SUSAN FENIMORE   Mount Vernon: a Letter to the Children of America. New York, 1859. 16mo., plts., green cloth, 1st ed., inscr'd by author, nice copy, brown-coated endpapers. Butterfield 21-146 1978 $20

COOPER, W. R.   An Archaic Dictionary: Biographical, Historical and Mythological. Bagster, 1876. Orig. cloth, 8vo. Howes 194-793 1978 £6.50

COOPERATIVE Achievement Tests. 1940. Complete set of all tests, bound in hard covered vol. Austin 80-880 1978 $27.50

COPE, GILBERT   Historic Homes and Instiutions and Genealogical and Personal Memoirs of Chester and Delaware Counties, Pa. New York, 1904. 2 vols., illus., 4to., rebound. MacManus 239-1425 1978 $95

COPE, GILBERT   Historic Homes and Institutions and Genealogical and Personal Memoirs of Chester and Delaware Counties, Pa. Illus. New York and Chicago, 1904. 2 vols., 4to., orig. 1/2 mor., edges rubbed, rebacked. Americanist 102-85 1978 $90

COPELAND, J. M.   Sir Toby's Lampoons and Laments. Toronto, 1932. Frontis. Hood 116-678 1978 $12.50

COPELAND, S.   A History of the Island of Madagascar... 1822. 8vo, half calf, folding map. Edwards 1012-312 1978 £120

COPEMAN, FRED   Reason in Conflict. London, (1948). Illus. Biblo 251-326 1978 $12.50

COPERNICUS, NICOLAUS   Astronomia Instraurata. Amsterdam, 1617. 4to., text diagrs., full antique calf, lib. stamp erased from margin of title, occas. light browning, but very good copy, 3rd ed. Norman 5-62 1978 $1,750

COPIES Or Extracts of Correspondence Relative to the Affairs of British North America. 1839. Sm. folio, half calf. Edwards 1012-417 1978 £95

COPLEY, FREDERICK S.   A Set of Alphabets of All the Various Hands of Modern Use. New York, (1870). Oblong 8vo., orig. cloth. Morrill 241-93 1978 $20

COPLEY, JOSIAH   Kansas and the Country Beyond on the Line of the Union Pacific Railway.... Philadelphia, 1867. Folding map, original printed wr., 1st ed. Ginsberg 14-284 1978 $125

COPP, ELBRIDGE J.   Reminiscences of the War of the Rebellion, 1861-1865. Nashua, 1911. Orig. cloth, 8vo., illus., 1st ed. Morrill 241-94 1978 $12.50

COPPARD, ALFRED EDGAR   Cherry Ripe, Poems. Monmouthshire, 1935. 8vo, two-tone cloth, leather back, printed in cherry-red, green and black on Barcham Green handmade paper, wood-engravings by Sylvia Marshall, 1 of 150 copies signed by author, fine. Duschnes 220-74 1978 $65

COPPARD, ALFRED EDGAR   Clorinda Walks in Heaven. (London), Golden Cockerel Press, 1922. 8vo, yellow boards and cloth, 1st binding, 1 of 1200 copies, fine. Duschnes 220-69 1978 $30

COPPARD, ALFRED EDGAR   Collected Poems. London, 1928. 8vo, blue cloth, uncut, ownership inscription on flyleaf, Fine, d.w., 1st ed. Desmarais 1-102 1978 $10

COPPARD, ALFRED EDGAR   Consequences. Boston, 1933. 8vo, cloth, d.j., frontis. by Eric Ravilious, some foxing, fine. Duschnes 220-73 1978 $10

COPPARD, ALFRED EDGAR   Count Stefan. Golden Cockerel, 1928. 12mo., marbled paper over bds., #351 of 600 numbered copies, illus. by Robert Gibbings. Battery Park 1-116 1978 $45

COPPARD, ALFRED EDGAR   Dunky Fitlow. London, 1933. Near mint in darkened d.w. Desmarais B-159 1978 $15

COPPARD, ALFRED EDGAR   Easter Day. (1931). Cloth-backed bds., very good, worn slipcase, first English ed. Bell Book 16-180 1978 £12.50

COPPARD, ALFRED EDGAR   Easter Day. (London, 1931). Quarto, boards, cloth back, author's signature, Ltd. ed., only ed., fine. Duschnes 220-72 1978 $30

COPPARD, ALFRED EDGAR   Emergency Exit. New York, 1934. 8vo, brown cloth, gilt stamped, minor foxing of edges, 1st Amer. ed., fine, no. 258 of 350 signed by Coppard. Desmarais 1-99 1978 $30

COPPARD, ALFRED EDGAR   Emergency Exit. New York, 1934. No. 68 of 350 copies, signed by the author, cloth, very good. Bell Book 16-181 1978 £17.50

COPPARD, ALFRED EDGAR   Fares Please! 1931. Fine, d.w., first English ed. Bell Book 16-182 1978 £10

COPPARD, ALFRED EDGAR   Fishmonger's Fiddle. London, 1925. 8vo, boards, cloth back, paper label, bookplate, uncut, Fine, d.w., 1st ed. Desmarais 1-103 1978 $12.50

COPPARD, ALFRED EDGAR   Fishmonger's Fiddle: Tales. New York, 1925. First U.S. ed., cloth-backed bds., very good. Bell Book 16-183 1978 £8.50

COPPARD, ALFRED EDGAR   Fishmonger's Fiddle. London, 1925. Bkplt., fine in darkened d.w. Desmarais B-162 1978 $12.50

COPPARD, ALFRED EDGAR   Hips & Haws. Berkshire, Golden Cockerel Press, 1922. 12 mo, boards, cloth back, d.j., 1 of 480 copies, 1st ed., fine. Duschnes 220-70 1978 $15

COPPARD, ALFRED EDGAR   The Hundredth Story. Golden Cockerel Press, 1931. 8vo, engrs., decor. bds., mor. back, fine, ltd. numbered copy. Quaritch 979-163 1978 $80

COPPARD, ALFRED EDGAR   The Man From Kilsheelan. London, 1930. 8vo, buckram, backstrip faded, woodcut by Robert Gibbings, 1 of 550 copies signed by author, 1st ed., fine. Duschnes 220-71 1978 $15

COPPARD, ALFRED EDGAR   Pelagea & Other Poems. Golden Cockerel, 1926. 8vo., pattern paper over bds., d.w., #185 of 425 numbered copies, prtd. & illus. by Robert Gibbings, very fine. Battery Park 1-114 1978 $75

COPPARD, ALFRED EDGAR   Pink Furniture. London, 1930. 8vo, full vellum dust-stained, uncut, boards warped, good, ltd. ed., 1st ed., no. 127 of 250 copies, signed by Coppard. Desmarias 1-100 1978 $20

COPPARD, ALFRED EDGAR   Ring the Bells of Heaven. White Owl Press, 1933. Bds., very good, worn d.w., first English ed. Bell Book 16-184 1978 £8.50

COPPARD, ALFRED EDGAR   Rummy. Golden Cockerel Press, 1932. 8vo., 1st ed., engrs., cloth, mor. back, fine, orig. glassine wrs., ltd. to 250 copies prtd. on handmade paper, signed by author & artist. Quaritch 979-164 1978 $110

COPPARD, ALFRED EDGAR   Rummy: that noble game expounded in prose, poetry, diagram and engraving. Golden Cockerel Press, 1932. Very good, one of 1000 copies, first English ed. Bell Book 16-185 1978 £6.50

COPPARD, ALFRED EDGAR   Silver Circus. London, 1928. 8vo, silver boards and cloth back, paper label, uncut, unopened, fine, d.w., 1st ed. Desmarais 1-101 1978 $10

COPPARD, ALFRED EDGAR   Silver Circus: tales. 1928. No. 19 of 125 copies numbered & signed by the author, full vellum, t.e.g., leather label, near fine, d.w., first English ed. Bell Book 16-186 1978 £32.50

COPPARD, ALFRED EDGAR   Silver Circus. London, 1928. Nice in chipped d.w. Desmarais B-160 1978 $10

COPPEE, CAPT. HENRY   Field Manual of Courts-Martial. Phila., 1863. Bell Wiley's copy. Broadfoot's 44-689 1978 $26.00

COPPENS, CHARLES   A Brief Text-Book of Logic and Mental Philosophy. 1891. Austin 80-881 1978 $10

COPPEY, HYPOLITE.   Monsieur de Raousset en Sonore. Mexico, 1855. Original printed wr., rebacked, laid in half morocco slipcase. Ginsberg 14-7 1978 $375

COQUEREL, A.   Rembrandt et l'Individualisme dans l'Art. Paris, 1869. 8vo., orig. covers. Van der Peet H-64-19 1978 Dfl 40

COQUIOT, GUSTAVE   Suite Provinciale. Paris, 1927. Sm. 4to., uncut, orig. wr., slipcase, ltd. ed., only 550 numbered copies, copy on valin de Rives paper, illus. with lg. pen & ink drwgs. by Marc Chagall. Goldschmidt 110-11 1978 $160

CORASII, IOANNES   Tolosatis Iureconsulti clarissimi, in titulum FF. de seruitutib. Leyden, 1548. 1st ed., folio, full contemporary blind-stamped calf, rebacked, red morocco spine label, gilt, ties lacking, exceedingly rare. Bennett 20-51 1978 $250

CORBET, JOHN   An Historicall Relation of the Military Government of Gloucester. 1645. First ed., sm. 4to., half sprinkled calf. F. Edwards 1013-270 1978 £90

CORBET, RICHARD   Poems. 1672. 3rd. ed., corrected & enlarged, sm. 12mo, publisher's woodcut device on title, plain calf, paper somewhat browned. Hannas 54-69 1978 £65

CORBETT, E. A.   McQueen of Edmonton. Toronto, 1934. Illus. Hood's 115-246 1978 $10

CORBETT, JULIAN STAFFORD   Drake and the Tudor Navy. 1898. First ed., frontispieces, plts., illus., 2 vols., 8vo., orig. cloth, largely unopened. F. Edwards 1013-46 1978 £20

CORBETT, JULIAN STAFFORD   Drake and the Tudor Navy. London, 1898. 2 vols., illus., 8vo., 1st ed. Morrill 239-352 1978 $25

CORBETT, JULIAN STAFFORD   Drake and the Tudor Navy. 1917. Illus., 2 vols., cr. 8vo. George's 635-808 1978 £10.50

CORBETT, JULIAN STAFFORD   England in the Mediterranean, A Study of the Rise and Influence of British Power Within the Straits 1603-1713. 1904. 2 vols., folding map, octavo, good. Upcroft 10-272 1978 £25

CORBETT, JULIAN STAFFORD   Official History of the Great War. 1920-31. Maps, 5 vols. in 9, 8vo., orig. cloth. F. Edwards 1013-47 1978 £150

CORBIN, HORACE HARLAN   The Perception of Grouping and Apparent Movement in Visual Depth. Paper. Austin 80-882 1978 $10

CORBIN, JOHN   The Return of the Middle Class. 1922. Austin 80-522 1978 $10

CORBIN, JOHN   School Boy Life in England. An American View. New York, 1898. Ownership inscription, very fine in torn d.w. Desmarais B-163 1978 $10

CORBITT, DAVID LEROY   The Formation of North Carolina Counties 1663-1943. Raleigh, 1950. Broadfoot 50-42 1978 $12

CORBY, W.   Memoirs of Chaplain Life. Notre Dame, 1894. Erasure on front f/l, Bell Wiley's copy. Broadfoot's 44-560 1978 $25

CORDAEUS, MAURICIUS   Tomus III Gynaeciorum, in Quo Hippocratis Coi, Medicorum Principis, Liber De Morbis Mulierum Explicatur. Basle, 1586. 4to., vellum, 3rd vol. Salloch 345-52 1978 $75

CORDASCO, FRANCESCO   A Bibliography of Robert Watt, M. D., Author of the Bibliotheca Britannica. New York, 1950. Portr., 8vo., ed. ltd. to 250 copies. Morrill 239-53 1978 $7.50

CORDELL, EUGENE F.   The Medical Annals of Maryland, 1799-1899... Baltimore, 1903. 1st ed., thick 8vo., illus., orig. cloth, fine. MacManus 239-1836 1978 $35

CORDELL, RICHARD A.   W. Somerset Maugham. London, 1937. First ed., orig. binding, nice. Rota 211-379 1978 £6

CORDIER, ALBERT HAWES   A Wyoming Big Game Hunt. [Kansas City], 1907. Orig. pr. pict. wr., tied, 1st ed. Ginsberg 14-1073 1978 $125

CORDIER, FRANCOIS SIMON   Les Champignons de la France. Paris, 1870. 4to., 1/2 green hardgrain mor., illus. with chromolithos. by A. D. Cordier, glossary, bibliography, index, clean, well preserved. Goldschmidt 110-14 1978 $185

CORDIER, MATHURIN   Corderii Colloquiorum Centuria Selecta;.... Boston, 1724. 1st Amer. ed., original full calf over oak, missing front fly-leaf, rear fly-leaf torn, light browning, remarkably fine, rare. Victoria 34-181 1978 $350

CORELLI, MARIE   "Temporal Power." A Novel. New York, 1902. 1st ed., bind. slightly soiled, good. Biblo BL781-911 1978 $9

COREY, ALBERT B.   The Crisis of 1830-1842 in Canadian-American Relations. New Haven, Toronto, London, 1941. 1st ed. Hood 117-561 1978 $45

COREY, D. P.   History of Malden, Mass. Malden, 1899. Illus., uncut, lib. marks, fine. MacManus 239-1035 1978 $35

COREY, LEWIS   The House of Morgan. 1930. Illus. with photos. Austin 80-523 1978 $10

CORIAT, ISADOR H.   The Meaning of Dreams. 1915. Austin 80-884 1978 $10

CORIAT, ISADOR H.   What is Psychoanalysis? 1917. Austin 80-885 1978 $10

CORIOLIS, G. G. DE   Du Calcul de l'Effet des Machines, ou considerations sur l'emploi des moteurs et sur leur evaluation. Paris, 1829. 4to., old qtr. calf, rubbed, first ed. Gurney 75-28 1978 £65

CORK AND ORRERY, JOHN BOYLE, 5th EARL OF   Remarks on the Life and Writings of Dr. Jonathan Swift. 1752. 8vo., cont. calf gilt, fine, first London ed. P.M. Hill 142-221 1978 £38

CORKE, HELEN   Lawrence and Apocalypse. London, (1933). 12mo., cloth, 1st ed., lower hinge chipped. J.S. Lawrence 38-L132 1978 $20

CORLE, EDWIN   Desert Country. New York, (1941). Biblo 247-198 1978 $15

CORLE, EDWIN   Listen, Bright Angel. New York, 1946. Cloth, 1st ed. Ginsberg 14-8 1978 $7.50

CORLE, EDWIN   People on the Earth. Santa Barbara and New York, (1950). Ltd. to 1,500 copies, very good, d.w. Biblo BL781-910 1978 $10

CORNARO, LEWIS   Discourses on a Sober and Temperate Life. 1798. Sm. 8vo., woodcuts, contemp. tree calf, rebacked. Quaritch 979-32 1978 $55

CORNELIO, VITTORIO   Osservazioni Odontalgiche Sulle Cause Della Carie Con un Appendice Sulla Formazione Della Doppia Serie Dei Denti Umani e Sulla Origine Della Destruzione Della Radice Dei Denti Lattei. Torino, 1813. Copperplts., 8vo., contemp. half calf, 1st ed., very scarce, wormholes, some rather large. Offenbacher 30-27 1978 $275

CORNEILLE, PIERRE ET THOMAS   Chefs-D'Oeuvre... Paris, 1828. Frontis., eng. & title vignette, browned, sig. of Henry Halford Vaughan, contemp. 1/2 green morocco, worn. Eaton 45-119 1978 £5

CORNELIUS, CHARLES OVER   Early American Furniture. New York, (1926). 1st ed., illus., fine. MacManus 239-650 1978 $17.50

CORNELIUS, CHARLES OVER   Early American Furniture. New York, 1926. Illus. Baldwins' 51-47 1978 $12.50

CORNELL, ETHEL L.   The Work of the School Psychologist. 1942. Pamphlet. Austin 80-886 1978 $8.50

CORNFORD, FRANCES   Travelling Home, and other poems. Cresset Press, 1948. Drawings, very good, d.w., first English ed. Bell Book 16-188 1978 £6.50

THE CORNHILL Magazine. 1860-69. Vols. 1-20, plts., illus., contemp. half green calf, 8vo. Howes 194-757 1978 £85

CORNISH, C.   Animal Artisans and Other Studies of Birds and Beasts. London, 1907. Illus., 8vo., orig. cloth. Book Chest 17-97 1978 $20

CORNWALL, BARRY   A Memoir of Charles Lamb. 1866. 1st. ed., frontis, orig. brown cloth, little rubbed, lib. label inside front cover. Jarndyce 16-805 1978 £12.50

CORNWALL, BRUCE   Life Sketches of Pierre Barlow Cornwall. San Francisco, 1906. Half morocco, author's copy with his bookplate. Ginsberg 14-285 1978 $125

CORNWALLIS, CHARLES EARL   Answer to Sir Henry Clinton's Narrative of the Campaign in 1781 in North America. Philadelphia, 1866. Fine, ltd. to 250 copies. MacManus 239-561 1978 $45

CORNWALLIS, CHARLES EARL   An Answer to that Part of the Narrative of Lieut.-Gen. Sir Henry Clinton Which Relates to the Conduct of Lieut.-Gen. Earl Cornwallis... 1783. 1st. ed., modern bds., name on title, orig. cloth, 8vo. Edwards 1012-483 1978 £85

CORNWALLIS-WEST, GEORGE   Fortune's Favourites. 1933. 1st. ed., 8vo, orig. green cloth, fine copy, inscribed by author. Sawyer 299-140 1978 £17.50

CORONATION of the Empress Elizabeth I. St. Petersburg, 1744. Orig. ed., folio, Russian test throughout, vignettes and plates by Ivan Sokolov, Grigory Kachalov and C. A. Wortmann, contemp. Russian brown mor., gilt spine in compart., gilt edges. Quaritch 978-135 1978 $3,950

CORONELLI, VINCENZO   Isola di Rodi Geografica-Storica, Antica, e Moderna, Coll'Altre Adiacenti Gia.... Venezia, 1688. 8vo., orig. soft bds., plts., nice, first ed. King 7-30 1978 £100

CORP, H.   The Antidote to the Miseries of Human Life, in the History of the Widow Placid, and her Daughter Rachel. 1808. Fcap. 8vo., orig. bds. George's 635-1279 1978 £6

CORPUS Christi: A Guide. Corpus Christi, 1942. Illus. Jenkins 116-1012 1978 $13.50

CORPUS Vasorum Antiquorum. Baltimore, 1934. Folio, plt. Allen 234-242 1978 $20

CORRESPONDENCE Between His Majesty's Government and the Government of New Granada... 1837. Sm. folio, modern blue cloth. Edwards 1012-636 1978 £45

CORRESPONDENCE Relative to Entrance into Canton, 1850-1855. 1857. Sm. folio, sewn as issued. Edwards 1012-183 1978 £20

CORRESPONDENCE Relative to the Negotiation of the Question of Disputed Right to the Oregon Territory... 1846. Sm. folio, binder's cloth. Edwards 1012-405 1978 £150

CORRESPONDENCE Respecting Sir Bartle Frere's Mission to the East Coast of Africa, 1872-73. 1873. Folding map, 8vo, binders' cloth. Edwards 1012-282 1978 £60

CORSI, EDWARD   In the Shadow of Liberty. 1935. Illus., orig. ed., ex-lib. Austin 79-163 1978 $8.50

CORTI, EGON CAESAR CONTE   Das Haus Rothschild in der Zeit Seiner Blute, 1830-1871. Leipzig, 1928. First ed., illus. Biblo 247-672 1978 $17.50

CORTISSOZ, ROYAL   Augustus Saint-Gaudens. Boston, 1907. Illus., 4to., covers dampstained, 1st ed. Morrill 241-96 1978 $12.50

CORVISART, JEAN NICOLAS
Please turn to
CORVISART DES MARETS, JEAN NICOLAS

CORVISART DES MARETS, JEAN NICOLAS   Essai sur les maladies et les lesions organiques du coeur et des gros vaisseaux. Paris, 1806. 1st ed., contemp. half calf, marbled bds., gilt back, red and green mor. labels. Gilhofer 75-28 1978 SFr 1,200

CORVO, FREDERICK BARON PSEUD.
Please turn to
ROLFE, FREDERICK WILLIAM

CORWIN, EDWARD S.   The Constitution and What It Means Today. Princeton, 1920. 12mo., 1st ed. Biblo 251-327 1978 $9.50

CORWOOD, J. O.   Karzan, the Wolf Dog. New York, (1941). Hood 116-465 1978 $12.50

CORY, WILLIAM JOHNSON   Ionica. 1858. 1st. ed., sm. 8vo, orig. green cloth, spine rubbed & faded, covers slightly stained, transcript in author's hand on back fly-leaf, fair copy, rare. Sawyer 299-i18 1978 £95

COS, J. CHARLES   The Irish Church. Chesterfield, (1868). 8vo., unbound. P. M. Hill 142-82 1978 £5

COSSINS, GEORGE   A Boer ot To-Day. London, 1900. Cr. 8vo, orig. cloth, few pages roughly opened, covers dull. K Books 239-105 1978 £5

COSSLEY-BATT, JILL L.   The Last of the California Rangers. New York, 1928. Illus., d.j., 1st ed. MacManus 239-1902 1978 $12.50

COSTAIN, A. J.   Lord Roberts. London, (1925). Cr. 8vo, pictorial cloth. K Books 239-106 1978 £5

COSTAIN, T. B.   The Black Rose. Garden City, 1945. 1st ed. Hood 116-462 1978 $10

COSTANSO, MIGUEL   The Spanish Occupation of California:... San Francisco, 1934. Illus., folding map, orig. boards, ltd. to 550 copies. Ginsberg 14-94 1978 $100

COSTE, JEAN-FRANCOIS   Oratio Habita in Capitolio Guliemopolitano in Comitiis Universitatis Virginiae, die XII Junii M.DCC.LXXXII. Lugduni Batavorum, 1783. 8vo., stitched, unopened in cloth fldr., 1st ed., partly waterstained. Offenbacher 30-28 1978 $250

COSTELLO, LOUISA STUART   Memoirs of Eminent Englishwomen. 1844. 1st. ed., 2 vols., frontis, foxed, plts., pink cloth, little marked. Jarndyce 16-406 1978 £8.50

COSTELLO, LOUISA STUART   Venice and the Venetians. London, 1851. 8vo., cloth, blind stamped sides, a.e.g., plts. King 7-346 1978 £15

THE COSTUME of Great Britain. London, 1804. Hand-colored plts., 3rd state, 1st ed., folio, mild waterstaining, contemp. red straight-grained mor., gilt decor. on bds. & spine, fine. Current Misc. 8-13 1978 $950

COSTUME of the Lower Order in Paris. (London, c.1810-1819). 12mo, plates, superb full-leather binding by R. Wallis, with gilt rules, ornaments, ornatley dec. gilt spine with raised bands, apparently the only complete copy. Victoria 34-183 1978 $500

COSTUMES Des Dames Parisiennes, ou l'Ami de la Mode. Paris, (1803). Plts., 32mo., full orig. green mor., rare. Argosy Special-27 1978 $150

COT, PIERRE   Triumph of Reason. 1944. Austin 80-69 1978 $12.50

COTE, N. O.   Political Appointments, Parliaments, and the Judicial Bench in the Dominion of Canada, 1896 to 1917. Ottawa, 1917. Ex-lib., some wear. Hood 116-21 1978 $17.50

COTES, ROGER   Harmonia Mensurarum.... Cambridge, 1722. 4to., engrav. plt., very nice, contemp. calf, gilt borders, repaired and rebacked, new leather label. Quaritch 977-143 1978 $200

COTES, ROGER   Hydrostatical and Pneumatical Lectures. London, 1738. With appendix, 8vo., ads, fldg. plts., contemp. calf, gilt, joints cracked, occas. very light foxing, but fine copy, 1st ed. Norman 5-*38 1978 $375

COTES, ROGER   Hydrostatical and Pneumatical Lectures by.... London, 1738. 1st ed., octavo, folding plates, full contemporary paneled calf, rebacked, bookplate, former owner's name and date on title. Bennett 20-52 1978 $275

COTHREN, WILLIAM   History of Ancient Woodbury, Conn., from the First Indian Deed in 1659 to 1854... Waterbury, 1854. 3 vols., illus., ports., rebound, lib. marks, very good. MacManus 239-960 1978 $125

COTMAN, JOHN SELL   Engravings of Sepulchral Brasses in Norfolk and Suffolk... 1839. 2 vols., folio, coloured frontis., tinted plts., half mor. Quaritch 983-7 1978 $900

COTTE, CHARLES   A History of Ancient Europe from the Earliest Times to the Subversion of the Western Empire. 1815. First ed., 3 vols., contemp. calf, one joint cracked, 8vo. Howes 194-223 1978 £18

COTTEAU, E.   Un Touriste dans l'Extreme-Orient: Japon, Chine, Indochine et Tonkin (1881-1882). Paris, 1884. Half calf, maps, plts., illus., binding rubbed, 8vo. Van der Peet 127-64 1978 Dfl 45

COTTEN, SALLIE SOUTHALL   The White Doe; or, the Legend of Virginia Dare. Philadelphia, 1901. Illus., lacks 1 flyleaf. Broadfoot 50-43 1978 $10

COTTERELL, HOWARD HERSCHEL   National Types of Old Pewter. Boston, 1925. 1st Amer. ed., quarto, illus., fine. Victoria 34-182 1978 $35

COTTERELL, HOWARD HERSCHEL   Pewter Down the Ages From Mediaeval Times to the Present Day With Notes on Evolution. Boston & New York, (1932). 159 plts. Baldwins' 51-48 1978 $55

COTTERILL, H. B.   Ancient Greece. 1913. Plt. Allen 234-246 1978 $7.50

COTTIER, ELIE   L'Histoire D'Un Vieux Metier. 8vo., wr., illus. Battery Park 1-446 1978 $150

COTTIN, SOPHIE RISTAUDE DE   Elizabeth; or, the Exiles of Siberia: A Tale Founded Upon Facts. Windsor, 1815. Sq. 24mo., marbled paper over oak, gilt lettered leather spine, gauffered edges, some rubbing of cover paper and page darkening. Victoria 34-184 1978 $40

COTTIN, SOPHIE RISTAUDE DE   Elizabeth, or the Exiles of Siberia. London, n.d. (early 1800's). Frontis. & engraved plates hand-colored, disbound. Greene 78-169 1978 $35

COTTLE, JOSEPH 1770-1853   Poems, Containing John the Baptist. Bristol, 1795. First ed., frontis., sm. 8vo., orig. half mor., very good, rare. Howes 194-1432 1978 £45

COTTMAN, GEORGE S.   Centennial History and Handbook of Indiana.... Indianapolis, 1915. Clean, orig. binding. Hayman 71-342 1978 $20

COTTON, CHARLES   The Genuine Poetical Works of... 1765. 5th ed., corrected, illus., 9 plts., 1 fldg., contemp. calf, gilt spine, worn. Eaton 45-120 1978 £9

COTTON, CHARLES   Genuine Poetical Works. 1771. 6th. ed., 8 plts., one fldg., full modern calf. Eaton 45-121 1978 £10

COTTON, CHARLES   Poems from the Works of Charles Cotton. 1922. Decorations by Lovat Fraser, cloth-backed bds., covers rubbed & soiled, good, first English ed. Bell Book 17-586 1978 £6.50

COTTON, H.   Typographical Gazetteer. Oxford, 1831-66. 2nd ed., 2 vols., vol. 1 in binder's cloth, vol. 2 in orig. cloth, spine soiled, hinges sprung, 8vo. George's 635-1198 1978 £25

COTTON, HENRY A.   The Defective Delinquent and Insane. Princeton University Press, 1921. 1st ed. in frayed dust jacket. Austin 80-887 1978 $27.50

COTTON, JESSIE CHILD   Selected Poems. New York, 1940. 1st ed., author's signed pres. Biblo BL781-912 1978 $10

COTTON, JOHN   First Edition of the First Anglo-American Law Code. N.P., 1641. 1st ed., sm. 4 to., sound, modern mor., many side-notes cut into with loss of 1 or 2 letters, catchwords and signatures also cut into. Quaritch Summer, 1978-8 1978 $1,700

COTTON, JOHN   A Practical Commentary, or An Exposition With Observations, Reasons and Uses Upon the First Epistle General of John. 1656. Folio, recent half crimson morocco, gilt over marbled bds., marginal repair to few leaves, nice copy. Fenning 32-77 1978 £48

THE COTTON Colours of the Cassella Color Company, New York, 182 and 184 Front Street. New York, 1913. 2nd ed., 8vo., orig. cloth. Morrill 241-571 1978 $20

COTUGNO, DOMENICO   De aquaeductibus auris humanae internae dissertatio. Naples, 1761. Very rare 1st ed., 8vo, engraved folding plates, contemp. half-calf, lightly rubbed. Gilhofer 75-29 1978 SFr 1,700

COUCH, JONATHAN   A History of the Fishes of the British Islands. London, 1868. 1st. ed., coloured plts., 4 vols., roy. 8vo, 1 vol. little faded. Traylen 88-557 1978 £250

COUES, E.   Avifauna Columbiana:.... 1883. Maps, chipped spine, uncolored map lacking small piece and repaired, 8vo, orig. cloth, 2nd ed., entirely rewritten. Book Chest 17-100 1978 $55

COUES, E. Field Ornithology Comprising a Manual of Instruction for Procuring, Preparing & Preserving birds and a Check List of North American Birds. Salem, 1874. Illus, 8vo, orig. cloth. Book Chest 17-99 1978 $35

COUGHLIN, CHARLES E. An Answer to Father Coughlin's Antics. 1940. Paper. Austin 79-164 1978 $8.50

COUGHLIN, CHARLES E. By the Sweat of Thy Brow. Oct. 1930-Feb. 1931. Paper. Austin 79-165 1978 $8.50

COUGHLIN, CHARLES E. Eight Lectures on Labor, Capital, and Justice. 1934. Paper. Austin 79-166 1978 $8.50

COUGHLIN, CHARLES E. Father Coughlin's Radio Sermons. 1931. Cloth. Austin 79-167 1978 $10

COUGHLIN, CHARLES E. Money. 1936. Paper. Austin 79-168 1978 $8.50

COUGHLIN, CHARLES E. A Series of Lectures on Social Justice. 1935. Paper. Austin 79-169 1978 $10

COUILLARD-DESPRES, A. Charles de Saint-Etienne de la Tour... St. Hyacinthe, (1932). Hood's 115-334 1978 $35

COULSON, JOHN Clevedon: A Poem. Clevedon, 1870. Orig. limp purple cloth wrappers, good. Jarndyce 16-407 1978 £9.50

COULTAS, HARLAND The Home Naturalist; With Practical Instructions For Collecting, Arranging and Preserving Natural Objects... (1877). Frontis, illus., 8vo, orig. red cloth, gilt, edges gilt, nice copy. Fenning 32-78 1978 £14

COULTER, E. MERTON Effects of Secession Upon the Commerce of the Mississippi Valley. Miss., 1916. Wrs., pres. from author to Bell Wiley, Bell Wiley's copy. Broadfoot's 44-93 1978 $7

COULTER, E. MERTON Planter's Wants in the Days of the Confederacy. Savannah, 1928. Wrs., pres. copy from author to Bell Wiley, reprint. Broadfoot's 44-95 1978 $10

COULTER, J. M. Morphology of Gymnosperms. London, 1917. Illus., roy. 8vo. Troylen 88-558 1978 £9

COULTER, J. Adventures on the Western Coast of South America and The Interior of California... 1847. 2 vols., sm. 8vo, orig. cloth, covers faded. Edwards 1012-12 1978 £85

COULTER, JOHN The Complete Story of the Galveston Horror. N.P., (1900). Orig. binding, clean. Hayman 71-725 1978 $8.50

COULTER, JOHN M. Evolution, Heredity and Eugenics. 1916. Illus. Austin 80-889 1978 $10

COULTER, M. Story of the Plant Kingdom. Illinois, 1935. 8vo, orig. cloth. Book Chest 17-494 1978 $10

COULTON, G. G. Life in the Middle Ages. 1931. Plts., 4 vols. Allen 234-1186 1978 $15

COULTON, G. G. The Medieval Scene; an informal introduction to the Middle Ages. Cambridge, 1930. Plts., illus., 8vo. Upcroft 12-83 1978 £4.50

COULTON, G. G. The Medieval Village. Cambridge, 1931. Plts., illus., 8vo. Upcroft 12-84 1978 £10

COULTON, G. G. Medieval Panorama, the English Scene from Conquest to Reformation. Cambridge, 1943. Plts., text illus., 8vo. George's 635-611 1978 £5

COULTON, G. G. Social Life in Britain from the Conquest to the Reformation. Cambridge, 1919. Illus., covers marked, 8vo. George's 635-612 1978 £7.50

THE COUNTRIES of Europe, and the Manners and Customs of its Various Nations. London, n.d. 2nd ed., sq. 12mo, plates, original full leather with gilt rules, modest rubbing, illus., very good. Victoria 34-185 1978 $125

A COUNTRY Holiday. London, c.1875. Illus. by Fred Grey, color plates, spine sewing, spine chips. Victoria 34-186 1978 $60

COUPER, WILLIAM Claudius Crozet, Soldier-Scholar-Educator-Engineer (1789-1864). Charlottesville, 1936. Wrs., Bell Wiley's copy. Broadfoot's 44-96 1978 $14

COURIER, P. L. Oeuvres. Paris, 1876. 3 vols., sm. cr. 8vo, blind-stamp on titles, red morocco, edges & joints very slightly rubbed. Eaton 45-122 1978 £10

COURIER De L'Art. Paris, 1883. 4to., cloth. Van der Peet H-64-118 1978 Dfl 50

COURMOS, JOHN Autobiography. 1935. Illus. Austin 79-175 1978 $12.50

COURNOS, JOHN Short Stories out of Soviet Russia. New York, 1929. Very nice, torn d.w., first ed., orig. binding. Rota 211-80 1978 £12.50

COURSEY, O. W. Beautiful Black Hills. Mitchell, (1926). Cloth, fine bright copy of 1st (and only?) ed. Hayman 73-136 1978 $17.50

COURSEY, O. W. "Wild Bill", James Butler Hickok. Mitchell, (1924). Cloth, little rubbed, very scarce. Hayman 72-156 1978 $35

COURT, W. H. B. The Rise of the Midland Industries, 1600-1838. 1938. 8vo. George's 635-307 1978 £6

COURT and City Register, or, Gentleman's Complete Annual Calendar for 1781. 1781. Fcap. 8vo., old sheep, worn. George's 635-613 1978 £5

THE COURT of Adultery: A Vision. 1778. Fourth ed., 4to., new bds., half-title. P. M. Hill 142-85 1978 £18

COURTELINE, G. Oeuvres. Paris, 1963. 2 vols., 8vo., cloth, slipcases, illus. by Dignimont. Van der Peet H-64-419 1978 Dfl 200

COURTIN, ANTOINE DE The Rules of Civility; or, The Maxims of Genteel Behaviour, as they are Practis'd and Observ'd by Persons of Quality. 1703. 1st. ed. of this translation, 12mo, initial & final blank leaves, contemp. panelled sheep. Hannas 54-70 1978 £32

COURTIVRON, GASPARD LE COMPASSEUR DE CREQUI-MONTFORT, MARQUIS DE Traite d'Optique ou l'on Donne la Theorie de la Lumiere Dans le Systeme Newtonien, Avec de Nouvelles Solutions des Principaux Problemes de Dioptrique & de Catoptrique. Paris, 1752. Fldg. copperplts., woodcut diagrams, 4to., contemp. calf, back gilt, 1st ed. Offenbacher 30-108 1978 $175

COURTY, A. Diseases of the Uterus, Ovaries and Fallopian Tubes. Philadelphia, 1883. Translated from third ed. Rittenhouse 49-161 1976 $15

COUSENS, HENRY The Antiquities of Sind. Calcutta, 1929. Plts., several coloured, roy. 4to., qtr. leather gilt. K Books 244-78 1978 £35

COUSIN, VICTOR Fragmens Philosophiques. Paris, 1826. 8vo., bds., 1st ed. Salloch 348-40 1978 $45

COUSINS, FRANK The Colonial Architecture of Salem. Boston, 1919. Illus., ltd. to 1,200 copies, t.e.g. MacManus 239-651 1978 $35

COUSTAU, PIERRE Petri Costalii Pegma, Cum narrationibus philosophicis. Lyons, 1555. 8vo, Italic and Roman letter, woocut emblems, orig. limp vellum, 1st ed. Quaritch 978-39 1978 $1,250

COUTANT, C. G. The History of Wyoming. Laramie, 1899. 1 page loose, scarce, map and plts. Biblo 248-233 1978 $125

COUTO, JOSE FERRER DE Cuestiones De Mejico, Venezuela Y America En General:.... Madrid, 1861. Full mottled calf. Jenkins 116-255 1978 $60

COUTS, CAVE J. From San Diego to Colorado in 1849. Los Angeles, 1932. Illus., maps, original boards, cloth spine, 1st ed. Ginsberg 14-287 1978 $50

COVELLO, LEONARD A High School and Its Immigrant Community. 1936. Austin 79-176 1978 $7.50

COVENT Garden Drollery. 1927. Ltd. ed. of 575 copies, octavo, good. Upcroft 10-37 1978 £10

COVENT Garden Drollery. 1928. Ltd. ed. of 400 copies, octavo, good. Upcroft 10-38 1978 £10

COVENANTERS-Presbyterus Triall; or the Occasion and Motives of Conversion to the Catholic Faith of a Person of Quality in Scotland... Paris, 1657. Old calf, edges gilt, preface signed F.W.S. Baldwins' 51-340 1978 $50

COVINGTON, D. B. The Argus Book Shop. Frontis., 1 of 350 signed & numbered copies, cloth, very fine. Battery Park 1-34 1978 $35

COW, JOHN Remarks on the Manner of Fitting Boars for Ships of War and Transport... London, 1829. 12mo., first ed., new bds., plts. Paine 78-17 1978 $22.50

COWAN, B. O. Record of Shorthorn Prize Winners. Chicago, (1919). Cloth, illus., 1st ed., very good copy from the John C. Burns Collection & autographed by him, scarce. Dykes 34-107 1978 $22.50

COWAN, LUCY M. D. Revolutionary Soldiers of Warren County, Pa. New York, 1916. Illus., ltd. to 300 copies, scarce. MacManus 239-1426 1978 $32.50

COWAN, ROBERT ERNEST A Bibliography of the History of California. 1510-1930. San Francisco, 1933. 2 vols., lg. 8vo., buckram. MacManus 238-895 1978 $75

COWARD, NOEL Present Indicative. 1937. Plts., very good, worn d.w., first English ed. Bell Book 16-197 1978 $7.50

COWARD, NOEL Private Lives. 1930. Covers faded, else good, first English ed. Bell Book 16-198 1978 $6.50

COWARD, NOEL Terribly Intimate Portraits. N.Y., (1922). 1st ed., 8 vo., illus., cloth over bds., very good. Houle 10-75 1978 $37.50

COWARD, NOEL The Vortex: A Play in Three Acts. 1925. First ed., cr. 8vo., fine, d.w., orig. cloth. Howes 194-758 1978 £15

COWARD, NOEL The Vortex. 1925. Covers somewhat soiled, good, first English ed. Bell Book 16-199 1978 $8.50

COWDRY, E. V. Problems of Aging. 1939. Illus., ex-lib., worn. Austin 80-890 1978 $17.50

COWELL, RUSSELL H. The Life, Speeches, and Public Services of James A. Garfield... Boston, 1881. 1/2 leather, minor wear. Hayman 71-165 1978 $8.50

COWLEY, ABRAHAM Poemata Latina. London, 1668. 1st. collected ed., engraved portrait by Faithorne, 8vo, contemp. calf, spine little defective. Traylen 88-213 1978 £65

COWLEY, ABRAHAM The Works. 1668. First collected ed., engrav. portrait, 5 parts in 1 vol., folio, 19th cent. half calf. Howes 194-30 1978 £35

COWLEY, ABRAHAM The Works. 1688-89. Folio, frontis, portrait, sound 19th. century calf, good. Jarndyce 16-11 1978 £32

COWLEY, ABRAHAM The Workes... 9th edition. 1700. Folio, frontis, portrait, orig. calf, black label, very good. Jarndyce 16-12 1978 £45

COWLEY, ABRAHAM The Works of... 1700. 9th. ed., folio, frontis, eng. full calf, blind-lines, raised bands, Zaehnsdorf binding. Eaton 45-123 1978 £50

COWLEY, HANNAH A School for Greybeards; or, The Mourning Bride: A Comedy. Dublin, 1787. 1st. Irish ed., 12mo, wrapper, fine. Fenning 32-79 1978 £9.50

COWLEY, MALCOLM Exile's Return. 1934. First ed., tattered d.j. Austin 82-1161 1978 $20

COWLEY, MALCOLM Exile's Return. New York, (1934). 1st ed. Biblo 251-434 1978 $27.50

COWLEY, W. H. Personnel...Bibliographical Index. 1932. Austin 80-891 1978 $37.50

COWPER, WILLIAM Cowper, Illustrated by a Series of Views, in, or near, the Park of Weston-Underwood, Bucks. 1803. Plts., 8vo., contemp. half calf, spine worn, joints cracked. Howes 194-230 1978 £12.50

COWPER, WILLIAM Cowper, Illustrated by a Series of Views, In, or Near, The Park of Weston-Underwood, Bucks. 1810. 1st. ed., engraved title, plts., uncut, orig. blue printed bd., cream paper spine defective at base. Jarndyce 16-408 1978 £24

COWPER, WILLIAM Memoir of the Early Life of William Cowper. Philadelphia, 1816. 12mo., orig. bds., untrimmed, fr. cover loose, back hinge weak, 1st Amer. ed. Morrill 239-354 1978 $17.50

COWPER, WILLIAM Olney Hymns, in Three Books. 1779. 3 parts in 1 vol., thk. 12mo., contemp. calf, rebacked and repaired, very fair, first ed. Howes 194-231 1978 £90

COWPER, WILLIAM Poems, by... 1788. 4th ed., 2 vols., vignette on t.p. of vol. 2, sign. of Lord M. Walsingham, mottled calf, joints & edges rubbed. Eaton 45-125 1978 £35

COWPER, WILLIAM Poems. 1798. New ed., plts., 2 vols., sm. 8vo., orig. bds., entirely uncut, backs worn, joints cracked, first illus. ed. Howes 194-227 1978 £15

COWPER, WILLIAM Poems. 1806. New ed., plts., 2 vols., contemp. calf, first ed. to contain Fuseli illus. Howes 194-228 1978 £25

COWPER, WILLIAM Poems. Edinburgh, 1818. 2 vols., frontis., 12mo., full calf. K Books 244-79 1978 £10

COWPER, WILLIAM Poems. 1820. 2 vols., frontis, vignette half-titles, head & tail pieces, 8 eng. plts., contemp. sky-blue morocco, gilt panelled, joints tender, rubbed, a.e.g. Eaton 45-124 1978 £15

COWPER, WILLIAM The Works of William Cowper. London, 1817. 11 vols., sm. 8vo., uniformly bound eds., full blue calf with gilt ruled borders & blindstamped inner border, paneled gilt spines, bindings somewhat scuffed, interiors complete with ribbon bookmarks very fine. Current 24-12 1978 $60

COX, E.H.M. The Gardener's Chapbook. London, 1931. 8vo, orig. cloth. Book Chest 17-489 1978 $18

COX, E.H.M. A History of Gardening in Scotland. London, 1935. 8vo., cloth, frontis., illus. on plts. Van der Peet H-64-299 1978 Dfl 60

COX, E.H.M. The Library of Edmund Gosse. London, 1924. Frontis. Battery Park 1-324 1978 $50

COX, E.T. First Annual Report of the Geological Survey of Indiana. Indianapolis, 1869. Plt., fldg. maps, 2 vols., 8vo., orig. bds., cloth back, ribbon ties, covers soiled. Morrill 239-440 1978 $25

COX, E.T. Second Report of the Geological Survey of Indiana, Made During the Year 1870. Indianapolis, 1871. Maps, plts., 8vo., spine faded, Raphael Pumpelly's copy. Morrill 239-441 1978 $25

COX, GEORGE VALENTINE The Prayer-Book Epistle Paraphrased in Verse. 1846. 12mo., orig. cloth, half-title. P. M. Hill 142-266 1978 £8

COX, GEORGE VALENTINE Recollections of Oxford. London, 1868. 1st ed., full polished calf. Greene 78-170 1978 $40

COX, ISAAC J. The Journeys of Rene Robert Cavelier Sieur de LaSalle. New York, 1922. 2 vols. MacManus 239-245 1978 $15

COX, ISAAC J. The West Florida Controversy, 1798-1813. A Study in American Diplomacy. Baltimore, 1918. 1st ed., lg. fold. map, orig. cloth, hinges tape-reinforced, very good. MacManus 239-1806 1978 $35

COX, J. C. English Church Furniture. 1907. Illus., 8vo. Upcroft 12-89 1978 £6.50

COX, JACOB D. Atlanta. New York, 1882. Bell Wiley's copy. Broadfoot 46-59 1978 $10

COX, JACOB D. The March to the Sea, Franklin and Nashville. New York, 1892. Bell Wiley's copy. Broadfoot 46-58 1978 $10

COX, JACOB D. The Second Battle of Bull Run as Connected with the Fitz-John Porter Case, a paper. Cincinnati, 1882. Bell Wiley's copy. Broadfoot 46-60 1978 $10

COX, JOHN W. Mechanical Aptitude. 1928. Austin 80-892 1978 $17.50

COX, M. L. History of Hale County, Texas. Plainview, 1937. Decorated cloth, near mint, 1st ed., autographed. Jenkins 116-542 1978 $85

COX, ROSS Adventures on the Columbia River,.... New York, 1832. Original cloth boards, 1st Amer. ed. Ginsberg 14-289 1978 $200

COX, ROSS The Columbia River... London, 1832. 2nd. ed., 2 vols., 8vo, modern half calf, gilt backs. Deighton 5-33 1978 £95

COX, SAMUEL HANSON   Quakerism Not Christianity: or, Reasons for Renouncing the Doctrine of Friends. New York, 1833. 8vo., orig. bds., cloth back, occas. dampstains & foxing. 1st ed.   Morrill 241-97 1978 $15

COX, SAMUEL S.   A Discourse on Old and New Landmarks;--Delivered in Tammany Hall, July 4, 1884. Wr., colorful 4-page program laid in. Butterfield 21-234 1978 $7.50

COX, SAMUEL S.   Eight Years in Congress, from 1857-1865. Memoir and Speeches. New York, 1865. Cloth. Hayman 72-157 1978 $12.50

COX, SAMUEL S.   The Four New Stars: Address...At Huron, Dakota. New York, 1889. Pictorial wr. Ginsberg 14-309 1978 $75

COX, SANDFORD C.   Recollections of the Early Settlement of the Wabash Valley. Lafayette, 1860. 1st ed., orig. cloth, front hinge cracked, nice. MacManus 239-975 1978 $42.50

COX, SIDNEY   Robert Frost: Original Ordinary Man. New York, 1929. 4to, boards, d.w. very slightly torn at top, else near Mint, signed by author, 1st ed., no. 877 of 1000 copies signed by author. Desmarais 1-177 1978 $30

COX, W.   Fearsome Creatures of the Lumber-Woods. Washington, 1910. 8vo, orig. cloth. Book Chest 17-101 1978 $25

COXE, DANIEL   A Description of the English Province of Carolana. Full modern calf, map is not present. Wolfe 39-110 1978 $650

COXE, ELIZABETH ALLEN   Memories of a South Carolina Plantation During the War. N.P., 1912. Illus., ltd. ed., pres. from author, new cloth. Broadfoot's 44-608 1978 $80

COXE, WILLIAM   History of the House of Austria, from the Foundation of the Monarchy by Rhodolph of Hapsburg to the death of Leopold II, 1218-1792. 1807. 3 vols., 4to., full calf, spines gilt, a little rubbed. George's 635-614 1978 £32.50

COXE, WILLIAM   Memoirs of John Duke of Marlborough. 1820. Contemp. tan calf, 7 vols., 8vo. and 4to., plts., port. frontis. F. Edwards 1013-358 1978 £200

COXE, WILLIAM   Travels Into Poland, Russia, Sweden, and Denmark. London, 1774-90. 1st ed., 3 vols., 4to, engraved maps, engraved plts., contemporary diced calf, sides ruled in gilt, marbled endpapers, vol. 3 neatly rebacked, joints little cracked, some foxing & offsetting, generally very good copy, bookplt. of Bishop of Durham. Dieghton 5-117 1978 £195

COXHEAD, A. C.   Thomas Stothard, R.A. London, 1906. Illus., roy. 8vo., orig. cloth. K Books 244-352 1978 £15

COXHEAD, M.   Garden Fancies. London, 1909. 12mo, orig. cloth. Book Chest 17-499 1978 $9

COYNE, J. STIRLING   Cockneys in California, "A Piece of Golden Opportunity" in One Act... New York, [c.1860]. Original wr. Ginsberg 14-95 1978 $30

COZZENS, JAMES GOULD   Guard of Honor. New York, 1948. Paper-clip mark on 1st few pages, very good in chipped d.w. Desmarais B-166 1978 $10

COZZENS, JAMES GOULD   The Just and the Unjust. New York, 1942. Fine in chipped d.w. Desmarais B-167 1978 $7.50

COZZENS, JAMES GOULD   The Just and the Unjust. New York, (1942). 1st ed., d.w. Biblo BL781-913 1978 $10

COZZENS, JAMES GOULD   The Just and The Unjust. New York, (1942). 8vo, cloth, d.j., 1st ed., fine. Duschnes 220-76 1978 $17.50

CRABB, GEORGE   A Family Encyclopaedia. New York, 1831. 8vo., woodcuts, contemp. tree calf, gilt on spine, worn & hinges cracked, lightly browned & foxed, marginal waterstain, signatures of former owners & bkplts, internally a good copy. Zeitlin 245-49 1978 $85

CRABBE, GEORGE   The Borough: A Poem. 1810. 2nd. ed., revised, 8vo, half-title, orig. bds., spine worn & roughly repaired, uncut, water-stains in upper margin. Hannas 54-72 1978 £25

CRABBE, GEORGE   The Borough: A Poem, in Twenty-Four Letters. 1810. 1st. ed., 8vo, half-title, contemp. diced calf, gilt, rebacked with orig. spine remounted, slight foxing at end. Hannas 54-71 1978 £35

CRABBE, GEORGE   English Synonymes. 1918. Illus., 2nd. ed., buckram. Eaton 45-127 1978 £8

CRABBE, GEORGE   Poems. 1807. 1st. ed., 8vo, half-title, inserted contents leaf, contemp. half calf, very worn, some foxing throughout, paper rather browned. Hannas 54-73 1978 £15

CRABBE, GEORGE   Poems. 1808. 3rd. ed., half title, foxing of few pages, tree calf, black label, v.g. Jarndyce 16-411 1978 £12.50

CRABBE, GEORGE   Poems. 1808. 3rd. ed., orig. half blue morocco, v.g. Jarndyce 16-410 1978 £15

CRABBE, GEORGE   The Poems of George Crabbe. London, 1909. New ed., portrait, uncut, cloth bds., nice. Limestone 9-71 1978 $10

CRABBE, GEORGE   The Poetical Works... 1834. 8 vols., fine eng. frontis., vignette t.p.s., half titles, orig. brown cloth, fine. Jarndyce 16-415 1978 £35

CRABBE, GEORGE   The Poetical Works of the Rev. George Crabbe With His Letters, and Journals, and His Life. London, 1847. New ed., 8 vols., 12mo., engraved frontis, 1/2 tan calf with marbled bds. & edges, raised bands on spine, bindings scuffed, interiors better than fine, nice reading set. Current 24-13 1978 $45

CRABBE, GEORGE   Readings in Crabbe. Quaritch, 1882. 12mo, blue cloth. Eaton 45-128 1978 £4

CRABBE, GEORGE   Tales. 1812. 1st. ed., 8vo, half-title, contemp. tree calf, rebacked, sm. tear in 2 leaves, paper slightly foxed. Hannas 54-74 1978 £20

CRABBE, GEORGE   Tales. 1820. 2 vols., fscp. 8vo., full contemp. fawn calf. Howes 194-759 1978 £16

CRABBE, GEORGE   Tales of the Hall. 1819. 1st. ed., 2 vols., half titles, orig. calf, v.g. Jarndyce 16-412 1978 £34

CRABBE, GEORGE   Tales of the Hall. 1819. 1st. ed., 2 vols., orig. half calf, spines gilt, v.g. Jarndyce 16-413 1978 £30

CRABBE, GEORGE   Tales of the Hall. 1819. 1st. ed., 2 vols., 8vo, lacks half-titles, contemp. calf, rebacked, breaking again. Hannas 54-75 1978 £12.50

CRABBE, GEORGE   Tales of the Hall. 1819. 1st. ed., 2 vols., light spotting, contemp. tree calf, u-cover of vol. 1 slightly scruffed, gilt spines. Eaton 45-129 1978 £20

CRABBE, GEORGE   Tale of the Hall. 1819. 1st. ed., 2 vols., some spotting, contemp. calf, gilt spine, joints cracked. Eaton 45-126 1978 £25

CRABBE, GEORGE   Universal Technological Dictionary. 1823. 1st. ed., 2 vols., 4to, 60 full page engraved plts., orig. half calf, marbled bds. rubbed otherwise v.g. Jarndyce 16-409 1978 £35

CRABBE, GEORGE   The Works. 1823. 1st. ed., 8vols., half titles, uncut, orig. grey bds., portions of spines defective on 3 vols., otherwise v.g., orig. condition. Jarndyce 16-414 1978 £18

CRABBE, GEORGE   The Works of Rev. George Crabbe. London, 1823. 8 vols., orig. bds., vols. 1-5 rebacked, vols. 6-8 have orig. backs & worn labels, good tight set. Limestone 9-70 1978 $95

CRADDOCK, CHARLES EGBERT PSEUD.
Please turn to
MURFREE, MARY NOAILLES

CRADLEBAUGH, JOHN   Utah and the Mormons. Washington, 1863. Half mor., 1st ed. Ginsberg 14-1000 1978 $175

CRAFFONARA, G.   I Piu celebri Quadri dell diverse scuole Italiane riuniti nell' Apparamento.... 1820. Plts., folio, orig. bds. worn. George's 635-15 1978 £18

CRAFTS, LELAND W.   Recent Experiments in Psychology. 1938. Illus. Austin 80-893 1978 $10

CRAIG, ALEC   The Banned Books Of England. London, 1937. 1st ed., very good or better. Limestone 9-110 1978 $22

CRAIG, BILL   Land of Far Distance. New York, 1934. Cloth, pic. end sheets, illus., 1st Amer. ed., very good copy, bkplt. of Enaid Jones. Dykes 34-115 1978 $12.50

CRAIG, EDWARD GORDON   The Art of the Theatre... 1905. Plts., sm. 4to, orig. printed wrappers, unusually fine copy. Traylen 88-215 1978 £21

CRAIG, EDWARD GORDON   Books and Theatres. 1925. First ed., plts., orig. buckram-backed bds., 8vo. Howes 194-760 1978 £10

CRAIG, EDWARD GORDON   Books and Theatres. 1925. Plts., text illus., cloth-backed bds., covers somewhat browned, very good, first English ed. Bell Book 17-184 1978 £12.50

CRAIG, EDWARD GORDON   Books and Theatres. 1925. D.w. Battery Park 1-349 1978 $35

CRAIG, GERALD S.   Tentative Course of Study in Elementary Science for Grades I and II. 1927. Paper. Austin 80-894 1978 $10

CRAIG, GERALD S.   Tentative Course of Study in Elementary Science for Grades III and IV. 1927. Austin 80-895 1978 $10

CRAIG, GERALD S.   Tentative Course of Study in Elementary Science for Grades V and VI. 1927. Paper. Austin 80-896 1978 $10

CRAIG, LOCKE   Memoirs and Speeches of..., Governor of N.C... Asheville, 1923. Lower margin stained. Broadfoot 50-110 1978 $10

THE CRAIG & RICHARDS GRANITE CO.   Designers, Sculptors and Manufacturers of Mausoleums, Sarcophagi, Monuments, and Headstones in All Kinds of Fine Granite. Quincy, n.d. (ca. 1900). Oblong 8vo., orig. wrs. Morrill 241-167 1978 $10

CRAIGE, JOHN H.   What the Citizen Should Know About the Marines. 1941. Illus. by Charles E. Pont. Austin 80-73 1978 $8.50

CRAIGHEAD, JAMES R. E.   Black Hawk. A Romance of the Black Hawk War... Creston, (1930). Cloth, 1st ed., fine, pic. bookplt., scarce. Dykes 35-157 1978 $10

CRAIGIE, PEARL MARY TERESA   A Bundle of Life. New York, 1894. 1st Amer. ed., orig. binding. Greene 78-224 1978 $15

CRAIGIE, PEARL MARY TERESA   The Dream and the Business. New York, 1906. 1st Amer. ed., cloth, spine faded, good. Greene 78-225 1978 $20

CRAIK, DINAH MARIA (MULOCK)   Christian's Mistake. New York, 1856. Orig. cloth, contemp. inscrip., 1st Amer. ed. Greene 78-262 1978 $20

CRAIK, DINAH MARIA (MULOCK)   John Halifax, Gentleman. 1856. 3 vols., sm. 8vo., 1st ed., orig. cloth, backs repaired, slipcase, bkplts., A.L.s. inserted. Quaritch 979-102 1978 $170

CRAIK, DINAH MARIA (MULOCK)   John Halifax, Gentleman. London, 1856. 3 vols., orig. cloth, 1st ed., covers worn. MacManus 238-361 1978 $135

CRAIK, DINAH MARIA (MULOCK)   A Life for a Life. London, 1859. 3 vols., orig. cloth, spines faded, 1st ed., very good. MacManus 238-362 1978 $125

CRAIK, DINAH MARIA (MULOCK)   An Unsentimental Journey Through Cornwall. 1884. 1st ed., 4to., half title, orig. blue cloth, gilt, good except for scuffing of front cover. Jarndyce 16-899 1978 £6

CRAIK, GEORGINA M.   A Woman's Thoughts About Women. n.d. 1st ed., frontis, orig. purple cloth, gilt. Jarndyce 16-416 1978 £14.50

CRAIK, ROBERT   Papers and Addresses. Montreal, 1907. Orig. binding. Wolfe 39-361 1978 $17.50

CRAKELT, WILLIAM   Entick's New Spelling Dictionary. 1798. Sq. 12mo., sheep rebacked. P. M. Hill 142-95 1978 £14

CRAMER, JOHANN ANDREAS   Anfangsgrunde der Probierkunst. Leipzig, 1794. 8vo., fldg. copperplts., contemp. bds., rubbed & light foxing, but very good copy, 1st ed. Norman 5-63 1978 $375

CRAMER'S Pittsburgh Almanack, for...1815... Pittsburgh, (1814). Sewed. Hayman 72-9 1978 $22.50

CRAMER'S Pittsburgh Almanack, for...1820. Pittsburgh, (1819). Wrs. loose. Hayman 72-11 1978 $27.50

CRAMER'S Pittsburgh Almanack, for 1821. Pittsburgh, (1820). Wrps. Hayman 71-9 1978 $35

CRANBROOK Papers. Detroit, 1900-1901. Thin 4tos., orig. hand-dec. wrs., uncut, unopened, very slight wr. wear, nos. 2 through 10. Americanist 102-35 1978 $50

CRANE, GEORGE W.   Psychology Applied. Northwestern University Press, 1932. Austin 80-897 1978 $10

CRANE, GEORGE W.   Psychology Applied. Chicago, Northwestern University Press, 1943. Illus. Austin 80-898 1978 $10

CRANE, HART   The Collected Poems. New York, (1933). Cloth, very good. Dawson's 447-214 1978 $25

CRANE, HART   The Collected Poems of Hart Crane. Boriswood, 1938. Orig. linen, spine somewhat dull, good, scarce, first English ed. Bell Book 17-189 1978 £27.50

CRANE, HART   White Buildings. New York, 1926. 8vo, decor. boards, cloth back, d.w. sun faded, Fine, 1st ed. Desmarais 1-108 1978 $275

CRANE, JAMES M.   The Past, The Present and The Future of the Pacific. San Francisco, 1856. Cloth. Ginsberg 14-96 1978 $275

CRANE, LEO   Desert Drums. Boston, 1928. Illus., 1st ed. MacManus 239-1154 1978 $25

CRANE, LEO   Indians of the Enchanted Desert. Boston, 1925. 1st ed., illus., orig. pic. cloth, fine. MacManus 239-1155 1978 $25

CRANE, MILLARD E.   1850-1950...Historical Sketch of the Village of Fonda. (Fonda), 1950. Fldg. map laid in, wr. Butterfield 21-280 1978 $10

CRANE, NATHALIA   An Alien from Heaven. New York, 1929. 1st ed., spine faded, slightly frayed d.w. Biblo BL781-914 1978 $12

CRANE, NATHALIA   Lava Land and Other Poems. New York, 1925. 1st ed. Biblo BL781-915 1978 $8.50

CRANE, NATHALIA   Venus Invisible and Other Poems. New York, 1928. Illus., 1st ed. Biblo BL781-916 1978 $10

CRANE, STEPHEN   The Black Riders and Other Lines. Boston, 1895. 12mo., orig. bds., 1st ed., 1 of 500 copies, spine slightly darkened and worn, otherwise fine. MacManus 238-454 1978 $275

CRANE, STEPHEN   George's Mother. New York, 1896. Orig. tan cloth, 1st ed., very nice. MacManus 238-455 1978 $30

CRANE, STEPHEN   Great Battles of the World. Philadelphia, 1901. Illus. by Joan Sloan, orig. dec. cloth, 1st ed., fine. MacManus 238-463 1978 $55

CRANE, STEPHEN   The Little Regiment and Other Episodes of the American Civil War. New York, 1896. Orig. cloth, soiled, 1st ed., 2nd print., good. MacManus 238-456 1978 $30

CRANE, STEPHEN   Maggie. A Girl of the Streets. New York, 1896. Orig. cloth, spine ends a bit worn, 2nd ed., 2nd state, fine. MacManus 238-457 1978 $40

CRANE, STEPHEN   Maggie. A Girl of the Streets. New York, 1896. Orig. cloth, soiled, 2nd ed., 1st state, inscription, good. MacManus 238-458 1978 $45

CRANE, STEPHEN   The Monster & Other Stories. New York, 1899. 1st ed., plts., illus., orig. decor. cloth, excellent copy, octagonal lea. book label of Efrem Zimbalist, 8vo. Americanist 103-119 1978 $85

CRANE, STEPHEN   The Monster and Other Stories. New York, 1899. Orig. pict. cloth, 1st ed., near-fine. MacManus 238-461 1978 $50

CRANE, STEPHEN   The O'Ruddy. A Romance. New York, (1903). Orig. pict. cloth, 1st ed., mint copy, orig. fragmented d.j. laid in. MacManus 238-464 1978 $75

CRANE, STEPHEN   The Red Badge of Courage. New York, Grabhorn Press. One of 980 numbered copies. Battery Park 1-136 1978 $75

CRANE, STEPHEN   The Third Violet. New York, 1897. Orig. cloth, 1st ed., covers slightly soiled, else very good. MacManus 238-459 1978 $37.50

CRANE, STEPHEN   Whilomville Stories. New York and London, 1900. Illus. by Peter Newell, orig. cloth, 1st ed., fine. MacManus 238-462 1978 $45

CRANE, W. J. E.   Bookbinding for Amateurs. London. Engrs. Battery Park 1-275 1978 $35

CRANE, WALTER   The Alphabet of Old Friends. London, (1875). 1st ed., quarto, color plates, colored pictorial wrappers by Crane, spine sewn, spine edge chipped, fine. Victoria 34-189 1978 $75

CRANE, WALTER   The Book of Wedding Days. London, 1889. 1st ed., large quarto, printed entirely in red, over-all cover designs by Crane, spine edges and tips worn in spots, fine, scarce. Victoria 34-190 1978 $60

CRANE, WALTER   The First of May, A Fairy Masque. Presented in a Series of 52 Designe by Walter Crane. London, 1881. Oblong elephant folio, loose in sheets as issued, printed on India paper and mounted, 1 of 200 copies, signed by author, original portfolio, boards showing wear, fine. Duschnes 220-77 1978 $225

CRANE, WALTER   Flora's Feast:.... London, 1899. Square octavo, orig. pict. boards designed by Crane, drawings in color, rubbed, blue cloth spine. Totteridge 29-25 1978 $50

CRANE, WALTER   Goody Two Shoes Picture Book: Containing Goody Two Shoes, Aladdin, and The Yellow Dwarf. London, (1901). Quarto, brown pict. cloth, color plts. and pict. endpapers by Crane, front hinge weak, corners bumped, fine. Duschnes 220-78 1978 $85

CRANE, WALTER   Kunst en Samenleving. Amsterdam, 1903. Sm. 8vo., calf backed decor. bds., richly gilt tooled spine & corners, woodcut vignettes, uncut, Jugend-stil binding & endpapers, very attractive copy. Van der Peet H-64-119 1978 Dfl 275

CRANE, WALTER   A Masque of Days. Cassell, 1901. Impl. 8vo., 1st ed., coloured pic. borders, orig. picture bds., torn d.w. Quaritch 979-104 1978 $120

CRANE, WALTER   Of the Decorative Illustration of Books Old and New. London, Chiswick Press, 1896. Illus., newly rebound in cloth. Battery Park 1-35 1978 $45

CRANE, WALTER   Pan-Pipes. London, 1883. 1st ed., oblong quarto, front free endpaper frayed, inner hinges cracked, light edge chipping of cover boards. Victoria 34-191 1978 $50

CRANE, WALTER   Pan-Pipes. London, n.d. 2nd ed., very fine internally, covers fine and bright. Victoria 34-192 1978 $35

CRANE, WALTER   The Shepheard's Calendar. London, 1898. 1st ed., plates, multi-colored cover drawings, very good. Victoria 34-193 1978 $45

CRANE, WALTER   The Song of Sixpence Toy Book. London, c.1875. Plates, rebound with original Crane designed covers laid-down, text and plates almost mint, rubbed. Victoria 34-194 1978 $100

CRANE, WALTER   This Little Pig Went to Market. London, c.1875. Color plates, colored pictorial wrappers loose, small chip, scarce, 1st ed. Victoria 34-196 1978 $45

CRANE, WALTER   Wayfarer's Love. 1904. 4to., parchment with pic. design in gilt on upper cover, ltd. to only 100 copies signed by editor. Quaritch 979-105 1978 $60

CRANMER, THOMAS   A Defence of the Trve Catholike Doctrine of the Sacrament of the body and blood of our saviour Christ. 1550. First ed., black letter, historiated woodcut border, sm. Qto., 17th cent. panelled calf, worn and repaired. Thomas 37-66 1978 £225

CRANTZ, DAVID   The History of Greenland. London, 1767. 2 vols., 1st ed. in English, 8vo., fldg. maps, fldg. plts., very neatly rebacked, interiors fine. Current 24-210 1978 $425

CRANTZ, DAVID   The History of Greenland... 1767. 1st. ed. in English, maps, plts., 2 vols., contemp. calf, gilt spines, 8vo, sm. split in 1 joint. Edwards 1012-570 1978 £225

CRANTZ, DAVID   History of Greenland, Containing a Description of the Country & Its Inhabitants. London, 1767. Fldg. maps, fldg. copper-plts., 2 vols., 8vo., contemp. calf, 1st ed. in English. Argosy Special-29 1978 $300

CRANTZ, DAVID   The History of Greenland... London, 1820. 2 vols., 8vo, aquatint frontispieces, aquatint plts., engraved plt., folding engraved map, neatly repaired, sl. staining in text, half calf, marbled bds., morocco labels, gilt. Deighton 5-207 1978 £95

CRANWELL, JOHN PHILIPS   The Destiny of Sea Power. 1941. Austin 80-74 1978 $8.50

CRAPSEY, ADELAIDE   Verse. Rochester, 1915. 8vo, gray cloth, t.e. g., uncut, Fine, d.w., 1st ed. Desmarais 1-107 1978 $40

CRAUFORD, JAMES   The History of the House of Este.... London, 1681. Engraved portrait, 8vo, contemp. calf. Traylen 88-449 1978 £36

CRAUFURD, QUINTON   Sketches Chiefly Relating to the History, Religion, Learning, And Manners of the Hindoos... 1792. 2nd. ed., enlarged, 2 vols., 8 vo, engraved vignette title-pgs., folding engraved plt., half calf, gilt backs. Deighton 5-69 1978 £35

CRAVATH, PROSPER   Early Annals of Whitewater. Whitewater, 1906. Illus. MacManus 239-1141 1978 $25

CRAVEN, ELIZABETH   A Journey Through the Crimea to Constantinople. London, 1789. 1st. ed., 4to, engraved map, engraved plt., contemporary calf, neatly rebacked, morocco label, gilt, bookplt. Deighton 5-70 1978 £145

CRAVEN, THOMAS   Modern Art. New York, 1934. Illus., 8vo., 1st ed., orig. cloth. Morrill 241-98 1978 $10

CRAVEN, THOMAS   A Treasury of American Prints. New York, (1939) Spiral binding, d.w., 4to., etchings, lithographs. Biblo 247-405 1978 $27.50

CRAVEN, THOMAS   A Treasury of Art Masterpieces. New York, 1939. Folio, plts. in color, 1st ed. Biblo BL781-580 1978 $16.50

CRAVEN, WESLEY FRANK   The Southern Colonies in the 17th Century, 1607-1689. Baton Rouge, 1949. First ed., fine, d.w., illus. Biblo 247-27 1978 $17.50

CRAWFORD, CHARLES   A Dissertation of the Phaedon of Plato... London, 1773. 8vo., contemp. calf, 1st ed. Salloch 348-41 1978 $165

CRAWFORD, CLAUDE C.   Learning a New Language. 1930. Austin 80-899 1978 $12.50

CRAWFORD, CLAUDE C.   The Technique of Study. 1928. Austin 80-900 1978 $8.50

CRAWFORD, D.   Thinking Black. London, 1912. 1st. ed., 8vo, gilt cloth, 21 colored & other plts., slightly shaken. K Books 239-107A 1978 £7

CRAWFORD, D.   Thinking Black. London, 1914. 2nd. ed., 8vo, 21 coloured and other plts., gilt cloth, slightly shaken, lower cover marked. K Books 239-107 1978 £5

CRAWFORD, FRANCIS MARION   Casa Braccio. New York, 1895. 1st ed., 2 vols., orig. cloth, good set. Greene 78-25 1978 $45

CRAWFORD, FRANCIS MARION   A Cigarette-Maker's Romance. 1890. 1st ed., 2 vols., half titles, names cut from leading free endpapers, orig. light blue cloth, Grant's lib. labels. Jarndyce 16-418 1978 £14.50

CRAWFORD, FRANCIS MARION   Greifenstein. London, 1889. 1st Eng. ed., orig. cloth. binding. Greene 78-26 1978 $25

CRAWFORD, FRANCIS MARION   Marzio's Crucifix. 1887. 1st ed., 2 vols., orig. blue cloth, v.g. Jarndyce 16-417 1978 £20

CRAWFORD, FRANCIS MARION   Marzio's Crucifix. London, 1887. First Eng. ed., red cloth binding. Greene 78-27 1978 $15

CRAWFORD, FRANCIS MARION   Sant'Ilario. London, 1889. First Eng. ed., red cloth binding, spine faded. Greene 78-28 1978 $15

CRAWFORD, FRANCIS MARION   With the Immortals. 1888. 1st ed., 2 vols., half titles, orig. dark blue cloth, v.g. Jarndyce 16-419 1978 £30

CRAWFORD, GEO. W.   Letter from the Secretary of War...Respecting the Claims of Texas to the Territory of New Mexico, and Orders Relative Thereto. Washington, 1850. Jenkins 116-999 1978 $8.00

CRAWFORD, KENNETH G.   The Pressure Boys. The Inside Story of Lobbying in America. New York, (1939). Biblo BL781-197 1978 $7.50

CRAWFORD, LEWIS F.   Rekindling Camp Fires. 1st trade ed., fine in d.w., reinforced, scarce. Dykes 34-20 1978 $30

CRAWFORD, LEWIS F.   Rekindling Camp Fires. Bismarck, (1926). Mor. & cloth, marbled end sheets, gilt top, illus., #54 of 100 numbered copies signed by author, fine copy, slipcase, rare. Dykes 34-19 1978 $125

CRAWFORD, MARY CAROLINE   Famous Families of Massachusetts. Boston, 1930. Illus., 2 vols., 8vo., 1st ed. Morrill 239-507 1978 $20

CRAWFORD, MARY CAROLINE   Social Life in Old New England. Boston, 1914. 1st. ed., profusely illus. Baldwins; 51-395 1978 $8.50

CRAWFORD, O. G. S.   Topography of Roman Scotland, North of the Antoine Wall. 1949. Plt. Allen 234-1515 1978 $12.50

CRAWFORD, RUTH   The Immigrant in St. Louis. Paper. Austin 79-178 1978 $27.50

CRAWFORD, T. HARTLEY   Annual Report of...Commissioner of Indian Affairs, Transmitted with the Message of the President...1838-1839. Washington, 1838. Original printed wr. Ginsberg 14-290 1978 $225

CRAWLEY, ERNEST   The Mystic Rose. 1927. 2 vols., new ed. enlarged. Austin 80-901 1978 $27.50

CREAGER, CHARLES E.   The Fourteenth Ohio National Guard.... Columbus, 1899. Clean, shaken, spotted & little worn, orig. binding. Hayman 71-531 1978 $10

THE CREAM of the Jest:.... Derby, n.d. (1826). 12mo, full red crushed levant, gilt, spine and inner dentelles gilt, t.e.g., by Worsfold, 1st ed., hand-colored frontispiece by George Cruikshank, bound in is original pencil sketch for frontispiece, signed at bottom by Cruikshank, half-title present, original printed front wrapper (rubbed), bound in. Ximenes 47-160 1978 $250

CREASEY, EDWARD   The Fifteen Decisive Battles of the World. London, 1905. Frontis., cr. 8vo., prize tree calf gilt. K Books 244-80 1978 £6

CREASY, E. S.   The Fifteen Decisive Battles of the World. 1853. Fourth ed., 8vo., orig. cloth. F. Edwards 1013-272 1978 £15

CREDIT Mobilier Investigation. Washington, 1873. Disbound. Ginsberg 14-860 1978 $12.50

CREEL, GEORGE   Sam Houston: Colossus in Buckskin. New York, 1928. Illus. Jenkins 116-678 1978 $15

CREENEY, W. F.   Illustrations of Incised Slabs on the Continent of Europe from Rubbings and Tracings. 1891. Folio, lithographic plts., orig. printed bds., cloth back. Quaritch 983-8 1978 $95

CREER, LELAND H.   Utah and the Nation. Seattle, 1929. Wr. Ginsberg 14-1001 1978 $15

CREIGHTON, D. G.   British North America at Confederation. Ottawa, 1939. Card cover. Hood 117-562 1978 $35

CREIGHTON, MANDELL   A History of the Papacy during the Period of the Reformation. 1882. 5 vols., 8vo. George's 635-1047 1978 £8.50

CREIGHTON, MANDELL   A History of the Papacy from the Great Schism to the Sack of Rome. 1897. New ed., six vols., 8vo. Upcroft 12-91 1978 £30

CREIGHTON, MANDELL,   Queen Elizabeth. Paris, 1896. Quarto, quarter red mor. over cloth boards, gilt-ruled, gilt spine lettering, orig. pr. wr. bound in, sole ed., hand-colored frontis., illus., fine. Bennett 7-31 1978 $175

CREIGHTON, W. B.   All in the Day's Work; Brief Essays for Busy People. Toronto, 1923. Hood 116-679 1978 $7.50

CRELL, CARL JUSTUS LUDWIG VON   Commentatio de Optima Extracta Parandi Methodo. Dieterich, (1793). Copperplt., 4to., contemp. wrs., 1st ed. Offenbacher 30-29 1978 $95

CREMATION. History of the Movement in Lancaster, Pa. with an Account of the Building, Furnace, Other Apparatus and the Processes. Lancaster, 1886. Illus., paper covers, top one detached. Rittenhouse 49-22 1976 $27.50

CREMONY, JOHN   Life Among the Apaches. San Francisco, 1868. Green cloth, gilt title on backstrip. Jenkins 116-25 1978 $150

CRERAR, T. A.   The Future of Canadian Mining... Ottawa, 1936. Card cover, illus. Hood's 115-700 1978 $12.50

CRESCENT Iron Manufacturing Company, with Statistics of Other Manufacturing Companies, Wheeling, Va. Boston, 1855. Plan, fldg. map, 8vo., orig. wrs., ex-lib. Morrill 239-637 1978 $15

CRESCI, GIOVANNI FRANCESCO   Essemplare di piu Sorti Lettere. Rome, 1568. Oblong sm. 4to., vellum, woodcut borders, rare, fourth ed. Schumann 511-13 1978 sFr 8750

CRESCIMBENI, GIOVANNI MARIA   Historia della Chiesa di S. Giovanni avanti Porta Latina. Roma, 1716. 4to., vellum, woodcut initials, plts., very good, first ed. King 7-159 1978 £35

CRESSON, CHARLES M.   Results of Examinations of Water from the River Schuylkill. Philadelphia, 1875. Paper, orig. covers, tables. Rittenhouse 49-163 1976 $15

CRESSWELL, BEATRIX F.   Alexis and His Flowers. 1891. 1st. ed., illus., 8vo, orig. cloth, gilt edges, gilt, fine copy. Fenning 32-80 1978 £6

CRESSWELL, NICHOLAS   Journal, 1774-77. New York, 1924. Portrait, spine dull, 8vo. George's 635-615 1978 £6.50

CRESSY, GEORGE BABCOCK   China's Geographic Foundations: A Survey of the land and its people. New York, 1934. Cloth, very good, some ink underlining, 9th printing, illus. Dawson's 449-27 1978 $10

CRESSY, HUGH E.   The Church History of Brittany from the beginning of Christianity to the Norman Conquest. 1668. Thk. folio, strongly bound in 18th cent. mottled calf over thick bds.,neatly rebacked, orig. mor. letteringpiece preserved, sole ed., rare. Howes 194-31 1978 £90

CRESWELL, HENRY   The Sins of the Fathers. London, 1885. 3 vols., orig. cloth, 1st ed., covers a bit worn and soiled, lib. labels. MacManus 238-340 1978 $85

CRESWICKE, LOUIS   The Life of the Right Honourable Joseph Chamberlain. London, c.1904. 4 vols., portraits, illus., roy. 8vo, orig. gilt cloth, bright set. K Books 239-108 1978 £7

CRESWICKE, LOUIS   South Africa and the Transvaal War. London, c.1900. 8 vols., numerous maps, coloured & other plts., roy. 8vo., orig. gilt cloth, illus. K Books 239-109 1978 £18

CREUZBAUR, ROBERT   Route from the Gulf of Mexico and the Lower Mississippe Valley to California and the Pacific Ocean, with Directions to Travellers. New York, 1849. Original cloth, maps lacking, extremely rare, 1st and only ed. Jenkins 116-258 1978 $2,000

CREVECOEUR, JEAN HECTOR ST. JOHN DE.
Please turn to
CREVECOEUR, MICHEL GUILLAUME ST. JEAN DE

CREVECOEUR, MICHEL GUILLAUME ST. JEAN DE   Letters from an American Farmer. London, 1782. 1st ed., 8vo., fldg. maps, rebound in 3/4 green mor. with marbled bds., bkplt. of owner, signed, near mint. Current Misc. 8-14 1978 $1,250

CREVECOEUR, MICHEL GUILLAUME ST. JEAN DE   Lettres d'un Cultivateur Americain Addresses a Wm. S.....on, Esq. depuis L'Annee 1770 Jusqu'en 1786. Paris, 1787. 3 vols., 8vo., full calf, plts., maps. Wolfe 39-110a 1978 $300

CREVECOEUR, MICHEL GUILLAUME ST. JEAN DE   Voyage dans la Haute Pensylvanie et dans L'Etat de New-York depuis l'annee 1785 jusqu'en 1798. Paris, 1801. 1st ed., 3 vols., 8vo., very good copy, contemp. marbled bds. backed in calf. Current Misc. 8-15 1978 $485

CREVIER, JEAN BAPTISTE LOUIS   Histoire des Empereurs Romans, Depuis Auguste Jusqu'a Constantin. Paris, 1750-1756. 6 vols., sm. 4to., half calf bindings, lg. engr. fldg. maps, scarce. Van der Peet H-64-300 1978 Dfl 325

CREWDSON, CHARLES N.   Tales of the Road. Chicago, 1905. Orig. binding, 2nd. ed., clean, fine, bright copy. Hayman 71-170 1978 $7.50

CREWE, MARQUESS OF   Lord Rosebery. 1931. 1st ed., 2 vols., d.w., very good, octavo bound in cloth. Hyland 128-456 1978 £6

CREWSON, E. A.   Old Times. Kansas City, 1893. Orig. binding, clean. Hayman 71-171 1978 $7.50

CRICHTON, ALEXANDER   An Inquiry into the Nature and Origin of Mental Derangement. London, 1798. 2 vols., 8vo., orig. bds., edges untrimmed, rebacked with contemp. paper, titles handwritten, covers slightly rubbed, some light stains, lst ed., very scarce. Morrill 239-55 1978 $250

CRICHTON, ARTHUR   The Festival of Flora. London, 1818. 2nd ed., 12mo, pictorial hand-colored t.p., hand-colored plates, no earlier printing is recorded, marbled boards, fine. Victoria 34-198 1978 $225

CRICHTON, PATRICK   Observations on a Machine for the Speedy Conveyance of Troops. Edinburgh, 1804. 8vo., plts., half calf. F. Edwards 1013-273 1978 $55

THE CRIES of York (In Two Parts). York, c.1810. Illus, sq.16mo, wrappers, plain original wrappers, stitching gone, tipped-in newspaper clipping. Victoria 34-199 1978 $65

CRIMONT, RAPHEAL   Prayers in the Crow Indian Language Composed by the Missionaries of the Society of Jesus. DeSmet Mission, 1891. Disbound, lst ed., only 700 copies printed. Ginsberg 14-401 1978 $100

CRIPPS, WILFRED JOSEPH   Old English Plate; Ecclesiastical, Decorative, and Domestic: Makers and Marks. New York, 1903. 127 illus., 8th ed. Baldwins' 51-49 1978 $20

CRISP, QUENTIN   All This and Bevin Too. 1943. Drawings by Mervyn Peake, wraps, good, inscribed by author, first English ed. Bell Book 17-720 1978 £40

CRISP, WILLIAM   Notes Towards a Secoana Grammar. London, 1905. 4th. ed., cr. 8vo, orig. cloth. K Books 239-110 1978 £9

CRISPIN, EDMUND   The Case of the Gilded Fly. 1944. Covers somewhat rubbed & soiled, good, first English ed. Bell Book 17-980 1978 £28.50

CRISPIN, EDMUND   The Moving Toyshop. 1946. Very good, scarce, first English ed. Bell Book 16-237 1978 £18.50

CRISSEY, FORREST   Alexander Legge 1880-1933. Chicago, 1936. Illus., original cloth, lst ed. Ginsberg 14-477 1978 $10

CRISSEY, FORREST   Since Forty Years Ago. Chicago, 1915. Illus. Biblo 248-45 1978 $22.50

CRISSEY, FORREST   Tattlings of a Retired Politician. Being the Letters ...of Hon. William Bradley, Ex-governor and Former Veteran of Practical Politics.. Chicago, 1904. Cloth. Hayman 72-158 1978 $8.50

CRITTENDEN, CHARLES CHRISTOPHER   North Carolina Newspapers Before 1790. Chapel Hill, 1928. New cloth. Broadfoot 50-46 1978 $10

CROABBON, A.   Science du Point d'Honneur. Paris, 1894. 8vo., half calf. Van der Peet H-64-607 1978 Dfl 60

CROCE, BENEDETTO   Theory and History of Historiography. 1921. 8vo. George's 635-616 1978 £5

CROCKER, HENRY RADCLIFFE   Atlas of the Diseases of the Skin. Edinburgh and London, 1896. Lg. folio, 2 vols., color plts., contemp. half-calf, bds. in margin a bit faded, fine set, lst ed. Gilhofer 74-88 1978 sFr 1,100

CROCKETT, DAVID   Col. Crockett's Exploits and Adventures in Texas.... Philadelphia, 1836. Foxed, lst ed. Jenkins 116-259 1978 $100

CROCKETT, DAVID   Davy Crockett's 1837 Almanack, Vol. I, No. 3. Nashville. Lacks back cover. Baldwins' 51-521 1978 $75

CROCKETT, SAMUEL R.   The Isle of the Winds. New York, 1900. lst Amer. ed., cloth, good condition. Greene 78-171 1978 $15

CROCKETT, SAMUEL R.   Sir Toady Crusoe. 1905. First ed., illus. by Gordon Browne, orig. pict. cloth, gilt top, spine faded, 8vo. Howes 194-974 1978 £5

CROCKETT, SAMUEL R.   The Stickit Minister's Wooing. New York, 1900. lst Amer. ed., orig. cloth, name on end paper, good. Greene 78-172 1978 $10

CROES, ROBERT B.   The Anniversary Lecture, Pronounced Before the Historical Society of the County of Vigo, Indiana, on the 14th of March, 1844. Cincinnati, 1845. Prtd. wrs., illus. Hayman 73-309 1978 $15

CROFTS, FREEMAN WILLS   The Groote Park Murder. 1923. Good, first English ed. Bell Book 17-228 1978 £18.50

CROFTS, FREEMAN WILLS   Inspector French and the Cheyne Mystery. 1926. Very good, first English ed. Bell Book 16-238 1978 £7.50

CROFUT, FLORENCE S. MARCY   Guide to the History and Historic Sites of Connecticut. 1937. 1st ed., 2 vols., 4to., illus., orig. cloth, front flyleaves lacking, else very good set. MacManus 239-95 1978 $40

CROIL, JAMES   Dundas; or, A Sketch of Canadian History.... Montreal, 1861. Endpaper missing, cover scuffed. Hood's 115-795 1978 $40

CROIL, JAMES   Steam Navigation and its Relation to the Commerce of Canada and the United States. Toronto, 1895. Illus., portraits, ex-library, very good, orig. binding. Wolfe 39-111 1978 $30

CROISET, M.   Essai sur la vie et les Oeuvres de Lucien. 1882. Allen 234-562 1978 $15

CROKER, JOHN WILSON   Correspondence Between the Right Hon. J. W. Croker and the Right Hon. Lord John Russell,.... London, 1854. 8vo, disbound, lst ed., scarce. Ximenes 47-61 1978 $27.50

CROKER, T. C.   Researches in the South of Ireland. (1824). Reprint, octavo bound in cloth. Hyland 128-936 1978 £7

CROLY, DAVID G.   Seymour and Blair. New York, 1868. Portrs., facsimile, sm. 8vo., lst ed., orig. cloth. Morrill 241-662 1978 $10

CROLY, GEORGE   Salathiel. 1829. 3 vols., orig. half calf, marbled bds., spines gilt, red labels, fine. Jarndyce 16-423 1978 £48

CROLY, GEORGE   Tales of the Great St. Bernard. 1828. 3 vols., full contemp. calf, pres. copy inscribed by author, 8vo. Howes 194-763 1978 £35

CROMMELIN, HENRIETTA DE LA CHEROIS   The Freaks of Lady Fortune. London, 1889. 2 vols., orig. cloth, lst ed., labels removed, but very good. MacManus 238-341 1978 $65

CROMWELL, OLIVER   The Letters and Speeches of .... 1904. 3 vols., octavo, good. Upcroft 10-41 1978 £25

CROMWELL, THOMAS KITSON   Excursions in the County of Essex. 1818-19. First ed., map, 2 vols., sm. 8vo., contemp. half calf. Howes 194-1376 1978 £30

CROMWELL, THOMAS KITSON   Excursions in the County of Kent. 1822. First ed., contemp. half calf, sm. 8vo., maps, plts. Howes 194-1377 1978 £18

CROMWELL, THOMAS KITSON   Excursions in the County of Norfolk. 1818-19. First ed., contemp. half calf, sm. 8vo., 2 vols. Howes 194-1378 1978 £30

CROMWELL, THOMAS KITSON   Excursions in the County of Suffolk. 1818-19. First ed., maps, 2 vols., sm. 8vo., contemp. half calf, spines gilt. Howes 194-1379 1978 £35

CROMWELL, THOMAS KITSON   Excursions in the County of Surrey. 1821. First ed., sm. 8vo., contemp. half calf, maps, minor foxing. Howes 194-1380 1978 £18

CROMWELL, THOMAS KITSON   Excursions in the County of Sussex. 1822. First ed., contemp. half calf, sm. 8vo., maps, minor damp staining of few plts. Howes 194-1381 1978 £18

CRONAU, RUDOLF   Drei Jahrhunderte Deutschen Lebens in Amerika. Berlin, 1909. Illus. Austin 79-179 1978 $47.50

CRONBACH, LEE J.   Essentials of Psychological Testing. 1949. Illus. Austin 80-902 1978 $10

CRONICA DEL REY JUAN II   Comienca la Cronica del serenisimo rey don Juan el segundo. Logrono, 1517. Folio, Gothic letter, woodcuts, clean tears in upper and outer margin of title repaired, English early 19th-century red mor., gilt panelled sides and spine, gilt edges, by Lewis, lst ed. Quaritch 978-40 1978 $4,800

CRONIN, A. J.   Grand Canary. London, 1933. 1st ed., 8vo., d.j., fine, Zane Grey's copy. Houle 10-78 1978 $45

CRONIN, A. J.   Hatter's Castle. London, 1931. lst ed., 8vo., d.j., worn, fine copy, very scarce. Current Misc. 8-52 1978 $75

CROOKS, ESTHER J.   The Ring Tournament in the United States. Richmond, (1936). Illus., 8vo., d.w., lst ed., orig. cloth. Morrill 241-99 1978 $7.50

CROPPER, JAMES   Relief for West-Indian Distress,.... London,
1823. 8vo, disbound, lst ed., half-title present. Ximenes 47-62 1978 $75

CROS, L.   l'Indochine francaise pour tous (comment aller,
et que faire en Indo-Chine). Paris, 1931. Numerous illus., map, 8vo, orig.
covers. Van der Peet 127-65 1978 Dfl 45

CROSBY, ERNEST HOWARD   The Crosby Family of New York. N.P., n.d.
4to., plts., wr., chipped. Butterfield 21-191 1978 $7.50

CROSBY, HARRY   Mad Queen. Paris, 1929. 8vo, orig. printed
wrs., illus. in color by Caresse Crosby, I of 100 copies, lst ed., bookplt., fine.
Duschness 220-23 1978 $150

CROSBY, PERCY   A Cartoonist's Philosophy. McLean, (1931).
8vo., illus. by author, lst ed., orig. cloth. Morrill 241-100 1978 $12.50

CROSBY, THOMAS   Among the An-ko-me-nums or Flathead Tribes
of Indians of the Pacific Coast. Toronto, 1907. Illus., ex-lib. Hood's 115-746
1978 $30

CROSBY, THOMAS   David Sallosalton. (Toronto, 1906). Card
cover, illus. Hood's 115-926 1978 $15

CROSKEY, JOHN W.   History of Blockley. A History of the Philadelphia General Hospital, 1731-1928. Philadelphia, 1929. 4to., illus. Mac-
Manus 239-1428 1978 $25

CROSLAND, T. W. H.   McClure's Children's Annual for 1903. New
York. Thick quarto, colored pict. linen, color plts. by W. Heath Robinson. Victoria 34-516 1978 $20

CROSS, ANDREW JAY   Dynamic Skiametry in Theory and Practice.
New York, 1911. Illus., 8vo., lst ed. Morrill 239-56 1978 $15

CROSS, AUSTIN F.   Snobs and Spines. Toronto, 1937. Hood 116-
680 1978 $7.50

CROSS, E. F. H.   Fire and Frost; Stories, Dialogues, Satires, Essays,
Poems... Toronto, 1898. Hood 116-681 1978 $10

CROSS, JOHN   History of the Variolous Epidemic...Chicken Pox.
London, 1820. Half leather, modern bds., rubber stamp on title, presented by
author. Rittenhouse 49-164 1976 $95

CROSS, LAUNCELOT   Characteristics of Leigh Hunt... 1878. Orig.
cloth, good. Jarndyce 16-759 1978 £6.50

CROSSMAN, EDWARD C.   The Book of the Springfield Military and Sporting
Rifles. North Carolina, (1932). Illus. Baldwins' 51-50 1978 $12.50

CROUSE, N. M.   In Quest of the Western Ocean. London, 1928.
Hood 116-616 1978 $45

CROWDER, W.   A Naturalist at the Seashore. New York, (1928).
8vo, orig. cloth. Book Chest 17-102 1978 $20

CROWE, F. J. W.   Masonic Clothing and Regalia, British and Continental. Edinburgh, 1900. 4to., plts., cloth. Quaritch 983-61 1978 $135

CROWE, J. A.   Raphael, his Life and Works. 1882. 2 vols.,
8vo. George's 635-205 1978 £5

CROWE, PAT   Spreading Evil: Pat Crowe's Autobiography.
New York, 1927. Original cloth. Ginsberg 14-291 1978 $25

CROWE, W. L.   The Mormon Waterloo:.... St. Paul, c.1902.
Orig. cloth, lst ed. Ginsberg 14-645 1978 $25

CROWE, WILLIAM   Lewesdon Hill A Poem. Oxford, 1788. 2nd. ed.,
4to, fully rebound in half morocco, marbled bds., fine modern binding. Jarndyce
16-64 1978 £45

CROWELL, I. H.   Braided and Interbraided Rugs. Toronto, 1945.
Pamphlet, illus. Hood 117-618 1978 $7.50

CROWELL, JOHN   Speech of Mr...., of Ohio, on Slavery in the
District of Columbia. Delivered in the House...July 26, 1848. N.P., n.d.
(Washington, 1848?). Unbound as issued. Hayman 72-710 1978 $12.50

CROWINSHIELD, MRS. SCHUYLER   Latitude 19. New York, 1898. Orig.
binding, clean, cover dampstained at top. Hayman 71-222 1978 $7.50

CROWLEY, ALEISTER   Ambergris: A Selection from the Poems. 1910.
First ed., portrait, cr. 8vo., orig. bds., spine slightly worn. Howes 194-764
1978 £22

CROWLEY, ALEISTER   Moonchild: a prologue. Mandrake Press, 1929.
Good, d.w., scarce, first English ed. Bell Book 16-204 1978 £35

CROWNE, WILLIAM   A true Relation of all the remarkable Places
and Passages observed in the Travels of the Right Honourable Thomas Lord Howard,
Earl of Arundell. N.P., 1637. Sm. 4 to., good, modern sprinkled calf, lst ed.
Quaritch Summer, 1978-9 1978 $550

CROWNINSHIELD, MARY BRADFORD   All Among the Lighthouses... Boston,
n.d. (1886). Sq. 8vo., dec. cloth, maps, lst ed. Paine 78-18 1978 $17.50

CROWQUILL, ALFRED   Seymour's Humorous Sketches. London, 1888.
Etched plates, plates on heavy paper in virtually mint condition, red cloth with
gilt and black vignettes by Seymour, fine. Victoria 34-200 1978 $35

CROWTHER, SAMUEL   Prohibition and Prosperity. 1930. Austin 80-
531 1978 $8.50

CROY, HOMER   Jesse James was my Neighbor. New York,
(1949). lst ed., d.w., fine. Biblo 248-267 1978 $17.50

CROZET, J. M.   Neue Reise Durch Die Sudsee, 1771-72... Leipzig, 1783. Engraved frontis, orig. wrappers, spine slightly defective, text little
browned, 8vo. Edwards 1012-365 1978 £60

CRUICKSHANK, A.   Wings in the Wilderness. New York, 1947.
Worn, faded binding, 8vo, orig. cloth. Book Chest 17-103 1978 $22

CRUICKSHANK, A. H.   Philip Massinger. 1920. Portrait, facsimiles,
octavo, good. Upcroft 10-277 1978 £6

CRUIKSHANK, ERNEST ALEXANDER   The Political Adventures of John Henry.
Toronto, 1936. Orig. binding. Wolfe 39-112 1978 $35

CRUIKSHANK, GEORGE   The Bachelor's Own Book. Glasgow, (c. 1880).
Plts., orig. pict. cloth, gilt, 8vo. George's 635-1533 1978 £7.50

CRUIKSHANK, GEORGE   Bentley's Miscellany. New York, 1838-1841.
lst Amer. ed., 8 vols., mint conditioned plates by Cruikshank, Crowquill & Leech,
lst Amer. printing, text fine and crisp, marbled boards, sheepskin spines, fine.
Victoria 34-201 1978 $95

CRUIKSHANK, GEORGE   Comic Almanack for 1845. Illus., orig. red
printed wrappers, spine missing. Jamdyce 16-437 1978 $9.50

CRUIKSHANK, GEORGE   The Comic Almanack and Diary. London, 1850.
Plates and illus., orange cloth with gilt design by artist, lacks f.p. Victoria
34-203 1978 $7.50

CRUIKSHANK, GEORGE   Der Freischutz Travestie: By Septimus Globus,
Esq...and the Original Tale Whereon the German Opera is Founded. 1824. Lg.
8vo., etchings by Cruikshank, coloured, mod. bds., leather back, good. Quaritch 983-313 1978 $250

CRUIKSHANK, GEORGE   A Discovery Concerning Ghosts; with a Rap at the
"Spirit-Rappers"... 1863. 8vo., lst ed., engravings by author, mod. cloth bind.
with orig. blue wrs. bound in. Quaritch 983-312 1978 $75

CRUIKSHANK, GEORGE   A Handbook for Posterity. 1896. Etchings on
glass, orig. qtr. roan. George's 635-133 1978 £15

CRUIKSHANK, GEORGE   George Cruikshank's Omnibus. 1842. lst. ed.,
engravings, half maroon morocco, little rubbed but nice & clean. Jarndyce 16-
434 1978 £40

CRUIKSHANK, GEORGE   Omnibus. 1885. New ed., ltd. to 300 copies,
India paper impressions, plts., woodcuts in text, by Cruikshank, imp. 8vo., qtr.
calf, marbled bd. sides, edges slightly rubbed, t.e.g., others untrimmed.
George's 635-1534 1978 £25

CRUIKSHANK, GEORGE   Punch and Judy... 1828. 2nd ed., 8vo., plts.
by Cruikshank, frontis., leather labels, gilt top. Quaritch 983-314 1978 $60

CRUIKSHANK, GEORGE   Songs, Naval and National, of the late Charles
Dibdin. London, 1841. Fine etched plates and illus., handsome tan leather, gilt
borders, ornately decorated spine, upper hinge cracked, fine and solid. Victoria
34-204 1978 $40

CRUIKSHANK, GEORGE   Sunday in London... 1833. Illus. by Cruikshank,
8vo., contemp. bds., cloth back, paper label. Quaritch 983-315 1978 $60

CRUIKSHANK, GEORGE — George Cruikshank's Table-Book. 1845. 1st. ed., 4to, vignettes, full pages plts., generally foxed, engraved title, half green calf, marbled bds., spine gilt, label. Jarndyce 16-436 1978 £38

CRUIKSHANK, GEORGE — George Cruikshank's Table Book. 1845. 1st. ed., engraved frontis, plts., illus., orig. half calf, cloth bds., plts. clean & bright. Jarndyce 16-435 1978 £40

CRUIKSHANK, ISAAC — The Turtle Dove; or Cupid's Artillery Levelled Against Human Hearts, Being a New and Original Valentine Writer... (1820?). Sm. 8vo., 1st ed., hand-coloured frontis. by Cruikshank, mod. bds., leather back. Quaritch 983-316 1978 $85

CRUIKSHANK, J. R. — Commercial Tourist...; or, Gentleman Traveller. A Satirical Poem, in Four Cantos... 1822. 2nd ed., enlarged, 8vo., coloured plts., half red mor., gilt panelled back, gilt top by Bamford, sm. marginal tears. Quaritch 983-317 1978 $250

CRUIKSHANK, R. — Sketches from Mr. Mathews at Home! An Excellent Collection of Recitations, Anecdotes, Songs... 1822. Sm. 8vo., fold. frontis. in colour by Cruikshank, mod. bds., leather back. Quaritch 983-318 1978 $120

CRUMP, C. G. — The History of the Life of Thomas Elwood. 1900. Octavo, good. Upcroft 10-52 1978 £5

CRUMP, H. J. — Colonial Admiralty Jurisdiction in the Seventeenth Century. 1931. Octavo, good. Upcroft 10-279 1978 £8.50

CRUMP, CAPT. R. P. — The Snively Expedition. New York, 1949. 12mo, printed wr., limited to 100 copies, none for sale. Jenkins 116-264 1978 $35

CRUMPTON, H. J. — The Adventures of Two Alabama Boys.... Montgomery, 1912. Illus., original cloth, 1st ed. Ginsberg 14-292 1978 $75

CRUTCHER, HESTER B. — A Guide for Developing Psychiatric Social Work in State Hospitals. Utica, State Hospitals Press, 1933. Paper. Austin 80-903 1978 $10

CRUTCHLEY, JOHN — General View of the Agriculture in the County of Rutland. London, 1794. 4to., stitched and uncut as issued, orig. cloth. K Books 244-81 1978 £14

CRUTTWELL, MAUD — Antonio Pollaiuolo. 1907. Illus., cr. 8vo. George's 635-200 1978 £5

CRYER, M. H. — Internal Anatomy of the Face. Philadelphia, 1916. Second ed., revised and enlarged. Rittenhouse 49-165 1976 $15

CUBBERLEY, ELLWOOD P. — A Brief History of Education. 1922. Austin 80-904 1978 $10

CUBBERLEY, ELWOOD P. — The Principal and His School. 1923. Austin 80-905 1978 $10

CUBBERLEY, ELLWOOD P. — State School Administration. 1927. Austin 80-907 1978 $10

CULBERT, JANE F. — The Visiting Teacher at Work. 1929. Austin 80-908 1978 $10

CULBERSON, C. A. — Address at the Iroquios Club Banquet, Chicago. Washington, 1904. Printed wr. Jenkins 116-268 1978 $25

CULIN, STEWART — Korean Games With Notes onCorresponding Games of China and Japan. Philadelphia, 1895. Fully illus., ltd. 550 copies. Baldwins' 51-51 1978 $47.50

CULIN, STEWART — Korean Games... Philadelphia, 1895. Illus., plts. mostly in color, dec. cloth, spine stained, spine split at top, one of 500 numbered copies, signed by author with pres. Dawson's 127-211 1978 $125

CULIN, STEWART — A Trooper's Narrative of Service in the Anthracite Coal Strike, 1902. Philadelphia, (1903). 1st ed., illus., orig. cloth, very good. MacManus 239-1429 1978 $30

CULL, MARY — Poems. 1854. 1st. ed., orig. green dull cloth, good. Jarndyce 16-450 1978 £12.50

CULLEN, COUNTEE — The Black Christ, and other poems. 1929. Very good, cloth-backed bds., first English ed. Bell Book 17-192 1978 £8.50

CULLEN, COUNTEE — Color. New York, (1925). 8vo, decor. boards and cloth, 1st ed., bookplt., fine. Duschnes 220-80 1978 $27.50

CULLEN, J. B. — The Story of the Irish in Boston. Boston, 1889. Illus. MacManus 239-215 1978 $25

CULLEN, MARGARET — Home, a Novel. 1804. 3rd. ed., 5 vols., half titles, orig. half calf, red labels, v.g. Jarndyce 16-451 1978 £36

CULLEN, THOMAS STEPHEN — Cancer of the Uterus, Its Pathology, Symptomatology, Diagnosis and Treatment. Philadelphia, 1909. Rittenhouse 49-166 1976 $15

CULLEN, WILLIAM — A Methodical System of Nosology. Stockbridge, (1808). 12mo, contemp. calf, scarce Amer. ed. Morrill 239-57 1978 $40

CULLEN, WILLIAM — Synopsis and Nosology, being an Arrangement and Definition of Diseases. Springfield, 1793. 12mo., 2nd ed., contemp. calf, worn & upper cover detached, lightly browned, good copy from the library of Dr. Alfred M. Hellman, rare Amer. ed. Zeitlin 245-51 1978 $150

CULLOM, MR. — Remarks of..., of Tennessee, on the Bill Making Appropriation for Certain Harbors and Rivers. Delivered in the House...April 20, 1844. Washington, 1844. Disbound. Hayman 72-668 1978 $7.50

CULLUM, GEORGE W. — Campaigns of the War of 1812-15, Against Great Britain... New York, 1879. 1st ed., illus., nice copy, rebound. MacManus 239-470 1978 $35

CULLUM, GEORGE W. — Register of the Officers and Graduates of the U.S. Military Academy. New York, 1850. 3/4 leather, scuffed, Bell Wiley's copy. Broadfoot's 44-99 1978 $20

CULLEY, JOHN H. — Cattle, Horses & Men of the Western Range. Los Angeles, (1940). Cloth, illus., frontis., 1st ed., fine copy, slipcase. Dykes 34-73 1978 $125

CULPEPER, NICHOLAS — The Complete Herbal. London, 1850. Engraved frontis. foxed and water stained, hand coloured plts., 4to., recent green cloth. K Books 244-82 1978 £35

CULVER, HENRY B. — The Book of Old Ships and Something of Their Evolution and Romance. New York, 1924. Pic. bds., lg. 4to., uncut, Flotilla ed., ltd., orig. signed drawing by Gordon Grant bound in. MacManus 239-1743 1978 $60

CULVER, HENRY B. — Contemporary Scale Models of Vessels of the Seventeenth Century. New York, 1926. Plts., folio, new buckram, ltd. ed. F. Edwards 1013-52 1978 £35

CULVER, HENRY B. — Contemporary Scale Models of Vessels of the Seventeenth Century... New York, (1925). Folio, one of 1000 copies. Baldwins' 51-506 1978 $85

CULVERWELL, ROBERT JAMES — On Single and Married Life. New York, (1862). 12mo., orig. wrs. Morrill 239-58 1978 $15

CUMBERLAND, RICHARD — Calvary; Or The Death of Christ. 1800. 2 vols., engraved frontispiece & plts., orig. calf, black & green labels, new ed., v.g. Jarndyce 16-65 1978 £12

CUMBERLAND, RICHARD — The Posthumous Dramatick Works. 1813. 1st. ed., 2 vols., half titles, orig. bds., uncut, blue cloth spines, good. Jarndyce 16-453 1978 £38

CUMINGS, SAMUEL — The Western Pilot, Containing Charts of the Ohio River,... Cincinnati, 1832. Maps, plates, very good rebound copy. Nestler Rare 78-60 1978 $85

CUMMING, A. — Hardy Chrysanthemums. New York, 1939, 45. 8vo, orig. cloth. Book Chest 17-493 1978 $9

CUMMING, CONSTANCE FREDERICA GORDON
Please turn to
GORDON-CUMMING, CONSTANCE FREDERICA

CUMMING, G. L. — It Goes Where you Hit It. 1948. Illus. Hood 117-619 1978 $10

CUMMING, ROUALEYN GORDON — Five Years of a Hunters Life in the Far Interior of South Africa. New York, 1850. 2 vols., additional illus. titles, 12mo, age-marked, some spotting, some inner margins strengthened, old style half calf. K Books 239-111 1978 £45

CUMMING, ROUALEYN GORDON   Five Years of a Hunter's Life in the Far Interior of South Africa.... London, 1851. 3rd ed., 2 vols., respined, sm. 8vo., orig. cloth, bookplt. of TD Carter. Book Chest 17-104 1978 $75

CUMMINGS, E. C.   Fairy Tales. New York, (1950). Illus. in color by John Eaton, spine sunned, very fine. Victoria 34-205 1978 $25

CUMMINGS, EDWARD ESTLIN   Eimi. (New York, 1933). Orig. cloth, 1st ed., 1 of 1,381 copies, signed by author, fine, somewhat soiled, worn d.j. Mac-Manus 238-632 1978 $75

CUMMINGS, EDWARD ESTLIN   The Enormous Room. New York, (1922). 1st ed., tan cloth stamped in black, d.j. remnants laid in, censored word blacked out, very good. Houle 10-384 1978 $175

CUMMINGS, EDWARD ESTLIN   The Enormous Room. New York, (1934). 12mo., first Modern Library ed., d.w. Biblo 247-509 1978 $10

CUMMINGS, EDWARD ESTLIN   The Enormous Room. New York, 1934. New ed., very good, d.w. Bell Book 17-194 1978 £7.50

CUMMINGS, HOMER   Address of..., Temprary Chairman of the Democratic National Convention, San Francisco, June 28, 1920. N.P., n.d. Clean, orig. binding, pres. copy. Hayman 71-661 1978 $7.50

CUMMINS, ELLA STERLING MIGHELS   The Story of the Files:.... [San Francisco], 1893. Illus., original pictorial cloth, 1st ed., full page presentation inscription on front flyleaf from author. Ginsberg 14-98 1978 $100

CUMMINS, ROBERT H.   Journal Written During a Tour of the Great Lakes in Aug., 1855. (New York), 1895. Orig. wrs., tall 8vo., uncut, scarce. Americanist 102-36 1978 $20

CUNARD, NANCY   Poems (Two) 1925. London, Aquila Press, 1930. One of 150 copies, this being unnumbered and marked for presentation, imp. 8vo., decor. paper bds., very nice, author's signed autograph pres. inscription. Rota 211-83 1978 £40

CUNDALL, H. M.   Birket Foster, R.W.S. London, 1906. 1st trade ed., lg. 8vo., orig. dec. cloth, spine faded, illus. Americanist 102-10 1978 $32.50

CUNDALL, H. M.   Birket Foster. London, 1906. Lg. paper copy, portrait, 73 coloured plts., 100 black & white illus. also an orig. etching by Birket Foster, lg. & thick 4to, orig. white cloth, cellophane dust cover, ltd. ed. of 500 numbered copies. Traylen 88-376 1978 £65

CUNDALL, H. M.   Kate Greenaway Pictures. 1921. 4to., portr. frontis., cloth, fine with d.w. Quaritch 979-181 1978 $105

CUNDALL, JOSEPH   On Bookbindings Ancient and Modern, Abridged... Philadelphia and Paris, n.d. Orig. illuminated parchment wrs., uncut, illus. Americanist 102-23 1978 $20

CUNHA, FELIX   Osler as a Gastroenterologist. San Francisco, 1948. 8vo., portr., orig. bds., fine uncut copy. Zeitlin 245-181 1978 $12.50

CUNN, SAMUEL   An Appendix to the English Translation of Commandine's Euclid.... London, 1725. 8vo., woodcut diagrams, new bds., first ed. Quaritch 977-152 1978 $100

CUNNINGHAM, A.   Les Francais au Tonkin et dans la Chine Meridionale. Hanoi, 1903. Numerous plts., illus., 8vo., orig. covers. Van der Peet 127-66 1978 Dfl 45

CUNNINGHAM, ALLAN   The Cabinet Gallery of Pictures,.... London, 1833-4. 1st ed., octavo, full red mor., gilt decor., gilt spines, hinges and edges slightly rubbed, gilt tops, bookplate of Robert Hoe, plates lightly foxed. Totter-idge 29-28 1978 $350

CUNNINGHAM, CHARLES E.   Timothy Dwight, 1752-1817. New York, 1942. Illus., 1st ed. Biblo BL781-235 1978 $9.50

CUNNINGHAM, EUGENE   Triggernometry. New York, 1934. Illus., 1st ed., binding somewhat worn. Nestler Rare 78-61 1978 $25

CUNNINGHAM, JOHN 1729-1773   Poems, Chiefly Pastoral. Newcastle, 1771. 2nd ed., 8vo., 19th Cent. half russia, uncut, frontis. P. M. Hill 142-268 1978 £40

CUNNINGHAM, JOHN 1729-1773   Poems, Chiefly Pastoral. Newcastle, 1766. 1st ed., 1st issue, 8vo., frontis. by Isaac Taylor, contemp. bds., new calfspine, signature of James Tyler. Hannas 54-77 1978 £85

CUNNINGHAM, JOHN WILLIAM   The Velvet Cushion. 1814. Second ed., 8vo., orig. bds., uncut, backstrip worn. P. M. Hill 142-83 1978 £7

CUNNINGHAM, PETER   The Story of Nell Gwyn: and the Sayings of Charles the Second. 1853. 1st. ed., engraved frontis, orig. green cloth, v.g. Jarndyce 16-454 1978 £12

CUNNINGHAM, WILLIAM   Alien Immigrants to England. London, 1897. Maps, illus., 1st ed. Austin 79-180 1978 $17.50

CUNNINGHAM, WILLIAM   Alien Immigrants to England. 1897. Maps, illus., cr. 8vo. George's 635-617 1978 £5

CUNNINGHAM, WILLIAM   The Growth of English Industry and Commerce in Modern Times. Cambridge, 1907. 2 vols., 8vo. George's 635-309 1978 £7.50

CUNNINGHAM, WILLIAM   The Use and Abuse of Money. 1891. English. Austin 80-532 1978 $11

CUNNINGHAME-GRAHAM, ROBERT BONTINE
Please turn to
GRAHAM, ROBERT BONTINE CUNNINGHAME

CUNYNGHAME, HENRY H.   European Enamels. 1906. Plts., 3 coloured, roy. 8vo, orig. cloth, gilt, t.e.g., nice copy. Fenning 32-81 1978 £21

CURATE, JACOB   Scotch Presbyterian Eloquence Display'd. Rotterdam, 1738. 8vo., unbound, frontispiece. P. M. Hill 142-84 1978 £12

CURETON, THOMAS KIRK   How to Teach Swimming and Diving. 1934. Vol. I - indexed, self contained. Austin 80-910 1978 $12.50

CURIE, EVE   Journey Among Warriors. 1943. 1st ed. Austin 80-77 1978 $7.50

CURIE, EVE   Madame Curie. New York, 1937. Illus., 8vo., very nice, orig. box, partly broken, 1st Amer. ed., autographed by author. Morrill 239-356 1978 $10

CURIE, MARIE   Oeuvres. Paris, 1908. 8vo., frontis. photogravure & plts., orig. prtd. wrs., uncut & mostly unopened, spine repaired, but fine copy, 1st ed. Norman 5-69 1978 $300

CURIE, MARIE   Oeuvres. Old cloth binding. Norman 5-69a 1978 $250

CURIE, MARIE   Recherches sur les Substances Radioactives. Paris, 1904. Diagrs. in text, contemp. half red mor., fine copy, 8vo., 2nd ed. Norman 5-66 1978 $275

CURIE, MARIE   Traite de Radioactivite. Paris, 1910. 2 vols., 8vo., frontis. photogravure, photolitho. plts., text illus., orig. prtd. wrs., uncut, spines repaired, but fine set in cloth drop-box, 1st ed. Norman 5-67 1978 $575

CURIE, PIERRE   Oeuvres, Publiees Par Les Soins de la Societe Francaise de Physique. Paris, 1908. Fine heliogravure portr., plts., text-illus., royal 8vo., half shagreen, fine copy. Offenbacher 30-30 1978 $150

CURIONE, LODOVICO   Lanotomia delle Cancellaresche Corsiue and Altre Maniere di Lettere. Rome, 1588. Oblong 4to., cont. vellum, plts., first ed., with 6 preliminary printed pages. Schumann 511-15 1978 sFr 6,250

CURIOSITIES Of Entomology. London, n.d. 10 coloured plts., thin 8vo, gilt edges. Traylen 88-559 1978 £10

CURLE, RICHARD   Collecting American First Editions, Its Pitfalls & Pleasures. 8vo., cloth, t.e.g., 1 of 1250 numbered copies, signed by author, illus. Battery Park 1-350 1978 $50

CURLEY, EDWIN A.   Nebraska, Its Advantages, Resources and Drawbacks. New York, 1875. Gilt decor., cloth, maps, illus., 1st Amer. ed., scarce, very good, slipcase. Dykes 34-247 1978 $40

CURRAN, CHARLES A.   Personality Factors in Counseling. 1945. Austin 80-912 1978 $10

CURRAN, EDWARD LODGE   Address by Rev. Edward Lodge Curran, Ph.D. Before Citizens U. S. A. Chicago, 1944. Austin 79-182 1978 $11

CURRAN, EDWARD LODGE   Facts About Communism. Ca. 1935. Paper. Austin 79-183 1978 $12.50

CURRAN, EDWARD LODGE   Orthodox Americanism. Brooklyn, ca. 1945. Paper. Austin 79-184 1978 $12.50

CURRAN, JEAN A.   Widening Horizons in Medical Education.   New York, 1948. Rittenhouse 49-169 1976 $10

CURRENT, ANNIE E.   Genealogy of the Current and Hobson Families. New Castle, 1906. Cloth, very scarce. Hayman 73-223 1973 $35

CURRENT, RICHARD NELSON   Old Thad Stevens, A Story of Ambition. Madison, 1942. Pres. copy from author to Bell Wiley. Broadfoot's 44-100 1978 $16

CURRIE, BARTON   Booth Tarkington. New York, 1932. Illus., 8vo., orig. tissue d.w., boxed, fine, lst ed. Morrill 241-663 1978 $27.50

CURRIE, BARTON   Fishers of Books. Boston, 1931. 8vo., orig. cloth, paper label, 1st ed. MacManus 238-898 1978 $12.50

CURRIE, BARTON   Fishers of Books. Boston, 1931. 8vo., cloth, illus., lst trade ed. Battery Park 1-351 1978 $25

CURRIE, BARTON   Fishers of Books. Boston, 1931. Orig. cloth, d.j., lst ed., pres. copy, T.L.s. from Currie laid in. MacManus 238-899 1978 $35

CURRIE, BARTON   Fishers of Books. 2 vol. ed., 1 of 365 numbered sets, signed by author, illus., spines darkened. Battery Park 1-352 1978 $75

CURRIE, E. A.   The Story of Laura Secord, and Canadian Reminiscences. St. Catharines, 1913. Illus., decorated cover. Hood's 115-247 1978 $27.50

CURRIE, MARGARET   Margaret Currie, Her Book. Toronto, 1924. Hood 116-682 1978 $7.50

CURRIER, A. H.   The Life of Constans L. Goodell, D.D. New York, (1887). Clean, worn at extremities, cover little soiled, back inner hinges weak, orig. binding. Hayman 71-178 1978 $7.50

CURRIER, ERNEST M.   Marks of Early American Silversmiths. Portland, 1938. Illus., 1st ed., 4to., frontis. port., illus., orig. cloth, nice copy. MacManus 239-653 1978 $75

CURRIER AND IVES   Best Fifty Lithographs. New York, (c.1933). Illus., 4to. Biblo BL781-706 1978 $18.50

CURRIER AND IVES   Clipper Ship Prints Including Other Merchant Ships. New York, 1930. 1st ed., sm. folio, illus., orig. gilt pic. cloth, ltd. to 500 copies, fine. MacManus 239-1744 1978 $60

CURRIER AND IVES   Clipper Ships. London, 1932. 4to., plts. in color, damp stain at bottom of front cover. Biblo BL781-707 1978 $16.50

CURRY, A. C.   Toronto Year Book, 1932; The Story of a City. Toronto, 1932. Illus., card cover. Hood 116-732 1978 $35

CURRY, CHARLES   John Brown Baldwin- Lawyer, Soldier, Statesman. Staunton, Va., 1928. Wraps, Bell Wiley's Copy. Broadfoot's 44-101 1978 $12.00

CURRY, MARGARET   The History of Platte County, Nebraska. Culver City, (1950). Illus., 1st ed., fine, inscribed by author, slip case, pic. fabricoid. Dykes 35-42 1978 $100

CURSON, HENRY   A Compendium of the Laws and Government, Ecclesiastical, Civil and Military of England, Scotland and Ireland... London, 1699. Sm. 8vo, contemp. calf, joints cracked. Traylen 88-465 1978 £110

A CURSORY View of James MacKintosh's Celebrated Speech..As Counsel for Mr. Peltier with such Extracts from It May Serve as a Beacon to Direct Irishmen. Dublin, 1804. 1st ed, plain wr., very good, octavo bound in cloth. Hyland 128-47 1978 £12

CURTI, MARGARET WOOSTER   Child Psychology. 1938. Illus. Austin 80-913 1978 $10

CURTIS, ALFRED A.   Life and Characteristics of Right Reverend Alfred A. Curtis, DD. 1913. Ex-lib. Austin 79-185 1978 $15

CURTIS, C.   Nature & Development of Plants. New York, 1925. 8vo, orig. cloth. Book Chest 17-496 1978 $10

CURTIS, C. H.   Orchids for Everyone. London, 1910. Plates, many in color, 8vo., orig. cloth. Book Chest 17-108 1978 $65

CURTIS, CHARLES P.   Hunting in Africa East and West. Boston, 1925. 33 plts., dec. cloth, 8vo. K Books 239-112 1978 £16

CURTIS, CHARLES P., JR.   Lions Under the Throne. A Study of the Supreme Court. Boston, 1947. Biblo BL781-811 1978 $7.50

CURTIS, FRANCIS   The Republican Party, a History of Its Fifty Years Existence... New York, 1904. Portrs., t.e.g., fine set. MacManus 239-108 1978 $40

CURTIS, GEORGE MUNSON   Early Silver of Connecticut and Its Makers. Meriden, 1913. 33 plts., worn ex-lib. copy. Baldwins' 51-52 1978 $27.50

CURTIS, GEORGE TICKNOR   Life of James Buchanan, Fifteenth President of the United States. New York, 1883. 1st ed., 2 vols., illus., errata slip in vol. I, orig. cloth, ex-lib., but good. MacManus 239-730 1978 $25

CURTIS, GEORGE TICKNOR   Pleas for Religious Liberty and the Rights of Conscience. Washington, 1886. Orig. pr. front wr., lst ed. Ginsberg 14-1103 1978 $35

CURTIS, GEORGE WILLIAM   Comprising Nile Notes, Howadji in Syria, Lotus-Eating, Potiphar Papers, Prue and I. New York, 1856. 5 vols., 12mo., contemp. calf, pres. inscrip. each vol. Morrill 239-357 1978 $57.50

CURTIS, GEORGE WILLIAM   The Duty of the American Scholar to Politics and the Times. New York, 1856. 8vo., unbound, lst ed. Morrill 241-102 1978 $7.50

CURTIS, GEORGE WILLIAM   Trumps. New York, 1861. Illus., 8vo., contemp. marbled bds., lea. back & corners, few signatures, lst ed., pres. from Curtis to his wife. Morrill 239-358 1978 $22.50

CURTIS, GEORGE WILLIAM   Washington Irving. New York, Devinne Press, 1901. Full lea., t.e.g., other edges uncut, 1 of 344 copies prtd. on handmade paper. Battery Park 1-65 1978 $50

CURTIS, JOHN G.   History of the Town of Brookline Mass. Boston, 1933. Illus., maps, fine. MacManus 239-1017 1978 $12.50

CURTIS, MATTOON M.   The Book of Snuff and Snuff Boxes... New York, (1935). Roy. 8vo., illus., cloth. Quaritch 983-123 1978 $80

CURTIS, NEWTON MARTIN   The Capture of Fort Fisher. Boston, 1900. Wrs. Bell Wiley's copy. Broadfoot 46-62 1978 $20

CURTIS, NEWTON MARTIN   From Bull Run to Chancellorsville. New York, 1906. Bell Wiley's copy. Broadfoot's 44-556 1978 $26

CURTIS, WILLIAM ELEROY   Abraham Lincoln. Philadelphia, (1902). Illus. Biblo 248-60 1978 $16.50

CURTIUS, ERNST   History of Greece. 1899. 5 vols. Allen 234-254 1978 $20

CURTIUS, L.   Die antike Kunst... Berlin, 1923. 4to., plain and coloured plts., bds., linen back. Quaritch 983-9 1978 $65

CURTIUS RUFUS, QUINTUS   Historiarum libri Accuratissime editi D. Heinsius. Leyden, Elzevir Press, 1633. Eng. title, map, 12mo., cont. calf, rebacked, occasional browning of text. Howes 194-543 1978 £12.50

CURTIUS RUFUS, QUINTUS   Quinto Curtio da P. Candido di Latino in volgare tradooto et novamente correcto. Venice, Aug., 1531. 8 vo., good condition, contemp. Venetian binding, dark brown mor. Schafer 19-13 1978 sFr. 2,600

CURTIUS RUFUS, QUINTUS   De Rebus Gestis Alexandri Regis Macedonum... Leiden, 1696. Engr. plts., old calf, covers detached, spine split. Allen 234-255 1978 $12.50

CURWEN, HENRY   A History of Booksellers. Rebound preserving most of orig. binding, ex-lib., with library markings, foxing. Battery Park 1-353 1978 $25

CURWEN, HENRY   Sorrow and Song: Studies in Literary Struggle. 1875. lst. collected ed., 2 vols., 8vo, orig. green cloth, inside joints weak, nice copy. Fenning 32-82 1978 £16

THE CURWEN Press Almanack, 1926. London, n.d. 1 of 425 copies, sm. 8vo., orig. cloth-backed bds., bookplt of Howard R. Spohn. Americanist 102-37 1978 $30

CURWOOD, JAMES OLIVER   The Ancient Highway. 1925. Frontis., first ed., fine, d.j. Austin 82-320 1978 $12.50

CURWOOD, JAMES OLIVER   The Courage of Marge O'Doone. New York, 1929. Hood's 115-425 1978 $7.50

CURWOOD, JAMES OLIVER   The Plains of Abraham. 1928. First ed., very good, d.j. Austin 82-321 1978 $12.50

CURWOOD, JAMES OLIVER   The River's End. Toronto, 1922. Browned, orig. cloth. Eaton 45-131 1978 £5

CURZON, GEORGE NATHANIEL   Modern Parliamentary Eloquence. 1914. Orig. cloth, 8vo. Howes 194-766 1978 £7.50

CUSACK, M. F.   A History of the Irish Nation. London, (1868). Illus., stout 4to., half hard-grain mor., gilt spine. K Books 244-353 1978 £15

CUSHING, CALEB   British and American Commision on the Hudson's Bay and Puget's Sound Agricultural Companies Claims. [Washington, 1868]. Orig. pr. wr., 1st ed. Ginsberg 14-809 1978 $75

CUSHING, CALEB   British and American Joint Commission for the Settlement of the Claims of the Hudson's Bay and Puget's Sound Agricultural Companies. Montreal, 1869. Disbound, 1st ed. Ginsberg 14-810 1978 $40

CUSHING, CALEB   The History and Present State of the Town of Newburyport. Newburyport, 1826. 12mo. Biblo 247-107 1978 $37.50

CUSHING, CALEB   Outlines of the Life and Public Services, Civil and Military, of William Henry Harrison. Boston, 1840. Portr., 16mo., orig. wrs., some foxing, 1st ed. Morrill 241-103 1978 $20

CUSHING, CALEB   Outlines of the Life and Public Services, Civil and Military, of William Henry Harrison, of Ohio. Washington, 1840. Sewn. Hayman 73-137 1978 $12.50

CUSHING, CALEB   Supplement and Appendix to the Arguments in Behalf of the United States in the Matter of the Claims of the Hudson's Bay and Puget's Sound Agricultural Companies. [Washington, 1868]. Orig. pr. wr., 1st ed. Ginsberg 14-811 1978 $35

CUSHING, E. H.   The New Texas School Reader. Houston, 1864. Original printed boards. Jenkins 116-275 1978 $850

CUSHING, FRANK HAMILTON   My Adventures in Zuni. Santa Fe, 1941. Illus., original cloth, 1st ed., limited to 400 copies. Ginsberg 14-293 1978 $150

CUSHING, HARVEY WILLIAMS   Collection of Books and Manuscripts. New York, 1943. Rittenhouse 49-170 1976 $20

CUSHING, HARVEY WILLIAMS   From a Surgeon's Journal, 1915-1918. Boston, 1936. Rittenhouse 49-173 1978 $15

CUSHING, HARVEY WILLIAMS   The Life of Sir William Osler. Oxford, 1925. Third impression, two vols., orig. binding. Wolfe 39-355 1978 $35

CUSHING, HARVEY WILLIAMS   Life of Sir William Osler. Oxford, 1926. 4th impression, 2 vols. Baldwins' 51-183 1978 $30

CUSHING, HARVEY WILLIAMS   The Medical Career, and Other Papers. Boston, 1940. 8vo., d.w., 1st ed. Morrill 239-60 1978 $15

CUSHING, HARVEY WILLIAMS   Meningiomas, Their Classification, Regional Behaviour, Life History and Surgical End Results. Baltimore, 1938. Rittenhouse 49-171 1976 $50

CUSHING, HARVEY WILLIAMS   Papers Relating to the Pituitary Body, Hypothalamus and Parsympathetic Nervous System. Springfield, 1932. Rittenhouse 49-172 1976 $60

CUSHING, HARVEY WILLIAMS   The Pituitary Body and Its Disorders. Philadelphia & London, (1912). 8vo., color frontis., fldg. plt., illus., orig. red cloth, gilt on spine, very good copy, 1st ed. Zeitlin 245-52 1978 $115

CUSHING, HARVEY WILLIAMS   Tumors of the Nervous Acusticus and the Syndrome of the Cerebellopontile Angle. Philadelphia, 1917. Ex-library, worn. Rittenhouse 49-174 1976 $25

CUSHING, HARVEY WILLIAMS   Tumors of the Nervus Acusticus and the Syndrome of Cerebellopontile Angle. Philadelphia, 1917. Rittenhouse 49-175 1978 $40

CUSHING, JAMES R.   Historical Discourse; Delivered Oct. 29, 1851, at the One Hundred and Fiftieth Anniversary of the Organization of the First Congregational Church... Portland, 1851. Unbound as issued. Hayman 72-444 1978 $7.50

CUSHING, THOMAS   History of the Counties of Gloucester, Salem and Cumberland, New Jersey. Philadelphia, 1883. Rebound, 4to., ports., scarce. MacManus 239-1253 1978 $175

CUSHMAN, H.B.   History of the Choctaw, Chicksaw, and Natchez Indians. Greenville, 1899. Original cloth, gilt, blindstamped panels, marbled edges, rare and basic. Jenkins 116-276 1978 $200

CUSHMAN, JOSEPH AUGUSTINE   Monograph of the Foraminiferal Family Polymorphinidae Recent & Fossil. Washington, 1930. Plts., spine chipping, 8vo., orig. cloth. Book Chest 17-106 1978 $25

CUSHMAN, ROBERT   The Sin and Danger of Self-Love Described in a Sermon Preached at Plymouth, in New England, 1621. Boston, 1846. 8vo., unbound. Morrill 241-104 1978 $7.50

CUSHMAN, SAMUEL   The Gold Mines of Gilpin County, Colorado. Central City, 1876. Original wr. bound in cloth, 1st ed. Ginsberg 14-256 1978 $175

CUSHNY, ARTHUR R.   Pharmacology and Therapeutics or the Action of Drugs in Health and Disease. Philadelphia, 1936. Rittenhouse 49-177 1976 $10

CUSSOMS, JOHN   United States "History" as a Yankee Makes and Takes It. Glen Allen, 1900. Wraps chipped, Bell Wiley's copy. Broadfoot's 44-691 1978 $15.00

CUSSONS, JOHN   Jack Sterry, the Jessie Scout. Richmond, 1908. Bell Wiley's copy. Broadfoot 46-63 1978 $16

CUST, A. M.   The Ivory-Workers of the Middle Ages. 1902. Illus., 8vo. Upcroft 12-94 1978 £6.50

CUST, LIONEL   The Master E. S. and the "Ars Moriendi". Oxford, 1898. Thin quarto, orig. pr. blue boards, cloth spine, bookplate of Virtue and Cahill Library and release stamp. Totteridge 29-29 1978 $50

CUST, NINA   Gentlemen Errant. 1909. Plt. Allen 234-1191 1978 $10

CUSTARD, ETHELINDA   The Discipline of Storms. New York... Indianapolis, 1859. Cloth, worn & other defects, poor copy, covers badly worn, spine chipped & repaired, foxed throughout. Hayman 73-177 1978 $12.50

CUSTER, ELIZABETH B.   "Boots and Saddles" or Life in Dakota with General Custer. New York, (1885). dec. cloth, 1st ed., 8vo., nice. Paine 78-37 1978 $18.50

CUSTER, ELIZABETH B.   "Boots and Saddles", or Life in Dakota with General Custer. New York, 1885. Portr., maps, cloth. Hayman 73-138 1978 $8.50

CUSTER, GEORGE   My Life on the Plains...With Indians. New York, 1874. First ed., 8vo., fine., orig. cloth, plts. Paine 78-38 1978 $50

CUTBUSH, JAMES   The American Artist's Manual... Philadelphia, 1814. 2 vols., nice set, cloth, some foxing, illus., 1st ed. MacManus 239-655 1978 $100

CUTBUSH, JAMES   A System of Pyrotechny, Comprehending the Theory and Practice, with the Application of Chemistry. Philadelphia, 1825. 8vo., plt., half antique calf, gilt, foxing, but very good copy, contemp. signature, lib. stamp, 1st ed. Norman 5-70 1978 $175

CUTCHINS, JOHN A.   A Famous Command, The Richmond Light Infantry Blues. Richmond, 1934. Pres. copy from author to another person. Broadfoot's 44-658 1978 $30

CUTHBERTSON, CATHERINE   Santo Sebastiano; or, The Young Protector. London, 1806. 1st. ed., 5 vols., sm. 8vo, contemp. half calf, worming at beginning and end of vol. 1, affecting text. Trayeln 88-216 1978 £85

CUTLER, CARL C.   Greyhounds of the Sea... New York, 1930. 1st ed., 4to., illus., scarce. MacManus 239-1745 1978 $40

CUTLER, R. KING   Address of...U.S. Senate of Louisiana. New Orleans, 1865. Disbound, 1st ed. Ginsberg 14-496 1978 $75

CUTLER, T. W.   A Grammar of Japanese Ornament and Design. 1880. Folio, plts., some coloured, orig. dec. cloth, gilt top.   Quaritch 983-139 1978 $450

CUTTEN, GEORGE BARTON   Mind: Its Origin and Goal. Yale University Press, 1925. Austin 80-914 1978 $8.50

CUTTEN, GEORGE BARTON   Three Thousand Years of Mental Healing. 1911. Illus. Austin 80-915 1978 $15

CUTTER, EPHRAIM   Monography Thyrotomy, for the Removal of Laryngeal Growths, Modified. Boston, 1871. 8vo., orig. wrs., 1st ed.   Morrill 239-61 1978 $7.50

CUTTER, WILLIAM RICHARD   Genealogical and Personal Memoirs Relating to the Families of Boston and Eastern Massachusetts. New York, 1908. 4 vols., 4to., half lea., some covers damps tained.   Morrill 241-327 1978 $25

CUTTING, ELISABETH   Jefferson Davis, Political Soldier. New York, 1930. Illus., presen. copy signed by author. Bell Wiley's copy. Broadfoot 46-64 1978 $20

CUTTS, E. L.   Scenes and Characters of the Middle Ages. 1872. Illus., 8vo. George's 635-618 1978 £5.25

CUVIER, GEORGES   The Animal Kingdom. London, 1837. 4 vols. in 2 vols. rebound in bright orange cloth, 8vo., orig. cloth, plts., most colored. Book Chest 17-107 1978 $135

CUVIER, GEORGES   Essay on the Theory of the Earth, with Geological Illustrations, by Professor Jameson. Edinburgh & London, 1827. Fifth ed., 8vo., contemp. calf, plts. Gurney 75-29 1978 £20

CYON, ELIE DE   Les Nerfs Du Coeur Anatomie Et Physiologie Avec Une Preface Sur Les Rapports De La Medecine Avec La Physiologie Et La Bacteriologie. Paris, 1905. 8vo., illus., buff prtd. wrs., light browning, bkplts. of Drs. E. F. Horine & C. B. Chapman, very good, uncut, mostly unopened copy, 1st ed.   Zeitlin 245-53 1978 $75

CYON, ELIE DE   Die Nerven Des Herzens. Berlin, 1907. 8vo., illus., black pebbled cloth, fine copy, bkplts. of Drs. E. F. Horine & C. B. Chapman, 1st ed. Zeitlin 245-54 1978 $65

THE CYPRESS HILLS CEMETERY   Catalogue for 1880. New York, 1880. Folded map frontis., pict. wr., good. Butterfield 21-491 1978 $20

THE CYPRESS HILLS CEMETERY   "Here Would I Wish to Sleep. This is the Spot..." New York, 1863. Wr., stained. Butterfield 21-490 1978 $15

D

D., H. PSEUD.
Please turn to
DOOLITTLE, HILDA

DABAYRAC, NICOLAS　　Sargines, Ou L'Eleve de L'Amour. Hambourg, Paris, 1793. 6mo., 2 eng. plts., 1/2 red morocco. Eaton 45-440 1978 £10

DABNEY, J. E.　　Mountain Spirits : A Chronicle of Corn Whiskey from King James' Ulster Plantation to America's Appalachians and the Moonshine Life. Photos. Broadfoot 50-49 1978 $9

DABNEY, ROBERT L.　　Life and Campaigns of Lieut.-Gen. Thomas J. Jackson. New York, 1866. Bell Wiley's copy. Broadfoot 46-65 1978 $25

DABNEY, VIRGINIUS　　Liberalism in the South. Chapel Hill, 1932. Fine, some underlining. MacManus 239-1800 1978 $8.50

DABOLL, NATHAN　　Daboll's Schoolmaster's Assistant. Ithaca, 1837. Lea., little scuffed. Hayman 73-139 1978 $10

DABOLL, S. B.　　Past and Present of Clinton County, Michigan. Chicago, 1906. Morocco. Hayman 71-464 1978 $62.50

DA COSTA, EMANUEL MENDES
Please turn to
MENDES DA COSTA, EMANUEL

DA COSTA, JOHN CHALMERS　　Poems of John Chalmers DaCosta. Philadelphia, 1942. Rittenhouse 49-178 1976 $10

DACUS, JOSEPH A.　　Illustrated Lives and Adventures of Frank and Jesse James and the Younger Brothers. St. Louis, 1882. Bell Wiley's copy. Broadfoot 46-496 1978 $20

DACUS, JOSEPH A.　　Life and Adventures of Frank and Jesse James the Noted Western Outlaws. Indianapolis, 1880. New cloth, inscribed. Hayman 72-162 1978 $17.50

DAFFAN, KATIE　　Texas Heroes. Ennis, 1924. 1st ed., illus. Jenkins 116-280 1978 $7.50

DAFFORNE, J.　　Pictures by Sir A. W. Callcott. (c. 1860). Roy. 4to., plts. George's 635-103 1978 £8.50

DAFOE, JOHN WESLEY　　Clifford Sifton, In Relation to His Times. Toronto, 1931. Lib. bookplate. Hood's 115-248 1978 $40

DAFOE, JOHN WESLEY　　Clifford Sifton, in Relation to His Times. Toronto, 1931. Hood 117-294 1978 $45

D'AGAPEYEFF, A.　　Maps. London, (1942). Illus. Biblo 247-449 1978 $15

DAGLISH, ERIC FITCH　　How to See Beasts. 1933. Wood engrav. by author, bds., covers soiled, good, first English ed. Bell Book 16-483 1978 £5

DAHL, BASIL　　To the Toilers and Other Verses. Berkeley Heights. Frontis., bds., cloth spine, no. 248 of an ed. ltd. to 450 copies prtd. on Canterbury laid Book. Battery Park 1-217 1978 $125

DAHL, BORGHILD　　I Wanted to See. 1944. Austin 80-917 1978 $7.50

DAHL, BORGHILD　　Karen. 1947. Austin 79-186 1978 $8.50

DAHLBERG, MARY　　Dagger. N. Y., 1930. 1st ed., 8 vo., art deco d.j., very good-fine. Houle 10-79 1978 $15

DAHLINGER, CHARLES W.　　The New Agrarianism. 1913. Austin 80-533 1978 $11

DAHN, FELIX　　A Struggle for Rome. London, 1878. 3 vols., orig. cloth, 1st ed. in English, good. MacManus 238-189 1978 $85

DAILEY, W. N. P.　　History of Montgomery Classis-R.C.A. to Which is Added Sketches of Mohawk Valley Men and Events of Early Days. Amsterdam, n.d. (ca. 1915). Stiff wr., many illus. Butterfield 21-273 1978 $7.50

DAINOW, MORLEY　　Self-Organization for Business Men. 1924. Austin 80-534 1978 $10

DAKERS, E. K.　　Titus Oates. 1949. Illus., octavo, good. Upcroft 10-406 1978 £6

D'ALBERTI DI VILLANOVA, FRANCESCO
Please turn to
ALBERTI DI VILLANOVA, FRANCESCO D'

DALE, DAPHNE　　Youth's Golden Days. Original Stories and Sketches. London-New York-Chicago, (1894). Illus., pict. bds. in color, little rubbed. Hayman 72-378 1978 $7.50

DALE, E.　　National Life and Character in the Mirror of Early English Literature. Cambridge, 1907. 8vo. Upcroft 12-95 1978 £8.50

DALE, EDWARD EVERETT　　The Range Cattle Industry. Norman, 1930. Illus., map, original cloth, faded, 1st ed., presentation copy signed by the author. Ginsberg 14-327 1978 $50

DALE, EDWARD EVERETT　　The Range Cattle Industry. Norman, 1930. Pic. cloth, decor. end sheets, maps, illus., rare, fine copy, slipcase. Dykes 34-21 1978 $100

DALE, HARRISON CLIFFORD　　The Ashley-Smith Explorations and the Discovery of a Central Route to the Pacific 1822-1829. Glendale, 1941. Illus., original cloth. Ginsberg 14-328 1978 $65

DALE, NELLIE　　Steps to Reading. (London), (1889). Sm. 8vo, t.p. in color and color plates, pictorial linen wrappers, very good. Victoria 34-195 1978 $30

D'ALEMBERT, JEAN LEROND
Please turn to
ALEMBERT, JEAN LEROND D'

DALI, SALVADOR　　Hidden Faces. 1947. Frontis. by author, very good, slightly worn d.w., first English ed. Bell Book 17-199 1978 £12.50

DALIZE, RENE　　Ballade du Pauvre Macchabe Mal Enterre. Paris, 1919. 4to., full cloth, partly uncut, orig. fr. wr. bound in, ltd. ed., 135 copies prtd., 1 of 110 on Arches paper, signed by Derain, orig. woodcuts by Andre Derain, cloth binding & fr. wr. slightly dulled. Goldschmidt 110-15 1978 $310

DALL, CAROLINE H.　　Otis. N.P., (1892). Illus., 8vo., 1st ed. Morrill 239-508 1978 $7.50

DALL, IAN　　Sun Before Seven. London, (1936). Illus., 1st ed. Biblo BL781-920 1978 $9

DALLAM, JAMES　　A Digest of the Laws of Texas, Containing a Full and Complete Compilation of Land Laws, Together with Opinions of the Supreme Court. Balitmore, 1845. Full calf, 1st ed. Jenkins 116-283 1978 $485

DALLAS, ROBERT CHARLES　　Recollections of the Life of Lord Byron, from the Year 1808 to the End of 1814.... Philadelphia, 1825. 1st US ed., orig. calf, 8vo. Americanist 101-29 1978 $35

D'ALLEMAGNE, HENRY RENE
Please turn to
ALLEMAGNE, HENRY RENE D'

DALRYMPLE, ALEXANDER　　An Historical Collection of the Several Voyages and Discoveries in the South Pacific Ocean. 1770-71. Engraved plts., 2 vols. in one, 4to, calf, rebacked, some browning. Edwards 1012-13 1978 £950

DALRYMPLE, DAVID, LORD HAILES 1726-1792
Please turn to
HAILES, DAVID DALRYMPLE, LORD 1726-1792

DALRYMPLE, JOHN 1726-1810   Memoirs of Great Britain and Ireland (1681-92). Edinburgh, 1771-73. 2 vols., first ed., 4to., early 19th cent. half calf, rebacked. Howes 194-234 1978 £52

DALRYMPLE, JOHN, 5TH EARL OF STAIR 1720-1789
Please turn to
STAIR, JOHN DALRYMPLE, 5TH EARL OF

D'ALTON, E. A.   History of Ireland from the Earliest Times to the Present Day. Dublin, (c. 1910). Map, coloured frontispiece, illus., 3 vols. in 6. George's 635-619 1978 £10.50

DALTON, HENRY G.   The History of British Guiana. London, 1855. 1st. ed., 2 vols., 8vo, folding map, engraved plts., orig. embossed red cloth, spines lettered in gilt, neatly recased, foot of spines repaired, cover trifle soiled. Deighton 5-34 1978 £65

DALTON, J. G.   Lyra Bicyclica: Forty Poets on the Wheel. Boston, 1880. 12mo., ex-lib., orig. cloth, 1st ed., pres. copy. Morrill 241-52 1978 $12.50

DALTON, JOHN 1766-1844   Meteorological Observations and Essays. Manchester, 1834. Second ed., 8vo., orig. bds., repaired, lib. stamp on title. Quaritch 977-91 1978 $100

DALTON, JOHN 1766-1844   A New System of Chemical Philosophy. London, 1842. Part I, 8vo., plts., orig. cloth, uncut, unopened, very good copy, 2nd ed. Norman 5-71 1978 $375

D'ALTON, JOHN 1792-1867   The History of the County of Dublin. Dublin, 1838. 1st. ed., 8vo, orig. cloth, neatly rebacked retaining orig. backstrip, nice. Fenning 32-83 1978 £24

D'ALTON, JOHN 1792-1867   The History of Co. Dublin. (1838). Reprint, octavo bound in cloth. Hyland 128-922 1978 £10

DALTON, JOHN 1792-1867   Memoir of John Dalton. London, 1856. 8vo., frontis. portr., orig. cloth, spine repaired, very good copy, 1st ed. Norman 5-72 1978 $75

DALY, ELIZABETH   Arrow Pointing Nowhere. New York, (1944). 1st ed. Biblo BL781-929 1978 $9

DALY, FREDERIC   Henry Irving in England and America 1838-84. 1884. First ed., portrait, cr. 8vo., orig. cloth gilt. Howes 194-1268 1978 £6.50

DALY, THOMAS AUGUSTINE   Canzoni. 1906. Illus., in Italian dialect. Austin 79-188 1978 $10

DALY, THOMAS AUGUSTINE   Carmina. 1912 (1909). Inscr. by Daly dated March 4, 1914, in Italian & Irish dialect. Austin 79-189 1978 $20

DALY, THOMAS AUGUSTINE   Madrigali. 1912. Illus., in Italian and Irish dialect, inscr'd by Daly. Austin 79-190 1978 $20

DALZELL, JAMES MC CORMICK   His Autobiography, Poems and Comic War Papers. Sketch of John Gray, Washington's Last Soldier.... Cincinnati, 1888. Cloth, spotted, some wear. Hayman 72-535 1978 $10

DALZELL, JAMES MC CORMICK   His Autobiography, Poems and Comic War Papers. Cincinnati, 1888. Bell Wiley's copy. Broadfoot's 44-588 1978 $16

LES DAMES de Byron; or, Portraits of the Principle Female Characters in Lord Byron's Poems... London, 1836. 4to., illus., orig. pub. full mor., 1st ed., extremities and edges a bit rubbed, inner hinges cracked. MacManus 238-183 1978 $35

DAMON, SAMUEL C.   A Trip from the Sandwich Islands to Lower Oregon and Upper California;.... Honolulu, 1849. Modern half morocco, 1st ed. Ginsberg 14-329 1978 $750

DAMPIER, WILLIAM   A New Voyage Round the World. London, 1927. 4to., vellum spine, cloth bds., illus., maps, fine copy, ltd. to 975 numbered copies, orig. pub. in 1697. MacManus 239-1746 1978 $65

DAMPIER, WILLIAM   Voyages and Discoveries by... London, 1931. 4to., vellum spine, cloth bds., illus., fold. maps, fine unopened copy, ltd. to 975 copies, orig. pub. in 1699. MacManus 239-1747 1978 $65

DAMPIER-WHETHAM, WILLIAM CECIL DAMPIER   A History of Science. 1930. Austin 80-919 1978 $10

DAMROSCH, FRANK   Some Essentials in the Teaching of Music. 1916. Austin 80-920 1978 $10

DAMROSCH, WALTER   My Musical Life. 1923. Illus., orig. ed. Austin 79-191 1978 $10

DANA, CHARLES L.   The Peaks of Medical History. New York, 1928. Second ed. Rittenhouse 49-179 1976 $15

DANA, J. C.   Notes on Bookbinding for Libraries. 1906. Battery Park 1-276 1978 $35

DANA, RICHARD HENRY 1815-1882   Two Years Before the Mast. New York, 1840. Black cloth, bkplt., good sound copy, two-part case with mor. back, A.L.s. from author laid in. Dawson's 447-216 1978 $275

DANA, RICHARD HENRY 1815-1882   Two Years Before the Mast. A Personal Narrative. Boston, 1869. Orig. cloth, rev'd. ed., spine faded, otherwise very good. MacManus 238-465 1978 $35

DANA, RICHARD HENRY 1815-1882   Two Years Before the Mast. A Personal Narrative. Boston, 1911. 2 vols., 1 of 350 numbered lg. paper sets, orig. cloth backed bds., uncut, nice. Americanist 102-38 1978 $125

DANA, RICHARD HENRY 1815-1882   Two Years Before the Mast. New York, 1936. 8vo., full color cream mor., gilt slipcase, ltd. to 1,000, bound by William Wheeler, 1st ed., collector's cond. Desmarais 1-112 1978 $100

DANCE OF DEATH   The Dances of Death... London, 1803. Quarto, frontis., plts. by Hans Holbein, gilt and blind stamped diamond in panel binding, rebacked. Bennett 20-107 1978 $95

DANCE OF DEATH   The Dance of Death Printed at Paris in 1490. Washington, 1945. Ed. ltd. to 200 numbered copies, reproduction made from copy in Lessing J. Rosenwald Collection, near mint, warping of full vellum covers, scarce. Current 24-224 1978 $175

DANCER, THOMAS   The Medical Assistant or Jamaica Practice of Physic. St. Jago de la Vega, 1809. 4to., old calf, gilt-ruled, gilt on spine, worn, minor foxing, bkplt. & library stamp, very good copy internally, pres. inscr., partially trimmed, 2nd ed., very rare. Zeitlin 245-302 1978 $875

DANDINI, GIROLAMO   Voyage Du Mont Liban... Paris, 1685. Sm. 8vo, engraved title, contemp. red morocco, gilt panelled spine. Edwards 1012-64 1978 £270

DANE, CLEMENCE   Fate Cries Out. 1935. First ed., signed pres. copy with signed type written letter, cr. 8vo., d.j. George's 635-1311 1978 £6

DANE, G. EZRA   Ghost Town. New York, (1948). Illus. Biblo 247-199 1978 $16.50

DANFORTH, C. H.   Hair – with Special Reference to Hypertrichosis. Chicago, 1925. Rittenhouse 49-180 1976 $10

D'ANGOULEME, MARGUERITE
Please turn to
MARGUERITE D'ANGOULEME

DANGUY, H.   Le Nouveau visage de la Cochinchine. Saigon, 1929. 8vo, orig. covers. Van der Peet 127-68 1978 Dfl 25

DANIEL, EDWARD M.   Speeches and Orations of John Warwick Daniel. Lynchburg, Va., 1911. Bell Wiley's copy. Broadfoot 46-66 1978 $20

DANIEL, F. E.   Recollections of a Rebel Surgeon. Chicago,
1901. Bell Wiley's copy. Broadfoot 46-67 1978 $30

DANIEL, GEORGE   Merrie England in the Olden Time. 1842. 2
vols., 8vo., 1st ed., portr., plts., illus., orig. brown ribbed cloth, decor. in
blind, fine set, pres. inscr. from Daniel. Quaritch 979-106 1978 $115

DANIEL, GEORGE   Merrie England in the Olden Time... 1842. 2
vols., 8vo., 1st ed., orig. brown ribbed cloth, fine, pres. inscription from Daniel,
plts. Quaritch 983-319 1978 $145

DANIEL, JOHN W.   Life, Services, and Character of Jefferson
Davis. Richmond, Va., 1890. Wraps, Bell Wiley's Copy. Broadfoot's 44-102
1978 $10.00

DANIEL, LIZZIE C.   Confederate Scrap-Book. Richmond, 1893.
Frontis., scarce, fine. MacManus 239-870 1978 $27.50

DANIEL, SAMUEL   The Poetical Works. 1718. 2 vols., 12mo.,
19th-century half calf, first ed. P. M. Hill 142-269 1978 £30

DANIEL B. Updike and the Merrymount Press. Grolier Club, 1940. Illus., one of
150 copies on machine made paper, cream bds., signed by Updike. Battery Park 1-
150 1978 $150

DANIEL Webster...for Young Americans. Boston, 1903. Illus. Biblo BL781-228
1978 $12

DANIELL, L. E.   Texas, The Country and Its Men:.... Austin,
1922. Original full morocco, gilt, marbled edges, fine copy, 1st ed, many unique
illus. Jenkins 116-297 1978 $150

DANIELL, RAYMOND   Civilians Must Fight. 1941. Austin 80-78 1978
$7.50

DANIELLI, J. F.   Cell Physiology and Pharmacology. New York,
1950. Library marks. Rittenhouse 49-181 1976 $15

DANIELS, G. W.   The Early English Cotton Industry. Manchester,
1920. Illus., cr. 8vo., stiff wrappers. George's 635-310 1978 £5

DANIELS, HARRIET MCDOUAL   Muller Hill. New York, 1943. 1st ed. in
dust jacket. Butterfield 21-262 1978 $12.50

DANIELS, JOSEPHUS   Editor in Politics. Chapel Hill, 1941. Illus.
Broadfoot 50-50 1978 $10

DANIELS, JOSEPHUS   The Navy and the Nation. New York, 1919.
Broadfoot 50-52 1978 $9

DANIELS, JOSEPHUS   Shirt-Sleeve Diplomat. Chapel Hill, 1947.
Broadfoot 50-53 1978 $10

DANIELS, JOSEPHUS   Tar Heel Editor. Chapel Hill, 1939. Illus.
Broadfoot 50-54 1978 $10

DANIELS, JOSEPHUS   The Wilson Era. Chapel Hill, 1944. 2 vols.
Broadfoot 50-55 1978 $18

DANIELS, WILLIAM HAVEN   Memorials of Gilbert Haven, Bishop of the Methodist Episcopal Church... Boston, 1880. Cloth. Hayman 72-167 1978 $12.50

DANIELSON, RICHARD   Martha Doyle and Other Sporting Memories.
N. Y., Derrydale Press, (1938). 1 of 1,200 numbered copies, 4to., red
buckram, leather labels, ink inscription, as new. Houle 10-85 1978 $60

DANKERS, JASPAR   Journal of a Voyage to New York and a Tour in
Several of the American Colonies in 1679-80. Brooklyn, 1867. Fldg. color plts.,
1st ed., crisp copy. Butterfield 21-133 1978 $35

DANNAY, FREDERIC
Please turn to
QUEEN, ELLERY PSEUD.

D'ANNUNZIO, GABRIELE
Please turn to
ANNUNZIO, GABRIELE D'

DANTE ALIGHIERI   The Canzoniere. 1835. Lg. 12mo., contemp.
blind- and gilt-tooled calf, frontispiece, plt. P. M. Hill 142-270 1978 £42

DANTE ALIGHIERI   The Commediae and Canzoniere. 1890. 2 vols.,
portrait, 8vo. George's 635-1288 1978 £5.25

DANTE ALIGHIERI   La comedia ...con la nova espositione di
Alessandro Vellutello. Venice, 1544. 4 to., italic letter, large woodcuts,
very good, contemp. vellum, repair to spine, 1st Vellutello ed. Quaritch
Summer, 1978-10 1978 $1,850

DANTE ALIGHIERI   La Comedia, con la Nova Espositione di Alessandro Vellutello; con Gratia de la Illustrissima Signoria di Vinegia. Venice,
1544. Woodcuts, thick 4to., old vellum, 1st ed., fine copy. Argosy Special-
33 1978 $450

DANTE ALIGHIERI   La Commedia. Venice, 1751. 3 vols., sm.
8vo., contemp. half calf. Howes 194-537 1978 £25

DANTE ALIGHIERI   La Divina Commedia di Dante Alighieri Novamente corretta spiegata e defesa da F.B.L.M.C. Roma, 1791. 3 vols., 4to.,
calf, blind-stamped, raised bands on spine, very good, vignette. King 7-160
1978 £80

DANTE ALIGHIERI   The Divina Commedia. 1802. Portrait, 3 vols.,
contemp. tree calf, spines gilt, first ed. of first complete English translation, 8vo.
Howes 194-235 1978 £35

DANTE ALIGHIERI   La Divina Commedia Di Dante Alighieri Con
Comento Analitico. 1826/7. 1st. ed., 2 vols., orig. half cloth, grey bds.,
paper labels, uncut, local wear on 1 hinge, fine, orig. condition. Jarndyce 16-
980 1978 £65

DANTE ALIGHIERI   La Divina Commedia con note di Paolo Costa.
Firenze, 1839. 3 vols., 16mo., calf, blind-stamped border on sides, very good.
King 7-161 1978 £20

DANTE ALIGHIERI   Dante's Divina Commedia. 1862. 2 vols., half
titles, orig. green cloth, v.g. Jarndyce 16-957 1978 £12.50

DANTE ALIGHIERI   La Divina Commedia of the Divine Comedy of...
in Italian and English. The Nonesuch Press, 1928. 4to., illus. after drawings of
Sandro Botticelli, full orange vellum, 1 of 1,475 copies, very slightly soiled and
rubbed, uncut, fine. MacManus 238-833 1978 $175

DANTE ALIGHIERI   The Divine Comedy. (New York, 1944). Color
illus., drawings, 8vo., half cloth over dec. bds., box, v.g. Houle 10-147 1978
$20

DANTE ALIGHIERI   The Divine Comedy. New York, 1948. 4to.,
illus. by Gustave Dore. Biblo 251-218 1978 $16.50

DANTE ALIGHIERI   La Divina Comedia or The Divine Comedy of
Dante Alighieri in Italian & English. One of 1475 copies on Van Gelder mount-
made paper, in orange vellum. Battery Park 1-216 1978 $275

DANTE ALIGHIERI   L'Enfer. Paris, 1950. Etchings by Edouard
Goerg, one of an ed. of 250 copies on velin du Marais, specially watermarked, this
copy marked, two vols., folio, unbound sheets, in portfolios, fine, in lithographed
chemises and slipcases. Rota 212-11 1978 £200

DANTE ALIGHIERI   The Vision;.... London, 1814. 3 vols., 24mo.,
orig. grey bds., printed paper labels, bit worn but sound, 1st complete ed., very
good copy. Ximenes 47-47 1978 $375

DANTE ALIGHIERI   The Vision. 1831. Third ed., 3 vols., sm.
8vo., orig. cloth, printed labels. Howes 194-767 1978 £8.50

DANTE Gabriel Rossetti. London, n.d. Plts., cloth over bds., very good
or better. Limestone 9-248 1978 $20

DA PONTE, LORENZO   Memoirs of Lorenzo Da Ponte. 1929. Illus.
Austin 79-193 1978 $15

DAPPER, OLFERT   Description De L'Afrique. Amsterdam, 1688.
Plts., maps, engrs., folio, contemp. calf, illus. Salloch 345-53 1978 $750

DARBISHIRE, H. The Early Lives of Milton. 1932. Octavo, good. Upcroft 10-42 1978 £10

DARBY, WILLIAM Dixons of Dixon's Ford; with "The Soldier's Tale". Harrisburg, 1878. 1st ed., 4to, orig. plain wrs., front wrap worn, back wrap gone, 8vo. Americanist 101-41 1978 $30

DARBY, WILLIAM A Tour from the City of New York, to Detroit... 1818. New York, 1819. Maps, first ed., with errata slip, orig. bds., worn, text uncut, foxed, maps very good, scarce. Biblo 247-41 1978 $75

DARCET, JEAN Memoire sur l'Action d'un feu egal, Violent, et Continue Pendant Plusieurs Jours sur und Grand Nombre de Terres, de Pierres, & Chaux Metalliques. Paris, 1766. 8vo., half antique calf, gilt, fine copy, 1st ed. Norman 5-73 1978 $300

DARGAN, OLIVE TILFORD From My Highest Hill. Philadelphia, 1925. Illus., ex-lib. Broadfoot 50-56 1978 $14

THE DARK Side of the Moon. New York, 1947. First Amer. ed., orig. binding, spine and edges of covers faded, nice, torn d.w. Rota 211-93 1978 £5

D'ARLES, HENRI
Please turn to
BEAUDE, HENRI 1870-

DARLEY, F.O.C. A Selection of War Lyrics. New York, 1864. 1st ed., plates by Darley, orig. leather, impressed designs and gilt lettered, gilt dentells, very fine internally. Victoria 34-312 1978 $32.50

DARLEY, JOHN G. Clinical Aspects and Interpretation of the Strong Vocational Interest Blank. 1941. Paper. Austin 80-921 1978 $10

DARLEY, JOHN G. Testing and Counseling in the High-School Guidance Program. 1943. Austin 80-922 1978 $7.50

DARLINGTON, CYRIL DEAN Genes, Plants and People. London, 1950. 8vo, orig. cloth. Book Chest 17-500 1978 $10

DARLINGTON, RICHARD A Full Description of the Great Tornado in Chester County, Pa. West Chester, 1877. 1st ed., orig. pict. wrs., illus., scarce, 8vo. Americanist 101-42 1978 $30

DARMON, J.E. Dictionnaire des Estampes & Livres Illustres sur les Ballons & Machines Volantes, des Debuts Jusques vers 1880. Montpellier, 1929. 8vo., plts., illus., orig. pict. wrs., ltd. to 1,112 copies. Quaritch 977-212 1978 $100

DARRELL, WILLIAM A Gentleman Instructed in the Conduct of a Virtuous and Happy Life. London, 1709. sm. 8vo, 4th ed., dedication by George Hickes, superb contemporary full leather binding, gilt ornaments, marbled endpapers, rare. Victoria 34-213 1978 $85

DART, JOHN d.1730 History and Antiquities of the Cathedral Church of Canterbury, and the Once-adjoining Monastery. 1726. Roy. folio, lg. paper, engraved plts., modern panelled calf. Quaritch 983-34 1978 $420

DARTHENAY Memoire sor la Ville...
Please turn to
MOUSSINOT, ABBE

DARTON, WILLIAM A Present for a Little Boy. London, 1830. 12mo, engravings, original plain wrappers, one leaf with taped tear. Victoria 34-215 1978 $100

DARWIN, CHARLES The Descent of Man, and Selection in Relation to Sex. ondon, 1871. 2 vols., 8vo., woodcut illus., orig. green blind-stamped cloth, gilt on spines, library stamps, very good copy laid in green cloth box, 1st ed., 1st issue, 2500 copies prtd. Zeitlin 245-56 1978 $250

DARWIN, CHARLES The Decent of Man and Selection in Relation to Sex. (2nd ed. 1874) 1920. Illus. Austin 80-923 1978 $10

DARWIN, CHARLES The Descent of Man and Selection in Relation to Sex. New York, 1890. New ed., revised and augmented. Rittenhouse 49-189 1976 $10

DARWIN, CHARLES Different Forms of Flowers on Plants of the Same Species. New York, 1889. Rittenhouse 49-186 1976 $10

DARWIN, CHARLES Effects of Cross and Self Fertilisation in the Vegetable Kingdom. New York, 1889. Rittenhouse 49-191 1976 $10

DARWIN, CHARLES Formation of Vegetable Mould, Through the action of Worms, with Observations on Their Habits. London, 1882, 1897. 8vo, orig. cloth. Book Chest 17-112 1978 $20

DARWIN, CHARLES Geological Observations on Coral Reefs, Volcanic Islands, and on South America... 1851. 1st. collected ed., maps, plts., orig. cloth, 8vo, faded, 4 plts., browned, 2 pg. of index badly opened. Edwards 1012-638 1978 £250

DARWIN, CHARLES Geological Observations. New York, 1891. Third ed. Rittenhouse 49-194 1976 $12.50

DARWIN, CHARLES Journal of Researches into the Natural History and Geology of the Countries visited during the Voyage of H.M.S. Beagle round the World.... New York, 1846. 2 vols., fcap. 8vo. George's 635-945 1978 £12.50

DARWIN, CHARLES Journal of Researches Into the Natural History and Geology of the Countries Visited During the Voyage of H.M.S. Beagle, Round the World... 1891. 8vo, orig. cloth, plts. Edwards 1012-639 1978 £15

DARWIN, CHARLES Journal of Researches into the Natural History and Geology of the Countries Visited During the Voyable of H.M.S. Beagle Roung the World. New York, 1891. New ed. Rittenhouse 49-192 1976 $12.50

DARWIN, CHARLES Journal of Researches Into the Natural History and Geology of the Countries Visited During the Voyage of HMS Beagle 'Round the World Nelson. 1900. Austin 80-924 1978 $12.50

DARWIN, CHARLES Journal of Researches into the Natural History and Geology of the Countries Visited During the Voyage of HMS Beagle Round the World Under the Command of Capt. Fitz Roy R.N. 1915. Illus. Austin 80-925 1978 $12.50

DARWIN, CHARLES The Life and Letters. 1919. Vol. 1 & Vol. 2, orig. ed. Austin 80-927 1978 $25

DARWIN, CHARLES The Movement and Habits of Climbing Plants. London, 1888. 8vo, orig. cloth. Book Chest 17-113 1978 $20

DARWIN, CHARLES Movements and Habits of Climbing Plants. New York, 1891. Second ed., revised. Rittenhouse 49-188 1976 $10

DARWIN, CHARLES Observations Geoligiques sur les Iles Volcaniques Explorees par l'Expedition du "Beagle".... Paris, 1902. 1st French ed., octavo, original green blindstamped publisher's cloth, unopened copy. Bennett 20-54 1978 $65

DARWIN, CHARLES On the Fertilisation of Orchids by Insects. New York, 1889. Second ed., revised. Rittenhouse 49-187 1976 $10

DARWIN, CHARLES On The Orgin of Species by Means of Natural Selection.... London, 1859. 1st ed., 8 vo., full leather by the Rose Bindery, bookplate, presented by Lothario Aemilio Weber, lacks the 32-page publisher's catalog, very good, scarce. Ballinger 11-D 1978 $1,000

DARWIN, CHARLES On the Origin of Species by Means of Natural Selection. London, 1859. Original cloth, recased, first ed. Rota 212-12 1978 £1,000

DARWIN, CHARLES The Origin of the Species by Means of Natural Selection.... London, 1859. 12mo, half-title and folding diagram, contemp. dark dark green half mor., bound without inserted adver., 1st ed. Quaritch 978-41 1978 $1,700

DARWIN, CHARLES The Original of Species, by Means of Natural Selection. New York, 1889. Vols. 1 & 2. Rittenhouse 49-184 1976 $10

DARWIN, CHARLES The Origin of Species by Means of Natural Selection. New York, n.d. Reprinted from the 6th London ed. Rittenhouse 49-185 1976 $7.50

DARWIN, CHARLES   On the Various Contrivances by which British and Foreign Orchids are Fertilised by Insects. London, 1862. First ed., plt., illus., spine faded, gilt decor. cover, 8vo. K Books 244-83 1978 £45

DARWIN, CHARLES   Power of Movement in Plants. New York, 1888. Rittenhouse 49-190 1976 $10

DARWIN, CHARLES   Structure and Distribution of Coral Reefs. New York, 1889. Third ed. Rittenhouse 49-193 1976 $12.50

DARWIN, CHARLES   The Variation of Animals and Plants under Domestication. London, 1868. 1st ed., 1st issue, octavo, 2 vols., woodcuts, original green publisher's cloth, gilt spine titles, fine set. Bennett 20-55 1978 $475

DARWIN, CHARLES   Variation of Animals and Plants Under Domestication. New York, 1890. Second ed., revised, two vols. Rittenhouse 49-195 1976 $10

DARWIN, ERASMUS   The Botanic Garden. London, 1791. Quarto, orig. calf, newly rebacked, engraved frontis. and plates, five plts. engraved by Blake, covers worn, bookplts., some foxing, fine. Duschness 220-24 1978 $375

DARWIN, ERASMUS   The Temple of Nature. New York, 1804. Top hinge weak, ususal wear. Rittenhouse 49-196 1976 $55

DARWIN, FRANCIS   Life and Letters of Charles Darwin. New York, 1891. Two vols. Rittenhouse 49-197 1976 $15

DARWIN, GEORGE HOWARD   The Tides and Kindred Phenomena in the Solar System. 1898. 1st. ed., half title, orig. blue cloth, v.g. Jarndyce 16-456 1978 £6.50

DASHIELL, JOHN FREDERICK   Direction Orientation in Maze Running by the White Rat. John Hopkins Press, 1930. Paper, 1st ed. Austin 80-928 1978 $17.50

DASHIELL, JOHN FREDERICK   An Experimental Manual in Psychology. 1931. Austin 80-929 1978 $17.50

DASHIELL, JOHN FREDERICK   Fundamentals of General Psychology. 1937. Illus. Austin 80-930 1978 $10

DASHIELL, JOHN FREDERICK   Fundamentals of Objective Psychology. 1928. Illus. Austin 80-931 1978 $10

D'ASSIGNY, MARIUS   The Poetical History: Being a Compleat Collection of all the Stories.... London, 1699. Sm. 8vo, 7th ed., calf, cover loose, very good. Victoria 34-217 1978 $45

DATI, CARLO   Delle Lodi del Commendatore Cassiano dal Pozzo. Florence, 1664. 4to., engraved frontis., half mor., 1st ed. Gilhofer 74-35 1978 sFr 900

DAUDET, ALPHONSE   Die Abenteuer des Herrn Tartarin aus Tarascon. Berlin, 1921. Sm. 4to., orig. pict. bds., illus. by Grosz, well preserved. Goldschmidt 110-31 1978 $100

DAUDET, ALPHONSE   La Petite Paroisse. Paris, 1895. 1/2 cloth, marbled bds., orig. yellow wrappers, bound in. Eaton 45-136 1978 £5

DAUDET, ALPHONSE   Port Tarascon. New York, 1891. 8vo., cloth, 1st ed., 1st state, frontis. J. S. Lawrence 38-794 1978 $50

DAUDET, ALPHONSE   Tartarin de Tarascon. Paris, 1939. Lg. 8vo., orig. covers, illus. in color by Dubout. Van der Peet H-64-421 1978 Dfl 55

DAUFES, E.   La Garde indigene de l'Indochine; de sa creation a nos jours. Avignon, 1933-1934. 2 vols., large 8vo, orig. covers, numerous plts. Van der Peet 127-70 1978 Dfl 195

D'AULNOY, MARIE CATHERINE JUMELLE DE BERNEVILLE, COMTESSE
Please turn to
AULNOY, MARIE CATHERINE JUMELLE DE BERNEVILLE, COMTESSE D'

DAUMIER, HONORE VICTORIN   Der Maler Daumier. Herausgegeben von E. Fuchs. Munich, 1927. Lg. folio, plts., cloth. Quaritch 983-174 1978 $115

DAUMIER, HONORE VICTORIN   Der Maler Daumier. Herausgegeben von E. Fuchs. Munich, 1927-30. Plts., 2 vols., lg. folio, bds., pres. copy signed by author. Quaritch 983-173 1978 $160

DAUSQUERIUS, CLAUDIUS   Terra, et Aqua, Seu Terrae Flutantes. Tornaci Nerviorum (Tournai), 1633. 4to., contemp. limp vellum, 1st ed., very rare, very good copy. Offenbacher 30-31 1978 $275

DAUTREMER, J.   Une Colonie modele; La Birmanie; Sous le regime britannique. Paris, n.d. (c. 1915). Half calf, gilt, folding map, plts., 8vo. Van der Peet 127-71 1978 Dfl 65

D'AUVERGNE, EDWARD   The History of the Campagne in the Spanish Netherlands. 1694. Sm. 4to., wrappers. F. Edwards 1013-275 1978 £20

DAVAINE, C.   Recherches sur la Generation des Huitres, Memoire lu a la Societe de Biologie, le 31 juillet 1852. Paris, 1853. Lg. 8vo., old red qtr. calf, gilt, plts., signed pres. inscription from author, first ed. Gurney 75-30 1978 £25

DAVALLON, BERQUIN   Vue De La Colonie Espangole Du Mississippi,.... Paris, 1803. Colored maps, orig. wr., joints frayed, chipping at spine. Jenkins 116-370 1978 $850

DAVENANT, CHARLES   Discourses on the Publick Revenues, and on the Trade of England. 1698. First ed., tables, 2 vols., contemp. calf, 2 joints cracked, rare. Howes 194-32 1978 £125

DAVENANT, CHARLES   An Essay upon the Probably Methods of making a People Gainers in the Ballance of Trade. 1700. Second ed., tables, contemp. calf gilt, joints cracked, 8vo. Howes 194-33 1978 £85

DAVENANT, CHARLES   Reflections Upon the Constitution and Management of the Trade to Africa... 1709. Sm. folio, half calf. Edwards 1012-252 1978 £200

DAVENANT, WILLIAM   The Works of... 1673-2. Sm. folio, 3 parts inl, lacks portrait, old calf, joints cracked, ownership inscpt. in ink dated 1703. Eaton 45-138 1978 £35

DAVENPORT, BISHOP   History of the United States... Philadelphia, 1851. New ed., rev'd., printed bds. worn. Hayman 72-169 1978 $7.50

DAVENPORT, BISHOP   A New Gazetter, or Geographical Dictionary of North America and the West Indies. Philadelphia, 1836. 1st of this ed., fine, orig. calf, illus., lg. color fold. map. MacManus 239-111 1978 $30

DAVENPORT, BISHOP   A Pocket Gazeteer, or Traveller's Guide Through North America and the West Indies. Trenton & Baltimore, 1834. Full calf, rubbed, wanting the map. Wolfe 39-113 1978 $15

DAVENPORT, CHARLES BENEDICT   Heredity in Relation to Eugenics. 1911. Illus. Austin 80-932 1978 $10

DAVENPORT, CYRIL   Cameos. London, 1900. Illus., plts., 8 in color. Baldwins' 51-54 1978 $17.50

DAVENPORT, J. WALKER   Snakes of Bexar County, Texas. San Antonio, 1943. Color illus. Jenkins 116-104 1978 $8.50

DAVENPORT, MARCIA   East Side West Side. N. Y., 1947. 1st ed., 8 vo., d.j., very good. Houle 10-80 1978 $15

DAVENPORT ADAMS, W. H.   Famous Regiments of the British Army: Their Origin and Services. (c. 1864). Portrait plts., sm. 8vo., orig. cloth. F. Edwards 1013-276 1978 £12

DAVEY, HUMPHREY   Salmonia. London, 1829. Second ed., orig. grey bds. Wolfe 39-9a 1978 $50

DAVEY, RICHARD PATRICK BOYLE Cuba, Past and Present. 1898. Fldg. map, plts., orig. cloth, 8vo., cover faded. Edwards 1012-707 1978 £25

DAVEY, RICHARD PATRICK BOYLE History of Mourning. (c. 1885). Tinted frontis., many illus., 4to., orig. bds., worn. George's 635-1290 1978 £7.50

DAVEY, RICHARD PATRICK BOYLE The Nine Days' Queen. London, 1910. 2nd ed., illus., good. Sexton 7-226 1978 £8

DAVEY, NORMAN Desiderium. Cambridge, 1920. Grey bds., cloth spine, corners bumped, blind-stamp on f.e.p. Eaton 45-139 1978 £5

DAVID, FRANCOIS ANNE Les Antiquites D'Herculanum... Paris, 1780-1803. 1st ed., 12 vols., 4to, 872 plts., contemp. French mottled calf, gilt, slight wear at some head & tail bands. Hannas 54-78 1978 £250

DAVID, HENRY The History of the Haymarket Affair. New York, (1936). 1st ed. Biblo 251-329 1978 $20

DAVID, L. -O. Melanges Historiques et Litteraires. Montreal, 1917. Orig. binding. Wolfe 39-115 1978 $12

DAVID, MAURICE Who Was "Columbus"? New York, (1933). Illus. Biblo 251-32 1978 $15

DAVID, MAURICE Who Was "Columbus"? 1933. Austin 79-194 1978 $27.50

DAVID Armstrong or Before the Dawn. Edinburgh, 1880. 2 vols., orig. cloth, 1st ed., vol. I a little soiled, otherwise very good. MacManus 238-334 1978 $60

DAVIDOFF, LEO M. Brain Tumors. State Hospitals Press, 1931. Illus. Austin 80-933 1978 $37.50

DAVIDSON, ALEXANDER A Complete History of Illinois fron 1673 to 1873. Springfield, 1877. 1st ed., thick 8vo, orig. 3/4 calf, marbled bds. MacManus 239-210 1978 $45

DAVIDSON, ALEXANDER A Complete History of Illinois from 1673 to 1873. Springfield, 1875. Lea., little scuffed but solid. Hayman 73-235 1978 $20

DAVIDSON, G. M. The Traveller's Guide Through the Middle and Northern States and the Provinces of Canada. Saratoga Springs, 1837. 7th ed., marbled bds., 3/4 lea., gold stamping. Hood 117-727 1978 $45

DAVIDSON, GABRIEL Our Jewish Farmers and the Story of the Jewish Agricultural Society. 1943. Austin 79-195 1978 $12.50

DAVIDSON, JAMES W. The Island of Formosa Past and Present.... London and New York, 1903. Cloth, worn, hinges weakening, signed and dated by author. Dawson's 449-28 1978 $100

DAVIDSON, JAMES W. The Island of Formosa Past and Present.... N.P., 1903. Cheap reprint, probably a piracy, no folding map, cloth (unevenly faded). Dawson's 449-29 1978 $30

DAVIDSON, JO Spanish Portraits. New York, (1938). Plts., 4to., wraps, good. Bell Book 17-454 1978 $25

DAVIDSON, JOHN The Last Ballad and Other Poems. London & New York, 1899. 1st ed., laid paper, blue gilt decorated buckram, very good or better. Limestone 9-72 1978 $30

DAVIDSON, JOHN The Last Ballad and Other Poems. 1899. 1st. ed., cr. 8vo, maroon cloth, gilt upper cover. Eaton 45-140 1978 £6

DAVIDSON, JOHN Notes Taken During Travels in Africa. 1839. Plts., 4to, rebacked, plts. & few pgs. slightly foxed, orig. cloth. Edwards 1012-237 1978 £185

DAVIDSON, JOHN Selected Poems. London, 1904. 1st ed., upper cover marked, very good or better. Limestone 9-73 1978 $13.50

DAVIDSON, LALLAH SHERMAN South of Joplin...a Tri-State Diggins's. New York, (1939). Illus., 1st ed., d.w. Biblo BL781-271 1978 $7.50

DAVIDSON, NORA FONTAINE Cullings from the Confederacy ...1862-1866. Washington, 1903. 8vo., orig. printed wrs., 1st ed. MacManus 238-901 1978 $15

DAVIDSON, THOMAS The Education of the Greek People. 1900. Austin 80-942a 1978 $11

DAVIDSON, THOMAS The Parthenon Frieze and Other Essays. London, 1882. 12mo., ex-lib., spine torn at top, good. Biblo BL781-363 1978 $8.50

DAVIE, IAN Oxford Poetry 1942-1943. Oxford, 1943. First ed., wrappers, backstrip faded, covers somewhat marked and worn, nice. Rota 211-17 1978 £6

DAVIE, JOHN CONSTANSE Letters From Paraguay.... London, 1805. 1st. ed., 8vo, half-title, half red roan, marbled sides, lettered in gilt on spine, sl. cracking of one joint, some rubbing of cover. Deighton 5-36 1978 £135

DAVIE, JOHN CONSTANSE Letters From Paraguay... 1805. 8vo, modern half mor. Edwards 1012-640 1978 £100

DAVIE, MAURICE R. Social Aspects of Mental Hygiene. Yale University Press, 1925. Austin 80-934 1978 $12.50

DAVIES, A. MERVYN A Biography of Clive of Plassey. New York, 1939. Biblo 247-669 1978 $15

DAVIES, CHARLES Elements of Surveying, and Navigation. New York, 1846. Rev. ed., orig. sheep, 8vo., good. Paine 78-40 1978 $12.50

DAVIES, CHARLES Intellectual Arithmetic. 1862. Old text book. Austin 80-935 1978 $10

DAVIES, E. The Bishop of Africa. Reading, (1885). Portr., sm. 8vo., 1st ed. Morrill 239-360 1978 $12.50

DAVIES, EDWARD W. LEWIS Paul Pendril: or, Sport and Adventure in Corsica. London, 1866. 8vo., original blue cloth, 1st ed., fine copy. Ximenes 46-68 1978 $40

DAVIES, GERALD S. Renascence. The Sculptured Tombs of the 15th Century in Rome. New York, 1916. Lg. 8vo., illus., good. Biblo BL781-733 1978 $17.50

DAVIES, HUGH WILLIAM Berhard von Breydenbach and his Journey to the Holy land 1483-4. London, 1911. Ltd. to 200 copies, plts., roy. 4to., orig. cloth, mor. back, t.e.g. Forster 130-166 1978 £90

DAVIES, J. C. The Baronial Opposition to Edward II; its character and policy; a study in administrative history. Cambridge, 1918. 8vo. Upcroft 12-96 1978 £12.50

DAVIES, J. C. Episcopal acts and cognate documents relating to Welsh dioceses 1066-1272. 1946-8. 2 vols., roy. 8vo. Upcroft 12-98 1978 £15

DAVIES, J. J. History and Business Directory of Madison County, Iowa. Des Moines, 1869. Folding map, original cloth, faded, 1st ed. Ginsberg 14-408 1978 $100

DAVIES, JOHN Historic Prologues. 1821. 8vo., orig. bds., new backstrip, uncut, fine. P. M. Hill 142-86 1978 £12

DAVIES, JOHN A Tahitian and English Dictionary, with Introductory Remarks on the Polynesian Language and a short Grammar of the Tahitian Dialect. Tahiti, 1851. 8vo., crushed green mor., 1st ed. Quaritch 978-145 1978 $350

DAVIES, JOSEPH E.   Mission to Moscow. New York, 1941. 8vo, orig. cloth, title faded from spine, pres. copy to Mrs. Winston Churchill, 10th printing, plts. Sawyer 298-69 1978 £110

DAVIES, R. A.   The Great Mackenzie in Word and Photograph. Toronto, 1947. Photos by G. Zuckerman. Hood 117-884 1978 $12.50

DAVIES, RHYS   A Bed of Feathers. Mandrake Press, (1929). 12mo., cloth-backed gilt bds., fine, first English ed. Bell Book 16-213 1978 £6.50

DAVIES, RHYS   Daisy Matthews and Three Other Tales. Golden Cockerell Press, 1932. Ltd. to 325 copies and signed by author, wood-engravings by Agnes Miller Parker, orig. qtr. mor., patterned cloth sides, t.e.g., other uncut. George's 635-898 1978 £35

DAVIES, RHYS   The Stars, the World, and the Women. 1930. One of 550 copies numbered & signed by author, roy. 8vo., buckram gilt, t.e.g., covers little marked, else very good, first English ed. Bell Book 17-201 1978 £7.50

DAVIES, RHYS   Tale. 1930. No. 17 of 100 copies only, signed by author, very good, somewhat browned wraps, first English ed. Bell Book 17-202 1978 £17.50

DAVIES, RHYS   The Things Men Do: short stories. 1936. Very good, worn d.w., inscribed by author, first English ed. Bell Book 16-216 1978 £7.50

DAVIES, RHYS   The Withered Root. London, 1927. 1st ed., fine, d.j., scarce. Ballinger 11-123 1978 £27.50

DAVIES, THOMAS   Memoirs of the Life of David Garrick. 1780. First ed., portrait, 2 vols., contemp. sheep, red mor. labels, joints cracked, 8vo. Howes 194-279 1978 £45

DAVIES, THOMAS   Memoirs of the Life of David Garrick. London, 1808. Fair reading copy only, scarce, 2 vols., illus. Biblo 247-899 1978 $42.50

DAVIES, WILLIAM HENRY   New Poems. 1907. 12mo., very good, first English ed. Bell Book 16-217 1978 £6

DAVIES, WILLIAM HENRY   The True Traveller. 1912. First ed., cr. 8vo. George's 635-1312 1978 £5

DAVILA, ENRICO CATERINO   The Historie of the Civill Warres of France. 1647. First English ed., thk. folio, contemp. calf, neatly rebacked, orig. label preserved, very good, uncropped. Howes 194-34 1978 £55

DAVILA, ENRICO CATERINO   The History of the Civil Wars of France.... (London), 1678. Quarto, woodcut initials, contemp. calf, rubbed. Bennett 20-57 1978 $150

DAVILA, ENRICO CATERINO   Historia delle Guerre Civili di Francia. London, 1755. Quarto, 2 vols., rubicated t.p., marginally indexed, full contemporary calf, gilt-panelled spine. Bennett 20-56 1978 $125

DAVILA, ENRICO CATERINO   Historia delle Guerre Civili di Francia. 1755. 2 vols., 4to., contemp. calf, rebacked. Howes 194-236 1978 £42

DAVIN, NICHOLAS FLOOD   The Irishman in Canada. (1877). Reprint, octavo bound in cloth. Hyland 128-939 1978 £10

DAVIS, A.   Antiquities of Central America, and the Discovery of New England by the Northmen, 500 Years Before Columbus. Boston, 1842. Ninth ed., printed wrappers. Wolfe 39-114 1978 $25

DAVIS, C. O.   The Life and Times of Patuone. Auckland, 1876. 12mo, orig. cloth, orig. photo. Edwards 1012-351 1978 £30

DAVIS, CALVIN   Junior High School Education. 1924. Austin 80-937 1978 $7.50

DAVIS, CHARLES E., JR.   Three Years in the Army, the Story of the Thirteenth Massachusetts Volunteers. Boston, 1894. Ex libris, Bell Wiley's copy. Broadfoot's 44-526 1978 $30

DAVIS, CHARLES G.   Ships of the Past. Salem, 1929. 1st ed., 4to., illus., plts., orig. full leatherette, bookplt., very fine. MacManus 239-1748 1978 $75

DAVIS, CHARLES G.   The Ways of the Sea. New York, 1930. 8vo., good., illus. Paine 78-41 1978 $17.50

DAVIS, CHARLES H.   Narrative of the North Polar Expedition, 1870-73... Washington, 1876. Maps, wood engravings, other plts., tail-pieces, thick imp. 8vo, orig. cloth, some spotting, mainly affecting tissues of plts. Edwards 1012-571 1978 £70

DAVIS, CHARLES H. S.   History of Wallingford, Conn. from Its Settlement in 1670... Meriden, 1870. Illus., recased. MacManus 239-958 1978 $50

DAVIS, DANIEL   A Manual of Magnetism, Including Galvanism, Magnetism, Electro-Magnetism, Electro-Dynamics, Magneto-Electricity, and Thermo-Electricity. Boston, 1847. 2nd ed., orig. illus., sm. 8vo., damp-stained, orig. cloth. Morrill 241-105 1978 $15

DAVIS, E. E.   A Study of Rural Schools in Williamson County. Austin, 1922. Jenkins 116-1477 1978 $7.50

DAVIS, EDWARDS   Lovers of Life. New York, (1934). 1st ed., signed. Biblo 251-437 1978 $15

DAVIS, EVELYN   Spirit of the Big Bend: Chronology of Presidio's Outstanding Dates. San Antonio, 1948. 1st ed., wr., illus. Jenkins 116-1108 1978 $10

DAVIS, FORREST   How War Came. 1942. Austin 80-79 1978 $12.50

DAVIS, FREDERICK H.   Myths & Legends of Japan. 1912. Coloured plts., 8vo, orig. cloth, gilt, t.e.g., very good copy. Fenning 32-85 1978 £7.50

DAVIS, GEORGE   Recollections of a Sea Wanderer's Life:.... New York, 1887. Illus., original pictorial cloth, 1st ed. Ginsberg 14-330 1978 $100

DAVIS, GEORGE L.   The Day-Star of American Freedon; Early Growth of Toleration in the Province of Maryland. New York, 1855. Orig. cloth, lib. stamp. MacManus 239-1829 1978 $12.50

DAVIS, HASSOLDT   Nepal, Land of Mystery. 1942. Illus., 8vo, orig. cloth, fine copy in d.w. Edwards 1012-95 1978 £15

DAVIS, HENRY   Moral and Pastoral Theology. 1936. 4 vols., 8vo. George's 635-1049 1978 £5

DAVIS, HENRY EDWARDS 1756-1784   An Examination of the Fifteenth and Sixteenth Chapters of Mr. Gibbon's History of the Decline and Fall of the Roman Empire. 1778. First ed., orig. bds., entirely uncut, partly unopened, 8vo. Howes 194-286 1978 £30

DAVIS, HENRY WILLIAM CHARLES   Medieval England, a New Edition of Barnard's Companion to English History. Oxford, 1924. Illus., 8vo. George's 635-718 1978 £6

DAVIS, J. LEE   Bits of History and Legends Around and About the Natural Bridge of Virginia from 1730 to 1950. (Lynchburg, 1949). Illus., 8vo., 1st ed., orig. cloth. Morrill 241-598 1978 $12.50

DAVIS, J. LUCIUS   The Trooper's Manual. Richmond, 1861. Embossed seal on front fly, Bell Wiley's copy. Broadfoot 46-455 1978 $125

DAVIS, J. P.   Corporations, a Study of the Origin and Development of Great Business Combinations and of their Relation to the Authority of the State. New York, 1905. 2 vols., 8vo. George's 635-311 1978 £12.50

DAVIS, J. R. AINSWORTH   The Natural History of Animals. London, 1903-04. 4 vols., in 8, illus., coloured plts., roy. 8vo., decor. cloth gilt, bright set. K Books 244-84 1978 £16

DAVIS, JEFFERSON   Report on the Commission to Examine into the Organization, System of Discipline, and Course of Instruction of the U. S. Military Academy at West Point. Washington, 1860. Cloth, fine. Jenkins 116-300 1978 $37.50

DAVIS, JEFFERSON   The Rise & Fall of the Confederate Government. New York, 1881. 2 vols., 3/4 lea., marble bds., fine set. Bell Wiley's copy. Broadfoot 46-70 1978 $125

DAVIS, JEFFERSON   The Rise and Fall of the Confederate Government. New York, 1881. Hinges cracked, cover worn, G. G. Vest's copy. Broadfoot's 44-106 1978 $45

DAVIS, JEFFERSON   The Rise & Fall of the Confederate Government. Richmond, 1938. 2 vols., United Daughters of the Confederacy Memorial Ed. Bell Wiley's copy. Broadfoot 46-71 1978 $50

DAVIS, JOHN   Historical Records of the Second Royal Surrey. 1877. Coloured plts., 8vo., orig. cloth, repaired. F. Edwards 1013-571 1978 £22

DAVIS, JOHN   Travels of Four Years and a Half in the United States of America during 1798, 1799, 1800, 1801, and 1802. New York, 1909. Untrimmed, orig. cloth-backed bds., very fine. MacManus 239-113 1978 $30

DAVIS, JOHN A.   How Management Can Integrate Negroes in War Industries. (Albany, 1942). Wr. Butterfield 21-70 1978 $7.50

DAVIS, JOHN FRANCIS   The Chinese: A General Description of the Empire of China and its Inhabitants. London, 1836. 2 vols., cloth, spines tanned and worn, joints worn in vol.1. Dawson's 449-30 1978 $80

DAVIS, L. D.   The History of the Methodist Episcopal Church in Cortland. Syracuse, 1855. 18mo., top of spine chipped. Butterfield 21-148 1978 $15

DAVIS, LOYAL   Annals of Roetgenology–A Series of Monographis Atlases. Volume Fourteen–Intracranial Tumors. New York, 1933. Library marks. Rittenhouse 49-199 1976 $20

DAVIS, LOYAL   Intracranial Tumors. Annals of Roentgenology, Volume XIV. New York, 1933. Rittenhouse 49-200 1976 $25

DAVIS, LOYAL   J. B. Murphy. Stormy Petrel of Surgery. New York, 1938. Rittenhouse 49-201 1976 $7.50

DAVIS, LOYAL   Principles of Neurological Surgery. Philadelphia, 1946. Third ed., thoroughly revised, ex-library. Rittenhouse 49-202 1976 $10

DAVIS, MARCELLUS L.   The Stranger. Philadelphia, (1938). Illus., tall thin 8vo., slightly soiled, orig. cloth, very good. Americanist 103-91 1978 $20

DAVIS, MATTHEW L.   Memoirs of Aaron Burr... New York, 1836. 1st ed., 2 vols., ports. MacManus 239-732 1978 $35

DAVIS, NATHAN   Carthage and Her Remains... 1861. Maps, plts., 2 coloured, orig. cloth, 8vo., spine faded. Edwards 1012-238 1978 £15

DAVIS, NATHAN   Carthage and Her Remains: Being an Account of the Excavations and Researches on the Site of the Phoenician Metropolis in Africa, and Other Adjacent Places. 1861. 8vo., maps, plts., calf gilt, gilt panelled back, a little rubbed. Quaritch 983-10 1978 $130

DAVIS, NATHAN   Inscriptions in the Phoenician Character, Now Deposited in the British Museum, Discovered on the Site of Carthage... 1863. Oblong folio, plts., cloth, mor. back. Quaritch 983-11 1978 $55

DAVIS, PARKE H.   Football the American Intercollegiate Game. New York, 1911. Illus. Baldwins' 51-542 1978 $10

DAVIS, RICHARD HARDING   About Paris. 1895. Illus., first ed. Austin 82-322 1978 $17.50

DAVIS, RICHARD HARDING   About Paris. New York, 1895. Illus. by Chas. Dana Gibson, stitching weak, orig. cloth gilt. Eaton 45-141 1978 £5

DAVIS, RICHARD HARDING   Captain Macklin. 1902. Frontis., illus., first ed. Austin 82-323 1978 $12.50

DAVIS, RICHARD HARDING   The Deserter. 1917. Bds. Austin 82-324 1978 $10

DAVIS, RICHARD HARDING   The Exiles and Other Stories. New York, 1894. Cloth. Hayman 73-179 1978 $10

DAVIS, RICHARD HARDING   In The Fog. New York, 1901. 1st ed., illus., frontispiece, uncut, blue pictorial cloth, lightly spotted else very good or better. Limestone 9-74 1978 $15

DAVIS, RICHARD HARDING   The Princess Aline. 1895. Illus. Austin 82-325 1978 $12.50

DAVIS, RICHARD HARDING   Ranson's Folly. 1902. Illus., first ed. Austin 82-326 1978 $12.50

DAVIS, RICHARD HARDING   The Rulers of the Mediterranean. 1893. Illus., first ed. Austin 82-327 1978 $17.50

DAVIS, RICHARD HARDING   The Scarlet Car. New York, 1907. Cloth, 1st ed. Hayman 72-172 1978 $7.50

DAVIS, RICHARD HARDING   Soldiers of Fortune. 1902. Illus. Austin 82-328 1978 $12.50

DAVIS, RICHARD HARDING   Van Bibber and Others. 1892. Frontis., first ed. Austin 82-329 1978 $17.50

DAVIS, RICHARD HARDING   Vera the Medium. 1908. Illus., fine, first ed. Austin 82-330 1978 $17.50

DAVIS, RICHARD HARDING   Vera the Medium. New York, 1908. Illus. by Frederick Dorr Steele, 1st ed., earliest bind. Americanist 102-46 1978 $20

DAVIS, RICHARD HARDING   The White Mice. 1909. Illus., first ed. Austin 82-331 1978 $15

DAVIS, SUSAN BURDICK   Wisconsin Lore for Boys and Girls. Milwaukee, 1931. First ed., author's signed pres., illus. Biblo 247-561 1978 $15

DAVIS, TARRINGS   History of Blair County, Pa. Harrisburg, 1931. 2 vols. MacManus 239-1433 1978 $45

DAVIS, THEODORE M.   The Tomb of Queen Tiyi. London, 1910. Plts., folio. Traylen 88-9 1978 £20

DAVIS, THOMAS   General View of the Agriculture of Wiltshire. 1811. Coloured map, plt., orig. bds., entirely uncut, upper joint weak, 8vo. Howes 194-122 1978 £25

DAVIS, VARINA   Jefferson Davis – A Memoir. NY, 1890. Binding tight, unusually good. Broadfoot's 44-107 1978 $50.00

DAVIS, VARINA   Jefferson Davis, Ex-President of the Confederate States of America. New York, (1890). Illus., 2 vols., thick 8vo., ex-lib., 1st ed., orig. cloth. Morrill 241-106 1978 $27.50

DAVIS, WILLIAM M.   Nimrod of the Sea.. New York, 1874. Cloth covers stained, 8vo., good internally. Paine 78-42 1978 $32.50

DAVIS, WILLIAM T.   Ancient Landmarks of Plymouth. Boston, 1899. 2nd ed., illus., orig. cloth, very good. MacManus 239-278 1978 $17.50

DAVIS, WILLIAM T.   The Church of St. Andrew, Richmond, Staten Island. Staten Island, 1925. 8vo., illus., 1st ed. Morrill 239-549 1978 $10

DAVIS, WILLIAM W. H.   History of Bucks County, Pa. New York, 1905. 2nd ed., rev'd. and enlarged, 3 vols., nice set, cloth, illus., very scarce. MacManus 239-1434 1978 $200

DAVIS, WILLIAM W. H.   History of Doylestown, Old and New, From Its Settlement to the Close of the 19th Century. Doylestown, (1904). Illus., fine, orig. cloth, scarce. MacManus 239-1435 1978 $65

DAVIS-DUBOIS, RACHEL   Neighbors in Action. 1950. Austin 79-197 $10

DAVISON, FRANK DALBY   Man-Shy. London, 1934. 8 vo., illus., d.j., very good, Zane Grey's copy. Houle 10-83 1978 $12.50

DAVISON, GIDEON MINOR   Tournee a la mode dans les Etats-Unis.... Paris, 1829. Orig. printed wrs., uncut. Wolfe 39-116 1978 $65

DAVISON, GIDEON MINOR   The Traveller's Guide Through the Middle and Northern States and the Provinces of Canada. Saratoga Springs, 1837. 7th. ed., marbled bds., 3/4 leather, gold stamping. Hood's 115-964 1978 $45

DAVISON, LAWRENCE H.   Movements in European History. Oxford, 1921. Sm. 8vo., cloth, 1st ed., 1st state in brown cloth. J.S. Lawrence 38-L66 1978 $150

DAVISON, S.   American Industries in the Technological Era. New York, 1936. Annotated bibliography. Hood 117-30 1978 $12.50

DAVY, HUMPHRY   Consolations in Travel. 1838. Fourth ed., calf gilt, sm. 8vo. P. M. Hill 142-87 1978 £12

DAVY, HUMPHRY   Electro-Chemical Researches, on the Decomposition of the Earth, with Observations on the Metals Obtained from the Alkaline Earth, and on the Amalgam Procured from Ammonia. (London, 1808). 4to., bds., 1st ed. Gilhofer 74-111 1978 sFr 250

DAVY, HUMPHRY   Elements of Agricultural Chemistry. London, 1813. Lg. 4to., engr. plts., orig. bds., new calf, spine, title page lightly foxed, light foxing on plts., but fine, lg. paper copy, 1st ed. Norman 5-74 1978 $300

DAVY, HUMPHRY   Elements of Agricultural Chemistry. 1814. Plts., contemp. half calf, 8vo., second ed. Howes 194-123 1978 £35

DAVY, HUMPHRY   On the Analysis of Soils, as Connected with their Improvement. London, 1805. 4to., plt., new wrappers. Quaritch 977-92 1978 $85

DAVY, HUMPHRY   On the Safety Lamp for Coal Miners. London, 1818. 1st ed., tall 8vo., orig. gray bds. with brown cloth, ink notation, light foxing, interior otherwise very fine, binding firm, fine copy, rare in orig. bds. Current 24-120 1978 $1,485

DAVY, HUMPHRY   Researches, Chemical and Philosophical. London, 1800. 1st ed., 8vo., ads, later full brown calf, inlaid avocado-green diamond pattern, fine, very scarce. Current 24-121 1978 $1100

DAVY, HUMPHRY   Researches, Chemical and Philosophical... London, 1839. 8vo., frontis. illus., orig. stamped cloth, rebacked with orig. back-strip mostly preserved, library stamps & bkplt., very good copy, 2nd ed., rare. Zeitlin 245-57 1978 $250

DAVY, JOHN   An Account of the Interior of Ceylon, and of Its Inhabitants... 1821. Folding map, 14 plts., 2 coloured, 1 folding, 4to, half morocco, t.e.g., other uncut, spine darkened, some slight foxing. Edwards 1012-125 1978 £90

DAVY, JOHN   Notes and Observations on the Ionian Islands and Malta... London, 1842. 1st. ed., 2 vols., engraved frontispieces, orig. blind stamped cloth, gilt backs, some fading, weating & staining of covers. Deighton 5-118 1978 £198

DAVYS, JOHN   An Essay on the Art of Decyphering. London. 4to., uncut, stitched as issued. K Books 244-85 1978 £60

DAWBARN, WILLIAM   Essays, Tales.... 1872. 2nd ed., covers faded, 8vo. George's 635-1291 1978 £5.25

DAWES, CHARLES G.   Notes as Vice President, 1928-1929. Boston, 1935. 1st ed., spine faded, illus. Biblo 248-95 1978 $16.50

DAWES, RUFUS R.   Service with the Sixth Wisconsin Volunteers. Marietta, 1936. Illus., Bell Wiley's copy. Broadfoot's 44-675 1978 $40

DAWKINS, W. BOYD   Cave Hunting. London, 1874. Illus., rebound in red lib. buckram. Baldwins' 51-341 1978 $17.50

DAWLEY, T. R.   Dawley's Tenpenny Toy Books, No. 4. New York, c.1865. Plates, wrappers. Victoria 34-220 1978 $27.50

DAWN To Daylight: or Glemas From the Poets of Twelve Centuries. n.d. (c.1870s). Roy. 8vo, wood-eng. by John Leighton, contemp. mottled calf, gilt panelled, rubbed. Eaton 45-142 1978 £15

DAWSON, C.   The Glory of the Trenches, an Interpretation. Toronto, 1918. Hood 116-117 1978 $12.50

DAWSON, C.   The Test of Scarlet; A Romance of Reality. New York, 1919. Hood's 115-427 1978 $10

DAWSON, GEORGE FRANCIS   Life and Services of Gen. John A. Logan as Soldier and Statesman. Chicago, 1887. Illus., 8vo., 1st ed. Morrill 239-362 1978 $10

DAWSON, J.   Australian Aboriginies: The Languages and Customs of Several Tribes of Aborigines in the The Western District of Victoria, Australia. Melbourne, Sydney, and Adelaide, 1881. Portraits, 4to, rebacked, orig. cloth, slightly worn, few wormholes. Edwards 1012-329 1978 £60

DAWSON, JOHN WILLIAM   Acadian Geology. London, 1868. Second ed., map, illus., 8vo., orig. cloth. K Books 244-131 1978 £30

DAWSON, JOHN WILLIAM   A Handbook of the Geography and Natural History of the Province of Nova Scotia. Pictou, 1863. Sixth ed., map, orig. binding. Wolfe 39-117 1978 $17.50

DAWSON, NICHOLAS   Narrative of Nicholas "Cheyenne" Dawson (Overland to California in '41 & '49, and Texas in '51).... San Francisco, 1933. Limited to 500 copies, reissue of rare 1901 ed., mint copy, d.j. Jenkins 116-306 1978 $55

DAWSON, SAMUEL EDWARD   The St. Lawrence Basin and Its Borderlands, Being the Story of Their Discovery, Exploration and Occupation. London, 1905. Illus., maps. Hood 116-519 1978 $17.50

DAWSON, SAMUEL EDWARD   The Saint Lawrence. New York, (1905). Orig. cloth, maps, illus., 8vo., almost fine, 1st ed. Morrill 241-107 1978 $15

DAWSON, SAMUEL EDWARD   The Saint Lawrence, Its Basin and Border-lands. New York, (1905). 1st ed., illus., orig. pic. cloth, very good. MacManus 239-114 1978 $22.50

DAWSON, SAMUEL EDWARD   A Study, with Critical and Explanatory Notes, of Lord Tennyson's Poem, the Princess. Montreal, 1884. 2nd ed. Hood 116-686 1978 $12.50

DAWSON, SARAH MORGAN   A Confederate Girl's Diary. Boston, 1913. 1st ed., illus. MacManus 239-871 1978 $20

DAWSON, SIMON JAMES   Report on the Exploration of the Country Between Lake Superior and the Red River Settlement and Between the Latter Place and the Assiniboine and Saskatchewan. Toronto, 1859. Large folding map, half morocco, paper label on front cover. Ginsberg 14-331 1978 $200

DAWSON, SIMON JAMES   Rapport sur l'exploration de la Contree... Toronto, 1859. Plates, large folding map, original half calf. Ginsberg 14-332 1978 $275

DAWSON, SIMON JAMES   Rapport Sur L'Exploration de la Contree Situee entre le lac Superior et la colonie de la Riviere Rouge et entre.... Toronto, 1859. Folding maps, original half calf, French ed. Ginsberg 14-333 1978 $125

DAWSON, W. H.   Cromwell's Understudy; The Life and Times of General John Lambert and the Rise and Fall of the Protectorate. 1938. Plts., octavo, good. Upcroft 10-283 1978 £8.50

DAWSON, W. J.   A Prophet in Babylon; a Story of Social Service.
New York, 1907. 2nd ed., slightly scuffed. Hood 116-466 1978 $7.50

DAWSON, W. S.   Aids to Psychiatry. 1934. 3rd ed. Austin 80-
938 1978 $10

DAWSON, WILLIAM C.   Speech on the Bill...Supression and Prevention of
Indian Hostilities for the Year 1838, and to Carry into Execution the Treaty Made
with the Cherokees in 1835... Washington, 1838. 8vo., unbound. Morrill 241-
108 1978 $10

DAY, C. W.   Five Years' Residence in the West Indies. 1852.
Engraved plts., spotted, 2 vols., sm. 8vo, orig. cloth, name on half-titles.
Edwards 1012-709 1978 £40

DAY, CATHERINE M.   Pioneers of the Eastern Townships. Montreal,
1863. Orig. binding. Wolfe 39-142 1978 $75

DAY, D.   Plants of Buffalo & Vicinity. Buffalo, 1882.
8vo, wr. Book Chest 17-502 1978 $12

DAY, F. P.   A Good Citizen. The Josiah Wood Lectures.
Sackville, 1947. Hood 116-687 1978 $7.50

DAY, FRANK MILES   American Country Houses of Today. New York,
1912. Illus., 4to., bind. worn, good. Biblo BL781-539 1978 $37.50

DAY, H. W.   The Sight Singing Manual... Cincinnati, (1849).
Wrs. worn and soiled. Hayman 72-717 1978 $7.50

DAY, HOLMAN F.   Verse Stories of the Plain Folk Who Are Keeping
Bright the Old Home Fires Up In Maine. Boston, 1904. 1st. ed. Baldwins' 51-
396 1978 $10

DAY, J. WENTWORTH   Sporting Adventure. London, 1937. 1st ed.,
plts., drawings, green cloth, gilt embossed, very good or better. Limestone 9-
75 1978 $25

DAY, L. W.   Story of the One Hundred and First Ohio Infantry.
Cleveland, 1894. Bell Wiley's copy. Broadfoot 46-356 1978 $35

DAY, LEWIS F.   Alphabets Old and New for the Use of Craftsmen..
Batsford, (1910). 8vo, orig. cloth, 3rd. ed., good. Sexton 7-13 1978 £6

DAY, LEWIS F.   The Art of William Morris. London, (1899).
Illus., 4to., binder's cloth, good, first ed. Rota 211-416 1978 £20

DAY, S. P.   English America: or, Pictures of Canadian Places
and People. London, 1864. 2 vols., orig. covers worn. Hood 116-618 1978
$175

DAY, SHERMAN   Historical Collections of the State of Pennsylvania... Philadelphia, 1843. Woodcuts, modern half leather, blank corner of
title restores, upper margin of 3 leaves torn, affecting headings, some spotting in
text, 8vo. Edwards 1012-484 1978 $20

DAY, SHERMAN   Historical Collections of the State of Pennsylvania... Philadelphia, (1843). MacManus 239-1437 1978 $35

DAY, SHERMAN   Historical Collections of the State of Pennsyl-
vanis... Philadelphia, (1843). 1st ed., thick 8vo., illus., full contemp. calf,
covers rubbed but a nice copy. MacManus 239-1436 1978 $60

DAY, THOMAS   The Dying Negro,.... London, 1773. 4to,
disbound, 1st ed., very rare. Ximenes 47-70 1978 $450

DAY, THOMAS   The Dying Negro... 1774. 4to, 2nd. ed.,
disbound, title & following leaf faintly stained. Hannas 54-310 1978 £32

DAY, THOMAS   The Dying Negro... 1793. 1st. complete ed.,
8vo, frontispiece, disbound. Hannas 54-311 1978 £20

DAY, THOMAS   The Forsaken Infant; or Entertaining History of
Little Jack. New York, 1819. 16mo, f.p., t.p. vignette, wrapper, almost fine.
Victoria 34-221 1978 $75

DAY, THOMAS   The History of Sanford and Merton;.... London,
1788-1790. 12mo, rebound in fine full leather, unlettered, all texts fine, scarce.
Victoria 34-223 1978 $110

DAY, THOMAS   The History of Sandford and Merton. Edinburgh,
1792. Plts., sm. 8vo., contemp. sheep, very good. P. M. Hill 142-88 1978
£75

DAY, THOMAS   The History of Sanford and Merton; A Work
Intended for the Use of Children. London, 1815. Engraved f.p., scarce one vol.
issue, rebacked in gilt and impressed designs, fine crisp copy. Victoria 34-222
1978 $35

THE DAY Breaking if not the Sun Rising of the Gospel with the Indians in New
England. New York, 1865. 4to., cloth, orig. wrs., bound in, ex-lib., ltd. to
250 copies. MacManus 239-1162 1978 $30

DAY LEWIS, CECIL   Country Comets. 1928. Orig. green bds., very
good, later issue, first English ed. Bell Book 16-218 1978 £6

DAY-LEWIS, CECIL   Noah and the Waters. 1936. 1st ed., covers
dull, 8vo. George's 635-1325 1978 £5

DAY LEWIS, CECIL   Noah and the Waters. Hogarth Press, 1936.
Very good, d.w., first English ed. Bell Book 16-219 1978 £10

DAY LEWIS, CECIL   Poems, 1943-47. 1948. Very good, d.w., first
English ed. Bell Book 16-220 1978 £4

DAY LEWIS, CECIL   A Time to Dance, and other poems. Hogarth
Press, 1935. Very good, first English ed. Bell Book 17-204 1978 £8.50

DEACON, WILLIAM ARTHUR   Pens and Pirates. Toronto, 1923. Hood 117-
469 1973 $10

DEACON, WILLIAM ARTHUR   Peter McArthur. Toronto, n.d. Ex-lib.
Hood's 115-249 1978 $10

DEADERICK, J. B.   The Truth about Shiloh. Memphis, Tn., 1942.
Pres copy, pict. cover, Bell Wiley's Copy. Broadfoot's 44-109 1978 $10.00

DEADLINE Delayed. 1947. Newspaper writers in various aspects of the war.
Austin 80-247 1978 $10

THE DEAF And Dumb Boy. 1851. 1st. ed., 2 vols., frontis, orig. pink cloth,
heads of spines rubbed & weakening of inner hinges, otherwise good. Jarndyce
16-264 1978 £20

DEALEY, JAMES Q.   A Text Book of Sociology. 1905. Austin 80-939
1978 $12.50

DEAN, AMOS   The History of Civilization. Albany, 1868-69.
7 vols., orig. terra-cotta cloth, ex-lib., lightly worn, sound cond. Butterfield
21-42 1978 $45

DEAN, MRS. ANDREW   The Grasshoppers. New York, 1895. 1st Amer.
ed., illus. by Walter B. Russell, orig. cloth, clipped pages, marginal tears, good.
Greene 78-173 1978 $15

DEAN, BASHFORD   A Bibliography of Fishes. New York, 1916-23.
3 vols., cloth. MacManus 238-920 1978 $125

DEAN, ELIZABETH LIPPINCOTT   Dolly Madison, The Nations Hostess. Boston,
(1923). Illus. from photos. Baldwins' 51-180 1978 $7.50

DEAN, HENRY CLAY   Crimes of the Civil War, and Curse of the
Funding System. Baltimore, Md., 1868. Bell Wiley's copy. Broadfoot 46-72
1978 $35

DEAN, JOHN   Value of Different Kinds of Prepared Vegetable
Food. Cambridge, 1854. 8vo., sewn, pres. from Dean. Morrill 239-62 1978
$8.50

DEANE, JOHN MARSHALL   A Journal of the Campaign in Flanders, A.D.
MDCCVIII. 1846. 8vo., cloth, orig. paper wrappers bound in, annotated in pencil,
ltd. ed. of 75 copies, few spots of wax on upper cover, o/w good copy, rare.
Sawyer 298-70 1978 £250

DEARBORN, HENRY ALEXANDER SCAMMELL　　The Life of William Bainbridge, Esq. of the United States Navy. Princeton, 1931. Illus. MacManus 239-1749 1978 $12.50

DEARBORN, HENRY ALEXANDER SCAMMELL　　Militia Laws of the United States of the Commonwealth of Massachusetts... Boston, 1840. Orig. marbled bds., covers, spine worn & loose. Baldwins' 51-304 1978 $17.50

DEARBORN, NATHANIEL　　Boston Notions; Being an Authentic and Concise Account of "That Village", from 1630 to 1847. Boston, 1848. Maps, plts., portraits, illus., 12mo, orig. leather, rebacked, sides worn, outer margin of 1 map frayed. Edwards 1012-485 1978 £20

DEARDEN, HAROLD　　The Technique of Living. 1924. Austin 80-940 1978 $10

DEARDEN, ROBERT R.　　The Guiding Light on The Great Highway. Philadelphia, (1929). Illus. Baldwins' 51-55 1978 $15

DEARDEN, ROBERT R.　　The Guiding Light on the Great Highway. Philadelphia, n.d. 8vo., orig. cloth, illus., pres. copy from author. MacManus 238-861 1978 $15

THE DEATH-BED of a Modern Free-Thinker. Woodbridge, (c. 1830). 8vo., unbound. P. M. Hill 142-90 1978 £6

DEAVER, JOHN BLAIR　　Surgical Anatomy. Philadelphia, 1901-1903. 3 vols., tall & thick 8vo., fine plts., orig. vellum over bds., gilt lettered, inscr. of orig. owner, dated 1903, very good copy, 1st ed. Zeitlin 245-58 1978 $75

DEAVER, JOHN BLAIR　　Surgical Anatomy of the Head and Neck. Philadelphia, 1904. Binding worn, patched, but still firm. Rittenhouse 49-204 1976 $20

DEBAR, J. H.　　The West Virginia Hand-Book and Immigrant's Guide. Parkersburg, 1870. Orig. binding, clean, considerably worn. Hayman 71-768 1978 $12.50

DE BOSSCHERE, JEAN
Please turn to
BOSSCHERE, JEAN DE

DE BOYER, JEAN BAPTISTE, MARQUIS D'ARGENS
Please turn to
ARGENS, JEAN BAPTISTE DE BOYER, MARQUIS D'

DE BURY, RICHARD
Please turn to
AUNGERVILLE, RICHARD

DE CASSERES, BENJAMIN　　Anathema! New York, 1928. 8vo, cloth, slipcase, 1 of 1250 copies signed by author, 1st ed., fine. Duschnes 220-231 1978 $27.50

DE CHANAL, FRANCOIS VICTOR ADOLPHE
Please turn to
CHANAL, FRANCOIS VICTOR ADOLPHE DE

DE CHARRIERE, ISABELLE
Please turn to
CHARRIERE, ISABELLA AGNETA (VAN TUYLL) DE

DE CHAZEAU, MELVIN G.　　Jobs and Markets. 1946. Austin 80-535 1978 $10

DE CILLIS, OLGA ELENA　　Absolute Threshold for the Perception of Tactual Movement. 1944. Paper. Austin 80-941 1978 $12.50

DECISION of the Four Judges in the Case of M'Garrahan v Maguire on Applications being Made for a New Trial. Dublin, 1828. T.p. repaired, 1/4 leather, good, octavo bound in cloth, reprint. Hyland 128-36 1978 £10

DECK, R.　　Pageant in the Sky. New York, 1941. 8vo, orig. cloth. Book Chest 17-118 1978 $12.50

DECKER, HEINRICH　　Barock-Plastik in den Aepenlandern. Vienna, (1943). 4to. Biblo BL781-734 1978 $20

DECLARATION Of Sentiments of the American Ant-Slavery Society. (New York, c.1845). Unbound. Hayman 71-698 1978 $10

DECLARATION Sur le Subiet et la Forme de l'Entree de Son Altesse Imperiale en France, et de sa Retraitte Apres l'Accomodement Fait entre la Regence... Cambrai, 1649. 4to. Gilhofer 74-65b 1978 sFr 100

DE COMBLES, DE LEON
Please turn to
COMBLES, DE d. 1770?

DECOU, GEORGE　　Moorestown, N.J., and Her Neighbors. Philadelphia, (1929). Illus., scarce. MacManus 239-1254 1978 $30

DECRETO De 20 De Noviembre De 1838 Sobre Ejercicio De La Facultad Coactiva Y Su Reglamento De 31 De Diciembre Del Mismo Ano. Saltillo, 1879. Printed wr., ornate borders. Jenkins 116-224 1978 $20

DEDEM DE GELDER, LE BARON DE　　Un General Hollandais Sous le Permier Empire. Paris, 1900. 8vo., orig. covers, frontis., portr. Van der Peet H-64-303 1978 Dfl 60

THE DEDICATION Exercises of the Actors' Monument to Edgar Allen Poe Sculptured by Richard Henry Park and Unveiled at the Metropolitan Museum...May 4, 1885. New York, 1885. Uncut, wr. Butterfield 21-539 1978 $7.50

DEDICATION of the New Buildings of the Harvard Medical School. Boston, 1906. Rittenhouse 49-333 1976 $10

DEDICATION of the New York (City) Normal College Edifice, October 29, 1873. (New York), 1873. Orig. cloth, fine, text loose, two mounted photo. prints. Butterfield 21-493 1978 $12.50

DEEDES, CHARLES P.　　History of the King's Own Yorkshire Light Infantry, Vol. IV. (1946). 8vo., orig. cloth, port. frontis. F. Edwards 1013-520 1978 £10

DEEPING, WARWICK　　Uther and Igraine. London, 1903. Pictorial cloth. Eaton 45-143 1978 £5

DEERE, GEORGE H.　　Autobiography of... Riverside, 1908. Illus., original cloth, 1st ed. Ginsberg 14-335 1978 $15

DEFARGUES, J. H.　　Traite de l'Ecriture sur l'Enseignement, ou Nouvelle Methode plus Claire et plus Facile que Toutes Celles qui ont Parues Jusqu'a Present. Versailles and Paris, 1787. Folio, early 19th cent. bds., calf back, first ed., rare, plts. Schumann 511-17 1978 sFr 1500

A DEFENCE of the Drama, Containing Mansel's Free Thoughts,.... New York, 1826. 8vo, original grey boards, cream printed paper backstrip, 1st ed., fine copy, entirely uncut, unopened, printed spine, unusual. Ximenes 47-306 1978 $75

DE FLIPPI, FILIPPO　　Karakoram and Western Himalaya 1909. London, 1912. 2 vols., imp.8vo, folding coloured maps, lg. folding plts., quarter parchment, green buckram sides, t.e.g., others uncut, spines trifle chafed & soiled, lib. labels removed, embossed institutional stamps in margins, o/w fine. Deighton 5-209 1978 £115

DEFOE, DANIEL　　Account of the Conduct of Robert Earl of Oxford. London, 1715. 8vo, modern half calf. Traylen 88-220 1978 £42

DEFOE, DANIEL　　The Advantages of the Present Settlement, and The Great Danger of a Relapse. London, 1689. 1st. ed., sm. 4to, marbled wrps. Traylen 88-221 1978 £145

DEFOE, DANIEL　　The Compleat Mendicant: or, Unhappy Beggar. London, 1699. 8vo, 19th-century half calf (covers loose), half morocco slipcase, (spine case defective), 1st ed. Ximenes 47-72 1978 $275

DEFOE, DANIEL　　The Dyet of Poland, a Stayr. Dantzick, 1705. 4to., 1st ed., full red levant mor., scarce, bkplt. of Viscount Hambleden, tall copy. Quaritch 979-109 1978 $545

DEFOE, DANIEL   Eleven Opinions about Mr. H____y (Harley).
1711. 8vo., 1st ed., unbound. Quaritch 979-110 1978 $85

DEFOE, DANIEL   The Fortunes and Misfortunes of the Famous Moll
Flanders. 1923. Orig. buckram gilt, gilt top, ed. ltd. to 775 copies, 8vo.
Howes 194-771 1978 £7.50

DEFOE, DANIEL   The History and Remarkable Life of the Truly
Honourable Colonel Jack. 1923. Ltd. to 775 copies, orig. buckram gilt, gilt
top, 8vo. Howes 194-772 1978 £7.50

DEFOE, DANIEL   The History of the Great Plague In London.
1754. 8vo., orig. marbled bds., uncut, worn, backstrip repaired, second ed.
P. M. Hill 142-91 1978 £60

DEFOE, DANIEL   The History of the Life and Adventures of Mr.
Duncan Campbell, a Gentleman. 1720. 8vo., contemp. panelled calf, frontispiece, plts., fine, first ed. P. M. Hill 142-300 1978 £200

DEFOE, DANIEL   The History of the Wars, of His Present Majesty
Charles XII. King of Sweden; from His First Landing in Denmark, to His Return from
Turkey to Pomerania. London, 1715. Full contemp. blind-stamped calf, 1st ed.,
very fine. MacManus 238-111 1978 $175

DEFOE, DANIEL   A Journal of the Plague Year:.... London,
1722. Octavo, some light foxing, full early calf, expertly rebacked, slipcase, 1st
ed., very good. Bennett 7-32 1978 $550

DEFOE, DANIEL   A Journal of the Plague Year. N.P., 1722.
8 vo., Narcissus Luttrell's copy, bound with 3 plague pamphlets, 18th century
half calf, marbled bds., rehinged, 1st ed. Quaritch Summer,1978-12 1978
$3,000

DEFOE, DANIEL   A Letter from Captain Tom to the Mobb. 1710.
Sm. 8vo., 1st ed., modern wrs., uncut, very rare. Quaritch 979-111 1978 $630

DEFOE, DANIEL   The Wonderful Life and Most Surprising Adventures
of Of(sic) that Renowned Hero, Robinson Crusoe. 1791. 12mo, inscriptions, board
paper mostly gone, upper cover hangs by threads, good, firm copy, unrecorded.
Victoria 34-228 1978 $32.50

DEFOE, DANIEL   The Life and Adventures of Robinson Crusoe. London, 1804. 2 vols., illus. by Stothard, lg. paper ed., 3/4 leather, badly worn,
some foxing, but fine, scarce. Biblo BL781-921 1978 $137.50

DEFOE, DANIEL   The Life and Adventures of Robinson Crusoe.
London, 1820. 2 vols., octavo, full contemp. calf, gilt, illus. Bennett 7-33
1978 $175

DEFOE, DANIEL   The Life and Adventures of Robinson Crusoe.
1820. Plts., 19th cent. full polished calf, vignettes, 2 vols., 8vo. Howes 194-
1410 1978 £48

DEFOE, DANIEL   Robinson Crusoeus. 1823. Fcap. 8vo., half
calf. George's 635-1292 1978 £5.25

DEFOE, DANIEL   Bysh's Edition of the Life of Robinson Crusoe, of
York,.... London, c.1830. 16mo, hand-colored cuts, plates, wrappers with
original stitching, completely firm, spine paper gone, minor foxing, dust soiling.
Victoria 34-226 1978 $30

DEFOE, DANIEL   The Life and Surprising Adventures of Robinson
Crusoe. 1831. First ed., engrav. frontis., woodcuts in text by George Cruikshank, 2 vols., sm. 8vo., orig. cloth, paper labels, spines faded but an excellent
copy, edges untrimmed. George's 635-1535 1978 £25

DEFOE, DANIEL   Robinson Crusoe in Arabic. (Malta, 1835).
4 woodcut illus., pencil note on f.e.p. attributes illus. to Bewick, inscribed, sm.
cr. 8vo., cloth, worn. Eaton 45-21 1978 £30

DEFOE, DANIEL   Robinson Crusoe. Mainz, c.1840's. Oblong
12mo, in German, lithographed plates, papered pictorial boards, minor spine defects.
Victoria 34-227 1978 $35

DEFOE, DANIEL   The Life and Adventures of Robinson Crusoe.
1840. Lg. 8vo., half roan, marbled sides, uncut, plts., illus. P. M. Hill 142-
92 1978 £18

DEFOE, DANIEL   The Adventures of Robinson Crusoe. London,
1864. 8vo., full blue mor., richly gilt tooled spine, marbled edges, colored
frontis., fine colored plts., woodcuts, rare, binding shaved, b & w plts. foxed.
Van der Peet H-64-304 1978 Dfl 195

DEFOE, DANIEL   Memoirs of the Conduct of Her Late Majesty and
Her Last Ministry, Relating to the Separate Peace with France. 1715. 8vo., 1st
ed., modern half calf, top rough gilt, other edges uncut. Quaritch 979-112
1978 $190

DEFOE, DANIEL   No Queen: or, No General. 1712. 8vo., 1st
ed., modern bds., lea. back. Quaritch 979-113 1978 $135

DEFOE, DANIEL   Reflections Upon the Late Great Revolution.
London, 1689. 1st. ed., half title, sm. 4to, contemp. panelled calf, rebacked.
Traylen 88-223 1978 £175

DEFOE, DANIEL   The Re-Representation: or, a Modest Search after
the Great Plunderers of the Nation. 1711. 8vo., 1st ed., rebound in cloth, calf
back. Quaritch 979-114 1978 $105

DEFOE, DANIEL   The Secret History of the October Club: from its
Original to this time. 1711. Sm. 8vo., 1st ed., disbound. Quaritch 979-116
1978 $65

DEFOE, DANIEL   The Secret History of State Intrigues in the Management of the Scepter, in the late Reign. 1715. Sm. 8vo., modern marbled bds.,
signature of former owner. Quaritch 979-115 1978 $170

DEFOE, DANIEL   Some Reflections on a Pamphlet Lately Published..
London, 1697. 2nd. ed., sm. 4to, modern quarter calf. Traylen 88-224 1978
£26

DEFOE, DANIEL   A Tour Through the Whole Island of Great Britain.
1769. 7th. ed., 4 vols., orig. calf, red labels, hinges slightly weak in vol. 1,
slight worming in lower margins vols. 1 & 2, o/w v.g. Jarndyce 16-66 1978 £40

DEFOE, DANIEL   A Tour Thro' The Whole Island of Great Britain...
London, 1927. Maps, 2 vols., roy. 8vo, cloth spines, mottled bds., t.e.g., frayed
d.w., ltd. ed. of 1000 copies. Traylen 88-225 1978 £48

DEFOE, DANIEL   A True Collection of the Writings of the Author
of the True Born Englishman. London, 1703. Portrait, 8vo, old calf, joints
repaired. Traylen 88-226 1978 £50

DEFOE, DANIEL   A True Collection of the Writings of the Author of
the True Born English man. 1705. Second ed., portrait, rebound in half calf antique, contents age-browned, 8vo. Howes 194-237 1978 £25

DEFOE, DANIEL   The Two Great Questions Consider'd. London,
1700. 1st. ed., sm. 4to, marbled wrappers, some foxing. Traylen 88-227 1978
£160

DEFOE, DANIEL   The Vision. N. P., n.d. (Edinburgh, 1706?
Nov.). Sm. 4to., conjugate bifolium, disbound, 1st issue, 1st ed., extremely
rare. Quaritch 979-117 1978 $1,000

DEFOREST, JOHN WILLIAM   History of the Indians of Connecticut, From the
Earliest Period to 1850. Hartford, 1851. 1st ed., illus., nice, orig. cloth.
MacManus 239-1156 1978 $45

DE FOREST, JOHN WILLIAM   A Union Officer in the Reconstruction.
New Haven, 1948. Bell Wiley's copy. Broadfoot 46-73 1978 $15

DE FOREST, JOHN WILLIAM   A Volunteer's Adventures. New Haven, 1946.
Bell Wiley's copy. Broadfoot's 44-439 1978 $12

DE FOREST, JOHN WILLIAM   A Volunteers Adventures. New Haven, 1946.
Bell Wiley's copy. Broadfoot 46-315 1978 $8

DE FOREST, L. E.   Society of Mayflower Descendants in the State
of New York. Sixth Record Book, Sept. 1926. New York, 1926. Illus., bound.
Biblo BL781-55 1978 $10

DE GARMO, CHARLES   Interest and Education. 1902. Austin 80-943
1978 $10

DE GARMO, CHARLES   Principles of Secondary Education. 1907. Austin 80-944 1978 $10

DE GARMO, W. B.   Abdominal Hernia, Its Diagnosis and Treatment.
Philadelphia, 1907. Rittenhouse 49-205 1976 $10

DE GOLYER, EVERETT   The Antiquity of the Oil Industry. Godley, 1947.
Original wr., limited to 300 copies, printed by Carl Hertzog, revised ed., mint
copy. Jenkins 116-618 1978 $125

DEGRAND, P. P. F.   Proceedings of the Friends of a Rail-road to San
Francisco, at the Public Meeting, Held at the U.S. Hotel, in Boston, April 19, 1849
including an Address to the People of the United States;.... Boston, 1849.
Folding map, original front wr. bound in half morocco, 2nd ed. Ginsberg 14-99
1978 $125

DE GROOT, HENRY   Recollections of California Mining Life: Primitive
Placers and First Important Discovery of Gold. San Francisco, 1884. Illus.,
orig. pr. pict. wrs., 1st ed. Ginsberg 14-100 1978 $125

DEGROOT, HENRY   Sketches of the Washoe Silver Mines. San
Francisco, 1860. Wrs., ltd. to 200 numbered copies, few copies of the orig.
are known. Hayman 73-141 1978 $7.50

DE GUERVILLE, AMEDEE BAILLOT
Please turn to
GUERVILLE, AMEDEE GUILLOT DE

DE GUINGAND, SIR FRANCIS   Operation Victory. 1947. Austin 80-83
1978 $11

DEGUISE, CHARLES   Helika. Memoire d'un vieux maitre d'ecole.
Montreal, 1872. Wolfe 39-118 1978 $30

DEHAN, RICHARD   That Which Hath Wings. New York, 1918. First
American ed., inner hinges sprung. Biblo 247-651 1978 $9.50

DE JARNETTE, DANIEL C.   The Monroe Doctrine. Richmond? 1865. Wrs.,
Bell Wiley's copy. Broadfoot 46-462 1978 $40

DEKKER, THOMAS   Dramatic Works. 1873. 4 vols., rebound in
cloth, ex-lib. copy, title-pgs. soiled. Eaton 45-144 1978 £35

DEKKER, THOMAS   The Magnificent Entertainment.... 1604. Sm.
4to., brown hardgrain mor. gilt, by Riviere, from the lib. of William Herbert with
his signature. Thomas 37-39 1978 £1000

DEKKER, THOMAS   The Second Part of the Honest Whore.
N.P., 1630. Sm. 4 to., lacks terminal blank L4, satisfactory, full red mor.
by Sangorski, 1st and only ed. Quaritch Summer, 1978-13 1978 $900

DE KRUIF, PAUL   Men Against Death. New York, (1932). Illus.,
8vo., cloth, 1st ed. Salloch 345-55 1978 $10

DE KRUIF, PAUL   Microbe Hunters. New York, (1926). 8vo.,
d.w., 1st ed. Morrill 239-63 1978 $12.50

DE LA CROIX, PETIS   The History of Genghizcan the Great. 1722.
Folding map, calf, rebacked, 8vo, bookplt. of Sir Foster Cunliffe. Edwards
1012-208 1978 £90

DELAFIELD, JOHN   An Inquiry Into The Origin of the Antiquities of
America... New York, 1839. 1st. ed., folding frontis, plts., 5 in colour, 4to,
spine faded & repaired. Edwards 1012-391 1978 £45

DELAGE, F.   La Troisieme guerre de religion en Limousin, combat de La Roche-l'Abeille, 1569. Limoges, (c. 1935). Map, plts., 8vo.
George's 635-622 1978 £5

DE LA MARE, COLIN   They Walk Again; ghost stories. London, 1931.
Nice, first ed., orig. binding, neatly mounted on front and rear end-papers are
portions of d.w. Rota 211-20 1978 £5

DE LA MARE, WALTER   Broomsticks and Other Tales. London, 1925.
8vo, light brown cloth, gilt stamped cover and spine, Fine, inscribed by author,
1st ed. Desmarais 1-116 1978 $40

DE LA MARE, WALTER   Broomsticks & Other Tales. 1925. One of 278
copies numbered & signed by author, wood-engrav. by Bold, orig. linen-backed
bds., leather label, t.e.g., very nice, first English ed. Bell Book 17-206 1978
£12.50

DE LA MARE, WALTER   The Burning Glass and Other Poems. London,
1945. 1st ed., very good or better. Limestone 9-77 1978 $12.50

DE LA MARE, WALTER   The Collected Tales of... New York, 1950.
1st Amer. ed. Biblo 251-438 1978 $15

DE LA MARE, WALTER   Come Hither: A Collection of Rhymes and Poems
for the Young of All Ages. 1923. First ed., illus., 2 vols., orig. holland backed
bds., special ed., ltd. to 350 numbered copies signed by author, 8vo. Howes
194-774 1978 £28

DE LA MARE, WALTER   Come Hither. 1923. Illus. with woodcuts,
author's signed pres. copy, orig. cloth, slightly rubbed. Eaton 45-147 1978 £30

DE LA MARE, WALTER   The Connoisseur, and other stories. 1926. Qtr.
buckram gilt, fine, worn d.w., signed by author, first English ed. Bell Book 17-
207 1978 £15

DE LA MARE, WALTER   The Connoisseur, and other Stories. 1926. First
ed., gilt bds., buckram back, repaired d.w., 8vo. Howes 194-775 1978 £6

DE LA MARE, WALTER   Crossings. New York, 1923. 1st ed., fine
colored f.p., B&W plates, fine. Victoria 34-481 1978 $35

DE LA MARE, WALTER   Crossings. London, 1923. 1st trade ed.,
uncut, spine label slightly worn, else very good or better. Limestone 9-78
1978 $20

DE LA MARE, WALTER   Crossings, a Fairy Play. London, 1923. Near
fine in darkened d.w., Forrest Reid's copy with his signature on flyleaf. Desmarais B-172 1978 $25

DE LA MARE, WALTER.   Crossings, A Fairy Play. London, 1923. 8vo,
boards, cloth back with leather label, near Fine, somewhat darkened and rubbed
d.w., Forrest Reid's copy with signature, 1st ed. Desmarais 1-115 1978 $25

DE LA MARE, WALTER   Desert Islands and Robinson Crusoe. London,
1930. Green cloth, t.e.g., others uncut, 1st ed., 1 of 650 signed. Bradley 49-
73 1978 $65

DE LA MARE, WALTER   Desert Islands and 'Robinson Crusoe'. 1930.
One of 650 copies numbered & signed by author, roy. 8vo., cloth gilt, t.e.g.,
very nice, first English ed. Bell Book 17-208 1978 £55

DE LA MARE, WALTER   Ding Dong Bell. 1924. One of 300 copies
numbered & signed by the author, linen-backed bds., very good, first English ed.
Bell Book 16-222 1978 £17.50

DE LA MARE, WALTER   Down-Adown-Derry. 1st ed., color plts., text
illus., fine. Victoria 34-482 1978 $40

DE LA MARE, WALTER   Early One Morning. New York, 1935. 8vo, red
cloth, gilt lettering on spine, Fine, inscribed to Hugh Palmer from Charles Warren
Everett, 1st ed., collector's cond. Desmarais 1-117 1978 $20

DE LA MARE, WALTER   Flora: A Book of Drawings. (1919). 4to., color
plts. by Pamela Bianco, bds., covers soiled, internally v.g., first Eng. ed. Bell
Book 16-479 1978 £10

DE LA MARE, WALTER   Henry Brocken. London, (1924). 8vo, boards,
cloth back, leather label, uncut, illus. by Martin Ellis, no. 183 of 250 signed
copies, 1st ed., collector's cond. Desmarais 1-118 1978 $30

DE LA MARE, WALTER   Henry Brocken. One of 250 copies numbered &
signed by author, plts., orig. linen-backed bds., leather label, nice, largely unopened, first English ed. Bell Book 17-209 1978 £12.50

DE LA MARE, WALTER   Inward Companion. London, 1950. Nice in
torn d.w. Desmarais B-173 1978 $10

DE LA MARE, WALTER   The Lord Fish. London, 1933. Ex-lib., near
fine in d.w. Desmarais B-174 1978 $12.50

DE LA MARE, WALTER   Poems. London, 1906. Nice, first ed., orig.
binding. Rota 212-13 1978 £35

DE LA MARE, WALTER   Poems 1901 to 1918. 1920. 2 vols., very good, first English ed. Bell Book 16-223 1978 £5

DE LA MARE, WALTER   Poems, 1901 to 1918. London, 1920. 8vo, 2 vols., gray stamped cloth, near Mint, slightly rubbed d.w., signed and dated by author, A.L.s. laid in, 1st ed. Desmarais 1-120 1978 $95

DE LA MARE, WALTER   Poems. London, 1906. Small 8vo., green cloth, gilt stamped cover and spine, ownership inscription, light foxing, 1st ed., collector's cond. Desmarais 1-119 1978 $45

DE LA MARE, WALTER   The Return. 1910. 1st. ed., cloth. Eaton 45-149 1978 £20

DE LA MARE, WALTER   The Riddle, and Other Stories. 1923. Cloth, very good, signed & dated by author. Eaton 45-145 1978 £10

DE LA MARE, WALTER   Songs of Childhood. London, 1923. Lmtd. to 310 copies, signed by author, color plates by Estella Canziani, vellum-backed boards, fine in dj. Victoria 34-229 1978 $125

DE LA MARE, WALTER   Songs of Childhood. London, 1923. Illus. by Estella Canziana, new ed., ltd. ed. of 310 copies, signed by author, coloured plts., illus., orig. qtr. parchment, 8vo. K Books 244-87 1978 £16

DE LA MARE, WALTER   Stuff and Nonsense and So On. 1927. End-paper signed, woodcuts by Bold, bookplt. cloth, sm. stain on spine. Eaton 45-146 1978 £7.50

DE LA MARE, WALTER   The Three Mulla-Mulgars. London, 1910. 1st ed., color plates by Monseil, inner hinges cracked, dust soiled, very good. Victoria 34-231 1978 $20

DE LA MARE, WALTER   This Year: Next Year. New York, (1937). 1st Amer. ed., color plates or illus. by Harold Jones, fine. Victoria 34-230 1978 $25

DE LA MARE, WALTER   The Traveller; a poem. London, 1946. Drawings by John Piper, fine, frayed d.w., inscribed by the author, first ed., orig. binding. Rota 211-86 1978 £25

DE LA MARE, WALTER   The Traveller. 1946. 1st. ed., lithos by John Piper, spine a shade worn & discoloured, otherwise v.g. Jarndyce 16-1207 1978 £8.50

DE LA MARE, WALTER   The Veil, and other poems. 1921. One of 250 copies, numbered & signed by author, orig. linen-backed bds., leather label, nice, first English ed. Bell Book 17-210 1978 £12.50

DE LA MARE, WALTER   The Veil and Other Poems. 1921. Paper covered bds., buckram spine. Eaton 45-148 1978 £5

DELAMBRE, JEAN-BAPTISTE   Histoire de l'Astronomie. Paris, 1827. 5 vols., 4to., old cloth, uncut, little worn, but fine set, 1st ed. Norman 5-76 1978 $375

DELAMBRE, JEAN BAPTISTE   Rapport Historique sur les Progres des Sciences Mathematiques Depuis 1789. Paris, 1810. 4to., lg. copy, rebound, half calf. Quaritch 977-93 1978 $125

DELAMOTTE, FREEMAN GAGE   Mediaeval Alphabets and Initials for Illuminators. London, 1861. Sq. 12mo., cloth, gilt, title page, plts. in color, fr. hinge broken, fine. Duschnes 220-158 1978 $45

DE LA MOTTE FOUQUE, FRIEDRICH
Please turn to
LA MOTTE FOUQUE, FRIEDRICH DE

DELAND, MARGARET   "Confession." N.P., n.d. (Hampton, ca. 1925). 16mo., orig. wrs., 1st ed. Morrill 239-363 1978 $12.50

DELAND, MARGARET   The Kays. New York, 1926. 8vo., orig. bds., cloth back, 1 of 250 copies of the pres. ed. signed by publishers. Morrill 239-364 1978 $13.50

DELAND, MARGARET   The Old Garden and Other Verses by.... London, 1893. Small octavo, orig. decor. cloth cover, cloth spine, colour lithographs by Walter Crane. Totterdige 29-26 1978 $75

DELANY, MARY   Letters from Mr. Delany to Mrs. Frances Hamilton, 1779-1788. 1820. First ed., portrait, orig. bds., entirely uncut, very good, rare, 8vo. Howes 194-238 1978 £25

DELANEY, JOHN P.   The Blue Devils in Italy. Washington, (1947). Illus. Biblo 247-783 1978 $17.50

DELANNOY, BURFORD   The Margate Mystery. New York, 1901. 1st ed., few pages roughly opened. Biblo 251-443 1978 $17.50

DELANO, ALONZO   The Miner's Progress: or, Scenes in the Life of a California Miner. Sacramento, 1853. Woodcuts, front wrapper by Charles Nahl, original printed wr. Ginsberg 14-101 1978 $550

DELANO, ALONZO   Old Block's Sketch Book. Santa Ana, 1947. Illus., original cloth. Ginsberg 14-102 1978 $17.50

DELANY, MARY GRANVILLE PENDARVES   Autobiography and Correspondence. 1861. Portraits, 3 vols., stitching loose, 8vo. George's 635-1243 1978 £10.50

DELANY, PATRICK   Observations upon Lord Orrery's Remarks on the Life and Writings of Dr. J. Swift. 1754. First ed., contemp. calf, label missing, joints cracked, 8vo. Howes 194-483 1978 £40

DELAPLAINE, EDWARD S.   Francis Scott Key, Life and Times. New York, 1937. Illus., ltd. to 500 copies, signed by author, fine. MacManus 239-780 1978 $35

DELAPLAINE, EDWARD S.   The Life of Thomas Johnson... New York, 1927. 1st ed., illus., fine, ltd. to 500 copies, signed by author. MacManus 239-779 1978 $35

DELAPLAINE, EDWARD S.   The Life of Thomas Johnson. New York, 1927. 9 illus., pres. copy. Baldwins' 51-280 1978 $15

DELAPORTE, L.   La Mesopotamie. Les Civilisations Babylonienne et Assyrienne. Paris, 1923. Illus., bound. Biblo BL781-364 1978 $12

DELAPORTE, YVES   Les Vitraux de la Cathedrale de Chartres. Paris, 1926. Paper covers torn, text fine, wrs., 4to. Biblo 247-310 1978 $52.50

DE LA RAMEE, LOUISE   Ariadne the Story of a Dream. 1877. 1st ed., 3 vols., half titles, lacking leading free endpapers, lib. labels on inner covers, orig. blue cloth, leading bds. blocked in black, gilt spines, rubbed, fair to good copy. Jarndyce 16-921 1978 £25

DE LA RAMEE, LOUISE   Critical Studies. London, 1900. 8vo, original pale green cloth, 1st ed. Ximenes 47-220 1978 $30

DE LA RAMEE, LOUISE   Folle-Farine. Philadelphia, 1871. 1st Amer. ed., 3 vols in 1, orig. cloth, very good. Greene 78-89 1978 $20

DE LA RAMEE, LOUISE   Idalia. Philadelphia, 1867. Cloth worn, lacks end paper, some interior soil, 1st Amer. ed., 3 vols. in 1. Greene 78-90 1978 $15

DE LA RAMEE, LOUISE   Pascarel. Only a Story. Philadelphia, 1873. 1st Amer. ed., 3 vols. in 1, green cloth, some shelf wear, good. Greene 78-91 1978 $20

DE LA RAMEE, LOUISE   Ruffino, Etc. London, 1890. Orig. cloth, 1st ed., covers slightly soiled, but very good. MacManus 238-366 1978 $75

DE LA RAMEE, LOUISE   A Tale of a Toad. London, Corvinus Press, 1939. One of 24 copies printed on Auvergne paper, folio, patterned cloth bds., mor. spine, nice, first ed. Rota 212-42 1978 £150

DE LA RAMEE, LOUISE   The Tower of Taddeo. London, 1892. 3 vols., orig. cloth, 1st ed., covers soiled, labels removed. MacManus 238-367 1978 $85

DE LA RAMEE, LOUISE   Views and Opinions. London, 1895. Orig. cloth, 1st ed., fine. MacManus 238-368 1978 $40

DE LA RAMEE, LOUISE　　A Village Commune. London, 1881. 2 vols., orig. cloth, 1st ed., spines a little faded and rubbed, otherwise very good. Mac-Manus 238-364 1978 $185

DE LA RAMEE, LOUISE　　Wanda. London, 1883. 3 vols., orig. cloth, a bit stained, 1st ed., very good. MacManus 238-365 1978 $150

DE LA RAMEE, PIERRE
Please turn to
LA RAMEE, PIERRE DE

DE LA ROCHE, MAZO　　Delight. New York, 1926. 1st ed. Hood 116-467 1978 $15

DE LA ROCHE, MAZO　　Delight. New York, 1926. 1st Amer. ed., d.w. Biblo BL781-923 1978 $9

DELAVAN, EDWARD C.　　Some Considerations Respecting the Construction of the Albany and Susquehanna Rail-Road. Albany, 1852. Self-wr., lg. fldg. map, very good. Butterfield 21-152A 1978 $25

DELAVOYE, ALEX M.　　Records of the 90th Regiment. 1880. Roy. 8vo., orig. cloth, spine faded. F. Edwards 1013-540 1978 £30

DEL BENE, BARTOLOMMEO　　Civitas Veri Sive Morum. Paris, 1609. Plts. by Thomas de Leu, folio, contemp. calf, gilt. Salloch 348-42 1978 $2,250

DE LEE, JOSEPH BOLIVAR　　The Principles and Practices of Obstetrics. Philadelphia, 1918. Third ed., thoroughly revised. Rittenhouse 49-207 1976 $10

DE LEON, THOMAS C.　　Belles, Beaux and Brains of the 60's. New York, 1909. Portraits, soiled cover, Bell Wiley's copy. Broadfoot's 44-111 1978 $14

DELESCHAMPS, PIERRE　　Des Mordans..ou Traite Complete de la Gravure. Paris, 1836. Plts., 8vo., orig. printed wrs. Schumann 511-18 1978 sFr 250

DELETANVILLE, THOMAS　　A New French Dictionary: In Two Parts... 1804. 4th. ed., revised, improved, contemp. calf, gilt spine, joints weak & rubbed. Eaton 45-151 1978 £8

DELEUZE, J. P. F.　　Practical Instruction in Animal Magnetism. 1843. Austin 80-947 1978 $37.50

DELHI, ARNE　　Selections of Byzantine Ornament. 1890. 2 vols., 4to., plts. loose in portfolio. Allen 234-1197 1978 $30

DELIGHTFUL Adventures, Histories, Anecdotes, and Memoirs, From Absolute Facts. N.P., 1744. 1st ed., 12mo, frontispiece, blank corners torn off, modern bds., sm. holes in one leaf, very good copy. Hannas 54-79 1978 $25

DE LILLE, JACQUES　　Le Malheur et la Pitie, Poeme en Quatre Chants. Londres, 1803. 1st. London ed., lg. 4to, thick paper, 5 plts., slightly foxed & waterstained, contemp. red-straight-grained morocco, blind-tooled & gilt, joints & corners slightly rubbed. Hannas 54-80 1978 £55

DELILLE, JACQUES　　Oeuvres. Paris, 1804-22. Plts., 12 vols., full contemp. straight-grained mor., 8vo. Howes 194-538 1978 £48

DE LINT, J. G.
Please turn to
LINT, JAN GERARD DE

DELISLE, ALEX. M.　　Speech of...in Support of the Petition for a Rail Road Between Quebec, Montreal, Bytown and Georgian Bay. Montreal, 1853. Wrs. Hood 117-728 1978 $55

DELITZSCH, FRIEDRICH　　Babel und Bibel. Two Lectures. 1903. Illus. Biblo BL781-365 1978 $10

DELL, FLOYD　　The Golden Spike. 1934. First ed., very good, d.j. Austin 82-332 1978 $37.50

DELL, FLOYD　　Intellectual Vagabondage. 1926. Austin 82-333 1978 $12.50

DELL, FLOYD　　King Arthur's Socks and Other Village Plays. 1912. Austin 82-334 1978 $17.50

DELL, FLOYD　　Runaway. 1925. Signed, ltd. to 250 copies. Austin 82-335 1978 $95

DELLE Rime Piacevoli del Berni, Casa, Mavro, Varchi, Dolce, Et d'altri Autori. Vicenza, 1603. 3 vols., 12mo., marbled bds., calf spine, very good. King 7-93 1978 £50

DELLENBAUGH, FREDERICK SAMUEL　　Breaking the Wilderness, the Story of the Conquest of the Far West,... New York, (1905). Illus., maps, uncut, fine. MacManus 239-1911 1978 $25

DELLENBAUGH, FREDERICK SAMUEL　　A Canon Voyage. New Haven, 1926. Illus. Biblo 247-203 1978 $15

DELLENBAUGH, FREDERICK SAMUEL　　Fremont and '49, the Story of a Remarkable Career and Its Relation to the Exploration and Development of our Western Territory, esp. California. New York, 1914. 1st ed., illus., maps, fine untrimmed copy, orig. pict. cloth, t.e.g., scarce. MacManus 239-1912 1978 $37.50

DELLENBAUGH, FREDERICK SAMUEL　　The Romance of the Colorado River. The Story of Its Discovery in 1540.... New York, 1909. 3rd ed., illus., fold. map, orig. pict. cloth, fine. MacManus 239-1913 1978 $25

DEL MAR, ALEXANDER　　Report on the Present Condition and Prospects of the Silver Mines of Middlesex Nevada. San Francisco, 1879. Folding map, orig. pr. wr., 1st ed. Ginsberg 14-730 1978 $75

DE LOLME, JOHN LEWIS　　The Constitution of England... 1784. 4th. ed., frontispiece portrait, orig. half calf, marbled bds., maroon labels, slight weakening of hinges, o/w v.g., from lib. of Lord Dacre with his bookplt. Jarndyce 16-67 1978 £10.50

DE LONG, GEORGE W.　　The Voyage of the Jeanette. London, 1883. 1st. ed., 2 vols., 8vo, tinted lithograph plt., other plts., portraits, folding & other maps, illus., lib. stamps, modern half calf, gilt backs. Deighton 5-155 1978 £125

DELORME, R.　　Le Musee de la Comedie Francaise. Paris, 1878. Lg. 8vo., half blue mor., gilt ribbed spine. Van der Peet H-64-120 1978 Dfl 55

DELOUME, A.　　Les Manieurs d'Argent a Rome Jusqu'a l'Empire. 1892. Buckram. Allen 234-262 1978 $10

DE LA TOUR, IMBART
Please turn to
IMBART DE LA TOUR, PIERRE

DE LUC, JEAN ANDRE　　Recherches sur les modifications de l'atomsphere. Geneva, 1772. 1st ed., 2 vols., 4 to., very fine copy, contemp. polished calf, gilt back with red morocco title label. Schafer 19-47 1978 sFr. 1,900

DE LUC, JEAN ANDRE　　Recherches Sur les Modifications de l'Atmosphere. Geneva, 1772. 2 vols., 4to., plts., contemp. bds., 1st ed., fine, uncut copy. Gilhofer 74-112 1978 sFr 750

DELWORTH, C. D.　　Christian Unity. Toronto, 1899. Paper cover. Hood 117-343 1978 $20

DEMAREST, WILLIAM H. S.　　The Anniversary of New Brunswick, N.J... New Brunswick, 1932. Illus. MacManus 239-1255 1978 $25

DEMAREST, WILLIAM H. S.　　A History of Rugers College... New Brunswick, 1924. 1st ed., royal 8vo., illus., orig. cloth, fine. MacManus 239-1256 1978 $15

DEMARQUAY, JEAN-NICOLAS　　Traite des Tumeurs de l'Orbite. Paris, 1860. 8vo., orig. prtd. wrs., uncut, 1st ed., fine copy. Offenbacher 30-116 1978 $115

DEMAUS, R.　　William Tindale... 1904. Plts., octavo, good. Upcroft 10-288 1978 £5

DE MENT, J. Handbook of Uranium Minerals, An Exposition and Catalog. Portland, 1947. Wrappers, errata sheet tipped in. Hood's 115-701 1978 $12

DEMIDOFF, E. Hunting Trips in the Caucasus. London, 1898. 8vo., cloth, illus., map. Van der Peet H-64-305 1978 Dfl 30

DE MILLE, JAMES A Castle in Spain. New York, n.d.(c.1883). 1st Amer. ed.(?), illus. by E.A. Abbey, orig. cloth, tall 8vo. Greene 78-174 1978 $20

DE MILLE, JAMES A Strange Manuscript Found in a Copper Cylinder. New York, 1888. 1st Amer. ed., illus. by Gilbert Gaul, blue cloth, worn spine, good. Greene 78-175 1978 $45

DEMING, CLARENCE Yale Yesterdays. New Haven, 1915. Illus., edges rubbed. Biblo BL781-25 1978 $10

DEMING, HENRY CHAMPION Eulogy of Abraham Lincoln... Hartford, 1865. Orig. cloth- covered wrps., gilt stamped. Hayman 71-420 1978 $20

DE MOIVRE, ABRAHAM
Please turn to
MOIVRE, ABRAHAM DE

DEMOLDER, E. La Route d'Emeraude. Bruxelles, 1925. 4to., cloth portfolio, cloth slipcase, illus. by A. Delstanche, ltd. ed. of 50 numbered copies only, prtd. on "Hollande". Van der Peet H-64-420 1978 Dfl 275

DEMONFERRAND, JEAN BAPTISTE FIRMIN Manuel D'Electricite Dynamique, Ou Traite Sur l'Action Mutuelle Des Conducteurs Electriques Et Des Aimans, Et Sur Une Nouvelle Theorie Du Magnetisme. Paris, 1823. Copperplts., 8vo., half mor., 1st ed., occas. foxing. Offenbacher 30-4 1978 $225

A DEMONSTRATION of the Necessity of a Legislative Union of G.B. & I.... Dublin, 1799. 1st ed., plain wr. Hyland 128-356 1978 £8

DE MORGAN, AUGUSTUS A Budget of Paradoxes. 1872. 8vo., orig. cloth, shaken. Quaritch 977-144 1978 $85

DE MORGAN, AUGUSTUS Memoir. London, 1882. 8vo., ads, illus., orig. cloth, gilt, very good copy. Norman 5-77 1978 $75

DE MORGAN, J. Les Premieres Civilisations. Etudes sur la Prehistorie et l'Histoire... Paris, 1909. Maps, 4to., orig. wrs. Biblo BL781-367 1978 $27.50

DE MORGAN, WILLIAM It Never Can Happen Again. London, 1909. 2 vols., 1st ed., color portrait, very good or better. Limestone 9-79 1978 $37.50

DEMOSTHENES Demosthenis, Graecorum Oratorum Principis, Olynthiacae Orationes Tres,.... London, 1571. Sm. 4to., half morocco, (spine defective), 1st Latin ed., bookplate of John Camp Williams, internally very good copy. Ximenes 47-74 1978 $150

DEMOSTHENES Opera, quae ad Nostram Aetatem Pervenerunt, Omnia Una cum Ulpiani Rhetoris Mommentariis,.... Basileae, (ca. 1549). 1st Latin translation, folio, five parts in one vol., full old vellum, repaired. Bennett 20-58 1978 $375

DEMPSTER, THOMAS Jo. Baptistae Passerii Pisaurensis Nob.... Lucae, 1767. Folio, bds., half calf edges rubbed, plts., very wide margins. King 7-163 1978 £70

DE MUSSET, ALFRED
Please turn to
MUSSET, ALFRED DE

DENHAM, DIXON Narrative of Travels and Discoveries in Northern and Central Africa, In the Years 1822, 1823, and 1824.... London, 1826. 2nd. ed., 2 vols, 8vo, coloured view, engraved plts., maps, one laid down on linen, some soiling, half calf, gilt backs. Deighton 5-10 1978 £70

DENHAM, GEORGE Intervalla. 1898. Half title, orig. cloth, v.g., uncut, pres. copy from editor. Jarndyce 16-459 1978 £5

DENHAM, THOMAS The Temporal Government of the Pope's State. 1788. 8vo., contemp. half calf, marbled sides. P.M. Hill 142-93 1978 £25

DENHARDT, ROBERT MOORMAN The Horse of the Americas. Norman, 1947. Cloth, illus., 1st ed., fine, d.w., scarce. Dykes 35-218 1978 $22.50

DENHARDT, ROBERT MOORMAN The Horse of the Americas. Norman, 1947. 1st ed., cloth, illus., fine copy in d.w., scarce. Dykes 34-224 1978 $22.50

DENIEFFE, J. A Personal Narrative of the Irish Revolutionary Brotherhood. (1906). Reprint, octavo bound in cloth. Hyland 128-940 1978 £6

DENINA, CARLO Dell'Impiego delle Persone. Torino, 1803. 2 vols. in 1, 12mo., marbled bds., calf spine, very good. King 7-164 1978 £25

DENISE, M. FERDINAND Les Californies, L'Oregon et L'Amerique Russe. [Paris, 1849]. Boards, 1st ed. Ginsberg 14-336 1978 $75

DENISON, GEORGE T. Canada and Her Relations to the Empire. Toronto, 1895. Hood 116-619 1978 $15

DENISON, GEORGE T. Soldiering in Canada, Recollections and Experiences. Toronto, 1900. Ex-lib, cover scuffed. Hood's 115-99 1978 $20

DENISON, GEORGE T. The Struggle for Imperial Unity; Recollections and Experiences. London, 1909. Hood 116-620 1978 $30

DENISON, GEORGE T. The Struggle for Imperial Unity. London, 1909. Orig. binding. Wolfe 39-121 1978 $22.50

DENISON, JESSE W. First Annual Report to the Stockholders of the Providence Western Land Company. Providence, 1857. Original printed wr., 1st ed. Ginsberg 14-409 1978 $75

DENISON, MARY ANDREWS Out of Prison. Boston, 1864. Cloth, worn, cover worn, but good tight copy. Hayman 73-180 1978 $12.50

DENISON, MERRILL Klondike Mike; an Alaskan Odyssey. New York, 1943. Hood 116-73 1978 $12.50

DENNE, SAMUEL Observations on Paper-Marks in a Letter to Mr. Gough. Cloth plts., 4 are fldg., watermarks, newly bound in cloth. Battery Park 1-447 1978 $100

DENNETT, TYLER John Hay, from Poetry to Politics. New York, 1934. Bell Wiley's copy. Broadfoot 46-497 1978 $10

DENNIS, CLARA Cape Breton Over. Toronto, 1943. Illus. with photos. Hood's 115-209 1978 $12.50

DENNIS, CLARA More About Nova Scotia. Toronto, 1937. Illus. Hood 117-240 1978 $17.50

DENNIS, G.R. The House of Cecil. 1914. Illus., 8vo. George's 635-594 1978 £5

DENNIS, GEORGE Cities & Cemeteries of Etruria. n.d. 2 vols., Everyman Ed. Allen 234-305 1978 $10

DENNIS, JOHN Appius and Virtinia. A Tragedy. London, (1709). 4to., mod. cloth, 1st ed., some browning throughout. MacManus 238-113 1978 $75

DENNIS, JOHN Rinaldo and Armida. A Tragedy. London, 1709. 4to., mod. cloth, 1st ed., some foxing and soiling throughout. MacManus 238-114 1978 $100

DENNISON, W. Gold Treasure of the Late Roman Period. 1918. 4to., plts. Allen 234-266 1978 $15

DENNY, CECIL E. The Law Marches West. Toronto, 1939. Ex-lib. but clean and tight. Hood 117-235 1978 $35

DENNY, EDWARD Hymn & Poems. n.d. (c.1845). 2nd. ed., orig. green cloth, inscription on endpaper, otherwise v.g. Jarndyce 16-460 1978 £9.50

DENNY, HAROLD N. Dollars for Bullets. The Story of American Rule in Nicaragua. New York, 1929. Illus., maps. Biblo BL781-106 1978 $9.50

DENNY, NATHANIEL P.   Address Delivered Before the Worcester Agricultural Society, September 25, 1822... Worcester, n.d. (1822?). Sewed. Hayman 72-176 1978 $10

DENSMORE, FRANCES   Chippewa Music. Washington, 1910. Cloth. Hayman 73-142 1978 $7.50

DENSMORE, FRANCES   Chippewa Music. Washington, 1910. Illus., inscription, cloth. Biblo BL781-68 1978 $12

DENSMORE, FRANCES   Chippewa Music - II. Washington, 1913. Illus., #53, cloth. Biblo BL781-69 1978 $14.50

DENT, JOHN CHARLES   The Last Forty Years, Canada Since the Union of 1841. Toronto, 1881. 2 vols., leather spines and corners. Hood 116-621 1978 $125

DENT, JOHN CHARLES   The Last Forty Years. Toronto, 1881. 2 vols., 3/4 lea., restored, gold inlay decor. on covers, marbled edged pages, bkplt. of John A. Macdonald. Hood 117-563 1978 $125

DENT, JOHN CHARLES   The Story of Upper Canadian Rebellion... Toronto, 1885. 2 vols., orig. decorated gilt-stamped bds. Hood's 115-587 1978 $75

DENTON, B. E.   A Two-Gun Cyclone. Dallas, [1927]. Illus., original pictorial cloth, 1st ed. Ginsberg 14-337 1978 $30

DENTON, DANIEL   A Brief Description of New York, Formerly Called New Netherlands with the Places Thereunto Adjoining. New York, 1845. 4to., spine torn, 1 of 100 lg. paper copies. Morrill 241-408 1978 $25

DENUNCE, M.   Spina Bifida: Anatomie Pathologique et Embryogenie. Paris & Bordeaux, n.d. Paper covers, uncut. Rittenhouse 49-209 1976 $25

DE PALENCIA, ISABEL
Please turn to
PALENCIA, ISABEL DE

DE PALMA, ANTHONY F.   Surgery of the Shoulder. Philadelphia, 1950. Rittenhouse 49-210 1976 $15

DEPERTHES, J. L. H. S.   Histoire Des Naufrages Ou Recueil Des Relations Les Plus Interessantes des Naufrages... Paris, 1788-89. 3 vols., 6 engraved plts., contemp. calf, gilt, panelled spines, red & green letter-pieces, slightly worn, 8vo. Edwards 1012-14 1978 £160

DE PEYSTER, JOHN WATTS   History of the Life of Leonard Torstenson. Poughkeepsie, 1855. 1st ed., pres. copy from author, inscr'd, backstrip worn. Austin 79-201 1978 $47.50

DEPIERRIS, H. A.   Le Tabac. Paris, 1898. 8vo., orig. covers. Van der Peet H-64-306 1978 Dfl 30

DE PLESSIS, C. N. J.   Uit De Geschiedenis Van De Zuid-Afrikaansche Republiek En Van De Afrikaanders. Amsterdam-Pretoria, 1898. 8vo, orig. cloth, plts. Edwards 1012-297 1978 £25

DEPONS, FRANCOIS   Travels In Parts of South America, 1801-4... Phillips, 1806. 8vo, modern half calf, some browning in text, maps. Edwards 1012-641 1978 £25

DEPOSITIO Cornut Typographici. Merrymount Press, 1911. 1 of 250 copies on Glaslan paper, bound in bds., 8vo. Battery Park 1-144 1978 $50

DEPPING, J. B.   Evening Entertainments. Philadelphia, 1833. New ed., woodcuts by Atherton, large pictorial cover label, upper cover hinge partly cracked, endpaper lacking, good. Victoria 34-236 1978 $10

DE PUY, HENRY FARR   A Bibliography of the English Colonial Treatise with the American Indians. Including a Synopsis of Each Treaty. New York, 1917. Orig. cloth, 1st ed., ltd. to 125 copies. MacManus 238-903 1978 $50

DE PUY, HENRY WALTER   The Mountain Hero and His Associates. Boston, 1855. 1st. ed., frontis. Baldwins' 51-171 1978 $20

DE QUILLE, DAN PSEUD.
Please turn to
WRIGHT, WILLIAM

DE QUINCEY, THOMAS   Collected Writings. Edinburgh, 1896-97. 14 vols., cr. 8vo., half calf, portrait. Howes 194-778 1978 £60

DE QUINCEY, THOMAS   Confessions of an Opium-Eater. E. Aurora, 1898. 1 of 925 numbered copies signed by Elbert Hubbard, from the library of DeWitt Miller with signature, orig. suede-backed bds., uncut, 8vo., very good. Americanist 103-80 1978 $30

DE QUINCEY, THOMAS   The Confessions of an English Opium-Eater. London, (1930). Illus., 1st of this illus. ed., top of spine nicked. Biblo BL781-640 1978 $10

DE QUINCEY, THOMAS   The Confessions of an English Opium Eater. 1948. Wood-engravings by Blair Hughes-Stanton, cloth gilt, very good, worn d.w., first English ed. Bell Book 17-490 1978 £6.50

DERBER, MILTON   The Aged and Society. 1950. Paper. Austin 80-950 1978 $12.50

DERBY, ALICE G.   A Bibliography of Ohio Geology. Columbus, 1906. Cloth. Hayman 73-523 1978 $10

DERBY, STANLEY EDWARD, 14TH EARL OF   Translations of Poems, Ancient and Modern. London, 1862. 8vo, orig. blue cloth, 1st ed., privately pr., presentation copy, inscribed on front flyleaf to John Murray. Ximenes 47-300 1978 $50

DERCUM, FRANCIS X.   A Clinical Manual of Mental Diseases. Philadelphia, 1914. Mark on spine. Rittenhouse 49-211 1976 $10

DERCUM, FRANCIS X.   An Essay on the Physiology of Mind. Philadelphia, 1922. Rittenhouse 49-212 1976 $7.50

DERCUM, FRANCIS X.   A Textbook on Nervous Diseases. 1895. Illus. with engrs. & colored plts., front cover off. Austin 80-952 1978 $37.50

DERENNES, CHARLES   The Life of the Bat. With Fronts From a Wood Block by E.F. Daglish. London, (1925). 1st print. in Eng., orig. bind. Americanist 102-13 1978 $30

DE RETZ, CARDINAL   Memoirs. 1723. 1st. ed., lg. 12mo, 4 vols., frontispiece portrait, orig. panelled calf, dark red labels, slight rubbing of leading hinge vol. 1, o/w fine & attractive set. Jarndyce 16-68 1978 £30

DERHAM, T.   Physico-Theology. (1732). Lacks title, new buckram, 8vo. George's 635-1051 1978 £7.50

DERHAM, WILLIAM   Artificial Clock-Maker. London, 1734. 4th ed., 12mo, contemp. brown calf, recently rebacked, binder's ticket, two-wing cloth wr., brown quarter mor. slip case. Totteridge 29-31 1978 $550

DERHAM, WILLIAM   Astro-Theology. London, 1715. 8vo., folding plts., slightly soiled, contemp. calf, repaired. Quaritch 977-178 1978 $65

DERHEIMS, JEAN LAMBERT   Histoire Naturelle Et Medicale Des Sangsues. Paris, 1825. 8vo., litho. plts., orig. prtd. wrs., spine strengthened with library tape, light browning, dampstain, ex-lib., very good copy, 1st ed., rare. Zeitlin 245-59 1978 $27.50

DE RICCI, SEYMOUR
Please turn to
RICCI, SEYMOUR DE

DERLETH, AUGUST   Not Long for this World. Sauk City, 1948. Black cloth, 1st ed., 1 of 2000, typewritten letter signed by Derleth laid in, fine in dust jacket. Bradley 49-76 1978 $50

DE ROOS, JOHN FREDERICK FITZGERALD
Please turn to
DE ROS, JOHN FREDERICK FITZGERALD

DE ROS, JOHN FREDERICK FITZGERALD   Personal Narrative of Travels in the United States and Canada in 1826, with Remarks on the Present State of the American Navy. London, 1827. 3rd ed., 3/4 lea., marbled bds., plts., maps, index, plts., slightly stained. Hood 117-564 1978 $200

DE ROS, JOHN FREDERICK FITZGERALD   Personal Narrative of Travels in the United States and Canada in 1826. London, 1827. Third ed., marbled bds., half calf. Wolfe 39-123 1978 $160

DERRAH, ROBERT H.   By Trolley Through Western New England. Boston, 1904. Maps, illus., 12mo., orig. wrs., 1st ed. Morrill 241-328 1978 $17.50

DERRY, JOSEPH TYRONE   The Strife of Brothers, a poem. New York, 1906. Illus. Bell Wiley's copy. Broadfoot 46-74 1978 $20

DERRY, JOSEPH TYRONE   The Strife of Brothers. Presen. copy from author, Ex libris. Bell Wiley's copy. Broadfoot 46-74A 1978 $10

DE RUPERT, A. E. D.   Californians and Mormons. New York, 1881. Original pictorial cloth, 1st ed. Ginsberg 14-338 1978 $35

DE SAUSSURE, MRS. NANCY (BOSTICK)   Old Plantation Days. Being Recollections of Southern Life Before the Civil War. New York, 1909. Orig. binding. Wolfe 39-126 1978 $15

DESBOIS, PIERRE   Aspects du Vieux Paris. Paris, 1923. 4to., 3/4 mor., uncut, orig. wr. & backstrip bound in, bound by Gruel, ltd. ed., 330 numbered copies issued, on handmade velin d'Arches paper, orig. etchings by Desbois. Goldschmidt 110-16 1978 $125

DESCARTES, RENE   Discours de la Methode. Paris, 1948. 4to., orig. wr., uncut, in sheets, slipcover & case, ltd. ed. of 222 copies prtd., 1 of 185 numbered copies on Montval paper, illus. by Roger Vieillard, fresh copy. Goldschmidt 110-75 1978 $300

DESCARTES, RENE   Lettres. Paris, 1724. Vols. I, II, IV, V. 4 vols. of 5, fold. plts., 8vo., contemp. calf spines gilt with labels. Salloch 348-46 1978 $60

DESCARTES, RENE   Meditationes De Prima Philosophia.... Amsterdam, 1678. 4to., marbled bds., leather label. Salloch 348-44 1978 $75

DESCARTES, RENE   Le Monde, ou le Traite de la Lumiere, et Des Autres Principaux Objets des sens. Paris, 1664. 8vo., text woodcuts, contemp. mottled calf, richly gilt spine, head & foot skillfully repaired, very fine copy, 1st ed., 1st issue. Norman 5-80 1978 $1,000

DESCARTES, RENE   Musicae Compendium. Amsterdam, 1683. 4to., wrs. Salloch 348-45 1978 $200

DESCARTES, RENE   Opera Philosophica. (Amstelodami, 1672). 4to., 3 works in 1 vol., woodcuts, decor. ornaments, bound together in contemp. panelled calf, worn, hinges cracked, ownership inscr., very good copy from the library of Dr. Alfred M. Hellman, Latin ed. Zeitlin 245-60 1978 $225

DESCARTES, RENE   Specimina Philosophiae: Seu Dissertatio de Methodo. Amsterdam, 1644. 4to., woodcuts, diagrs. in text, full antique calf, gilt, old signature crossed out on title, but fine copy, 1st ed. in Latin. Norman 5-78 1978 $1,000

DESCARTES, RENE   Tractatus de Homine, et de Formatione Foetus. Amsterdam, 1677. Sm. 4to., woodcuts, contemp. calf, newly rebacked, corners repaired, third Latin ed. Quaritch 977-19 1978 $300

DESCAVES, LUCIEN   The Colour of Paris. London, 1925. Illus., bottom of spine torn. Biblo BL781-629 1978 $10

DE SCHWEINITZ, EDMUND   The History of the Church Known as the Unitas Fratrum, Etc. Pethlehem, 1885. Fine, orig. cloth. MacManus 239-1440 1978 $30

DE SCHWEINITZ, EDMUND   The Life and Times of David Zeisberger. Philadelphia, 1870. 1st ed., cloth, very good. MacManus 239-1226 1978 $45

DE SCHWEINITZ, GEORGE EDMUND   Pulsating Exophthalmos. Philadelphia, 1908. Library marks on spine. Rittenhouse 49-213 1978 $25

DESCRIPTION Generale et Particuliere de la France, Department du Rhone. Paris, 1781. Half title, engraved headpieces, lg. folio, half roan, rubbed, upper cover detached. George's 635-623 1978 £10.50

DESCRIPTION of a View of the City of Quebec. London, 1831. Plain wrappers, engrav. fold. frontis. Wolfe 39-451 1978 $50

DESCRIPTION of Faribault and Vicinity. Faribault, 1884. Illus., original pictorial printed wr., 1st ed. Ginsberg 14-549 1978 $75

A DESCRIPTION of the Memorable Sieges and Battles in the North of England. Bolton, 1785. 8vo., later half calf, frontispiece, plt., torn and much repaired, text rather thumbed and browned, scarce. P. M. Hill 142-94 1978 £18

A DESCRIPTION of the Town of Berkely with a History of the University of California Presenting the Natural and Acquired Advantages of a Most Attractive Place of Residence. San Francisco, 1881. Original printed wr., 1st ed. Ginsberg 14-103 1978 $100

A DESCRIPTIVE and Historical Sketch of Boston Harbor and Surroundings. Boston, (1885). Illus., fldg. map, 12mo., orig. wrs. Morrill 241-329 1978 $17.50

DESCRIPTIVE Catalogue of Grape Vines and Small Fruits. Fredonia, (1883). Color plts. Butterfield 21-444 1978 $25

DESCRIPTIVE Catalogue of Stereoscopic Views. Cooperstown, n.d. (A 1890). 24mo., inserted pict. ad, pict. wr., minor chipping. Butterfield 21-342 1978 $15

DESCRIPTIVE Guide to the Collections in the Geological Hall of the American Museum of Natural History. N.P., n.d. (c. 1870). Printed wrs., fold. plt. Hayman 72-178 1978 $7.50

DE SELINCOURT, ERNEST   Wordsworthian and other Studies. 1947. Orig. ed., 8vo., orig. cloth. Howes 194-780 1978 £6

A DESERET Second Book. (Salt Lake City), 1868. Prtd. bds., prtd. in Deseret phonetic alphabet. Hayman 73-458 1978 $50

DESGODETZ, ANTOINE   Les Edifices Antiques de Rome Dessines et Mesures Tres Exactement Par Antoine Desgodetz Architecte. Paris, 1682. Lg. folio, first ed., mottled calf, very good. King 7-274 1978 £450

DE SHANE, BRIAN   De Sade...
Please turn to
EGAN, BERESFORD PATRICK

DESHIELDS, JAMES T.   Border Wars of Texas. Tioga, Texas, 1912. 1st ed., illus., orig. pict. cloth, spine ends wearing, corners bumped, hinges weakening but intact, stains on lower cover, interior very good. Limestone 9-82 1978 $55

DESHIELDS, JAMES T.   Cynthia and Parker: The Story of Her Capture at the Massacre of the Inmates of Parker's Fort. St. Louis, 1886. Illus., dark green cloth, blind embossed bands and gilt title and vignette, rare work, nice condition. Jenkins 116-697 1978 $125

DESHIELDS, JAMES T.   They Sat in High Places: The Presidents and Governors of Texas. San Antonio, 1940. 1st ed., inscribed and signed by author, mint copy. Jenkins 116-319 1978 $75

DESHOULIERES, MME. ANTOINE (DU LIGER DE LA GAROE)   Oeuvres Choisies... Geneva, 1777. 12mo., engr. frontis., contemp. calf, gilt panelled, worn. Eaton 45-154 1978 £5

DESJARDINS, L. G.   England, Canada and the Great War. Quebec, 1918. Hood 117-119 1978 $17.50

DESLANDES, ANDRE FRANCOIS BOUREAU   Essai Sur La Marine Des Anciens et Particulierement sur leurs Vaisseaux de Guerre. Paris, 1768. Plts., 8vo., contemp. calf. F. Edwards 1013-59 1978 £80

DESLANDES, M.   Reflexions sur les Grands Mommes Qui Mort en Plaisantant. Amsterdam, 1776. Nouvelle ed., orig. binding, some wear. Rittenhouse 49-214 1976 $85

DESMARETS DE SAINT SORLIN, ARMAND   Livre de Touttes sortes de Chiffres par Alphabets Redoubles Dessignes. Paris, 1664. 8vo., full blue mor. Janssenist binding, inner gilt dentelles, first ed., splendid copy. Schumann 511-19 1978 sFr 1,750

DESMARETS DE SAINT SORLIN, ARMAND   Livre de Touttes Sortes de Chiffres par Alphabets Redoubles. Paris, 1664. 8vo., engraved plts., dark blue mor., gilt edges, rare 1st ed. Gilhofer 74-36 1978 sFr 2,800

DE SMET, PIERRE JEAN
Please turn to
SMET, PIERRE JEAN DE

DESMOND, CHARLES   Wooden-Shipbuilding. New York (1919). 4to., orig. cloth, good. Paine 78-43 1978 $27.50

DES RIVIERES-BEAUBIEN, HENRY   Traite sur les lois Civiles du Bas-Canada. Vol. I only. Montreal, 1832. Orig. binding, autograph signature of Wm. Bignell on title page. Wolfe 39-125 1978 $50

DES RIVIERES-BEAUBIEN, HENRY   Traite sur les lois Civiles du Bas-Canada. Vol. I & II (of 3). Montreal, 1832. Orig. plain bds., uncut. Wolfe 39-124 1978 $150

DESRUELLES, H. M. J.   Traite Pratique des Maladies Veneriennes. Paris, 1836. Engr. plts., 8vo., old bds., calf back. Morrill 239-64 1978 $9

DE STAEL, MME.
Please turn to
STAEL-HOLSTEIN, ANNE LOUISE GERMAINE NECKER, BARONNE DE

DETAILED Description of Boston's Great Health Palace. Boston, n.d. (circa 1890?). Wrs. Hayman 73-255 1978 $7.50

DETAILLE, EDOUARD   Types et Uniformes. Paris, 1885-89. 2 vols., folio, contemp. full mor., coloured plts. F. Edwards 1013-280 1978 £550

DE TAVEL, DURET   Calabria During a Military Residence of Three Years. London, 1832. 1st ed., 8vo., frontis., scattered foxing, contemp. marbled bds., calf spine. Current 24-177 1978 $110

DETJEN, MARY E. F.   Home Room Guidance Programs for the Junior High School Years. 1940. Austin 80-958 1978 $10

DETROIT River Scenes. (Columbus, 1887). Orig. binding, clean. Hayman 71-466 1978 $15

DEUTSCH, ALBERT   The Mentally III in America. 1937. Illus., 1st ed. in slightly frayed dust jacket. Austin 80-959 1978 $17.50

DEUTSCH, ALBERT   Sex Habits of American Men. 1948. Austin 80-960 1978 $10

DEUTSCH, HELENE   Psycho-Analysis of the Neuroses. Hogarth Press, 1932. Very good, first English ed. Bell Book 16-442 1978 £4.50

DEUTSCH, HELENE   The Psychology of Women. 1944. Vol. I, self-contained, indexed. Austin 80-961 1978 $8.50

DEUTSCHLANDS Gegner im Weltkriege. Berlin, (c. 1925). Coloured plts., folio, orig. cloth. F. Edwards 1013-281 1978 £25

DEVENS, R. M.   Our First Century: Being a Popular Descriptive Portraiture of the One Hundred Great and Memorable Events...in the History of our Country. Springfield, 1878. Plts., portrs., 4to., rebound in buckram, dampstains. Morrill 241-111 1978 $10

DEVEREAUX, MARY   Lafitte of Louisiana. 1902. Illus., first ed., fine. Austin 82-336 1978 $17.50

DEVEY, JOSEPH   The Physical and Metaphysical Works of Lord Bacon. London, 1904. 8vo., cloth. Salloch 348-9 1978 $12

DEVEY, LOUISA   Life of Rosina, Lady Lytton. 1887. Orig. cloth, portrait, 8vo. Howes 194-1018 1978 £5.50

DEVINE, EDWARD T.   The Normal Life. 1917. 2nd ed. rev. Austin 80-962 1978 $10

DE VINNE, THEODORE LOW   Christopher Plantin & the Plantin-Moretus Museum at Antwerp. New York, Grolier Club, 1888. Illus., 1 of 300 copies, tall 8vo., orig. wrs. over light bds., unopened copy, excellent copy. Americanist 103-30 1978 $75

DE VINNE, THEODORE LOW   Correct Composition. New York, 1910. New cloth. Battery Park 1-361 1978 $25

DE VINNE, THEODORE LOW   The Invention of Printing. New York, 1876. 2nd ed., illus., slightly rubbed. Battery Park 1-358 1978 $200

DE VINNE, THEODORE LOW   Manual of Printing Office Practice. (New York, 1883). 8vo., cloth binding. Battery Park 1-359 1978 $25

DE VINNE, THEODORE LOW   Plain Printing Types. New York, 1900. New cloth. Battery Park 1-360 1978 $25

DE VINNE, THEODORE LOW   The Practice of Typography. New York, 1900. 1st ed., illus., former owner's ink note, 8vo., orig. cloth, very good. Americanist 103-75 1978 $25

DE VINNE, THEODORE LOW   The Practice of Typography: a Treatise on Title-Pages with Numerous Illus. in Facsimile & Some Observations on the Early & Recent Printing of Books. New York, De Vinne Press, 1902. 1st enlarged trade ed., 8vo., orig. cloth, very good. Americanist 103-76 1978 $30

DE VINNE, THEODORE LOW   The Printers' Price List. New York, 1871. 2nd ed., 8vo., cloth. Battery Park 1-357 1978 $200

DE VINNE, THEODORE LOW   The Printers' Price List. New York, 1871. 2nd ed., orig. lea. decor. 17th Cent. style, rebacked with cloth, scarce, 8vo., very good. Americanist 103-120 1978 $75

DE VOTO, BERNARD   Across the Wide Missouri. Cambridge, 1947. Thick 8vo., pict. wrs., map endpapers, contemp. watercolor paintings by Alfred Jacob Miller and others, advance copy, fine. Duschnes 220-82 1978 $17.50

DE VOTO, BERNARD   Across the Wide Missouri. Boston, 1947. Ltd. ed., signed, illus. Biblo 247-205 1978 $75

DE VOTO, BERNARD   The Year of Decision, 1846. Boston, 1943. First ed., fine, d.w. Biblo 247-38 1978 $15

DEVOY, J.   Recollections of an Irish Rebel. (1910). Reprint, octavo bound in cloth. Hyland 128-942 1978 £10

DEVRAIGNE, LOUIS   L'Obstetrique a Travers Les Ages. Paris, 1939. First ed. Rittenhouse 49-216 1976 $65

DE VRIES, HUGO
Please turn to
VRIES, HUGO DE

DEWAR, G. A. B.   Wild Life in Hampshire Highlands. London, 1899. 1st. ed., chapter headings & endpapers by Arthur Rackham, plts., 8vo. Traylen 88-564 1978 £14

DEWAR, LINDSAY   Psychology for Religious Workers. 1932. Austin 80-963 1978 $10

DEWART, E. H.   Songs of Life: a Collection of Poems. Toronto, 1869. Cover scuffed. Hood 116-815 1978 $25

DEWEES, WILLIAM POTTS   A Compendious System of Midwifery. Philadelphia, 1826. 8vo., plts., contemp. calf, gilt, lightly browned, fixed with dampstains, good copy from the library of Dr. Alfred M. Hellman, 2nd ed. Zeitlin 245-61 1978 $65

DEWEES, WILLIAM POTTS   Midwifery. Philadelphia, 1828. Third ed., plts. Rittenhouse 49-217 1976 $20

DEWEES, WILLIAM POTTS   A Treatise on the Diseases of Females. Philadelphia, 1828. Engr. plts., 8vo., new buckram, foxed, plts. stained, 2nd ed. Morrill 239-65 1978 $27.50

DEWEES, WILLIAM POTTS   A Treatise on the Diseases of Females. Philadelphia, 1843. Eighth ed. Rittenhouse 49-218 1976 $10

DEWEES, WILLIAM POTTS   A Treatise on the Physical and Medical Treatment of Children. Philadelphia, 1832. 4th ed., 8vo., contemp. calf, foxed. Morrill 239-66 1978 $12.50

DEWEY, DAVIS RICH   Financial History of the United States. 1918. 6th ed. Austin 80-541 1978 $10

DEWEY, EDWARD R.   Cycles. 1947. Ex-lib. Austin 80-964 1978 $7.50

DEWEY, EVELYN   The Dalton Laboratory Plan. 1922. Austin 80-965 1978 $10

DEWEY, EVELYN   Methods and Results of Testing School Children. 1920. Austin 80-967 1978 $27.50

DEWEY, EVELYN   New Schools for Old. 1919. Austin 80-966 1978 $10

DEWEY, JOHN   Applied Psychology. n.d. (1886). Austin 80-987 1978 $17.50

DEWEY, JOHN   Characters and Events. 1929. 2 vols., 1st ed. Austin 80-978 1978 $27.50

DEWEY, JOHN   Characters and Events. 1929. Vol. II only, ex-lib. Austin 80-978a 1978 $8.75

DEWEY, JOHN   Democracy and Education. 1920 (1916). Austin 80-982 1978 $7.50

DEWEY, JOHN   Ethics. 1908. Austin 80-989 1978 $10

DEWEY, JOHN   Experience and Nature. 1925. Austin 80-985 1978 $12.50

DEWEY, JOHN   How We Think. 1910. Orig. unrev. ed. Austin 80-973 1978 $10

DEWEY, JOHN   Human Nature and Conduct. 1922. 1st ed. in slightly frayed dust jacket. Austin 80-972 1978 $25

DEWEY, JOHN   Individualism Old and New. 1930. Hard cover ed. Austin 80-974 1978 $10

DEWEY, JOHN   Interest and Effort in Education. 1913. Austin 80-975 1978 $7.50

DEWEY, JOHN   Moral Principles in Education. 1909. Austin 80-977 1978 $7.50

DEWEY, JOHN   Problems of Men. 1946. 1st ed. in dust jacket. Austin 80-979 1978 $10

DEWEY, JOHN   Progressive Education and the Science of Education. 1928. Pamphlet. Austin 80-980 1978 $10

DEWEY, JOHN   Psychology. 1887 (1886). Backstrip worn. Austin 80-981 1978 $17.50

DEWEY, JOHN   Psychology. 1891. Amer. book, 3rd rev. ed. Austin 80-983 1978 $17.50

DEWEY, JOHN   Psychology of Numbers. (1895) 1909. Austin 80-988 1978 $12.50

DEWEY, JOHN   The Quest for Certainty. 1929. 1st ed. Austin 80-984 1978 $17.50

DEWEY, JOHN   The School and Society. 1915. Rev. ed. Austin 80-986 1978 $7.50

DEWEY, LAURIN   Special Report of the Warden of the Ohio Penitentiary, on Prisons and Prison Discipline. Columbus, 1851. Wrps. Hayman 71-183 1978 $15

DEWEY, ORVILLE   A Discourse on Slavery and the Annexation of Texas. New York, 1844. Sewn. Ginsberg 14-952 1978 $150

DEWEY, SQUIRE P.   The Bonanza Mines and the Bonanza Kings of California. [San Francisco, 1880]. Original cloth, inscribed presentation copy. Ginsberg 14-104 1978 $125

DEWITT, DAVID M.   The Impeachment and Trial of Andrew Johnson. New York, 1903. 1st ed., scarce, fine. MacManus 239-123 1978 $45

DEWITZ, A. VON   In Danisch Westindien. Niesky, 1882. 1st ed., sm. 8vo., scarce, illus., frontis., shelf wear to extremities, black mor. spine, black bds. with minor defects, interior & plts. fine. Current 24-110 1978 $190

DEXTER, GRANT   Canada and the Building of Peace. Toronto, (1944). Card cover. Hood 117-565 1978 $12.50

DEXTER, HENRY M.   The England and Holland of the Pilgrims. Boston, 1905. Illus., 8vo., ex-lib., 1st ed. Morrill 239-366 1978 $10

DEXTER, T. P. G.   Psychology in the School Room. (1898) 1902. Austin 80-993 1978 $10

DEZALLIER D'ARGENVILLE, ANTOINE JOSEPH   The Theory and Practice of Gardening.... 1728. 2nd ed., folding engraved plts., illus., 4to., recent half calf, nice copy. Fenning 32-86 1978 £165

D'HORMOYS, PAUL   Une Visite chez Soulouque. Souvenirs d'un Voyage dans l'ile d'Haiti. Paris, 1859. 18mo., blue cloth, blue marbled bds. Gilhofer 74-61 1978 sFr 200

DIARY of Ephraim Shelby Dodd, Member of Company D, Terry's Texas Rangers, 1862-64. Austin, 1914. Printed wr., fine copy, scarce. Jenkins 116-1486 1978 $27.50

THE DIARY of Philip Leget Edwards. San Francisco, Grabhorn Press, 1932. Cloth & marbled bds., frontis. in color, #4, Rare Americana Series, very good copy, slipcase. Dykes 34-290 1978 $75

DIARY of the Besieged Resident in Paris. 1871. Covers faded, 8vo. George's 635-809 1978 £7.50

A DIARY Of The Wreck of His Majesty's Ship "Challenger", on the Western Coast of South America, in May, 1835... 1836. Folding litho. plts., contemp. half calf, 8vo, slightly worn. Edwards 1012-634 1978 £90

DIAZ, ABBY MORTON   The William Henry Letters. Boston, 1870. 1st ed., illus., f.p. tissue guards foxed. Victoria 34-243 1978 $45

DIAZ DEL CASTILLO, BERNAL   The True History of the Conquest of Mexico, Written in 1568... 1800. 4to, vellum over bds., slightly spotted, uncut. Edwards 1012-689 1978 £120

DIBBLEE, GEORGE BINNEY   The Psychological Theory of Value. 1924. Austin 80-994 1978 $27.50

DIBDIN, CHARLES   The Professional Life of .... 1803. 1st. ed., 4 vols., frontis, portraits, rebound in cloth without the prints. Eaton 45-155 1978 £40

DIBDIN, CHARLES   The Songs. 1839. 2 vols. in 1, vignette t.p.s., numerous woodcuts throughout, orig. half calf, marbled bds., good. Jarndyce 16-464 1978 £12

DIBDIN, T. C.   Progressive Drawing Book. 1852. Lithographs, stained, no text, sm. oblong folio, binders cloth. George's 635-17 1978 £12.50

DIBDIN, THOMAS FROGNALL   An Annotated List of the Publications of... Thomas Frognall Dibdin. Cambridge, 1965. Sm. folio, cloth, ex-lib. copy. Battery Park 1-367 1978 $100

DIBDIN, THOMAS FROGNALL   A Bibliographical, Antiquarian, & Picturesque Tour in France & Germany. London, 1821. Illus., engr. plts., 5 vols., thick lg. 8vo., full tree calf, 1st ed., rare lg. paper issue, India-proof state, A.L.s. tipped in. Argosy Special-34 1978 $1,000

DIBDIN, THOMAS FROGNALL   A Bibliographical Antiquarian and Picturesque Tour in France and Germany. London. Sm. 8vo., 3 vols. Battery Park 1-368 1978 $150

DIBDIN, THOMAS FROGNALL   Bibliomania. London, 1876. 8vo., 3/4 lea., marbled paper over bds., t.e.g., frontis., fine copy. Battery Park 1-364 1978 $150

DIBDIN, THOMAS FROGNALL   An Introduction to the Knowledge of Rare and Valuable Editions of the Greek and Latin Classics. 1803. 3rd ed., 2 vols. bound in one. Battery Park 1-365 1978 $100

DIBDIN, THOMAS FROGNALL   The Last of the Last of the Three Dibdins. n.d. 1st. ed., engraved portrait, fully rebound in half calf, marbled bds., v.g. Jarndyce 16-466 1978 £36

DIBDIN, THOMAS FROGNALL   The Library Companion. London, 1825. 2nd ed., 2 vols., lg. paper copy, binding rubbed. Battery Park 1-366a 1978 $200

DIBDIN, THOMAS FROGNALL   Reminiscences of a Literary Life. 1836. 1st. ed., 2 vols., frontis portrait, engraved front vol. 2, illus., full calf, red & green labels, spines gilt, one sm. section of hinge split, otherwise fine. Jarndyce 16-465 1978 £65

DIBDIN, THOMAS FROGNALL   Venetian Printers, a Conversation on the Fourth Day of the Bibliographical Decameron, with Annotations. Press of W. E. Rudge, 1924. 1 of 223 copies, signed inscr., folio, orig. decor. heavy wrs., uncut, 8vo., very good. Americanist 103-137 1978 $50

DICEY, EDWARD   A Month in Russia During the Marriage of the Czarevitch. London, 1867. Orig. oval photos, 8vo., orig. cloth, 1st ed. Morrill 241-112 1978 $30

DICEY, EDWARD   The Story of the Khedivate. London, 1902. 1st. ed., 8vo., orig. brown cloth, cover little soiled, lib. label removed, lib. stamp on some leaves. Deighton 5-11 1978 £22

DICK, ERNST   The Interest Standard of Currency. 1926. Austin 80-544 1978 $12.50

DICK, EVERETT   The Dixie Frontier. A Social History of the Southern Frontier from the First Transmontane Beginnings to the Civil War. New York, 1948. 1st ed., illus., d.j., scarce. MacManus 239-1801 1978 $20

DICK, EVERETT   The Long Drive. Reprinted from Collections of the Kansas State Historical Society, Vol. XVII, 1926-28. Wrs., illus., 1st separate prtg., fine copy, scarce. Dykes 34-288 1978 $10

DICK, HARRY B.   Dick's Games of Patience or Solitaire with Cards. New York, (1898). Illus., 8vo., gashes on binding. Morrill 239-357 1978 $10

DICK Tracy on Voodoo Island. Radine, (1944). Spine rubbed at edges & split half inch at top of spine edges, good or better. Bernard 5-336 1978 $9

DICKENS, CHARLES   The Adventures of Oliver Twist; or, the Parish Boy's Progress. London, 1846. Illus. by George Cruikshank, orig. dec. cloth, 1st octavo ed., recased, covers frayed and worn, rare. MacManus 238-198 1978 $85

DICKENS, CHARLES   American Notes for General Circulation. London, 1842. 2 vols., orig. cloth, 1st ed., 1st issue, covers very worn, spine torn on vol. I, faded, half mor. slipcase. MacManus 238-196 1978 $85

DICKENS, CHARLES   American Notes. Leipzig, 1842. Copyright ed., green cloth bds., red leather spine, v.g. Jarndyce 16-508 1978 £8.50

DICKENS, CHARLES   American Notes. London, 1884. Orig. pict. wrappers, author's copyright ed. Wolfe 39-128 1978 $10

DICKENS, CHARLES   Autumn Leaves. (1836). Folio, disbound, worn. Jarndyce 16-586 1978 £5.50

DICKENS, CHARLES   La Bataille de la Vie. Paris, 1853. First French ed., orig. yellow wraps, nice. Bell Book 17-275 1978 £10

DICKENS, CHARLES   The Battle of Life. London, 1846. 12mo., orig. gilt pict. cloth, 1st ed., 4th issue, spine ragged. MacManus 238-199 1978 $45

DICKENS, CHARLES   Bleak House. Leipzig, 1852. 1st Tauchnitz ed. of 4 vols. in 2, orig. cloth binding, marble-stained edges, gilt filigree design on spine, gilt lettering, very fine set. Greene 78-29 1978 $175

DICKENS, CHARLES   Bleak House. 1852-53. 20 parts in 19, 8vo., 1st ed., illus., orig. green paper wrs., lea. case, very good copy. Quaritch 979-119 1978 $750

DICKENS, CHARLES   Bleak House. 1853. Orig. 20 parts in 19, plts., quite unfoxed, all contents neat & clean, fine set boxed. Jarndyce 16-526 1978 £230

DICKENS, CHARLES   Bleak House. 1853. First ed., plts., contemp. calf, thick 8vo., plts. foxed as usual. Howes 194-781 1978 £24

DICKENS, CHARLES   Bleak House. 1853. 1st. ed., illus. by H. K. Browne, half title, untrimmed in orig. green cloth, spine little rubbed, otherwise v.g. Jarndyce 16-527 1978 £55

DICKENS, CHARLES   Bleak House. 1853. 1st. ed., illus. by H. K. Browne, half black calf, raised bands gilt, red label, fine. Jarndyce 16-528 1978 £50

DICKENS, CHARLES   Bleak House. 1853. 1st. ed., illus. by H. K. Browne, half maroon morocco, rebacked, good. Jarndyce 16-529 1978 £17.50

DICKENS, CHARLES   Bleak House. London, 1853. Quarter calf, marbled bds., plts. foxed, sm. bkplt. Dawson's 447-217 1978 $100

DICKENS, CHARLES   Bleak House. New York, n.d. (1853). Paper covers intact, edge fraying, good cond., 2 illus. by H.K. Browne. Greene 78-176 1978 $30

DICKENS, CHARLES   Bleak House. n.d. Orig. illus., orig. green cloth, v.g. Jarndyce 16-570 1978 £6.50

DICKENS, CHARLES   A Child's History of England. 1854-59. 3 vols., half titles, frontis, orig. pink cloth, gilt imprint, good. Jarndyce 16-531 1978 £48

DICKENS, CHARLES   The Chimes. London, 1845. 12mo., orig. gilt pict. cloth, 1st ed., 2nd issue, front flyleaf lacking, otherwise very good. MacManus 238-197 1978 $25

DICKENS, CHARLES   The Chimes. New York, 1845. 1st. American ed., tall 8vo., orig. grey printed wrappers, generally little worn, preserved in attractive half mock-vellum, brown label, Suzannet Bookplt. Jarndyce 16-514 1978 £18.50

DICKENS, CHARLES   The Chimes. A Goblin Story. Some Bells that Rang on On Old Year Out & A New Year In. New Year, 1845. 2nd Amer. ed., orig. pict. wrs., uncut 8vo., frayed edges, foxed, cloth folder, slip case. Greene 78-179 1978 $125

DICKENS, CHARLES   A Christmas Carol. N. Y., 1902. 8vo., watered silk ends, t.e.g., gilt stamped limp brown suede, edges slightly rubbed, else very good. Houle 10-87 1978 $20

DICKENS, CHARLES   A Christmas Carol in Prose, Being a Ghost Story of Christmas. New York, Press of the Woolly Whale, 1930. #76 of 250 copies, 1st folio, orig. vellum-backed cloth, uncut, 8vo., very good. Americanist 103-111 1978 $75

DICKENS, CHARLES   A Christmas Carol. San Francisco: The Grabhorn Press, 1950. Folio, dec. paper bds., green cloth back, ltd. to 250 copies, spine faded, else fine, uncut copy, bookplt. Howell 5-31 1978 $50

DICKENS, CHARLES   A Christmas Carol. London. Illus. by John Leech, orig. brown cloth, gilt, a.e.g., plts. hand coloured. Wolfe 39-129 1978 $150

DICKENS, CHARLES   Christmas Numbers From Household Words 1851-1858. 1851-58. Orig. front wrapper bound in, blue binders cloth, good. Jarndyce 16-576 1978 £12.50

DICKENS, CHARLES   The Cricket on the Hearth. A Fairy Tale of Home. London, 1846. 1st ed., illus., red cloth, edges gilt, spine damage. Greene 78-180 1978 $45

DICKENS, CHARLES   A Curious Dance Around A Curious Tree. (1860). 1st. ed., 1st. issue, orig. purple paper wrappers, dark purple crushed morocco, gilt borders, dentelles & spine, t.e.g., fine copy, rare. Jarndyce 16-539 1978 £160

DICKENS, CHARLES   David Copperfield. 1850. 1st. ed., illus. by H.K. Browne, 3 vols., half black calf, raised bands, gilt, red labels, fine. Jarndyce 16-523 1978 £75

DICKENS, CHARLES   David Copperfield. 1850. 1st. ed., 1 vol. in 2,
illus. by H.K. Browne, half calf, marbled bds., 1 gathering springing in vol. 1,
spine little rubbed. Jarndyce 16-524 1978 £45

DICKENS, CHARLES   David Copperfield. 1921. Ltd. ed. no. 75 of
275 copies, frontis, half title, uncut, grey bds., paper label, v.g. Jarndyce 16-
592 1978 £14

DICKENS, CHARLES   Dombey & Son. 1846-8. Orig. 20 parts in 19,
orig. green wrappers, plts., some foxing to plts. & little wear to spines, v.g. in
brown cloth box. Jarndyce 16-518 1978 £340

DICKENS, CHARLES   Dombey and Son. 1848. 1st. ed., illus. by
H.K. Browne, half title, recent half brown calf, brown label, cloth covered bds.,
good. Jarndyce 16-522 1978 £24

DICKENS, CHARLES   Dombey and Son. 1848. 1st. ed., frontis,
engraved title & plts., half green morocco, fine copy, extra illus. by Phiz. Jarndyce 16-519 1978 £48

DICKENS, CHARLES   Dombey and Son. 1848. 1st. ed., illus. by
Phiz, half green calf, red label, fine copy. Jarndyce 16-521 1978 £33

DICKENS, CHARLES   Dombey and Son. 1848. 1st. ed., 2 vols.,
illus. by H.K. Browne, half black calf, raised bands, gilt, red labels, local damage
to section of spine otherwise v.g. Jarndyce 16-520 1978 £38

DICKENS, CHARLES   Dombey and Son. n.d. Orig. illus., orig.
green cloth, v.g. Jarndyce 16-568 1978 £7.50

DICKENS, CHARLES   Great Expectations. 1861. 3 vols., vol. 1 3rd
ed., vol. 2 4th. ed., vol. 3 1st. ed., half calf, marbled bds., red labels, spines
gilt, handsome set. Jarndyce 16-540 1978 £95

DICKENS, CHARLES   Great Expectations. 1861. 3 vols., 5th. ed.,
orig. purple cloth, spines dulled & generally rubbed. Jarndyce 16-541 1978
£12.50

DICKENS, CHARLES   Hard Times. For These Times. London, 1854.
Orig. cloth, 1st ed., covers worn, extremities worn. MacManus 238-201 1978
$100

DICKENS, CHARLES   Hard Times. 1854. 1st. ed., half title, orig.
light green cloth, dulled, otherwise v.g. Jarndyce 16-530 1978 £75

DICKENS, CHARLES   The Haunted Man & The Ghost's Bargain. 1848.
Engravings, fscp. 8vo., orig. decor. cloth, good, first English ed. Bell Book 16-
266 1978 £17.50

DICKENS, CHARLES   Hunted Down: A Story. (1870). 1st. English
ed., half title, orig. green printed wrappers, bound in half green morocco, leading
hinge little rubbed, spine gilt, v.g. Jarndyce 16-550 1978 £60

DICKENS, CHARLES   Hunted Down. A Story. With Some Account of
Thomas Griffiths Wainewright, the Poisoner. London, n.d. Orig. green printed
wrs., 1st Eng. ed., orig. pub. in 1861, nice, bookplt. removed. MacManus
238-203 1978 $50

DICKENS, CHARLES   The Keepsake. 1852. London, 1852. Orig.
dec. cloth, illus., 1st ed., hinges slightly torn, but good, mor. slipcase. Mac-
Manus 238-200 1978 $50

DICKENS, CHARLES   The Letters. 1880-82. Vol. 1- 1st. ed., vol. 2-
2nd. ed., vol. 3 - 1st. ed., half titles, orig. purple cloth, rubbed but sound, lib.
labels removed. Jarndyce 16-559 1978 £13.50

DICKENS, CHARLES   The Library of Fiction, or, Family Story-Teller.
1836-37. 1st. ed., 2 vols., illus. by Seymour, half black calf, bds. little rubbed,
good. Jarndyce 16-472 1978 £68

DICKENS, CHARLES   The Life and Adventures of Martin Chuzzlewit.
London, 1884. 1st ed., 1st issue, illus. by Phiz, quarter calf, marbled boards,
two owners' bookplates, edges rubbed. Greene 78-182 1978 $75

DICKENS, CHARLES   Martin Chuzzlewit. 1844. 1st. ed., 1st. issue,
illus. by Phiz, half title, half straight-grained red morocco, attractively gilt,
corners little rubbed, otherwise very good, tall, clean, copy. Jarndyce 16-511
1978 £45

DICKENS, CHARLES   Martin Chuzzlewit. 1844. 1st. ed., illus. by
Phiz, some foxing, half green calf, maroon labels, good. Jarndyce 16-512 1978
£28

DICKENS, CHARLES   The Life and Adventures of Martin Chuzzlewit.
1844. Illus. by Phiz, 1st. ed., half calf, spine gilt, blue label, fine copy. Jarndyce 16-510 1978 £60

DICKENS, CHARLES   Martin Chuzzlewit. 1850. Half dark green
morocco, new frontis by Frank Stone, new preface, good. Jarndyce 16-513 1978
£10.50

DICKENS, CHARLES   Martin Chuzzlewit. n.d. Orig. illus., orig.
green cloth, v.g. Jarndyce 16-567 1978 £8.50

DICKENS, CHARLES   The Life and Adventures of Nicholas Nickleby.
1839. 1st. ed., frontis portrait & illus. by Phiz, half calf, spine gilt, blue label,
fine copy. Jarndyce 16-496 1978 £60

DICKENS, CHARLES   Nicholas Nickleby. 1839. 1st. ed., bound
into 2 vols., frontis, portrait, illus. by Phiz, extra illus. by "Peter Palette", orig.
full dark blue straight-grained morocco, gilt borders & spines, hinges rubbed, plts.
clean & bright. Jarndyce 16-495 1978 £65

DICKENS, CHARLES   Nicholas Nickleby. 1839. Illus. by Phiz,
2 vols., half black calf, raised bands, gilt, red label. Jarndyce 16-497 1978
£45

DICKENS, CHARLES   Nicholas Nickleby. n.d. (c.1880). 4to, orig.
maroon cloth folder, lacking ties, India proofs from orig. steel plts., v.g. Jarndyce 16-498 1978 £35

DICKENS, CHARLES   Nicholas Nickleby. n.d. Orig. illus., orig.
green cloth, v.g. Jarndyce 16-563 1978 £7.50

DICKENS, CHARLES   The Life of Our Lord. London, 1934. 8vo,
purple cloth, gilt stamped, fine, d.w., 1st ed. Desmarais 1-121 1978 $15

DICKENS, CHARLES   The Life of Our Lord. London, 1934. Cloth,
printed on Japon vellum, scarce dj. Greene 78-183 1978 $55

DICKENS, CHARLES   The Life of Our Lord. London, 1934. Fine in
d.w. Desmarais B-181 1978 $15

DICKENS, CHARLES   The Life of Our Lord. 1st Amer. ed., frontis.,
small octavo, orig. green cloth, gilt lettering, spine faded, d.j. faded and repaired
with scotch tape. Totteridge 29-32 1978 $7.50

DICKENS, CHARLES   The Life of Our Lord. London, 1934. Illus.,
1st ed., square octavo, orig. red cloth, d.j. Totteridge 29-33 1978 $20

DICKENS, CHARLES   The Life of Our Lord Written During the Years
1846-1849...for His Children & now first published. New York, 1934. 1st Amer.
Ltd. ed., paper covered boards, t.e.g., printed by Updike, mint cond., boxed.
Greene 78-184 1978 $35

DICKENS, CHARLES   Little Dorrit. London, 1855-57. Illus. by H.
K. Browne, orig. pict. wrs., 1st ed., 1st issue, errata slip, 20 parts in 19, 1 back
wr. missing, general wear and foxing. MacManus 238-202 1978 $250

DICKENS, CHARLES   Little Dorrit. 1857. 1st. ed., 1st. issue, illus.
by H. K. Browne, some foxing to plts., & outer edges to 2 pgs., little worn,
untrimmed in orig. green cloth, slight fading otherwise v.g. Jarndyce 16-532
1978 £50

DICKENS, CHARLES   Little Dorrit. 1857. 1st. ed., illus. by H. K.
Browne, half black calf, marbled bds., raised spines gilt, red label, very slight
damp stain to outer corner of some plts., otherwise fine handsome copy. Jarndyce
16-533 1978 £55

DICKENS, CHARLES   Little Dorrit. 1857. 1st. ed., illus. by H. K.
Browne, frontis & engraved title foxed, otherwise clean & bright, half green calf,
hinges weak, lacks label. Jarndyce 16-536 1978 £16

DICKENS, CHARLES   Little Dorrit. 1857. 1st. ed., illus. by H. K. Browne, orig. half calf, good.   Jarndyce 16-534 1978 £38

DICKENS, CHARLES   Little Dorrit. 1857. 1st. ed., illus. by H. K. Browne, some little foxing, half maroon morocco, rubbed at head & tail of spine. Jarndyce 16-535 1978 £20

DICKENS, CHARLES   Little Dorrit. n.d. Orig. illus., orig. green cloth, little rubbed, good.   Jarndyce 16-571 1978 £5.50

DICKENS, CHARLES   The Loving Ballad of Lord Bateman. 1851. 2nd. ed., plts. by George Cruikshank, half title, orig. straigh-grained green cloth, gilt imprint, fine.   Jarndyce 16-525 1978 £18

DICKENS, CHARLES   Master Humphrey's Clock. 1840. 1st. ed., orig. 88 weekly parts, illus. by H.K. Browne, orig. white printed wrappers, little wear to corners of part I, otherwise very good set, boxed.   Jarndyce 16-499 1978 £580

DICKENS, CHARLES   Master Humphrey's Clock. 1840-41. 1st. ed., frontis & illus. by Cattermole & Browne, orig. cloth, binding variant, hinges slightly frayed in places, heads & tails little worn, gatherings springing in vol. I, good.   Jarndyce 16-502 1978 £25

DICKENS, CHARLES   Master Humphrey's Clock. London, 1840-41. Illus. by George Cattermole and H. K. Browne, 4to., 3 vols., orig. pict. cloth, 1st bound ed., extremities worn, fair copy.   MacManus 238-194 1978 $75

DICKENS, CHARLES   Master Humphrey's Clock. 1840/1. 1st. ed., illus. by George Cattermole & Hablot Browne, 3 vols. as 2, orig. half calf, marbled bds., good.   Jarndyce 16-500 1978 £45

DICKENS, CHARLES   Master Humphrey's Clock. 1840-1. 1st. ed., 3 vols., illus. by Cattermole, Phiz, orig. brown cloth, one hinge little worn. Jarndyce 16-503 1978 £32

DICKENS, CHARLES   Master Humphrey's Clock. 1840-41. 1st. ed., 3 vols., illus. by Cattermole, Hablot Browne, half tan calf, black labels, cloth bds., v.g.   Jarndyce 16-501 1978 £28.50

DICKENS, CHARLES   Memoirs of Joseph Grimaldi. London, 1838. Illus. by George Cruikshank, 2 vols., orig. pink cloth, 1st ed., 1st issue, spines faded, somewhat foxed, slightly worn, but fine.   MacManus 238-192 1978 $185

DICKENS, CHARLES   Memoirs of Joseph Grimaldi. 1838. 1st. ed., 2 vols., frontis portrait, illus. by George Cruikshank, orig. green calf, spines gilt, red labels, some foxing otherwise v.g.   Jarndyce 16-487 1978 £75

DICKENS, CHARLES   Memoirs of Joseph Grimaldi. 1846. Illus. by George Cruikshank, new coloured frontis, half calf, green cloth bds., new ed. Jarndyce 16-488 1978 £27

DICKENS, CHARLES   Mrs. Lirriper's Lodgings. 1863. Orig. blue paper wrappers, v.g.   Jarndyce 16-580 1978 £12.50

DICKENS, CHARLES   Mrs. Lirriper's Legacy. 1864. Blue paper, orig. blue wrappers, mint.   Jarndyce 16-581 1978 £18.50

DICKENS, CHARLES   Mr. Pickwick. n.d. (c. 1910). Colour plts. by Frank Reynolds, no. 70 of 350 copies, signed by artist, 4to., full vellum gilt, silk ties missing, t.e.g., very good, first English ed.   Bell Book 17-499 1978 £35

DICKENS, CHARLES   The Mudfog Papers. 1880. 1st. ed., half dark blue morocco, gilt by Zaehnsdorf, preserving orig. red cloth covers & spine, at back of vol., v.g.   Jarndyce 16-551 1978 £28

DICKENS, CHARLES   Mugby Junction. 1866. Orig. blue wrappers, v.g.   Jarndyce 16-582 1978 £9.50

DICKENS, CHARLES   The Mystery of Edwin Drood. 1870. 1st. ed., portrait & illus. by S. L. Fildes, orig. half black calf, red label, marbled bds., wide margined copy totally free from foxing.   Jarndyce 16-548 1978 £35

DICKENS, CHARLES   The Mystery of Edwin Drood. 1870. 12 illus. by S.L. Fildes, portrait, 1st. ed., orig. half calf, marbled bds., black label, v.g. Jarndyce 16-547 1978 £40

DICKENS, CHARLES   The Mystery of Edwin Drood. 1870. Orig. 6 parts, poor, made up set, worn, complete with nearly all adverts.   Jarndyce 16-546 1978 £25

DICKENS, CHARLES   The Mystery of Edwin Drood. London, 1870. Illus. by S. L. Fildes, orig. cloth, 1st ed., covers worn, but good.   MacManus 238-204 1978 $75

DICKENS, CHARLES   The Mystery of Edwin Drood. 1870. 1st. ed., frontis portrait, engraved title & plts., by S. L. Fildes, half red calf, little rubbed. Jarndyce 16-549 1978 £20

DICKENS, CHARLES   The Mystery of Edwin Drood. 1870. First ed., plts., orig. green pict. cloth, nice, portrait, 8vo.   Howes 194-783 1978 £30

DICKENS, CHARLES   No Thoroughfare. 1867. Orig. blue wrappers, good.   Jarndyce 16-583 1978 £12

DICKENS, CHARLES   The Nonesuch Dickens; the complete Works and Letters. London, Nonesuch Press, 1937-38. Illus. from orig. plts., one of 877 sets, 23 vols., lg. 8vo., bound in buckram, very nice, first ed.   Rota 211-445 1978 £1500

DICKENS, CHARLES   Oliver Twist. 1839. 2nd. ed., 3 vols., illus. by G. Cruikshank, some foxing throughout, half green morocco, little rubbed. Jarndyce 16-505 1978 £22

DICKENS, CHARLES   Oliver Twist. 1839. 2nd. ed., 3 vols., illus. by Cruikshank, half titles, orig. brown ribbed cloth, some foxing to plts., good. Jarndyce 16-504 1978 £42

DICKENS, CHARLES   Oliver Twist. 1863. Illus. by George Cruikshank, half black calf, raised bands, gilt, red label, fine. Jarndyce 16-506 1978 £28

DICKENS, CHARLES   Oliver Twist. n.d. 24 illus. on steel by G. Cruikshank, new & revised ed., half red calf, marbled bds., spine gilt, blue label, fine.   Jarndyce 16-507 1978 £30

DICKENS, CHARLES   Oliver Twist. n.d. Orig. illus., orig. green cloth, v.g.   Jarndyce 16-562 1978 £7.50

DICKENS, CHARLES   Our Mutual Friend. 1865. First ed., 2 vols., contemp. half calf, rubbed, plts., 8vo.   Howes 194-784 1978 £18

DICKENS, CHARLES   Our Mutual Friend. 1865. 1st. ed., 2 vols. in I, illus. by Marcus Stone, engraved title facsimile of part issue front wrappers, half calf, spine gilt, green label, fine copy.   Jarndyce 16-544 1978 £45

DICKENS, CHARLES   Our Mutual Friend. 1865. 1st. ed., 2 vols., half titles, illus. by Marcus Stone, some rubbing to heads & tails of spines, good copy in orig. purple cloth.   Jarndyce 16-543 1978 £32

DICKENS, CHARLES   Our Mutual Friend. 1st. ed., 2 vols., illus. by Marcus Stone, half black calf, raised bands gilt, red labels, v.g.   Jarndyce 16-542 1978 £60

DICKENS, CHARLES   Our Mutual Friend. n.d. Orig. illus., orig. green cloth, v.g.   Jarndyce 16-572 1978 £7.50

DICKENS, CHARLES   The Personal History and Experience of David Copperfield the Younger. New York, 1850. Amer. ed., 7 issues, engravings, covers detached, spine flaking, damp stains, good.   Greene 78-186 1978 $50

DICKENS, CHARLES   The Pic-Nic Papers. London, 1841. Illus. by George Cruikshank, Phiz, etc., 3 vols., orig. cloth, 1st ed., 2nd issue, back flyleaf missing in vol. I, spines torn, faded and slightly worn.   MacManus 238-195 1978 $75

DICKENS, CHARLES   Pickwick Papers. 1837. 1st. ed., frontis, engraved title & plts. by Seymour & Phiz, some foxing, slight wear to outer margin of last plt., orig. half green calf, spine gilt, black label, fine attractive copy. Jarndyce 16-479 1978 £45

DICKENS, CHARLES   Pickwick Papers. 1837. 1st. ed., illus. by Seymour & Phiz, half title, uncaptioned plts., some foxing, half dark blue calf little rubbed.   Jarndyce 16-480 1978 £40

DICKENS, CHARLES   Pickwick Papers. 1845. Early ed., engraved frontis vignette title & illus. by Phiz., orig. half calf, red label, engraved title bears the date 1837. Jarndyce 16-481 1978 £15

DICKENS, CHARLES   Pickwick Papers. 1847. Frontis, half title, orig. green cloth, spine filt, new frontis by G. R. Leslie, new preface. Jarndyce 16-482 1978 £8.50

DICKENS, CHARLES   Pickwick Papers. n.d. (c.1880). Orig. maroon cloth folder, lacking ties, India proofs printed from orig. steel plts., v.g. Jarndyce 16-484 1978 £30

DICKENS, CHARLES   The Pickwick Papers. 1931. 20 parts, text reprinted with facsimiles of plts., orig. wrappers. Jarndyce 16-483 1978 £12.50

DICKENS, CHARLES   Pickwick. n.d. Orig. illus., orig. green cloth, good. Jarndyce 16-561 1978 £8.50

DICKENS, CHARLES   Pictures From Italy. 1846. 1st. ed., vignette title & illus. by Samuel Palmer, half title, orig. blue cloth, little worn at head & tail of hinges. Jarndyce 16-516 1978 £16

DICKENS, CHARLES   Pictures From Italy. 1846. 1st. ed., half title, vignette illus. on wood by Samuel Palmer, orig. blue cloth, v.g. Jarndyce 16-515 1978 £38

DICKENS, CHARLES   Pictures from Italy. London, 1846. Octavo, full early polished calf, gilt rules, edges marbled, hinges restored masterfull, 1st Book ed. Bennett 7-35 1978 $95

DICKENS, CHARLES   The Poor Traveller: Boots at the Holly-Tree Inn... 1864. Orig. green wrappers. Eaton 45-156 1978 £5

DICKENS, CHARLES   The Posthumous Papers of the Pickwick Club. 1826-7. 1st. ed., orig. 20 parts in 19, illus., orig. wrappers, some parts carefully respined, boxed, good set. Jarndyce 16-478 1978 £580

DICKENS, CHARLES   The Posthumous Papers of the Pickwick Club. London, 1837. Illus. by R. Seymour and Phiz, octavo, bound in full polished calf, inner gilt dentelles, gilt rules, spines gilt, fine, rare, early issue of 1st ed. Bennett 7-36 1978 $500

DICKENS, CHARLES   The Postumous Papers of the Pickwick Club. London, 1837. 1st ed., 2 vols., plts., some hand-colored, 1st state, steel engrs., full tan calf, rebacked with contemp. gilt-decor. backs laid down. Current Misc. 8-16 1978 $485

DICKENS, CHARLES   The Posthumous Papers of The Pickwick Club. London, 1837. 8vo, bound in dark green mor., gilt, decor. silk doublures, t.e.g., engraved plts. by Seymour and Browne, captioned; two by Buss, colored suite of illus. by Frederick W. Pailthorpe, 1st English ed. in book form, fine. Duschnes 22-83 1978 $550

DICKENS, CHARLES   The Posthumous Papers ot the Pickwick Club. London, 1910. 2 vols., sm. folio, picture cloth, 24 coloured plts. & numerous black & white illus. by Cecil Aldin, pres. prize label on fly leaf. Traylen 88-363 1978 £21

DICKENS, CHARLES   The Posthumous Papers of the Pickwick Club. London, 1931-32. Illus., 20 parts, orig. wrs., Lombard St. ed., ltd. to 1,000 copies, fine. MacManus 238-206 1978 $50

DICKENS, CHARLES   Sketches by Boz. 1836. 2nd. ed., 2 vols., illus. by George Cruikshank, plts. little browned, half red morocco, good. Jarndyce 16-474 1978 £25

DICKENS, CHARLES   Sketches by Boz. 1836-7. 1st. & 2nd. series, 3 vols., illus. by George Cruikshank, orig. marbles bds., new corners & spines, gilt, black labels, v.g. Jarndyce 16-475 1978 £54

DICKENS, CHARLES   Sketches by Boz. 1839. 1st. one vol. ed., illus. by George Cruikshank, half green morocco, cloth bds., fine. Jarndyce 16-476 1978 £54

DICKENS, CHARLES   Sketches by Boz. 1850. Half dark green morocco, new frontispiece by Cruikshank, new preface. Jarndyce 16-477 1978 £10.50

DICKENS, CHARLES   Sketches by Boz. 1870. Orig. illus., orig. green cloth, good. Jarndyce 16-560 1978 £10

DICKENS, CHARLES   Sketches of Young Gentlemen. Dedicated to the Young Ladies. London, 1838. Illus. by "Phiz", red mor., marbled endpapers, 1st ed., spine worn. MacManus 238-193 1978 $65

DICKENS, CHARLES   Sketches of Young Gentlemen. 1838. Illus. by Phiz, 2nd. ed., orig. printed blue card binding, sm. portion missing from bottom of spine, otherwise v.g., orig. condition. Jarndyce 16-491 1978 £30

DICKENS, CHARLES   Sketches of Young Gentlemen. 1838. 3rd. ed., illus. by Phiz, attractively rebound in half blue morocco, marbled bds., good. Jarndyce 16-492 1978 £25

DICKENS, CHARLES   Sketches of Young Couples... 1840. 1st. ed., half title, orig. printed blue card binding, lacks backstrip otherwise v.g., orig. condition, illus. by Phiz. Jarndyce 16-493 1978 £40

DICKENS, CHARLES   Sketches of Young Ladies. In Which These Interesting Members of the Animal Kingdom are Classified. London, 1837. Illus. by Phiz, 12mo., old 3/4 mor., 1st ed., covers worn. MacManus 238-205 1978 $65

DICKENS, CHARLES   Speech of Charles Dickens Esq. at the Anniversary Festival of the Hospital for Sick Children. 1858. Unbound pamphlet as issued, orig. sewing intact, no sign of any loss, very scarce. Jarndyce 16-537 1978 £90

DICKENS, CHARLES   The Speeches (1841-1870). 1884. Half title, orig. dull blue cloth, spine darkened, good. Jarndyce 16-554 1978 £9.50

DICKENS, CHARLES   The Strange Gentleman... c. 1871. Orig. white wrappers, v.g., slight wear to spine. Jarndyce 16-552 1978 £9.50

DICKENS, CHARLES   Sunday Under Three Heads. As It Is; As Sabbath Would Make It; As It Might Be Made. London, 1836. Illus. by H. K. Browne, 12mo., orig. pict. wrs., cover partially detached, slightly soiled, 1st ed., nice, scarce, half-mor. case. MacManus 238-191 1978 $150

DICKENS, CHARLES   A Tale of Two Cities. London, 1859. 8vo, orig. blue wrs., 8 parts in 7, illus. by H. K. Browne, enclosed in green 3/4 leather solander case with wrs., 1st ed., fine. Duschnes 220-84 1978 $1,500

DICKENS, CHARLES   A Tale of Two Cities. 1860. 2nd. ed., illus. by H. K. Browne, orig. half blue morocco, marbled bds., fine, plts. exceptionally clean. Jarndyce 16-538 1978 £44

DICKENS, CHARLES   The Unpublished Letters of Charles Dickens to Mark Lemon. 1927. 4to, ltd. ed. of 520 copies, facsimile illus., orig. half vellum, purple cloth covered bds., v.g., this copy unnumbered. Jarndyce 16-591 1978 £24

DICKENS, CHARLES   The Village Coquettes. (1836). Rebound in half maroon calf, v.g. Jarndyce 16-473 1978 £8.50

DICKENS, CHARLES   Wellerisms From Pickwick and Master Humphrey's Clock. (1895). 3rd. ed., illus., orig. bright blue cloth, gilt, little rubbed. Jarndyce 16-485 1978 £5.50

DICKENS, CHARLES   Young Gentlemen of the Nineteenth Century. 1839. 1st. ed., illus., unopened, orig. green printed bds., slightly rubbed, rare, v.g. Jarndyce 16-494 1978 £65

DICKENS, EDWIN   The Mystery of Edwin Drood. London, 1870. First Book Ed., engraved frontispiece & title page, quarter calf & cloth, edges rubbed, spine seam starting, interior foxing, w/owner's bookplate. Greene 78-31 1978 $35.00

DICKENS, MAMIE   My Father As I Recall Him. Westminster, (1895). 1st ed., uncut, gilt pictorial cloth, portrait, illus., very good or better. Limestone 9-84 1978 $25

DICKENSON, JONATHAN   God's Protecting Providence... Philadelphia, 1868. Facs. ed., contemp. 3/4 calf, marbled bds., very good. MacManus 239-1157 1978 $45

DICKENSON, JONATHAN   The Shipwreck and Dreadful Sufferings of Robert Barrow, with Divers Others Persons, Amongst the Inhuman Cannibals of Florida. Salem, 1826. Hayman 73-561 1978 $125

DICKERSON, OLIVER M.   American Colonial Government 1696-1765. Cleveland, 1912. Cloth, 1st ed. Hayman 73-143 1978 $25

DICKINSON, THE BROTHERS   Dickinson's Comprehensive Pictures of the Great Exhibition of 1851. London, 1854. 2 vols. in 1, roy. folio, hand finished plts., very slight foxing on margin of frontispiece, otherwise very clean, half mor. gilt. Quaritch 977-213 1978 $2,000

DICKINSON, E. M.   A Patriot's Mistake; Reminiscences of the Parnell Family. 1905. Light marks on cover, good, octavo bound in cloth. Hyland 128-330 1978 £5

DICKINSON, EMILY   Bolts of Melody. New York, 1945. 8vo, cloth, d.j., 1st ed., fine. Duschnes 220-87 1978 $17.50

DICKINSON, EMILY   Further Poems of Emily Dickinson Withheld from Publication by Her Sister Lavinia. Boston, 1929. Near fine in damaged d.w. Desmarais B-185 1978 $15

DICKINSON, EMILY   Letters of... Boston, 1894. 12mo, 2 vols., orig. cloth, 1st ed., 1st print., covers soiled, otherwise good. MacManus 238-467 1978 $60

DICKINSON, EMILY   A Masque of Poets. Including Guy Vernon, a Novelette in Verse. Boston, 1878. 12mo, orig. cloth, very slightly rubbed, 1st ed., "Red Line Ed." of which only 500 copies were printed. MacManus 238-466 1978 $150

DICKINSON, EMILY   Poems. Second Series. Boston, 1892. 8vo, green cloth, gilt stamped cover and spine, bevelled edges, uncut, t.e.g., ownership inscription, spine spotted, 1st ed., collector's cond. Desmarais 1-122 1978 $20

DICKINSON, EMILY   Selected Poems. 1924. Cloth-backed bds., printed label chipped, very good, first English ed. Bell Book 17-277 1978 £8.50

DICKINSON, EMILY   The Single Hound. Poems of a Lifetime. Boston, 1914. Orig. cloth-backed bds., 1st ed., covers slightly stained. MacManus 238-468 1978 $150

DICKINSON, G. LOWES   Poems. N.P.(London), 1896. 8vo, original grey printed wrappers, 1st ed., presentation copy, inscribed by author, laid-in one-page letter from author, nice copy, very scarce. Ximenes 47-75 1978 $150

DICKINSON, H. W.   Robert Fulton, Engineer and Artist. London, 1913. Illus., bookplt., fine. MacManus 239-755 1978 $22.50

DICKINSON, ROBERT LATOU   The Single Woman. Baltimore, 1934. Rittenhouse 49-219 1976 $10

DICKINSON, S. N.   The Boston Almanac for the Year 1846. Boston, 1846. 16mo, orig. cloth, fold. maps, very good. MacManus 239-280 1978 $15

DICKINSON, S. N.   Boston Almanac for 1849. Boston, 1849. 16mo, folding map, orig. cloth. Edwards 1012-473 1978 £20

DICKINSON, WILLIAM   Ode Gratulatoria, in Magnae Britanniae Imperium Fauste & Feliciter Adunatum. Londini, 1707. 1st. ed., folio, disbound. Hannas 54-82 1978 £45

DICKINSON, ZENAS CLARK   Economic Motives. Cambridge, Harvard University Press, 1924. Austin 80-545 1978 $27.50

DICKSON, ALBERT JEROME   Covered Wagon Days. Cleveland, 1929. Cloth. Hayman 73-145 1978 $30

DICKSON, ALBERT JEROME   Covered Wagon Days... Cleveland, 1929. Illus. Biblo 247-207 1978 $35

DICKSON, CARTER   The Red Widow Murders. 1935. Good, first English ed. Bell Book 17-231 1978 £18.50

DICKSON, FRANK D.   Functional Disorders of the Foot. Philadelphia, 1944. Second ed., library marks. Rittenhouse 49-220 1976 $9

DICKSON, HARRIS   An Old-Fashioned Senator, a Story-Biography of John Sharp Williams. New York, 1925. Bell Wiley's copy. Broadfoot 46-499 1978 $8

DICKSON, HARRIS   The Story of King Cotton. 1937. Illus. with photos. Austin 80-546 1978 $11

DICKSON, LEONARD EUGENE   Algebraic Invariants. 1914. Austin 80-995 1978 $17.50

DICKSON, R. W.   A Grammar of the First Principles of Agriculture, Intended Chiefly for the Use of Young Persons. London, 1810. 1st ed., 12mo, double-folded f.p. and engraved plates, full original leather, scarce. Victoria 34-244 1978 $17.50

DICKSON, R. W.   Practical Agriculture or, a Complete System of Modern Husbandry... London, 1805. Engraved plts., hand coloured plts., 2 vols., thick 4to, half calf, leather labels, old bd. sides, some slight foxing. Traylen 88-565 1978 £130

DICKSON, ROBERT   Who Was Scotland's First Printer? London, 1881. 12mo, orig. wrs., 1st ed. Morrill 241-113 1978 $7.50

DICKSON, SAMUEL HENRY   Essays on Life, Sleep, Pain.... Philadelphia, 1852. Rittenhouse 49-222 1976 $35

DICKSON, VIRGIL E.   Mental Tests and the Classroom Teacher. 1923. Austin 90-996 1978 $7.50

DICKSON, WILLIAM   Mitigation of Slavery, in 2 Parts. 1814. 8vo, binders' cloth. Edwards 1012-253 1978 £90

DICTAMEN de la Comision de Libertad de Imprenta,.... Mexico, 1822. 8vo, new quarter mor., very rare. Quaritch 978-104 1978 $350

DICTIONARY of Music and Musicians. 1894. Woodcuts, illus., 4 vols., 8vo. George's 635-1401 1978 £15

DIDEROT, DENIS   Principes de la Philosophie Morale;.... Amsterdam, 1745. 8vo, frontis., vignettes and plate by Durand engraved by Fessard, contemp. French citron mor., triple-line gilt borders, flat spine, longitudinal brown leather label, marbled endpapers, gilt edges, 1st ed. Quaritch 978-42 1978 $1,350

DIEBOW, HANS   Die Juden in U.S.A. Berlin, 1939. Illus., photos, paper, in German. Austin 79-208 1978 $37.50

DIEFENDORF, A. ROSS   Clinical Psychiatry. (1907) 1918. New ed., rev. Austin 80-997 1978 $17.50

DIEFENDORF, MARY R.   The Historic Mohawk. New York, 1910. 1st ed., illus., orig. cloth, fine. MacManus 239-342 1978 $30

DIEFFENBACH, WILLIAM H.   Hydrotherapy. New York, (1909). Illus., 8vo., 1st ed. Morrill 239-67 1978 $8.50

DIEREVILLE, N. DE   Relation du Voyage du Port Royal de L'Acadie ou de la Nouvelle France. Amsterdam, 1710. Contemp. calf, engrav. frontis. Wolfe 39-130 1978 $200

DIETZ, AUGUST   Catalog and Hand-Book (Specialized) of the Postage Stamps and Envelopes of the Confederate States of America. Richmond, Va., 1945. Bell Wiley's Copy. Broadfoot's 44-112 1978 $20.00

DIEZ, ERNST   Iranische Kunst. Vienna, (1944). Illus., color plts., portion of back cover torn away. Biblo BL781-369 1978 $12

DIGBY, KENELM 1603-1665   Remedes Souverains et Secrets Experimentez. Paris, 1689. 12mo., cont. calf, gilt dec. spine, some sections browned, rare ed. in French. Zeitlin 245-62 1978 $275

DIGBY, KENELM HENRY   Evenings on the Thames. 1860. 1st. ed., 2 vols., orig. blue cloth, good. Jarndyce 16-598 1978 £10.50

A DIGEST-of the Laws, Decisions and Usages of the R. W. G. Lodge of North America, and the Grand Lodge of Ohio, Independent Order of Good Templars. Cleveland, 1868. Cloth. Hayman 72-528 1978 $7.50

DIGGES, DUDLEY   The Compleat Ambassador;.... London, 1655. Folio, full old calf, engraved frontis., sole ed. Bennett 7-37 1978 $325

DIGGES, GEORGE A.   Historical Facts Concerning Buncombe County Government. Asheville, 1935. Illus., lower margin stained. Broadfoot 50-58 1978 $25

DIGGES, LEONARD   A Geometrical Practical Treatise Named Pantometria. London, 1591. Folio, text woodcuts, eighteenth century sprinkled calf, second ed., lower part of several leaves waterstained. Quaritch 977-145 1978 $1,250

DILL, SAMUEL   Roman Society from Nero to Marcus Aurelius. 1937. Endpaper spotted. Allen 234-277 1978 $15

DILLENBACK, N. P.   Consumption, Bronchitis, Asthma, Catarrh, and Clergymans's Sore Throat. Boston, 1866. Rittenhouse 49-223 1976 $15

DILLINGHAM, WILLIAM H.   An Oration Delivered Before the Society of the Sons of New England of Philadelphia. Philadelphia, 1847. Wrs. Hayman 73-146 1978 $7.50

DILLMONT, TH. DE   L'Art Chretien en Egypte, Le Filet-Richelieu, Le Triest, Ire et IIme series. Mulhouse, 1910. 4 vols., 4to., loose in portfolios as issued. George's 635-256 1978 £6

DILLON, VISCOUNT   An Almain Armourer's Album... 1905. Folio, colour plts., signature on flyleaf, vellum gilt, gilt top, soiled, but a good copy. Quaritch 983-125 1978 $450

DILLON, EDWARD   Glass. 1907. Roy. 8vo., plts., some coloured, marginal annotation, cloth. Quaritch 983-99 1978 $90

DILLON, F.   Sketches in The Island of Madeira. 1850. Litho. title, tinted litho. plts., folio, orig. cloth, morocco back, binding repaired, slight foxing. Edwards 1012-314 1978 £450

DILNOT, GEORGE   Triumphs of Detection. London, 1929. Illus., Ist ed. Biblo 251-291 1978 $17.50

DILTHEY, WILHELM   Die Geistige Welt... Leipzig, 1924. 2 vols., vols. 5 and 6, 4to., cloth. Salloch 348-49 1978 $35

DILTHEY, WILHELM   Weltanschauungslehre... Leipzig, 1931. Vol. 8. Salloch 348-50 1978 $11

DILWORTH, W. H.   The Life of Alexander Pope. 1760. 12mo., 19th century calf gilt, nice, portrait, scarce. P. M. Hill 142-205 1978 £38

DIMOCK, HEDLEY S.   The Modern Child and Religion. 1934. Paper. Austin 90-998 1978 $7.50

DINESEN, ISAK   Seven Gothic Tales. New York, 1934. Ist Amer. ed., d.w. frayed. Biblo 251-459 1978 $15

DINNEEN, JOSEPH F.   The Purple Shamrock. 1949. Austin 79-209 1978 $10

DINNEEN, MAURICE   The Catholic Total Abstinence Movement in the Archdiocese of Boston. Boston, Press of E. L. Grimes, 1908. Illus. Austin 79-210 1978 $27.50

DINNEEN, JOSEPH F.   The Purple Shamrock. The Hon. James Michael Curley of Boston. New York, (1949). Illus., 1st ed. Biblo BL781-199 1978 $7.50

DINSDALE, ALFRED   First Principles of Television. 1932. 8vo., plts., binders cloth. Quaritch 977-214 1978 $30

DINSDALE, ALFRED   Television. London, 1926. 8vo., illus., orig. prtd. bds., pict. d.w. worn, good copy, Ist ed. Norman 5-**11 1978 $200

DINSDALE, ALFRED   Television. London, 1926. First ed., plts., cr. 8vo., rather dusty, orig. printed card covers, rather stained. K Books 244-96 1978 £45

DINSDALE, ALFRED   Television. London, 1928. Second ed., plts., cr. 8vo. K Books 244-97 1978 £30

DINSDALE, ALFRED   Television. London, The Television Press, Ltd., 1928. 2nd ed., 12mo., illus., fine copy, orig. blue cloth. Current Misc. 8-42 1978 $150

THE DIOCESAN and Federal Organization of the Protestant Episcopal Church in Pennsylvania. Chester, 1880. Wrs. Hayman 73-603 1978 $7.50

DIODORUS SICULUS   Bibliothecae Historicae Libri. 1746. 2 vols., folio, new buckram, some foxing, in Greek & Latin. Allen 234-1518 1978 $50

DIOGENES LAERTIUS   Vitae et Sententiae Philosophorum. Venice, 1475. Folio, old calf, gilt spine & borders, lower cover little damaged, fine copy. Traylen 88-431 1978 £1350

DION CASSIUS COCCEIANUS
Please turn to
CASSIUS DIO COCCEIANUS

DIONIS, PIERRE   Traite General Des Accouchemens... Paris, 1718. 8vo., frontis. portr., engr. plts., contemp. calf, worn, marginal wormtrails, some browning, good & complete copy, Ist ed., very rare. Zeitlin 245-63 1978 $350

DIPMAN, CARL W.   The Modern Hardware Store. New York, 1929. Illus., 8vo., Ist ed. Morrill 239-368 1978 $12.50

DIRCKS, HENRY   The Life, Times and Scientific Labours of the Second Marquis of Worcester. 1865. Plts., illus., octavo, good. Upcroft 10-159 1978 £20

DIRECTORY of Canastota and Wampsville. Canastota, 1914. Ads, wr. Butterfield 21-263 1978 $7.50

DIRECTORY of Seneca Falls and Waterloo. Syracuse, 1886. Some pages pasted on bds., spine partly worn, internally fine. Butterfield 21-411 1978 $25

DIRECTORY of the City of Bucyrus, Ohio. Norwalk, 1914. Bds., little soiled. Hayman 72-534 1978 $8.50

DIRINGER, DAVID   The Illuminated Book. New York. Plts. Battery Park 1-369 1978 $50

DISCLOSURE of the Real Parties to the Purchase and Sale of the Trademen's Bank. (New York, 1826). Sewn, uncut, very good. Butterfield 21-481 1978 $20

DISCOVERIES Concerning Ghosts with a Rap at the Spirit Rappers. 1863. Ist ed., bound from orig. part preserving blue printed paper wrappers, gap in binding at end, where some illus. have been removed, half calf, marbled bds., good condition. Jarndyce 16-440 1978 £15

DISCURSO Sobre La Arquitectura Naval Antigua Y Moderna Prolusion Academica.. Dixo Don Cipriano Vimercati',.... En Madrid, 1787. Red leather binding, gold design. Nestler Rare 78-197 1978 $35

DISINFECTION and Disinfectants. Concord, 1888. Illus., ex-lib., back cover waterstained, Ist ed. Morrill 239-69 1978 $10

DISRAELI, BENJAMIN   Commentaries on the Reign of Charles the First, King of England. 1851. New ed., 2 vols., orig. patterned cloth, mint. Jarndyce 16-608 1978 £34

DISRAELI, BENJAMIN   Coningsby; or the New Generation. London, 1844. 3 vols., later 3/4 calf, 1st ed., rare. MacManus 238-207 1978 $250

DISRAELI, BENJAMIN   Coningsby... 1844. 2nd. ed., 3 vols., orig. grey bds., green cloth spines, paper labels, inner hinges little weak, some marking of endpapers, externally v.g. Jarndyce 16-618 1978 £42

DISRAELI, BENJAMIN   Constitutional Refore: Five Speeches, (1859-65). 1866. Ist. ed., orig. crushed red morocco, half title, gilt borders, dentelles & spine by Riviere, t.e.g., fine. Jarndyce 16-611 1978 £34

DISRAELI, BENJAMIN   Contarini Fleming. New York, 1832. 1st. American ed., 2 vols., orig. salmon pink cloth, paper labels, fine. Jarndyce 16-601 1978 £65

DISRAELI, BENJAMIN   Contarini-Fleming. 1853. New ed., half calf, good. Jarndyce 16-607 1978 £15

DISRAELI, BENJAMIN   Endymion. 1880. 1st. ed., 3 vols., half-titles, orig. red cloth, spines faded, stitching weak in vol. 2. Eaton 45-157 1978 £10

DISRAELI, BENJAMIN   Endymion. London, 1880. 1st ed., 3 vols., scarlet cloth binding, spine damage, good tight copies. Greene 78-32 1978 $75

DISRAELI, BENJAMIN   Endymion. 1880. 3 vols., half titles, orig. red cloth, couple of sm. marks, otherwise fine bright copy. Jarndyce 16-617 1978 £24

DISRAELI, BENJAMIN   Inaugural Address Delivered to the University of Glasgow, Nov. 19, 1873. 1873. 2nd. ed., untrimmed in crushed red morocco, gilt borders, dentelles & spine by Riviere, t.e.g., fine. Jarndyce 16-616 1978 £40

DISRAELI, BENJAMIN   The Letters of Runnymede. 1836. 1st. ed., sm. portion torn from 1st. advt., orig. patterned cloth, good. Jarndyce 16-604 1978 £85

DISRAELI, BENJAMIN   Lord George Bentinck: A Political Biography. Colburn, 1852. 1st. ed., 8vo, orig. cloth, binding lightly stained & inside joints weak, very good copy. Fenning 32-87 1978 £32

DISRAELI, BENJAMIN   Lord George Bentinck: A Political Biography. 1852. 1st. ed., rebound in half calf, hand-marbled bds. Jarndyce 16-606 1978 £18

DISRAELI, BENJAMIN   Lothair. 1870. 1st. ed., 3 vols., half titles, orig. green cloth, good. Jarndyce 16-613 1978 £35

DISRAELI, BENJAMIN   Lothair. New York, 1870. 1st Am. ed., 3 vols. in 1, orig. cloth. Greene 78-33 1978 $20

DISRAELI, BENJAMIN   Lothair. 1870. 2nd. ed., 3 vols., half titles, orig. half red calf, marbled bds., fine. Jarndyce 16-614 1978 £27

DISRAELI, BENJAMIN   Lothair. 1870. 2nd. ed., 3 vols., half titles, orig. green cloth. Jarndyce 16-615 1978 £18

DISRAELI, BENJAMIN   Novels and Tales. 1900. 11 vols., 8vo., Hughenden ed., half mor., gilt tops. Quaritch 979-120 1978 $170

DISRAELI, BENJAMIN   Novels & Tales Bradenham Edition. 1926-7. 12 vols., orig. black cloth, blocked in blind & gilt, untrimmed, t.e.g., fine set. Jarndyce 16-620 1978 £90

DISRAELI, BENJAMIN   The Revolutionary Epick. 1834. 1st. ed., 4to, 2 parts in 1 vol., half titles, orig. publisher's cloth, slight wear to top section of leading hinge otherwise very good copy, extremely rare, only 50 copies. Jarndyce 16-602 1978 £340

DISRAELI, BENJAMIN   The Revolutionary Epick. 1864. Half title, untrimmed in crushed red morocco, gilt borders, dentelles & spines by Riviere, t.e.g., fine. Jarndyce 16-603 1978 £32

DISRAELI, BENJAMIN   Tancred: or, The New Crusade. 1847. 1st. ed., half green calf, red labels, marbled bds., v.g. Jarndyce 16-605 1978 £65

DISRAELI, BENJAMIN   Tancred. 1847. 3 vols., contemp. half calf, contrasting labels, good, first English ed. Bell Book 17-280 1978 £25

DISRAELI, BENJAMIN   The Voyage of Captain Popanilla. 1828. 1st. ed., orig. half calf, rebacked, new endpapers, Rowland Hill's copy, signed by him. Jarndyce 16-600 1978 £78

DISRAELI, ISAAC   Amenities of Literature Consisting of Sketches and Characters of English Literature. London, 1863. 2 vols., new ed., orig. red cloth, frontis., binding stain. Greene 78-188 1978 $25

DISRAELI, ISAAC   Curiosities of Literature. Paris, 1835. 3 vols., diced calf, gilt spines, 8vo. K Books 244-99 1978 £18

DISRAELI, ISAAC   Curiosities of Literature. 1858. 3 vols., new ed., frontis, half titles, orig. green cloth, v.g. Jarndyce 16-610 1978 £5.50

DISRAELI, ISAAC   Curiosities of Literature. London, 1865-66. New ed., 3 vols., red cloth, spine damage, good. Greene 78-189 1978 $35

D'ISRAELI, ISAAC   Domestic Anecdotes of the French Nation During the Last 30 Years... 1794. 1st. ed., half calf, spine worn, otherwise sound. Jarndyce 16-75 1978 £15.50

DISRAELI, ISAAC   The Illustrator Illustrated. 1838. 1st. ed., half title, uncut, in contemp. half green morocco, good. Jarndyce 16-599 1978 £15

D'ISRAELI, ISAAC   Literary Miscellanies. 1801. Sm. 8vo., new ed., contemp. calf, rubbed, joints cracked, label missing. Howes 194-245 1978 £10

DISTANT, W. L.   Rhopalocera Malayana... London, 1882-1886. Coloured plts., woodcuts, lg. & thick 4to, old brown calf, red leather label. Traylen 88-566 1978 £225

THE DISTINCT Symptoms of the Gravel and Stone, Explained to the Patient.... London, 1759. 8vo., wrappers. Gurney 75-31 1978 £20

DISTURNELL, JOHN   The Great Lakes... Philadelphia, 1871. Fldg. map. Hood 117-729 1978 $45

DITCHFIELD, P. H.   The Old English Country Squire. 1912. Colored illus., 8vo. George's 635-625 1978 £6.50

DITCHFIELD, P. H.   The Parish Clerk. 1907. Illus., 8vo. George's 635-626 1978 £6.50

DITMARS, R.   A Review of the Box Turtles. Soft cloth binding, tall 8vo, scarce. Book Chest 17-120 1978 $28

DIVEN, A. S.   Speeches of Hon. A. S. Diven, of New York on the Appropriation Bill and the Confiscation of Rebel Property. Washington, 1862. Disbound. Bell Wiley's copy. Broadfoot 46-75 1978 $10

DIVERSI avvisi particolari dall'Indie di Portogallo,... Venice, 1565. 8vo, half vellum, very rare ed. Gilhofer 75-3 1978 SFr 1,300

DIVINE Service Book for the Armed Services. Ottawa, 1950. Hood 117-120 1978 $12.50

DIX, J.   Flowers in Colour. New York, 1948. 4to, orig. cloth, colour plts. Book Chest 17-505 1978 $10

DIX, JOHN A.   Speech of...President of the Mississippi and Missouri Railroad Company,.... New York, 1856. Original printed wr., 1st ed. Ginsberg 14-410 1978 $60

DIXON, CHARLES   The Game Birds and Wild Fowl of the British Islands... London, 1895. Coloured illus. by A. T. Elwes, 8vo, orig. cloth, good. Sexton 7-195 1978 £12

DIXON, CHARLES D.   The Menace: An Exposition of Quackery Nostrum, Exploitation and Reminiscences of a Country Doctor. San Antonio, 1914. Plts., illus., tall thin 8vo., orig. cloth, 1st ed., pres. copy. Argosy Special-36 1978 $75

DIXON, CLIVE   The Leaguer of Ladysmith. London, (1900). Oblong 4to, orig. pictorial coloured bds., 18 coloured plts. K Books 239-118 1978 £20

DIXON, EDWARD H.   Back-Bone. New York, (1866). Orig. mounted photo of author, autographed, 8vo., foxed, 1st ed. Morrill 239-69 1978 $15

DIXON, EDWARD H.   The Scalpel. New York, January 1849 to August 1850. 1st 8 nos. bound in red lea. & bds. Butterfield 21-401 1978 $35

DIXON, EDWARD H.   Scenes in the Practice of a New York Surgeon. New York, 1855. Some shabbiness. Rittenhouse 49-224 1976 $20

DIXON, GEORG   Der Kapitaine Portlock's und Dixon's Reise um die Welt Besonders nach der Nordwestlichen Kuste von America...1785-1788. Berlin, 1790. German text, map, plts., old plain wrs., rebacked with cloth, waterstained, lacking plt. 7. Dawson's 127-253 1978 $75

DIXON, GEORGE   Voyage Round the World... 1789. 1st. ed., engraved plts., 4to, calf. Edwards 1012-15 1978 £450

DIXON, J. H.   Chronicles and Stories of the Craven Dales. (1881). Half title, orig. blue gilt, dec. bds., mint. Jarndyce 16-621 1978 £8.50

DIXON, R. HOMER   The Border or Riding Clans. Albany, 1889. Sm. 4to., uncut, unopened, orig. binding. Wolfe 39-131 1978 $25

DIXON, SAM HOUSTON   Romance and Tragedy of Texas History. Houston, 1924. Fine, 1st ed. Jenkins 116-325 1978 $45

DIXON, THOMAS   The Black Hood. 1924. First ed. Austin 82-342 1978 $10

DIXON, THOMAS   The Clansman. 1905. Illus., first ed., very good. Austin 82-343 1978 $12.50

DIXON, THOMAS   The Clansman. 1905. Illus. Austin 82-345 1978 $8.50

DIXON, THOMAS   Companions. 1931. First ed. Austin 82-346 1978 $12.50

DIXON, THOMAS   Comrades. 1909. Illus. in color. Austin 82-347 1978 $10

DIXON, THOMAS   The Fall of a Nation. 1916. Illus. Austin 82-349 1978 $12.50

DIXON, THOMAS   The One Woman. 1903. Illus., first ed. Austin 82-350 1978 $10

DIXON, THOMAS   The One Woman. 1903. Austin 82-351 1978 $7.50

DIXON, THOMAS   The Traitor. 1907. Illus. Austin 82-352 1978 $8.50

DIXON, THOMAS   The Victim. 1914. Illus. Austin 82-354 1978 $8.50

DIXON, W. MACNEILE   The English Parnassus. Oxford, 1921. 2nd impression of 1st ed., very good or better. Limestone 9-97 1978 $10

DIXON, W. MACNIELLE   The Human Situation. 1937. Austin 80-999 1978 $8.50

DIXON, WILLIAM HEPWORTH   British Cyprus. 1879. 1st. ed., 8vo, coloured frontis, recent bds., very good copy. Fenning 32-88 1978 £16.50

DOBB, MAURICE   Political Economy and Capitalism. New York, (1937). Biblo BL781-812 1978 $7.50

DOBBINS, W. W.   History of the Battle of Lake Erie... Erie, 1913. Illus. MacManus 239-471 1978 $15

DOBBS, ARTHUR   An Account of the Countries Adjoining Hudson's Bay... 1744. Folding map, 4to, calf, one joint repaired. Edwards 1012-421 1978 £1200

DOBELL, BERTRAM   The Laureate of Pessimism: a Sketch of the Life and Character of James Thomson. 1910. Fine, unopened, wraps, first English ed. Bell Book 17-862 1978 £5.50

DOBELL, WILLIAM   The Art of William Dobell. Sydney, 1946. Very good, coloured & numerous b/w plts., d.w., first English ed. Bell Book 17-026 1978 £5

DOBIE, CHARLES CALDWELL   San Francisco, a Pageant. 1934. Illus., very good. Austin 82-923 1978 $12.50

DOBIE, JAMES FRANK   Apache Gold & Yaqui Silver. Boston, 1939. Letter from Dobie to Wiley laid in. Bell Wiley's copy. Broadfoot 46-501 1978 $35

DOBIE, JAMES FRANK   Bigfoot Wallace and the Hickory Nuts. Austin, 1936. Printed wr., limited to 300 numbered autographed copies, mint. Jenkins 116-1582 1978 $300

DOBIE, JAMES FRANK   Coronado's Childred: Tales of Lost Mines and Buried Treasures of the Southwest. New York, 1931. Illus., bookplt. of John William Rogers. Jenkins 116-326 1978 $25

DOBIE, JAMES FRANK   Coyote Wisdom. Austin, 1938. Mint copy, d.j., 1st ed. Jenkins 116-329 1978 $65

DOBIE, JAMES FRANK   Guide to Life and Literature of the Southwest. Austin, 1943. 1st ed., printed wr., scarce issue in wrappers, not meant for sale, illus. Jenkins 116-333 1978 $50

DOBIE, JAMES FRANK   He Belongs to the Texas Folk-Lore Society. Austin, 1937. Illus. by Ben C. Mead. Jenkins 116-334 1978 $12.50

DOBIE, JAMES FRANK   John C. Duval: First Texas Man of Letters. Dallas, 1939. Illus. by Tom Lea, 1st ed., rare, autographed by Dobie. Jenkins 116-336 1978 $125

DOBIE, JAMES FRANK   The Longhorns. Boston, 1941. 1st ed., signed by Dobie, illus., spine a bit stained. Jenkins 116-338 1978 $25

DOBIE, JAMES FRANK   Mustangs and Cow Horses. Austin, 1940. Fabricoid, pic. end sheets, illus., 1st ed., fine copy in reinforced dull pic. d.w., protected with plastic cover, slipcase, very scarce. Dykes 34-226 1978 $75

DOBIE, JAMES FRANK   A Texan in England. London, 1946. 1st English ed., illus., tom d.j. Jenkins 116-1538 1978 $17.50

DOBIE, JAMES FRANK   A Vaquero of the Brush Country. Dallas, 1929. Cloth & bds., map end sheets, 1st ed., 1st issue, very good copy, slipcase. Dykes 34-54 1978 $100

DOBIE, JAMES FRANK   A Vaquero of the Brush Country. London, 1949. 1st English ed., d.j. Jenkins 116-345 1978 $15

DOBLADO, DON LEUCADIO   Letters from Spain. 1822. 8vo., orig. bds., uncut, backstrip partly defective, first ed. P. M. Hill 142-41 1978 £16

DOBREE, BONAMY   Essays in Biography 1680-1726. Oxford, 1925. Plts., orig. cloth, 8vo. Howes 194-805 1978 £5

DOBSON, ALBAN   A Bibliography of the First Editions by Austin Dobson. London, First Edition Club, 1925. one of 500 numbered copies, 8vo., orig. red cloth, v.g. Houle 10-89 1978 $75

DOBSON, AUSTIN   The Ballad of Beau Brocade. London, 1892. Illus., 1st Amer. ed. Biblo BL781-635 1978 $27.50

DOBSON, AUSTIN   Collected Poems. London, 1897. 1st ed., covers rubbed. Biblo 251-460 1978 $20

DOBSON, AUSTIN   De Libris: prose & verse. Covers dull, good, illus., plts., first English ed. Bell Book 16-485 1978 £4

DOBSON, AUSTIN   Eighteenth Century Vignettes. New York, 1892. No. 55 of 250, very good. Ballinger 11-129 1978 $17.50

DOBSON, AUSTIN   The Story of Rosina and Other Verses. New York, 1895. Illus., 1st Amer. ed. Biblo BL781-636 1978 $22.50

DOBSON, AUSTIN   The Story of Rosina and Other Verses. London, 1895. 1 of 250 numbered copies on Arnold handmade paper, illus. by Hugh Thomson, 4 to., orig. white cloth, stamped in gilt, bookplate, fine, scarce, tight, clean. Houle 10-337 1978 $130

DOBSON, AUSTIN   Vignettes in Rhyme and Verse de Societe (Now Fist Collected). London, 1873. Sm. 8vo, orig. brown decor. cloth, 1st ed., primary binding, one of 500 copies, very good copy. Ximenes 47-76 1978 $45

DOBSON, AUSTIN   Vignettes in Rhyme and Vers de Societe. London, 1873. 12mo., orig. cloth, 1st ed., spine slightly soiled, but very good. MacManus 238-208 1978 $85

DOBSON, EDWARD   The Students Guide to the Practice of Measuring and Valuing Artificers' Works. 1858. 3rd. ed., folding engraved plts., illus., 8vo, orig. cloth, nice copy. Fenning 32-89 1978 £24

DOBSON, SUSANNAH   The Life of Petrarch. London, 1799. 2 vols., vignettes, plts., good, contemp. calf, 8vo. K Books 244-354 1978 £12

DOBSON, SUSANNAH   The Life of Petrarch. 1799. 4th ed., copper-plts., 2 vols., half calf, rubbed, joints cracked, 8vo. George's 635-1450 1978 £7.50

DOBSON, SUSANNAH   Petrarch's View of Human Life. London, 1791. 8vo., bds. Salloch 348-192 1978 $50

DOCK, LAVINIA   A History of Nursing. 1907. Austin 80-963a 1978 $27.50

DOCK, LAVINIA   A History of Nursing. 1912. Illus., vol. 3 only. Austin 80-963b 1978 $12.50

DOCKERAY, FLOYD C.   General Psychology. 1935. Rev. ed. Austin 80-1001 1978 $10

DR. STRONG'S, The Saratoga Springs Sanitarium, Saratoga Springs, N. Y. (New York, ca. 1901). Illus., oblong 8vo., orig. wrs. Morrill 239-70 1978 $10

THE DOCUMENTARY History of the State of New York. Albany, 1850-51. Taller quarto ed. in green cloth, complete resetting of type, bindings chipped, sm. tears, all sound, maps, plts. complete. Butterfield 21-154 1978 $35

DOCUMENTS Accompanying a Report of the Committee Appointed to Enquire into the Expediency or Inexpediency of Giving Further Time to Persons Entitled to Military Land Warrants, to Obtain and Locate the Same. Made the 30th December, 1801. (Washington, 1801). Mod. bds., very rare. Hayman 72-554 1978 $50

DODD, GEORGE   The Curiosities of Industry and the Applied Sciences. 1854. 8vo. George's 635-314 1978 £6

DODD, GEORGE   Novelties, Inventions and Curiosities in Arts and Manufactures. 1853. 3rd. ed., half title, sm. 8vo, wrapper, orig. printed paper label mounted on upper cover, very good copy. Fenning 32-90 1978 £9.50

DODD, LEE WILSON   The Golden Complex. 1927. Austin 80-1002 1978 $8.50

DODD, WILLIAM   The Beauties of History;.... London, 1800. 3rd ed., engravings, f.p. lacking, calf, upper hinge cracked, very good. Victoria 34-245 1978 $35

DODD, WILLIAM   The Beauties of Shakspeare, Regularly Selected From Each Play. Chiswick, 1818. 12mo, contemp. green calf, gilt, little worn. Hannas 54-85 1978 £7.50

DODD, WILLIAM   The Sisters. 1781. 8vo., recent half calf, nice, plts., reprint. P. M. Hill 142-186 1978 £70

DODD, WILLIAM   Thoughts in Prison: In Five Parts, Viz. The Imprisonment. The Retrospect. Publick Punishment. The Trial. Futurity... London, 1777. 8vo., orig. blue-grey paper wrs., uncut, 1st ed., wrs. soiled, worn at extremities, but good. MacManus 238-115 1978 $200

DODD, WILLIAM E.   Ambassador Dodd's Diary. 1941. Austin 80-86 1978 $8.50

DODD, WILLIAM E.   The Old South. New York, 1937. Cloth, 1st prtg., worn & torn dust jacket, book is fine. Hayman 73-147 1978 $7.50

DODDRIDGE, MR.   Speech of Mr Doddridge, in the Case of Samuel Houston, Charged with a Contempt and Breech of the Privileges of the House... Washington, 1832. Sm. tear repaired. Jenkins 116-687 1978 $85

DODDRIDGE, JOSEPH   Settlement of Western Country... Bowling Green, n.d. (c. 1919). Cloth. Hayman 72-199 1978 $15

DODDRIDGE, PHILIP   Some Remarkable Passages in the Life of the Honourable Col. James Gardiner. 1747. Sm. 8vo., second ed., contemp. calf, worn, rebacked. F. Edwards 1013-303 1978 £10

DODDRIDGE, PHILIP   Some Remarkable Passages in the Life of the Honourable Col. James Gardiner, Who was Slain at the Battle of Preston-Pans... Boston, 1748. 3rd ed., blank wrs., light dampstaining on first few leaves. Hayman 72-201 1978 $75

DODGE, D. STUART   Memoria's of William E. Dodge. New York, (1887). Cloth, little rubbed. Hayman 73-148 1978 $10

DODGE, GRENVILLE M.   The Battle of Atlanta and Other Campaigns. Council Bluffs, 1910. Illus., 1st ed., bookplt., fine. MacManus 239-872 1978 $32.50

DODGE, GRENVILLE M.   Sketch of the Military Service of Major General Wager Swayne. New York, (1903). Wrs. Hayman 73-111 1978 $8.50

DODGE, MARY ABIGAIL   Biography of James G. Blaine. Norwich, 1895. Cloth. Hayman 72-200 1978 $10

DODGE, MARY MAPES   Along the Way. New York, 1879. 12mo., first ed., covers worn. Biblo 247-563 1978 $17.50

DODGE, MARY MAPES   Hans Brinker; or, The Silver Skates. New York, c.1870. Illus. by Darley and Nast, fine gilt windmill on cover, very good. Victoria 34-246 1978 $15

DODGE, MARY MAPES   Hans Brinker or the Silver Skates. 1897. Orig. illus. Austin 82-355 1978 $12.50

DODGE, MARY MAPES   The Land of Pluck. New York, 1894. 1st ed., fine, 1st issue orange binding. Victoria 34-247 1978 $20

DODGE, MARY MAPES   Rhymes and Jingles. New York, 1876. 2nd ed., excellent illus., tips rubbed, fine, bright copy, scarce. Victoria 34-248 1978 $17.50

DODGE, RAYMOND   The Craving for Superiority. Yale University Press, 1931. Austin 80-1003 1978 $8.50

DODGE, RAYMOND   Psychological Effects of Alcohol. 1915. 1st ed. Austin 80-1004 1978 $75

DODGE, RICHARD IRVING   The Black Hills. New York, 1876. Illus., folding map, tinted paltes, original cloth, 1st ed. Ginsberg 14-340 1978 $100

DODGE, RICHARD IRVING   A Living Issue. Washington, 1882. Original printed wr., 1st ed., privately printed. Ginsberg 14-341 1978 $250

DODGE, THEODORE ARYAULT   Caesar. 1892. 2 vols. Allen 234-150 1978 $30

DODGSON, CAMPBELL   Woodcuts and Metal Cuts of the 15th Century, chiefly of the German School. London, 1914. Plts., cr. 4to., orig. cloth, fine. Forster 130-196 1978 £20

DODGSON, CHARLES LUTWIDGE   Alice's Adventures in Wonderland. Boston, 1869. 2nd Amer. ed., Tenniel illus., green cloth, covers heavily rubbed, rear inner hinge cracked, text very fine. Victoria 34-142 1978 $30

DODGSON, CHARLES LUTWIDGE   Alice's Adventures in Wonderland. New York, 1901. 1st ed., plts. by Peter Newell, white "vellum" with impressed gilt vignettes, covers dust soiled, spine darkened, very good. Victoria 34-143 1978 $22.50

DODGSON, CHARLES LUTWIDGE   Alice's Adventures in Wonderland. London, (1907). Illus. by Arthur Rackham, coloured plts., text illus., 8vo., orig. cloth. K Books 244-62 1978 £20

DODGSON, CHARLES LUTWIDGE   Alice's Adventures in Wonderland. 1914. Lg. 8vo., illus., orig. vellum, ltd. ed., printed on hand-made paper. Howes 194-710 1978 £7.50

DODGSON, CHARLES LUTWIDGE   Alice's Adventures in Wonderland. Philadelphia, 1923. Illus. in color by Gertrude A. Kay, orig. drwgs. by John Tenniel, 1st of this ed., 1 plt. loose. Biblo 251-220 1978 $17.50

DODGSON, CHARLES LUTWIDGE   Alice's Adventures Under Ground. 1886. Sm. 8vo., 1st ed., illus. by author, orig. cloth gilt, black endpapers, clean copy, facsimile of orig. ms. Quaritch 979-122 1978 $120

DODGSON, CHARLES LUTWIDGE   Alice's Adventures Under Ground. London, 1886. Illus. by author, red cloth, edges gilt, 1st ed., covers soiled & worn. Bradley 49-78 1978 $20

DODGSON, CHARLES LUTWIDGE   Le Avventure d'Alice nel poese delle Meraviglie. London, 1872. 1st ed. in Italian, same binding and illus. as 1st English ed., fine. Victoria 34-144 1978 $80

DODGSON, CHARLES LUTWIDGE   Doublets. A Word-Puzzle. London, 1879. 12mo., orig. cloth, very slightly soiled, 1st pub. ed., fine. MacManus 238-211 1978 $75

DODGSON, CHARLES LUTWIDGE   An Easter Greeting to Every Child Who Loves "Alice." (Oxford, 1876). 16mo., 1st ed., slightly foxed. MacManus 238-210 1978 $150

DODGSON, CHARLES LUTWIDGE   The Hunting of the Snark. 1876. Sm. 8vo., 1st ed., illus., orig. grey cloth, gilt edges, good copy. Quaritch 979-124 1978 $140

DODGSON, CHARLES LUTWIDGE   The Hunting of the Snark. 1948. Illus. by Mervyn Peake, fcap. 8vo. George's 635-196 1978 £5

DODGSON, CHARLES LUTWIDGE   The Lewis Carroll Picture Book: A Selection from the Unpublished Writings & Drawings,…. London, 1899. 1st ed., about fine. Victoria 34-145 1978 $25

DODGSON, CHARLES LUTWIDGE   The New Belfry of Christ Church. Oxford, 1872. 1st ed., 1st issue, almost fine. MacManus 238-209 1978 $85

DODGSON, CHARLES LUTWIDGE   Rhyme? and Reason? 1883. Sm. 8vo., 1st ed., illus., clean copy, orig. cloth, very slightly soiled. Quaritch 979-123 1978 $40

DODGSON, CHARLES LUTWIDGE   The Russian Journal and other selections. 1935. First U.S. ed., nice. Bell Book 16-150 1978 £12.50

DODGSON, CHARLES LUTWIDGE   Sylvie and Bruno and Sylvie and Bruno Concluded. London, 1889, 1893. 8vo., red cloth stamped in gilt, a.e.g., 2 vols., 1st ed., red cloth slipcase, illus. by Harry Furniss, Collector's condition. Desmarais 1-72 1978 $140

DODGSON, CHARLES LUTWIDGE   Sylvie and Bruno Concluded. London, 1893. Cloth, frontis. browned from tissue guard. Dawson's 447-218 1978 $50

DODGSON, CHARLES LUTWIDGE   Sylvie and Bruno Concluded. London, 1893. Illus. by Harry Furniss, 1st ed. Biblo BL781-1023 1978 $67.50

DODGSON, CHARLES LUTWIDGE   Through the Looking Glass. New York, 1902. Illus., plts., frontis. portrait, full white gilt stamped Japan vellum bds., t.e.g., fine. Houle 10-59 1978 $85

DODGSON, CHARLES LUTWIDGE   The 'Wonderland' Postage-Stamp-Case. 1889-90. 2 parts, 12mo., 1st ed., orig. card end-wrs., orig. envelope. Quaritch 979-125 1978 $120

DODGSON, CHARLES LUTWIDGE   Complete Works. Nonesuch Press, n.d. Illus. by John Tenniel, red buckram, very good, worn d.w., first English ed. Bell Book 16-149 1978 £8.50

DODSLEY, J.   A Collection of Poems. 1775. 6 vols., contemp. tree calf, vignettes, 8vo. Howes 194-246 1978 £32

DODSLEY, ROBERT   The Preceptor. 1783. Frontispieces, plts., 2 vols. in 3, maps, contemp. calf, spines gilt, seventh ed., 8vo. Howes 194-247 1978 £48

DODSLEY, ROBERT   The Preceptor. 1783. Seventh ed., 3 vols., 8vo., 18th century tree calf, gilt backs, plts., maps. P. M. Hill 142-96 1978 £85

DODSLEY, ROBERT   A Select Collection of Old English Plays. 1874-76. Fourth ed., 15 vols., contemp. mor., orig. issue, very scarce. Howes 194-248 1978 £100

DODSLEY, ROBERT   Select Collection of old English Plays. 1874-76. 15 vols., 8vo., 1st ed., facsimiles, cloth, good, clean set. Quaritch 979-126 1978 $220

DODSON, JAMES   The Anti-logarithmic Canon. London, 1742. Sm. folio, clean, contemp. calf, neatly repaired. Quaritch 977-147 1978 $100

DOENGES, WILLY   Meissner Porzellan. Zweite Auflage. Dresden, (1921). Illus., some in color. Biblo BL781-572 1978 $20

DOFLEIN, FR.   Ostasienfahrt. Leipzig, 1906. Cloth, illus., maps, plts., 8vo. Van der Peet 127-295 1978 Dfl 65

DOGERTY, ROBERT   Siege at Chepachet. N.P. (Rhode Island?), n.d. (ca. 1844). 8vo, original tan pictorial wrappers, (somewhat worn and soiled), 1st ed., very scarce. Ximenes 47-77 1978 $45

DOGLIONI, G. N.   L'Anno Dove si ha Perfetto…. Venice, 1587. Sm. 4to., woodcuts, early vellum, ties missing. Quaritch 977-179 1978 $275

DOGNIN, P.   Note Sur la Faune des Lepidopteres de Loja (Equateur) et descriptions d'especes nouvells. Paris, 1887-96. Folio, uncut, 8vo., orig. cloth, color plts. Book Chest 17-124 1978 $225

DOHERTY, H. E.   The Aylwards and Their Orphans. Quebec, 1863. Orig. printed wrappers. Wolfe 39-27 1978 $35

DOHERTY, HENRY L.   Principles and Ideas for Doherty Men. 1923. 6 vols., illus. Austin 80-553 1978 $47.50

DOHERTY, T.   Anatomical Works. Illus. by G. Stubbs, folio, 8vo, orig. cloth. Book Chest 17-373 1978 $85

DOHRING, K.   Buddhistische Tempelanlagen in Siam. Bangkok, 1920. 4to., boards, plts. Van der Peet 127-73 1978 Dfl 100

DOHRING, K.   Siam, Land und Volk - Die bildende Kunst. Darmstadt-Hagen-Gotha, 1923. 2 vols., 4to., orig. boards, rare. Van der Peet 127-74 1978 Dfl 85

DOIGE, THOMAS   An Alphabetical List of the Merchants, Traders, and Housekeepers, Residing in Montreal. Montreal, 1819. Sm. 8vo., contemp. calf. Wolfe 39-132a 1978 $1,600

DOLCE, LODOVICO   Dialogo nel quale si ragiona del modo di accrescere e conservar la memoria. Venice, 1562. 8 vo., woodcut illus., fine, French 18th century green mor., rare 1st ed. Quaritch Summer, 1978-14 1978 $1,000

DOLE, ESTHER MOHR   Maryland During the American Revolution. 1941. Illus. by George B. Keester. Baldwins' 51-281 1978 $15

DOLL, EDGAR A.   Clinical Studies in Feeble-Mindedness. 1917. Illus., some waterstains on fore edge. Austin 80-1005 1978 $12.50

DOLL, EDGAR A.   Twenty Five Years - The Vineland Laboratory 1906-31. 1932. Austin 80-1006 1978 $27.50

DOLL, JOSEPH   Leichter Unterricht In Der Vokal Musik, Enthaltend, Die Vornehmsten Kirchen-Melodien…. Harrisburg, 1821. 1 copy only, oblong large 8vo, orig. calf-backed decor. boards, rubbed & loose, good complete copy. Americanist 101-104 1978 $95

DOLLARD, JOHN   Criteria for the Life History. Yale University Press, 1935. 1st ed. in dust jacket. Austin 80-1007 1978 $20

DOLLARD, JOHN   Fear in Battle. 1944. Paper. Austin 80-1008 1978 $15

DOLLARD, JOHN   Personality and Psyche Therapy. 1950. Austin 80-1009 1978 $12.50

DOLMAN, ALFRED   In The Footsteps of Livingstone. London, 1924. 5 maps, plts., illus., 8vo, orig. cloth, some pages roughly opened, some age-marking, reasonable ex-lib. K Books 239-119 1978 £10

LE DOMAINE Colonial Francais. Paris, 1929-30. 4 vols., 4to., half green mor, plts., maps, ltd. publication. Van der Peet 127-296 1978 dFl 350

DOMENECH, EMMANUEL HENRI DIEUDONNE   Journal D'un Missionaire au Texas et au Mexique. Paris, 1857. Original printed wrs., 1st ed., map. Jenkins 116-361 1978 $135

DOMENECH, EMMANUEL HENRI DIEUDONNE   Seven Years' Residence in the Great Deserts of North America…. London, 1860. 2 vols., illus., map, colored plts., orig. cloth, 1st ed. Ginsberg 14-342 1978 $150

DOMESTIC Missionary Society of Massachusetts: The Sixth Annual Report, June 24, 1824.   Springfield, 1824. 8vo, wrappers. Edwards 1012-487 1978 £12

DONAHUE, WILMA   Planning the Older Years. 1950. Austin 80-1010 1978 $12.50

DONALDSON, ALFRED L.   A History of the Adirondacks. 1921. 2 vols., 1st ed., illus., bibliography, maps, good. Nestler Rare 78-110 1978 $125

DONALDSON, J. W.   New Cratylus, or Contributions Towards a More Accurate Knowledge of the Greek Language. 1869. 3rd ed., new buckram. Allen 234-282 1978 $10

DONALDSON, THOMAS   The George Catlin Indian Gallery in the U.S. National Museum with Memoir and Statistics. Washington, 1887. Illus., nice, cloth, sm. thick 4to. MacManus 239-1158 1978 $50

DONDERS, FRANZ CORNELIUS   On the Anomalies of Accomodation and Refraction of the Eye. London, 1864. 8vo., illus., orig. blind-stamped brown cloth, gilt lettering on backstrip, light browning, good copy, 1st ed. Zeitlin 245-64 1978 $75

DONEHOO, GEORGE P.   A History of the Cumberland Valley in Pennsylvania. Harrisburg, 1930. 1st ed., 2 vols., 4to., illus., orig. cloth, fine. MacManus 239-1430 1978 $85

DONHAM, WALLACE BRETT   Business Adrift. 1931. Austin 80-554 1978 $8.50

DONI, ANTON FRANCESCO   I Marmi. Venice, 1552-53. 4 to., woodcuts, cont. vellum over bds., first ed., v.f. Schafer 19-16 1978 sFr 1600

DONKIN, MAJOR ROBERT   Military Collections and Remarks. New York, 1777. 8vo, original drab paper wrappers, hand lettered on the spine, green cloth folding case, 1st ed., very fine uncut copy, exceptionally fresh original condition, engraved frontispiece by J. Smith. Ximenes 47-78 1978 $900

DONNE, JACK   A Defence of Women for Their Inconstancy & Their Paintings. Franfrolico Press, 1925. 12mo., thin, cloth. Battery Park 1-94 1978 $50

DONNE, JOHN   Complete Poetry and Selected Prose. 1929. Sm. 8vo., ed. de luxe, prtd. on spec. paper, levant mor., back little faded, ltd. to 675 copies. Quaritch 979-241 1978 $175

DONNE, JOHN   The Holy Sonnets of John Donne. Golden Cockerel Press, 1938. 8vo., illus., cloth, d.w., bkplt., ltd. to 550 copies signed by artist. Quaritch 979-167 1978 $175

DONNE, JOHN   Love Poems. Soho, 1923. Decor. bds., vellum spine, near fine. Dawson's 447-98 1978 $45

DONNE, JOHN   Paradoxes and Problemes. 1923. 8vo., woodcuts, bds., fine, ltd. to 645 copies. Quaritch 979-242 1978 $115

DONNE, JOHN   Poems. 1938. 2 vols., orig. cloth, 8vo. Howes 194-808 1978 £7.50

DONNE, JOHN   The Poetry of John Donne. Sm. folio, #29 of 50 numbered copies, Beckett text paper, decor. cut in oake-woode, bds. Battery Park 1-181 1978 $100

DONNEGAN, JAMES   New Greek and English Lexicon. London, 1831. Second ed., qtr. calf, spine sunned, top and base of backstrip chafed, 8vo. K Books 244-101 1978 £5

DONNELLE, A. J.   Cyclorama of General Custer's Last Fight Against the Sioux Indians,... Boston, 1889. Folding chart, illus., orig. pr. pict wr., water staining, 1st ed. Ginsberg 14-1093 1978 $75

DONNELLY, IGNATIUS   The Great Cryptogram... 1888. 2 vols., orig. red cloth, corners & edges worn, portraits & facsimiles. Eaton 45- 160 1978 £12

DONNELLY, IVON A.   Chinese Junks and Other Native Craft. Shanghai, (1924). First ed., 8vo, good, illus., orig. cloth. Paine 78-44 1978 $17.50

DONNER, ETTA   Hinterland Liberia. London, 1939. Plts, 8vo, orig. cloth, shaken & covers dull. K Books 239-120 1978 £6

DONOHOE, THOMAS   The Iroquois and the Jesuits. Buffalo, 1895. 1st ed., orig. cloth, good. MacManus 239-1159 1978 $35

DONOVAN, EDWARD   An Epitome of the Natural History of the Insects of China. 1798. 4to., 1st issue, hand-coloured plts., stains on two plts., contemp. diced russia. Quaritch 983-320 1978 $3,500

DONOVAN, EDWARD   An Epitome of the Natural History of the Insects of India and the Islands in the Indian Seas... 1800(-04). Roy. 4to., hand-coloured plts., some spotting on a few plts., contemp. quarter mor., uncut, orig. issue. Quaritch 983-321 1978 $3,500

D'OOGE, M. L.   Acropolis of Athens. 1908. Plt., binding slightly dented. Allen 234-283 1978 $12.50

DOOLEY, JOHN   John Dooley, Confederate Soldier. (Washington), Georgetown University Press, 1945. Orig. cloth, portr., 8vo., 1st ed. Morrill 241-115 1978 $15

DOOLITTLE, HILDA   Collected Poems of H.D. New York, 1925. 1st ed., front inner hinge split, spine dull. Biblo BL781-947 1978 $17.50

DOOLITTLE, HILDA   The Flowering of the Rod. 1946. Stiff wraps, very good, first English ed. Bell Book 16-426 1978 £5.50

DOOLITTLE, HILDA   Sea Gardens. London, 1916. 8vo, green boards, uncut, printed at Chiswick Press, 2 small smudges on cover, 1st ed., Collector's cond. Desmarais 1-123 1978 $150

DOOLITTLE, HILDA   Sea Garden. 1916. Covers faded, orig. wraps, backstrip defective, good, scarce, first English ed. Bell Book 16-427 1978 £30

DOOLITTLE, HILDA   Sea Garden. London, 1916. Stiff wrappers, first ed., nice. Rota 212-29 1978 £35

DOORLY, E.   The Insect Man. Cambridge, 1936. Woodcuts by R. Gibbings, cr. 8vo. George's 635-974 1978 £7.50

DOORNINCK, P. N. VAN   Inventaris van het oud Archief der Gemeente Spaarn Woude en Haarlemmerliede, met Lijsten van Schouten en Predikanten. Haarlem, 1894. 8vo., orig. covers. Van der Peet H-64-309 1978 Dfl 35

DOORNINCK, P. N. VAN   Inventaris van het oud Archief der Gemeente Wijk aan Zee en Wijk aan Duin met Lijsten der Schouten, Predikanten, enz. Haarlem, 1899. 8vo., orig. covers. Van der Peet H-64-311 1978 Dfl 35

DORAN, JOHN   In and About Drury Lane. Boston, n.d. Ltd. ed., 2 vols., illus., 8vo., light dampstains on covers, orig. cloth. Morrill 241-664 1978 $7.50

DORAN, JOHN   Memories of Our Great Towns... 1878. 1st. ed., half title, orig. tan calf, gilt borders & coat-of -arms, gilt spine, green label, fine. Jarndyce 16-622 1978 £18

DORAN, JOHN   "Their Majesties' Servants". 1864. First ed., portraits, 2 vols., contemp. full coarse-grained mor. gilt, gilt tops, 8vo. Howes 194-1262 1978 £28

DORAN, JOHN   Their Majesties Servants. 1888. Portraits, wood engravings, 3 vols., imp. 8vo., 2 spines faded. George's 635-1402 1978 £60

DORAN, JOHN   "Their Majesties' Servants". London, 1888. Enlarged ed., 8 vo., orig. gilt stamped yellow cloth, uncut, illus., copper plt. engraved portraits, wood engravings, 3 vols., very good. Houle 10-91 1978 $45

DORCUS, ROY M.   Textbook of Abnormal Psychology. 1939. 2nd ed. Austin 80-1011 1978 $10

DORCUS, ROY M.   Textbook of Abnormal Psychology. Baltimore, 1950. Fourth ed. Rittenhouse 49-225 1976 $10

DORE, J. R.   Old Bibles, an Account of the Early Versions of the English Bible. 1888. 2nd ed., facs., lg. cr. 8vo., spine worn. George's 635-1054 1978 £5.25

DOREMUS, PHILIP   Reminiscences of Montclair. Montclair, 1908. Illus. MacManus 239-1257 1978 $22.50

DOREY, ALICE ANN   Light and Shadow. Toronto, 1949. Card cover, inscribed and signed. Hood 116-817 1978 $7.50

DORFMAN, JOSEPH   The Economic Mind in American Civilization 1606-1865. 1946. Vol. 2, 1st ed. Austin 80-555 1978 $27.50

DORFMAN, JOSEPH   The Economic Mind in American Civilization. New York, 1946. 2 vols. MacManus 239-128 1978 $25

DORGELES, R.   Chez les Beautes aux Dents limees. Paris, n.d. (c. 1930). Rare, 8vo, orig. covers. Van der Peet 127-75 1978 Dfl 30

DORLAND, A. G.   A Hundred Years of Quaker Education in Canada.. 1942. Hood's 115-385 1978 $7.50

DORMER, E. W.   Gray of Reading... 1923. 4to, good. Upcroft 10-294 1978 £12.50

DORNBLASER, THOMAS F.   My Life-Story for Young and Old. N.P., 1930. Cloth, light marginal dampstains on some leaves, pres. copy. Hayman 73-149 1973 $10

DORNBLASER, THOMAS F.   Sabre Strokes of the Pennsylvania Dragoons, in the War of 1861-1865. Philadelphia, 1884. Bell Wiley's copy. Broadfoot 46-361 1978 $27

DORNBURGH, HENRY   Why the Wilderness is Called Adirondack. Glens Falls, 1885. Wr., good. Nestler Rare 78-111 1978 $35

DORNBURGH, HENRY   Why the Wilderness is Called Adirondack. Glens Falls, 1885. Pink prtd. wr., near mint. Butterfield 21-11 1978 $35

DORR, BENJAMIN   Historical Account of Christ Church, Phila.,... 1695-1841; and of St. Peter's and St. James's Until the Separation of the Churches. New York, 1841. Port., cloth. MacManus 239-1616 1978 $15

DORR, RHETA LOUISE (CHILDE)   Susan B. Anthony...The Woman Who Changed the Mind of a Nation. New York, 1928. Illus. Biblo 251-310 1978 $15

DORRANCE, A.   Gardening in the Greenhouse. New York, 1935. 8vo, orig. cloth. Book Chest 17-501 1978 $9

DORRINGTON, THEOPHILUS d. 1715   Observations concerning the present state of Religion in the Romish Church. 1699. Contemp. panelled calf, first ed., 8vo. Howes 194-35 1978 £52

D'ORSAY, LAURENCE   Mistress of Spears. A Tale of the Amazulu. Kansas City, (1930). 1st ed., author's signed pres. Biblo BL781-949 1978 $10

DORSET, CATHARINE ANN   The Peacock "At Home"I or Grand Assemblage of Birds. Philadelphia, 1814. Original English plates, sewn, wrappers rubbed & frayed, incorrectly attributed to "Roscoe" on wrapper and t.p., scarce. Victoria 34-251 1978 $55

DORSEY, GEORGE A.   The Arapaho Sun Dance; the Ceremony of the Offerings Lodge. Chicago, 1903. Wrs., illus., few plts. in color, lacks back cover. Biblo BL781-70 1978 $17.50

DORSEY, GEORGE A.   Traditions of the Shidi Pawnee. New York, 1904. Fine, orig. cloth, scarce. MacManus 239-1160 1978 $40

DORSEY, JOHN MORRIS   The Foundations of Human Nature. 1935. Austin 80-1012 1978 $10

DORSEY, JOHN SYNG   Elements of Surgery. Philadelphia, 1823. Two vols., plts., third ed., slight bend to lower cover on Vol. 2. Rittenhouse 49-228 1976 $30

DORSEY, SARAH A.   Recollections of Henry Watkins Allen, Brig. Gen. CSA, Ex-Gov. of LA. New York, 1866. Bell Wiley's copy. Broadfoot 46-77 1978 $30

DORSON, RICHARD M.   America Begins. New York, (1950). Fine, d.w., illus. Biblo 247-39 1978 $15

DOS PASSOS, JOHN   Adventures of a Young Man. New York, (1939). 1st ed., covers faded, spotted. Biblo 251-461 1978 $10

DOS PASSOS, JOHN   The Big Money. New York, 1936. 16mo, blue cloth, stated 1st ed., spine slightly faded, near Fine. Desmarais 1-126 1978 $15

DOS PASSOS, JOHN   First Encounter. New York, n.d. (ca. 1945). 1st ed., d.w. Biblo 251-462 1978 $15

DOS PASSOS, JOHN   The 42nd Parallel. New York, 1930. 8vo, marbled boards, cloth back, spine label darkened and somewhat chipped, stated 1st ed., nice, collector's cond. Desmarais 1-125 1978 $17.50

DOS PASSOS, JOHN   Manhattan Transfer. New York, (1946). 12mo., 1st Penguin paperback ed., orig. wrs. Biblo 251-463 1978 $7.50

DOS PASSOS, JOHN   1919. 1932. First ed., good. Austin 82-1162 1978 $20

DOS PASSOS, JOHN   One Man's Initiation---1917. London, (1920). Orig. cloth, d.j., a little torn, 1st ed., 1,250 copies printed, very nice. MacManus 238-633 1978 $150

DOS PASSOS, JOHN   Orient Express. 1927. Blue cloth backstrip, pink bds., backstrip faded and bds. faded, else v.g., first ed., illus. in color. Austin 82-1164 1978 $35

DOS PASSOS, JOHN   Streets of Night. 1923. First ed., v.g. Austin 82-1165 1978 $35

DOS PASSOS, JOHN   Three Soldiers. New York, (1921). Orange-stamped black cloth, top edges stained orange, 1st ed., 1st state, fine & bright in scarce dust jacket. Bradley 49-80 1978 $60

DOSKER, HENRY   Levensschets Van Rev. A. C. Van Raalte, D. D. 1893. Frontis., in Dutch. Austin 79-211 1978 $75

DOSSIE, R.   The Handmaid to the Arts, Teaching. I... 1764. 2 vols., 8vo., contemp. calf, repaired. Quaritch 983-175 1978 $190

DOSTOEVSKY, AIMEE   Fyodor Dostoevsky: A Study. 1921. First ed., orig. cloth, 8vo. Howes 194-811 1978 £6

DOSTOEVSKY, FYODOR   The Grand Inquisitor. N.P., (London), 1930. 8vo., full vellum, 1st ed., 1 of 300 no. copies, vellum warping. J.S. Lawrence 38-L31 1978 $100

DOSTOEVSKY, FYODOR   Poor Folk. 1894. Sm. 8vo., orig. yellow cloth stamped in black, cover dust soiled, first English ed. Howes 194-810 1978 £15

DOTY, LOCKWOOD L.   History of Livingston County...from Its Earliest Traditions, to Its Part in the War for Our Union. Geneseo, 1876. Engr. portrs., orig. cloth, rubbed along edges, good sound copy. Butterfield 21-252 1978 $65

DOTY, LOCKWOOD L.   A History of the Big Tree Treaty. (Dansville, 1897). Plts., orig. cloth, scarce. Butterfield 21-253 1978 $25

DOTY, WILLIAM J.   The Historic Annals of Southwestern New York. 3 vols., lg. 4tos., illus., very fine. MacManus 239-1099 1978 $75

DOUBLEDAY, ABNER   Chancellorsville and Gettysburg. New York, 1892. Bell Wiley's copy. Broadfoot 46-79 1978 $10

DOUBLEDAY, ABNER   Reminiscences of Forts Sumter & Moultrie in 1860-61. New York, 1876. Bell Wiley's copy. Broadfoot 46-78 1978 $18

DOUBLEDAY, ABNER   Reminiscences of Forts Sumter and Moultrie in 1860-'61. New York, 1876. Frontis., map, 8vo., ex-lib., 1st ed., orig. cloth. Morrill 241-116 1978 $12.50

DOUCET, R.   Les Institutions de la France au XVIe siecle. 1948. 2 vols., binder's buckram, spines faded. George's 635-627 1978 £6.50

D'OUDEGHERST, P.   Les Chroniques et Annales de Flandres: Contenant les Heroiques et Tres Victorieux Exploicts des Forestiers, & Comtes de Flandres. Anvers, 1571. 8vo., full brown calf, lace-work border on both sides, richly gilt tooled, scarce, signed binding by De Samelany & J. Weckesser, very fine, attractive binding. Van der Peet H-64-514 1978 Dfl 1450

DOUGAL, WM. H.   Off for California: The Letters, Log and Sketches of William H. Dougal, Gold Rush Artist... Oakland, 1949. Illus., folding plates, long 8vo cloth, 1st ed., limited to 600 copies. Ginsberg 14-106 1978 $35

DOUGHERTY, RAYMOND PHILIP   Records from Erech. 1920. Autographed texts, plts., ex-lib., backstrip worn, otherwise good. Austin 80-1013 1978 $47.50

DOUGHTY, ARTHUR GEORGE   Cheadle's Journal of a Trip Across Canada, 1862-63. Ottawa, 1931. Orig. ed., fold. map, illus. Hood 116-847 1978 $45

DOUGHTY, ARTHUR GEORGE   Documents Relating to the Constitutional History of Canada, 1819-1828. Ottawa, 1935. Card cover. Hood's 115-7 1978 $40

DOUGHTY, ARTHUR GEORGE   The King's Book of Quebec. Ottawa, 1911. 2 vols., plts., some coloured, fold. map, card covers. Hood 116-520 1978 $55

DOUGHTY, CHARLES MONTAGU   The Dawn in Britain. London, 1943. Tall 8vo., blue cloth, gilt lettering on spine and cover, new ed. in 1 vol., fine lightly worn d.w., no. 304 of 535 copies. Desmarais 1-127 1978 $25

DOUGHTY, CHARLES MONTAGU   Mansoul or the Riddle of the World. London, 1920. Fine, chipped d.w. Desmarais B-189 1978 $20

DOUGHTY, CHARLES MONTAGU   Travels in Arabia Deserta. London, 1921. 8vo., green gilt stamped cloth, 2 vols., 1st ed., unopened, uncut, fine, orig. maps, plans and charts, laid in holograph postcard. Desmarais 1-129 1978 $300

DOUGHTY, CHARLES MONTAGU   Travels in Arabia Deserta. London, 1936 (1943). New ed., 2 vols., maps, plts., 4to., nice, d.w., orig. cloth. K Books 244-355 1978 £35

DOUGHTY, CHARLES MONTAGU   Travels in Arabia Deserta. New York, n.d. 16mo., gilt stamped blue cloth, thin-paper ed., 1 vol., complete and unabridged, badly torn d.w. and box, 1st ed., collector's cond. Desmarais 1-130 1978 $25

DOUGHTY, DOROTHY   The American Birds of... 1962. Ltd. to 1500 copies, 4to, subscribers ed., fine copy in slip box. Baldwins' 51-58 1978 $200

DOUGHTY, WILLIAM H.   The Physical Geography of the North Pacific Ocean,... Augusta, 1867. Original printed wr., inscribed presentation copy from author. Ginsberg 14-343 1978 $100

DOUGLAS, ALFRED BRUCE   Collected Poems. 1919. Sm. 8vo., 1st ed., portr. frontis., orig. cloth, back slightly darkened, pres. inscr. by Alfred Douglas, A.L.s. loosely inserted. Quaritch 979-346 1978 $75

DOUGLAS, ALFRED BRUCE   In Excelsis. 1924. Very good, d.w., first English ed. Bell Book 16-268 1978 £4.50

DOUGLAS, ALFRED BRUCE   In Excelsis. 1924. 1st. ed., 8vo, orig. cloth, d.w., pres. copy from author, inscription on f/l. Sawyer 299-119 1978 £65

DOUGLAS, ALFRED BRUCE   Lyrics. 1935. First ed., portrait, 8vo., d.j. George's 635-1313 1978 £5

DOUGLAS, ALFRED BRUCE   My Friendship with Oscar Wilde. New York, 1932. Fine copy, light foxing, d.w. chipped & lightly soiled. Desmarais B-666 1978 $35

DOUGLAS, ALFRED BRUCE   Sonnets. 1909. Orog. bds., uncut, binding trifle soiled, 8vo., second ed. Howes 194-812 1978 £7

DOUGLAS, ALFRED BRUCE   Sonnets. 1935. First ed., frontis., 8vo., d.j. George's 635-1314 1978 £5.25

DOUGLAS, C. H.   Social Credit. New York, 1933. Rev'd. 2nd ed. Hood 116-346 1978 $20

DOUGLAS, GEORGE A. H.   Sir William Wallace, and Other Poems. Glasgow, (1877?). 1st. & only ed., 8vo, orig. blue cloth, gilt, nice copy. Fenning 32-92 1978 £10.50

DOUGLAS, JAMES   The History of the Lateral Operation.... London, 1726. 4to., bds., first ed. Gurney 75-33 1978 £80

DOUGLAS, JAMES   New England and New France: Contrasts and Parallels in Colonial History. New York, 1913. Illus., maps. MacManus 239-129 1978 $25

DOUGLAS, JAMES   Old France in the New World. Cleveland/London, 1906. Second ed., illus., orig. binding. Wolfe 39-134 1978 $20

DOUGLAS, JOHN   A Letter Addressed to Two Great Men, on the Prospect of Peace; and on the Terms Necessary to be Insisted Upon in the Negociation. London, 1760. 3/4 leather, mottled bds. Hood 116-118 1978 $85

DOUGLAS, JOHN   Select Works. Salisbury, 1820. Portrait, thk. 4to., contemp. straight grained mor., gilt edges, portrait and title browned. Howes 194-250 1978 £30

DOUGLAS, M.   Across Greeland's Ice-Fields; the Adventures of Nansen and Peary on the Great Ice-Cap. London, Edinburgh, 1897. Illus., dec. hard cover. Hood 116-76 1978 $15

DOUGLAS, M.   The Frozen North. Boston, n.d. Illus. with maps, coloured plts. & engrs., decor. cover. Hood 117-92 1978 $30

DOUGLAS, M.   The White North, with Nordenskiold, De Long and Nansen. London, 1899. B/W plts. Hood 117-93 1978 $25

DOUGLAS, NEIL   Lavinia, a poem; and an Asiatic Petition. Edinburgh, 1799. 8vo, disbound, 1st ed., uncommon. Ximenes 47-79 1978 $50

DOUGLAS, NORMAN   Birds and Beasts of the Greek Anthology. (Florence), 1927. One of 500 copies, unnumbered & unsigned, author's annotated copy, patterned bds., manuscript corrections, first ed. Rota 212-15 1978 £350

DOUGLAS, NORMAN   Capri. Florence, 1930. One of 103 copies on Binda handmade paper, portrait of the author, signed by author, plts., 4to., orig. blue linen, leather label, internally a very nice, unopened copy, first English ed. Bell Book 16-269 1978 £75

DOUGLAS, NORMAN   Contributions to an Avifauna of Baden. London, 1894. Reprinted, orig. binding, sewn, nice. Rota 212-14 1978 £200

DOUGLAS, NORMAN   D. H. Lawrence and Maurice Magnus. 1924. 1st. ed., 1st. issue, beige paper wrappers, spine unlettered, v.g. Jarndyce 16-1223 1978 £15

DOUGLAS, NORMAN   D.H. Lawrence and Maurice Magnus: A Plea for Better Manners. (Florence), 1924. 12mo., wrs., 1st ed., 1st issue, bookplt. J.S. Lawrence 38-L135 1978 $65

DOUGLAS, NORMAN   D.H. Lawrence and Maurice Magnus: A Plea for Better Manners. (Florence), 1924. 12mo., wrs., 1st ed., 1st issue, worn along front hinge. J.S. Lawrence 38-L136 1978 $55

DOUGLAS, NORMAN   D. H. Lawrence and Maurice Magnus: A Plea for Better Manners. (Florence), 1924. 12mo., wrs., 1st ed., 1st issue, fine. J.S. Lawrence 38-L134 1978 $75

DOUGLAS, NORMAN   D. H. Lawrence and Maurice Magnus: A Plea for Better Manners. Florence, 1924, (1925). 8vo., tan pr. wr., 1st ed., partially unopened, near Mint, inscribed. Desmarais 1-131 1978 $65

DOUGLAS, NORMAN   D.H. Lawrence and Maurice Magnus: A Plea for Better Manners. (Florence), 1925. 8vo., wrs., 1st ed., 2nd issue, unopened, fine. J.S. Lawrence 38-L137 1978 $35

DOUGLAS, NORMAN   D.H. Lawrence and Maurice Magnus: A Plea for Better Manners. (Florence), 1925. 8vo., wrs., 1st ed., 2nd issue. J.S. Lawrence 38-L138 1978 $15

DOUGLAS, NORMAN   D. H. Lawrence and Maurice Magnus. 1925. Wrs., scarce. Biblo BL781-951 1978 $32.50

DOUGLAS, NORMAN   Experiments. London, 1925. 8vo, red cloth, d.w. darkened and chipped top and bottom, 1st English ed., collector's cond. Desmarais 1-132 1978 $75

DOUGLAS, NORMAN   How About Europe? 1930. Near fine, first English ed. Bell Book 17-284 1978 £5.50

DOUGLAS, NORMAN   In the Beginning. 1927. 8vo., 1st ed., decor. bds., light foxing, near fine, orig. glassine d.w. repaired, ltd. to 700 copies numbered & signed by author. Quaritch 979-127 1978 $70

DOUGLAS, NORMAN   In the Beginning. London, 1927. Orig. bds., 1st ed., ltd. to 750 signed copies, spine a bit worn. MacManus 238-634 1978 $60

DOUGLAS, NORMAN   In the Beginning. 1928. Fine, d.w., first English ed. Bell Book 16-271 1978 £12.50

DOUGLAS, NORMAN   Late Harvest. London, 1946. 8vo, red cloth, gilt stamped, covers slightly warped, d.w. chipped at bottom of spine, 1st ed., collector's cond. Desmarais 1-133 1978 $25

DOUGLAS, NORMAN   London Street Games. London, 1916. 8vo, tan buckram, t.e.g., uncut, unopened, unusually Fine, 1 of 500 copies, 1st ed. Desmarais 1-134 1978 $70

DOUGLAS, NORMAN   London Street Games. 1931. 2nd. ed., d.w., fine. Jarndyce 16-1218 1978 £6.50

DOUGLAS, NORMAN   Looking Back. 1934. 1st. 1 vol. ed., d.w., rubbed & price cut out, good. Jarndyce 16-1221 1978 £14

DOUGLAS, NORMAN   Looking Back. London, 1934. First trade ed., orig. binding, nice. Rota 211-90 1978 £7.50

DOUGLAS, NORMAN   Nerinda. Florence, 1929. One of 475 copies numbered & signed by author, roy. 8vo., bds., leather labels, near fine in slipcase. Bell Book 16-272 1978 £55

DOUGLAS, NORMAN   One Day. 1929. 1st. ed., brown bds., head and tail of spine shade bumped, verge paper ed., no. 209 of 500. Jarndyce 16-1224 1978 £20

DOUGLAS, NORMAN   One Day. France, Hours Press, 1929. 1 of 200 signed copies on velin de rives paper, sm. 4to., orig. lea. covers, some fading, pic. endpapers, illus., very good. Americanist 103-31 1978 $60

DOUGLAS, NORMAN   One Day. Hours Press, 1929. One of 300 numbered copies on Verge de Vidalon paper, puce colored bds. Battery Park 1-170 1978 $150

DOUGLAS, NORMAN   Paneros. 1921. No. 294 of 650 copies, portrait, qtr. buckram, t.e.g., fine, d.w., first English ed. Bell Book 16-274 1978 £22.50

DOUGLAS, NORMAN   Paneros. London, 1931. 1st. ed., 650 numbered copies, portrait, roy. 8vo, dec. bds., buckram spine faded. Traylen 88-229 1978 £30

DOUGLAS, NORMAN   Some Limericks. N.P., 1929. 8vo, grey cloth boards, red lettering, top edges stained yellow, 2nd Continental ed., no. 288 of 1,000 copies, collector's cond. Desmarais 1-135 1978 $75

DOUGLAS, NORMAN   South Wind. New York, 1928. New ed., coloured plts. by Valenti Angelo, roy. 8vo, black cloth gilt, very good. Bell Book 17-285 1978 £18.50

DOUGLAS, NORMAN   South Wind. Chicago, 1929. New ed., coloured frontispieces, plts., 2 vols., roy. 8vo, buckram gilt, fine, unopened, sl. chipped d.w., worn slipcase. Bell Book 17-286 1978 £65

DOUGLAS, NORMAN   Summer Islands. 1931. 1st. ed., paper label on spine slightly rubbed, spine slightly sunned, good. Jarndyce 16-1222 1978 £6.50

DOUGLAS, NORMAN   Summer Islands: Ischia and Ponza. London, 1931. One of 500 numbered copies, first ed., orig. binding, head and foot of spine faded, nice, torn d.w. Rota 211-89 1978 £15

DOUGLAS, NORMAN   Summer Islands: Ischia and Ponza. Harmsworth, 1931. No. 107 of 500 numbered copies, frontis., spine faded, very good, first English ed. Bell Book 17-287 1978 £25

DOUGLAS, NORMAN   Summer Islands: Ischia and Ponza. 1931. Near fine, worn d.w., first English ed. Bell Book 16-275 1978 £15

DOUGLAS, NORMAN   Summer Islands: Ischia and Ponza. London, n.d. (1931). 8vo, original blue cloth, printed paper label, dust jacket, 1st ed., one of 500 numbered copies, frontispiece; extra label tipped-in, fine copy. Ximenes 47-80 1978 $50

DOUGLAS, NORMAN   They Went. 1920. Very good, first English ed. Bell Book 17-288 1978 £18.50

DOUGLAS, NORMAN   They Went. 1920. 1st. ed., orig. cloth, spine faded & covers slightly marked. Eaton 45-163 1978 £5

DOUGLAS, NORMAN   Together. 1923. 1st. ed., red cloth, slightly marked & spine little sunned, some light foxing. Jarndyce 16-1220 1978 £8

DOUGLAS, NORMAN   Together. 1923. 1st. ed., cloth, inscription on f.e.p., good. Eaton 45-164 1978 £12

DOUGLAS, R.   Nipigon to Winnipeg; a Canoe Voyage Through Western Ontario by Edward Umfreville in 1784. Ottawa, 1929. Card cover. Hood 116-733 1978 $22.50

DOUGLAS, R.   Twenty Years of York Factory, 1694-1714, Jeremie's Account of Hudson Strait and Bay. Ottawa, 1926. Illus., maps. Hood 116-573 1978 $30

DOUGLAS, R. K.   Catalogue of Chinese Printed Books, Manuscripts and Drawings. London, 1877. Roy. 4to., orig. cloth. Forster 130-197 1978 £15

DOUGLAS, R. K.   Catalogue of Japanese Printed Books and Manuscripts; Supplement 1899-1903. London, 1898-1904. 2 vols., roy. 4to., orig. cloth. Forster 130-198 1978 £25

DOUGLAS, ROBERT B.   The Chevalier de Pontgibaud. A French Volunteer in the War of Independence. Paris, 1898. Cloth, 2nd ed. Hayman 72-617 1978 $12.50

DOUGLAS, STEPHEN A.   Popular Sovereignty in the Territories. New York, 1859. 8vo., unbound. Morrill 241-118 1978 $10

DOUGLAS, STEPHEN A.   Popular Sovereignty in the Territories...Federal and Local Authority. New York, 1859. Disbound. Hayman 73-287 1978 $7.50

DOUGLAS, THOMAS, EARL OF SELKIRK
Please turn to
SELKIRK, THOMAS DOUGLAS, EARL OF

DOUGLAS, W.   Duelling in the Army. London, 1887. 8vo., cloth, binding poor & worn. Van der Peet H-64-312 1978 Dfl 40

DOUGLAS, WILLIAM   Freemasonry in Manitoba, 1864-1925. Winnipeg, 1925. Illus. Hood's 115-997 1978 $25

DOUGLAS-LITHGOW, R. A.   Nantucket, a History. New York, 1914. Map, illus. MacManus 239-1040 1978 $17.50

DOUGLASS, BENJAMIN   History of Wayne County, Ohio, from the Days of the Pioneers and First Settlers to the Present Time. Indianapolis, 1878. Leather, nice. Hayman 72-587 1978 $65

DOUGLASS, FREDERICK   Oration, Delivered in Corinthian Hall, Rochester ...July 5th, 1852. Rochester, 1852. Wr., clean, sound, near fine copy. Butterfield 21-235 1978 $175

DOUGLASS, HARL ROY   American Public Education. 1948. Austin 30-1014 1978 $10

DOUMER, P.   l'Indo-Chine francaise (Souvenirs). Paris, 1905. 4to, frontisp., plts., colored map, orig. covers. Van der Peet 127-76 1978 Dfl 75

DOUMER, P.   Situation de l'Indo-Chine (1897-1901). Hanoi, 1902. Large 8vo, half blue mor., num. tables. Van der Peet 127-77 1978 Dfl 85

DOURISBOURE, L'ABBE P.   Les Sauvages Ba-Hnars (Cochinchine orientale). Paris, 1929. Ports., plts., 8vo, orig. covers. Van der Peet 127-78 1978 Dfl 45

DOVE, KARL   Das Klima des Aussertropischen Sudafrika. Gottingen, 1888. Amateur half cloth, 8vo, folding maps. K Books 239-122 1978 £12

DOVE, P. E.   Domesday Studies; being the papers read at the meetings of the Domesday Commemoration, 1886. 1888-91. 2 vols., 4to., map. Upcroft 12-113 1978 £25

DOVER, ROBERT 1575-1641 Annalia Dubrensia. Cheltenham, 1878. Plts., sm. 4to., contemp. cloth, gilt edges. Howes 194-813 1978 £15

DOVES PRESS Catalogue Raisonne of Books Printed and Published at the Doves Press 1900-1911. (Hammersmith), 1911. Orig. linen-backed bds. Americanist 102-42 1978 $150

DOW, CHARLES MASON Anthology and Bibliography of Niagara Falls. Albany, 1921. Illus., 2 vols., 8vo. Morrill 239-561 1978 $15

DOW, CHARLES MASON Anthology and Bibliography of Niagara Falls. Albany, 1921. 2 vols. Butterfield 21-303 1978 $12.50

DOW, GEORGE FRANCIS Every Day Life in the Massachusetts Bay Colony. Boston, 1935. Illus., limited to 100 copies, very good. Nestler Rare 78-195 1978 $48

DOW, GEORGE FRANCIS The Pirates of the New England Coast, 1630-1730. Salem, 1923. 1st ed., illus. MacManus 239-1751 1978 $60

DOW, GEORGE FRANCIS Slave Ships and Slaving. Salem, 1927. 50 plts., roy. 8vo, covers dull, orig. cloth. K Books 239-123 1978 £15

DOW, GEORGE FRANCIS Slave Ships and Slaving. Salem, 1927. 1st ed., 4to., illus., plts., orig. cloth-backed marbled bds., pub. box, fine copy, 1 of 97 copies printed on rag paper. MacManus 239-1750 1978 $225

DOW, GEORGE FRANCIS Whale Ships and Whaling. Salem, 1925. Baldwins' 51-507 1978 $67.50

DOW, LORENZO The Dealings of God, Man, and the Devil as Exemplified in the Life, Experience, and Travels of... Norwich, 1833. Orig. calf. MacManus 239-130 1978 $40

DOW, LORENZO History of Cosmopolite: Or The Writings of Rev. Lorenzo Dow... Cincinnati, 1849. 6th. ed., new clean, rebound. Hayman 71-186 1978 $12.50

DOWDING, C. V. Book of Practical Television. London, 1935. 8vo., plts., text-illus., cloth. Quaritch 977-215 1978 $35

DOWELL, BENJAMIN F. The Petition of B. F. Dowell and Others Asking Pay for Two Companies of Oregon Volunteers and Their Expenses,.... Jacksonville, 1869. Orig. pict. pr. wr. Ginsberg 14-814 1978 $225

DOWELL, S. A History of Taxation and Taxes in England from the Earliest Times to the Present Day. 1884. 4 vols., covers faded, 8vo. George's 635-315 1978 £15

DOWLING, ROBERT The Mystery of Killard. 1879. 1st. ed., 3 vols., half titles, orig. olive cloth, black & gilt imprint, v.g. Jarndyce 16-623 1978 £45

DOWNES, RANDOLPH C. Council Fires on the Upper Ohio. Pittsburgh, 1940. Illus. MacManus 239-1161 1978 $17.50

DOWNEY, FAIRFAX Indian Fighting Army. New York, 1941. 1st. ed., top & bottom spine rubbed, illus. from drawings by Frederic Remington. Baldwins' 51-559 1978 $25

DOWNEY, FAIRFAX Portrait Of An Era As Drawn By C. D. Gibson. New York & London, 1936. 1st ed., illus., d.j., very good or better. Limestone 9-119 1978 $25

DOWNEY, JUNE E. The Kingdom of the Mind. 1927. 1st ed. in frayed dust jacket, illus. Austin 80-1015 1978 $12.50

DOWNEY, JUNE E. The Will Temperment and Its Testing. 1923. 1st ed. Austin 80-1016 1978 $20

DOWNEY, S. W. Prospectus of the Wyoming Central Land and Improvement Company. St. Louis, 1884. Orig. pr. wr., 1st ed. Ginsberg 14-1075 1978 $175

THE DOWNFALL of Henry Ward Beecher. New York, (1874). Uncut, orig. pict. yellow wr. Butterfield 21-482a 1978 $35

DOWNIE, WILLIAM Hunting for Gold:.... San Francisco, 1893. Illus., original cloth, 1st ed. Ginsberg 14-344 1978 $85

DOWNING, ANDREW JACKSON The Architecture of Country Houses. New York, 1852. Illus., orig. cloth, neatly recased. George's 635-80 1978 £25

DOWNING, ANDREW JACKSON The Fruits and Fruit Trees of America.... New York, 1847. Illus., orig. cloth, fine. MacManus 239-15 1978 $25

DOWNING, ANDREW JACKSON The Horticulturist, and Journal of Rural Art and Taste. Albany, July 1846-December 1852. 7 vols., signed & unsigned writings, illus., orig. cloth, some chipping, library numbers on spines, good sound set. Butterfield 21-155 1978 $150

DOWNING, ANDREW JACKSON A Treatise on the Theory and Practice of Landscape Gardening, Adapted to North America. New York, 1853. 5th ed., illus., 8vo., foxed, binding faded, orig. cloth. Morrill 241-666 1978 $27.50

DOWNING, HARRIET Mary; or Female Friendship: A Poem. 1816. 1st. ed., 4to, half title, uncut, orig. brown bds., paper spine, label, hinges little weak, otherwise v.g. Jarndyce 16-624 1978 £32

DOWNING, JACK My Thirty Years Out of the Senate. New York, 1859. Illus. by J. H. Howard, 1st ed., 12mo., pres. incrip. to W. W. Seaton from the author, fr. cover soiled & faded, text intact. Current 24-104 1978 $145

DOWNS, E. C. Four Years a Scout and Spy. Zanesville, 1866. Cloth, some wear, 1st ed. Hayman 73-105 1978 $27.50

DOWSE, THOMAS STRETCH Neuralgia. 1880. Austin 80-1017 1978 $27.50

DOWSETT, H. M. Wireless Telephony and Broadcasting. London, 1923. 2 vols., plts., charts, text-illus., roy. 8vo., orig. cloth. K Books 244-103 1978 £16

DOWSON, ERNEST Decorations; in verse and prose. London, 1899. Orig. white parchment, covers just a little marked, internally nice, preserved in cloth folder and slipcase, scarce, first ed. Rota 212-16 1978 £55

DOWSON, ERNEST Dilemmas. Stories and Studies in Sentiment. London, 1895. Orig. cloth, 1st ed., covers stained. MacManus 238-212 1978 $50

DOWSON, ERNEST The Pierrot of the Minute. New York, The Grolier Club, 1923. 1 of 300 copies, prtd. on Antique laid paper, thin 12mo., marbled paper over bds., boxed. Battery Park 1-22 1978 $175

DOWSON, ERNEST The Pierrot of the Minute. New York, Grolier Club, 1923. 1 of 300 copies, orig. flexible marbled bds., 8vo., very good. Americanist 103-138 1978 $50

DOY, JOHN The Narrative of...of Lawrence, Kansas. New York, 1860. Orig. front wr. bound in half calf, 1st ed., inscribed by author. Ginsberg 14-442 1978 $200

DOYLE, ARTHUR CONAN Adventures of Gerard. London, n.d. (1903). 1st ed., very good, bookplt., signature on flyleaf. MacManus 238-214 1978 $65

DOYLE, ARTHUR CONAN The Adventures of Sherlock Holmes. New York, (1950). Near mint, slipcase. Bernard 5-84 1978 $20

DOYLE, ARTHUR CONAN The Great Boer War. London, 1901. 10th impression, maps, backstrip faded, orig. cloth, 8vo. K Books 239-124A 1978 £5

DOYLE, ARTHUR CONAN The Great Boer War. London, 1902. Complete ed., 8vo, orig. cloth, maps. K Books 239-124B 1978 £7

DOYLE, ARTHUR CONAN The Great Shadow and Beyond the City. Bristol, n.d. Illus. by James Greig and Paul Hardy, very good, first English ed. Bell Book 17-289 1978 £16.50

DOYLE, ARTHUR CONAN His Last Bow: some reminiscences of Sherlock Holmes. 1917. Covers faded, lower joint split, good, first English ed. Bell Book 17-290 1978 £26.50

DOYLE, ARTHUR CONAN His Last Bow. 1917. Near fine copy, first English ed. Bell Book 16-980 1978 £45

DOYLE, ARTHUR CONAN   The Hound of the Baskervilles. London, 1902. First ed., plts., orig. cloth, nice, 8vo. K Books 244-74 1978 £125

DOYLE, ARTHUR CONAN   The Land of Mist. New York, 1926. Good or better. Bernard 5-85 1978 $12.50

DOYLE, ARTHUR CONAN   The Last Galley. 1911. Plts. in colour, cloth, some foxing, good, first English ed. Bell Book 16-276 1978 £8.50

DOYLE, ARTHUR CONAN   The Refugees. New York, 1893. 1st Am. ed., illus., orig. blue cloth, very good. Greene 78-34 1978 $30

DOYLE, ARTHUR CONAN   Rodney Stone. London, 1896. 8vo, blue cloth, gilt lettering, illus., front and rear hinge started, uncut, 1st ed., collector's cond. Desmarais 1-136 1978 $50

DOYLE, ARTHUR CONAN   Rodney Stone. 1896. Plts., front hinge weak, good, first English ed. Bell Book 16-278 1978 £15

DOYLE, ARTHUR CONAN   Round the Fire Stories. 1908. Pict. cloth, covers damp-mottled, else good, first English ed. Bell Book 16-279 1978 £12.50

DOYLE, ARTHUR CONAN   Round the Red Lamp: facts and fancies of medical life. 1894. Covers little dull, very good, first English ed. Bell Book 16-280 1978 £15

DOYLE, ARTHUR CONAN   The Sign of Four. 1894. New ed., orig. blue cloth blocked in black & gilt, good copy. Jarndyce 16-625 1978 £10.50

DOYLE, ARTHUR CONAN   Sir Nigel. 1906. First ed., plts., cr. 8vo., orig. cloth, spine faded. Howes 194-815 1978 £6

DOYLE, ARTHUR CONAN   The Speckled Band: an adventure of Sherlock Holmes. 1912. First acting ed., very good, wraps. Bell Book 16-281 1978 £4.50

DOYLE, ARTHUR CONAN   The Stark Munro Letters. 1895. 1st ed., half title, frontis., orig. dark green cloth, lettering gilt, very good. Jarndyce 16-626 1978 £18.50

DOYLE, ARTHUR CONAN   The Stark Munro Letters. 1895. First ed., frontis., cr. 8vo., orig. dark green cloth, nice. Howes 194-816 1978 £12

DOYLE, ARTHUR CONAN   The Stark Munro Letters. 1895. Frontis., good, first English ed. Bell Book 17-291 1978 £15

DOYLE, ARTHUR CONAN   The Stark Munro Letters. London, 1895. Illus., orig. cloth, 1st ed., spine slightly frayed, otherwise fine. MacManus 238-213 1978 $35

DOYLE, ARTHUR CONAN   Through the Magic Door. 1907. Plts., pict. cloth, good, first English ed. Bell Book 16-282 1978 £10

DOYLE, ARTHUR CONAN   The Tragedy of the Korosko. London, 1898. 1st ed., illus., gilt decorative red pictorial cloth, very good or better. Limestone 9-91 1978 $35

DOYLE, ARTHUR CONAN   Uncle Bernac: a memory of the Empire. 1897. Plts., cloth, good, first English ed. Bell Book 16-283 1978 £6.50

DOYLE, ARTHUR CONAN   The White Company. London, 1905. 26th ed., illus., cr. 8vo., prize calf gilt. K Books 244-73 1978 £7

DOYLE, ARTHUR CONAN   Works... New York, (1902). Author's ed., 1 of 1,000 numbered sets, 13 vols., uncut, t.e.g., slightly rubbed. Americanist 102-43 1978 $125

DOYLE, ARTHUR CONAN   Works. 1903. Plts., 12 vols., orig. salmon silk cloth, gilt tops, ed. ltd. to 1,000 numbered sets signed by author, 8vo. Howes 194-814 1978 £75

DOYLE, BERNARD   Comb Making In America. 1925. Privately printed, 4to. Baldwins' 51-59 1978 $22.50

DOYLE, JAMES E.   A Chronicle of England, B.C. 55-A.D. 1485. London, 1864. 1st ed., color illus., engraved and printed by Edmund Evans, thick quarto, orig. John Leighton binding, blocked in gold on covers and spine, edges lightly rubbed, inner hinge cracked, text very fine. Victoria 34-252 1978 $150

DOYLE, JOHN H.   A Story of Early Toledo. Bowling Green, (1919). Cloth, ex-lib., not a bad copy. Hayman 73-550 1978 $10

DOYLE, RICHARD   The Foreign Tour of Messrs. Brown, Jones & Robinson. n.d. (1854). 1st. ed., half title, orig. maroon cloth, gilt imprint, lacks leading free endpaper. Jarndyce 16-627 1978 £22

DOYLE, RICHARD   Manners and Customs of ye Englyshe. 1849. Plts. by R. Doyle, 2 vols. in 1, oblong imp. 8vo., full mor. gilt rubbed. George's 635-137 1978 £15

DOZY, G. J.   De Familie Dozy. den Haag, 1911. Lg. 8vo., cloth, portr., text illus., illus. on plts., front cover discolored. Van der Peet H-64-313 1978 Dfl 45

DRAFT ELECTRIC LIGHT CO.   The Draft System of Electrical Railway Propulsion. Marion, (1888). Oblong 8vo, fine illus., front cover loose. Baldwins' 51-373 1978 $50

DRAKE, CHARLES D.   Address of Charles D. Drake, on the Birthday of Washington. N.P., n.d. (St. Louis, 1862?). Sewed. Hayman 71-188 1978 $10

DRAKE, CHARLES D.   Please Circulate. The Veto Power: Its Nature and History; the Danger to the Country from Its Exercise, and the True Position of Parties and Presidential Candidates in Relation to It. (Washington, 1848). Unbound as issued. Hayman 72-628 1978 $15

DRAKE, DANIEL   Pioneer Life in Kentucky. A Series, of Reminiscental Letters from...M.D. of Cincinnati to His Children... Cincinnati, 1870. 1st ed., cloth, frontis. MacManus 239-1817 1978 $50

DRAKE, DANIEL   A Systematic Treatise. Cincinnatti, 1850. Thick 8vo., maps, modern tan lea., gilt lettered, ownership inscr., maps lightly browned, unusually well-preserved copy, 1st ed. Zeitlin 245-65 1978 $275

DRAKE, FRANCIS S.   Dictionary of American Biography... Boston, 1879. Thick 4to, scarce, orig. cloth, some wear. MacManus 239-131 1978 $30

DRAKE, FRANCIS S.   Tea Leaves: Being a Collection of Letters and Documents Relating to the Shipment of Tea to the American Colonies in the Year 1773. Boston, 1884. Illus., fine. MacManus 239-563 1978 $35

DRAKE, H. B.   Korea of the Japanese. London, (1930). Cloth, faded, hinges weak, plts. Dawson's 127-212 1978 $17.50

DRAKE, JOSEPH RODMAN   The Culprit Fay and other Poems. New York, 1835. 4to, orig. brown cloth, covers worn and faded, foxing, frontis. loose, 1st ed., collector's cond. Desmarais 1-137 1978 $40

DRAKE, JOSEPH RODMAN   The Culprit Fay and Other Poems. Grolier Club, 1923. Frontis., portr., illus. by E. E. Winchell, 8vo., 1 of 300 copies on English handmade paper, bound in Japanese paper bds. with parchment paper spine. Battery Park 1-148 1978 $75

DRAKE, M.   A History of English Glass-Painting... 1912. Folio, plain and coloured plts., half parchment, sl. soiled. Quaritch 983-100 1978 $145

DRAKE, NATHAN   Noontide Leisure... 1824. 1st. ed., 2 vols., half titles, half maroon morocco, spines gilt, but rubbed. Jarndyce 16-628 1978 £15

DRAKE, NATHAN   Shakespeare and his Times. 1817. First ed., frontis., 2 vols., 4to., uncut, orig. bds., rebacked with cloth. Howes 194-1446 1978 £32

DRAKE, ST. CLAIR   Black Metropolis. New York, (1945). Biblo 251-63 1978 $15

DRAKE, SAMUEL ADAMS   The Benefactors of the World. Chicago, (1902). Cloth. Hayman 73-150 1978 $7.50

DRAKE, SAMUEL ADAMS   The Heart of the White Mountains Their Legend and Scenery. New York, 1882. Illus. by W. H. Gibson, lg. 4to, orig. pic. cloth, fine. MacManus 239-330 1978 $30

DRAKE, SAMUEL ADAMS   The Heart of the White Mountains. New York, 1882. 4to., illus. Biblo BL781-141 1978 $9.50

DRAKE, SAMUEL ADAMS   The Making of the Ohio Valley States 1660-1837.
New York, 1894. Cloth, covers faded and soiled, free endpaper lacking in front.
Hayman 72-202 1978 $7.50

DRAKE, SAMUEL ADAMS   Old Boston Taverns & Tavern Clubs. 1917. Illus.,
maps, good. Nestler Rare 78-241 1978 $12

DRAKE, SAMUEL G.   The History and Antiquities of Boston..to 1770.
Boston, 1856. Lg. 8vo., engravings, 3/4 leather, rubbed. Biblo BL781-132
1978 $27.50

DRAKE, SAMUEL G.   The History and Antiquities of Boston. Boston,
1856. 4to, 1st ed., illus., plts. MacManus 239-289 1978 $35

DRALSE DE GRANDPIERRE, SIEUR   Relation De Divers Voyages Faits Dans L'Afrique... Paris, 1718. Thick sm. 8vo, half calf. Edwards 1012-254 1978 £120

DRANE, AUGUSTA T.   Songs in the Night, and Other Poems. 1876.
1st. ed., 8vo, orig. cloth, gilt, very good copy. Fenning 32-94 1978 £8.50

DRANE, R.   The Collection of Old Worcester Porcelain Formed
by the Late....Exhibited by Albert Amor, St. James Street, London. 1922. 4to.,
plts., cloth. Quaritch 983-Addenda g 1978 $80

DRANNAN, W. F.   Capt...., Chief of Scouts as Pilot to Emigrant
and Government Trains, Across the Plains of the Wild West of Fifty Years Ago.
Chicago, (1910). Cloth, little rubbed. Hayman 72-203 1978 $10

DRAPER, J.   History of Spencer, From Its Earliest Settlement
to the Year 1841... Worcester, 1841. MacManus 239-1052 1978 $32.50

DRAPER, JOHN WILLIAM   A History of the Intellectual Development of
Europe. London, 1891. 2 vols., 8vo., cloth. Salloch 50-51 1978 $30

DRAPER, JOHN WILLIAM   Scientific Memoirs, Being Experimental Contributions to a Knowledge of Radiant Energy. New York, 1878. 8vo., frontis.,
portr., text illus., orig. cloth, very good copy, 1st ed. Norman 5-82 1978
$85

DRAPER, JOHN WILLIAM   A Treatise on the Forces Which Produce the Organization of Plants. New York, 1844. 4to., handcolored frontis., plts., orig.
cloth, gilt, hinges repaired, some foxing, very good copy, 1st ed. Norman 5-81
1978 $150

DRAPER, JOHN WILLIAM   A Treatise on the Forces Which Produce the
Organization of Plants.. New York, 1844. Engr. color frontis., engr. plts.,
tall 4to., orig. cloth, 1st ed. Argosy Special-37 1978 $150

DRAYTON, G.   Three Meridians. Toronto, 1950. Card cover.
Hood 117-795 1978 $7.50

DRAYTON, MICHAEL   Minor Poems of .... Oxford, 1907. Octavo,
good. Upcroft 10-47 1978 £5

DRAYTON, MICHAEL   Nimphidia, The Court of Faerie. 1921. 1st.
ed., sm. 8vo, no. 337 of 510 copies, paper label slightly imperfect, vellum spine
discoloured, otherwise v.g. Jarndyce 16-1197 1978 £5.50

DRAYTON, MICHAEL   Poemes, Lyrick and Pastorall. 1891. From the
ed. of (1605?), sm. 4to., orig. wrappers. Howes 194-1212n 1978 £7.50

DRAYTON, MICHAEL   Poems. N.P., 1605. 8 vo., good, fresh,
contemp. calf, neatly rebacked, 1st ed. Quaritch Summer,1978-15 1978
$1,200

DRAYTON, MICHAEL   Poems. London, 1608. Title within woodcut
border, engraved title pg. of later edition tipped in as frontis, sm. 8vo, 19th.
century calf gilt, gilt edges, joints worn. Traylen 88-230 1978 £495

DRAYTON, MICHAEL   Poems. 1888. Reprinted from orig. ed. of 1605,
part I only, sm. 4to., orig. wrappers. Howes 194-1212m 1978 £7.50

DRAX, PETER   Murder by Chance. n.d. Very good, worn d.w.,
first English ed. Bell Book 17-234 1978 £6.50

THE DREAM City. St. Louis, (1893). Orig. binding, clean. Hayman 71-205
1978 $22.50

DREER, FERDINAND JULIUS   A Catalogue of the Collection of Autographs...
Philadelphia, 1890-1893. 2 vols., 4to., orig. cloth, ltd. to 200 no. sets, 1 spine
spotted. MacManus 238-908 1978 $40

DREISER, THEODORE.   An American Tragedy. New York, 1925. 8vo,
2 vols., black cloth, 1st issue with white end papers, spines darkened, front hinge
of vol. I weakened, 1st ed., collector's cond. Desmarais 1-138 1978 $22.50

DREISER, THEODORE   An American Tragedy. New York, 1925. No.
471 of ed. ltd. to 795 copies, vol. I signed by author, newly rebound in simulated
leather, uncut, two vols. Wolfe 39-135 1978 $50

DREISER, THEODORE   An American Tragedy. New York, 1925. 8vo,
blue boards, 3/4 cloth, 1 of 795 copies signed by author, 2 vols., fine. Duschnes
220-89 1978 $125

DREISER, THEODORE   Chains: Lesser Novels and Stories. New York,
1927. Decor. bds., cloth spine, bkplt., very fine in worn slipcase, 1 of 440
copies signed by author. Dawson's 447-219 1978 $60

DREISER, THEODORE   The Color of a Great City. New York,1923.
8vo, black cloth, gilt stamped, illus. by C. B. Falls, spine faded, uncut, unopened, near fine, 1st ed. Desmarais 1-139 1978 $20

DREISER, THEODORE   Dawn. New York, (1931). 1st ed. Biblo
BL781-952 1978 $12

DREISER, THEODORE   Epitaph. A Poem. New York, (1929). 4to.,
orig. calf, extremities a little rubbed, 1st ed., 1 of 200 numbered copies, leather,
signed by author, fine. MacManus 238-636 1978 $55

DREISER, THEODORE   Epitaph. New York, Heron Press, (1929). 1 of
200 copies bound in black Japanese silk, 1 of 900 prtd. on Keijyo Kami paper,
signed by author, mint in worn slipcase. Dawson's 447-220 1978 $50

DREISER, THEODORE   A Gallery of Women. New York, 1929. 2 vols.,
orig. parchment-backed bds., 1st ed., ltd. to 560 copies, signed by author, uncut, fine. MacManus 238-635 1978 $60

DREISER, THEODORE.   A Gallery of Women. New York, 1929. 8vo,
2 vols., brown cloth, gilt stamped, orig. d.w., split box, 1st ed., collector's
cond. Desmarais 1-140 1978 $25

DREISER, THEODORE   A Gallery of Women. New York, 1929. Thick
8vo, parchment-backed boards, 1 of 560 copies signed by author, 1st ed., 2 vols.,
fine. Duschnes 220-91 1978 $65

DREISER, THEODORE   Hey Rub-A-Dub-Dub: A Book of the Mystery and
Wonder and Terror of Life. New York, 1920. 8vo, blue cloth, ownership
inscription, 1st ed., collector's cond. Desmarais 1-141 1978 $20

DREISER, THEODORE   A Hoosier Holiday. New York, 1916. Illus.,
bds., blue cloth back, text & binding 2nd state. Dawson's 447-221 1978 $25

DREISER, THEODORE   Sister Carrie. New York, Limited Editions Club,
1939. Ltd. ed., signed by the artist, bookplate, illus. by Reginald Marsh. Biblo
247-585 1978 $47.50

DREISER, THEODORE   Twelve Men. New York, 1919. First ed.,
edges rubbed. Biblo 247-536 1978 $20

DREISER, THEODORE   Twelve Men. New York, (1928). 1st Modern
Library ed. Biblo 251-464 1978 $8.50

DRELINCOURT, CHARLES 1595-1669   Les Consolations de l'Ame Fidele, contre
les Frayeurs de la Mort. Paris, 1669. Portrait, 4to., contemp. calf, one joint
cracked. Howes 194-540 1978 £30

DRELINCOURT, CHARLES 1595-1669   De Divinis qpud Hippocratem Dogmates
Sermo quem Graece Habuit Septimo idus Martius 1689. 1689. 12mo., old calf.
George's 635-1055 1978 £6

DREPPERD, CARL W.   Early American Prints. New York, (1930).
Cloth, piece torn from bottom corner of one leaf, illus., 1st prtg. Hayman 73-
152 1978 $7.50

DREPPERD, CARL W.   Pioneer America. New York, 1949. 2300 illus.
Baldwins' 51-60 1978 $12.50

DREPPERD, CARL W.   Pioneer America. Its First Three Centuries. New York, 1949. Illus., 1st ed., fine, d.w., boxed. Biblo BL781-530 1978 $24.50

DRESCELIUS, P. J.   De Zonne-Bloem of de overeenkomst van der Menschelyken wil met der Godolyken.... (1796). Engravings, 12mo., calf. George's 635-1056 1978 £5

DRESSER, JOHN   Report on a Recent Discovery of Gold Near Lake Megantic, Quebec. Ottawa, 1908. Printed wrappers frayed, loose. Wolfe 39-143 1978 $15

DREW, ELIZABETH   T. S. Eliot: the design of his poetry. 1950. Very good, d.w., first English ed. Bell Book 16-314 1978 £5.50

DREW, JOHN   Practical Meteorology. 1840. Second ed., 8vo., orig. cloth, uncut, bright, frontispiece, plts. P. M. Hill 142-173 1978 £35

DREXEL, JEREMIAS   Orbis Phaethon Hoc est De Universis Vitiis Linguae. Coloniae, 1634. 2nd ed., small octavo, engraved pictorial initials, full early calf, gilt-ruled spine and title on spine label, gilt. Bennett 20-59 1978 $175

DRIGGS, B. W.   History of Teton Valley, Idaho. Caldwell, 1926. Illus., original cloth, 1st ed. Ginsberg 14-402 1978 $45

DRIGGS, HOWARD R.   Rise of the Lone Star: A Story of Texas Told by Its Pioneers. New York, 1936. Illus., 1st ed., d.j. Jenkins 116-364 1978 $12.50

DRINKER, ELIZABETH   Extracts from the Journal....1759-1807. Philadelphia, 1889. 1st ed., scarce & valuable, soil marks on cover, orig. binding, 8vo. Americanist 101-44 1978 $55

DRINKWATER, JOHN   All About Me. 1928. 3rd imp., drawings, covers somewhat soiled, good, signed by the author, first English ed. Bell Book 16-285 1978 £5

DRINKWATER, JOHN   Claud Lovat Fraser. London, Curwen Press, 1923. Frontis., 1 of 450 numbered copies signed by both John Drinkwater & Albert Rutherston. Battery Park 1-105 1978 $175

DRINKWATER, JOHN   The Life and Adventures of Carl Laemmle. London, (1931). Illus., 8vo., bkplt., 1st ed. Morrill 239-369 1978 $7.50

DRINKWATER, JOHN   Lincoln. The World Emancipator. Boston, 1920. Bkplt., fine in torn d.w. Desmarais B-196 1978 $10

DRINKWATER, JOHN   Patriotism in Literature. 1924. Pres. copy inscribed from the author, fscp. 8vo., very good, first English ed. Bell Book 16-286 1978 £15

DRINKWATER, JOHN   Persephone. (Mt. Vernon, 1926). Cloth, fine, 1 of 550 copies, signed by Drinkwater. Dawson's 447-143 1978 $50

DRINKWATER, JOHN   The Pilgrim of Eternity. 1925. 8vo., plts., cloth, dust wrapper, bkplt., signed pres. inscr. from author. Quaritch 979-76 1978 $40

DRINKWATER, JOHN   The World's Lincoln. New York, The Bowling Green Press, 1928. 8vo., bds., fine copy, one of 800 copies. Battery Park 1-127 1978 $25

DROBA, DANIEL D.   Czech and Slovak Leaders in Metropolitan Chicago. Chicago, 1934. Illus. with photos. Austin 79-212 1978 $47.50

DROCHON, J. E.   Un Chevalier apotre, Celestin-Godefroy Chicard, Missionnaire du Yun-Nan. Paris, 1891. Nouv. ed., large 8vo, portrs., map, illus., rare, orig. covers. Van der Peet 127-79 1978 Dfl 75

THE DROLL Story-Teller; or, New Oddest of All Oddities. London, n.d. (ca. 1822). 12mo, half green morocco, gilt, by Wallis, 1st ed., hand-colored frontispiece by George Cruikshank, fine copy. Ximenes 47-161 1978 $125

DRUCKER, PETER F.   The New Society. 1950. Austin 80-558 1978 $8.50

DRUITT, ROBERT   Principles and Practice of Modern Surgery. Philadelphia, 1858. New Amer. ed. Rittenhouse 49-230 1976 $15

DRUMM, STELLA M.   Down the Sante Fe Trail and Into Mexico. The Diary of Susan Shelby Magoffin... New Haven, 1926. Illus., map. MacManus 239-1914 1978 $35

DRUMMOND, HENRY   Addresses. Toronto, 1891. Hood 117-471 1973 $10

DRUMMOND, HENRY   Tropical Africa. New York, 1889. 6 maps, cr. 8vo, orig. cloth. K Books 239-125 1978 £5

DRUMMOND, HENRY   Tropical Africa. London, 190-. Maps, cr. 8vo, orig. cloth. K Books 239-125A 1978 £5

DRUMMOND, WILLIAM 1585-1649   The Poems. 1790. Sm. 8vo., early 19th cent. half calf, spine worn, joints weak. Howes 194-251 1978 £7.50

DRUMMOND, WILLIAM 1770?-1828   The Oedipus Judaicus. 1811. Plts., some foxing, full green calf, gilt, 8vo. George's 635-1424 1978 £18.50

DRUMMOND, WILLIAM HENRY   The Habitant and Other French Canadian Poems. New York and London, 1898. Illus. Hood 116-820 1978 $10

DRUMMOND, WILLIAM HENRY   Johnnie Couteau, and Other Poems. New York, 1901. Illus. by Frederick S. Coburn, 8vo., orig. bds., calf back, spine slightly rubbed, otherwise nice, 1 of 1000 autographed copies. Morrill 239-370 1978 $10

DRURY, A. W.   History of the Church of the United Brethren in Christ. Dayton, Ohio, 1931. Orig. cl. Ginsberg 16-860 1978 $50.00

DRURY, ANNA H.   The Blue Ribbons, A Story of the Last Century. (1855). 1st. ed., plts., cr. 8vo, orig. cloth, gilt & silver, edges gilt, very good. Fenning 32-95 1978 £8

DRURY, DR. J   Illustrations of Natural History. London, 1770, 1782. 1st ed., half contemp. calf over marbled bds., one cover detached, fresh, hand-colored engraved plates, Vol. 1 & Vol. 3, rare colored issue. Houle 10-385 1978 $750

DRURY, JOHN   Midwest Heritage. New York, (1948). First ed., fine, d.w., 4to., engravings. Biblo 247-210 1978 $17.50

DRURY, P. SHELDON   The Startling and Thrilling Narrative of the Dark and Terrible Deeds of Henry Madison,.... Philadelphia, [1857]. Frontis, woodcuts by Miller, original printed wr., 1st ed. Ginsberg 14-107 1978 $250

DRURY, ROBERT   Madagascar; or Robert Drury's Journal During Fifteen Years Captivity on That Island. London, 1890. 13 illus., backstrip dull, slightly frayed at extremities, orig. cloth, 8vo. K Books 239-126 1978 £8

DRURY, ROBERT   The Pleasant and Surprising Adventures of Mr. Robert Drury... 1743. Folding map, engraved plts., calf, rebacked, 8vo. Edwards 1012-313 1978 £120

DRYDEN, JOHN   Absalom and Achitophel. 1682. 3rd. ed., 4to, disbound, sm. tear in margin of title. Hannas 54-90 1978 £25

DRYDEN, JOHN   Albion and Albanius: An Opera. 1691. 1st. quarto ed., disbound, some foxing. Hannas 54-91 1978 £45

DRYDEN, JOHN   All For Love. N.P., 1678. N.P., 1678. Sm. 4 to., tear to C1 affecting 1 letter, closed tear to H2, very good large copy, modern mottled calf, cloth folder, slipcase, 1st ed. Quaritch Summer, 1978-41 1978 $550

DRYDEN, JOHN   All for Love, or the World Well Lost. San Francisco, 1929. Frontis., sm. folio, vellum backed red paper bds., ltd. to 250, slipcase. Howell 5-19 1978 $60

DRYDEN, JOHN   The Conquest of Granada by the Spaniards. In Two Parts. 1678. Third ed., 2 parts in 1 vol., sm. 4to., newly bound in qtr. calf antique style. Howes 194-36 1978 £32

DRYDEN, JOHN   Don Sebastian. 1692. 2nd. ed., 4to, disbound, heavily foxed throughout, stains on few leaves. Hannas 54-92 1978 £10

DRYDEN, JOHN   Fables: Ancient & Modern. London, 1700. 1st ed., thick folio, full contemp. blind stamped calf, rebacked, rubbed, gilt stamped label on spine, engraved portrait. Houle 10-93 1978 $225

DRYDEN, JOHN   Fables Ancient and Modern... London, 1700.
Full brown crushed mor., a.e.g., 1st ed. MacManus 238-116 1978 $150

DRYDEN, JOHN   Fables ancient and modern. 1713. Engraved
frontispiece, contemp. panelled calf, head of spine trifle worn, second ed. Howes
194-37 1978 £30

DRYDEN, JOHN   The Fables of John Dryden,.... London, 1797.
1st ed., large quarto, bound in contemp. full straight-grained mor., gilt borders
on covers, gilt spine, gilt dentelles, leather hinges, offsetting from plates, orig.
tissue guards present, gilt edges. Totteridge 29-35 1978 $225

DRYDEN, JOHN   The Indian Emperour... London, 1681. Sm. 4to,
new quarter morocco, lg. & good copy, leaf B2 is torn & repaired. Trayley 88-
231 1978 £50

DRYDEN, JOHN   King Arthur: Or, the British Worthy. 1691.
1st. ed., 2nd. issue, disbound, foxed throughout, line of imprint cropped, scribbles
on half-title. Hannas 54-93 1978 £65

DRYDEN, JOHN   The Miscellaneous Works Containing All His
Original Poems, Tales & Translations. 1767. 4 vols., orig. calf, spine gilt, red
& green labels, fine. Jarndyce 16-76 1978 £38

DRYDEN, JOHN   The Murmurers. 1689. 1st. ed., folio, disbound,
wormholes in lower margin. Hannas 54-98 1978 £65

DRYDEN, JOHN   Oedipus: A Tragedy. 1679. First ed., newly
bound in qtr. calf antique style, good. Howes 194-39 1978 £52

DRYDEN, JOHN   The State of Innocence, and Fall of Man; an
Opera. 1678. Sm. 4to., newly bound in qtr. calf antique style. Howes 194-38
1978 £28

DRYDEN, JOHN   Troilus and Cressida. N.P., 1679. Sm.
4to., fine large copy, some bottom edges uncut, new half mor., 1st ed.
Quaritch Summer, 1978-42 1978 $550

DRYDEN, JOHN   The Vindication: or the Parallel of the French
Holy-League, and the English League and Covenant, Turn'd Into A Seditions Libell.
1683. 1st. ed., 4to, disbound, scribbles on initial blank leaf. Hannas 54-94
1978 £75

DRYDEN, JOHN   The Works, Now First Collected. 1808. Illus.,
portrait, 18 vols., tall 8vo., contemp. diced russia, gilt frame sides, first Scott
ed. Howes 194-818 1978 £200

DUANE, ALEXANDER   A New Classification of the Motor Anomalies of
the Eye Based Upon Physiological Principles. (New York, 1897). 8vo., orig.
gray prtd. wrs., very good. Zeitlin 245-66 1978 $25

DUANE, WILLIAM   A Handbook for Infantry. Philadelphia, Pa.,
1814. Plts., fine copy, uncut, orig. bds. Bell Wiley 's copy. Broadfoot 46-503
1978 $30

DUANE, WILLIAM   A Military Dictionary,.... Philadelphia, 1810.
Thick 8vo, contemporary tree calf, spine gilt, 1st ed., foxed, very good copy.
Ximenes 47-82 1978 $100

DUANE, WILLIAM   Mississippi Question. Philadelphia, 1803. Disbound, 1st ed. Ginsberg 14-498 1978 $47.50

DUANE, WILLIAM N.   Poems of the Mohawk Valley
Please turn to
CAMP, PHINEAS 1788-1868

DU BARRY, MARIE JEANNE   Letters to and From the Countess du Barry. 1779.
Contemp. half calf, spine worn, 8vo. Howes 194-252 1978 £10

DUBBERLEY, ELLWOOD P.   Readings in the History of Education. 1920.
Illus. Austin 80-906 1978 $10

DUBLIN, LOUIS I.   American People. 1936. Austin 80-559 1978
$12.50

DUBLIN, LOUIS I.   A Family of Thirty Million: The Story of Metropolitan Life Insurance Company. 1943. Austin 80-560 1978 $7.50

DUBLIN, LOUIS I.   Population Problems. 1926. Austin 80-561 1978
$12.50

DUBOIS, CARDINAL   Memoirs of .... New York, 1929. 8vo, orig.
cloth, 2 vols., full page drawings by Lui Trugo, good. Sexton 7-140 1978 £15

DU BOIS, HENRI PÈNE   Four Private Libraries of New York. New York,
Devinne Press, 1892. 1st series, frontis. in color, 1 of 200 copies on Japan vellum,
orig. wrs., binding intact. Battery Park 1-69 1978 $100

DU BOIS, HENRI PÈNE   Four Private Libraries in New York. 1 of 800
numbered copies on Holland paper, newly rebound in marbled paper over bds.,
cloth spine. Battery Park 1-70 1978 $50

DUBOIS, J. A.   Description of the Character, Manners and Customs of the People of India... 1817. 4to, half calf. Edwards 1012-96 1978 $45

DUBOIS, JACQUES   Livre de la Generation de l'Homme... Paris,
1559. 8vo., old calf, gilt back, fine copy, 1st French ed. Gilhofer 74-101
1978 sFr 1,500

DUBOIS, PAUL   The Psychic Treatment of Nervous Disorders.
1909. 6th rev. Austin 80-1019 1978 $12.50

DUBOIS, PAUL   The Psychological Origin of Mental Disorders.
1913. Austin 80-1020 1978 $10

DU BOIS, W. E. BURGHARDT   Darkwater. Voices from Within the Veil.
New York, 1920. 1st ed. MacManus 239-836 1978 $15

DU BOIS, W. E. BURGHARDT   John Brown. Philadelphia, 1909. First ed.,
very good. Austin 82-356 1978 $27.50

DUBOR, M.   Views of the Remains of Ancient Buildings in
Rome, and Its Vicinity. London, 1820. Folio, coloured aquatint views, red
half morocco, matching bds., sl. waterstaining, red morocco label, gilt. Deighton 5-120 1978 £325

DUBREUIL, JEAN   Perspective Practical. London, 1672. Plts.,
illus., title in red & black, 4to, contemp. calf, gilt panelled sides, spine &
corners neatly repaired. Traylen 88-373 1978 £150

DUBUISSON, PAUL ULRICH   Abrege de la Revolution de l'Amerique Angloise,
depuis le Commencement de l'annee 1774... Paris, 1778. 12mo., orig. mottled
brown calf, gilt back. Gilhofer 74-63 1978 sFr 250

DUCATI, PERICLE   L'Arte Classica. Turin, 1939. Illus., 3rd ed.,
some underscoring, used. Biblo BL781-373 1978 $27.50

DU CELLIER, M. F.   Historie des classes laborieuses en France, depuis
la conquete de la Gaule par Jules Cesar jusqua nos jours. 1860. Half mor., 8vo.
George's 635-316 1978 £8.50

DU CHAILLU, PAUL B.   Adventures in The Great Forest of Equatorial
Africa and the Country of the Dwarfs. London, 1890. Map, illus., gilt-decor.
cover, 8vo. K Books 244-104 1978 £12

DU CHAILLU, PAUL B.   Explorations and Adventures in Equitorial Africa...
the Gorilla...and Other Animals. New York, 1861. 1st U.S. ed., lg. 8vo.,
orig. pict. cloth, illus., spine ends and edges rubbed. Americanist 102-2 1978
$55

DU CHAILLU, PAUL B.   Explorations & Adventures in Equatorial Africa.
London, 1861. 2nd ed., map, frontispiece, plts., good, old style half calf, 8vo.
K Books 244-356 1978 £30

DU CHAILLU, PAUL B.   Ivar the Viking. 1893. Austin 82-357 1978
$12.50

DU CHAILLU, PAUL B.   The Land of the Midnight Sun; Summer and Winter
Journeys Through Sweden, Norway, Lapland and Northern Finland. New York,
1882. Illus., map, 2 vols., covers dec. Hood 116-77 1978 $30

DU CHAILLU, PAUL B.   Lost in the Jungle. New York, 1877. Illus.,
cr. 8vo, gilt-dec. cloth. K Books 239-127 1978 £8

DU CHAILLU, PAUL B.   My Apingi Kingdom: With Life in the Great
Sahara. New York, 1871. Many illus., cr. 8vo, gilt dec. cloth. K Books
239-128 1978 £8

DU CHAILLU, PAUL B.   Stories of the Gorilla Country. New York, 1868.
1st ed., illus., tips rubbed, very good copy. Victoria 34-253 1978 $55

DU CHAILLU, PAUL B.   Stories of the Gorilla Country.   New York, 1877.
Illus., cr. 8vo, gilt-dec. cloth.   K Books 239-129 1978 £8

DU CHAILLU, PAUL B.   Wild Life Under the Equator.   London, 1869.
Illus., cr. 8vo, gilt cloth.   K Books 239-130 1978 £8

DU CHAILLU, PAUL B.   Wild Life Under the Equator.   New York, 1875.
Illus., cr. 8vo, gilt cloth.   K Books 239-130A 1978 £8

DUCHAT, YVES   Histoire de la Guerre Sainct, faite par les Francois
& autres Chrestiens.... Paris, 1620. Contemp. vellum, letterine piece, thk. sm.
8vo., upper portions of some leaves dampstained, first ed. Howes 194-541 1978
£35

DU CHATELET, MARQUISE GABRIELLE-EMILIE.   Institutions de Physique.   Paris,
1740. 1st ed., Chatelet's 1st book, octavo, rebacked calf, gilt spine, crisp.
Bennett 20-60 1978 $375

DUCHAUSSOIS, PIERRE   Apotres Inconnus.   Paris, (1924). Card cover.
Hood's 115-54 1978 $15

DUCHAUSSOIS, PIERRE   Aux Glaces Polaires, Indiens et Esquimaux.
Paris, Lyon, (1921). Card cover, folding map. Hood's 115-53 1978 $22.50

DUCHENNE DE BOULOGNE, GUILLAUME BENJAMIN AMAND   Physiologie
des Mouvements Demontree a l'aide de L'experimentation.... Paris, 1867. 8vo.,
woodcuts, contemp. quarter mor., orig. printed wrs. bound in.   Quaritch 977-20
1978 $850

DUCHENNE DE BOULOGNE, GUILLAUME BENJAMIN AMAND   Physiology
of Motion Demonstrated by Means of Electrical Stimulation and Clinical Observation and Applied to the Study of Paralysis and Deformities.   Philadelphia, 1949.
8vo., frontis. portr., illus., modern half brown calf, gilt lettering on spine, fine
copy, #498 of 1500 copies prtd.   Zeitlin 245-67 1978 $75

DUCHESNE, LOUIS MARIE OLIVIER   The Beginnings of the Temporal Sovereignty
of the Popes, A.D. 754-1073. 1908. Some annotation, 8vo. Upcroft 12-115
1978 £7.50

DU CHOUL, GUILLAUME   Discous Sur La Castrametation Et Discipline Militaire Des Romains. 1672. 2 parts in 1 vol., illus., thick sm. 4to., contemp.
sprinkled calf. F. Edwards 1013-284 1978 £85

DUCK, STEPHEN   Poems on Several Occasions.   London, 1736.
4to, 19th-century half calf, 1st ed., frontispiece portrait engraved by Bickham,
very good copy. Ximenes 47-83 1978 $275

DUCKETT, E. S.   Anglo-Saxon saints and scholars.   New York,
1947. 8vo. Upcroft 12-116 1978 £7.50

DUCKETT, G. F.   Record-evidences, among archives of the ancient
abbey of Cluni from 1077 to 1534. 1886. Royal 8vo. Upcroft 12-120 1978
£6.50

DUCKWORTH, W. L. H.   Studies from the Anthropological Laboratory.
Cambridge, 1904. Illus. Austin 80-1021 1978 $27.50

DUCLOS, CHARLES PINEAU   The History of Lewis XI. 1746. 1st. English ed.,
2 vols., 8vo, contemp. calf, nearly broken. Hannas 54-99 1978 £8.50

DUDEVANT, MME.
Please turn to
SAND, GEORGE

DUDLEY-GORDON, TOM   I Seek My Prey in the Waters. 1943. Austin
80-89 1978 $11

DUDYCHA, GEORGE J.   An Objective Study of Punctuality in Relation to
Personality and Achievement. 1936. Paper. Austin 80-1022 1978 $12.50

DUEHREN, E.   Der Marquis de Sade und Seine Zeit.   Berlin,
1922. Sm. 8vo., half cloth. Van der Peet H-64-314 1978 Dfl 45

DUER, WILLIAM ALEXANDER   A Letter, Addressed to Cadwallader D. Colden
in Answer to the Strictures... Albany, 1817. Good. Nestler Rare 78-204 1978
$55

DUER, WILLIAM ALEXANDER   The Life of William Alexander, Earl of Stirling;
Major General in the Army of the United States During the Revolution with Selections from His Correspondence... New York, 1847. Hood 116-212 1978 $65

DUER, WILLIAM ALEXANDER   The Life of William Alexander, Earl of Stirling...
New York, 1847. Port., maps.   MacManus 239-564 1978 $30

DUERER, ALBRECHT   Della Simmetria De I Corpi Hvmani, Libri Quattro. Venice, 1591. Folio, full and double page woodcut diagrams, Italic letter,
1st ed. in Italian. Quaritch 978-47 1978 $1,750

DUERER, ALBRECHT   Ephrussi, C. Albert Durer et ses Dessins.   Paris,
1882. 4to., frontis., plts., half mor. Quaritch 983-178 1978 $120

DUERER, ALBRECHT   Etliche Underricht zu Befestigung der Stett.
(Nuremberg, 1527). Folio, fldg. woodcuts, all drawn & engr. by author, limp
vellum, fine copy, 1st ed., 2nd issue. Norman 5-84 1978 $4,000

DUERER, ALBRECHT   Underweysung der Messung. (Nuremberg),
1525. Folio, text woodcuts by author, contemp. blindstamped calf over oak bds.,
orig. bosses, rebacked, endpapers renewed, clasps restored, lower margin of
title restored, occas. light foxing & soiling, but very good copy in fine contemp.
binding, 1st ed., 2nd issue. Norman 5-83 1978 $7,500

DUERER, ALBRECHT   De Urbibus, Arcibus, Castellisque Condendis Ac
Muniendis Rationes. Paris, 1535. Fldg. plts., woodcuts, thin folio, vellum,
1st ed. in Latin. Salloch 345-57 1978 $1,400

DUFF, EDWARD GORDON   Caxton's Tully of Old Age and Friendship. 1481.
(London): 1912. Fold frontis., orig. half-calf, rubbed, 1st ed., foxing. Mac-
Manus 238-910 1978 $40

DUFF, EDWARD GORDON   A Century of the English Book Trade. Short No-
tices of all Printers, Stationers, Book-Binders, and Others Connected with It...
London, 1905. 8vo., orig. cloth-backed bds., 1st ed., bookplt. and signature of
Cyril Bathurst Judge. MacManus 238-911 1978 $35

DUFF, EDWARD GORDON   A Century of the English Book Trade. London,
1948. Fscap. 4to., orig. bds., holland back, fine. Forster 130-1 1978 £8

DUFF, J. W.   Literary History of Rome in The Silver Age. 1935.
Allen 234-287 1978 $10

DUFF, LOUIS BLAKE   The County Kerchief. Toronto, 1949. 8 illus.
Hood's 115-635 1978 $12.50

DUFF, SHIELA, GRANT   A German Protectorate, The Czechs Under Nazi
Rule. 1942. 1st. ed., 8vo, orig. cloth, pres. copy to Winston Churchill.
Sawyer 298-72 1978 £82

DUFFERIN SCHOOL OLD BOYS' ASSOCIATION   Diamond Jubilee Yearbook,
1877-1937, Vol. XIV. Toronto, (1937). Hood's 115-386 1978 $7.50

DUFFY, HERBERT S.   William Howard Taft. New York, 1930. Illus.,
1st ed., spine faded. Biblo 248-101 1978 $17.50

DUFFY, HERBERT S.   William Howard Taft. New York, 1930. Clean,
orig. binding. Hayman 71-191 1978 $7.50

DUFRENE, MAXIMILLIAN   Secessus Triduani Sacerdotales Octo. Augsburg,
1746. Sm. thk. 8vo., contemp. vellum over wooden bds., one inner hinge weak,
some foxing, clasps missing. Howes 194-542 1978 £15

DUFRENOY, MME.   Etrennes a ma Fille ou Soirees Amusantes de la
Jeunesse. Paris, 1816. Vol. I (of 2), 2nd ed., color plates, all hand-colored,
gilt-decorated calf worn. Victoria 34-254 1978 $25

DU FRESNOY, C. A.   The Art of Painting ..with Remarks: Translated into English... 1716. Sm. 8vo., frontis., foxed and slightly soiled, some light
marginal water staining, but good copy, contemp. panelled calf. Quaritch 983-
177 1978 $160

DUFTY, JOSEPH   A Blighted Life, and Other Poems. (1871). 1st.
ed., orig. dark green cloth, inner hinge weak, otherwise v.g. Jarndyce 16-629
1978 £8.50

DUGAN, WILLIAM JAMES   Electro-Therapeutics Handbook. Philadelphia,
1910. Rittenhouse 49-232 1976 $10

DUGAS, GEORGE   The Canadian West. Montreal, 1905. Ex-lib.,
trans. from French. Hood 117-386 1978 $25

DUGAS, GEORGE   Monseigneur Provencher et les Missions de la
Rivere-Rouge. Montreal, 1889. Orig. cl, 1st ed. Ginsberg 16-961 1978
$100.00

DUGAS, GEORGE   La Premiere Canadienne Au Nord-Ouest ou Bio-
graphie de Marie-Anne Gaboury. Winnipeg, 1945. Card cover, troisieme ed.
Hood's 115-998 1978 $17.50

DUGDALE, WILLIAM   The History of Imbanking and Drayning of Divers
Fenns and Marshes.... 1662. Folio, portrait, maps, fine large copy, superbly
bound in early 19th century russia, blind & gilt panelled sides and spine, gilt edges,
scarce. Quaritch 977-216 1978 $950

DUGDALE, WILLIAM   The History of St. Paul's Cathedral in London.
1818. Thk. folio, strongly bound in half mor., gilt top, very good, one of a sm.
number of lg. paper copies, plts. Howes 194-253 1978 £55

DUGDALE, WILLIAM   Monasticon Anglicanum... 1846. 6 vols. in 8,
folio, port., lg. plts., black mor. Quaritch 983-12 1978 $800

DUGDALE, WILLIAM   A Perfect Copy of All Summons of the Nobility
to the Great Councils and Parliaments of this Realm, from the XLIX of King Henry
the IIId until these Present Times. 1685 (1794). Folio, full contemp. diced russia,
good. Howes 194-254 1978 £50

DUGDALE, WILLIAM   A Short View of the Late Troubles in England.
1681. Folio, portrait, contemp. calf, neatly rebacked, first ed. Howes 194-40
1978 £52

DUGG, E. GORDON   William Caxton. Caxton Club, 1905. 4to.,
plts., frontis., 1 of 252 copies prtd. from type on American handmade paper,
prospectus laid in. Battery Park 1-193 1978 $250

DUGMORE, ARTHUR RADCLYFFE   Nature and the Camera. New York, 1902.
Photos by author, soiled binding, 8vo., orig. cloth. Book Chest 17-126 1978
$25

DUGMORE, ARTHUR RADCLYFFE   Wild Life and the Camera. Philadelphia,
1912. Spine worn, ex-lib with stamps, 8vo., orig. cloth. Book Chest 17-127
1978 $25

DUGMORE, H. H.   The Reminiscences of an Albany Settler. Graham's Town, 1871. 8vo, orig. cloth, lacks free end-paper, rather thumbed & worn,
sound. K Books 239-131 1978 £35

DUGUET, JACQUES JOSEPH   The Institution of a Prince. 1740. 1st. English
ed., 2 vols., 8vo, half-titles, contemp. calf. Hannas 54-100 1978 £25

DUGUET, RAYMOND   La Poligamye aux Etats-Unis. Paris, 1922.
Orig. pr. wr., 1st ed. Ginsberg 14-646 1978 $30

DUHAMEL, G.   Vie et Aventures de Salavin. Paris, 1955. 5
vols., bds. porfolios, bds. slipcases, 1 of 4900 copies on "Velin Chiffon", rare.
Van der Peet H-64-424 1978 Dfl 250

DU HAMEL, JEAN BAPTISTE.   De Meteoris et Fossilibus libri duo.... Parisiis,
1660. 1st ed., quarto, diagrams in text, ornamental head- and tail-pieces, initials,
old half vellum. Bennett 20-61 1978 $340

DUHAMEL, JEAN PIERRE FRANCOIS GUILLOT   Geometrie Souterraine. Paris,
1787. 4to., orig. bds., uncut, plts., first ed., rare. Gurney 75-34 1978 £70

DUHRING, HENRY   The Art of Living. 1843. Lg. 12mo., orig.
cloth, fine. P. M. Hill 142-98 1978 £12

DUINKERKEN, A. VAN   Bloemlezing uit de Katholieke Poezie van de
Vroegste Tijden tot Heden. Bilthoven, 1936-1939. 3 vols., lg. 8vo., half calf,
uncut, spines shaved. Van der Peet H-64-371 1978 Dfl 95

DUIS, E.   The Good Old Times in McLean County, Illinois.
Bloomington, 1874. Rebound. MacManus 239-968 1978 $40

DUJARDIN, EDOUARD   Pour la Vierge du Roc Ardent. Paris, 1889. Sm.
folio, frontis. etching with water colour by Louis Anquetin, uncut, orig. plain
paper wr., one of 55 copies, inscribed with signed poem by author. Quaritch 978-
45 1978 $425

DUJARDIN, EDOUARD   Reponse de la bergere au berger. Paris, 1892.
Small folio, colour lithograph frontis. by Maurice Denis, uncut, orig. plain
paper wr. Quaritch 978-46 1978 $750

DU JON, FRANCOIS
Please turn to
JUNIUS FRANCISCUS

DUKE, BASIL W.   History of Morgan's Cavalry. Cincinnati, Oh.,
1867. Badly worn copy, Bell Wiley's Copy. Broadfoot's 44-118 1978 $20.00

DUKE, JANE TAYLOR   Kenmore and the Lewises. New York, 1949.
First ed., d.w., illus. Biblo 248-211 1978 $15

DUKE, WILLIAM   Remarks Upon Education With Respect to the
Learned Languages Shewing Their Importance to Good Literature and a Due Cultivation of the Human Understanding. Philadelphia, 1795. Disbound. Baldwins'
51-431 1978 $75

DUKER, ABRAHAM G.   Governments-in-Exile on Jewish Rights. 1942.
Paper. Austin 79-217 1978 $12.50

DUKER, ABRAHAM G.   Jewish Post-War Problems. 1942. Paper.
Austin 79-214 1978 $10

DULAC, EDMUND   The Love of the Foolish Angel. (London), 1929.
1st ed., 8vo, B&W f.p., colored cloth covers faded, fine copy, scarce. Victoria
34-257 1978 $45

DULAC, EDMUND   Picture-Book for the French Red Cross. London,
(1915). 1st ed., quarto, plates, tipped-in portrait of Dulac, covers heavily dust-
soiled, text fine. Victoria 34-258 1978 $50

DULAC, EDMUND   Picture Book for the French Red Cross. (1915).
Portrait, coloured plts., 4to. George's 635-138 1978 £10.50

DULAC, EDMUND   The Queen's Book of the Red Cross. (London,
1939). 1st ed., color plates by Dulac and others, covers faded, fine. Victoria
34-259 1978 $17.50

DU LAC, FRANCOIS MARIE PERRIN
Please turn to
PERRIN DU LAC, FRANCOIS MARIE

DULAURE, JACQUES-ANTOINE   The Gods of Generation. 1933. Austin
80-1023 1978 $17.50

DULLES, ELEANOR LANSING   The Dollar, the Franc and Inflation. 1933.
1st ed. in dust jacket. Austin 80-562 1978 $27.50

DULLES, F. R.   Lowered Boats. New York, (1933). Covers
stained, 8vo., illus., good. Paine 78-45 1978 $15

DUMAS, ALEXANDRE 1802-1870   Count of Monte Cristo. (Mt. Vernon),
1941. Illus. by Lynd Ward, 1 of 1,500 numbered copies signed by Ward, 4to.,
orig. black cloth, bookplates, slipcase, 4 vols., fine. Houle 10-358 1978 $125

DUMAS, ALEXANDRE 1802-1870   Memoirs of a Physician. 1847-47-48. First
ed., 3 vols. in 1, sm. 8vo., cont. half calf, v.g. Fenning 32-98 1978 £10

DUMAS, ALEXANDRE 1802-1870   The Romances. Boston, c. 1900. Ltd. illus.
lib. ed., colour frontis., plts., 60 vols., full crushed levant mor., gilt tops, 8vo.
Howes 194-820 1978 £300

DUMAS, ALEXANDRE 1802-1870   The Three Musketeers. Maastrich for The
Limited Editions Club, 1932. 4to., 2 vols., illus. in color by Pierre Falke, orig.
dec. cloth, pub. box, 1 of 1,500 copies, signed by illustrator, fine. MacManus
238-821 1978 $25

DU MAURIER, DAPHNE   The Du Mauriers. 1937. Covers dull, else good,
first English ed. Bell Book 17-294 1978 £6.50

DU MAURIER, DAPHNE   The Loving Spirit. 1931. Good, scarce, first
English ed. Bell Book 16-294 1978 £12.50

DU MAURIER, DAPHNE   Rebecca. London, 1938. 1st ed., scarce. Biblo BL781-954 1978 $113

DU MAURIER, GEORGE   English Society. London, 1897. Oblong folio,
orig. cloth. K Books 244-357 1978 £10

DU MAURIER, GEORGE   Peter Ibbetson. London, 1892. Illus. by author, 2 vols., orig. cloth, 1st ed., 1st bind., very good set. MacManus 238-215 1978 $85

DU MAURIER, GEORGE   Peter Ibbetson. 1892. Illus. by the author, 2 vols., orig. pict. cloth, nice, first English ed. Bell Book 16-295 1978 £12.50

DU MAURIER, GEORGE   Trilby, A Novel. New York, 1894. 8vo, stamped tan cloth, illus. by author, cover foxed, good, 1st ed., collector's cond. Desmarais 1-142 1978 $10

DU MAURIER, GEORGE   Trilby. London, 1894. 3 vols., orig. cloth, extremities and spine edges worn, 1st ed., few inner hinges cracked, otherwise good. MacManus 238-216 1978 $150

DU MAURIER, GEORGE   Trilby A Novel. 1895. Illus., untrimmed, orig. dark blue cloth, gilt imprint, fine copy. Jarndyce 16-630 1978 £10.50

DUMAURIER, GEORGE   Trilby. New York, 1895. Decor. covers rubbed & soiled, good. Desmarais B-200 1978 $10

DUMBRILLE, DOROTHY   All This Difference. Toronto, 1945. Illus. by S. McCormick. Hood's 115-430 1978 $20

DUMBRILLE, DOROTHY   Stairway to the Stars. Toronto, 1946. Signed by author. Hood's 115-865 1978 $15

DUMBRILLE, DOROTHY   Watch the Sun Rise! A Collection of Poems. Alexandria, 1943. Illus., signed by author. Hood 116-821 1978 $15

DUMOND, DWIGHT L.   America in Our Time, 1896-1946. New York, (1947). Biblo BL781-49 1978 $9

DUMONT, A.   Melanges d'Archeologie et d'Epigraphie, Reunis Par T. Homolle. 1892. Plt., edges browned. Allen 234-288 1978 $25

DU MONT, J.   The Basis of Combination in Chess. London, (1938). 8vo., orig. cloth. K Books 244-358 1978 £5

DUMONT, THERON Q.   The Advanced Course of Personal Magnetism. 1917. Austin 80-1024 1978 $10

DUMOULIN, STEPHANE   Le Tonkin; Exploration du Mekong. Paris, 1888. 4to, half calf, illus., plts. Van der Peet 127-80 1978 Dfl 85

DUMOURIER, GENERAL   Memoirs of General Dumourier Written By Himself. Dublin, 1797. 2 parts in 1 vol., 8vo., contemp. calf. F. Edwards 1013-285 1978 £20

DUMOURIEZ, CHARLES F.   The Life of General Dumouriez. 1796. 1st. ed., 3 vols., 8vo, recently & neatly bound in contemp. style bds., paper labels, uncut, fine copy. Fenning 32-99 1978 £24

DUMVILLE, BENJAMIN   The Science of Speech. 1909. Austin 80-1025 1978 $7.50

DUNANT, JEAN HENRI   Un Souvenir de Solferino, Geneva, 1862. 4to., map, half-cloth, marbled bds., fine, rare, 1st ed. Gilhofer 74-89 1978 sFr 3,500

DUNANT, JEAN HENRI   Un Souvenir de Solferino. Geneve, 1862. Royal 8vo., full red mor., 1st ed., very rare, inscr'd on title page, few stains, otherwise fine cond. Offenbacher 30-32 1978 $850

DUNAWAY, WAYLAND F.   The Scotch-Irish of Colonial Pennsylvania. Chapel Hill, 1944. MacManus 239-1441 1978 $17.50

DUNBAR, CHARLES F.   Chapters on the History of Banking. 1891. Austin 80-563 1978 $15

DUNBAR, FLANDERS   Psychosomatic Diagnosis. New York, 1943. Rittenhouse 49-233 1976 $10

DUNBAR, PAUL LAWRENCE   Folks from Dixie. (1898). First ed., English issue, colour frontis., plts., cr. 8vo., orig. pict. cloth. Howes 194-821 1978 £6.50

DUNBAR, PAUL LAWRENCE   The Uncalled. A Novel. New York, 1898. 1st ed., 12mo., orig. dec. cloth, fine. MacManus 238-469 1978 $45

DUNBAR, SEYMOUR   A History of Travel in American Showing Development of Travel and Transportation. Indiana, (1915). 1st. ed., illus., maps, color plts., 4 vols. Baldwins' 51-10 1978 $50

DUNBAR, SEYMOUR   A History of Travel in America. Indianapolis, 1915. 4 vols., orig. cloth, illus., some in color. MacManus 239-132 1978 $70

DUNBAR, SEYMOUR   A History of Travel in America. 1937. 1 vol. ed., illus., maps. Nestler Rare 78-112 1978 $20

DUNBAR, WILLIAM   The Poems of .... 1932. Good, octavo. Upcroft 10-48 1978 £5

DUNCAN, BINGHAM   Letters of General J.E.B. Stuart to His Wife. Atlanta, 1943. Wrs, Bell Wiley's copy. Broadfoot's 44-119 1978 $14

DUNCAN, DOROTHY   Bluenose. Toronto, 1946. Illus. Hood 117-242 1978 $22.50

DUNCAN, DOROTHY   Partner in Three Worlds. New York and London, 1944. Signed by author. Hood's 115-251 1978 $20

DUNCAN, FRANCIS   Our Garrisons in the West. London, 1864. Orig. binding somewhat worn, inside clean & tight, lg. fldg. map. Hood 117-566 1978 $100

DUNCAN, GEORGE W.   John Archibald Campbell. Montgomery, Ala., 1905. Wraps, uncut, Bell Wiley's Copy. Broadfoot's 44-120 1978 $12.00

DUNCAN, JOHN M.   Travels through Part of the United States and Canada in 1818 and 1819. New York, 1823. 2 vols., rebound. Hood 117-567 1978 $200

DUNCAN, LOUIS C.   The Medical Department of the United States Army in the Civil War. Washington, 1910 (?). Lacks wrs., Bell Wiley's copy. Broadfoot's 44-121 1978 $30

DUNCAN, LOUIS C.   Medical Men in the American Revolution, 1775-1783. Carlisle Barracks, 1931. 8vo., orig. wrs., ex-lib., 1st ed. Morrill 239-71 1978 $15

DUNCAN, N.   The Best of a Bad Job; a Hearty Tale of the Sea. Toronto, 1912. Slightly worn. Hood 116-469 1978 $7.50

DUNCAN, N.   Harbour Tales Down North. New York, 1918. Illus. Hood 116-470 1978 $15

DUNCAN, ROBERT   Medieval Scenes. San Francisco, (1950). 8vo., red paper wrs., sewn as issued, 1st ed., ltd. to 250 copies, signed by author, spine faded, light stain on front free endpaper, else fine. Howell 5-20 1978 $125

DUNCAN, WILLIAM   The Elements of Logick. London, 1748. 1st ed., octavo, full contemp. calf, rebacked, preserving original spine. Bennett 20-234 1978 $125

DUNCOMBE, MRS. JOHN   The Village Gentleman, and the Attorney at Law. A Narrative. London, 1808. 2 vols., 12mo., contemp. calf, 1st ed., covers worn, otherwise very good. MacManus 238-217 1978 $100

DUNCUM, BARBARA M.   The Development of Inhalation Anaesthesia With Special Reference to the Years 1846-1900. London, 1947. 8vo, orig. cloth, d.w., illus., good. Sexton 7-196 1978 £18

DUNDAS, DAVID   Instructions and Regulations for the Formations and Movements of the Cavalry. 1797. First ed., plts., 8vo., contemp. vellum, brass clasps. F. Edwards 1013-286 1978 £45

DUNDONALD, THOMAS COCHRANE, 10TH EARL OF   The Autobiography of a Seaman. London, 1860. 2nd ed., 2 vols., 8vo., orig. cloth, maps, good. Sexton 7-166 1978 £12.50

DUNGLISON, ROBLEY   Dictionary of Medical Science. Philadelphia, 1866. Tight, clean. Rittenhouse 49-235 1976 $25

DUNGLISON, ROBLEY   Dictionary of Medical Science. Philadelphia, 1866. No ed. specified on title, leather, clean, tight. Rittenhouse 49-241 1976 $15

DUNGLISON, ROBLEY   Dictionary of Medical Science. Philadelphia, 1874. Bit shabby. Rittenhouse 49-238 1976 $10

DUNGLISON, ROBLEY   History of Medicine. To the Commencement of the 19th Century. Philadelphia, 1872. First ed., cloth on spine loose at title, still partly attached. Rittenhouse 49-240 1976 $67.50

DUNGLISON, ROBLEY   History of Medicine...to the Commencement of the 19th Century. Philadelphia, 1872. Rittenhouse 49-239 1976 $75

DUNGLISON, ROBLEY   New Remedies-The Method of Preparing & Administering Them. Philadelphia, 1839. Binding much dried out, foxed, needs rebinding. Rittenhouse 49-237 1976 $35

DUNGLISON, ROBLEY   New Remedies: The Method of Preparing and Administering Them. Philadelphia, 1841. Rittenhouse 49-236 1976 $45

DUNGLISON, ROBLEY   The Practice of Medicine: A Treatise of Special Pathology and Therapeutics. Philadelphia, 1844. 2 vols., very clean. Rittenhouse 49-234 1976 $40

DUNHAM, B. MABEL   Mills and Millers of Western Ontario. Ontario, 1946. Card cover. Hood's 115-801 1978 $10

DUNHAM, FRANCIS LEE   An Approach to Social Medicine. 1925. 1st ed. in dust jacket. Austin 80-951 1978 $17.50

DUNHAM, JOSIAH   An Oration for the Fourth of July, 1798. Hanover, n.d. (1798). 8vo, disbound, 2nd ed., very scarce. Ximenes 47-84 1978 $35

DUNHAM, KATHARINE   Journey to Accompong. New York, (1946). Drawings. Biblo 247-286 1978 $17.50

DUNHAM, MABEL   Grand River. Toronto, 1945. Illus. by Edward Cleghorn. Hood 117-730 1978 $7.50

DUNHAM, MABEL   The Trail of the King's Men. Toronto, n.d. Hood's 115-431 1978 $17.50

DUNIWAY, CHARLES   The Development of the Freedom of the Press in Massachusetts. N.P., 1906. Good. Nestler Rare 78-8 1978 $20

DUNLAP, JACK W.   Handbook of Statistical Nomographs, Tables and Formulas. 1932. Austin 80-1027 1978 $27.50

DUNLAP, KNIGHT   Elements of Psychology. 1936. Illus., 1st ed. Austin 80-1029 1978 $17.50

DUNLAP, KNIGHT   The Elements of Scientific Psychology. 1922. 1st ed. Austin 80-1034 1978 $37.50

DUNLAP, KNIGHT   Mysticism, Freudianism & Scientific Psychology. 1920. 1st ed. in frayed dust jacket. Austin 80-1030 1978 $22.50

DUNLAP, KNIGHT   Personal Beauty and Racial Betterment. 1920. 1st ed. in dust jacket. Austin 80-1031 1978 $20

DUNLAP, KNIGHT   Social Psychology. 1925. 1st ed. Austin 80-1032 1978 $22.50

DUNLAP, KNIGHT   A System of Psychology. 1912. Austin 80-1033 1978 $12.50

DUNLAP, ORRIN E.   The Grandeurs of Niagara. Buffalo, 1901. Side-opening 4to. Butterfield 21-304 1978 $15

DUNLAP, WILLIAM   Diary. 1766-1839. New York, 1931. 3 vols., illus., orig. cloth, special ed. ltd. to 100 sets, very fine. MacManus 239-133 $65

DUNLAP, WILLIAM   History of the New Netherlands, Province of New York, and State of New York, to the Adoption of the Federal Constitution. New York, 1839-40. Portr., plt., fldg. maps, 2 vols., 8vo, orig. bds., cloth backs, backs faded, occas. light foxing, 1st ed. Morrill 239-550 1978 $50

DUNLAP, WILLIAM   Memoirs of Charles Brockden Brown, The American Novelist. 1822. 1st. U.K. ed., 8vo, recent calf-backed marbled bds., nice copy. Fenning 32-100 1978 £24.50

DUNLOP, H.   Let's Arrange Flowers. New York, 1943. 8vo, orig. cloth. Book Chest 17-507 1978 $8.50

DUNLOP, J. C.   History of Roman Literature from Its Earliest Period to the Augustan Age. 1823. 2 vols. Allen 234-290 1978 $12.50

DUNLOP, J. C.   History of Roman Literature from Its Earliest Period to the Augustan Age. 1828. 3 vols., ex-lib., buckram. Allen 234-289 1978 $10

DUNN, ALAN   Rejections. New York, 1931. 4to., 1st ed. Biblo 251-164 1978 $15

DUNN, E. J.   The Bushman. London, 1931. 4to, frontispieces, 33 plts., illus. K Books 239-133 1978 £8

DUNN, H. H.   The Crimson Jester: Zapata of Mexico. New York, 1933. 1st ed. Jenkins 116-1511 1978 $45

DUNN, JOHN   Brief, In Reference to Bill Pending Before Congress as to Private Land Claims. [Chicago, 1880]. Disbound, 1st ed. Ginsberg 14-756 1978 $55

DUNN, NATHAN   A Descriptive Catalogue of the Chinese Collection in Philadelphia. Philadelphia, 1839. Wrs., leather spine, small parts of spine missing, joints splitting, foxed. Dawson's 449-32 1978 $75

DUNN, WILLIAM E.   Spanish and French Rivalry in the Gulf Region of the U. S., 1678-1702:.... Austin, 1917. Wr. Jenkins 116-367 1978 $45

DUNNE, FINLEY PETER   Dissertations. 1906. First ed. Austin 82-358 1978 $12.50

DUNNE, FINLEY PETER   Mr. Dooley in Peace and War. Boston, 1898. First ed. Austin 82-359 1978 $10

DUNNE, FINLEY PETER   Mr. Dooley in the Hearts of His Countrymen. 1899. Austin 82-361 1978 $8.50

DUNNE, FINLEY PETER   Mr. Dooley on Making a Will and Other Necessary Evils. 1919. First ed. Austin 82-362 1978 $12.50

DUNNE, FINLEY PETER   Mr. Dooley's Opinions. 1901. First ed., very good. Austin 82-363 1978 $20

DUNNE, FINLEY PETER   Mr. Dooley's Philosophy. 1900. Austin 82-365 1978 $8.50

DUNNE, FINLEY PETER   Observations by Mr. Dooley. 1902. Rose cloth, first ed., very good, frayed d.j. Austin 82-366 1978 $37.50

DUNNE, J. W.   An Experiment With Time. London, 1927. Nice, first ed., orig. binding, bookplt. Rota 212-17 1978 £21

DUNNE, J. W.   The New Immortality. 1938. Very good, slight worn d.w., first English ed. Bell Book 17-296 1978 £5

DUNNE, J. W.   The Serial Universe. 1938. 1st Amer. ed. in repaired dust jacket, cover faded some. Austin 80-1035 1978 $15

DUNNING, ALBERT E.   Congregationalists in America. New York, (1894). 1st ed., illus., orig. 3/4 calf, very good copy. MacManus 239-91 1978 $22.50

DUNNING, WILLIAM ARCHIBALD   Essays on the Civil War and Reconstruction and Related Topics. NY, 1898. Bell Wiley's Copy. Broadfoot's 44-122 1978 $9.00

DUNSANY, EDWARD JOHN MORETON DRAX PLUNKETT   The Blessing of Pan. 1927. Frontis., fine, first English ed. Bell Book 17-297 1978 £15

DUNSANY, EDWARD JOHN MORETON DRAX PLUNKETT   The Book of Wonder. Boston, n.d. Illus. by S. H. Sime, one signature loose, name in ink on flyleaf, dated 1917. Biblo 251-479 1978 $12.50

DUNSANY, EDWARD JOHN MORETON DRAX PLUNKETT   The Charwoman's Shadow. New York, 1926. 1st Amer. ed., covers faded, edges rubbed. Biblo 251-480 1978 $15

DUNSANY, EDWARD JOHN MORETON DRAX PLUNKETT   Fifty-One Tales. New York, 1915. 1st Amer. ed., binding rubbed. Biblo 251-481 1978 $16.50

DUNSANY, EDWARD JOHN MORETON DRAX PLUNKETT   Fifty-One Tales. 1915. Portrait, linen-backed bds., covers somewhat browned, good, first English ed. Bell Book 17-298 1978 £16.50

DUNSANY, EDWARD JOHN MORETON DRAX PLUNKETT   The Fourth Book of Jorkens. Sauk City, 1948. One of 3,000 copies, very good, d.w. Bernard 5-382 1978 $30

DUNSANY, EDWARD JOHN MORETON DRAX PLUNKETT   The Gods of Pegana. London, 1911. 8vo., bds., cloth back, 2nd ed., ownership inscription, covers lightly worn, fine. Desmarais 1-146 1978 $20

DUNSANY, EDWARD JOHN MORETON DRAX PLUNKETT   The Gods of Pegana. Boston, n.d. 1st Amer. ed., illus. by S. H. Sime. Biblo 251-482 1978 $17.50

DUNSANY, EDWARD JOHN MORETON DRAX PLUNKETT   Guerrilla. Indian-apolis, (1944). 1st Amer. ed., d.w. Biblo 251-465 1978 $15

DUNSANY, EDWARD JOHN MORETON DRAX PLUNKETT   The Last Book of Wonder. Boston, (1916). 1st Amer. ed., illus. by S. H. Sime. Biblo 251-483 1978 $15

DUNSANY, EDWARD JOHN MORETON DRAX PLUNKETT   My Ireland. New York, 1937. Illus., 1st Amer. ed. Biblo 251-466 1978 $17.50

DUNSANY, EDWARD JOHN MORETON DRAX PLUNKETT   Plays of Gods and Men. 1917. Portrait, linen-backed bds., spine faded, very good, first English ed. Bell Book 17-299 1978 £12.50

DUNSANY, EDWARD JOHN MORETON DRAX PLUNKETT   Plays of Gods & Men. Dublin, 1917. 8vo., boards, cloth back, foxed, bookplate, 1st ed., collector's cond. Desmarais 1-147 1978 $15

DUNSANY, EDWARD JOHN MORETON DRAX PLUNKETT   Rory and Bran. New York, (1937). 1st Amer. ed. Biblo 251-484 1978 $15

DUNSANY, EDWARD JOHN MORETON DRAX PLUNKETT   The Story of Mona Sheehy. New York, 1940. 1st Amer. ed., d.w. Biblo 251-485 1978 $18.50

DUNSANY, EDWARD JOHN MORETON DRAX PLUNKETT   Tales of War. Dublin, 1918. 8vo., bds., cloth back, d.w. spine severed, light edge browning, 1st ed., collector's cond. Desmarais 1-148 1978 $30

DUNSANY, EDWARD JOHN MORETON DRAX PLUNKETT   Tales of War. Boston, 1918. 1st Amer. ed. Biblo 251-486 1978 $15

DUNSANY, EDWARD JOHN MORETON DRAX PLUNKETT   Time and the Gods. Boston, n.d. Illus. by S. H. Sime. Biblo 251-487 1978 $15

DUNSFORD, MARTIN   Historical Memoirs of the Town and Parish of Tiverton, in the County of Devon. Exeter, 1790. Engrav. title, second ed., plts., 4to., old style half calf. K Books 244-105 1978 £70

DUNTHORNE, GORDON   Flower and Fruit Prints of the 18th and Early 19th Centuries: Their History, Makers and Uses, with a Catalogue Raisonne of the Works in Which They are Found. Washington, 1938. Folio, orig. cloth, slipcase, fine. MacManus 238-912 1978 $225

DUNTON, JOHN   A True Journall of the Sally Fleet with the Pro-ceedings of the Voyage. 1637. Plt., sm. 4to., modern half mor. F. Edwards 1013-61 1978 £350

DUPATY, J. B.   Lettres sur l'Italie. Paris, 1822. 3 vols. in 1, sm. 12mo., shell patterned bds., half calf, good. King 7-348 1978 $25

DUPIN, CHARLES   Mathematics Practically Applied to the Useful and Fine Arts. London, 1827. 8vo., plts., orig. cloth, a trifle worn. Quaritch 977-217 1978 $70

DUPIN, LOUIS ELLIES   Bibliotheque Universelle des Historiens;.... Amsterdam, 1708. 1st folio ed., quarto, maps, full contemporary flecked calf, morocco spine-label, gilt, finely engraved pictorial t.p.   Bennett 20-62 1978 $200

DUPIN, LOUIS ELLIES   A Compleat History of the Canon and Writers... 1699-1700. 1st. English ed., 2 vols. in 1, folio, contemp. calf, heavily scored by sharp knife removing strips of leather. Hannas 54-101 1978 £15

DUPIN, LOUIS ELLIES   A New History of Ecclesiastical Writers... 1696-95-99. 3rd. ed., 13 vols. in 4, folio, lacking 1 leaf, contemp. panelled calf, lacks labels, slightly worn, minor worming in 2 vols., fine unused set. Hannas 54-102 1978 £65

DU PONT, B. G.   Du Pont de Nemours. N.P., (1933). 1st ed., 2 vols., illus., orig. leatherette, pub. box, very fine. MacManus 239-745 1978 $45

DU PONT, H. A.   The Campaign of 1864 in the Valley of Virginia and the Expedition to Lynchburg. New York, 1925. Port., maps, fine, d.j. MacManus 239-873 1978 $22.50

DU PONT, H. A.   The Early Generations of the Du Pont and Allied Families. New York, 1923. 2 vols., frontis., scarce. MacManus 239-920 1978 $100

DU PONT, H. A.   Rear-Admiral Samuel Francis DuPont, United States Navy. New York, 1926. Stained cover, Bell Wiley's copy. Broadfoot's 44-123 1978 $10

DUPONT, MAURICE   Decoration coreenne. Paris, n.d. Plates, loose in wrs., (little chipped), encased in folding cloth covers, marbled board slip case with leather spine. Dawson's 127-213 1978 $135

DUPORT, JAMES 1606-79   Sive Metaphrasis Libri Psalmorum Graecis Versibus Contexta. Cambridge, 1666. First ed., 4to., engraved portrait, contemp. calf, neatly rebacked, orig. label. Howes 194-41 1978 £35

DUPPA, RICHARD   The Classes and Orders of the Linnaean System of Botany. London, 1816. Plts., some colored, 8vo., contemp. straight-grain mor., a.e.g., 1st ed., light cover wear, some light offsetting from plts., else fine, bookplts. Howell 5-21 1978 $400

DU PREL, CARL   Die Philosophie Der Mystik. Leipzig, 1910. Salloch 348-53 1978 $22.50

DUPREZ, M. F.   Report on Atmospheric Electricity. (Washington), n.d. 8vo., sewn, ex-lib. Morrill 241-120 1978 $7.50

DUPUY, W. A.   The Nation's Forests. 1938. Ex-lib. Austin 80-565 1978 $10

DUPUYTREN, GUILLAUME   Lectures on Clinical Surgery. Washington, 1835. Rittenhouse 49-242 1976 $25

DUPUYTREN, GUILLAUME   On Lesions of the Vascular System, Diseases of the Rectum, and Other Surgical Complaints. London, 1854. 8vo., orig. green stamped cloth with gilt insignia, gilt lettering on spine, very good uncut copy with bkplts. of Drs. James Gilpin Houseman & Alfred M. Hellman. Zeitlin 245-68 1978 $75

DUPUYTREN, GUILLAUME   On the Injuries and Diseases of Bones. London, 1847. 8vo., orig. green blind-stamped cloth, gilt lettering on spine, light brown-ing, bkplts. of Drs. James Gilpin Houseman & Alfred M. Hellman, very good copy. Zeitlin 245-69 1978 $65

DURAND, H.   Wild Flowers & Ferns. New York, 1925. 8vo, orig. cloth. Book Chest 17-508 1978 $12.50

DURANDI, JACOPO   Delle Antiche Citta di Pedona, Caburro, Germ-anicia.... 1769. 8vo., vellum, illus., plt., first ed. King 7-166 1978 £20

DURANDRUEL, GALERIE   Recueil D'estampes Gravees a L'eau-Forte. Paris, London, 1873. 6 vols., 4to., contemp. 3/4 hardgrain mor., uncut, orig. etchings, prtd. on verge paper. Goldschmidt 110-5 1978 $475

DURANDUS, GUILELMUS BP OF MENDE
Please turn to
DURANTIS, GUILELMUS BP OF MENDE

DURANG, MARY   The Rainbow of Charity.... Philadelphia, (1857).
Hand-colored plates, very good.   Victoria 34-263 1978 $15

DURANT, WILL   Adventures in Genius. 1931. Illus., first ed.,
signed by author. Austin 82-367 1978 $12.50

DURANT, WILL   Transition. 1927. 352 pages. Austin 82-368
1978 $7.50

DURANTIS, GUILELMUS BP OF MENDE   Rationale divinorum officiorum.   Venice, 1494. Folio, quarter calf with marbled bds., front fly-leaf repaired, rear
leaves lightly stained, woodcut initials. Bennett 20-63 1978 $1,575

DURBIN, E. F. M.   Purchasing Power and Trade Depression.   London,
1933. 1st ed. Austin 80-566 1978 $17.50

DURER, ALBRECHT
Please turn to
DUERER, ALBRECHT

D'URFEY, THOMAS   Songs Compleat, Pleasant and Divertive.   1719
(1875). 6 vols., sm. 8vo., portr. frontis., half vellum, gilt tops, bkplt. Quaritch 979-130 1978 $175

DURHAM, EARL OF   Report on the Affairs of British North America,
from the.... Toronto, 1839. 3/4 leather, marbled bds. & end-papers. Hood's
115-589 1978 $90

DURHAM, JAMES 1622-58   The Blessednesse of the Death of these that die in
the Lord.... (Glasgow), 1681. First ed., sm. 8vo., 19th cent. calf, corner of
one leaf torn with loss of a few words, good. Howes 194-42 1978 $35

DURHAM, ROBERT LEE   The Call of the South. 1908. Illus., first ed.
Austin 82-369 1978 $20

DURKIN, D. L.   The Fighting Men of Canada. Toronto, 1918.
Hood 116-822 1978 $12.50

DURKIN, HELEN E.   Trial and Error, Gradual Analysis and Sudden
Reorganization. 1937. Paper. Austin 80-1037 1978 $12.50

DURKIN, JOSEPH T.   John Dooley, Confederate Soldier, His War
Journal. Washington, 1945. Bell Wiley's copy. Broadfoot's 44-651 1978 $20

DURNO, J.   A Description of a New-Invented Stove-grate,....
London, 1753. 8vo, disbound, 1st ed., small repair to the verso of the t.p., very
good copy of a rare tract. Ximenes 47-85 1978 $250

DURO, CESAREO FERNANDEZ
Please turn to
FERNANDEZ DURO, CESAREO

DURRANT, VALENTINE   A Modern Minister. 1878. 1st. ed., 2 vols.,
illus., half titles, half dark blue calf, maroon labels, v.g. Jarndyce 16-631
1978 £30

DURRBACH, F.   Inscriptions de Delos. 1926. Folio, buckram.
Allen 234-291 1978 $25

DURRELL, LAWRENCE   Panic Spring. New York, (1937). Orig. binding. Wolfe 39-136 1978 $150

DURRELL, LAWRENCE   Unckebunck: a biography in little. Fortune
Press, 1938. Near fine, d.w., rare, first English ed. Bell Book 17-303 1978
£85

DURRETT, REUBEN T.   The Centenary of Louisville. Louisville, 1893.
4to., ports., #8, orig. wrs., unopened, covers slightly frayed. Biblo BL781-249
1978 $45

DURRIE, DANIEL S.   A History of Madison, the Capital of Wisconsin.
Madison, 1874. Fine, orig. cloth. MacManus 239-1139 1978 $30

D'URVILLE, M. DUMONT   Voyage Pittoresque Autour De Monde... Paris,
1846. Maps, illus., 2 vols., imp. 8vo, half calf. Edwards 1012-16 1978 £75

DURY, ANDREW   A New, General and Universal Atlas. 1761.
Sm. oblong 8vo, pictorial engraved title-pg., engraved maps, coloured in outline,
contemporary speckled calf, gilt border, gilt back, raised bands. Deighton 5-182
1978 £165

DU SOMMERARD, A.   Les Arts au Moyen Age, en ce qui Concerne Prin-
cipalement le Palais Romain de Paris, L'Hotel de Cluny. 1846. Vol. 5 only, half
mor. Allen 234-1213 1978 $9.50

DUSS, JOHN S.   The Harmonists. A Personal History. Harrisburg, 1943. 1st ed. MacManus 239-1442 1978 $22.50

DU TERTRE, J. B.   Histoire General Des Isles de S. Christophe...
Paris, Jacques Langlois, 1654. Sm. 4to, limp vellum, maps, slight browning.
Edwards 1012-712 1978 £500

DUTREUIL DE RHINS, J. L.   Le Royaume d'Annam et les Annamites. Paris,
1879. Half cloth, folding map, plts., 8vo. Van der Peet 127-83 1978 Dfl 50

DUTROCHET, RENE JOACHIM HENRI   Essai Sur Une Nouvelle Theorie de la
Voix, Avec l'Expose Des Divers Systemes Qui Ont Paru Jusqu'a ce Jour sur cet
Objet. Paris, 1806. Lg. 4to., contemp. blue wrs., uncut, 1st ed., very scarce,
some foxing. Offenbacher 30-33 1978 $200

DUTROCHET, RENE JOAQUIM HENRI   Recherches Anatomiques et Physiologiques sur la Structure Intime des Animaux et des Vegetaux et sur leur Motilite.
Paris, 1824. Fldg. table, copperplts., designed by author, 8vo., 3/4 calf, back
gilt, 1st ed., some foxing. Offenbacher 30-34 1978 $275

DUTTON, SAMUEL W. S.   The History of the North Church in New Haven.
New Haven, 1842. Later 3/4 mor., marbled bds., very good. MacManus 239-
100 1978 $10

DUTTON, WILLIAM S.   Du Pont...One Hundred and Forty Years. New
York, 1942. Biblo BL781-83 1978 $7.50

DUTUIT, E.   La Collection Dutuit. Paris, 1899. Ltd. to
350 copies, plts., illus., med. folio, orig. bds. Forster 130-2 1978 £75

DUVAL, E. W.   T. E. Lawrence, a Bibliography. New York,
Spiral Press, (1938). Arrow Eds., one of 500 copies prtd., very fine. Battery
Park 1-466 1978 $95

DUVAL, JULES   Histoire De L'Emigration. Paris, 1862. In
French. Austin 79-218 1978 $47.50

DUVERNEY, JOSEPH-GUICHARD   Traite de l'Organe de l'Ouie, Contenant
la Structure, les Usages & les Maladies de Toutes les Parties de l'Oreille. Paris,
1683. Lg. fldg. anatomical copperplts., 12mo., contemp. calf, worn, back gilt,
1st ed. Offenbacher 30-35 1978 $875

DWIGGINS, WILLIAM ADDISON   Form Letters. New York, 1930. Illus.,
signed. Battery Park 1-75 1978 $45

DWIGGINS, WILLIAM ADDISON   The Pictorial Life of Benjamin Franklin.
Philadelphia, 1923. 4to., bds., cloth spine, illus., frontis. in color, fine.
Battery Park 1-74 1978 $45

DWIGGINS, WILLIAM ADDISON   22 Printers Marks and Seals Designed and
Drawn by W. A. Dwiggins. New York, 1929. 1st ed., ltd. to 350 numbered
copies signed by author, 8vo., unpaginated, partially uncut, orig. black gilt decor.
bds., blue cloth spine, interior near mint. Current 24-215 1978 $150

DWIGGINS, WILLIAM ADDISON   W.A.D. to RR. 1940. Thin 4to. Battery
Park 1-77 1978 $45

DWIGGINS, WILLIAM ADDISON   What are the Dwiggins Marionettes? Puterschein Hingham Press. Sm. folio, folded, wr., very fine. Battery Park 1-73
1978 $50

DWIGHT, H. G.   The Emperor of Elam and Other Stories. 1920.
Austin 82-370 1978 $12.50

DWIGHT, HENRY OTIS   The Encyclopedia of Missions. New York, 1904.
2nd. ed., orig. binding, clean. Hayman 71-192 1978 $10

DWIGHT, MARGARET VAN HORN   A Journey to Ohio in 1810, as Recorded in the Journal of. New Haven, 1912. Ltd. to 600 copies, bds. MacManus 239-379 1978 $17.50

DWIGHT, MARGARET VAN HORN   A Journey to Ohio in 1810. New Haven, 1914. Biblo 248-246 1978 $7.50

DWIGHT, T.   A Sermon Delivered in Boston, Sept. 16, 1813, Before the American Board of Commissioners for Foreign Missions... Boston, 1813. 8vo, orig. cloth, wrappers. Edwards 1012-488 1978 £15

DWIGHT, THEODORE F.   Critical Sketches of Some of the Federal & Confederate Commanders. Boston, 1895. Bell Wiley's copy. Broadfoot 46-81 1978 $16

DWIGHT, TIMOTHY   The Conquest of Canaan; a Poem, in Eleven Books. Hartford, 1785. Orig. leather, rubbed, 1st ed. MacManus 238-470 1978 $85

DWIGHT, TIMOTHY   Greenfield Hill: a Poem, in Seven Parts. New York, 1794. 8vo, disbound, 1st ed. Ximenes 47-86 1978 $75

DYBOWSKI, J.   La Route Du Tchad... Paris, 1893. Folding map, portrait, illus., roy. 8vo, morocco spine. Edwards 1012-255 1978 £25

DYCE, ALEXANDER   Remarks on Mr. J. P. Collier's and Mr. C. Knight's Editions of Shakespeare. London, 1844. 8vo, original green cloth, printed paper label, 1st ed., nice copy, partly unopened. Ximenes 47-87 1978 $30

DYCHE, THOMAS   English Particles Latiniz'd: .... London, 1713. Sm. 8vo, contemporary sheepskin, cracked at hinges, very fine, firm. Victoria 34-266 1978 $35

DYCHE, THOMAS   A Guide to the English Tongue. Gainsborough, 1811. 12mo, woodcut portrait, illus., orig. sheep, very worn, 2 parts. Hannas 54-186 1978 £12.50

DYE, E. E.   McLoughlin and Old Oregon. Chicago, 1903. 5th ed. Hood 117-295 1978 $17.50

DYER, CHARLES N.   History of the Town of Plainfield, Hampshire Co., Mass., From Its Settlement to 1891. Northampton, 1891. Illus. MacManus 239-1045 1978 $27.50

DYER, D. B.   "Fort Reno";.... New York, 1896. Illus., orig. cloth, 1st ed. Ginsberg 14-796 1978 $125

DYER, E. J.   The Routes and Mineral Resources of North Western Canada. London, 1898. Lacking fold. map and frontis. Hood 116-78 1978 $85

DYER, ELISHA   Official Register of Rhode Island Officers and Men Who Served in the U. S. Army & Navy from 1861 to 1866. Providence, 1893 & 1895. New cloth, 2 vols., Bell Wiley's copy. Broadfoot 46-369 1978 $50

DYER, FRANK LEWIS   Edison, His Life and Inventions. New York, 1910. Illus., 2 vols. MacManus 239-749 1978 $22.50

DYER, GILBERT 1743-1820   Vulgar Errors, Ancient and Modern. Exeter, 1816-14. First ed., 3 parts in 1 vol., half calf, gilt top, 8vo. Howes 194-255 1978 £15

DYER, JOHN P.   From Shiloh to San Juan, The Life of "Fightin' Joe" Wheeler. University, La., 1941. Bell Wiley's copy. Broadfoot 46-82 1978 $20

DYER, MARY M.   A Portraiture of Shakerism, ... N.P. (Concord), 1822. 12mo, contemporary half calf (bit rubbed, but sound), 1st ed., light browning, very good copy. Ximenes 47-88 1978 $175

DYER, T. F. T.   British Popular Customs, Present and Past. Bohn, 1900. Cr. 8vo. George's 635-1425 1978 £5.50

DYER, T. H.   Pompeii, its History, Buildings and Antiquities. 1867. Map, engraved plts., wood-engravings, cr. 8vo., full crimson calf, gilt, a little rubbed. George's 635-503 1978 £5

DYER, W.   All Around Robin Hood's Barn. New York, 1926. 1st ed., drawings by Charles Livingston Bull, 8vo, orig. cloth. Book Chest 17-129 1978 $35

DYESS, WILLIAM E.   The Dyess Story. 1944. Austin 80-90 1978 $11

DYKES, WILLIAM RICKATSON   Notes on Tulip Species. London, 1930. Folio, d.w., coloured plts. Traylen 88-567 1978 £75

DYOTT, WILLIAM   Dyott's Diary, 1781-1845. 1907. Portrait, 2 vols., 8vo. George's 635-810 1978 £7.50

E

E., A. PSEUD.
Please turn to
RUSSELL, GEORGE WILLIAM

EACHARD, L.   The Gazeteer's. 1706. Bottom of title missing, 18mo. George's 635-1464 1978 £5

EADE, CHARLES   The Unrelenting Struggle. 1942. Austin 80-58 1978 $10

EADIE, TOM   I Like Diving. Boston, 1929. Illus., orig. cloth, 8vo., d.w., 1st ed. Morrill 241-122 1978 $12.50

EADMER THE MONK   Eadmeri Monarchi Cantuariensis Historiae Novorum sive Sui Saeculi Libri VI. London, 1623. 1st ed., title in red & black, folio, contemp. calf. Traylen 88-232 1978 £60

EAGEN, CHARLES   Statement of the Financial Condition of the Territory of Washington,... Olympia, 1864. Disbound, 1st ed. Ginsberg 14-1028 1978 $100

EARHART, AMELIA   The Fun Of It. New York, 1932. Illus. Biblo 247-652 1978 $15

EARHART, J. F.   The Harmonizer. Cincinnati, 1897. Complimentary copy by Ault & Wiborg Co., 12mo., cloth, prtd. on various colored paper. Battery Park 1-467 1978 $250

EARLE, ALICE MORSE   Costume of Colonial Times. New York, 1894. 1st. ed. Baldwins' 51-61 1978 $12.50

EARLE, ALICE MORSE   Home Life in Colonial Days. New York, 1898. Illus. Baldwins' 51-62 1978 $10

EARLE, ALICE MORSE   Old Time Gardens. New York, 1901. 1st ed., illus., contemp. 3/4 mor., cloth, 1 of 350 copies on lg. paper, library stamps, otherwise a fine copy. MacManus 239-657 1978 $35

EARLE, ALICE MORSE   Old Time Gardens. New York, 1901. Illus., 8vo, orig. cloth. Book Chest 17-131 1978 $28

EARLE, ALICE MORSE   Old Time Gardens Newly Set Forth. New York, 1901. 1st. ed., very good copy. Baldwins' 51-64 1978 $12.50

EARLE, ALICE MORSE   Stage-Coach and Tavern Days. New York, 1901. Illus. Baldwins' 51-63 1978 $12.50

EARLE, ALICE MORSE   Sun-Dials and Roses of Yesterday. New York, 1902. 8vo, orig. cloth. Book Chest 17-130 1978 $25

EARLE, ALICE MORSE   Two Centuries of Costume in America 1620-1820. New York, 1903. Illus., orig. cloth, fine set, rebacked. MacManus 239-658 1978 $40

EARLE, ALICE MORSE   Two Centuries of Costume in America. New York, 1903. 1st. ed., illus., 2 vols. Baldwins' 51-65 1978 $20

EARLE, ALICE MORSE   Two Centuries of Costume in America. New York, (1910). 2 vols. in 1, minor rubbing. Baldwins' 51-66 1978 $17.50

EARLE, C.   A Third Pot-Pourri. New York, 1903. Faded binding, 8vo, orig. cloth. Book Chest 17-132 1978 $18.50

EARLE, FERDINAND   The Lyric Year. One Hundred Poems... New York, 1912. 1st ed., 2nd state. Biblo BL781-955 1978 $12

EARLE, JOHN   English Prose: its Elements, History and Usage. 1890. Orig. cloth, 8vo. Howes 194-822 1978 £6.50

EARLE, JOHN   Microcosmography: or, A Piece of the World Discover'd. 1732. 12mo, buckram, slightly foxed. Hannas 54-103 1978 £17.50

EARLE, JOHN   Micro-Cosmographie. 1903. 1st. ed., ltd. 250 copies, 1/4 vellum, orig. grey bds., spine darkened, otherwise v.g. Jarndyce 16-1198 1978 £12.50

EARLE, SWEPSON   The Chesapeake Bay Country. Baltimore, 1929. Thick royal 8vo., illus., maps, orig. cloth, very good. MacManus 239-1802 1978 $35

EARLE, THOMAS   Annals of the General Society of Mechanics and Tradesmen of the City of New York, from 1785 to 1880. New York, 1882. Plts., 4to., 1st ed., orig. cloth. Morrill 241-696 1978 $50

EARLE, THOMAS   The Life, Travels and Opinions of Benjamin Lundy, Including His Journeys to Texas and Mexico.... Philadelphia, 1847. Later half mor., 1st ed., color map. Jenkins 116-1572 1978 $250

EARLY, JUBAL A.   The Heritage of the South. Lynchburg, 1915. Bell Wiley's copy. Broadfoot 46-83 1978 $20

EARLY Coastwise and Foreign Shipping of Salem. Salem, 1934. 8vo., orig. cloth, fine. Paine 78-46 1978 $20.00

EARLY Drawings and Pictures of London, with Some Contemporary Furniture. 1920. 4to., plts., buckram. Quaritch 983-212 1978 $55

EARLY Records of the City and County of Albany and...Rensselaerswyck. Albany, 1916. Vol. 2 only, fine copy. Butterfield 21-23 1978 $20

EARLY English Text Society. London, 1864-1890. Orig. series vols. 1-94, lacking vols. 2, 3, and 79, and extra series vols. 1-58, 8vo, half morocco. Traylen 88-233 1978 £750

EARLY Records of the City and County of Albany and...Rensselaerswyck. Albany, 1918. Vol. 3 only, mint copy. Butterfield 21-24 1978 $25

EARLY Records of the City and County of Albany and...Rensselaerswyck. Albany, 1919. Vol. 4 only, as new. Butterfield 21-25 1978 $15

EARLY Venetian Pictures and Other Works of Art. 1912. 4to., plts., buckram, uncut. Quaritch 983-270 1978 $75

EARLY Scenes in Church History. Salt Lake City, 1882. Orig. cloth, 1st ed. Ginsberg 14-647 1978 $20

EARNEST, ERNEST   John and William Bartram, Botanists and Explorers. Philadelphi, 1940. Orig. cloth, ports. MacManus 239-1365 1978 $15

EARP, WILBUR F.   The Lord Paramount. 1936. Austin 80-568 1978 $10

EAST, EDWARD M.   Heredity and Human Affairs. 1927. Austin 80-1038 1978 $10

EAST-India Register and Army List for 1855. 1855. Thick sm. 8vo, morocco. Edwards 1012-97 1978 £20

THE EASTERN Townships Gazeteer and General Business Directory. St. Johns, 1867. Folio, marbled bds., cloth back, covers worn, map, very scarce. Wolfe 39-144 1978 $500

EASTERBY, W.   The History of the Law of Tithes in England. Cambridge, 1888. 8vo. Upcroft 12-124 1978 £7.50

EASTERN COMMERCIAL TEACHERS ASSOC. 11th Yearbook - 1938: Modernizing Business Education. Austin 80-1039 1978 $10

EASTERN COMMERCIAL TEACHERS ASSOC. 12th Yearbook - 1939: Improvement of Classroom Teaching in Business Education. Austin 80-1040 1978 $10

EASTERN COMMERCIAL TEACHERS ASSOC.   15th Yearbook - 1942: Unite Planning in Business Education. Austin 80-1041 1978 $10

EASTLAKE, CHARLES L.   Beitrage zur Geschichte der Olmalerei. Wien, 1907. Biblo 251-198 1978 $17.50

EASTMAN, H.   New England Ferns and Their Common Allies. New York, 1904. Poor binding, 8vo, orig. cloth. Book Chest 17-133 1978 $12

EASTMAN, MARY H.   Chicora And Other Regions of the Conquerors and the Conquered. 1854. 1st. ed., engraved plts., imp. 8vo, orig. cloth, slightly scuffed & dust-soiled. Edwards 1012-552 1978 £75

EATON, A. W. H.   Acadian Ballads and Lyrics in Many Moods. Toronto, 1930. Hood 116-823 1978 $25

EATON, C. ANNE   Continental Adventures. 1826. 3 vols., 8vo, light foxing in 2 vols., contemp. 1/2 calf, marbled bds. & edges. Eaton 45-167 1978 £30

EATON, ELON HOWARD   Birds of New York. Albany, 1910-14. 2 vols., thick 4to., color plts., nice set, scarce. Butterfield 21-69 1978 $100

EATON, LILLEY   Genealogical History of the Town of Reading, Mass... Boston, 1874. Illus., ports., orig. cloth, lib. marks, very good. MacManus 239-1047 1978 $42.50

EATON, MOSES   Five Years on the Erie Canal:.... Utica, 1845. Binding quite worn. Nestler Rare 78-114 1978 $55

EATON, MOSES   Five Years on the Erie Canal. Utica, 1846. 16mo., orig. cloth, scarce. Butterfield 21-90 1978 $45

EATON, MOSES   Manual of Botany, for North America... Albany, 1833. 6th ed., illus., orig. full calf, scuffed, but nice. MacManus 239-56 1978 $30

EATON, SEYMOUR   The Traveling Bears in the East and West. New York, (1915). 1st ed., illus. by V. Floyd Campbell, colored f.p., minor cover defects, very good. Victoria 34-267 1978 $30

EATON, WALTER PRICHARD   In Berkshire Fields. New York, (1920). Illus., in color, 1st ed., orig. cloth-backed pic. bds., nice. MacManus 239-293 1978 $15

EBEN, FREDERIC   The Swedish Army. 1808. Coloured aquatint plts., 4to., contemp. half calf, marbled bds., fine, rare. F. Edwards 1013-288 1978 £2,750

EBERHART, RICHARD   A Bravery of Earth. 1930. Very good, nice d.w., first English ed. Bell Book 17-306 1978 £65

EBERHART, RICHARD   Poems, New and Selected. Norfolk, 1944. 32mo, green pr. wr., Mint, signed by author, 1st ed., collector's cond. Desmarais 1-152 1978 $40

EBERLE, FREDERICK   Trial of Frederick Eberle & Others at a Nidi Prius Court, Held at Phila.,.... Philadelphia, 1817. 1st ed., 2-tone cloth with added endpapers, uncut copy, orig. binding, 8vo. Americanist 101-159 1978 $30

EBERLE, JOHN   A Treatise on the Practice of Medicine. Philadelphia, 1831. 2nd ed., 8vo., contemp. calf, 2 vols., heavily foxed. Morrill 239-72 1978 $15

EBERLEIN, HAROLD DONALDSON   The Church of Saint Peter in the Great Valley. Richmond, 1944. First ed., illus., orig. cloth, v.g. MacManus 239-1444 1978 $15

EBERLEIN, HAROLD DONALDSON   The Colonial Homes of Philadelphia and Its Neighborhood. Philadelphia, 1912. Illus., fine copy. MacManus 239-1443 1978 $45

EBERLEIN, HAROLD DONALDSON   Colonial Interiors. New York, 1938. First ed., 3rd series, lg. 4to., plts., signed by authors, 8vo., orig. binding. Americanist 101-5 1978 $45

EBERLEIN, HAROLD DONALDSON   Details of the Architecture of Tuscany. New York, 1923. Plts., sm. folio, Baldwin's 51-68 1978 $20

EBERLEIN, HAROLD DONALDSON   Details of the Architecture of Tuscany. New York, (1923). Folio, photos, bind. worn, contents v.g. Biblo BL781-540 1978 $35

EBERLEIN, HAROLD DONALDSON   Diary of Independence Hall. Philadelphia, (1943). Illus., from photos., engrs., 8vo., 1st ed., pres. copy from authors. Morrill 239-577 1978 $10

EBERLEIN, HAROLD DONALDSON   Historic Houses of the Hudson Valley. New York, 1942. Plts., sm. folio. Baldwin's 51-412 1978 $20

EBERLEIN, HAROLD DONALDSON   Manor Houses and Historic Homes of Long Island and Staten Island. Philadelphia, 1928. 1st ed., ltd. ed., illus. MacManus 239-659 1978 $25

EBERLEIN, HAROLD DONALDSON   Manor Houses and Historic Homes of Long Island and Staten Island. Philadelphia, 1928. 75 illus., ltd. ed. Baldwins' 51-411 1978 $27.50

EBERLEIN, HAROLD DONALDSON   The Manors and Historic Homes of the Hudson Valley. Philadelphia, 1924. 1st ed., ltd. ed., illus., fine untrimmed copy. MacManus 239-660 1978 $35

EBERLEIN, HAROLD DONALDSON   The Manors and Historic Homes of the Hudson Valley. Philadelphia, 1924. Illus., ltd. ed. Baldwins' 51-410 1978 $32.50

EBERLEIN, HAROLD DONALDSON   Portrait of a Colonial City. Philadelphia 1670-1838. Philadelphia, (1939). Illus., plts., 1st ed., 4to., orig. cloth, fine, untrimmed copy, ltd. ed., scarce. MacManus 239-1646 1978 $100

EBERLEIN, HAROLD DONALDSON   Portrait of a Colonial City. Philadelphia, (1939). 252 illus., maps, 4to., binding faded & some stains, inscribed to Edward L. Davis. Baldwins' 51-432 1978 $65

EBERLEIN, HAROLD DONALDSON   The Practical Book of American Antiques. n.d. Rev'd ed., illus. Biblo BL781-531 1978 $10

EBERLEIN, HAROLD DONALDSON   The Practical Book of Chinaware. Philadelphia, 1925. Illus., first ed. Baldwin's 51-70 1978 $15

EBERLEIN, HAROLD DONALDSON   The Practical Book of Early American Arts & Crafts. 1916. Illus., good. Nestler Rare 78-259 1978 $20

EBERLEIN, HAROLD DONALDSON   The Practical Book of Garden Structure and Design. Philadelphia, 1937. Illus., quarto, orig. cloth, v.g. Americanist 103-37 1978 $30

EBERLEIN, HAROLD DONALDSON   The Practical Book of Period Furniture. Philadelphia, (1914). 5th impression, illus. Baldwins' 51-69 1978 $10

EBERLEIN, HAROLD DONALDSON   The Practical Book of Period Furniture. Philadelphia, (1914). 250 illus. Baldwins' 51-67 1978 $12.50

EBERS, GEORG   Cleopatra A Romance. n.d. (1894). 1st. English ed., 2 vols., orig. blue cloth, v.g. Jarndyce 16-632 1978 £18.50

EBERS, GEORG   Die Heiroglyphischen Schriftzeichen der Egypter. Leipzig, 1890. Illus., covers rubbed. Biblo BL781-374 1978 $10

EBERSTADT, CHARLES   A Letter That Founded A Kingdom. New York, 1950. Orig. wr., 100 copies printed. Ginsberg 14-648 1978 $10

EBERT, ADOLF   Allgemeine Geschichte der Literatur des Mittelalters im Abendlande. 1889. Vol. I only, shaken, browned. Allen 234-1214 1978 $12.50

EBSWORTH, J. W.   Westminister Drolleries; Both Parts of 1671, 1672; Being a Choice Collection of Songs and Poems. 1875. Ltd. to 400 copies, octavo, good. Upcroft 10-182 1978 £10

EBURNE, RICHARD   A Plaine Pathway to Plantations. Hengstridge in the Countie of Somerset, 1624. 1st ed., sm. 4to, divided into 3 parts, minor soiling & spotting, ink notation dates, rebound in full red mor., single fillet border, corded, binding fine, scarce. Current 24-78 1978 $4,500

EBY, C. S.   The World Problem and the Divine Solution. Toronto, 1914. Hood 116-292 1978 $7.50

EBY, FREDERICK   The Development of Education in Texas. New York, 1925. Jenkins 116-374 1978 $65

EBY, FREDERICK   The History and Philosophy of Education. 1940. Illus. Austin 80-1043 1978 $12.50

ECCENTRIC Tales, From the German. . . with Illustrations by George Cruikshank, from sketches by Alfred Crowquill. London, 1827. 8vo, half dark green crushed levant, gilt, spine gilt, silk endpapers, t.e.g., by Riviere, 1st ed., outer edges uncut. Ximenes 47-174 1978 $275

ECK, TH. G. VAN   De Familie Van Eck. den Haag, 1929. 8vo., orig. covers, portrs. Van der Peet H-64-316 1978 Dfl 40

ECKARDT, ANDREAS   A History of Korean Art. London and Leipzig, 1929. Illus., plts., cloth, little faded. Dawson's 127-214 1978 $100

ECKEL, EDWIN C.   Iron Ores. New York, 1914. Orig. cloth, maps, illus., 8vo., ex-lib., 1st ed. Morrill 241-123 1978 $10

ECKEL, JOHN C.   The First Editions of the Writings of Charles Dickens. Their Points and Values. London, and New York, 1932. Revised and Enlarged, illus. and facsimilies, 8vo, 3/4 mor., d.j., slipcase, 1 fo 250 copies signed by author, bottom of backstrip rubbed, fine. Duschnes 220-86 1978 $125

ECKENRODE, HAMILTON JAMES   James Longstreet: Lee's War Horse. Chapel Hill, 1936. Bell Wiley's copy. Broadfoot's 46-84 1978 $45

ECKENRODE, HAMILTON JAMES   The Political History of Virgina During the Reconstruction. Baltimore, 1904. New cloth, Bell Wiley's copy. Broadfoot's 44-664 1978 $26.00

ECKENRODE, HAMILTON JAMES   The Revolution in Virginia. Boston, 1916. First ed., very scarce. MacManus 239-1879 1978 $37.50

ECKENRODE, HAMILTON JAMES   Rutherford B. Hayes, Statesman of Reunion. New York, 1930. Bell Wiley's copy. Broadfoot 46-507 1978 $8

ECKENRODE, HAMILTON JAMES   Rutherford B. Hayes Statesman of Reunion. New York, 1930. Illus., scarce. MacManus 239-767 1978 $22.50

ECKERMANN, J. P.   Conversations of Goethe with Eckermann and Soret. 1850. 2 vols., orig. cloth, rebacked, orig. backstrips preserved, 8vo. Howes 194-893 1978 £25

ECKFELDT, JOHN W.   Cobbs Creek in the Days of the Old Powder Mill. Philadelphia, 1917. Illus., scarce, rebacked. MacManus 239-1607 1978 $20

ECKHEL, L'ABBE   Choix des pierres gravees du cabinet imperial des antiques. Vienne, 1788. Plts., folio, half roan rubbed, sides faded, edges uncut, dust-soiled. George's 635-18 1978 £65

AN ECONOMIC Survey of Collin County. Austin, 1949. Wr. Jenkins 116-227 1978 $12.50

AN ECONOMIC Survey of Parker County. Austin, 1948. Fine folding map. Jenkins 116-1049 1978 $30

AN ECONOMIC Survey of Red River County. Austin, 1949. Wr., scarce. Jenkins 116-1159 1978 $12.50

AN ECONOMIC Survey of Rockwall County. Austin, 1949. Wr. Jenkins 116-1189 1978 $12.50

AN ECONOMIC Survey of Smith County. Austin, 1949. Wr. Jenkins 116-1250 1978 $12.50

AN ECONOMIC Survey of Taylor County. Austin, 1949. Wr., scarce. Jenkins 116-1312 1978 $12.50

ECONOMY of the Hands and Feet, Fingers and Toes. London, 1830. Rittenhouse 49-24 1975 $75

EDDINGTON, A. S.   The Nature of the Physical World. 1929. Austin 80-1044 1978 $7.50

EDDINGTON, A. S.   New Pathways in Science. 1935. Austin 80-1045 1978 $12.50

EDDINGTON, A. S.   Report on the Relativity Theory of Gravitation. 1920. 8vo., orig. printed wrappers, spine worn, second ed. Quaritch 977-94 1978 $50

EDDY, A. D.   "Black Jacob", a Monument of Grace. Philadelphia, 1842. 18mo., orig. bds., lea. back. Butterfield 21-71 1978 $65

EDDY, RICHARD   History of the Sixtieth Regiment New York State Volunteers. Philadelphia, 1864. Spine chipped, Bell Wiley's copy. Broadfoot's 44-557 1978 $25

EDDY, RICHARD   Universalism in America. Boston, 1886. 2nd ed., 2 vols., orig. cloth, very good set. MacManus 239-464 1978 $40

EDDY County...The Most Southeastern County in the Territory. Santa Fe, 1901. Illus., orig. self pr. wr., 1st ed. Ginsberg 14-1109 1978 $85

EDE, CHARLES   The Art of the Books...in Europe & America 1939-1950. 4to., illus. Battery Park 1-371 1978 $50

EDEL, ABRAHAM   Aristotle's Theory of the Infinite. New York, 1934. Author's signed pres., covers torn, wrs. Biblo 251-258 1978 $12.50

EDELSTEIN, HYMAN   Spirit of Israel, and Other Poems. Toronto, 1950. Hood 117-797 1978 $15

EDEN, EMILY   Portraits of the Princes & People of India. London, 1844. 1st. ed., lg. folio, contemporary coloured lithograph title-pg., contemporary coloured lithograph plts., red half morocco, gilt borders, matching bds. Deighton 5-72 1978 £655

EDEN, EMILY   The Semi-Attached Couple. Boston, 1861. 2nd Am. ed., orig. cloth, spine ends worn, interior good, scarce, 2 vols. in 1. Greene 78-35 1978 $30

EDEN, EMILY   'Up the Country'. 1865. 3rd. ed., 2 vols., half title, orig. red cloth, v.g. Jarndyce 16-633 1978 £14.50

EDGAR, A.   The Bibles of England, a Plain Account for Plain People of the Principal Versions of the Bible in English. 1889. 8vo. George's 635-1057 1978 £6

EDGAR, J. G.   Cressy and Poictiers; or,.... London, 1865. 1st ed., plates by Gustave Dore and Robert Dudley, text illus., very good. Victoria 34-249 1978 $50

EDGAR, MATILDA   Ten Years of Upper Canada in Peace and War, 1805-1815, Being the Ridout Letters. Toronto, 1890. Orig. binding, new endpapers. Hood's 115-802 1978 $65

EDGAR, MATILDA   Ten Years of Upper Canada in Peace and War, 1805-1815, Being the Ridout Letters. London, 1891. Orig. binding. Hood 117-732 1978 $65

EDGAR, P.   The Art of the Novel From 1700 to the Present Time. New York, 1933. Hood's 115-336 1978 $22.50

EDGAR, W.   The Story of a Grain of Wheat. New York, 1903. 8vo, orig. cloth. Book Chest 17-509 1978 $10

EDGEWORTH, MARIA   Belinda. 1811. 3rd. ed., 3 vols., half titles, orig. half calf, red labels, marbled bds., good. Jarndyce 16-635 1978 £32

EDGEWORTH, MARIA   The Bracelets. Philadelphia, 1804. 1st Amer. ed., 16mo, engraved f.p., marbled boards rubbed, spine paper mostly gone, copy shaky, text lightly foxed but very good. Victoria 34-268 1978 $85

EDGEWORTH, MARIA   Castle Rackrent; An Hibernian Tale. 1800. 2nd. ed., orig. half calf, marbled bds. Jarndyce 16-634 1978 £28

EDGEWORTH, MARIA   Memoirs of Richard Lovell Edgeworth, Esq..... Boston, 1821. 1st Amer. ed., original boards moderately worn, book split in two halves. Victoria 34-270 1978 $35

EDGEWORTH, MARIA   Orlandino. Edinburg, 1848. 1st ed., lithographed f.p., marbled boards, red leather spine, spine mostly gone, very good. Victoria 34-271 1978 $32.50

EDGEWORTH, MARIE   The Parent's Assistant; or, Stories for Children.
New York, 1835. New Am. ed., orig. cloth. Greene 78-36 1978 $35

EDGEWORTH, MARIA   Popular Tales. London, 1805. Second ed., 3
vols., cr. 8vo., contemp. half leather, some staining of cover, one leaf loose.
K Books 244-109 1978 £18

EDGEWORTH, MARIA   Practical Education. 1801. Second ed., plts.,
3 vols., cloth, mor. labels, 8vo. Howes 194-256 1978 £42

EDGEWORTH, MARIA   Rosamond, Part I. Boston, 1813. 16mo, printed
boards, leather spine amateurishly replaced, text almost fine. Victoria 34-272
1978 $15

EDGEWORTH, MARIA   Rosamond. London, 1821. 2 vols., 12mo, 1st ed.,
1st issue, marbled boards, green roan spine, heavily rubbed, text very good and
firm. Victoria 34-273 1978 $55

EDGEWORTH, MARIA   Tales of Fashionable Life. London, 1809. 3
vols., 1st ed., contemporary 3/4 leather, marbled paper boards, lightly foxed,
almost fine set. Victoria 34-274 1978 $150

EDGEWORTH, MAIRA   Tales of Fashionable Life. Paris, 1831. Uniform
quarter mor. & cloth, very good. Greene 78-37 1978 $95

EDGEWORTH, MARIA   Tomorrow: or, The Danges of Delay. New
Brunswick, 1807. 12mo, 1st Amer. ed., calf, foxed, very good. Victoria 34-275
1978 $35

EDGEWORTH, RICHARD LOVELL   Essay on Irish Bulls. 1802. 8vo., old calf,
rebacked, a little thumbed and age-soiled, first ed. P. M. Hill 142-99 1978
£15

EDGEWORTH, RICHARD LOVELL   Essays on Irish Bulls. London, 1803. 2nd
ed., corrected, original roan-backed bds., heavily rubbed, leaves stained, text
very good and solid, extensively corrected and scarce. Victoria 34-269 1978
$20

EDIE, LIONEL   The Stabilization of Business. 1923. 1st ed.
Austin 80-571 1978 $17.50

EDINBURGH Delineated: Comprising Fifty Views...of the Scottish Metropolis.
Edinburgh and London, c. 1850. Contemp. half calf, plts., 8vo. Howes 194-
1382 1978 £21

THE EDINBURGH Imperial Atlas. Edinburgh, c. 1840. Hand-coloured maps,
lg. folio, worn half roan, 8vo. K Books 244-340 1978 £35

EDLAND, H.   Encyclopedia of Roses in Natural Color. 8vo,
orig. cloth. Book Chest 17-510 1978 $10

EDMAN, IRWIN   Human Traits and Their Social Significance.
1920. Austin 80-1047 1978 $7.50

EDMEADES, J. F.   Some Historical Records of the West Kent Yeomanry 1797-1909. 1909. Coloured plts. & frontis., 8vo., orig. cloth. F. Edwards 1013-562 1978 £20

EDMONDS, C. R.   Diseases of Animals in South Africa. London,
1922. Illus., 8vo, orig. cloth, covers beetle attacked. K Books 239-136 1978
£5

EDMONDS, J. M.   Twelve War Epitaphs. Ashendene Press, 1916/
1918. Fine. Duschnes 220-6 1978 $550

EDMONDS, S. EMMA E.   Nurse and Spy in the Union Army. Hartford,
1865. Cloth, slightly worn. Hayman 73-106 1978 $8.50

EDMONDS, WALTER D.   The Big Barn. Boston, 1930. 1st ed., roughly
opened in several places. Butterfield 21-173 1978 $12.50

EDMONDS, WALTER D.   Drums Along the Mohawk. Boston, 1836. 1st
prtg., near mint. Butterfield 21-174 1978 $20

EDMONDS, WALTER D.   Mostly Canallers, Collected Stories. Boston,
1934. 1st ed., torn & frayed dust jacket. Butterfield 21-176 1978 $10

EDMONDS, WALTER D.   The Wedding Journey. Boston, 1947. 1st ed.,
lightly chipped dust jacket. Butterfield 21-178 1978 $15

EDMONDS, WALTER D.   Young Ames. Boston, 1942. Owner's name on
title page, 1st ed. in dust jacket. Butterfield 21-179 1978 $8

EDMONDSON, JOSEPH   A Complete Body of Heraldry... London, 1780.
Portrait, engraved plts., 2 vols., folio, contemp. tree calf, fully gilt spine,
leather labels, little worn. Traylen 88-451 1978 £100

EDMONDSTON, ARTHUR   A View of the Ancient and Present State of the
Zetland Islands... Edinburgh, 1809. 1st. ed., 2 vols., 8vo, engraved map, gilt,
polished half calf, marbled bds., gilt backs, morocco labels. Deighton 5-208
1978 £85

EDMONSTON-SCOTT, W. J.   Elements of Negro Religion. Edinburgh, 1910.
Frontis, orig. cloth, 8vo, covers little marked. K Books 239-137 1978 £14

EDMONSTONE, SIR ARCHIBALD   A Journey to Two of the Oases of Upper Egypt.
London, 1822. 8vo, original grey boards, printed paper label, 1st ed., very fine
copy. Ximenes 47-91 1978 $75

EDMUNDSON, G.   Anglo-Dutch Rivalry during the first half of the
17th Century. Oxford, 1911. Covers stained, 8vo. George's 635-319 1978 £5

EDO Jidai Shoki Eiri-Bon Hyakushu. Kyoto, 1927. 2 vols., plts., sewn, fold.
case, one of 270. Dawson's 449-112 1978 $125

EDOUART, AUGUST   Ancestors in Silhouette. London, 1921. 1st ed.,
4to., illus., orig. pic. cloth, very good, A.L.s. from author. MacManus 239-
662 1978 $60

EDSON, NEWELL W.   Sex Conduct. 1912. Paper. Austin 80-1048
1978 $10

EDWARDS, AMELIA B.   Lord Brackenbury. 1880. 1st. ed., 3 vols.,
half red morocco, heads of spines trifle worn, otherwise good. Jarndyce 16-637
1978 £25

EDWARDS, AMELIA B.   A Midsummer Ramble in the Dolomites. London,
(1890). Frontis., map, plts., illus., roy. 8vo., decor. cloth. K Books 244-359
1978 £8

EDWARDS, AMELIA B.   A Thousand Miles Up the Nile. London, 1891.
70 illus., roy. 8vo, gilt cloth, corners chafed. K Books 239-138 1978 £9

EDWARDS, ANNIE   A Blue Stocking. New York, 1877. 1st Am. ed.,
orig. wrappers, lacking spine, covers worn, interior good. Greene 78-38 1978
$45

EDWARDS, B. B.   The Missionary Gazeteer. Boston, 1832. Illus.
by engravings, backstrip worn, orig. binding. Wolfe 39-176 1978 $50

EDWARDS, BRYAN   An Historical Survey of the French Colony in the
Island of St. Domingo... 1797. 1st. ed., 4to, modern half calf. Edwards
1012-736 1978 £75

EDWARDS, BRYAN   The History Civil and Commercial of the British
Colonies in the West Indies: In Two Volumes.... London, 1793. 2 vols., 4to.,
maps and plates, contemp. sprinkled calf, repaired. Quaritch 978-153 1978
$325

EDWARDS, BRYAN   The History, Civil and Commercial, of the
British Colonies in the West Indies. 1807. 4th. ed., folding maps, plts., 3 vols.,
8vo, contemp. calf, rebacked, corners repaired, red labels, browning on some
plts. Edwards 1012-713 1978 £150

EDWARDS, MRS. C. M.   My Sister Margaret. A Temperance Story. New
York, (1859). Cloth, some dampstaining. Hayman 72-205 1978 $8.50

EDWARDS, E. D.   The Dragon Book. London, (1946). Covers sl.
stained. Biblo 247-919 1978 $12.50

EDWARDS, E. I.   Desert Yarns. Los Angeles, 1946. Cloth,
dec. bds., #98 of ltd. ed. of 250 no. copies, fine. Dykes 35-44 1978 $27.50

EDWARDS, F. W.   British Blood-Sucking Flies. 1939. Plts., roy. 8vo. George's 635-973 1978 £10.50

EDWARDS, GEORGE T.   Music and Musicians of Maine... Portland, 1928. 1st ed., illus. MacManus 239-274 1978 $17.50

EDWARDS, H. SUTHERLAND   The Lyrical Drama. 1881. 1st. ed., 2 vols., orig. blue cloth, good. Jarndyce 16-912 1978 £24

EDWARDS, J. G.   Historical Essays in Honour of James Tait. 1933. 4to., plts. Upcroft 12-129 1978 £20

EDWARDS, JOHN N.   Shelby and His Men. Kansas City, Mo., 1897. Bell Wiley's copy. Broadfoot 46-85 1978 $30

EDWARDS, JONATHAN   A Treatise Concerning Religious Affections.... Philadelphia, 1794. Contemp. calf, rubbed, good sound copy, orig. binding, 8vo. Americanist 101-45 1978 $25

EDWARDS, LIONEL   Famous Fox-hunters. 1932. Contemp. pict. and drawings by author, 4to. George's 635-1506 1978 £7.50

EDWARDS, NEVILLE   The Transvaal in War and Peace. London, 1900. Illus., 4to, dec. cloth, rather shabby. K Books 239-140A 1978 £10

EDWARDS, NEVILLE   The Transvaal in War and Peace. London, 1900. Very well illus. from photos, 4to, dec. cloth, g.e. K Books 239-140 1978 £15

EDWARDS, OSMAN   The Value of Dickens. Hastings, 1912. 12mo, pr. red wr. Totteridge 29-34 1978 $7.50

EDWARDS, PHILIP LEGET   The Diary of... San Francisco, 1932. Cloth, marbled bds., label, very good, slip case. Dykes 35-79 1978 $75

EDWARDS, TRYON   Reasons for Thankfulness. Rochester, 1837. Disbound, lightly foxed on title page. Hayman 73-475 1978 $7.50

EDWARDS, W. F.   W. F. Edwards' Tourists' Guide and Directory of the Truckee Basin. Truckee, 1883. Illus., original cloth, 1st ed. Ginsberg 14-108 1978 $125

EDWARDS, W. H.   A Voyage Up The River Amazon... 1847. 1st. London ed., sm. 8vo, orig. cloth, spine faded. Edwards 1012-642 1978 £35

EDWARDS, WILLIAM FREDERICK   De l'Influence des Agens Physiques sur la Vie. Paris, 1824. 8vo., wrappers bound in, qtr. calf, plt., pres. copy with inscription from author, first ed. Gurney 75-35 1978 £145

EDWARDS, WILLIAM H.   Timothy and Rhoda Ogden Edwards of Stockbridge, Mass., and Their Descendants. Cincinnati, 1903. 1st ed., illus., orig. cloth, covers soiled, but good copy. MacManus 239-921 1978 $17.50

EDWARDS, WILLIAMS   Personal Adventures During the Indian Rebellion in Rohilcund, Futteghur, and Oude. 1859. 3rd. ed., revised, orig. cloth, v.g. Jarndyce 16-638 1978 £14

EDWIN Davis French: A Memorial His Life..His Art. New York, Devinne Press, 1907. Portrs., plts., engr., 1 of 475 numbered copies. Battery Park 1-66 1978 $75

EDYE, L.   The Historical Records of the Royal Marines, Vol. 1 1664-1701. 1893. Roy. 8vo., orig. cloth, portraits, coloured plts. F. Edwards 1013-554 1978 £25

EELKING, MAX VON   The German Allied Troops in the...War of Independence 1776-1783. Albany, 1893. Untrimmed copy, rebound. MacManus 239-565 1978 $30

EELS, MYRON   A Reply to Professor Bourne's "The Whitman Legend." Walla Walla, 1902. Wrps., scarce. Hayman 71-194 1978 $12.50

EELLS, SAMUEL   Oration Delivered Before the Biennial Convention of the Alpha Delta Phi Society. Cincinnati, 1839. Disbound. Hayman 73-508 1978 $12.50

EGAN, BERESFORD PATRICK   De Sade. Fortune Press, n.d. Portr., plts., 1 of 1600 copies, 4to., buckram, very good, d.w., 1st Eng. ed. Bell Book 16-983 1978 £25

EGAN, MAURICE F.   Jasper Thorn. Philadelphia, (1897). Orig. binding, clean, couple of damp spots on spine. Hayman 71-224 1978 $8.50

EGAN, PIERCE   Pierce Egan's Finish to the Adventures of Tom, Jerry, and Logic in their Pursuits Through Life in and out of London. London, (1871). Lg. 8vo., a.e.g., handcolored illus. by Robert Cruikshank, full brown calf binding, gilt decor. spine, binding firm, plts. clear & bright. Current 24-216 1978 $185

EGAN, PIERCE   Life in London. 1821. First ed., woodcuts, coloured plts. by I.R. and G. Cruikshank, half calf, spine rubbed, 8vo. George's 635-1302 1978 £175

EGAN, PIERCE   The Life of an Actor. 1903. Coloured plts., sm. 8vo., half maroon calf gilt, gilt top. Howes 194-1263 1978 £7.50

EGAN, PIERCE   Walks through Bath, Describing Everything Worthy of Interest... Bath, 1819. 8vo., lg. paper, plts., cont. calf. Quaritch 983-322 1978 $195

EGE, RALPH   Pioneers of Old Hopewell, N.J.... Hopewell, 1908. 1st ed., port., very scarce. MacManus 239-1259 1978 $85

EGEDE, HANS   Omstaedelig Og Udforlig Relation... Copenhagen, 1738. Sm. 4to, contemp. calf, browning in text. Edwards 1012-572 1978 £480

EGERTON, F. CLEMENT C.   African Majesty: A Record of Refuge at the Court of the King of Bangante in the French Cameroons. London, 1938. 2 maps, 123 illus., roy. 8vo, orig. cloth, covers dull. K Books 239-141 1978 £8

EGERTON, H. E.   Federations and Unions within the British Empire. Oxford, 1911. Lacks prelims. before title, 8vo. George's 635-629 1978 £5.25

EGERTON, MARY MARGARET   The Book of Costume. London, 1847. Illus., engrs. on wood, 8vo., half mor, all edges gilt, new ed. Morrill 239-371a 1978 $35

EGGLESTON, EDWARD   The Circuit Rider. A Tale of the Heroic Age. New York, 1874. Orig. cloth, illus., 1st ed., state B, very nice. MacManus 238-471 1978 $30

EGGLESTON, EDWARD   The Circuit Rider: A Tale Of The Heroic Age. New York, 1874. 1st Amer. ed., original gilt pictorial cloth. Jenkins 116-1540 1978 $45

EGGLESTON, EDWARD   The Faith Doctor. A Story of New York. New York, 1891. Orig. dec. cloth, minor wear to extremities, 1st ed., nice. Mac-Manus 238-473 1978 $27.50

EGGLESTON, EDWARD   The Hoosier School-boy. New York, 1883. 2nd print., illus., orig. cloth, good. MacManus 238-472 1978 $30

EGGLESTON, GEORGE CARY   The History of the Confederate War Its Causes and Its Conduct. New York, 1910. 2 vols., 1st ed., scarce. MacManus 239-874 1978 $50

EGGLESTON, GEORGE CARY   Two Gentlemen of Virginia. 1908. Illus., first ed. Austin 82-371 1978 $17.50

EGGLESTON, GEORGE CARY   The Wreck of The Red Bird. New York, 1882. 1st ed., plates, tips rubbed, inner hinges cracked, very good. Victoria 34-276 1978 $10

EGGLESTON, NATHANIEL H.   Religion in Politics. A Discourse to the Congregational Church and Society, in Madison Wis... Madison, 1856. Wrs. Hayman 72-801 1978 $10

EGLE, WILLIAM H.   History of the Counties of Dauphin and Lebanon.. Penna... Philadelphia, 1883. 4to., rebound, ports., illus. MacManus 239-1445 1978 $125

EGLE, WILLIAM H.   Pennsylvania in the War of the Revolution.
Harrisburg, 1896. 2 vols., illus., maps, rebound. MacManus 239-566 1978
$50

EGLESFIELD, F.   Monarchy Revived Being the Personal History of
Charles the Second from His Earliest Years to His Restoration to the Throne. London, 1822. Reprint of 1661 ed., 8vo., fine red binding, narrow gilt border, ports.
on china paper. Van der Peet h64-318 1978 Dfl 95

EHLE, BOYD   Dominie Jacob Ehle and His Descendents. 1930-
35. Folded facsimile, wrs., very good. Butterfield 21-277b 1978 $15

EHLERS, E.   Zur Kenntnis der Pedicellineen. Gottingen,
1890. Ex-lib with small stamp on title, large 4to, waterstained, marbled boards,
cloth spine, 8vo, orig. cloth. Book Chest 17-136 1978 $35

EHRENBURG, ILYA   The Love of Jeanne Ney. 1929. Fine, d.w.,
first English ed. Bell Book 16-301 1978 £10

EHRENFELD, RICHARD   Grundriss Einer Entwicklungsgeschichte Der
Chemischen Atomisk. Heidelberg, 1906. 8vo., plts., modern cloth, very good
copy. Norman 5-14 1978 $40

EHRICH, LOUIS R.   The Question of Silver.... New York, 1896.
2nd ed., rev'd., cloth. Hayman 72-645 1978 $7.50

EHRMANN, THEOPHIL FRIEDRICH   Neueste Kunde Von Africa. Prag, 1811.
5 folding maps, 6 folding & other plts., calf, 8vo, several rubber stamps. K Books
239-143 1978 £35

EICHHORN, IO GODOFR   Antiqua Historia ex ipsis Veterum Scriptorum Latinorum Narrationibus Contexta. Gottingae, 1811. 2 vols., 8vo., marbled bds.,
calf spine and tips. King 7-350 1978 £20

EIFFEL, GUSTAVE   Nouvelles Recherches sur la Resistance de l'Air
et l'Aviation Faites au Laboratoire d'Auteuil. Paris, 1914. 2 vols., lg. 4to.,
frontis., fldg. transparent grid laid in, photos & diagrs. in text, atlas, orig.
cloth, slightly worn, fine set, lst ed. Norman 5-*10 1978 $400

EIFFEL, GUSTAVE   Recherches Experimentales sur la Resistance de
l'Air Executees a la Tour Eiffel. Paris, 1907. 4to., heliogravures, diagrs.,
text illus., orig. cloth-backed prtd. bds., hinges weak, but fine copy, lst ed.,
pres. copy. Norman 5-*7 1978 $250

EIFFEL, GUSTAVE   Recherches Experimentales sur la Resistance de
l'Air Executees a la Tour Eiffel. Paris, (1909 or 1910). 8vo., photo. plts., fldg.
diagr., text illus., contemp. half mor., little rubbed, very good copy. Norman
5-*8 1978 $150

EIFFEL, GUSTAVE   La Resistance de l'Air. Paris, 1910. 8vo.,
ads, fldg. diagrs., text illus., orig. cloth, gilt, fine copy, lst ed., inscr'd by
author. Norman 5-*9 1978 $200

EIGHTH Annual Report of the State Commissioner of Common Schools to the
Governor of the State of Ohio. Columbus, 1862. Wrs. Hayman 73-525 1978
$7.50

EINHARD   De Vita et Gestis Caroli Magni, Cum Commen-
tario Joh. Utrecht, 1711. Quarto, engraved folding plate, folding geneological
table, full contemporary blind-stamped calf, from library of Andrew Fletcher with
his signature on recto of back cover. Bennett 20-64 1978 $200

EINSTEIN, ALBERT   Entwurf einer Verallgemeinerten Relativitats-
theorie und einer Theorie der Gravitation. Leipzig and Berlin, 1913. 8vo., orig.
printed wrappers, wrappers a little foxed. Quaritch 977-95 1978 $875

EINSTEIN, ALBERT   The Evolution of Physics. 1938. Illus., lst ed.
Austin 80-1050a 1978 $10

EINSTEIN, ALBERT   Investigations on the Theory of the Brownian
Movement. London, (1926). 8vo., ads, orig. cloth, gilt, uncut, fine copy,
lst ed. in English. Norman 5-*13 1978 $85

EINSTEIN, ALBERT   Mein Weltbild. Amsterdam, 1934. 8vo.,
orig. wrs., lst ed. Salloch 348-55 1978 $100

EINSTEIN, ALBERT   Neue Moglichkeit fur eine Einheitliche Feldtheorie von Gravitation und Elektrizitat. Berlin, 1928. Offprint, 8vo., orig.
prtd. wrs., fine copy, lst ed. Norman 5-90 1978 $250

EINSTEIN, ALBERT   Relativity. London, (1920). Spec. appendix,
8vo., ads, frontis. portr., diagrs., orig. cloth, gilt, uncut, very good copy,
lst ed. in English. Norman 5-*11 1978 $85

EINSTEIN, ALBERT   The Theory of Relativity. (Berlin), 1921. 8vo.,
frontis. portr., orig. prtd. wrs., slightly stained & spine repaired, but fine copy,
inscr'd in Russian by translator, lst ed. in Russian. Norman 5-*12 1978 $200

EINSTEIN, ALBERT   Uber die Specielle und die Allgemeine Relati-
vitatstheorie. Braunschweig, 1917. 8vo., orig. prtd. wrs., uncut, spine repaired, very good copy, lst ed. Norman 5-88 1978 $150

EINSTEIN, ALBERT   Zur Einheitlichen Feldtheorie. Berlin, 1929.
Offprint, 8vo., orig. prtd. wrs., fine copy, lst ed. Norman 5-91 1978 $300

EINSTEIN, LEWIS   The Italian Renaissance in England – Studies.
New York, 1902. Plts., octavo, good. Upcroft 10-298 1978 £8.50

EISELE, WILBERT E.   The Real "Wild Bill" Hickok. Denver, 1931.
Pic. cloth, illus., lst ed., fine, d.w. Dykes 35-103 1978 $15

EISELEY, LOREN   The Brown Wasps. Mount Horeb, Perishable
Press, 1969. 12mo., marbled paper over bds., one of 200 copies on handmade
Charter Oak paper, frontis., very fine. Battery Park 1-223 1978 $150

EISENBERG, PHILIP   Expressive Movements Related to Feeling of
Dominance. 1937. Paper. Austin 80-1052 1978 $12.50

EISENDRATH, M. N.   The Never Failing Stream. Toronto, 1939.
Inscribed & signed by author. Hood's 115-928 1978 $10

EISENHOWER, DWIGHT D.   Crusade in Europe. New York, 1948. Very
fine in torn d.w. Desmarais B-216 1978 $10

EISENHOWER, DWIGHT D.   The Prayer of... (New York), n.d. Wrs.,
near mint. Dawson's 447-66 1978 $10

EISENSCHIML, OTTO   The American Iliad. Indianapolis, 1947.
Bell Wiley's copy. Broadfoot 46-86 1978 $14

EISENSCHIML, OTTO   In the Shadow of Lincoln's Death. New York,
1940. lst ed., illus., orig. cloth, very good, inscribed by author. MacManus
239-875 1978 $37.50

EISENSON, JON   Examining for Aphasia. 1946. Austin 80-1053
1978 $12.50

EISENSON, JON   The Psychology of Speech. 1947. Austin 80-
1055 1978 $10

EISSLER, M.   The Cyanide Process for the Extraction of Gold
and Its Practical Application on the Witwatersrand Gold Fields in South Africa.
London, 1895. Cr. 8vo., orig. cloth, folding & other plts., illus. K Books 239-
144 1978 £14

EKELOF, A.   Ett Ai I Stilla Hafvet. Stockholm, 1872. Plts.,
4to, cover soiled, waterstain affecting text and plts., tear in 1 leaf repaired, orig.
cloth. Edwards 1012-17 1978 £150

EKINS, JEFFERY   The Loves of Medea and Jason... London, 1771.
4to., mod. bds., lst ed., very good. MacManus 238-117 1978 $45

EKWALL, EILERT   English Place-Names in '-ing'. 1923. Roy.
8vo., cloth. Howes 194-823 1978 £8.50

ELAM, CHARLES   A Physician's Problems. Boston, 1871. Cloth,
little worn, light dampstains, pencil underlining, poor. Hayman 72-206 1978
$7.50

ELAND, G.   Shardeloes Papers of the 17th and 18th Centuries.
1947. Table, illus., octavo, good. Upcroft 10-299 1978 £5

ELDER, J. R.   The Highland Host of 1678. 1914. Octavo, good.
Upcroft 10-300 1978 £5.50

ELDER, WILLIAM   Biography of Elisha Kent Kane. Philadelphia, 1858. Illus. Baldwins' 51-177 1978 $10

ELDER, WILLIAM   Debt and Resources of the United States: and the Effect of Secession Upon the Trade and Industry of the Loyal States. N.P., n.d. (1863?). Disbound. Hayman 72-124 1978 $7.50

ELDERTON, W. PALIN   Primer of Statistics. 1914. Illus., 3rd ed. Austin 80-1057 1978 $8.50

ELECTRIC Railway and Lighting Properties. Boston, 1909. Maps, 12mo., orig. limp lea. Morrill 239-371b 1978 $10

ELEGANT Extracts from Rebel Writers. No. 1. (Washington, n.d., 1868?). Unbound as issued. Hayman 72-638 1978 $8.50

ELEVEN Miniature Biographies as Issued by Knapp & Co.... New York, 1888. 11 vols., 2 11/16 x 1 7/16th inches, lacks wrs. Morrill 241-367 1978 $13.50

ELGEE, FRANK   Early Man in North-East Yorkshire. Gloucester, 1930. Frontis, plts., illus., 4to. Traylen 88-10 1978 £10

ELGOOD, GEORGE S.   Italian Gardens. New York & London, 1907. Sm. folio, plts. in color, drawings. Baldwins' 51-71 1978 $17.50

ELIAS, E. L.   The Book of Polar Exploration. London, 1928. 8vo., cloth, colored frontis., colored plts., illus. on plts., map on endpapers. Van der Peet H-64-319 1978 Dfl 85

ELIAS, J. E.   Het Geslacht Elias. den Haag, 1937. Lg. 8vo., plts., orig. covers, text illus., genealogical table. Van der Peet H-64-320 1978 Dfl 45

ELIAS, JULIUS   Die Handzeichnungen Max Leibermanns. Berlin, 1922. Lg. 4to., publisher's 3/4 hardgrain mor., ltd. ed. of 430 numbered copies prtd., well preserved. Goldschmidt 110-45 1978 $300

ELIOT, F. P.   Six Letters on the Subject of the Armed Yeomanry. 1797. Plts., 8vo., half mor., uncut, first complete collected ed. F. Edwards 1013-291 1978 £35

ELIOT, GEORGE   Adam Bede. 1859. 1st. ed., 3 vols., half titles, orig. half brown calf, hinges little rubbed, black labels. Jarndyce 16-640 1978 £58

ELIOT, GEORGE   Adam Bebe. 1859. 3 vols., sm. 8vo., 1st ed., orig. cloth enclosed in cloth case, very good copy, scarce. Quaritch 979-132 1978 $1,500

ELIOT, GEORGE   Adam Bede. London, n.d. Thick, large 8vo, ornate gilt spine, fine. Victoria 34-109 1978 $25

ELIOT, GEORGE   Daniel DeRonda. 1876. 1st. ed., 4 vols., half calf, cloth bds. rubbed, good. Jarndyce 16-650 1978 £35

ELIOT, GEORGE   Early Essays. N.P., 1919. Orig. cloth, 1st ed., 1 of 220 copies, fine. MacManus 238-223 1978 $45

ELIOT, GEORGE   Essays and Leaves from a Note-Book. Edinburgh, 1884. Orig. cloth, 1st ed., very good. MacManus 238-222 1978 $85

ELIOT, GEORGE   Essays & Leaves From a Note-Book. 1884. 2nd. ed., half title, orig. brown cloth, v.g. Jarndyce 16-654 1978 £5

ELIOT, GEORGE   Felix Holt, The Radical. 1866. 1st. ed., 3 vols., half titles, orig. brown cloth, very slight fraying of hinge vol. 1, otherwise v.g. Jarndyce 16-646 1978 £110

ELIOT, GEORGE   Felix Holt, The Radical. 1866. 1st. ed., 3 vols., half titles, new matching endpapers, orig. brown cloth, Mudies' labels, v.g. Jarndyce 16-647 1978 £75

ELIOT, GEORGE   Felix Holt the Radical. 1866. 3 vols., sm. 8vo., 1st ed., orig. cloth uncut, very good copy, bkplts. Quaritch 979-133 1978 $180

ELIOT, GEORGE   George Elliot's Life Related in Her Letters & Journals. New York, 1885. Fragile paper covers, fine. Greene 78-197 1978 $35

ELIOT, GEORGE   Impressions of Theophrastus Such. Edinburgh, 1879. Orig. cloth, 1st ed., covers slightly worn, else very good. MacManus 238-221 1978 $85

ELIOT, GEORGE   Impressions of Theophrastus Such. 1879. 1st. ed., half calf, spine gilt, v.g. Jarndyce 16-652 1978 £12.50

ELIOT, GEORGE   Impressions of Theophrastus Such. 1879. 1st. ed., half title, orig. cloth, little worn & spine dulled, good. Jarndyce 16-653 1978 £16.50

ELIOT, GEORGE   The Legend of Jubal and Other Poems. Edinburgh, 1874. 1st. ed., with errata slip, 1/2 calf with lib. crest on upper cover. Eaton 45-168 1978 £15

ELIOT, GEORGE   The Legend of Jubal & Other Poems. 1874. 1st. ed., half title, orig. purple cloth, little rubbed, good. Jarndyce 16-649 1978 £15

ELIOT, GEORGE   Middlemarch. 1881. Cr. 8vo., half calf gilt. Howes 194-824 1978 £7.50

ELIOT, GEORGE   The Mill on the Floss. New York, 1860. 1st Amer. ed., 3 vols. in 1, orig. cloth, shelf wear, foxing. Greene 78-198 1978 $45

ELIOT, GEORGE   The Mill on the Floss. Edinburgh and London, 1860. 3 vols., 8vo., orig. cloth, 1st ed., extremities of spine a bit worn, but very good set. MacManus 238-218 1978 $150

ELIOT, GEORGE   The Mill on the Floss. 1860. 1st. ed., 3 vols., half titles, half calf, brown labels, marbled endpapers & edges, fine attractive set. Jarndyce 16-641 1978 £68

ELIOT, GEORGE   Novels. (c. 1890). 7 vols., 8vo., vellum backs. Quaritch 979-131 1978 $300

ELIOT, GEORGE   Novels of George Eliot. New York, n.d. 12 vols., octavo, half calf, marbled boards. Bennett 7-38 1978 $250

ELIOT, GEORGE   Romola. 1863. 1st. ed., 3 vols., calf, gilt borders, dentelles & spines, red & green labels, t.e.g., fine copy. Jarndyce 16-645 1978 £140

ELIOT, GEORGE   Scenes of Clerical Life. 1858. 1st. ed., 2 vols. bound as 1, half title, orig. half red morocco, marbled bds., slightly rubbed, o/w v.g. Jarndyce 16-639 1978 £68

ELIOT, GEORGE   Silas Marner: The Weaver of Raveloe. 1861. 1st. ed., half title, orig. brown cloth little dulled & sm. ink stain on bottom of back bd., excellently recased with matching cloth, good. Jarndyce 16-643 1978 £52

ELIOT, GEORGE   Silas Marner; the Weaver of Raveloe. Edinburgh, 1861. Orig. cloth, 1st ed., bind. slightly worn, otherwise very good. MacManus 238-219 1978 $200

ELIOT, GEORGE   Silas Marner: The Weaver of Raveloe. Edinburgh & London, 1861. Orig. ripple-grained cinnamon-colored cloth, top & fore-edges untrimmed, spine gilt, cream-colored end papers, 1st ed., brown half-mor. slipcase. Bradley 49-85 1978 $425

ELIOT, GEORGE   Silas Marner: The Weaver of Raveloe. 1861. 1st. ed., half title, orig. brown cloth, one gathering slightly springing o/w v.g. Jarndyce 16-642 1978 £70

ELIOT, GEORGE   Silas Marner: The Weaver of Raveloe. 1861. 1st. ed., half brown morocco, gilt bands, marbled bds., v.g. Jarndyce 16-644 1978 £52

ELIOT, GEORGE   The Spanish Gypsy. A Poem. Edinburgh, 1868. Orig. cloth, 1st ed., extremities and edges slightly worn. MacManus 238-220 1978 $75

ELIOT, GEORGE   The Spanish Gypsy. 1868. 2nd. ed., half title, orig. blue cloth, hinges very slightly rubbed, otherwise v.g. Jarndyce 16-648 1978 £8.50

ELIOT, GEORGE   Works. (London, 1863). 29 vols., 8vo., and sm. 8vo., 3/4 tan mor., gilt spines, orig. cloth covers, first eds., very fine. Howell 5-25 1978 $1000

ELIOT, JOHN   The Parlement of Pratlers. London, Westminster Press, 1928. 1 of 625 numbered copies, illus. by Hal Collins, pattern paper over bds., cloth spine, edges show fraying. Battery Park 1-95 1978 $75

ELIOT, THOMAS STEARNS   After Strange Gods. London, 1934. 8vo, black orig. cloth, fore and bottom edges uncut, Fine, author crossed out his printed name on t.p. and added his signature, 1st ed., collector's cond. Desmarais 1-156 1978 $125

ELIOT, THOMAS STEARNS   After Strange Gods: a primer of modern heresy. 1934. Very good, worn d.w., first English ed. Bell Book 16-302 1978 £20

ELIOT, THOMAS STEARNS   After Strange Gods. London, 1934. Very fine in chipped d.w. Desmarais B-217 1978 $60

ELIOT, THOMAS STEARNS   After the Torchlight. New Haven, 1933. 12mo., handwritten, orig. watercolour frontis., decor. in colours & gold, decor. paper wrs., #1 of 2 copies. Quaritch 979-261 1978 $275

ELIOT, THOMAS STEARNS   Anabasis; a poem. London, 1930. One of 350 numbered copies, signed by Eliot, fine, worn slipcase, first ed, orig. binding. Rota 212-19 1978 £65

ELIOT, THOMAS STEARNS   Animula. (1929). Coloured illus. by Gertrude Hermes, woodcut on wrapper, sm. 8vo., orig. lemon wrappers. Howes 194-826 1978 £7.50

ELIOT, THOMAS STEARNS   Ash-Wednesday. New York, Fountain Press, 1930. 1st ed., 1 of 600 signed, cellophane dust jacket, publisher's tan cardboard box, cloth wr. & slipcase. Bradley 49-86 1978 $395

ELIOT, THOMAS STEARNS   Ash-Wednesday. New York, 1930. Orig. cloth, 1st ed., 1 of 600 copies signed by poet, spine slightly worn, but fine. MacManus 238-638 1978 $175

ELIOT, THOMAS STEARNS   Ash Wednesday. 1930. Fine, somewhat frayed d.w., first English ed. Bell Book 17-307 1978 £27.50

ELIOT, THOMAS STEARNS   The Classics and the Man of Letters. London, 1942. 12mo., orig. wrs., 1st ed., 1st issue, fine. MacManus 238-639 1978 $35

ELIOT, THOMAS STEARNS   The Cocktail Party. London, (1950). 1st ed., d.w. slightly frayed, ink inscr. on flyleaf. Biblo 251-472 1978 $32.50

ELIOT, THOMAS STEARNS   The Cocktail Party. London, 1950. 4th impression, very fine in torn d.w. Desmarais B-218 1978 $10

ELIOT, THOMAS STEARNS   Death by Water. New Haven, 1932. 12mo., handwritten & illuminated in gold & colours, orig. watercolour frontis., decor. paper wrs., Prokosch bkplt., #2 of 5 copies, "color model" for frontis. laid in. Quaritch 979-262 1978 $260

ELIOT, THOMAS STEARNS   East Coker. 1940. Orig. wraps, covers somewhat browned, spine partly split & piece missing from head of lower cover, else good, first English ed. Bell Book 17-308 1978 £15

ELIOT, THOMAS STEARNS   East Coker. London, 1940. 2nd impression of 1st ed., printed wr., very good or better. Limestone 9-95 1978 $8

ELIOT, THOMAS STEARNS   Elibabethan Essays. 1934. Very good, first English ed. Bell Book 16-303 1978 £6.50

ELIOT, THOMAS STEARNS   The Family Reunion. 1939. Very good, d.w., first English ed. Bell Book 16-304 1978 £12.50

ELIOT, THOMAS STEARNS   For Lancelot Andrewes: Essays on Style and Order. 1928. First ed., cr. 8vo., orig. blue cloth, printed label, d.w. Howes 194-827 1978 £28

ELIOT, THOMAS STEARNS   For Lancelot Andrewes, Essays on Style and Order. London, 1928. 8vo, dark blue cloth slightly soiled, spine faded, some foxing, edges uncut, 1st ed., collector's cond. Desmarais 1-157 1978 $35

ELIOT, THOMAS STEARNS   Four Quartets. 1944. Covers dusty, good, first English ed. Bell Book 16-305 1978 £6.50

ELIOT, THOMAS STEARNS   The Idea of a Christian Society. 1939. First ed., name on endpaper, 8vo. George's 635-1315 1978 £5

ELIOT, THOMAS STEARNS   Journey of the Magi. (1927). Coloured frontis. by E. McKnight Kauffer, no. 341 of 350 copies, bds., near fine, first English ed. Bell Book 16-306 1978 £22.50

ELIOT, THOMAS STEARNS   Journey of the Magi. (1927). First ed., illus. by E. McKnight Kauffer, fscp. 8vo., orig. yellow wrappers. Howes 194-828 1978 £7.50

ELIOT, THOMAS STEARNS   Milton. 1947. First ed., roy. 8vo., orig. wrappers, only 500 copies printed. Howes 194-829 1978 £12.50

ELIOT, THOMAS STEARNS   Murder in the Cathedral. London, (1935). Purple cloth, 1st complete ed., 3000 copies only, light foxing on end papers, fine in fairly good dust jacket. Bradley 49-87 1978 $15

ELIOT, THOMAS STEARNS   Murder in the Cathedral. 1935. Very good, first English ed. Bell Book 17-309 1978 £6.50

ELIOT, THOMAS STEARNS   Murder in the Cathedral. 1935. First complete ed., orig. cloth, fine, d.w., 8vo. Howes 194-830 1978 £25

ELIOT, THOMAS STEARNS   Notes towards the Definition of Culture. 1948. Very good, d.w., first English ed. Bell Book 16-307 1978 £7.50

ELIOT, THOMAS STEARNS   Notes Towards the Definition of Culture. London, 1948. Ownership inscription, fine in lightly soiled d.w. Desmarais B-223 1978 $15

ELIOT, THOMAS STEARNS   O City City. New Haven, 1932. 12mo., handwritten, orig. watercolour frontis., decor. in colours & gold., decor. paper wrs., #2 of 2 copies. Quaritch 979-263 1978 $260

ELIOT, THOMAS STEARNS   Old Possum's Book of Practical Cats. London, 1939. 8vo, tan decorated cloth, bookplate of Eric Quayle, endpapers browned, d.w. soiled, 1st ed., collector's cond. Desmarais 1-158 1978 $80

ELIOT, THOMAS STEARNS   Old Possum's Book of Practical Cats. (New York, 1939). Orig. binding. Wolfe 39-177 1978 $20

ELIOT, THOMAS STEARNS   Old Possum's Book of Practical Cats. 1940. First illus. ed., sm. 4to., orig. cloth, colour plts. Howes 194-831 1978 £12

ELIOT, THOMAS STEARNS   Poems. New York, 1920. Tan paper bds., 1st Amer. ed., light foxing, fine copy, scarce. Bradley 49-88 1978 $95

ELIOT, THOMAS STEARNS   Poems. New York, 1920. Cr. 8vo., orig. tan bds., very good, rare. Howes 194-832 1978 £65

ELIOT, THOMAS STEARNS   The Sacred Wood: Essays on Poetry and Criticism. 1920. First ed., sm. 8vo., orig. cloth. Howes 194-833 1978 £35

ELIOT, THOMAS STEARNS   The Sacred Wood. New York, 1921. Blue cloth, 1st ed., 1 of 365 copies, dust jacket, scarce. Bradley 49-89 1978 $195

ELIOT, THOMAS STEARNS   A Song for Simeon. (1928). First ed., coloured illus., fscp. 8vo., orig. blue wrappers. Howes 194-834 1978 £7.50

ELIOT, THOMAS STEARNS   Sweeney Agonistes: fragments of an Aristophanic melodrama. 1932. Bds., fine, d.w., signed by the author, first English ed. Bell Book 16-309 1978 £60

ELIOT, THOMAS STEARNS   Sweeney Agonistes: Fragments of an Aristophanic Medodrama. 1932. First ed., sm. 8vo., orig. bds. Howes 194-835 1978 £15

ELIOT, THOMAS STEARNS   Sweeney Agonistes. 1932. Bds., very good, worn d.w., first English ed. Bell Book 17-310 1978 £15

ELIOT, THOMAS STEARNS   Sweeney Agonistes. Fragments of an Aristophanic Melodrama. London, 1932. Ownership inscription, fine. Desmarais B-225 1978 $65

ELIOT, THOMAS STEARNS   Thoughts After Lambeth. (1931). First ed., orig. wrappers, 8vo. Howes 194-836 1978 £7.50

ELIOT, THOMAS STEARNS   Two Poems. (Cambridge), 1935. 12mo., 1st ed., decor. paper wrs., ltd. to 22 copies, proof copy. Quaritch 979-264 1978 $700

ELIOT, THOMAS STEARNS   The Undergraduate Poems. Cambridge, 1949.
1 of 1,000 copies, 1st ed., collector's cond., reprinted from Harvard Advocate
(Nov. 1948). Desmarais 1-159 1978 $100

ELIOT, THOMAS STEARNS   The Waste Land. Greenwich, 1922. Tall 8vo.,
very minor water-stains, prtd. wrs. with minor edge chipping, else fine. Current
24-14 1978 $250

ELIOT, THOMAS STEARNS   The Waste Land. Hogarth Press, 1923. Orig.
marbled bds., good, about 460 copies were printed, first English ed. Bell Book
16-311 1978 £150

ELIOT, THOMAS STEARNS   The Waste Land. Hogarth Press, 1923. 8vo.,
1st English ed., orig. bds., back faded, bkplt. of Richard Hughes. Quaritch
979-347 1978 $300

ELIOT, THOMAS STEARNS   What is a Classic? 1945. Very good, d.w.,
first English ed. Bell Book 16-312 1978 £6.50

ELIOT, THOMAS STEARNS   What is a Classic? London, 1945. 4to, ordinary issue, blue cloth, edges minimally soiled, small ownership sign. in ink on
front free endpaper, d.w. soiled with small tears, 1st ed., collector's cond.
Desmarais 1-160 1978 $20

ELIOT, WILLIAM G.   The Story of Archer Alexander. Boston, 1885.
Baldwins' 51-379 1978 $17.50

ELIS, J.   Articulorum XXXIX, eccesiae Anglicanae defensio
una cum nova corundem versionae. Cantabrigiae, 1694. 12mo., old calf worn.
George's 635-1058 1978 £6.50

ELKIN, W. M.   Eddie Newton's Ride. 1934. One of 300, signed
by Newton. Battery Park 1-426 1978 $35

ELKINGTON, JOSEPH   The Doukhobors. Leach, 1903. Illus. with
photos by author, maps, 1st ed., inscr. by author, ex-lib., blind stamp on title
page. Austin 79-221 1978 $75

ELKINS, STEPHEN B.   Admission of New Mexico as a State-Her Resources
and Future. Washington, 1874. Orig. pr. wr., 1st ed. Ginsberg 14-757 1978
$75

ELLACOMBE, HENRY N.   The Plant-Lore and Garden-Craft of Shakespeare.
(1896). Plts., illus., 8vo, orig. cloth, gilt, t.e.g., nice copy. Fenning 32-
101 1978 £14

ELLENWOOD, JAMES W.   There's No Place Like Home. 1942. Austin 80-
1060 1978 $8.50

ELLESMERE, EARL OF   Translations From the German; and Original
Poems. 1824. Lib. stamp on title-pg., 1/2 russia, rubbed. Eaton 45-170 1978
£5

ELLET, ELIZABETH   Pioneer Women of the West. New York, 1856.
Rebound copy, clean. Hayman 71-196 1978 $12.50

ELLICOTT, ANDREW   The Journal of...(The) Late Commissioner on
Behalf of the US During.... Philadelphia, 1803. 1st ed., contemp. calf, 4to,
joints partly open, maps & plates, 8vo. Americanist 101-46 1978 $475

ELLIE, LT.   Le Général Gallieni: Le Tonkin-Madagascar.
Paris, 1900. Numerous plts., illus., 8vo, orig. covers. Van der Peet 127-85
1978 Dfl 65

ELLINGTON, GEORGE   The Women of New York, or the Under-World of
the Great City. New York, 1869. Engrs., 8vo, 1st ed., orig. cloth. Morrill 241-409 1978 $30

ELLIOT, A. MARSHALL   Methods of Teaching Modern Languages. Austin
80-1061 1978 $15

ELLIOT, CHARLOTTE   Medusa and Other Poems. London, 1878.
1st ed., orig. gilt cloth, very good or better. Limestone 9-96 1978 $20

ELLIOT, DANIEL GIRAUD   A Monograph of the Felidae or Family of the Cats.
1833. Imp. folio, 61 x 48 cms., hand-coloured plts. by Smit, contemp. crimson
mor. extra, fully gilt spine, orig. printed wrs. boud in, bookplt. of John Aspinall,
Elliot's signature on t.p. Quaritch 983-323 1978 $15,000

ELLIOT, FRANCES   The Diary of an Idle Woman in Sicily. Bristol,
1885. 1st. ed., 2 vols., orig. brown cloth, v.g. Jarndyce 16-655 1978 £24

ELLIOT, G.   The Romance of Plant Life. New York, 1907.
8vo, orig. cloth. Book Chest 17-513 1978 $10

ELLIOT, JONATHAN   The Debates, Resolutions and Other Proceedings
in Convention on the Adoption of the Federal Constitution...General Convention
at Philadelphia, 1787. Washington, 1828. Virginia Vol. II, full lea., Bell
Wiley's copy. Broadfoot 46-508 1978 $20

ELLIOT, MARY   Elliott's Tales, for Boys. London, c.1820.
12mo, double-folded engraved copper plates, marbled boards, red-roan spine,
fine, crisp copy. Victoria 34-277 1978 $185

ELLIOTT, A. E.   Into the Sunshine. Toronto, 1948. Wrs.
Hood 117-798 1978 $7.50

ELLIOTT, C.   Fading Trails. New York, 1942. Plates by W.
Weber, 8vo, orig. cloth. Book Chest 17-138 1978 $15

ELLIOTT, CHARLES WYLLYS   Mysteries. New York, 1852. 8vo., orig.
cloth, 1st ed. Morrill 241-127 1978 $25

ELLIOTT, CHARLES WYLLYS   Mysteries: or Glimpses of the Supernatural.
New York, 1852. Ads, cloth covers shaken, but holding. Butterfield 21-392
1978 $15

ELLIOTT, CHARLES WYLLYS   The New England History, from the Discovery of
the Continent by the Northmen, A.D. 986, to the Period When the Colonies Declared Their Independence, A.D. 1776. New York, 1857. 1st ed., 2 vols.,
illus., orig. cloth, spines worn, front inner hinges of vol. I cracked, bookplts.,
removed, else good set. MacManus 239-134 1978 $37.50

ELLIOTT, DANIEL GIRAUD   The New and Heretofore Unfigured Species of
the Birds of North America. New York, (1866)-1869. Coloured plts., 2 vols. in
1, lg. folio, cloth, unusually clean & free from foxing. Traylen 88-648 1978
£5250

ELLIOTT, EDWARD   Biographical Story of the Constitution... New
York, (1910). Cloth. Hayman 72-207 1978 $7.50

ELLIOTT, J. W.   Mother Goose's Nursery Rhymes and Nursery Sons,
set to music. New York, n.d. Profusely illus., pictorial gilt cloth, fine.
Victoria 34-282 1978 $15

ELLIOTT, C. B.   Travels in The Three Great Empires of Austria,
Russia, and Turkey. London, 1838. 1st. ed., 2 vols., 8vo, tinted lithograph
plts., maps, quarter calf, gilt backs. Deighton 5-121 1978 £40

ELLIOTT, MARY   The Rose, containing Original Poems for Young
People. London, (1824). 1st ed., 12mo, hand-colored plates, printed and decor.
wrappers are stained and darkened, spine very neatly repaired, folding board
box with gilt leather spine. Victoria 34-278 1978 $225

ELLIOTT, MARY   The Sailor Boy and Other Tales. Philadelphia,
1847. 16mo, printed wrappers, very good, foxed. Victoria 34-279 1978 $8.50

ELLIOTT, O. L.   "The Mississippi Girl." (Toledo, 1947). Orig.
binding, clean. Hayman 71-197 1978 $12.50

ELLIOTT, SIMON B.   The Important Timber Trees of the United States.
1912. Illus. Austin 80-572 1978 $12.50

ELLIS, MRS.   Social Distinction, or Hearts and Homes. n.d.
(1848-9). 1st. ed., 3 vols., frontis, engraved titles & plts. in all vols., red calf,
gilt emblems & borders, gilt spines, green labels, a.e.g., good. Jarndyce 16-656
1978 £27.50

ELLIS, A. B.   The Tshi-Speaking Peoples of the Gold Coast of
West Africa. London, 1887. Map, cover little dull, 8vo, orig. cloth. K Books
239-145 1978 £20

ELLIS, A. B.   The Yoruba-Speaking Peoples of the Slave Coast
of West Africa. London, 1894. Modern half calf, 8vo, 2 maps. K Books 239-
146 1978 £20

ELLIS, A. C.   The University of Texas Community Song Book.
Austin, 1918. Jenkins 116-1374 1978 $8.50

ELLIS, A. G.   A Descriptive List of the Arabic Manuscripts
Acquired...since 1894. London, 1912. Med. 8vo., orig. cloth. Forster 130-
200 1978 £5

ELLIS, A. CASWELL   Money Value of Education. 1917. Paper. Austin 80-1062 1978 $10

ELLIS, ASA, JR.   The Country Dyers Assistant. Brookfield, (1798). 1st ed., paper re-inforced spine, good copy. Nestler Rare 78-249 1978 $275

ELLIS, CHARLES   Richmond, and Other Poems. 1845. Coloured Baxter frontis, 2 plts., 1/2 pale calf, gilt spine, blue label, joints slightly rubbed. Eaton 45-171 1978 £20

ELLIS, EDWARD S.   The Camp-Fires of General Lee, from the Peninsula to Appomattox Court-House. Philadelphia, Pa., 1886. Bell Wiley's copy. Broadfoot 46-87 1978 $16

ELLIS, ELMER   Henry Moore Teller, Defender of the West. Caldwell, 1941. Cloth, illus., 1st ed., fine. Dykes 35-139 1978 $10

ELLIS, ELMER   Henry Moore Teller, Defender of the West. Caldwell, 1941. Cloth, little worn dust jacket. Hayman 73-156 1978 $8.50

ELLIS, F. S.   The History of Reynard the Fox, His Family, Friends and Associates. London, 1894. 1st ed., quarto, full maroon mor., gilt lettering on spine, gilt top, other edges uncut, orig. covers bound in at rear. Totteridge 29-37 1978 $125

ELLIS, FRANKLIN   History of Lancaster County, Penna. With Biographical Sketches. Philadelphia, 1883. Illus., maps, nice copy, rebound. MacManus 239-1532 1978 $125

ELLIS, FRANKLIN   History of Monmouth County, New Jersey. Philadelphia, 1885. Thick 4to., illus., ports., later cloth, very good. MacManus 239-1260 1978 $150

ELLIS, GEORGE   History of the Late Revolution in the Dutch Republic. London, 1789. 1st ed., octavo, original boards, rebacked, fine copy, tall, wide-margined, uncut. Bennett 20-65 1978 $150

ELLIS, GEORGE   Specimens of Early English Metrical Romances. 1805. First ed., 3 vols., sm. 8vo., contemp. tree calf, spines rubbed and trifle chipped, labels missing. Howes 194-258 1978 £21

ELLIS, GEORGE   Specimens of Early English Metrical Romances. 1848. New ed., 8vo., contemp. calf, coloured frontispiece. P. M. Hill 142-102 1978 £12

ELLIS, GEORGE EDWARD   Letters Upon the Annexation of Texas, Addressed to Hon. John Quincy Adams. Boston, 1845. Orig. blue pr. wr. Ginsberg 14-953 1978 $275

ELLIS, GEORGE W.   King Philip's War... New York, (1906). 1st ed., fold. map, illus., orig. cloth, very good. MacManus 239-135 1978 $22.50

ELLIS, HAVELOCK   George Chapman; An Essay. Nonesuch Press, 1934. Roy. 8vo, orig. bds., slip-case, one of 700 copies, good. Upcroft 10-301 1978 £16

ELLIS, HAVELOCK   Kanga Creek. Berkeley Heights, Oriole Press, 1933. 8vo., pattern paper over bds., cloth spine, d.w., copy no. 17 of an ed. ltd. to 250 numbered copies, prtd. on Arak paper, signed, inscr'd pres. copy by Harry Weinberger. Battery Park 1-218 1978 $125

ELLIS, HAVELOCK   More Essays of Live and Virtue. London, 1931. First ed., orig. binding, spine faded, very good. Rota 211-96 1978 £5

ELLIS, HAVELOCK   Psychology of Sex. London, 1933. First ed., orig. binding, spine darkened, nice. Rota 211-97 1978 £6

ELLIS, HAVELOCK   Stories and Essays. New Jersey, 1924. 2 vols., 1 of 305 sets, near mint. Desmarais B-227 1978 $10

ELLIS, HENRY   Journal of the Late Embassy, Lord Amherst's, to China... 1817. 4to., port., map, coloured plts., some light marginal staining of port., half calf. Quaritch 983-324 1978 $375

ELLIS, HENRY   Journal of the Proceedings of the Late Embassy to China comprising a Correct Narrative of the Public Transactions of the Embassy, of the Voyage to and from China and of the Journey from the Mouth of the Pei-Ho to the Return to Canton. London, 1817. 1st ed., 4to., colored aquatints, maps, diced brown calf, fine, hand-colored plts. Current Misc. 8-17 1978 $495

ELLIS, HENRY J.   Index to the Charters and Rolls in the Dept. of Manuscripts, British Museum. London, 1900-1912. 2 vols., thick roy. 8vo. Traylen 88-45 1978 £18

ELLIS, J. M.   Facepowder and Gunpowder. Toronto, 1947. Illus., inscribed and signed by Ellis. Hood 116-119 1978 $12.50

ELLIS, JOHN   Directions for bringing over seeds and plants, from the East Indies and other distant countries.... London, 1770. Plts., half leather, scuffed. Dawson's 127-254 1978 $600

ELLIS, JOHN   The Ellis Correspondence. 1829. 2 vols., half calf, portrait, 8vo. Howes 194-839 1978 £21

ELLIS, JOHN S.   Our County. Its History and Early Settlement by Townships. (Muncie, 1898). Orig. poems, cloth, moderate wear. Hayman 73-310 1978 $30

ELLIS, O. O.   The Plattsburg Manual. New York, 1917. First ed., illus. Biblo 247-765 1978 $17.50

ELLIS, R. W.   The Physical Features and Geology of the Route of the Proposed Ottawa Canal Between the St. Lawrence River and Lake Huron. 1895. Folding map. Hood's 115-965 1978 $10

ELLIS, SUMNER   Life of Edwin H. Chapin. Boston, 1882. Orig. cl., 1st ed. Ginsberg 16-850 1978 $10.00

ELLIS, T. P.   The Welsh Benedictines of the Terror. 1936. Roy. 8vo, 4 plts., good. Upcroft 10-303 1978 £8.50

ELLIS, TRISTRAM J.   On a Raft, and Through the Desert. London, Ye Leadenhall Press, 1881. Illus. by author, ltd. ed. of 25 copies, signed by author, 2 vols., lg. 4to., orig. gilt-lettered parchment. K Books 244-111 1978 £80

ELLIS, WILLIAM   The Country Housewife's Family Companion... Domestick Concerns of a Country Life. London, ca. 1750. Engr. frontis, 8vo., full calf, rebacked. Argosy Special-38 1978 $100

ELLIS, WILLIAM   Narrative of a Tour through Hawaii... London, 1826. Illus., map, plts., hlf. leather, plts. foxed. Dawson's 127-255 1978 $200

ELLIS, WILLIAM   Philo-Socrates: A Series of Papers Etc. 1864. 1st. ed., 4 vols., half titles, orig. green cloth, v.g. Jarndyce 16-657 1978 £9

ELLIS, WILLIAM   Polynesian Researches... 1830. 2 vols., maps, plts., illus., maroon morocco, 8vo., plts., foxed & slightly dampstained. Edwards 1012-368 1978 £100

ELLIS, WILLIAM   Polynesian Researches, During a Residence of Nearly Six Years in the South Sea Islands... 1830. 2 vols., folding engraved map, engraved plts., woodcut illus., bds., neatly rebacked, retaining orig. printed labels, defective. Deighton 5-99 1978 £90

ELLIS, WILLIAM   Polynesian Researches During a Residence of Nearly Eight Years in the Society and Sandwich Islands. London, 1853. 4 vols., plts., fold. maps, illus., 12mo., full calf antique, gilt spines, red mor. spine labels, 3rd ed., light foxing, else fine. Howell 5-23 1978 $350

ELLIS, WILLIAM   Three Visits to Madagascar During the Years 1853-1854-1856. London, 1858. Map, folding frontis, 14 plts., 11 text-illus., old style half calf, 8vo. K Books 239-148 1978 £30

ELLIS, WILLIAM   Three Visits to Madagascar furing the Years 1853-1854-1856. London, 1859. Frontis., map, portrait, plts., illus., roy. 8vo., orig. cloth, good, backstrip rather creased, covers dusty. K Books 244-361 1978 £18

ELLISON, D. J.   Italy Through the Stereoscope. New York & London, (1903). 1st. ed., 8vo, orig. cloth, gilt, lg. folding maps, orig. cloth box constructed to simulate 3 bound volumes, fine unmarked copy. Fenning 32-102 1978 £95

ELLISON, JEROME   The Dam. 1941. First ed., d.j. Austin 82-373 1978 $12.50

ELLISON, ROBERT S.   Fort Bridger Wyoming, A Brief History... Casper, 1931. Illus., folding map, orig. pr. pict. wr., 1st ed. Ginsberg 14-1076 1978 $17.50

ELLSBERG, E.   Hell on Ice: The Sage of the Jeannette. 1938. 8vo, orig. cloth, end-paper cloth. Edwards 1012-573 1978 £10

ELMER, J.   Tales of Weights and Prices. London, 1758. 1st ed., sq. 12mo, contemporary calf, gilt-ruled borders, cover hinges cracked, very good, solid copy. Victoria 34-577 1978 $35

ELMER, LUCIUS Q. C.   The Constitution and Government of the Province and State of New Jersey... Newark, 1872. Rebound. MacManus 239-1261 1978 $27.50

ELMER, LUCIUS Q. C.   History of the Early Settlement and Progress of Cumberland County, N.J.... Bridgeton, 1869. 1st ed., cloth, very fine. Mac-Manus 239-1262 1978 $45

ELMER, LUCIUS Q. C.   History of the Early Settlement & Progress of Cumberland County, N. J.; & of the Currency of this & the Adjoining Colonies. Bridgeton, 1869. 1st ed., tall thin 8vo., orig. owner's embossed stamp, orig. cloth, very good. Americanist 103-63 1978 $42.50

ELMES, JAMES   Memoirs of the Life and Works of Sir Christopher Wren. 1823. 1st. ed., 4to, fine frontis portrait, plts., orig. full calf, gilt borders & spine, maroon label, leading hinge weakening otherwise v.g. Jarndyce 16-1186 1978 £58

ELSCHER, K.   Kunst der Renaissance. Potsdam, 1924. Sm. 4to., cloth, illus., colored plts. Van der Peet H-64-28 1978 Dfl 30

ELSINORE, San Diego County, California (A Good City to Go to and Grow Up In). [Elsinore, c.1895]. Oblong 16mo. original printed wr. Ginsberg 14-109 1978 $20

ELSKAMP, MAX   Dominical. Antwerp, 1892. Sm. 8vo., orig. wr., uncut, 1st ed., issued in 103 numbered copies. Goldschmidt 110-72 1978 $300

ELSON, J. M.   National Reference Book on Canadian Men and Women with Other General Information. (Montreal), 1936. 5th. ed., photos, ex-lib. Hood's 115-11 1978 $40

ELSON, JOHN   Riders of the Dawn. Toronto, 1934. Inscr'd & signed. Hood 117-799 1978 $12.50

ELTON, LORD   Imperial Commonwealth. New York, (1946). Biblo 247-682 1978 $15

ELTON, CHARLES I.   An Account of Shelley's visits to France, Switzerland, and Savoy, in the Years 1814 and 1816. London, 1894. 1st ed., photogravure portrait, illus., etchings, pen & ink sketches, laid paper, uncut, orig. gold tooled cloth, very good or better. Limestone 9-266 1978 $30

ELWES, ALFRED   Stories of An Old Maid, Related to Her Nephews and Nieces. New York, 1856. Orig. binding, plts., frontispieces engraved, clean. Hayman 71-268 1978 $12.50

ELWES, HENRY JOHN   The Trees of Great Britain and Ireland. Edinburgh, 1906-13. Plts., 7 vols. in 15 parts, roy. 4to., orig. wrappers, in portfolios with ties as issued. George's 635-1532 1978 £300

ELWES, HENRY JOHN   The Trees of Great Britain and Ireland. Edinburgh, 1906-13. Portrait, coloured frontis, coloured title-pgs., monochrome plts. from photos & other plts., 7 vols., 4to, parts in printed wrappers in printed bd. cases, issued to 244 subscribers only. Traylen 88-568 1978 £200

ELWOOD, MURIEL   Deeper the Heritage. New York, 1947. Hood 117-512 1978 $10

ELY, RICHARD T.   An Introduction to Political Economy. Chautauqua Press, 1889. Austin 80-573 1978 $7.50

ELYOT, THOMAS   The Castell of Health. London, 1587. 8vo., old calf with repairs. Schafer 19-48 1978 sFr. 3,000

EMANUEL, WALTER   A Dog Day. London, 1924. illus. by Cecil Aldin, good-very good. Houle 10-2 1978 $10

EMBURY, AYMAR II   One Hundred Country Houses. Modern American Examples. New York, 1909. Illus., bind. poor, good. Biblo BL781-541 1978 $15

EMDEN, PAUL H.   Randlords. London, 1935. 7 plts., covers slightly marked, orig. cloth, 8vo. K Books 239-149 1978 £6

EMERSON, CHARLES L.   Rise and Progress of Minnesota Territory. St. Paul, 1855. Original printed wr. laid in half morocco slipcase, 1st ed. Ginsberg 14-551 1978 $500

EMERSON, G.   Report on the Trees and Shrubs. Boston, 1846. Re-spined, ex-lib with stamps, plates, 8vo, orig. cloth. Book Chest 17-140 1978 $65

EMERSON, G. D.   The Niagara Frontier Landmarks Association. A Record of Its Work. Buffalo, 1906. Illus. Hood 116-734 1978 $65

EMERSON, JOSEPH   The Evangelical Primer. Boston, 1819. 10th ed., cuts, original marbled paper wrappers, paper chipped at tips, very good. Victoria 34-281 1978 $25

EMERSON, JOSEPH   The Evangelical Primer. Boston, 1828. 16mo, woodcuts, sewn, spine paper gone, corner of rear wrapper gone, very good. Victoria 34-280 1978 $15

EMERSON, NANNETTE SNOW   A History of Dungeon Rock. Boston, 1856. First ed., orig. wrs., sound. Limestone 9-328 1978 $25

EMERSON, PETER HENRY   Naturalistic Photography For Students of the Art. London, 1889. 1st ed., 8 vo., orig. tan cloth, uncut, spine sunned, else very good. Houle 10-99 1978 $160

EMERSON, RALPH WALDO   Essays. Boston, 1841. Orig. cloth, 1st ed., bind. F, bookplt., cloth faded, a little rubbed, otherwise nice, half-mor. slipcase. MacManus 238-474 1978 $225

EMERSON, RAPLH WALDO   Essays. Hammersmith, Doves Press, 1906. 8vo, full tan mor. binding, gilt tooling, spine inlaid with dark brown leather lettered in gilt, cockerel endleaves, 1 of 300 copies, fine. Duschnes 220-88 1978 $350

EMERSON, RALPH WALDO   Fortune of the Republic. Lecture Delivered at the Old South Church, March 30, 1878. Boston, 1878. 12mo., orig. cloth, 1st ed. MacManus 238-477 1978 $35

EMERSON, RALPH WALDO   The Heart of Emerson's Journals. Boston, 1926. 1st ed. Biblo BL781-956 1978 $9.50

EMERSON, RALPH WALDO   Poems. Boston, 1847. 1st American ed., 1st issue with 4 pages of ads dated Jan., 1847, 8 vo., full modern crushed red levant mor., green watered silk doublures, edges gilt, cloth slipcase, fine copy. Houle 10-100 1978 $475

EMERSON, RALPH WALDO   Poems. Boston, 1847. Orig. bds., 8vo., paper label, 1st ed., spine restored, but very good. MacManus 238-475 1978 $175

EMERSON, RALPH WALDO   Records of a Lifelong Friendship 1807-1882. N.P., 1910. 1st printing, no. 10 of a limited ed. of 780 copies, very good. Nestler Rare 78-9 1978 $15

EMERSON, RALPH WALDO   Society and Solitude. Twelve Chapters. Boston, 1870. Orig. cloth, very slightly rubbed, 1st print., fine. MacManus 238-476 1978 $35

EMERSON, WILLIAM   An Historical Sketch of the First Church in Boston. Boston, 1812. Orig. bds., joint tender. Wolfe 39-178 1978 $60

EMERSON, WILLIAM   The Principles of Mechanics.... 1811. 6th. ed., folding engraved plts., 4to, orig. bds., uncut, neatly rebacked, nice copy. Fenning 32-104 1978 £32

EMERY, WALTER B.   Nubian Treasure. London, 1948. Orig. cloth, 8vo, 48 plts., 10 maps. K Books 239-150 1978 £8

THE EMIGRANTS... London, 1794. 2 vols., 12mo., full contemp. calf, 1st ed. MacManus 238-91 1978 $250

EMIGRATION; or, England and Paris, a Poem. London, 1816. 8vo, disbound, 1st ed., very scarce. Ximenes 47-248 1978 $45

EMILY, a Tale for Young Persons. 1825. 12mo., contemp. roan, half-title, frontispiece. P. M. Hill 142-74 1978 £12

EMMA Willard and Her Pupils... New York, n.d. (1898). Illus., lg. thick 4to., orig. cloth, fine. MacManus 239-829 1978 $40

EMMET, ROSINA   Pretty Peggy and Other Ballads. New York, (1880). 8vo, very good. Victoria 34-283 1978 $22.50

EMMONS, CHARLES P.   Sketches of Bunker Hill Battle and Monument.... Charlestown, 1844. 4th ed., orig. binding, clean. Hayman 71-198 1978 $7.50

EMMONS, NATHANAEL   A Discourse delivered on the day of the Annual Fast in Massachusetts, April 7, 1803. Wrentham, 1803. 8vo., wrappers, uncut. P. M. Hill 142-17 1978 £7

EMORY, WILLIAM H.   Notes of a Military Reconnissance from Ft. Leavenworth.... Washington, 1848. 1st ed. Jenkins 116-392 1978 $165

THE EMPIRE State from New York to Niagara Falls. Gloversville and Portland, 1906. Side-opening 8vo. Butterfield 21-457 1978 $12.50

EMRICH, DUNCAN   It's an Old Wild West Custom. New York, (1949) First ed., fine, d.w. Biblo 247-213 1978 $16.50

ENBERG, LARS MAGNUS   Svensk Spraklara, Utgifven af Svenska Akademien. Stockholm, 1836. 1st. ed., 8vo, contemp. half cloth, worn. Hannas 54-187 1978 £10

ENCAUSSE, GERARD   Papus, The Tarot of the Bohemians. London, 1910. Cr. 8vo, orig. cloth, gilt dec., good. Sexton 7-64 1978 £8.50

ENCINAS, DIEGO MIGUEL BRINGAS DE MANZANEDA Y
Please turn to
BRINGAS DE MANZANEDA Y ENCINAS, DIEGO MIGUEL

ENCYCLOPAEDIA Britannica. Edinburgh, 1771. First ed., 3 vols., plts., 4to., fine old style calf. K Books 244-112 1978 £500

ENCYCLOPAEDIA Britannica. Eleventh & Twelfth Editions. 1910-22. Illus., plts., maps, 32 vols., sm. 4to., orig. publishers half mor. Howes 194-841 1978 £65

ENCYCLOPAEDIA of Sport and Games. 1911. Colour plts., illus., 4 vols, imp. 8vo. George's 635-1501 1978 £10.50

ENDE, CASPARUS VAN DEN   Le Gazophilace de la Langue Francoise et Flamande. Rotterdam, 1681. 4to, additional engraved title, contemp. vellum, soiled loosening. Hannas 54-188 1978 £20

ENESEE, PSEUD.
Please turn to
EMERSON, NANNETTE SNOW

ENGEL, S.   Essai Sur Cette Question: Quand Et Commend L' Amerique A-T-Elle Ete Peuplee D'Hommes Et D'Animaux? Amsterdam, 1767. 5 vols. bound in 4, red mor. gilt, fine set. Salloch 345-58 1978 $250

ENGELBACH, LEWIS   Naples and the Campagna Felice. 1815. Maps, fine aquatint plts., all beautifully hand coloured, tall 8vo., contemp. full calf. Howes 194-1406 1978 £175

ENGELHARDT, ZEPHYRIN   San Luis Rey Mission. San Francisco, 1921. Cloth, 1st ed. Hayman 73-75 1978 $12.50

ENGELS, FREDERICK   The Origin of the Family Private Property and the State. Chicago, 1902. Austin 80-574 1978 $11

ENGERTH, WILHELM   Bildliche Darstellungen Der Einfachen Maschinen In Isometrischer Projektion. Vienna, (1845). Color plts., big sq. folio, orig. prtd. wrs. laid in loosely. Salloch 345-59 1978 $30

ENGLAND, JANE   The Sjambok. London, (1929). Cr. 8vo, 3rd. impression, orig. cloth, rather foxed. K Books 239-151 1978 £5

ENGLAND, JOSEPH W.   The First Century of the Philadelphia College of Pharmacy, 1821-1921. Philadelphia, 1922. Rittenhouse 49-247 1976 $12.50

ENGLE, PAUL   American Child. New York, (1945). Blue bds. & cloth, pres. copy, inscr. by poet, mended jacket. Bradley 49-91 1978 $10

ENGLEFIELD, HENRY C.   Diescription of the Picturesque Beauties, Antiquities, and Geological Phenomena, of the Isle of Wight. 1816. Roy. 4to., maps, plts., some in colour, slight foxing, contemp. blind stamped calf gilt. Quaritch 983-13 1978 $540

ENGLEHEART, NATHANIEL B.   A Concise Treatise on Eccentric Turning. 1867. 2nd. ed., plts., illus., 4to, orig. cloth, gilt, fine copy. Fenning 32-105 1978 £14.50

ENGLISH, ARTHUR   The Vanished Race. Montreal, 1927. Hood 116-409 1978 $35

ENGLISH Advice to the Freeholders of England. 1715. 8vo., newly bound in cloth, mor. back, uncut. Quaritch 979-12 1978 $40

ENGLISH Catalogue of Books. London, 1896-1966. 60 vols., mostly orig. cloth, lacks vols. for 1947 and 1949-1951, roy. 8vo. Traylen 88-46 1978 £50

ENGLISH Incunabula in the John Rylands Library. A Catalogue of Books Printed in England and of English Books Printed Abroad Between the Years 1475 and 1500... Manchester, 1930. Folio, orig. cloth, 1st ed., ex-lib. MacManus 238-951 1978 $40

ENGLISH Mezzotint Portraits from Circa 1750 to 1830. 1902. Roy. 4to., plts., buckram, unopened. Quaritch 983-181 1978 $65

ENNERSLEY, W. E.   Edward's Cross. New York, 1824. Narrow 8vo., frontis., orig. ochre wrs., fine. Quaritch 979-87 1978 $65

THE ENQUIRER: Devoted to Free Discussion as to the Kind of Wine Proper to be Used at the Lord's Supper, &c. Albany, 1841. Folio, colored plts. Butterfield 21-46 1978 $65

AN Enquiry Into The Causes of the Miscarriage of the Scots Colony at Darien. Glasgow, 1700. 1st. ed., 8vo, panelled calf, morocco label gilt, head of back defective. Deighton 5-35 1978 £115

AN ENQUIRY into the Reasons of the Conduct of Great Britain, with Relation to the Present State of Affairs in Europe. 1727. 8vo., slightly dust-stained. Quaritch 979-193 1978 $20

AN ENQUIRY: or, a Discourse between a Yeoman of Kent, and a Knight of a Shire upon the Prorogation of the Parliament to 2nd May 1693. (1693). Stained, sm. 4to., disbound. George's 635-639 1978 £8.50

AN ENQUIRY Relative to the Highways in the Shire of Berwick. N.P., n.d. (ca. 1780). 8vo, sewn, as issued, 1st ed., fine copy, uncut and unopened. Ximenes 47-273 1978 $40

ENRIGHT, MAURICE   The Ridgefield Tavern. Brooklyn, 1903. Illus. by Katherine Enright, 8vo., orig. wrs., 1st ed. Morrill 239-372 1978 $12.50

ENSKO, STEPHEN G. C.   American Silversmiths and Their Marks. New York, 1927. Part 2 only. Baldwins' 51-74 1978 $75

ENSKO, STEPHEN G. C.   American Silversmiths and Their Marks. New York, 1927-1948. Privately printed, 3 vols. Baldwins' 51-73 1978 $225

ENSKO, STEPHEN G. C.   American Silversmiths and Their Marks. New York, 1948. Part 3 only. Baldwins' 51-75 1978 $125

ENSKO, STEPHEN G. C.   American Silversmiths and Their Marks III. New York, 1948. Illus., maps. Biblo 251-250 1978 $77.50

ENSKO, STEPHEN G. C.   English Silver, 1675-1825. New York, (1937). Illus. Biblo BL781-532 1978 $28.50

ENTERTAINING a Nation. The Career of Long Branch, N.J. (Bayonne), 1940. Illus., map, 1st ed., fine, d.j. MacManus 239-1292 1978 $25

EOBANUS HESSUS   Saluberrima Bonae Valetudinis Tuendae Praecepta.
Frankfurt, 1568. Sm. 8vo., wrs. Salloch 345-60 1978 $90

EPHINGEN, JORG VON   The Diary of Jorg von Ehingen. Oxford, 1929.
4to., plts., portraits. Upcroft 12-131 1978 £9

EPICTETUS   The Discourses. 1902. 2 vols., lg. 8vo., orig.
qtr. vellum, gilt tops, ed. ltd. to 250 copies, printed on handmade paper. Howes
194-845 1978 £12.50

EPICTETUS   Enchiridion... Basel, 1563. 3 parts in 1 vol.,
lg. 8vo., first ed., orig. cont. blind stamped pigskin over bds., woodcuts, fine.
Schafer 19-17 1978 sFr 3500

EPICTETUS   Epictetus His Morals, with Simplicius His
Comment. London, 1694. 8vo, contemporary calf, spine gilt, 1st ed., fine copy.
Ximenes 47-92 1978 $125

EPICTETUS   Epicteti quae supersunt dissertationes ab Arriano
Collectae nec non Enchiridion et Fragmenta Graece et Latine. 1741. 2 vols.,
cr. 4to., contemp. calf, very good. Howes 194-259 1978 £38

EPICTETUS   All The Works of .... 1759. 2nd. ed., 4to,
orig. calf, head rubbed, brown label, good sound copy. Jarndyce 16-52 1978
£40

EPICTETUS   The Works of.... 1807. 4th. ed., 2 vols.,
orig. calf, good. Jarndyce 16-381 1978 £18

EPICURUS   The Extant Remains of the Greek Text. New
York, Limited Editions Club, 1947. Prtd. in black & red, decor. in gold, ltd.,
numbered ed., signed by Bruce Rogers, 8vo., black calf, slipcase. Salloch 345-
61 1978 $75

EPICURUS   Morals, Collected and Englished by Walter
Charleton. London, 1926. Ltd. to 750 copies, bookplate. Biblo 247-466 1978
$27.50

EPIGRAMMATUM Delectus ex Omnibus tum veteribus, tum recentionibus poetis
accurate decerptus. 1503. Engraved frontis. of coat of arms, 12mo., contemp.
calf. George's 635-463 1978 £8

EPIPHANIUS, SAINT   Contra octoaginta Haereses opus, Panarium, sive
Arcula, aut Capsula Medica appellatum. Basle, 1578. Folio, old blind stamped
calf, sometime rebacked. Howes 194-544 1978 £35

EPISTOLAE Diversorum Philosophorum, Oratorum. Venice, 1499. 1st ed., 4to, 2
vols., blindstamped calf, gilt ornaments, gilt edges, marginal wormholes carefully
repaired. Gilhofer 75-32 1978 SFr 6,400

EPISTOLAE Diversorum Philosophorum Oratorum. Venice, 1499. 2 vols. in 1,
4to., full straight-grained blue mor., gilt inner dentelles, silk endleaves, signed
by Bozerian. Salloch 348-56 1978 $2,500

EPISTOLARUM Obscurorum Virorum ad Dm. M. Ortuinum Gratium, Vol. 2 only.
1710. 12mo., contemp. panelled calf. George's 635-1303 1978 £5

EPITOME instituti societatis Jesu. Bruselles, 1690. Woodcut device on title,
sm. 8vo., old vellum, spine defective. George's 635-1082 1978 £10.50

EPPES, SUSAN BRADFORD   Through Some Eventful Years. Macon, Ga.,
1926. Bell Wiley's copy. Broadfoot 46-88 1978 $35

EPPES, SUSAN BRADFORD   Through Some Eventful Years. Macon, 1926.
Letter from Eppes relative laid in, ex libris, Bell Wiley's copy. Broadfoot's 44-126
1978 $25

EPSTEIN, RALPH C.   Industrial Profits. 1934. Austin 80-575 1978
$20

EQUICOLA, MARIO   Libro de natura de amore. Venice, 1525.
4 to., very fine, orig. contemp. Venetian gilt calf binding, 1st ed.. Schafer
19-18 1978 sFr. 2,200

ERASMUS, DESIDERIUS   Eloge de la Folié. Paris, 1944. Tall 8vo., half
vellum, bds. slipcase, frontis. portr. of Erasmus, ltd. ed. of 1025 numbered copies.
Van der Peet H-64-426 1978 Dfl 75

ERASMUS, DESIDERIUS   Adagiorum Opus... Lyons, 1541. Folio, old
mor. Salloch 348-57 1978 $300

ERASMUS, DESIDERIUS   L'Eloge De La Folie... Amsterdam, 1731.
Nouvelle ed., 8vo., marbled bds. Salloch 348-58 1978 $235

ERASMUS, DESIDERIUS   Familiarium colloquiorum opus (Colloquia aliquot
nova). (Paris, 1531). Exceedingly rare ed., oblong 12mo, 2 parts in one vol., red
mor., gilt panels, spine, edges and inside dentelles. Gilhofer 75-33 1978 SFr
3,000

ERASMUS, DESIDERIUS   Lingua. Basle, 1547. 8vo., mod. 1/2 mor.
Salloch 348-59 1978 $225

ERASMUS, DESIDERIUS   Moriae Encomium:.... London, 1709. Octavo,
calf, previously rebacked, covers detached but present, bookplt., plts. Totteridge
29-38 1978 $60

ERASMUS, DESIDERIUS   The Praise of Folly. London, 1887. Illus., half
blue mor., gilt dec. spine, 8vo. K Books 244-114 1978 £16

ERASMUS, DESIDERIUS   The Praise of Folly. London, 1887. 8vo., orig.
cloth, plts., good. Sexton 7-16 1978 £10

ERASMUS, DESIDERIUS   Twenty Two Select Colloquies. 1711. Engrav.
portrait, contemp. calf, red mor. label, 8vo. Howes 194-260 1978 £25

ERCKMANN, EMILE   The Conscript. London, 1870. First Smith Elder
ed., green bubble grain cloth, plts. by Riou. Greene 78-39 1978 $70

ERCKMANN, EMILE   Les Deux Freres, Paris, 1873. Paris, 1872. 2
vols. in 1, new 1/2 green calf, extra gilt spine, fine binding. Eaton 45-175 1978
£12

ERCKMANN-CHATRIN, MM. The Illustrious Dr. Matheus. London,
(1880). Engravings, fancy gilt cover, only English-language ed., very good
or better. Limestone 9-99 1978 $20

ERCOLANI, GIROLAMO   Le Eroine della Solitudine Sacra. Venezia,
1664. 12mo., vellum, illus. King 7-36 1978 £35

ERDMANN, BENNO   Logische Elementarlehre Logik I. Halle,
1907. 2nd rev'd. ed., thick tall 8vo., cloth. Salloch 348-60 1978 $40

ERDMANN, OTTO LINNE   Ueber das Nickel, Seine Gewinnung im Grossen
und Technische Benutzung, Vorzuglich zu Weisskupfer (Argentan, Neusilber).
Leipzig, 1827. 1st ed., nice, uncut copy, stamp & owner's signature on title.
Offenbacher 30-36 1978 $75

ERIZZO, SEBASTIANO   Trattato Dell'Instrumento et Via Inventrice De
Gli Antichi. Venice, 1554. 1st ed., quarto, woodcut initials and ornaments,
contemporary limp vellum. Bennett 20-66 1978 $475

ERIZZO, SEBASTIANO   Trattato Dell'Istrumento Et Via Inventrice Degli
Antichi. Venice, 1554. 4to., vellum. Salloch 345-63 1978 $185

ERMAN, ADOLF   Life in Ancient Egypt. London, 1894. Plts.,
illus., roy. 8vo. Traylen 88-11 1978 £20

ERNEST Harcourt, or the Loyalist's Son. Philadelphia, 1843. Pamphlet binder.
Austin 82-94 1978 $20

ERNESTUS, IO. AU.   Clavis Ciceroniana, Sive Indices Rerum et Verbo-
rum Philologico-Critici in Opera Ciceronis Accedunt, Graeca Ciceronis Reces
Sariis Observationibus Illustrata. Halae, 1757. 8vo., full old vellum. Van der
Peet H-64-321 1978 Dfl 45

ERNST, J. J.   Insectes d'Europe, Chenilles, Crisalides, Papil-
lons et Sphinx,...Decrets par le R. P. Engramelle. 1779-93. 8 vols. in 6, roy.
4to., plain and hand-coloured frontis., plts., half vellum, green leather labels,
bds. sides, uncut, fine. Quaritch 983-325 1978 $5,500

ERNST, MORRIS   American Sexual Behavior and the Kinsey Report.
1948. Austin 80-1042a 1978 $8.50

ERNST, MORRIS L.   Too Big. Boston, 1940. 1st ed., d.w. Biblo
BL781-813 1978 $10

ERNST, MORRIS L.   The Ultimate Power.   New York, 1937.
Biblo 251-332 1978 $9.50

ERRAPATER   Book of Knowledge. 1735. Engraved frontis.,
cuts in text, a few pages defective, 12mo., old calf, worn. George's 635-933
1978 £5

ERSKINE, LORD   Speeches when at the Bar, against constructive
Treason. (c. 1835). 4 vols., 8vo. George's 635-1281 1978 £8.50

ERSKINE, JOHN ELPHINSTONE   Journal of a Cruise among the Islands of the
Western Pacific, London, 1853. 1st ed., octavo, frontispiece, plates, lithographs,
wood-engravings, folding map, full polished calf, rubbed, double gilt fillets,
gilt-tooled paneled spine with black leather label, marbled edges and end papers,
gilt on spine mostly rubbed off. Bennett 20-67 1978 $285

ERTZ, SUSAN   Now East, Now West. 1927. Slightly foxed,
cloth. Eaton 45-176 1978 £5

ERVINE, ST. JOHN   Private Enterprise. London, (1948). 1st ed.,
d.w. Biblo 251-474 1978 $8.50

ERWIN, MARIE H.   Wyoming Historical Blue Book: A Legal and
Political History of Wyoming, 1868-1943. Denver, [1943]. Illus., orig. cloth,
1st ed. Ginsberg 14-1077 1978 $40

ERWIN, MILO   History of Williamson Co., Illinois... Marion,
1876. 1st ed., 3/4 mor. MacManus 239-972 1978 $45

ESCOTT, T. H. S.   Personal Forces of the Period. London, 1898.
1st ed., stain across bottom of upper cover, very good or better. Limestone
9-98 1978 $12.50

ESDAILE, JAMES   Mesmerism in India, and its Practical Application
in Surgery and Medicine. London, 1846. Sm. 8vo., orig. brown blind-stamped
cloth, gilt lettering on spine, pencilled notes, very good copy, 1st ed. Zeitlin
245-72 1978 $285

ESDAILE, K. A.   Roubiliac's Work at Trinity College. Cambridge,
1924. Thin sq. cr. 8vo., orig. cloth, backed bds., plts., good. Sexton 7-17 1978
£10

ESHER, REGINALD VISCOUNT   The Tragedy of Lord Kitchener. 1921. 1st. ed.,
4th printing, plts., 8vo., orig. cloth, occasional light foxing. Sawyer 298-73
1978 £27

ESHLEMAN, CLAYTON   T'ai. Cambridge, (1969). 1 of 99 numbered
copies signed by author, 1st ed., 8 vo., bds., glassine jacket, as new. Houle
10-101 1978 $85

ESHLEMAN, H. FRANK   Historic Background and Annals of the Swiss and
German Pioneer Settlers of Southeastern Pennsylvania... Lancaster, 1917. Mac-
Manus 239-1449 1978 $25

ESNAULT-PELTERIE, ROBERT   l'Astronautique. Paris, 1930. 8vo., lg. fldg.
charts, orig. prtd. wrs., uncut, fine copy, 1st ed. Norman 5-94 1978 $125

ESNAULT-PELTERIE, ROBERT   L'exploration Par Fusees de la Tres Haute Atmosphere et de la Possiblite des Voyages Interplanetaires. Paris, 1928. 8vo., 8
cancel leaves inserted in addition to orig. misprinted text, orig. prtd. wrs., uncut, spine repaired, but fine copy, 1st ed. Norman 5-93 1978 $250

ESNAULT-PELTERIE, ROBERT   L'exploration Par Fusees de la Tres Haute Atmosphere et de la Possiblite des Voyages Interplanetaires. Fine cond., but without
extra cancel leaves. Norman 5-93a 1978 $175

ESNAULT-PELTRIE, ROBERT   Notice sur les Travaux Scientifiques. Paris,
1918-36. 2 vols., 4to., fldg. diagrs., text photos & diagrs., orig. prtd. wrs., a
little chipped at head & foot of spine, very good copies, inscr'd by author. Norman 5-**13 1978 $300

ESPEJO, ANTONIO DE   New Mexico. Lancaster, 1928. Orig. cloth, 1
of 200 numbered copies, signed by F. W. Hodge. Ginsberg 14-758 1978 $125

ESPENSHADE, A. H.   Penna. Place Names. State College, (1925).
Map, scarce. MacManus 239-1450 1978 $22.50

ESPINOSA, J. MANUEL   Crusaders of the Rio Grande:... Chicago,
1942. Illus., orig. cloth, 1st ed. Ginsberg 14-1110 1978 $65

ESPINOSA DE LOS MONTEROS, CARLOS   Esposicion que Sobre las Provincials
de Sonora y Sinaloa,.... Mexico, 1823. Tables, 1st ed., full mo, extremely rare
and valuable. Ginsberg 14-347 1978 $1,000

ESPOSITO, COLONEL VINCENT J.   The West Point Atlas of American Wars
1689-1900, NY,1959. Maps, Bell Wiley's Copy.Broadfoot's 44-128 1978 $100.00

ESPY, ARTHUR   The Legislative Investigations of Cincinnati in
the Years 1906 and 1908. Cincinnati, 1910. Cloth. Hayman 73-505 1978 $7.50

ESQUEMLING, JOHN
Please turn to
EXQUEMELIN, ALEXANDRE OLIVIER

ESQUIVEL, FRANCISCO DE   Relacion de la Invencion de los Cverpos Santos,
Que en los anos 1614, 1615, y 1616.... 1617. 4to., limp vellum, good, illus.
King 7-277 1978 £35

AN ESSAY for Regulating and making more useful the Militia of this Kingdom.
1701. Second ed. corrected, 4to., unbound. P. M. Hill 142-174 1978 £12

AN ESSAY In the Writings and Genius of Shakespeare... 1770. Orig. half calf,
spine worn, 2nd. ed. Jarndyce 16-192 1978 £22

ESSAYS & Observations on the Following Subjects Viz. on Trade, Husbandry of
Flax, Raising Banks Against Tides & Floods, Hops..Published By A Society of Gen-
tlemen in Dublin. London, 1740. Reprint, plts., modern 1/2 leather, very good.
Hyland 128-550 1978 £75

ESSAYS of the Year, 1929-30. Argonaut Press, 1930. One of 250 numbered
copies on lg. paper, very good, first English ed. Bell Book 16-011 1978 £6.50

ESSAYS On The Repeal of the Union, To Which the Association Prized Were
Awarded... 1845. 1st. collected ed., 8vo, orig. green cloth, uncut, fine.
Fenning 32-280 1978 £24

ESSE, JAMES   Hunger. Dublin, 1918. 12mo, printed wrs., 1st
ed., fine. Duschnes 220-289 1978 $30

ESSEX, W. H.   Illustrations of the Architectural Ornaments and
Embellishments, and Painted Glass of the Temple Church London... 1845. 4to.,
coloured and plain plts., orig. cloth. Quaritch 983-103 1978 $135

THE ESTABLISHMENT of a General Packet Station, on the South-West coast of
Ireland. 1836. 8vo., new bds., map. F. Edwards 1013-64 1978 £30

ESTABROOKS, HENRY L.   Adrift in Dixie: Or, A Yankee Officer Among
The Rebels. New York, 1866. Ex libris, Bell Wiley's copy. Broadfoot's 44-529
1978 $14

ESTENSI, GLI STATI   Tariffa de Medicamenti Portati Dalla Farmacopea.
Modena, 1839. Rittenhouse 49-250 1976 $15

ESTIENNE, CHARLES   De Dissectione Partium Corparis Humani libri
tres. Paris, 1545. Rare, 1st ed., folio, woodcuts, old calf, gilt panels. Gilhofer
75-34 1978 SFr 17,000

ESTIENNE, CHARLES   Vinetum. Sylva, Frutetum, Collis. De Re Hor-
tensi. Seminarium. Arbutum, Fonticulus, Spinetum. Pratum, Lacus, Arundinetum.
Paris, 1537-1543. 6 works in 1 vol., 8vo., full red mor., gilt edges, fine copy.
Salloch 345-62 1978 $1,250

ESTIENNE, HENRI   The Act of Making Devises... London, 1646.
1st. ed. in English, engraved title by Marshall, engraved vignette, plts., sm. 4to.,
old quarter calf, 1st. few leaves stained. Traylen 88-238 1978 £145

ESTIENNE, HENRI   Fragmenta Poetarum veterum Latinorum, quorum
opera non extant.... (Geneva), 1564. Sm. 8vo., full turquoise mor., all edges
gilt, marginal stains on a few leaves, first ed. Howes 194-546 1978 £85

ESTIENNE, HENRI   Poesis philosophica, vel saltem reliquiae poesis
philosophicae,.... (Geneva), 1573. 1st ed., 8vo, contemp. vellum, fine.
Gilhofer 75-35 1978 SFr 850

ESTIMATE of the Cost of an Armory.   Raleigh, 1861. Wrs., disbound, Bell Wiley's copy. Broadfoot 46-350 1978 $10

ESTVAN, B.   War Pictures from the South. NY, 1863. Cracked front hinge, paper labels worn, cover faded, Bell Wiley's Copy. Broadfoot's 44-129 1978 $20.00

ETCHINGS of Rembrandt. A Chronological Listing. London, n.d. 4to., plts. Biblo BL781-718 1978 $16.50

ETHEREGE, GEORGE   The Dramatic Works. Oxford, 1927. 2 vols., cr. 8vo., orig. holland backed bds. Howes 194-848 1978 £12.50

ETHEREGE, GEORGE   She Wou'd if She Cou'd. 1671. 2nd. ed., 4to, half cloth, few page numerals cut into. Hannas 54-104 1978 £45

ETHEREGE, GEORGE   The Works of ... 1704. 1st. collected ed., 8vo, contemp. calf, rehinged new end-papers, 1st. part-title misbound in front. Hannas 54-105 1978 £85

ETHNOGRAPHICAL Album of the Weapons, Tools, Ornaments, Articles of Dress Etc. of the Natives of the Pacific Islands. Landscape folio, 4 vols. in 2, ltd. to 350 copies. Traylen 88-491 1978 £95

ETIENNE, J. D.   Traite des Mines a l'Usage des Jeunes Militaires. Berne, 1779. Plts., 4to., contemp. half calf. F. Edwards 1013-293 1978 £80

ETLING, MARY   Battles--How They are Won. 1944. Maps, illus. Austin 80-95 1978 $10

THE ETONIAN. 1823. 3rd ed., 3 vols., post 8vo., half calf, rubbed. George's 635-1295 1978 £15

ETOURNEAU, MONS.   Les Mormons. Paris, 1856. Illus., orig. pr. wr., 1st ed. Ginsberg 14-1104 1978 $85

ETTING, FRANK M.   An Historical Account of the Old State House of Penna. Now Known as the Hall of Independence. Philadelphia, 1891. Illus., 4to., nice. MacManus 239-1602 1978 $15

ETZENHOUSER, R.   From Palmyra, New York, 1830, To Independence, Missouri, 1894... Independence, 1894. Orig. wr., 1st ed. Ginsberg 14-649 1978 $75

ETZENSBERGER, R.   Up the Nile by Steam. London, (1872). Maps, 12mo., orig. limp cloth, binding partly faded. Morrill 241-129 1978 $15

EUCLIDES   The Elements of Geometrie...Faithfully Translated into the English Toung. London, 1570. 56 of 60 cut-outs, folio, early paneled calf, hinges weak, 1st ed. in English, some stains, bkplt. Offenbacher 30-37 1978 $2,000

EUCLIDES   The Elements of Euclid, Explained and Demonstrated in a New and Most Easie Method. London, 1685. 12mo., plts., contemp. panelled calf, joints repaired, first ed. Quaritch 977-150 1978 $175

EUCLIDES   The Elements of Euclid, Explained in a New But Most Easie Method. London, 1696. Sm. 8vo., frontispiece, light age-staining, recent panelled calf, second ed. Quaritch 977-151 1978 $135

EUCLIDES   The Elements of Euclid.... 1829. 8vo., very good, wrapper, diagrams. Fenning 32-106 1978 £6.50

EUCLIDES   Euclidis Megarensis.... Paris, 1566. Folio, old calf, repaired, numerous diagrams, large, crisp and clean copy. Quaritch 977-149 1978 $550

EUCLIDES   Orontii Finsei Delphinatis.... Paris, 1551. Sm. 4to., woodcut diagrams, a few sm. damp stains, top margins rather frayed, old limp vellum, third ed. Quaritch 977-148 1978 $325

EUGENE, OF SAVOY, PRINCE Memoirs. 1811. 8vo., contemp. calf, portrait, fine. P. M. Hill 142-104 1978 £16

EULER, LEONHARD   Institutiones Calculi Differentialis cum eius usu in Analysi Finitorum ac Doctrina Serierum. Petersbury, 1755. 4to., nineteenth century half calf. Quaritch 977-153 1978 $600

EULER, LEONHARD   Introductio in analysin infinitorum. Lausanne, 1748. 2 vols., 4 to., 1st ed., fine clean copy, orig. publisher's card-boards. Schafer 19-49 1978 sFr. 3,300

EULER, LEONHARD   Methodus Inveniendi Lineas Curvas. Geneva, 1744. 4to., fldg. copperplts., contemp. vellum, occas. light foxing, but fine copy, 1st ed. Norman 5-96 1978 $2,000

EULER, LEONHARD   Tentamen Novae Theoriae Musicae ex Certissimis Harmoniae Principiis. Petropoli (St. Petersburg), 1739. 4to., plts., contemp. vellum, light dampstaining, but fine copy with wide margins, 1st ed. Norman 5-95 1978 $500

EURIPIDES   Hecuba, Orestes et Phoenissae, collatis decem Msstis textum et scholia emendavit.... Cantabrigae, 1726. Contemp. calf, 8vo. George's 635-464 1978 £5.25

EURIPIDES   Tragoediae XIX. 1597. Vol. 1 only, vellum, time-darkened. Allen 234-319 1978 $30

EURIPIDES   The Tragedies of .... 1781/1783. Vol. 1, 1st. ed., 4to, engraved frontis, vol. 2 - 1st. ed., 4to, half-title, half calf, marbled bds., hinges of vol. 1 weakening, o/w good. Jarndyce 16-165 1978 £18

EUROPEAN Civilisation, its Origin and Development. 1935. Folding maps, 7 vols., spines faded, 8vo. George's 635-640 1978 £70

EUROPEAN War; Despatches Between British Government and Ambassadors; Speeches Delivered in the Imperial House of Commons. Ottawa, 1914. Hood 116-120 1978 $15

EUSEBIUS   The Auncient Ecclesiastical Histories of the First Six Hundred Years after Christ. 1619. Folio, partly printed in black letter, contemp. sheep, neatly rebacked with calf, new endpapers. Howes 194-44 1978 £65

EUSTACE, JOHN CHETWODE   A Classical Tour through Italy. London, 1815. 2 vols., third ed., 8vo., bds., paper back, worn, uncut. King 7-352 1978 £25

EUSTACE, JOHN CHETWODE   A Letter From Paris to George Petrie. 1814. 1st. ed., lib. stamps on 1 blank, uncut in orig. brown wrappers, paper label, v.g. Jarndyce 16-658 1978 £12.50

EUSTATHII De Ismeniae et Esmenes Amoribus. 1618. 1st ed., octavo, full contemp. calf, rebacked, gilt cartouches on both covers, spine gilt-ruled, very nice, bookplate. Bennett 20-82 1978 $150

EUSTATHIUS, MACREM BOLITES   Gli Amori d'Ismenio composti per Evstathio Philosopho et di Greco tradotti per Lelio Carani. Florence, 1550. 8vo, Italic letter, contemp. French vellum gilt, spine gilt, gilt centre and corner-pieces, lacking ties, gilt edges. Quaritch 978-51 1978 $550

EUTROPIUS   A Breviary of Roman History. London, 1684. 1st. ed., fcap. 8vo, contemp. calf, rebacked. Traylen 88-239 1978 £58

EUTROPIUS   Eutropius's Compendious History of Rome. Boston, 1793. 1st Amer. ed., 8vo, 1" lacking in upper spine, text very good. Victoria 34-163 1978 $22.50

EVACUATION Day 100 Years Ago. New York, 1883. Illus. by Howard Pyle, good. Nestler Rare 78-172 1978 $25

EVANGELICAL LUTHERAN SYNOD OF MIAMI   Proceedings of the Third and Fourth Sessions of the..., Convened in Tarlton, May 8, 1846. Baltimore, 1847. Disbound. Hayman 72-565 1978 $12.50

EVANGELICAL LUTHERAN SYNOD OF MIAMI   Proceedings of the Fifth Session of the..., Convened in Hamilton, April 17th, 1848. Dayton, 1848. Disbound. Hayman 72-566 1978 $10

EVANGELICAL LUTHERAN SYNOD OF NORTHERN INDIANA   Minutes of the Second Convention of the Evangelical Lutheran Synod of Northern Indiana, Held in the Luteran Church in Albion, Ind., September 18-20, A.D. 1856. Indianapolis, 1856. Disbound. Hayman 72-358 1978 $12.50

EVANGELICAL LUTHERAN SYNOD OF NORTHERN INDIANA   Minutes of the 5th Annual Convention of the Evangelical Lutheran Synod of Northern Indiana, Held in the Methodist Episcopal Church in Cicero, Indiana, Sept. 22-25, A.D., 1859. Indianapolis, 1859. Disbound. Hayman 72-359 1978 $15

EVANGELICAL LUTHERAN SYNOD OF NORTHERN INDIANA   Proceedings of the Ninth Annual Convention of the....Held in Spencerville, Indiana, from Sept. 29 to Oct. 4, 1863. Indianapolis, 1863. Disbound. Hayman 72-360 1978 $12.50

EVANGELICAL LUTHERAN SYNOD OF NORTHERN INDIANA   Proceedings of the 10th Annual Convention of the...Held in Camden, Indiana, from September 27 to Oct. 1, 1864. Fort Wayne, 1864. Disbound. Hayman 72-361 1978 $12.50

EVANGELICAL LUTHERAN SYNOD OF NORTHERN INDIANA   Proceedings of the 11th Annual Convention of the....Convened in Cicero, Hamilton County, Indiana, Oct. 16 to 21, 1866. Indianapolis, 1866. Disbound. Hayman 72-363 1978 $12.50

EVANS, ABEL   The Apparition. (Oxford), 1710. 8vo., unbound, first ed. P. M. Hill 142-272 1978 £40

EVANS, ABEL   The Apparition. 1710. 2nd. ed., rebound in half calf, marbled bds., v.g. Jarndyce 16-77 1978 £24

EVANS, ARTHUR   The Palace of Minos. 1921-36. 5 vols. in 7, imp. 8vo., map, coloured and plain plts., illus., cloth, vol. I loose. Quaritch 983-14 1978 $1,000

EVANS, ARTHUR F.   The History of the Oil Engine. London, (1932). 8vo., illus., orig. cloth, d.w., very good copy. Norman 5-212 1978 $40

EVANS, CLEMENT A.   Confederate Military History.... New York, 1962. Reprint, Bell Wiley's copy. Broadfoot's 44-130 1978 $125

EVANS, CLEMENT A.   Confederate Military History,...North Carolina. Atlanta, 1899. Vol. IV, rebound. Broadfoot 50-348 1978 $25

EVANS, CLEMENT   Confederate Military History Vol. VIII, Tennessee. Atlanta, 1899. 3/4 lea., Bell Wiley's copy. Broadfoot 46-378 1978 $20

EVANS, ELWOOD   The State of Washington. (Tacoma, 1893). Wrps., little soiled. Hayman 71-761 1978 $12.50

EVANS, F. M. G.   The Principal Secretary of State, a Survey of the Office 1558-1680. Manchester, 1923. Illus., 8vo. George's 635-642 1978 £5

EVANS, F. W.   Compendium of the Origin, History...with Biographies. New Lebanon, 1867. 16mo., prtd. wr., nice copy. Butterfield 21-415 1978 $20

EVANS, GEORGE C.   History of Jefferson, N.H. Manchester, 1927. Illus. MacManus 239-1071 1978 $17.50

EVANS, H. W.   The Attitude of the Knights of the Ku Klux Klan Toward the Roman Catholic Hierarchy. n.d. ca. 1923. Austin 79-227 1978 $20

EVANS, HENRY O.   Iron Pioneer: Henry W. Oliver, 1840-1904. New York, 1942. Illus., 1st ed. Biblo BL781-89 1978 $9

EVANS, J.   Monastic Life at Cluny 910-1157. Oxford, 1931. Plts., 8vo. Upcroft 12-137 1978 £8.50

EVANS, J. T.   The Church Plate of Breconshire. 1912. Sm. 4to., plts. Biblo 247-325 1978 $72.50

EVANS, LUTHER   Texas Centennial Exhibition Held at the Library of Congress. Washington, 1946. Illus. Jenkins 116-424 1978 $18.50

EVANS, MARY ANNE
Please turn to
ELIOT, GEORGE

EVANS, NATHANIEL   Poems of Several Occasions with Some Other Compositions. Philadelphia, 1772. Contemp. calf, rubbed, 1st ed., few stains, lacks leaf of errata. MacManus 238-478 1978 $75

EVANS, NELSON W.   A History of Scioto County, Ohio, Together with a Pioneer Record of Southern Ohio. Portsmouth, 1903. Cloth, very scarce. Hayman 72-571 1978 $70

EVANS, OLIVER   The Young Mill-Wright & Millers Guide. Philadelphia, 1821. 4th ed., very good, binding very worn. Nestler Rare 78-192 1978 $95

EVANS, THEOPHILUS   A View of the Primitive Ages. Ebensburg, 1834. 8vo., contemp. calf, some foxing, 1st ed. in English. Morrill 241-130 1978 $10

EVANS, THOMAS   Old Ballads, Historical and Narrative, With Some of Modern Date:.... 2 vols., octavo, title vignettes engraved by Isaac Taylor, contemp. blond calf, spines gilt, marbled endpapers, mor. labels, 1st ed. Bennett 7-39 1978 $200

EVANS, W. F.   The Divine Law of Cure. Boston, 1886. Cloth. Hayman 73-158 1978 $8.50

EVANS, WILLIAM   Benefaction of William Evans, and the Evans Festival. Syracuse, 1858. Wr. Butterfield 21-264 1978 $12.50

EVANS, WILLIAM   Supplementary Volume to A Treatise on the Theory and Practice of Agriculture, Adapted to the Cultivation and Economy of the Animal and Vegetable Productions... Montreal, 1836. Plain cloth, lib. bind. Hood 116-348 1978 $175

EVANS, WILLIAM FRANKLIN   Border Skylines: Fifty Years of "Tallying Out" on the Bloys Round-up. Dallas, 1940. Illus., original cloth, 1st ed. Ginsberg 14-348 1978 $30

EVAN-THOMAS, OWEN   Domestic Utensils of Wood. XVIth to XIXth Century... 1932. 4to., plts., illus., cloth, d.w. Quaritch 983-Addenda h 1978 $150

EVANTUREL, EUDORE   Premieres Poesies 1876-1878. Quebec, 1878. Wolfe 39-179 1978 $20

EVE, GEORGE W.   Decorative Heraldry. London, 1897. No. 60 of 130 copies prtd. on Japanese vellum, illus., newly bound in marbled paper over bds. & cloth. Battery Park 1-290 1978 $125

EVELYN, JOHN   Fumifugium: Or, the Inconvenience of AER, and Smoake of London Dissipated Together with Some Remedies Humbly Proposed By..., Esq; to His Sacred Majestie... (The Swan Press: 1930). Orig. cloth-backed gray bds., d.j., somewhat soiled, 1 of 100 copies, very good. MacManus 238-846 1978 $17.50

EVELYN, JOHN   The Life of Mrs. Godolphin... London, 1847. Illus., frontis., full brown mor., 1st ed., bookplts., hinges weak, otherwise nice. MacManus 238-119 1978 $30

EVELYN, JOHN   Memoirs, Illustrative of the Life and Writings of John Evelyn, Esq. 1818. 2 vols., 4to., 1st ed., fldg. pedigree, plts., contemp. mottled calf, panelled backs, gilt & blind panelled sides, unusually clean copy. Quarity 979-137 1978 $400

EVELYN, JOHN   Miscellaneous Writings. London, 1825. Plts., facsimile frontis, thick 4to., orig. bds., uncut. Traylen 88-241 1978 £35

EVELYN, JOHN   The Miscellaneous Writings of, Author of Sylva, or, a Discourse of Forest Trees. London, 1825. 4to., contemp. bds., illus., calf back & corners, ex-lib., crudely rebacked with white tape, foxed, 1st ed. Morrill 241-131 1978 $25

EVELYN, JOHN   Sylva, or a Discourse of Forest-Trees, and the Propagation of Timber in His Majesties Dominions. London, 1664. 1st. ed., title in red & black with engraved arms, folio, old calf rebacked, good copy. Traylen 88-569 1978 £225

EVELYN, JOHN   Sylva, or a Discourse of Forest-Trees and the Propagation of Timber in His Majesties Dominions. York, 1786. Portrait, engraved plts., 2 vols., 4to, half brown morocco, gilt tops, very fine copy. Traylen 88-570 1978 £150

EVELYN, JOHN   Silva. York, 1812. Plts., 2 vols., 4to., contemp. half russia, rebacked. Howes 194-262 1978 £38

EVENKELLIUS, ACATIUS   The Schoole of Potentates. London, 1650. Sm. 8vo, corner torn from N2 and N3 just affecting numeral, old sheep, later label, stamp in gilt on sides, illus. Traylen 88-242 1978 £125

L'EVENTAIL et la Fourrure chez Paquin, 1911. Paris, 1911. Folio, plts. coloured in pochoir, orig. dec. bds., ltd. to 300 numbered copies. Quaritch 978-10 1978 $1,550

EVENTFUL Narratives. Salt Lake City, 1887. Orig. cloth, 1st ed. Ginsberg 14-650 1978 $25

EVERETT, ALEXANDER H. An Address Delivered Before the Peithessophian and Philoclean Societies of Rutgers College, on the Literary Character of the Scriptures. New York, 1838. 8vo., orig. wrs., 1st ed. Morrill 241-397 1978 $7.50

EVERETT, CHARLES C. Eulogy on Abraham Lincoln...Before the Citizens of Bangor...June 1st, 1865. Bangor, 1865. Wrs., sm. piece chipped from corner of back wr. Hayman 72-425 1978 $17.50

EVERETT, CHARLES C. A Sermon in Commemoration of the Death of Abraham Lincoln... Bangor, 1865. Disbound, 600 copies published. Hayman 71-421 1978 $12.50

EVERETT, EDWARD A Eulogy on the Life and Character of John Quincy Adams.... Boston, 1848. Sewed. Hayman 71-201 1978 $7.50

EVERETT, GEORGE The Path-Way to Peace and Profit. 1694. Sm. 4to., half calf. F. Edwards 1013-65 1978 £300

EVERETT, GEORGE H. Health Fragments. New York, 1874. Illus., 8vo., 1st ed. Morrill 239-78 1978 $15

EVERETT, HENRY The History of the Somerset Light Infantry 1685-1914. 1934. Coloured plts., imp. 8vo., portraits, publisher's half mor. F. Edwards 1013-490 1978 £50

EVERITT, GRAHAM English Caricaturists and Graphic Humourists of the 19th Century. 1886. Illus., coloured plts., 4to., orig. cloth, neatly recased. George's 635-19 1978 £45

EVERITT, GRAHAM English Caricaturists and Graphic Humourists of the 19th Century. 1893. Second ed., illus., roy. 8vo., orig. cloth gilt, covers dull & somewhat worn, hinges sprung, else good. Bell Book 17-146 1978 £15

EVERSON, WILLIAM The Waldport Poems. Waldport, Untide Press, 1944. Illus., wrs., slightly tattered, browned & soiled, internally fine, 1 of 975 copies prtd. Dawson's 447-223 1978 $30

EVERY Boy's Book of Sport and Pastime. London, 1905. 2nd ed., illus., thick 8vo. Victoria 34-411 1978 $30

EVES, C. WASHINGTON The West Indies. 1893. 3rd. ed., folding maps, plts., sm. 8vo, orig. cloth, spine faded. Edwards 1012-716 1978 £25

EVIDENCE Concerning Projected Railways Across the Sierra Nevada Mountains, From Pacific Tide Waters in California,.... Carson City, 1865. Half morocco. Ginsberg 14-110 1978 $275

L'EVOLUTION de l'Humanite'. 1920-23. Text illus., 9 vols., cr. 8vo., orig. cloth, spines dull. George's 635-946 1978 £20

EVREINOFF, N. Histoire du Theatre Russe. Paris, 1947. 8vo., orig. covers. Van der Peet H-64-124 1978 Dfl 30

EWALD, A. C. The Rt. Hon. Benjamin Disraeli, Earl of Beaconsfield and his Times. 1882. Portraits, 5 vols., roy. 8vo. George's 635-624 1978 £5.25

EWALD, OSKAR Die Franzoesische Aufklaerungs-Philosophie. Munich, 1925. 8vo., cloth. Salloch 348-62 1978 $10

EWART, JOHN S. The Independence Papers. Ottawa, 1930-32. 2 vols. Hood's 115-590 1978 $65

EWART, JOHN S. The Kingdom of Canada, Imperial Federation, the Colonial Conferences, the Alaska Boundary, and Other Essays. Toronto, 1908. Hood 116-623 1978 $35

EWART, JOHN S. The Manitoba School Question... Toronto, 1894. Hood's 115-999 1978 $100

EWART, JOHN S. The World of Famine and The Duty of Canada. Ottawa, 1917. Covers mended. Hood's 115-591 1978 $10

EWART, T. S. A Flag For Canada... Ottawa, 1947. Hood's 115-592 1978 $10

EWBANK, THOMAS Life in Brazil.... New York, 1856. Orig. binding, clean, illus., moderate wear at top of spine, sm. dampstain at upper corner of some leaves. Hayman 71-202 1978 $15

EWIN, DAVID The Story of George Gershwin. N. Y., Holt, (1943). 1st ed., illus., d.j., good-fine. Houle 10-121 1978 $20

EWING, E. E. Bugles and Bells. Cincinnati, 1899. Cloth, written mostly in verse, scarce. Hayman 73-116 1973 $27.50

EWING, HORATIA Melchior's Dream and Other Tales. 1862. 1st. ed., illus., half title, orig. blue cloth, v.g. Jarndyce 16-659 1978 £8.50

EWING, JAMES Neoplastic Diseases. Philadelphia & London, (1940). Thick 8vo., illus., orig. green cloth, gilt lettering, library stamps, good copy. Zeitlin 245-73 1978 $75

EWING, JOHN The Royal Scots 1914-1919. 1925. Frontis., plts., 2 vols., 8vo., orig. cloth. F. Edwards 1013-480 1978 £12

EX-LEGIONNAIRE 1384. London, c.1930. 8vo, orig. cloth, covers spotted. K Books 239-153 1978 £5

AN EXAMINATION and Explanation of the South-Sea Company's Scheme, for Taking in the Publick Debts. London, 1720. 8vo, modern boards, 3rd ed. Ximenes 47-293 1978 $40

AN EXAMINATION of Some of the Provisions of the "Act to Create a Fund for the Benefit of the Creditors of Certain Monied Corporations, and for Other Purposes". New-York, 1829. Disbound. Hayman 73-476 1978 $12.50

EXECUTIVE and Congressional Directory of the Confederate States. N.P., 1899. Wrs., Bell Wiley's copy. Broadfoot's 44-85 1978 $16

EXECUTIVE Proceedings, Correspondence and Documents, Relating to Oregon, from which the Injuction of Secrecy has been Removed. Washington, 1846. Disbound. Ginsberg 14-815 1978 $25

EXEMPLAR of Berlin Woolwork. c.1864. Oblong 8vo., hand-coloured designs, contemp. cloth, a little worn. Quaritch 983-59 1978 $240

EXHIBITION Illustrative of Early English Portraiture. 1909. Roy. 4to., plts., buckram. Quaritch 983-236 1978 $65

EXHIBITION Of American Sculpture. 1923. Orig. paper covers, 4to. Baldwins' 51-153 1978 $25

EXHIBITION of Early German Art. 1906. Roy. 4to., plts., buckram. Quaritch 983-188 1978 $75

EXHIBITIONS of Pictures by Masters of the Netherlandish and Allied Schools of the XVth and early XVIth Centuries. 1892. Roy. 4to., plts., buckram. Quaritch 983-225 1978 $50

EXIDEUIL, PIERRE D' The Human Pair in the work of Thomas Hardy. (1930). Some foxing, else very good, first English ed. Bell Book 17-441 1978 £12.50

EXPOSITION d'art Canadien, Musee du jeu de Paume. Paris, 1927. Colored card cover, sepia plts. Hood 117-176 1978 $30

EXPOSITION Universelle De 1867. Paris, Rio de Janeiro, London, Norwich, 1867-68. 20 brochures bound in 2 thick vols., 8vo., half cloth, very good cond. Offenbacher 30-125 1978 $125

AN EXPOSURE of Some of the Numerous Mistatements and Misrepresentations Contained in a Pamphlet Commonly Known by the Name of Mr. Marryat's Pamphlet, entitled "Thoughts on the Abolition of the Slave Trade." London, 1816. 8vo, sewn, as issued, 1st ed., very fine copy, uncut and unopened. Ximenes 47-293 1978 $85

EXQUEMELIN, ALEXANDRE OLIVIER   Bucaniers of America... London, 1684.
4to., cont. calf, plts., tall copy, first ed. F. Edwards 1012-714 1978 £300

EXQUEMELIN, ALEXANDRE OLIVIER   Bucaniers of America. London, 1684.
1st ed. in English, sm. 4to., 2 vols. in 1, portrs., plts., maps, sm. engr., full
red mor., very scarce, complete. Current Misc. 8-18 1978 $1,375

EXQUEMELIN, ALEXANDER OLIVIER   The History of the Bucaniers of America.
London, 1741. Plts., maps, 2 vols., 12mo., contemp. calf, 4th English ed.
Morrill 241-132 1978 $160

EXQUEMELIN, ALEXANDRE OLIVIER   The History of the Bucaniers of America.
London, 1810. 12mo., old mor. dec. in gilt, slightly rubbed, frontis. Americanist 102-91 1978 $40

EXQUEMELIN, ALEXANDRE OLIVIER   The History of the Buccaneers of America
.... Boston, (?1853). 8vo., orig. cloth, illus., some browning in text. Edwards 1012-715 1978 £30

EXTRACTS from the Diary of Roger Payne. New York, 1928. Decor. bds.,
gilt, 1 of 175 numbered copies prtd. on handmade paper, bkplt., very fine copy.
Battery Park 1-161 1978 $45

EYCLESHYMER, A. C.   Cross-Section Anatomy. New York, 1911. Thick
sm. folio, illus., rebound in buckram, plts. Rittenhouse 49-252 1976 $75

EYKYN, T.   Parts of the Pacific, By a Peripatetic Parson.
1896. Map, illus., orig. cloth, 8vo. Edwards 1012-369 1978 £18

EYLAND, SETH   The Evolution of a Life Described in the
Memoirs of Major Seth Eyland. New York, 1884. Bell Wiley's copy. Broadfoot 46-91 1978 $10

EYRE, JAMES K., JR.   The Roosevelt-MacArthur Conflict. Chambersburg, (1950). Cloth., 1st ed., signed by author, slightly worn d.j. Hayman 72-
209 1978 $8.50

EYRE, JOHN   Man's Ruin and Recovery, or Paradise Lost and
Restored. Buffalo, 1835. 2nd ed., uncut, unopened, orig. plain wr., dusty,
good. Butterfield 21-83 1978 $27.50

EYRE, VINCENT   The Military Operations at Cabul... 1843.
2nd. ed., folding plan, sm. 8vo, calf gilt, g.e. Edwards 1012-118 1978 £30

EYRE, VINCENT   The Military Operations at Cabul... 1843.
5th. ed., folding map, 8vo, orig. cloth, gilt, very good. Fenning 32-108
1978 £9.50

EYRE-TODD, GEORGE   The Highland Clans of Scotland.... New York,
1923. 122 illus., 2 vols. Baldwins' 51-342 1978 $22.50

EYTH, K.   Die Dekorationsmalerei der Kunstgewerbliche
Seite. Leipzig, 1894. 2 vols., lg. 8vo., plts., orig. covers, spine damaged.
Van der Peet H-64-30 1978 Dfl 50

EYTON, THOMAS C.   A History of the rarer British Birds. 1836. 8vo.,
woodcuts, qtr. green calf. George's 635-1006 1978 £25

F

FABES, GILBERT H.   Modern First Editions: Points and Values, Second Series. London, (1931). Orig. cloth, d.j., 1st ed., 1 of 1,000 copies, fine. MacManus 238-917 1978 $20

FABES, GILBERT H.   The Romance of a Bookshop. 1904-1929. N.P., 1929. 4to., orig. cloth, illus., signed by William and Gilbert Foyle. MacManus 238-916 1978 $30

FABRI, MARCELLO   L'Inconnu Sur Les Villes. Paris, 1921. Orig. paper covers, tattered. Eaton 45-180 1978 £5

FABRICIUS AB AQUAPENDENTE, HIERONYMUS   The Embryological Treatises of Hieronymus Fabricius of Aquapendente. Ithaca, Cornell University Press, 1942. Thick 4to., reproduc. of portr. & all plts., orig. cloth, fine copy. Zeitlin 245-74 1978 $100

FABRICIUS AB AQUAPENDENTE, HIERONYMUS   Oevvres Chirvrgicales. A Lyon, 1666. Thick 8vo., contemp. sprinkled calf, gilt on spine, very worn, browned, marginal worming, signatures of early owners & bkplt. of Dr. Alfred M. Hellman, rare French ed. Zeitlin 245-75 1978 $275

FABRY VON HILDEN, WILHELM   Observationum & Curationum Chirurgicarum Centuriae. Basle, 1606. 8vo., old limp vellum, portrait, woodcuts, first ed. Gurney 75-36 1978 £75

FABYAN, ROBERT   The Chronicle of Fabian, Whiche He Nameth the Concordaunce of Histories, Newly Perused. London, 1559. Folio, 17th-century calf, spine gilt (neatly rebacked, preserving the original spine), in cloth case, 4th and last early ed., minor worming, very fine copy, crisp, unsophisticated, from library of Narcissus Luttrell, with his stamped monogram on the t.p. Ximenes 47-93 1978 $1800.00

FACSIMILE of the Laws and Acts of...New York. De Vinne Press. One of 212 copies on English handmade paper, bound in white vellum. Battery Park 1-141 1978 $125

FACTS About Minnesota Condensed and Compiled from Official Records. St. Paul, 1879. Large folding map, original printed wr., 1st ed. Ginsberg 14-552 1978 $100

FACTS About South Dakota:.... Aberdeen, 1890. Original printed wr. in cardboard binder, 1st ed. Ginsberg 14-312 1978 $125

FACTS and Figures on the Subject of Ohio Taxation. N.P., n.d. (1854?). Stitched as issued, foxed, some dampstains. Hayman 73-527 1978 $7.50

"FACTS are Stubborn Things." London, n.d. (ca. 1791). 8vo., unbound, some leaves trimmed close. Morrill 239-79 1978 $25

FACTS Tending to Prove That General Lee, Was Never Absent From This Country, Fro Any Length of Time. London, 1813. Good. Nestler Rare 78-164 1978 $30

FADEN, W.   Petit Neptune Francais... London, 1793. 4to., orig. bds., spine miss., old cloth case, lacks plt. no 16, uncut, frontis. loose. Paine 78-47 1978 $125.00

FAGES, PEDRO   The Colorado River Campaign: 1781-1782. Berkeley, 1913. Illus., original printed wr. Ginsberg 14-111 1978 $15

FAGNIEZ, G.   Etudes sur l'industrie et la classe industrielle a Paris au XIIIe et au XIVe siecle. 1877. 8vo. George's 635-321 1978 £6

FAHEY, DENIS   The Rulers of Russia. 1940. Amer. ed., 34d ed. Austin 79-229 1978 $17.50

FAIR, A. A.   Spill the Jackpot! New York, 1941. 1st ed. Biblo 251-446 1978 $12.50

FAIRBAIRN, JAMES   Fairbairn's Crests of the Leading Families in Great Britain and Ireland... New York, 1911. Newly bound in lib. buckram, 2 vols. in 1. Baldwins' 51-250 1978 $75

FAIRBAIRN, WILLIAM   Iron, Its History, Properties, & Processess of Manufacture. Edinburgh, 1869. 3rd. ed., folding plts., illus., 8vo, orig. cloth, slight wear at corners, nice copy. Fenning 32-109 1978 £18

FAIRBANKS, GEORGE R.   History of Florida from its Discovery...to the Close of the Florida War, in 1842. Philadelphia, 1871. 1st ed., 8vo., orig. cloth, very good. Americanist 103-123 1978 $37.50

FAIRBRIDGE, DOROTHEA   Historic Houses of South Africa. Oxford, 1922. 4to., coloured and plain plts., cloth. Quaritch 983-36 1978 $125

FAIRBRIDGE, DOROTHEA   The Pilgrims' Way in South Africa. London, 1928. 4to, coloured frontis, 32 photos, illus., orig. cloth. K Books 239-155 1978 £7

FAIRCHILD, HENRY P.   Immigrant Backgrounds. 1927. Austin 79-230 1978 $17.50

FAIRCHILD, JAMES H.   Oberlin: The Colony and the College. Oberlin, 1883. Orig. binding, clean. Hayman 71-533 1978 $15

FAIRCHILD, T. B.   A History of the Town of Cuyahoga Falls, Summit Co., Ohio. Cleveland, 1876. Orig. cloth, fine, very scarce. MacManus 239-1108 1978 $50

FAIRHOLME, GEORGE   New and Conclusive Physical Demonstrations both of the Fact and Period of the Mosaic Deluge. 1837. 8vo., old qtr. calf, frontispiece, plt., illus. P. M. Hill 142-118 1978 £25

FAIRHOLT, F. W.   Gog and Magog. London, 1859. 1st ed., sm. 8vo, almost fine, very scarce. Victoria 34-286 1978 $65

FAIRLESS, MICHAEL   The Roadmender. London, 1920. Handmade paper, t.e.g., cloth-backed paper bds., unnumbered copy of ed. ltd. to 1,025 copies, very good or better. Limestone 9-102 1978 $22.50

FAIRLIE, GERARD   Captain Bulldog Drummond. 1945. Fine, d.w., first English ed. Bell Book 17-795 1978 $8.50

FAIRMAN, CHARLES E.   Art and Artists of the Capitol of the United States. Washington, D.C., 1927. Illus., lg. 4to. MacManus 239-663 1978 $35

FAITHFULL, EMILY   Three Visits to America. Edinburgh, 1884. Bell Wiley 's copy. Broadfoot 46-509 1978 $20

FAITHORN, JOHN   Facts and Observations on Liver Complaints and Bilious Disorders. Philadelphia, 1822. 8vo., orig. bds., untrimmed, foxed, 2nd Amer. ed. Morrill 239-80 1978 $12.50

FALCONAR, MARIA   Poetic Laurels for Characters of Distinguished Merit;.... London, 1791. 4to, early stiff marbled wrappers, calf spine (worn at the foot), 1st ed., scarce. Ximenes 47-94 1978 $90

FALCONER, J. D.   On Horseback Through Nigeria or Life and Travel in the Central Sudan. London, 1911. Map, 32 illus., rather foxed, gilt-dec. covers, 8vo, shabby, corners bumped. K Books 239-157 1978 £8

FALCONER, ROBERT   University Federation in Toronto. 1940. Hood 116-368 1978 $7.50

FALCONER, THOMAS   Oregon Question:.... London, 1845. Folding map, half mor., 2nd ed. Ginsberg 14-816 1978 $100

FALCONER, WILLIAM   The Ship-Wreck. New York, 1800. Engr. plts., 12mo., contemp. calf, gilt decor. spine. Morrill 241-667 1978 $20

FALCONER, WILLIAM   The Shipwreck, a Poem. 1804. Plts., vignettes, 8vo., contemp. straight-grained mor. F. Edwards 1013-67 1978 £35

FALCONER, WILLIAM   The Shipwreck. 1811. Plts., vignettes, tall 8vo., full contemp. diced russia, gilt edges, a half-inch portion missing from head of spine. Howes 194-263 1978 £15

FALKE, J. V.   Hellas Und Rom. Stuttgart, n.d. (ab. 1900). 8vo., folio, cloth, richly ornamented, plts., text illus. Van der Peet H-64-324 1978 Dfl 45

FALL River, Massachusetts. Providence, (1901). Prtd. on one side only, wrs., photo. views. Hayman 73-411 1973 $8.50

A FALLEN Angel. A Novel. London, 1878. 3 vols., orig. cloth, 1st ed., lib. labels removed, but good. MacManus 238-333 1978 $80

FALLON, JOHN T.   List of Synonyms of Organizations in the Volunteer Service of the United States. Washington, 1885. Cracked hinges, ex libris, Bell Wiley's Copy. Broadfoot's 44-132 $25.00

FALLOPPIO, GABRIELE   De Morbo Gallico. Patavii, 1563-1564. Sm. 4to., modern bds., browned, stains, wormhole, fine copy, 1st eds. Zeitlin 245-76 1978 $750

FALLOWS, SAMUEL   Hot Shot Fired at Fashion's Follies and Society's Abominations... Newark, 1890. Orig. binding, clean, moderate wear. Hayman 71-213 1978 $12.50

FALLS, CYRIL   Military Operations Macedonia. 1933-35. 4 vols., 8vo., orig. cloth, fine, orig. d.j., plts., coloured maps. F. Edwards 1013-392 1978 £55

THE FALLS of Niagara: Being a Complete Guide to all the Points of Interest Around and in the Immediate Neighbourhood of the Great Cataract. New York/Toronto, (n.d.). Oblong 12mo., cloth, loose in case, plts. Wolfe 39-391 1978 $40

FALSHAW, G.   Leconte de Lisle et l'Inde. 1923. Roy. 8vo. George's 635-1379 1978 £5

FAMILY Record of the Maltby-Morehouse Family. A List of Pedigrees...Arranged for the Children of George Ellsworth Maltby and Georgia Lord Morehouse Maltby... (1895). Signature, rebound copy. Biblo BL781-60 1978 $20

FANNING, LEONARD M.   The Rise of American Oil. New York, (1948). Rev. ed. Biblo BL781-84 1978 $9

FANNING, NATHANIEL   Fanning's Narrative, the Memoirs of... New York, 1913. Hinges cracked. Broadfoot 50-65 1978 $100

FANSHAWE, ANN   The Memoirs of .... 1907. Plts., tables, octavo, good. Upcroft 10-55 1978 £10

FARADAY, CORNELIA B.   European Carpets and Rugs. Grand Rapids, 1929. Lg. 4to., illus., some in color, fine. MacManus 239-664 1978 $45

FARADAY, MICHAEL   Faraday's Diary. 1932-36. 8 vols., 8vo., plts., cloth, reproductions of Faraday's numerous marginal sketches. Quaritch 977-97 1978 $175

FARADAY, MICHAEL   Experimental Researches in Chemistry and Physics. London, 1859. 8vo., plts., orig. cloth, gilt, occas. light foxing, but fine copy, 1st ed. in book form. Norman 5-100 1978 $200

FARADAY, MICHAEL   Experimental Researches in Electricity. London, 1832. Offprint, 4to., copperplts., orig. wrs., uncut, unopened, spine restored, wrs. chipped & soiling in margin of title, very good copy, half mor. box, inscr'd from author, 1st ed. Norman 5-97 1978 $2,000

FARADAY, MICHAEL   Experimental Researches in Electricity. (London, 1832-1852). 1st ed., 4to., bds., complete set, very rare, preserved in cloth box. Gilhofer 75-37 1978 SFr 12,000

FARADAY, MICHAEL   Experimental Researches in Electricity. London, (1832)-52. Complete set of 29 offprints, lg. 4to., plts., contemp. half mor., richly gilt spine, little rubbed, some plts. foxed, but fine copy, occas. pencil annotations, 1st eds. inscr'd by author. Norman 5-98 1978 $3,500

FARADAY, MICHAEL   Experimental Researches in Electricity. London, 1839. 3 vols., 8vo., engr. plts., orig. blindstamped cloth, Vol. I rebacked, retaining orig. spine, but fine set, 1st ed. in book form. Norman 5-99 1978 $750

FARAGO, LADISLAS   Abyssinia on the Eve. London, 1935. 8vo., orig. cloth, maps, plts., covers dull. K Books 239-158 1978 £5

FARAGO, LADISLAS   The Axis Grand Strategy. 1942. Austin 80-96 1978 $12.50

FARAGO, LADISLAS   German Psychological Warfare. 1942. Austin 80-97 1978 $27.50

FARBER, JAMES   Texas C.S.A., A Spotlight on Disaster. New York, 1947. Bell Wiley's copy. Broadfoot's 44-638 1978 $22

FARBER, JAMES   Texas, C.S.A. New York, 1947. Limited ed. Jenkins 116-428 1978 $20

FARET, NICOLAS   The Honest Man: Or, The Art to please in Court. London, 1632. 12mo, contemp. calf gilt, panelled sides with corner fleurons, gilt edges, 1st ed. in English. Quaritch 978-52 1978 $900

FARFAN, AGUSTIN   Tractado Breve De Medicina (Mexico, 1592). Madrid, 1944. Facsimile ed., 4to., wrs. Salloch 345-65 1978 $55

FARGO, CLARENCE H.   The Story of the Delaware Valley. (Frenchtown, 1936). 1st ed., errata, orig. cloth, fine, only 100 copies printed. MacManus 239-1263 1978 $25

FARGUS, FREDERICK JOHN   Called Back. New York, 1884. 1st Amer. ed., mustard cloth, back cover warped, good. Greene 78-167 1978 $65

FARINGTON, JOSEPH   Diary. (1922). Vols. 1-4, portrait, illus., covers faded and stained. George's 635-20 1978 £10.50

FARINGTON, JOSEPH   Views of the Lakes Etc. 1789. Oblong folio, full red morocco, fine modern binding, plts., fine. Jarndyce 16-78 1978 £240

FARIS, JOHN T.   Old Churches and Meeting-Houses in and Around Philadelphia. Philadelphia, 1926. Inscribed copy. Baldwins' 51-433 1978 $15

FARIS, JOHN T.   Old Churches and Meeting Houses in and Around Philadelphia. Philadelphia, 1926. Colored frontis., illus. MacManus 239-1451 1978 $15

FARIS, JOHN T.   Old Roads Out of Philadelphia. Philadelphia, 1917. 117 illus., map. Baldwins' 51-434 1978 $15

FARIS, JOHN T.   Old Roads Out of Philadelphia. Philadelphia, (1917). Illus., map. MacManus 239-1452 1978 $10

FARIS, JOHN T.   Old Trails and Roads in Penn's Land. Philadelphia, 1927. Illus. MacManus 239-1454 1978 $15

FARIS, JOHN T.   The Romance of Old Philadelphia. Philadelphia, 1918. Colored frontis., illus. MacManus 239-1453 1978 $10

FARIS, JOHN T.   Seeing Pennsylvania. Philadelphia, 1919. Illus., maps. MacManus 239-1455 1978 $7.50

FARJEON, ELEANOR   Mrs. Malone; a poem. London, 1950. Wrappers, very nice, first ed., author's signed autograph pres. inscription. Rota 211-106 1978 £10

FARJEON, ELEANOR   Pan-Worship and other poems. London, 1908. First ed., orig. binding, very nice, author's contemp. autograph pres. inscription. Rota 211-105 1978 £30

FARJEON, JEFFERSON   The Compleat Smuggler. Indianapolis, 1938. 8vo., orig. cloth, frontis., plts., illus. F. Edwards 1013-70 1978 £10

FARKAS, KARL   "Farkas Entdeckt Amerika". N. P., 1941. Illus., paper, in German. Austin 79-232 1978 $20

FARLEY, JAMES A.   Jim Farley's Story. New York, (1948). Author's signed pres. Biblo 251-80 1978 $10

FARLEY, JOHN M.   History of St. Patrick's Cathedral. New York, (1908). Illus. Biblo BL781-159 1978 $10

FARMAN, HENRY   Catalogue de la Societe "Jero"-Aeroplanes Henry & Maurice Farman. Antwerp, (1913). 4to., illus., orig. printed wrs. sewn with blue cord, buckram case. Quaritch 977-218 1978 $250

FARMER, J. B.   The Book of Nature Study. (c. 1932). Colored plts., text illus., 6 vols., roy. 8vo. George's 635-994 1978 £5.25

FARMER, JOHN   Twelve Sonnets on Colyton Church, with Notes, Illustrative and Descriptive. London, 1842. 12mo, original green cloth wrappers, 1st ed., signed by Mary Farmer, wood-engraved frontispiece, very good copy. Ximenes 47-95 1978 $22.50

FARMER, JOHN S.   The Public School Word Book. 1900. Buckram, privately issued for subscribers. Eaton 45-181 1978 £5

FARMER, JOHN S.   Slang and its Analogues Past and Present. 1890-1903. Orig. ed., only 750 sets printed, 7 vols., sm. 4to., half contemp. mor. Howes 194-796 1978 £120

FARMER, THOMAS D. J.   A History of the Parish of St. John's Church, Ancaster, with Many Biographical Sketches of Those...Who...Established and Maintained it. Guelph, 1924. Hood 117-349 1978 $35

THE FARMERS and Mechanics Almanac, for...1840... Philadelphia, (1839). Pict. wrs. Hayman 72-14 1978 $8.50

THE FARMER'S Calendar, for...1850. Richmond, (1849). Illus. Hayman 72-15 1978 $20

THE FARMER'S Edition of the British Almanac of the S.P.C.K. for the Year 1831. London, (1830). 12mo., old cloth. K Books 244-335 1978 £10

THE FARMERS Journal. Bath, 1852-53. Vol. I, scarce, foxed, new cloth. Broadfoot 50-66 1978 $75

FARMILOE, EDITH   All the World Over. London-New York, n.d. 1st ed., oblong quarto, color plates. Victoria 34-287 1978 $22.50

FARNAM, HENRY W.   The Economic Utilization of History. Yale University Press, 1913. Ex-lib. Austin 80-578 1978 $11

FARQUHAR, GEORGE   Sir Henry Wildair: Being the Sequel of the Trip to the Jubilee. London, 1701. Quarto, quarter modern calf, grey mottled boards, inner margin of title-page strengthened, lightly foxed, 1st ed. Bennett 7-40 1978 $195

FARQUHAR, GEORGE   The Complete Works of... Bloomsbury: The Nonesuch Press, 1930. 2 vols., 4to., buckram-backed bds., paper labels, 1 of 1,000 sets, labels a bit worn, uncut, fine. MacManus 238-834 1978 $100

FARRAR, ADAM S.   A Critical History of Free Thought in Reference to the Christian Religion... New York, 1883. Cloth, scarce. Hayman 72-210 1978 $8.50

FARRAR, CHARLES A. J.   Through the Wilds. 1892. Illus., lacks frontis., very good. Austin 82-375 1978 $27.50

FARRAR, F. W.   A Tale of College Life. Edinburgh, 1859. 1st. ed., half calf, red label, v.g. Jarndyce 16-660 1978 £26

FARRELL, F. A.   The 51st (Highland) Division, War Sketches. Edinburgh, 1920. Plates, 4to. George's 635-811 1978 £15

FARRELL, HUGH   What Price Progress? 1926. Austin 80-579 1978 $10

FARRELL, JAMES T.   Bernard Clare. N. Y., (1946). 1st ed., 8 vo., d.j., short tear, else very good-fine. Houle 10-103 1978 $25

FARRELL, JAMES T.   Gas-House McGinty. Cleveland, (1943). Author's signed pres. Biblo BL781-968 1978 $9.50

FARRELL, JAMES T.   The Name is Fogarty. 1950. Inscribed by Farrell, first ed., d.j., v.g. Austin 82-1166 1978 $47.50

FARRELL, JAMES T.   The Road Between. 1949. First ed., pres. copy signed by Farrell. Austin 82-1167 1978 $27.50

FARRELL, JAMES T.   When Boyhood Dreams Come True. New York, (1946). Gray cloth, 1st ed., fine in dust jacket. Bradley 49-95 1978 $10

FARRELL, JAMES T.   Young Lonigan: a Boyhood in Chicago Streets. New York, 1932. Brown cloth, 1st ed., 1st state, fine in dust jacket, scarce. Bradley 49-96 1978 $150

FARRELL, M.   Financial Statement of Dakota County for the Year 1895. Farmington, 1896. Original front printed wr., 1st ed. Ginsberg 14-553 1978 $37.50

FARRELLY, M. J.   The Settlement After the War in South Africa. London, 1900. 8vo, orig. cloth, heavy foxing, spine dull. K Books 239-159 1978 £8

FARREN, HARRY DESMOND   Sabotage. 1942. Paper. Austin 80-98 1978 $10

FARRER, REGINALD JOHN   Alpines and Bog-Plants. London, 1908. Illus., cloth faded, 8vo. K Books 244-116 1978 £6

FARRER, REGINALD JOHN   The English Rock-Garden. 1919. Plates, 2 vols., 8vo. George's 635-952 1978 £25

FARRER, REGINALD JOHN   The English Rock-Garden. 1922. Covers worn. George's 635-953 1978 £12.50

FARRER, REGINALD JOHN   In Old Ceylon. 1908. 8vo., orig. cloth, 19 plts., fine copy. Edwards 1012-126 1978 £18

FARRER, WILLIAM   Outline Itinerary of King Henry the First. 1919. Allen 234-1287 1978 $7.50

FARRINGTON, E.   The Gardener's Omnibus. 1938. 4to, orig. cloth. Book Chest 17-516 1978 $12.50

FARRINGTON, E.   The Gardener's Travel Book. 1938. 8vo, orig. cloth. Book Chest 17-517 1978 $9.50

FARRINGTON, SELWYN KIP   Atlantic Game Fishing. New York, 1937. 1st ed., thick quarto, cloth, gilt, color plts., fine. Duschnes 220-140 1978 $60

FARRINGTON, SELWYN KIP   The Ducks Came Back. New York, (1945). Colored front by Lynn Bogue Hunt, 8vo, orig. cloth. Book Chest 17-144 1978 $40

FAST, HOWARD   The Unvanquished. New York, (1942). 1st ed., sm. nick at top of fr. cover. Biblo 251-494 1978 $9.50

FAST Life: An Autobiography..Together with Details of the Amours of the Marquis of Waterford... c.1860. Reprint, octavo bound in cloth. Hyland 128-752 1978 £5

FATHERLESS Fanny. London, n.d. (c.1825). Engraved plates, soiled & mended, quarter calf, worn at edges. Greene 78-1 1978 $35

FATIO, G.   Geneve et les Pays-Bas. Geneve-Haarlem, 1928. Sm. 4to., half calf, copy of the Luxe-ed., ltd. & numbered, plts., vignettes. Van der Peet H-64-325 1978 Dfl 75

FATTORUSSO, J.   Wonders of Italy. The Monuments of Antiquity, the Churches, the Palaces, the Treasures of Art. Florence, (1949). Illus., some color plts., 9th ed., rev'd. and enlarged. Biblo BL781-659 1978 $13.50

FAU, JULIEN   Anatomie des Formes Exterieures du Corps Humain, a l'Usage des Peintres et des Sculpteurs. Paris, 1845. 8vo., folio, plts., half-calf, fine, 1st ed. Gilhofer 74-90 1978 sFr 550

FAUCHER DE SAINT-MAURICE, N. H. E.   Relation de ce qui s'est Passe lors des Fouilles Faites par ordre du Gouvernement....Quebec, 1879. Illus. Wolfe 39-181 1978 $30

FAUGHNAN, THOMAS   Stirring Incidents in the Life of a British Soldier. Toronto, 1885. Light staining on a few pgs. Hood 116-688 1978 $7.50

FAUJAS DE SAINT-FOND, BARTHELMY   Description des Experineces de la Machine Aerostatique de MM. Montgolfier. Paris, 1783. 8vo., contemp. calf, back gilt, plts., first ed., very fine. Gurney 75-37 1978 £325

FAUJAS DE SAINT-FOND, BARTHELEMY   Description des Experiences de la Machine Aerostatique de MM. de Montgolfier et de Celles Auxquelles cette Decouverte a Donne Lieu. Paris, 1784. 8vo., frontis., plts., fldg. table, early 19th Cent. half mor., gilt, frontis. stained & repaired in margin, but very good copy, pirated 2nd ed. Norman 5-**15 1978 $175

FAULK, JOHANNES DANIEL   Characteristics of Goethe. London, 1833. 1st English ed., 8 vo., 3/4 brown mor. over marbled bds., raised bands, gilt stamped title, t.e.g., 3 vols., fine. Houle 10-104 1978 $175

FAULKNER, CHARLES JAMES   The Speech of ..., of Berkeley, in the House of Delegates of Virginia, on the Policy of the State with Respect to Her Slave Population... Richmond, 1832. Stitched. Hayman 72-211 1978 $50

FAULKNER, H.   The Mysteries of the Flowers. New York, (1917). Signed, 8vo, orig. cloth. Book Chest 17-145 1978 $18.50

FAULKNER, VIRGINIA   The Barbarians. 1935. Ex-lib. Austin 82-376 1978 $12.50

FAULKNER, VIRGINIA   Friends and Romans. New York, 1934. 1st ed., signed, bind. faded, good. Biblo BL781-970 1978 $9

FAULKNER, WILLIAM   Pylon. New York, 1935. Nice in well-worn d.w. Desmarais B-232 1978 $55

FAULKNER, WILLIAM   Absalom, Absalom! New York, 1936. First US ed., good. Bell Book 17-337 1978 £15

FAULKNER, WILLIAM   As I Lay Dying. New York, (1930). Tan cloth, top edges stained dark brown, 1st ed., 1st issue, fine copy in dust jacket, black cloth protective box. Bradley 49-97 1978 $600

FAULKNER, WILLIAM   Doctor Martino and Other Stories. New York, 1934. 1st ed., small octavo, blue cloth, d.j. slightly chipped at head of spine. Totteridge 29-39 1978 $125

FAULKNER, WILLIAM   Doctor Martino and Other Stories. New York, 1934. Black & red cloth, gilt top edges stained black, others uncut, 1st ed., 1 of 350 numbered copies signed by author, Michael Sadleir's copy with bkplt., almost fine, unopened copy, black cloth protective box. Bradley 49-99 1978 $685

FAULKNER, WILLIAM   The Hamlet. New York, 1940. Black cloth, 1st ed., very good, without dust jacket. Bradley 49-101 1978 $35

FAULKNER, WILLIAM   The Hamlet. Name on flyleaf, spine dull. Bradley 49-102 1978 $20

FAULKNER, WILLIAM   Knight's Gambit. New York, (1949). Orig. cloth, d.j., chipped, 1st ed., 1st print., bookplt. MacManus 238-643 1978 $35

FAULKNER, WILLIAM   Light in August. New York, 1932. First U.S. ed., good. Bell Book 17-339 1978 £47.50

FAULKNER, WILLIAM   Light in August. (New York), (1932). Orig. cloth, 1st ed., near-fine, somewhat worn, d.j. MacManus 238-641 1978 $135

FAULKNER, WILLIAM   The Marionettes. Charlottesville, University Press, 1975. 1st facsimile & 1st published ed., 4to., loose cut leaves in box, as issued, ed. ltd. to 126 copies, prtd. on Arches paper, mustard-colored slipcase, mint. Current 24-15 1978 $385

FAULKNER, WILLIAM   Sanctuary. New York, (1931). Magenta bds., gray cloth spine, very good. Bradley 49-109 1978 $150

FAULKNER, WILLIAM   Sanctuary. New York, (1932). Biblo BL781-971 1978 $12

FAULKNER, WILLIAM   Soldiers' Pay. New York, 1926. Blue cloth, stamped in yellow, fore-edges untrimmed, 1st ed., scarce, lettering flaked from spine, blue buckram box. Bradley 49-111 1978 $250

FAULKNER, WILLIAM   The Sound and the Fury. London, 1931. 1st English ed., 1st issue in black cloth, top edge stained in red, very good-fine. Houle 10-105 1978 $55

FAULKNER, WILLIAM   These 13. New York, (1931). Orig. cloth, 1st ed., 1 of 299 copies signed by author, covers slightly faded and soiled, otherwise very good. MacManus 238-640 1978 $375

FAULKNER, WILLIAM   This Earth: a Poem. New York, 1932. Illus., uncut & unopened, stiff tan wrs., sewn, 1st ed., fine. Bradley 49-112 1978 $125

FAULKNER, WILLIAM   The Unvanquished. 1938. Spine little faded, very good, first English ed. Bell Book 17-341 1978 £28.50

FAULKNER, WILLIAM   The Wild Palsm. New York, 1939. First U.S. ed., good, worn d.w. Bell Book 17-342 1978 £55

FAULKNER, WILLIAM   The Wild Palms. New York, (1939). Orig. cloth, d.j., torn, 1st ed., 1st print., bookplt. MacManus 238-642 1978 $50

FAULKNER-HORNE, SHIRLEY   Green Trail. London, (1947). Illus. by Peter Biegel, 1st ed., author's signed pres. Biblo 251-524 1978 $15

FAULL, J. H.   The Natural History of the Toronto Region. Ontario Canada. Toronto, 1913. Fold. maps, bound. Hood 116-736 1978 $25

FAULMANN, KARL   Illustrirte Geschicte der Schrift. 1880. Illus. Battery Park 1-469 1978 $100

FAUNA Of British India, Including Ceylon and Burma. London, 1889. 2 vols., illus., roy. 8vo, covers badly spotted, clean inside, scarce. Traylen 88-571 1978 £15

FAURE, GIAMBATTISTA   Congetture Fisiche intorno alle Cagioni de' Fenomeni osservati in Roma nella Macchina Elettrica. Rome, 1747. 4to., old marbled bds., back torn, first ed. Gurney 75-38 1978 £55

FAUSBOLL, V.   Tha Dhammapada, Being a Collection of Moral Verses in Pali. London, 1900. 8vo., very fine dark blue velvet binding, luxurious. Van der Peet H-64-326 1978 Dfl 195

FAUST, ALBERT B.   The German Element in the United States. Boston, (1909). Illus., 2 vols. MacManus 239-138 1978 $35

FAUTEUX, AEGIDIUS   Les Chevaliers de Saint-Louis en Danada. Montreal, 1940. Wolfe 39-184 1978 $35

FAUTEUX, AEGIDIUS   The Introduction of Printing into Canada. Montreal, (1929). Six chapters, each as a separate brochure, in orig. cardboard slipcase. Wolfe 39-185 1978 $85

FAUTEUX, AEGIDIUS   Journal du Siege de Quebec. Quebec, 1922. Wolfe 39-183 1978 $35

FAUVEL-GOURAUD, FRANCIS   Phreno-Mnemotechny, or, the Art of Memory. New York, 1845. Portr., 8vo., backstrip with several tears, 1st ed. Morrill 239-375 1978 $30

FAUX, W.   Early Western Travels. Cleveland, 1904. Clean, orig. binding. Hayman 71-732 1978 $10

FAVILL, JOHN   Henry Baird Favill...1860-1916. Chicago, 1917. 8vo., 1st ed. Morrill 239-81 1978 $12.50

FAWCETT, EDGAR   Fantasy and Passion. Boston, 1878. 1st. ed., sm. 8vo, orig. reddish brown cloth, gilt, monogram on spine, slight wear to spine, very good copy. Fenning 32-111 1978 $8.50

FAWCETT, HENRY   Manual of Political Economy. 1876. 5th rev. ed., enlarged, English. Austin 80-580 1978 $11

FAY, AMY   Music-Study in Germany. New York, 1908. 18th ed. Biblo 247-880 1978 $13.50

FAY, BERNARD   Franklin the Apostle of Modern Times. Boston, 1929. Illus. MacManus 239-160 1978 $7.50

FAY, SIDNEY B.   The Origins of the World War. New York, 1928. 2 vols., illus. Biblo 247-766 1978 $25

FAY, THEODORE SEDGWICK   Dreams and Reveries of a Quiet Man. New York, 1832. First ed., very good, half-calf and marbled boards, library labels neatly mounted inside front cover. Greene 78-40 1978 $65

FAYLE, CHARLES ERNEST   Charles Wright, A Memoir. 1943. 1st ed., ltd. 500 copies, port., d. w. loose inserts, 3 typed copies of letters from G.B.S. to Wright in 1885, good. Hyland 128-820 1978 £12.50

FAYLE, CHARLES ERNEST   Seaborne Trade, 1914-18. 1920-24. 4 vols., 8vo., orig. cloth, coloured maps. F. Edwards 1013-71 1978 £35

FEA, A.   King Monmouth; Being a History of the Career of James Scott, 'The Protestant Duke', 1649-1685. 1902. Plts., illus., rear bd. spotted, octavo, good. Upcroft 10- 307 1978 £5

FEARING, KENNETH   The Big Clock. New York, (1946). 1st ed., spine dull. Biblo BL781-972 1978 $8.50

FEARN, FRANCES   Diary of a Refugee. New York, 1910. Inscribed pres. copy by son-in-law of author, Bell Wiley's copy. Broadfoot's 44-133 1978 $50

FEARN, JOHN   A Rationale of the Laws of Cerebral Vision. London, (ca. 1830). Fldg. plts., 8vo., orig. bds. Morrill 239-82 1978 $15

FEARON, HENRY BRADSHAW   Sketches of America. London, 1818. Light underlinings, binding quite worn, 1st ed., front cover detached. Nestler Rare 78-115 1978 $85

FEATHERSTONHAUGH, GEORGE WILLIAM   Excursion through the Slave States. New York, 1844. Rear board detached, 3/4 leather, front hinge cracked, Bell Wiley's copy. Broadfoot's 44-134 1978 $30

FEATLEY, DANIEL   The House of Mourning. 1640. (Part titles dated 1639). 1st. ed., folio, contemp. calf, rebacking slightly damaged by worm. Hannas 54-106 1978 £38

FEAVEARYEAR, A. E.   The Pound Sterling, a History of English Money. Oxford, 1931. 8vo. George's 635-322 1978 £6

FECHHEIMER, HEDWIG   Kleinplastik der Aegypter... Berlin, 1922. Covers rubbed, front inner hinge cracked, otherwise good. Biblo BL781-376 1978 $15

THE FEDERALIST. New York, 1788. 1st ed., 12mo., 2 vols., rebound in new full calf by Bayntun, inner dentelles in gilt, marbled endpapers, text a bit browned, near fine copy. Current 24-79 1978 $2,750

FEE, WALTER R.   The Transition from Aristocracy to Democracy in New Jersey... Somerville, 1933. 1st ed., frontis., map, orig. cloth, fine. MacManus 239-1264 1978 $25

FEHR, B.   Die Englische Literatur des 19. Berlin, 1923. 4to., cloth, plts., some in color, text illus. Van der Peet H-64-394 1978 Dfl 95

FEIKEMA, FEIKE   The Golden Bowl. St. Paul, 1944. First ed., long inscription signed by author. Austin 82-379 1978 $27.50

FEILD, ROBERT D.   The Art of Walt Disney. London, 1945. Plts. some in colour, portrait, sm. folio, dec. cloth. Traylen 88-372 1978 £30

FEILING, K.   A History of the Tory Party 1640-1714. Oxford, 1924. Octavo, good. Upcroft 10-308 1978 £8.50

FEININGER, ANDREAS   Feininger on Photography. Chicago & New York, (1949). 1st ed., illus., 4to., orig. cloth. Morrill 241-668 1978 $15

FELDMAN, HERMAN   Racial Factors in American Industry. 1931. 1st ed. Austin 79-236 1978 $15

FELICIANO DA LAZESIO, FRANCESCO   Libro di Arithmetica & Geometria Speculativa & Praticale. Venice, 1550. Sm. 4to., woodcut illus., nice, vellum, lea. label. Quaritch 977-161 1978 $250

FELICIO DOS SANTOS, J.   Memorials Do Districto Diamantino Da Comarca do Serro Frio.... Rio de Janeiro, 1868. 8vo., marbled bds., leather spine. Edwards 1012-645 1978 £30

FELIPPE, BARTOLOME   Tractado del Conseio y Delos Consejeros Delos Principes. Ciombra, 1584. 4to., errata leaf, vellum, 1st gatherings remargined, 1st ed. Gilhofer 74-12 1978 sFr 1,000

FELL, SARAH   Household Account Book. Cambridge, 1920. Roy. 8vo., orig. canvas-backed bds., paper label rubbed. George's 635-1305 1978 £8.50

FELLIG, ARTHUR   Naked City. N. Y., (1945). 1st ed., 4 to., cloth, pictorial endpapers, illus., very good. Houle 10-106 1978 $85

FELLOWES, WILLIAM DORSET   Paris; During the Interesting Month of July 1815. 1815. Coloured plts., 8vo., contemp. half calf. F. Edwards 1013-295 1978 £30

FELLOWS, HENRY PARKER   Boating Trips on New England Rivers. Boston, 1884. Maps, illus., 8vo., orig. cloth, 1st ed. Morrill 241-134 1978 $20

FELLTHAM, OWEN   Resolves [Divine, Morall, Political]. London, 1631. Octavo, woodcut initials, dak blue mor. with decor. gilt borders, gilt-tooled paneled spine, folding red cloth box in slipcase of full red mor., both lined in red felt, exceptionally fine. Bennett 7-41 1978 $275

FELT, JOSEPH B.   An Historical Account of Massachusetts Currency. Boston, 1839. 1st ed., tall 8vo., t.e.g., bound in 1/2 blue calf with marbled bds., matching endpapers, interior clean, some wear, fine copy. Current 24-94 1978 $185

FELTHAM, JOHN   A Guide to all the Watering and Sea-Bathing Places. London, (1803). Plts., maps, 12mo., half calf, one section loose, 8vo. K Books 244-117 1978 £40

FELTON, J. B.   Oration Delivered at the 4th Anniversary of the College of California...And the Addresses at the Festival... San Francisco, 1858. Orig. pr. front wr., 1st ed. Ginsberg 14-1088 1978 $45

FENELON, FRANCOIS DE SALIGNAC DE LA MOTHE   The Adventures of Telemachus, the Son of Ulysses. 1768. First ed. of this translation, 4to., contemp. calf-backed bds., very good, vignettes. Howes 194-264 1978 £48

FENELON, FRANCOIS DE SALIGNAC DE LA MOTHE   The Adventures of Telemachus, the Son of Ulysses. 1778. Sixth ed., 12mo., contemp. half roan, spine gilt ruled. Howes 194-265 1978 £8.50

FENELON, FRANCOIS DE SALIGNAC DE LA MOTHE-   Demonstration de l'existence de Dieu. Amsterdam, 1713. 1st Amsterdam ed., 12mo, rehinged period calf, gilt-stamped spine, exceedingly scarce. Bennett 20-69 1978 $150

FENELON, FRANCOIS DE SALIGNAC DE LA MOTHE   Dialogues of the Dead. 1776. 2 vols., 12mo., contemp. mottled sheep, nice. P. M. Hill 142-105 1978 £15

FENELON, FRANCOIS DE SALIGNAC DE LA MOTHE   Dialogues Sur L'Eloquence en General, et Sur Celle de la Chaire En Particulier. Paris, 1718. 1st. ed., 12mo, lacks final blank leaf, contemp. calf, lacks label. Hannas 54-107 1978 £20

FENELON, FRANCOIS DE SALIGNAC DE LA MOTHE   Instructions for the Education of Daughters. 1750. 12mo, contemp. red sheep, very worn, gilt spine with tooling of Foulis bindery. Hannas 54-108 1978 £12.50

FENELON, FRANCOIS DE SALIGNAC DE LA MOTTE   La Vie Des Anciens Philosophie. Munich, 1925. 8vo., cloth, pres. bookplt., fine. Salloch 348-63 1978 $50

FENN, GEORGE MANVILLE   The Vicar's People: A Story of a Stain. London, 1881. 1st ed., 3 vols., very scarce three-decker, almost fine set. Victoria 34-288 1978 $100

FENNELL, JAMES   Something. Boston, 1809, 1810. Boards, calf spine, worn. Eaton 45-182 1978 £20

FENNER, PHYLLIS R.   Cowboys, Cowboys, Cowboys...Roundups and Rodeos, Branding... New York, (1950). Illus., 1st ed. Biblo BL781-273 1973 $9.50

FENNING, DANIEL   The Young Gentleman's Volunteer Universal Spelling-Book... 1785. Engraved frontis, illus., fully rebound in half calf, marbled bds., v.g. Jarndyce 16-70 1978 £45

FENNING, DANIEL   The Young Man's Book of Knowledge... 1764. 1st.ed., plts., 3 of which are folding, lg. 12mo, contemp. unlettered calf, slight wear to joints, very good copy. Fenning 32-112 1978 £38.50

FENNO-GENDROT, ALMIRA TORREY BLAKE   The Ancestry and Allied Families of Nathan Blake 3rd and Susan (Torrey) Blake, Early Residents of East Corinth, Vermont. Boston, 1916. Illus., 8vo. Morrill 239-629 1978 $15

FENOLLOSA, ERNEST F.   Epochs of Chinese & Japanese Art: An Outline History of East Asiatic Design. New York, (1913). 2 vols., boards, cloth spine and tips, moderate wear, new and revised ed. Dawson's 449-34 1978 $95

FENTON, I. D.   Adventures of Mr. Colonel Somerset in Caffraria, During the War. 1858. 8vo., orig. cloth, spine slightly faded. Edwards 1012-298 1978 $30

FENTON, RICHARD   Memoirs of an Old Wig. London, 1815. 1st ed., half-calf with marbled boards, decor. gilt spine, owner's bookplate, excellent. Greene 78-200 1978 $90

FENWICK, R. O.   The Goblin Groom. Edinburgh, 1809. 4to., 1st ed., full polished calf, gilt extra, all edges gilt, pres. inscr., bkplt. Quaritch 979-138 1978 $85

FERBER, EDNA   Great Son. New York, 1945. Very nice in chipped d.w. Desmarais B-237 1978 $7.50

FERBER, EDNA   Show Boat. Garden City, 1926. Very good, chipped & lightly soiled dw. Bernard 5-519 1978 $8.50

FERGUSON, CHARLES D.   The Experiences of a Forty-niner During the Thirty Four Years Residence in California and Australia. Cleveland, 1888. Illus., original cloth, 1st ed. Ginsberg 14-112 1978 $75

FERGUSON, CHARLES D.   The Experiences of a Forty-Niner During Thirty-Four Years Residence in California and Australia. Cleveland, 1888. Illus., 1st ed. MacManus 239-1915 1978 $30

FERGUSON, ERNA   Murder and Mystery in New Mexico. Albuquerque, (1948). Cloth, map, frontis., fine, d.w., scarce. Dykes 35-200 1978 $22.50

FERGUSON, JAMES   The Art of Drawing in Perspective Made Easy to Those Who Have no Previous Knowledge of the Mathematics... Edinburgh, 1823. New ed., sm. 8vo., plts., a little foxed, contemp. bds., uncut, partially unopened. Quaritch 983-182 1978 $90

FERGUSON, JAMES   An Introduction to Electricity. 1775. 2nd. ed., 6 sections, folding engraved plts., 8vo, contemp. sheep, little worn but sound, good copy. Fenning 32-113 1978 $21.50

FERGUSON, JAMES   Lectures on Select Subjects in Mechanics, Hydrostatics, Pneumatics, and Optics:.... London, 1760. 1st ed., octavo, plates, tables, full expertly restored early calf, gilt spine panels, bookplate of Ragley Hall. Bennett 20-70 1978 $300

FERGUSON, JAMES   Record of the 9th (Volunteer) Battalion (Highlanders) the Royal Scots... Edinburgh, 1909. 4 coloured & 20 other plts., gilt cloth, 8vo, spine faded. K Books 239-161 1978 £15

FERGUSON, JOHN   Bibliotheca Chemica: A Catalogue of the Alchemical, Chemical and Pharmaceutical Books in the Collection of the Late James Young. Glasglow, 1906. 2 vols., 4to., photogravure portrs., publisher's half mor., uncut, little rubbed, foxing, fine set with bkplts. of Sir William Crookes, 1st ed. Norman 5-103 1978 $250

FERGUSON, JOHN M.   Landmarks of Economic Thought. 1946. Austin 80-582 1978 $10

FERGUSON, ROBERT   Arctic Harpooner...1879. University of Pennsylvania, 1938. 8vo., illus., margins wrinkled. Pd ne 78-48 1978 $18.50

FERGUSON, ROBERT   An Enquirie into and Detection of the Barbarous Murder of the Late Earl of Essex. 1684. First ed., sm. 4to., 19th cent. half calf, uncropped. Howes 194-43 1978 £55

FERGUSON, ROBERT   Harpooner. A Four-Year Voyage on the Barque Kathleen, 1880-1884. Philadelphia, 1936. Illus. MacManus 239-1752 1978 $15

FERGUSON, SAMUEL   Laws of the Western Gael, and Other Poems. London, 1865. 1st. ed., sm. 8vo, cloth, new cloth spine, pres. inscription on f/l. Traylen 88-244 1978 £10

FERGUSON, W. K.   Renaissance in Historical Thought. 1948. Allen 234-1233 1978 $8.50

FERGUSSON, B.   Beyond the Chindwin. London, 1945. Cloth, plts., illus., map, 8vo. Van der Peet 127-90 1978 Dfl 30

FERGUSSON, J.   Illustrations of the Rock-Cut Temples of India... 1845. Without text vol., tinted litho plts., lg. folio, orig. printed bds., rebacked cloth, slightly worn, some foxing. Edwards 1012-98 1978 £100

FERGUSSON, R. MENZIES   Rambles in the Far North. Paisley, 1884. 8vo., frontis., decor. cover. K Books 244-118 1978 £6

FERGUSSON, ROBERT   Scots Poems. London, (c. 1920). Illus., color plts., sm. 8 vo., d.j., fine. Houle 10-108 1978 $20

FERGUSSON, ROBERT   The Works of ... 1810. New ed., frontis portrait, 19th. century half calf, marbled bds., slipcase, good. Jarndyce 16-661 1978 £24

FERNANDEZ DE SAN SALVADOR, AUGUSTIN P.   Los Jesuitas Quitados Y Restituidos Al Mundo. Mexico, 1816. Full tooled calf. Ginsberg 14-113 1978 $350

FERNANDEZ DE VELASCO Y PIMENTAL, DON BERNARDINO   Deleyte de la Discrecion y Facil Escuela de Agudeza que en Ramillete Texido de Ingeniosas Promptitudes. Madrid, 1764. 3rd ed., quarto, full contemporary calf, gilt-panelled spine, all edges red, rubbed. Bennett 20-71 1978 $85

FERNANDEZ DURO, CESAREO   Don Francisco Fernandez de la Cueva, Duque de Albuquerque. Madrid, 1884. Folio, printed wr., uncut. Jenkins 116-437 1978 $85

FERNOW, BERTHOLD   Documents Relating to the...Dutch and Swedish Settlements on the Delaware River. Albany, 1877. Tall thick 4to., good clean copy, orig. cloth. Butterfield 21-157 1978 $35

FERRABOSCHI, M.   Architettura della Basilica di S. Pietro in Vaticano... 1812. Roy. folio, engraved plts., some minor foxing, red mor. gilt. Quaritch 983-37 1978 $2,100

FERRAND, JACQUES   De La Maladie D'Amovr, ov Melancholie erotique. Paris, 1623. 8vo., woodcut ornaments & initials, modern 3/4 green mor., gilt lettering, lightly browned, very good copy with bkplts. of A. Renaud & Dr. Alfred M. Hellman, rare revised ed. Zeitlin 245-77 1978 $375

FERRAR, M. L.   Officers of the Green Howards, Alexandra.... Belfast, 1931. Plts., 8vo., orig. cloth, frontis. F. Edwards 1013-494 1978 £15

FERRAR, NICHOLAS   The Story Books of Little Gidding. 1899. Plts., octavo, good. Upcroft 10-56 1978 £7.50

FERRARIUS, OCTAVIUS   De Re Vestiaria Libri Tres. Patavii, 1642. 8vo., vellum, first ed., woodcut initials. King 7-38 1978 £30

FERRARS, M.   Burma. London, 1900. 4to, cloth, gilt, illus., plts. Van der Peet 127-91 1978 Dfl 185

FERREL, WILLIAM   Popular Essays on the Movements of the Atmosphere. Washington, 1882. 4to., orig. wrs. Morrill 241-135 1978 $12.50

FERRI, A.   De Sclopetorum Sive Archibusorum Vulneribus, Eiusdem de Caruncula Sive Callo Quae Cervici Vesicae Innasuntur. Rome, 1552. Sm. 4to., woodcuts, rebound in half vellum. Quaritch 977-21 1978 $850

FERRIAR, JOHN   An Essay Towards a Theory of Apparitions. 1813. 8vo., contemp. half red roan. P. M. Hill 142-106 1978 £42

FERRIAR, JOHN   Illustrations of Sterne: With Other Essays and Verses. 1812. 2nd. ed., 2 vols. in 1, half titles, uncut in orig. (later remainder?) brown cloth, dulled. Jarndyce 16-662 1978 £12.50

FERRIAR, JOHN   Illustrations of Sterne; With Other Essays and Verses. 1812. 2nd. ed., 2 vols. in 1, half title, 19th. century cloth, good. Jarndyce 16-663 1978 £18

FERRIAR, JOHN   Illustrations of Sterne: with Other Essays and Verses. London, 1812. 2 vols., 8vo., orig. cloth-backed bds., uncut, vol. II unopened, 2nd ed. MacManus 238-147 1978 $50

FERRIER, SUSAN EDMONDSTONE   The Inheritance. 1824. 3 vols., sm. 8vo., 1st ed., contemp. bds., calf backs. Quaritch 979-139 1978 $115

FERRIER, SUSAN EDMONDSTONE   The Inheritance. Edinburgh, 1824. 3 vols., octavo, half early calf over marbled boards, 1st ed., fine. Bennett 7-42 1978 $185

FERRIER, SUSAN EDMONDSTONE   Marriage. Edinburgh, 1818. 3 vols., 12mo, contemp. half-calf over marbled boards, spines gilt-ruled, all edges marbled, 1st ed. Bennett 7-43 1978 $165

FERRIS, BENJAMIN   A History of the Original Settlements on the
Delaware from its Discovery by Hudson.... Wilmington, 1846. Illus. by maps,
drawings, orig. full calf, neatly rebacked. Baldwins' 51-220 1978 $65

FERRIS, BENJAMIN G.   Utah and the Mormons. New York, 1854. 12mo,
original dark brown cloth, 1st ed., very fine copy. Ximenes 47-97 1978 $45

FERRIS, BENJAMIN G.   Utah and the Mormons:.... New York, 1854.
Plates, orig. cloth, 1st ed. Ginsberg 14-1002 1978 $50

FERRY, J.   Le Tonkin et la Mere Patrie. Paris, 1890.
8vo, orig. covers. Van der Peet 127-297 1978 Dfl 55

FESS, SIMEON DAVIDSON   A Compendium of United States History Arranged
in Topical Outline. Ada, 1891. Flexible cloth, pencil notes on flyleaf. Hayman
73-528 1978 $8.50

FESS, SIMEON DAVIDSON   Ohio. Chicago & New York, 1937. 5 vols.,
orig. binding, 1st. vol. is chipped at top of spine, o/w very good set. Hayman
71-536 1978 $25

FETES de Versailles. (Paris, 1674-79). 3 series in 1 vol., folio, double-
page engraved plts., contemp. mottled calf, gilt borders, orig. issue, attractive copy. Quaritch Summer,1978-16 1978 $6,250

FEUDAL Days; or, the Noble Outlaw. London, n.d. (ca. 1810). 12mo, original
grey printed wrappers, cloth slipcase, green morocco spine, 1st ed.(?), chapbook,
very fine copy, Cohn's own collection. Ximenes 47-99 1978 $150

A FEW Historic Records of the Church in the Diocese of Texas During the Rebellion,
.... New York, 1865. Front wraps & first few pages torn at outer margin, wraps
soiled, Bell Wiley's copy. Broadfoot's 44-639 1978 $20

A FEW Thought on an Union..Observations Upon Mr. Weld's Pamphlet of "No
Union". Dublin, 1799. 1st ed., plain wrs. Hyland 128-765 1978 £10

FEWSTER, E.   Litany Before the Dawn of Fire. Toronto, 1942.
Card cover. Hood 117-803 1978 $7.50

FEWSTER, E. P.   My Garden Dreams. Ottawa, 1926. Marginal
illus. Hood 117-622 1978 $12.50

FFOULKES, CHARLES JOHN   Armour & Weapons. Oxford, 1909. 8vo.,
cloth, frontis., plts., text illus., pencil underlining throughout. Van der Peet
H-64-327 327 1978 Dfl 45

FIALETTI, ODOARDO   Il Vero Modo et Ordine per Disegnare Tutte le
Parti del Corpo Humano. Venice, 1608. Oblong 4to., plts., old half-vellum,
marbled bds., lightly rubbed, fine clean copy, rare 1st ed. Gilhofer 74-38 1978
sFr 2,800

FIAMELLI, GIOVANNI FRANCESCO   La Riga Mathematica di Gio. Roma,
1605. 1st ed., quarto, full contemporary vellum, fine, rare. Bennett 20-72 1978
$270

FIAMMA DE Divino Amore. Bologna, 1536. Very rare 1st ed., limp vellum, woodcuts, fine. Gilhofer 75-38 1978 SFr 2,300

FICHTE, JOHANN GOTTLIEB   Das System Der Sittenlehre. Jena and Leipzig,
1798. 8vo., bds. Salloch 348-65 1978 $300

FICHTE, JOHANN GOTTLIEB   Ueber den Begriff der Wissenschaftslehre oder der
sogenannten Philosophie. 1st ed., 8vo, contemp. boards, uncut copy, lightly
browned. Gilhofer 75-39 1978 SFr 550

FICINO, MARSILIO   De Immortalitate Animorum. Paris, 1559.
Thick 8vo., greem 1/2 mor., vellum label, light stains on last few pgs. Salloch
348-67 1978 $225

FICINO, MARSILIO   De Triplici Vita: Sana, Longa and Celitus...
Strasbourg, 1511. 4to., calf, armorial bind., fine. Salloch 348-66 1978 $400

FICK, ADOLF EUGEN   Lehrbuch der Anatomie und Physiologie der Sinne-
sorgane. Lahr, 1864. Woodcut illus., stereoscopic pictures, 8vo., contemp.
cloth, back gilt, 1st ed., fine copy. Offenbacher 30-38 1978 $145

FICKE, ARTHUR DAVISON   Mr. Faust. A Play. New York, 1913. 1st ed.,
edges rubbed, name on flyleaf. Biblo BL781-974 1978 $10

FICKLEN, JOHN ROSE   History of Reconstruction in Louisiana. Baltimore, 1910. Wrs., Bell Wiley's copy. Broadfoot 46-336 1978 $16

FICKLIN, O. B.   Remarks of Mr..., of Illinois, Delivered in the
House...January 10, 1844. N.P., n.d. Disbound. Hayman 72-669 1978
$8.50

FIDLER, N. D.   Law and The Practice of Nursing. Toronto, 1947.
Hood's 115-636 1978 $10

FIDLER, PAUL E.   Inventory of Federal Archives in the States:
The Farm Credit Administration, Texas. San Antonio, 1940. Jenkins 116-438
1978 $8.50

FIELD, AL G.   Watch Yourself Go By. Columbus, 1912. Cl.,
orig. binding. Hayman 71-245 1978 $10

FIELD, ANNE P. L.   The Story of Canada Blackie. New York, (1915).
Sm. 8vo., 1st ed. Morrill 239-376 1978 $15

FIELD, CYRUS W.   Testimonial of Friendship to, on the Eve of His
Departure on a Tour Round the World. New York, October 26, 1880. New
York, 1880. 8vo., orig. wrs. Morrill 241-136 1978 $7.50

FIELD, EDWARD   Diary of Colonel Israel Angell Commanding the
Second Rhode Island Reg. During the Revolution. Providence, 1899. Illus. Mac-
Manus 239-568 1978 $30

FIELD, EDWARD   Revolutionary Defences in Rhode Island...
Providence, 1896. Illus., maps, fine. MacManus 239-569 1978 $27.50

FIELD, EDWARD   State of Rhode Island the Providence Plantations
at the End of the Century. Boston, 1902. Illus., maps, 3 vols., 4tos, fine set.
MacManus 239-422 1978 $50

FIELD, EUGENE   Culture's Garland. Being Memoranda of the
Gradual Rise of Literature, Art, Music and Society in Chicago, and Other Western
Ganglia. Boston, 1887. 12mo., orig. printed wrs., 1st ed., spine a bit defec-
tive, but good, scarce. MacManus 238-479 1978 $45

FIELD, EUGENE   Echoes from the Sabine Farm...Horatian Lyrics
Now for the First Time Discreetly and Delectable Done Into English Verse... New
Rochelle, 1891. 1st ed., 1 of 70 paper copies, signed by Wilson, inscription,
orig. d.w., a little worn. Americanist 102-48 1978 $85

FIELD, EUGENE   A Little Book of Profitable Tales. New York,
1890. 12mo, cloth, gilt, t.e.g., 1st trade ed., slightly worn, fine. Duschnes
220-95 1978 $10

FIELD, EUGENE   A Little Book of Profitable Tales. New York,
1895. 12mo., etched portr., 1st ed. Biblo 251-497 1978 $12.50

FIELD, EUGENE   A Little Book of Tribune Verse. Denver, 1901.
8vo., orig. bds., vellum back & corners, bottom blank margin dampstained, otherwise nice, 1 of 750 lg. paper copies. Morrill 239-377 1978 $12.50

FIELD, EUGENE   Lullaby-Land: songs of childhood. 1898. Drawings by Charles Robinson, 12mo., orig. pict. cloth gilt, t.e.g., covers dull, good,
first English ed. Bell Book 17-500 1978 £5

FIELD, EUGENE   My Book. N.P., n.d. 4to, full blue mor., very
near Mint, 2 letters laid in, 1st ed., collector's cond. Desmarais 1-161 1978 $75

FIELD, EUGENE   Poems. New York, 1912. 8vo., 1/2 mor.,
marbled boards and end papers, raised bands, uncut, unopened, insignificant
rubbing of corners, Mint, 1st ed. Desmarais 1-162 1978 $20

FIELD, EUGENE   Songs and Other Verse. New York, 1896. 1st
ed., ink inscr. on flyleaf. Biblo 251-498 1978 $17.50

FIELD, EUGENE   The Tribune Primer. New York, The Marion
Press, 1900. Sq. 12mo., boards, 3/4 leather, worn, 1 of 25 copies on Japan paper,
fine. Duschnes 220-96 1978 $37.50

FIELD, KATE   Pen Photographs of Charles Dickens ' Readings
Taken From Life. 1871. 1st. American ed., frontis portrait, illus., orig. blue
cloth, fine copy, slight damage to bottom edges of few pages. Jarndyce 16-587
1978 £14

FIELD, MICHAEL   Julia Domina. Vale Press, 1903. Illus.,
signed, fine paper, prtd. bds., 1 of 240 copies, bkplts. of two previous owners.
Battery Park 1-232 1978 $250

FIELD, MICHAEL   The Race of Leaves. Vale Press. 8vo., one
of 280 copies, floral paper over bds. Battery Park 1-231 1978 $200

FIELD, RACHEL   All This and Heaven Too. New York, 1938. 1st
ed., d.w. Biblo BL781-975 1978 $10

FIELD, RACHEL   All Through the Night. New York, 1940. 1st
ed., illus., pictorial dust jacket. Victoria 34-289 1978 $7.50

FIELD, RACHEL   Branches Green. New York, 1934. 1st ed.,
plates and illus. by Dorothy Lathrop, fine, dust jacket. Victoria 34-290 1978
$25

FIELD, RACHEL   God's Pocket. New York, 1934. Biblo 247-
102 1978 $13.50

FIELD, RACHEL   Prayer for a Child. New York, 1944. 1st ed.,
fine. Victoria 34-450 1978 $25

FIELD, RICHARD   Of the Church, Five Bookes. Oxford, 1635.
Third ed., folio, cont. calf, good. Howes 194-45 1978 £40

FIELD, RICHARD S.   The Provincial Courts of New Jersey, ... New
York, 1849. Inscribed. MacManus 239-1265 1978 $40

FIELD, THOMAS W.   The Battle of Long Island. Brooklyn, 1869.
Plts., fldg. maps, 1st ed., nice copy. Butterfield 21-373 1978 $45

FIELD FORCE PUMP CO.   Catalogue No. 32. (Elmira, c. 1912). Wrps.,
illus. Hayman 71-100 1978 $8.50

THE FIELD Book. London, 1833. First ed., steel engrav. frontis., text-illus.,
roy. 8vo., orig. cloth. K Books 244-119 1978 £20

FIELDING, HENRY   Amelia. London, 1752. 1st. ed., 4 vols., sm.
8vo, contemp. calf, gilt spines, red leather labels. Traylen 88-246 1978 £150

FIELDING, HENRY   Amelia. 1752. 1st. ed., 4 vols., orig. speckled
calf, very fine. Jarndyce 16-80 1978 £200

FIELDING, HENRY   Amelia. London, 1752. 4 vols., 12mo., full
calf, red. mor. labels, 1st ed., fine, very faint foxing, sm. bookplt. MacManus
238-121 1978 $400

FIELDING, HENRY   An Apology for the Life of Mrs. Shamela Andrews.
(Waltham St. Lawrence): The Golden Cockerel Press, 1926. Orig. cloth-backed
bds., 1 of 450 copies, fine. MacManus 238-793 1978 $45

FIELDING, HENRY   The History of the Adventures of Joseph Andrews.
1751. Plts., 2 vols., 12mo., contemp. calf, joints cracked, labels missing, fifth
ed. Howes 194-266 1978 £21

FIELDING, HENRY   The History of Tom Jones, A Foundling. London,
1749. 1st. issue of 1st. ed., 6 vols., sm. 8vo, contemp. mottled calf, gilt spines,
leather labels, unusually nice copy. Traylen 88-247 1978 £525

FIELDING, HENRY   The History of Tom Jones, A Foundling. 1749.
1st. ed., 6 vols., later half calf, very attractively recased, spines extra gilt.
Jarndyce 16-79 1978 £580

FIELDING, HENRY   The History of Tom Jones, a Foundling. 1749.
2nd. ed., 6 vols., 12mo, lacks final blank leaves in 3 vols., brown crushed morocco,
gilt, a.e.g., water-stains on bindings & text. Hannas 54-109 1978 £110

FIELDING, HENRY   The History of Tom Jones, A Foundling. London,
1749. 6 vols., contemp. mottled calf, spines gilt, extremities worn, joints tender,
2nd ed. Bennett 7-44 1978 $285

FIELDING, HENRY   The History of Tom Jones, A Foundling. 1750.
4 vols., 12mo, cancel titles, contemp. calf, some foxing throughout, 4th. ed.
Hannas 54-110 1978 £45

FIELDING, HENRY   The History of Tom Jones, A Foundling. Leipzig,
1844. (Wrapper dated 1917). 2 vols., sq. 8vo, orig. printed wrappers, uncut.
Hannas 54-111 1978 £6

FIELDING, HENRY   A Journey from This World to the Next. Waltham St. Lawrence: The Golden Cockerel Press, 1930. Illus., orig. buckram, 1 of
500 copies, spine darkened, but very good. MacManus 238-794 1978 $30

FIELDING, HENRY   The Miser. 1733. 1st. ed., 8vo, disbound.
Hannas 54-112 1978 £65

FIELDING, HENRY   The Novels. Boston and New York, 1926. 10
vols., illus., orig. cloth-backed bds., 1 of 520 lg. paper sets, covers slightly
soiled, otherwise good. MacManus 238-122 1978 $200

FIELDING, HENRY   Novels. Oxford, 1926. Shakespeare Head ed.,
10 vols., 8vo, buckram, ltd. ed. of 1030 copies. Traylen 88-245 1978 £98

FIELDING, HENRY   Pasquin. 1736. 1st. ed., 8vo, disbound, paper
little browned. Hannas 54-113 1978 £45

FIELDING, HENRY   A Proposal for Making an Effectual Provision for
the Poor,... London, 1753. 1st ed., thin octavo, orig. drab grey wr., chipped
and strengthened, map neatly repaired, uncut, two wing cloth wr., brown quarter
mor. slipcase, gilt lettering on spine. Totteridge 29-40 1978 $300

FIELDING, HENRY   The Temple Beau. 1730. 8vo., unbound, first
ed. P. M. Hill 142-107 1978 £75

FIELDING, MANTLE   Dictionary of American Painters, Sculptors, and
Engravers. Philadelphia, n.d. 1st ed., 4to., illus., plts., cloth, ltd. to 700
copies, very good. MacManus 239-665 1978 $35

FIELDING, MANTLE   Gilbert Stuart's Portraits of George Washington.
Philadelphia, 1923. 1st ed., illus., t.e.g., uncut, orig. 3/4 cloth and parchment, very fine, ltd. to 350 signed copies. MacManus 239-706 1978 $100

FIELDING, SARAH   The Adventures of David Simple Containing an
Account of His Travels Through the Cities of London and Westminster... 1744.
2nd. ed., 2 vols., orig. calf, hinges weakening, front endpapers becoming loose.
Jarndyce 16-81 1978 £65

FIELDING, SARAH   The History of the Countess of Dellwvn. 1759.
1st. ed., 2 vols., orig. calf, hinges weakening, o/w v.g. Jarndyce 16-82
1978 £325

FIELDING, THEODORE HENRY ADOLPHUS Cumberland, Westmorland, and
Lancashire Illustrated, Exhibiting the Scenery of the Lakes, Antiquities, and Other
Picturesque Objects. 1822. Folio, lg. paper, plts., hand-coloured, contemp.
red straight-grained mor., uncut. Quaritch 983-326 1978 $1,690

FIELDING, THEODORE HENRY ADOLPHUS A Picturesque Tour of the English
Lakes, Containing a Description of the Most Romantic Scenery of Cumberland,
Westmorland, and Lancashire.... 1821. 4to., coloured plts., fine copy, orig.
red cloth gilt. Quaritch 983-327 1978 $1,250

FIELDING, THEODORE HENRY ADOLPHUS Synopsis of Practical Perspective,
Lineal and Aerial. 1839. 8vo., colour and plain plts., some plts. lightly spotted
pres. copy from author, orig. cloth, 2nd ed. Quaritch 983-183 1978 $65

FIELDS, J. C.   Proceedings of the International Mathematical
Congress Held in Toronto, August 11-16, 1924. Toronto, 1928. 2 vols., illus.,
inscribed by editor. Hood 116-921 1978 $60

FIELDS, JAMES I.   In & Out Doors with Charles Dickens. Boston,
1876. 12 mo., green cloth, good. Greene 78-181 1978 $30

FIELDS, JAMES T.   Poems. Boston, 1849. 1st ed., binding A,
inscr., nice copy, 8vo. Americanist 103-32 1978 $45

FIELDS, JAMES T.   Yesterdays with Authors. Boston, (1900). 1 vol.
extended to 2, extra-illus., octavo, bound in full purple mor. by W. Root, gilt
spines, gilt edges, slipcase. Totteridge 29-41 1978 $250

FIENNES, GERARD   Sea Power and Freedom... New York, 1918.
1st ed., illus., orig. cloth, fine. MacManus 239-1753 1978 $10

FIFTEENTH Annual Fair of the Tippecanoe Co. Agricultural Association... LaFayette, (1881). Illus. Hayman 72-365 1978 $12.50

FIFTIETH Anniversary of the First Baptist Church, Bloomfield, N.J., 1851-1901.
MacManus 239-1243 1978 $10

FIFTY Texas Rarities. Ann Arbor, 1946. From the library of Everett D. Graff,
prtd. white wrs., 1st ed., scarce, crease on corner of back cover. Bradley 49-
26 1978 $50

FIGARO Illustree. (Paris, 1899-1907). 8 vols., 8vo., imp. folio, gilt ornam
cloth bindings, colored plts., other plts., text illus. in color & b & w, nice set.
Van der Peet H-64-328 1978 Dfl 750

FIGGIS, DARRELL   The Paintings of William Blake. 1925. 4to.,
plts., color and black and white, bds., buckram back with dust wr. Quaritch
979-51 1978 $180

FIGGIS, J. N.   The Divine Right of Kings. Cambridge, 1914.
2nd. ed., octavo, good. Upcroft 10-310 1978 £5

FIGUEROA, REV. GREGORY   The Church and the Synagogue in St. Ambrose.
Washington, 1949. Cloth. Ginsberg 16-962 1978 $10.00

FILENE, A. LINCOLN   A Merchant's Horizon. 1924. Austin 80-583
1978 $10

FILENE, CATHERINE   Careers for Women. Boston, 1920. Rear cover
stained. Biblo BL781-814 1978 $8.50

FILENE, EDWARD A.   Successful Living in This Machine Age. 1931.
Austin 80-584 1978 $8.50

FILENE, EDWARD A.   The Way Out... 1925. Austin 80-585 1978
$8.50

FILICAIA, VINCENZIO DA   Poesie Toscane. Firenze, 1797. 4to., vellum,
backstrip defective at head, first ed. King 7-168 1978 £50

FILISOLA, VICENTE   Memorias Para la Historia de la Guerra de Tejas.
Mexico, 1849. Original full mottled calf. Jenkins 116-440 1978 $450

FILLMORE, JOHN COMFORT   Piano-forte Music. Philadelphia, 1892. 8vo.
Morrill 239-378 1978 $10

FILSON, JOHN   The Discovery and Settlement of Kentucky.
Paris, 1875. French ed., 3/4 leather. Broadfoot 50-67 1978 $300

FINAN, J.   Maize in the Great Herbals. 1950. 8vo, orig.
cloth. Book Chest 17-154 1978 $17.50

FINANCE Accounts of Ireland for the Year Ended 5th January, 1803. Octavo
bound in cloth, reprint. Hyland 128-403 1978 £15

FINCH, ANNE   Countess of Winchelsea. London, 1713. 8vo.,
1st ed., 1st issue, contemp. calf, gilt, slightly worn, sound. Quaritch 979-140
1978 $1,260

FINCH, EDITH   Wilfrid Scawen Blunt 1840-1922. 1938. Map,
plts., 8vo., orig. cloth. Howes 194-647 1978 £7.50

FINCHAM, HENRY W.   Artists and Engravers of British and American Book
Plates... London, 1897. 4to., orig. cloth, 1st ed., ltd. to 1,050 copies, covers
spotted, but good. MacManus 238-868 1978 $65

FINCHAM, HENRY W.   Artists and Engravers of British and American Book
Plates. London, 1897. 1st ed., large quarto, profusely illus. Victoria 34-291
1978 $50

FINDEN, EDWARD   The Ports, Harbours, Watering-Places, and Coast
Scenery of Great Britain. 1842. 2 vols., 4to., plts., some foxing, half calf
gilt, rubbed. Quaritch 983-328 1978 $380

FINDEN, EDWARD   The Ports, Harbours, Watering Places and Coast
Scenery of Great Britain. 1842. Plts., 2 vols. in 1, 4to., orig. mor., binding
broken, some foxing. Howes 194-1383 1978 £130

FINDEN, W.   Tableaux, of National Character, Beauty, and
Costume. 1843. 2 vols., folio, black calf, rubbed, rebacked cloth, unlettered.
George's 635-142 1978 £20

FINDING List of the Willard Library of Evansville, Indiana. Evansville, 1892.
Wrps., soiled, little worn. Hayman 71-344 1978 $7.50

FINDLAY, A. G.   A Directory for the Navigation of the North
Pacific Ocean... London, 1886. Plts., 3rd ed., lg. 8vo., cloth, fine. Paine
78-51 1978 $62.50

FINDLAY, A. G.   A Directory for the South Pacific Ocean....
London, n.d. (1884). 5th ed., lg. 8vo., cloth, fine, plts. Paine 78-52 1978
$65

FINDLAY, H.   Garden Making & Keeping. New York, 1932.
8vo, orig. cloth. Book Chest 17-519 1978 $8.50

FINDLAY, JAMES   Directory to Gentlemen's seats, Villages...in
Scotland.... Edinburgh, c. 1843. Map, newly bound in bds., 8vo. K Books
244-120 1978 £8

FINDLAY, JAMES   Directory to Gentlemen's Seats, Villages...in
Scotland. London, c. 1851. New bds., 8vo., map. K Books 244-121 1978
£6

FINDLAY, QUAY H.   Mule Skinners, Supply Company, 135th Field
Artillery. Cleveland, 1920. Flexible cloth. Hayman 72-808 1978 $10

FINDLAY, WILLIAM   Robert Burns and the Medical Profession. Paisley,
1898. Portraits, cr. 4to., orig. cloth. K Books 244-362 1978 £8

FINDLEY, PALMER   The Story of Childbirth. New York, 1933.
Somewhat worn. Rittenhouse 49-254 1976 $12.50

FINE, ORONCE   De Mundi Sphaera.... Paris, 1555. Sm. 4to.,
woodcuts, sm. waterstains on titlepage & a few other leaves, but good copy, early
limp bds., second ed. Quaritch 977-180 1978 $325

FINE, ORONCE   Protomathiesis:.... Paris, 1530-1532. 1st ed.,
contemp. limp vellum, upper part of spine repaired, folio, woodcuts. Gilhofer
75-40 1978 SFr 9,000

FINE Paper and the Printer; A Guide to Basic Understanding of Fine Papers as
Applied to the Printing Trade in Canada. Calgary, n.d. Hood's 115-161 1978
$12.50

FINEBERG, SOLOMAN A.   Overcoming Anti-Semitism. 1943. Austin
79-241 1978 $10

FINEGAN, JAMES E.   Tammany at Bay. New York, 1933. Illus.,
1st ed. Biblo 251-70 1978 $16.50

FINES Imposed and Deductions Made From Mail-Contractors. (Washington, 1873).
Disbound. Hayman 71-435 1978 $7.50

FINGER, CHARLES J.   Highwaymen. New York, 1923. 8vo., d.w.,
1st ed. Morrill 239-379 1978 $13.50

FINGER, CHARLES J.   Romantic Rascals. New York, 1927. Illus. by
Paul Honore, 8vo., d.w., 1st ed. Morrill 239-380 1978 $13.50

FINGER, CHARLES J.   Seven Horizons. New York, 1930. Illus., 8vo.,
1st ed. Morrill 239-381 1978 $8.50

FINK, LEO G.   Old Jesuit Trails in Penn's Forest. New York,
1936. Illus., scarce. MacManus 239-1457 1978 $30

FINLAY, G.   History of the Byzantine Empire from DCCXVI to MLVII. London, 1853. 8vo., cloth. Van der Peet H-64-330 1978 Dfl 40

FINLAY, M.   Our American Maples & Some Others. New York, 1934. 8vo, orig. cloth. Book Chest 17-520 1978 $9

FINLAYSON, GEORGE   The Mission to Siam and Hue, The Capital of Cochin China... London, 1826. 8vo, half-title, some spotting, half calf, gilt back. Deighton 5-73 1978 £45

FINLAYSON, H.   The Red Centre. Sydney, 1936. Folding map, 3rd ed., 8vo, orig. cloth. Book Chest 17-155 1978 $25

FINLEY, JAMES B.   Autobiography of... or, Pioneer Life in the West. Cincinnati, n.d. (1890's?). Cloth, slightly rubbed. Hayman 72-249 1978 $7.50

FINLEY, JOHN   The French in the Heart of America. New York, 1915. 1st ed., orig. cloth, very good. MacManus 239-139 1978 $20

FINLEY, MARTHA   Elsie's Motherhood. New York, 1876. 1st ed., 5th vol., very scarce, light cover fading and spotting. Victoria 34-292 1978 $25

FINN, F.   Hutchinson's Animals of all Countries. (c. 1930). Coloured plts., illus., 4 vols., 4to. George's 635-1018 1978 £5.25

FINNEMORE, JOHN   Two Boys in War-Time. London, 1900. 6 plts., cr. 8vo, dec. cloth, lacks lst. free end-paper, covers bit marked. K Books 239-162 1978 £5

FINNEY, CHARLES G.   The Circus of Dr. Lao. New York, 1935. 1st ed., fine copy, slightly torn dust jacket. Victoria 34-293 1978 $65

FINNIE, RICHARD   Lure of the North. Philadelphia, 1940. Illus. Hood 117-94 1978 $25

FIRBANK, RONALD   The Artificial Princess. 1934. First ed., fine, d.w., orig. cloth, 8vo. Howes 194-855 1978 £7.50

FIRBANK, RONALD   The Artifical Princess. 1934. Good, first English ed. Bell Book 16-336 1978 £12.50

FIRBANK, RONALD   Concerning the Eccentricities of Cardinal Pirelli. 1926. Frontis. portrait by Augustus John, near fine, worn d.w., 1000 copies pr., first English ed. Bell Book 17-343 1978 £38.50

FIRBANK, RONALD   Odette d'Antrevernes. London, 1905. One of 10 large paper copies on japon vellum, full cream vellum, very nice, first ed. Rota 212-20 1978 £300

FIRBANK, RONALD   Prancing Nigger. New York, 1924. First U.S. ed., very good, somewhat worn d.w. Bell Book 17-345 1978 £42.50

FIRBANK, RONALD   The Works of Ronald Firbank. 1929. No. 157 of 235 sets, portraits, 5 vols., yellow buckram, covers stained, internally very good. Bell Book 17-981 1978 £58.50

FIREBAUGH, ELLEN M.   The Physician's Wife and Things that May Pertain to her Life. Philadelphia, 1894. Illus. with photo-engrs., 8vo., fr. cover slightly soiled, lst ed. Morrill 239-83 1978 $10

FIRENZUOLA, AGNOLO   Opere di Messer Agnolo Fi renzuola Fiorentino. Firenze, 1763. 3 vols., 8vo., vellum. King 7-169 1978 £15

FIRESTONE, HARVEY S.   Men and Rubber. 1926. 1st ed. Austin 80-586 1978 $12.50

THE FIRM of John Dickinson and Company Limited. 1896. Illus., roy. 8vo. George's 635-312 1978 £6

FIRMIN, EMILE   Le Kansas en 1889. Topeka, 1889. Illus., large folding map, orig. pr. wr., lst ed. Ginsberg 14-1100 1978 $125

FIRST EDITION CLUB   Bibliographical Catalogue of First Editions, Proof Copies and Manuscripts of Books by Lord Byron Exhibited at the 4th Exhibition Held by the First Edition Club. Jan. 1925. London, First Edition Club, 1925. Ltd. to 500 copies, cr. 4to., orig. buckram, t.e.g. Forster 130-306 1978 £28

THE FIRST Prospectus of The Limited Editons Club. (Boston, 1929). Thin 8vo, marbled boards, cloth spine, t.e.g., fine. Duschnes 220-208 1978 $10

THE FIRST Published Life of Abraham Lincoln Written in the Year MDCCCLX. (Detroit), The Cranbrook Press, 1900. Ed. ltd. to 245 copies, 4to., lst ed., full green levant with elab. gilt fillets on bds., endpapers of dark green moire satin, portr. of Lincoln on porcelain, few hairline cracks, very fine, green cloth slipcase. Current Misc. 8-54 1978 $850

THE FIRST Railroad in Germany Between Nuremburg and Furth; with Title in French, German and English. c.1845. Peepshow, 7-1/2 x 5ins., hand-coloured, excellent cond., orig. wr., slip-case, corners slightly worn, label. Quaritch 983-353 1978 $700

FIRST Record Book of the "Old Dutch Church of Sleepy Hollow"...Now the First Reformed Church of Tarrytown. 1901. 4to., plts., uncut & partly unopened, orange cloth. Butterfield 21-465 1978 $25

FIRST Report of the Special Committee Appointed to Inquire into the Causes Which Retard the Settlement of the Eastern Townships, of Lower Canada. Toronto, 1851. Modern cloth. Wolfe 39-162 1978 $50

FIRST And Second Books of Homilies. Oxford, 1844. Calf, octavo, good. Upcroft 10-83 1978 £8.50

FIRTH, C. H.   Essays - Historical and Literary. Oxford, 1938. Octavo, good. Upcroft 10-316 1978 £8.50

FIRTH, C. H.   The House of Lords During the Civil War. 1910. Octavo, good. Upcroft 10-314 1978 £6

FIRTH, RAYMOND   Malay Fishermen... London, (1946). As new, d.j., 8vo., plts., maps. Paine 78-53 1978 $17.50

FISCH, MAX H.   Nicolaus Pol Doctor 1494. New York, (1947). Illus., 8vo. Morrill 239-84 1978 $12.50

FISCHEL, OSKAR   Modes and Manners of the Nineteenth Century. 1790-1914. 4 vols., fully illus. Baldwins' 51-78 1978 $75

FISCHEL, OSKAR   Modes and Manners of the XIXth Century as represented in the pictures and engravings of the time. 1909. Coloured illus., 3 vols., recased, now rubbed. George's 635-240 1978 £21

FISCHER, BERNHARD   Der Sektionskurs kurze Anleitung zur Pathologisch-Anatomischen Untersuchung Menschlicher Leichen. Munich, 1922. Second ed. Rittenhouse 49-255 1976 $15

FISCHER, E. S.   Elements of Natural Philosophy. Boston, 1827. "Courtlandt Van Rennselaer" copy, interleaved with his mms. notes, orig. calf with label YD Clark Binder, waxed. Baldwins' 51-413 1978 $50

FISCHER, EMIL   Untersuchungen in der Puringruppe. Berlin, 1907. 8vo., orig. cloth, very good copy, lst collected ed. Norman 5-106 1978 $125

FISCHER, EMIL   Untersuchungen Uber Aminosauren, Polypeptide und Proteine. Berlin, 1906-23. 2 vols., 8vo., orig. cloth, vol. 2 somewhat loose in case, very good set, lst collected ed. Norman 5-105 1978 $125

FISCHER, EMIL   Untersuchungen Uber Kohlenhydrate und Fermente. Berlin, 1909-22. 2 vols., 8vo., orig. cloth, gilt, fine set, lst collected ed. Norman 5-107 1978 $125

FISCHER, EMIL   Untersuchungen Uber Triphenylmethanfarbstoffe, Hydrazine und Indole. Berlin, 1924. 8vo., orig. cloth, very good copy, lst collected ed. Norman 5-108 1978 $85

FISCHER, H.   Der Bergspiegel eine Ausiese. Munchen, 1929. Photographs, orig. linen, 8vo. George's 635-1513 1978 £5

FISCHER, HANS   Die Chemie des Pyrrols. Leipzig, 1934-37. 2 vols., 8vo., orig. cloth, gilt, very good set, lst ed., band I and band II. Norman 5-109 1978 $75

FISCHER, LOUIS   Down of Victory. 1942. Austin 80-99 1978
$10

FISCHER, M.   Report as to Socorro County (New Mexico).
Socorro, 1881. Orig. pr. wr., 1st ed. Ginsberg 14-759 1978 $250

FISCHER, OTTO   Die Kunst Indiens, Chinas und Japans. Berlin,
(1928). Half-tone plts., gravure or mounted color plts., boards, cloth spine and
tips, somewhat scuffed, hinges weak. Dawson's 127-299 1978 $65

FISCHER-HANSEN, CARL   Om Amerika. New York, 1903. Frontis.,
in Danish. Austin 79-245 1978 $37.50

FISH, A.   Henrietta Rae, Mrs. Ernest Normand. 1905.
8vo., coloured and plain plts., cloth, inscribed by Miss Rae. Quaritch 983-239
1978 $50

FISH, HAMILTON   The New York Privateers 1756-1763... New
York, 1945. One of 400, signed by author, fine, 8vo., orig. cloth, illus.
Paine 78-55 1978 $35

FISHBERG, MAURICE   The Jews. 1911. 1st Amer. ed. Austin 79-
246 1978 $20

FISHER, ALLAN G. B.   The Clash of Progress and Security. Macmillan,
1935. 1st. ed., 8vo, orig. cloth, nice copy. Fenning 32-114 1978 £6

FISHER, ALLAN G. B.   Economic Progress and Social Security. Macmillan, 1945. 1st. ed., 8vo, orig. cloth, spine faded, nice. Fenning 32-115
1978 £6

FISHER, BEN VON D.   The Runkle Family. 1899. Illus. Austin
79-247 1978 $47.50

FISHER, C. E.   Kanzas and the Constitution. Boston, 1856.
Disbound, 1st ed. Ginsberg 14-443 1978 $20

FISHER, GEORGE ADAMS   The Yankee Conscript. Philadelphia, 1864.
Hinges cracked, cover worn, Bell Wiley's copy. Broadfoot's 44-136 1978 $14

FISHER, HARRISON   Fair Americans. New York, 1911. 1st ed.,
quarto, color plates, faded, very good. Victoria 34-294 1978 $65

FISHER, IRVING   Booms and Depressions. Adelphi, 1932. 1st
ed. in slightly frayed dust jacket. Austin 80-587 1978 $15

FISHER, IRVING   Elementary Principles of Economics. 1928. Illus.
Austin 80-588 1978 $10

FISHER, IRVING   Money Illusion. Adelphi, 1928. 1st ed. Austin 80-589 1978 $12.50

FISHER, IRVING   The Nature of Capital & Income. 1906. Austin
80-590 1978 $12.50

FISHER, IRVING   100% Money. Adelphi, 1935. 1st ed. Austin
80-591 1978 $27.50

FISHER, IRVING   The Purchasing Power of Money. 1920. New,
rev. ed. Austin 80-594 1978 $12.50

FISHER, IRVING   Stable Money. Adelphi, 1934. 1st ed. Austin
80-592 1978 $20

FISHER, IRVING   The Stock Market Crash-and After. 1930. Illus.,
1st ed. Austin 80-593 1978 $22.50

FISHER, L. E.   The Background of the Revolution for Mexican
Independence. Boston, 1934. Jenkins 116-445 1978 $85

FISHER, PETER   History of New Brunswick, as Originally Published
in 1825... St. John, 1921. Hood 116-213 1978 $45

FISHER, PHILIP A.   Record of the Descendants of Josua, Anthony and
Cornelius Fisher of Dedham, Mass., 1636-1640. Everett, 1898. Covers worn.
Baldwins' 51-251 1978 $25

FISHER, R.   Introduction to a Catalogue of the Early Italian
Prints in the B.M. London, Chiswick Press, 1886. Roy. 8vo., orig. buckram,
back inner hinge cracked, text fine. Forster 130-201 1978 £10

FISHER, SYDNEY GEORGE   Men, Women and Manners in Colonial Times.
Philadelphia, 1898. 2 vols., illus. MacManus 239-140 1978 $15

FISHER, SYDNEY GEORGE   The Struggle for American Independence.
Philadelphia, 1908. 2 vols., illus., fine. MacManus 239-570 1978 $37.50

FISHER, SYDNEY GEORGE   The Trial of the Constitution. Philadelphia,
1862. 1st. ed., orig. cloth, pres. copy from author. Baldwins' 51-11 1978 $17.50

FISHER, SYDNEY GEORGE   The True Benjamin Franklin. Philadelphia,
1899. Illus., orig. cloth, good copy. MacManus 239-164 1978 $8.50

FISHER, SYDNEY GEORGE   The True History of the American Revolution.
Philadelphia and London, 1902. Illus., maps, stain on cover. Hood's 115-103
1978 $10

FISHER, THOMAS   The Negro's Memorial, or, Abolitionist's
Catechism; by an Abolitionist. London, 1825. 8vo, contemporary diced russia,
gilt, 1st ed., presentation copy, inscribed by the author, very good copy, very
scarce. Ximenes 47-102 1978 $225

FISHER, VARDIS   April. A Fable of Love. New York, 1937.
Orig. mor., extremities rubbed, 1st ed., 1 of 50 numbered copies signed by author,
rubbing, fine. MacManus 238-646 1978 $50

FISHER, VARDIS   City of Illusion. New York, 1941. First ed.,
orig. binding, fine. Rota 211-108 1978 £5

FISHER, VARDIS   Dark Bridwell. Cambridge, Mass., 1931. First
ed., orig. binding, nice. Rota 211-107 1978 £5

FISHER, VARDIS   The Golden Rooms. N. Y., (c. 1944).
1st Armed Services ed., No. 713, oblong 16 mo., pictorial wrappers, fine.
Houle 10-109 1978 $20

FISHER, VARDIS   In Tragic Life. 1932. 1st trade ed. in cloth,
some corner creases else very good, d.w. Dykes 35-141 1978 $15

FISHER, VARDIS   In Tragic Life. 1932. Mor., gilt top, 1 of
25 no. copies of 1st ed. signed by author, inscription by author, a little worn at
spine, else fine, slipcase. Dykes 35-140 1978 $50

FISHER, VARDIS   No Villain Need Be. New York, 1936. Orig.
mor., top of spine chipped, 1st ed., 1 of 75 numbered copies, signed by author,
fine. MacManus 238-645 1978 $40

FISHER, VARDIS   Passions Spin the Plot. 1934. Mor., gilt
top, 1 of 75 no. copies of 1st ed. signed by author, bookplt., inscribed, top of
spine worn else fine, slipcase. Dykes 35-142 1978 $45

FISHER, VARDIS   We are Betrayed. New York, (1935). Orig.
mor., a bit rubbed, 1st ed., 1 of 75 numbered copies, signed by author, fine.
MacManus 238-644 1978 $40

FISHER, W. E. GARRETT   The Transvaal and the Boers. London, 1900.
Folding map, some foxing, few ink-notes at beginning & end, covers slightly marked,
orig. cloth, 8vo. K Books 239-163 1978 £11

FISHER, WALTER M.   The Californians. London, 1876. Original
cloth, 1st ed. Ginsberg 14-115 1978 $35

FISK, JAMES LIBERTY   Expedition of Captain Fisk to the Rocky Mountains
Washington, 1864. Disbound, 1st ed. Ginsberg 14-349 1978 $40

FISKE, CHRISTABEL F.   Vassar Mediaeval Studies. 1923. Allen 234-
1236 1978 $10

FISKE, GERTRUDE HORSFORD   Studies in the Bi-Literal Cipher of Francis Bacon..
Boston and London, 1913. 4to, numerous plts., bds., parchment spine, frayed.
Eaton 45-183 1978 £15

FISKE, JOHN   The American Revolution. Boston, 1894. 2 vols.
Hood 116-122 1978 $20

FISKE, JOHN   The Dutch and Quaker Colonies in America.
Boston, 1899. 2 vols., illus., maps. MacManus 239-141 1978 $17.50

FISKE, JOHN   Old Virginia and her Neighbors. Cambridge,
1900. 1 of 250 numbered copies printed on large paper at Riverside Press, 4 to.,
cloth over bds., uncut, illus., maps, 2 vols., very good. Houle 10-110
1978 $60

FITCH, JOHN   Annals of the Army of the Cumberland.
Phila, 1864. Steel engravings, ex libris, Bell Wiley's Copy. Broadfoot's 44-137
1978 $25.00

FITCH, LYLE   Planning for Jobs. 1946. Ex-lib. Austin 80-596
1978 $12.50

FITCH, SAMUEL SHELDON   Six Lectures on the Uses of the Lungs. New York,
1847. Illus., sm. 8vo., 1st ed. Morrill 239-85 1978 $10

FITCH, WILLIAM   Mineral Waters of the U.S. & American Spas.
1927. Illus. good. Nestler Rare 78-215 1978 $35

FITCH, WILLIAM CLYDE   The Knighting of the Twins and Ten Other Tales.
Boston, (1891). Author's 1st book, illus. by Virginia Gerson, very fine. Victoria
34-295 1978 $65

FITCH, WILLIAM E.   Some Neglected History of North Carolina...
New York, 1914. Fold. maps, scarce. MacManus 239-613 1978 $37.50

FITCH-BREWER, ANNETTE   The Story of a Mother-Love. (Jefferson, 1913).
Cloth, scarce. Hayman 72-250 1978 $15

FITCHETT, W. H.   Fights for the Flag. London, 1898. Sm. 8vo.,
full calf, gilt tooled spine, gilt borders, a.e.g., frontis. portr., 2nd impr. Van
der Peet H-64-331 1978 Dfl 70

FITCHETT, W. H.   How England Saved Europe, the Story of the Great
War (1793-1815). 1900. Plans, portraits, 4 vols., cr. 8vo. George's 635-644
1978 £7.50

FITE, DAVID   Social & Industrial Conditions in the North
During the Civil War. NY, 1910. Bell Wiley's Copy. Broadfoot's 44-139 1978
$25.00

FITE, EMERSON DAVID   A Book of Old Maps. Cambridge, 1926. First
ed., folio, maps. Biblo 247-450 1978 $150

FITE, EMERSON DAVID   The Presidential Campaign of 1860. NY, 1911.
Bell Wiley's Copy. Broadfoot's 44-138 1978 $16.00

FITHIAN, PHILIP VICKERS   Journal and Letters, 1773-1774: A Plantation
Tutor of the Old Dominion. Williamsburg, 1943. 1st of this ed., fine, d.w.,
illus. Biblo 248-212 1978 $23.50

FITTER, R.   British Birds in Colour. London, n.d. 8vo,
orig. cloth. Book Chest 17-156 1978 $20

FITZ-ADAM, ADAM   The World. London, 1782. New ed., 4 vols.,
12mo., contemp. calf. K Books 244-464 1978 £20

FITZ-ADAM, ADAM   The World. 1789. 4 vols., orig. calf, v.g.
Jarndyce 16-54 1978 £32

FITZGERALD, EDWARD   Pedro Calderon de la Barca. N.P., (1865).
8vo., contemp. wrs., rebacked, mor. slipcase, extremely rare, 1st ed., pres.
copy inscr. Quaritch 979-142 1978 $850

FITZGERALD, EDWARD   Polonius. 1852. Sm. 8vo., very fine copy,
orig. cloth, mor. case, pres. copy inscr. Quaritch 979-141 1978 $600

FITZGERALD, FRANCIS SCOTT KEY   All the Sad Young Men. New York,
1926. Orig. cloth, 1st ed., fine. MacManus 238-648 1978 $100

FITZGERALD, FRANCIS SCOTT KEY   All the Sad Young Men. New York,
1926. 8vo., cloth, 1st ed., 1st state, very fine copy. J. S. Lawrence 38-F5
1978 $185

FITZGERALD, FRANCIS SCOTT KEY   All the Sad Young Men. New York,
1926. 8vo., cloth, 1st ed., 1st state, some foxing. J. S. Lawrence 38-F6 1978
$100

FITZGERALD, FRANCIS SCOTT KEY   All the Sad Young Men. New York,
1926. 8vo., cloth, 1st ed., later state. J. S. Lawrence 38-F7 1978 $50

FITZGERALD, FRANCIS SCOTT KEY   The Beautiful and the Damned. New
York, 1922. Orig. cloth, 1st ed., 2nd print., 1st state, slightly soiled and worn.
MacManus 238-647 1978 $100

FITZGERALD, FRANCIS SCOTT KEY   The Beautiful and Damned. New York,
1922. First U.S. ed., very good. Bell Book 17-346 1978 £37.50

FITZGERALD, FRANCIS SCOTT KEY   The beautiful and damned. New York,
1922. 8vo., green cloth, 1st issue, covers somewhat worn and darkened, hinges
beginning to split, penciled ownership inscription, good only, 1st ed. Desmarais
1-164 1978 $45

FITZGERALD, FRANCIS SCOTT KEY   The Beautiful and Damned. New York,
1922. 8vo., gilt-stamped cloth, d.j., 1st ed., signed by author, rare d.j., very
fine copy. J. S. Lawrence 38-F18 1978 $2,000

FITZGERALD, FRANCIS SCOTT KEY   The Crack-Up. (New York, 1945).
Tall 8vo., cloth-backed decor. bds., d.j., 1st ed., 1st prtg., d.j. reinforced
with tape. J. S. Lawrence 38-F25 1978 $75

FITZGERALD, FRANCIS SCOTT KEY   The Crack-Up. (New York, 1945).
Tall 8vo., cloth-backed decor. bds., d.j., 1st ed., 1st prtg., pencilled inscr.
J. S. Lawrence 38-F26 1978 $50

FITZGERALD, FRANCIS SCOTT KEY   The Crack-Up. (New York, 1945).
Tall 8vo., cloth, d.j., 1st full-cloth ed., later prtg., fine copy. J. S. Lawrence 38-F27 1978 $35

FITZGERALD, FRANCIS SCOTT KEY   The Evil Eye. Cincinnati, New York &
London, 1915. 4to., cloth-backed bds., 1st ed., fine copy, cloth fldg. box,
rare. J. S. Lawrence 38-F40 1978 $1,400

FITZGERALD, FRANCIS SCOTT KEY   The Evil Eye. (Cincinnati, New York
& London), 1915. 4to., cloth-backed bds., 1st ed., covers rebacked. J. S.
Lawrence 38-F41 1978 $50

FITZGERALD, FRANCIS SCOTT KEY   Fie! Fie! Fi-Fi! Cincinnati, New
York, London, 1914. 4to., orig. cloth-backed bds., 1st ed., fine copy. J. S.
Lawrence 38-F42 1978 $850

FITZGERALD, FRANCIS SCOTT KEY   Flappers and Philosophers. New York,
1920. 8vo., cloth, 1st ed., 3rd prtg., pres. copy, inscr. & signed. J. S.
Lawrence 38-F47 1978 $650

FITZGERALD, FRANCIS SCOTT KEY   Flappers and Philosophers. New York,
1920. First U.S. ed., sm. nick at head os spine, else very good. Bell Book 17-
348 1978 £70

FITZGERALD, FRANCIS SCOTT KEY   Flappers and Phylosophers. New York,
1920. Green cloth, 1st ed., fine copy, scarce, nice cond. Bradley 49-121 1978
$135

FITZGERALD, FRANCIS SCOTT KEY   The Great Gatsby. New York, 1925.
8vo., gilt-stamped cloth, d.j., 1st ed., 1st prtg., fine copy, 1st issue d.j.
J. S. Lawrence 38-F52 1978 $1,000

FITZGERALD, FRANCIS SCOTT KEY   The Great Gatsby. New York, 1925.
First U.S. ed., good. Bell Book 17-349 1978 £75

FITZGERALD, FRANCIS SCOTT KEY   The Great Gatsby. New York, 1925.
8vo., gilt-stamped cloth, d.j., 1st ed., 2nd prtg., scarce, 3,000 copies, 2nd
issue d.j. J. S. Lawrence 38-F53 1978 $500

FITZGERALD, FRANCIS SCOTT KEY   The Great Gatsby. New York, 1925.
8vo., cloth, 1st ed., 1st prtg., dampstain on front cover. J. S. Lawrence 38-
F54 1978 $100

FITZGERALD, FRANCIS SCOTT KEY   The Great Gatsby. New York, 1925.
8vo., cloth, 1st ed., 2nd prtg. J. S. Lawrence 38-F55 1978 $100

FITZGERALD, FRANCIS SCOTT KEY   The Great Gatsby. New York, (1945).
12mo., pic. wrs., 1st paperback ed., spine sunned & worn. J. S. Lawrence 38-
F57 1978 $10

FITZGERALD, FRANCIS SCOTT KEY   The Last Tycoon. New York, 1941.
8vo., cloth, 2nd Amer. ed., William McFee's copy, letters from McFee about
book tipped in, d.j. photo. J. S. Lawrence 38-F68 1978 $150

FITZGERALD, FRANCIS SCOTT KEY   The Portable F. S. F.   New York, 1945. 1st of this ed.   Biblo 251-499 1978 $10

FITZGERALD, FRANCIS SCOTT KEY   Safety First.   Cincinnati, New York, London, (1916).   4to., orig. cloth-backed bds., 1st ed., fine copy, cloth fldg. case.   J. S. Lawrence 38-F99 1978 $1,200

FITZGERALD, FRANCIS SCOTT KEY   Tales of the Jazz Age.   New York, 1922. 1st issue, very good.   Bernard 5-95 1978 $65

FITZGERALD, FRANCIS SCOTT KEY   Tales of the Jazz Age.   New York, 1922.   8vo., cloth, 1st ed., 1st prtg.   J. S. Lawrence 38-F100 1978 $125

FITZGERALD, FRANCIS SCOTT KEY   Tales of the Jazz Age.   New York, 1922.   8vo., cloth, 1st ed., 2nd prtg.   J. S. Lawrence 38-F101 1978 $35

FITZGERALD, FRANCIS SCOTT KEY   Tales of the Jazz Age.   New York, 1922.   8vo., green cloth, 1st ed.   J. S. Lawrence 38-F102 1978 $25

FITZGERALD, FRANCIS SCOTT KEY   Tales of the Jazz Age.   1922.   First ed. Austin 82-1169 1978 $60

FITZGERALD, FRANCIS SCOTT KEY   Tales of the Jazz Age.   New York, 1922.   First U.S. ed., very good.   Bell Book 17-350 1978 £65

FITZGERALD, FRANCIS SCOTT KEY   Taps at Reveille.   New York, 1935.   1st ed., orig. cloth, d.j., 1st state, very good.   MacManus 238-649 1978 $200

FITZGERALD, FRANCIS SCOTT KEY   Taps at Reveille.   New York, 1935. 8vo., cloth, d.j., 1st ed., 1st state, from the library & with bkplt. of Arthur Mizener, fine copy.   J. S. Lawrence 38-F103 1978 $475

FITZGERALD, FRANCIS SCOTT KEY   Taps at Reveille.   New York, 1935. 8vo., cloth, d.j., 1st ed., 2nd state, dampstain.   J. S. Lawrence 38-F104 1978 $185

FITZGERALD, FRANCIS SCOTT KEY   Tender is the Night.   New York, 1934. 8vo., cloth, 1st ed., 1st prtg.   J. S. Lawrence 38-F108 1978 $150

FITZGERALD, FRANCIS SCOTT KEY   Tender is the Night.   New York, 1934. 8vo., gilt-stamped cloth, d.j., 1st ed.   J. S. Lawrence 38-F106 1978 $400

FITZGERALD, FRANCIS SCOTT KEY   This Side of Paradise.   New York, 1920. 8vo., orig. cloth, d.j., 1st ed., 1st prtg., signed by author, fine copy.   J. S. Lawrence 38-F112 1978 $1,500

FITZGERALD, FRANCIS SCOTT KEY   This Side of Paradise.   New York, 1920. 8vo., green cloth, third printing, ownership inscription, good only, 1st ed., collector's cond.   Desmarais 1-165 1978 $60

FITZGERALD, FRANCIS SCOTT KEY   This Side of Paradise.   1921.   Good, covers stained, first English ed.   Bell Book 16-340 1978 £25

FITZGERALD, FRANCIS SCOTT KEY   This Side of Paradise.   New York, 1920. 8vo., cloth, 1st ed., photo of author & signed by him.   J. S. Lawrence 38-F113 1978 $650

FITZGERALD, FRANCIS SCOTT KEY   This Side of Paradise.   (New York, 1948). 12mo., pic. wrs., 1st Dell prtg., fine copy.   J. S. Lawrence 38-F114 1978 $15

FITZGERALD, FRANCIS SCOTT KEY   The Vegetable: or, From President to Postman.   New York, 1923.   8vo., gilt-stamped cloth, d.j., 1st ed., 1st prtg., very fine copy.   J. S. Lawrence 38-F119 1978 $450

FITZGERALD, HUGH   Governors I Have Known.   Austin, 1927.   Political illus. by John Knott.   Jenkins 116-447 1978 $20

FITZGERALD, PERCY   Bozland.   London, 1895.   8vo, original dark blue-green cloth, 1st ed., fine copy.   Ximenes 47-104 1978 $17.50

FITZGERALD, PERCY   The Kembles.   (1871).   Plts., 2 vols., half green calf rubbed, 8vo.   George's 635-1409 1978 £10.50

FITZGERALD, PERCY   The Life of George the Fourth, including His Letters & Opinions with a View of the Men, Manners & Politics of His Reign. New York, 1881.   Paper covers, damp stain, sound.   Greene 78-201 1978 $20

FITZGERALD, PERCY H.   Autobiography of A Small Boy.   Boston, 1869. 1st Amer. ed., very good.   Victoria 34-296 1978 $20

FITZGERALD, ROBERT   Aqua Salsa Dulcorata...   London, 1683.   4to., 1/2 calf, 1st ed. in Latin, very rare.   Salloch 345-66 1978 $600

FITZGERALD, THOMAS   Poems on Several Occasions.   1736.   Half red morocco, rubbed, marbled bds., black label, 2nd. ed.   Jarndyce 16-83 1978 £43

FITZGERALD, THOMAS   Poems on Several Occasions.   1736.   2nd. ed., orig. red morocco, gilt borders, a.e.g.   Jarndyce 16-84 1978 £50

FITZ-GERALD, S. J. ADAIR   Dickens and the Drama.   London, 1910. 1st ed., orig. blind stamped red cloth, gilt stamped spine, illus., portraits, some foxing, else very good.   Houle 10-88 1978 $20

FITZGERALD, ZELDA   Save Me the Waltz.   New York, 1932.   8vo., cloth, d.j., 1st ed., fine copy.   J. S. Lawrence 38-F134 1978 $300

FITZHERBERT, ANTHONY   La Novel Natura Breuium de Judge Tresreuerend Monsieur Anthony Fitzherbert Dernierement Reuieu & Corrigee Per Laucteur... London, 1616.   Partly black letter, 8vo, contemp. mottled calf, gilt, new label, joints weak.   Traylen 88-466 1978 £140

FITZHERBERT, WILLIAM   Maxims and Reflections.   1785.   New ed., sm. 8vo., contemp. tree calf, fine.   P. M. Hill 142-108 1978 £18

FITZOSBORNE, THOMAS   The Letters of Sir Thomas Fitzosborne on Several Subjects.   1776.   Contemp. calf, rebacked, contrasting label, 8vo.   Howes 194-388 1978 £15

FITZPATRICK, C. J.   Fifty Years of Suretyship and Insurance: U. S. Fidelity and Guarantee Co.   Baltimore, 1946.   Index.   Austin 80-597 1978 $10

FITZPATRICK, J. P.   The Transvaal From Within.   London, 1899. 5th. impression, little dusty & age-marked, orig. cloth, 8vo.   K Books 239-164 1978 £6

FITZPATRICK, PATRICK VINCENT   Thaumaturgus.   London, 1828.   8vo, modern half calf, 1st ed., presentation copy, inscribed by author.   Ximenes 47-105 1978 $35

FITZPATRICK, PERCY   Jock of the Bushveld.   London, 1908.   5th. impression, plts., text-illus., gilt cloth, covers little dull, 8vo.   K Books 239-165 1978 £5

FITZPATRICK, W.J.   Correspondence of Daniel O'Connell.   1888. 2 vols., ex lib., very good, octavo bound in cloth, reprint.   Hyland 128-218 1978 £12

FITZPATRICK, WILLIAM J.   The Life of Charles Lever.   n.d.   New ed., frontis portrait, orig. cloth.   Jarndyce 16-814 1978 £10

FITZPATRICK, WILLIAM J.   The Life, Times and Correspondence of the Right Rev. Dr. Doyle, Bishop of Kildare and Leighlin.   Dublin, 1861.   1st. ed., 2 vols., 8vo, orig. cloth, gilt, portrait, plts., nice copy.   Fenning 32-116 1978 £12.50

FITZSIMONS, F. W.   Snakes.   London, (1932).   44 illus., 8vo, orig. cloth, covers dull, tear in upper joint.   K Books 239-166 1978 £5

THE FIVE Cotton States and New York.   N.P., 1861.   8vo., unbound, 1st ed. Morrill 241-86 1978 $17.50

FIVE Points in the Record of North Carolina in the Great War of 1861-65. Goldsboro, 1904.   New cloth.   Bell Wiley's copy.   Broadfoot 46-92 1978 $20

FLACCUS, LOUIS W.   The Spirit and Substance of Art.   New York, 1931.   Rev'd. and enlarged ed., illus.   Biblo BL781-587 1978 $10

FLAGG, CHARLES A.   A Guide to Massachusetts Local History.   Salem, (1907).   1st ed., fold. maps, orig. cloth, very good.   MacManus 239-288 1978 $40

FLAMANT, PIERRE RENE   Memoire Pratique sur le Forceps.   Strasbourg, 1816. Copperplt., 8vo., modern bds., 1st ed., very good copy, inscr'd by author to Jean Sedillot.   Offenbacher 30-39 1978 $115

FLAMSTEED, JOHN   Historiae Coelestis Libri Duo Quorum Prior Exhibet Catalogum Stellarum Fixarum.... London, 1712. Folio, portrait, plts., some slight dampstaining towards end, slightly later sheep backed bds., joints split, worn, uncut, preserved in buckram box, heavily annotated by Edmond Halley, pp 269/70 mended with slight loss of text.   Quaritch 977-181 1978 $18,000

FLANAGAN, JOHN T.   America is West. 1945. Austin 82-380 1978 $17.50

FLANDERS, HELEN H.   Vermont Folk-songs and Ballads.   Brattleboro, (1931). Biblo 248-74 1978 $10

FLANDERS, HENRY   The Lives and Times of the Chief Justices of the Supreme Court of the United States. Philadelphia, 1875. 2 vols., orig. cloth, some wear. MacManus 239-142 1978 $27.50

FLANIGAN, J. H.   Mormonism Triumphant! Liverpool, 1849. Cloth, 1st ed. Ginsberg 14-651 1978 $85

FLATAU, EDWARD   Neurologische Schemata fur die arztliche Praxis. Berlin, 1915. Rittenhouse 49-257 1976 $15

FLATMAN, THOMAS   Poems and Songs. 1682. 8vo, contemp. calf, rebacked. Hannas 54-116 1978 £85

FLAUBERT, GUSTAVE   Un Coeur Simple. Eragny Press, 1901. 12mo., woodcut frontis. & border, bds., linen back, little light foxing, ltd. to 226 copies. Quaritch 979-134 1978 $190

FLAUBERT, GUSTAVE   Un Coeur simple. Eragny Press, 1901. Ltd. to 226 copies, woodcut frontis., sm. 8vo., orig. linen-backed bds., edges uncut. George's 635-886 1978 £65

FLAUBERT, GUSTAVE   La Legende de Saint Julien L'Hospitalier. Eragny Press, 1900. Ltd. to 226 copies, inscribed pres. copy from Lucien and Esther Pissarro, woodcut frontis., sm. 8vo., orig. linen-backed bds., edges uncut and partly unopened. George's 635-887 1978 £110

FLAUBERT, GUSTAVE   Madame Bovary. Paris, 1857. 8 vo., contemp. marbled paper bds., black mor. spine, 1st ed., pres. copy from author, with autograph inscription. Quaritch Summer,1978-17 1978 $11,500

FLAUBERT, GUSTAVE   Salambo. Waltham St. Lawrence: The Golden Cockerel Press, (1931). 4to., wood engravings by Robert Gibbings, orig. cloth-backed printed bds., 1 of 500 copies, t.e.g., corners a bit rubbed, but nice. Mac-Manus 238-795 1978 $45

FLAUBERT, GUSTAVE   La Tentation de Saint Antoine. Paris, 1938. Folio in orig. pict. wr., in sheets, uncut, deluxe ed. issued in 220 copies, 1 of 185 numbered copies on Arches paper, illus. by Odilon Redon on mounted China paper, very fine copy. Goldschmidt 110-56 1978 $5,000

FLAUBERT, GUSTAVE   Complete Works. New York and London, 1904. Coloured titles and frontis., plts., 10 vols., demy 8vo., half mor., best English ed. Howes 194-859 1978 £70

FLAUBERT, GUSTAVE   Complete Works. 1926. Coloured frontis., plts., 10 vols., orig. silk cloth gilt, gilt tops, ltd. to 500 sets. Howes 194-860 1978 £35

FLAVEL, EDMUND M.   Navigation Spiritualized. 1796. First ed., sm. 8vo., contemp. bds., new calf back. F. Edwards 1013-73 1978 £95

FLAVEL, JOHN   A Token for Mourners. Salem, 1802. 12mo., orig. bds., calf back. Morrill 241-139 1978 $7.50

FLAVEL, JOHN   A Token for Mourners. Ver., 1813. 12mo, marbled paper over oak, covers worn, text very good. Victoria 34-297 1978 $15

FLAXMAN, JOHN   Anatomical Studies of the Bones and Muscles, for the Use of Artists. London, 1833. Folio, portrait, plts., portrait and several plts. foxed, orig. cloth, repaired. Quaritch 977-22 1978 $375

FLAXMAN, JOHN   Compositions from the Divine Poem of Dante Alighieri containing Hell, Purgatory and Paradise. 1807. Plts., foxed, sm. oblong folio, half calf, covers detached, lacks spine. George's 635-143 1978 £20

FLAXMAN, JOHN   Compositions from the Tragedies of Aeschylus. 1831. Oblong 4to., engr. plts., half mor., base of spine chipped, plts. rehinged & foxed throughout. Allen 234-A 1978 $32.50

FLAXMAN, JOHN   Illustrations of the Divine Poem of Dante. 1867. Plts., folio, loose in case due to gutta percha binding. George's 635-144 1978 £18

FLAXMAN, JOHN   Lectures on Sculpture. London, 1829. Frontispiece, lithographs, plts., 1st ed., 8 vo., 3/4 green calf over marbled bds., bookplates of Sir Henry Doulton, fine. Houle 10-111 1978 $195

FLAXMAN, JOHN   Lectures on Sculpture. 1892. Plts., cr. 8vo., full calf, gilt. George's 635-264 1978 £7.50

FLECHIER, VALENTIN ESPRIT   The Life of the Emperour Theodosius the Great. 1693. Cont. panelled calf, nice, sole ed. in English, 8vo. Howes 194-46 1978 £55

FLECKER, JAMES ELROY   Don Juan: A Play in Three Acts. London, 1925. 8vo, green cloth, gilt lettering on spine and cover, foxing, Fine in d.w., 1st ed., collector's cond. Desmarais 1-167 1978 $12.50

FLECKER, JAMES ELROY   Don Juan: A Play in Three Acts. London, 1925. Fine in chipped d.w. Desmarais B-247 1978 $12.50

FLECKER, JAMES ELROY   The Golden Journey to Samarkand. London, 1913. 8vo., blue cloth, 1st ed. skillfully repaired d.w., presentation inscription and A.L.s. from Edward Marsh to Edmund Gosse, collector's cond. Desmarais 1-168 1978 $200

FLECKER, JAMES ELROY   The Last Generation. 1908. 1st. ed., 12mo, red cloth, 2 bookplts. Eaton 45-184 1978 £15

FLECKER, JAMES ELROY   The Old Ships. London, (1915). 4to, pr. paper covers, uncut, covers worn and shipped, 1st ed., collector's cond. Desmarais 1-169 1978 $30

FLEETWOOD, WILLIAM   Chronicon Preciosum. 1707. First ed., contemp. panelled calf, corners worn, rebacked, rough paper label, 8vo. George's 635-324 1978 £37.50

FLEETWOOD, WILLIAM   A Compleat Collection of the Sermons, Tracts, and Pieces of All Kinds. 1737. Folio, contemp. calf, joints weak, first collected ed. Howes 194-267 1978 £35

FLEETWOOD, WILLIAM   A Compleat Collection of the Sermons, Tracts, and Pieces of All Kings. 1737. 1st. ed., folio, 19th century half calf, corners little rubbed, o/w good sound copy. Jarndyce 16-86 1978 £15.50

FLEETWOOD, WILLIAM   Four Sermons... 1712. 1st. ed., orig. panelled calf, red label, v.g. Jarndyce 16-85 1978 £12.50

FLEG, EDMOND   The Wall of Weeping. London, 1929. 8vo, original black cloth, 1st ed., one of 750 copies numbered and signed by author and translator, very nice copy, slightly torn and spotted dust jacket. Ximenes 47-343 1978 $12.50

FLEMING, ALEXANDER   Penicillin: Its Practical Application. London, 1946. First ed., cover marked slightly. Rittenhouse 49-258 1976 $35

FLEMING, C. E.   One-Night Camps vs. Established Bed-Grounds on Nevada Sheep Ranges. Carson City, 1918. Wrs., illus., 1st ed., fine copy from the Allred Collection, rare. Dykes 34-274 1978 $25

FLEMING, ETHEL   New York. New York, 1929. Illus., 4to., 1st ed., bind. spotted, front inner hinge weak. Biblo BL781-160 1978 $17.50

FLEMING, GEORGE THORNTON   History of Pittsburgh and Environs. New York, 1922. Cloth, half leather, good cond., 4 vols., ports., illus., 4to. Mac-Manus 239-1652 1978 $35

FLEMING, JOHN   Botanical Guide to the Wild Flowers in the West of Scotland. Glasgow, 1880. Cr. 8vo., orig. cloth. K Books 244-363 1978 £6

FLEMING, MAY AGNES   Maude Percy's Secret. New York, 1884. 1st ed., very good or better. Limestone 9-107 1978 $15

FLEMING, PETER   The Flying Visit. 1940. Drawings by David Low, very good, worn d.w., first English ed. Bell Book 17-594 1978 £7.50

FLEMING, SANFORD   Report and Documents in Reference to the Canadian Pacific Railway. Ottawa, 1880. Maps, plts. Hood 116-624 1978 $100

FLEMING, SANFORD   Report in Reference to the Canadian Pacific Railway. Ottawa, 1879. Orig. printed wrappers, fold. map. Wolfe 39-468a 1978 $60

FLEMING, THOMAS   Around the "Pan" With Uncle Hank. New York, (1901). Orig. binding, clean, illus. Hayman 71-208 1978 $10

FLEMING, W. S.   God In Our Public Schools. 1942. Austin 79-249 1978 $12.50

FLEMING, WALTER L.   Civil War and Reconstruction in Alabama. Cleveland, 1911. Rear board stained, Bell Wiley's copy. Broadfoot's 44-417 1978 $36.00

FLEMING, WALTER L.   The Constitution and the Ritual of the Knights of the White Camelia. Morgantown, 1904. Wrs., Bell Wiley's copy. Broadfoot's 44-146 1978 $15

FLEMING, WALTER L.   Jefferson Davis' Camel Experiment. Baton Rouge, 1909. Wrs., Bell Wiley's copy. Broadfoot's 44-145 1978 $7

FLEMING, WALTER L.   Jefferson Davis' First Marriage. N.P., n.d. c.1914. Wrs., Bell Wiley's copy. Broadfoot's 44-143 1978 $10

FLEMING, WALTER L.   Jefferson Davis, The Negroes and the Negro Problem. Baton Rouge, 1908. Wrs., Bell Wiley's copy. Broadfoot's 44-144 1978 $12

THE FLEMISH Stained Glass Windows. New York, (1925). Black & white plts., 8vo., orig. wrs., ex-lib. Morrill 239-551 1978 $7.50

FLEMMING, LEONARD   The Call of the Veld. London, 1903. 2nd. ed., 29 illus., orig. cloth, 8vo. K Books 239-168 1978 £6

FLENTJE, ERNST L.   Check List of Government Publications Relating to the Discovery of the Territory West of the Mississippi River, Arranged Chiefly from Poores "Index". Chicago, 1949. Marginal notes in pen, very good. Nestler Rare 78-63 1978 $85

FLETCHER, DANIEL   Reminiscences of California and the Civil War. Ayer, 1894. Frontis, original cloth, 1st ed. Ginsberg 14-350 1978 $40

FLETCHER, GILES   Christ's Victorie, and Triumph in Heaven, and Earth, Over, and After Death. Cambridge, 1610. First ed., first issue, sm. 4to., 2 parts in 1 vol., newly rebound in panelled mottled calf antique, fine, rare. Howes 194-47 1978 £325

FLETCHER, IFAN KYRLE   Ronald Firbank: a memoir. 1930. Portraits, very good, worn d.w., first English ed. Bell Book 16-338 1978 £18.50

FLETCHER, J.S.   When Charles the First Was King. London, 1892. 1st ed., 3 vols., cloth, marbled boards, spine edges worn, interiors good. Greene 78-41 1978 $75

FLETCHER, JOHN   Monsieur Thomas: a Comedy. London, 1639. Complete, fine, 4to., 19th Cent. calf, gilt dentelles, 1st ed. Argosy Special-39 1978 $400

FLETCHER, JOHN   Studies on Slavery... Natchez, 1852. Baldwins' 51-380 1978 $42.50

FLETCHER, JOHN GOULD   The Black Rock; poems. London, 1928. First ed., orig. binding, nice, d.w. Rota 211-112 1978 £7.50

FLETCHER, PHINEAS   Venus and Anchises... 1926. Plts., octavo, good. Upcroft 10-57 1978 £5

FLETCHER, THOMAS   Poems on Several Occasions, and Translations. 1692. Sm. 8vo., early panelled calf, scarce, sole ed. Howes 194-48 1978 £60

FLETCHER, W.   The Picturesque Primer. London, (1828). 1st ed., color plates, marbled boards, red-roan spine, minor spine defects, very scarce. Victoria 34-298 1978 $425

FLETCHER, WILLIAM YOUNGER   Bookbinding in France. London, 1894. Roy. 8vo., plts., illus., linen, mor. back, soiled and rubbed. Forster 130-6 1978 £10

FLEURIEU, C. P.C. DE   Decouvertes Des Francois en 1768 & 1769... Paris, 1790. 4to., calf, rebacked & repaired, folding plts. & charts. Edwards 1012-372 1978 £300

FLEXNER, ABRAHAM   Medical Education. A Comparative Study. New York, 1925. Library marks. Rittenhouse 49-259 1976 $10

FLEXNER, JAMES THOMAS   John Singleton Copley. Boston, 1948. Illus., 4to., pic. d.w., color fronts., plts., very good. Americanist 103-12 1978 $25

FLEXNER, SIMON   William Henry Welch and the Heroci Age of American Medicine. New York, 1941. Some fading on spine. Rittenhouse 49-260 1976 $12.50

FLIGHT, EDWARD G.   The True Legend of St. Dunstan & The Devil. 1871. Illus. by George Cruikshank, 3rd. ed., orig. brown cloth block in black & gilt, v.g. Jarndyce 16-443 1978 £9.50

FLINDERS, MATTHEW   A Voyage to Terra Australia;.... 1814. 2 vols., royal 4to., imperial folio atlas, plates, occasional spotting, contemp. diced-russia gilt, Atlas vol. in orig. drab paper boards, orig. printed paper label on upper cover, spire renewed, 1st ed. Quaritch 978-54 1978 $8,500

FLINT, THOMAS   Diary of Dr. Thomas Flint: California to Maine and Return, 1851-1855. Los Angeles, 1923. Illus., orig. pr. wr. bound in cardboard covers, 1st ed. Ginsberg 14-1096 1978 $35

FLINT, TIMOTHY   Francis Barrian: or, the Mexican Patriot. Philadelphia, 1834. 2 vols., original boards, linen backed paper labels, 2nd ed. Jenkins 116-1547 1978 $475

FLINT, TIMOTHY   Recollections of the Last Ten Years Passed in Occasional Residences and Journeyings in the Valley of the Mississippi,... Boston, 1826. Half Calf, 1st ed. Ginsberg 14-352 1978 $125

FLINT, WILLIAM RUSSELL   Judith. 1928. Ltd. ed., 4 coloured plts. by author, 4to., vellum, orig. d.w., pres. copy from author, inscription in pencil. Sawyer 299-120 1978 £35

FLINT, WILLIAM RUSSELL   Minxex Admonished or Beauty Reproved. 1955. Ltd. ed. of 550 copies, coloured frontis, coloured title illus., other illus., lg.8vo, orig. red cloth gilt, pres. copy from author. Sawyer 299-121 1978 £160

FLITNER, JOHANN   Nebvlo Nebvlonyn... Frankfurt, 1620. 8vo., Roman and Italic letter, plts., early vellum, lacking ties, first ed. Quaritch 978-55 1978 $450

FLOHERTY, JOHN J.   The Courage and the Glory. 1942. Illus. with photos. Austin 80-101 1978 $8.50

FLORENCE and Some Tuscan Cities. London, c.1905. Painted by Col. R. C. Goff. Biblo BL781-622 1978 $12

FLORENCE of Worcester, Chronicle, with the two Continuations. 1854. Cr. 8vo., orig. cloth, hinges sprung. George's 635-550 1978 £5.25

FLORENTIN, P.   Album de Dessins en Cheveux. Paris, n.d. (1863). Plts., two with gold coloring, lg. 4to., orig. stamped cloth. Schumann 511-20 1978 sFr 1,125

FLORENZ, KARL   Geschichte de japanischen litteratur. Leipzig, 1909. 2nd ed., cloth, (somewhat stained, worn, and foxed, hinges weak or splitting). Dawson's 449-115 1978 $7.50

FLORIAN, JEAN PIERRE CLARIS DE   Kedar et Amela. Paris, 1901. One of 350 copies, unnumbered, cloth, orig. silk wrs., fine. Bell Book 17-362 1978 £12.50

THE FLORICULTURAL Cabinet and Florists' Magazine. Vols. V and VI. London, 1837-8. 2 vols. in one, hand-coloured plts., occasional age-marking throughout, half green calf, 8vo. K Books 244-364 1978 £35

FLORIJN, J.   Gronbeginselen der Hoogere Meetkunde Bevatten- de de Voornaamste Eigenschappen der Kegelsneden en van Eenige Andere Kromme Lijnen op een zeer Gemaklijke en Nieuwe Wijze Beweezen, en tot Dienst var Eerstbeginnenden Opgesteld. Rotterdam, 1794. 8vo., full old calf, fldg. plts. Van der Peet H-64-332 1978 Dfl 110

FLORUS, LUCIUS ANNAEUS   Epitome Rerum Romanarum ex. 1822. 2 vols., new buckram, blind stamp on titles. Allen 234-1522 1978 $17.50

FLORUS, LUCIUS ANNAEUS   Rerum Romanarum Liber IV. 1715. 16mo., new buckram, rubber stamp on title. Allen 234-1521 1978 $8.50

FLORUS, LUCIUS ANNAEUS   The Roman Histories of ... Dewe, n.d. (1621?). lst. English ed., 12mo, engraved title, contemp. calf, spine worn & repaired, some light water-stains, 2nd. issue. Hannas 54-117 1978 £45

FLORUS Anglo-Bavaricus. Liege, 1685. Vellum, tips of spine defective. Allen 234-1238 1978 $17.50

FLORY, M. A.   A Book about Fans...Fan-Painting...Fan-Collec- ting. New York, 1895. Ltd. to 150 copies on hand-made paper. Biblo BL781- 591 1978 $95

FLOURENS, MARIE-JEAN-PIERRE   Memoires d'Anatomie et de Physiologie Comparees. Paris, 1844. Copperplts., all but one handcolored, folio, half vellum, orig. prtd. wrs. bound in, uncut, lst ed., fine. Offenbacher 30-41 1978 $160

FLOWER, DESMOND   A Thousand Years of French Books. N.P., 1948. Orig. pictorial wr., very good or better. Limestone 9-301 1978 $10

FLOWER, FRANK A.   Edwin McMasters Stanton, The Autocrat of Rebel- lion, Emancipation, and Reconstruction. Akron, 1905. Orig. binding, cl., sl. wear, scarce. Hayman 71-250 1978 $15

FLOWER, FRANK A.   Edwin McMasters Stanton. Akron, 1905. Illus., scarce. MacManus 239-818 1978 $17.50

FLOWER, GEORGE   History of the English Settlement in Edwards County Illinois, Founded in 1817 and 1818. Chicago, 1882. Nice untrimmed copy, newly rebound. MacManus 239-211 1978 $27.50

FLOWER, WILLIAM HENRY   An Introduction to the Osteology of the Mammal- ia. London, 1885. Third ed., text illus., full prize calf, backstrip chafed at head and base, 8vo. K Books 244-122 1978 £7

THE FLOWER Basket, A Fairy Tale. London, 1816. 12mo, lst ed., roan-backed boards rubbed, text very good. Victoria 34-300 1978 $50

FLOYD, FRED C.   History of the Fortieth (Mozart) Regiment New York Volunteers. Boston, 1909. 8vo., illus., ex-lib., nice, orig. cloth. Morrill 241-410 1978 $25

FLOYER, JOHN   The History of Cold Bathing. London, 1715. 4th ed., 8vo., contemp. calf, fr. cover loose, back hinge cracked. Morrill 239-86 1978 $40

FLUCKINGER, F. A.   Pharmaeographia, a History of the Principal Drugs of Vegetable Origin.... 1879. 8vo. George's 635-991 1978 £6.50

FLUKER, ANNE   Confed'ric Gol'. Macon, Ga., 1926. Bell Wiley's copy. Broadfoot 46-93 1978 $20

FLYCHE, ALBERT   Burma Past and Present... London, 1878. lst. ed., 2 vols., 8vo, engraved portraits, plts., illus., 10 coloured, coloured folding map, orig. green cloth, gilt, joints of vol. 2 repaired, lib. labels removed. Dieghton 5-75 1978 £38

FOCH, MARSHAL   The Principles of War. 1920. Maps, diagrams, 2nd ed., 8vo. George's 635-812 1978 £5.25

FOCILLON, H.   Peintures Romanes des Eglises de France. 1938. Photos, 4to., illus. Allen 234-1239 1978 $17.50

FOLEY, D.   Garden Flowers in Color. New York, 1943. 8vo, orig. cloth. Book Chest 17-523 1978 $9

FOLEY, D.   Vegetable Gardening in Color. New York, 1942. 8vo, orig. cloth. Book Chest 17-525 1978 $10

FOLEY, MARTHA   The Best American Short Stories of 1942. Austin 82-159 1978 $10

FOLEY, MARTHA   The Best American Short Stories of 1943. First ed., very good, frayed d.j. Austin 82-159a 1978 $15

FOLEY, MARTHA   The Best American Short Stories of 1943. Austin 82-160 1978 $8.50

FOLEY, MARTHA   The Best American Short Stories of 1944. Austin 82-161 1978 $10

FOLEY, MARTHA   The Best American Short Stories, 1944. Boston, 1944. lst ed., d.w., frayed. Biblo BL781-977 1978 $10

FOLEY, MARTHA   The Best American Short Stories for 1945. Austin 82-162 1978 $10

FOLEY, MARTHA   The Best American Short Stories of 1946. Austin 82-163 1978 $7.50

FOLEY, MARTHA   The Best American Short Stories of 1946. Austin 82-166 1978 $12.50

FOLEY, MARTHA   The Best American Short Stories for 1947. Austin 82-164 1978 $10

FOLEY, MARTHA   The Best American Short Stories of 1948. Austin 82-165 1978 $10

FOLEY, MARTHA   The Best American Short Stories of 1950. First ed, very good, frayed d.j., inscribed by Foley. Austin 82-167 1978 $27.50

FOLEY, MARTHA   The Best American Short Stories of 1950. Austin 82-168 1978 $12.50

FOLEY, P. K.   American Authors. 1795-1895... Boston, 1897. Orig. cloth, paper label, 1st ed., ltd. to 500 copies, bookplt., extremities worn, but good. MacManus 238-921 1978 $50

FOLIGNO, C.   Latin thought during the Middle Ages. Oxford, 1929. Plts., 8vo. Upcroft 12-145 1978 £5

FOLK, EDGAR ESTES   A Catalogue of the Library of Charles Lee Smith. Wake Forest, 1950. Pres. copy, cover faded. Broadfoot 50-69 1978 $25

FOLLETT, FREDERICK   History of the Press in Western New York From the Beginning to the Middle of the 19th Century. 1920. Reprint of 1847 ed., limited to 91 copies, lacks backstrip. Nestler Rare 78-116 1978 $45

FOLLIE, LOUIS GUILLAUME DE LA
Please turn to
LA FOLLIE, LOUIS GUILLAUME DE

FOLSOM, CHARLES FOLLEN   Studies of Criminal Responsibility and Limited
Responsibility. c. 1909. Rittenhouse 49-267 1976 $15

FOLSOM, GEORGE F.   Mexico in 1842...A Sketch of Its History, ...
New York, 1842. Folding map in color, orig. cloth, 1st ed. Jenkins 116-453
1978 $350

FOLSOM, JOSEPH F.   Bloomfield Old and New... Bloomfield, 1912.
Illus. MacManus 239-1266 1978 $25

FOLSON, GEORGE   History of Saco and Biddeford... Saco, 1830.
Frontis., contemp. 3/4 calf, marbled bds., 1 signature loose, otherwise good.
MacManus 239-992 1978 $75

FOLTZ, JONATHAN MESSERSMITH   The Endem c Influence of Evil Government
... New York, 1843. 8vo., litho. frontis. by author, orig. black blind-stamped
cloth, gilt lettering on spine, pres. copy inscr. by author, signature & bkplt. of
Louis H. Roddis, USN, very good copy, 1st ed. Zeitlin 245-79 1978 $150

FONER, PHILIP S.   Jack London American Rebel. New York, 1947.
Very good, dw. Bernard 5-168 1978 $15

FONSECA, CHRISTOPHER DE   A Discourse of Holy Love, By Which the Soul is
United Unto God. London, 1652. Engraved frontis, title printed in red & black,
sm. 8vo, old calf, later rebacking. Traylen 88-248 1978 £68

FONTAINE, F. G. DE   History of American Abolitionism. New York,
1861. 8vo., unbound. Morrill 241-141 1978 $15

FONTAINE, FRANCIS   Etowah: A Romance of the Confederacy.
Atlanta, Ga., 1887. Sm. snag on spine, Bell Wiley's Copy. Broadfoot's
44-147 1978 $20.00

FONTAINE, MLLE. G.   Collection de Cent Especes ou Varietes du Genre
Camellia... Bruzelles, A. Mertens, 1845. Hand-coloured litho. plts., 4to,
contemp. half red morocco, gilt, Belgium Royal Monogram on spine, few slight
marginal stains, fine. Traylen 88-649 1978 £9000

FONTANA, CARLO   Utilissimo trattato dell'acque correnti, ...
Rome, 1696. 1st ed., light browning, contemp. vellum. Gilhofer 75-41 1978
SFr 1,600

FONTANINI, GIUSTO   Biblioteca dell'Eloquenza Italiana di Monsignore
Giusto Fontanini Arcivescovo D'Ancira con le Annotazione del Signor Apostolo
Zeno Istorico e Poeta Cesareo Cittadino Veneziano. Venezia, 1753. 2 vols.,
4to., marbled soft bds., very good. King 7-170 1978 £70

FONTENELLE, BERNARD LE BOVIER DE   A Discovery of New Worlds. 1688.
Sm. cr. 8vo., browned, errata, 1f, old calf, spine defective. Eaton 45-187
1978 £50

FONTENELLE, BERNARD LE BOVIER DE   Entretiens sur la Pluralite des Mondes.
Paris, 1686. 12mo., frontis., cont. calf, richly gilt spine, rubbed, fine, first
ed. Norman 5-110 1978 $850

FONTENAY, GUY DE   Magnum Collectorium Historicum Ex Multifario
Diversorum Autorum Editione Conformatum... Paris, 1521. 8vo., 1/2 mor., rare.
Salloch 348-69 1978 $500

FONTENAY LE MARMION   Cartulaire de la Seigneurie de Fontenay Le Marmion, Provenant des Archives de Matignon. 1895. 4to., new buckram. Allen
234-1241 1978 $15

FONTENELLE, BERNARD LE BOVIER DE   Oeuvres. Paris, 1758. Nouvelle ed.,
10 vols., engr. plts., 8vo., contemp. marbled calf, backs gilt. Salloch 345-69
1978 $300

FOOT, JESSE   The Lives of Andrew Robinson Bowes and the
Countess of Strathmore. (1815). Engraved portrait, orig. bds., 8vo. George's
635-1232 1978 £7.50

FOOT, JOHN   An Appeal to the Public, touching the Death of
Mr. George Clarke.... London, 1769. 8vo., disbound, third ed. Gurney 75-
39 1978 £20

FOOTE, A. E.   The Naturalists' Agency Catalogue. Part First:
Minerals. Philadelphia, 1876. Orig. prtd. wrs., illus., 8vo., very good.
Americanist 103-60 1978 $22.50

FOOTE, ANDREW H.   Africa and the American Flag. New York, 1854.
Orig. binding. Wolfe 39-187 1978 $20

FOOTE, E. B.   Sammy Tubbes The Boy Doctor and "Sponsie",
The Troublesome Monkey. New York, 1874. 1st ed., illus. by H. L. Stephens,
very good. Victoria 34-301 1978 $30

FOOTE, HENRY STUART   Casket of Reminiscences. Washington, 1874.
Bell Wiley's copy. Broadfoot 46-94 1978 $20

FOOTE, HENRY STUART   Texas and The Texans: or, Advance of the Anglo-
Americans to the Southwest... Philadelphia, 1841. 2 vols., 1st ed., contemp.
half morocco. Jenkins 116-1548 1978 $350

FOOTE, HENRY STUART   Texas and the Texans;... Philadelphia, 1841.
2 vols., 1st ed. Nestler Rare 78-64 1978 $85

FOOTE, HENRY STUART   Texas and the Texans: or, Advance of the Anglo-
Americans to the Southwest. Philadelphia, 1841. 2 vols, original cloth, 1st ed.
Jenkins 116-454 1978 $325

FOOTE, SAMUEL   Dramatic Works. n.d. 4 vols., l. plt. general
title & divisional titles, half titles, new grey cloth with paper labels on spines.
Eaton 45-189 1978 £40

FOOTE, WILLIAM HENRY   Sketches of North Carolina Historical and Biographical. New York, 1846. Spine repaired with leather. Broadfoot 50-70b
1978 $40

FOOTE, WILLIAM HENRY   Sketches of North Carolina Historical and Biographical. New York, 1912. Broadfoot 50-70a 1978 $15

FOOTNER, HULBERT   The Doctor who Held Hands, a Madame Storey
Novel. Garden City, 1929. Cloth, 1st ed., nice, little worn d.j. Hayman 72-
185 1978 $7.50

FOOTNER, HULBERT   Maryland Main and the Eastern Shore. New
York, 1942. 1st ed., illus., uncut. MacManus 239-1834 1978 $15

FOOTNER, HULBERT   Salute to a Maryland House of 1650. New York,
1939. 1st. ed., illus. Baldwins' 51-283 1978 $10

FOPPEMA, Y.   Spijkerschrift. Amsterdam, 1946. 8vo., orig.
covers. Van der Peet H-64-373 1978 Dfl 40

FORAIN, JEAN LOUIS   Album...H. Simonis Empis...Paris. Paris,
c. 1896. Folio, lithographs, orig. dec. wr. bearing colour repeat of title design,
cloth case, one of 50 copies signed by artist, fine. Quaritch 978-56 1978 $450

FORAIN, JEAN-LOUIS   Nous, vous, eux! Paris, 1893. Large 4to, lithographs, half cark blue mor., t.e.g., other edges uncut, orig. decorated wr. bound
in, one of 50 copies on papier du Japon signed by artist. Quaritch 978-58 1978
$400

FORAIN, JEAN LOUIS   Les Temps Difficiles (Panama)... Paris, 1893.
Lg. 4to., half dark blue mor., t.e.g., others uncut, orig. dec. wr., lithographs,
in 2 states, one of ltd. number on papier de Chine. Quaritch 978-57 1978
$300

FORAKER, JOSEPH B.   Notes of a Busy Life. Cincinnati, 1916. 2 vols.,
cloth, 1st vol. 3rd ed., 2nd vol. 2nd ed., pres. inscription. Hayman 72-253
1978 $10

FORBES, ALLAN   Boston and Some Noted Emigres. Boston,
1938. Illus., paper. Austin 79-250 1978 $12.50

FORBES, ALLAN   France and New England. Boston, 1925-1929.
Illus., 3 vols., tall 8vo., orig. wrs. Morrill 241-142 1978 $12.50

FORBES, ALLAN   Towns of New England and Old England, Ireland, and Scotland. New York, 1921. Illus., 2 vols., 4to., nice. Morrill 239-334 1978 $10

FORBES, ARCHIBALD   My Experiences of the War Between France and Germany. 1871. 2 vols., thick 8vo., orig. cloth. F. Edwards 1013-296 1978 £12

FORBES, B. C.   Automotive Giants of America. 1926. Austin 80-601 1978 $8.50

FORBES, CHARLES   Iceland; Its Volcanoes, Geysers, and Glaciers. 1860. 8vo, engraved vignette title-pg., folding engraved map, engraved plts., engraved illus., half calf, gilt back. Deighton 5-122 1978 £28

FORBES, CHARLES S.   The Second Battle of Bennington. St. Albans, 1877. Illus., 12mo, 1st ed., fldg. map. Morrill 239-635 1978 $9

FORBES, DUNCAN   A Letter to a Bishop. 1732. 8vo., unbound, first ed., scarce. P. M. Hill 142-109 1978 £21

FORBES, ESTHER   America's Paul Revere. Boston, 1946. Quarto, color plates by Ward, very fine copy, ragged d.j. Victoria 34-839 1978 $30

FORBES, ESTHER   Paul Revere...and the World He Lived In. Boston, 1942. 1st ed., illus. Biblo 251-98 1978 $12.50

FORBES, FRANCIS   The Improvement of Waste Lands. 1778. First ed., contemp. calf, 8vo. Howes 194-124 1978 £45

FORBES, FREDERICK E.   Five Years in China; From 1842 to 1847. 1848. Coloured frontis, illus., 8vo, contemp. half calf, nice copy. Fenning 32-117 1978 £42.50

FORBES, HARRIETTE M.   Gravestones of Early New England and the Men Who Made Them, 1653-1800. Boston, 1927. Sm. 4to., illus., ltd. ed., boxed. Biblo 247-103 1978 $35

FORBES, HARRIETTE M.   Gravestones of Early New England and the Men Who Made Them. N.P., 1927. Limited 780 copies, binding worn. Nestler Rare 78-11 1978 $25

FORBES, JAMES   L'Eglise catholique en ecosse a la fin du XVIe siecle, Martyre de Jean Oglvie. 1885. Portrait, half calf, 8vo. George's 635-1106 1978 £5.50

FORBES, JAMES   Oriental Memoirs... 1813. Portrait, plts., 2 in colour, 4 vols., 4to, contemp. diced calf gilt, rebacked, some foxing & offsetting. Edwards 1012-18 1978 £750

FORBES, JAMES   Recent Disturbances and Military Executions in Ceylon. 1850. 8vo, calf, joint repaired, coloured illus., pen & ink sketches. Edwards 1012-127 1978 £75

FORBES, MANSFIELD D.   Clare College 1326-1926. Cambridge, 1928 & 1930. 2 vols., 4to, orig. buckram backed bds., plts., illus., good. Sexton 7-102 1978 £45

FORBES, PATRICK   6th Guards Tank Brigade, The Story of Guardsmen in Churchill Tanks. (1946). Roy. 8vo, orig. cloth, coloured frontis, photos, maps, pres. copy to Winston Churchill. Sawyer 298-76 1978 £135

FORBES, ROSITA   From Red Sea to Blue Nile. 1925. 1st. ed., 61 illus., map, 8vo, orig. cloth, occasional spots, o/w good copy, inscribed by author. Sawyer 299-123 1978 £18

FORBES, WILLIAM ALEXANDER   The Collected Scientific Papers of the late William Alexander Forbes.... London, 1885. 1st ed., octavo, frontispiece portrait, plates, many hand-colored, numerous illus., 3/4 grained calf over pebbled cloth, gilt rules. Bennett 20-74 1978 $125

FORBES-LINDSAY, C. H.   America's Insular Possessions. Philadelphia, 1906. 2 vols., illus., decor. cloth, backstrips dull. Dawson's 127-256 1978 $20

FORBES-ROBERTSON, DIANA   War Letters from Britain. 1941. Austin 80-102 1978 $7.50

FORBIN, COUNT DE   Voyage a Siam. Paris, 1853. Cloth, ex-library copy, somewhat soiled, waterstained, 8vo. Van der Peet 127-94 1978 Dfl 40

FORBIN, COUNT DE   Voyage Dans Le Levant, 1817-18. Paris, 1819. Folding plan, modern half calf, 8vo. Edwards 1012-47 1978 £30

FORBUSH, EDWARD HOWE   Birds of Massachusetts and Other New England States. (Boston), 1925, 1927 & 1929. 1st ed., 4to., 3 vols., color plts. from drwgs. by Louis Agassiz, illus., maps, worn with weak hinges, orig. green cloth, gilt lettering on bds. & spines. Current 24-254 1978 $235

FORBUSH, EDWARD HOWE   Useful Birds and Their Protection. 1907. Large 8vo, orig. cloth, colored front., plts. Book Chest 17-158 1978 $35

FORCE, M. F.   From Fort Henry to Corinth. New York, 1881. Bell Wiley's copy. Broadfoot 46-95 1978 $10

FORCE, PETER   The National Calendar, and Annals of the United States; for 1823. Washington City, 1823. 12mo, rebound, illus. MacManus 239-144 1978 $20

THE FORCE of Example;.... London, 1797. 12mo, contemporary sheep, 1st ed., foxed, engraved frontispiece. Ximenes 47-100 1978 $125

FORCELLIN, E.   Totius Latinitatis Lexicon, in Hac Editione Post Tertiam Auctam et Emendatam a J. Furlanetto, Cura V. de-Vit. 1858-75. 4to., 6 vols., new buckram. Allen 234-G 1978 $150

FORD, ANDREW E.   History of the Origin of the Town of Clinton, Mass. Clinton, 1896. Illus., fine, orig. cloth. MacManus 239-1022 1978 $35

FORD, CHARLES H.   A Night with Jupiter & Other Fantastic Stories. New York, 1945. Signed with inscription by bookman-author, Tony Buttitta; illus., very good. Bernard 5-100 1978 $25

FORD, FORD MADOX   Ancient Lights and Certain New Reflections. 1911. Plts., t.e.g., good, scarce, first English ed. Bell Book 17-363 1978 £45

FORD, FORD MADOX   The Fifth Queen Crowned. London, 1908. First ed., orig. binding, spine faded, nice, scarce. Rota 211-113 1978 £25

FORD, FORD MADOX   The Fifth Queen and the Fifth Queen Crowned. London, (1953). 2 vols., 1st pub. in 1906, orig. cloth bind. for 1st ed. is worn and soiled, some dampstaining affecting the 1st and last pgs. MacManus 238-653 1978 $250

FORD, FORD MADOX   Great Trade Route. 1937. Coloured frontis., very good, first English ed. Bell Book 16-348 1978 £15

FORD, FORD MADOX   Great Trade Route. New York, 1937. First U.S. ed., coloured frontis., drawings, fine, worn d.w. Bell Book 17-364 1978 £35

FORD, FORD MADOX   Great Trade Route. London, (1937). 1st ed., bind. slightly rubbed. Biblo BL781-978 1978 £16.50

FORD, FORD MADOX   Joseph Conrad: A Personal Remembrance. 1924. First ed., portrait, cr. 8vo., orig. cloth. Howes 194-756 1978 £6

FORD, FORD MADOX   Ladies Whose Bright Eyes: A romance. 1911. Covers little soiled, good, first English ed. Bell Book 16-350 1978 £25

FORD, FORD MADOX   Last Post. 1928. Very good, first English ed. Bell Book 17-365 1978 £17.50

FORD, FORD MADOX   A Little Less Than Gods. New York, 1928. First U.S. ed., spine faded, else very good. Bell Book 17-366 1978 £15

FORD, FORD MADOX   A Man Could Stand Up. A Novel. London, (1926). Orig. cloth, d.j., 1st ed., fine. MacManus 238-651 1978 $55

FORD, FORD MADOX   A Man Could Stand Up. London, 1926. Orig. cloth, 1st ed., very fine. MacManus 238-652 1978 $50

FORD, FORD MADOX   A Mirror to France. 1926. Coloured frontis., very good, first English ed. Bell Book 16-351 1978 £10

FORD, FORD MADOX   A Mirror to France. 1926. Coloured frontis., near fine, worn d.w., first English ed. Bell Book 17-367 1978 £35

FORD, FORD MADOX   New York is not America. London, 1927. Fine, first ed., orig. binding. Rota 211-114 1978 £15

FORD, FORD MADOX   No More Parades. London, (1925). Orig. cloth, 1st ed., very fine. MacManus 238-650 1978 $50

FORD, FORD MADOX   No More Parades. 1925. Good, first English ed. Bell Book 16-352 1978 £15

FORD, FORD MADDOX   On Heaven and other poems written on active service. London, 1918. Spine severely faded, very good, first ed., orig. binding. Rota 212-21 1978 £35

FORD, FORD MADOX   Some Do Not. 1924. Covers faded, good, first English ed. Bell Book 16-353 1978 £15

FORD, FORD MADOX   The Young Lovell: a romance. 1913. Good, very scarce, first English ed. Bell Book 17-368 1978 £47.50

FORD, HARVEY S.   What the Citizen Should Know About the Army. 1942. Rev. ed., illus. Austin 80-103 1978 $8.50

FORD, HENRY   The International Jew. n.d. Abridged from orig., hardcover ed. Austin 79-251 1978 $12.50

FORD, HENRY   Moving Forward. 1930. 1st ed. Austin 80-602 1978 $10

FORD, HENRY   My Life and Work. Garden City, 1927. Austin 80-603 1978 $7.50

FORD, HENRY   Henry Ford's Own Story. 1917. Austin 80-604 1978 $12.50

FORD, JAMES L.   Hypnotic Tales and Other Tales. New York, 1891. Cloth. Hayman 73-181 1978 $15

FORD, JAMES L.   The Literary Shop and Other Tales. New York, 1894. Cloth. Hayman 73-182 1978 $10

FORD, JOHN   Fame's Memorial. Kent, Lee Priory Press, 1819. 8vo., contemp. half calf, rebacked, some foxing, neat library stamp. Quaritch 979-146 1978 $50

FORD, JOHN S.   Origin and Fall of the Alamo. San Antonio, 1895. Orig. pictorial wr. Jenkins 116-456 1978 $135

FORD, PAUL LEICESTER   Bibliography of. A List of Books Written By, or Relating to Benjamin Franklin. Brooklyn, 1889. ltd. to 500 copies, rebound. MacManus 239-157 1978 $30

FORD, PAUL LEICESTER   Bibliotheca Hamiltoniana. New York, 1886. 1st ed., ltd. to 500 numbered copies, cloth, nice copy. MacManus 239-190 1978 $35

FORD, PAUL LEICESTER   Janice Meredith, A Story of the American Revolution. New York, 1899. Orig. binding, clean, 1st. ed. Hayman 71-251 1978 $7.50

FORD, PAUL LEICESTER   The Journals of Hugh Gaine: Printer. New York, 1902. 1st ed., 2 vols., illus., tall 8vo., 1 of 380 copies, pres. card tipped in. Argosy Special-42 1978 $125

FORD, PAUL LEICESTER   A List of Books Written By, or Relating to Benjamin Franklin. Brooklyn, 1889. 8vo., mod. buckram, 1st ed., ltd. to 500 copies. MacManus 238-924 1978 $30

FORD, PAUL LEICESTER   The Many Sided Franklin. New York, 1899. 1st ed., illus., uncut. MacManus 239-163 1978 $12.50

FORD, PAUL LEICESTER   The New England Primer. New York, 1899. 1st ed., illus., fine copy, orig. cloth-backed bds. MacManus 239-145 1978 $30

FORD, PAUL LEICESTER   The Story of an Untold Love. Boston, 1897. Cloth, in red binding with quills in fr. cover ornament stamped in dull opaque violet, second prtg. Hayman 73-133 1978 $7.50

FORD, PAUL LEICESTER   Wanted – a Chaperon. New York, 1902. Cloth, little faded, slight wear, frontis., 1st ed. Hayman 72-254 1978 $7.50

FORD, TIREY L.   Dawn and the Dons. San Francisco, 1926. Cloth, pic. bds., 1st ed., some corner wear, else very good. Dykes 35-45 1978 $7.50

FORD, WILLIAM   A Description of Scenery in the Lake District. Carlisle, 1840. Second ed., coloured maps, vignette views, 12mo., recased in orig. cloth, pict. engrav. paper label on upper cover. K Books 244-123 1978 £15

FORD, WORTHINGTON CHAUNCEY   A Cycle of Adams Letters 1861-1865. 1920. 2 vols. Austin 82-19 1978 $27.50

FORDHAM, E. W.   Songs Of The Specials. London, 1916. 1st ed., orig. pictorial wr., illus., fragile, worn at edges, very good or better. Limestone 9-109 1978 $15

FORDHAM, ELIAS PYM   Personal Narrative of Travels in Virginia, Maryland, Pennsylvania, Ohio, Indiana, Kentucky. Cleveland, 1906. Cloth, 1st prtg. Hayman 73-216 1978 $25

FORDYCE, A. D.   Memorials of the Late Hugh Mair, D.D. Toronto, 1879. Hood's 115-930 1978 $10

FORDYCE, ALEXANDER DINGWALL   Family Record of the Name of Dingwall Fordyce. Fergus, 1885. Orig. photo, modern buckram, long autograph pres. inscription signed by author. Wolfe 39-188 1978 $100

FOREIGN Conspiracy Against the Liberties of the United States. New York, 1835. 12mo., old marbled cloth, corrected with notes by author. Morrill 241-376 1978 $12.50

FOREMAN, CAROLYN THOMAS   The Cross Timbers. Muskogee, 1947. 1st ed., scarce. Jenkins 116-457 1978 $45

FOREMAN, CAROLYN THOMAS   The Cross Timbers. N.P., 1947. Folding map, 1st ed., signed by author. Jenkins 116-1549 1978 $50

FOREMAN, CAROLYN THOMAS   Oklahoma Imprints. 1835-1907. A History of Printing in Oklahoma Before Statehood. Norman, 1936. 8vo., orig. cloth, 1st ed. MacManus 238-1016 1978 $25

FOREMAN, GRANT   The Adventures of James Collier, First Collector of the Port of San Francisco. Chicago, 1937. Original cloth, 1st ed., one of 250 copies. Ginsberg 14-248 1978 $40

FOREMAN, GRANT   A Pathfinder in the Southwest... Norman, 1941. Cloth, fold. map, illus., fine. Dykes 35-220 1978 $22.50

FOREMAN, GRANT   Pioneer Days in the Early Southwest. Cleveland, 1926. 1st ed., autographed. Jenkins 116-459 1978 $65

FOREMAN, JOHN   The Philippine Islands, a Political, Geographical, Ethnographical, Social & Commercial History...Embracing the Whole Period of Spanish Rule. New York, 1899. 2nd ed., maps, illus., lg. thick 8vo., orig. pic. cloth, bkplt., very good. Americanist 103-71 1978 $20

FORESTER, C. S.   Lord Hornblower. London, 1946. Fine, first ed., orig. binding. Rota 211-117 1978 £5

FORESTER, C. S.   Napoleon and his Court. 1924. Plts., near fine, very scarce, first English ed. Bell Book 17-369 1978 £45

FORESTER, E. M.   Sinclair Lewis Interprets America. (Cambridge, 1932). Stapled, self-wrs., 1st ed., 1 of 100, fine copy. Bradley 49-123 1978 $85

FORESTER, THOMAS   Norway and Its Scenery. London, 1853. 1st. ed., 8vo, mezzotint plts., tree calf, gilt borders, panelled back, morocco label, end-papers & edges, inner hinges strengthened. Deighton 5-123 1978 £58

FORESTI, ANTONIO   La Strada al Santuario mostrata a' Cherici, che aspirano al Sacerdozio. Perugia, 1766. Cr. 8vo., contemp. vellum. Howes 194-548 1978 £15

FORESTI DA BERGAMO, JACOBO FILIPPO   Supplementum Chronicarum. Venice, 1492-93. Folio, complete, frontis., wormed, half calf spine over old vellum. Bennett 20-24 1978 $1,750

FORESTI DA BERGAMO, JACOBO FILIPPO   Supplementum Chronicorum.... Paris, 1535. Woodcut portraits in text, folio, 19th cent. buff calf over thick bds., rebacked, orig. label remounted, fine. Howes 194-549 1978 £250

FORGERON, P.   Als ik Kan. Burxelles, 1941. 4to., slipcase, ltd. ed. of 300 numbered copies on "Simili-Japon", orig. covers, text in French. Van der Peet H-64-427 1978 Dfl 125

FORGES and Furnaces in the Province of Penna. Philadelphia, 1914. Uncut, illus. MacManus 239-1459 1978 $50

FORLONG, JAMES GEORGE ROCHE   Rivers of Life. 1882. Maps, illus., stained, 2 vols. and slipcase of maps, 4to., half mor. George's 635-1426 1978 £80

FORMAN, H. BUXTON   The Books of William Morris. Pictorial illus., ltd. to 500 copies. Traylen 88-492 1978 £10

FORMAN, HENRY CHANDLEE   Jamestown and St. Mary's, Buried Cities of Romance. Baltimore, 1938. Photos, sketches, maps by author, 8vo., binding lightly stained, 1st ed. Morrill 239-638 1978 $15

FORMBY, H.   Ancient Rome and its Connection with the Christian Religion. 1880. Plts., cuts in text, roy. 4to. George's 635-1173 1978 £12.50

FORMILLI, C. T. G.   The Stones of Italy. London, 1927. Thick 8vo, orig. dec. cloth, good. Sexton 7-8C 1978 £8.50

FORMULAIRE de Prieres a L'Usage des Pensionnaires des Religieuses Ursulines. Quebec, 1799. Nouvelle ed., old bds. crudely covered in modern cloth, pages 315-18 missing. Wolfe 39-490 1978 $350

FORNEY, M. N.   The Car-builder's Dictionary. New York, 1879. Oblong 8vo., figures, decor. cloth, a little worn. Quaritch 977-219 1978 $125

FORREST, EARLE R.   Lone War Trail of Apache Kid. Pasadena, (1947). Illus. by C.M. Russell, 1st ed., ltd. to 250 copies, signed by authors, illus., fine., d.j. MacManus 239-1163 1978 $40

FORREST, GEORGE   The Life of Lord Roberts. London, 1914. 8 plts., roy. 8vo, gilt cloth, bright copy. K Books 239-169 1978 £7

FORRESTER, MRS.   June. 1883. 1st. ed., 3 vols., half titles, orig. dull blue cloth, blocked in gilt, very slight rubbing, bright blue endpapers, v.g. Jarndyce 16-666 1978 £48

FORRESTER, MRS.   My Lord and My Lady. Philadelphia, 1882. 1st Amer. ed., orig. cloth, very good. Greene 78-202 1978 $15

FORRESTER, IZOLA   This One Mad Act. The Unknown Story of John Wilkes Booth and His Family. Boston, 1937. 1st ed., illus. MacManus 239-723 1978 $17.50

FORSDIKE, SIDNEY   The Effects of Radium Upon Living Tissues with Special Reference to Its Use in the Treatment of Malignant Disease. New York, 1923. 8vo., plts., orig. blue cloth, gilt lettering, ex-lib., very good copy. Zeitlin 245-80 1978 $35

FORSEY, E. A.   Unemployment In the Machine Age: Its Causes. Toronto, 1936. Hood's 115-297 1978 $12.50

FORSTER, CHARLES FFRENCH BLAKE   The Irish Chieftan; or, A Struggle for the Crown... Dublin, 1872. 1st. ed., roy. 8vo, orig. green cloth, gilt, little foxing, nice copy. Penning 32-118 1978 £28.50

FORSTER, EDWARD JACOB   A Manual for Medical Officers of the Militia of the United States. New York, 1877. Sm. 8vo., 1st ed., pres. from author. Morrill 239-87 1978 $25

FORSTER, EDWARD MORGAN   Abinger Harvest. 1936. Very good, first English ed. Bell Book 16-356 1978 £16.50

FORSTER, EDWARD MORGAN   Alexandria; a history and a guide. Alexandria, 1922. Nice, scarce, first ed., orig. binding. Rota 212-22 1978 £50

FORSTER, EDWARD MORGAN   Alexandria: A History and a Guide. Alexandria, 1938. Maps, plts., orig. printed bds., spine faded, 8vo., second ed. Howes 194-861 1978 £20

FORSTER, EDWARD MORGAN   Aspects of the Novel. Good, first English ed. Bell Book 16-357 1978 £24

FORSTER, EDWARD MORGAN   The Celestial Omnibus and Other Stories. London, 1911. Orig. cloth, 1st ed., 1st impression, very good. MacManus 238-654 1978 £50

FORSTER, EDWARD MORGAN   The Eternal Moment. London, 1928. Orig. cloth, 1st ed., signature, front cover a bit spotted, but very good. MacManus 238-656 1978 £30

FORSTER, EDWARD MORGAN   The Eternal Moment, and other stories. 1928. Cloth gilt, very good, first English ed. Bell Book 17-371 1978 £18.50

FORSTER, EDWARD MORGAN   A Letter to Madan Blanchard. Hogarth Press, 1931. Very good, wraps, first English ed. Bell Book 17-372 1978 £7.50

FORSTER, EDWARD MORGAN   The Longest Journey. 1907. Good, first English ed. Bell Book 16-358 1978 £45

FORSTER, EDWARD MORGAN   The Longest Journey. New York, 1922. First U.S. ed., very good. Bell Book 17-373 1978 £15

FORSTER, EDWARD MORGAN   The New Disorder. New York, 1949. Frontispiece portrait specially drawn by Paul Cadmus, one of 1,200 copies, wrappers, inscribed by author, first ed. Rota 212-23 1978 £75

FORSTER, EDWARD MORGAN   Nordic Twilight. 1940. First ed., cr. 8vo., orig. wrappers. Howes 194-863 1978 £5

FORSTER, EDWARD MORGAN   A Passage to India. London, 1924. Orig. cloth, 1st ed., front cover slightly faded and worn. MacManus 238-655 1978 $85

FORSTER, EDWARD MORGAN   Pharos & Pharillon. Hogarth Press, 1923. Cloth-backed bds., good, first English ed. Bell Book 16-359 1978 £32.50

FORSTER, EDWARD MORGAN   Pharos and Pharillon. Hogarth Press, 1923. Second ed., orig. blue wraps, covers somewhat soiled & creased, good, 1000 copies printed. Bell Book 17-374 1978 £12.50

FORSTER, EDWARD MORGAN   A Room with a View. 1908. Good, first English ed. Bell Book 16-360 1978 £37.50

FORSTER, EDWARD MORGAN   The Story of the Siren. Richmond, Hogarth Press, 1920. 8vo., 1st ed., orig. blue wrs., fine copy, scarce, only 500 copies prtd. Quaritch 979-147 1978 $240

FORSTER, EDWARD MORGAN   Virginia Woolf. 1942. First ed., cr. 8vo., orig. wrappers. Howes 194-865 1978 £5

FORSTER, EDWARD MORGAN   Virginia Woolf. Cambridge, 1942. Wraps, backstrip chipped, else very good, first English ed. Bell Book 17-375 1978 £5.50

FORSTER, GUIDO F.   Naval Reserve Guide. Cornell Maritime Press, 1943. Illus. Austin 80-104 1978 $10

FORSTER, H. G.　　　A Layman's Theology.　Toronto, 1946.　Wrs.
Hood 116-293 1978 $7.50

FORSTER, JOHN　　　Arrest of the Five Members by Charles the First...
1860. Octavo, good.　Upcroft 10-318 1978 £10

FORSTER, JOHN　　　The Life of Charles Dickens.　1872-3-4.　3 vols.,
vol. 3 - 1st. ed., frontis, illus., half titles, orig. purple cloth, heads & tails
frayed, all vols. loosening.　Jarndyce 16-556 1978 £5.50

FORSTER, JOHN　　　The Life of Charles Dickens.　1872-3-4.　3
vols., vols. 2 & 3 1st. eds., frontis & illus., orig. purple cloth, faded but sound.
Jarndyce 16-555 1978 £14.50

FORSTER, JOHN　　　Sir John Eliot; a Biography 1590-1632.　1864.
2 vols., 2 portraits, octavo, good.　Upcroft 10-319 1978 £12.50

FORSTER, JOHN　　　The Statesmen of the Commonwealth of England....
1862. 5 vols., engraved frontis to each vol., orig. half calf, marbled bds., v.g.
Jarndyce 16-667 1978 £22

FORSTER, THOMAS I. M.　　　Medicina Simplex; or, The Pilgrims Waybook...
1832. 1st. ed.?, half title, 12mo, wrapper, edges uncut, very good copy.
Fenning 32-119 1978 £16.50

FORSTNER, FREIHERRN　　The Journal of Submarine Commander von Forstner.
Boston, 1917. Orig. cloth, illus., 12mo., 1st Amer. ed.　Morrill 241-143 1978
$8.50

FORSYTH, JOSEPH BELL　　A Few Months in the East.　Quebec, 1861.　Plts.,
two-line autograph inscription by author, orig. binding.　Wolfe 39-189 1978 $75

FORT, PAUL　　　Le Livre des Ballades.　Paris, (1921).　Quarto,
limited to 1,300 copies, tipped-in color plates, original pictorial wrappers,
glassene dust jacket.　Victoria 34-677 1978 $200

FORT, TOMLINSON　　A Dissertation on the Practice of Medicine.　Milledgeville, 1849. Thick 8vo., contemp. calf, worn, covers detached, internally
very good copy with bkplt. of Medical Society of County of Kings, 1st ed.,
scarce. Zeitlin 245-81 1978 $250

FORT Sumter Memorial　New York, 1915.　Ltd. to 750 copies, plts.　Bell
Wiley's copy.　Broadfoot 46-97 1978 $30

FORTESCUE, JOHN WILLIAM　The County Lieutenancies and the Army, 1803-
14. 1909. 8vo.　George's 635-813 1978 £8.50

FORTESCUE, JOHN WILLIAM　A History of the British Army.　1899-1923.
Vols. 1-11 with maps to Vols. IX and X, lacks Vols. 12-13 and 5 vols. of maps.
George's 635-814 1978 £60

FORTESCUE, JOHN WILLIAM　A History of the British Army.　1899-1930.　13
vols. in 20, 8vo., orig. cloth, fine.　F. Edwards 1013-297 1978 £350

FORTIA D'URBAN, MARQUIS DE　Essai sur l'Origine de l'Ecriture, sur Son
Introduction dans la Grece et son Usage jusqu'au Temps d'Homere. Paris, 1832.
8vo., plts., cont. calf, blind tooled border, first ed.　Schumann 511-21 1978
sFr 525

FORTIE, MARIUS　　　Black and Beautiful.　London, 1938.　2 maps,
illus., orig. cloth, 8vo, covers slightly marked.　K Books 239-171 1978 £6

FORTIER, ALCEE　　　A History of Louisiana.　Paris & New York, 1904.
Maps, plts., few in color, 4 vols., 4to., orig. half mor., marbled bd. sides,
backstrips partly torn & chipped, interior fine, ed. Royale, 1 of 200 copies on
handmade paper.　Morrill 239-484 1978 $125

FORTIS, ALBERTO　　　Voyage en Dalmatie.　Berne, 1778.　2 vols.,
8vo., mottled calf, plts., very good, first French translation.　King 7-353 1978
£100

FORTREY, SAMUEL　　England's Interest & Improvement 1663.　1907.
Paper.　Austin 80-606 1978 $10

THE FORTY and Four Thoroughbred Yearlings... (Lexington, 1914). Wrs.　Hayman 73-353 1973 $3.50

FOSCA, F.　　　Tintoret.　1929.　Plts., 4to., wrappers a little
worn.　George's 635-215 1978 £7.50

FOSCOLO, UGO　　　Ricciada.　London, 1820.　8vo, spotted, purple
morocco gilt, joints rubbed.　Eaton 45-188 1978 £20

FOSCOLO, UGO　　　Dei Sepoleri Poesie di Ugo Foscolo D'Ippolito
Pindemonte e di Giovanni Torti.... Venezia, 1824. Sm. 8vo., marbled bds.,
calf spine, very good.　King 7-171 1978 £20

FOSTER, BIRKET　　　Sabbath Bells.　n.d.　New ed., illus. by Birket
Foster, orig. cloth, gilt.　George's 635-146 1978 £7.50

FOSTER, C. L.　　　Letters from the Front, Being a Record of the
Part Played by Offices of the Bank in the Great War, 1914-19.　Toronto, 1920-21.
Illus., 2 vols.　Hood 117-123 1978 $30

FOSTER, DANIEL　　　A Sermon Preached Before His Excellency John
Hancock, Esq. Governour of the Commonwealth of Massachusetts, May 26, 1790.
Boston, 1790. Sewed.　Hayman 71-252 1978 $15

FOSTER, G.　　　Links of Empire.　Toronto, 1924.　Hood 116-625
1978 $7.50

FOSTER, GENEVIEVE　　　Abraham Lincoln's World.　New York, (1944).
Signed by author, illus., lg. 8vo, fine.　Bernard 5-165 1978 $15

FOSTER, HANNAH　　　The Coquette; or, The History of Eliza Wharton.
Exeter, 1828. 11th ed., author's first book, f.p. engraved by Abel Brown, very
good.　Victoria 34-302 1978 $10

FOSTER, HANNAH　　　The Coquette; or, the History of Eliza Wharton.
Boston, 1855. Portr., sm. 8vo.　Morrill 239-385 1978 $10

FOSTER, JOHN WELLS　　Report on the Geology and Topography of a Portion of the Lake Superior Land District, in the State of Michigan.　Washington,
1850, 1851. Two parts, fold. map, plts., orig. binding.　Wolfe 39-276 1978
$75

FOSTER, JOHN Y.　　　New Jersey and the Rebellion.　Newark, 1868.
Ex libris, one hinge starting, tips of spine worn, Bell Wiley's copy.　Broadfoot's
44-552 1978 $15.00

FOSTER, JOSHUA JAMES　　Chats on Old Miniatures.　London, 1908.　8vo.,
illus., pict. cloth.　K Books 244-124 1978 £7

FOSTER, JOSHUA JAMES　　A Dictionary of Painters of Miniatures.　1926.
Portrait, roy. 8vo.　George's 635-21 1978 £25

FOSTER, JOSHUA JAMES　　The Stuarts.　London-New York, 1902.　2 vols.,
8vo., folio, cloth, illus., plts., frontis's.　Van der Peet H-64-127 1978 Dfl
175

FOSTER, JOSHUA JAMES　　Wessex Worthies.　London, 1920.　Plts.,
frontispiece, uncut, t.e.g., orig. parchment backed green buckram, gilt
design, No. 204 of DeLuxe Ed. ltd. to 50 copies, signed, very good or
better.　Limestone 9-140 1978 $80

FOSTER, MICHAEL　　　Claude Bernard, Masters of Medicine.　New
York, 1899.　Rittenhouse 49-268 1976 $12.50

FOSTER, P. C.　　　The Foster Family.　Santa Barbara, 1925.　Illus.,
original cloth.　Ginsberg 14-116 1978 $150

FOSTER, S.　　　Elliptical, or Azimuthal Horologiography.　Lon-
don, 1654. 4 parts in 1 vol., sm. 4to., diagrams, light waterstaining throughout,
more severe on a few leaves at beginning and end, contemp. calf, repaired.　Quaritch 977-182 1978 $300

FOSTER, STEPHEN　　　A Treasury of Stephen Foster.　New York, (1946).
Illus. by William Sharp, 4to, very good or better in dw.　Bernard 5-101 1978
$7.50

FOSTER, STEPHEN S.   The Brotherhood of Thieves. Boston, 1844. First ed., 12mo., wrs. Biblo 247-91 1978 $50

FOSTER, WARREN WODEN   Some Descendants of Arthur Warren of Weymouth, Massachusetts Bay Colony. Washington, 1911. Baldwins' 51-269 1978 $17.50

FOSTER, WILLIAM TRUFANT   Business Without a Buyer. 1927. 2nd rev. ed., illus. with graphs. Austin 80-605 1978 $11

FOSTER-MELLIAR, A.   The Book of the Rose. London, 1902. Orig. cloth, 2nd ed., illus., sm. 8vo. Morrill 241-144 1978 $7.50

FOTHERGILL, JESSIE   The First Violin. New York, 1878. 1st Amer. ed., fine. Victoria 34-303 1978 $17.50

FOUCART, PAUL   De la Fonction Industrielle des Femmes. Paris, 1882. 8vo., orig. prtd. wrs., uncut, light foxing, very good copy, pres. inscrip. Norman 5-303 1978 $75

FOULKE, ROY A.   The Sinews of American Commerce. 1941. Illus., photos, with slipcase. Austin 80-612 1978 $12.50

FOULON, P.   Angkor, dans la Foret. Hanoi, 1931. Large 8vo, color plts., ltd. and numbered ed., orig. covers. Van der Peet 127-95 1978 Dfl 45

FOUNDATIONS of British Foreign Policy from Pitt (1792) to Salisbury (1902). Cambridge, 1938. 8vo. George's 635-647 1978 £8.50

FOUNTAIN, P.   The Great North-West and the Great Lake Region of North America. 1904. Orig. cloth, 8vo, spine faded. Edwards 1012-422 1978 £15

FOUQUE, FRIEDRICH DE LA MOTTE
Please turn to
LA MOTTE FOUQUE, FRIEDRICH DE

FOUR Papers on Acting. New York, 1926. 4 vols., 1st ed., uncut, unopened, bds., fine, all mint in protective tissues. Limestone 9-300 1978 $50

FOURCROY, ANTOINE-FRANCOIS DE   Elementary Lectures on Chemistry and Natural History. Edinburgh, 1785. Many additions, notes, illus. by translator, 2 vols., 8vo., contemp. half calf, rebacked, corners restored, some foxing, but very good set, 1st ed. in English. Norman 5-113 1978 $375

FOURCROY, ANTOINE-FRANCOIS DE   Lecons Elementaires d'Histoire Naturelle et de Chimie. Paris, 1782. 8vo., 2 vols., fldg. tables, fldg. plt., contemp. calf, gilt, hinges repaired, tables foxed, dampstaining, but very good set in cloth box, sm. stamp on titles, 1st ed. Norman 5-112 1978 $450

FOURCROY, ANTOINE FRANCOIS DE   Philosophie Chimique, ou Verites Fondamentales de la Chimie Moderne, Disposees Dans un Nouvel Ordre. Paris, 1792. Sm. 8vo., contemp. calf, 1st ed., 1st issue, very rare. Offenbacher 30-42 1978 $275

FOURCROY, ANTOINE FRANCOIS DE   The Philosophy of Chemistry. London, 1795. 8vo., orig. bds., uncut, rebacked, fine, first ed. in English. Norman 5-114 1978 $300

FOURCROY, ANTOINE-FRANCOIS DE   Systeme des Connaisances Chimiques, et de Leurs Applications au Phenomenes de la Nature et de l'Art. Paris, (1800-1802). 11 vols., 8vo., old bds., very good set, 1st ed. Norman 5-115 1978 $850

FOURIER, JEAN BAPTISTE JOSEPH   Theorie analytique de la chaleur. Paris, 1822. Very rare 1st ed., engraved plts., half-calf, contemp. blank wr. bound in, light spots, very fine, uncut, 4to. Gilhofer 75-42 1978 SFr 1,600

FOURIER, JEAN BAPTISTE JOSEPH   Theorie Analytique de la Chaleur. Paris, 1822. Copperplts., 4to., old half calf, hinges weak, 1st ed., extremely rare, library stamps. Offenbacher 30-43 1978 $1,250

FOURNEL, VICTOR   Les Artistes Francais Contemporains. Tours, 1884. Royal 8vo., polychrome & gilt publisher's stamped cloth, one hinge weak, illus. with orig. etchings. Goldschmidt 110-5 1978 $50

FOURNIER, ALFRED   Die Vererbung der Syphilis. Leipzig and Wien, 1892. Tall 8vo., orange paper with upper cover of orig. wr. bound in, spine broken, v.g., uncut. Zeitlin 245-83 1978 $35

FOURNIER, EDOUARD   L'Art De La Reliure en France aux Dernier Siecles. Paris, 1888. 16mo., newly rebound, marbled paper over bds., 3/4 cloth, pages waterstained. Battery Park 1-277 1978 $75

FOURNIER, JEAN ALFRED
Please turn to
FOURNIER, ALFRED

FOURNIER, JOSEPH LEOPOLD   Dissertation Inauguralis Chemico-Medica de Metallis. Viennae, 1777. 8vo., contemp. decor. paper wrs., 1st ed. Offenbacher 30-44 1978 $115

FOURTH Annual Fair of the Carroll County Voluntary Agricultural Association.. Delphi, Indiana. Lafayette, 1877. Wrps., lacks back wrapper. Hayman 71-338 1978 $8.50

FOWLER, ELLEN THORNEYCROFT   Concerning Isabel Carnaby. New York, 1899. 1st Amer. ed., cloth, some binding soil, interior good. Greene 78-203 1978 $20

FOWLER, ELLEN THORNEYCROFT   A Double Thread. New York, 1899. 1st Amer. ed., orig. cloth. Greene 78-204 1978 $15

FOWLER, GENE   Beau James. New York, 1949. 1st ed., signed by author, part of flyleaf cut away, d.w. Biblo BL781-181 1978 $9

FOWLER, H. N.   A Handbook of Greek Archaeology. New York, (1909). Illus. Biblo BL781-378 1978 $9

FOWLER, HENRY WATSON   A Dictionary of Modern English Usage. Oxford, 1926. 8vo, original dark blue cloth, stamped in gilt, 1st ed., printed on onion-like paper, very fine bright copy. Ximenes 47-106 1978 $30

FOWLER, O. S.   The Self-Instructor in Phrenology and Physiognomy. New York, 1890. Rittenhouse 49-269 1976 $7.50

FOWLER, WILLIAM C.   History of Durham, Conn., From the First Grant of Land in 1662 to 1866. Hartford, 1866. Orig. cloth., lib. marks, fine. MacManus 239-945 1978 $40

FOX, CHARLES JAMES   A History of the Early Part of the Reign of James the Second. London, 1808. 1st ed., 4to., old half lea. with marbled bds., scuffed, engr. portr., very good. Americanist 103-33 1978 $40

FOX, CHARLES JAMES   A History of the Early Part of the Reign of James the Second;.... London, 1808. Large quarto, engraved frontis. portrait, contemp. calf, fine, one of 50 large paper copies, armorial bookplate, 1st ed. Bennett 7-45 1978 $225

FOX, CHARLES JAMES   A History of the Early Part of the Reign of James the Second;.... London, 1808. 1st ed., fine, large quarto, frontis., contemp. calf, gilt borders, rebacked preserving orig. gilt-tooled paneled spine, bookplate. Bennett 20-75 1978 $225

FOX, CHARLES JAMES   A History of the Early Part of the Reign of James the Second. London, 1808. 1st ed., portrait frontispiece, 4to., contemp. calf, good. K Books 244-365 1978 £18

FOX, CYRUS T.   Reading and Berks County Penna. New York, 1925. 3 vols., illus., 4tos., very fine. MacManus 239-1371 1978 $85

FOX, DIXON RYAN   The Minutes of the Court of Sessions (1657-1696) Westchester County, New York. White Plains, 1924. Bound. Biblo 248-84 1978 $17.50

FOX, FRANK   Australia. London, (1927). Second ed., illus. in color. Biblo 247-684 1978 $15

FOX, GEORGE   George Fox's Book of Miracles. Cambridge, 1948. Plts., octavo, good. Upcroft 10-61 1978 £6.50

FOX, GEORGE   A Journal or Historical Account of the Life, Travels, Sufferings, Christian Experiences, and Labour of Love in the Work of the Ministry of ... 1765. 3rd. ed., folio, calf, worn, title dust-soiled, G.M. Trevelyan's signature on end-paper. Hannas 54-118 1978 £38

FOX, GEORGE   The Journal of .... Cambridge, 1911. Plts., octavo, good, 2 vols. Upcroft 10-59 1978 £15

FOX, GEORGE HENRY   Photographic Illustrations of Skin Diseases. New York, 1880. Plts., 4to., half lea., 1st ed. Morrill 239-88 1978 $75

FOX, GEORGE HENRY   Photographic Illustrations of Skin Diseases. New York, 1885. 2nd ed., 4to., hand-colored phto. plts. on heavy paper, contemp. half lea., gilt lettering, worn, light browning, dampstains, good copy internally, signatures of former owners, rare. Zeitlin 245-84 1978 $85

FOX, HERBERT   Disease in Captive Wild Mammals and Birds. Philadelphia, (1923). Tall thick 8vo., illus., orig. blue cloth, gilt-lettered spine, fine copy, 1st ed. Zeitlin 245-85 1978 $45

FOX, HERBERT   Disease in Captive Wild Mammals and Birds. Philadelphia, 1923. Cover a little worn, internally clean, a trifle loose. Rittenhouse 49-271 1976 $65

FOX, HERBERT   Disease in Captive Wild Mammals and Birds. Philadelphia, 1923. First ed., unusued copy. Rittenhouse 49-272 1976 $85

FOX, J. C.   The Lady Ivie's Trials For the Great Part of Shadwell in the County of Middlesex Before Lord Chief Justice Jeffreys in 1684. Oxford, 1929. Map, illus., octavo, good. Upcroft 10-62 1978 £9

FOX, JOHN, JR.   The Little Shepherd of Kingdom Come. New York, 1931. 1 of 512 numbered copies signed by N. C. Wyeth, illus. by Wyeth, 4 to., half vellum on cloth, t.e.g., uncut, mostly unopened, color plts., fine. Houle 10-377 1978 $325

FOX, LAWRENCE K.   South Dakota Historical Collections... Pierre, 1938. Cloth, vol. 19, 1st ed., very good, scarce. Dykes 35-230 1978 $25

FOX, MARIA   Memoirs. 1846. Half roan, rubbed, 8vo. George's 635-1067 1978 £6.50

FOX, PAUL   The Poles in America. 1922. Illus., 1st ed., ex-lib. Austin 79-255 1978 $10

FOX, WILLIAM F.   Regimental Losses 1861-1865. Albany, NY, 1866. Hinges cracked, frayed margins, Bell Wiley's Copy. Broadfoot's 44-150 1978 $30.00

THE FOX and the Geese. New York, c.1850's. 12mo, illus. yellow wrappers, spine partly split, fine. Victoria 34-304 1978 $35

FOX-DAVIES, ARTHUR CHARLES   Armorial Families. London, 1929. 7th ed., 2 vols., 4to. Baldwins' 51-252 1978 $75

FOX-DAVIES, ARTHUR CHARLES   Art of Heraldry, Encyclopaedia of Armory. 1904. Folio, plts., some colored & illus., rebacked. Allen 234-1297 1978 $60

FOXCROFT, CHARLES T.   The Night Sister and other Poems. 1918. First ed., sm. 8vo., orig. limp bds., d.w., rare. Howes 194-867 1978 £6.50

FOXE, JOHN   An Abridgment of the Book of Martyrs. New York, 1810. Engr. frontis. by Peter Maverick, 8vo., contemp. calf. Morrill 239-387 1978 $12.50

FOXE, JOHN   An Abridgment of The Book of Martyrs. New-York, 1810. Thick 8vo, calf, 1st Amer. ed., foxed and lightly rubbed, very good firm copy. Victoria 34-305 1978 $25

FOXE, JOHN   'The Book of Martyrs'. London, 1641. 3 vols., small folio, modern brown buckram, leather title labels. Totteridge 29-43 1978 $200

FOXE, JOHN   Fox's Book of Martyrs. Philadelphia, (1829). Engr. plts., engr. vignettes, 2 vols. in 1, 4to., contemp. calf, bottom inch of spine lacking. Morrill 239-388 1978 $25

FRACASTORUS, GIROLAMO   Anthologia Seu Selecta Quaedam Poemata Italorum Qui Latine Scripserunt. Londini, 1684. 12mo., contemp. panelled calf, worn. Quaritch 977-23 1978 $50

FRACASTORO, GIROLAMO   Homocentrica Eiusdem de Causis Criticorum Dierum per ea quae in nobis sunt. Venice, 1538. Sm. 4to., very slight waterstaining, orig. limp vellum, first ed. Quaritch 977-183 1978 $2,250

FRACASTORO, GIROLAMO   Opera Omnia. Venice, 1574. 2nd ed., 4to., 3/4 calf, woodcut portr. Salloch 345-71 1978 $350

FRACKER, GEORGE   A Voyage to South America, with an Account of a Shipwreck in the River La Plata, in the Year 1817. Boston, 1826. 12mo, half morocco, 2nd ed., revised, very good copy, rare title. Ximenes 47-107 1978 $150

FRADENBURGH, J. N.   Departed Gods. Cincinnati, 1891. Orig. binding, clean, minor spotting on cover. Hayman 71-253 1978 $8.50

FRADRYSSA, G. V.   Roman Catholicism Capitulating Before Protestantism. Mobile, 1908. Trans. from Spanish. Austin 79-256 1978 $12.50

FRAGMENTS of Experience. Salt Lake City, 1882. Cloth, 1st ed. Ginsberg 14-652 1978 $15

FRAGMENTS of Family and Contemporary History. Pittsburgh, 1867. 12mo., 1st ed., orig. cloth. Morrill 241-499 1978 $10

FRAME, S. J.   The Future of the Anglo-Saxon Race. Toronto, 1936. Inscribed by author. Hood's 115-931 1978 $12.50

FRANCE, ANATOLE   Crainquebille. New York, Limited Editions Club, 1949. Ltd. ed., signed by artist, 4to., illus. by Bernard Lamotte. Biblo 247-588 1978 $32.50

FRANCE, ANATOLE   Golden Tales. New York, 1927. Illus. with plates by L. A. Patterson, gilt stamped black cloth, very good. Houle 10-255 1978 $12.50

FRANCE, ANATOLE   Mother of Pearl. 1929. Plts. by Frank C. Pape, roy. 8vo., decor. cloth gilt, very good, first English ed. Bell Book 17-498 1978 £8.50

FRANCE, ANATOLE   Penguin Island. New York: The Limited Editions Club, 1947. Sm. 4to., illus., orig. leather-backed silk-covered bds., pub. box, 1 of 1,500 copies, fine. MacManus 238-822 1978 $15

FRANCE, ANATOLE   Thais. London, (1928). Fine, d.w., illus. Biblo 247-352 1978 $17.50

FRANCE, ANATOLE   Well of Saint Clare. London & New York, 1928. Illus., gilt stamped black cloth, fine. Houle 10-253 1978 $15

FRANCE, ANATOLE   Works. London, 1924. 39 vols., sm. 8vo. Traylen 88-249 1978 £20

FRANCESCO D'ASSISI, SAINT   I Fioretti del glorioso Poverello di Cristo S. Francesco di Assisi. 1922. 8vo., prtd. in red & black, woodcut illus., vellum, sm. bkplt., fine clean copy, 240 copies prtd. on paper. Quaritch 979-7 1978 $450

FRANCESCO D'ASSISI, SAINT   Fioretti di San Francesco Ne' quali si contiene la Vita.... Venetia. 12mo., recent limp vellum, woodcut vignette, illus. King 7-172 1978 £55

FRANCESCO D'ASSISI, SAINT   Un Mazzeto di certi Fioretti del glorioso Poverello di Cristo San Francesco di Assisi insieme col Cantico al sole del Medesimo. 1904. 4to., woodcuts, bds. Quaritch 979-8 1978 $450

FRANCESCO DE VIERI FIORENTINO, D.   Trattato delle Metheore. Fiorenza, 1573. Woodcut illus., 16mo., later 1/2 vellum. Argosy Special-41 1978 $150

FRANCHI, DIEGO DE   Historia del Patriarcha S. Giovangualberto del Monastico Ordine di Vallombrosa. Florence, 1640. Lg. 4to., illus., frontis., contemp. calf, fine, 1st ed. Gilhofer 74-131 1978 sFr 2,000

FRANCHOT, C. P.   "Stanislas Pascal Franchot Arrives".   December 1940. Fldg. family chart. Butterfield 21-192 1978 $10

FRANCIS OF ASSISI
Please turn to
FRANCESCO D'ASSISI, SAINT

FRANCIS, G.   The Dictionary of the Arts, Sciences and Manufactures. 1842. Engravings in text, binders buckram, 8vo. George's 635-1467 1978 £6

FRANCK, DR.   Notice sur les Grains de Sante du Docteur Franck. Paris, 1807. Paper covers. Rittenhouse 49-273 1976 $12.50

FRANCK, G. F.   Exercitatio Medica de Pericardio, atque Experimenta & Observationibus novissimis circa id habitis. Altdorf, 1690. 4to., disbound. Gurney 75-40 1978 £20

FRANCK, HARRY A.   Glimpses of Japan and Formosa. New York, (1924). Cloth, spine extremities frayed. Dawson's 449-118 1978 $10

FRANCK DE FRANCKENAU, GEORG   Tractatus Philologico-Medicus De Cornutis in Quo Varia Curiosa. Heidelbergae, 1676. Sm. 4to., fine woodcut, modern plain wrs., light foxing, very good. Zeitlin 245-86 1978 $35

FRANCOIS, JEAN   Dictionnaire Roman, Walon, Celtique et Tudesque.... 1777. 4to., calf, good, first ed. King 7-354 1978 £80

FRANK, DOCTOR   Health in Our Homes. Boston, 1887. 12mo., covers dampstained, 1st ed. Morrill 239-89 1978 $8.50

FRANK, HERMAN   Jewish Typography & Bookmaking Art. New York, 1938. Illus., 8vo. Battery Park 1-473 1978 $50

FRANK, LEONHARD   Brother and Sister. London, 1930. First English ed., one of 500 numbered copies, signed by author, very nice, slipcase, orig. binding. Rota 211-119 1978 £6

FRANK, TENNEY   Economic Survey of Ancient Rome. 1944. Vol. 6, index, only. Allen 234-343 1978 $10

FRANK, WALDO   City Block. Darien, 1922. Tan bds., cloth spine, 1st ed., 1 of 1250, inscr. by author, spine faded. Bradley 49-124 1978 $8.50

FRANK, WALDO   Holiday. New York, (1923). Orig. cloth, 1st ed. MacManus 238-657 1978 $20

FRANKAU, JULIA   Eighteenth Century Colour Prints. 1900. Pictures printed in colours from copperplts., imp. 4to. George's 635-147 1978 £100

FRANKAU, JULIA   William Ward, A.R.A., James Ward, R.A., Their Lives and Works. 1904. Plts., roy. 8vo., 2 vols., half red crushed mor., red cloth sides, t.e.g., fine. George's 635-148 1978 £190

FRANKLIN, AUGUSTUS   The American Farier...For The...Farmer,.... Strasburg, 1803. 1st & only ed., contemp scuffed calf decor. on spine w/gilt sunbursts, orig. binding, 8vo. Americanist 101-49 1978 $90

FRANKLIN, BENJAMIN   Autobiography, Edited From His Manuscript,.... Philadelphia, 1868. 1st complete ed., slight wear to ends of spine, orig. binding, 8vo. Americanist 101-50 1978 $25

FRANKLIN, BENJAMIN   Autobiographical Writings. New York, 1945. Biblo 247-46 1978 $12.50

FRANKLIN, BENJAMIN   Autobiography. Berkeley, 1949. First of this ed., d.w. Biblo 247-47 1978 $12.50

FRANKLIN, BENJAMIN   Correspondence inedite et secrete du Docteur B. Franklin,.... Paris, 1817. 1st ed., octavo, 2 vols., frontis. in each vol., orig. plain paper wr., folding cloth box, fine. Bennett 20-76 1978 $350

FRANKLIN, BENJAMIN   Experiments and Observations on Electricity, Made at Philadelphia in America, and Communicated in Several Letters to Peter Collinson of London. London, 1751-54. 4to., 3 vols. in 1, full antique calf, 18th Cent. style, title of pt. 1 washed, few minor tears repaired, but fine set, handsomely bound, 1st ed. Norman 5-116 1978 $8,500

FRANKLIN, BENJAMIN   Familiar Letters and Miscellaneous Papers. 1833. Orig. cloth backed bds., first English ed., some foxing of text, 8vo. Howes 194-868 1978 £20

FRANKLIN, BENJAMIN   Facsimile of Poor Richard's Almanack for 1733. N.P., DeVinne Press, 1894. One of 144 copies, orig. bds., uncut, illus., fronts signed by arts, 8vo., very good. Americanist 103-34 1978 $85

FRANKLIN, BENJAMIN   Oeuvres de M. Franklin.... Paris, 1773. 1st ed., quarto, 2 vols. in 1, engraved portrait and plates by F. N. Martinet, contemporary half-calf over boards, rebacked, morocco title-label on spine, a bit rubbed, rare. Bennett 20-77 1978 $750

FRANKLIN, BENJAMIN   Political, Miscellaneous, and Philosophical Pieces. London, 1779. 4to., frontis. portr., plts., fldg. table, contemp. calf, rubbed, rebacked, frontis. lightly foxed, very good copy, 1st ed. Norman 5-117 1978 $500

FRANKLIN, BENJAMIN   The Way to Wealth. Nottingham, c.1800-10. Uncut chapbook, about fine. Victoria 34-306 1978 $30

FRANKLIN, BENJAMIN   The Way to Wealth: The Preface to Poor Richard's Almanack for.... New York, 1930. 1 of 390 copies, signed by Preissig, lg thin folio, orig. cloth-backed boards, orig. box, 8vo. Americanist 101-51 1978 $30

FRANKLIN, BENJAMIN   Works...Consisting of His Life, Written by Himself...(&) Essays. New York, 1794. 2nd Amer. ed., 2 vols. in 1, old calf, spine repaired w/leather, marginal defects & tears, complete, with portr. engr. by Tanner. Americanist 101-52 1978 $40

FRANKLIN, BENJAMIN   The Works of the Late Dr..., Consisting of His Life, Written by Himself. Charlestown, 1798. Frontis. port., contemp. calf, marginal wear, but nice. MacManus 239-152 1978 $40

FRANKLIN, BENJAMIN   The Complete Works, in Philosophy, Politics, and Morals. London, 1806. 3 vols., 8vo., index misbound at end of Vol. 3 instead of Vol. 1, portr., plts., fldg. map, fldg. table, old half calf, gilt, little foxing, but fine set, handsomely bound, 1st ed. Norman 5-*18 1978 $375

FRANKLIN, BENJAMIN   The Works of... Boston, 1825. Port., orig. calf-backed bds. MacManus 239-150 1978 $25

FRANKLIN, BENJAMIN   The Works of...Containing Several Political and Historical Tracts... London, 1840. 10 vols., rebound, ex-lib. MacManus 239-151 1978 $85

FRANKLIN, CHARLES H.   Study on Project of Publication, The War of the Rebellion. Washington, 1931. Bell Wiley's Copy. Broadfoot's 44-151 1978 $25.00

FRANKLIN, COLIN   The Private Presses. D.w., very fine. Battery Park 1-372 1978 $25

FRANKLIN, J. BENJAMIN   A Cheap Trip to the Great Salt Lake City. Ipswich, (1864). Orig. pr. wr., 3rd ed. Ginsberg 14-1003 1978 $75

FRANKLIN, JEAN DWIGHT   Why. Derrydale Press, 1929. 1 of 1000 copies, 16mo., bds., fine. Battery Park 1-62 1978 $50

FRANKLIN, JOHN   Narrative of a Journey to the Shores of the Polar Sea in the Year 1819, 20, 21, and 22. London, 1823. 1st ed., thick 4to., engr. plts., minor dampstaining, maps, hand-colored engrs., full early 19th Cent. calf. Current Misc. 8-20 1978 $675

FRANKLIN, JOHN   Narrative of a Journey to the Shores of the Polar Sea,... Philadelphia, 1824. Illus., engraved frontis., folding map, half mor., 1st Amer. ed. Ginsberg 14-1097 1978 $175

FRANKLIN, JOHN   Some Private Correspondence of ...   and Lady Jane Franklin. Sydney, 1947. Illus., 2 parts, orig. printed wrappers, 8vo., ltd. ed. of 200 copies.   Edwards 1012-331 1978 £20

FRANKLIN, JOHN HOPE   The Free Negro in North Carolina 1790-1860. Chapel Hill, 1943. Broadfoot 50-71 1978 $20

FRANKLIN DEBATING SOCIETY   The Constitution and By-Laws of ...of Germantown. Germantown, (1830). Later 3/4 mor. and marbled bds., bookplt. MacManus 239-1461 1978 $15

FRANKLYN, JULIAN   Shield and Crest, An Account of the Art and Science of Heraldry. 1960. 1st. ed., coloured plts., coloured frontis, 8vo., orig. cloth, pres. copy to Winston Churchill, fine copy. Sawyer 298-77 1978 £165

FRANKS, DAVID   The New York Directory... New York, 1786. Cloth. MacManus 239-370 1978 $20

FRANTZIUS, FRITZ VON   The Book of Truth and Facts. Chicago, 1916. Austin 79-258 1978 $20

FRANZ, JOSEPH   Emperor and Empress. Cortege Historique de la Ville de Vienne a l'Occasion des Noces d'Argent de leurs Majestes Francois-Joseph I et Elisabeth... Paris, (c.1800). Roy. folio, plts., dec. borders, 3/4 levant mor., ltd. to 550 no. copies. Quaritch 983-185 1978 $125

FRANZIUS, JOHANNES GEORGIUS FRIDERICUS   Scriptores Physignomoniae Veteres Ex Recensione Camille Perussci.... Altenbvrgi, 1780. 8vo., cloth, good. King 7-355 1978 £25

FRANZOSIUS, HIERONYMUS   De Motu Cordis, et Sanguinis in Animalibus. Pro Aristotele, & Galeno Adversus Anatomicos Neotericos Libri Duo. Veronae, n.d. (1652). Woodcuts, 4to., old limp bds., uncut, only ed., extremely rare, very fine copy. Offenbacher 30-64 1978 $1,200

FRARY, I. T.   Early Homes of Ohio. Richmond, (1936). 1st ed., illus., orig. cloth, d.j., fine. MacManus 239-666 1978 $37.50

FRARY, I. T.   Ohio in Homespun & Calico. 1942. Illus., signed by author. Austin 80-615 1978 $12.50

FRASER, AGNES R.   Donald Fraser of Livingstonia. London, 1934. Orig. cloth, 8vo., 2 plts., map. K Books 239-172 1978 £5

FRASER, MRS. ALEXANDER   A Maddening Blow. London, 1878. 3 vols., orig. cloth, 1st ed., lib. labels removed, covers a little soiled, otherwise very good. MacManus 238-342 1978 $85

FRASER, AUGUSTA ZELIA   Lucilla. An Experiment. London, 1859. 2 vols., orig. cloth, 1st ed., front inner hinge of vol. I cracked, otherwise fine, bookplts. MacManus 238-351 1978 $85

FRASER, CLAUD LOVAT   The Book of Lovat. London, 1923. 4to., frontis., pict. cover in color, decor. endpaper in color, d.w., worn. Battery Park 1-105 1978 $100

FRASER, CLAUD LOVAT   The Printed Work of Claud Lovat Fraser. London, 1923. Erratum slip laid in , frontis., 1 of 275 numbered & signed copies. Battery Park 1-104 1978 $125

FRASER, CLAUD LOVAT   Sixty-three Unpublished Designs. London, First Edition Club. 1 of 500 numbered copies, prtd. on Ingres paper dyed by hand, bound in paper bds. Battery Park 1-103 1978 $75

FRASER, DOUGLAS C.   Impressions, Nigeria 1925. London, 1926. Map, plts., orig. cloth, 8vo. K Books 239-173 1978 £8

FRASER, GEORGIA   The Stone House at Gowanus, Scene of the Battle of Long Island... New York, 1909. Illus., uncut. MacManus 239-571 1978 $15

FRASER, MRS. HUGH   A Diplomat's Wife in Japan: Letters from home to home. London, 1899. 2nd ed., 2 vols., illus., decor. cloth, spine faded. Dawson's 449-119 1978 $50

FRASER, I. F.   The Spirit of French Canada, a Study of the Literature. New York, Toronto, 1939. Ex-lib. Hood 117-476 1978 $25

FRASER, JESSIE   Not Counting the Cost. New York, 1895. 1st Amer. ed., quarter calf, marbled boards, edges rubbed. Greene 78-112 1978 $20

FRASER, JOHN   Canadian Pen and Ink Sketches. Montreal, 1890. Hinge on front cover worn. Hood's 115-594 1978 $30

FRASER, JOHN   Youth's Golden Cycle... Philadelphia & Chicago, 1885. Orig. binding, clean. Hayman 71-254 1978 $8.50

FRASER, JOHN FOSTER   The Conquering Jew. 1915. Austin 79-259 1978 $12.50

FRASER, L. M.   Economic Thought and Language. 1947. Austin 80-616 1978 $12.50

FRASER, MARY C.   Seven Years on the Pacific Slope. c.1914. Plts., 8vo., orig. cloth, nice copy. Fenning 32-120 1978 £9.50

FRASER, R. W.   Illustrative Views in Tinted Lithography of Interesting and Romantic Parish Kirks and Manses in Scotland... Edinburgh, c.1850. 4to., plts., some slight foxing, orig. cloth, mor. back. Quaritch 983-329 1978 $70

FRASER, W. A.   The Blood Lilies. Toronto, 1903. Illus. Hood 116-471 1978 $10

FRASER, W. A.   Mooswa and Others of the Boundaries. New York, 1900. Cloth. Hayman 73-217 1978 $10

FRASER-TYTLER, C. C.   Margaret. 1872. 1st. ed., 2 vols., orig. blue cloth, little dulled, otherwise v.g. Jarndyce 16-669 1978 £25

FRAUENSTAEDT, J.   Schopenhauer-Lexikon. Leipzig, 1871. 2 vols., 8vo., 1/2 cloth. Salloch 348-241 1978 $40

FRAUNHOFER, JOSEPH   Neue Modifikation des Lichtes durch gegenseitige Einwirkung und Beugung der Strahlen, und Gesetze derselben. (Munich, 1821-2). 4to., old half cloth, plts., very rare. Gurney 75-41 1978 £265

FRAZEE, W. D.   Reminiscences and Sermons. Nashville, 1892. Orig. cl., 1st ed. Ginsberg 16-863 1978 $25.00

FRAZER, LADY   Leaves from the Golden Bough. 1924. Plts. by H. M. Brock, 8vo. George's 635-1428 1978 £5.50

FRAZER, JAMES GEORGE   The Golden Bough:.... London, 1890. 1st ed., 2 vols, 8vo., orig. ed.'s cloth. Gilhofer 75-44 1978 SFr 850

FRAZER, JAMES GEORGE   The Golden Bough, a Study in Magic and Religion. 1923-27. 11 vols. (ex 13), some spines worn, some covers faded, 8vo. George's 635- 1427 1978 £25

FRAZER, JAMES GEORGE   The Gorgon's Head and other Literary Pieces. 1927. Portrait, 8vo. George's 635-1342 1978 £6.50

FRAZER, JAMES GEORGE   Graecia Antiqua. 1930. Plt. Allen 234-719 1978 $20

FRAZER, WILLIAM   Fireside Musings of "Uncle" Rastus and "Aunt" Randy. Charlotte, N. C., 1925. Bell Wiley's copy. Broadfoot 46-511 1978 $10

FRAZER, WILLIAM   The Possumist and Other Stories. Charlotte, N. C., 1924. Bell Wiley's copy. Broadfoot 46-510 1978 $10

FREART, ROLAND   A Parallel of the Ancient Architecture with the Modern, in a Collection of Ten Principal Authors Who Have Written Upon the Five Orders... 1664. Folio, plts., light ink spotting on 2 leaves, 19th century calf antique, gilt edges, 1st ed. in English. Quaritch 983-38 1978 $1,200

FREDERIC, HAROLD   The Damnation of Theron Ware.   Chicago, 1896.
Green cloth, top edges gilt, others uncut, lst ed., very good.   Bradley 49-125
1978 $20

FREDERIC, HAROLD   In the Valley.   1890.   Illus. by Howard Pyle, first
ed.   Austin 82-388 1978 $125

FREDERIC, HAROLD   In the Valley.   New York, 1890.   Illus. by
Howard Pyle, 12mo., orig. cloth, lst ed., bind. B, very good, signature on flyleaf.   MacManus 238-480 1978 $85

FREDERIC, HAROLD   Mrs. Albert Grundy.   Observations in Philistia.
London, (New York?), 1896. 12mo., orig. tan dec. buckram, lst ed., covers
and spine darkened.   MacManus 238-482 1978 $75

FREDERIC, HAROLD   The Young Emperor William II of Germany. A
Study in Character Development on a Throne.   New York, 1891.   Orig. cloth,
1st Amer. ed., very good.   MacManus 238-481 1978 $50

FREDERICK II, KING OF PRUSSIA   The Posthumous Works.   1789. 13 vols.,
contemp. diced calf, backs worn, lacks portrait, 8vo.   Howes 194-278 1978 £55

FREDERICK, COLONEL   The Description of Corsica with an Account of
its Union to the Crown of Great Britain.   London, 1795. 8vo., green mor., first
ed.   King 7-356 1978 £120

FREDERICK, J. GEORGE   Business Research and Statistics.   1920. Austin
80-617 1978 $10

FREDERICK, J. GEORGE   Modern Industrial Consolidation.   1926. lst ed.,
inscr'd by author.   Austin 80-618 1978 $17.50

FREDERICKSON, A. D.   Ad Orientem.   1889. Coloured plts., litho.
plts., illus., 8vo, orig. cloth, covers slightly soiled.   Edwards 1012-204 1978
£25

FREDUR, THOR   Sketches From Shady Places.   1879. lst. ed.,
half title, fine in orig. brown cloth.   Jarndyce 16-830 1978 £20

FREE CHURCH OF SCOTLAND   Report of the Proceedings of the General Assembly.   Edinburgh, 1846. 8vo., unbound.   Morrill 241-145 1978 $20

FREE THOUGHT PRESS   The Story of the Inquisition.   Free Thought
Press, 1928. Illus.   Austin 79-260 1978 $12.50

FREEBURG, VICTOR O.   William Henry Welch at Eighty. A Memorial
Record of Celebrations Around the World in His Honor.   New York, 1930. Rittenhouse 49-274 1976 $20

FREEDLEY, EDWIN T.   Philadelphia & Its Manufacturers: A Hand-book....
Philadelphia, 1858. lst ed., illus., neatly rebacked, 8vo. Americanist 101-154
1978 $35

FREEDLEY, EDWIN T.   Philadelphia and Its Manufactures...   Philadelphia, 1859. Illus., nice copy, orig. cloth, some wear on spine.   Mac Manus
239-1643 1978 $45

FREEMAN, A. MARTIN   Thomas Love Peacock.   London, 1911.
1st ed., very good, orig. cloth.   Limestone 9-228 1978 $30

FREEMAN, DOUGLAS SOUTHALL   A Calendar of Confederate Papers
Richmond, Va., 1908. New cloth, Bell Wiley's Copy.   Broadfoot's 44-155
1978 $40.00

FREEMAN, DOUGLAS SOUTHALL   George Washington, a Biography.   New
York, 1948. First ed., illus., 2 vols., vol. 1 and 2 only.   Biblo 247-165 1978
$28.50

FREEMAN, DOUGLAS SOUTHALL   George Washington, a Biography.   New York,
1948-51. First eds., fine, boxed, illus., vols. 1-6, lacking vol. 7.   Biblo 247-
164 1978 $125

FREEMAN, DOUGLAS SOUTHALL   George Washington.   New York, 1948-
1952. 6 vols., lst ed., 8vo., black & white plts., maps, endpapers, blue cloth,
near very fine.   Current 24-108 1978 $80

FREEMAN, DOUGLAS SOUTHALL   Lee's Lieutenants.   New York, 1942-43-44..
3 vols., clean, lst. ed., lst. vol. signed by author, slightly worn d.j.   Hayman
71-123 1978 $45

FREEMAN, DOUGLAS SOUTHALL   Lee's Lieutenants.   New York, 1944. 3
vols., illus.   MacManus 239-876 1978 $40

FREEMAN, DOUGLAS SOUTHALL   Lee's Lieutenants.   New York, 1944.
Illus., 3 vols., 8vo.   Morrill 239-390 1978 $25

FREEMAN, DOUGLAS SOUTHALL   R. E. Lee, a Biography.   New York, 1936.
4 vols., illus., maps.   MacManus 239-877 1978 $35

FREEMAN, DOUGLAS SOUTHALL   R. E. Lee, a Biography.   New York,
1948. 4 vols., Pulitzer Prize ed.   Bell Wiley's copy.   Broadfoot 46-99 1978
$75

FREEMAN, DOUGLAS SOUTHALL   R. E. Lee, a Biography.   New York, n.d.
Illus., 4 vols., 8vo., nice.   Morrill 239-389 1978 $25

FREEMAN, DOUGLAS SOUTHALL   The South to Posterity.   New York
1939. Presen. copy from author.   Bell Wiley's copy.   Broadfoot 46-98 1978 $25

FREEMAN, E. A.   History of Federal Government, from Foundation
of the Achaian League to Disruption of the U.S.   1863. Ex-lib., buckram, maps.
Allen 234-344 1978 $8.50

FREEMAN, E. A.   The Reign of William Rufus and the Accession of
Henry I.   Oxford, 1882. 2 vols., prize calf, spine faded.   George's 635-649
1978 £18

FREEMAN, E. H.   The Veil of Secrecy Removed...Only True and
Authentic History of Edward H. Rulloff.   Binghamton, 1871. Plts., ads, prtd.
wr., little chipped.   Butterfield 21-75 1978 $35

FREEMAN, F.   Yaradee; a Plea for Africa, in familiar Conversations on the Subject of Slavery and Colonization.   Philadelphia, 1836. 12mo,
original violet patterned cloth, lst ed., fine copy.   Ximenes 47-109 1978 $65

FREEMAN, J. J.   A Narrative of the Persecution of the Christians
in Madagascar.   London, 1840. 12mo, lacks frontis, foxed, binders cloth, reading
copy.   K Books 239-175 1978 £7

FREEMAN, JAMES E.   Gatherings From an Artist's Portfolio.   New
York, 1877. lst. ed., orig. green cloth, inscribed pres. copy from author to Mrs.
Thomas Barnes, A.L.S. to the lady's husband, 8vo, illus., photos.   Jarndyce
16-671 1978 £36

FREEMAN, MARY E. WILKINS   "Doc" Gordon.   New York, 1906. Cloth., lst
ed.   Hayman 72-220 1978 $8.50

FREEMAN, NATHANIEL C.   Parnasus in Philadelphia, A Satire.   Philadelphia,
1854. lst ed., orig. boards, spine wear, w/sign. & contemp. comments of H.
Sharpless, 8vo.   Americanist 101-54 1978 $40

THE FREEMAN'S Almanac: for...1838... Cincinnati, (1837). Sewed. Hayman
72-13 1978 $15

THE FREEMAN'S Almanack: for...1839. Cincinnati, (1838). Hayman 73-14
1978 $12.50

FREEZE, JOHN G.   A History of Columbia Co., Pa., From the Earliest Times.   Bloomsburg, 1883. Illus., rebound.   MacManus 239-1423 1978
$55

FREGE, FRIEDRICH LUDWIG GOTTLOB
Please turn to
FREGE, GOTTLOB

FREGE, GOTTLOB   Funktion und Begriff.   Jena, 1891. Rare first ed.,
orig. pr. wr.   Gilhofer 75-46 1978 sFr 700

FREGE, GOTTLOB   Die Grundlagen de Arithmetik.   Breslau, 1884.
lst ed., half-cloth, marginal repairs, pencil entries on last blank page.   Gilhofer
75-45 1978 SFr 900

FREGOSO, BAPTISTA   De Dictus Factisque Memorabilibus Collectanea a
Camillo Gilino latina facta. Milano, 1509. Folio, old vellum, 1st ed. Gilhofer
74-64 1978 sFr 1,000

FREHERO, MARQUARDO   Tractatus de Fama Publica, In Quo Tota Vis
Communis Opinionis Hominum.... Francofurti, 1588. Folio, full stiff vellum,
Andrew Fletcher's copy with signature on rear endpaper. Bennett 20-78 1978
$325

FREIND, JOHN   Emmenologia. London, 1720. 8vo., fine, contemp. calf. Quaritch 977-24 1978 $125

FREIND, JOHN   Historia Medicinae. Venetiis, 1735. Rittenhouse 49-275 1976 $75

FREIND, JOHN   Nine Commentaries Upon Fevers; and Two Epistles Concerning the Smallpox, Addressed to Dr. Mead. London, 1730. 8vo., vignette, some very light dampstaining, tree calf, newly rebacked. Quaritch 977-
25 1978 $85

FREINET, E.   l'Enfant Artiste. Cannes, n.d. 8vo., cloth,
plts., some in color. Van der Peet H-64-35 1978 Dfl 55

FREKE, WILLIAM   Select Essays Tending to the Universal Reformation
of Learning. 1693. 8vo., contemp. sprinkled sheep, nice, only ed., scarce.
P. M. Hill 142-3 1978 £140

FRELIGH, M.   Homoeopathic Practice of Medicine. New York,
1862. 9th ed., revised & enlarged, 8vo., old bds., roan back & corners. Morrill 239-90 1978 $15

FRELINGHUYSEN, THEODORE   An Address Delivered Before the Philoclean
and Peithessophian Societies, of Rutgers College. New Brunswick, 1831. 8vo.,
orig. wrs., 1st ed. Morrill 241-398 1978 $7.50

FREMANTLE, ANNE   Come to Dust. 1941. First ed. Austin 82-385
1978 $17.50

FREMANTLE, ANNE   James and Joan. 1948. First ed. Austin 82-386
1978 $12.50

FREMANTLE, ARTHUR JAMES L.   Three Months in the Southern States: April-
June 1863. Edinburgh, 1863. Bell Wiley's copy. Broadfoot 46-100 1978 $75

FREMANTLE, ARTHUR JAMES L.   Three Months in the Southern States: April-
June, 1863. New York, 1864. Modern cloth, 1st Amer. ed., rebound copy.
Hayman 73-107 1978 $27.50

FREMANTLE, ARTHUR JAMES L.   Three Months in the Southern States: April-
June, 1863. New York, 1864. 1st ed. Jenkins 116-469 1978 $45

FREMONT, JOHN CHARLES   Life, Explorations and Public Services of...
Boston, 1856. First ed., binding worn, marginal stains, foxing, good used copy,
scarce. Biblo 247-215 1978 $32.50

FREMONT, JOHN CHARLES   A Report on an Exploration of the Country Lying,
between the Missouri River and the Rocky Mountains,.... Washington, 1843.
Illus., plates, map, original printed wr., mended, half morocco slipcase, 1st ed.
Ginsberg 14-354 1978 $225

FRENCH, ALLEN   The First Year of the American Revolution.
Boston, 1934. Maps. MacManus 239-572 1978 $27.50

FRENCH, D. G.   Standard Canadian Reciter... Toronto, 1918.
Bound. Hood's 115-337 1978 $20

FRENCH, G. R.   A Catalogue of the Antiquities and Works of Art.
1869. Plts., 2 vols., 4to., half calf. F. Edwards 1013-298 1978 £40

FRENCH, GEORGE   An Answer to a Scurrilous Libel, Intitled a Letter
to Mr. G. French... London, 1719. 1st ed., 8vo, contemporary panelled calf,
neatly rebacked, gilt. Deighton 5-37 1978 £55

FRENCH, HENRY W.   Our Boys in Ireland. New York, (1891). Lg.
8vo., orig. cloth-backed pic. covers, illus., very good. Americanist 103-36
1978 $25

FRENCH, J. W.   Modern Power Generators, Steam, Electric and
Internal-Combustion and Their Application to Present-Day Requirements. 1908.
2 vols., 4to., illus., orig. Art Nouveau decor. cloth. Quaritch 977-220 1978
$150

FRENCH, J. W.   Modern Power Generators, Steam, Electric and
Internal Combustion.... 1908. Coloured plts., 2 vols., folio. George's 635-
972 1978 £35

FRENCH, JOHN HOMER   Gazetteer of the State of New York. Syracuse,
1860. Plts., "7th Ed.", 1/2 lea., nice sound copy, no foxing. Butterfield 21-
181 1978 $35

FRENCH, JONATHAN   The True Republican.... Philadelphia, 1858.
Full leather covers, rubbed but solid and tight copy, illus. with portraits. Hayman 71-257 1978 $10

FRENCH, SAMUEL LIVINGSTON   Reminiscences of Plymouth, Luzerne County.
(Plymouth, 1915). Illus, 8vo., 1st ed. Morrill 239-578 1978 $8.50

FRENCH Art of the Eighteenth Century. 1914. 4to., plts., buckram. Quaritch
983-186 1978 $75

FRENCH Equatorial Africa and Cameroons. 1942. Maps, illus., orig. cloth, 8vo.
Edwards 1012-256 1978 £20

FREND, WILLIAM   An Account of the Proceedings of the University
of Cambridge Against William Frend. Cambridge, 1793. Half vellum, maroon
label, good. Jarndyce 16-88 1978 £15

FREND, WILLIAM   Peace & Union... Cambridge, 1793. Rebound
in grey bds., 2nd. ed., v.g. Jarndyce 16-87 1978 £16

FRENEAU, PHILIP   The Miscellaneous Works of Mr. Philip Freneau
Containing His Essays, and Additional Poems. Philadelphia, 1788. 1st ed., 8vo.,
extra thick paper ed., internally fine copy, lightly scuffed 19th Cent. calf.
Current Misc. 8-21 1978 $150

FRENEAU, PHILIP   The Poems of ..., Poet of the American Revolution. Princeton, 1902-1907. 3 vols., orig. cloth, 1st ed., ltd. to 1,250 sets,
scarce. MacManus 238-484 1978 $150

FRENEAU, PHILIP   Poems Written Between the Years 1768 and 1794...
Monmouth, 1795. Old calf, 1st of this ed., good, front and rear blank pgs. missing, scarce. MacManus 238-483 1978 $150

FRERE, BENJAMIN   The Adventures of a Dramatist, on a Journey to
the London Managers. London, 1813. 2 vols. in one, 12mo, contemporary half
calf (trifle worn), spine gilt, 1st ed., very good, very rare. Ximenes 47-110
1978 $250

FRESENBORG, BERNARD   "Thirty Years in Hell". St. Louis, (1904).
Cloth. Hayman 73-219 1978 $7.50

FRESHFIELD, DOUGLAS W.   The Exploration of the Caucasus. London &
New York, 1896. 1st. ed., 2 vols., imp. 8vo, 4 coloured folding maps, plts.,
illus., orig. two-tone green buckram, gilt, t.e.g., others uncut, spine trifle
faded, one inner hinge trifle cracked, internally good copy. Dieghton 5-74
1978 £65

FREUD, SIGMUND   Die Frage Der Laienanalyse. Vienna, 1926.
8vo., cloth, 1st ed. Salloch 345-72 1978 $45

FREUD, SIGMUND   A General Introduction to Psychoanalysis. New
York, (1920). 8vo., frontis, orig. blue cloth, gilt lettering on upper cover,
ex-lib., good copy. Zeitlin 245-87 1978 $65

FREUD, SIGMUND   Das Ich Und Das Es. Leipzig, Wien, Zurich,
1923. 8vo., illus., orig. prtd. orange wrs., light browning, very good unopened
& uncut copy, 1st ed. Zeitlin 245-88 1978 $195

FREUD, SIGMUND   Die Infantile Cerebrallahmung. Wien, 1897.
8vo., modern white simulated lea. binding, gilt lettered, margins lightly browned, very good copy, lst ed., rare.   Zeitlin 245-89 1978 $350

FREUD, SIGMUND   The Interpretation of Dreams. London, 1921.
Thick 8vo., cloth.   Salloch 345-73 1978 $25

FREUD, SIGMUND   Die Traumdeutung. Leipzig und Wien, 1900.
8vo., orig. black pebbled cloth, gilt lettering on spine, former owner's embossed stamp, fine copy laid in green cloth case, lst ed., 600 copies prtd.   Zeitlin 245-90 1978 $4,500

FREUD, SIGMUND   Uber Psychoanalyse, Funf vorlesungen gehalten zur 20 jahrigen Grundungsfeier der Clark University in Worcester, Mass. September 1909. Leipzig und Wien, 1920. 8vo., orig. grey-green prtd. wrs., pencil underlining & marks, very good, uncut copy, lst ed.   Zeitlin 245-91 1978 $30

FREWEN, MORETON   Melton Mowbray, and Other Memories. London, 1924. Illus., orig. cloth, lst ed.   Ginsberg 14-699 1978 $85

FREY, ALBERT R.   Sobriquets and Nicknames. n.d.   Cloth, shabby.   Eaton 45-193 1978 £8

FREY, CL.   Pirates et Rebelles au Tonkin, nos Soldats au Yen-The. Paris, 1892. 8vo., orig. covers.   Van der Peet 127-298 1978 Dfl 60

FREY, CARROLL   A Bibliography of the Writings of H. L. Mencken. Philadelphia, 1924. Orig. cloth-backed bds., paper labels, lst ed., #2 of 85 lg. paper copies signed by Mencken and Frey, bookplts., rubbed, otherwise very good.   MacManus 238-984 1978 $250

FREYTAG, GUSTAV   Debit and Credit. New York, 1858. Orig. binding, clean, cover chipped around edges.   Hayman 71-225 1978 $7.50

FRIAR, JOHN G.   A Practical Spanish Grammar for Border Patrol Officers. 1949. Paper.   Austin 79-261 1978 $10

THE FRIAR and Boy; or, The Young Piper's Pleasant Pastime;.... London, c.1750. 12mo, large woodcut, excellent copy, 3/4 leather and marbled boards, fine.   Victoria 34-311 1978 $450

FRIDOLIN, STEPHAN   Schatzbwhalter oder Schrein der wahren Reichtumer des Heils und ewiger Seligkeit. Numberg, 1491. lst and only ed., rare, folio, woodcuts, old vellum.   Gilhofer 75-47 1978 SFr 55,000

FRIEDELL, EGON   Cultural History of the Modern Age. 1930. Vol. I only.   Allen 234-1246 1978 $8.50

FRIEDELL, EGON   A Cultural History of the Modern Age. 1930. 3 vols., roy. 8vo.   George's 635-650 1978 $8.50

FRIEDLANDER, ALFRED   Hypotension. Baltimore, 1927. 8vo., d.w., lst ed.   Morrill 239-91 1978 $7.50

FRIEDLANDER, LUDWIG   Roman Life & Manners Under the Early Empire. 1913. 4 vols., tops of 2 spines slightly torn.   Allen 234-348 1978 $30

FRIEDLANDER, M. J.   Die Altniederlandische Malerei. Leiden, 1944. 4to., orig. covers, plts.   Van der Peet H-64-37 1978 Dfl 50

FRIEDLAENDER, PAUL   Platon. I: Eidos, Paideia, Dialogos. II: Die Platonischen Schriften. Berlin and Leipzig, 1928-1930. 4to., cloth.   Salloch 348-199 1978 $60

FRIEDMAN, ELISHA M.   International Commerce and Reconstruction. 1920.   Austin 80-619 1978 $10

FRIEDMANN, HERBERT   The Natural History Background of Camouflage. 1942. Illus., paper.   Austin 80-106 1978 $7.50

THE FRIENDLY Couriere: By Way of Letters From Persons in Town to their Acquaintance in the Country. 1711. lst. ed., 8vo., modern bds., water-stained.   Hannas 54-135 1978 £55

FRIENDS OF AMERICAN ART   First Yearbook. Chicago, 1910-11. Illus.   Biblo BL781-594 1978 $10

FRIENDS OF DEMOCRACY   The Case Against Joseph E. McWilliams. n.d. ca. 1940. Illus. with photos, facsimiles.   Austin 79-461 1978 $12.50

FRIENDS OF DEMOCRACY   Father Coughlin. Kansas City, n.d. ca. 1940. Illus., paper.   Austin 79-170 1978 $27.50

FRIENDSHIP'S Offering: a Christmas, New Year, and Birthday Present, for MDCCCLIV. Philadelphia, 1854. Orig. red lea., rubbed, plts. engr. by Sartrain.   Hayman 73-220 1978 $10

FRIES, ADELAIDE L.   Records of the Moravians in North Carolina. 1947. Illus., lst ed.   Austin 79-495 1978 $27.50

FRIPP, E. I.   Master Richard Quyny, Bailiff of Stratford-Upon-Avon and Friend of Shakespeare. Oxford, 1924. Illus., octavo, good.   Upcroft 10-323 1978 £6

FRIPP, E. I.   Shakespeare Studies; Biographical and Literary. 1930. 34 plts., octavo, good.   Upcroft 10-324 1978 £6.50

FRISBIE, LEVI   Inaugural Address, Delivered in the Chapel of the University at Cambridge, November 5, 1817. Cambridge, 1817. Disbound, sm. library stamp on back page.   Hayman 73-221 1978 $10

FRISI, PAOLO   Elogio del Galileo. Livorno (Leghorn), 1775. 8vo., orig. wrs., uncut, very light dampstaining, but fine copy, lst ed., Livorno issue.   Norman 5-120 1978 $95

FRISI, PAOLO   Traite des Rivieres et des Torrens. Paris, 1774. 4to., half calf.   F. Edwards 1013-75 1978 £70

FRISI, PAOLO   A Treatise on Rivers and Torrents. London, 1818. 4to., plts., orig. cloth backed bds., uncut.   Quaritch 977-221 1978 $250

FRISWELL, HAIN   Ghost Stories and Phantom Fancies. 1858. Orig. pict. bds., backstrip missing, good, first English ed.   Bell Book 17-327 1978 £15

FRITH, JOHN   A Boke Made by Johan Fryth, Prysoner in the Tower of London,.... London, 1548. 8vo, 18th-century calf, 3rd ed., one signature misbound, fine copy complete with final leaf.   Ximenes 47-111 1978 $350

FRITSCH, GUSTAV THEODOR   Die Elektrischen Fische. Leipzig, 1887-1890. Folio, 2 vols., litho. plts., woodcuts, orig. cloth-backed prtd. bds., very good, unopened & uncut copy, lst ed.   Zeitlin 245-92 1978 $175

FRITTS, FRANK   Fifth Avenue to Farm. 1938. Ex-lib.   Austin 80-620 1978 $10

FRITZ, SAMUEL   Journal of the Travels and Labours of...in the River of the Amazons Between 1686 and 1723. London, 1922. Maps, orig. cloth.   Biblo BL781-109 1978 $15

FROGER, PIERRE   Panaches et Culottes de Peau. Angers, 1946. Hand-coloured plts. by author, 8vo., orig. wrappers, uncut, preserved in leather folder.   F. Edwards 1013-299 1978 £38

FROISETH, JENNIE A.   The Women of Mormonism.... Detroit, 1882. Orig. binding, lst. ed., clean, illus.   Hayman 71-257 1978 $15

FROISSART, JOHN   Chronicles of England, France, Spain and the Adjoining Countries. London, 1839. 2 vols., t.e.g., 4to., color extra plts., bound from orig. 16 parts of 1838, wrs. bound in at back of each vol., bound in 3/4 maroon mor., near mint.   Current 24-218 1978 $145

FROISSART, JOHN   Chronicles of England, France, Spain and the adjoining Countries from the latter part of the Reign of Edward II to the Coronation of Henry IV. 1839. Text illus., 2 vols., roy. 8vo., half mor., spines stained.   George's 635-651 1978 £20

FROISSART, JOHN   Froissart's Cronycles of England, Fraunce, Spayne, Portyngale, Scotlande, Bretayne, Flaunders & Other Places Adjoynynge. Oxford, 1927-28. 8vo., bds., cloth backs, paper labels, as issued, maps and coats-of-arms by Paul Woodroffe and colored by hand, 1 of 350 sets on Kelmscott handmade paper, 8 vols., very fine.   Duschnes 220-281 1978 $550

FROISSART, JOHN   Illuminated Illustrations of Froissart Selected from the Ms. in the British Museum by H. N. Humphreys... London, 1844 & '45. 2 vols., t.e.g., 4to., handcolored plts., orig. wrs. bound in, some soiling & spotting on wrs., plts. perfect, green cloth with red mor. spines, very scarce. Current 24-219 1978 $285

FROLICH, L.   Girofle-Girofla. Paris, n.d. Plates and pictorial wrappers all by Frolich, very good. Victoria 34-313 1978 $22.50

FROLICH, L.   Nous n'Irons Plus au Bois. Paris, n.d. Book of 8 color plates, pictorial wrappers all by Frolich, all scarce, very good. Victoria 34-312 1978 $22.50

FROLICH, L.   Le Roi Dagobert. Paris, n.d. Book of plates and pictorial wrappers by Frolich, very minor margin edge waterstain, very good. Victoria 34-314 1978 $200

FROM Dixie Richmond, 1893. Orig. articles. Bell Wiley's copy. Broadfoot 46-101 1978 $15

FROM Mine to Mint...The Dime Savings Mining Co. New York, [ca. 1900]. Illus., original printed wr., 1st ed. Ginsberg 14-403 1978 $35

FROM Niagara to the Sea, Official Guide, 1898. Montreal, 1898. Wrappers with pictorial design. Hood's 115-966 1978 $25

FROM Puget Sound to the Rhine. N.P. (Denver), n.d. Orig. binding, clean, slightly soiled. Hayman 71-797 1978 $8.50

FRONTIER Forts of Pennsylvania. 1896. Illus., color plts., maps, 2 vols., front hinge cracked, vol. I., covers rubbed. Baldwins' 51-437 1978 $75

FROST, AARON   Idaho Springs: Its Mines and Mineral Waters. Georgetown, 1880. Original printed wr., illus., 1st ed., rare. Ginsberg 14-257 1978 $175

FROST, ARTHUR BURDETT   The A. B. Frost Portfolio. New York, 1904. Lg. folio, contained in orig. bds., few tears & dampstains in margins of plts., folio covers loose, worn in spots. Morrill 239-392 1978 $50

FROST, ARTHUR BURDETT   Stuff and Nonsense. New York, (1884). Illus., 4to., orig. pict. bds., 1st ed., covers a bit stained and worn, but very good. MacManus 238-485 1978 $50

FROST, DONALD MC KAY   Notes on General Ashley: The Overland Trail and South Pass. Worcester, 1945. Original boards with cloth backstrip, one of 50 copies. Ginsberg 14-355 1978 $75

FROST, JOHN   An Abridgment of Elements of Criticism.... New York, 1848. New ed., clean. Hayman 71-258 1978 $7.50

FROST, JOHN   The Book of the Navy; Comprising a General History of the American Marine. New York, 1842. 1st ed., text and plts. foxed, bind. worn. Biblo BL781-52 1978 $34.50

FROST, JOHN   Lives of American Merchants, Eminent for Integrity, Enterprise and Public Spirit. New York, 1844. 12mo, frontis., orig. cloth, very good. MacManus 239-170 1978 $15

FROST, R. W.   Concerning McMaster, the University's Past and Present in Facts and Figures. Hamilton, 1947. Card cover, illus. Hood 116-369 1978 $7.50

FROST, ROBERT   Closed for Good. 1948. 16mo, pr. wrs., wood engravings by Thomas Nason, 1st eds., fine cond. Duschnes 220-106 1978 $30

FROST, ROBERT   Collected Poems. New York, 1930. Cloth, sm. bkplt, near fine, 1 of 1000 numbered copies signed by Frost. Dawson's 447-225 1978 $50

FROST, ROBERT   Complete Poems, 1949. New York, 1949. First U.S. ed., portrait, very good. Bell Book 17-383 1978 £15

FROST, ROBERT   Come In and Other Poems. (New York, 1943). Illus., pic. tan buckram, 1st ed., fine in chipped dust jacket. Bradley 49-126 1978 $10

FROST, ROBERT   Come In and Other Poems. (New York), 1943. Illus., cloth, very fine in fine d.w. Dawson's 447-226 1978 $25

FROST, ROBERT   From Snow to Snow. New York, 1936. 4to, green cloth, gilt inscription, Nice in rubbed and slightly chipped d.w., 1st ed., collector's cond. Desmarais 1-171 1978 $15

FROST, ROBERT   A Further Range. New York, 1936. First U.S. ed., very good, slightly worn d.w. Bell Book 17-384 1978 £15

FROST, ROBERT   A Further Range. New York, (1936). Cloth, ink inscr. Dawson's 447-227 1978 $15

FROST, ROBERT   A Masque of Mercy. New York, (1947). Orig. cloth-backed bds., 1st ed., 1 of 751 numbered copies, signed by author, boxed. MacManus 238-658 1978 $60

FROST, ROBERT   A Masque of Mercy. New York, (1947). Bds., cloth back, mint in glassine wr. & slipcase, 1 of 751 numbered copies signed by author. Dawson's 447-228 1978 $45

FROST, ROBERT   A Masque of Mercy. New York, 1947. No. 580 of 751 copies signed by author, 4to., cloth-backed bds., fine, worn slipcase. Bell Book 17-385 1978 £38.50

FROST, ROBERT   A Masque of Mercy. New York, 1947. 8vo, blue cloth, stated 1st pr., faded on spine of d.w., Mint, 1st ed. Desmarais 1-173 1978 $15

FROST, ROBERT   A Masque of Reason. New York, (1945). Cloth, worn & slightly torn d.w. Dawson's 447-229 1978 $15

FROST, ROBERT   A Mask of Reason. New York, 1945. 8vo, blue cloth, stated 1st printing, Fine , d.w., 1st ed., collector's cond. Desmarais 1-174 1978 $12.50

FROST, ROBERT   A Masque of Reason. New York, 1945. Fine in torn d.w. Desmarais B-256 1978 $15

FROST, ROBERT   Mountain Interval. New York, 1916. 8vo, blue cloth, gilt lettering on cover and spine, 1st issue, ownership inscription, 1st ed., collector's cond. Desmarais 1-175 1978 $40

FROST, ROBERT   Mountain Interval. New York, (1916). Cloth, fine, 1st state, rare. Dawson's 447-230 1978 $85

FROST, ROBERT   New Hampshire, a Poem With Notes and Grace Notes. New York, 1923. Woodcuts by J. J. Lankes, 1st ed., signed by Frost, corners bumped. Americanist 102-50 1978 $100

FROST, ROBERT   The Poems of Robert Frost. New York, 1946. First U.S. ed., very good, d.w., inscribed by author. Bell Book 17-386 1978 £22.50

FROST, ROBERT   Steeple Bush. New York, 1947. 8vo, green cloth, near Mint, d.w., 1st ed. Desmarais 1-176 1978 $30

FROST, ROBERT   Steeple Bush. New York, 1947. Orig. cloth-backed bds., 1st ed., 1 of 751 numbered copies, signed by author, boxed. MacManus 238-659 1978 $60

FROST, ROBERT   Steeple Bush. New York, 1947. Bds., cloth spine, near mint in glassine wr. & slipcase, 1 of 751 numbered copies signed by author. Dawson's 447-231 1978 $75

FROST, ROBERT   Steeple Bush. New York, (1947). Cloth, fine in very good d.w., 1st trade ed. Dawson's 447-232 1978 $30

FROST, ROBERT   West-Running Brook. New York, 1928. 1st ed., 2 vols., ltd. to 1000 signed copies, 8vo., t.e.g., signed by Frost, near mint copy, green cloth slipcase, scarce, crudely repaired publisher's box. Current Misc. 8-22 1978 $885

FROST, ROBERT   West-Running Brook. New York, (1928). Bds., cloth back, very good in d.w., clean & bright, 2nd state, 1st ed. Dawson's 447-233 1978 $15

FROST, ROBERT   A Witness Tree. New York, (1942). Cloth, fine in very good d.w. Dawson's 447-234 1978 $30

FROST, T.   The Realm of the Ice King. (1875). Sm. 8vo., folding map, illus., dec. cloth. Edwards 1012-574 1978 £12

FROST, WALTER   Bacon Und Die Naturphilosophie. Munich, 1927. Salloch 348-10 1978 $11

FROST & ADAMS, CO.   Descriptive Catalogue. Boston, 1914. Illus., sm. 8vo., orig. wrs. Morrill 241-15 1978 $12.50

FROTHINGHAM, OCTAVIUS BROOKS Gerrit Smith. New York, 1878. 1st ed., illus., orig. cloth, rubbed, but very good. MacManus 239-816 1978 $17.50

FROTHINGHAM, RICHARD, JR. The History of Charlestown, Mass. Charlestown, 1845. Illus., fold. map, rebound, lib. marks. MacManus 239-1019 1978 $40

FROTHINGHAM, WASHINGTON History of Montgomery County. Syracuse, 1892. 1st ed., thick 4to., illus., t.e.g., rebound, fine. MacManus 239-1094 1978 $60

FROTIER DE LA COSTE-MESSELIERE, PIERRE Les Tresors de Delphes. Paris, (1950). 4to., plts. Biblo BL78-366 1978 $22.50

FROUDE, JAMES ANTHONY The English in the West Indies. 1888. 1st. ed., illus. engraved on wood by G. Pearson, half title, orig. green cloth, lib. label removed from upper cover, very slight wear to top of leading hinge, otherwise good. Jarndyce 16-1167 1978 £20

FROUDE, JAMES ANTHONY The English in the West Indies, or the Bow of Ulysees. 1888. 1st. ed., vignette, woodcut plts., orig. cloth, 8vo, label removed from front cover. Edwards 1012-717 1978 £18

FROUDE, JAMES ANTHONY History of England from the Fall of Wolsey to the Death of Elizabeth. 1858. 12 vols., covers faded and rubbed, 8vo. George's 635-652 1978 £7.50

FROUDE, JAMES ANTHONY History of England from the Fall of Wolsey to the Death of Elizabeth. 1898. 12 vols., cr. 8vo., some spines badly stained. George's 635-653 1978 £5

FROUDE, JAMES ANTHONY Life and Letters of Erasmus. New York, 1894. 1st Amer. ed., fr. inner hinge sprung. Biblo 251-263 1978 $17.50

FROUDE, JAMES ANTHONY Short Studies on Great Subjects. 1903. 4 vols., cr. 8vo. George's 635-1343 1978 £5.25

FROUDE, JAMES ANTHONY Short Studies on Great Subjects. 1905. Half blue prize calf, rubbed, 8vo. George's 635-1344 1978 £7.50

FROUDE, JAMES ANTHONY Thomas Carlyle: A History of the First Forty Years of His Life....with, A History of His Life in London.... 1882-85. Library ed., plts., 4 vols., 8vo., orig. cloth. Howes 194-707 1978 £25

FRUEDENTHAL, ELSBETH E. The Aviation Business. 1940. Austin 80-621 1978 $12.50

FRY, CAROLINE   The Listener. New York, 1852. Orig. cloth, illus, 2 vols. in 1. Greene 78-42 1978 $25

FRY, CHRISTOPHER   The Lady's Not for Burning. London, 1949. Fine in lightly soiled d.w. Desmarais B-261 1978 $12.50

FRY, CHRISTOPHER   Thor, with Angels; a play. Canterbury, 1948. One of 750 copies, wrappers, fine, first ed. Rota 211-128 1978 £12

FRY, F. M.   A Historical Catalogue of the Pictures, Hearse-Cloths and Tapestry at Merchants Taylors' Hall. 1907. Illus., roy. 8vo. George's 635-22 1978 £7.50

FRY, HENRY P.   The Modern Ku Klux Klan. Boston, (1922). Orig. cloth, fine copy. MacManus 239-171 1978 $17.50

FRY, ROGER   Giovanni Bellini. 1899. Plts., sm. 4to., cloth-backed bds., covers somewhat rubbed & soiled, else good, first English ed. Bell Book 16-365 1978 £10.50

FRY, ROGER   Giovanni Bellini. 1899. Plts., sq. 8vo. George's 635-94 1978 £5.25

FRY, ROGER   Last Lectures. Cambridge, 1939. Roy. 8vo. George's 635-149 1978 £15

FRY, ROGER   Vision and Design. 1920. Illus., 4to. George's 635-150 1978 £22.50

FRY, THOMAS   Domestic Portraiture. 1833. 8vo., contemp. blue calf gilt, slightly rubbed. P. M. Hill 142-114 1978 £12

FRYER, JOHN   A New Account of East-India and Persia... 1698. Portrait, maps, plts., sm. folio, calf, rebacked & repaired, some slight browning. Edwards 1012-65 1978 £375

FUCHS, EDWARD   Die Karekatur Der Europaischen Voiker. Berlin, (1901). 500 illus., spine chipped & worn. Baldwins' 51-80 1978 $20

FUCHS, EMIL   Concerning the Art of Etching. (New York), 1926. Plts., 8vo., orig. wrs. Morrill 239-393 1978 $10

FUCHS, LEONHARD   Plantarum Eefigies... Lyons, 1551. 16mo., woodcuts, gatherings misbound, cont. Lyonese calf, clean and crisp, second ed. Quaritch 978-59 1978 $1,700

FUENTES, MANUEL E.   Lima: Sketches of the Capital of Peru... Paris, 1866. Woodcut frontis, coloured title, portrait, litho. plts., imp. 8vo, orig. printed bds., cloth spine, crease down centre, cover slightly dust-soiled. Edwards 1012-646 1978 £50

FUESS, CLAUDE MOORE   Daniel Webster. Boston, 1930. Illus., 2 vols. MacManus 239-826 1978 $22.50

FUILLEVERT, S.   Fuillevert's Science of Palmistry. Chicago, 1897. Illus., 8vo., sm. stain fr. cover. Morrill 239-394 1978 $9.50

FUJIMOTO, T.   The Nightside of Japan. London, 1927. Illus., cloth, front endpaper browned, little bumped, 3rd printing. Dawson's 449-122 1978 $30

FULGOSUS, BAPTISTA   De dictus factisque memorabilibus collectanea. Milan, 1509. 1st ed., folio, Roman letter, rare, very good, full old vellum. Bennett 20-79 1978 $850

FULKERSON, H. S.   A Civilian's Recollections of the War Between the States. Louisiana, 1939. Cover spotted, Bell Wiley's Copy. Broadfoot's 44-157 1978 $70.00

A FULL And Interesting Account of the Great Hippopotamus, or River Horse.... London, 1764. 8vo, 4 wood engraved vignettes, some spotting, orig. printed green paper wrapper, wood engraved illus. Deighton 5-15 1978 £35

FULL And True Relation of the Revolution in the Kingdom of Siam... 1690. Sm. 4to, modern calf. Edwards 1012-148 1978 £200

FULLER, B. A. G.   History of Greek Philosophy. 1923-31. 3 vols. in 1. Allen 234-350 1978 $20

FULLER, CLAUD E.   Firearms of the Confederacy. Huntington, 1944. Bell Wiley's copy. Broadfoot's 44-159 1978 $60

FULLER, EMELINE L.   Left by the Indians or Rapine, Massacre and Cannibalism on the Overland Trail in 1860. New York, 1936. Reprint of 1892 ed., illus., original wr., ed. limited to 200 copies. Ginsberg 14-356 1978 $25

FULLER, FREDERICK L.   My Half Century as an Inventor. 1938. Austin 80-623 1978 $17.50

FULLER, GEORGE W.   A Bibliography of Bookplate Literature. Spokane, 1926. One of 500 numbered copies signed by editor, very fine. Battery Park I-374 1978 $75

FULLER, HENRY CLAY   Adventures of Bill Longley, Captured by Sheriff Milton Mast and Deputy Bill Burrows...And Was Executed... Nacogdoches, n.d. Original pict. wr., near mint. Jenkins 116-832 1978 $35

FULLER, HIRAM   Belle Brittan on a Tour at Newport and Here and There. 1858. First ed. Austin 82-387 1978 $27.50

FULLER, IGNATIUS   Peace and Holiness; In Three Sermons Upon Several Occasions. 1672. First ed., contemp. sheep, 8vo. Howes 194-49 1978 £22

FULLER, J. D. P.   The Movement for the Acquisition of all Mexico, 1846-1848. Baltimore, 1936. Wr. Jenkins 116-919 1978 $45

FULLER, J. F. C.   Armoured Warfare. 1943. 8vo., orig. cloth. F. Edwards 1013-300 1978 £10

FULLER, J.F.C.   The Generalship of Ulysses S. Grant. London, 1929. Bell Wiley's copy. Broadfoot's 44-160 1978 $20

FULLER, JOHN   The History of Berwick upon Tweed. Edinburgh, 1799. Engrav. frontispiece, plts., good uncut copy, orig. bds., later cloth backstrip, 8vo. K Books 244-366 1978 £20

FULLER, O. MUIRIEL   John Muir of Wall Street. 1927. Austin 79-264 1978 $10

FULLER, ROBERT   An Account of the Imprisonment and Sufferings of Robert Fuller... Boston, 1833. 8vo., unbound, 1st ed. Morrill 239-92 1978 $30

FULLER, ROBERT H.   Jubilee Jim. The Life of Colonel James Fisk, Jr. New York, 1928. Illus., 1st ed. Biblo BL781-85 1978 $10

FULLER, THOMAS   The Church History of Britain From the Birth of Jesus Christ Until the Year MDCXLVIII. 1837. Plts., new ed., with author's corrections, orig. cloth, spines dull, octavo, good. Upcroft 10-63 1978 £10

FULLER, THOMAS   The Church History of Britain from the Birth of Jesus Christ until 1648. 1842. Engraved plts., 3 vols., half calf, a little rubbed. George's 635-1068 1978 £12.50

FULLER, THOMAS   The Historie of the Holy Warre. Cambridge, 1640. 2nd. ed., engraved title by Marshall, folding map, sm. folio, green morocco, gilt extra, gilt edges, frontis. Traylen 88-250 1978 £130

FULLER, THOMAS   The History of the University of Cambridge.... 1940. Plts., octavo, good. Upcroft 10-64 1978 £15

FULLER, THOMAS   The History of the Worthies of England. 1840. New ed., portrait, stained, 3 vols., contemp. half calf, labels rubbed, 1 missing, scarce, 8vo. Howes 194-871 1978 £35

FULLER, THOMAS E.   The Right Honourable Cecil John Rhodes. London, 1910. Orig. cloth, 8vo, plts. K Books 239-177 1978 £7

FULLERTON, EDITH LORING   How to Make a Vegetable Garden. New York, 1905. Illus., 4to., orig. cloth, 1st ed. Morrill 241-146 1978 $10

FULLERTON, GEORGIANA   Too Strange Not to be True. New York, 1865. 1st Am. ed., 3 vols. in 1, orig. cloth, spine damaged, good copy. Greene 78-43 1978 $45

FULLERTON, W. Y.   The Christ of the Congo River. London, 1928. 2 folding maps, cr. 8vo, orig. cloth. K Books 239-178 1978 £6

FULTON, CHARLES J.   History of Jefferson County, Iowa... Chicago, 1914. Vol. I of II. Hayman 72-369 1978 $15

FULTON, JAMES A.   Uncle Sam, Banker 1910-1940. McKeesport, 1915. Cloth. Hayman 73-222 1978 $8.50

FULTON, JOHN FARQUHAR   Harvey Cushing. Springfield, 1946. First ed., thick 8vo., illus., d.j., fine. Houle 10-112 1978 $35

FULTON, JOHN FARQUHAR   Harvey Cushing, A Biography. Springfield, 1946. D.j., some slight signs of wear. Rittenhouse 49-276 1976 $15

FULTON, JOHN FARQUHAR   Muscular Contraction and the Reflex Control of Movement. Baltimore, 1926. Tall 8vo., illus., orig. green cloth, gilt on spine, bkplt. & library stamps, good copy, 1st ed. Zeitlin 245-304 1978 $85

FULTON, JUSTIN D.   Washington in the Lap of Rome. Boston, (1888). Illus., orig. cloth. MacManus 239-31 1978 $17.50

FULTON, JUSTIN D.   Show Your Colors; or, a Story of Boston Life. New York, (1875). Orig. binding, clean, little rubbed. Hayman 71-383 1978 $7.50

FULTON, ROBERT   Torpedo War, and Submarine Explosions. New York, 1810. Sm. oblong folio, plts., full blue mor., gilt, sm. blindstamp on title, fine copy, 1st ed. Norman 5-*19 1978 $1,500

FUMAGALLI, GIUSEPPE   L'arte della legatura alla corte degli Estensi.... Firenze, 1913. Plts., illus., med. 4to., Cockerell bds., mor. back gilt, orig. wrappers bound in. Forster 130-9 1978 £85

FUNCK-BRENTANO, FRANTZ   Les Lettres de Cachet a Paris. Paris, 1903. Plts., lg. 4to., orig. bds., untrimmed, ex-lib. Morrill 239-396 1978 $17.50

FUNCK-BRENTANO, FRANTZ   The Renaissance. 1936. Top of spine worn. Allen 234-1250 1978 $7.50

FURIETTI, J. A.   De Musiuis. Rome, 1752. 4to., plts., contemp. half calf, a little worn. Quaritch 983-15 1978 $300

FURLONG, CHARLES WELLINGTON   Let 'Er Buck, a Story of the Passing of the Old West. New York, 1921. Cloth. Hayman 72-258 1978 $10

FURLONG, LAWRENCE   The American Coast Pilot. 2nd ed., buckram, 8vo, good. Paine 78-7 1978 $145.00

FURMAN, MOORE   The Letters of Moore Furman, Deputy Quarter-Master General of New Jersey in the Revolution. 1912. Ltd. to 350 copies, good. Nestler Rare 78-163 1978 $85

FURNEAUX, W.   Butterflies and Moths (British). London, 1897. New ed., plts., coloured, text illus., full red calf, 8vo. K Books 244-127 1978 £12

FURNISS, HARRY   The Confessions of a Caricaturist. 1901. 1st. ed., illus., 2 vols., roy. 8vo, orig. cloth, gilt, t.e.g., nice copy. Fenning 32-121 1978 $18.50

FURNISS, HARRY   The Two Pins Club. 1925. Frontis. & drawings by author, very good, first English ed. Bell Book 16-484 1978 £5.50

FURNISS, WILLIAM   The Old World or Scenes and Cities in Foreign Lands. 1849. Illus. Austin 82-389 1978 $12.50

FURNISS, WILLIAM   Waraga, or the Charms of the Nile. New York, 1850. 8 tinted lithographs, cr. 8vo, orig. cloth, rather age-browned, backstrip laid down. K Books 239-179 1978 £10

FURNIVALL, FREDERICK JAMES   Early English Meals and Manners. (1868). Reprint 1931. 8vo. Upcroft 12-151 1978 £10

FURNIVAL, W. J.   Leadless Decorative Tiles, Faience, and Mosaic, Comprising Notes and Excerpts on the History and Materials, Manufacture and Use of Ornamental Flooring Tiles... 1904. 4to., plain and coloured plts., cloth, gilt top. Quaritch 983-82 1978 $180

FURSE, CHARLES WELLINGTON   Illustrated Memoirs of... A.R.A. with Critical Papers and Fragments... 1908. Roy. 4to., plts., buckram. Quaritch 983-187 1978 $30

FURST, HERBERT   The Modern Woodcut. New York, 1924. 4to., illus., orig. pic. cloth, bookplt. removed, very good. MacManus 239-667 1978 $50

FURST, HERBERT   The Woodcut. London, 1927-29. Ltd. 101, good condition. Baldwins' 51-192 1978 $90

FURTHER Papers Relating to the Rebellion in China. 1863. Sm. folio, binders' cloth. Edwards 1012-190 1978 £60

FURTHER Papers Relative to the Recent Discovery of Gold in Australia. London, 1852. Sm. folio, folding engraved map, coloured in outline, bds. Deighton 5-101 1978 £95

FURTHER Queries Upon the Present State of the New English Affairs by S. E. New York, 1865. 8vo., orig. wrs., dampstained, 1 of 250 copies initialled by Joseph Sabin. Morrill 241-147 1978 $12.50

FUTHEY, J. SMITH   Historical Discourse. Philadelphia, 1870. Baldwins' 51-438 1978 $22.50

FUTHEY, J. SMITH   Historical Discourse...the 150th Anniversary of the Upper Octorara Presbyterian Church, Chester County, Pa. Philadelphia, 1870. Tall 8vo., illus., scarce, orig. cloth, very good. Americanist 103-68 1978 $22.50

FUTHEY, J. SMITH   History of Chester County, Penna, with Genealogical.... Philadelphia, 1881. 1st ed., thick 4to, orig. quarter morocco, rubbed, worn, maps & illus. Americanist 101-55 1978 $185

FUTHEY, J. SMITH   History of Chester County, Pa., With Genealogical and Biographical Sketches. Philadelphia, 1881. Illus., lg. 4to., bound in 2 vols., cloth. MacManus 239-1413 1978 $225

FYLEMAN, ROSE   Fairies and Chimneys. London, (1918). 1st book ed., minor cloth rubbing, very good. Victoria 34-318 1978 $20

FYLER, A.   The History of the 50th Regiment from the earliest date to the Year 1881. 1895. Coloured plt., illus., roy. 8vo., red cloth. F. Edwards 1013-519 1978 £50

G

G., MME. C.   Dix Contes pour l'Enfance. Tours, 1857. 12mo,
French binding of impressed boards, heavily decor. in gilt on covers and spine,
very good. Victoria 34-319 1978 $25

GABORIAU, EMILE   Baron Trigault's Vengeance. N. Y., 1913.
Illus., plts., gilt stamped red cloth, t.e.g., very good. Houle 10-113
1978 $10

GABORIAU, EMILE   The Clique of Gold. N. Y., 1913.
Illus., plts., 8 vo., gilt stamped blue cloth, fine. Houle 10-114 1978 $10

GABRIELSON, IRA N.   The Fisherman's Encyclopedia. New York,
(1950). Lg. 4to., deluxe ed., dec. leatherette, orig. owner's name stamped on
cover, illus., plts., some in color. Americanist 102-110 1978 $27.50

GADDIS, MAXWELL P.   Brief Recollections of the Late Rev. George W.
Walker. Cincinnati, 1871. 5th ed., cloth, some edge wear. Hayman 73-531
1978 $8.50

GADDIS, MAXWELL P.   Foot-Prints of an Itinerant. Cincinnati, 1857.
Orig. cl. Ginsberg 16-864 1978 $15.00

GAER, JOSEPH   Heart Upon the Rock. 1950. Austin 79-265
1978 $11

GAETZ, ANNIE L.   The Park Country. (Vancouver, B. C., 1948).
Bds., 1st ed., fine copy in d.w., reinforced, sm. ed., scarce. Dykes 34-96
1978 $35

GAG, WANDA   Millions of Cats. New York, (1928). 1st ed.,
fine copy. Victoria 34-320 1978 $60

GAGE, THOMAS   The English-American His Travail By Sea and
Land... London, 1648. 1st. ed., sm. folio, rare blank A1, contemporary mottled
calf, neatly rebacked, raised bands, green morocco label gilt, "Sr. Henry Blount"
on lower margin of title pg. Deighton 5-38 1978 £585

GAGE, THOMAS   The History of Rowley, Anciently Including
Bradford, Roxford, and Georgetown, From the Year 1639 to the Present Time.
Boston, 1840. Litho. grontis., errata leaf, old 1/2 calf, very good. MacManus
239-1048 1978 $50

GAGE, THOMAS   A New Survey of the West-Indies:.... London,
1677. 3rd ed., octavo, folding map, contemporary calf, rubbed. Bennett 20-80
1978 $500

GAGLIARDELLI, SALVADORE   Soprascritte di Lettere in Forma Cancelleresca,
Corsiva, Appartenenti ad Ogni Grado di Persona. N.P., (Florence), n.d. (1583).
Oblong 4to., old limp vellum, calligraphic specimens. Schumann 511-22 1978
sFr 5,600

GAGNON, ERNEST   Chansons Populaires du Canada. Quebec, 1865.
Wolfe 39-192 1978 $95

GAGNON, ERNEST   Chansons Populaires du Canada. Quebec, 1880.
Deuxieme ed. Wolfe 39-192a 1978 $50

GAGNON, ERNEST   Lettres de Voyage. Quebec, 1876. Wolfe 39-
193 1978 $25

GAINE, HUGH   Hutchins Improved: Being an Almanack..for..1792.
Nestler Rare 78-117 1978 $15

GAINES, HELEN F.   Elementary Cryptanalysis. Boston, 1942. Biblo
BL781-782 1978 $8.50

GAINSBOROUGH, THOMAS   A Collection of Prints, Illustrative of English
Scenery... London, n.d.(1820). Folio, soft ground etchings, 37 in colour,
contemporary straigh grained crimson morocco, gilt line & decorative borders,
all edges gilt, rubbed, lower joints worn. Deighton 5-124 1978 £325

GAIRDNER, J.   History of the Life and Reign of Richard the Third.
Cambridge, 1898. Revised ed., portraits, 8vo. Upcroft 12-153 1978 £8.50

GAITSKELL, C. D.   Arts and Crafts in Our Schools. Toronto, 1949.
Illus. Hood's 115-389 1978 $10

GALANI, CLEMENTIS   Clementis Galani, Surrentini, Clerici Regularis.
1686. Sm. 8vo., marbled bds., calf spine, good. King 7-278 1978 £25

GALDSTON, IAGO   Progress in Medicine. A Critical Review of the
Last Hundred Years. New York, 1940. D.j. fresh, unmarked. Rittenhouse 49-
278 1976 $12.50

GALE, NORMAN   A Book Of Quatrains. Old Bilton, Rug-
by, (1909). Wove Basingwerk Parchment, uncut, orig. green cloth, gilt, very
good or better. Limestone 9-111 1978 $27.50

GALE, NORMAN   A Country Muse. Second Series. Westminster,
1895. Orig. cloth, paper label, 1st of this ed., 1 of 50 lg. paper copies, fine.
MacManus 238-224 1978 $50

GALE, THOMAS A.   The Wonder of the 19th Century! Erie, 1860.
Wr., boxed, very good. Nestler Rare 78-206 1978 $25

GALE, ZONA   Miss Lulu Bett. New York, 1930. Author's
signed pres. Biblo BL781-980 1978 $12.50

GALE, ZONA   Mothers to Men. 1911. First ed., v.g. Austin
82-1169 1978 $27.50

GALE, ZONA   Portage, Wisconsin and Other Essays. New York,
1928. 1st ed. Biblo BL781-981 1978 $10

GALEN, CLAUDIUS
Please turn to
GALENUS

GALENUS   Lanatomie Des Os Du Corps Humain. Lyons,
1541. Sm. 8vo., full red mor., 1st ed. Salloch 345-74 1978 $600

GALET   Le Corps de l'Homme, Traite Complet d'Anatomie
et de Physiologie Humaines,... Paris, 1844. 4 vols., sm. folio, frontis., contemp. red half-mor., marbled bds., gilt back, fine, 1st ed. Gilhofer 74-91
1978 sFr 2,300

GALEZOWSKI, XAVIER   Du Diagnostic des Maladies des Yeux par la Chro-
matoscopie Retinienne, Precede d'une Etude sur les Lois Physiques et Physiologiques
des Couleurs. Paris, 1868. Fldg. plt., tints, 8vo., orig. red cloth, 1st ed.
Offenbacher 30-117 1978 $150

GALIANI, FERDINAND   De' Doveri de' Principi Neutrali Verso I Principi
Guerreggianti... (Naples?), 1782. Lg. 4to., half calf, lightly worn, lib. stamp
on t.p., 1st ed. Gilhofer 74-13 1978 sFr 500

GALILEI, GALILEO   Dialogo...Sopra i Due Massimi Sistemi Del
Mondo Tolemaico, e Copernicano. Florence, 1632. 4to., text diagrs., frontis.
supplied in facsimile, contemp. or early 18th Cent. bds., spine repaired, occas.
browning, but very good copy, 1st ed. Norman 5-119 1978 $2,500

GALILEI, GALILEO   Memorie e Lettere Indite Finora o Disperse....
Modena, 1818-21. 1st ed., quarto, 2 vols., portraits, plts, full crimson mor. with
gilt fillets, 2nd vol. mostly unopened, fine, wide margined. Bennett 20-81 1978
$1,200

GALILEI, GALILEO   Les Nouvelles Pensees De Galilee, Mathemati-
cien et Ingenieur du Duc de Florence. Paris, 1639. Fldg. plt., 8vo., vellum.
Salloch 345-75 1978 $2,200

GALILEI, GALILEO   Systema Cosmicum. Strassburg, 1635. 4to.,
frontispiece, portrait, woodcuts, text browned, contemp. vellum, repaired, library
stamp removed leaving a grey stain, first Latin ed. Quaritch 977-184 1978
$2,000

GALLAND, S.   Le Novelle e la Favole Indiane di Bidpai e di
Lokman. Venezia, 1730. 1st Italian ed., 2 vols., sm. 12mo, original marbled
boards, gilt-decorated leather spines, lightly foxed, fine copy, rare. Victoria
34-321 1978 $75

GALLATIN, A.   The Right of the United States of America to the Northeastern Boundary Claimed by Them.   New York, 1841. Folded map. Hood's 115-595 1978 $27.50

GALLATIN, ALBERT EUGENE   Whistler's Pastels, and other modern profiles. New York, 1913. New ed., 1 of 400 copies, plts., very good, unopened. Bell Book 16-676 1978 £22.50

GALLATIN, E. L.   What Life Has Taught Me.   Denver, [1900]. Illus, original cloth, signed by author. Ginsberg 14-357 1978 $150

GALLEGHY, JOSEPH   The Adventures of Steve Waterhouse, or the Surprising Career of a Texas-man. San Antonio, 1947. 1st ed., autographed. Jenkins 116-477 1978 $15

GALLENGA, ANTONIO   History of Piedmont. London, 1855. 3 vols., folding map, tables, 8vo., orig. cloth. K Books 244-128 1978 £16

GALLI DA BIBIENA, FERDINANDO   Direzione a' Giovani Studenti nel Disegno dell'Architettura Civile... Bologna, 1764.1753. Cont. bds., fine, uncut, 2 vols., engravings, second and third eds. Gilhofer 74-28 1978 sFr 900

GALLOIS, LEONARD   Histoire de Napoleon d'apres Lui-meme. Paris, 1828. 2 parts in 1 vol., 8vo., contemp. half calf. F. Edwards 1013-383 1978 £15

GALLOWAY, SAMUEL   Address Delivered Before the Graduates of the Union Literary Society of Miami University. Springfield, 1838. Disbound. Hayman 72-544 1978 $10

GALLUP, JOSEPH A.   Sketches of Epidemic Diseases in the State of Vermont. Boston, 1815. 8vo., contemp. calf, 1st ed. Morrill 239-93 1978 $65

GALLUP, JOSEPH A.   Sketches of Epidemic Diseases in the State of Vermont from this First Settlement in the Year 1815.... Boston, 1815. Rittenhouse 49-279 1976 $50

GALSWORTHY, JOHN   The Apple Tree. Sydney, 1941. 12mo., 1st Australian ed., name on flyleaf. Biblo BL781-982 1978 $10

GALSWORTHY, JOHN   Author and Critic. New York, 1933. 8vo., cloth, gilt, 1 of 300 copies, 1st ed., fine. Duschnes 220-111 1978 $15

GALSWORTHY, JOHN   Author and Critic. New York, 1933. Cloth, thin. Battery Park 1-172 1978 $45

GALSWORTHY, JOHN   Awakening. London, (1920). 1st ed., orig. pictorial bds., illus., very good or better. Limestone 9-112 1978 $30

GALSWORTHY, JOHN   Captures. 1923. Bookplt., very fine, d.w., half-mor. slipcase, first English ed. Bell Book 16-367 1978 £15

GALSWORTHY, JOHN   Caravan: The Assembled Tales of John Galsworthy. London, 1925. 16mo, green cloth, Fine in d.w., 1st ed., collector's cond. Desmarais 1-179 1978 $10

GALSWORTHY, JOHN   Caravan: Assembled Tales. 1925. First ed., 8vo., orig. cloth, spine faded. Howes 194-873 1978 £4

GALSWORTHY, JOHN   The Collected Poems of John Galsworthy.   New York, 1934. Fine in soiled d.w. Desmarais B-268 1978 $12.50

GALSWORTHY, JOHN   A Commentary. 1908. First ed., cr. 8vo., orig. cloth, last 2 leaves foxed. Howes 194-874 1978 £6.50

GALSWORTHY, JOHN   A Commentary. London, 1930. 8vo, red cloth, uncut, unopened, d.w. damaged, Good, 1st ed., ed. limited to 275 copies and this is no. 128, signed by author, collector's cond. Desmarais 1-180 1978 $22.50

GALSWORTHY, JOHN   A Commentary. 1930. Orig. buckram, gilt top, fine, torn d.w., special ed., ltd. to 250 copies signed by the author, 8vo. Howes 194-875 1978 £9

GALSWORTHY, JOHN   Ex Libris John Galsworthy. London, 1933. Paper wrs., near mint. Desmarais B-269 1978 $7.50

GALSWORTHY, JOHN   Flowering Wilderness. London, 1932. Fine in d.w. Desmarais B-267 1978 $10

GALSWORTHY, JOHN   The Forsyte Saga. London, 1922. One of 275 numbered copies on India paper, signed by author, full limp green calf, very nice, first ed. Rota 212-25 1978 £65

GALSWORTHY, JOHN   From the Four Winds. London, 1897. Orig. cloth, 1st ed., 500 copies printed, bind. a little worn, but good, Florence Henniker's signature on the flyleaf. MacManus 238-660 1978 $250

GALSWORTHY, JOHN   International Thought. Cambridge, 1923. 8vo, grey paper wr., front wr. darkened and slightly chipped with one two inch tear, very Good, 1st ed., collector's cond. Desmarais 1-181 1978 $17.50

GALSWORTHY, JOHN   The Land: A Plea by John Galsworthy. London, 1918. Stitched, covers slightly dust-stained, Fine, 1st ed., collector's cond. Desmarais 1-182 1978 $20

GALSWORTHY, JOHN   A Modern Comedy. 1929. First ed., table, cr. 8vo., orig. cloth. Howes 194-876 1978 £5

GALSWORTHY, JOHN   A Motley. London, 1910. Nice, author's signed autograph pres. inscription, orig. binding, first ed. Rota 212-26 1978 £50

GALSWORTHY, JOHN   Over The River. London, 1933. 1st ed., d.j., very good or better. Limestone 9-114 1978 $12

GALSWORTHY, JOHN   Over the River. London, 1933. 8vo, boards, vellum back somewhat dust-stained, Nice, no. 104 of 375 copies, 1st ed., collector's cond. Desmarais 1-183 1978 $25

GALSWORTHY, JOHN   The Plays of John Galsworthy. London, 1929. 8vo, green cloth, uncut, unopened, mint, slightly stained d.w., 1st ed., handmade paper signed by Galsworthy, ltd. to 1275 copies and this is no. 341. Desmarais 1-184 1978 $30

GALSWORTHY, JOHN   The Plight of the Miners, A National Danger. London, 1928. Fragile, Mint, 1st ed., collector's cond. Desmarais 1-185 1978 $7.50

GALSWORTHY, JOHN   The Roof. London, (1929). First ed., d.w. Biblo 247-544 1978 $15

GALSWORTHY, JOHN   The Silver Spoon. London, 1926. Fine in chipped & soiled d.w. Desmarais B-265 1978 $10

GALSWORTHY, JOHN   The Slaughter of Animals for Food. London, (1913). Mint, green cloth slipcase, scarce, 1st ed., collector's cond. Desmarais 1-186 1978 $25

GALT, JOHN   Collection of the Works. Edinburgh and London, 1895. Portrait, illus., 8 vols., 12mo., orig. cloth. Howes 194-879 1978 £25

GALT, JOHN   The Last of the Lairds... 1826. 1st. ed., half title, half dark blue calf, red label, v.g. Jarndyce 16-672 1978 £52

GALT, JOHN   Letters From the Levant... 1813. Map, half calf, 8vo. Edwards 1012-49 1978 £45

GALT, JOHN   The Life of Lord Byron. 1830. Sm. 8vo., contemp. cloth and label, rather worn and soiled, portraits. P. M. Hill 142-60 1978 £18

GALT, JOHN   The Member: An Autobiography. 1832. 1st. ed., polished calf, green label, spine faded. Jarndyce 16-674 1978 £40

GALT, JOHN   The Omen. Edinburgh, 1825. 8vo, Victorian half calf, spine gilt, 1st ed., pages somewhat stained, very good copy. Ximenes 47-112 1978 $125

GALT, JOHN   Voyages and Travels, 1809-11... 1812. 4to, engraved plts., bds., roan back & corners. Edwards 1012-48 1978 £75

GALTON, FRANCIS   Hereditary Genius. London, 1869. 8vo., orig. maroon cloth with center gilt inset, faded, light foxing, bkplt. & library stamps, good copy, with A.L.s., 1st ed., rare. Zeitlin 245-93 1978 $275

GALTON, FRANCIS   Inquiries Into Human Faculty and Its Development. London, n.d. Published as second ed. Rittenhouse 49-280 1976 $7.50

GALTON, FRANCIS   The Narrative of An Explorer In Tropical South
Africa. London, 1853. 1st. ed., 8vo, tinted lithograph frontispiece, tinted lithograph plts., woodcut plt., folding coloured map, half calf, gilt back.   Deighton
5-13 1978 £58

GALTON, FRANCIS   Narrative of an Explorer in Tropical South Africa,
Being an Account of A Visit to Damaraland in 1851. London, 1889. Cr. 8vo, illus.,
orig. cloth, little shaken. K Books 239-180 1978 £8

GALVEZ, BERNARDO DE   Instructions for Governing the Interior Provinces
of New Spain, 1786. Berkeley, 1951. Limited to 500 numbered copies.   Jenkins
116-487 1978 $100

GALVEZ, BERNARDO DE   Instruccion Formada en Virtud de Real Orden de
S. M.,.... Mexico, 1786. Folio, half morocco slipcase, signed at end with
holograph signature of Francisco Fernandez de Cordova, considerably rare.
Ginsberg 14-358 1978 $5,000

GALY-CAZALAT, ANTOINE   Memoire Theorique et Pratique sur les Bateaux
A Vapeur. Paris, 1837. Plts., 4to., orig. wrappers, roughly rebacked, worn,
unopened, preserved in new cloth box. F. Edwards 1013-76 1978 £120

GAMBOLD, JOHN   The Martyrdom of St. Ignatius. 1773. 8vo.,
contemp. calf, vignette on title-page. P. M. Hill 142-115 1978 £25

GAMBRALL, THEODORE C.   Church Life in Colonial Maryland.   Baltimore,
1885. 1st ed.   MacManus 239-1827 1978 $15

GAMBRALL, THEODORE C.   Studies in the Civil, Social and Ecclesiastical
History of Early Maryland. New York, 1893. Fine. MacManus 239-1842
1978 $20

GAMBRELL, HERBERT   Anson Jones The Last President of Texas.
Garden City, 1948. 1st. ed., orig. binding, minor wear on one edge, clean.
Hayman 71-726 1978 $7.50

GAMBRILLO, M. D.   Archivi Del Futurismo. Rome, (1958-62).
4 to., d.j., 2 vols., fine, illus., reproductions (some in color).   Houle
10-116 1978 $135

GAMBS, JOHN S.   Beyond Supply and Demand.   Columbia University
Press, 1946.   Austin 80-626 1978 $12.50

GAMES and Songs of American Children. New York, 1883. Octavo, orig. pict.
tan cloth, spine faded and chipped. Totteridge 29-44 1978 $60

GAMIO, MANUEL   Mexican Immigration to the United States.
University of Chicago Press, 1930. 1st ed. Austin 79-267 1978 $12.50

THE GAMUT, or, Scale of Music; To Which is Added, A Number of Easy Tunes.
Albany, c. 1815. Orig. wr. worn. Nestler Rare 78-94 1978 $75

GANNETT, HENRY   A Gazetteer of West Virginia.   Washington,
1904. Wrs.   Hayman 73-736 1978 $12.50

GANONG, WILLIAM FRANCIS   Histories, New Brunswick Localities. 1906-
08. 3/4 leather, plts., maps. Hood's 116-215 1978 $225

GANONG, WILLIAM FRANCIS   The History of Caraquet and Pokemouche.
St. John, 1948. Hood's 117-244 1978 $7.50

GANONG, WILLIAM FRANCIS   The Identity of the Animals and Plants Mentioned by the Early Voyagers to Eastern Canada and Newfoundland. 1909. Hood's
116-216 1978 $12.50

GANONG, WILLIAM FRANCIS   A Monograph of the Origin of Settlements in
the Province of New Brunswick. 1904. Maps. Hood's 116-217 1978 $65

GANSON, EVE   Desert Mavericks. Santa Barbara, 1928.
Cloth, illus., 1st ed., fine. Dykes 35-47 1978 $7.50

GANTT, E. W.   Address of...C. S. A., First Published October
7, 1863, at Little Rock... Philadelphia, 1863. Sewn as issued. Ginsberg 14-30
1978 $75

GARBER, JOHN P.   The Valley of the Delaware and Its Place in
American History. Philadelphia, (1934). Illus., nice copy, d.j. MacManus
239-1463 1978 $20

GARCIA, GREGORIO   Origen de los Indios de el Nuevo Mundo,....
Madrid, 1729. Complete with all engravings, preliminary leaves, half morocco,
2nd ed., additions and corrections by Andres Gonzales Barcia. Ginsberg 14-359
1978 $650

GARCIA, GUSTAVE   The Actors' Art... 1882. 1st. ed., 4to,
folding frontispiece, numerous illus., half morocco, orig. printed wrappers bound
in. Hannas 54-326 1978 £15

GARCIA AB ORTO, DEL HUERTO   Aromatum Et Simplicium Aliquot Medicamentorum Apud Indos Nascentium Historia. Antwerp, 1567. Woodcuts, sm. 8vo.,
vellum with label, extremely rare. Salloch 345-76 1978 $500

GARCIA DE PALACIO, DIEGO   Instruccion Nautica Para Navegar (Mexico,
1587). Madrid, 1944. Facsimile ed., ltd., numbered ed., 4to., wrs., uncut.
Salloch 345-77 1978 $85

GARCILASO DE LA VEGA   La Florida Del Inca. Madrid, 1723. Folio,
title in red & black, limp vellum, dust-soiled, tear in 1 leaf repaired, stain in
margins of last 5 pgs. Edwards 1012-489 1978 £125

GARD, WAYNE   Frontier Justice. Norman, 1949. First ed., fine,
d.w., illus. Biblo 247-218 1978 $18.50

GARD, WAYNE   Sam Bass. Boston, 1936. 1st ed., illus., fine.
MacManus 239-1916 1978 $25

GARDEN, ALEXANDER   Anecdotes of the American Revolution. Charleston, 1828. Errata slip, cloth. Broadfoot 50-73 1978 $100

THE GARDEN, an Illustrated Weekly Journal of Horticulture in all its Branches.
London, 1883. Vol. 24, coloured plts., illus., 4to., orig. cloth. K Books 244-
129 1978 £20

A GARDEN Book for Houston. Houston, 1939. Cloth. Jenkins 116-573 1978
$12.50

THE GARDEN Club of America. (Philadelphia, 1938). Portr., 8vo., orig. bds.,
cloth back, 1st ed. Morrill 241-163 1978 $10

GARDENS Old and New, the Country House and its Garden Environment. (1900).
Illus., folio, covers stained and rubbed. George's 635-954 1978 £5.25

GARDINER, D.   The Oxinden Letters 1607-1642... 1933. Plts.,
octavo, good. Upcroft 10-67 1978 £8

GARDINER, RALPH   Englands Grievance Discovered, In Relation to
the Coal Trade... Newcastle, 1796. Folding map, plts., roy. 8vo., half calf,
uncut. Traylen 88-73 1978 £45

GARDINER, ROBERT WILLIAM   Categorical Minute of the Motion of the House of
Commons.... 1859. 1st. ed., roy. 8vo., unbound, sewn as issued, nice copy.
Fenning 32-122 1978 £10.50

GARDINER, S. R.   The Fall of the Monarchy of Charles I, 1637-49.
1882. 2 vols., 8vo. George's 635-654 1978 £15

GARDINER, WILLIAM   The Music of Nature. Boston, 1841. Illus.,
8vo., rebacked with most of orig. backstrip preserved. Morrill 241-670 1978
$10

GARDINER, WREY   New Road 5. London, (1949). First ed., illus.
Biblo 247-608 1978 $15

GARDINER, WREY   Thirteen Stories. London, 1944. First ed., orig.
binding, very nice, d.w. Rota 211-21 1978 £5

GARDNER, ARTHUR   The Peaks, Lochs, & Coasts of the Western Highlands. Edinburgh, 1928. Plts., binders cloth, 8vo. K Books 244-130 1978 £7

GARDNER, ARTHUR H.   Wrecks Around Nantucket. Nantucket, (1930).
Map, illus., fine, wrs. MacManus 239-1755 1978 $15

GARDNER, AUGUSTUS KINSLEY   The French Metropolis. New York, 1850.
2nd ed., illus., steel engrs., 8vo., orig. cloth, occas. foxing. Morrill 241-
149 1978 $10

GARDNER, EDMUND G.   Dante's Ten Heavens: A Study of the Paradiso.
1898. 8vo., orig. cloth. Howes 194-768 1978 £6

GARDNER, EDMUND G.   The Story of Florence. London, (1903). Illus. Biblo BL781-620 1978 $12

GARDNER, ERLE STANLEY   The Case of the Sulky Girl. New York, 1933. Canadian ed., orig. binding. Wolfe 39-200 1978 $15

GARDNER, ERLE STANLEY   Turn on the Heat. 1940. Very good, d.w., first English ed. Bell Book 16-243 1978 £10

GARDNER, F. LEIGH   Bibliotheca Astrologica. London, 1911. Frontis, 8vo, orig. cloth, good. Sexton 7-65 1978 £8.50

GARDNER, JOHN STARKIE   Armour in England from the Earliest Times to the Reign of James the First. 1897-98. Coloured plts., illus., 2 vols. in 1 as issued, roy. 8vo. George's 635-241 1978 £10

GARDNER, JOHN STARKIE   Foreign Armour in England. 1897. Roy. 8vo, coloured plts., mod. half calf. Quaritch 983-126 1978 $40

GARDNER, JOHN STARKIE   Foreign Armour in England. 1898. Coloured plts., text illus., roy. 8vo., covers faded. George's 635-242 1978 £6.50

GARDNER, JOHN STARKIE   Old Silver-Work. 1903. Plts., lg. 4to., buckram, t.e.g., covers little soiled, nice, first English ed. Bell Book 17-812 1978 £50

GARDNER, PERCY   Sculptured Tombs of Hellas. London, 1896. Plts. Biblo BL781-379 1978 $25

GARDNER, SAMUEL   English Gothic Foliage Sculpture. Cambridge, 1927. Cr. 8vo, orig. cloth, plts., good. Sexton 7-18 1978 £5

GARDNER, W. H.   Gerard Manley Hopkins: a study of poetic idiosyncrasy in relation to poetic tradition. 1944. Very good, d.w., buckram, first English ed. Bell Book 16-447 1978 £5.50

GARDNER, W. J.   A History of Jamaica from Its Discovery by Christopher Columbus to the Year 1872. London, 1909. 1st ed., orig. cloth, fine. MacManus 239-218 1978 $30

GARDNER, W. M.   British Coal-Tar Industry, its Origin, Development and Decline. 1915. Illus., 8vo. George's 635-291 1978 £5.25

GARDNER, WILL   The Coffin Saga. Cambridge, (1949). First ed., d.w. Biblo 247-104 1978 $17.50

GARDNER-SHARP, ABBIE   History of the Spirit Lake Massacre and Captivity of Miss Abbie Gardner. Des Moines, 1895. 4th ed., illus., bookplt., orig. cloth, fine. MacManus 239-1164 1978 $25

GARFIELD, JAMES ABRAM   The Works. Boston, 1882. 1st ed., 2 vols., frontis., ports., orig. cloth, hinges in vol. II cracking, else very good set. MacManus 239-174 1978 $32.50

GARFIELD, JAMES RUDOLPH   Report of the Commissioner of Corporations on The Beef Industry. Washington, D. C., 1905. Cloth, 1st ed., fine copy from the Allred Collection, scarce. Dykes 34-150 1978 $50

GARFIELD, JAMES RUDOLPH   Report of the Commissioner of Corporations on The Beef Industry. Wrs. fraying, text fine. Dykes 34-151 1978 $40

GARGAZ, PIERRE-ANDRE   A Project of Universal and Perpetual Peace. New York, 1922. Uncut, unopened. MacManus 239-149 1978 $15

GARGAZ, PIERRE-ANDRE   A Project of Universal & Perpetual Peace Written by...a Former Galley Slave, & Printed by Benj. Franklin at Passy in... 1782. New York, 1922. Excellent uncut copy in slightly worn box, 1 of 1250 copies, fldg. facsimile, Victor Paltsits' copy, inscr., 8vo., orig. cloth, very good. Americanist 103-124 1978 $22.50

GARIN, FRANCOYS   Complainte et Enseignements. Paris, 1832. Sm. 4to., rebound in buckram, leather label, margins browned, ltd. to 100 no. copies only, rare, facsimile. Howes 194-906 1978 £14

GARIOT, J. B.   Treatise on the Diseases of the Mouth. Baltimore, 1843. 8vo., old half calf, rubbed, rebacked. Gurney 75-43 1978 £75

GARLAND, C. M.   Depressions and Their Solution... 1935. Austin 80-628 1978 $10

GARLAND, HAMLIN   The Light of the Star. 1904. Frontis., first ed., v.g. Austin 82-1171 1978 $27.50

GARLAND, HAMLIN   A Little Norsk or Ol' Pap's Flaxen. New York, 1892. Orig. dec. bds., 1st ed., nice, scarce. MacManus 238-486 1978 $30

GARLAND, HAMLIN   Trail-makers of the Middle Border. New York, 1926. Illus., 1st ed., front inner hinge split. Biblo BL781-984 1978 $9

GARLAND, JAMES   Tregarthen Hall, A Novel. 1871. 1st. ed., 3 vols., half titles, orig. green cloth, v.g. Jarndyce 16-675 1978 £48

A GARLAND of New Songs. Newcastle upon Tyne, c.1800. Chapbook, large cover woodcut, slight paper darkening. Victoria 34-323 1978 $225

THE GARLAND of Rachel, by Divers Kindly Hands. Portland, Mosher Press, 1902. 1 of 450 copies, orig. parchment wrs. with silk ties, rare, 8vo., very good. Americanist 103-62 1978 $75

GARMANN, CHRISTIAN FRIEDRICH   De Miraculis Mortuorum. Lipsiae, 1670. Woodcut, 4to., 3/4 vellum, 1st ed., paper browned. Offenbacher 30-53 1978 $275

GARNEAU, FRANCOIS XAVIER   Histoire du Canada Depuis sa Decouverte Jusqu'a nos Jours. Quebec, 1852. Second ed. Wolfe 39-195 1978 $100

GARNEAU, FRANCOIS XAVIER   Histoire du Canada. Paris, 1928. 2 vols., bound in black fab., with orig. wrappers inside. Hood's 115-596 1978 $60

GARNEAU, FRANCOIS XAVIER   History of Canada, From the Time of Its Discovery Till the Union Year 1840-41.... Montreal, 1862. 2nd ed., folding map, portrait, 2 vols., orig. cloth, 8vo. Edwards 1012-423 1978 £20

GARNER, ELVIRA   Ezekiel. New York, (1937). 1st ed., color illus., very fine, dj. Victoria 34-324 1978 $20

GARNER, JAMES WILFORD   Reconstruction in Mississippi. New York, 1901. Hinges cracked, Bell Wiley's copy. Broadfoot's 44-541 1978 $50

GARNEREY, AUGUST   Livre d'Amour ou Folastreries du Vieux Temps. Paris, (1821). Hand-colored plates, lovely gilt impressed cathedral-design full calf binding, text foxed, minor spine wear, fine copy. Victoria 34-503 1978 $100

GARNETT, DAVID   The Grasshoppers Come. London, 1931. Fine in chipped d.w. Desmarais B-270 1978 $12.50

GARNETT, DAVID   Lady into Fox. 1922. Sm. 8vo., 1st ed., illus., bkplt. of Richard Hughes. Quaritch 979-148 1978 $20

GARNETT, DAVID   A Man in the Zoo. 1924. Sm. 8vo., 1st ed., wood engrs., cloth, bkplt. of Richard Hughes. Quaritch 979-149 1978 $20

GARNETT, DAVID   The Man in the Zoo. London, 1924. Fine in torn & darkened d.w. Desmarais B-271 1978 $10

GARNETT, DAVID   A Rabbit in the Air. London, 1932. First ed., illus., cr. 8vo., very good, d.w., orig. cloth. Howes 194-883 1978 £5

GARNETT, DAVID   The Sailor's Return. 1925. First ed., frontis., cr. 8vo., fine, d.w., orig. cloth. Howes 194-884 1978 £5

GARNETT, DAVID   The Sailor's Return. 1925. One of 160 numbered copies signed by author, buckram, a.e.g., very good, first English ed. Bell Book 16-368 1978 £8.50

GARNETT, EDWARD   The Breaking Point: a censured play. 1907. Orig. linen, very good, first English ed. Bell Book 17-387 1978 £6

GARNETT, EDWARD   Papa's War & other satires. n.d. (c. 1918). Sm. 4to., bds., very good, first English ed. Bell Book 17-388 1978 £5

GARNETT, EDWARD   The Trial of Jeanne d'Arc and Other Plays. London, 1931. 8vo, marbled boards, 1/4 vellum, Fine, special ed., no. 4 of 100 copies, 1st ed., collector's cond. Desmarais 1-187 1978 $35

GARNETT, EDWARD   The Trial of Jeanne d'Arc and Other Plays. London, 1931. Good in torn d.w. Desmarais B-272 1978 $12.50

GARNETT, PORTER   A Documentary Account of the Beginnings of the Laboratory Press, Carnegie Institute of Technology.   Pittsburgh, 1927. Marbled bds., very good, 1 of 160 copies. Dawson's 447-88 1978 $135

GARNETT, PORTER   The Fine Book: A Symposium. Pittsburgh, 1934. Full brown mor., bookplts., one of 225 copies. Dawsons 447-87 1978 $200

GARNETT, PORTER   Papers of the San Francisco Committee of Vigilance of 1851. Berkeley, 1910-1911. Illus., original printed wr. Ginsberg 14-119 1978 $15

GARNETT, R. S.   Letters about Shelley interchanges by three friends: Edward Dowden, Richard Garnett and Wm. Michael Rossetti. 1917. 8vo., orig. cloth. Howes 194-1196 1978 £5

GARNETT, RICHARD   Idylls and Epigrams. 1869. Sm. cr. 8vo., cloth. Eaton 45-194 1978 £5

GARNETT, RICHARD   Poems. London & Boston, 1895. 1st ed., uncut, orig. gilt buckram, unopened, ltd. to 350 copies, U. K., very good or better. Limestone 9-116 1978 $45

GARNETT, RICHARD   Twilight of the Gods, and Other Tales. London, 1888. Orig. blue cloth, good. Greene 78-205 1978 $50

GARRARD, APSLEY CHERRY   The Worst Journey in the World: Antarctic, 1910-1913. 1922. 1st. ed., map, illus., some in colour, 2 vols., 8vo, orig. cloth. Edwards 1012-568 1978 $50

GARRARD, LEWIS H.   Chamberburg in the Colony and the Revolution. Philadelphia, 1856. 1st ed. MacManus 239-1464 1978 $20

GARRARD, LEWIS H.   Wah-to-Yah and the Taos Trail. San Francisco, 1936. Illus., original boards, cloth spine, limited ed. of 550 copies. Ginsberg 14-360 1978 $75

GARRETSON, JAMES EDMUND   A System of Oral Surgery. Philadelphia, 1881. Thick 8vo., plts. 3rd ed., woodcut illus., contemp. calf, library stamps, inscr's, good copy. Zeitlin 245-94 1978 $85

GARRETT, A. C.   Lecture on Texas: Its Climate, Soil Resources, and How to Get and Enjoy Them. St. Louis, 1883. Pr. wr., rare, very fine. Jenkins 116-492 1978 $125

GARRETT, FYDELL E.   The Story of an African Crisis. London, 1897. New enlarged, revised ed., few illus., cr. 8vo., slight foxing, pictorial covers little dull. K Books 239-181 1978 £20

GARRETT, FYDELL E.   The Story of An African Crisis. 1897. Illus., 8vo, orig. pictorial cloth, very good copy. Fenning 32-123 1978 £14

GARRETT, GARET   A Bubble That Broke the World. Boston, 1932. 1st ed. Austin 80-629 1978 $12.50

GARRETT, GARET   Where the Money Grows. 1911. 1st ed. Austin 80-630 1978 $10

GARRETT, PATRICK FLOYD   Pat. F. Garrett's Authentic Life of Billy the Kid. New York, 1927. Photos, scarce reissue of 1882 ed. Jenkins 116-117 1978 $35

GARRETT, SAMUEL BOND   Bond Genealogy. Muncie, 1913. Cloth. Hayman 73-225 1978 $22.50

GARRICK, DAVID   The Fairies. 1755. 2nd. ed., 8vo, disbound. Hannas 54-136 1978 £10

GARRICK, DAVID   Lethe. 1749. 1st. authorized ed., 8vo, half-title, dust-soiled, modern limp calf. Hannas 54-137 1978 £35

GARRICK, DAVID   Pineapples of Finest Flavour. Cambridge, 1930. One of 400 numbered copies, 4to., cloth, plts., fine. Houle 10-120 1978 $45

GARRIGOU-LAGRANGE, R.   Theologia fundamentalis secundum S. Thomae doctrinam.... Romae, 1945. 2 vols., roy. 8vo., half leather, spines faded. George's 635-1142 1978 £7.50

GARRIOCH, A. C.   The Correction Line. Winnipeg, 1933. Illus. Hood 116-848 1978 $45

GARRIOCH, A. C.   A Hatchet Mark in Duplicate. Toronto, 1929. Owners' names on flyleaf. Hood 117-892 1978 $15

GARRISON, E. W.   Memoir of Mrs. Rebekah P. Pinkham, Late Consort of Rev. E. Pinkham, of Sedgwick, Me. Portland, 1840. Portr., 12mo., binding partly faded, some foxing, 1st ed., orig. cloth. Morrill 241-151 1978 $13.50

GARRISON, ELISHA E.   The Riddle of Economics. 1932. Austin 80-631 1978 $8.50

GARRISON, FIELDING HUDSON   History of Medicine. Philadelphia, 1917. Worn, underlined, second ed., revised and enlarged. Rittenhouse 49-285 1976 $9

GARRISON, GEORGE P.   The Lot of the Reformer. Austin, 1891. Orig. printed wr. Jenkins 116-494 1978 $8.50

GARRITY, DEVIN A.   New Irish Poets. New York, 1948. Woodcuts. Biblo 247-822 1978 $15

GARROD, H. W.   The Profession of Poetry and other Lectures. 1929. Orig. cloth, 8vo., d.w. Howes 194-886 1978 £6.50

GARSTON, EDGAR   Greece Revisited and Sketches in Lower Egypt in 1840 With Thirty - Six Hours of a Campaign in Greece in 1825. London, 1842. 1st. ed., 2 vols., 8vo, lithograph frontispieces, lithograph plt., some staining, half polished half calf, marbled bds., marbled paper missing from lower bd. of vol. 2, gilt back, marbled edges. Deighton 5-210 1978 £68

GARTZ, KATE CRANE   The Parlor Provocateur. Pasadena, (1923). 1st ed. Biblo 251-335 1978 $15

GARVEY, MICHAEL ANGELO   The Silent Revolution:.... London, 1852. 8vo, original violet cloth, spine evenly faded, 1st ed., very good copy. Ximenes 47-113 1978 $65

GARVIN, JAMES LOUIS   The Economic Foundations of Peace. 1919. Austin 80-632 1978 $12.50

GARWOOD, DARRELL   Crossroads of America...Kansas City. New York, (1948). Illus. Biblo 247-219 1978 $12.50

GARZONI, TOMASO   L'Hospidale De'Pazzi Incvrabili. Venezia, 1589. 8vo., woodcut, contemp. vellum, gilt lettering on spine, browned, little foxing, fine copy. Zeitlin 245-95 1978 $450

GASCOIGNE, HENRY BARNET   Gascoigne's Path to Naval Fame. Warwick, 1825. Second ed., plts., 8vo., contemp. calf, blind-stamped. F. Edwards 1013-77 1978 £55

GASCOYNE, DAVID   Poems, 1937-1942. London, 1943. Coloured plts., sm. 4to., cloth-backed bds., good, first English ed. Bell Book 17-389 1978 £16.50

GASCOYNE, DAVID   Poems 1937-1942. 1943. First ed., plts. in colour, first issue, fine, frayed d.w., orig. cloth, 8vo. Howes 194-887 1978 £20

GASCOYNE, DAVID   A Vagrant and other poems. 1950. Very good, d.w., first English ed. Bell Book 17-390 1978 £8.50

GASELEE, S.   An Anthology of Medieval Latin. 1925. 8vo. Upcroft 12-157 1978 £4

GASK, NORMAN   Old Silver Spoons of England. London, 1926. Plts., illus., 4to, half orange morocco, cloth sides, few pages little foxed. Traylen 88-377 1978 £30

GASKELL, ELIZABETH CLEGHORN   Mary Barton: A Tale of Manchester Life. London, 1848. 2 vols., orig. cloth, 1st ed., bookplts., spines faded and chipped, inner hinges cracking, covers a little soiled, rare. MacManus 238-225 1978 $250

GASKELL, ELIZABETH CLEGHORN   Ruth. A Novel. London, 1853. 3 vols., orig. cloth, spines faded and slightly torn, 1st ed., inner hinges cracked in vol. I, otherwise good. MacManus 238-226 1978 $225

GASKELL, ELIZABETH CLEGHORN   Wives and Daughters: An Every-Day Story. London, 1866. Illus. by George Du Maurier, 2 vols., orig. cloth, 1st ed., spines worn and repaired, recased. MacManus 238-227 1978 $135

GASKELL, PHILLIP   John Baskerville: A Bibliography. 4to, plts., full-size facsimile. Traylen 88-493 1978 £12

GASKIN, MRS. ARTHUR   Horn-Book Jingles. London, 1896-7. 1st ed., tall, narrow 8vo, plates on thick paper, ornately decorated pictorial impressed cloth covers lightly rubbed, fine. Victoria 34-325 1978 $125

GASPARIN, AGENOR DE   The Uprising of a Great People. New York, 1862. New Amer. ed., cloth, unusually good copy. Hayman 73-224 1978 $12.50

GASPEY, THOMAS   Takings. 1821. First ed., contemp. half calf, etchings, 8vo., spine chipped at head and foot. Howes 194-1386 1978 £15

GASQUET, FRANCIS AIDAN   Collectana Anglo-Premonstratensia. 1904-6. 8vo. Upcroft 12-158 1978 £20

GASQUET, FRANCIS AIDAN   The Eve of the Reformation; Studies in the Religious Life and Thought of the English People. 1900. Octavo, good. Upcroft 10-328 1978 £6.50

GASQUET, FRANCIS AIDAN   Eve of the Reformation. 1927. Allen 234-1253 1978 $8.50

GASQUET, FRANCIS AIDAN   Henry VIII & the English Monasteries. 1910. New buckram. Allen 234-1291 1978 $15

GASQUET, FRANCIS AIDAN   The Old English Bible and other essays. 1908. 2nd ed., 8vo. Upcroft 12-159 1978 £5

GASS, JACOB   Chronicon Ephratense; a History of the Community of Seventh Day Baptists at Ephrata, Lancaster, Penna. Lancaster, 1889. 1st ed. in Eng., binder's cloth, very good, ltd. ed. MacManus 239-1446 1978 $65

GASS, PATRICK   Gass's Journal of the Lewis and Clark Expedition. Chicago, 1904. Illus., orig. cloth, scarce, very fine. MacManus 239-175 1978 $45

GASSENDI, PIERRE   Institutio Astronomica, Juxta Hypotheses Tam Veterum Quam Recentiorum. 1635. 8vo., woodcut plts., text woodcuts, contemp. panelled calf, unlettered, joints split, first printing in England. Quaritch 977-186 1978 $850

GASSENDI, PIERRE   Tychonis Brahei, Equitis Dani, Astronomorum Coryphaei, Vita. Hagae-Comitum, 1655. Portrs., 4to., half vellum, fine copy. Offenbacher 30-54 1978 $275

GASTRELL, FRANCIS   The Religious Education of Poor Children Recommended in a Sermon...June 5, 1707. London, 1707. 2nd ed., 12mo., unbound. Morrill 241-152 1978 $7.50

GATES, CHARLES M.   Messages of the Governors of the Territory of Washington to the Legislative Assembly 1854-1889. Seattle, 1940. Illus., wr. Ginsberg 14-1029 1978 $20

GATES, REGINALD RUGGLES   Human Genetics. Volume 1 & 2. New York, 1948. Rittenhouse 49-287 1976 $25

GATES, SUSA YOUNG   The Life Story of Brigham Young. New York, 1930. Illus. Baldwins' 51-188 1978 $15

GATES' Ninth Annual Mexico Tours, an Ideal Winter Tour. N.P., n.d. (Toledo, c.1902). Wrps. Hayman 71-459 1978 $7.50

GATHORNE-HARDY, ROBERT   Paradisus Dubitantis: an Heroic Poem. N.P., 1929. 8vo, original white boards, decorated in blue and green (spine a bit dull), 1st ed., nice copy, very scarce. Ximenes 47-114 1978 $30

GATINEAU, FELIX   Histoire Des France-Americains De Southbridge, Massachusetts. Framingham, Lakeview Press, 1919. Many illus., in French. Austin 79-269 1978 $47.50

GATTERER, JOHANN CHRISTOFF 1727-99   Elementa Artis Diplomaticae Universalis. Gottingen, 1765. Sm. 4to., contemp. half sheep, plts., first ed. Howes 194-244 1978 £45

GATTERMANN, L.   Die Praxis Des Organischen Chemikers. Berlin, 1940. Slight burn upper edge. Rittenhouse 49-288 1976 $10

GATTI, ATTILIO   The Wrath of Moto. New York, 1941. 1st ed., illus. by Paul Bransom, fine, dj. Victoria 34-326 1978 $10

GATTY, C. T.   George Wyndham Recognita. 1917. 1st Public ed., from Green-Armytage Collection, 2 A.l.s. from author, pencilled notes by G-A, d.w., very good, octavo bound in cloth. Hyland 128-827 1978 £15

GATTY, HAROLD   The Raft Book. 1943. Illus. Austin 80-107 1978 $17.50

GATTY, MARGARET (SCOTT)   The Book of Sun-dials. 1900. Enlarged and reedited, roy. 8vo., plts., illus., cloth. Quaritch 983-83 1978 $120

GAUDEN, JOHN   A Discourse of Artificial Beauty, in Point of Conscience between Two Ladies. London, 1662. 8vo, contemporary calf, rebacked (corners rubbed), 2nd ed. Ximenes 47-115 1978 $200

GAUGUIN, P.   Noa Noa. den Haag, n.d. 4to., bds., colored plts. Van der Peet H-64-39 1978 Dfl 45

GAUL, ENRIQUE F.   Leonardo Nieman. Mexico, n.d. Sq. 4to., color plts., text in Spanish and English. Biblo BL781-666 1978 $17.50

GAULTIER, P.   Le Rire et la Caricature. Paris, 1911. 8vo., orig. covers, illus. Van der Peet H-64-273 1978 Dfl 35

GAUNT, WILLIAM   British Painting From Hogarth's Day To Ours. London, 1945. Illus., 1st ed., orig. buckram, nearly fine. Limestone 9-117 1978 $15

GAUSS, KARL FRIEDRICH   Determinatio Attractionis, Guam in Punctum Quodvis Positionis Datae Exerceret Planeta, si Eius Massa per Totam Orbitam, Ratione Temporis, Quo Singulae Partes Describuntur, Uniformiter Esset Dispertita. Gottingen, 1818. 4to., bds., orig. ed. Gilhofer 74-5 1978 sFr 900

GAUSS, KARL FRIEDRICH   General Investigations of Curved Surfaces of 1827 and 1825. 1902. Sq. 4to., 1/2 red crushed levant. Argosy Special-43 1978 $75

GAUSS, KARL FRIEDRICH   Intensitas vis magneticae terrestris ad mensuram absolutam revocata. Gottingen, 1883. 4 to., 1st ed., modern half vellum. Schafer 19 -50 1978 sFr. 1,400

GAUSS, KARL FRIEDRICH   Methode des Moindres Carres. Paris, 1855. 8vo., recent mor. backed cloth. Quaritch 977-154 1978 $55

GAUSS, KARL FRIEDRICH   Principia Generalia Theoriae Figurae Fluidorum in Statu Aequilibrii. Gottingen, 1830. 4to., bds., 1st ed. Gilhofer 74-113 1978 sFr 950

GAUTIER, THEOPHILE   The Dead Leman. Portland, Mosher Press, 1903. 1 of 425 copies on Japan vellum, 12mo., wraps, good. Bell Book 16-659 1978 £5.50

GAUTIER, THEOPHILE   Fortunio ou l'Eldorado. Paris, 1929. Lg. 8vo., bds. portfolio, bds. slipcase, litho. plts. by Ch. Guerin, ltd. ed. of 225 copies, 1 of 25 copies on "Japon", extra set of lithos. on "Chine". Van der Peet H-64-428 1978 Dfl 145

GAUTIER, THEOPHILE   Poesier Nouvelles. Paris, 1866. 1/2 calf, corners repaired & rebacked, gilt spine, lib. crest on upper cover. Eaton 45-195 1978 £10

GAUTIER, THEOPHILE   Tableaux de Siege. Paris, 1871. 1/2 calf, rebacked, corners repaired, lib. crest on upper cover. Eaton 45-196 1978 £8

GAUVREAU, EMILE   The Wild Blue Yonder. 1944. Austin 80-109 1978 $8.50

GAVANTI, BARTOLOMMEO   Thesaurus sactorum rituum cum novis observationibus et addit. Rome, 1736-38. Quarto, 4 vols., full contemp. vellum, titles gilt-stamped on spines, edges mottled green and red. Bennett 20-83 1978 $350

GAVARD, CH.   Galerie des Marechaux de France. Paris, 1839. Sm. quarto, portrait plates, modern half-calf and marbled boards, very good. Victoria 34-327 1978 $40

GAVARNI, GUILLAUME SULPICE CHEVALIER   Masques et Visages. Paris, 1857. 8vo., orig. covers, drawings. Van der Peet H64-274 1978 Dfl 45

GAVIN, ANTONIO   A Short History of Monastical Orders... London, 1693. 1st. ed., sm. 8vo, modern half purple morocco, gilt, g.t. Traylen 88-253 1978 £30

GAVIT, JOHN PALMER   Americans From Abroad. Chicago, 1926. Austin 79-270 1978 $12.50

GAVITT, ELNATHAN C.   Crumbs from My Saddle Bags, or, Reminiscences of Pioneer Life and Biographical Sketches. Toledo, 1884. Cloth. Hayman 72-262 1978 $35

GAWAIN AND THE GREEN KNIGHT   Sir Gawain and the Green Knight. Oxford, 1925. First ed., orig. binding, nice, scarce. Rota 211-707 1978 #30

GAWSWORTH, JOHN   Apes, Japes and Hitlerism: a study and bibliography of Wyndham Lewis. 1932. Covers dull, good, first English ed. Bell Book 16-567 1978 £10

GAWSWORTH, JOHN   Mishka and Madelaine: A Poem Sequence For Marcia. 1932. Ltd. ed. of 25 copies, 13 illus. by Tristam Rainey, 4to, orig. green cloth, gilt, fine copy, Japon vellum paper, signed by author & artist. Sawyer 299-141 1978 £35

GAWSWORTH, JOHN   The Twyn Barlwm Press, 1931-32. 1933. Very good, 1 of 50 numbered copies signed by Arthur Machen, wraps, first English ed. Bell Book 16-608 1978 £15

GAY, F. DREW   The Prince of Wales in India. Detroit, 1878. Illus., 8vo., orig. cloth, spine faded. Morrill 241-153 1978 $10

GAY, JOHN   Achilles. 1723. 8vo., 1st ed., green mor., gilt panelled back gilt edges, very good copy. Quaritch 979-150 1978 $200

GAY, JOHN   The Beggar's Opera. London, 1733. 3rd. ed., thin 8vo., full brown morocco, gilt edges, inside gilt borders, 1st. ed. with music. Traylen 88-252A 1978 £20

GAY, JOHN   The Beggar's Opera. 1921. Coloured plts. by Lovat Fraser, roy. 8vo., cloth-backed bds., very good, first English ed. Bell Book 16-594 1978 £10

GAY, JOHN   The Beggar's Opera Caricatures. London, (1922). First ed., 4to., loose as issued, orig. portfolio, half cloth over bds., plts. clean, v.g. Houle 10-102 1978 $85

GAY, JOHN   The Beggar's Opera. London, (1922). Caricature portrs., tall 8vo., plts., contained loose as issued in orig. portfolio of bds., cloth back, 1st ed. Morrill 239-398 1978 $20

GAY, JOHN   The Beggar's Opera. Paris: The Limited Editions Club, 1937. Sm. folio, illus., orig. embossed cloth, pub. box, 1 of 1,500 copies, fine. MacManus 238-823 1978 $20

GAY, JOHN   Fables. Stockdale, 1793. 2 vols., roy. 8vo., engr., plts., full modern blind stamped mor., gilt tops. Quaritch 979-151 1978 $385

GAY, JOHN   Fables by John Gay,.... London, 1793. Octavo, full brown calf, decor. covers and spine in the style of Edwards of Halifax, front joint cracked, off-setting of plts. Totteridge 29-45 1978 $250

GAY, JOHN   Poems on Several Occasions. 1720. 2 vols. in 1, 4to., plts., contemp. panelled calf, rebacked. Howes 194-280 1978 £50

GAY, MARY A. H.   Life in Dixie During the War. 1863-1864-1865. Atlanta, 1892. Sm. 8vo., binding partly worn, 1st ed., orig. cloth. Morrill 241-154 1978 $27.50

GAY, VERBON F.   The Story of Rainbow Corner. London, Nov. 1942 to Dec. 1943. Austin 80-110 1978 $10

GAY, ZHENYA   170 Cats. New York, (1939). 1st ed., almost fine. Victoria 34-328 1978 $20

GAY-LUSSAC, JOSEPH LOUIS   Recherches Physico-Chymiques. Paris, 1811. 2 vols., 8vo., fldg. plts., contemp. calf, richly gilt spines & borders, little rubbed & lightly foxed, but fine set in special prize binding, 1st ed. Norman 5-122 1978 $375

GAY-LUSSAC, JOSEPH LOUIS   Recherches Physico-Chimiques, Faites sur la Pile. Paris, 1811. 2 vols., fldg. copperplts., 8vo., contemp. calf, 1st ed., fine. Offenbacher 30-56 1978 $450

GAYA, LOUIS DE   Traite des Armes, des Machines de Guerre.... Paris, 1678. Sm. 8vo., contemp. calf, plts. F. Edwards 1013-304 1978 £160

GAYA, LOUIS DE   A Treatise of the Arms and Engines of War... 1678. First Eng. ed., John Evelyn's copy, plts., sm. 8vo., cont. sprinkled sheep. F. Edwards 1013-305 1978 £750

GAYARRE, CHARLES   Histoire de la Louisiane. Nouvelle Orleans, 1846-47. 2 vols. in 1, cloth with original printed wr. bound in, 1st ed. Jenkins 116-497 1978 $175

GAYARRE, CHARLES   Louisiana: Its History as a French Colony. New York, 1852. Map, 1st ed., dampstaines and foxing on bind. Biblo BL781-250 1978 $27.50

GAYER, ARTHUR D.   Monetary Policy and Economic Stabilization. 1937. 2nd rev. ed., ex-lib., library binding. Austin 80-634 1978 $17.50

GAZET, ANGELIN   Pia Hilaria. London, Cambridge, 1657. 2 books in 1 vol., 1st. title printed in red & black, sm. 8vo., contemp. calf. Traylen 88-254 1978 £40

GAZETTE Francoise. New York, 1926. Limited to 300 copies. Nestler Rare 78-159 1978 $45

GAZIUS, ANTONIUS   Florida Corona Que Ad Sanitatis Hominum Conservationem Ac Longevam Vitam Perducendam Sunt Pernecessaria Continens. (1514). 4to., woodcut, old sprinkled bds., lightly browned, sm. worm-holes, ownership inscr., good copy from the library of Dr. Alfred M. Hellman, scarce. Zeitlin 245-97 1978 $350

GEARY, JOHN W.   A Sketch of the Early Life and of the Civil and Military Services of Major General...., [Philadelphia, 1866]. Original printed pictorial wr., 1st ed. Ginsberg 14-361 1978 $75

GEDDES, MICHAEL   The Church History of Ethiopia. 1696. First ed., cont. calf, 8vo. Howes 194-50 1978 £35

GEDDIE, JOHN   The Lake Regions of Central Africa. London, 1881. 32 illus., cr. 8vo., dec. cloth gilt. K Books 239-183 1978 £15

GEDDIE, WILLIAM   A Bibliography of Middle Scots Poets. Edinburgh, 1912. Half mor. MacManus 238-928 1978 $35

GEDENKBOEK-Tachtig Jaar Stork. Hengelo, 1943. 4to., cloth, illus. on plts., text illus. Van der Peet H-64-335 1978 Dfl 65

GEDENKBOEK ter Herinnering aan het Tienjarig Bestaan van de Nederlandsche Vereeniging voor Radiotelegrafie, 1916-1926. Zutphen, 1926. 8vo., cloth, illus. Van der Peet H-64-334 1978 Dfl 65

GEDNEY, L. C.   The Town Records of Hopewell, N.J. New York, 1931. MacManus 239-1267 1978 $30

GEE, EDWARD   An Answer to the Compiler of the Nubes Testium.. 1688. 1st. ed., 4to, wrappers, fine copy. Fenning 32-124 1978 £8.50

GEE, JOSHUA   Israel's Mourning for Aaron's Death. Boston, 1728. 8vo, disbound, 1st ed, minor soiling, sound copy. Ximenes 47-117 1978 $100

GEER, J. J.   Beyond the Lines. Philadelphia, 1863. New cloth, 1st ed., rebound copy. Hayman 73-109 1978 $15

GEER, J. J. DE   Proeve Eener Geschiedenis van het Geslacht Nijenrode. Utrecht, (1854). 8vo., orig. covers, fldg. genealogical table, torn. Van der Peet H-64-336 1978 Dfl 40

GEESON, J. E.   The Old Fort at Toronto, 1793-1906. Toronto, 1906. Card cover, illus. Hood 117-734 1978 $17.50

DIE GEFAHR in den Strassen.... Philadelphia, 1810. 1st & only US German-lang. ed., orig. plain stiff wraps, woodcut vignette on t.p. to Ales. Anderson, 8vo. Americanist 101-72 1978 $50

DIE GEFAHR in de Strassen. Phiadelphia, 1810. 1st and only ed., 16mo, t.p. woodcut, fine. Victoria 34-329 1978 $45

GEFAHR in Den Strassen, nebst Einigen andern Erzaehlungen. Philadelphia, 1810. Woodcut, 18mo., orig. pink stiff wrs., German-American ed. Argosy Special-44 1978 $75

GEFFROY, GUSTAVE   Les Bateaux de Paris. Paris, 1903. 1st ed. ltd. to 184 copies, 4to., a.e.g., copy #1 & only copy on China paper, illus., wood engrs., bound in full crimson levant, spine with raised bands, brocaded red satin endpapers, ribbon bkmark., near mint throughout, blue cloth fldg. box. Current 24-220 1978 $1,285

GEGENBAUR, CARL   Lehrbuch Der Anatomie Des Menschen. Leipzig, 1899. 2 vols., 8vo., illus., some in color, half brown mor., ex-lib., good copy. Zeitlin 245-98 1978 $37.50

GEGENHEIMER, ALBERT F.   Wm. Smith Educator and Churchman 1727-1803. Philadelphia, 1943. MacManus 239-1466 1978 $12.50

GEHLE, FREDERICK W.   Our Dubbledam Journey. 1941. Austin 79-271 1978 $10

GEIB, H. V.   Soil Survey of Harris County, Texas. Washington, 1928. Wr., large folding map. Jenkins 116-574 1978 $10

GEIGER, BENNO   Magnasco. Bergamo, 1949. Text in Italian, plts., some in color, sm. folio, half brown lea. & tan buckram, 1st ed., 1 of 1500 signed by author. Bradley 49-130 1978 £110

GEIKIE, ARCHIBALD   Outlines of Field Geology. London, 1879. Second ed., illus., 8vo., orig. cloth. K Books 244-132 1978 £6

GEIKIE, JAMES   The Great Ice Age and Its Relation to the Antiquity of Man. London, 1894. 3rd. ed., maps, charts, illus., thick 8vo. Traylen 88-574 1978 £15

GEIKIE, JAMES   Prehistoric Europe. London, 1881. Plts., illus., 1st. ed., 8vo. Traylen 88-575 1978 £15

GEIL, WILLIAM EDGAR   Eighteen Capitals of China. London, 1911. Cloth, joints and edges worn, hinges weak, slight foxing. Dawson's 449-35 1978 $35

GEIL, WILLIAM EDGAR   The Great Wall of China. New York, 1909. Plts., Cloth, front hinge weak. Dawson's 449-36 1978 $40

GEISER, SAMUEL W.   Horticulture and Horticulturists in Early Texas. Dallas, 1945. Wr. Jenkins 116-498 1978 $8.50

GEISER, SAMUEL W.   Naturalists of the Frontier. Dallas, 1937. 1st ed. Jenkins 116-499 1978 $25

GEISER MANUFACTURING CO.   1895 Price List of Repairs for Machinery Manufactured by the..., Waynesboro, Pa. N.P., (1895). Pict. wrs., little rubbed at bottom of front wr. Hayman 72-102 1978 $10

GEIST, SAMUEL H.   Ovarian Tumors. New York, 1942. Rittenhouse 49-290 1976 $25

GELINAS, GRATIEN   Tit-Coq. Montreal, 1950. Card cover, 1st ed., photos. Hood 117-477 1978 $10

GELINAS, GRATIEN   Tit-Coq. (Montreal, 1950). Illus. Wolfe 39-197 1978 $25

GELLER, G. G.   Sarah Bernhardt. London, (1933). First ed., illus. Biblo 247-894 1978 $17.50

GELLERMANN, WILLIAM   Martin Dies. New York, 1944. D.j. Jenkins 116-1551 1978 $20

GELLERT, CHRISTLIEB EHREGOTT   Chimie Metallurgique.... Paris, 1758. 2 vols., 12mo., contemp. calf, plts., woodcuts, first French ed. Gurney 75-44 1978 £80

GELLHORN, MARTHA   The Wine of Astonishment. 1948. First ed. Austin 82-392 1978 $11

GELSEMIUM Sempervirens. Boston, 1883. 12mo., 1st ed. Morrill 239-95 1978 $15

GEMMA FRISIUS   Les Principes d'Astronomie et Cosmographie.... Paris, 1582. 8vo., contemp. limp vellum, woodcuts, second? French ed., fine. Gurney 75-45 1978 £165

GEMMILL, J. A.   Canadian Parliamentary Companion for 1887. Ottawa, 1887. Cover stained. Hood 116-13 1978 $25

GEMS for the Young Folks. Salt Lake City, 1881. Orig. cloth, 1st ed. Ginsberg 14-653 1978 $15

GEMS of Colorado Scenery...Wash Drawings by Mr. Geo. Berger. Denver, n.d. (c. 1900?). Wrs., 8th ed. Hayman 72-147 1978 $7.50

GENEALOGY of a Branch of the Randall Family. (Norwich, 1879). 1st ed., orig. wrs., worn, very good, scarce. MacManus 239-936 1978 $85

GENERAL MOTORS   The War Effort of the Overseas Division. 1944. Illus. Austin 80-112 1978 $10

A GENERAL Collection of Voyages and Discoveries Made by the Portuguese and the Spaniards, During the 15th and 16th Centuries. 1789. 2 engraved portraits, maps, plts., 4to, contemp. tree calf, spine gilt. Edwards 1012-35 1978 £150

GENERAL Description of the City of Nassau and Island of New Providence,.... New York, 1871. Sm. 8vo., orig. pr. and engraved wr. Quaritch 978-155 1978 $80

GENERAL Regulations and Orders for the Army. 1822. 8vo., contemp. half calf. F. Edwards 1013-306 1978 £20

THE GENERAL Review Maneuvers: or the Whole Evolutions of a Battalion of Foot... London, 1789. Illus. with 16 copper-plts. in color, orig. full calf, 8vo, fine copy, rare. Baldwins' 51-306 1978 $150

GENLIS, STEPHANIE FELICITE DUCREST DE SAINT AUBIN   Adelaide and Theodore. 1784. 3 vols., 12mo, contemp. tree calf, gilt backs, old lib. labels inside covers, very nice. P. M. Hill 142-100 1978 £30

GENLIS, STEPHANIE FELICITE DUCREST DE SAINT AUBIN   Annales de la Vertu.... Paris, 1786. 3 vols., 12mo., recent bds., nice copy. Fenning 32-125 1978 £18.50

GENLIS, STEPHANIE FELICITE DUCREST DE SAINT AUBIN   Dictionnaire Critique et Raisonne des Etiquettes de la Cour.... Paris, 1818. Ed. orig., 2 vols., contemp. mottled calf, labels missing, text and contents good, 8vo. Howes 194-550 1978 £15

GENLIS, STEPHANIE FELICITE DUCREST DE SAINT AUBIN   The Duchess de la Valliere, and Madame de Maintenon, Romances. 1837. 2 vols., lg. 12mo., 19th-century deep pink calf, gilt backs. P. M. Hill 142-187 1978 £38

GENT, THOMAS   Historia Compendiosa Romana:.... (York, c.1772). 2nd vol., woodcuts and plates, rebound in full leather, fine copy, rare. Victoria 34-330 1978 $135

GENTHE, ARNOLD   Impressions of Old New Orleans. New York, 1926. Plts., illus., 4to., green paper bds., green cloth back, 1st ed., light cover wear, else fine. Howell 5-26 1978 $75

GENTIL, FRANCOIS   The Retir'd Gard'ner. 1706. Two vols., 8vo., contemp. panelled calf, good, frontispieces, plts., woodcuts. P. M. Hill 142-116 1978 £175

GENTILE, DON S.   One-Man Air Force. 1944. Illus. Austin 80-113 1978 $7.50

GENTILERICCIO, PIERGIROLAMO   Della Filosofia Di Amore. Venice, 1618. Plts., 8vo., vellum with label, 1st ed. Salloch 348-71 1978 $125

GENTILLET, INNOCENT   Commentariorum De Regno... N.P., (Lausanne), 1577. 8vo., vellem, old owner's name on title. Salloch 348-72 1978 $80

GENTLE Annie Melodist No. 2. New York, 1859. 12mo, orig. red cloth. Baldwins' 51-343 1978 $25

GENTRY, T.   Intelligence in Plants and Animals. New York, 1900. 8vo, orig. cloth. Book Chest 17-161 1978 $25

GEOFFREY Franklin. Chiswick Press, 1933. Plts., orig. buckram, 8vo. Howes 194-869 1978 £6

GEOFFROY SAINT-HILAIRE, ETIENNE   A Collection of Fifteen Monographs of the Great Zoologist, Anatomist and Biologist, Dealing with his Research and Investigations on the Formation of Monstrosities. (ca. 1820-1834). 8vo., mostly in orig. wrs., good, uncut cond. Zeitlin 245-99 1978 $150

THE GEOGRAPHICAL And Historical Dictionary of America and the West Indies... 1812. 5 vols., 4to, contemp. calf, sides of 1 vol. somewhat worn, rebacked, Admiralty lib. stamp on front fly-leaves, with folio Atlas, maps. Edwards 1012-381 1978 £1500

THE GEOGRAPHICAL Annual. London, 1836. Coloured engrav. title, coloured maps, sm. 8vo., neatly recased in orig. green mor., 8vo. K Books 244-367 1978 £20

GEOGRAPHICAL Handbook Series For Official Use Only. 1941-46. Maps, 8vo, orig. cloth, 58 vols., illus. Edwards 1012-19 1978 £750

GEOGRAPHICAL Handbook Series. 1943. Maps, illus., 8vo, orig. cloth. Edwards 1012-151 1978 £20

A GEOMETRICAL Decimal Interest Table. Utica, 1815. 16mo, original marbled wr. (somewhat worn), 1st ed. Ximenes 47-270 1978 $90

GEORGE, HENRY   The Land Question. (1881). Austin 80-635 1978 $11

GEORGE, HENRY   Moses. 1918. Austin 80-636 1978 $7.50

GEORGE, HENRY   Our Land and Land Policy. (1871) 1902. Austin
80-637 1978 $12.50

GEORGE, HENRY   A Perplexed Philosopher. 1892. Austin 80-638
1978 $27.50

GEORGE, HENRY   Progress and Poverty. 1881 (1879). Austin 80-
639 1978 $12.50

GEORGE, HENRY   Protection or Free Trade. 1886. 1st ed. Austin
80-640 1978 $27.50

GEORGE, HENRY   Protection or Free Trade? (Washington, 1892).
Unbound as issued. Hayman 71-655 1978 $7.50

GEORGE, HENRY   The Science of Political Economy. 1898. 1st ed.
Austin 80-641 1978 $27.50

GEORGE, HENRY   The Science of Political Economy. Toronto,
1898. Ex-library, rebound in buckram. Wolfe 39-201 1978 $75

GEORGE, HENRY   Social Problems. 1884. 1st English ed. Austin
80-642 1978 $27.50

GEORGE, HENRY JR.   The Life of Henry George. 1900. Austin 80-
643 1978 $10

GEORGE, JOHN NIGEL   English Pistols and Revolvers, an Historical Outline of the Development and Design of English Hand Firearms from the 17th Century.
Onslow, 1938. Plates, roy. 8vo. George's 635-816 1978 £15

GEORGE, JOHN NIGEL   English Pistols and Revolvers. 8vo, 26 plts.,
Traylen 88-494 1978 £5

GEORGETOWN Directory. Georgetown, 1924. Foxed. Jenkins. 116-1478 1978
$37.50

GEORGIA. LAWS   Georgia-Acts of the General Assembly of the
State of Georgia, Passed in Milledgeville, at an Annual Session in November and
December, 1862...Milledgeville, 1863. Wrs., Bell Wiley's copy. Broadfoot
46-445 1978 $50

GEORGIA. LAWS   Georgia-Acts of the General Assembly of the
State of Georgia, Passed in Milledgeville at an Annual Session in November and
December, 1863...Milledgeville, 1864. Wrs., Bell Wiley's copy. Broadfoot 46-
446 1978 $50

GEORGIAN Poetry 1911-1922. London, 1912-1922. 5 vols., laid paper,
uncut, orig. gilt bds., very good or better. Limestone 9-120 1978 $45

GEORGIUS, D. I.   D. Paulus Apostolus in mari, quod nunc venetus
sinus dicitus, naufragus et melitae Dalmatensis insulae. Venetiis, (1730). Engraved frontis., text wormed, 4to., old vellum, loose in case, wormed. George's
635-1069 1978 £5

GERARD DE NERVAL   Les Chimeres. Paris, n.d. (1947). 4to., orig.
covers, ltd. to 360 numbered copies. Van der Peet H64-442 1978 Dfl 45

GERARD, ALEXANDER   An Essay on Taste. London & Edinburgh, 1759.
First ed., title-leaf frayed and soiled, somewhat thumbed and dusty throughout, old
style half calf, 8vo. K Books 244-368 1978 £38

GERARD, ALEXANDER   An Essay on Taste. Edinburgh, 1780. Third ed.,
8vo., contemp. calf, fine. P. M. Hill 142-302 1978 £48

GERARD, DOROTHEA   An Arranged Marriage. New York, 1895. 1st
Amer. ed., quarter calf, marbled boards, good. Greene 78-206 1978 $10

GERARD, F.   The School of Man. 1753. 2nd. ed., 12mo,
contemp. calf, upper joint cracked. Eaton 45-211 1978 £10

GERARD, JOHN   The Herball or Generall Historie of Plantes.
London, 1633. Folio, woodcuts, contemp. calf rebacked in antique style, fine,
first ed. Quaritch 977-26 1978 $2,000

GERARD, MORICE   Dr. Manton. London, 1907. First ed., orig.
binding, very good. Rota 211-135 1978 £6

GERBIER, BALTHAZAR   The None-Such Charles His Character.... London, 1651. Engraved portrait, engraved plt. inserted, 1st. ed., fcap. 8vo, contemp.
calf, rebacked. Traylen 88-255 1978 £68

GERBRANDY, P. S.   National and International Stability. Cambridge,
1944. 12mo. Biblo 251-336 1978 $8.50

GERHARDT, CHARLES   Charles Gerhardt, sa vie, son Oeuvre, sa
Correspondance. Paris, 1900. 8vo., portr., fldg. diagr., buckram, fine copy,
1st ed., inscr'd by co-author Gerhardt. Norman 5-124 1978 $40

GERHARDT, CHARLES   Triate de Chimie Organique. Paris, 1853-56.
4 vols., 8vo., text illus., contemp. half mor., gilt, occas. light foxing, but
fine set, 1st ed. Norman 5-123 1978 $250

GERIN-LAJOIE, A.   Catechisme Politique;...Canada... Montreal,
1851. Orig.pr. wrps., 1st ed. Ginsberg 16-840 1978 $45.00

GERLI, A.   Opuscoli di Agostino Gerli. Parma, 1785.
Folio, plts., vignettes, unpressed, orig. limp bds., uncut, mor. backed box. Quaritch 977-223 1978 $2,500

GERMAN STORIES. 1826. 3 vols., 1st. ed., half calf, black labels, marbled
bds., fine. Jarndyce 16-678 1978 £25.50

GERMAINS, VICTOR WALLACE   The Truth About Kitchener. 1925. 1st. ed.,
8vo, orig. wine cloth, spine slightly faded, nick in top of upper cover, pres. copy
to Winston Churchill. Sawyer 298-78 1978 £105

GERNING, JOHANN ISAAC VON   A Picturesque Tour Along the Rhine, from
Mentz to Cologne.... 1820. 4to., map., coloured plts. by Schuetz, some very
minor offsetting or slight foxing on 1 of 2 plts., calf gilt spine. Quaritch 983-
331 1978 $5,500

GERNON, BLAINE B.   Lincoln in the Political Circus... Chicago,
1936. 1st ed., d.j., ltd. to 1,000 copies. MacManus 239-878 1978 $22.50

GEROULD, WINIFRED G.   A Guide to Trollope. London, 1948.
1st ed., fine, d.j. Limestone 9-304 1978 $22.50

GERRISH, THEODORE   Army Life. Portland, (1882). 8vo., 1st ed.,
orig. cloth. Morrill 241-158 1978 $15

GERSHAW, F. W.   A Brief History of Southern Alberta-"The Short
Grass Area". N. P., n.d. Cloth, illus., 1st ed., fine copy, scarce. Dykes
34-97 1978 $25

GERSHWIN, GEORGE   George Gershwin. New York, 1938. Sq.
quarto, 2-color cloth, covarrubias caricature of Gershwin, repro. of paintings
by George Gershwin, 1st ed., fine. Duschnes 220-114 1978 $65

GERSON, JOHANNES   Opera. (Strassburg), 1488. 1st illus. ed.,
folio, contemp. calf, blind-stamped over wooden bds., rebacked in contemp. style,
woodcut portrait, all bosses, clasps and straps present, rubricated throughout in red
and blue, floriated initials with burnished gold on each vol., some slight staining,
beautiful set. Bennett 20-84 1978 $7,500

GERSTER, ARPAD   Rules of Aseptic and Antiseptic Surgery. New
York, 1891. Third ed., top spine cloth missing. Rittenhouse 49-292 1976 $10

GERTRUDE, MARY   Philip Randolph: A Tale of Virginia. New York,
1845. 1st ed., almost fine. Victoria 34-332 1978 $30

GERVASI, FRANK   But Soldiers Wondered Why. 1943. 1st ed.
Austin 80-114 1978 $10

GERVASI, FRANK   War Has Seven Faces. 1942. Austin 80-115
1978 $8.50

GESCHICHTE Der Martyrer, Nach Dem...Original Des...Johann Fox Und And-
erer...Besonders Fur Den Gemeinen Deutschen Mann, in Den Vereinigten Staaten..
Aus Dem Englischen Ubersetzt... Cincinnati, 1830. 1st ed., 2 vols. in 1, orig.
calf, slight wear, woodcuts. Americanist 102-106 1978 $30

GESCHICHTE Der Vereinigten Staaten Von Nord-Amerika,.... Philadelphia,
1838. 1st ed., contemp. calf, rebacked with orig. spine retained, woodcuts, 8vo.
Americanist 101-75 1978 $20

GESCHICKTER, CHARLES F.   Tumors of Bone. Philadelphia, 1949. Third ed.
Rittenhouse 49-293 1976 $15

GESNER, ABRAHAM   A Practical Treatise on Coal, Petroleum, and
Other Distilled Oils. New York, 1861. 8vo., woodcut frontispiece, illus., orig.
cloth. Quaritch 977-224 1978 $350

GESNER, KONRAD   Vogelbuch. Zuerich, 1557. Woodcuts, tall folio, bds., 1st German ed. Salloch 345-78 1978 $800

GESSLER, CLIFFORD   Hawaii, Isles of Enchantment. 1937. Illus., very good, d.j. Austin 82-925 1978 $12.50

GESSNER, CONRAD
Please turn to
GESNER, KONRAD

GESSNER, ROBERT   Some of My Best Friends are Jews. 1936. Illus. with photos taken by author, covers worn around edges. Austin 79-278 1978 $12.50

GESSNER, ROBERT   Youth is the Time. 1945. First ed., d.j. Austin 82-393 1978 $12.50

GESSNER, SALOMON   The Death of Abel. 1766. Eighth ed., 12mo., contemp. calf, gilt panelled back, label missing. Howes 194-283 1978 £10

GESTA Romanorum, or, Entertaining Moral Stories. 1877. Cr. 8vo., orig. cloth, hinges sprung. George's 635-551 1978 £5.25

GESTA Romanorum. 1924. Allen 234-1257 1978 $7.50

GETCHELL, F. H.   Illustrated Encyclopedia of the Science and Practice of Obstretrics. Philadelphia, 1890. Large octavo, covers loose, ends of spine frayed. Rittenhouse 49-294 1976 $25

GETHIN, GRACE   Misery is Vertues Whetstone. 1703. Third ed., 2 parts in 1 vol., sm. 4to., 19th cent. blind tooled navy calf, portrait. Howes 194-284 1978 £40

GHELEN, SIGISMUND   Notitia Utraque cum Orientis tum Occidentis ultra Arcadii Honoriique Caesarum tempora,.... Basle, 1552. 1st complete ed., folio, Froben's device on title and colophon leaf, woodcuts by Conrad Schnitt, contemp. full calf, blind line panels, gilt central medallions on both covers, rebacked preserving original spine, few strips of leather scraped, fine. Bennett 20-235 1978 $950

GHENT, PERCY   John Reade and His Friends. (Toronto), 1925. Inscribed and signed by author. Hood 116-690 1978 $30

GHENT, W. J.   The Early Far West. New York, 1936. Illus., binding faded. Biblo 248-250 1978 $15

GHENT, W. J.   The Early Far West. A Narrative Outline 1540-1850. New York, 1936. Cloth, light flecking. Hayman 72-264 1978 $7.50

GHIRARDELLI, G. B. F.   Il Constantino, tragedia. 1660. Engraved title, 24mo., old vellum. George's 635-1349 1978 £5.50

GHISLAIN DE BUSBECQ, OGIER
Please turn to
BUSBECQ, OGIER GHISLAIN DE

GIACOMELLI, R.   Gli Scritti. Rome, 1936. Lg. 8vo., illus., orig. prtd. wrs., uncut, very good copy. Norman 5-L27 1978 $45

GIACOMETTI, ALBERTO   Paris Sans Fin. Paris, 1969. Sm. folio in sheets, uncut, in orig. wr., slipcover & case, ltd. ed. issued in 270 copies, 1 of 250 numbered copies on velin d'Arches paper, with signature stamp of artist, illus. with orig. litho. by Giacometti, excellent state of preservation. Goldschmidt 110-24 1978 $7,500

GIARRE, GAETANO   Alfabeto di Lettere Iniziali Adorno di Animali e Proseguito da Vaga Serie di Caratteri. Florence, 1797. Sm. folio, plts., cont. paper wrs., spine defective, wrs. somewhat frayed, first ed. Schumann 511-23 1978 sFr 2,600

GIBBENS, ALVARO F.   Historic Blennerhassett Island Home Near Parkersburg, W. Va. Parkersburg, 1924. Wrs. Hayman 73-737 1978 $8.50

GIBBINGS, ROBERT   Coconut Island. 1936. First ed., wood-engrav. by author, covers a trifle soiled. George's 635-153 1978 £6

GIBBINGS, ROBERT   Coming Down the Wye. 1942. First ed., wood-engravings by the author, maps, d.j. George's 635-154 1978 £5

GIBBINGS, ROBERT   John Graham (Convict) 1824. 1937. First ed., wood-engravings by the author, covers a trifle dull. George's 635-156 1978 £5

GIBBINGS, ROBERT   Iorana! 1932. First English ed., roy. 8vo., wood-engravings by author, orig. cloth-backed bds., d.j. George's 635-155 1978 £15

GIBBINGS, ROBERT   Lovely is the Lee. 1945. First ed., wood-engravings by author, d.j. George's 635-157 1978 £5

GIBBINGS, ROBERT   Over the Reefs. 1948. First ed., wood-engravings by the author, d.j. George's 635-158 1978 £5

GIBBINGS, ROBERT   Over the Reefs. 1948. Engrav. by author, cloth gilt, fine, d.w., first English ed. Bell Book 16-369 1978 £4.50

GIBBINGS, ROBERT   Sweet Thames Run Softly. 1940. First ed., wood-engravings by the author, covers a little dull. George's 635-159 1978 £5

GIBBINGS, ROBERT   A True Tale of Love in Tonga. 1935. First ed., wood-engravings by the author, orig. cloth-backed bds. George's 635-160 1978 £6

GIBBINS, H. DE B.   Industrial History of England. 1894. 3rd ed. Austin 80-644 1978 $10

GIBBON, EDMUND   Miscellaneous Works. 1796. 2 vols., 4to., recent half calf, silhouette portrait, good. P. M. Hill 142-119 1978 £50

GIBBON, EDWARD   The History of the Decline and Fall of the Roman Empire. 1776-88. 6 vols., 4to., 1st ed., portr., maps, contemp. half calf, some browning, good sound set. Quaritch 979-153 1978 $840

GIBBON, EDWARD   The History of the Decline & Fall of the Roman Empire. 1776-89. 6 vols., 4to., orig. calf, some hinges little weak, maroon & green labels, spine little rubbed, good set. Jarndyce 16-92 1978 £120

GIBBON, EDWARD   The History of the Decline and Fall of the Roman Empire. London, 1778-88. 6 vols., quarto, contemp. brown full calf, blind stamped, plts. Totteridge 29-46 1978 $875

GIBBON, EDWARD   Decline & Fall of the Roman Empire. 1816. New ed., 12 vols., old calf, joints cracked. Allen 234-360 1978 $35

GIBBON, EDWARD   The Decline and Fall of the Roman Empire. Halifax, 1848. 4 vols., portrait, new binders cloth. George's 635-465 1978 £12.50

GIBBON, EDWARD   The Decline and Fall of the Roman Empire. 1896-1900. 8 vols., cr. 8vo. George's 635-466 1978 £25

GIBBON, EDWARD   Decline & Fall of the Roman Empire. n.d. 3 vols., modern library ed. Allen 234-358 1978 $15

GIBBON, EDWARD   Miscellaneous Works. Dublin, 1796. 3 vols., frontispiece, contemp. tree calf, first Dublin ed., 8vo. Howes 194-285 1978 £25

GIBBON, EDWARD   Miscellaneous Works. London, 1796. 2 vols., quarto, portrait, full spanish calf (rebacked, orig. spine laid in), 1st ed. Bennett 7-47 1978 $250

GIBBON, EDWARD   Miscellaneous Works With Memoirs of His Life and Writings. 1796. Illus., 1st. ed., 2 vols., 4to, orig. calf, v.g. Jarndyce 16-91 1978 £36

GIBBON, EDWARD   Private Letters 1753-94. 1897. 2nd ed., frontispieces, 2 vols., 8vo. George's 635-1242 1978 £12

GIBBON, FREDERICK P.   The 42nd Division, 1914-1918. (c. 1920). Port. frontis., plts., 8vo., orig. decor. cloth. F. Edwards 1013-588 1978 £12

GIBBON, JOHN MURRAY   Canadian Folk Songs, Old and New... Toronto, 1929. Hood 116-826 1978 $15

GIBBON, JOHN MURRAY   Canadian Mosaic. Toronto, (1938). Colour illus., maps, d.j., orig. binding. Wolfe 39-203 1978 $45

GIBBON, JOHN MURRAY   The Order of Good Cheer. Toronto, 1929. Illus., paper. Austin 79-279 1978 $11

GIBBONS, HERBERT A.   John Wanamaker. New York, 1926. 2 vols., illus., fine. MacManus 239-825 1978 $22.50

GIBBONS, JAMES   Our Christian Heritage. Baltimore, 1889. Frontis. Austin 79-280 1978 $10

GIBBONS, STELLA   Conference at Cold Comfort Farm. 1949. Very good, d.w., first English ed. Bell Book 16-370 1978 £5

GIBBS, ARCHIE   U-Boat Prisoner. 1943. Austin 80-116 1978 $8.50

GIBBS, EVELYN   The Teaching of Art in Schools. London, 1937. Sm. 4to, orig. cloth, d.w., plts., good. Sexton 7-19 1978 £7.50

GIBBS, GEORGE   Memoirs of the Administrations of Washington and John Adams... New York, 1846. 2 vols., fine set, orig. cloth, 1st ed. Mac-Manus 239-178 1978 $60

GIBBS, JOSIAH WILLARD   Elementary Principles in Statistical Mechanics Developed with Especial Reference to the Rational Foundation of Thermodynamics. New York, 1902. 8vo., orig. cloth, gilt, slightly worn, fine copy, 1st ed. Norman 5-*22 1978 $150

GIBBS, JOSIAH WILLARD   The Scientific Papers. New York, 1906. 2 vols., lg. 8vo., frontis. portr., orig. cloth, slightly worn, but fine set, 1st ed. Norman 5-125 1978 $175

GIBNEY, JOHN   Practical Observations on the Use and Abuse of Cold & Warm Sea-Bathing in Various Diseases... 1813. 1st. ed., uncut & largely unopened, orig. bds., spine defective at head & tail. Jarndyce 16-679 1978 £22

GIBSON, A. M.   A Political Crime the History of the Great Fraud. New York, 1885. 1st ed., orig. cloth, rubbed. MacManus 239-179 1978 $30

GIBSON, CHARLES DANA   Gibson Cartoons. 1914. Plts., 4to., pict. bds., soiled. George's 635-121 1978 £6.50

GIBSON, E.   Codex juris ecclesiastici anglicani. (1713). Vol. 2 only, folio, contemp. calf, worn. George's 635-1070 1978 £8.50

GIBSON, EVA KATHARINE   Zauberlinda the Wise Witch. Chicago-Lansing, (1901). 1st ed., fine copy. Victoria 34-331 1978 $40

GIBSON, FRANCIS   Memoirs of the Bastile... 1802. 1st. ed., 8vo, 3 plts., orig. wrappers, lacks backstrip, uncut. Hannas 54-126 1978 £12.50

GIBSON, J. M.   Northland Songs, No. 1. Toronto, 1936. Illus. card cover. Hood's 115-869 1978 $15

GIBSON, J. T.   History of the Seventy-Eight Pennsylvania Volunteer Infantry. Pittsburg, 1905. Plts., new cloth, library stamp, Bell Wiley's copy. Broadfoot 46-365 1978 $20

GIBSON, J. W.   Recollections of a Pioneer. (St. Joseph, 1912). Cloth, decor. end sheets, 1st ed., fine copy, scarce, slipcase. Dykes 34-23 1978 $150

GIBSON, J. Y.   The Story of the Zulus. Pietermaritzburg, 1903. Plts., final gathering weak, 8vo., orig. cloth. K Books 244-369 1978 £20

GIBSON, J. Y.   The Story of the Zulus. London, 1911. New ed., revised & extended, 11 plts., orig. cloth, 8vo. K Books 239-185 1978 £15

GIBSON, JOHN   Guide and Directory of the State of Louisiana and the Cities of New Orleans and Lafayette... New Orleans, 1838. Illus., plates, half calf, 1st ed. Ginsberg 14-499 1978 $250

GIBSON, JOHN   History of York County Pennsylvania. Chicago, 1886. 4to., illus., maps, fine, orig. 1/2 leather. MacManus 239-1732 1978 $135

GIBSON, KATHARINE   The Goldsmith of Florence. New York, 1929. 4to, decorations by Kalman Kubinyi. Baldwins' 51-81 1978 $20

GIBSON, R. W.   Francis Bacon: A Bibliography of his Works and of Baconiana to the Year 1750. Oxford, 1950. With this copy is the excessively scarce "Supplement", cover soil. Ballinger 11-8 1978 $90

GIBSON, W. H.   Highways and Byways or Saunterings in New England. New York, 1883. Scarce, orig. gold stamped binding, gilt edges, 4to. Book Chest 17-162 1978 $58

GIBSON, W. H.   My Studio Neighbors. New York, 1898. Illus. by author, 8vo, orig. cloth. Book Chest 17-163 1978 $18

GIBSON, W. H.   Our Native Orchids. New York, 1905. 8vo, orig. cloth. Book Chest 17-164 1978 $25

GIBSON, W. W.   Home. 1920. Illus., title page, dec. bds., cloth spine, no. 66 of ltd. ed. of 300 copies. Eaton 45-38 1978 £20

GIBSON, W. W.   Home; poems. London, Beaumont Press, 1920. One of 260 numbered copies on handmade paper, nice, author's signed autograph pres. inscription, first ed., orig. binding. Rota 211-138 1978 £25

GIBSON, W. W.   I Heard a Sailor. London, 1925. Very fine. Desmarais B-274 1978 $10

GIBSON, WILLIAM   Conscience: a Poetical Essay. Cambridge, 1772. 4to, disbound, 1st ed. Ximenes 47-118 1978 $45

GIBSON, WILLIAM   The True Method of Dieting Horses. London, 1731. 3rd ed., orig. leather, crudely taped at spine, 8vo. Book Chest 17-165 1978 $95

GIDDINGS, JOSHUA R.   The Exiles of Florida: or, Crimes Committed by Our Government Against the Maroons... Columbus, 1858. 1st ed., illus., ex-lib. MacManus 239-1813 1978 $17.50

GIDDINGS, JOSHUA R.   Upon the Annexation of Texas. Washington, 1844. Wr. Jenkins 116-500 1978 $22.50

GIDE, ANDRE   Montaigne: An Essay in Two Parts. London, 1929. 8vo, green cloth, Fine, no. 69 of 800 copies, signed by Gide, 1st ed., collector's cond. Desmarais 1-188 1978 $35

GIDE, ANDRE   Oscar Wilde, A Study. Oxford, 1905. 1 of only 50 numbered copies, large handmade paper signed by Sturat Mason, 1st publication in English, sm. 4 to., illus., 3/4 Japan vellum over cloth, t.e.g, uncut, bookplate, good-fine. Houle 10-370 1978 $125

GIDE, ANDRE   Robert. Paris, (1930). Ltd. ed., no, 1740, 1/2 half calf, orig. wraps. bound in, booklabels of Roger Senhouse and Montague Shearman. Eaton 45-203 1978 £6

GIDEON, SAMUEL E.   Landmarks in Austin, Texas. Austin, 1925. Pict. wr. Jenkins 116-1375 1978 $8.50

GIERKE, OTTO   Natural Law and The Theory of Society, 1500-1800. Cambridge, 1934. 2 vols., tall 8vo., cloth. Salloch 348-73 1978 $25

GIFFEN, ROBERT   The Case Against Bimetallism. London, 1892. Inner hinges split, good. Biblo BL781-818 1978 $9.50

GIFTS of Genius: A Miscellany of Prose and Poetry, by American Authors. New York, (1859). Text very good, covers worn. 34-333 1978 $10

GIGLIOLI, C. H. D.   Naples in 1799. London, 1903. 8vo., cloth, illus. Van der Peet H-64-338 1978 Dfl 60

GILBERT, DAVID   Valedictory Address to the Graduates of the Medical Department of Pennsylvania College, 3/5/52. Philadelphia, 1852. Rittenhouse 49-295 1976 $10

GILBERT, F. C.   Practical Lessons from the Experience of Israel for the Church of To-Day. Lancaster, 1902. Illus. Austin 79-281 1978 $27.50

GILBERT, GEORGE   Cathedral Cities of England. New York, 1907. Illus. in color, 1st Amer. ed., inner hinges split. Biblo BL781-621 1978 $12

GILBERT, HENRY   King Arthur's Knights. Edinbrugh, 1911. Illus. in color by Walter Crane, first ed., full red crushed levant, raised bands, fine, handsome copy, exhibition binding. Houle 10-76 1978 $235

GILBERT, J. T.   Documents Relating to Ireland, 1795-1804. (1893). Reprint, octavo bound in cloth. Hyland 128-945 1978 £6.40

GILBERT, J. T.   A Jacobite Narrative of the War in Ireland, 1688-1691. (1892). Octavo bound in cloth, reprint. Hyland 128-947 1978 £6.50

GILBERT, J. WARREN   The Blue and Gray. N.P., 1922. Fldg.
map, illus. Bell Wiley's copy. Broadfoot 46-108 1978 $10

GILBERT, JOSIAH   The Dolomite Mountains. London, 1864. 1st.
ed., 8vo., half-title, vignette title-pg., coloured lithograph plts., coloured lithograph folding maps, illus., polished half calf, marbled sides, panelled back, gilt,
t.e.g. Deighton 5-125 1978 £65

GILBERT, STUART   James Joyce's Ulysses: a study. New York,
1931. First U.S. ed., spine faded, very good. Bell Book 17-521 1978 £12.50

GILBERT, WILLIAM   The Magic Mirror. London, 1866. 1st ed.,
illus., orig. cloth, gilt edges, rubbed edges, good. Greene 78-207 1978 $65

GILBERT, WILLIAM   De Magnete. London, 1600. Sm. folio,
printer's device on title, woodcuts, fldg. diagr., contemp. reversed calf, rubbed,
rebacked, fine copy, 1st ed. Norman 5-126 1978 $7,500

GILBERT, WILLIAM   On the Loadstone. New York, 1893. 8vo.
liv, frontis. portr., text illus., orig. cloth, gilt, uncut, fine copy, 1st ed. in
English. Norman 5-127 1978 $175

GILBERT, WILLIAM H.   Peoples of India. 1944. Illus., paper. Austin
80-117 1978 $8.50

GILBERT, WILLIAM SCHWENCK   The "Bab" Ballads. London, 1869. Illus. by
author, first ed., orig. binding, nice. Rota 211-139 1978 £35

GILBERT, WILLIAM SCHWENCK   The Bab Ballads. More Bab Ballads. London,
1869, (1873). Illus. by author, 2 vols., orig. pict. cloth, 1st ed., covers darkened, bookplts. removed, otherwise good. MacManus 238-228 1978 $125

GILBERT, WILLIAM SCHWENCK   "His Excellency." An Entirely Original
Comic Opera in Two Acts. London, 1894. Orig. printed wrs., 1st ed., wr. wea
wear, fine. MacManus 238-230 1978 $85

GILBERT, WILLIAM SCHWENCK   The Mikado. 1911. Coloured plts. by
Russell Flint, 4to., decor. cloth gilt, spine faded, joints split at head, good,
first English ed. Bell Book 17-488 1978 £10

GILBERT, WILLIAM SCHWENCK   New and Original Extravaganzas. Boston,
(1931). Orig. cloth, sm. 8vo., ex-lib. Morrill 241-159 1978 $7.50

GILBERT, WILLIAM SCHWENCK   Ruddigore; or, the Witch's Curse!....
London, (1887). Orig. printed wrs., 2nd ed., rare, covers slightly worn, but
fine. MacManus 238-229 1978 $60

GILBERT, WILLIAM SCHWENCK   Savoy Operas. London, 1909. Sm. 4to.,
illus. in color by W. Russell Flint, name on t.p. Biblo BL781-618 1978 $62.50

GILBERT, WILLIAM SCHWENCK   Songs of a Savoyard. 1890. 8vo., frontis.,
illus., decor. cloth, gilt edges, somewhat used. Quaritch 979-154 1978 $40

GILBERT, WILLIAM SCHWENCK   The Yeomen of the Guard or The Merryman
and His Maid. London, 1929. 8vo., cloth, d.j., illus. in color by Flint,
drawing in pen and ink by Charles E. Brock. 220-98 1978 $25

GILCHRIST, ALEXANDER   Life of William Blake. London, 1863. First
ed., 8vo., 3/4 blue calf, 2 vols., v.g., illus., orig. cloth bound in. Houle 10-
380 1978 $200

GILCHRIST, ALEXANDER   Life of William Blake. 1880. Second ed.,
portrait, illus., lg. 8vo., 2 vols., orig. cloth, uncut, scarce. Howes 194-1427
1978 £85

GILCHRIST, ALEXANDER   Life of William Blake... 1880. New ed., 2
vols., illus., 8vo., cloth, ex-lib. stamp, v.g. Quaritch 983-298 1978 $350

GILCHRIST, ALEXANDER   Life of William Blake with Selections from his
Poems and Other Writings. 1880. 2 vols., 8vo., best ed., portr., cloth, ex-
lib. stamp, very good copy. Quaritch 979-52 1978 $275

GILCHRIST, ALEXANDER   The Life of William Blake. London, 1907.
Numerous repro. from Blakes pictures, thick 8vo, cloth, gilt, t.e.g., fine.
Duschnes 220-28 1978 $37.50

GILCHRIST, EBENEZER   The Use of Sea Voyages in Medicine.... 1771.
8vo., contemp. calf. F. Edwards 1013-78 1978 £100

GILDER, RICHARD WATSON   Grover Cleveland: A Record of Friendship.
New York, 1910. 1st ed., illus. Biblo 248-92 1978 $17.50

GILDER, RICHARD WATSON   Letters. 1916. Illus., first ed. Austin 82-394
1978 $12.50

GILDER, RICHARD WATSON   The New Day. A Poem in Songs and Sonnets.
New York, 1876. Sq. 12mo., orig. pict. cloth, 1st ed., near-fine. MacManus
238-487 1978 $50

GILDER, RODMAN   The Battery. Boston, 1936. Illus. MacManus
239-360 1978 $17.50

GILES, ALFRED E.   Marriage. Boston, 1882. Disbound, 1st ed.
Ginsberg 14-654 1978 $35

GILES, DOROTHY   Singing Valleys. 1940. Austin 80-645 1978
$10

GILES, HARRY F.   The Beauties of the State of Washington. Olympia, 1915. Illus., orig. pr. pict. wr., 1st ed. Ginsberg 14-1030 1978 $22.50

GILES, HERBERT A.   A Chinese Biographical Dictionary. New York,
n.d. Cloth, very good, reprint of 1898 ed. Dawson's 449-37 1978 $25

GILES, J. A.   Six Old English Chronicles. 1848. Frontis.,
cr. 8vo., orig. cloth. George's 635-559 1978 £5.50

GILES, JAMES   Drawings of Aberdeenshire Castles. Aberdeen,
1936. Portrait frontis., map, plts., some coloured, 4to., orig. cloth. K Books
244-139 1978 £12

GILHAM, MAJOR WILLIAM   Manual of Instruction for the Volunteers and
Militia of the United States. Phila., 1861. Illus., charts, New cloth, library
stamp on title page, Bell Wiley's Copy. Broadfoot's 44-165 1978 $50.00

GILKIN, IWAN   La Damnation de l'Artiste. Brussels, 1890.
4to., contemp. brown mor., lg. inlaid panel of brown calf on both sides, uncut,
orig. wr. bound in, bound by H. Beenkens, 1st ed., only 150 numbered copies prtd.,
1 of preferred 10 copies on Japan paper. Goldschmidt 110-57 1978 $1,600

GILL, C.   Studies in Midland History. Oxford, 1930.
Sketch maps, illus., 8vo. George's 635-659 1978 £6.50

GILL, CHARLES   Notes Historiques sur L'Origine de la Famille Gill
de Saint-Francois du Lac et Saint-Thomas de Pierreville et Histoire de ma propre
Famille. Montreal, 1887. 12mo. Wolfe 39-198 1978 $45

GILL, ERIC   Art and Manufacture. 1929. First ed., wood-
engravings by Gill, sm. 8vo., orig. paper wrappers. George's 635-163 1978
£7.50

GILL, ERIC   Art and Prudence. Golden Cockerel Press, 1928.
Narrow 8vo., engrs. by author, buckram, fine with d.w., ltd. to 500 copies.
Quaritch 979-165 1978 $220

GILL, ERIC   Art-Nonsense and Other Essays. 1929. First ed.,
wood-engravings, orig. blue buckram, spine faded, top edges trimmed, others uncut. George's 635-164 1978 £45

GILL, ERIC   Art Nonsense and Other Essays. London, 1929.
1st. ed., lg. 8vo, orig. buckram, d.w. Traylen 88-256 1978 £30

GILL, ERIC   Beauty Looks After Herself. 1933. First ed.,
signed by Gill, line-drawings by Gill, cr. 8vo. George's 635-165 1978 £12.50

GILL, ERIC   Clothes. 1931. First ed., wood-engravings by
Gill, cr. 8vo., spine faded. George's 635-166 1978 £10

GILL, ERIC   Engravings. Bristol, Fanfare Press, 1929. One
of only 80 special copies on Batchelor handmade paper, signed by artist, folio, half
vellum, black cloth sides, very nice, first ed. Rota 212-27 1978 £600

GILL, ERIC   Engravings by Eric Gill. Bristol, 1929. Lg. 4to.,
1st ed., engrs., cloth, 490 copies prtd. Quaritch 979-155 1978 $400

GILL, ERIC   Engravings 1928-1933. 1934. 4to., illus., cloth,
little used. Quaritch 979-156 1978 $250

GILL, ERIC   The Future of Sculpture. 1928. One of only 55 copies printed, inscribed by author, map, cr. 8vo., orig. black cloth, covers badly stained. George's 635-167 1978 £10.50

GILL, ERIC   In a Strange Land. 1944. First ed., wood-engravings by Gill, cr. 8vo. George's 635-168 1978 £6.50

GILL, ERIC   Last Essays. London, (1942). Cloth, very fine, slightly soiled d.w. Dawson's 447-42 1978 £17.50

GILL, ERIC   The Law the Lawyers Know About. Ditchling, St. Dominic's Press, 1929. Sm. 4to., wood engrs. by Eric Gill, sewn. Quaritch 979-281 1978 $15

GILL, ERIC   Letters. 1947. Plts., very good, defective d.w., first English ed. Bell Book 16-371 1978 £4.50

GILL, ERIC   Letters. 1947. Illus., cr. 8vo. George's 635-169 1978 £5

GILL, ERIC   The Lord's Song: a sermon. Golden Cockerel Press, 1934. One of 500 numbered copies, frontis. engrav. by author, white buckram gilt, very good, first English ed. Bell Book 17-391 1978 £65

GILL, ERIC   Sacred and Secular. 1940. Illus., cr. 8vo. George's 635-170 1978 £5

GILL, ERIC   Sculpture. Ditchling, Suxxex, (1923). Sm. 4to., linen, bkplt., edges slightly darkened. Quaritch 979-282 1978 $120

GILL, ERIC   Songs Without Clothes. Sussex, 1921. First ed., orig. wrappers, printed d.w. with hand-coloured design, only 240 copies were printed, 8vo. Howes 194-889 1978 £30

GILL, ERIC   Unemployment. London, 1933. 12mo, pr. wrs., wood-engraving by author, 1 of 2000 copies, fine. Duschnes 220-115 1978 $27.50

GILL, HELEN   The Establishment of Counties in Kansas, 1855-1903. N.P., n.d. Maps, original wr. Ginsberg 14-444 1978 $7.50

GILL, W.   The River of the Golden Sand... 1880. 2 vols., 8vo, half calf, frontispieces, vignettes on titles, maps. Edwards 1012-136 1978 £60

GILLESPIE, NOEL A.   Endotracheal Anaesthesia. 1950. Second ed., revised and enlarged. Rittenhouse 49-296 1976 $10

GILLESPIE, ROBERT   Round about Flakirk. Glasgow, 1868. Fcap. 8vo., good, orig. cloth. K Books 244-370 1978 £8

GILLESPIE, W. M.   A Treatise on Land-Surveying. New York, 1858. Engravings, ex-library, very good, sixth ed., orig. binding. Wolfe 39-205 1978 $30

GILLET, E.   A Sermon Delivered Before the Maine Missionary Society, at Their Annual Meeting in Bath, June 27, 1810. Hallowell, 1810. 8vo, orig. cloth, wrappers. Edwards 1012-490 1978 £15

GILLET, RANSOM H.   Democracy in the United States. New York, 1868. Frontis. portr. Butterfield 21-197 1978 $15

GILLETT, ELDER C. E.   Pioneering. Elgin, 1929. Illus., orig. cloth, 1st ed. Ginsberg 14-1098 1978 $60

GILLETT, JAMES B.   Six Years with the Texas Rangers. Austin, 1921. Illus., original cloth, 1st ed. Jenkins 116-501 1978 $75

GILLETT, JAMES B.   Six Years with the Texas Rangers. Austin, (1921). Cloth, illus., 1st ed., scarce, fine, plastic cover, slipcase. Dykes 35-237 1978 $75

GILLETTE, MRS. F. E.   Das "Weisse Haus" Kochbuch... Chicago, 1891. Cloth, slightly soiled. Hayman 72-154 1978 $12.50

GILLIES, JOHN   The History of Ancient Greece. 1786. 1st. ed., 2 vols., 4to, orig. calf, brown & green labels, fine folding maps, leading hinge to vol. 1 cracked, otherwise fine. Jarndyce 16-94 1978 £30

GILLIES, JOHN   The History of Ancient Greece, its Colonies and Conquests, from the earliest Accounts till the Division of the Macedonian Empire in the East. 1801. Engraved portrait, map, 4 vols., contemp. tree calf, spines gilt, a little rubbed. George's 635-467 1978 £15

GILLIMORE, PARKER   The Hunter's Arcadia. London, 1886. Illus., dec. cloth, rather thumbed, shaken & worn, 8vo. K Books 239-187 1978 £8

GILLIMORE, PARKER   Prairie Farms and Prairie Folk. London, 1872. 1st. ed., 2 vols., sm. 8vo, engraved frontispieces, vignette title-pgs., quarter calf, gilt back. Deighton 5-39 1978 £30

GILLIS, J. D.   The Cape Breton Giant; A Truthful Memoir. Halifax, (1926). Card cover. Hood's 115-212 1978 $20

GILLIS, JAMES MELVILLE   The U.S. Naval Astronomical Expedition to the Southern Hemisphere, 1849-52. Washington, 1855. 2 vols., 4to, orig. cloth, tear in 1 spine repaired, blank margin of 1 leaf restored. Edwards 1012-647 1978 £100

GILLISS, WALTER   Recollections of the Gilliss Press and Its Work During Fifty Years 1869-1919. New York, 1926. 8vo., orig. leather-backed bds., 1st ed., ltd. to 300 copies, plts. MacManus 238-929 1978 $45

GILLIS, WALTER   Recollections of the Gillis Press and Its Work During Fifty Years 1869-1919. Grolier Club, 1926. Frontis. portr., plts., illus., 1 of 300 copies on Eltham handmade paper, new lea. spine. Battery Park 1-149 1978 $75

GILLMORE, INEZ HAYNES   The Ollivant Orphans. New York, 1915. First ed., frontis. Biblo 247-548 1978 $15

GILLMORE, QUINCY ADAMS   Official Report to the US Engineer Dept., of the Seige and Reduction of Fort Pulaski, Georgia. New York, 1862. Wrs., maps, colored plts., new cloth, Bell Wiley's copy. Broadfoot's 46-324 1978 $33

GILLMORE, QUINCY ADAMS   A Practical Treatise on Roads, Streets and Pavements. New York, 1888. 6th. ed., clean, orig. binding. Hayman 71-266 1978 $8.50

GILMAN, CAROLINE (HOWARD)   Recollections of a Southern Matron. New York, 1838. Half black leather & marbled bds. Baldwins' 51-523 1978 $15

GILMAN, CAROLINE (HOWARD)   Recollections of a Southern Matron. New York, 1838. Cover stained, sm. holes in spine, Bell Wiley's copy. Broadfoot's 44-708 1978 $12

GILMAN, CHANDLER R.   A Medico-Legal Examination of the Case of Charles B. Huntington, with Remarks on Moral Insanity and on the Legal Test of Sanity. New York, 1857. 8vo., orig. wrs., 1st ed. Morrill 239-96 1978 $10

GILMAN, DANIEL C.   Statement of the Progress and Conditon of the University of California. Berkeley, 1875. Original printed wr., 1st ed. Ginsberg 14-121 1978 $65

GILMAN, HAROLD   Paintings and Drawing in the Collection of Edward le Bas. 1965. Folio, sm. 8vo., colour reproductions, half mor. portfolio, ltd. to 105 copies. Quaritch 983-332 1978 $400

GILMAN, SAMUEL   Pleasures and Pains of the Student's Life. Boston, 1852. 8vo., unbound, title bit dust soiled, 1st ed., pres. to John Pierpont. Morrill 239-400 1978 $12.50

GILMER, JOHN A.   State of the Union Speech of Hon. John A. Gilmer, of North Carolina. Washington, 1861. Wrs. Bell Wiley's copy. Broadfoot 46-109 1978 $8

GILMORE, BARBARA   A Puritan Town and Its Imprints. Northampton, 1942. Fine. MacManus 239-296 1978 $10

GILMORE, JAMES   Down in Tennessee, and Back by Way of Richmond. New York, 1864. Bell Wiley's copy. Broadfoot 46-111 1978 $30

GILMORE, JAMES   My Southern Friends. New York, 1863. Bell Wiley's copy. Broadfoot 46-110 1978 $12

GILMORE, JAMES A.   John Sevier as a Commonwealth-Builder. New York, 1887. 1st ed., covers worn, fair copy, map. Biblo 248-209 1978 $17.50

GILMORE, JAMES R.   Personal Recollections of Abraham Lincoln and the Civil War. Boston, 1898. Illus. Baldwins' 51-202 1978 $12.50

GILMORE, MINNIE   Pipes from Prairie-Land, and Other Places.   New York, (1886). Cloth, slightly soiled. Hayman 72-265 1978 $7.50

GILMORE, P. S.   History of the National Peace Jubilee and Great Musical Festival, Held in the City of Boston, June, 1869, to Commemorate the Restoration of Peace Throughout the Land. Boston, 1871. Orig. cloth, 8vo., illus., 1st ed. Morrill 241-160 1978 $25

GILPIN, LAURA   The Rio Grande, River of Destiny: An Interpretation of the River, The Land, and the People. New York, 1929. Illus., maps, 1st ed., d.j. Jenkins 116-502 1978 $45

GILPIN, RICHARD   Daemonologia Sacra, or a Treatise of Satans Temptations. London, 1677. Thick 4to., disbound, 1st ed. Argosy Special-45 1978 $125

GILPIN, WILLIAM   An Essay Upon Prints... 1768. Sm. 8vo., contemp. calf, gilt dec. spine, fine copy. Quaritch 983-189 1978 $200

GILPIN, WILLIAM   An Essay on Prints. London, 1792. Fourth ed., old calf, covers worn and loose, scarce. Biblo 247-407 1978 $32.50

GILPIN, WILLIAM   Observations on the Western Parts of England. 1808. Second ed., tinted aquatint plts., contemp. calf, rebacked, 8vo. Howes 194-1387 1978 £30

GILPIN, WILLIAM   Observations, Relative Chiefly to Picturesque Beauty, Made in the Year 1772, on Several Parts of England... 1792. 2 vols., 4to., lg. paper, plts., sm. blind stamp, calf, 3rd ed. Quaritch 983-190 1978 $115

GILPIN, WILLIAM   Remarks on Forest Scenery, and Other Woodland Views, Illustrated by the Scenes of New Forest in Hampshire. 1791. 2 vols., 8vo., tinted plts., contemp. tree calf, gilt, 1st ed. Quaritch 983-191 1978 $125

GILPIN, WILLIAM   Remarks on Forest Scenery and other Woodland Views. 1808. Third ed., map, tinted aquatints, 2 vols., orig. bds., rebacked, uncut, 8vo. Howes 194-1388 1978 £38

GILSON, E.   The Spirit of Mediaeval Philosophy. 1936. 8vo. Upcroft 12-162 1978 £7.50

GINGERICH, MELVIN   The Mennonites in Iowa. 1939. Austin 79-283 1978 $27.50

GINZBERG, ELI   Grass on the Slag Heaps...Welsh Miners. New York, 1942. Biblo BL781-816 1978 $8.50

GINZBERG, ELI   The Illusion of Economic Stability. New York, 1939. Biblo BL781-819 1978 $10

GIOJA, MELCHIORRE   Filosofia della Statistica. Milano, 1826. 2 vols., 4to., vol. I: contemp. half-calf; vol. II: Orig. printed wrs., uncut, lightly loose, 1st ed. Gilhofer 74-14 1978 sFr 400

GIORDA, JOSEPH   A Dictionary of the Kalispel or Flat-Head Indian Language, Compiled by the Missionaries of the Society of Jesus. St. Ignatius Mission, 1877-1879. Plain wr., 1st ed. Ginsberg 14-615 1978 $375

GIORDA, JOSEPH   Lu Tel Kaimintis Kolinzuten Kuitlt Smimii. St. Ignatius, 1879. Half morocco, 1st ed. Ginsberg 14-616 1978 $175

GIORDA, JOSEPH   Smiimii Lu Tel Kaimintis Kolinzuten. St. Ignatius Mission, 1876. Original printed wr., 1st ed. Ginsberg 14-617 1978 $175

GIORDA, JOSEPH   Szmimeie-S Jesus Christ:.... St. Ignatius Mission, 1880. Disbound. Ginsberg 14-618 1978 $40

GIORNALE Araldico-Storico-Gealogico. 1912-13. Sewn, colored plt. Allen 234-1260 1978 $10

GIOTTO DI BONDONE   Frescoes. New York, (1950). Folio, cloth, color plts. Biblo 251-245 1978 $25

GIOVIO, PAOLO   Lettera di Paolo Giovio Vescovo di Nocera Sul Vitto Umano a Felice Trofino.... 1808. 4to., marbled bds., calf spine, very good. King 7-174 1978 £25

GIPSON, FRED   "The Cow Killers." With the Aftosa Commission in Mexico. Austin, 1956. Fine illus., illus. by Bill Leftwich, 1st ed., mint. Jenkins 116-503 1978 $10

GIPSON, FRED   Fabulous Empire. Boston, 1946. Cloth, 1st ed., fine copy in d.w., reinforced, scarce. Dykes 34-82 1978 $27.50

GIPSON, FRED   Fabulous Empire: Colonel Zack Miller's Story. Cambridge, 1946. 1st ed., d.j., author's scarce 1st book. Jenkins 116-1552 1978 $25

GIPSON, LAWRENCE H.   Lewis Evans... Philadelphia, 1939. Lg. 4to., maps. MacManus 239-1467a 1978 $40

GIRADOUX, JEAN   Amica America. 1918. Ltd. ed. of 500 copies no. 70, illus. in text, wraps., ink sign. on upper cover. Eaton 45-204 1978 £5

GIRALDI CINTHIO, GIOVANBATTISTA   De Gli Hecattommithi di M. Giovanbattista Gyraldi Cinthio Nobile Ferrarese. Mondovi, 1565. 2 vols., 8vo., sm. stamps on each title, 17th cent. vellum, first ed., very rare, complete, excellent. Quaritch 978-60 1978 $1,600

GIRALDUS CAMBRENSIS   Historical Works. 1913. Cr. 8vo., orig. cloth. George's 635-552 1978 £6.50

GIRAUD, A.   Le Laurier. Bruxelles, 1916. 4to., fine green half mor., gilt, t.e.g., portr., ltd. ed. of 160 numbered copies only. Van der Peet H-64-430 1978 Dfl 175

GIRDLER, TOM   Boot Straps, an Autobiography. 1943. Austin 80-646 1978 $8.50

GIRL SCOUTS OF AMERICA   Handbook For Girl Scouts. 1917. 2nd. ed.? Baldwins' 51-344 1978 $37.50

GIRL SCOUTS OF AMERICA   Scouting For Girls. New York, 1929. 3rd. abridged ed., very good copy, except an inch tear at top of frontispiece. Baldwins' 51-345 1978 $22.50

THE GIRL'S Own Annual. 1888/9. Half leather, very good, reprint. Hyland 128-867 1978 £25

THE GIRL'S Own Annual. 1888/9. Original gilt decor. binding, good, reprint. Hyland 128-866 1978 £35

A GIRL'S Room. Boston, (1886). 1st ed., profusely illus., almost fine. Victoria 34-336 1978 $12.50

GIROD, ARMURY   Notes Diverses sur le Bas-Canada. Village Debartzch, 1835. 4to., printed wrappers, uncut, sewn. Wolfe 39-476 1978 $150

GIROUARD, DESIRE   Lake St. Louis Old and New. Montreal, 1893. Illus., Columbian ed., 4to., orig. cloth. Wolfe 39-206 1978 $95

GIROUARD, DESIRE   Supplement au "Lake St. Louis". Montreal, 1900. Printed wrappers, illus., fold. plan, uncut. Wolfe 39-207 1978 $35

GIROUARD, DESIRE   Le Vieux Lachine et le Massacre du 5 Aout 1689. Montreal, 1889. Printed wrappers, illus., fold. plan. Wolfe 39-208 1978 $30

GISBERT, BLAISE   Christian Eloquence in Theory and Practice. 1718. 8vo., contemp. panelled calf. P. M. Hill 142-120 1978 £28

GISBORNE, THOMAS   Walks in a Forest... 1801. 5th. ed., illus. by S. Gilpin, orig. mottled calf, gilt borders & spine, v.g. Jarndyce 16-681 1978 £22

GISSING, ALGERNON   Second Selves. London, (1908). Orig. cloth, 1st ed., good. MacManus 238-231 1978 $45

GISSING, GEORGE   Demos. A Story of English Socialism. London, 1886. 3 vols., orig. cloth, 1st ed., lib. labels removed, but good. MacManus 238-232 1978 $275

GISSING, GEORGE   Denzil Quarrier. A Novel. London, 1892. Orig. cloth, 1st ed., rare, spine slightly dull, else very good. MacManus 238-237 1978 $125

GISSING, GEORGE   The Emancipated. A Novel. London, 1890. 3 vols., orig. cloth-backed bds., 1st ed., ex-lib. copy, bookplts., otherwise very good. MacManus 238-233 1978 $225

GISSING, GEORGE   The Immortal Dickens. London, (1925). Orig. cloth, paper label, 1st ed. MacManus 238-245 1978 $20

GISSING, GEORGE   In the Year of the Jubilee. London, 1894. 3 vols., orig. cloth, 1st ed., bind. a bit worn, lib. label removed, otherwise very good. MacManus 238-238 1978 $235

GISSING, GEORGE   Letters of ... to Members of His Family... London, 1927. Orig. cloth, spine a little worn, but good. MacManus 238-246 1978 $20

GISSING, GEORGE   New Grub Street. A Novel. London, 1891. 3 vols., orig. cloth, extremities and edges a bit worn, 1st ed., inner hinges cracked, but good copy, Augustine Birrell's bookply. in each vol., half mor. slip-case. MacManus 238-235 1978 $500

GISSING, GEORGE   New Grub Street. A Novel. London, 1891. 3 vols., orig. cloth, recased, worn, 1st ed., good working copy, lib. labels removed. MacManus 238-234 1978 $150

GISSING, GEORGE   New Grub Street. A Novel. London, 1891. 3 vols., orig. cloth, 2nd ed., very fine. MacManus 238-236 1978 $150

GISSING, GEORGE   The Paying Guest. London, 1895. 12mo., orig. cloth, 1st ed., covers somewhat worn and soiled. MacManus 238-239 1978 $75

GISSING, GEORGE   The Private Papers of Henry Ryecroft. Westminster, 1903. Orig. cloth, 1st ed., spine worn, front inner hinge cracked, bookstamp. MacManus 238-242 1978 $50

GISSING, GEORGE   The Private Papers of Henry Ryecroft. 1903. First ed., orig. cloth, 8vo., hinges little strained. Howes 194-890 1978 £25

GISSING, GEORGE   Sleeping Fires. New York, 1896. Orig. cloth, spine darkened. Greene 78-208 1978 $10

GISSING, GEORGE   The Town Traveler. London, 1898. Orig. cloth, 1st ed., spine faded, covers soiled and worn. MacManus 238-241 1978 $50

GISSING, GEORGE   Veranilda. London, 1904. 1st ed., orig. cloth, spine worn. Greene 78-44 1978 $40

GISSING, GEORGE   Veranilda. A Romance. London, 1904. Orig. cloth, 1st ed., good. MacManus 238-243 1978 $35

GISSING, GEORGE   The Whirlpool. London, 1897. Orig. cloth, 1st ed., good, covers worn. MacManus 238-240 1978 $50

GISSING, GEORGE   Will Warburton. London, 1905. Orig. cloth, 1st ed., very good. MacManus 238-244 1978 $45

GIST, W. W.   The Ages of the Soldiers in the Civil War as Contained in Iowa Journal of History. Cardboard covers, Bell Wiley's copy. Broadfoot's 44-491 1978 $8.00

GITLOW, BENJAMIN   I Confess. The Truth About American Communism. New York, (1940). 1st ed., signed by Sidney Hillman. Biblo BL781-817 1978 $10

GIVRY, GRILLOT DE   Witchcraft, Magic & Alchemy. Boston, 1931. 1st US ed., 4to., color plts., illus., orig. cloth, very good. Americanist 103-125 1978 $50

GLADDEN, WASHINGTON   Commencement Days. 1916. Austin 82-397 1978 $12.50

GLADDEN, WASHINGTON   The Great Commoner of Ohio. (Columbus, 1893). Wrs., slight wear. Hayman 73-534 1978 $8.50

GLADDEN, WASHINGTON   Santa Claus on a Lark. 1890. Illus. Austin 82-398 1978 $12.50

GLADSTONE, W. E.   The State in its relations with the Church. 1838. Half calf, a little rubbed, 8vo. George's 635-1072 1978 £10.50

GLANVIL, BARTHOLOMAEUS
Please turn to
BARTHOLOMAEUS ANGLICUS

GLANVILL, JOSEPH   Sadducismus Triumphatus. 1726. 2 parts, 4th ed., plts., cont. panelled calf, 8vo. Howes 194-51 1978 £85

GLANVILL, JOSEPH   Scepsis Scientifica. 1665. Sm. 4to., half calf, v.g. Howes 194-52 1978 £135

GLAREANUS, HENRICUS   De Geographia Liber Unus. Freiburg, 1539. Woodcut diagrams, sm. 4to., vellum, light waterstains. Salloch 345-79 1978 $500

GLAS, GEORGE   The History of the Discovery and Conquest of the Canary Islands... 1764. 1st. ed., folding map, 4to, calf, rebacked. Edwards 1012-315 1978 £150

GLAS, GEORGE   The History of the Discovery and Conquest of the Canary Islands... London, 1764. 4to, folding engraved map, plts., some spotting, mottled half calf, marbled bds., gilt back, morocco label gilt, joints weak. Deighton 5-14 1978 £145

GLASCOCK, W. N.   Naval Sketch-Book; or, The Service Afloat and Ashore. 1826. 2nd. ed., 2 vols., sm. 8vo, contemp. half calf, some spotting in text. Edwards 1012-424 1978 £40

GLASER, CHRISTOPHLE   Traite de la Chimie. Paris, 1663. 8vo., plts., contemp. vellum, some dampstaining, but very good copy, 1st ed. Norman 5-*23 1978 $750

GLASGOW, MAUDE   The Scotch-Irish in Northern Ireland and in the American Colonies. 1936. 1st ed. Austin 79-285 1978 $20

GLASENAPP, H. VON   Die Literaturen Indiens. Potsdam, 1929. 4to., cloth, plts., some in color, text illus. Van der Peet H-64-465 1978 Dfl 70

GLASER, CURT   Die Altdeutsche Malerei. 1924. 4to., illus. Allen 234-1261 1978 $30

GLASGOW, ELLEN   The Deliverance. N. Y., 1904. 1st ed., illus., color plts., gilt stamped red cloth, very good. Houle 10-123 1978 $20

GLASS, H. A.   The Barbone Parliament.... 1899. Octavo, good. Upcroft 10-329 1978 £6.50

GLASS, MONTAGUE   Y'Understand. 1925. Austin 79-287 1978 $10

GLASSCOCK, C. B.   The Big Bonanza...the Comstock Lode. Indianapolis, (1931). Illus., 1st ed. Biblo BL781-274 1978 $9.50

GLASSCOCK, C. B.   Gold In Them Hills, The Story of the West's Last Wild Mining Days. Indianapolis, (1932). Orig. binding, clean, light flecking on cover. Hayman 71-269 1978 $7.50

GLASSER, OTTO   Medical Physics. Chicago, 1944. Used copy. Rittenhouse 49-297 1976 $20

GLATZER, NAHUM N.   In Time and Eternity. 1946. Austin 79-288 1978 $10

GLAZEBROOK, RICHARD   Dictionary of Applied Physics. London, 1922-23. 5 vols., 8vo., fully illus., cloth, first issue. Quaritch 977-98 1978 $75

GLEASON, C. W.   How to Acquire and Preserve Health. N.P., 1874. Finely executed woodcuts. Rittenhouse 49-298 1976 $9

GLEICHEN, WILHELM FRIEDRICH VON   Das Neueste Aus Dem Reiche Der Pflanzen, Oder Mikroskopische Untersuchungen und Beobachtungen der Geheimen Zeugungstheile der Pflanzen. N.P., 1764-1766. Color plts., folio, contemp. bds. Salloch 345-80 1978 $1,200

GLEIG, G. R.   A Narrative of the Campaigns of the British Army at Washington and New Orleans... 1826. 2nd. ed., orig. bds., slightly soiled, rebacked, 8vo. Edwards 1012-491 1978 £45

GLEIG, G. R.   Sale's Brigade in Afghanistan... 1846. Sm. 8vo, half calf. Edwards 1012-121 1978 £20

GLEIG, GEORGE   A Critique on the Poems of Robert Burns. Edinburgh, 1812. 8vo., contemp. half sheep, gilt back, hinges worn, frontispiece, plts. P. M. Hill 142-55 1978 £36

GLEIG, ROBERT   The Country Curate. 1830. 1st. ed., 2 vols.,
orig. half calf, marbled bds., good. Jarndyce 16-684 1978 £38

GLEN, A. R.   Under the Pole Star: The Oxford University
Arctic Expedition, 1935-6. 1937. Maps, plts., roy. 8vo, orig. cloth. Edwards
1012-575 1978 £12

GLEN, A. R.   Young Men in the Arctic... London, 1935.
Illus., spine mended. Hood 116-80 1978 $10

GLENN, THOMAS   Merion in the Welsh Tract... Norristown,
1896. Scarce, ltd. to 500 copies. MacManus 239-1560 1978 $60

GLENTWORTH, JAMES B.   A Statement of the Frauds on the Elective Franchise in the City of New York in the Fall of...1838 and Spring of 1839. (New
York, 1841). Sewn, self-wr. Butterfield 21-500 1978 $12.50

GLICK, CARL   Swords of Silence: Chinese secret societies, past
and present. New York, (1947). Cloth, very good. Dawson's 449-38 1978
$12.50

GLISAN, RODNEY   Journal of Army Life. San Francisco, 1874.
Illus., original pictorial cloth, 1st ed. Ginsberg 14-364 1978 $50

GLOAG, JOHN   A History of Cast Iron in Architecture. 1948.
4to., coloured plts., illus., cloth, d.w. Quaritch 977-225 1978 $70

GLOAG, JOHN   A History of Cast Iron Architecture. London,
(1948). 507 plts., 4to. Baldwins' 51-83 1978 £42.50

GLOB SILVER MINING CO.   Reports of the General Superintendant and Trustees
of the Glob Silver Mining Co., Organized under the Laws of the State of New
York. New York, 1865. Map, orig. wr. laid in half mor case. Ginsberg 14-731
1978 $125

GLOBENSKY, C. A. M.   La Rebellion de 1837 a Saint-Eustache. Quebec,
1883. Printed cloth, portraits. Wolfe 39-474 1978 $55

GLOBUS, SEPTIMUS   Der Freischuta Travestie. London, 1824. 8vo,
full dark green crushed levant, gilt, spine and inner dentelles gilt, t.e.g., by
Riviere (hinges trifle rubbed), 1st ed., plates etched by George Cruikshank, very
scarce. Ximenes 47-219 1978 $225

GLORIOSO, IOANNES CAMILLUS   De Cometis Dissertatio Astronomico-
Physica Publica Habita in Gymnasio Patavino Anno Domini MDCXIX. Venteiis,
1624. 4to., modern vellum, 1st ed., scarce, fine. Offenbacher 30-47 1978
$450

GLOUX, OLIVER 1818-1883
Please turn to
AIMARD, GUSTAVE

GLOVER, ANNA   An Account of John Glover of Dorchester and His
Descendants. Boston, 1867. Biblo BL781-58 1978 $27.50

GLOVER, JOHN M.   Administration of the Mint Bureau. Speech of...,
of Missouri, in the House...March 3, 1879. Washington, 1879. Stapled as issued, inscribed by author. Hayman 72-266 1978 $7.50

GLOVER, RICHARD   Leonidas. 1739. 4th. ed., half-title, calf,
hinges weak, spine rubbed, text v.g. Jarndyce 16-95 1978 £5

GLOVER, RICHARD   Medea. 1762. Thick paper, disbound, 2nd. ed.
Hannas 54-140 1978 £12.50

GLOVER, T. R.   Challenge of the Greek & Other Essays. 1942.
Allen 234-363 1978 $7.50

GLOVER, T. R.   A Corner of Empire. London, 1937. Hood
117-735 1978 $35

GMELIN, LEOPOLD   Hand-Book of Chemistry. London, 1848-72.
19 vols., 8vo., plts., orig. cloth, gilt, some vols. loose in case, but very good
set, 1st ed. in English. Norman 5-129 1978 $475

GNUDI, MARTHA TEACH   The Life and Times of Gaspare Tagliacozzi Surgeon
of Bologna 1545-1599. New York, (1950). Folio, plts., guardsheets, prtd. in
Italy on Handmade paper, vellum with overlapping edges, fine, unopened & uncut copy from the library of Dr. Gnudi, plain cardboard box, 1 of 4 lg. paper
copies. Zeitlin 245-255 1978 $900

GNUDI, MARTHA TEACH   The Life and Times of Gaspare Tagliacozzi Surgeon
of Bologna 1545-1599. New York, (1950). 4to., plts., full stamped red mor.,
gilt-rule, gilt corner fleurons, gilt lettering, boxed, #1 of 15 special copies prtd.
Zeitlin 245-256 1978 $450

GOAD, CHARLES E.   Atlas of the City of Toronto & Suburbs. Montreal,
1884. Atlas folio, covers worn, maps. Wolfe 39-213 1978 $250

GOAD, JOHN   Astro-Meteorologica, or, Aphorism's and Dis-
courses of Bodies Coelestial, Their Natures and Influences. 1686. 1st. ed., folio,
contemp. calf, neatly recased with new endpapers, neat repair to sm. blank portion
of title, very good copy. Fenning 32-127 1978 £245

GOBART, LAURENT, S. J.   Tractatus Philosophicus de Barometro. Amstelodami, 1702. Engrs., 12mo., contemp. half pigskin, 1st ed., nice copy. Offenbacher 30-57 1978 $135

GOD and Nature's Sovereign Remedials. New York, 1864. 12mo., orig. wrs.
Morrill 239-97 1978 $10

GODCHARLES, FREDERIC A.   Chronicles of Central Pennsylvania. New
York, (1944). Illus., 4 vols., 4to., scarce. MacManus 239-1468 1978 $75

GODCHARLES, FREDERIC A.   Daily Stories of Pennsylvania. Milton, 1924.
MacManus 239-1469 1978 $12.50

GODDARD, PLINY EARLE   Indians of the Southwest. New York, 1921.
Illus. Biblo 251-43 1978 $12.50

GODDARD, ROBERT H.   A Method of Reaching Extreme Altitudes. Washington, D. C., 1919. 8vo., photolitho. plts., illus., orig. prtd. wrs., repaired,
few minor tears in wrs., repaired, but fine copy in cloth case, 1st ed. Norman
5-*24 1978 $1,000

GODDARD, ROBERT H.   A Method of Reaching Extreme Altitudes. Washington, 1919. 8vo., plts., orig. wrs., minor tear in upper wrapper. Quaritch
977-226 1978 $1,350

GODDARD, WILLIAM G.   An Address, in Commemoration of the Death of
William Henry Harrison, President of the United States. Delivered Before the City
Council and Citizens of Providence... Providence, 1841. Wrs., light dampstains.
Hayman 72-267 1978 $12.50

GODEE-MOLSBERGEN, E. C.   South-African History Told in Pictures. Amsterdam, 1913. Very well illus., folio, 8vo, orig. cloth, covers little scuffed. K
Books 239-188 1978 £15

GODEFROY, G.   Les Orfevres de Lyon 1306-1791) et de Trevoux
1700-1786... Paris, 1965. 4to., map, plts., orig. wrs., ltd. to 700 copies.
Quaritch 983-127 1978 $190

GODEFROY, JACQUES   The History of the United Provinces of Achaia.
1673. 4to., new bds. P. M. Hill 142-4 1978 £38

GODFREY, CARLOS E.   The Commander-in-Chiefs Guard. Washington,
D.C., 1904. 1st ed., illus., orig. cloth, very good. MacManus 239-573 1978
$40

GODOLPHIN, JOHN   A View of the Admiral Jurisdiction. 1685.
Second ed., sm. 8vo., contemp. calf. F. Edwards 1013-80 1978 £60

GODOLPHIN, SIDNEY   The Poems of .... Oxford, 1931. Octavo,
good. Upcroft 10-71 1978 £5

GODSELL, PHILLIP H.   Arctic Trader, the Account of Twenty Years with
the Hudson's Bay Company. Toronto, 1943. Illus., ex-lib. Hood 116-81 1978
$15

GODSELL, PHILLIP H.   The Romance of the Alaska Highway. Toronto,
1944. Hood's 115-967 1978 $15

GODWIN, FRANCIS   A Catalogue of the Bishops of England, since the
first planting of Christian religion in this Island, ... Londini, 1601. Quarto, in
eights, early pressed vellum, expertly rebacked, bookplate, 1st ed. Bennett 7-48
1978 $250

GODWIN, FRANCIS   A Catalogue of the Bishops of England, ...
Londini, 1601. 1st ed., quarto, early pressed vellum, rebacked, English black-
letter face, bookplate. Bennett 20-85 1978 $250

GODWIN, FRANCIS   A Catalogue of the Bishops of England... 1601.
First ed., sm. 4to., recently rebound in full calf antique style. Howes 194-54
1978 £65

GODWIN, MARY WOLLSTONECRAFT 1797-1851
Please turn to
SHELLEY, MARY WOLLSTONECRAFT GODWIN

GODWIN, WILLIAM   The Adventures of Caleb Williams... 1832.
Frontis & engraved title, half calf, black label, little rubbed. Jarndyce 16-687
1978 £12.50

GODWIN, WILLIAM   An Enquiry Concerning Political Justice, and Its
Influence on General Virtue and Happiness. London, 1793. 1st. ed., 2 vols., 4to,
half calf, red & green lettering-pieces. Traylen 88-74 1978 £650

GODWIN, WILLIAM   Enquiry Concerning Political Justice and Its
Influence on Morals and Happiness. Philadelphia, 1796. 1st Amer. ed., 2 vols.,
8vo, marbled calf with labels, spine gilt. Salloch 348-75 1978 $150

GODWIN, WILLIAM   Enquiry Concerning Policital Justice and Its
Influence on Morals and Happiness. London, 1798. 3rd. ed., 2 vols., 8vo,
modern half calf, old board sides. Traylen 88-75 1978 £40

GODWIN, WILLIAM   Enquiry Concerning Political Justice and Its
Influence on Morals and Happiness. 1842. 4th. ed., 2 vols. in I, uncut &
unopened, orig. green cloth, spine dulled, good. Jarndyce 16-686 1978 £18

GODWIN, WILLIAM   Fleetwood... 1832. Frontis, engraved title,
orig. pink cloth, black labels, new preface, v.g. Jarndyce 16-688 1978 £18.50

GODWIN, WILLIAM   History of the Commonwealth of England...
1824-28. 1st. ed., 4 vols., half titles, very good set, orig. blue cloth, paper
labels, little rubbed. Jarndyce 16-685 1978 £62

GODWIN, WILLIAM   History of the Commonwealth of England, From
Its Commencement to the Restoration of Charles the Second. 1824-28. 4 vols.,
half cloth, bd. sides, octavo, good. Upcroft 10-332 1978 £40

GODWIN, WILLIAM   Life of Geoffrey Chaucer. 1803. First ed., 2
vols., portraits, 4to., contemp. half calf, rebacked, orig. labels. Howes 194-
206 1978 £65

GODWIN, WILLIAM   Mandeville. 1817. 3 vols., 12mo., 1st ed.,
orig. bds., internally fresh, uncut. Quaritch 979-161 1978 $230

GODWIN, WILLIAM   Mandeville. Edinburgh, 1817. 3 vols., 12mo.,
19th-century full mottled calf gilt, t.e.g., many other edges uncut, first ed. P.
M. Hill 142-303 1978 £185

GODWIN, WILLIAM   Mandeville. Edinburgh, 1817. Three vols., sm.
8vo., half calf, rebacked, very good, first ed. Rota 212-28 1978 £160

GODWIN, WILLIAM   Mandeville: A Tale of the Seventeenth Century
in England. Edinburgh, 1817. First ed., 3 vols., sm. 8vo., contemp. calf, rebacked, rare. Howes 194-287 1978 £85

GODWYN, THOMAS   Moses and Aaron. 1672. 8th. ed., 4to, recent
bds., neat annotations, nice copy. Fenning 32-128 1978 £14.50

GOEBBELS, JOSEPH   Vom Kaiserhof zur Reichskanzlei. Munich, 1935.
Biblo 247-688 1978 $17.50

GOERCH, CARL   Down Home. Raleigh, 1943. Illus. Broadfoot
50-75 1978 $10

GOETHE, JOHANN WOLFGANG VON   A Dramatic Poem. 1834. 2nd ed.,
rebound in red buckram. Eaton 45-205 1978 £8

GOETHE, JOHANN WOLFGANG VON   Faustus. 1821. Plts., drawn and
engraved by Henry Moses, 4to., orig. bds., worn, spine defective. George's
635-195 1978 £12.50

GOETHE, JOHANN WOLFGANG VON   Faust: a Tragedy. 1839, 1843. 2
vols. in 1, lg. 8vo., half mor. gilt, illus. P. M. Hill 142-273 1978 £38

GOETHE, JOHANN WOLFGANG VON   Faust, A Dramatic Poem. 1867. 1st
ed., orig. red cloth block in gilt, a.e.g., signed by translator John W. Grant,
fine & attractive copy. Jarndyce 16-696 1978 £10.50

GOETHE, JOHANN WOLFGANG VON   Faust, a Drama. 1906. Plts. drawn
by Gilbert James, cr. 8vo. George's 635-187 1978 £5.25

GOETHE, JOHANN WOLFGANG VON   Faust. Berlin, 1926-1927. 2 vols.,
folio, text vol. in orig. full red mor., uncut, bound by Ulber-Sochting, Berlin,
plts. vol. in orig. white pigskin portfolio, uncut, ltd. ed., issued in 150
numbered copies, plt. vol. prtd. in 50 copies only, orig. lithos. by Max Slevogt,
prtd. on handmade paper, lithos. prtd. on China paper, etchings on velin paper,
exceptionally fresh & clean. Goldschmidt 110-69 1978 $4,000

GOETHE, JOHANN WOLFGANG VON   Goethe's Schriften. Leipzig, 1787-
90. 8 vols., sm. 8vo, plates by Chodowiecki, occasional light spotting, contemp.
German half calf, 1st authorized collection. Quaritch 978-64 1978 $4,250

GOETHE, JOHANN WOLFGANG VON   Goethe's neue Schriften. Berlin,
1792-1800. 7 vols., sm. 8vo, folding plates of music, contemp. paper boards,
leather labels, 2nd authorized collection. Quaritch 978-65 1978 $975

GOETHE, JOHANN WOLFGANG VON   The Sorrows of Werter: A German
Story. 1783. 4th ed., 2 vols., orig. speckled calf, maroon labels, fine.
Jarndyce 16-96 1978 £48

GOETHE, JOHANN WOLFGANG VON   Torquato Tasso, A Dramatic Poem.
1833. 2nd. ed., green morocco, gilt borders, hinges rubbed, good. Jarndyce 16-
690 1978 £10.50

GOETHE, JOHANN WOLFGANG VON   Werther, Traduction de L'Allemand de
Goete, Par C. Aubry.... Paris, 1797. 2 vols., calf, 3 1/2 x 5 1/4", contemp.
gilt spines, 4 eng. Eaton 45-206 1978 £25

GOETHE, JOHANN WOLFGANG VON   West-oestlicher Divan. Stuttgart,
1819. 8vo, some spotting, contemp. half calf, gilt spine, 1st ed., very rare 1st
issue. Quaritch 978-66 1978 $775

GOETHE, JOHANN WOLFGANG VON   Zur Farbenlehre. Tubingen, 1810.
1st ed., engr. plts., mostly colored by hand, contemp. half calf, 2 vols., 8vo,
atlas in 4to. Gilhofer 75-49 1978 SFr 5,800

GOETHE, JOHANN WOLFGANG VON   Zur Naturwissenschaft uberhaupt,
besonders zur Morphologie. Stuttgart, 1817-1824. Extremely rare complete set of
1st issues, engraved full-page plate, orig. pr. wr., preserved in two boxes. Gilhofer 75-50 1978 SFr 5,500

GOFF, G. I.   Historical Records of the 91st Argyllshire Highlanders. 1891. 8vo., coloured frontis. & plts., orig. cloth. F. Edwards 1013-
541 1978 £30

GOGARTY, OLIVER ST. JOHN   Elbow Room. Dublin, Cuala Press, 1939.
One of 450 copies, linen-backed bds., fine, unopened. Bell Book 17-394 1978
£37.50

GOGARTY, OLIVER ST. JOHN   Going Native. New York, 1940. 8vo,
blue cloth, gilt lettering, uncut, Fine, inscribed by Gogarty, 1st ed., collector's
cond. Desmarais 1-190 1978 $20

GOGARTY, OLIVER ST. JOHN   I Follow St. Patrick. London, 1938. Illus.,
fldg. map, blue cloth, 1st ed., fine in dust jacket. Bradley 49-133 1978 $15

GOGARTY, OLIVER ST. JOHN   James Augustine Joyce. Dallas, 1949. One
of 1050 copies, fine, wraps. Bell Book 16-519 1978 £8.50

GOGARTY, OLIVER ST. JOHN   Others to Adorn. 1938. Very good, worn
d.w., first English ed. Bell Book 17-395 1978 £8.50

GOGH, VINCENT VAN   The Complete Letters of... Greenwich, n.d.
Fine set. Biblo 251-254 1978 $87.50

GOGH, VINCENT VAN   Letters to Emile Bernard. 1938. Plts., 4to.
George's 635-220 1978 £12.50

GOGOARTY, OLIVER ST. JOHN   Elbow Room. Cuala Press, 1939. Illus.,
1 of 450 copies, fine. Battery Park 1-50 1978 $100

GOGOL, NIKOLAI   Dead Souls. Chichikov's Journeys; or, Home
Life in Old Russia. New York: The Limited Editions Club, 1944. 8vo., 2 vols.,
illus. in color by Lucille Corcos, orig. cloth-backed bds., pub. box, 1 of 1,200
copies, signed by illustrator, fine. MacManus 238-824 1978 $27.50

GOLD, MICHAEL   Jews Without Money. New York, (1930). Wood
cuts by Howard Simon, worn d.j., orig. binding. Wolfe 39-212 1978 $20

GOLD, P. D.   In Florida's Dawn. Jacksonville, 1926.
Inscribed copy. Baldwins' 51-524 1978 $12.50

GOLDBERG, ISAAC   The Man Mencken. New York, 1925.
2nd printing of 2nd month of publication, portrait, illus., very good or better. Limestone 9-197 1978 $25

GOLDEN, PETER   The Voice of Ireland. New York, (1915). 8vo,
soiled gray-green cloth, signed, 1st ed., collector's cond. Desmarais 1-191
1978 $30

GOLDEN COCKEREL PRESS   Prospectus for the Season 1933. (Waltham St.
Lawrence, 1933). 4to., illus., orig. pict. wrs., very good. MacManus 238-801
1978 $12.50

GOLDENSON, S. H.   Moral and Spiritual Foundations for the World
of Tomorrow. New York, 1945. Biblo 251-693 1978 $15

GOLDER, FRANK ALFRED   Bering's Voyages. New York, 1922. 2 vols.,
12mo., orig. cloth, good, plts. Paine 78-57 1978 $22.50

GOLDER, FRANK ALFRED   The March of the Mormon Battalion From Council
Bluffs to California... New York, (1928). 1st ed., illus., scarce. MacManus
239-1917 1978 $27.50

GOLDER, JOHN   The Life of the Hon. Wm. Tilghman, Late
Chief Justice of...Penna... Philadelphia, 1829. 1st ed., portr., orig. cloth-
backed bds., uncut, 8vo., very good. Americanist 103-38 1978 $25

GOLDING, LOUIS   Poems Drunk and Drowsy. London, n.d. (1934).
8vo, original cream parchment boards, 1st ed., one of 25 copies printed on Japon
vellum paper, numbered and signed by author, illus. by Hugh Easton. Ximenes
47-119 1978 $35

GOLDING AND COMPANY   Catalogue and Price-List of Machinery, Tolls, Material....Boston, Mass... N.P., (1897). Wrs., illus. Hayman 72-105 1978
$15

GOLDONI, CARLO   The Liar. London, 1922. 1st ed., full color,
plates, spine label darkened, very fine copy. Victoria 34-307 1978 $40

GOLDONI, CARLO   The Liar. A Comedy in Three Acts. New York,
1922. Illus., 1st Amer. ed., bind. dust-faded, edges rubbed. Biblo BL781-986
1978 $10

GOLDONI, CARLO   The Liar: a comedy. 1922. Coloured frontis.,
drawings by Claud Lovat Fraser, sm. 4to., cloth-backed bds., covers faded &
rubbed, good, first English ed. Bell Book 17-587 1978 $6.50

GOLDSCHEIDER, LUDWIG   Etruscan Sculpture. 1941. Folio, illus. Allen
234-306 1978 $15

GOLDSCHEIDER, LUDWIG   Roman Portraits. 1940. Folio, plt., shaken.
Allen 234-365 1978 $15

GOLDSCHMIDT, ALFONS   Die Dritte Eroberung Amerikas. Berlin, 1929.
Illus. Biblo BL781-63 1978 $9.50

GOLDSMID, E.   Bibliotheca Curiosa. Edinburgh, 1886-88. Ltd.
to 200 copies on thick paper, 3 vols. in 1, new buckram, 8vo. George's 635-
1199 1978 £45

GOLDSMITH, ELIZABETH E.   Sacred Symbols in Art. New York, (1912).
12mo., illus., 2nd ed., rev'd. and enlarged. Biblo BL781-599 1978 $10

GOLDSMITH, J. PSEUD.
Please turn to
PHILLIPS, SIR RICHARD

GOLDSMITH, OLIVER   Abridgement of his History of England, from the
Invasion of Julius Caesar, to the Death of George II. Derby, 1816. Sm. 8vo.,
frontis, early calf, hinges worn. Quaritch 979-89 1978 $95

GOLDSMITH, OLIVER   Citizen of the World. Chiswick, 1819. 2 vols.,
engrav. title, 12mo., full calf. K Books 244-141 1978 £11

GOLDSMITH, OLIVER   The Deserted Village. London, (1927). 4to.,
orig. bds., tissue d.w., fine. Morrill 239-401 1978 $15

GOLDSMITH, OLIVER   Englands Historia i Bref Fran En Fader Till Dess
Son. Stockholm, 1825-27. 1st Swedish ed., 3 vols. in 2, sm. 8vo, contemp.
half calf, slightly worn, oil stain on 8 last leaves of vol. 2. Hannas 54-141 1978
£18

GOLDSMITH, OLIVER   An Enquiry into the Present State of Polite Learning in Europe. 1774. Second ed., 8vo., calf, rebacked, corners rubbed, tall
copy. P. M. Hill 142-122 1978 £38

GOLDSMITH, OLIVER   Essays. London, 1765. Contemp. calf, 12mo.,
strip of calf gone from back cover, 1st ed. Americanist 102-53 1978 $175

GOLDSMITH, OLIVER   Essays by... Collecta Revirescunt. London,
1765. 12mo., full contemp. calf, gilt, 1st ed. MacManus 238-124 1978 $200

GOLDSMITH, OLIVER   Essays. 1765. 1st. ed., 12mo, engraved title,
foxed, contemp. mottled calf, rebacked, corner of 2 leaves torn. Hannas 54-
142 1978 £65

GOLDSMITH, OLIVER   Essays. 1766. 2nd. ed., 19th. century half
calf, v.g. Jarndyce 16-97 1978 £38

GOLDSMITH, OLIVER   Essays. 1775. Orig. calf, rebacked, v.g.
Jarndyce 16-98 1978 £12.50

GOLDSMITH, OLIVER   The Good Natur'd Man: A Comedy. 1768.
1st. ed., 4th. impression, 8vo, half-title, disbound. Hannas 54-143 1978 £45

GOLDSMITH, OLIVER   The Grecian History, From the Earliest State to
The Death of Alexander the Great. Hartford, 1826. 2 vols. in 1 as issued, leather, orig. binding. Hayman 71-270 1978 $12.50

GOLDSMITH, OLIVER   Grekiska Historian i Sammandrag. Stockholm,
1806. 1st. Swedish ed., 8vo, contemp. half calf, holes in margin of title repaired.
Hannas 54-144 1978 £15

GOLDSMITH, OLIVER   The History of England to the Death of George II.
1800. 3 vols., contemp. calf, rubbed, 8vo. George's 635-662 1978 £5

GOLDSMITH, OLIVER   A History of the Earth and Animated Nature.
1857. Coloured plts., sewing loose in places, 2 vols., roy. 8vo., covers worn.
George's 635-995 1978 £12.50

GOLDSMITH, OLIVER   A History of the Earth, and of Animals, in General.
Chambersburg, n.d. (ca. 1820s-1830s). 8vo., contemp. calf. Morrill 241-161
1978 $12.50

GOLDSMITH, OLIVER   The Life of Richard Nash, Of Bath. Bath, 1762.
First ed., first issue, portrait, contemp. calf, label missing, upper joint cracked,
very good, 8vo. Howes 194-290 1978 £145

GOLDSMITH, OLIVER   Miscellaneous Works. Glasgow, 1816. 4 vols.,
portrait, contemp. calf gilt, 8vo. Howes 194-288 1978 £26

GOLDSMITH, OLIVER   The Poems. 1822. Engraved by Finden, orig.
red calf, gilt borders & spine, attractive, good. Jarndyce 16-692 1978 £9.50

GOLDSMITH, OLIVER   Poems and Plays. 1889. Etchings, one of 150
numbered copies on large paper, 2 vols., quarter parchment, internally very good,
first English ed. Bell Book 17-404 1978 £6

GOLDSMITH, OLIVER   The Poetical and Dramatic Works. 1786. 2
vols., portrait, contemp. tree calf, labels missing, 8vo. Howes 194-289 1978
£15

GOLDSMITH, OLIVER   The Poetical Works. 1785. Complete in 1 vol.,
2nd. ed., 1st. leaf repaired, edges tattered, modern full pale calf, gilt spine.
Eaton 45-209 1978 £30

GOLDSMITH, OLIVER   Poetical Works. Hereford, 1799. 12mo., woodcuts, green mor., gilt panelled back, gilt edges. Quaritch 979-29 1978 $185

GOLDSMITH, OLIVER   Poetical Works. Gloucester, 1809. Sm. 8vo.,
woodcuts, orig. bds., good clean copy. Quaritch 979-30 1978 $95

GOLDSMITH, OLIVER　　　Poetical Works. 1866. Sm. 4to, orig. cloth stamped in black & gold on upper cover. Eaton 45-208 1978 £5

GOLDSMITH, OLIVER　　　The Roman History Abridged for the Use of Schools. London, 1786. 4th. ed., plts., sm. 8vo, orig. calf. Traylen 88-140 1978 £9

GOLDSMITH, OLIVER　　　The Roman History, from the Foundation of the City of Rome to the Destruction of the Western Empire. 1769. 2 vols., fine, contemp. polished calf, first ed., 8vo. Howes 194-291 1978 £65

GOLDSMITH, OLIVER　　　The Roman History, From the Foundation of the City of Rome, to the Destruction of the Western Empire. 1769. 1st. ed., 2 vols., 8vo, contemp. calf, slightly worn, some damp-stains affecting index leaves, final end-papers & lower cover of vol. I. Hannas 54-145 1978 £16

GOLDSMITH, OLIVER　　　The Roman History, from the Foundation of the City of Rome to the Destruction of the Western Empire. 1786. New ed., 2 vols., contemp. calf, labels missing, joints partly cracked, 8vo. Howes 194-292 1978 £20

GOLDSMITH, OLIVER　　　She Stoops to Conquer... Dublin, 1773. 1st. Dublin ed., 12mo, disbound, waterstained. Hannas 54-146 1978 £15

GOLDSMITH, OLIVER　　　She Stoops to Conquer or the Mistakes of a Night. London, (1912). Illus. by Hugh Thomson, frontis., lg. 4to, orig. full vellum, t.e.g., gilt-stamped, deluxe ed., ltd. to 350 copies, signed by artist, covers warped and lightly soiled. Howell 5-28 1978 $200

GOLDSMITH, OLIVER　　　The Traveller, or a Prospect of Society. 1765. 4to., 1st ed., dark green mor. gilt edges. Quaritch 979-172 1978 $150

GOLDSMITH, OLIVER　　　The Traveller,.... London, 1765. 1st Pub. ed., thin quarto, bound in elaborately gilt decor. green levant by Stikeman, spine cracked, gilt top. Totteridge 29-48 1978 $325

GOLDSMITH, OLIVER　　　The Traveller, a Poem. 1770. Engraved title-page, 4to, wrapper, fine. Fenning 32-129 1978 £10.50

GOLDSMITH, OLIVER　　　The Traveller. 1774. 4th. ed., half-title, water-stains across top corner, rebound in brown bds. Jarndyce 16-99 1978 £10.50

GOLDSMITH, OLIVER　　　The Vicar of Wakefield. 1787. 8th. ed., cr. 8vo, title medallion portrait, old bds., green parchment spine, worn. Eaton 45-210 1978 £8

GOLDSMITH, OLIVER　　　The Vicar of Wakefield. Berlin, 1789. Sm. 8vo, frontispiece, contemp. half calf, slightly worn. Hannas 54-147 1978 £15

GOLDSMITH, OLIVER　　　The Vicar of Wakefield. 1832. Illus. by George Cruikshank, half calf, green labels, v.g. Jarndyce 16-432 1978 £12.50

GOLDSMITH, OLIVER　　　The Vicar of Wakefield. Philadelphia, (1929). Quarto, 1st Amer. ed., plates and pictorial endpapers, fine copy. Victoria 34-690 1978 $60

GOLDSMITH, OLIVER　　　The Vicar of Wakefield. Philadelphia, (1929). Mint, colored pict. d.j., orig. box with d.j. plate, folding protective glassene wr., slight cracking of box edges. Victoria 34-691 1978 $175

GOLDSMITH, OLIVER　　　Works. London, 1848. 4 vols., small octavo, full tan mor., contrasting labels, gilt and blind stamping, very good. Bennett 7-49 1978 $45

GOLDSON, WILLIAM　　　Observations on The Passage Between the Atlantic and Pacific Oceans... Portsmouth, 1793. 4to, folding map, browned, full blue morocco. Edwards 1012-392 1978 £1100

GOLDSTEIN, DAVID　　　Jewish Panorama. Boston, 1940. Ex-lib. Austin 79-291 1978 $12.50

GOLDSTEIN, DAVID　　　Socialism. Boston, 1911. 2nd ed. Austin 79-290 1978 $12.50

GOLDWATER, BARRY　　　Arizona Portraits. N.P., 1940. Orig. pict. folio cloth tied at spine, 1st ed., illus. Ginsberg 14-9 1978 $45

GOLOVNIN, VASILY MIKHAILOVICH　　　Narrative of My Captivity in Japan, During the Years 1811, 1812, and 1813.... London, 1818. 2 vols., 8vo., half calf, gilt backs. Deighton 5-76 1978 £75

GOLTZIUS, HUBERTUS　　　Los vivos retratos de todos los Emperadores. Antwerp, 1560. Folio, medallion portraits in chiaroscuro, contemp. vellum bds., 1st Spanish ed., very good. Quaritch Summer, 1978-20 1978 $2,250

GOMEZ DE LUQUE, GONZALO　　　Librero Primero delos famosos hechos del principe Celidon de Iberia. Alcala, 1583. Small 4to, repair to lower outer corner of one leaf restored in skillful pen-facsimile, English 19th-century red mor. gilt, gilt edges, only ed. Quaritch 978-63 1978 $1,250

GOMME, GEORGE LAURENCE　　　The Gentleman's Magazine Library. London, 1889. 8vo., white cloth dust soiled, 1st ed. Morrill 239-402 1978 $20

GONCOURT, EDMOND LOUIS ANTOINE DE　　　L'Amour au Dix-Huitieme Siecle. Paris, 1875. Half calf, gilt, text in eng. border, very slightly rubbed. Eaton 45-212 1978 £10

GONCOURT, EDMOND LOUIS ANTOINE DE　　　La Saint-Huberty d'apres sa Correspondance et ses Papiers de Famille. Paris, 1882. 8vo., illus. border to each page, half mor., embroidered silk covers, worn, facsimile letter. Eaton 45-213 1978 £5

GONNER, E. C. K.　　　Common Land and Inclosure. 1912. 8vo. George's 635-325 1978 £7.50

GONVOT, C. -N.　　　Manuel de Legislation Militaire. Paris, 1828. 8vo., contemp. calf, rebacked. F. Edwards 1013-308 1978 £12

GONZALES, J. ELEUTERIO　　　Coleccion de Noticias Y Documentos Para La Historia Del Estado De N. Leon. Monterey, 1867. 1/2 calf, orig. boards, worn. Jenkins 116-506 1978 $200

GONZALES, P. DIEGO PABLO　　　Manual Para Administrar a Los Indios del Idioma Cahita los Santos Sacramentos,.... Mexico, 1740. Vellum, 1st ed. Ginsberg 14-366 1978 $3,500

GOOCH, G. P.　　　Before the War, Studies in Diplomacy. Vol. 2, Coming of the Storm. 1938. 8vo. George's 635-663 1978 £5

GOOCH, G. P.　　　History and Historians in the 19th Century. London, 1920. Second ed. Biblo 247-690 1978 $17.50

GOOD, JOHN MASON　　　The Book of Nature. 1828. 2nd. ed., 3 vols., fine set, half green calf, spine decorated in blind & gilt, black labels. Jarndyce 16-693 1978 £28

GOOD, JOHN MASON　　　Study of Medicine. Volumes I, II, III and IV. London, 1840. Fourth ed., unusually good. Rittenhouse 49-300 1976 $25

THE GOOD-NATURED Little Boy. New Haven, 1826. Sq.24mo, wrappers illus., good. Victoria 34-337 1978 $15

GOODE, JOHN　　　Recollections of a Lifetime. New York and Washington, 1906. 1st ed., port. MacManus 239-1877 1978 $27.50

GOODE, KENNETT M.　　　Showmanship in Business. 1936. Austin 80-647 1978 $10

GOODELL, EDWIN B.　　　Montclair. The Evolution of a Suburban Town. Montclair, 1934. 1st ed., illus., orig. cloth, very good. MacManus 239-1268 1978 $32.50

GOODEN, STEPHEN　　　The Revelation of St. John the Divine:.... 1939. 3 engravings, signed and dated in pencil. Quaritch 978-67 1978 $750

GOODENOUGH, CAROLINE LEONARD　　　High Lights on Hymnists and Their Hymns. (New Bedford, 1931). Orig. cloth, 8vo., 1st ed. Morrill 241-162 1978 $15

GOODLAND, ROGER　　　A Bibliography of Sex Rites and Customs. London, 1931. 4to., d.w., nice, 1st ed. Morrill 239-98 1978 $35

GOODLAND, ROGER　　　A Bibliography of Sex Rites and Customs. 1931. 4to. George's 635-1203 1978 £35

GOODMAN, ABRAM VOSSEN　　　American Overture. 1947. Illus. Austin 79-293 1978 $12.50

GOODMAN, JACK   While You Were Gone. 1946. Austin 80-118 1978 $8.50

GOODMAN, NATHAN G.   Benjamin Franklin Reader. New York, (1945). Drawings. Biblo BL781-50 1978 $7.50

GOODRICH, PHINEAS G.   History of Wayne County, Pa. Honesdale, 1880. Orig. cloth, very scarce. MacManus 239-1470 1978 $60

GOODRICH, SAMUEL GRISWOLD   The Balloon Travels of Robert Merry and His Young Friends Over Various Countries in Europe. 1860. Illus., first ed. Austin 82-969 1978 $27.50

GOODRICH, SAMUEL GRISWOLD   Les Contes de Pierre Parley sur l'Amerique. Boston, 1832. Sq. 12mo., hand colored frontis., illus., woodcuts, orig. cloth, rubbed. Victoria 35-581 1978 $125

GOODRICH, SAMUEL GRISWOLD   History of the Indians, of North and South America. Boston, 1853. 12mo., orig. cloth, illus., headband worn. Edwards 1012-553 1978 £10

GOODRICH, SAMUEL GRISWOLD   Lives of Celebrated American Indians... Boston, 1843. Leather bind. little scuffed. Hood's 116-413 1978 $75

GOODRICH, SAMUEL GRISWOLD   A Pictorial Geography of the World. Boston, 1849. Illus., calf, very good. Victoria 34-601 1978 $25

GOODRICH, SAMUEL GRISWOLD   Recollections of a Lifetime. New York, 1857. 2 vols., illus., scarce, fine set, orig. cloth. MacManus 239-757 1978 $30

GOODRICH, SAMUEL GRISWOLD   The Second Book of History. Boston, 1841. Illus., upper bd. cover loose, spine worn. Victoria 35-561 1978 $8.50

GOODRICH, SAMUEL GRISWOLD   Tales About Europe, Asia, Africa and America. London, 1837. Thick 12mo., engrvs., maps. Victoria 35-583 1978 $45

GOODRICH, SAMUEL GRISWOLD   Tales About Ireland and the Irish. London, n.d. 8vo., color frontis., orig. cloth. Emerald 68-871 1978 £8.50

GOODSPEED, CHARLES   Yankee Bookseller. N.P., 1937. Illus., dull binding. Nestler Rare 78-14 1978 $10

GOODSPEED, GEORGE S.   A History of the Ancient World. New York, 1904. Illus., maps. Biblo BL781-383 1978 $9

GOODSPEED, T. H.   Plant Hunters in the Andes. (1950). 8vo, orig. cloth, end-paper maps, illus. Edwards 1012-648 1978 £15

GOODWIN, CARDINAL   The Trans-Mississippi West 1803-1853. A History of Its Acquistion and Settlement. New York, 1922. Cloth, minor wear, 1st ed., maps, ex-lib., good. Hayman 72-268 1978 $10

GOODWIN, C. C.   As I Remember Them. Salt Lake City, 1913. Cloth. Hayman 72-269 1978 $22.50

GOODWIN, C. C.   The Comstock Club. Salt Lake City, 1891. First ed. Biblo 247-220 1978 $37.50

GOODWIN, DANIEL R.   Southern Slavery in its Present Aspects... Philadelphia, 1864. 1st ed. MacManus 239-837 1978 $25

GOODWIN, HERMON CAMP   Pioneer History. New York, 1859. Portrs., 1st ed., orig. cloth, worn & chipped, sound. Butterfield 21-149 1978 $25

GOODWIN, HERMON CAMP   Pioneer History; or, Cortland County and the Border Wars of New York. New York, 1859. Ports., 1st ed. Biblo BL781-161 1978 $30

GOODWIN, JOHN   Right & Might Well Met. 1648. 1st. ed., sm. 4to, later half blue calf, good. Jarndyce 16-15 1978 £32

GOODWIN, MAUD WILDER   The Colonial Cavalier. Boston, 1895. 2nd ed., illus., spine faded, very good or better. Limestone 9-121 1978 $25

GOODWIN, MAUD WILDER   Historic New York During Two Centuries. New York and London, (1898). 2 vols. in 1, plts., maps, fine copy. Butterfield 21-501 1978 $20

GOODWIN, MAUD WILDER   Sir Christopher. Boston, 1901. 1st. ed., orig. binding, clean. Hayman 71-226 1978 $7.50

GOODWIN, RUTHERFORD   A Brief & True Report Concerning Williamsburg in Virginia. Richmond, 1941. 4th & abridged ed., bds. Hayman 73-715 1978 $7.50

GOODWIN, WILLIAM B.   The Ruins of Great Ireland in New England. Boston, (1946). Binding rubbed, spotted, illus., maps, sm. 4to. Biblo 247-289 1978 $37.50

GOPPERT, H. R.   Die Fossile Flora der Permischen Formation. Cassel, 1864-1865. Illus., litho. plts. out of text, front cover damaged, back-cover gone, soiled copy. Van der Peet H-64-339 1978 Dfl 95

GORDIS, ROBERT   The Jew Faces a New World. 1941. 1st ed., inscr'd by author. Austin 79-294 1978 $22.50

GORDON, ADAM LINDSAY   Poems. Melbourne and London, (1884). Cr. 8vo., red calf gilt. K Books 244-142 1978 £6

GORDON, ALEXANDER   The History of Peter the Great, Emperor of Russia. Aberdeen, 1755. 2 vols., 8vo, contemporary calf, gilt, 1st ed. Ximenes 47-120 1978 $100

GORDON, ALFRED   Poems. Toronto, 1915. Card cover. Hood 116-827 1978 $15

GORDON, C. G.   The Journals of, At Kartoum... 1885. 2 maps, illus., thick 8vo, half red morocco, t.e.g., spine slightly damaged. Edwards 1012-283 1978 £45

GORDON, C. G.   The Journals of Major-General .... London, 1885. Maps, illus., cr. 8vo, orig. cloth, rather shabby working copy. K Books 239-189 1978 £5

GORDON, C. W.   The Life of James Robertson, Missionary Superintendent in Western Canada. Toronto, 1908. Illus. Hood 116-244 1978 $15

GORDON, ELIZABETH PUTNAM   The Story of the Life and Work of Cordelia A. Greene, M. D. Castile, 1925. Illus., 8vo., 1st ed., pres. copy. Morrill 239-99 1978 $10

GORDON, GEORGE H.   History of the Campaign of the Army of Virginia Under John Pope, Brigadier General...from Cedar Mountain to Alexandria, 1862. Boston, 1880. Maps, 8vo., ex-lib., orig. cloth. Morrill 241-164 1978 $10

GORDON, H. LAING   Sir James Young Simpson and Chloroform, 1811-1872. Masters of Medicine. London, 1897. Rittenhouse 49-303 1976 $15

GORDON, JAMES   "Dr. Gordon's Journal Overland From India in the Year 1828 Through Egypt, Syria, Asia Minor, to Constantinople to England". (1827-28). Darwings, 4to, half roan, rebacked. Edwards 1012-66 1978 £60

GORDON, JAMES   The Character of a Generous Prince Drawn from the great Lines of Heroick Fortitude. 1703. 8vo., contemp. sprinkled calf. P. M. Hill 142-123 1978 £48

GORDON, JOHN   Joseph Conrad. The Making of a Novelist. Cambridge, 1940. Near mint in d.w. Desmarais B-153 1978 $25

GORDON, JOHN B.   Reminiscences of the Civil War. New York, 1903. 1st ed., illus., nice untrimmed copy, orig. cloth. MacManus 239-879 1978 $32.50

GORDON, PATRICK   Geography Anatomizd: Or, The Geographical Grammar. London, 1735. 14th. ed., 8vo, half-title, folding engraved maps by Senex, engraved head & tailpieces, contemporary speckled calf, gilt line borders, back defective, morocco label defective, joints weak. Deighton 5-211 1978 £65

GORDON, PATRICK   Geography Anatomiz'd. 1737. Contemp. calf, joints cracked, fifteenth ed., maps, 8vo. Howes 194-293 1978 £30

GORDON, SETON   The Cairngorm Hills of Scotland. London, (1925). Illus., plts., roy. 8vo., gilt cloth. K Books 244-372 1978 £6

GORDON, THOMAS   The Independent Whig. Hartford, 1816.
1st Amer. ed., 4 vols. in 1, 8vo., contemp. calf. Morrill 241-671 1978 $17.50

GORDON, THOMAS F.   A Gazetteer of...Pennsylvania. Philadelphia,
1832. 1st ed., lg 8vo, old calf, worn, name on t.p., colored folding map, errata
leaf, scarce. Americanist 101-59 1978 $40

GORDON, THOMAS F.   Gazetteer of the State of New York. Philadelphia, 1836. Plans, colored fldg. state map frontis., splendid cond., illus., old
lea., neatly rebacked with orig. spine & label laid down, from the library of
Benjamin De Forest Curtiss, scarce. Butterfield 21-198 1978 $125

GORDON, THOMAS F.   The History of Pennsylvania, From Its Discovery
by Europeans to the Declaration of Independence in 1776. Philadelphia, 1829.
1st ed., fine copy, 3/4 mor. MacManus 239-1471 1978 $40

GORDON, W. FR.   Thailand; Das neue Siam. Leipzig, 1942.
Boards, map, 8vo. Van der Peet 127-99 1978 Dfl 15

GORDON, W. J.   Perseus the Gorgon Slayer. London, n.d.
Quarto, chromolithographed illus., colored pictorial boards, light edge chips,
fine copy. Victoria 34-751 1978 $25

GORDON, WELCHE   Jesse James and His Band of Notorious Outlaws.
Chicago, 1892. Cloth, little worn. Hayman 72-271 1978 $25

GORDON, WILHELMINA   Daniel M. Gordon, his Life. Toronto, 1941.
Illus. Hood 117-300 1978 $15

GORDON, WILLIAM   The Plan of a Society for Making Provision for
Widows, ... Boston, 1772. 8vo, half brown morocco, 1st ed., signed by author
at end of preface, author-made manuscript corrections, very good, rare. Ximenes
47-121 1978 $250

GORDON-CUMMING, CONSTANCE FREDERICA   Two Happy Years in Ceylon.
1892. Map, foxed, plts., 2 vols., 8vo., orig. cloth. Edwards 1012-124 1978
£30

GORDON-CUMMING, CONSTANCE FREDERICA   Wanderings in China. 1886.
2 vols., illus., 8vo., orig. cloth. Edwards 1012-188 1978 £30

GORE, CATHERINE GRACE FRANCES (MOODY)   Cecil, A Peer, A Sequel to
Cecil. 1841. First ed., 3 vols., orig. half mor., half titles, tops of spines rubbed
else v.g. Jarndyce 16-694 1978 £42

GORE, CATHERINE GRACE FRANCES (MOODY)   The Courtier of the Days of
Charles II and Other Tales. New York, 1839. First American ed., orig. cloth,
2 vols., very good, note signed by Gore. Greene 78-45 1978 $120

GORE, CATHERINE GRACE FRANCES (MOODY)   New Year's Day. London,
(1846). Dec. cloth, first ed., illus. by G. Cruikshank, stamped in gilt. Greene
78-210 1978 $80

GORE, CATHERINE GRACE FRANCES (MOODY)   Paris in 1841. London, c.
1842. Frontispiece, plts., orig. cloth, covers rather dull, 8vo. K Books 244-
144 1978 £10

GORE, CATHERINE GRACE FRANCES (MOODY)   The Tuileries. New York,
1831. First Amer. ed., 2 vols., half calf, bds., damp stains. Greene 78-46
1978 $55

GORER, E.   Chinese Porcelain and Hard Stones. 1911. 2 vols.
vols., roy. 4to., text in Eng. and French, coloured plts., buckram, ltd. ed. of
1,000 copies signed by author, this is #480. Quaritch 983-140 1978 $1,200

GORER, GEOFFREY   Africa Dances. London, 1935. Maps, plts., 8
vo, orig. cloth. K Books 239-190 1978 £6

GORGES, RAYMOND   The Story of a Family Through Eleven Centuries.
Boston, 1944. Illus. by portraits. Baldwins' 51-253 1978 $27.50

GORHAM, GEORGE O.   Life and Public Services of Edwin M. Stanton.
Boston, 1899. Ports., maps, 2 vols., scarce. MacManus 239-907 1978 $35

GORKI, MAXIM   Reminiscences of Leonid Andreyev. New York,
1928. 12mo, boards and cloth, 1 of 400 copies, corners bumped, fine. Duschnes
220-194 1978 $37.50

GORKI, MAXIM   Reminiscences of My Youth. 1924. First English
ed., orig. cloth, 8vo. Howes 194-899 1978 £6.50

GORRINGE, H. H.   Egyptian Obelisks. London, 1885. Illus.,
engravings, chromo-litho., lg. 4to. Traylen 88-13 1978 £50

GORTER, JOHANNES DE   Medicina Dogmatica. Patavii, 1755. 4to.,
contemp. calf, blind-stamped border, gilt on spine, gilt dentelles, worn, sound
copy, sm. ownership label inside cover "Giuseppe Trombara Chirurgo", Padua ed.
Zeitlin 245-100 1978 $125

GORTER, JOHANNES DE   De Perspiratione Insensibili Editio Secunda Italica.
Patavii, 1755. 4to., fldg. engr. plts., contemp. plain bds., fine, uncut copy,
rare. Zeitlin 245-101 1978 $165

GORTON ANGIER, A.   The Far East Revisited. London, 1903. 8vo.,
cloth, illus., maps. Van der Peet H-64-340 1978 Dfl 85

THE GOSHEN MANUFACTURING COMPANY   1914 Catalog. (Goshen? 1914).
Wrps., dampstain at bottom of front wrapper & title-pg. Hayman 71-339 1978
$7.50

GOSLIN, OMAR   Our Towns Business. 1939. Austin 80-650 1978
$10

GOSLIN, RYLLIS   Don't Kill the Goose. 1939. Illus. with charts &
graphs, ex-lib. Austin 80-649 1978 $10

GOSLING, WILLIAM G.   The Life of Sir Humphrey Gilbert, England's
First Empire Builder. 1911. Illus., octavo, good. Upcroft 10-335 1978 £8

GOSNELL, HARPUR ALLEN   Before the Mast in the Clippers... New York,
1937. Illus., maps, ltd. to 950 copies, fine. MacManus 239-1757 1978 $75

GOSNELL, HARPUR ALLEN   Guns on the Western Waters – The Story of River
Gunboats in the Civil War. Baton Rouge, 1949. Typed review by Wiley laid in,
Bell Wiley's copy. Broadfoot's 44-170 1978 $15

GOSNELL, HARPUR ALLEN   Rebel Raider. Chapel Hill, 1948. Bell
Wiley's copy. Broadfoot 46-112 1978 $12

GOSNELL, R. E.   The Story of Confederation, with a Post-script on
the Quebec Situation. N.P., 1918. Hood 116-522 1978 $10

GOSS, WARREN LEE   The Soldiers Story of His Captivity at Andersonville, Bell Isle, and Other Rebel Prisons. Boston, 1871. Full leather scuffed,
pencil notation on front fly/leaf, Bell Wiley's copy. Broadfoot's 44-521 1978 $12

GOSSE, EDMUND   From Shakespeare to Pope: An Inquiry into the
Causes and Phenomena of the Rise of Classical Poetry in England. 1885. First ed.,
cr. 8vo., orig. cloth. Howes 194-900 1978 £5

GOSSE, EDMUND   Gray. London, 1882. 1st ed., orig.
red cloth, very good or better. Limestone 9-129 1978 $22

GOSSE, EDMUND   Life of William Congreve. 1924. Second ed.,
cr. 8vo., orig. cloth. Howes 194-751 1978 £5

GOSSE, EDMUND   Memoir of Thomas Lodge. 1882. Thin 4to,
quarter leather, only few copies printed. Traylen 88-294 1978 £6

GOSSE, EDMUND   Silhouettes. London, 1925. 1st ed.,
d.j., very good or better. Limestone 9-122 1978 $15

GOSSE, PHILIP 1879-   My Private Library. London, 1926. Orig. cloth,
1st ed., 1 of 300 copies signed by author. MacManus 238-933 1978 $50

GOSSE, PHILIP 1879-   The Pirate's Who's Who Giving Particulars of the
Lives and Deaths of the Privates and Buccaneers. Boston, 1924. Illus., orig.
cloth. MacManus 239-1758 1978 $15

GOSSE, PHILIP HENRY   The Monuments of Ancient Egypt, and Their
Relation to the Word of God. London, 1855. 1st ed., 120 illus., 12mo, orig.
cloth. K Books 239-191 1978 £10

GOSSELIN, A.   Champlain et Hudson. – La Decouverte du lac
Cahmplain, et Celle de la Riviere Hudson...1609-1909. 1909. Card cover.
Hood 116-523 1978 $7.50

GOSSELIN, A.   L'Abbe Holmes et L'Instruction Publique. 1907.
Hood 116-370 1978 $10

GOSTLING, GEORGE   Extracts from the Treaties Between Great Britain and Other Kingdoms and States of Such Articles as Relate to .... London, 1792. 1st ed., quarto, bound in contemp. full red straight-grained mor. by Kalthoeber, gilt edges, leather inner hinges bookplate of Richard Prime. Totteridge 29-47 1978 $325

GOTCH, J. A.   Early Renaissance Architecture in England. 1901. Plts., text illus., roy. 8vo. George's 635-81 1978 £10.50

GOTHEIN, E.   Schriften zur Kulturgeschichte der Renaissance, Reformation und Gegenreformation. 1924. 2 vols. Allen 234-1262 1978 $10

GOTHEIN, MARIE LUISE   A History of Garden Art. London, (1928). 2 vols., illus., orig. ed., gilt-decor, blue cloth, 8vo., orig. cloth. Book Chest 17-167a 1978 $130

GOTHEIN, MARIE LUISE   A History of Garden Art...... London, (1928). Orig. ed., plain green cloth, 8vo. Book Chest 17-167b 1978 $110

THE GOTHIC Renaissance: Its Origin, Progress, and Principles. 1860. 8vo, unbound, sewn as issued, nice copy. Fenning 32-130 1978 £8.50

GOTTSCHALK, LOUIS   Lafayette and the Close of the American Revolution. (1942). 1st ed., orig. cloth, d.j., fine. MacManus 239-574 1978 $22.50

GOTTSCHALK, LOUIS   Lafayette Joins the American Army. (1937). 1st ed., illus., orig. cloth, d.j., fine. MacManus 239-576 1978 $22.50

GOTTSCHALK, MAX   Jews in the Post-War World. Dryden Press, 1945. Austin 79-295 1978 $12.50

GOTZ, W.   Die Verkehrswege im Dienste des Welthandels. 1888. Half calf, worn, maps. Allen 234-367 1978 $25

GOUDGE, ELIZABETH   The Bird in the Tree. London, (1940). 1st ed., Biblo BL781-987 1978 $9

GOUDSMIT, S.   De Gast-Vertellers, een Serie Pogingen tot een Eenigzins Fatsoenlijk Cabaret in Klein Kwarto. Laren, 1924. 8vo., bds., illus. by C. Beekman, signed by author & artist, rare. Van der Peet H-64-374 1978 Dfl 65

GOUDY, FREDERIC WILLIAM   The Alphabet: 15 Interpretive Designs Drawn & Arranged with Explanatory Text & Illustrations. New York, Village Press, 1918. Sm. folio, uncut, 8vo., orig. cloth, very good. Americanist 103-127 1978 $40

GOUDY, FREDRIC WILLIAM   Bertha M. Goudy, a Memorial. One of 300 copies printed on Hulbut Permanent Record Book paper, frontis., illus., signed and dated by Goudy. Battery Park 1-129 1978 $75

GOUDY, FREDERIC WILLIAM   The City of Crafts. New York, 1922. Illus. by George Ilian. Battery Park 1-123 1978 $25

GOUDY, FREDERIC WILLIAM   Elements of Lettering. New York, Marchbanks Press, 1922. 1st ed., folio, nice, unopened copy, slightly worn box, 8vo., orig. cloth, very good. Americanist 103-128 1978 $40

GOUDY, FREDERIC WILLIAM   A Half Century of Type Design and Typography 1895-1945. 1946. 2 vols., cloth, fine, bookplates of Will Ransom, one of 825 numbered sets. Dawson's LA 447-175 1978 $60

GOUGE, WILLIAM M.   The Fiscal History of Texas. Philadelphia, 1852. 1st ed., orig. cloth, recased, rebacked, very good or better. Limestone 9-123 1978 $80

GOUGET, A. Y. DE   The Origin of Laws, Arts, And Sciences, and Their Progress Among the Most Antient Nations. Edinburgh, 1775. Plts., tables, 3 vols., 8vo, contemp. calf, leather labels, joints weak & little worn. Traylen 88-257 1978 £48

GOUGH, JOHN   A Treatise of Arithmetic Theory & Practice.... Philadelphia, 1788. 1st US ed., contemp. calf, scuffed, joint weak, name &c, written on t.p., 8vo. Americanist 101-60 1978 $28.50

GOUGH, JOHN B.   Autobiography and Personal Recollections... Springfield, 1869. Illus., 1/2 leather, free endpaper lacking in front, otherwise attractive. Hayman 72-270 1978 $8.50

GOUGH, JOHN B.   Sunlight and Shadow... London, 1881. Orig. binding, clean, bookplate on front endpaper. Hayman 71-271 1978 $8.50

GOUGH, T. B.   Boyish Reminiscences of His Majesty the King's Visit to Canada in 1860. Toronto, n.d. Illus. Hood 117-569 1978 $15

GOULARD, THOMAS   A Treatise on the Effects and Various Preparations of Lead. London, 1773. Sm. 8vo., contemp. calf, gilt on spine, light browning, minor stains, good copy from library of Dr. Alfred M. Hellman. Zeitlin 245-102 1978 $45

GOULD, B. A.   War Thoughts of an Optimist... Toronto, 1915. Hood's 115-108 1978 $12.50

GOULD, GEORGE M.   Concerning Lafcadio Hearn. Philadelphia, (1908) 1st ed., illus., dw, orig. binding, 8vo. Americanist 101-61 1978 $20

GOULD, GEORGE M.   Concerning Lafcadio Hearn. 1908. Plts., very good, first English ed. Bell Book 16-430 1978 £10

GOULD, GEORGE M.   The Jefferson Medical College of Philadelphia. New York and Chicago, 1904. Illus., 2 vols. Rittenhouse 49-305 1976 $50

GOULD, JAY   History of Delaware County, and Border Wars of New York.... 1856. Good. Nestler Rare 78-120 1978 $120

GOULD, JOHN   The Birds of Asia. London, 1850-1883. 7 vols., lg. folio, half green morocco, gilt, slight foxing at beginning & end of some vols., 530 full pg. coloured litho. plts., fine copy. Traylen 88-576 1978 $26,000

GOULD, JOHN   The Birds of Asia. London, 1861. Thin atlas folio, orig. pr. boards, brown cloth spine torn, hand-colored lithographs. Totteridge 29-49 1978 $750

GOULD, JOHN   The Birds of Europe. London, 1837. 5 vols., impl. folio, contemp. full crimson morocco, gilt, g. e., 448 hand-coloured lithos., beautiful set, orig. subscriber's copy only 286 printed copies. Traylen 88-577 1978 $15,000

GOULD, JOHN   A Monograph of the Odontophorinae or Partridges of America. London, 1850. Hand-coloured litho. plts., lg. folio, half dark green morocco, gilt spine, gilt edges, fine copy. Traylen 88-578 1978 $5500

GOULD, JOHN   A Monograph of the Trochilidae or Family of Humming Birds. London, 1849. 5 vols., complete in orig. 25 parts, 360 hand-coloured litho. plts., lg. folio, fine. Traylen 88-579 1978 £15,000

GOULD, JOHN   A Monography of the Trochildae, or Family of Humming Birds. 1861 and 1887. 6 vols., imp. folio, hand-coloured plts., contemp. half dark green mor. gilt. Quaritch 983-333 1978 $43,000

GOULD, R. F.   The History of Freemasonry, its Antiquities, Symbols, constitutions.... (1900). 6 vols., roy. 4to., coloured plts. George's 635-1429 1978 £12

GOULD, R. F.   The History of Freemasonry. Edinburgh, n.d. 3 vols., sm. 4to., half red calf binding, gilt tooled front covers, gilt tooled spines, a.e.g., frontis. portrs., nice set, bindings on joints shaved, some slight occas. foxing. Van der Peet H-64-341 1978 Dfl 275

GOULD, RUPERT THOMAS   Enigmas. Another Book of Unexplained Facts. London, 1929. Rittenhouse 49-306 1976 $15

GOULD, RUPERT THOMAS   The Marine Chronometer--Its History and Development. Illus., plts., 8vo. Traylen 88-495 1978 £10

GOULDSBURY, C. E.   Tigerland: Reminiscences of Forty Years' Sport and Adventure in Bengal. 1913. 8vo, orig. cloth, plts. Edwards 1012-100 1978 £12

GOURDON, H.   l'Indochine. Paris, 1931. Plts., maps, 8vo., orig. covers. Van der Peet 127-100 1978 Dfl 35

GOURLAY, ROBERT   Statistical Account of Upper Canada. London, 1822. Vol. 2 (only), modern buckram, uncut, coloured frontis., map, some damp and light fox marks. Wolfe 39-214 1978 $250

GOURLAY, ROBERT FLEMING   The Banished Briton and Neptunian: Being a Record of the Life, Writings, Principles, and Projects of... Boston, 1843. Originally issued in 38 parts, parts 1-12 bound with orig. covers, re-spined & inscribed by author, part 32 inscribed & signed by author. Hood's 115-807 1978 $500

GOURLIE, N.   A Winter with Finnish Laps. London, 1939. 1st ed., 8vo., cloth, frontis portr., illus., plts., fldg. map. Van der Peet H-64-342 1978 Dfl 40

GOURMONT, REMY DE   The Horses of Diomedes. Boston, 1923. 1st Amer. ed., bookplt. Biblo BL781-988 1978 $9.50

GOURMONT, REMY DE   A Night in the Luxembourg. Boston, 1919. 1st Amer. ed., bookplt. partially removed. Biblo BL781-989 1978 $10

GOURMONT, REMY DE   A Virgin Heart. New York, 1921. 1st Amer. ed., some damp stains on cover, d.w. Biblo BL781-1013 1978 $10

GOUROU, P.   Esquisse d'une Etude de l'Habitation Annamite, dans l'Annam septentrienal et central du Thanh Hoa au Binh Dinh. Paris, 1936. 4to, plts, orig. covers. Van der Peet 127-101 1978 Dfl 45

GOURVITCH, PAUL PENSAC   How Germany Does Business. 1919. Austin 80-651 1978 $10

GOVER, R. S.   George Romney. 1904. Photogravures and half-tone engravings, roy. 4to. George's 635-207 1978 £12.50

THE GOVERNMENT of Montgomery County, Maryland. N.P., 1941. Cloth, ex-lib., not a bad copy. Hayman 73-410 1973 $8.50

GOVERNMENT Telegraph. N.P., (ca. 1888). 8vo., sewn. Morrill 239-403 1978 $8.50

GOW, A. S. F.   A. E. Housman: A Sketch. 1936. Portrait, orig. buckram, d.w., 8vo. Howes 194-946 1978 £5

GOWANLOCK, T.   Two Months in the Camp of Big Bear. Parkdale, 1885. Parts 1 & 2 in 1 vol., orig. binding, scuffed, illus. Hood's 115-1000 1978 $75

GOWER, JOHN   De Confessione Amantis. London, 1554. Wood-cut title, black letter, folio, modern full calf, antique style, leather label. Traylen 88-258 1978 £350

GOWER, RICHARD HALL   A Treatise on the Theory & Practice of Seaman-ship, Together with a System of Naval Signals. London, 1808. 3rd ed., illus., light dampstains, rebinding needed. Nestler Rare 78-191 1978 $75

GOZZI, CARLO   The Memoirs. Nimmo, 1890. First English ed., hand-coloured engrav., 2 vols., roy. 8vo., orig. cloth, paper labels, unopened, one of only 210 numbered lg. paper copies. Howes 194-1266 1978 £55

GRAAF, REGNER DE   De Virorum Organis Generatione Inservientibus de Clysteribus et de usu Siphonis in Anatomia. Leiden and Rotterdam, 1668. Sm. 8vo., portrait, plts., very sm. waterstain in foremargins, very attractive, contemp. calf, gilt spine, foot of spine chipped, first ed. Quaritch 977-27 1978 $850

A GRABHORN Bag. (San Francisco, 1941). Paper fldr., decor. bd. portfolio, 1 of 200 copies. Dawson's 447-52 1978 $60

GRACE, E. G.   Charles m. Schwab. New York, 1947. Austin 80-652 1978 $10

GRACIAN, BALTASAR   Obras De Lorenzo Gracian. Antwerp, 1669. 2 vols., thick 4to., marbled calf, backs gilt, with labels, 3rd complete ed. Salloch 348-76 1978 $400

GRADUALE Minus Lexiviense. Lisieux, 1752. Lg. folio, full lea. with metal bosses, lacking clasps, lower portion of spine torn, minor marginal stains. Allen 234-1264 1978 $60

GRAECAE Grammatrices rudimenta, in usum Scholiae Regiae Westmonasteriensis. 1707. Sm. 8vo., contemp. calf. George's 635-468 1978 £8

GRAESSE, J. G. T.   Fuhrer fur Sammler von Porzellan und Fayence, Steinzeug, Steingut usw. Berlin, 1919. 5th ed., illus., bds., spinal extremities worn. Biblo BL781-573 1978 $30

GRAESSE, J. G. T.   Orbis Latinus, Oder, Verzeichnis der Wichtigsten Lateinischen Orts- und Laendernamen. 1922. Buckram, browned. Allen 234-368 1978 $15

GRAFFMAN, CARL SAMUEL   Skottska Vuer Tecknade efter Naturen Under en Resa i Skottland ar 1830 af C.S. Graffman. Stockholm, n.d. (1831-33). 1st. ed., folio, engraved title, loose, 24 plts., contemp. half calf, rubbed. Hannas 54-294 1978 $50

GRAFTON, C. C.   Works. 1914. Cathedral ed., 8 vols, 8vo. George's 635-1073 1978 £12

GRAFTON, C. S.   The Canadian "Emma Gees": A History of the Canadian Machine Gun Corps. London, Ontario, 1938. Photos & maps. Hood's 115-109 1978 $45

GRAHAM, ALBERT ADAMS   History of Richland County, Ohio... Mans-field, (1880). 1st ed., thick 4to., illus., errate leaf, orig. 3/4 calf and cloth, very good. MacManus 239-1114 1978 $100

GRAHAM, ALBERT ADAMS   History of Richland County, Ohio. Mansfield, 1880. Orig. binding, clean. Hayman 71-580 1978 $60

GRAHAM, ANGUS   The Golden Grindstone, the Adventures of George M. Mitchell. Toronto, 1935. Illus., maps. Hood 117-301 1978 $22.50

GRAHAM, AUDREY   Historic St. John's at York Mills, 1816-1843. Toronto, n.d. Illus. Hood 117-351 1978 $15

GRAHAM, B. N. GORDON   Hunter at Heart. London, 1950. Plts., illus., d.w., orig. cloth, 8vo. K Books 244-145 1978 £5

GRAHAM, E.   The Harrow Life of Henry Montague Butler. 1920. Plts., spine faded, 8vo. George's 635-1235 1978 £5.25

GRAHAM, E. P.   A Sketch of Saint John's Parish as a Memorial of Its Centennial 1823-1923 and of the Consecreation of the Church 1924. Canton, 1924. Wrs., pres. copy. Hayman 73-574 1978 $7.50

GRAHAM, G. H.   Larry; or, the Avenging Terrors. Toronto, 1923. Hood 116-473 1978 $7.50

GRAHAM, GERALD S.   Empire of the North Atlantic. Toronto, 1950. 1st ed. Hood 117-570 1978 $35

GRAHAM, HENRY   The Annals of the Yeomanry Cavalry of Wiltshire. Liverpool and Devizes, 1886-1908. 2 vols., 8vo., orig. cloth, portrait frontis., plts., mint. F. Edwards 1013-573 1978 £40

GRAHAM, HENRY   History of the Sixteenth, the Queen's Light Dragoons, 1759 to 1912; 1912 to 1925. Devizes, 1912-26. Coloured plts., 2 vols., 4to., orig. cloth, frontis. port. F. Edwards 1013-471 1978 £115

GRAHAM, J.   A History of the Siege of Londonderry and Defence of Enniskillen in 1688-89. Dublin, 1829. Engraved portrait and title, fcap. 8vo. George's 635-817 1978 £8.50

GRAHAM, J. D.   Report on the Subject of the Boundary Line Between the U.S. and Mexico. Washington, 1852. Folding maps, original cloth, gilt, 1st ed., fine. Jenkins 116-1553 1978 $125

GRAHAM, JAMES A.   The...Papers 1861-64. Chapel Hill, 1920. New cloth. Broadfoot 50-362 1978 $15

GRAHAM, LLOYD   Niagara Country. New York, 1949. Hood's 115-808 1978 $15

GRAHAM, MARIA   Journal of a Residence in Chile, 1822... 1824. Plts., vignettes, 4to, contemp. diced calf, browning on some plts. & title, dis-colouration in margin of 4 plts. Edwards 1012-649 1978 £265

GRAHAM, MARIA   Journal of a Residence in Chile, During the Year 1822 and a Voyage from Chile to Brazil in 1823. London, 1824. 1st ed., sm. 4to., marbled edges, fine sm. woodcut text illus., full brown calf contemp. bind-ing, blind-tooled diamond pattern on covers, fine cond., some light foxing on 2 plts. only. Current 24-178 1978 $345

GRAHAM, MARIA   Journal of a Residence in India. Edinburgh, 1812. 4to, contemporary half calf, spine gilt, 1st ed., hand-colored frontispiece, engraved plates (borders foxed), very good copy. Ximenes 47-122 1978 $90

GRAHAM, MARIA   Journal of a Residence in India. Edinburgh, 1813. 2nd. ed., 4to, hand coloured engraved frontispiece, engraved plts., orig. bds., edges uncut, roughly rebacked with tape, edges of cover worn, some foxing of plis. Deighton 5-77 1978 £110

GRAHAM, MARIA   A Short History of Spain. 1828. 1st. & only ed., illus., 2 vols., lg. 12mo, cont. half calf, gilt, nice copy. Fenning 32-123 1978 £16

GRAHAM, ROBERT BONTINE CUNNINGHAME   Doughty Deeds. London, 1925. 1st ed., illus., d.j., very good or better. Limestone 9-124 1978 $20

GRAHAM, ROBERT BONTINE CUNNINGHAME   Father Archangel of Scotland, and Other Essays. London, 1896. 8vo., maroon cloth, gilt lettering on cover and spine, pencil marking in margin, 1st ed., collector's cond. Desmarais 1-192 1978 $30

GRAHAM, ROBERT BONTINE CUNNINGHAME   The Ipane. 1899. First ed., cr. 8vo., binders cloth, orig. wrappers bound in. George's 635-1310 1978 £5

GRAHAM, ROBERT BONTINE CUNNINGHAME   Los Caballos de la Conquista. Buenos Aires, (1946). Tall 8vo., stiff paper covers and pict. wrs., scuff on spine, fine, 1st ed., collector's cond. Desmarais 1-193 1978 $25

GRAHAM, ROBERT BONTINE CUNNINGHAME   Notes On The District of Men-teith. Stirling & Canada, 1907. New 2nd ed., illus., foldout map, uncut, t.e.g., orig. cloth, sev. leaves carelessly opened, very good or better. Lime-stone 9-125 1978 $45

GRAHAM, ROBERT BONTINE CUNNINGHAME   Portrait of a Dictator. Lon-don, 1933. 8vo., red cloth, frontis. portrait loose, fine, 1st ed., collector's cond. Desmarais 1-195 1978 $15

GRAHAM, ROBERT BONTINE CUNNINGHAME   Rodeo. London, 1936. 1st ed., portrait, d.j., very good or better. Limestone 9-127 1978 $13.50

GRAHAM, STEPHEN   The Death of Yesterday. London, 1930. First ed., orig. binding, very nice. Rota 211-145 1978 £5

GRAHAM, STEPHEN   Priest of the Ideal. London, 1921. 8vo, dark blue cloth, corners bumped, bookplate, repro. with inscription to Charles Wilson by author, 1st ed., collector's cond., d.w. Desmarais 1-196 1978 $25

GRAHAM, STEPHEN   Tramping with a Poet in the Rockies. New York, 1922. Green cloth, 1st ed., very good. Bradley 49-189 1978 $15

GRAHAM, THOMAS   On the Absorption and Dialytic Separation of Gases by Colloid Sepia. (London, 1866). 4to., old wrappers, torn. Gurney 75-46 1978 £35

GRAHAM, WALTER ARMSTRONG   Siam. 1924. Map, plts., 8vo., orig. cloth, 2 vols. Edwards 1012-149 1978 £45

GRAHAM, WILLIAM ALEXANDER   The Story of the Little Big Horn. New York, (1926). Illus., maps, stain on front cover. Baldwins' 51-561 1978 $20

GRAHAME, JAMES   The History of the Rise and Progress of the United States...Till the British Revolution in 1688. London, 1827. 2 vols., 8vo., orig. bds., cloth backs, spines faded, 1st ed. Morrill 241-166 1978 $32.50

GRAHAME, JAMES   The History of the Rise and Progress of the United States of North America, till the British Revolution of 1688. London, 1827. 2 vols., 1st ed., orig. full dec. calf, rubbed. MacManus 239-180 1978 $50

GRAHAME, JAMES   The Siege of Copenhagen. Edinburgh, 1808. Second ed., 4to., wrappers. F. Edwards 1013-81 1978 £10

GRAHAME, KENNETH   The Wind in the Willows. London, (1908). Frontis., 8vo., gilt-pic. cloth, uncut, 1st ed. Argosy Special-47 1978 $400

GRAHAME, KENNETH   The Wind in the Willows. 1908. First ed., frontis., full mor., spine panelled in gilt, gilt top, other edges untrimmed, rare, 8vo. Howes 194-902 1978 £165

GRAHAME, KENNETH   The Wind in the Willows. London, (1908). 2nd ed., untrimmed edges, moderate edge rubbing, very good. Victoria 34-340 1978 $50

GRAHAME, KENNETH   The Piper at the Gates of Dawn. London, n.d. One of 100 numbered copies, wrappers, fine, orig. glassene wrapper, first ed. Rota 211-146 1978 £15

GRAHAME, KENNETH   The Headswoman. 1921. 1st illus. ed., qtr. buckram, coloured woodcuts, some foxing, very good, first English ed. Bell Book 16-378 1978 £4

GRAMLING, OLIVER   Free Men are Fighting. 1942. Austin 80-119 1978 $8.50

GRAMM, CARL H.   The Germans in New Brunswick, N.J. Cleveland, 1930. D.j. MacManus 239-1270 1978 $25

GRAMMATICA Busbeiana, auctior et emendatior. 1702. Contemp. calf, a little rubbed, 8vo. George's 635-469 1978 £7.50

GRAMONDO, GABRIEL BARTHOLOMAEO   Historiarum Galliae ab Excessu Henrici IV:.... Toulouse, 1643. 1st ed., folio, full contemp. calf, engrav. t.p., running heads, woodcut devices and initials, Andrew Fletcher copy with signature on t.p., exceedingly rare. Bennett 20-86 1978 $850

GRAND, GORDON   The Southborough Fox and Other Colonel Weatherford Stories. New York, Derrydale Press, 1939. 1 of 1450 copies, drwgs. Battery Park 1-63 1978 $85

GRAND Bal des Artistes Travesti Transmental... Paris, 1923. 4to., illus. by Picasso and others, typed and auto. poems by Tzara and others, orig. wrs. Quaritch 978-127 1978 $130

GRAND Civic and Military Demonstration in Honor of the Removal of the Remains of James Monroe, Fifth President of the United States, from New York to Virginia. New York, 1858. Errata, mod. cloth. Hayman 72-477 1978 $8.50

GRAND GEOGRAPHIE Bong Illustree. Paris, 1911-1914. 5 vols., folio, half calf, illus., colored plts., map. Van der Peet 127-280 1978 Dfl 450

GRAND Rapids, Mich., As It Is. 1894. Grand Rapids, 1894. Oblong 4to., orig. wrs. Morrill 239-523 1978 $17.50

GRAND-CARTERET, JOHN   Vieux Papiers Vielles Images Cartons d'un Collection eur. Paris, 1896. 4to., cloth, dec. endpapers, orig. pict. wr. bound in. Battery Park 1-443a 1978 $275

GRANDAMI, JACQUES   Nova Demonstratio Immobilitatis Terrae Petita ex Virtute Magnetica. Flexiae (La Fleche), 1645. 4to., engr. title, plts., text illus., old half mor., rubbed, but very good copy, 1st ed. Norman 5-**16 1978 $450

GRANDEAU, LOUIS   Instruction Pratique sur l'Analyse Spectrale, Comprenant: I. la Description des Appareils. Paris, 1863. Colored litho. plt., fldg. copperplts., 8vo., orig. prtd. wrs., uncut, 1st ed., scarce. Offenbacher 30-58 1978 $125

GRANDI, GUIDO   Geometrica Demonstratio Theorematum Hugenianorum Circa Logisticam.... Florence, 1701. 4to., woodcut diagrams, light waterstain on half title, contemp. vellum. Quaritch 977-155 1978 $75

GRANGE, AMY MARY   A Modern Galahad. 1895. 1st. ed., 8vo, orig. cloth, nice copy. Fenning 32-134 1978 £6

GRANGER, GORDON   General Orders No. 11. Galveston, 1865. Small quarto. Jenkins 116-1156 1978 $17.50

GRANITE CURLING CLUB OF TORONTO   Constitution, Rules and Regulations. Toronto, 1892. Hood 117-626 1978 $12.50

GRANNAN, JOSEPH C.   Grannan's Warning Against Fraud and Valuable Information. Akron, 1891. Portr., 8vo., orig. cloth, nice. Morrill 241-168 1978 $30

GRANNIS, C. B.   Heritage of the Graphic Arts. Battery Park 1-375 1978 $19.95

GRANT, AMY G.   Letters from Armageddon, a Collection Made During the World War. Boston, 1930. Illus. Hood 117-125 1978 $25

GRANT, ANNE (MAC VICAR)   Letters From the Mountains... 1806. 1st. ed., 3 vols., half calf, rebacked, good. Jarndyce 16-695 1978 £25

GRANT, ANNE (MAC VICAR)   Letters From the Mountains... 1809. 4th. ed., 3 vols., title-pgs. browned, contemp. calf, gilt spines, joints weak. Eaton 45-215 1978 £35

GRANT, ANNE (MAC VICAR)   Memoirs of an American Lady... 1808. 1st. ed., 2 vols., 12mo, modern half calf, text soiled. Edwards 1012-492 1978 £40

GRANT, ANNE (MC VICKAR)   Memoirs of an American Lady... London, 1817. 2 vols., 3rd. ed., orig. bds., leather spine scuffed. Hood's 115-597 1978 $75

GRANT, ANNE (MAC VICAR)   Poems on Various Subjects. Edinburgh, 1803. 8vo., 1st ed., orig. bds. Quaritch 979-173 1978 $65

GRANT, ANNE (MAC VICAR)   Poems on Various Subjects. Edinburgh, 1803. 8vo., orig. bds., uncut, backstrip partly defective, first ed. P. M. Hill 142-274 1978 £20

GRANT, BLANCHE C.   Kit Carson's Own Story of His Life... Taos, 1926. Dec. wrs., illus., 1st ed., very good, very scarce. Dykes 35-201 1978 $50

GRANT, CHARLES   The History of Mauritius... 1801. Folding maps, 4to, calf, rebacked, lacking portrait, maps repaired, & laid down. Edwards 1012-317 1978 £40

GRANT, GEORGE M.   Ocean to Ocean. Toronto, 1873. 1st. ed., maps, plts., orig. cloth, 8vo, name on title, one joint slightly worn. Edwards 1012-425 1978 £40

GRANT, GEORGE M.   Ocean to Ocean, Sandford Fleming's Expedition Through Canada in 1872. Toronto, 1877. Enlarged and rev'd. ed., illus., dark green plain bind., plts. Hood 116-850 1978 $30

GRANT, GEORGE M.   Ocean to Ocean; Sanford Fleming's Expedition Through Canada in 1872. Toronto, 1925. Rev. ed., illus., deluxe numbered ed. Hood's 115-58 1978 $40

GRANT, GEORGE M.   Picturesque Canada. Toronto, 1875. 36 parts as originally issued, plts. & pages clean, covers worn at edges. Hood's 115-173 1978 $150

GRANT, GORDON   The Ship Book. Springfield, n.d. Colored pictorial boards, very good. Victoria 34-342 1978 $12.50

GRANT, GORDON   The Story of the Ship. New York, (1919). Large quarto, plates, very good. Victoria 34-341 1978 $15

GRANT, JAMES   Cassell's Old and New Edinburgh. London, c. 1885. 3 vols., wood-engrav. 4to., half dark hard-grain mor., gilt spines. K Books 244-373 1978 £15

GRANT, JAMES   Memoirs and Adventures of Sir John Hepburn. Edinburgh, 1851. 1st. ed., 8vo, half morocco, gilt spine, a.e.g. Hannas 54-150 1978 £10

GRANT, JAMES   Sketches in London. 1838. 1st. ed., illus. by
Phiz & others, orig. brown cloth, some foxing to plts., otherwise v.g. Jarndyce
16-821 1978 £35

GRANT, JAMES   Sketches in London. 1838. Engraved frontis.
title and plts., half calf, 8vo. George's 635-1350 1978 £18

GRANT, M. H.   The Makers of Black Basaltes. 1910. 4to.,
frontis., plts., cloth, orig. ed. Quaritch 983-104 1978 $165

GRANT, ROBERT   History of Physical Astronomy. London, (1852).
8vo., diagrs., contemp. half calf, richly gilt spine, little rubbed, fine copy, 1st
ed., signed by William Thomson, Lord Kelvin. Norman 5-*41 1978 $175

GRANT, ROBERT   Unleavened Bread. New York, 1900. 1st. ed.,
orig. binding, clean. Hayman 71-227 1978 $7.50

GRANT, ULYSSES SIMPSON   Letters to His Father and His Youngest Sister,
1857-78. New York, 1912. Portrs., 8vo., orig. cloth, 1st ed. Morrill 241-
170 1978 $10

GRANT, ULYSSES SIMPSON   Personal Memoirs. New York, 1885. 1st ed.,
numbered copy, illus., 2 vols. Baldwins' 51-203 1978 $20

GRANT, ULYSSES SIMPSON   Personal Memoirs of... New York, 1885.
2 vols., illus., maps, 1st ed. Biblo 251-28 1978 $17.50

GRANT, ULYSSES SIMPSON   Personal Memoirs. New York, 1885-1886.
Maps, illus., 2 vols., 8vo., 1st ed., orig. cloth. Morrill 241-672 1978 $12.50

GRANT, ULYSSES SIMPSON   Report of Lieutenant General U. S. Grant,
of the Armies of the United States 1864-65. Washington, 1865. New cloth.
Bell Wiley's copy. Broadfoot 46-115 1978 $20

GRANT, WILLIAM D.   Christendom Anno Domini MDCCCCI... Toronto,
1902. Vol. 1 only, illus. Hood 116-294 1978 $7.50

GRANVILLE, A. B.   Autobiography. London, 1874. 8vo., ex-lib.,
1st ed. Morrill 239-101 1978 $15

GRANVILLE, A. B.   Graphic Illustrations of Abortion and the Diseases
of Menstruation. London, 1833. Plts., copperplts., 4to., old marbled bds.,
mor. back & corners, 1st ed. Morrill 239-100 1978 $75

GRANVILLE, GEORGE, VISCOUNT LANSDOWNE
Please turn to
LANSDOWNE, GEORGE GRANVILLE, VISCOUNT

GRANVILLE, MARY
Please turn to
DELANY, MARY GRANVILLE PENDARVES

GRANVILLE BAKER, B.   A Winter in Portugal. London, n.d. 8vo.,
pict. cloth, colored frontis., orig. drwgs. by author, map. Van der Peet H-64-
343 1978 Dfl 45

GRAPHIC Illustrations of Warwickshire. Birmingham, 1829. 4to., plts., contemp.
tree calf. Quaritch 983-378 1978 $240

GRAS, N. S. B.   The Early English Customs System. Cambridge,
Mass., 1918. 8vo. Upcroft 12-169 1978 £20

GRAS, N. B. S.   Industrial Evolution. Oxford, 1930. Ex-lib.
Austin 80-654 1978 $10

GRATACAP, L. P.   The Evacuation of England. The Twist in the Gulf
Stream. New York, 1908. 1st ed., front flyleaf missing, writing on half-t.p.
Biblo BL781-962 1978 $9.50

GRATIANI, ANTONII MARIAE   De Vita Johannis Francisci Commendoni Cardin-
alis.... Parisiis, 1669. 1st ed., quarto, portrait of Commendone, original
boards, later paper spine, rare, Fletcher of Saltoun copy. Bennett 20-87 1978
$550

GRATIUS, ORTWIN d. 1541   Fasciculus Rerum Expetendarum & Fugiendarum.
1690. 2 vols., folio, contemp. panelled calf, rebacked. Howes 194-1434 1978
£55

GRATTAN, THOMAS COLLEY   The Heiress of Bruges... 1831. 2nd. ed., 3
vols., orig. half calf, marbled bds., raised bands gilt, red labels, apart from slight
defect on lower side of one bd. fine copy. Jarndyce 16-697 1978 £34

GRATTAN, THOMAS COLLEY   Highways and By-ways. 1823. 8vo., 1st ed.,
orig. bds., worn, uncut, slight foxing, slight worming, inscr., good copy. Quaritch 979-174 1978 £20

GRATTAN, THOMAS COLLEY   Jacqueline of Holland. 1831. 3 vols. in 1,
titles lightly foxed, 1/2 green morocco, gilt spine, corners rubbed, bookplt.
Eaton 45-216 1978 £30

GRATTAN, THOMAS COLLEY   Legends of the Rhine and of the Low Countries.
1832. Foxed, 3 vols., post 8vo., half cloth, 2 vols. lack lettering-pieces.
George's 635-1351 1978 £10.50

GRATZ, SIMON   A Book About Autographs. Philadelphia, 1920.
8vo., orig. cloth, 1st ed., ltd. to 500 no. copies, illus. MacManus 238-935
1978 $25

GRAVE, CHARLES   Blue Jackets and Others. 1927. 4to., drawings.
George's 635-122 1978 £5

GRAVELL, M. C. F. W.   Der Mensch. Berlin, 1818. 8vo., orig. green
lea., gilt on spine, gilt dentelles, very good copy, 3rd ed. Zeitlin 245-104
1978 $45

GRAVES, A.   A Century of Loan Exhibition, 1813-1912. 1913-
15. 5 vols., 4to., half leaf green mor., gilt spines and tops, orig. issue, ltd. to
250 copies. Quaritch 983-194 1978 $275

GRAVES, MRS. A. C.   Seclusaval, or the Arts of Romanism. Nashville,
1879. Orig. binding, clean. Hayman 71-228 1978 $12.50

GRAVES, J. A.   Out of Doors, California and Oregon. Los
Angeles, 1912. Cloth, bds., mor. title label, gilt top, illus., 1st ed., bookplt.,
some underlining, very good, plastic d.w. Dykes 35-49 1978 $12.50

GRAVES, R. J.   Clinical Lectures. Philadelphia, 1838. Rittenhouse 49-307 1976 $10

GRAVES, RICHARD   The Festoon: A Collection of Epigrams, Ancient
and Modern. 1767. Second ed., 12mo., new calf antique. P. M. Hill 142-
275 1978 £42

GRAVES, ROBERT   But It Still Goes On. London, 1930. First ed.,
orig. binding, second state, pp. 157/8 cancelled, spine marked, nice. Rota 211-
147 1978 £7.50

GRAVES, ROBERT   But it Still Goes On: an accumulation. 1930.
Very good, first English ed. Bell Book 16-379 1978 £15

GRAVES, ROBERT   Collected Poems, 1914-47. 1948. Fine, first
English ed., d.w. Bell Book 16-381 1978 £18.50

GRAVES, ROBERT   Count Belisarius. 1938. 1st. ed., maps, cloth.
Eaton 45-218 1978 £6

GRAVES, ROBERT   Count Belisarius. 1938. Pres. copy inscribed by
author, covers little marked & rubbed, else very good, first English ed. Bell Book
17-409 1978 £25

GRAVES, ROBERT   Country Sentiment. 1920. Bds., good, first
English ed. Bell Book 16-382 1978 £30

GRAVES, ROBERT   Fairies and Fusiliers. 1917. Very good, d.w.,
first English ed. Bell Book 16-384 1978 £55

GRAVES, ROBERT   Fairies and Fusiliers. New York, 1919. Second
printing, first Amer. ed., newscuttings laid in. Limestone 9-131 1978 $30

GRAVES, ROBERT   The Golden Fleece. 1944. Very good, worn
d.w., first English ed. Bell Book 16-385 1978 £7.50

GRAVES, ROBERT   Good-Bye to all That. 1929. First ed., illus.,
maps, orig. cloth, binding dust-soiled, 8vo. Howes 194-903 1978 £7.50

GRAVES, ROBERT   Good-Bye to All That: an autobiography. 1929.
Maps, plts., good, first English ed. Bell Book 17-410 1978 £50

GRAVES, ROBERT   Good-Bye to All That: an autobiography. 1929.
Maps, plts., very good, d.w., first English ed., 2nd issue. Bell Book 16-386
1978 £17.50

GRAVES, ROBERT   Lars Porsena. n.d. (1927). 12mo., bds., good,
first English ed. Bell Book 16-387 1978 £12

GRAVES, ROBERT   Lars Porsena or The Future of Swearing. n.d.
(1927). 1st. ed., sm. 8vo, paper label on spine worn, spine rubbed at head & tail,
good. Jarndyce 16-1200 1978 £12

GRAVES, ROBERT   Mrs. Fisher. 1928. 12mo., bds., very good,
repaired d.w., first English ed. Bell Book 17-411 1978 £20

GRAVES, ROBERT   Mrs. Fisher, or the Future of Humour. 1928.
12mo, rebound later in cloth. Eaton 45-217 1978 £8

GRAVES, ROBERT   Mock Beggar Hall. Hogarth Press, 1924. 4to.,
orig. decor. bds., sound copy, signed by Graves. Quaritch 979-354 1978
$210

GRAVES, ROBERT   On English Poetry. 1922. Very good, orig.
decor. cloth, first English ed., first issue. Bell Book 16-388 1978 £21

GRAVES, ROBERT   Over the Brazier. 1916. Second impression, orig. wraps, very good, first English ed. Bell Book 17-412 1978 £40

GRAVES, ROBERT   The Reader over your Shoulder: a handbook for writers of English prose. 1943. Fine, d.w., first English ed. Bell Book 16-392 1978 £12.50

GRAVES, ROBERT   The Shout. London, 1929. Orig. patterned bds., d.j., 1st ed., 1 of 530 copies signed by author, fine. MacManus 238-661 1978 $125

GRAVES, ROBERT   A Survey of Modernist Poetry. 1927. Cloth-backed bds., good, first English ed. Bell Book 17-416 1978 £35

GRAVES, ROBERT   Welchman's Hose. 1925. One of 525 copies, cloth backed bds., good, first Eng. ed., wood engravings. Bell Book 16-394 1978 £50

GRAVES, ROBERT   Welchman's Hose. 1925. Sm. 4to., 1st ed., wood engrs., decor. bds., cloth back, fine copy, ltd. to 525 copies. Quaritch 979-175 1978 $200

GRAVES, WILLIAM W.   The First Protestant Osage Missions, 1820-1837. Oswego, 1949. Original cloth, 1st ed. Ginsberg 14-445 1978 $15

GRAVESON, I. H. A. DE   Historia ecclesiastica veteris testamenti. Remondiniana, 1762. Half title, text printed in dble-columns, 3 vols. in 1, lg. 8vo., old vellum, worn. George's 635-1074 1978 £6.50

GRAVIER, GABRIEL   Decouvertes et Etablissements de Cavalier de La Salle de Rouen dans L'Amerique du Nord. Paris, 1870. Illus., fold. maps, orig. binding. Wolfe 39-215 1978 $95

GRAVIERE, E. JURIEN DE LA   Guerres Maritimes.... Paris, (c. 1850). 2 vols., sm. 8vo., half calf. F. Edwards 1013-82 1978 £30

GRAY, ASA   Field, Forest, and Garden Botany, a Simple Introduction to the Common Plants of the United States East of the Mississippi, Both Wild and Cultivated. New York, 1869. 8vo., orig. cloth, 2nd ed. Morrill 241-171 1978 $10

GRAY, ASA   Manual of the Botany of the Northern United States. New York, 1857. Plts., 8vo., cloth. Salloch 345-83 1978 $90

GRAY, B. K.   A History of English Philanthropy, from the Dissolution of the Monasteries to the taking of the First Census. 1905. 8vo. George's 635-326 1978 £5.25

GRAY, CHARLES   Poems. Cupar, 1811. 8vo., orig. bds., uncut, fine, first ed. P. M. Hill 142-276 1978 £38

GRAY, F.   My Two African Journeys. England, (1928). Faded, stained binding, 8vo, orig. cloth. Book Chest 17-168 1978 $25

GRAY, FRANCIS C.   An Address to the Massachusetts Charitable Fire Society, at Their Annual Meeting, Oct. 10, 1817. Boston, 1817. Disbound. Hayman 73-412 1978 $10

GRAY, GEORGE W.   The Advancing Front of Medicine. New York, 1941. Rittenhouse 49-308 1976 $10

GRAY, HENRY   Anatomy, Descriptive and Surgical. Philadelphia, 1859. First Amer. ed., re-hinged, orig. bds. & title strip. Rittenhouse 49-309 1976 $450

GRAY, HENRY   Anatomy, Descriptive and Surgical. Philadelphia, 1859. Tall 8vo., wood engrs., modern cloth, pencil ownership inscr. of R. G. Cutter, library bkplt. & stamps, minor stains, good copy, rare 1st Amer. ed. Zeitlin 245-305 1978 $575

GRAY, HUGH   Letters from Canada, Written During a Residence There in the Years 1806, 1807, 1808.... London, 1809. 3/4 leather, fold. map. Hood 116-627 1978 $250

GRAY, JAMES   An Introduction to Arithmetic. Edinburgh, 1824. Nineteenth ed., 18mo., sheep. K Books 244-374 1978 £10

GRAY, JAMES   Pine, Stream and Prairie. Wisconsin and Minnesota in Profile. New York, 1945. Illus., map, 1st ed. Biblo BL781-275 1978 $10

GRAY, JOHN CHIPMAN   The Nature and Sources of the Law. New York, 1921. 2nd ed. Biblo 251-338 1978 $15

GRAY, L. L.   Old Indianola. San Antonio, 1950. Cloth, d.j. Jenkins 116-183 1978 $12.50

GRAY, MAXWELL   The Last Sentence. 1893. 2nd. thousand, 3 vols., half titles, orig. cloth, vol. I little loose otherwise good. Jarndyce 16-698 1978 £14.50

GRAY, THOMAS   Elegy in a Country Church-Yard. New York, (1931). First ed. with illus. by John Vassos, sm. 4to. Biblo 247-356 1978 $20

GRAY, THOMAS   The Poems of Mr. Gray. York, 1775. Quarto, frontis. portrait, full contemp. tree calf, floral gilt borders and spine panels, masterfully rehinged, 1st ed. Bennett 7-50 1978 $200

GRAY, THOMAS   The Poems of Mr. Gray. London, 1775. Portr., 4to., contemp. marbled bds., calf back, occas. foxing. Morrill 239-404 1978 $30

GRAY, THOMAS   The Poems. Dublin, 1776. 2 vols. in 1, 12mo., 19th-century half calf, marbled sides, portrait. P. M. Hill 142-277 1978 £14

GRAY, THOMAS   The Works. 1814. 2 vols., 4to, l.p., frontis, plts., full morocco, worn, college arms on spines & upper covers, book label of Roger Senhouse with his pencil notes. Eaton 45-219 1978 £50

GRAY, THOMAS   Works, With Memoirs of His Life and Writings by William Mason. London, 1814. Plts., lg. paper copy, 2 vols., folio, orig. cloth, leather labels, rather worn, inscribed to Wm. Wordsworth from Saml. Rogers. Traylen 88-259 1978 £130

GRAY, W. FORBES   Scott in Sunshine and Shadow: The tribute of his friends. 1931. Plts., orig. cloth, 8vo. Howes 194-1167 1978 £5.50

GRAY, WALTER T.   The Bad Boy Abroad. New York, (1883). 12mo., orig. wrs. Morrill 239-405 1978 $7.50

GRAY, WILLIAM   Travels in Western Africa, 1818-21... 1825. 1st. ed., engraved folding map, plts., contemp. half calf, gilt spine, some foxing & offsetting in text, corners bruised & spine repaired, 8vo. Edwards 1012-257 1978 £150

GRAY, WOOD   The Hidden Civil War. New York, 1942. Illus., scarce. MacManus 239-880 1978 $25

GRAYDON, ALEXANDER   Memoirs of a Life, Chiefly Passed in Pennsylvania... Harrisburg, 1811. 1st ed., rebound, errata, fine. MacManus 239-1473 1978 $40

GRAYDON, ALEXANDER   Memoirs of His Own Time... Philadelphia, 1846. Nice copy, orig. cloth. MacManus 239-1474 1978 $40

GRAYSON, A. J.   "The Spirit of 1861" History of the Sixth Indiana Regiment in the Three Months Campaign in Western Virginia. Madison, 1875. Wrs., ex libris, cover loose and soiled, Bell Wiley's copy. Broadfoot's 44-478 1978 $16

GRAYSON, JENNIE T.   History of the Virginia State Society Daughters of the American Revolution... Charlottesville, 1930. Orig. binding, clean. Hayman 71-747 1978 $10

GREARD, V. C. O.   Meissonier. His Life and his Art. 1897. 4to., plts., illus., orig. cloth. F. Edwards 1013-362 1978 £25

THE GREAT American Scout and Spy, "General Bunker". New York, 1870. 3rd ed., illus., 8vo., orig. cloth. Morrill 241-509 1978 $22.50

THE GREAT North Platte Region of B and M Railroad Lands. [St. Louis, 1879?]. Illus., plates, maps, orig. pict. pr. wr., maps on rear wr. Ginsberg 14-710 1978 $125

THE GREAT NORTHWEST:.... Portland, 1867. Orig. front wr., 1st ed. Ginsberg 14-1113 1978 $225

THE GREAT Union Pacific Railroad Excursion to the Hundredth Meridian:.... Chicago, 1867. Illus., half mor., 1st ed. Ginsberg 14-990 1978 $125

GREAVES, RICHARD   Brewster's Millions. Chicago, 1903. 8vo, cloth, gilt, t.e.g., 1st ed., fine. Duschnes 220-201 1978 $25

GREDT, JOSEPH   Elementa Philosophiae Aristotelico-Thomisticae. Freiburg, 1909. 2 vols. Salloch 348-77 1978 $30

GREELEY, ADOLPHUS WASHINGTON   Three Years of Arctic Service.... 1886. 1st London ed., maps, illus., 2 vols., 8vo., decor. cloth. Edwards 1012-576 1978 £55

GREELEY, HORACE   The Great Industries of the United States. Hartford, 1872. Illus. MacManus 239-183 1978 $35

GREELY, A. W.   Report on the Climatic Conditions of the State of Texas. Washington, 1892. Folio, boards, leather label, color folding maps and charts. Jenkins 116-512 1978 $125

GREEN, A. S.   History of the Irish State to 1014. 1925. Map, 8vo. Upcroft 12-172 1978 £8.50

GREEN, ANNA KATHERINE   The Filigree Ball: Being a Full and True Account of the Solution of the Mystery Concerning the Jeffrey-Moore Affair. Indianapolis, (1903). Cloth, little worn, 1st ed. Hayman 72-186 1978 $7.50

GREEN, ANNA KATHARINE   The Step on the Stair. 1923. Very good, worn & repaired d.w., first English ed. Bell Book 16-244 1978 £15

GREEN, BERIAH   Iniquity and a Meeting: Discourse...in the Congregational Church, Whitesboro, Lord's Day, January 31, 1841. Whitesboro, Press of the Oneida Institute, 1841. Disbound. Butterfield 21-1 1978 $20

GREEN, BERIAH   Things for Northern Men to do (About Slavery). New York, 1836. Sewn, pink prtd. wr. Butterfield 21-2 1978 $25

GREEN, DUFF   Memorial of Duff Green, President of the Sabine and Rio Grande Railroad Company... Washington, 1860. Sewn. Jenkins 116-526 1978 $25

GREEN, EDWIN L.   A History of Richland County. Columbia, 1932. Illus., some penciling, otherwise fine. MacManus 239-1122 1978 $30

GREEN, ELMER   Adventures of Carl Rydell. London, 1924. Illus. Biblo 247-11 1978 $15

GREEN, GEORGE SMITH   The State of Innocence and Fall of Man. London, 1745. 8vo, old cloth backed bds., lacks last leaf of index to the notes. Sexton 7-146 1978 £8

GREEN, HARRY C.   The Pioneer Mothers of America. New York, (1912). 3 vols., illus., sm. 4tos, fine. MacManus 239-532 1978 $55

GREEN, HORACE   General Grant's Last Stand. New York, 1936. Illus. Biblo 248-20 1978 $17.50

GREEN, JOHN RICHARD   History of the English People. New York, n.d. Cloth, 4 vols., maps, edges rubbed, good. Biblo 247-691 1978 $20

GREEN, JONATHAN S.   Journal of a Tour on the North West Coast of America in the Year 1829:.... New York, 1916. Half mor., 1st ed., no. 10 of 10 copies on vellum. Ginsberg 14-1099 1978 $150

GREEN, JOSEPH REYNOLDS   The Soluble Ferments and Fermentation. Cambridge, University Press, 1899. 8vo., orig. cloth, gilt, uncut, worn but very good copy, 1st ed. Norman 5-*25 1978 $75

GREEN, M. P.   The Fight for Dominion. New York, (1899). Cloth, rubbed, inner hinges weak. Hayman 73-135 1978 $15

GREEN, PAUL   Salvation on a String and Other Tales of the South. 1946. First ed., ex-lib. Austin 82-400 1978 $12.50

GREEN, ROGER LANCELYN   Andrew Lang. Leicester, (1946). 1st ed., 8vo, colored f.p., mint copy, dj. Victoria 34-343 1978 $12.50

GREEN, SAMUEL ABBOTT   Groton Historical Series. A Collection of Papers Relating to the History of the Town of Gorton, Mass. 4 vols., orig. cloth, cloth-backed bds., 1 vol. in orig. wrs., lib. marks. MacManus 239-1029 1978 $100

GREEN, SAMUEL ABBOTT   John Foster, the Earliest American Engraver and the First Boston Printer. Boston, 1909. 1st ed., 4to., illus., orig. bind., scarce. Americanist 102-55 1978 $65

GREEN, SAMUEL ABBOT   Ten Fac-simile Reproductions Relating to Various Subjects. Boston, 1903. Facsimiles, 4to., ltd. to 125 copies. Morrill 241-331 1978 $25

GREEN, THOMAS J.   Journal of the Texian Expedition Against Mier.... Austin, 1935. Illus., scarce. Jenkins 116-526 1978 $35

GREEN, THOMAS M.   The Spanish Conspiracy: A Review of Early Spanish Movements in the Southwest,.... Cincinnati, 1891. Fine copy, 1st ed. Jenkins 116-527 1978 $135

GREEN, WILLIAM   The Annals of George III, from his Accession to 1801. 1805. Engraved frontis. offset, 2 vols., sm. 8vo., spanish calf, newly rebacked, dark green calf. George's 635-657 1978 £30

GREEN, WILLIAM   A Description of a Series of Sixty Small Prints of the Lakes Etched by...of Ambleside... 1814. Oblong 8vo., lg. paper, plts., half calf antique. Quaritch 983-195 1978 $190

GREENAWAY, KATE   Almanack for 1883. London, (1883). 16mo., orig. glazed pict. bds., 1st ed., fine. MacManus 238-248 1978 $50

GREENAWAY, KATE   Almanack for 1884. London, (1884). 16mo., orig. imitation green mor. gilt, 1st ed., fine. MacManus 238-250 1978 $45

GREENAWAY, KATE   Almanack for 1884. London, (1884). 16mo., orig. imitation white mor. gilt, 1st ed., fine. MacManus 238-249 1978 $40

GREENAWAY, KATE   Almanack for 1885. London, (1885). 16mo., orig. cloth-backed glazed pict. bds., 1st ed., almost fine. MacManus 238-251 1978 $50

GREENAWAY, KATE   Almanack for 1886. London, (1886). 16mo., orig. pict. white mor., 1st ed., near-fine. MacManus 238-252 1978 $50

GREENAWAY, KATE   Almanack for 1891. London, (1891). 16mo., orig. cloth-backed pict. bds., 1st ed., fine. MacManus 238-253 1978 $50

GREENAWAY, KATE   Almanack for 1892. London, (1892). 16mo., orig. pict. white mor., 1st ed., very good. MacManus 238-254 1978 $50

GREENAWAY, KATE   Birthday Book for Children. (1880). 24mo., coloured plts., illus., orig. cloth. Quaritch 979-177 1978 $80

GREENAWAY, KATE   Book of Games. London, n.d. Plates, spine cloth mottled, very good. Victoria 34-346 1978 $20

GREENAWAY, KATE   A Day in a Child's Life. London, (1881). 1st ed., cover soiling, tip rubbing, very good. Victoria 34-347 1978 $60

GREENAWAY, KATE   A Day in a Child's Life. (1881). 4to., 1st ed., coloured illus., decor. bds., good copy. Quaritch 979-178 1978 $120

GREENAWAY, KATE   Language of Flowers. London, (1884). 1st ed., front fly-leaf gone, very good. Victoria 34-348 1978 $45

GREENAWAY, KATE   Language of Flowers. (1884). Sm. 4to., 1st ed., coloured illus., orig. pic. bds., cloth back, contemp. inscr. Quaritch 979-179 1978 $80

GREENAWAY, KATE   Language of Flowers. London, n.d. 12mo., orig. cloth-backed glazed pict. bds., 1st ed., very good. MacManus 238-255 1978 $70

GREENAWAY, KATE   Marigold Garden. London, n.d. Almost fine. Victoria 34-349 1978 $25

GREENAWAY, KATE   Sixteen Examples in Colour of the Artist's Work. London, 1910. 1st ed., tipped-in color plates on dark brown paper, inscribed by Marion H. Spielmann, very good. Victoria 34-351 1978 $85

GREENAWAY, KATE   Under the Window. (1878). 4to., 1st ed., coloured illus., orig. pic. bds., sound copy. Quaritch 979-180 1978 $105

GREENAWAY, KATE   Under the Window. Pictures and Rhymes for Children. London, (1878). Illus. in color, orig. pict. bds., 1st ed., rear inner hinge cracked, extremities worn. MacManus 238-247 1978 $75

GREENAWAY, KATE   Under the Window. Pictures and Rhymes for Children. London, n.d. Illus. in color, 1st ed., inscription on half-t.p., bd., bind. rubbed. Biblo BL781-1025 1978 $37.50

GREENAWAY, KATE   Under the Window. London, n.d. Very good copy. Victoria 34-353 1978 $20

GREENBERG, BETTY D.   The Jewish Home Beautiful. 1941. Illus.
Austin 79-299 1978 $10

GREENE, CHARLES W.   A Sketch of Kingston and Its Surroundings.
Kingston, 1883. Orig. pr. wr., lst ed. Ginsberg 14-761 1978 $375

GREENE, EVARTS B.   American Population Before the Federal Census
of 1790. New York, 1932. MacManus 239-184 1978 $17.50

GREENE, EVARTS B.   A Guide to the Principal Sources for Early American History in the City of New York. New York, 1929. Orig. cloth, fine.
MacManus 239-364 1978 $25

GREENE, FRANCIS B.   History of Boothbay, Southport, and Boothbay
Harbor, Maine. Portland, 1906. 1st ed., illus., maps, orig. cloth, ports., fine.
MacManus 239-983 1978 $42.50

GREENE, FRANCIS VINTON   The Mississippi. New York, 1882. Fldg.
maps. Bell Wiley's copy. Broadfoot 46-119 1978 $14

GREENE, FRANCIS VINTON   The Revolutionary War and the Military Policy
of the United States. New York, 1911. Maps, lst ed., spine faded. Biblo
248-201 1978 $18.50

GREENE, GEORGE W.   Life of Nathanael Greene. Boston, 1848.
Very good or better. Limestone 9-329 1978 $25

GREENE, GRAHAM   Another Mexico. New York, 1939. First U.S.
ed., plts., very good. Bell Book 17-419 1978 £22.50

GREENE, GRAHAM   The Bear Fell Free. 1935. No. 176 of 250
copies numbered and signed by the author, cloth, near fine, d.w., first English ed.
Bell Book 16-395 1978 £120

GREENE, GRAHAM   British Dramatists. 1942. Bds., very good,
worn d.w., illus. in colour, first English ed. Bell Book 16-396 1978 £5

GREENE, GRAHAM   The Heart of the Matter. London, 1948. First
ed., orig. binding, nice, torn d.w. Rota 211-148 1978 £5

GREENE, GRAHAM   The Heart of the Matter. London, 1948. 16mo,
blue cloth, bookplate, d.w. somewhat darkened and rubbed, Fine, lst ed., collector's cond. Desmarais 1-198 1978 $25

GREENE, GRAHAM   Journey Without Maps. New York, 1936. First
U.S. ed., fine, d.w. Bell Book 17-422 1978 £32.50

GREENE, GRAHAM   The Little Fire Engine. (1950). Colour illus.,
oblong 4to., pict. bds., very good, first English ed. Bell Book 16-399 1978
£24

GREENE, GRAHAM   The Man Within. New York, 1929. First U.S.
ed., very good, d.w. Bell Book 17-423 1978 £40

GREENE, GRAHAM   Stamboul Train. 1932. Bookplate, else very
good, first English ed. Bell Book 17-427 1978 £17.50

GREENE, M. LOUISE   The Development of Religious Liberty in Connecticut. Boston, 1905. Orig. cloth. MacManus 239-94 1978 $17.50

GREENE, MAX   The Kanzas Region: Forest, Prairie, Desert,
Mountain, Vale and River. New York, 1856. Map, original cloth, lst ed.
Ginsberg 14-369 1978 $150

GREENE, NELSON   The Mohawk Turnpike Book. Without prospectus.
Butterfield 21-275 1978 $8.50

GREENE, NELSON   The Old Mohawk Turnpike Book. Fort Plain,
1924. Photo illus., maps, stiff wr., orig. prospectus laid in. Butterfield 21-274
1978 $12.50

GREENE, T. W.   A Brief Account of the Great Revival in Lawrence,
Kansas, February and March, 1872 in Connection with the Evangelistic Labors of
Rev. E. Payson Hammond... Lawrence, 1872. Original printed wr., lst ed.
Ginsberg 14-446 1978 $125

GREENE, WILLIAM CHASE   Achievement of Greece, a Chapter in Human
Experience. 1924. Ex-lib. Allen 234-371 1978 $7.50

GREENE, WILLIAM CHASE   Achievement of Rome. 1933. Allen 234-372
1978 $7.50

GREENE County 1803-1908. Xenia, 1908. Cloth, some flecking on cover.
Hayman 73-535 1978 $22.50

GREENER, W. W.   The Breech-Loader and how to use it. London,
1899. 8th ed., illus., cr. 8vo., orig. cloth, good. K Books 244-146 1978 £11

GREENFIELD, CHARLES D.   Resources of Montana. Helena, 1919. Illus.,
original printed wr. Ginsberg 14-619 1978 $25

GREENFIELD, K. R.   The Army Ground Forces, the Organization of
Ground Combat Troops, U. S. Army in WW II. Washington, 1947. Bell Wiley's
copy. Broadfoot 46-515 1978 $20

GREENIDGE, A. H. J.   Handbook of Greek Constitutional History. 1896.
Map, foxed, top of spine slightly worn. Allen 234-373 1978 $7.50

GREENLEAF, BENJAMIN   Introduction to the National Arithmetic, on the
Inductive System... Columbus, 1860. Pict. bds. rubbed. Hayman 72-274 1978
$8.50

GREENLEAF, BENJAMIN   A Key to the National Arithmetic... Boston,
1853. Orig. binding, clean, little rubbed. Hayman 71-276 1978 $7.50

GREENOUGH, W. P.   Canadian Folk-life and Folk-lore. New York,
1897. Illus., lst ed., dec. cover. Hood 116-525 1978 $20

GREENS For Christmas. (New York), Analectic Press, 1874. lst ed., 8vo.,
orig. cloth, very good. Americanist 103-9 1978 $30

GREENSHIELDS, J. B.   Annals of the Parish of Lesmahagow. Edinburgh,
1864. Plts., one coloured, 4to., covers dull. K Books 244-375 1978 £20

GREENSHTREET, W. J.   Isaac Newton 1642-1727. 1927. Plates, 8vo.
George's 635-988 1978 $5.25

GREENWELL, GRAHAM   An Infant in Arms, War Letters of a Company
Officer 1914-1918. London, 1935. lst. ed., 8vo, orig. cloth, illus., A.L.S.
from author. Sexton 7-147 1978 £10

GREENWOOD, GEORGE   The Tree-Lifter... 1844. lst. ed., folding
tinted litho. frontis, 8vo, orig. green cloth, nice copy. Fenning 32-135 1978
£28.50

GREENWOOD, JAMES   Legends of Savage Life. London, 1869. lst ed.,
binder's miniature bookplate present, inner hinge cracked, minor cover rubbing,
faint spots, very good. Victoria 34-356 1978 $85

GREENWOOD, JAMES   The London Vocabulary, English and Latin.
London, 1802. 22nd ed., original linen binding, very good. Victoria 34-355
1978 $55

GREENWOOD, JAMES   The Wilds of London. London, 1874. Illus.
by Alfred Concanen, orig. pict. cloth, binder's ticket inside cover. Greene
78-212 1978 $75

GREENWOOD, WALTER   The Cleft Stick. 1937. Plts. by Arthur Wragg,
orig. linen, fine, d.w., first English ed. Bell Book 17-504 1978 £6

GREER, JAMES K.   Bois D'Arc to Barb'd Wire. Dallas, 1936. lst
ed. Jenkins 116-1554 1978 $87.50

GREER, JAMES K.   Grand Prairie. Dallas, (1935). Cloth, maps,
illus., lst ed., spine faded, fine copy, scarce. Dykes 34-251 1978 $50

GREET, W. CABELL   War Words: Recommended Pronunciations. Columbia University Press, 1943. Ex-lib. Austin 80-120 1978 $10

GREG, WALTER WILSON   A Bibliography of the English Printed Drama to the
Restoration. London, 1939-1959 (reprint 1970). Frontis, plts., 4 vols., 4to.
Traylen 88-47 1978 £30

GREG, WALTER WILSON   A List of English Plays Written Before 1643 and
Printed Before 1700. London, 1900, (1899). 3/4 morocco, gilt spine, faded.
Eaton 45-222 1978 £10

GREGG, ALAN   Furtherance of Medical Research. New Haven,
1941. Rittenhouse 49-310 1976 $10

GREGG, FRANK M.   The Founding of a Nation. Cleveland, 1915.
2 vols., pres. inscrip. from Arthur H. Clark, fine copies in little worn dust jackets,
cloth. Hayman 73-237 1973 $25

GREGG, J. CHANDLER   Life in the Army in the Department of Virginia
and the Gulf, including Observations in New Orleans. Philadelphia, 1868.
Bell Wiley's copy. Broadfoot's 44-593 1978 $20

GREGO, J.   Rowlandson the Caricaturist: a Selection from
His Works, with Anecdotal Descriptions of His Famous Caricatures, and a Sketch of
His Life, Times, and Contemporaries. 1880. 2 vols., 4to, port., illus., red
mor. gilt. Quaritch 983-248 1978 $375

GREGOR, J.   Kulturgeschichte des Balletts. Wien, 1944.
8v9., cloth, colored plts., illus. Van der Peet H-64-135 1978 Dfl 55

GREGOROVIUS, FERDINAND   History of the City of Rome in the Middle Ages.
1894-1902. Vols. 1-7 only, top of one spine torn. Allen 234-1 1978 $85

GREGOROVIUS, FERDINAND   History of the City of Rome in the Middle Ages.
London, 1909. 13 vols., cr. 8vo. Traylen 88-260 1978 £125

GREGORY, DAMIEL SEELYE   The Crime of Christendom. Abbey Press, 1900.
Austin 79-300 1978 $47.50

GREGORY, DAVID   Astronomiae Physicae et Geometricae Elementa.
Oxford, 1702. Folio, contemp. panelled calf, rebacked, first ed. Quaritch
977-187 1978 $550

GREGORY, GEORGE   A Dictionary of Arts and Sciences. New York,
1821-22. 3 vols., 2nd Amer. ed., lg. thick 4tos., mod. cloth, illus., text
foxed. MacManus 239-669 1978 $85

GREGORY, GEORGE   Elements of the Theory and Practice of Physics.
Vol. 1 & 2. Philadelphia, 1831. Fresh, clean, tight. Rittenhouse 49-311 1976
$35

GREGORY, HORACE   Pilgrim of the Apocalypse. A Critical Study of
D.H. Lawrence. New York, 1933. 12mo., cloth, 1st ed. J.S. Lawrence 38-
L144 1978 $25

GREGORY, HORACE   Pilgrim of the Apocalypse. New York, 1933.
Near mint in d.w. Desmarais B-339 1978 $20

GREGORY, ISABELLA AUGUSTA (PERSSE)   A Book of Saints and Wonders.
London, 1907. First trade ed., orig. binding, good. Rota 211-153 1978 £5

GREGORY, ISABELLA AUGUSTA (PERSSE)   Coole. Dublin, Cuala Press, 1931.
First ed., woodcut, orig. linen-backed bds., ed. ltd. to 250 copies only. Howes
194-1433 1978 £45

GREGORY, ISABELLA AUGUSTA (PERSSE)   Coole. Dublin, Cuala Press, 1931.
One of 250 copies, fine, d.w., first ed., orig. binding. Rota 211-155 1978 £50

GREGORY, ISABELLA AUGUSTA (PERSSE)   The Kiltartan Poetry Book. Dublin,
Cuala Press, 1918. One of 400 copies, nice, first ed., orig. binding. Rota 211-
154 1978 £40

GREGORY, ISABELLA AUGUSTA (PERSSE)   New Comedies. Putham, 1913.
3rd printing, frontis, portraits, cloth, stained. Eaton 45-223 1978 £5

GREGORY, JOSHUA   Combustion from Heracleitos to Lavoisier.
London, 1934. Orig. cloth, 8vo., very good copy. Norman 5-60 1978 $25

GREGORY, OLINTHUS   A Treatise of Mechanics, Theoretical, Practical,
and Descriptive. London, 1826. Fourth ed., 2 vols. text, 1 vol. plts., 8vo.,
orig. cloth backed bds., printed paper labels, uncut, bookplt. of Sir Joseph Radcliffe. Quaritch 977-227 1978 $125

GREGORY, SAMUEL A. M.   History of Mexico (and the) Texian Revolution....
Boston, 1847. Pictorial wr., sewn. Jenkins 116-535 1978 $175

GREGORY, T. E.   The Gold Standard and Its Future. 1932. Austin
80-655 1978 $11

GREGORY, WILLIAM   Paddiana... 1848. 2nd. ed., 2 vols., frontis,
half titles, orig. green cloth, v.g. Jarndyce 16-699 1978 £32

GREGORY, WILLIAM   The Trial of Antichrist, Otherwise the Man of
Sin, for High Treason Against the Son of God... Toronto, 1853. Cover scuffed.
Hood 116-295 1978 $20

GREHAN, A.   Le Royaume De Siam. Paris, 1868. Roy. 8vo.,
plts., morocco-backed bds., cover slightly rubbed, dampstain in lower margin.
Edwards 1012-150 1978 £15

GRELOT, W. J.   A Late Voyage to Constantinople... London,
1683. 1st. English ed., 8vo, engraved portrait, engraved plts., some browning,
sl. staining of bottom margin, contemporary panelled calf, worn, neatly rebacked
in matching style, morocco label, gilt. Deighton 5-126 1978 £115

GRENFELL, WILFRED THOMPSON   Adrift on an Ice-Pan. Boston, 1935. Illus.
Hood's 117-98 1978 $25

GRENFELL, WILFRED THOMPSON   Down North on the Labrador. New York,
1911. Illus., ex-lib. Hood's 117-246 1978 $10

GRENFELL, WILFRED THOMASON   The Fishermen's Saint. New York, 1931.
Inscr'd & signed by author. Hood 117-478 1978 $40

GRENFELL, WILFRED THOMASON   Forty Years for Labrador. Boston, 1932.
Illus. Hood's 115-213 1978 $20

GRENFELL, WILFRED THOMASON   Tales of the Labrador. Boston, 1916. Frontis,
first ed., ex-lib. Austin 82-401 1978 $15

GRENVILLE, WILLIAM WYNDHAM   Nugae Metricae. 1824. 4to, privately
printed, ltd. ed. of 250 copies, orig. bds., leather spine, defective, upper joint
cracked. Eaton 45-224 1978 £8

GRENVILLE-HEARNE, GUNDRY.   Boy Sailors. Fortune Press, n.d. Qtr. buckram, very good, first English ed. Bell Book 16-362 1978 £5

GRESS, EDMUND G.   Fashions in American Typography. New York,
1931. Illus., bkplt. removed. Battery Park 1-471 1978 $35

GRESSWELL, E.   A View of the Early Parisian Greek Press. Oxford, 1833. 2 vols., newly rebound in cloth. Battery Park 1-377 1978 $150

GRESWELL, WILLIAM PARR   Annals of Parisian Typography, Containing an
Account of the Earliest Typographical Establishments of Paris; and Notices and Il-
lustations of the Most Remarkable Productions of the Parisian Gothic Press...
London, 1818. 8vo., later cloth, a.e.g., 1st ed. MacManus 238-937 1978
$60

GRESWELL, WILLIAM PARR   Memoirs of Angelus Politianus, Joannes Picus of
Mirandula.... Manchester, 1805. Second ed., newly bound in half calf, all
edges gilt, scarce, 8vo. Howes 194-300 1978 £28

GREVILLE, CHARLES CAVENDISH FULKE   The Greville Memoirs. London,
1875. 3rd ed., 3 vols., 8vo., orig. cloth. Morrill 241-172 1978 $12.50

GREVILLE, CHARLES CAVENDISH FULKE   The Greville Memoirs, a Journal of
the Reigns of King George IV, King William IV and Queen Victoria. 1913. 8
vols., portrait, cr. 8vo., spines faded. George's 635-665 1978 £6.50

GREVILLE, FULKE   Maxims, Characters, and Reflections, Critical,
Satyrical and Moral. 1756. First ed., contemp. calf, neatly rebacked, mor.
label, 8vo. Howes 194-301 1978 £38

GREVIN, A.   Et A. Huart, Les Parisiennes. Paris, n.d. (ab.
1900). Lg. thick 8vo., half calf, colored caricatural plts., rare, binding soiled,
bottom of spine damaged. Van der Peet H-64-275 1978 Dfl 85

GREW, NEHEMIAH   The Anatomy of Vegetables Begun. London,
1672. Sm. 8vo., plts., contemp. calf, repaired. Quaritch 977-99 1978 $450

GREY, C. H.   Hardy Bulbs. New York, 1938. 3 vols.,
8vo., orig. cloth, colored plts. Book Chest 17-173 1978 $200

GREY, RICHARD   Dr. R. Grey's Memoria Technica... Oxford,
1831. Lg. 12mo, orig. bds., uncut, printed paper label, headbands chipped, nice
copy. Fenning 32-137 1978 £6.50

GREY, RICHARD   Memoria Technica. London, 1730. 8vo., contemp. calf, rubbed, rebacked, first ed. Gurney 75-47 1978 $35

GREY, ZANE   Arizona Ames. N. Y., Harper, 1932.
1st ed., cloth, author's copy, inscribed by author's son. Houle 10-126
1978 $60

GREY, ZANE   Call of the Canyon. London, (c.1930).
8 vo., pictorial d.j., signed by author, top edge spotted. Houle 10-128
1978 $95

GREY, ZANE   Heritage of the Desert. N. Y., (c.1945).
1st Armed Services ed., No 997, oblong 16mo., printed wrappers, very good,
author's copy. Houle 10-130 1978 $45

GREY, ZANE   Tales of Swordfish and Tuna. New York,
Harper, 1927. 1st ed., illus., plts, d.j., fine, from author's library. Houle
10-137 1978 $225

GREY, ZANE   Tales of the Angler's Eldorado: New Zealand.
New York, Harper, 1926. Limited pres. 1st ed., 4 to., 3/4 red mor. over
marbled bds., raised bands, t.e.g., photographs, drawings, fine. Houle
10-136 1978 $295

GREY, ZANE   Tales of the Angler's Eldorado: New Zealand.
New York, Harper, 1926. From author's library, limited pres. 1st ed., 4 to.,
3/4 red mor. over marbled bds., raised bands, t.e.g., photographs, drawings,
mint copy. Houle 10-135 1978 $375

GREY, ZANE   Thundering Herd. New York, Harper, 1925.
8 vo., 1st ed., d.j., illus., signed by author, good-fine. Houle 10-138
1978 $150

GREY, ZANE   Trail Driver. London, (1936). 1st English
ed., 1st printing, 8 vo., pictorial d.j., fine, author's copy. Houle 10-139
1978 $60

GREY, ZANE   Trail of the Jaguar. Williamsport,n.d.
1 of 500 copies, 1st ed., stiff printed wrappers, fine. Houle 10-140 1978
$10

GREY, ZANE   The Young Pitcher. 1911. First ed. Austin 82-
402 1978 $20

GREY OF FALLODON, VISCOUNT   Fallodon Papers. 1926. Woodcuts by
Robert Gibbings, 8vo. George's 635-161 1978 £5

GRIDLEY, A. D.   History of the Town of Kirkland. New York
and Cambridge, 1874. Plts., chipped and lightly shaken, good copy, very scarce.
Butterfield 21-312 1978 $35

GRIEB, CONRAD K.   Uncovering the Forces for War. 1947. Paper.
Austin 79-301 1978 $27.50

GRIER, RICHARD   Notes Taken From Dr. Bartons Lectures Delivered
in the University of Pennsylvania, 1807. Note in front cover, Dr. Richard Grier
departed this life in Sept. 4, 1808. Baldwins' 51-356 1978 $300

GRIERSON, B. H.   Annual Report of Desertions in the Department of
Arizona, 1889. Los Angeles, 1889. Orig. pr. wrs., 1st ed. Ginsberg 14-11
1978 $150

GRIEVE, CHRISTOPHER MURRAY   Albyn, or Scotland and the Future. 1927.
Bds., 12mo., good, worn d.w., first English ed. Bell Book 16-602 1978 £16.50

GRIEVE, CHRISTOPHER MURRAY   Lucky Poet. 1943. Portrait, very good, first
English ed. Bell Book 16-603 1978 £30

GRIEVE, CHRISTOPHER MURRAY   Penny Wheep. 1926. Near fine, secondary
binding, light blue bds., first English ed. Bell Book 17-611 1978 £27.50

GRIEVE, CHRISTOPHER MURRAY   Scottish Eccentrics. London, 1936. Nice,
dust soiled d.w., orig. binding, first ed. Rota 212-38 1978 £50

GRIEVE, CHRISTOPHER MURRAY   To Circumjack Cencrastus. 1930. Good,
first English ed. Bell Book 16-604 1978 £15

GRIEWE, W. F.   History of South America. Cleveland, (1913).
Illus., spine dull. Biblo BL781-110 1978 $9

GRIFFIN, ALFRED   An Illustrated Sketch Book of Riley County,
Kansasm the "Blue Ribbon County". Manhattan, 1881. Illus., half morocco, 1st
ed. Ginsberg 14-447 1978 $175

GRIFFIN, APPLETON PRENTISS CLARK   A Catalogue of the Collection in the
Boston Athenaeum. Boston, 1897. Illus., fine untrimmed copy. MacManus 239-
489 1978 $27.50

GRIFFIN, EDWARD D.   The Kingdom of Christ: A Missionary Sermon...
Philadelphia, 1805. 8vo, orig. cloth, some spotting, wrappers. Edwards 1012-
493 1978 £20

GRIFFIN, EDWARD D.   A Sermon, Preached July 22, 1807, at the Funeral
of the Rev. Alexander MacWhorter, D. D., Senior Pastor of the Presbyterian
Church, in Newark. New York, 1807. Portrs., 8vo., 1st ed., orig. cloth.
Morrill 241-399 1978 $7.50

GRIFFIN, HAROLD   Alaska and the Canadian Northwest, Our New
Frontier. New York, 1944. Photos. Hood 116-82 1978 $15

GRIFFIN, JOHN S.   A Doctor Comes to California:.... San Francisco, 1943. Maps and frontis, original cloth. Ginsberg 14-122 1978 $25

GRIFFIN, JOHN SMITH   A Historical Sketch Descriptive of Jesuit Warfare
Together with a Defensive Appeal, Addressed to the Young Ministers and Intelligent
Laymen of the Congregational Churches of Oregon and Washington. Hillsboro,
1881. Original wr., slipcased, 1st ed. Ginsberg 14-372 1978 $150

GRIFFIN, MARTEN L.   J. Stephen Moylan, Muster-Master General Sec.
and Aide-de-camp to Washington. Philadelphia, 1909. Pres. copy. Baldwins'
51-307 1978 $20

GRIFFIN, MARTIN I.   Catholics and the American Revolution. Ridley
Park, 1907-9-11. Illus., 3 vols., orig. cloth, each vol. ltd. to 1,000 copies,
complete sets are extremely scarce. MacManus 239-577 1978 $100

GRIFFIN, RICHARD   Epitome of the Bill on Poor Law Medical Relief
Introduced Into Parliament by F. Pigott... 1860. 8vo, orig. printed wrapper, fine.
Fenning 32-138 1978 £8.50

GRIFFIN, ROBERT A.   School of the Citizen Soldier. 1942. Illus.
Austin 80-121 1978 $12.50

GRIFFISS, BARTOW   The New York Call Money Market. 1925. Illus.
Austin 80-656 1978 $11

GRIFFITH, ACTON F.   A Collection and Selection of English Prologues
and Epilogues. 1779. First ed., frontispiece, plts., 4 vols., sm. 8vo., contemp.
calf. Howes 194-302 1978 £35

GRIFFITH, ELIZABETH   The Morality of Shakespeare's Drama Illustrated.
London, 1775. 8vo, contemporary tree calf, tilt, spine gilt, 1st ed., very fine
copy. Ximenes 47-123 1978 $125

GRIFFITH, GEORGE DARBY   A Journey Across The Desert, From Ceylon to
Marseilles... London, 1845. 2 vols., 8vo, half-titles, tinted lithograph frontispieces, illus., some soiling, half calf, morocco labels, gilt. Deighton 5-183
1978 £55

GRIFFITH, JOHN   A Journal of the Life, Travels, and Labours in
the Work of the Ministry of ... London, 1779. 1st. ed., 8vo, contemp. calf,
very worn, names on title, water-stained at end. Hannas 54-151 1978 £15

GRIFFITH, R. EGLESFELD   Medical Botany. Philadelphia, 1847. Rittenhouse 49-312 1976 $35

GRIFFITH, THOMAS   Sketches of the Early History of Maryland.
Baltimore, 1821. Rebound, very good. Nestler Rare 78-39 1978 $22

GRIFFITHS, JOHN WILLIS   Treatise on Marine and Naval Architecture.
New York, 1851. Plts., 4to., cloth. F. Edwards 1013-83 1978 £65

GRIFFITHS, THOMAS S.   A History of Baptists in New Jersey. Hights-
town, 1904. Frontis., fine. MacManus 239-1271 1978 $27.50

GRIFONI, GIOVANNI POMPEO   Lettera, e Disegno di un' Apparato di Woulfe
Diretta al Meretiss., ed Eccellentiss. Siena, 1821. Lg. litho. plt., 8vo., contemp. wrs., uncut, 1st ed., very scarce, fine, uncut copy. Offenbacher 30-59
1978 $115

GRIGGS, NATHAN KIRK   Lyrics of the Lariat. New York, (1893). Two-
tone cloth, illus., 1st ed., 1st issue, fine copy, slipcase. Dykes 34-22 1978
$50

GRIGGS, WILLIAM   Portfolio of Italian & Sicilian Art. London,
1885-1890. Plts., folio, orig. fr. wrs., ex-lib., lacks backstrip, wr. fragile &
chipped. Morrill 239-407 1978 $25

GRIGSON, GEOFFREY   Visionary Poems and Passages. London, 1944.
First ed., orig. binding, nice, torn d.w., cover design and colour-lithographs by
John Craxton. Rota 211-25 1978 £6

GRIGSON, GEOFFREY   Visionary Poems and Passages. 1944. Coloured lithographs by John Craxton, pict. cloth, very good, first English ed. Bell Book 16-481 1978 £7.50

GRIMALDI, STACEY   Origines Genealogicae;.... London, 1828. Quarto, 3/4 contemp. calf and marbled boards, chipped at head of spine, extremities worn, Ist ed., pres. copy inscribed by author. Bennett 7-51 1978 $95

GRIMALIUS GOSLICIUS, LAURENTIUS   De Optimo Senatore Libri Duo. Venice, 1568. First ed., sm. 4to., contemp. calf, very good. Howes 194-551a 1978 £125

GRIMES, J. BRYAN   Notes on Colonial North Carolina 1700-1750. N.P., 1905. New cloth. Broadfoot 50-79 1978 $15

GRIMM, THE BROTHERS   Hansel and Gretel and Other Stories by the Brothers Grimm. London, (1918). Limited to 600 numbered copies, signed by author, Kay Nielsen, colored plates, thick quarto, pictorial white cloth in gilt and blue, covers slightly soiled, text plates and text virtually mint. Victoria 34-587 1978 $775

GRIMM, THE BROTHERS   Household Tales by the Brothers Grimm. 1946. Coloured plts. & text illus. by Mervyn Peake, sm. 4to., very good, first English ed. Bell Book 17-714 1978 £20

GRIMM, JACOB   Fairy Tales. Limited Editions Club, 1931. Illus. with hand-colored woodcuts, I of 1500 copies signed by book designer, full lea., boxed, 8vo., very good. Americanist 103-40 1978 $45

GRIMSCHITZ, BRUNO   Wiener Barockpaläste. Vienna, (1947). Sm. 4to., illus., spine torn. Biblo BL781-542 1978 $13.50

GRINDROD, RALPH B.   Bacchus. New York, 1840. Ist. American, from 3rd. English ed., clean, orig. binding. Hayman 71-278 1978 $15

GRINDLEY, H. M.   Scenery, Costumes, and Architecture, Chiefly on the Western Side of India. 1826-(1830). Folio, hand-coloured plts., red half mor. gilt, fine copy. Quaritch 983-334 1978 $2,450

GRISEWOOD, H.   Ideas and Beliefs of the Victorians. London, (1950). Biblo 251-339 1978 $15

GRISWOLD, ALEXANDER V.   A Charge, Addressed to the Clergy of the Protestant Episcopal Church in the Eastern Diocese, Delivered Before the Biennial Convention, in Portsmouth, N.H. Sept. 28, 1814... Boston, 1816. Disbound. Hayman 72-275 1978 $12.50

GRISWOLD, RUFUS WILMOT   The Republican Court or American Society in the Days of Washington. New York, 1855. Engrav. portraits, 4to., tooled mor. Wolfe 39-219 1978 $25

GRISWOLD, RUFUS WILMOT   The Republican Court; Or, American Society in the Days of Washington. New York, 1867. Morocco, rubbed, new ed., plts. Hayman 71-277 1978 $12.50

GROEDEL, J.   Bad-Nauheim. Its Springs and Their Uses. Bindernagel, 1909. Rittenhouse 49-314 1976 $10

GROEN, JAN VAN DER   Le Jardiner Du Pays-Bas,.... Brussels, 1672. Rare French trans., 5 parts in one vol., small 4to, old vellum. Quaritch 978-69 1978 $1,100

GROLIER CLUB   The United States Navy 1776 to 1815 Depicted in an Exhibition of American Naval Engagements and Naval Commanders Held at the Grolier Club... New York, 1942. 4to., illus., orig. bds., ltd. to 700 copies. MacManus 239-1793 1978 $45

GROLIER CLUB   The United States Navy, 1776 to 1815... New York, Grolier Club, 1942. Illus., 4to., orig. bds., ltd. to 700 copies. Morrill 241-586 1978 $25

GRONAU, G. RAFAEL   Des Meisters Gemalde. Stuttgart, 1909. 8vo., gilt decor. cloth, illus. Van der Peet H-64-43 1978 Dfl 45

GRONOVIUS, JACOBUS   Geographia Antiqua. Leyden, 1697. Engrs., 4to., vellum. Salloch 345-176 1978 $95

GRONOVIUS, JACOBUS   Georgraphica Antiqua. Leiden, 1700. Sm. 4to., parallel Greek & Latin texts, contemp. calf, rebacked. Howes 194-552 1978 £35

GRONOW, REES HOWELL   The Reminiscences and Recollections of Captain Gronow. London, 1900. Portr., illus., 2 vols., 8vo., orig. cloth. Morrill 241-173 1978 $15

GROOT, HUGO DE
Please turn to
GROTIUS, HUGO

GROSCLAUDE   Les Gaietes de L'Annee 1888. Paris, 1889. Sm. 8vo., illus. wrs., caricatural illus. Van der Peet H-64-276 1978 Dfl 45

GROSE, FRANCIS   The Antiquities of England and Wales, and Scotland. (c.1790-)97. 10 vols., 4to., plts., some hand coloured, half mor. gilt. Quaritch 983-16 1978 $3,800

GROSE, FRANCIS   The Antiquities of Scotland. 1797. Map coloured by hand, 2 vols., 4to., contemp. half calf. Howes 194-1389 1978 £85

GROSE, FRANCIS   A Classical Dictionary of the Vulgar Tongue. 1885. Half title, orig. pink bds., corners rubbed, leather spine. Jarndyce 16-701 1978 £9.50

GROSE, FRANCIS   A Provincial Glossary. 1790. Second ed., 19th cent. cloth-backed bds., leather label, entirely uncut, 8vo. Howes 194-303 1978 £20

GROSE, FRANCIS   A Provincial Glossary; With a Collection of Local Proverbs, and Popular Superstitions. 1811. 3rd. ed., 8vo, contemp. calf, rebacked. Hannas 54-190 1978 £20

GROSE, FRANCIS   A Provincial Glossary. 1811. New ed., 8vo., orig. bds., new backstrip, uncut. P. M. Hill 142-125 1978 £18

GROSLIER, G.   Eaux et Lumieres. Paris, 1931. Large 8vo., plts., orig. covers. Van der Peet 127-103 1978 Dfl 45

GROSS, ELBRIDGE HENRY   The Life of Paul Revere. Boston, 1891. Ist. ed., I of 200 copies on lg. paper, very fully illus., portraits, sm. thick quarto, front hinge starting in both vols., 2 vols., bookplate. Baldwins' 51-184 1978 $55

GROSS, SAMUEL DAVID   A Manual of Military Surgery. Philadelphia, 1861. Woodcuts, 12mo., spine faded, Ist ed. Morrill 239-102 1978 $60

GROSS, SAMUEL DAVID   A System of Surgery. Philadelphia, 1866. 2 vols., lg. 8vo., contemp. calf, dampstains, 4th ed., revised. Morrill 239-103 1978 $25

GROSS, SAMUEL DAVID   System of Surgery. Pathological, Diagnostic, Therapeutic, and Operative, Vol. 1 & 2. Philadelphia, 1882. Sixth ed., some mild scuffing. Rittenhouse 49-315 1976 $30

GROSSE, HENNING   Magica, seu mirabilium historiarum de spectris et apparitionibus spirituum;.... Eisleben,1597. 4to., very rare 1st ed., very fine copy, contemp. calf, front cover date "1599". Schafer 19-51 1978 sFr. 950

GROSSI, TOMMASO   Ildegonda. Milano, 1825. 8vo, 4 plts., 1/2 calf, gilt. Eaton 45-225 1978 £5

GROSSMITH, GEORGE   The Diary of a Nobody. Bristol, [1892]. 12mo, orig. cloth, light discoloration on free end-papers, felt-lined brown cloth slipcase backed with mor., Ist ed. Bennett 7-52 1978 $125

GROSTIZA, M. F.   Correspondencia Que La Mediado...Sobre El Paso Del Sabina Por Las Propas Que Mandaba El General Gaines. Philadelphia, 1836. Half morocco slipcase, map, Ist ed., extremely rare. Jenkins 116-507 1978 $750

GROSVENOR, BENJAMIN   Health. 1716. 12mo., contemp. panelled calf, first ed., fine. P. M. Hill 142-126 1978 £30

GROSVENOR, GERALD   Rudolpho. Boston, n.d. (c. 1867). Folio, woodcut illus., pr. wrs., back wr. missing. Paine 78-62 1978 $22.50

GROSZ, GEORGE   Ecce Homo. Berlin, 1923. 4to., orig. pict. flexible bd. wr., ltd. ed. issued in 5 different runs, excellent copy. Goldschmidt 110-26 1978 $550

GROSZ, GEORGE   Die Gezeichneten. Berlin, (1930). Illus., sm. 4to., prtd. paper cover with Grosz drwg., pres. copy. Argosy Special-48 1978 $200

GROSZ, GEORGE   Mit Pinsel und Schere. Berlin, 1922. Sm. 4to. in sheets, in orig. portfolio, photo plts. on coated paper, slight foxing on wr. Goldschmidt 110-27 1978 $150

GROSZ, GEORGE   Der Spiesser-Spiegel. Dresden, 1925. Quarto, cloth, gilt, repro. of drawings, 1st ed., fine. Duschnes 220-135 1978 $150

GROSZ, GEORGE   Der Spiesser-Spiegel. Dresden, 1925. Sm. 4to., orig. cloth, set of 60 plts. by Grosz. Goldschmidt 110-28 1978 $100

GROSZ, GEORGE   Uber alles die Liebe. Berlin, 1930. 4to., publisher's orange cloth, watercolors & drwgs. by G. Grosz. Goldschmidt 110-29 1978 $140

GROTE, GEORGE   Greece. New York, 1900. 11 vols., good, no. paper labels on spines. Biblo BL781-387 1978 $30

GROTH, JOHN   Studio: Europe. New York, 1945. Illus., by author, blue cloth, 1st ed., pres. inscr. signed by Groth, jacket chipped. Bradley 49-146 1978 $20

GROTIUS, HUGO   Apologeticus Eorum Qui Hollandiae Westfrisiae Que et Vicinis quibusdam nationibus ex legibus praefuerunt ante mutationem quae evenit anno 1618. Paris, 1622. 1st ed. in Latin, octavo, full contemp. limp vellum, Andrew Fletcher copy with signature, very fine. Bennett 20-88 1978 $750

GROTIUS, HUGO   Epistolae ad Gallos. Leiden, 1650. 16mo., vellum, rubbed. Allen 234-1273 1978 $30

GROTIUS, HUGO   Epistolae quotquot reperiri potuerunt. Amsterdam, 1687. Contemp. vellum, skilfully rebacked, thick folio, very good, first complete ed. Howes 194-553 1978 $80

GROTIUS, HUGO   Of the Rights of War and Peace. 1715. 3 vols., 8vo., contemp. calf gilt, early rebacking. P. M. Hill 142-128 1978 £30

GROTIUS, HUGO   Poemata, Collecta & magnam partem nunc primum edita a fratre... Leyden, 1617. 8vo, contemp. sign. on flyleaf of Nicholas Vilett, contemp. calf, repair to head of spine, 1st ed. Quaritch 978-70 1978 $475

GROTIUS, HUGO   The Rights of War and Peace. Washington, (1901). Ltd. autograph ed. Biblo 251-265 1978 $15

GROTIUS, HUGO   De Veritate Religionis Christianae. Parisiis, 1640. 1st ed., 12mo, full contemporary vellum, paper spine label, engraved regal device on t.p., Andrew Fletcher copy with his signature on t.p. Bennett 20-89 1978 $950

GROTIUS, HUGO   De Veritate Religionis Christianae. Amsterdam, 1675. 16mo., vellum, contemp. ink scorings. Allen 234-1272 1978 $25

GROTIUS, HUGO   De Veritate Religionis Christianae. 1772. Rebacked, 12mo., sheep. P. M. Hill 142-127 1978 £15

GROULX, L.   Les Ecoles des Minorites. Montreal, 1922. Vol. 2, card covers. Hood 116-526 1978 $17.50

GROUSSET, R.   De l'Inde au Cambodge et a Java. Monaco, 1950. 4to, boards, map, plts., ltd. and numbered ed. of 3,300 copies. Van der Peet 127-301 1978 Dfl 85

GROVER, EULALIE OSGOOD   The Sunbonnet Babies' Primer. Chicago-New York, (1902). 1st ed., illus. by Bertha Corbett, Neidlinger musical endpapers, slight dust soiling, spine tip rubbing, fine. Victoria 34-358 1978 $85

GROVER, FRANK R.   A Brief History of Les Cheneaux Islands. Evanston, 1911. Pict. bds., 200 copies prtd. Hayman 73-434 1978 $20

GROVER, LAFAYETTE   The Report of Governeor Grover to General Schofield on the Modoc War,.... Salem, 1874. Orig. wr. bound in half mor., 1st ed. Ginsberg 14-818 1978 $200

GROVES, E. L.   Everyday Children, A Book of Poems. Toronto, 1932. Illus. by children. Hood's 115-873 1978 $7.50

GROVES, PERCY   Historical Records of the 7th or Royal Regiment of Fusiliers. Guernsey, 1903. Coloured plts., thick 8vo., orig. cloth, faded, rebacked, orig. spine laid down. F. Edwards 1013-485 1978 £70

GROVES, PERCY   History of the 91st Princess Louise's Argyllshire Highlanders. 1894. Roy. 8vo., orig. cloth, coloured plts. F. Edwards 1013-542 1978 £60

GROVES, PERCY   History of the 93rd Sutherland Highlanders. 1895. Coloured plts., roy. 8vo., orig. cloth. F. Edwards 1013-545 1978 £60

GROVES, PERCY   History of the 2nd Dragoons.... London, 1893. 4to., orig. cloth backed bds., coloured plts. F. Edwards 1013-466 1978 £30

GROVES, PERCY J.   The War of the Axe. London, 1904. Cr. 8vo, dec. cloth, plts. K Books 239-193 1978 £5

GRUBB, I.   Quakerism and Industry, before 1800. 1930. 8vo. George's 635-327 1978 £8.50

GRUEL, LEON   Catalogue Des Reliures De Style et Objects artistiques en Cuir Cisele. Paris, 1893. Sq., 8 vo., illus., full plum mor. Houle 10-38 1978 $45

GRUEL, LEON   Quelques notes sur les reliures executees pour Marguerite de Valois, Reine de France et de Navarre. Paris, 1922. Ltd. to 170 copies, plts., med. 4to., orig. wrs. Forster 130-12 1978 £4

GRUNDY, FELIX   Speech of Mr. Grundy, of Tennessee, on Mr. Foot's Resolution, Proposing an Inquiry into the Expediency of Abolishing the Office of Surveyor General of Public Lands... Washington, 1830. Double columns, disbound. Hayman 73-240 1978 $15

GRUNER, L.   Decorations de Palais et d'Englises en Italie.... Paris and London, 1854. Plts., 9 which are beautifully coloured, atlas folio, half red morocco, worn & little warped, some staining principally in margin. Traylen 88-380 1978 £60

GRYNAEUS, SIMON   Lexicon Graecum. Basle, 1539. 1st ed., old vellum, lightly worn, lower margin of title repaired, 4to. Gilhofer 75-51 1978 SFr 400

GRYNAEUS, SIMON   Novus Orbis Regionum Ac Insularum Veteribus Incognitarum una Tabula Cosmographica.... Basileae, 1537. Folio, contemp. blind-stamped pigskin, red morocco spine label, gilt, very lightly worn at extremities, lacking clasps. Bennett 20-90 1978 $3,500

GRYNNE, JOHN   Military Memoirs of the Great Civil War. Edinburgh, 1822. 1st. ed., 4to, contemp. half russia, gilt spine, little foxed at beginning & end, lacks final end-paper. Hannas 54-293 1978 £20

GUADAGNINI, ARCIPRETE   La Falsita dalla asserta Lega di Teologi Anti-molinisti.... (c. 1750). 8vo., marbled bds., calf spine, good. King 7-175 1978 £25

GUAGNINO, ALESSANDRO   Sarmatiae Europeae Descripto,.... (Cracow), 1578. Very rare 1st ed., contemp. vellum, rebacked, two leaves torn and repaired, light browning, folio, 6 parts in 1 vol., very fine. Gilhofer 75-52 1978 SFr 2,300

GUALTEROTTI, RAFFAELE   Lvniverso ouero Il Polemidoro Poema Eroico Con licenza de Superiori.... 1600. 4to., calf, illus., first ed. King 7-44 1978 £50

GUALTERUZZI, CARLO   Libro di Novelle e di Bel Parlar Gentile. Firenze, 1724. 8vo., half vellum, bds., good tall copy. King 7-176 1978 £25

GUARAS, ANTONIO DE   The Accession of Queen Mary... 1892. Sm. 4to, folding facsimile, sm. tear in head of spine, ltd. to 350 copies, good. Upcroft 10-73 1978 £8.50

GUARINI, GIOVANNI BATTISTA   Alda Guarini Veronensis. Basil, July, 1517. Sm. 4to., extremely rare ed., modern half vellum. Schafer 19-19 1978 sFr 1,500

GUARINI, GIOVANNI BATTISTA   Il Pastor Fido. Paris, 1680. 6mo, engraved titles & printed, eng. plts., head & tail pieces, contemp. leather, gilt spine, defective at head, some worming in both covers, end-papers scribbled on. Eaton 45-226 1978 £20

GUARINI, GIOVANNI BATTISTA   Il Pastor Fido Tragicommedia.... Roma, 1797. Sm. 8vo., calf, very good, plts. King 7-177 1978 £25

GUARINI, GIOVANNI BATTISTA   Il Pastor Fido Tragicommedia Pastorale. 1828. Sm. 8vo., marbled bds., calf spine, very good. King 7-178 1978 £20

GUARMANI, CARLO CLAUDIO CAMILLO   Northern Naid.   London, Argonaut Press, 1938. Ltd. ed., map in pocket, plts., 4to., orig. cloth.   K Books 244-377 1978 £35

GUAZZO, STEFANO   De Civili Conversatione Dissertationes Politicae. Jena, 1606. Thick 8vo., blind-stamped pigskin, orig. dated bind. of 1606. Sallocy 348-80 1978 $75

GUAZZO, STEFANO   La Ciuil Conuersatione. Venetia, 1628. Sm. 8vo., vellum. King 7-45 1978 £20

GUBBELS, JAC L.   American Highways and Roadsides.   Boston, 1938. Jenkins 116-536 1978 $7.50

GUEDE, DOCTEUR   J. Casanova. Paris, 1912. Paper wraps., both covers detached. Eaton 45-227 1978 £5

GUEDY, H.   Le Palais du Louvre. (1900). Plts., folio, half roan, rubbed. George's 635-82 1978 £5.25

GUER, JEAN ANTOINE   Storia Serio-Critico-Giocosa Dell'Anima Delle Bestie. Napoli, 1752-1753. Sm. 8vo., 2 vols., contemp. vellum, gilt on spines, foxed, good copy, ex-lib., rare Italian ed. Zeitlin 245-106 1978 $75

GUERARD, ALBERT   The France of Tomorrow. Cambridge, 1942. First ed. Biblo 247-692 1978 $15

GUERBER, H. A.   Myths of Northern Lands. New York, (1895). Illus., 8vo., orig. cloth, former owner's notes. Morrill 241-174 1978 $7.50

GUERBER, H. A.   Myths of the Norsemen from the Eddas and Sagas. London, 1912. 1st ed., thick octavo, illus., bound in 3/4 vellum by Bates, gilt decorated spine, leather label chipped, very good. Victoria 34-361 1978 $30

GUERIN, MAURICE DE   The Centaur and the Bacchante. Portland, Mosher Press, 1897. 2nd ed., 1 of 425 copies on Japan vellum, 12mo., wraps., near fine, defective slipcase. Bell Book 16-658 1978 £5

GUERIN, THOMAS   Feudal Canada, the Story of the Seigniories of New France. Montreal, 1926. Card cover. Hood 116-527 1978 $40

GUERINIERE, M. DE LA   Elemens de Cavalerie. Bruxelles, 1791. Nouvelle ed., orig. blank wrs., fldg. plts. Hayman 73-241 1978 $40

GUERRA, FATHER JOSPEH   Fecunda Nube Del Cielo Guadalupano Y Mystica Paloma Del Estrechs Palomar.... Mexico, (1726). Vellum. Jenkins 116-882 1978 $2.250

GUERRY DE MAUBREUIL, MARIE-ARMAND   Translation of an Address to the Congress: To All Powers of Europe. London, 1818. 1st ed., 4to, contemp. tree calf, gilt spine. Hannas 54-128 1978 £25

GUERVILLE, AMEDEE GUILLOT DE   New Egypt. London, 1906. Illus., 8vo., orig. cloth. K Books 239-113 1978 £8

GUEST, DAVID   A Textbook of Dialectical Materialism. 1939. Austin 80-657 1978 $10

GUETTARD, J. E.   Observations sur les Plantes. Paris, 1747. 2 vols., 12mo., contemp. calf, plts., first ed. Gurney 75-48 1978 £75

GUEVARA, ANTONIO DE   Il Dispregio della Corte, e Lode della Villa. Berscia, 1602. 12mo., stiff paper covers. King 7-46 1978 £20

GUEZ, JEAN LOUIS, SIEVR DE BALZAC
Please turn to
BALZAC, JEAN LOUIS GUEZ, SIEVR DE

GUGGENHEIM, SIEGFRIED   Dem Andenken An Meinen Freund Und Lehrer Dr. Max Dienemann. Frankfurt am Main, 1948. Paper, in German. Austin 79-303 1978 $27.50

GUGGISBERG, F. G.   "The Shop". The Story of the Royal Military Academy. 1900. Coloured plts., illus., 8vo., orig. cloth. F. Edwards 1013-320 1978 £15

GUIDE To Public Vital Statistics in Texas. San Antonio, 1941. Jenkins 116-537 1978 $12.50

GUICCIARDINI, FRANCESCO   Dell'Historia D'Italia Di.... Venice, 1564. 1st ed., quarto, full old calf, decorative gilt spine with raised bands, joints weak, title laid down and crease on printer's device, Andrew Fletcher's copy, signed. Bennett 20-91 1978 $400

GUICCIARDINI, FRANCESCO   The History of ... 1599. 2nd. ed., folio, 18th. century panelled calf, fine. Jarndyce 16-16 1978 £250

GUICCIARDINI, LODOVICO   Descrittione... di tutti i Paesi Bassi... Con piu carte di Geographia del paese, & col ritratto naturale di piu terre principali. Antwerp, 1567. Folio, woodcuts, very rare 1st ed., fine copy, contemp. limp vellum. Schafer 19-20 1978 sFr. 4,800

GUIDE, PHILIPPE   Observations Anatomiques Faites sur Plusieurs Animaux au Sortir de la Machine Pneumatique. Paris, 1674. Fldg. copperplt., 12mo., modern bds., 1st ed. Offenbacher 30-60 1978 $175

A GUIDE for Emigrants to Minnesota, by a Tourist. St. Paul, 1857. Map, original printed wr., 1st ed. Ginsberg 14-554 1978 $150

THE GUIDE Into Tongues... 1627. 2nd. ed., folio, title in woodcut border mounted, marginal tears to few leaves repaired, full panelled calf, little rubbed, good. Jarndyce 16-13 1978 £140

GUIDE to Church Vital Statistics Records in North Dakota. Bismarck, 1942. Original wr., 1st ed. Ginsberg 14-315 1978 $15

A GUIDE to New Rochelle and Its Vicinity. New York, 1842. 18mo., 1st ed., vignette, orig. cloth. Morrill 241-404 1978 $10

GUIDE to the City of New York. New York, (n.d.). Printed in oil colours, map, orig. binding. Wolfe 39-390 1978 $75

A GUIDE To the Nations Birthplace. 1937. Illus., 1st. ed., d.j., maps, nice copy. Baldwins' 51-473 1978 $35

A GUIDE to the Sculptures of the Parthenon in the British Museum. London, 1908. Illus., bds., rubbed. Biblo BL781-334 1978 $9.50

GUIDE To The Streets, Street Pavements, Street Car Routes and House Numbers of Detroit With Other Interesting Information. (Detroit, 1905). Wrps., moderate wear. Hayman 71-465 1978 $7.50

GUIDI, GUIDO   De Anatome Corporis Humani Libri VII. Venice, 1611. 2 works in 1 vol., folio, woodcuts, title a little soiled, vellum, soiled, first ed. Quaritch 977-29 1978 $2,750

GUIDI, GUIDO   Chirurgia e Graeco in Latinum Conversa. Paris, 1544. Folio, roman letter, fine woodcuts, fine large copy, orig. dark calf, minor repair to head of spine, first ed. Quaritch 977-28 1978 $11,000

GUIDUCCI, MARIO   Discorso Delle Comete Fatto da lui Nell' Accademia Fiorentina nel suo Medesimo Consolato. Firenze, 1619. Woodcut diagrams, 4to., old limp bds., 1st ed., fine copy, from Riccardi library. Offenbacher 30-48 1978 $900

GUIGARD, JOANNIS   Armorial du Bibliophile. Paris, 1870-3. 2 vols. in 1, illus., roy. 8vo., half mor., rubbed, t.e.g. Forster 130-13 1978 £40

GUILD, GEORGE B.   A Brief Narrative of the Fourth Tennessee Cavalry Regiment. Nashville, 1913. Pres. copy from author to another person. Broadfoot's 44-614 1978 $100

GUILLAUME DE VAUDONCOURT, FREDERIC   Letters on the Internal Political State of Spain... 1825. Portrait, 8vo., recent bds. Fenning 32-140 1978 £12.50

GUILLEBERT, M. N.   Les Epistre de S. Paul aux Romains. Paris, 1633. Sm. 8vo., 7 x 4 1/2 inches, ruled in red throughout, contemp. French crimson mor., pict. title. Howes 194-554 1978 £30

GUILLET DE SAINT-GEORGE, GEORGE   Les Arts de L'Homme d'Epee. 1686. Fifth ed., plts., 12mo., contemp. sprinkled sheep. F. Edwards 1013-322 1978 £80

GUILLET, E. C.   The Great Migration; the Atlantic Crossing by Sailing Ship Since 1770. London, Toronto, 1937. Illus. Hood 116-628 1978 $25

GUILLIE, S.   Essai sur l'Instruction des Aveugles, ou Expose Analytique des Procedes Employes Pour les Instruire. Paris, 1817. 8vo., frontis., plts., contemp. quarter crimson mor., 1st ed. Quaritch 983-335 1978 $485

GUILLIE, S.   Essai sur l'Instruction des Aveugles, ou Expose Analytique des Procedes Employes pour les Instruire. Paris, 1817. 8vo., frontispiece, plts., contemp. quarter crimson mor., first ed. Quaritch 977-30 1978 $400

GUILLIM, JOHN   A Display of Heraldry. London, 1724. Folio, fine full red mor. binding, tooled gilt borders, gilt spine, inner gilt dentelles, possibly the royal copy, front hinge tender, large-paper copy, last and most complete ed., illus. colored by hand. Bennett 7-53 1978 $650

GUINEY, LOUISE IMOGEN   Goose-Quill Papers. Boston, 1885. 12mo., orig. cloth, paper label, 1st ed. MacManus 238-488 1978 $37.50

GUINNARD, A.   Three Years' Slavery Among the Patagonians... 1871. 8vo, orig. cloth, map. Edwards 1012-650 1978 £35

GUIRAND F.   Mythologie Generale. Paris, 1935. 4to., cloth, text illus., colored plts. Van der Peet H-64-344 1978 Dfl 60

GUISAN, GENERAL   Rapport Du .. A L'Assemblee Federale Sur Le Service Actif, 1939-45. Lausanne, (1946). Roy. 8vo, vellum backed bds. with red morocco lettering piece, pres. copy to Winston Churchill. Sawyer 298-79 1978 $92

GUITERMAN, ARTHUR   Brave Laughter. New York, 1943. 1st ed., d.w. Biblo BL781-991 1978 $9

GUIZOT, MADAME   A French Country Family. New York, 1868. 1st Amer. ed., orig. cloth, good. Greene 78-263 1978 $20

GUIZOT, MADAME   The Young Student. n.d. (1853). Frontis, stamped cloth. Eaton 45-228 1978 £5

GULICK, SIDNEY J.   The American Japanese Problem. 1914. Illus. with photos, 1st ed. Austin 79-304 1978 $22.50

GULICK, WILLIAM O.   Journal & Letters. N.P., 1942. Bell Wiley's copy. Broadfoot's 44-487 1978 $36

GUMMERE, AMELIA (MOTT)   Friends In Burlington. Philadelphia, 1884. Baldwins' 51-346 1978 $10

GUMMERE, AMELIA (MOTT)   The Quaker. Philadelphia, 1901. Scarce, re-backed. MacManus 239-670 1978 $30

GUMUCHIAN ET COMPAGNIE   Les Livres de l'Enfance du XV au XIX Siecle. Paris, (1930). Ltd. to 900 copies, lg. quarto, 2 vols., plts., litho color plate on upper wrs., papered spines heavily cracked, excellent set. Victoria 34-359 1978 $375

GUMUCHIAN ET COMPAGNIE   Les Livres de l'Enfance du XV au XIX Siecle. No. 62 of 100 copies, on Papier de Hollande, plts. printed on vellum like paper, 3/4 crushed levant, gilt rules, gilt dec. spines, almost mint. Victoria 34-360 1978 $500

GUNDER, CLAUDE A.   Life of Claude A. Gunder. Marion, 1908. Wrs. Hayman 73-314 1978 $7.50

GUNDOLF, FRIEDRICH   Paracelsus. Berlin, 1927. 8vo., orig. gilt-decor. cloth, 1st ed., fine copy. Salloch 345-144 1978 $15

GUNN, ALEXANDER   Memoirs of the Rev. John Henry Livingston. New York, 1856. New ed., portr. Butterfield 21-158 1978 $7.50

GUNN, DOUGLAS   San Diego: Climate, Resources, Topography, Productions... San Diego, 1886. Illus., folding panorama, original printed wr., 1st ed. Ginsberg 14-123 1978 $100

GUNN, JOHN   Gunn's Domestic Medicine, or Poor Man's Friend. Springfield, 1835. 4th ed., lea. Hayman 73-422 1978 $25

GUNN, ROBERT A.   The Nature and Treatment of Venereal Diseases. New York, 1874. 8vo., cover spots, 1st ed. Morrill 239-104 1978 $10

GUNNING, SUSANNAH   The Count de Poland. 1780. 1st. ed., 4 vols., half-titles, orig. half calf, red labels, marbled bds., hinges little weak, o/w fine, inscribed. Jarndyce 16-102 1978 £220

GUNTER, ARCHIBALD CLAVERING   The Princess of Copper. A Novel. New York, (1900). Cloth. Hayman 72-222 1978 $7.50

GUNTHER, JOHN   Eden for One. 1927. First ed. Austin 82-403 1978 $12.50

GUNTHER, ROBERT T.   Astrolabes of the World. Illus., plts., 2 vols. in 1, folio, ltd. to 350 copies. Traylen 88-497 1978 $45

GUNTON, K.   Fifty Drawings-Fifty Verses. 1937. Ltd. ed., signed by author and artist, orig. bds. George's 635-906 1978 $7.50

GURDON, THORNHAGH 1663-1733   The History of the High Court of Parliament, its Antiquity, Preheminence and Authority.... 1731. 2 vols., cr. 8vo., contemp. calf, first ed. Howes 194-304 1978 £30

GURKO, LEO   The Angry Decade. 1947. First ed. Austin 82-404 1978 $12.50

GURLAND, A. R. L.   Glimpses of Soviet Jewry. New York, 1948. 4to., wrs. Biblo 251-695 1978 $12.50

GURLEY, LEONARD B.   Memoir of William Gurley, Late of Milan, Ohio, a Local Minister of the Methodist Episcopal Church. Cincinnati, 1850. Cloth, faded and moderately worn. Hayman 73-536 1978 $22.50

GURLEY, P. D.   Faith in God. 1940. Limited to 300 copies. Nestler Rare 78-40 1978 $10

GURLITT, C.   Die Deutsche Kunst des Neunzehnten Jahrhunderts. Berlin, 1899. 8vo., half calf, plts. Van der Peet H-64-137 1978 Dfl 45

GURNEY, ALFRED   A Ramble Through the United States. [London, 1886]. Original pictorial cloth, 1st ed., privately printed with presentation inscription from author. Ginsberg 14-374 1978 $125

GURNEY, JOSEPH JOHN   A Winter In The West Indies... London, 1840. 2nd. ed., 8vo, frontispiece, half calf, rebacked, morocco label gilt. Deighton 5-212 1978 £65

GUROWSKI, ADAM   Diary from March 4, 1861 to Nov. 12, 1862. Boston, 1862. New cloth. Bell Wiley's copy. Broadfoot 46-120 1978 $14

GURTEEN, S. HUMPHREYS   A Handbook of Charity Organization. Buffalo, 1882. 8vo., binding partly dampstained, 1st ed. Morrill 239-408 1978 $15

GUTHLAC, SAINT   The Anglo-Saxon Version of the Life of. 1848. 8vo., orig. cloth. P. M. Hill 142-129 1978 £16

GUTHRIE, A. B.   The Way West. New York, (1949). First ed., d.w. frayed. Biblo 247-551 1978 $13.50

GUTHRIE, DOUGLAS   A History of Medicine. New York, 1947. Rittenhouse 49-317 1976 $17.50

GUTHRIE, E. J.   Old Scottish Customs, Local and General. London & Glasgow, 1885. Cr. 8vo., orig. cloth. K Books 244-376 1978 £8

GUTHRIE, JAMES   The Elf: a sequence of the seasons; summer, autumn, winter. 1902-04. Illus., 3 vols., linen-backed decor. bds., very nice, first English ed. Bell Book 16-698 1978 £65

GUTHRIE, JAMES   The Elf. Old Bourne Press. One of 250 copies, numbered, illus. in color. Battery Park 1-158 1978 $45

GUTHRIE, N. G.   Flake and Petal. Toronto, 1928. Signed by author. Hood 116-828 1978 $12.50

GUTHRIE, THOMAS ANSTEY   Love Among the Lions. New York, 1899. 1st Amer. ed., illus., 12mo. Biblo 251-393 1978 $17.50

GUTHRIE, THOMAS ANSTEY   A Lyre and Lancet. A Story in Scenes. London, 1895. 12mo., orig. cloth, 1st ed. MacManus 238-160 1978 $45

GUTHRIE, THOMAS ANSTEY   Voces Populi... London, 1890. Illus., orig. cloth-backed bds., a bit worn, 1st ed. MacManus 238-159 1978 $40

GUTIERREZ, ROBERT   The Clinical Management of Horseshoe Kidney.
New York, 1934. Rittenhouse 49-318 1976 $15

GUTMAN, SIDNEY   Seven Years' Harvest. 1934. Spine faded, some
foxing, good, first English ed. Bell Book 17-024 1978 £8.50

GUTTMACHER, MANFRED S.   America's Last King. New York, 1941. Illus.,
d.j., fine. MacManus 239-185 1978 $12.50

GUTTMANN, JULIUS   Die Philosophie Des Judentums. Munich,
1933. 8vo., cloth. Salloch 348-81 1978 $22.50

GUY, JOSEPH   Guy's School Geography. London, 1811. 2nd
ed., maps, 18mo., age-marking, old sheep. K Books 244-378 1978 £7

GUYON, JEANNE MARIE   The Life of Lady Guion. Bristol, 1772. 2 vols.
in 1, 8vo., contemp. calf rebacked, first ed. in English. P. M. Hill 142-130
1978 £38

GUYONNEAU DE PAMBOUR, FRANCOIS MARIE COMTE   A Practical Treatise
on Locomotive Engines. London, 1840. 2nd ed., 8vo., fldg. plts., orig. cloth,
slightly worn. Quaritch 977-246 1978 $85

GUYOT, YVES   Socialistic Fallacies. 1910. Ex-lib. Austin 80-
658 1978 $10

GUYOT, YVES   Where and Why Public Ownership Has Failed.
1914. Austin 80-659 1978 $10

GUYTON-MORVEAU, LOUIS B.   Treatise on the Means of Purifying Infected
Air, of Preventing Contagion, and Arresting Its Progress. London, 1802. Trans.
from French, 8vo., half antique calf, uncut, occas. light foxing, but fine copy,
discreet lib. stamp, 1st ed. in English. Norman 5-132 1978 $300

GWILT, F. G.   Constance; A Lay of the Olden Time. Montreal,
1874. Privately bound, gold stamping. Hood's 115-875 1978 $35

GWIN, WILLIAM M.   Arguments on the Subject of a Pacific Railroad
Before the Senate. Washington, 1860. Half mor. Ginsberg 14-861 1978 $75

GWINNETT, RICHARD   Pylades and Corinna: or, Memoirs of the Lives,
Amours, and Writings of..., Esq... London, 1736, 1732. Frontis. port., full
contemp. calf, 2 vols., 2nd ed. of vol. I, 1st ed. of vol. II. MacManus 238-
120 1978 $150

GWYNN, S.   Life and Friendship of Dean Swift. 1935. Very
good, octavo bound in cloth, reprint, d.w. Hyland 128-607 1978 £6

GYBBON-SPILSBURY, A.   The Tourmaline Expedition. London, 1906.
Folding map, gilt cloth, 8vo, 12 plts. K Books 239-195 1978 £15

GYLLIUS, P.   De Bosporo Thracid. 1632. 32mo., engraved
title, vellum. George's 635-470 1978 £8.50

H

HAAB, O.   An Atlas of Opthalmoscopy. New York, 1895.
Illus. in color, sm. 8vo., lst Amer. ed. Morrill 239-105 1978 $15

HAAS, J. H. L. DE   Collection d' Antiquites vente a Amsterdam 13
Mai 1914. Amsterdam, 1914. Illus., sm. folio. George's 635-24 1978 £5

HAAS, JAMES D.   Gleanings from Germany. 1839. 8vo., orig.
cloth, uncut, some foxing, inscribed copy. P. M. Hill 142-132 1978 £12

HAAS, R. B.   Catalog of the Published and Unpublished
Writings of Gertrude Stein. New Haven, 1941. 8 vo., wr., good. Houle
10-321 1978 $35

HABBERTON, JOHN   Four Irrespressibles, or, the Tribe of Benjamin.
Boston, (1877). Upper wrapper chipped at edges, lower one loose, very good, firm
copy. Victoria 34-363 1978 $40

HABBERTON, JOHN   Helen's Babies. Boston, (1876). lst ed., 2nd
issue., in wrappers, excellent firm copy with only minor wrapper chips, signed by
Habberton on wrapper. Victoria 34-362 1978 $55

HABERLANDT, G.   Physiological Plant Anatomy. London, 1914.
Illus., thick 8vo. Traylen 88-580 1978 £10

HABERLER, GOTTFRIED   Prosperity and Depression. 1946. 3rd enlarged
ed. Austin 80-661 1978 $12.50

HABERLY, LOYD   Daneway–A Fairy Play for Emery Walker. Seven
Acres Press, 1929. Tall 8vo., illus. by author, brown mor., gilt & blind tooled,
ltd. to 60 copies signed & dated 19th November, 1929 by printer. Quaritch
979-289 1978 $240

HABERMANN, JOHN   Christiche Morgen–und Abend–Gebeter, auf alle
Tage in der Woche. Germantown, 1733. Woodcut, pages browned, original
boards, leather spine, edges partly cracked. Victoria 34-364 1978 $35

HABESCI, ELIAS   The Present State of the Ottoman Empire. London, 1784. lst. English ed., 8vo, half-title, orig. circulating lib. labels on inside
front bd., half calf, gilt back. Deighton 5-127 1978 £75

HACK, MARIA   Harry Beaufoy: or, The Pupil of Nature. London,
1821. lst ed., roan-backed marbled boards, f.p. engraved by E. B. Hack, almost
fine. Victoria 34-365 1978 $40

HACKETT, ALICE PAYNE   Wellesley. Part of the American Story. New
York, 1949. Illus., lst ed. Biblo BL781-27 1978 $9.50

HACKNEY FURNISHING CO.   Guide to House, Cottage, Mansion & Hotel
Furnishing. c.1900. Illus., few coloured or tinted, oblong 4to, orig. printed
wrapper, nice clean copy. Fenning 32-141 1978 £24

HADDOCK, JOHN A.   The Growth of a Century: As Illustrated in the
History of Jefferson County...1793 to 1894. Philadelphia, 1894. Thick 4to.,
plts., brown lea., spine lightly faded, but very good copy, all edges gilt. Butterfield 21-227 1978 $75

HADDOCK, JOSEPH W.   Somnolism and Psycheism. London, 1851. Orig.
cloth, 8vo., woodcuts, second ed., plts. Gurney 75-49 1978 £20

HADER, BERTA   The Inside Story of the Hader Books. New York,
1937. lst ed., color, very good. Victoria 34-366 1978 $12.50

HADFIELD, JOSEPH   An Englishman in America, 1785, Being the
Diary of... Toronto, 1933. Hood's 115-610 1978 $35

HADLEY, JOHN   Restoration Love Songs. (Oxford), 1950. 8vo,
marbled boards, cloth back, leather label, uncut, t.e.g., colotype plates from
drawings by Whistler including double fold-out frontis., l/2 inch line of slight
water staining along bottom of front cover, else Mint, ed. ltd. to 660 copies this
is no. 149, inscribed by ed. to Charles Batey, from Batey's personal lib. with
bookplate, lst ed. Desmarais 1-421 1978 $50

HADZITS, GEORGE DEPUE   Our Debt to Greece and Rome. 1925-35. 39
vols. Allen 234-L 1978 $100

HAEBLER, KONRAD   Tyefounding and Commerce in Type During the
Early Years of Printing. New York, 1926. Thin quarto, blue wrs. chipped, lst
ed., fine. Duschnes 220-309 1978 $10

HAECKEL, ERNST   Kunstformen Der Natur. Leipzig, 1904. Litho.
plts., folio, l/2 lea., very beautiful & unusual vol. Salloch 345-85 1978 $450

HAECKEL, ERNST   The Riddle of the Universe. New York, 1901.
8vo., cloth, English translation. Salloch 345-87 1978 $17.50

HAECKEL, ERNST   Die Weltraetsel. Bonn, 1901. 7th ed., tall
8vo., cloth. Salloch 345-86 1978 $20

HAEDENS, KLEBER   Gerard De Nerval, ou la Sagesse Romantique.
Paris, 1939. Sm. 8vo, paper covers. Eaton 45-229 1978 £5

HAESER, HEINRICH   Lehrbuch Der Geschichte Der Medicin Und Der
Epidemischen Krankheiten. Jena, 1875. 3 vols., thick 8vo., half brown cloth,
marbled bds., light browning, some foxing, good uncut set, bkplts. of Dr. Alfred
M. Hellman, 3rd ed. Zeitlin 245-109 1978 $100

HAESER, HEINRICH   Lehrbuch der Geschichte der medicin und der
epidemischen Krankheiten. Jena, 1875-82. 8vo., 3 vols., orig. cloth, vol. 2
reapired, third ed. Gurney 75-50 1978 £105

HAFEN, LE ROY R.   The Far West and Rockies Historical Series 1820-
1875. Glendale, 1954-61. 15 vols., illus., maps, complete set. MacManus
239-1918 1978 $300

HAFEN, LE ROY R.   The Life Story of Thomas Fitzpatrick, Chief of
the Mountain Men. Denver, 1931. lst ed., 1 of 100 copies, signed by both
authors, illus. Biblo 248-255 1978 $200

HAFEN, LE ROY R.   The Mountain Men and the Fur Trade of the Far
West. Glendale, 1965-72. 10 vols., illus., fine. Biblo 247-222 1978 $200

HAGECIUS AB HAGEK, THADDAEUS   Aphorismorum Metoposcopicorum Libellus. Frankfurt, 1584. Woodcuts, 2nd ed., thin 8vo., l/2 calf. Salloch 345-
89 1978 $125

HAGEDORN, HERMANN   Roosevelt in the Badlands. Boston, 1921. lst.
trade ed., orig. binding, clean. Hayman 71-279 1978 $10

HAGEDORN, HERMANN   Roosevelt in the Bad Lands. Boston and New
York, 1921. Cloth, lst trade ed. Hayman 72-277 1978 $12.50

HAGEN, V. VON   South America Called Them. New York, 1945.
lst ed., 8vo, orig. cloth. Book Chest 17-176 1978 $35

HAGENBECK, CARL   Beasts and Men. London, 1909. Portrait frontis., plts., text illus., roy. 8vo., orig. cloth. K Books 244-147 1978 £12

HAGER, ALICE ROGERS   Wings Over the Americas. 1940. Illus. with
photos. Austin 80-663 1978 $10

HAGGAR, REGINALD G.   English Pottery Figures, 1660-1860. London, 1947.
Plts., 12mo., d.w., orig. cloth. Morrill 241-175 1978 $7.50

HAGGARD, ARTHUR   Comrades in Arms. London, 1899. Cr. 8vo,
dec.cloth, slight foxing, covers little dull. K Books 239-196 1978 £5

HAGGARD, HENRY RIDER   Allan Quatermain. London, 1887. lst ed.,
almost fine. Victoria 34-368 1978 $60

HAGGARD, HENRY RIDER   Alan Quartermain. 1887. lst. ed., cr. 8vo,
plts., spine faded. Traylen 88-262A 1978 £10

HAGGARD, HENRY RIDER   Allan's Wife and Other Tales. London, 1889.
Illus., orig. cloth, lst ed., fine. MacManus 238-259 1978 $75

HAGGARD, HENRY RIDER   Beatrice. London, 1893. New ed., rubbed cover, some interior foxing, very good or better. Limestone 9-136
1978 $10

HAGGARD, HENRY RIDER   Child of Storm. 1913. lst. ed., cr. 8vo, plts.
by A. C. Michael. Traylen 88-262B 1978 £6

HAGGARD, HENRY RIDER   Colonel Quaritch, V.C. A Tale of Country Life.
London, 1888. 3 vols., orig. cloth, lst ed., covers a bit soiled and stained,
otherwise good. MacManus 238-257 1978 $175

HAGGARD, HENRY RIDER   Finished. London, 1917. Illus., orig. cloth,
lst ed., covers slightly marked, but very good. MacManus 238-262 1978 $35

HAGGARD, HENRY RIDER　　Heart of the World.　New York, 1895.　1st ed., illus., orig. cloth, good copy.　Greene 78-48　1978 $85

HAGGARD, HENRY RIDER　　Jess.　1887.　1st. ed., cr. 8vo, spine faded & re-cased.　Traylen 88-262C　1978 £6

HAGGARD, HENRY RIDER　　King Solomon's Mines.　1885.　Frontis., covers somewhat soiled, good, first English ed.　Bell Book 17-433　1978 £25

HAGGARD, HENRY RIDER　　The Last Boer War.　London, 1900, principally 1881.　Cr. 8vo, frayed pictorial wrappers.　K Books 239-197　1978 £6

HAGGARD, HENRY RIDER　　The Mahatma and the Hare.　London, 1911. Orig. cloth, illus., 1st ed., fine.　MacManus 238-261　1978 $35

HAGGARD, HENRY RIDER　　Maiwa's Revenge; or the War of the Little Hand. London, 1888.　Orig. black cloth, 1st ed., fine.　MacManus 238-258　1978 $85

HAGGARD, HENRY RIDER　　Maiwa's Revenge; or, The War of the Little Hand. 1888.　1st. ed., 8vo, orig. pale green bds., printed in red, nice copy.　Fenning 32-142　1978 £18

HAGGARD, HENRY RIDER　　Mr. Meeson's Will.　London, 1888.　8vo, red decorated cloth, rear hinge started, shaken, 1st ed., collector's cond.　Demarais 1-203　1978 $60

HAGGARD, HENRY RIDER　　Mr. Meeson's Will.　1888.　First ed., plts., orig. pict. cloth, cover damp-stained, 8vo.　Howes 194-907　1978 £7.50

HAGGARD, HENRY RIDER　　Nada the Lily.　1892.　1st. ed., cr. 8vo, plts., binding faded.　Traylen 88-262D　1978 £8

HAGGARD, HENRY RIDER　　Pearl-Maiden: a tale of the fall of Jerusalem. 1903.　Plts., text somewhat foxed throughout, very good, first English ed.　Bell Book 16-405　1978 £8.50

HAGGARD, HENRY RIDER　　The People of the Mist.　New York, 1894.　1st Am. ed., illus. by Arthur Layard, orig. cloth, good.　Greene 78-49　1978 $25

HAGGARD, HENRY RIDER　　Regeneration.　London, 1910.　1st ed., almost fine, very scarce.　Victoria 34-369　1978 $90

HAGGARD, HENRY RIDER　　Stella Fregelius: a tale of three destinies.　1904. Very good, first English ed.　Bell Book 17-434　1978 £8.50

HAGGARD, HENRY RIDER　　A Winter Pilgrimage: an account of travels through Palestine, Italy, and the Island of Cyprus, accomplished in the year 1900. 1901.　Plts., t.e.g., very good, first English ed.　Bell Book 16-406　1978 £5

HAGGARD, HENRY RIDER　　A Winter Pilgrimmage.　London, 1901.　1st ed., photographs, fine, neatly rebacked in cloth dust jacket.　Victoria 34-370　1978 $50

HAGNER, CHARLES V.　　Early History of the Falls of Schuylkill, Manayunk, Schuylkill and Lehigh Navigation Companies, Etc.　Philadelphia, 1869. Illus.　MacManus 239-1475　1978 $20

HAGNER, LILLIE MAY　　Alluring San Antonio Through the Eyes of an Artist.　San Antonio, 1947.　Illus.　Jenkins 116-106　1978 $12.50

HAGOOD, JOHNSON　　Memoirs of the War of Secession From the Orig. Manuscripts of Johnson Hagood Brigadier-General C.S.A.　Columbia, 1910. Folding map & illus., Bell Wiley's copy.　Broadfoot's 44-610　1978 $60.00

HAHN, ALBERT　　The Economics of Illusion.　1949.　Austin 80-664 1978 $11

HAHN, EMILY　　Raffles of Singapore.　1946.　First ed., d.j., very good.　Austin 82-405　1978 $17.50

HAHN, J. E.　　The Intelligence Service within the Canadian Corps, 1914-1918.　Toronto, 1930.　Photos., fold. maps, signed by author.　Hood 116-123　1978 $20

HAHNEMANN, SAMUEL CHRISTIAN FRIEDRICH　　Hahnemann's Defence of the Organon of Rational Medicine, and of His Previous Homeopathic Works Against the Attacks of Professor Hecker.　Philadelphia, 1896.　Portr., 8vo., ex-lib.　Morrill 239-106　1978 $10

HAHNEMANN, SAMUEL CHRISTIAN FRIEDRICH　　The Lesser Writings...　New York, 1852.　Port., lg. 8vo., orig. 1/2 leather dec. in gilt, rubbed.　Americanist 102-70　1978 $25

HAHNEMANN, SAMUEL CHRISTIAN FRIEDRICH　　The Lesser Writings.　New York, 1852.　Thick 8vo., half mor., binding very worn, chip on upper spine. Rittenhouse 49-320　1976 $50

HAHNEMANN, SAMUEL CHRISTIAN FRIEDRICH　　Organon de rationellen Heilkunde.　Dresden 1810.　Extremely rare 1st ed., old boards, preserved in cloth box.　Gilhofer 75-53　1978 SFr 11,000

HAHNEMANN, SAMUEL CHRISTIAN FRIEDRICH　　Organon of Homeopathic Medicine.　New York, 1843.　2nd Amer. ed., 8vo., gilt-decor. orig. cloth. Salloch 345-90　1978 $60

HAHNEMANN, SAMUEL CHRISTIAN FRIEDRICH　　Organon of Homeopathic Medicine.　New York, Philadelphia, London, 1869.　Fourth Amer. ed., chip top of spine, endpapers cut.　Rittenhouse 49-319　1976 $10

HAIG-BROWN, R. L.　　Starbuck Valley Winter.　Toronto, 1946.　Illus. by Charles Defeo.　Hood 117-514　1978 $12.50

HAIGH, JAMES　　The Dier's Assistant in the Art of Dying Wool and Woollen Goods....　Poughkeepsie, 1813.　Good, hinges worn.　Nestler Rare 78-248　1978 $125

HAIGH, RICHMOND　　An Ehtiopian Saga.　London, 1919.　Sm. 8vo, orig. cloth.　K Books 239-198　1978 £6

HAIGH, S.　　Sketches of Buenos Ayres, Chile and Peru.　1831. Folding map, modern half leather, 8vo, map mounted on linen, 2 leaves repaired, few lib. stamps in text.　Edwards 1012-651　1978 £65

HAIGHT, CANNIFF　　Coming of the Loyalists.　Toronto, 1899.　U.E. Series no. 2, unopened.　Hood's 115-811　1978 $20

HAIGHT, CANNIFF　　Here and There in the Home Land; England, Scotland and Ireland, as Seen by a Canadian.　Toronto, 1895.　Illus.　Hood 116-691 1978 $10

HAIGHT, THERON WILBER　　Three Wisconsin Cushings.　N.P., 1910.　Ltd. to 2500 copies, new cloth, Bell Wiley's copy.　Broadfoot 46-394　1978 $15

HAILE, FR. BERNARD　　A Manual of Navaho Grammar.　St. Michael's, 1926.　Original printed wr., 1st ed.　Ginsberg 14-12　1978 $65

HAILE, M.　　Life and Letters of John Lingard, 1771-1851. (1911).　8vo.　George's 635-1089　1978 £5.25

HAILE, M.　　Life of Reginald Pole.　1911.　2nd. ed., plts., octavo, good.　Upcroft 10-343　1978 £10

HAILES, DAVID DALRYMPLE, LORD 1726-1792　　Annals of Scotland.　Edinburgh, London, 1776.　First ed., 4to., 19th cent. half calf.　Howes 194-233 1978 £22

HAILEY, FOSTER　　Pacific Battle Line.　1944.　Austin 80-124　1978 $8.50

HAIN, H. H.　　History of Perry County, Pa....　Harrisburg, 1922.　1st ed., sm thick 4to, mark on back cover, illus., orig. binding. Americanist 101-62　1978 $90

HAINES, C. GROVE　　The Origin and Background of the Second World War.　New York, 1943.　Maps, spine dull.　Biblo 247-785　1978 $15

HAINES, C. R.　　Dover Priory; a history of the Priory of St. Mary the Virgin and St. Martin of the New Work.　Cambridge, 1930.　Plts., illus., 8vo. Upcroft 12-178　1978 £12.50

HAINES, HERBERT　　A Manual of Monumental Brasses.　Oxford, 1861. 2 vols., illus.　Biblo 247-318　1978 $42.50

HAINES, RICHARD　　Genealogy of the Stokes Family...　Camden, 1903.　Illus., 4to.　MacManus 239-940　1978 $37.50

HAINES, T. L.　　The Royal Path of Life...　Chicago, 1882. Orig. binding, clean, moderate wear at extremities.　Hayman 71-281　1978 $8.50

HAIR, THOMAS H.　　Sketches of the Coal Mines in Northumberland and Durham.　London, 1839.　Folio, plts., plt. mounts foxed, half mor., 1st ed. Quaritch 983-336　1978 $1,450

HAIR, THOMAS H.　　Sketches of the Coal Mines in Northumberland & Durham.　Camden Town, London, 1839.　Folio, plts. & vignette printed on India paper and mounted, title washed and remounted, text and Plt. mounts foxed affecting the plts. themselves in about 15 cases, rebound in half mor., first ed.　Quaritch 977-229　1978 $1,200

HAJEK, LUBOR   Chinese Art. London, n.d. Cloth, spine and part of back cover faded, plts. Dawson's 449-42 1978 $27.50

HAKE, LUCY   Something New on Men and Manners, A Critique on the Follies and Vices of the Age Etc. 1828. 1st. ed., fully rebound in cloth, paper label, good. Jarndyce 16-703 1978 £14

HAKEWILL, GEORGE   An Apologie or Declaration of the Power and Providence of God in the Gouvernment of the World. London, 1635. 3rd ed., enlarged, frontis., folio, 1/2 calf with label. Salloch 348-82 1978 $185

HAKEWILL, JAMES   A Picturesque Tour of Italy from Drawings made in 1816-1817. London, 1820. 4to., polished calf, a.e.g., plts. King 7-357 1978 £175

HAKLUYT, RICHARD   The Principal Navigations, Voiages, Traffiques and Discoueries of the English Nation... 1598-1600. 2nd. ed., mostly black letter, woodcut initials, head & tail pieces, 3 vols., folio, half calf, slight damp-staining on corners of few leaves. Edwards 1012-20 1978 £1800

HAKLUYT, RICHARD   The Principal Navigations, Voyages, Traffiques and Discoueries of the English Nation. 1926. 8 vols., octavo, good. Upcroft 10-74 1978 £15

HAKUSEKI, ARAI
Please turn to
ARAI, HAKUSEKI

HAKUSUI, INAMI   The Japanese Sword. Tokyo, 1948. Illus. Baldwins' 51-87 1978 $20

HALDANE, VISCOUNT   The Philosophy of Humanism. New Haven, 1922. Salloch 348-83 1978 $12.50

HALDANE, J. S.   The Regulation of the Lung-Ventilation. London, 1905. 8vo., orig. printed wrapper, inscribed from author. Quaritch 977-31 1978 $125

HALDONE, J. B. S.   The Marxist Philosophy and the Sciences. 1939. Austin 80-665 1978 $12.50

HALE, ALBERT   Old Newburyport Houses. Boston, (1912). 4to., illus., scarce. MacManus 239-671 1978 $32.50

HALE, ANNIE RILEY   Excerpts from Rooseveltian Fact and Fable. New York, (1908). Wrs. Hayman 72-648 1978 $7.50

HALE, EDWARD EVERETT   The Brick Moon. Wood engrs., ltd. ed. Battery Park 1-179 1978 $35

HALE, EDWARD EVERETT   The Ingham Papers. Boston, 1869. Orig. cloth. MacManus 239-771 1978 $10

HALE, EDWARD EVERETT   Kanzas and Nebraska:.... Boston, 1854. Folding map, original cloth, 1st ed. Ginsberg 14-377 1978 $50

HALE, EDWARD EVERETT   Kansas and Nebraska: the History, Geographical and Physical Characteristics, and Political Position of Those Territories... Boston, 1854. Nice copy, orig. cloth, old lib. stamp, 1st ed., fold. map. Mac-Manus 239-1919 1978 $35

HALE, EDWARD EVERETT   Memories of a Hundred Years. New York, 1902. 1st ed., 2 vols., cloth, illus., very good. Greene 78-213 1978 $35

HALE, EDWARD EVERETT   Silhouettes and Songs Illustrative of the Months... Boston, 1876. Orig. pict. cloth, very good. MacManus 238-489 1978 $35

HALE, EDWIN M.   Saw Palmetto. Philadelphia, 1898. 12mo. Morrill 239-103 1978 $10

HALE, HORATIO   The Iroquois Book of Rites. Philadelphia, 1883. Wrs., frayed, damp-stained at lower margins, scarce. Biblo BL781-74 1978 $32.50

HALE, JOHN P.   Letter from John P. Hale of New Hampshire to His Constituents on the Proposed Annexation of Texas. Washington, 1845. Jenkins 116-1586 1978 $185

HALE, KATHERINE   Canadian Cities of Romance. Toronto, 1922. Drwgs. by Dorothy Stevens. Hood 117-571 1978 $25

HALE, KATHERINE   Isabella Valancy Crawford. Toronto, 1923. Hood 116-692 1978 $7.50

HALE, P. M.   The Woods and Timbers of North Carolina. Raleigh, 1890. Wrs., lg. fold. colored map, ex-lib., spine worn. Broadfoot 50-81 1978 $20

HALE, SALMA   Annals of the Town of Keene, from its First Settlement, in 1734, to the Year 1790. Concord, 1826. 8vo, disbound, 1st ed., light browning. Ximenes 47-124 1978 $60

HALE, SALMA   Annals of the Town of Keene, From Its First Settlement, in 1734, to 1790... Keene, 1851. Fine, rebound. MacManus 239-1072 1978 $35

HALE, WILLIAM J.   Farmer Victorious. 1949. Austin 80-666 1978 $7.50

HALE, WILLIAM J.   Prosperity Beckons. Stratford, 1936. Austin 80-667 1978 $8.50

HALEN, JUAN VAN   Narrative of Don Juan Van Halen's Imprisonment in the Dungeons of the Inquisition at Madrid... 1827. 1st. ed., 2 vols., 8vo, plts., frontispiece foxed & map little torn, contemp. half morocco, rubbed, corners of 1 leaf torn off & repaired. Hannas 54-152 1978 £25

HALES, A. G.   Campaign Pictures of the War in South Africa (1899-1900). London, 1900. Frontis, cr. 8vo, gilt cloth, slightly shaken, 1" tear in backstrip. K Books 239-199 1978 £8

HALES, STEPHEN   Statical Essays: containing Vegetable Statics. London, 1769. Vol. I fourth ed., Vol. II third ed., 8vo., contemp. calf, plts., rebacked and repaired. Gurney 75-51 1978 £165

HALES, STEPHEN   Vegetable Staticks. London, 1727. 8vo., copperplts. by Simon Gribelin, contemp. calf, rubbed, rebacked, lib. bklabel, neat stamp on title, very good copy, 1st ed. Norman 5-135 1978 $600

HALES, WILLIAM   Analysis Aequationum. Dublin, 1784. 4to., contemp. sprinkled calf. Quaritch 977-157 1978 $150

HALEVY, E.   Histoire du Peuple anglais au XIXe siecle, Vols. 1-3 to 1841 with the Epilogue 1895-1914. 1924-32. 5 vols., roy. 8vo., binder's buckram. George's 635-667 1978 £18

HALEVY, L.   l'Abbe Constantin. Paris, 1887. 4to., half mor., t.e.g., plts. by M. Lemaire. Van der Peet H-64-431 1978 Dfl 125

HALEVY, L.   Recits de Guerre - l'Invasion 1870-1871. Paris, (c. 1890). Illus., lg. 4to., orig. cloth. F. Edwards 1013-325 1978 £30

HALEY, J. EVETTS   Charles Goodnight, Cowman and Plainsman. Boston, New York, 1936. Cloth, map, illus., 1st ed., scarce, fine copy in orig. pic. d.w., reinforced, protected with plastic cover, slipcase. Dykes 34-24 1978 $75

HALEY, J. EVETTS   Charles Goodnight...Cowman and Plainsman. Norman, 1949. 1st U. of Oklahoma Ed., fine copy, d.w. Biblo 248-252 1978 $17.50

HALEY, J. EVETTS   Charles Goodnight, Cowman and Plainsman. 1st ed., spine browning, very good copy, slipcase. Dykes 34-25 1978 $50

HALEY, J. EVETTS   Some Southwestern Trails. El Paso, 1948. Oblong octavo, cloth in worn slipcase, 1st ed., spine sunned, limited to 500 copies bound in cloth. Jenkins 116-620 1978 $200

HALEY, J. EVETTS   The Xit Ranch of Texas, and the Early Days of the Llano Estacado. Chicago, 1929. 1st issue, "rare". Jenkins 116-548 1978 $185

HALFORD, HENRY   Essays and Orations. London, 1833. Portr., sm. 8vo., half calf, 2nd ed. Morrill 239-109 1978 $10

HALIBURTON, THOMAS CHANDLER   The Bubbles of Canada. London, 1839. 1st ed., orig. binding, some staining on front cover. Hood's 115-216 1978 $65

HALIBURTON, THOMAS CHANDLER   The Bubbles of Canada. 1839. 1st ed., half dark blue calf, maroon label, slight knock to spine, slight foxing to prelims o/w v.g. Jarndyce 16-704 1978 £38

HALIBURTON, THOMAS CHANDLER   The Bubbles of Canada. 1839. Lg. 8vo., cloth-backed bds., worn, uncut, printed label defective, first London ed. P. M. Hill 142-133 1978 £12

HALIBURTON, THOMAS CHANDLER   The Clockmaker. Philadelphia, 1838. Good copy. Austin 82-855 1978 $20

HALIBURTON, THOMAS CHANDLER   The Clockmaker. London, 1838-1840. 3 vols., rebound in contemp. 3/4 lea., 1st & 3rd are 1st eds., second series of 4th ed., lg. map in facsimile, beautiful set. Hood 117-515 1978 $300

HALIBURTON, THOMAS CHANDLER   The Clockmaker. 1839. 3rd ed. Austin 82-856 1978 $27.50

HALIBURTON, THOMAS CHANDLER   An Historical and Statistical Account of Nova-Scotia. Halifax, 1829. 2 vols., illus. by map & several engrs., orig. covers. Hood 117-247 1978 $325

HALIBURTON, THOMAS CHANDLER   The Letter Bag of The Great Western; or Life In a Steamer. London, 1840. 1st ed., orig. bds., faded. Hood's 115-217 1978 $70

HALIBURTON, THOMAS CHANDLER   The Letter Bag of the Great Western; or, Life in a Steamer. London, 1840. 1st London ed., half green leather, 8vo. Edwards 1012-393 1978 £25

HALIBURTON, THOMAS CHANDLER   Sam Slick the Clockmaker, His sayings and Doings. Toronto, n.d. (c. 1930). 3 vols. in 1. Hood 116-474 1978 $15

HALIFAX, GEORGE SAVILE, MARQUIS OF   The Complete Works... Oxford, 1912. Portrait, facsimiles, octavo, good. Upcroft 10-153 1978 £6

HALIFAX, GEORGE SAVILE, MARQUIS OF   The Complete Works. 1912. Orig. ed., portr., orig. buckram, prtd. label, scarce, 8vo. Howes 194-1153 1978 £8.50

HALIFAX, Nova Scotia, and Its Attractions. (Halifax, n.d., ca. 1900). Illus., oblong 8vo. Morrill 239-409 1978 $12.50

HALKERSTON, PETER   A Treatise on the History, Law and Privileges of the Palace and Sanctuary of Holyroodhouse. Edinburgh, 1831. 1st. ed., uncut in orig. bds., cloth spine label little worn, good. Jarndyce 16-995 1978 £18.50

HALL, ABRAHAM OAKEY   Horace Greeley Decently Dissected, in a Letter. New York, 1862. Wr. Butterfield 21-503 1978 $12.50

HALL, ANNA MARIA FIELDING   Midsummer Eve: A Fairy Tale of Love. 1848. Wood-eng., one joint splitting at head, orig. blue cloth, gilt. Eaton 45-230 1978 £6

HALL, ANNA MARIA FIELDING   Pilgrimages to English Shrines. 1850. 1st ed., illus. by F. W. Fairholt, half title, numerous vignettes, orig. brown cloth, blocked in gilt & blind, fine attractive copy. Jarndyce 16-709 1978 £16.50

HALL, ARTHUR VINE   Poems of a South African. Cape Town, 1942. 10th. ed., portrait frontis, lacks free end-paper, 8vo, orig. cloth. K Books 239-200 1978 £5

HALL, ASAPH   The Parallax of a Lyrae and 61 Cygni. Washington, 1882. 4to., orig. wrs. Morrill 241-176 1978 $10

HALL, BASIL   Account of a Voyage of Discovery to the West Coast of Corea.... London, 1818. Quarto, plts., uncolored maps, half calf, marbled bds., spine rubbed, bookplate of James, Earl of Southesk, exceptionally fine, first ed. Bennett 20-92 1978 $375

HALL, BASIL   Account of a Voyage of Discovery to the West Coast of Corea, and the Great Loo-Choo Island...;.... London, 1818. Color plts., repaired pages, newly rebound in calf and marbled boards. Dawson's 127-217 1978 $175

HALL, BASIL   Extracts From a Journal Written On The Coasts of Chili, Peru, and Mexico, 1820-22. Edinburgh, 1825. 4th. ed., folding map, 2 vols., sm. 8vo, contemp. half calf, rebacked, no half-title to vol. 2. Edwards 1012-652 1978 £55

HALL, BASIL   Patchwork. 1841. 1st. ed., 3 vols., half titles, half green morocco, green cloth bds., spines browned, otherwise v.g. Jarndyce 16-708 1978 £28

HALL, BASIL   Schloss Hainfield; or, A Winter in Lower Styria. Edinburgh, 1837. 2nd. ed., half title, uncut in orig. brown bds., paper label, leading hinge little worn, good. Jarndyce 16-707 1978 £16.50

HALL, BASIL   Travels in North America in the Years 1827 and 1828. Edinburgh, 1829. Three vols., contemp. marbled bds., half calf, joints cracked, coloured fold. map. Wolfe 39-222 1978 $100

HALL, BASIL   Travels in North America in 1827 and 1828. Edinburgh, 1829. 1st. ed., coloured folding map, 3 vols., contemp. calf, rebacked, morocco, 8vo. Edwards 1012-394 1978 £115

HALL, CHARLES E.   Progress of the Negro in Texas. Washington, 1933. Illus. Jenkins 116-553 1978 $15

HALL, CHARLES H.   The Dutch and the Iroquois. New York, 1882. Wrs. Biblo BL781-75 1978 $12.50

HALL, CHARLES FRANCIS   Narrative of the North Polar Expedition. Washington, 1876. 1st. ed., sm. 4to, maps, lithograph plts., steel engraved plts., wood engraved plts., gilt, tail-piece illus., orig. red cloth, neatly recased & repaired. Deighton 5-156 1978 $75

HALL, CHARLES H.   History of Wyoming Borough, Pa. West Pittston, 1935. Illus., orig. stiff wrs. MacManus 239-1477 1978 $15

HALL, CHARLES W.   Adrift in the Ice-Fields. Boston, New York, 1877. Illus., some wear. Hood 116-83 1978 $25

HALL, CLAUDE V.   The Early History of Floyd County. Canyon, 1947. Cloth, fine. Jenkins 116-450 1978 $12.50

HALL, CLAYTON C.   Baltimore Its History and Its People. New York, 1912. 3 vols., illus., maps, very fine, 3/4 leather. MacManus 239-996 1978 $80

HALL, CLAYTON C.   Narratives of Early Maryland, 1633-1684. New York, 1910. Map. MacManus 239-1837 1978 $15

HALL, CLIFTON R.   Andrew Jackson- Military Governor of Tennessee. Princeton, 1916. Slight discoloration, Bell Wiley's Copy. Broadfoot's 44-177 1978 $16.00

HALL, COURTNEY ROBERT   Confederate Medicine. Sept. 1935. Wrs. Bell Wiley's copy. Broadfoot 46-123 1978 $20

HALL, D. J.   Enchanted Sand: A New-Mexican Pilgrimage. London, [1932]. Illus., orig. cloth, 1st ed. Ginsberg 14-762 1978 $15

HALL, EDWARD H.   The Great West: A Guide for Emigrants, Travellers, and Miners to the Western States and Territories... London, 1870. Folding maps, original printed boards, revised ed. Ginsberg 14-378 1978 $125

HALL, EDWIN   The Ancient Historical Records of Norwalk, Conn... Norwalk, 1865. Illus., fold. map, 3/4 calf, lib. marks, fine. MacManus 239-954 1978 $45

HALL, EDWIN   The Puritans and Their Principles. New York, 1847. 3rd ed., orig. cloth, very good. MacManus 239-186 1978 $15

HALL, FANNY W.   Rambles in Europe. New York, 1838. 8vo., 2 vols., nice, 1st ed., pres. from author. Morrill 241-673 1978 $30

HALL, FREDERICK G.   The Bank of Ireland, 1783-1946...Dublin, 1949. Plts., illus., roy. 8vo, orig. cloth, d.w., nice. Fenning 32-143 1978 £12.50

HALL, GORDON   President Lincoln's Death; Its Voice to the People. Northampton, 1865. Wrps. Hayman 71-422 1978 $20

HALL, H. R.   The Civilization of Greece in the Bronze Age. 1928. Maps, illus., roy. 8vo. George's 635-1174 1978 £8.50

HALL, HUBERT   Court Life under the Plantagenets. 1890. 8vo, coloured plts., other illus. George's 635-668 1978 £5.25

HALL, HUBERT   Court Life under the Plantagenets. 1899. Plts., some in colour, illus., 8vo. Upcroft 12-181 1978 £7.50

HALL, HUBERT   Society in the Elizabethan Age. 1902. Colored plts., 8vo. George's 635-669 1978 £7.50

HALL, JAMES   Geology of New-York. Part IV. Albany, 1843. Tall thick 4to., very lg. "geological map", colored & folded, plts., orig. cloth, backstrip chipped, near-fine cond. Butterfield 21-294 1978 $65

HALL, JAMES   Notes and Observations on the Cohoes Mastodon. Albany, 1871. Plts., some folded. Butterfield 21-295 1978 $35

HALL, JAMES   Palaeontology. Albany, 1859-61. Vol. III, tall 4to., 2 vols., orig. cloth, plts. Butterfield 21-297 1978 $27.50

HALL, JAMES   Palaeontology of New-York. Part VI. Albany, 1852. Vol. II, tall thick 4to., plts., b & w, orig. cloth. Butterfield 21-296 1978 $22.50

HALL, JAMES NORMAN   High Adventure. Boston, 1918. Illus., 8vo., d.w., 1st ed. Morrill 239-294 1978 $15

HALL, JAMES NORMAN   Kitchener's Mob. Boston, 1916. Portr., 8vo., 1st ed. Morrill 239-410 1978 $7.50

HALL, JOHN   On the Education of Children, While Under the
Care of Parents or Guardians. New York, 1835. 12mo, original brown patterned
cloth (shelf label removed from foot of spine), 1st ed., old library bookplate.
Ximenes 47-125 1978 $35

HALL, JOHN   The History of the Civil War in America. London, 1780. 1st ed., 8vo., lg. fldg. map frontis, text clear, fine, contemp. marbled binding with 1/2 tan calf, some scuffing, very rare. Current 24-82 1978
$385

HALL, JOSEPH   Mundus alter et idem, sive Terra Australis.
(London, 1605?). Sm. 8 vo., good, German 18th century calf-backed bds.,
1st ed. Quaritch Summer,1978-21 1978 $1,600

HALL, JOSEPH   Occasional Meditations Set Forth by Robert Hall.
1633. Third ed., 12mo., contemp. calf. Howes 194-55 1978 £25

HALL, JOSEPH   A Recollection of Such Treatises as Have Been
Heretofore Severally Published, and Are Nowe Revised, Corrected, Augmented.
London, 1615. Engraved title by R. Elstrack, folio, contemp. calf, gilt centre
ornament on sides, gilt spine, slight repairs. Traylen 88-263 1978 £40

HALL, JOSEPH   Resolutions and Decisions of Divers Practicall
Cases of Conscience in Continuall Use Amongst Men... London, 1649. 1st. ed.,
printed within double-line borders, some cut into, ownership inscription dated 1695,
12mo, contemp. calf gilt, top of spine chipped, leather label. Traylen 88-264
1978 £48

HALL, JOSEPH   The Shaking of the Olive Tree. 1660. Sm. 4to.,
cont. calf, neatly rebacked. Howes 194-56 1978 £20

HALL, MARSHALL   A Descriptive, Diagnostic and Practical Essay on
Disorders of the Digestive Organs and General Health... Keene, 1823. 8vo.,
orig. bds., paper backstrip strengthened with tape, worn, lightly browned, foxed,
bkplt. of John Bell, M. D., good, uncut copy, 1st Amer. ed. Zeitlin 245-110
1978 $75

HALL, MARSHALL   A Descriptive, Diagnostic and Practical Essay on
Disorders of the Digestive Organs and General Health. Keene, 1823. 8vo.,
orig. bds., fr. cover stained, part of spine lacking, 1st Amer. ed. Morrill 239-
110 1978 $22.50

HALL, PRESCOTT F.   Immigration; and Its Effects Upon the United
States. 1908. 2nd. Austin 79-307 1978 $12.50

HALL, PETER   Picturesque Memorials of Salisbury. Salisbury,
1834. 4to., contemp. half calf, entirely uncut, plts., nice. Howes 194-1435
1978 £55

HALL, R. P.   A Treatise on the Hair. (Boston?), 1866. Sm.
8vo., orig. wrs. Morrill 239-111 1978 $12.50

HALL, RADCLYFFE   Miss Ogilvy Finds Herself. 1934. Very good,
d.w., first English ed. Bell Book 16-407 1978 £5.50

HALL, ROBERT   The Highland Sportsman and Tourist. Edinburgh,
1884. Map in pocket, plts., 8vo., 3rd ed., orig. cloth. K Books 244-148 1978
£6

HALL, MRS. SAMUEL CARTER
Please turn to
HALL, ANNA MARIA FIELDING

HALL, THORNTON   Enslavers of Kings. New York, 1914. Reproductions. Biblo 247-694 1978 $17.50

HALL, W. H.   The Nemesis in China. 1847. Plts., text
illus., sm. 8vo., orig. cloth. F. Edwards 1013-89 1978 £30

HALL, WILLIAM   Encyclopedia of English Grammar.... Columbus,
1850. Leather, 3 in. crack in lower joints. Hayman 71-527 1978 $10

HALL-STEVENSON, JOHN   The Works of..., Esq.... London, 1795. 3 vols.,
8vo., orig. grey bds., paper spines, a little worn, uncut, 1st collected ed. Mac-
Manus 238-125 1978 $200

HALLAM, ARTHUR HENRY   Remains in Verse and Prose. 1835. Full brown
morocco, all edges gilt. Baldwins' 51-347 1978 £65

HALLENBECK, CLEVELAND   Legends of the Spanish Southwest. Glendale,
1938. Illus., folding map, original cloth, 1st ed. Ginsberg 14-379 1978 $32.50

HALLENBECK, CLEVELAND   Alvar Nunez Cabezade Vaca: The Journey and
Route of the First European to Cross the Continent of North America, 1534-1536.
Glendale, 1940. Illus. original cloth, 1st ed. Jenkins 116-179 1978 $40

HALLENBECK, CLEVELAND   Spanish Missions Of The Old Southwest.
Garden City, 1926. 1st ed., illus., very good, d.j. Limestone 9-137
1978 $50

HALLENCK, FITZ-GREENE   Alnwick Castle, with Other Poems. New York,
1836. Orig. cloth, 1st of this ed., pres. copy, inscribed by author, bind. loose,
covers partly defective. MacManus 238-490 1978 $50

HALLER, ALBRECHT VON   Disputationum Anatomicarum Selectarum. Gottingae, 1746-1752. Copperplts., 4to., contemp. half vellum, fine & complete
set. Offenbacher 30-61 1978 $950

HALLIDAY, F. E.   Shakespeare and His Critics. 1949. Ltd. deluxe
ed. of 250 copies, full leather. Eaton 45-450 1978 £5

HALLIDAY, WILLIAM R.   Growth of the City State. 1923. 1st series.
Allen 234-391 1978 $7.50

HALLIER, FRANCOIS   Defensio Ecclesiasticae Hierarchiae Adversus
Hermanni Loemelii Spongiam. Paris, 1632. 4to., calf, first ed., woodcut head
pieces and initials. King 7-280 1978 £20

HALLIFAX, SAMUEL   Three Sermons Preached Before the University of
Cambridge,.... Cambridge, 1772. 4to, disbound, 1st ed. Ximenes 47-126
1978 $15

HALLIWELL-PHILLIPPS, J.   Illustrations of the Life of Shakespeare in a
Discursive Series of Essays... Part The First. 1874. 4to, engravings, blind-
stamp on title, author's pres. copy, orig. stamped cloth, rebacked. Eaton 45-
451 1978 £20

HALLOCK, CHARLES   The Fishing Tourist: Angler's Guide and Reference
Book. New York, 1873. 1st ed., old 1/2 mor., edges rubbed, frontis., illus.
Americanist 102-111 1978 $75

HALLOWELL, JOHN K.   Boulder County as It Is. Denver, 1882. Original
printed wr., 1st ed. Ginsberg 14-260 1978 $125

HALLOWELL, JOHN K.   Gunnison, Colorado's Bonanza County. Gunnison, 1883. Orig. pr. wr., 1st ed., author's ed. Ginsberg 14-261 1978 $125

HALLUM, JOHN   Reminiscences of the Civil War. Little Rock,
1903. Bell Wiley's copy. 44-431 1978 $45

HALOANDER, JO. A.   Institutionum Imperialium Analysis,....
Strassburg, 1575. Quarto in sixes, full contemp. limp vellum, exquisitely pr.,
Vvriot's dragon device on title, Fletcher of Saltoun copy with his signature on
back paste-down, 1st ed. Bennett 20-94 1978 $275

HALPINE, CHARLES GRAHAM The Life and Adventures, Songs, Services,
Speeches of Private Mile O'Reilly. NY, 1864. Comic illus. by E. K. Mullen,
orig. cloth binding, damp stained, good cond. Greene 78-323 1978 $65.00

HALSALLE, HENRY DE   The Romance of Modern First Editions. Philadelphia, 1931. Battery Park 1-355 1978 $25

HALSALLE, HENRY DE   The Romance of Modern First Editions. Philadelphia, (1931). Cloth., nice copy, slightly worn d.j. Hayman 72-174 1978
$8.50

HALSEY, FRANCIS WHITING The Old New York Frontier. New York, 1901.
1st ed., fold. map. MacManus 239-356 1978 $32.50

HALSEY, FRANCIS WHITING The Old New York Frontier...1614-1800. New
York, 1917. Maps, plts., later prtg. Butterfield 21-201 1978 $15

HALSEY, FRANCIS WHITING A Tour of Four Great Rivers. New York, 1906.
Maps, illus., ltd. to 785 copies, very scarce, bookplt. MacManus 239-187
1978 $37.50

HALSEY, LEWIS   The Falls of Taughannock. New York, 1866.
Sq. 18mo., illus., ads, pict. wr., fine copy. Butterfield 21-433 1978 $25

HALSEY, R. T. H.   The Homes of Our Ancestors. New York, 1937.
Illus. Biblo BL781-543 1978 $12

HALSTED, C. A.   Life of Margaret Beaufort, Countess of Richmond
and Derby, Mother of King Henry the Seventh... London, 1845. Portrait, 8vo,
polished calf. Traylen 88-265 1978 £6

HALSTED, WILLIAM STEWART Partial, Progressive and Complete Occlusion of
the Aorta and Other Large Arteries in the Dog by Means of the Metal Band. 1909.
Rittenhouse 49-323 1976 $25

HAMANN, RICHARD   Aegyptische Kunst. Wesen and Geschichte.
Berlin, (1944). Illus. Biblo BL781-389 1978 $14.50

HAMEL, FRANK   Famous French Salons. 1909. Plts., orig. cloth,
8vo. Howes 194-908 1978 £5

HAMERSLY, LEWIS R.   The Records of Living Officers of the U.S. Navy
and Marine Corps... Philadelphia, 1870. 8vo, orig. cloth. Edwards 1012-544
1978 £20

HAMERTON, PHILIP GILBERT   The Etcher's Handbook. 1881. 3rd. ed., plts.,
orig. purple cloth, faded, Dr. Arthur Evershed's copy signed by him. Jarndyce
16-710 1978 £9.50

HAMERTON, PHILIP GILBERT   The Graphic Arts. 1882. Lg. paper, plts.,
text illus., folio, orig. parchment, soiled and rubbed. George's 635-25 1978
£30

HAMERTON, PHILIP GILBERT   Man in Art. London, 1892. Lg. folio,
full vellum, uncut, unopened, plts. on Japan vellum, rare, deluxe ed., fine.
Houle 10-149 1978 $145

HAMERTON, PHILIP GILBERT   Portfolio Papers. London, 1889. 1st ed.,
8 vo., orig. gilt stamped cloth, frontispiece, very good. Houle 10-150
1978 $25

HAMERTON, PHILIP GILBERT   Wenderholme. Boston, 1876. 1st Amer. ed.(?),
3 vols. in 1, orig. cloth, mint. Greene 78-215 1978 $35

HAMILL, H. M.   The Old South. Nashville, n.d. (ca. 1904).
Portrs., 12mo., orig. wrs. Morrill 241-177 1978 $7.50

HAMILL, JOHN   The Strange Career of Mr. Hoover under Two
Flags. New York, 1931. Illus., wrs. Hayman 73-244 1978 $8.50

HAMILL, KATHERINE   Swamp Shadow. 1936. First ed., d.j. Austin
82-406 1978 $15

HAMILTON, A. J.   Origin and Objects of the Slaveholders' Conspiracy. New York, 1862. Yellow printed wr. Jenkins 116-558 1978 $65

HAMILTON, ALEXANDER   A New Account of the East Indies. London,
Argonaut Press, 1930. Ltd. ed., 2 vols., maps, plts., illus., 4to., orig. cloth.
K Books 244-379 1978 £30

HAMILTON, ALEXANDER   A New Account of the East Indies. 1930.
Maps, illus., 2 vols., 4to, orig. cloth, vellum spine, ltd. to 975 numbered
copies. Edwards 1012-161 1978 £65

HAMILTON, ALLAN MC LANE   The Intimate Life of Alexander Hamilton.
New York, 1911. Illus. Biblo 248-96 1978 $17.50

HAMILTON, ANDREW J.   On The State Of The Union. Washington, 1861.
Jenkins 116-557 1978 $17.50

HAMILTON, ANGUS   En Coree. Paris, n.d. (c. 1920). Illus.,
decor. cloth, moderate wear and soiling, a.e.g. Dawson's 127-219 1978 $55

HAMILTON, ANGUS   Korea. New York, 1904. Illus., cloth, somewhat worn, edges foxed. Dawson's 127-218 1978 $25

HAMILTON, BOB   Gene Autry and The Thief River Outlaws. 1944.
Illus., paper browning, else good. Austin 82-407 1978 $12.50

HAMILTON, CHARLES   Sketches of Life and Sport in South-Eastern Africa.
London, 1870. Illus. by Pierre Mejanel, frontispiece, 5 plts., cr. 8vo, neatly
recased in orig. cloth. K Books 239-201 1978 £43

HAMILTON, CHARLES E.   A Handy Guide to Papermaking with tr. of 1798.
Berkeley, 1948. Japanese ed., 12mo., 1 of 1000 copies. Battery Park 1-451 1978
$50

HAMILTON, CHARLES WILLIAM   A Summer in Northern Lands. Boston, (1922).
Illus. from photos, 8vo., 1st ed. Morrill 239-411 1978 $10

HAMILTON, CLAYTON   On the Trail of Stevenson. 1915. Drawings, first
ed., lg. paper ed. Austin 82-408 1978 $12.50

HAMILTON, CLAYTON   On the Trail of Stevenson. New York, 1916.
8vo, boards, cloth back, paper labels, illus. from drawings by Walter Hale, Fine,
1st ed., collector's cond. Desmarais 1-389 1978 $20

HAMILTON, D. E.   How the Fight Was Won; A General Sketch of
the Great War. Toronto, 1920. Card cover. Hood's 115-110 1978 $7.50

HAMILTON, ELIZABETH   The Cottagers of Glenburnie; A Tale for the
Farmer's Inglenook. Edinburgh, 1808. 8vo, contemporary tree calf, spine gilt,
1st ed., very good copy. Ximenes 47-127 1978 $125

HAMILTON, ELIZABETH   Memoirs of the Life of Agrippina, the Wife of
Germanicus. Bath, 1804. 1st. ed., 3 vols., 8vo, half-titles, contemp. mottled
calf with tree calf lozenges on all covers, one head-band worn, final gathering
heavily foxed. Hannas 54-153 1978 £40

HAMILTON, F. W.   The Origin and History of the First or Grenadier
Guards. 1874. Coloured plts., 3 vols., 8vo., full calf. F. Edwards 1013-475
1978 £85

HAMILTON, G. ROSTREVOR   The Latin Portrait. An Anthology Made by...
London: The Nonesuch Press, 1929. 12mo., orig. cream buckram, pub. box, ltd.
to 1,050 copies, fine. MacManus 238-836 1978 $25

HAMILTON, G. ROSTREVOR   The Latin Portrait. Nonesuch Press, 1929. No.
2 of 1050 copies, buckram, fine, unopened, worn slipcase, 12mo., first English ed.
Bell Book 16-679 1978 £5.50

HAMILTON, GAIL PSEUD.
Please turn to
DODGE, MARY ABIGAIL

HAMILTON, H.   The English Brass and Copper Trades to 1800.
1926. Illus., some scoring, newspaper cuttings inserted, covers faded, 8vo.
George's 635-328 1978 £8.50

HAMILTON, HENRY S.   Reminiscences of a Veteran. Concord, 1897.
Illus., original cloth, 1st ed. Ginsberg 14-380 1978 $75

HAMILTON, HUGH   Philosophical Essays. 1783. Fourth ed., plt.,
sm. 8vo., contemp. calf, upper joint cracked. Howes 194-305 1978 £10

HAMILTON, J. C.   The Prairie Province; Sketches of Travel from Lake
Ontario to Lake Winnipeg... Toronto, 1876. Fold. map. Hood 116-851 1978
$35

HAMILTON, J. TAYLOR   A History of the Church Known as the Moravian
Church...During the 18th and 19th Centuries. Bethlehem, 1900. Illus., scarce.
MacManus 239-1478 1978 $37.50

HAMILTON, JAMES   The Several Speeches of Duke Hamilton, Henry
Earl of Holland, and Arthur Lord Capel.... 1649. First ed., sm. 4to., uncut,
19th cent. calf. Howes 194-93 1978 £50

HAMILTON, JOSEPH GREGOIRE DE ROULHAC   The Papers of Thomas Ruffin.
Raleigh, 1918. 4 vols., few spots on covers. Broadfoot's 50-347 1978 $75

HAMILTON, JOSEPH GREGOIRE DE ROULHAC   William Richardson Davie: A
Memoir. Chapel Hill, 1907. New cloth. Broadfoot's 50-82 1978 $10

HAMILTON, KATE W.   The House That Jack Built. Philadelphia,
(1880). Orig. binding, clean. Hayman 71-284 1978 $7.50

HAMILTON, M. A.   A Self-Denying Ordinance. New York, 1895.
1st Amer. ed., quarter calf, marbled boards, good. Greene 78-214 1978 $10

HAMILTON, MILTON W.   The Country Printer New York State, 1785-1830.
New York, 1936. Orig. cloth, fine. MacManus 239-337 1978 $32.50

HAMILTON, MILTON W.   New York State, 1785-1830. Columbia University Press, 1936. Frontis., 1st ed. Butterfield 21-202 1978 $25

HAMILTON, STANISLAUS M.   Letters to Washington and Accompanying Papers.
Boston, 1898-1902. Illus., nice untrimmed set, 5 vols., t.e.g., very scarce.
MacManus 239-500 1978 $75

HAMILTON, THOMAS   Men and Manners in America. Edinburgh, 1834.
Two vols., second ed., marbled bds., half calf. Wolfe 39-223 1978 $35

HAMILTON, THOMAS   The Youth and Manhood of Cyril Thornton.
1827. 1st. ed., 3 vols., gilt borders & spines, black labels, v.g. Jarndyce 16-
711 1978 £38

HAMILTON, THOMAS   The Youth and Manhood of Cyril Thornton.
Edinburgh & London, 1827. 3 vols., lib. stamps on titles, 1/2 morocco, ex-lib.
binding. Eaton 45-231 1978 £30

HAMILTON, WALTER   Dated Book-Plates...with a Treatise on Their
Origin and Development. Part I.---Dated Book-Plates prior to 1700. Part II.---
Dated Book-Plates of the Eighteenth Century. Part III.---Dated Book-Plates of the
Nineteenth Century to 1895. London, 1895. Illus., 1st ed., covers soiled. Mac-
Manus 238-869 1978 $85

HAMILTON, WALTER   Parodies of the Works of English and American Authors. London, 1884-89. 1st Book ed., quarter calf, 6 vols in 3, cloth with all edges stained red, some shelf wear, interiors in good condition. Greene 78-50 1978 $125

HAMILTON, WALTON H.   Case of Bituminous Coal. 1925. 1st ed. Austin 80-669 1978 $12.50

HAMILTON, WALTON H.   The Pattern of Competition. 1940. 1st ed. in dust jacket. Austin 80-668 1978 $20

HAMILTON, WILLIAM   Observations on the Preparation, Utility and Administration of the Digitalis Purpurea, or Foxglove, in Dropsy of the Chest, Consumption, Hemorrhage, Scarlet Fever, Measles... London, 1807. 8vo., orig. blue bds., rebacked in gray paper, lightly foxed, dampstain, good copy, pres. inscr. from the author, bkplts of Drs. Carleton B. Chapman & Emmet Field Horine, 1st ed., rare. Zeitlin 245-112 1978 $127.50

HAMILTON, WILLIAM   The Poems and Songs. Edinburgh, 1850. 12mo., red cloth, printed label, uncut, fine. P. M. Hill 142-279 1978 £10

HAMILTON, WILLIAM B.   A Social Survey of Austin. Austin, 1913. Illus., scarce. Jenkins 116-1377 1978 $13.50

HAMILTON, WILLIAM R.   Lectures on Quaternions: Containing a Systematic Statement of a New Mathematical Method. Dublin, 1853. 8vo., inscribed by author, orig. cloth, spine faded, first ed. Quaritch 977-158 1978 $700

HAMILTON'S Historical, Descriptive and Practical Catechism of the Organ. (c. 1820). 12mo. George's 635-1404 1978 £6.50

HAMILTON, the Birmingham of Canada. Hamilton, 1892. Quarto, illus. Hood 116-744 1978 $45

HAMLEY, EDWARD BRUCE   The Operations of War Explained and Illustrated. 1872. Third ed., maps, sq. roy. 8vo., orig. cloth. F. Edwards 1013-326 1978 £15

HAMLIN, A. D. F.   A Text-Book of the History of Architecture. London, 1922. 8vo., cloth, illus., new rev. ed. Van der Peet H-64-139 1978 Dfl 30

HAMLIN, AUGUSTUS C.   Martyria. Boston, 1866. 1st ed., orig. cloth, illus. by author, sm. 8vo., ex-lib. Morrill 241-178 1978 $15

HAMLIN, AUGUSTUS C.   Martyria: or, Andersonville Prison. Boston, 1866. Illus. by author, new cloth. Bell Wiley's copy. Broadfoot 46-125 1978 $17

HAMLIN, PERCY   The Making of a Soldier: Letters of General R. S. Ewell. Richmond, 1935. Bell Wiley's copy. Broadfoot's 44-181 1978 $16

HAMLIN, SCOVILLE   The Menace of Overproduction. 1930. Austin 80-670 1978 $11

HAMMER, CHEVALIER J. VON   The History of the Assassins. 1835. Sm. 8vo, orig. bds., rebacked. Edwards 1012-67 1978 £50

HAMMER, VICTOR   Le Mystere de la Charite de Heanne d'Arc. New York, 1943. 8vo, 2-tone cloth, gilt, engraved by Victor Hammer, 1 of 500 copies, French text, fine. Duschnes 220-137a 1978 $60

HAMMER, WILLIAM J.   Radium and Other Radio-Active Substances. New York, 1903. Rittenhouse 49-325 1976 $35

HAMMERTON, JOHN ALEXANDER   Countries of the World. (c. 1930). New ed., illus., some coloured, 2 vols., 4to. George's 635-670 1978 £5.25

HAMMERTON, JOHN ALEXANDER   Peoples of All Nations. London, Amalgamated Press, n.d. c. 1924. 7 vols., sm. thick 4to., half black mor., colour plts. Sexton 7-150 1978 £25

HAMMERTON, JOHN ALEXANDER   A Popular History of the Great War. London, n.d. c. 1925. 6 vols., maps, illus., cr. 8vo., orig. cloth. Sexton 7-149 1978 £10

HAMMERTON, JOHN ALEXANDER   Universal History of the World. (c.1930). Color plts., illus., 8vols., orig. qtr. blue mor. George's 635-782 1978 £15

HAMMERTON, JOHN ALEXANDER   The War Illustrated: Album De Luxe... 1917-18. London, 1918. Vol. IX, illus. Hood's 116-124 1978 $25

HAMMERTON, JOHN ALEXANDER   Wonders of Animal Life. (c.1920). Color plts., illus., 2 vols., 4to. George's 635-1017 1978 £5.25

HAMMERTON, JOHN ALEXANDER   Wonders of the Past.... (c. 1925). Maps, coloured plts., illus., 2 vols., 4to. George's 635-1175 1978 £5.25

HAMMETT, CHARLES E.   The Controversy Touching The Old Stone Mill, In The Town of Newport, Rhode Island.... Newport, 1851. Illus. Baldwins' 51-399 1978 $50

HAMMETT, DASHIFLL   Creeps By Night. 1931. First ed. Austin 82-409 1978 $35

HAMMETT, DASHIELL   Creeps By Night. Cleveland, (1944). 1st Forum Books printing, 8 vo., d.j., printed on wartime paper, fine. Houle 10-151 1978 $45

HAMMETT, DASHIELL   The Glass Key. New York, 1934. 1st ed., 4th printing, d.j., very good. Houle 10-152 1978 $125

HAMMETT, DASHIELL   Red Harvest. New York, 1929. First U.S. ed., cloth, fine, d.w., scarce. Bell Book 17-243 1978 £135

HAMMETT, DASHIELL   Thin Man. New York, 1934. 1st ed., 1st issue, d.j., very good. Houle 10-153 1978 $350

HAMMETT, DASHIELL   The Thin Man. 1934. Scarce, very good, first English ed. Bell Book 16-246 1978 £55

HAMMETT, G. A.   Philosophy of Space and Time. Newport, 1849. Sm. 8vo., orig. wrs., 1st ed. Morrill 239-112 1978 $17.50

HAMMETT, R. W.   Romanesque Architecture of Europe. 1927. 4to., plts. Allen 234-1277 1978 $25

HAMMOND, HENRY   An Account of Mr. Cawdry's Triplex Diatribe Concerning Superstition, Wil-Worship and Christmas Festivall. London, 1655. Orig.? full calf, front cover broken loose. Baldwins' 51-348 1978 $50

HAMMOND, I. B.   Reminiscences of Frontier Life. Portland, 1904. Original printed wr., in half morocco slipcase. Ginsberg 14-381 1978 $85

HAMMOND, JABEZ D.   The History of Political Parties in the State of New York, From the Ratification of the Federal Constitution to December, 1840. Albany, 1842. 2 vols., 1st ed., bookplts., fine, orig. cloth. MacManus 239-345 1978 $55

HAMMOND, JABEZ D.   Letter to the Hon. John C. Calhoun, on the Annexation of Texas. Copperstown, 1844. Half mor., 1st ed. Ginsberg 14-955 1978 $300

HAMMOND, JABEZ D.   Life and Times of Silas Wright, Late Governor of...New York. Syracuse and New York, 1848. Portrs., orig. pict. cloth, 1st ed., nice copy. Butterfield 21-473 1978 $55

HAMMOND, JABEZ D.   Life and Times of Silas Wright, Late Governor of ...New York. Bound in publisher's sheep with lea. labels, worn but holding, labeled on spine as Vol. III. Butterfield 21-474 1978 $15

HAMMOND, JAMES   Love Elegies. (Edinburgh), 1743. 8vo., unbound. P. M. Hill 142-278 1978 £36

HAMMOND, MRS. JOHN HAYS   A Woman's Part in a Revolution. London, 1897. Cr. 8vo, orig. cloth, flamboyantly inscribed by author. K Books 239-203 1978 £18

HAMMOND, JOHN HAYS   The Truth About the Jameson Raid. Boston, 1918. Cr. 8vo, orig. bds. K Books 239-202 1978 £12

HAMMOND, JOHN LAWRENCE   The Skilled Labourer, 1760-1832. 1919. Spine dull, 8vo. George's 635-329 1978 £5.25

HAMMOND, JOHN LAWRENCE   The Village Labourer, 1760-1832, a Study in the Government of England before the Reform Bill. 1913. 8vo. George's 635-330 1978 £5.25

HAMMOND, JOHN MARTIN   The Colonial Mansions of Maryland and Delaware. Philadelphia, 1914. 1st ed., illus., plts., very fine, uncut, orig. pic. cloth, ltd. ed. MacManus 239-672 1978 $55

HAMMOND, JOHN MARTIN   Colonial Mansions of Maryland and Delaware. Philadelphia, 1914. 65 illus. Baldwins' 51-284 1978 $27.50

HAMMOND, JOHN MARTIN   Quaint and Historic Forts of North America. Philadelphia, 1915. Illus. MacManus 239-194 1978 $25

HAMMOND, JOHN W. Men and Volts. 1941. Illus. Austin 80-671 1978 $10

HAMMOND, JOHN WINTHROP Charles Proteus Steinmetz. 1924. Illus. Austin 79-309 1978 $10

HAMMOND, JOSEPH A Cornish Parish. London, 1897. Illus., 8vo., lst ed. Morrill 239-353 1978 $10

HAMMOND, OTIS GRANT History of the Seal and Flag of the State of New Hampshire. (Concord), 1916. 8vo., orig. bds., cloth back, illus. Morrill 241-390 1978 $10

HAMMOND, OTIS GRANT Letters and Papers of Major-General John Sullivan, Continental Army. Concord, 1930-31-39. 3 vols., frontis., orig. cloth, hinges weak, but very nice. MacManus 239-578 1978 $75

HAMMOND, ROBERT The Electric Light in Our Homes. London, (1884). 8vo., 3 orig. mounted photos & text illus., orig. cloth, gilt, occas. foxing, but fine copy, lst ed., pres. copy. Norman 5-136 1978 $95

HAMMOND, S. H. Hunting Adventures in the Northern Wilds... New York, 1856. Coloured title, coloured plts., 8vo., orig. cloth, cover faded, slightly worn. Edwards 1012-494 1978 £15

HAMMOND, SAMUEL H. Speech of Hon. Samuel H. Hammond of Steuben County on the Governor's Message. Albany, 1860. Butterfield 21-120 1978 $12.50

HAMNETT, NINA Laughing Torso: reminiscences. 1932. Plts., illus., bookplt., very good, first English ed. Bell Book 17-435 1978 £15

HAMPSON, R. T. Origines Patriciae, or, Deduction of European Titles of Nobility & Dignified Offices from Their Primitive Source. 1846. Ex-lib., buckram, lacks flyleaves. Allen 234-1278 1978 $7.50

HAMPTON, MOULTON The Mirror of the World; or, Stories From All Climes. Boston, 1856. Orig. binding, clean, little wear. Hayman 71-229 1978 $15

HAMSUN, KNUT August. 1932. Buckram, spine somewhat faded, very good, first English ed. Bell Book 16-410 1978 £6

HANAFORD, PHEBE A. Field, Gunboat, Hospital, and Prison. Boston, 1866. Portr., 8vo., orig. cloth, lst ed. Morrill 241-179 1978 $8.50

HANBURY, DANIEL Science Papers chiefly Pharmacological and Botanical. London, 1876. 8vo., full mor., portrait, illus., fine. Gurney 75-53 1978 £35

HANCE, ANTHONY M. Recollections of the Troop March of 1882. 1910. 1st ed., orig. wrs., good copy. MacManus 239-1480 1978 $20

HANCOCK, HARRIE I. Inspector Henderson, the Central Office Detective. New York, n.d. (circa 1900?). Pict. wrs., some wear, lacks back wr. Hayman 73-245 1978 $7.50

HANCOCK, SAMUEL The Narrative of Samuel Hancock, 1845-1860. New York, 1927. Map, lst ed., fine. MacManus 239-1920 1978 $20

HANCOCK, SAMUEL The Narrative of...1845-1860. New York, 1927. First ed., map. Biblo 247-223 1978 $17.50

HANCOCK, THOMAS Personal Narrative of the Origin and Progress of the Caoutchouc or India-Rubber Manufacture in England. London, 1857. 8vo., ads, frontis. litho. portr., engr. & litho. plts., some fldg., orig. blind-stamped cloth, spine repaired, but very good copy, lst ed. Norman 5-137 1978 $250

HANCOCK, WINFIELD The Civil Record of Major General Winfield S. Hancock, During His Administration in Louisiana and Texas. (Austin?), 1871. Printed wr., chipped along edge. Jenkins 116-560 1978 $85

HANCOCK, WINFIELD The Civil Record of Major-General ...During His Administration in Louisiana and Texas. N.P., 1880. Half mor., lst ed. Ginsberg 14-382 1978 $150

HAND, M. C. From a Forest to a City. Personal Reminiscences of Syracuse, New York. Syracuse, 1889. 1st ed., illus., orig. cloth, very fine. MacManus 239-1102 1978 $35

THE HAND Book to Monterey and Vicinity:.... Monterey, 1875. Original printed wr., lst ed. Ginsberg 14-124 1978 $100

A HANDBOOK For Posterity: or Recollections of "Twiddle Twaddle". 1876. lst ltd. ed., no. 42 of 50 on ordinary paper, hand-coloured, untrimmed, orig. half brown calf, t.e.g., fine copy. Jarndyce 16-444 1978 £65

HANDBUCH der Stadt Philadelphia und Imgebung...Centennial-Feier und Weltausstellung von 1876. Philadelphia, 1876. Illus., lg. fold. map in color, fine, orig. cloth-backed bds. MacManus 239-1613 1978 $22.50

HANDCOCK, P. S. P. Mesopotamian Archaeology. London, 1912. 8vo., plts., illus. Traylen 88-15 1978 £8

HANDEL, GEORGE F. The Sacred Oratorios, As Set to Music. 1799. lst. ed., 2 vols., frontis., plts., orig. tree calf, spines gilt, black labels. Jarndyce 16-104 1978 £35

HANDFORTH, THOMAS Mei Li. New York, 1938. lst ed., almost fine copy. Victoria 34-372 1978 $30

HANDS, WILLIAM HATTON Schediasms; Verse and Prose. 1824. Frontis, portrait, orig. bds., one joint cracked, soiled. Eaton 45-232 1978 £6

HANDY, ESAAC W. K. United States Bonds. Baltimore, 1874. Bell Wiley's copy. Broadfoot 46-126 1978 $50

HANDY, WILLOWDEAN C. L'Arts des Iles Marquises. Paris, 1938. Plts., French text, wrs. Dawson's 127-261 1978 $35

HANDZEICHNUNGEN alter Meister der Hollandischen Malerschule. Dritte Verbesserte Auflage. Leipzig, 1921. 6 vols., imp. 4to., leather backs. Quaritch 983-179 1978 $215

HANEY, LEWIS H. History of Economic Thought. 1936. 3rd enlarged ed., lst ed. Austin 80-672 1978 $27.50

HANEY, LEWIS H. Studies in the Industrial Resources of Texas... Austin, 1915. Illus., orig. pr. wr., lst ed. Ginsberg 14-956 1978 $10

HANEY, LEWIS H. Studies in the Industrial Resources of Texas. Austin, 1915. Wr., maps, charts. Jenkins 116-563 1978 $25

HANKIN, C. C. Life of Mary Anne Schimmelpenninck. 1860. Portrait, post 8vo. George's 635-1262 1978 £5

HANLEY, JAMES Captain Bottell. 1933. No. 42 of 99 copies only, numbered & signed by author, quarter buckram, t.e.g., very good, first English ed. Bell Book 17-437 1978 £42.50

HANLEY, JAMES The German Prisoner. London, (1930). 1 of 500 numbered copies signed by author, 1st ed., frontispiece, good-fine. Houle 10-154 1978 $85

HANLEY, JAMES The German Prisoner. London, (1930). One of 500 numbered copies, signed by the author, very nice, frontispiece by William Roberts, orig. binding, first ed. Rota 211-164 1978 £15

HANLEY, JAMES Quartermaster Clausen. White Owl Press, 1934. Bds., very good, d.w., first English ed. Bell Book 16-413 1978 £15

HANLEY, SYLVANUS Caliphs & Sultans... 1868. lst. ed., half title, orig. dull brown cloth, good. Jarndyce 16-712 1978 £7.50

HANMER, JOHN Sonnets. 1840. lst. ed., some slight foxing, orig. grained dark green cloth blocked in blind, gilt spine, v.g. Jarndyce 16-713 1978 £18.50

HANNA, CHARLES A. The Scotch-Irish or, the Scot in North Britain, North Ireland, and North America. New York, 1902. 2 vols., lst ed., illus., maps. MacManus 239-432 1978 $65

HANNAM, JOHN Reflections on Various Subjects. 1797. 8vo., contemp. marbled wrappers. P. M. Hill 142-134 1978 £25

HANNAY, J. B. Sex Symbolism in Religion. 1922. Portrait, text illus., 2 vols., 8vo. George's 635-1076 1978 £8.50

HANNAY, JAMES 1827-1873 Satire & Satirists. 1854. lst. ed., half title, orig. green cloth, little faded, otherwise v.g. Jarndyce 16-714 1978 £10.50

HANNAY, JAMES 1842-1910 The History of Acadia From Its First Discovery to Its Surrender to England by the Treaty of Paris. St. John, 1879. Insc. & signed by author. Hood's 115-218 1978 $70

HANNAY, JAMES 1842-1910   History of the War of 1812, Between Great Britain and the United States of America. Toronto, 1905. Illus. Hood's 115-111 1978 $30

HANNAY, JAMES 1842-1910   History of the War of 1812... Toronto, 1905. 1st ed., illus., uncut, orig. cloth, very good. MacManus 239-475 1978 $35

HANNAY, JAMES 1842-1910   Life of F. R. Wynne. 1897. 1st ed., signed pres. copy from author, octavo bound in cloth. Hyland 128-828 1978 £9.50

HANNAY, JAMES OWEN   Irishmen All. 1913. 1st ed., ex lib, cover dull, illus., text good. Hyland 128-839 1978 £12.50

HANNAY, JAMES OWEN   Irishmen All. 1914. F.p. damaged, very good, octavo bound in cloth. Hyland 128-840 1978 £7.50

HANNOVER, EMIL   Pottery and Porcelain, a Handbook For Collectors. London, 1925. 3 vols., roy. 8vo, coloured plts., illus. Traylen 88-381 1978 £80

HANNUM, ALBERTA   Spin A Silver Dollar. New York, 1945. 1st ed., illus., color plts., Yazz d.j., very good or better. Limestone 9-138 1978 $30

HANNUM, ANNA PASCHALL   A Quaker Forty-Niner. The Adventures of Charles Edward Pancoast on the American Frontier. Philadelphia, 1930. Illus., d.j. MacManus 239-1905 1978 $12.50

HANNUM, ANNA PASCHALL   A Quaker Forty-Niner. Philadelphia, 1930. Illus., map. Baldwins' 51-562 1978 $15

HANSBROUGH, VIVIAN   History of Greene County, Arkansas. Little Rock, 1946. 1st ed., cloth, illus., fine. Dykes 35-34 1978 $15

HANSCOM, ELIZABETH DEERING   The Heart of the Puritan. New York, 1917. Frontis., 8vo, 1st ed. Morrill 239-412 1978 $7.50

HANSELL, GEORGE H.   Reminiscences of Baptist Churches and Baptist Leaders in New York City and Vicinity. Philadelphia, 1899. Illus., orig. cloth. MacManus 239-371 1978 $12.50

HANSEN, LEONARDUS   Vita Mirabilis et Mors Pretiosa Venerabilis Sororis Rosae de S. Maria Limensis.... Rome, 1664. 4to, Roman letter, orig. limp vellum, cardinal's arms in gilt, 1st ed. Quaritch 978-125 1978 $250

HANSEN, MARCUS LEE   The Atlantic Migration, 1607-1860. Cambridge, 1940. Hood's 115-598 1978 $25

HANSEN, MARCUS LEE   The Atlantic Migration. Harvard University Press, 1940. Illus., 1st ed. in repaired dust jacket. Austin 79-312 1978 $27.50

HANSEN, MARCUS LEE   The Mingling of the Canadian and American Peoples. New Haven, 1940. Fldg. map, signed by Brebner. Hood 117-573 1978 $40

HANSFORD, PAMELA   Thomas Wolfe A Critical Study. London, (1947). Very good, dw. Bernard 5-301 1978 $15

HANSON, J. H.   Centennial Chronological Paragraph History of the City of St. Paul, Minnesota. St. Paul, 1876. Orig. wr., 1st ed. Ginsberg 14-555 1978 $50

HANSON, JOSEPH MILLS   The Conquest of the Missouri. Chicago, 1916. Map & illus., 3rd ed. Baldwins' 51-563 1978 $17.50

HANSON, O.   The Kachins; Their customs and traditions (Burma). Rangoon, 1912. Cloth, illus., plts., 8vo. Van der Peet 127-106 1978 Dfl 55

HANSON, WILLIS T.   The Early Life of John Howard Payne. Boston, 1913. Ltd. to 483 copies, 1/2 calf. MacManus 239-800 1978 $25

HANSON, WILLIS T.   A History of Schenectady During the Revolution. N. P., 1916. 8vo, 1st ed., ltd. to 1000 copies, orig. cloth. Morrill 241-411 1978 $25

HANSON, WILLIS T.   A History of Schenectady (NY) During the Revolution. 1916. Good. Nestler Rare 78-165 1978 $25

HANSTEEN, CHRISTOPHER   Untersuchungen uber den Magnetismus der Erde. Christiania, 1819. Fldg. copperplts., lg. engr. maps, 2 vols., 4to., obl. folio, contemp. wrs., rebacked, uncut, atlas stitched, 1st ed., text vol. very good cond., waterstain. Offenbacher 30-62 1978 $275

HANWAY, JONAS   An Historical Account of the British Trade Over The Caspian Sea... 1762. 3rd. ed., folding maps, engraved plts., 2 vols., 4to, contemp. calf, joints repaired. Edwards 1012-68 1978 £200

HANWAY, JONAS   Virtue in Humble Life. 1777. Second ed., 2 vols. in 1, frontispieces, thk. 4to., contemp. calf, pres. copy inscribed by author. Howes 194-306 1978 £80

HAPGOOD, HUTCHINS   The Spirit of Labor. 1907. First ed., very good, repaired frayed d.j. Austin 82-410 1978 $20

HAPGOOD, HUTCHINS   The Spirit of the Ghetto. 1909. Illus., 1st ed. of rev. ed., illuminated cover, bright. Austin 79-313 1978 $37.50

HAPGOOD, HUTCHINS   Types from City Streets. New York, 1910. 8vo., illus., 1st ed., orig. cloth. Morrill 241-180 1978 $10

HAPGOOD, HUTCHINS   A Victorian in the Modern World. 1939. First ed. Austin 82-411 1978 $12.50

HARBAUGH, H.   Harbaugh's Harfe Gedichte in Penna-Deutscher Mundart. Philadelphia, (1870). Partly translated. Baldwins' 51-440 1978 $10

HARBEN, WILL   Pole Baker. New York, 1905. Cloth, 1st ed. Hayman 73-186 1978 $7.50

HARBOR of Galveston: Resolution of the Legislature of Texas. Washington, 1874. Jenkins 116-479 1978 $7.50

HARCOURT-SMITH, SIMON   The Last Uptake. London, n. d. 1st ed., 4 to., orig. red cloth, gilt stamped spine, very good-fine, illus. by Rex Whistler, color. Houle 10-365 1978 $35

HARD, WALTER   The Connecticut. New York, (1947). Illus. by Douglas W. Gorsline, 1st ed., signed, d.w. frayed. Biblo 251-103 1978 $17.50

HARD, WALTER   A Mountain Township. 1933. First ed., with letter signed. Austin 82-412 1978 $20

HARDAKER, A.   A Brief History of Pawnbroking. 1892. Cr. 8vo. George's 635-331 1978 £5

HARDEE, W. J.   Rifle and Infantry Tactics. Raleigh, 1862. Orig. bds., Bell Wiley's copy. Broadfoot 46-456 1978 $100

HARDEE, W. J.   Rifle and Light Infantry Tactics. Philadelphia, Pa., 1860 & 1855. Fldg. maps, 1/2 lea., binding worn. Bell Wiley's copy. Broadfoot 46-127 1978 $50

HARDENBRASS AND HAVERILL; or, The Secret of the Castle, A Novel. 1817. 1st. ed., 4 vols., half titles, orig. half calf, v.g. Jarndyce 16-256 1978 £110

HARDIE, MARTIN   The British School of Etching. Illus., & signed by author, good. Sexton 7-24 1978 £8

HARDIE, MARTIN   John Pettie, R.A., R.S.A. 1908. Roy. 8vo., coloures plts., dec. cloth, gilt top. Quaritch 983-231 1978 $35

HARDIE, MARTIN   War Posters Issued by Belligerent and Neutral Nations 1914-1919. London, 1920. 1st ed., 4 to., orig. green cloth with pictorial design stamped in black & red, uncut, illus., color, bookplate, very good. Houle 10-155 1978 $125

HARDIMAN, J.   Irish Minstrelsy of Bardic Remains of Ireland. (1831). Octavo bound in cloth, reprint. Hyland 128-950 1978 £12.50

HARDIN, G. A.   History of Herkimer County, New York. Syracuse, 1893. Thick 4to., rebound, illus., fine. MacManus 239-1087 1978 $65

HARDIN, JOHN J.   On The Annexation of Texas. Washington, 1845. Wr. Jenkins 116-567 1978 $22.50

HARDIN, JOHN WESLEY   The Life of John Wesley Hardin, From the Original Manuscript, as Written by Himself. Sequin, 1896. 1st ed., original printed wr. bound in later cloth, illus., second issue. Jenkins 116-568 1978 $30

HARDING, EMILY J.   Fairy Tales of the Slav Peasants and Herdsmen. London, 1896. 1st ed., slight spine edge split and rubbing, very good. Victoria 34-378 1978 $30

HARDING, J. D.   Elementary Art; or the Use of the Lead Pencil Advocated and Explained. 1834. Folio, plts., some foxed, orig. cloth. Quaritch 983-196 1978 $250

HARDING, J. D.   Lessons on Trees. London, n.d. (c.1900). Illus. Biblo BL781-745 1978 $8.50

HARDMAN, FRANCIS   Border Life; or, Tales of the South-Western Border. Philadelphia, n.d. (c. 1880). Cloth. Hayman 72-280 1978 $12.50

HARDWICKE, COUNTESS   The Court of Oberon, or The Three Wishes. 1831. 1st ed., 4to, coloured frontis, orig. blue printed bds., loose, bds. detached. Jarndyce 16-715 1978 £10.50

HARDY, C.   Forest Life in Acadie: Sketches of Sport and Natural History in the Lower Provinces of the Canadian Dominion. 1869. 8vo, orig. cloth, coloured frontis, vignette on title, woodcut illus., cover faded. Edwards 1012-426 1978 £40

HARDY, R. W. H.   Travels in the Interior of Mexico, 1825-1828. 1829. Folding map, few repairs, plts., vignettes, contemp. calf, 8vo. Edwards 1012-690 1978 £95

HARDY, THOMAS   A Changed Man. The Waiting Supper and Other Tales... London, 1913. Frontis., orig. cloth, d.j., chipped at extremities, 1st ed., rear cover somewhat damp stained, else very good, scarce in d.j. MacManus 238-266 1978 $75

HARDY, THOMAS   A Changed Man, The Waiting Supper, and other tales. 1913. T.e.g., very good, covers little faded, first English ed. Bell Book 16-986 1978 $18.50

HARDY, THOMAS   A Desperate Remedy. Dorchester, 1922. 4to., illus., fine, wraps, first English ed. Bell Book 17-440 1978 £10

HARDY, THOMAS   The Dynasts. A Drama of the Napoleanic Wars. London, 1903-1906-1908. 3 vols., 8vo., orig. green cloth, 1st ed., vol. I rare 1st issue, covers a little faded, otherwise nice, cloth fold. boxes. MacManus 238-265 1978 $450

HARDY, THOMAS   The Dynasts. London, 1927. Large 8vo, 3 vols., decor. boards, vellum spine, pr. at Chiswick Press, orig. d.w.'s slightly chipped, uncut, unopened, near Mint, limited to 525 large signed paper copies, 1st ed., collector's cond. Desmarais 1-204 1978 $200

HARDY, THOMAS   The Famous Tragedy of the Queen of Cornwall. London, 1923. Orig. cloth, d.j., 1st ed., fine copy, half-mor. case. MacManus 238-268 1978 $75

HARDY, THOMAS   A Group of Noble Dames. New York, 1891. 1st Amer. ed., orig. cloth, good. Greene 78-54 1978 $25

HARDY, THOMAS   A Group of Noble Dames. New York, 1891. 8vo, green stamped cloth, near Mint, 1st ed., collector's cond. Desmarais 1-205 1978 $30

HARDY, THOMAS   Human Shows, Far Phantasies, Songs and Trifles. 1925. First ed., cr. 8vo., covers a little dull. George's 635-1317 1978 £10.50

HARDY, THOMAS   Human Shows Far Phantasies, Songs and Trifles. London, 1925. 8vo, green cloth, uncut, unopened, bookplates, front hinge started, near Mint, d.w., board slipcase, 1st ed., collector's cond. Desmarais 1-206 1978 $30

HARDY, THOMAS   Jude the Obscure. 1896. Good, covers somewhat worn, first English ed. Bell Book 16-416 1978 £16.50

HARDY, THOMAS   Late Lyrics and Earlier. 1922. First ed., orig. cloth, 8vo. Howes 194-912 1978 £10

HARDY, THOMAS   Moments of Vision and Miscellaneous Verses. London, 1917. 8vo, green cloth, uncut, Fine in board slipcase, 1st ed., collector's cond. Desmarais 1-207 1978 $30

HARDY, THOMAS   Old Mrs. Chundle, a Short Story. New York, 1929. Thin, tall 8vo, boards, cloth back, uncut, unopened, Fine, no. 15 of limited ed. of 742 numbered, 1st ed., collector's cond. Desmarais 1-208 1978 $30

HARDY, THOMAS   The Oxen. Hove, 1915. Orig. printed wrs., 1st separate ed., fine, half-mor. slipcase. MacManus 238-267 1978 $50

HARDY, THOMAS   Selected Poems. 1921. No. 774 of 1025 copies on handmade paper, full vellum, t.e.g., nice, first English ed. Bell Book 17-438 1978 £37.50

HARDY, THOMAS   Selected Poems. 1921. Portrait, orig. vellum, gilt top, other edges untrimmed, d.w., ltd. to 1025 numbered copies, 8vo. Howes 194-911 1978 £18

HARDY, THOMAS   Tess of the D'Urbervilles. New York, 1892. New ed., 3 vols. in I, illus., brick-colored cloth, good. Greene 78-216 1978 $25

HARDY, THOMAS   The Three Wayfarers; a play. Dorchester, 1935. First English ed., one of 250 numbered copies, wrappers, very nice. Rota 211-165 1978 £10

HARDY, THOMAS   The Trumpet Major. A Tale. London, 1880. 3 vols., orig. cloth, 1st ed., secondary bind., lib. labels, worn, half mor. slipcase. MacManus 238-263 1978 $185

HARDY, THOMAS   Two on a Tower. A Romance. London, 1882. 3 vols., orig. cloth, 1st ed., ex-lib. set, labels removed. MacManus 238-264 1978 $250

HARDY, THOMAS   Winter Words, in various moods and metres. New York, 1928. First U.S. ed., no. 461 of 500 copies, roy. 8vo., quarter imitation vellum, very good, defective slipcase. Bell Book 17-439 1978 £27.50

HARDY, THOMAS   Works. 1919-20. 37 vols., 8vo., Mellstock ed., portr., cloth, some browned, good bright set, 500 copies, 1st vol. signed by author. Quaritch 979-368 1978 $2,250

HARDY, W. J.   Bookplates. London, 1893. Orig. vellum-backed bds., illus. 1 of 150 lg. paper copies, covers a bit soiled. MacManus 238-871 1978 $50

HARDY, W. J.   Book-Plates. London, 1893. Plts., demy 8vo., orig. buckram, faded. Forster 130-106 1978 £10

HARDY, W. J.   Bookplates. London, 1897. 8vo., orig. cloth, 2nd ed., illus. MacManus 238-870 1978 $20

HARDY, W. J.   The Handwriting of the Kings and Queens of England. 1893. Photogravures and facsimiles, super imp. 8vo., covers stained. George's 635-671 1978 £8.50

HARE, A. J. C.   Memorials of a Quiet Life. 1877. Frontispieces, 3 vols., cr. 8vo., half calf, rubbed. George's 635-1245 1978 £8.50

HARE, A. J. C.   The Story of Two Noble Lives, being Memorials of Charlotte, Countess Canning, and Louisa Marchioness of Waterford. 1893. Lg. paper, plts. on India paper, illus., 3 vols., roy. 8vo., covers soiled. George's 635-1246 1978 £10.50

HARFORD, JOHN S.   The Life of Michael Angelo Buonarroti. 1858. 2nd. ed., plts., 2 folding, 2 vols., 8vo, orig. cloth, nice copy. Fenning 32-144 1978 £14.50

HARINGTON, JOHN   Nugae Antiquae.... 1769-79. 3 vols., 12mo., contemp. tree calf, one label missing, sm. hole in one leaf affecting 5 words only. Howes 194-307 1978 £30

HARINGTON, JOHN   Nugae Antiquae. 1804. 2 vols., lg. 8vo., contemp. half calf, good. P. M. Hill 142-135 1978 £55

HARIOT, THOMAS   A Brief and True Report of the New Found Land of Virginia. Ann Arbor, 1931. Facs. reproduction of rare 1588 ed., ltd. to 315 copies, boxed, stiff vellum wrs. MacManus 239-1865 1978 $25

HARK, ANN   Hex Marks the Spot. Philadelphia, (1938). 1st. ed., d.j. signed & inscribed by author, fine. Baldwins' 51-441 1978 $7.50

HARKNESS, JOHN GRAHAM   Stormont, Dundas and Glengarry. 1946. Orig. binding. Wolfe 39-225 1978 $65

HARLAN, GEORGE O.   Illustrated Horse-Owner's Guide; Being a Synopsis of the Diseases of Horses and Cattle... Toledo, 1879. Cloth, faded and worn. Hayman 72-281 1978 $7.50

HARLAN, JAMES   Speech of Hon. Jas. Harlan, of Iowa, in the Senate, January 11, 1861. (Washington, n.d.). Unbound as issued. Hayman 73-247 1973 $7.50

HARLAN, R.   The Affiliation of the Physical Sciences: Being the Introduction to Medical and Physical Researches. Philadelphia, 1835. Paper wrappers. Rittenhouse 49-330 1976 $17.50

HARLAND, MARION PSEUD.
Please turn to
TERHUNE, MARY VIRGINIA (HAWES)

HARLEIAN Miscellany; A Collection of Scarce, Curious and Entertaining Tracts, as Well in Manuscript as in Print. London, 1808-13. Printed on thick paper, 10 vols., 4to, polished tree calf, rebacked, leather label. Traylen 88-266 1978 £180

THE HARLEIAN Miscellany. London, 1809-1810. Orig. boards lacking spines, uncut, all half-titles present. Greene 78-217 1978 $175

HARLEY, GEORGE DAVIES   Poems, 1796. n.d. (1796?). 1st. ed., 12mo, probably lacking half-title, contemp. calf, rebacked. Hannas 54-327 1978 £60

HARLEY, LEWIS R.   The Life of Charles Thomson.... Philadelphia, (1900). 1st ed., ltd. to 500 copies, uncut, t.e.g., illus., orig. binding, 8vo. Americanist 101-63 1978 $35

HARLEY, TIMOTHY   Lunar Science: Ancient and Modern. London, 1886. 8vo., orig. cloth, 1st ed. Morrill 241-182 1978 $10

HARLOW, ALVIN F.   Old Bowery Days. New York, 1931. 1st ed. MacManus 239-355 1978 $27.50

HARLOW, SAMUEL   The Botanist & Physician. Kingston, 1831. Bds., rubbed, sm. hole in one leaf. Hayman 73-423 1978 $35

HARMAN, EDWARD GEORGE   Edmund Spenser and the Impresonations of Francis Bacon. 1914. Cloth, A.L.S. from author tipped in. Eaton 45-233 1978 £7

HARMAN, H. M.   The Story of the Church of St. George the Martyr of Toronto, Canada. Toronto, 1945. Illus. Hood 117-353 1978 $10

HARMER, S. F.   Cambridge Natural History. Cambridge, 1909. Profusely illus., 10 vols., roy. 8vo., fine set in half mor., cloth sides, contents lettered, gilt tops. Traylen 88-549 1978 £90

HARMON, DANIEL WILLIAMS   A Journal of Voyages and Travels in the Interior of North America.... Andover, 1820. Port., map, full comtemp. calf, 1st ed. Ginsberg 14-383 1978 $450

HARMON, DANIEL WILLIAMS   A Journal of Voyages and Travels in the Interior of North America. Toronto, 1911. Hood's 115-599 1978 $15

THE HARMONIST, a Select Collection of Ancient and Modern Glees, Catches.... (1788). 8 vols. in 2, half roan rubbed, 8vo. George's 635-1406 1978 £20

HARNISCH, A.   Gedichte fur Kinder mit 52 Abbildungen von A. Harnisch, und einum Anhange 112 ausgewahlte Kinderlieder enthaltend. Berlin, c.1835. 12mo, Hand-colored plates, 1835 inscription, 3/4 leather, marbled boards, very good. Victoria 34-374 1978 $350

HAROUTUNIAN, JOSEPH   Piety Versus Moralism. 1932. Ex-lib., some wear to backstrip. Austin 82-413 1978 $27.50

HARPER, CHARLES GEORGE   Half-Hours with the Highwaymen. 1908. Illus. by P. Hardy, the author and from old prints, 2 vols., orig. cloth rubbed, spine Vol. 2 discoloured, 8vo. George's 635-1282 1978 £18

HARPER, FRANK C.   Pittsburgh of Today. New York, 1931. 4 vols., 3/4 leather. Hayman 71-626 1978 $50

HARPER, GEORGE MC LEAN   William Wordsworth: His Life, Works and Influences. 1916. Plts., map, 2 vols., orig. cloth, 8vo. Howes 194-1348 1978 £8.50

HARPER, HENRY HOWARD   The Story of a Nephrectomy. Norwood, 1927. Portr., sm. 8vo., boxed. Morrill 239-113 1978 $12.50

HARPER, J. M.   The Battle of the Plains: The Greatest Event In Canadian History. Toronto, 1909. Illus. Hood's 115-112 1978 $20

HARRADEN, BEATRICE   Hilda Stratford. New York, 1897. 1st ed., illus., cloth, t.e.g., good. Greene 78-219 1978 $40

HARRADEN, BEATRICE   Ships that Pass in the Night. London, 1893. Orig. cloth, 1st ed., covers rubbed, but good. MacManus 238-270 1978 $45

HARRELL, JOHN M.   The Brooks and Baxter War, A History of the Reconstruction Period in Arkansa. St. Louis, 1893. Cover stained & worn, Bell Wiley's copy. Broadfoot's 44-432 1978 $50

HARRINGTON, CHARLES E.   Summering in Colorado. Denver, 1874. Cloth. Hayman 72-284 1978 $20

HARRINGTON, GEORGE F.   Inside: A Chronicle of Secession. New York, 1866. Illus. by Thomas Nast, binding faded, partly worn, 8vo., 1st ed. Morrill 239-293 1978 $10

HARRINGTON, JAMES   The Oceana of James Harrington, and His Other Works... London and Westminster, 1700. 1st. collected ed., folio, frontispiece, portrait, folding plt., contemp. calf, gilt spine, one joint repaired, other cracking. Hannas 54-155 1978 £85

HARRINGTON, JAMES   The Oceana and Other Works. 1747. 3rd. ed., folio, fine engraved frontis, portrait, orig. calf, brown label, fine copy. Jarndyce 16-105 1978 £60

HARRINGTON, JESSIE   Silversmiths of Delaware 1700-1850 and Old Church Silver in Delaware. N.P., 1939. Illus., orig. cloth, ltd. to 300 no. copies, fine. MacManus 239-673 1978 $75

HARRINGTON, JESSIE   Silversmiths of Delaware, 1700-1850. Camden. Illus., & marks, printed 1st. ed., 300 numbered copies, no. 123. Baldwins' 51-224 1978 $150

HARRINGTON, JOSEPH   Sermons...With a Memoir. Boston, 1854. Orig. cloth, 1st ed. Ginsberg 16-830 1978 $20.00

HARRINGTON, JOSEPH   Sermons...With a Memoir. Boston, 1854. Illus., original cloth, 1st ed. Ginsberg 14-125 1978 $20

HARRINGTON, KARL P.   Songs of the PsiUpsilon Fraternity. New York, 1908. Sm. 4to. Biblo BL781-34 1978 $9

HARRINGTON, MICHEAL   The Sea is Our Doorway. Toronto, 1947. Card cover. Hood 117-806 1978 $7.50

HARRIS, ALEX   A Biographical History of Lancaster County... Lancaster, 1872. Very scarce, rebound. MacManus 239-1531 1978 $50

HARRIS, ALEXANDER   A Review of the Political Conflict in America, from the Commencement of the Anti-slavery Agitation to the Close of Southern Reconstruction... New York, 1876. Cloth. Hayman 72-283 1978 $20

HARRIS, C. FISKE   Catalogue of American Poetry Comprising Duplicates from the Collection of C. Fiske Harris. Providence, 1883. 12mo., newly bound in cloth. Battery Park 1-326 1978 $50

HARRIS, C. T.   A Review of Four Lectures on Homoeopathy. Detroit, 1869. 8vo., orig. wrs., 1st ed. Morrill 239-115 1978 $17.50

HARRIS, CHAPIN A.   A Dictionary of Dental Science, Biography, Bibliography, and Medical Terminology. Philadelphia, 1849. Lg. 8vo., contemp. calf, occas. heavy dampstains, 1st ed. Morrill 239-114 1978 $15

HARRIS, DEAN   Pioneers of the Cross in Canada. St. Louis, 1912. Orig. cl. Ginsberg 16-841 1978 $15.00

HARRIS, FRANCIS   Lawson's History of North Carolina. Richmond, 1937. Map, plts. Broadfoot 50-121 1978 $35

HARRIS, FRANK   Frank Harris on Bernard Shaw. New York, 1931. Port. frontis., illus., 8vo, cloth, 1st Amer. ed., postcript by Shaw, fine. Duschnes 220-282 1978 $12.50

HARRIS, FRANK   Great Days. New York, (1920). Light blue cloth, later ed., very good in chipped dust jacket. Bradley 49-138 1978 $30

HARRIS, FRANK   Latest Contemporary Portraits. New York, (1927). Margins spotted, orig. cloth, signed pres. inscription & quotation from "Religio Medici". Eaton 45-234 1978 £15

HARRIS, FRANK   New Preface to "The Life and Confessions of Oscar Wilde." Fortune Press, 1927. Qtr. buckram, very good, first English ed. Bell Book 16-923 1978 £6.50

HARRIS, FRANK   Oscar Wilde: His Life and Confessions. New York, 1918. First ed., portraits, 2 vols., orig. green cloth, 8vo. Howes 194-1335 1978 £20

HARRIS, FRANK   Oscar Wilde, His Life and Confessions. New York, (1930). Biblo 247-869 1978 $9.50

HARRIS, H.   Essays and Photographs. London, 1901. Minor foxing, 8vo, orig. cloth. Book Chest 17-178 1978 $40

HARRIS, HENRY E.   Some Birds of the Canary Islands and South Africa. London, 1901. Orig. cloth, 8vo, frontispiece, 55 plts. K Books 239-205 1978 £18

HARRIS, I.　　　　Diet and High Blood Pressure.　London,
Hogarth Press, 1937. 1st ed., d.j., very good.　Houle 10-159　1978　$30

HARRIS, JAMES　　　　Hermes:....　London, 1751. 1st ed., octavo,
full contemp. calf.　Bennett 20-95　1978　$275

HARRIS, JAMES　　　　Hermes.　1771. Third ed., frontispiece, contemp. calf, good, 8vo.　Howes 194-308　1978　£25

HARRIS, JOEL CHANDLER　　　Aaron in the Wildwoods.　Boston & New York,
1897. 1st ed., 1st printing, illus., very good.　Victoria 34-375　1978　$22.50

HARRIS, JOEL CHANDLER　　　The Chronicles of Aunt Minervy Ann.　New York,
1899. 1st ed., issue "B", illus. by A. B. Frost, cover edges and spine darkened,
inner hinges cracked, text very good.　Victoria 34-376　1978　$7.50

HARRIS, JOEL CHANDLER　　　Daddy Jake the Runaway and Short Stories Told
After Dark.　New York, (1889). 4to., illus., orig. pict. bds., 1st ed., scarce,
covers worn, extremities chipped.　MacManus 238-492　1978　$100

HARRIS, JOEL CHANDLER　　　Gabriel Tolliver.　New York, 1902. 8vo.,
fr. hinge slightly cracked, 1st ed.　Morrill 239-414　1978　$15

HARRIS, JOEL CHANDLER　　　Nights with Uncle Remus Myths and Legends of the
Old Plantation.　Boston, 1883. Orig. pict. cloth, 1st ed., very good.　Mac-
Manus 238-491　1978　$45

HARRIS, JOEL CHANDLER　　　On the Plantation. A Story of a Georgia Boy's
Adventures During the War.　New York, 1892. Illus., frontis. port., orig. pict.
cloth, 1st ed., bookplt., fine.　MacManus 238-493　1978　$60

HARRIS, JOEL CHANDLER　　　On the Wing of Occasions.　New York, 1900.
Illus., orig. cloth, 1st ed., bind. D, green cloth, good.　MacManus 238-495
1978　$45

HARRIS, JOEL CHANDLER　　　On the Wing of Occasions.　New York, 1900.
Illus., 8vo., 1st ed.　Morrill 239-413　1978　$15

HARRIS, JOEL CHANDLER　　　On the Wing of Occasions.　NY, 1900 •
Illus, slightly worn, Bell Wiley's Copy.　Broadfoot's 44-186　1978　$10.00

HARRIS, JOEL CHANDLER　　　Told by Uncle Remus. New Stories of the Old
Plantation.　New York, 1905. Spine lightly sunfaded, near fine.　Desmarais B-
302　1978　$45

HARRIS, JOEL CHANDLER　　　Uncle Remus and His Friends. Old Plantation
Stories, Songs and Ballads with Sketches of Negro Character.　Boston, 1892. 1st
ed., illus. by A. B. Frost, orig. cloth, very good, bookplt.　MacManus 238-494
1978　$40

HARRIS, JOEL CHANDLER　　　Uncle Remus and His Friends.　Boston, 1892.
8vo, green stamped cloth, top and bottom of spine worn, ownership inscription, very
Good, 1st ed., collector's cond.　Desmarais 1-210　1978　$40

HARRIS, JOEL CHANDLER　　　Uncle Remus: His Songs and His Sayings.　New
York, 1881. 12mo., 1st issue, brown cloth with butterfly designed endpapers, top & bottom of spine worn, front bd. shows sm. tear in cloth, gilt & black
stamping, interior very good, good copy, scarce.　Current 24-17　1978　$185

HARRIS, JOEL CHANDLER　　　Uncle Remus His Songs and His Sayings.　New
York, 1881. 8vo, 1st ed., 1st issue, green stamped cloth, spot on spine, very
Fine, collector's cond.　Desmarais 1-211　1978　$150

HARRIS, JOHN　　　Lexicon Technicum.　London, 1704-10. 2
vols., folio, frontis. portr. by Robert White, copperplts., tables, woodcut text
illus., contemp. panelled calf, little rubbed, but fine set, 1st ed.　Norman 5-
138　1978　$1,650

HARRIS, JOHN　　　Lexicon Technicum.　London, 1704-10. First
ed., 2 vols., red and black titles, plts., woodcuts, folio, old style calf.　K Books
244-149　1978　£400

HARRIS, JULIA COLLIER　　　The Life and Letters of Joel Chandler Harris.
Boston, 1918. Bell Wiley's copy.　Broadfoot 46-521　1978　$15

HARRIS, LARRY　　　Pancho Villa and the Columbus Raid.　El Paso,
1949. Stiff wr.　Jenkins 116-583　1978　$17.50

HARRIS, MARK　　　Trumpet to the World.　1946. First ed., covers
soiled else good.　Austin 82-1172　1978　$27.50

HARRIS, PAUL P.　　　This Rotarian Age.　Chicago, 1935. 8vo.,
orig. cloth, 1st ed., autographed.　Morrill 241-508　1978　$15

HARRIS, SEYMOUR E.　　　Economic Planning.　1949. 1st ed.　Austin 80-
675　1978　$17.50

HARRIS, SEYMOUR E.　　　The National Debt and the New Economics.
1947. 1st ed.　Austin 80-676　1978　$20

HARRIS, SEYMOUR E.　　　The New Economics.　1948. Ex-lib.　Austin 80-
677　1978　$7.50

HARRIS, THADDEUS MASON　Biographical Memorials of James Oglethorpe,
Founder of the Colony of Georgia.　Boston, 1841. Illus., map, 1st ed., orig.
cloth.　MacManus 239-1808　1978　$35

HARRIS, THADDEUS MASON　　The Natural History of the Bible....　Boston,
1793. Foxing, full leather, 8vo, orig. cloth.　Book Chest 17-179　1978　$125

HARRIS, THOMAS LAKE　　　Conversation in Heaven.　Fountaingrove, 1894.
Orig. cloth, stained, first ed.　Ginsberg 14-126　1978　$75

HARRIS, THOMAS LAKE　　　The Great Republic: A Poem of the Sun.　New
York, 1867. Leather, 1st ed.　Ginsberg 14-127　1978　$100

HARRIS, THOMAS LAKE　　　A Lyric of the Golden Age.　New York, 1856.
Original cloth, 1st ed.　Ginsberg 14-128　1978　$125

HARRIS, THOMAS MEALEY　　　Assassination of Lincoln...　Boston, (1892).
1st ed., orig. cloth, illus.　MacManus 239-881　1978　$45

HARRIS, WILLIAM C.　　　Prison-Life in the Tobacco Warehouse at Richmond.　Philadelphia, 1862. New cloth, library stamp on title page, Bell Wiley's
copy.　Broadfoot 46-364　1978　$16

HARRIS, WILLIAM CORNWALLIS　The Highlands of Ethiopia.　1844. Folding
map, repaired, coloured portrait, tinted litho. plts., 3 vols., half green mor.,
8vo., repaired.　Edwards 1012-284　1978　£150

HARRIS, WILLIAM CORNWALLIS　Portraits of the Game and Wild Animals of
Southern Africa....　1840. 1st ed., 2nd issue, coloured litho. plts. by F.
Howard, lg. folio, contemp. half red mor., spine tooled in compartments in centre,
gilt, g.e., some foxing.　Edwards 1012-299　1978　£1700

HARRIS, WILLIAM CORNWALLIS　The Wild Sports of Southern Africa....
1839. 1st ed., folding map, plts., 3 tinted lithos., 8vo., orig. cloth, gilt, uncut,
binding little worn but sound, scarce.　Fenning 32-145　1978　£85

HARRIS, WILLIAM CORNWALLIS　The Wild Sports of Southern Africa.　London,
1852. 5th. ed., coloured vignette, coloured frontispiece, 24 coloured plts., roy.
8vo, modern half calf, in quarter leather slip-case, folding map.　K Books 239-
207　1978　£175

HARRIS, WILLIAM CORNWALLIS　The Wild Sports of Southern Africa.　London,
1852. Orig. cloth rebacked, coloured plts., folding map, lacking frontispiece,
slight foxing, age-marking.　K Books 239-207A　1978　£125

HARRISON, BENJAMIN　　　Message From...Transmitting Certain Reports
Upon the Condition of the Navajo Country.　Washington, 1893. Folding maps,
cloth with leather label, 1st ed.　Ginsberg 14-702　1978　$75

HARRISON, BENJAMIN　　　This Country of Ours.　New York, 1897. 1st ed.,
orig. cloth, fine.　MacManus 239-195　1978　$10

HARRISON, BENJAMIN　　　Turtle Mountain Indians.　Washington, 1893.
Disbound.　Ginsberg 14-1095　1978　$35

HARRISON, MRS. BURTON
Please turn to
HARRISON, CONSTANCE (CARY), MRS. BURTON HARRISON

HARRISON, CONSTANCE (CARY), "MRS. BURTON HARRISON"　　Recollections
Grave and Gay.　New York, 1912. Cloth, nice copy.　Hayman 73-249　1978
$10

HARRISON, E. S.　　　Central California, Santa Clara Valley:....
San Jose, [1887]. Illus., folding map, original printed wr.　Ginsberg 14-129
1978　$100

HARRISON, J. C.　　　Bird Portraits.　London, (1949). 4to, soiled
cloth.　Book Chest 17-180　1978　$18.50

HARRISON, J. HOUSTON　　　Settlers by the Long Grey Trail.　Dayton, 1935.
1st ed., thick 4to., illus., orig. cloth, fine.　MacManus 239-925　1978　$50

HARRISON, JOHN   The Laird of Restalrig's Daughter: A Legend of the Siege of Leith-Edinburgh. Edinburgh, 1857. 1st ed., inscribed by author, orig. cloth, good. Greene 78-220 1978 $65

HARRISON, JOSEPH T.   The Story of the Dining Fork. Cincinnati, 1927. Cloth, prtd. in ltd. ed., fine copy. Hayman 73-539 1978 $20

HARRISON, MARY K.   Mrs. Lorimer. A Study in Black & White. London. 1st ed., orig. cloth, very fine, signed letter. Greene 78-258 1978 $85

HARRISON, MATTHEW   The Rise, Progress, and Present Structure of the English Language. London, 1848. 8vo., ex-lib., 1st ed. Morrill 239-415 1978 $7.50

HARRISON, OLIVER   Sinclair Lewis. New York, 1925. 500 copies printed for pres. to American Booksellers, portrait, photos, orig. decorative bds., label, nice. Limestone 9-178 1978 $35

HARRISON, W. RANDLE   Suggestions for Illuminating. London, c. 1880. 2nd ed., coloured title, plts., 4to., orig. cloth, neatly rebacked. K Books 244-150 1978 £16

HARRISON, WILLIAM POPE   Theophilus Walton; or, the Majesty of Truth... Nashville, 1859. Cloth, faded and worn. Hayman 72-223 1978 $7.50

HARRISON, WILLIAM W.   The Royal Ancestry of George Leib Harrison of Philadelphia. Philadelphia, 1914. Cloth, 3/4 mor., ltd. to 100 copies. MacManus 239-926 1978 $60

HARRISON, WILMOT   Memorable London Houses. 1889. 1st. ed., no. 102 of 250 signed by author, 100 illus., uncut, laid paper, orig. cream cloth, bevelled bds. block in brown & gilt, covers little darkened, o/w v.g. Jarndyce 16-832 1978 £20

HARRISON, Waples and Allied Families. Philadelphia, 1910. 4to., illus., cloth, half mor., ltd. to 100 copies, scarce. MacManus 239-927 1978 $85

HARRISON-AINSWORTH, E. D.   The History and War Records of the Surrey Yeomanry 1797-1928. 1928. Maps, 8vo., orig. cloth, coloured plt., frontis. F. Edwards 1013-572 1978 £20

HARRISSE, HENRY   Decouverte et Evolution Cartographique de Terre-Neuve et Des Pays Circonvoisins, 1497-1501-1769. 4to., printed wrappers, illus., fine paper, uncut, unopened. Wolfe 39-227 1978 $130

HARRISSE, HENRY   Notes Pour Servir a L'Histoire a la Bibliographie et a la Cartographie de la Nouvelle-France.... Paris, 1872. Wolfe 39-228 1978 $25

HARROLD, E. W.   The Diary of Our Own Pepys:....Record of Canadian Life. Toronto, 1947. Hood 116-267 1978 $20

HARSHA, WILLIAM J.   Ploughed Under, the Story of an Indian Chief... New York, 1881. Cloth, little discolored., lacks flyleaves. Hayman 72-224 1978 $10

HARSHA, WILLIAM J.   A Timid Brave. New York, & London, 1886. Orig. binding, clean, cover little soiled, slightly worn. Hayman 71-230 1978 $7.50

HARSHBERGER, JOHN W.   The Vegetation of the New Jersey Pine-Barrens... Philadelphia, 1916. 1st ed., illus., orig. dec. cloth, very fine, scarce. MacManus 239-1272 1978 $50

HART, BURDETT   Congregationalism:..... St. Paul, 1859. Original printed wr., 1st ed. Ginsberg 14-556 1978 $35

HART, BURDETT   The Opening of the New Northwest. N.P., 1871. Disbound. Ginsberg 14-384 1978 $15

HART, CHARLES HENRY   Browere's Life Masks of Great Americans. 1899. 1st ed., ltd. to 347 copies, illus., nice copy, orig. vellum-backed bds. MacManus 239-674 1978 $37.50

HART, CHARLES HENRY   Memoirs of the Life and Works of Jean Antoine Houdon. Philadelphia, 1911. 1st ed., illus., orig. cloth, ltd. to 250 copies, cloth rubbed, but very good copy. MacManus 239-677 1978 $85

HART, GERALD E.   The Fall of New France, 1755-1760. Montreal, 1888. Ports., 3/4 leather, gilt edged pgs. Hood 116-528 1978 $40

HART, H. G.   The New Annual Army List. 1867. 8vo., full green calf, mor. label. F. Edwards 1013-330 1978 £30

HART, H. G.   The New Annual Army List, and Militia List, for 1869. 1869. 8vo., full green calf, mor. label. F. Edwards 1013-331 1978 £30

HART, HORACE   Bibliotheca Typographica. 1933. Battery Park 1-378 1978 $25

HART, JOHN A.   Pioneer Days in the Southwest from 1850 to 1879. Guthrie, 1909. Illus., original pictorial cloth, age stained. Ginsberg 14-385 1978 $60

HART, JOSEPH C.   Miriam-Coffin, or the Whale Fisherman. New York, 1835. 2 vols. in 1, 12mo., lib. buckram, 2nd ed., good. Paine 78-64 1978 $57.50

HART, JULIA CATHERINE BECKWITH   Tonnewonte. Watertown, Albany, 1824, 1825. Two vols. in one, contemp. bds., badly worn, detached, foxed, uncut. Wolfe 39-229 1978 $150

HART, SCOTT   Moon Is Waning. N. Y., Derrydale, (1939). 1 of 950 numbered copies, tall 8 vo., pictorial blue buckram, gilt, fine. Houle 10-86 1978 $45

HART, BASIL HENRY LIDDELL
Please turn to
LIDDELL HART, BASIL HENRY

HARTCLIFFE, JOHN   A Discourse Against Purgatory. 1685. 1st. ed., 4to, wrapper, fine. Fenning 32-146 1978 £8.50

HARTE, MRS. BAGOT   Bianco. 1893. 1st. ed., 2 vols., half titles, orig. dark green cloth, gilt spine, bright fine copy. Jarndyce 16-717 1978 £48

HARTE, BRET   Clarence. Boston, 1895. Ownership inscription, fr. hinge started, fine. Desmarais B-303 1978 $9

HARTE, BRET   Gabriel Conroy. Hartford, 1876. Illus., 8vo., 1st ed., 2nd binding. Morrill 239-416 1978 $10

HARTE, BRET   The Luck of Roaring Camp, and Other Sketches. Boston, Grolier Club, 1870. Maroon cloth, good solid copy. Dawson's 447-237 1978 $175

HARTE, BRET   The Luck of Roraring Camp, and Other Sketches. Boston, 1870. 12mo., orig. cloth, 1st ed., covers somewhat torn. MacManus 238-496 1978 $100

HARTE, BRET   Mr. Jack Hamlins Mediation. Boston, 1899. Ownership inscription, very fine. Desmarais B-304 1978 $12.50

HARTE, BRET   Plain Language from Truthful James. The Heathen Chinee. Chicago, 1870. Illus. by Joseph Hull, 1st ed., 1st print., fine, cloth case. MacManus 238-497 1978 $85

HARTE, BRET   Poems. Boston, 1871. Maroon cloth, bkplt., ink signature. Dawson's 447-238 1978 $25

HARTE, BRET   Stories In Light and Shadow. Boston & New York, 1898. 1st ed., shelfworn, interior clean, very good or better. Limestone 9-141 1978 $15

HARTE, BRET   A Waif of the Plains. London, 1890. 1st ed., illus., pictorial cover, very good or better. Limestone 9-142 1978 $45

HARTE, WALTER   An Essay on Satire, Particularly on the Dunciad. London, 1730. 8vo, disbound, 1st ed., small library blindstamp of the t.p., half-title spotted. Ximenes 47-128 1978 $75

HARTER, THOMAS H.   Boonastiel, a Volume of Legend, Story and Song in "Pennsylvania Dutch." N.P., 1904. 1st ed., illus., orig. bind. Americanist 102-56 1978 $22.50

HARTFORD in the Olden Time: Its First Thirty Years. Hartford, 1853. Map, plts., 8vo., 1st ed., pres. copy, orig. cloth. Morrill 241-89 1978 $20

HARTING, G.   The Tropical World. 1863. Woodcuts, 8vo. George's 635-997 1978 £8.50

HARTING, J.   British Animals Extinct Within Historic Times With Some Account of British Wild White Cattle. London, 1880. Illus. by Wolf & others, 8vo., orig. cloth. Book Chest 17-181 1978 $25

HARTLAUB, G. F.　　Gustave Dore. Leipzig, n.d. Lg. 8vo., half calf, illus. Van der Peet H-64-44 1978 Dfl 65

HARTLEY, D.　　Life and Work of the People of England. 1931. Illus., 2 vols., roy. 8vo., cover a little faded and worn. George's 635-672 1978 £6.50

HARTLEY, DAVID　　Speech & Motions Made in House of Commons, Monday 27 March 1775. (London), 1775. 2nd ed. Nestler Rare 78-166 1978 $125

HARTLEY, JOHN　　Geography for Youth, Adapted to the Different Classes of Learners. 1823. 12mo, contemp. calf, little worn but sound and nice clean copy. Fenning 32-147 1978 £8

HARTLEY, L. P.　　The Boat. 1949. Very good, first English ed. Bell Book 17-443 1978 £8.50

HARTLEY, L. P.　　Night Fears and other stories. 1924. Some foxing, nice, slip autographed by the author tipped in, first English ed. Bell Book 16-421 1978 £35

HARTLEY, L. P.　　The Shrimp and the Anemone. 1944. Very good, first English ed. Bell Book 17-444 1978 £8.50

HARTLEY, P. H. S.　　Johannes de Mirfield of St. Bartholomew's, Smithfield, his life and works. Cambridge, 1936. Plts., 8vo. Upcroft 12-186 1978 £10

HARTLEY, ROBERT M.　　Marriage and Birth Records...by Rev. James Dempster, 1778-1803. 1930-35. Index of names, wrs., very good. Butterfield 21-277d 1978 $10

HARTLIB, SAMUEL　　Samuel Hartlib His Legacy of Husbandry. London, 1655. 3rd and best ed., small quarto, old calf, rebacked, preserving original leather label, contemp. signature of Wm. Carter on title, armorial bookplate, pasted down, small rust stain on two leaves. Bennett 20-96 1978 $195

HARTMAN, WILLIAM D.　　Conchologia Cestrica. The Molluscous Animals and Their Shells, of Chester Co., Pa. Philadelphia, 1874. 1st ed., illus., orig. cloth, fine. MacManus 239-1411 1978 $20

HARTMANN, C. H.　　The Cavalier Spirit and Its Influence on the Life and Work of Richard Lovelace(1618-1658). 1925. Illus., octavo, good. Upcroft 10-353 1978 £7

HARTMANN, NICOLAI　　Ethik. Berlin, 1949. 3rd ed., thick 8vo., cloth. Salloch 348-84 1978 $25

HARTMANN, SADAKICHI　　Confucius. Los Angeles, 1923. Blue cloth, stab-bound with ribbons, 1 of 500 copies. Dawson's 447-239 1978 $25

HARTNELL, RICHARD　　Texas and California: Letters of William Kennedy, Nicholas Carter, and Richard Hartnell to the Times, with Sundry French and Other Extracts. London, 1841. Full Calf. Jenkins 116-1583 1978 $475

HARTNEY, HAROLD E.　　What the Citizen Should Know About the Air Forces. 1942. Illus. by Alan Haemer. Austin 80-127 1978 $8.50

HARTRANFT, M. V.　　Grapes of Gladness. Los Angeles, (1939). 1st ed., 8 vo., cloth over patterned bds., d.j., very good. Houle 10-330 1978 $95

HARTSHORNE, A.　　Old English Glasses. An Account of Glass Drinking Vessels in England, from Early Times to the End of the XVIIIth Century. 1897. Folio, coloured and plains plts., new half blue mor. Quaritch 983-106 1978 $200

HARTSHORNE, C. H.　　Ancient Metrical Tales. 1829. 8vo., contemp. half roan. P. M. Hill 142-280 1978 £25

HARTSHORNE, E. Y.　　The German Universities and National Socialism. 1937. Illus., tables, 8vo. George's 635-1296 1978 £5.25

HARTSOEKER, NICOLAAS　　Essay de Dioptrique. Paris, 1694. 4to., fldg. copperplt., text illus., full antique calf, gilt, some foxing, very good copy, 1st ed. Norman 5-139 1978 $650

HARTWIG, G.　　The Polar and Tropical Worlds; a Description of Man and Nature in the Polar and Equatorial Regions of the Globe. Guelph, 1874. 2 vols. in 1, new ed., tooled leather bind. Hood 116-84 1978 $15

HARTZLER, H. B.　　Moody in Chicago or the World's Fair Gospel Campaign... New York, (1894). Cloth, scarce. Hayman 72-330 1978 $10

HARVEY, D. C.　　The French Regime in Prince Edward Island. New Haven, 1926. Hood 116-219 1978 $45

HARVEY, D. C.　　Holland's Description of Cape Breton Island and Other Documents. Halifax, 1935. Card cover. Hood 116-220 1978 $50

HARVEY, F. L.　　Christchurch Cathedral, Fredericton, N. B. Fredericton, n.d. Card cover, illus. Hood 117-251 1978 $7.50

HARVEY, FRED　　First Families of the Southwest. Kansas City, [ca. 1908]. Colored plates, original tied pictorial printed wr. Ginsberg 14-386 1978 $35

HARVEY, FRED　　First Families of the Southwest. Kansas City, Missouri, (c. 1908). Color plts., orig. tied pictorial wr., very good or better. Limestone 9-143 1978 $30

HARVEY, GEORGE　　Henry Clay Frick, the Man. Portland, 1936. Fine in d.w. Biblo 247-50 1978 $27.50

HARVEY, GEORGE　　Henry Clay Frick...The Man. New York, 1936. Biblo 251-39 1978 $22.50

HARVEY, GEORGE　　Ossian's Fingal... 1814. 1st. ed., orig. tree calf, red label, v.g. Jarndyce 16-718 1978 £15

HARVEY, GIDEON　　The Disease of London. 1675. Sm. 8vo., well rebound in full dark polished calf, some age browning of contents, first ed., rare. Howes 194-57 1978 £120

HARVEY, JEAN-CHARLES　　Les Demi-Civilises. Montreal, 1934. Signed by author, card cover. Hood 116-475 1978 $10

HARVEY, JEAN CHARLES　　French Canada at War. Toronto, 1941. Card cover. Hood 116-529 1978 $7.50

HARVEY, OSCAR J.　　A History of Wilkes-Barre, Luzerne Co., Pennsylvania From Its First Beginnings... Wilkes-Barre, 1909-30. Illus., maps, 6 vols., 4tos., fine. MacManus 239-1481 1978 $150

HARVEY, W. H.　　Coin's Financial School. Chicago, (1894). Wrps. Hayman 71-286 1978 $7.50

HARVEY, WILLIAM 1578-1657　　Anatomical Exercises of Dr. William Harvey. 1928. Sm. 8vo., orig. niger mor., gilt top, fine. Quaritch 979-243 1978 $150

HARVEY, WILLIAM 1578-1657　　The Anatomical Exercises of Dr. William Harvey. Nonesuch Press, (1928). 8vo., engraved plt., orig. plum niger mor., 1500 copies printed. Quaritch 977-32 1978 $125

HARVEY, WILLIAM 1578-1657　　Exercitationes de Generatione Animalium Quibus Accedunt Quaedam de Partu. Londini, 1651. Sm. 4to., frontis., fine, mod. dark brown panelled calf, gilt lettered, v.g., first ed. Zeitlin 245-113 1978 $3,500

HARVEY, WILLIAM 1578-1657　　Exercitationes de Generatione Animalium. Amstelodami, 1651. Thick 24mo., contemp. vellum, 1st Elzevir ed. Argosy Special-49 1978 $850

HARVEY, WILLIAM 1578-1657　　Praelectiones Anatomiae Universalis By William Harvey. London, 1886. 4to., 3/4 red calf, gilt lettering on upper cover, gilt on spine, inscr., fine copy. Zeitlin 245-114 1978 $150

HARVEY, WILLIAM 1578-1657　　Works. London, 1847. Chipped top and bottom of spine, worn on corners. Rittenhouse 49-334 1976 $55

HARVEY, WILLIAM 1796?-1873　　London Scenes & London People. 1863. 1st ed., frontis & illus., orig. purple cloth, blocked in blind & gilt, red edges, v.g. Jarndyce 16-826 1978 £30

HARVEY, WILLIAM HENRY　　Phycologia Britannica.... London, 1846-1851. Coloured plts., 3 vols., 1st. ed., roy. 8vo, half green morocco, gilt spines. Traylen 88-582 1978 £320

HARVIE, JOSEPH C.　　The History of the Convict Hulk. 1897. Illus., photos, half roan, repaired, orig. wrapper bound in, 8vo. Edwards 1012-333 1978 £65

HARWELL, RICHARD BARKSDALE　　Confederate Music. Chapel Hill, 1950. Bell Wiley's copy. Broadfoot 46-131 1978 $20

HARWOOD, E. C.　　Cause and Control of the Business Cycle. 1932. Inscr'd by author, 1st ed. Austin 80-679 1978 $12.50

HASBACH, W. A History of the English Agricultural Labourer. 1920. 8vo. George's 635-332 1978 £8.50

HASBROUCK, STEPHEN Altar Fires Relighted. New York, 1912. 1st ed., 8vo., orig. cloth. Morrill 241-184 1978 $12.50

HASEY, JOHN F. Yankee Fighter. Garden City, 1944. Illus. Austin 80-128 1978 $8.50

HASKELL, ALLAN C. Graphic Charts in Business. 1922. Austin 80-681 1978 $12.50

HASKELL, BENJAMIN Essays on the Physiology of the Nervous System with an Appendix on Hydrophobia. Gloucester, 1856. 8vo., orig. wrs., sm. gash on spine, 1st ed. Morrill 239-116 1978 $25

HASKELL, FRANK ARETAS The Battle of Gettysburg. N.P., 1910. Illus., Bell Wiley's copy. Broadfoot's 44-676 1978 $22

HASKINS, C. H. A History of Higher Education in Pennsylvania. Washington, 1902. Illus., wrs., fine. MacManus 239-1482 1978 $22.50

HASKINS, C. H. The Normans in European History. Boston and New York, 1915. 8vo. Upcroft 12-188 1978 £6.50

HASKINS, R. W. New England and the West. Buffalo, 1843. Sewn as issued, 1st ed. Ginsberg 14-387 1978 $75

HASSALL, CHRISTOPHER Devil's Dyke; poems. London, 1936. First ed., orig. binding, spine darkened, very good, author's signed autograph inscription. Rota 211-175 1978 £6

HASSALL, J. Tour of the Grand Junction...With an Historical and Topographical Description of Those Parts of the Counties of Middlesex, Hertfordshire, Buckinghamshire, Bedfordshire, and Northamptonshire... 1819. 8vo., coloured plts., some minor foxing, slight marginal stain on 2 plts., red mor. gilt. Quaritch 983-337 1978 $965

HASSALL, W. O. Catulary of St. Mary Clerkenwell. 1949. Allen 234-1161 1978 $7.50

HASSARD, ALBERT R. Not Guilty and Other Trials. Toronto, 1926. Cover scuffed. Hood 117-395 1978 $20

HASSARD, ALBERT R. Not Guilty and Other Trials. Toronto, 1926. Cover scuffed. Hood's 115-640 1978 $20

HASSE, HEINRICH Schopenhauer. Munich, 1926. Salloch 348-85 1978 $15

HASSELL, J. The Camera, or, Art of Drawing in Water Colors... (1840). 8vo., plts., coloured aquatint, orig. cloth, gilt. Quaritch 983-197 1978 $150

HASSELT, M. VAN Belgique et Hollande. Paris, 1844. 8vo., bds. with calf spine, text in double column, plts. King 7-358 1978 £25

HASSIN, GEORGE B. Histopathology of the Peripheral and Central Nervous Systems. Baltimore, 1933. Rittenhouse 49-326 1976 $15

HASSIN, GEORGE B. Histopathology of the Peripheral and Central Nervous Systems. New York, 1940. Second ed., revised and entirely reset. Rittenhouse 49-327 1976 $20

HASSLER, EDGAR W. Old Westmoreland: A History of Western Pennsylvania During the Revolution. Pittsburgh, 1900. 1st ed., orig. cloth, very scarce. MacManus 239-1483 1978 $50

HASTINGS, LADY FLORA Poems. 1841. Half-calf, gilt spine, little rubbed. Eaton 45-235 1978 £6

HASTINGS, FRANK S. A Ranchman's Recollections: An Autobiography in Which Unfamiliar Facts Bearing upon the Origin of the Cattle Industry in the Southwest... Chicago, 1921. 1st ed., original pictorial cloth, illus., near mint. Jenkins 116-590 1978 $100

HASTINGS, FRANK S. A Ranchman's Recollections. Chicago, 1921. Pic. cloth, illus., frontis., 1st ed., fine copy, slipcase. Dykes 34-26 1978 $85

HASTINGS, FRANK WARREN Wed to a Lunatic. St. Johnsbury, 1895. 12mo., part of covers heavily dampstained, 1st ed. Morrill 239-422 1978 $15

HASTINGS, HUGH Military Minutes of the Council of Appointment of the State of New York. Albany, 1901. 4 vols. MacManus 239-350 1978 $37.50

HASTINGS, R. H. W. S. The Rifle Brigade in the Second World War 1939-1945. Aldershot, 1950. 8vo., plts., frontis., orig. cloth. F. Edwards 1013-546 1978 £12

HASTINGS, THOMAS The Mother's Nursery Songs. New York, 1835. 1st ed., 12mo, front fly-leaf gone, foxed, spine cloth chipped, scarce. Victoria 34-379 1978 $30

HATCH, ALDEN American Express. 1950. Illus., photos. Austin 80-680 1978 $7.50

HATCH, ERNEST F. G. Far Eastern Impressions: Japan-Korea-China. Chicago, 1905. Illus., folding map, cloth. Dawson's 127-302 1978 $12

HATCH, F. H. The Geology of South Africa. London, 1905. 2 coloured folding maps, folding table, 89 illus., g.t., 8vo, orig. cloth. K Books 239-208 1978 £12

HATCHER, EDMUND N. The Last Four Weeks of the War (Civil). Columbus, 1892. Orig. cloth, 8vo., 1st ed., illus. Morrill 241-185 1978 $17.50

HATCHER, EDMUND N. The Last Four Weeks of the War. Columbus, O., 1892. 3/4 leather, rubbed, Bell Wiley's Copy. Broadfoot's 44-189 1978 $18.00

HATCHER, HARLAN A Century of Iron and Men. Indianapolis, (1950). Cloth, 1st ed. Hayman 73-250 1973 $7.50

HATCHER, HARLAN The Great Lakes. London, 1944. Illus., maps. Hood's 115-969 1978 $17.50

HATCHER, HARLAN Lake Erie. Indianapolis and New York, (1945). 1st ed., dust jacket, American Lakes Series. Butterfield 21-241 1978 $7.50

HATCHER, MATTIE AUSTIN The Opening of Texas to Foreign Settlement, 1801-1821. Austin, 1927. Folding maps, plates. Jenkins 116-591 1978 $45

HATFIELD, EDWIN F. History of Elizabeth, New Jersey... New York, 1868. Illus. MacManus 239-1273 1978 $75

HATFIELD, MARCUS P. The Physiology and Hygiene of the House in which We Live. New York, 1887. Text illus., 8vo., 1st ed. Morrill 239-117 1978 $10

HATFIELD, R. G. The American House-Carpenter:.... New York, 1852. 5th ed., illus., blind stamped cloth binding, gold decoration and lettering, very good. Nestler Rare 78-258 1978 $45

HATHAWAY, KATHARINE BUTLER The Journals and Letters of the Little Locksmith. New York, 1946. Illus., 1st ed. Biblo BL781-1027 1978 $7.50

HATTERSLEY, CHARLES W. An English Boy's Life and Adventures in Uganda. London, c. 1910. 8vo, coloured frontis., & title, rather foxed, dec. cloth. K Books 239-210 1978 £6

HATTON, JOSEPH To-Day In America. London, 1881. 1st ed., 2 vols., 8vo, half calf, gilt backs. Deighton 5-40 1978 £30

HATTON, T. Water Colour Without a Master: Upwards of To Hundred Separate Objects in Landscape Shown Under Various Tints and Afterwards Composed Into Pictures... 1857. 4to., hand-coloured plts., orig. cloth, covers stained. Quaritch 983-198 1978 $120

HAUDICQUER DE BLANCOURT, JEAN The Art of Glass. London, 1699. Engr. copperplts., 8vo., contemp. calf panels with mod. polished calf back, 1st ed. in English, scarce. Argosy Special-50 1978 $250

HAUGEN, NILS P. Pioneer and Political Reminscences. 1930. Austin 79-315 1978 $12.50

HAUGLAND, VERN Letter from New Guinea. London, (1944). Cloth, worn, signed presentation from Evan R. Gill. Dawson's 127-262 1978 $10

HAUKSBEE, FRANCIS Pysico-Mechanical Experiments on Various Subjects. London, 1709. Copperplts., 4to., contemp. calf, rebacked, 1st ed., very rare. Offenbacher 30-66 1978 $450

HAULTAIN, A. Two Country Walks in Canada. Toronto, 1903. Illus., signed by author. Hood 117-628 1978 $15

HAULTAIN, T. A History of Riel's Second Rebellion and How it Was Quelled. Toronto, 1885. Parts 1 & 2, wrappers, wrapper on part 2 was loose been re-attached, plates very clean. Hood's 115-1003 1978 $125

HAUPTMANN, AUGUST   Neues Chymisches Kunst Project und sehr Wichtiges Bergk Bedencken. Leipzig, 1658. Sm. 8vo., frontis. & fldg. plts., full antique calf, fine copy, lst ed.? Norman 5-*27 1978 $750

HAUPTMANN, GERHART   Winterballads: eine dramatische dichtung. Berlin, 1917. 1st German ed., bds., very good. Bell Book 16-422 1978 £6.50

HAURISIUS, BENNO CASPAR   Scriptores Historiae Romanae Latini Veteres, qui extant omnes, notis illustrati. Heidelberg, 1743-48. Frontispiece, plts., 3 vols., thk. folio, contemp. vellum. Howes 194-555 1978 £60

HAUSENSTEIN, W.   Der Nackte Mensch in der Kunst Aller Zeiten. Munchen, n.d. (ab. 1910). 8vo., cloth, text illus. Van der Peet H-64-45 1978 Dfl 40

HAUSER, BENJAMIN GAYELORD   Keener Vision Without Glasses. New York, (1932). 8vo., d.w., tear in spine of d.w., lst ed., pres. copy. Morrill 239-118 1978 $7.50

HAUSER, EMIL D. W.   Diseases of the Foot. Philadelphia, 1939. Ex-library, firm, clean. Rittenhouse 49-335 1976 $10

HAUSER, EMIL D. W.   Diseases of the Foot. Philadelphia, 1950. Much used library copy, internally clean. Rittenhouse 49-336 1976 $8

HAUSER, HENRI   Les Debuts de l'age moderne. 1946. 3rd ed., map, binder's buckram. George's 635-676 1978 £6

HAUSER, HENRI   Germany's Commercial Grip on the World.... 1917. lst. ed. in English, 8vo, orig. cloth, nice copy. Fenning 32-148 1978 £8.50

HAUSER, HENRI   La Preponderance Espagnole, 1559-1660. 1940. 2nd ed., binder's cloth. George's 635-673 1978 £5

HAUSER, HENRI   Les sources de l'histoire de France, XVIe siecle, 1494-1610, III, les guerres de religion, 1559-89. 1912. Binder's buckram, 8vo. George's 635-675 1978 £6

HAUSER, HENRI   Les sources de l'histoire de France, XVIe siecle, 1494-1610, III, les guerres de religion, 1559-89. 1912. 8vo. George's 635-674 1978 £5

HAUSLEITTER, LEO   The Machine Unchained. 1933. Austin 80-682 1978 $7.50

HAUY, RENE JUST   Essai d'une Theorie sur la Structure des Crystaux, appliquee a plusieurs genres de substances crystallisees. Paris, 1784. Very rare lst ed., contemp. half-calf, 8vo, plts., very fine. Gilhofer 75-54 1978 SFr 4,900

HAUY, RENE JUST   Exposition Raisonee de la Theorie de l'Electricite et du Magnetisme, d'Apres les Principes de M. Aepinus. Paris, 1787. 8vo., plts., cont. half calf, rubbed, hinges repaired, inscription., first ed. Norman 5-140 1978 $275

HAUY, VALENTIN   Essai sur L'Education des Aveugles. Paris, 1786. 4to., contemp. mottled calf gilt spine, joints repaired, a little worn, first ed. Quaritch 977-33 1978 $700

HAUY, VALENTIN   Essai sur l'Education des Aveugles, ou Expose de Differens Moyens, Verifies par l'Experience, Pour les Mettre en Etat de Lire, a l'Aide du Tact... Paris, 1786. 4to., contemp. mottled calf, rubbed, back gilt, lst ed., very good copy. Offenbacher 30-118 1978 $600

HAVELL, E. B.   A Handbook of Indian Art. London, 1920. 8vo, plts. Traylen 88-382 1978 £10

HAVELL, E. B.   Indian Sculpture and Painting Illustrated by Typical Masterpieces... (1928). Roy. 8vo., coloured frontis., slight damp-markers on a few outer edges, cloth, d.w. Quaritch 983-141 1978 £90

HAVEN, C. C.   A New Historic Manual Concerning the Three Battles at Trenton and Princeton, New Jersey, During the War for American Independence... Tranton, 1871. Orig. cloth, illus. MacManus 239-579 1978 $35

HAVERGAL, F. R.   Kept for the Master's Use. Toronto, 1879. Hood 116-297 1978 $7.50

HAVIGHURST, WALTER   The Long Ships Passing. New York, 1942. Illus., lst ed., d. w. Biblo 251-41 1978 $12.50

HAVILAND, CHARLES EDWARD   Cat. de la Bibliotheque. Paris, 1923. 2 vols., plts., illus., imp. 8vo., marbled bds., cloth backs, orig. wrs. bound in. Forster 130-19 1978 £12

HAWEIS, H. R.   Sir Morell Mackenzie. London, 1894. Rittenhouse 49-341 1976 $25

HAWES, CHARLES BOARDMAN   The Dark Frigate. Boston, (1923). Illus., 8vo., lst ed. Morrill 241-187 1978 $12.50

HAWES, CHARLES BOARDMAN   Whaling. London, 1924. lst. ed., roy. 8vo, coloured frontispiece, coloured plts., one slightly defective, margin torn, orig. blue cloth, decorative gilt vignette, gilt back. Deighton 5-229 1978 £25

HAWES, JOEL   Lectures Addressed to the Young Men of Hartford and New Haven, and Published at Their United Request. Hartford, 1828. 2nd ed., bds. rubbed. Hayman 72-289 1978 $10

HAWES, MARY   Memoir of the Rev. Erskine J. Hawes... New York, 1862. Orig. cl., lst ed. Ginsberg 16-875 1978 $10.00

HAWKER, GEORGE   The Life of George Grenfell, Congo Missionary and Explorer. London, 1909. 5 maps, portrait, 70 illus., gilt cloth, 8vo, bright. K Books 239-211 1978 £9

HAWKER, ROBERT S.   The Cornish Ballads and Other Poems. 1869. Sm. 8vo., lst ed., orig. green cloth, very fresh unfaded copy. Quaritch 979-190 1978 $75

HAWKER, ROBERT S.   Stones Broken from the Rocks. Oxford, 1922. First ed., plts., cr. 8vo., orig. buckram backed bds. Howes 194-921 1978 £5

HAWKES, JOHN   The Goose on the Grave. Two Short Novels. (New York), (1945). Orig. cloth, 1st ed., signed by author, fine, tattered d.j. MacManus 238-662 1978 $25

HAWKESWORTH, JOHN   The Adventures of Telemachus,.... London, 1795. 2 vols. in one, quarto, brown full calf, blind and gilt stamped, gilt lettering on spine, bookplts. of Mary Macmillan Norton, coloured engravings. Totteridge 29-51 1978 $200

HAWKESWORTH, JOHN   Sammlung Interessanter... N.P., 1787. 8vo., contemp. bds., joint partly split, engraved folding map, woodcut vignette. Edwards 1012-373 1978 £60

HAWKINS, ALFRED   The Quebec Directory, and City and Commercial Register, 1847-8. Montreal, 1847. Orig. binding, front cover loose. Wolfe 39-451a 1978 $125

HAWKINS, ANTHONY HOPE   The Chronicles of Count Antonio. London, 1895. First ed., orig. binding, nice. Rota 211-195 1978 £5

HAWKINS, ANTHONY HOPE   The Dolly Dialogues. New York, 1894. lst Amer. ed., minor dust-soiling of tan cloth, very good. Victoria 34-671 1978 $17.50

HAWKINS, ANTHONY HOPE   The Dolly Dialogues. London, 1899. 3rd English ed., laid paper, bright crimson cloth, very good or better, with "Westminster Gazette" at base of spine. Limestone 9-153 1978 $22.50

HAWKINS, ANTHONY HOPE   The Heart of Princess Osra. London, 1896. First ed., orig. binding, covers and spine marked, nice. Rota 211-196 1978 £5

HAWKINS, ANTHONY HOPE   The Prisoner of Zenda. Bristol, Arrowsmith, (1894). Orig. cloth, author's signature, written on sm. piece of paper, pasted on title pg. Eaton 45-253 1978 £8

HAWKINS, ANTHONY HOPE   Rupert of Hentzau. Bristol, (1898). First ed., plts., orig. cloth, binding little dull, 8vo. Howes 194-944 1978 £5

HAWKINS, ANTHONY HOPE   Simon Dale. London, 1898. First ed., orig. binding, nice. Rota 211-197 1978 £5

HAWKINS, C. A.   Some Facts Concerning York and York County. York, 1901. Illus. MacManus 239-1484 1978 $12.50

HAWKINS, CHRISTOPHER   The Adventures of Christopher Hawkins...Details of His Captivity..Escape From the Jersey Prison Ship.... New York, 1864. Illus., light stain on bottom edge of binding, good. Nestler Rare 78-158 1978 $85

HAWKINS, E.   Select Papyri in the Hieratic Character from the Collections of the B.M. London, 1841-4. 3 parts in 1 vol., plts., roy. folio, half pigskin, t.e.g. Forster 130-208 1978 £95

HAWKINS, JOHN   A General History of the Science and Practice of Music. London, 1776. 5 vols., illus., lst ed., quarto, bound in brown tree calf, 2 covers detached, light offsetting of some plates. Totteridge 29-50 1978 $400

HAWKINS, JOHN   The Life of Samuel Johnson, LL.D. 1787. Lg. 8vo., 19th-century calf gilt, hinge cracked, very good, first ed. P. M. Hill 142-154 1978 £60

HAWKINS, JOHN   The Life of Samuel Johnson, LL.D. Dublin, 1787. First Dublin ed., contemp. sheep, label missing, upper joint little cracked. Howes 194-337 1978 £38

HAWKINS, JOHN PARKER   Memoranda Concerning Some Branches of the Hawkins Family and Connections. [Indianapolis, 1913]. Illus., original cloth, 1st ed., clipped signature and calling card of author. Ginsberg 14-388 1978 $75

HAWKINS, RICHARD   A Discourse of the Nationall Excellencies of England. London, 1658. 1st. ed., sm. 8vo, contemp. calf, old rebacking. Traylen 88-76 1978 £95

HAWKINS, WALLACE   The Case of John C. Watrous, United States Judge for Texas. Dallas, 1950. Cloth, 1 of 1200 copies. Hayman 73-695 1978 $10

HAWKINS, WILLIAM   Tracts in Divinity. Oxford, 1758. 1st. & only collected ed., 3 vols., 8vo, half calf, gilt, fine set. Fenning 32-149 1978 £110

HAWKS, FRANCIS L.   History of North Carolina. Fayetteville, 1857-1858. 2 vols., 1st ed., rebound. Broadfoot 50-86 1978 $40

HAWKS, JOHN   Orderly Book and Journal of. (New York), 1911. Orig. binding. Wolfe 39-226 1978 $45

HAWKS, WELLS   Moonshine Strategy and Other Stories. Baltimore, 1906. 1st ed., frontispiece, illus., pictorial cloth, good. Limestone 9-144 1978 $20

HAWLES, JOHN   Solicitor-General to the Late King William. London, 1771. 16mo., unbound. Morrill 241-188 1978 $10

HAWLEY, WALTER A.   Oriental Rugs, Antique and Modern. New York, 1922. 4to., maps, coloured and plain plts., cloth. Quaritch 983-63 1978 $180

HAWTHORNE, HILDEGARDE   Romantic Cities of California. 1939. Illus., first ed., v.g. Austin 82-926 1978 $20

HAWTHORNE, JULIAN   Archibald Malmaison. 1879. 1st. ed., half title, cont. half green morocco, hinges rubbed, good. Jarndyce 16-720 1978 £14.50

HAWTHORNE, JULIAN   Archibald Malmaison. New York, 1899. Illus., orig. dec. cloth, 1st illus. ed., fine. MacManus 238-498 1978 $40

HAWTHORNE, NATHANIEL   The Blithedale Romance. Boston, 1852. Orig. cloth, spine ends chipped, joints a little rubbed, 1st Amer. ed., fine. MacManus 238-505 1978 $35

HAWTHORNE, NATHANIEL   The Blithedale Romance. 1852. 1st. English ed., 2 vols., orig. brown cloth, very slight wear to hinges otherwise v.g. Jarndyce 16-719 1978 £42

HAWTHORNE, NATHANIEL   Doctor Grimshawe's Secret. Boston, 1883. 1st trade ed., orig. cloth, signature, very good. MacManus 238-511 1978 $27.50

HAWTHORNE, NATHANIEL   The House of the Seven Gables. A Romance. Boston, 1851. Orig. cloth, 1st ed., bind. A, covers a bit stained, spine ends slightly frayed, otherwise good. MacManus 238-502 1978 $200

HAWTHORNE, NATHANIEL   Life of Franklin Pierce. Boston, 1852. Orig. cloth, extremities of spine slightly worn, 1st ed., very nice. MacManus 238-506 1978 $85

HAWTHORNE, NATHANIEL   Life of Franklin Pierce. Boston, 1852. 8vo, original dark brown cloth, 1st ed., very good copy. Ximenes 47-129 1978 $50

HAWTHORNE, NATHANIEL   The Marble Faun. Boston and New York. 2 vols., portrait frontis., plts., gilt decor. cover, 8vo. K Books 244-151 1978 £10

HAWTHORNE, NATHANIEL   Mosses from an Old Manse. New York, 1846. 2 vols. in 1, orig. cloth, 1st 1 vol. ed., very slightly worn, near-fine. MacManus 238-500 1978 $150

HAWTHORNE, NATHANIEL   Our Old Home. Boston, 1863. Orig. cloth, 1st ed., 1st state, fine. MacManus 238-509 1978 $40

HAWTHORNE, NATHANIEL   Our Old Home. A Series of English Sketches. Boston, 1863. Orig. cloth, 1st ed., 2nd state, spine ends slightly worn. MacManus 238-508 1978 $22.50

HAWTHORNE, NATHANIEL   Our Old Home. 1890. 2 vols., buckram, plts., very good, first English ed. Bell Book 16-424 1978 £6.50

HAWTHORNE, NATHANIEL   Passages from the French and Italian Note-Books. Boston, 1872. 2 vols., orig. cloth, 1st ed., bind. A, front flyleaf in vol. I clipped, otherwise very good. MacManus 238-510 1978 $35

HAWTHORNE, NATHANIEL   The Scarlett Letter. A Romance. Boston, 1850. 8vo., orig. cloth, spine ends chipped, minor rubbing, 1st ed., covers a bit stained, slightly worn, bright copy. MacManus 238-501 1978 $200

HAWTHORNE, NATHANIEL   The Scarlet Letter. Boston, 1850. 1st ed., 12 mo., 1st issue, very fine copy or better, orig. brown cloth, binding firm, owner's inscrip., boxed in 1/2 maroon mor. slipcase, rare in this cond. Current 24-252 1978 $685

HAWTHORNE, NATHANIEL   The Scarlet Letter. London, (1859). Illus., purple cloth with gilt lettering & designs, edges gilt, good. Greene 78-221 1978 $50

HAWTHORNE, NATHANIEL   The Scarlet Letter. New York: Grabhorn Press, 1928. Illus., half niger mor. and cloth, ltd. to 980 copies, extremities of spine slightly rubbed, otherwise very good. MacManus 238-803 1978 $60

HAWTHORNE, NATHANIEL   The Scarlet Letter. New York, 1928. 8vo, buckram, 1/2 mor., uncut, unopened, illus. by Valenti Angelo, Mint in orig. heavy black paper d.w., no. 434 of 980 copies, inscrip. by Angelo, 1st ed., collector's cond. Desmarais 1-213 1978 $75

HAWTHORNE, NATHANIEL   The Scarlet Letter. New York, Grabhorn Press, 1928. Illus. with wood blocks by Valenti Angelo, 1 of 980 numbered copies, new lea. spine. Battery Park 1-135 1978 $125

HAWTHORNE, NATHANIEL   The Snow-Images and Other Twice-Told Tales. Boston, 1852. 1st ed., 1st issue, very good. Victoria 34-380 1978 $75

HAWTHORNE, NATHANIEL   Tanglewood Tales, for Girls and Boys; Being a Second Wonder-Book. Boston, 1853. 12mo., orig. cloth, 1st Amer. ed., spine slightly faded, otherwise fine. MacManus 238-507 1978 $175

HAWTHORNE, NATHANIEL   Transformation; or, The Romance of Monte Benj. London, 1860. Cloth binding, all spines damaged, 3 vols., interiors good clean, tight copies. Greene 78-324 1978 $60

HAWTHORNE, NATHANIEL   Transformation: or, The Romance of Monte Beni. Leipzig, 1860. Copyright ed., 2 vols., 16mo., orig. sepia colored photos bound in, bound in full vellum with elaborate gilt decor's on spine & bds., marbled end-papers, mint. Current 24-18 1978 $100

HAWTHORNE, NATHANIEL   True Stories from History and Biography. Boston, 1851. 12mo., orig. cloth, 1st ed., 2nd impression, very nice. MacManus 238-504 1978 $25

HAWTHORNE, NATHANIEL   True Stories from History and Biography. Boston, 1851. 12mo., orig. cloth, 1st ed., 1st impression, covers a bit worn and soiled, but very nice. MacManus 238-503 1978 $75

HAWTHORNE, NATHANIEL   Twice-Told Tales. Boston, 1837. 8vo., orig. cloth, spine ends neatly repaired, 1st ed., very fine, signature on endpaper. MacManus 238-499 1978 $325

HAWTHORNE, NATHANIEL   Twice Told Tales. Boston, 1837. 12mo, modern full claret mor., gilt. t. e.g., uncut, bound without ads, Fine, 1st ed., collector's cond. Desmarais 1-214 1978 $160

HAWTHORNE, NATHANIEL   A Wonder Book for Girls and Boys. Illus. by Walter Crane, 1st ed., octavo, orig. decor. cloth covers, color plts., bookplte. Totteridge 29-27 1978 $75

HAWTHORNE, NATHANIEL   A Wonder-Book for Girls and Boys. Boston, 1852. 8vo, original blue cloth, blue morocco slip-case, 1st ed., frontispiece and plates by Hammatt Billings. Ximenes 47-130 1978 $375

HAWTHORNE, NATHANIEL   A Wonder Book for Girls & Boys. Boston, 1893. 1st ed., color plates, headpieces, Art Nouveau pictorial cloth, covers rubbed, spine tips worn, text very good. Victoria 34-197 1978 $32.50

HAWTREY, R. G.   The Economic Problem. 1926. 1st. ed., 8vo, orig. cloth, pres. copy to Winston Churchill. Sawyer 298-82 1978 £75

HAY, J.   A Narrative of the Insurrection in the Island of Grenada... 1823. Modern half calf, 8vo, many pages browned or badly spotted. Edwards 1012-718 1978 £65

HAY, JOHN   The Bread-Winners. (1883). 1899. Austin 82-
414 1978 $11

HAY, JOHN   Castilian Days. 1871. First ed., first issue, good.
Austin 82-415 1978 $37.50

HAY, JOHN   Jim Bludso of the Prairie Belle, and Little Bree-
ches. Boston, 1871. 12mo., mod. half mor., orig. wrs. bound in, t.e.g., 1st
ed. MacManus 238-512 1978 $75

HAY, JOHN   A Poet in Exile: Early Letters... Boston, 1910.
1st ed., 1 of 440 copies, orig. bds., nice, boxed, illus. Americanist 102-57
1978 $35

HAYDEN, ARTHUR   Chats on English Earthenware. Toronto, (1909).
150 illus. Baldwins' 51-89 1978 $12.50

HAYDEN, ARTHUR   Chats on Old Furniture. London, (1925). Illus.,
4th ed., bind. torn otherwise good. Biblo BL781-596 1978 $8.50

HAYDEN, F. A.   Historical Record of the 76th "Hindoostan" Regiment from its formation in 1787 to 30th June 1881. Lichfield, (c. 1908). Maps,
8vo., orig. cloth backed bds. F. Edwards 1013-530 1978 $15

HAYDEN, F. A.   Historical Record of the 76th "Hindoostan" Regiment from its formation in 1787 to 30th June 1881. Lichfield, (c. 1908). 8vo.,
orig. cloth, coloured portrait & frontis. F. Edwards 1013-529 1978 £30

HAYDEN, JAMES R.   Venereal Diseases. Philadelphia, 1901. Third
revised ed., title page loose. Rittenhouse 49-338 1976 $9

HAYDEN, THOMAS   The Diseases of the Heart and of the Aorta.
Philadelphia, 1875. Illus., 2 vols., thick 8vo., cloth, one spine loose, first Amer.
ed. Rittenhouse 49-337 1976 $29

HAYDEN, WILLIAM R.   Clara Wharton. Boston, (1851). Portr., 8vo.,
unbound. Morrill 239-423 1978 $15

HAYDN, HIRAM   Manhattan Furlough. 1945. First ed., d.j.
Austin 82-417 1978 $12.50

HAYDN, HIRAM   Western Reserve University from Hudson to
Cleveland 1878-1890. (Cleveland), 1905. Cloth. Hayman 73-540 1978 $8.50

HAYDON, A. L.   The Riders of the Plains. London, 1918. Illus.
with photos, maps, diagrs., pages browned, cover scuffed, 7th impression. Hood
117-893 1978 $7.50

HAYES, A. A., JR.   New Colorado and the Santa Fe Trail. New
York, 1880. 1st ed., illus., map. MacManus 239-1921 1978 $25

HAYES, ALBERT H.   A Medical Treatise on Nervous Affections. Boston, 1870. Rittenhouse 49-339 1976 $15

HAYES, ALBERT H.   Sexual Physiology of Woman, and Her Diseases.
Boston, (1869). Fine tinted lithographs, 8vo., full orig. mor. Morrill 239-119
1978 $22.50

HAYES, ARTHUR J.   The Source of the Blue Nile. London, 1905.
2 folding maps, 47 illus., orig. cloth, 8vo. K Books 239-212 1978 £20

HAYES, ARTHUR J.   The Source of the Blue Nile. London, 1905.
Illus., top of spine chipped, 1st ed. Biblo BL781-391 1978 $24.50

HAYES, CARLTON J. H.   Wartime Mission in Spain. 1945. Austin 80-
129 1978 $8.50

HAYES, EDWARD   The Ballads of Ireland. 1857. 2nd. ed., cr. 8
vo, engraved title-pg., plts., 2 vols. bound in 1, contemp. half calf, gilt, some
light foxing, very good & sound copy. Fenning 32-150 1978 £9.50

HAYES, H. GORDON   Spending, Saving, & Employment. 1945. 1st ed.
Austin 80-684 1978 $12.50

HAYES, H. GORDON   Spending, Saving and Employment. 1947. Austin 80-715 1978 $12.50

HAYES, ISAAC ISRAEL   The Open Polar Sea. New York, 1867.
Maps, illus., 8vo., 1st ed. Morrill 241-674 1978 $15

HAYES, ISAAC ISRAEL   The Open Polar Sea: A Narrative of a Voyage
of Discovery Towards the North Pole... New York, 1867. 1st. ed., maps, plts.,
portraits, orig. cloth, 8vo, browned, spine slightly worn. Edwards 1012-577
1978 £12

HAYES, ISAAC ISRAEL   The Open Polar Sea... London, 1867. 1st.
English ed., 8vo, portrait, tinted maps, plts., bound in modern half calf, gilt,
little dust-soiling of some leaves. Deighton 5-157 1978 £40

HAYES, J. G.   The Conquest of the South Pole. 1936. 8vo,
orig. cloth, illus. Edwards 1012-578 1978 £15

HAYES, JOHN RUSSELL   Brandywine Days Or, The Shepherd's Hour-Glass.
Philadelphia, 1910. Illus. Baldwins' 51-442 1978 $10

HAYES, THOMAS   A Serious Address, on the Dangerous Consequences
of Neglecting Common Coughs and Colds, with...the Prevention and Cure of Con-
sumptions... Boston, 1796. 1st U.S. ed., blue marbled bds., leatherette spine.
Americanist 102-71 1978 $60

HAYET, ARMAND   Chansons de Bord Recueillies et Presentees par
le Capitaine au Long Cours, etc. Paris, 1927. 4to., orig. pict. wr., uncut,
ltd. ed., 1 of 500 numbered copies on velin Lafuma paper. Goldschmidt 110-44
1978 $50

HAYLEY, WILLIAM   Epistle to a Friend on the Death of John Thornton,
Esq. 1780. 1st. ed., 4to, rebound in brown bds., v.g. Jarndyce 16-106 1978
£24

HAYLEY, WILLIAM   The Life of George Romney, Esq. Chichester,
1809. 4to., frontis., plts., contemp. straight-grained green mor., gilt, edges
gilt, back faded. Quaritch 979-47 1978 $300

HAYLEY, WILLIAM   Ode. 1780. 4to., unbound, half-title, first
ed. P. M. Hill 142-281 1978 £18

HAYLEY, WILLIAM   Plays of Three Acts Written For a Private Theatre.
1784. 1st. ed., 4to, half titles, orig. calf, brown label, spine gilt, superb copy,
contemp. binding. Jarndyce 16-108 1978 £72

HAYLEY, WILLIAM   The Triumphs of Temper. 1781. 4to., contemp.
qtr. calf, marbled sides, spine rubbed, first ed. P. M. Hill 142-282 1978 £28

HAYLEY, WILLIAM   The Triumphs of Temper. 1788. 6th. ed.,
half title, orig. calf, maroon label, attractive copy. Jarndyce 16-109 1978
£9.50

HAYLEY, WILLIAM   The Triumphs of Temper. 1796. 9th. ed.,
orig. tree calf, very good. Jarndyce 16-110 1978 £8.50

HAYLEY, WILLIAM   The Triumphs of Temper. 1803. Sm. 8vo., plts.,
contemp. calf, rebacked, neat inscr. Quaritch 979-48 1978 $375

HAYM, R.   Hegel Und Seine Zeit. Berlin, 1857. 8vo.,
3/4 mor., 1st ed., rare. Salloch 348-86 1978 $125

HAYNE, M. H. E.   The Pioneers of the Klondyke... London, 1897.
1st. ed., cr.8vo, map, plts., orig. red cloth, gilt, spine faded, cover somewhat
soiled, lib. label removed, indelible lib. stamp in margins. Deighton 5-41 1978
£45

HAYNES, D. E. L.   The Parthenon Frieze. London, n.d. Photos.
Biblo BL781-392 1978 $13.50

HAYNES, DOROTHY K.   Thous Shalt Not Suffer a Witch, and other stories.
1949. Illus. by Mervyn Peake, covers little soiled, good, first English ed. Bell
Book 17-722 1978 £10

HAYNES, GEORGE H.   The Senate of the United States... Boston, 1938.
2 vols., illus., 1st ed. Biblo BL781-204 1978 $12

HAYNES, WILLIAMS   The Stone That Burns. 1942. Illus. Austin 80-
685 1978 $11

HAYS, I. MINIS   Calendar of the Papers of Benjamin Franklin in
the Library of the American Philosophical Society. Philadelphia, 1908. 1st ed.,
5 vols., illus., orig. cloth, very fine. MacManus 239-158 1978 $85

HAYTHORNE, G. V.   Land and Labour... Toronto, 1941. Ex-lib.
Hood's 115-299 1978 $15

HAYWARD, ABRAHAM   Biographical and Critical Essays. 1858-74.
Three series complete, 5 vols., orig. cloth, bindings faded, 2 vols. sometime
recased, 8vo. Howes 194-922 1978 £30

HAYWARD, ABRAHAM   More About Junius. 1868. Inscribed pres. copy
from author, orig. half calf, v.g. Jarndyce 16-722 1978 £15

HAYWARD, ABRAHAM   Selected Essays. 1878. 2 vols., 8vo., orig.
cloth, very good. P. M. Hill 142-137 1978 £16

HAYWARD, JOHN 1564(?)-1627   The Life and Reign of King Edward the Sixth,
.... London, 1636. 1st ed., 12mo., engraved frontispiece, engraved t.p. by
William Marshall, full early flecked roan. Bennett 20-97 1978 $195

HAYWARD, JOHN 1781-1862   The New England Gazetteer... Concord, 1839.
4th. ed., plts., illus., calf, some light browning in text, 8vo. Edwards 1012-
495 1978 £15

HAYWARD, JOHN 1905-   English Poetry. 1950. Illus., roy. 8vo., facsimiles, buckram, gilt top, ltd. to 550 numbered copies. Quaritch 979-191 1978
$160

HAYWARD, JOHN 1905-   English Poetry. 1950. Illus., ltd. to 550 copies,
roy. 8vo., orig. buckram. George's 635-1206 1978 £45

HAYWOOD, A. H.   Through Timbuctu and Across the Great Sahara.
London, 1912. Folding map, 45 illus., backstrip faded, orig. cloth, 8vo. K Books
239-213 1978 £14

HAYWOOD, ELIZA   The Fruitless Enquiry. 1767. 12mo, 2nd. ed.,
contemp. paper bds., sheep spine, worn, lib. label removed from inner cover,
uncut, 1 leaf torn across. Hannas 54-157 1978 £110

HAYWOOD, ELIZA   A Wife to Be Lett: A Comedy. 1724. 1st. ed.,
8vo, lacks leaf before title, half cloth, paper browned. Hannas 54-158 1978 £55

HAYWOOD, JOHN   A Manual of the Laws of North Carolina.
Raleigh, 1819. Foxed, full leather. Broadfoot 50-88 1978 $20

HAYWOOD, MARSHALL D.   Lives of the Bishops of North Carolina From the
Establishment of the Episcopate...to the Division of the Diocese. Raleigh, 1910.
Illus. MacManus 239-1847 1978 $20

HAZARD, CAROLINE   The Narragansett Friend's Meeting in the 18th
Century... Boston, 1899. MacManus 239-420 1978 $12.50

HAZARD, CAROLINE   Thomas Hazard Son of Robert Called College Tom.
Boston, 1893. 1st ed., illus., map, orig. cloth, fine copy. MacManus 239-
423 1978 $27.50

HAZARD, ELIZABETH   Autumn Musings and Other Poems. Philadelphia,
1874. 1st. ed., sm. 8vo, orig. cloth, gilt, tear in foot of spine, nice copy o/w.
Fenning 32-151 1978 £14.50

HAZARD, LUCY LOCKWOOD   The Frontier in American Literature. [New York,
1941]. Original cloth. Ginsberg 14-389 1978 $12.50

HAZARD, SAMUEL   Annals of Pennsylvania 1609-82. Philadelphia,
1850. MacManus 239-1485 1978 $30

HAZARD, SAMUEL   Annuals of Pennsylvania from the Discovery of
the Delaware, 1609-1682. Philadelphia, 1850. 1st. ed., orig. cloth, extremities
of backstrip chipped, covers rubbed, otherwise sound, clean copy. Baldwins' 51-
443 1978 $20

HAZELETT, C. WILLIAM   A Dynamic Capitalism. 1943. Austin 80-686
1978 $12.50

HAZELTON, GEORGE C.   The National Capital. New York, 1914. Cl.,
orig. binding, li. flecking on cover. Hayman 71- 289 1978 $7.50

HAZEN, E.   The Symbolical Primer:.... New York, (1830).
12mo, illus. wrappers, very good. Victoria 34-381 1978 $40

HAZEN, HENRY A.   History of Billerica, Mass... Boston, 1883.
Illus., orig. cloth, lib. marks, very good. MacManus 239-1012 1978 $40

HAZLETON, JNO. M.   A History of Linebred Anxiety 4th Herefords of
Straight Gudgell & Simpson Breeding. Kansas City, 1939. Fabricoid, illus. in
color, 1st ed., fine copy, scarce. Dykes 34-108 1978 $25

HAZLITT, WILLIAM 1778-1830   Characters of Shakespeare's Plays. London,
1817. First ed., 8vo., mod. calf, antique style, gilt top, others uncut, unusually
nice. Traylen 88-267 1978 £60

HAZLITT, WILLIAM 1778-1830   Lectures on the English Comic Writers. 1819.
First ed., orig. bds., entirely uncut, rebacked with calf, 8vo. Howes 194-923
1978 #45

HAZLITT, WILLIAM 1778-1830   Lectures on the English Poets. 1819. Second
ed., uncut, orig. bds., rebacked, 8vo. Howes 194-924 1978 £15

HAZLITT, WILLIAM 1778-1830   Political Essays. 1819. First ed., orig. bds.,
entirely unpressed and uncut, very good, 8vo. Howes 194-925 1978 £45

HAZLITT, WILLIAM 1778-1830   The Spirit of the Age. 1825. 8vo., first ed.,
ink inscription, half calf, rebacked. Eaton 45-237 1978 #40

HAZLITT, WILLIAM 1778-1830   Table-Talk. 1824. Second ed., 2 vols., mid
19th cent. half calf, yellow edges, 8vo. Howes 194-926 1978 £42

HAZLITT, WILLIAM CAREW   The Baron's Daughter. Edinburgh, 1877. 4to,
original blue cloth, 1st ed., original poetry, very scarce. Ximenes 47-131 1978
$27.50

HAZLITT, WILLIAM CAREW   Four Generations of a Literary Family.... 1896.
Plts., 2 vols., orig. green cloth, first ed., 8vo. Howes 194-927 1978 £15

HAZLIT, WILLIAM CAREW   Jocular Literature. Battery Park 1-261 1978
$22.50

HAZLIT, WILLIAM CAREW   Memoirs. 1867. 1st. ed., 2 vols., frontis portraits, orig. green cloth, good. Jarndyce 16-726 1978 £18

HAZLITT, WILLIAM CAREW   Studies in Jocular Literature. 1890. 4to., qtr.
roan, extra lg. paper, t.e.g., others uncut. P.M. Hill 142-136 1978 £24

HAZZLEDINE, GEORGE DOUGLAS   The White Man in Nigeria. London, 1904.
Folding map, 16 plts., dec. cloth, 8vo. K Books 239-214 1978 £10

HE mau Himeni Hawaii he mea hoolea'i i ke akua mau, ia Iehova. Oahu, 1830.
Calf (foxed), covers stained, joints worn. Dawson's 127-263 1978 $300

HEAD, BARCLAY V.   Historia Numorum. Oxford, 1911. Illus.,
thick 8vo. Traylen 88-383 1978 £30

HEAD, FRANCIS BOND   Bubbles from the Brunnens of Nassau, by an Old
Man. NY, 1836. Disbound. Greene 78-51 1978 $25.00

HEAD, FRANCIS BOND   The Emigrant. 1846. 1st. ed., sm. 8vo, half
morocco, faded. Edwards 1012-429 1978 £40

HEAD, FRANCIS BOND   The Emigrant. 1846. 8vo., half calf, first ed.
P. M. Hill 142-66 1978 £14

HEAD, FRANCIS BOND   A Narrative. 1839. 1st. ed., orig. cloth, 8vo,
spine slightly faded. Edwards 1012-428 1978 £75

HEAD, FRANCIS BOND   A Narrative of Upper Canada. London, 1839.
1st ed., royal 8vo., ads, text clear & fine, uncut edges, orig. green ribbed cloth,
gilt decor. fr. cover, spine faded to brown, binding firm, rare. Current 24-179
1978 $130

HEAD, FRANCIS BOND   A Narrative. London, 1839. Orig. cloth cover
worn. Hood 116-630 1978 $40

HEAD, GEORGE   Forest Scenes and Incidents, in the Wilds of
North America... 1838. 2nd. ed., folding map, sm. 8vo, contemp. calf.
Edwards 1012-427 1978 £50

HEADLAM, CUTHBERT   History of the Guards Division in the Great War,
1915-1918. 1924. Coloured frontis., maps, 2 vols., 8vo., orig. cloth, spines
faded. F. Edwards 1013-585 1978 £20

HEADLEE, THOMAS J.   The Mosquitoes of New Jersey and Their Control.
New Brunswick, 1945. Ex-library. Rittenhouse 49-343 1976 $12.50

HEADLEY, J. T.   The Second War with England. New York,
1853. 2 vols., illus., fine set, orig. cloth. MacManus 239-478 1978 $40

HEADLEY, P. C.   Public Men of Today... Hartford, 1884. Ports.,
full leather bind., leather little rubbed, good. Hayman 72-290 1978 $15

HEADLEY, RUSSELL   The History of Orange County. Middletown,
1908. Thick tall 8vo., engr. portrs. Butterfield 21-332 1978 $65

HEALES, A.   The Records of Merton Priory in the County of
Surrey, chiefly from early and unpublished documents. Oxford, 1898. Lg. 8vo.,
map, plts. Upcroft 12-190 1978 £15

HEALY, W. J.   Women of Red River. Winnipeg, 1923. Coloured
frontis., 1st ed. Hood 116-852 1978 $30

HEARN, LAFCADIO   The Boy Who Drew Cats. (Tokyo, 1898). Printed on crepe paper, large paper format, illus. in color, Ist ed., virtually mint. Victoria 34-382 1978 $75

HEARN, LAFCADIO   Editorials from the Kobe Chronicle. (New York, 1913). First ed., Itd. to 100 copies, orig. pr. wrs., buckram. Limestone 9-145 1978 $110

HEARN, LAFCADIO   Exotics and Retrospectives. Boston, 1898. Ownership inscription, near fine in torn d.w. Desmarais B-306 1978 $15

HEARN, LAFCADIO   Gibbeted: Execution of a Youthful Murderer. Los Angeles, 1933. Black cloth, good copy, I of 200 numbered copies. Dawson's 447-240 1978 $50

HEARN, LAFCADIO   Glimpses of Unfamiliar Japan. 1894. 2 vols., decor. cloth, covers somewhat soiled, good ex-lib. copy, first English ed. Bell Book 16-428 1978 £30

HEARN, LAFCADIO   Kokoro: Hints and Echoes of Inner Japanese Life. Boston, 1896. Decor. green cloth, t.e.g., Ist ed., spine faded, extra-illus. by former owner. Bradley 49-140 1978 $12.50

HEARN, LAFCADIO   Miscellanies. 1924. Tall 8vo, 2 vols., Ist. ed., near fine. Jarndyce 16-1201 1978 £15

HEARN, LAFCADIO   "Out of the East." Boston/New York, Cambridge, (1895). Green cloth, gilt, t.e.g., uncut. Wolfe 39-230 1978 $15

HEARN, LAFCADIO   The Romance of the Milky Way, and other studies & stories. New York, 1905. First U.S. ed., covers dull, good. Bell Book 16-429 1978 $8.50

HEARN, LAFCADIO   The Selected Writings of Lafcadio Hearn. New York, (1949). Name otherwise good in chipped & creased dw. Bernard 5-126 1978 $10

HEARN, LAFCADIO   Some Chinese Ghosts. Boston, 1887. 12mo., orig. cloth, Ist ed., fine, rare in this cond. MacManus 238-513 1978 $85

HEARN, WILLIAM EDWARD   The Government of England. Its Structure and Its Development. London, 1887. 2nd ed. Biblo BL781-821 1978 $9

HEARNE, SAMUEL   Journey from Prince of Wales's Fort, in Hudson's Bay, to the Northern Ocean. Dublin, 1796. 8vo., full modern speckled calf, fold. mpa, plts. Wolfe 39-231 1978 $250

HEARNE, SAMUEL   Voyage Du Fort Du Prince De Galles.... (Paris, 1799). 2 vols., 8vo, cloth, maps, plts., slight tear in I map reparied, short tear in 8 leaves at end of vol. I repaired, affecting few letters. Edwards 1012-431 1978 £95

HEARNE, SAMUEL   Voyage Du Fort Du Prince De Galles... (Paris, 1799). Folding maps, plts., 4to, old marbled paper over bds., parchment spine, uncut. Edwards 1012-430 1978 £250

HEARNE, THOMAS   Remarks and Collections, 1795-1735. Oxford, 1885-1921. II vols., 8vo. Traylen 88-268 1978 £48

HEART, JONATHAN   Journal of Captain Jonathan Heart on the March With His Company From Connecticut to Fort Pitt...1785.... Albany, 1885. Sq. 8vo., uncut, prtd. wrs., I of 150 copies only, out of print, inscr'd by Douglas Brymner. Butterfield 21-287 1978 $75

HEARTMAN, CHARLES F.   A Bibliography of First Printings of the Writings of Edgar Allan Poe. Mississippi, 1940. Orig. cloth, Ist ed., less than 350 copies printed. MacManus 238-1027 1978 $50

HEARTMAN, CHARLES F.   The Cradle of the United States 1765-1789... Perth Amboy, 1922. Rebound, 1st ed., Itd. to 100 copies. MacManus 238-941 1978 $60

HEARTMAN, CHARLES F.   The New England Primer Issued Prior to 1830. Ltd. to 300 copies, very good. Nestler Rare 78-16 1978 $28

HEATH, DUDLEY   Miniatures. 1905. Plts., II coloured, roy. 8vo., orig. cloth, gilt, t.e.g., nice copy. Fenning 32-152 1978 £12.50

HEATH, H.   The Caricaturist's Scrap Book. (London, 1840). Oblong folio, plts., orig. cloth. K Books 244-380 1978 £52

HEATH, T.   A History of Greek Mathematics. Oxford, 1921. 2 vols., spines faded, 8vo. George's 635-987 1978 £25

HEATH, WILLIAM   General Orders Issued by Major-General William Heath, When in Command of the Eastern Department, 23 May 1777 to 3 October 1777. Brooklyn, 1890. 8vo., orig. wrs., Itd. to 250 copies. Morrill 241-189 1978 $15

HEATH, WILLIAM   Memoirs. Boston, 1798. Cloth, library marks. MacManus 239-580 1978 $35

HEATH, WILLIAM   Memoirs. New York, 1901. 8vo., orig. cloth, Itd. to 500 copies. Morrill 241-190 1978 $25

HEATHCOTE, CHARLES W.   History of Chester County, Pa. West Chester, 1926. School edition, illus., maps. Baldwins' 51-444 1978 $12.50

HEATHCOTE, HENRY   Treatise on Stay-Sails for the Purpose of intercepting wind between the Square-Sails of Ships.... 1824. 8vo., contemp. half calf, plts. F. Edwards 1013-94 1978 £85

HEATHCOTE, NORMAN   St. Kilda. London, 1900. Map, plts., text-illus., gilt decor. cover, 8vo. K Books 244-152 1978 £7

HEAVENHILL, W. S.   Siege of the Alamo: A Mexican-Texan Tale. San Antonio, 1888. Original pictorial printed wr. Jenkins 116-1556 1978 $18.50

HEBARD, GRACE RAYMOND   The Bozeman Trail:.... Cleveland, 1922. 2 vols., illus., original cloth, slight discoloration on spine, Ist ed. Ginsberg 14-390 1978 $75

HEBARD, GRACE RAYMOND   Sacajawea. A Guide and Interpreter of the Lewis and Clark Expedition... Glendale, 1933. Illus., fold. map, orig. cloth, very fine unopened copy. MacManus 239-1922 1978 $35

HEBBEL, F.   Die Nibelungen. Munchen, 1912. Lg. 8vo., marbled bds., uncut, rare. Van der Peet H-64-466 1978 Dfl 300

HEBER, REGINALD   The Life of the Right Rev. Jeremy Taylor, D.D. 1828. 1/2 leather, (spine torn), text good, reprint. Hyland 128-642 1978 £5

HEBER, REGINALD   Narrative of a Journey Through the Upper Provinces of India,.... London, 1828. Ist ed., quarto, 2 vols., frontispiece portrait, plates, wood engravings, map, full green russia, a.e.g., plates somewhat foxed. Bennett 20-98 1978 $175

HEBER, REGINALD   Sermons on the Lessons, The Gospel, or the Epistle for Every Sunday in the Year. 1827. Ist. ed., 3 vols., orig. blue calf, v.g. Jarndyce 16-727 1978 £14.50

HEBER, REGINALD   Sermons preached in India. London, 1829. Frontispiece, half calf, endpapers discoloured, 8vo. K Books 244-153 1978 £7

HECHT, H.   Die Englische Literatur im Mittelalter. Potsdam, 1927. 4to., cloth, plts., some in color, text illus. Van der Peet H-64-395 1978 Dfl 55

HECKER, AUGUST FRIEDRICH   Ueber Die Nervenfieber, welche in Berlin im Jahre 1807 herrschten, nebst bemerkungen uber die reizende, starkende und schwachende kurmethode. Berlin, 1808. Sm. 8vo., sewn, orig. decor. wrs., browned, some dampstains, fraying, library stamp, good copy, Ist ed., rare. Zeitlin 245-116 1978 $75

HECKER, JUSTUS FRIEDRICH KARL   The Epidemics of the Middle Ages. London, 1844. 8vo., orig. green stamped cloth, gilt lettering on spine, good copy, bkplts. of Drs. James Gilpin Houseman & Alfred M. Hellman. Zeitlin 245-115 1978 $65

HECKER'S Croton Flour Mills, New York. New York, (1869). 16mo., orig. wrs., unnumbered pages. Morrill 239-383 1978 $10

HECKEWELDER, JOHN GOTTLIEB ERNESTUS 1743-1823   History, Manners, and Customs of the Indian Nations Who Once Inhabited Pennsylvania and the Neighbouring States. Philadelphia, 1876. New and revised ed., fine. MacManus 239-1165 1978 $40

HECKMANN, A.   Zuckerarbeiten und Eismeisselei. (Leipzig, 1925). Plts., many in color, illus., 4to. Morrill 239-424 1978 $10

HECQUET, PHILIPPE   Reflexions sur l'Usage de Opium,.... Paris, 1726. Ist ed., 12mo, full contemp. speckled calf, gilt spine panels, rare. Bennett 20-99 1978 $225

HEDBERG, ARVID   Stockholms bokbindare 1460-1700. Stockholm, 1949. Vol. I only (of 2), plts., imp. 8vo., orig. wrs. Forster 130-20 1978 £10

HEDDLE, M. FORSTER   The Mineralogy of Scotland. Edinburgh, 1901. 2 vols., maps, plts., illus., roy. 8vo., fine, orig. cloth. K Books 244-133 1978 £20

HEDENSTROM, S.   The Sport of Orienterring.   Toronto, 1948. Card cover, illus.   Hood 117-629 1978 $10

HEDERICH, BENJAMIN   Graecum lexicon manuale.... 1816. 4to., contemp. tree calf, spine defective.   George's 635-471 1978 £5.25

HEDGE, MARY ANN   Samboe; or, the African Boy. 1823. 1st. ed., 12mo, frontispiece, orig. quarter roan.   Hannas 54-312 1978 £24

HEDGES, M. H.   Dan Minturn. 1927. First ed. Austin 82-419 1978 $17.50

HEDIN, SVEN ANDERS   Big Horse's Flight: The Trail of War in Central Asia. London, 1936. Illus., folding map cloth, very good.   Dawson's 127-303 1978 $35

HEDIN, SVEN ANDERS   Central Asia and Tibet: Towards the Holy City of Lassa. London, 1903. 2 vols., illus., folding maps, cloth, preliminaries, edges foxed, generally very good.   Dawson's 127-304 1978 $125

HEDIN, SVEN ANDERS   The Flight of "Big Horse". New York, 1936. Binding faded, illus.   Biblo 251-8 1978 $15

HEDIN, SEVEN ANDERS   My Life As An Explorer. 1926. Coloured frontis., illus., maps, 8vo, orig. cloth, cover slightly worn.   Edwards 1012-137 1978 £15

HEDIN, SVEN ANDERS   Trans-Himalaya: Discoveries and Adventures in Tibet. London, 1910. 2 vols., illus., maps, cloth, spines a little faded, 1 hinge weakening, 2nd printing, very good.   Dawson's 127-305 1978 $135

HEDIN, SVEN ANDERS   Trans-Himalaya: Discoveries and Adventures in Tibet. London, 1913. Vol. 3, illus., maps, cloth, slight wear.   Dawson's 127-306 1978 $60

HEDRICK, ULYSSES PRENTISS   The Cherries of New York. Albany, 1915. Thick 4to., color plts., frontis. portr.   Butterfield 21-184 1978 $17.50

HEDRICK, ULYSSES PRENTISS   The Grapes of New York. Albany, 1908. Thick 4to., color plts., portr., scarce, covers lightly spotted.   Butterfield 21-185 1978 $50

HEDRICK, ULYSSES PRENTISS   The Land of the Crooked Tree. New York, 1948. 1st ed., nice copy in dust jacket, cloth.   Hayman 73-436 1978 $8.50

HEDRICK, ULYSSES PRENTISS   The Peaches of New York. Albany, 1917. Thick 4to., color plts., map, portr.   Butterfield 21-186 1978 $25

HEDRICK, ULYSSES PRENTISS   The Plums of New York. Albany, 1911. Color plts., frontis. portr.   Butterfield 21-187 1978 $20

HEDRICK, ULYSSES PRENTISS   The Small Fruits of New York. Albany, 1925. Color plts., frontis. portr., bkplt. removed.   Butterfield 21-188 1978 $35

HEDRICK, ULYSSES PRENTISS   Sturtevant's Notes on Edible Plants. Albany, 1919. Thick lg. 4to., bkplt. removed.   Butterfield 21-189 1978 $20

HEELY, EMMA A.   Paintings Copied from Engravings. Albany, 1847. 4to., orig. full mor., a.e.g.   Wolfe 39-233 1978 $500

HEENEY, CANON BERTAL   I Walk with a Bishop. Toronto, 1939. Orig. binding.   Wolfe 39-147 1978 $15

HEENEY, W. B.   What Our Church Stands for; the Anglican Church in Canadian Life. Toronto, 1932. Blank flyleaf missing.   Hood 116-298 1978 $10

HEEREN, A. H. L.   Historical Researches into the Politics, Intercourse, and Trade of the Principal Nations of Antiquity. Oxford, 1833. 3 vols., fold. map, 3/4 leather, bind. rubbed.   Biblo BL781-393 1978 $57.50

HEFFERMAN, BERNARD LEO A.M.   Some Cross-Bearers of the Finger Lakes Region. Chicago, 1925. Illus.   Austin 79-318 1978 $37.50

HEFNER-ALTENECK, J. H. VON   Serrurerie, ou les Ouvrages en Fer Forge du Moyen Age et de la Renaissance. Traduit par D. Ramee. 1870. Folio, plts., half mor., a little rubbed, gilt top.   Quaritch 983-Addenda i 1978 $450

HEGEL, GEORG WILHELM FRIEDRICH   Grundlinien der Philosophie des Rechts. Berlin, 1821. Rare 1st ed., contemp. boards, lightly rubbed, 8vo.   Gilhofer 75-55 1978 SFr 2,900

HEGEL, GEORG WILHELM FRIEDRICH   The Logic of... London, 1892. 2nd ed., 8vo., cloth.   Salloch 348-88 1978 $12.50

HEGEL, GEORG WILHELM FRIEDRICH   System der Wissenschaft... Bamberg and Wuerzburg, 1807. 8vo., half calf, first ed.   Salloch 348-87 1978 $1,200

HEHN, VICTOR   The Wanderings of Plants and Animals From Their First Home. London, 1888. Tall thick 8vo., cloth.   Salloch 345-91 1978 $40

HEIDEL, WILLIAM   The Heroic Age of Science. Baltimore, 1933. 8vo., cloth.   Norman 5-141 1978 $20

HEIDFELDIO, JOHANNE   Septimum Renata, Renovata,.... Herborn?, 1616. Octavo, full contemp. calf, blind-stamped on upper and lower covers, considered rare.   Bennett 20-100 1978 $125

HEIDRICH, E.   Alt-Niederlandische Malerei. Jena, 1910. Lg. 8vo., cloth, illus. on plts.   Van der Peet H-64-46 1978 Dfl 35

HEIGHWAY, OSBORN W. T.   Leila Ada: The Jewish Convert. Philadelphia, 1853.   Austin 79-319 1978 $17.50

HEILMAN, G. E.   Calendar of the Joel R. Poinsett Papers. Philadelphia, 1941.   Jenkins 116-1088 1978 $8.50

HEILNER, VAN CAMPEN   Adventures in Angling, a Book of Salt Water Fishing... Cincinnati, (1922). Illus., orig. blue cloth, color plts.   Americanist 102-112 1978 $20

HEILPERIN, MICHAEL A.   The Trade of Nations. 1947.   Austin 80-689 1978 $10

HEIMANN, EDUARD   History of Economic Doctrines. Oxford University Press, 1945. 1st ed.   Austin 80-690 1978 $12.50

HEIN, O. L.   Memories of Long Ago. New York, 1925. First ed., illus.   Biblo 247-52 1978 $15

HEINE, HEINRICH   Buch der Lieder...Hamburg bei Hoffman und Campe, 1827. Hamburg, 1827. 1st ed., 8vo, calf-backed boards, preserving the orig. grey wr.   Quaritch 978-74 1978 $1,800

HEINE, HEINRICH   Works. 1906. 12 vols., cr. 8vo., orig. cloth. Howes 194-928 1978 £30

HEINEMANN, FRITZ   Odysseus oder Die Zukunft Der Philosophie. Stockholm, 1939. 8vo., bds.   Salloch 348-89 1978 $7.50

HEINEN, HENRY   Gesundheits-schatzkammer.... Lancaster, 1831. 1st ed., old decor. calf, wear, 8vo.   Americanist 101-95 1978 $15

HEINONEN, A. I.   Finnish Friends in Canada. Toronto, 1930. Illus.   Hood 116-416 1978 $22.50

HEINSIUS, DANIEL   Heinsii Danielis Herodes Infanticida, Tragoedia. Batavorum, 1632. Octavo, full early-style calf, gilt-ruled, red and black t.p. Bennett 20-101 1978 $60

HEINZ, H. J.   Catalog of the Collection of Watches Belonging to...of Pittsburgh, Deposited by Him in the Carnegie Museum. (Pittsburgh), 1917. Plts., 8vo., orig. bds., white cloth back.   Morrill 241-609 1978 $30

HEISENBERG, W.   Die Physikalischen Prinzipien der Quanten Theorie. Leipzig, 1930. 8vo., photographic illus., orig. cloth, d.w., first ed. Quaritch 977-100 1978

HEISS, H.   Die Romanischen Literaturen des 19. und 20. Potsdam, 1935. 4to., cloth, plts., some in color, text illus.   Van der Peet H-64-467 1978 Dfl 70

HEISS, M.   The Four Gospels Examined and Vindicated on Catholic Principles. Milwaukee, 1863. Orig. cl., 1st ed.   Ginsberg 16-846 1978 $17.50

HEITMAN, FRANCIS B.   Historical Register of Officers of the Continental Army During the War of the Revolution... Washington, 1914. Rev'd and enlgd. ed., very nice copy, orig. cloth.   MacManus 239-581 1978 $80

HELD, JULIUS S.   17th and 18th Century Art. Baroque Painting – Sculpture – Architecture. Englewood Cliffs, n.d. 4to., illus., some in color, fine, d.w.   Biblo B L781-603 1978 $12

HELDENBUCH, Darinn Viel Seltzamer Geschichten und Kurtzweilige Historien, von den Grossen Helden und Rysen. Frankfurt on the Main, 1590. 4to., woodcuts, fine, orig. cont. vellum over thin bds.   Schafer 19-21 1978 sFr 4400

HELEN'S Dove and Other Stories. New York, n.d. Wrappers, illus., fine, scarce. Victoria 34-383 1978 $25

HELENA'S Social Supremacy:.... Helena, 1894. Illus., maps, original printed wr. Ginsberg 14-620 1978 $300

HELFENSTEIN, J. C. ALBERTUS   A Collection Of Choice Sermons.... Carlisle, 1832. Contemp. calf, rubbing, lst ed. in English, 8vo. Americanist 101-126 1978 $20

HELLEN, ROBERT   Observations on a Speech delivered the 26th Day of December 1769, in the House of Lords of Ireland. Dublin, 1770. Half roan, 8vo. Howes 194-309 1978 £10

HELLENBROECK, A.   Specimen of Divine Truths, Fitted for the Use of Those...Who Desire to Prepare Themselves for the Due Confession of Their Faith. New York, M DCC XCI. Printed "on fine paper with large, new type", old bds., rubbed & chipped, but holding. Butterfield 21-505 1978 $50

HELLER, OTTO   Der Untergang Des Judentums. Wien/Berlin, 1931. In German. Austin 79-321 1978 $27.50

HELLER, WILLIAM J.   Historic Easton From the Window of a Trolley Car. Easton, 1911. MacManus 239-1489 1978 $25

HELLFRIED, C. F.   Outlines of a Political Survey of the English Attack on Denmark in the Year 1807. London, 1809. 8vo., unbound, lst ed. Morrill 241-192 1978 $10

HELLMAN, GEORGE S.   Lanes of Memory. 1927. First ed. Austin 82-421 1978 $11

HELLMAN, GEORGE S.   Persian Conqueror. 1935. First ed. Austin 82-422 1978 $11

HELLWALD, F. VON   Hinterindische Lander und Volker; Reisen in den Fluss gebieten des Irawaddy und Mekong; in Annam, Kambodscha und Siam. Leipzig, 1876. Cloth, plts., illus., rare, 8vo. Van der Peet 127-108 1978 Dfl 70

HELM, MRS. MARY S.   Scraps of Early Texas History. Austin, 1884. Original cloth, foxed, scarce. Jenkins 116-597 1978 $275

HELMHOLTZ, HERMANN LUDWIG FERDINAND VON   Die Lehre Von Der Tonempfindungen also Physiologische Grundlage Fur Die Theorie Der Musik. Braunschweig, 1863. 8vo., woodcuts, contemp. half lea., gilt on backstrip, dampstained, good copy, ownership inscr. of Henry von Ende, dated 1863, lst ed. Zeitlin 245-320 1978 $950

HELMS, ANTON ZACHARIAS   Travels From Buenos Ayres by Potosi to Lima.... 1807. Modern half calf, 8vo. Edwards 1012-653 1978 £25

HELOT, JULES   Histoire Centennale du Sucre de Betterave. Paris, 1912. Heliotype reproductions of rare colored caricatures, old engrs., portrs. & photos, oblong folio, orig. black & red cloth, gilt pict. fr. cover. Offenbacher 30-149 1978 $150

HELPER, HINTON ROWAN   Compendium of the Impending Crisis of the South. New York, 1860. Wis. Bell Wiley's copy. Broadfoot 46-134 1978 $12

HELPER, HINTON ROWAN   The Impending Crisis of the South: How to Meet It. NY, 1860. Rebound, Bell Wiley's Copy. Broadfoot's 44-193 1978 $10.00

HELPER, HINTON ROWAN   The Impending Crisis of the South: How to Meet It. New York. lst ed. MacManus 239-838 1978 $30

HELPER, HINTON ROWAN   Nojoque: A Question for a Continent. NY, 1867. Slightly worn, Bell Wiley's Copy. Broadfoot's 44-192 1978 $14.00

HELPFUL Visions. Salt Lake City, 1887. Orig. cloth, lst ed. Ginsberg 14-655 1978 $15

HELPS, ARTHUR   Realmah. London, 1868. 2 vols., orig. cloth, lst ed., very good. MacManus 238-271 1978 $75

HELPS, ARTHUR   The Spanish Conquest in America and Its Relation to the History of Slavery and to the Government of Colonies. London and New York, 1900-1904. 4 vols., cloth, fldg. maps. Hayman 73-253 1978 $25

HELVETIUS, CLAUDE A.   Le Bonheur, Poeme en Six Chants... Londres, 1773. 8vo, half calf, fine copy. Fenning 32-154 1978 £32

HELYOT, R. P.   Histoire Abregee et Costumes Colories des Ordres Monastiques, Religieux et Militaires, Contenant L'Histoire Abregee de ces Divers Ordres, leurs Moeurs, leurs Regles... Paris, 1837. 2 vols., 4to., hand-coloured plts., orig. printed bds. Quaritch 983-64 1978 $930

HEMANS, FELICIA DOROTHEA   The Forest Sanctuary. 1825. Lg. 8vo., recent cloth, uncut, good, first ed. P. M. Hill 142-283 1978 £9

HEMANS, FELICIA DOROTHEA   The Sceptic; a Poem. 1820. 1st ed., half title, rebound in half brown cloth, marbled bds., good. Jarndyce 16-729 1978 £15

HEMANS, FELICIA DOROTHEA   Songs of the Affections, and Other Poems. Edinburgh, London, 1830. 12mo., old half calf, gilt, rubbed, hinge partly cracked, first ed. P. M. Hill 142-284 1978 £7

HEMANS, LAWTON T.   Life and Times of Stevens Thomson Mason the Boy Governor of Michigan. Lansing, 1920. Illus. MacManus 239-793 1978 $10

HEMINGWAY, ERNEST   Across the River and Into the Trees. New York, 1950. 16mo, black cloth, repaired and somewhat rumpled d.w., Nice, lst ed., collector's cond. Desmarais 1-215 1978 $10

HEMINGWAY, ERNEST   Across the River and Into the Trees. 1950. First ed., very good, d.j., owner's bookplate. Austin 82-423 1978 $20

HEMINGWAY, ERNEST   Across the River and Into the Trees. 1950. First ed. Austin 82-424 1978 $10

HEMINGWAY, ERNEST   A Farewell to Arms. New York, 1929. Black cloth, lst ed., lst state, exceptionally fine copy, lst state dust jacket. Bradley 49-141 1978 $525

HEMINGWAY, ERNEST   A Farewell to Arms. New York, 1929. Orig. cloth, lst ed., lst issue, good, defective d.j. MacManus 238-666 1978 $50

HEMINGWAY, ERNEST   A Farewell to Arms. New York, 1929. lst ed., lst issue, very good, scarce d.j. Ballinger 11-141 1978 $135.00

HEMINGWAY, ERNEST   A Farewell to Arms. New York, 1929. 8vo, black cloth, paper labels, spine and back cover slightly spotted, lst state, ownership inscription, Nice, lst ed., collector's cond. Desmarais 1-216 1978 $45

HEMINGWAY, ERNEST   A Farewell to Arms. New York, 1929. First U.S. ed., covers dull & little marked, else good. Bell Book 16-431 1978 $28.50

HEMINGWAY, ERNEST   A Farewell to Arms. 1929. First English ed., fine, frayed d.w., orig. cloth, 8vo. Howes 194-929 1978 £15

HEMINGWAY, ERNEST   A Farewell to Arms. New York, 1929. First US ed., very good. Bell Book 17-446 1978 £42.50

HEMINGWAY, ERNEST   A Farewell to Arms. 1929. Movie ed. Austin 82-425 1978 $10

HEMINGWAY, ERNEST   A Farewell to Arms. New York, 1929. Frnt. hinge cracked, d.j. Ballinger 11-142 1978 $95.00

HEMINGWAY, ERNEST   A Farewell to Arms. New York, 1932. Very good, somewhat soiled d.w. Bell Book 16-354 1978 £8.50

HEMINGWAY, ERNEST   A Farwell to Arms. (1929). 1949. Modern Standard Authors Edition, first ed., d.j., very good. Austin 82-426 1978 $20

HEMINGWAY, ERNEST   For Whom the Bell Tolls. New York, 1940. Beige buckram, lst ed., nice copy in dust jacket, chipped, lst state. Bradley 49-142 1978 $95

HEMINGWAY, ERNEST   For Whom the Bell Tolls. New York, 1940. 16mo, tan cloth, lst pr. with d.w. in lst state, near Mint, chipped and worn d.w., lst ed., collector's cond. Desmarais 1-217 1978 $70

HEMINGWAY, ERNEST   For Whom the Bell Tolls. 1940. First ed. Austin 82-427 1978 $12.50

HEMINGWAY, ERNEST   For Whom the Bell Tolls. New York, 1940. First U.S. ed., orig. linen, very good, worn d.w. Bell Book 17-447 1978 £35

HEMINGWAY, ERNEST   For Whom the Bell Tolls. 1941. Very good, worn d.w., first English ed. Bell Book 17-448 1978 £16.50

HEMINGWAY, ERNEST   For Whom the Bell Tolls. 1941. Very good, first English ed. Bell Book 16-432 1978 £6.50

HEMINGWAY, ERNEST   Green Hills of Africa. New York, 1935. 8vo, green cloth, lst issue, orig. d.w. is somewhat chipped and rumpled, nice, lst ed., collector's cond. Desmarais 1-218 1978 $50

HEMINGWAY, ERNEST   Green Hills of Africa. 1936. Drawings, buck-ram, very good, first English ed. Bell Book 17-449 1978 £22.50

HEMINGWAY, ERNEST   In Our Time: stories. 1926. Covers somewhat faded & marked, good, first English ed. Bell Book 16-433 1978 £28.50

HEMINGWAY, ERNEST   In Sicily. New York, 1949. Bkplt., near mint in d.w. Desmarais B-308 1978 $7.50

HEMINGWAY, ERNEST   Men Without Women. New York, 1927. Cloth, bookseller's stamp, else very good, 1st state. Dawson's 447-241 1978 $40

HEMINGWAY, ERNEST   The Sun Also Rises. New York, 1926. Covers soiled, spine faded, hinges sprung, good. Bell Book 17-452 1978 £26.50

HEMINGWAY, ERNEST   Three Stories and Ten Poems. (Paris, 1923). Wrappers, good, author's contemp. pres. inscription, rare, only 300 copies printed, first ed. Rota 212-30 1978 £2,650

HEMINGWAY, ERNEST   To Have and Have Not. New York, 1937. Orig. cloth, 1st ed., bookplt. removed, otherwise very fine. MacManus 238-667 1978 $25

HEMINGWAY, ERNEST   The Torrents of Spring. New York, 1926. Orig. cloth, 1st ed., bookplt. removed, otherwise very good. MacManus 238-665 1978 $100

HEMINGWAY, ERNEST   The Torrents of Spring. 1933. Covers somewhat soiled, good, d.w., first English ed. Bell Book 16-434 1978 £28.50

HEMINGWAY, ERNEST   Winner Take Nothing. New York, 1933. 8vo.; cloth, d.j. chipped, first ed., fine. Duschnes 220-139 1978 $75

HEMINGWAY, ERNEST   Winner Take Nothing. New York, 1933. First U.S. ed., fine, worn d.w. Bell Book 17-453 1978 £65

HEMINGWAY, ERNEST   Winner Take Nothing. New York, 1933. 1st ed. fine, d.j. Ballinger 11-143 1978 $75.00

HEMON, LOUIS   Maria Chapdelaine; a Tale of the Lake St. John Country. New York, 1927. Hood 116-477 1978 $17.50

HEMPEL, CHARLES JULIUS   New Homoeopathic Pharmacopoeia & Posology. New York, 1850. Sm. 8vo., spine slightly torn, 1st ed. Morrill 239-121 1978 $35

HEMPEL, CHARLES JULIUS   The Science of Homoeopathy. New York, 1874. Portr., 8vo. Morrill 239-122 1978 $27.50

HEMPEL, CHARLES JULIUS   A Treatise on the Use of Arnica in Cases of Con-tusions, Wounds, Strains, Sprains. New York, 1845. Illus., 8vo., unbound, 1st ed. Morrill 239-120 1978 $7.50

HEMPEL, JOHANNES   Die Althebraische Literatur und ihr Hellenistisch-Judisches Nachleben. Potsdam, 1930. 4to., cloth, plts., text illus. Van der Peet H-64-468 1978 Dfl 55

HEMSTERHUYS, FRANCOIS   Sophyle ou de la Philosophie...A Paris. Paris, 1778. 1st ed., 12mo, large paper, contemp. citron cor., gilt, a trifle rubbed, green mor. label, gilt edges. Quaritch 978-75 1978 $375

HENDERSON, ARCHIBALD   Bernard Shaw: playboy and prophet. New York, 1932. First U.S. ed., plts., spine faded, very good. Bell Book 16-775 1978 £7.50

HENDERSON, ARCHIBALD   North Carolina, the Old North State and the New. Chicago, 1941. 5 vols. Broadfoot 50-90 1978 $125

HENDERSON, ARCHIBALD   Old Homes and Gardens of North Carolina. Chapel Hill, 1939. Ltd. to 1,000 numbered copies, signed by Clyde Hoey, Governor, photos by Bayard Wootten. Broadfoot 50-91 1978 $150

HENDERSON, ARCHIBALD   Washington's Southern Tour 1791. Boston, 1923. 1st ed., lg. 4to, illus., very fine. MacManus 239-505 1978 $35

HENDERSON, C. L.   Ships Wake and Roads Lure. Montreal, 1937. Signed by author. Hood 117-807 1978 $15

HENDERSON, C. R.   The Social Spirit in America. Meadville, 1897. Cl., orig. binding. Hayman 71-290 1978 $7.50

HENDERSON, EBENEZER   The Annals of Dunfermline and Vicinity from the Earliest Authentic Period to the Present Time A.D. 1069-1878. Glasgow, 1879. Portrait frontis., plts., illus., stout 4to., orig. qtr. roan, internally good. K Books 244-381 1978 £15

HENDERSON, EBENEZER   Iceland; Or The Journal of a Residence in That Island, During the Years 1814 and 1815. Edinburgh, 1818. 1st. ed., 2 vols., 8vo, engraved plts., folding engraved map, some spotting & staining, sl. tear in one plt., map repaired, half calf, gilt backs. Deighton 5-128 1978 £95

HENDERSON, GEORGE COCKBURN   The Discoveries of the Fiji Islands.... 1937. Maps, illus., some folding, orig. cloth, 8vo. Edwards 1012-374 1978 £18

HENDERSON, GEORGE FRANCIS ROBERT   The Campaign of Fredericksburg Nov-Dec 1862 by a Line Officer. London, c. 1892. Cover faded, Bell Wiley's copy. Broadfoot's 44-196 1978 $90

HENDERSON, GEORGE FRANCIS ROBERT   The Science of War, A Collection of Essays and Lectures 1891-1903. London, 1916. Folding maps, Bell Wiley's copy, some pencil underlining. Broadfoot's 44-194 1978 $25

HENDERSON, GEORGE FRANCIS ROBERT   Stonewall Jackson and the American Civil War. London, 1905. 2 vols., illus., maps, fine. MacManus 239-882 1978 $22.50

HENDERSON, GEORGE FRANCIS ROBERT   Stonewall Jackson and the American Civil War. London, 1909. Maps, Bell Wiley's copy, 2 vols. Broadfoot's 44-195 1978 $30

HENDERSON, H. B.   World War II in Pictures. 1945. Illus., Vol. I only. Austin 80-130 1978 $10

HENDERSON, HELEN W.   The Pennsylvania Academy of the Fine Arts and Other Collections of Philadelphia. Boston, 1911. Illus. MacManus 239-1491 1978 $12.50

HENDERSON, HENRY F.   Religion in Scotland. Paisley, c. 1920. 8vo., orig. cloth. K Books 244-382 1978 £6

HENDERSON, J.   Great Men of Canada... Toronto, 1928, 1929. 1st. & 2nd. series, 2 vols., marginal sketches & plts. Hood's 155-17 1978 $35

HENDERSON, JUNIUS   Geology in Its Relation to Landscape. Boston, 1925. 8vo., ex-lib., 1st ed. Morrill 241-193 1978 $7.50

HENDERSON, PAUL C.   Landmarks on the Oregon Trail. New York, 1953. First ed., colored views, map, ltd. to 300 copies, signed by author and publisher, fine. Biblo 247-224 1978 $97.50

HENDERSON, PETER   Henderson's Handbook of Plants. New York, 1881. Orig. binding, minor wear, clean. Hayman 71-291 1978 $8.50

HENDERSON, PHILIP   And Morning in his Eyes: a Book about Christopher Marlowe. Boriswood, 1937. Plts., spine faded, scarce, orig. cloth, 8vo. Howes 194-1034 1978 £5.50

HENDRICK, BURTON J.   Bulwark of the Republic...the Constitution. Boston, 1937. Illus., 1st ed., d.w. Biblo BL781-65 1978 $9.50

HENDRICK, BURTON J.   The Life and Letters of Walter H. Page. New York, 1922. 2 vols., 3/4 mor. Broadfoot 50-93 1978 $20

HENDRICK, BURTON J.   Lincoln's War Cabinet. Boston, 1946. Bell Wiley's Copy. Broadfoot's 44-197 1978 $8.00

HENDRICK, BURTON J.   Statesmen of the Lost Cause: Jefferson Davis and His Cabinet. New York, 1939. 1st ed. Jenkins 116-601 1978 $8.50

HENDRICK, REE HERRING   Lineage and Tradition of the Herring, Conyers, Hendrick, Boddie, Perry, Crudup, Denson and Hilliard Families. N.P., 1916. Covers soiled. Broadfoot 50-94 1978 $40

HENDRICKS, GEORGE D.   The Bad Man of the West. San Antonio, 1950. Illus., d.j. Jenkins 116-602 1978 $10

HENDRICKSON, HENRY   Out from the Darkness. 1897. Frontis., 1st ed. Austin 79-322 1978 $27.50

HENDRY, FRANK C.   The Ocean Tramp. 1938. Roy. 8vo., orig. cloth, plts. F. Edwards 1013-95 1978 £15

HENDRYX, J. B.   Beyond the Outposts. London, n.d. Hood 117-516 1978 $12.50

HENFREY, H. W.   Guide to the Study and Arrangement of English Coins. 1870. Frontis., text figures, cr. 8vo., covers spotted, autograph letter from author tipped in. George's 635-262 1978 £6.50

HENKELS, STAN B.   The Bibliographer's Manual of American History, Containing an Account of All State, Territory, Town and County Histories, Etc. Philadelphia, 1907-1910. 5 vols., 4to., uncut, labels a bit worn.   MacManus 238-874 1978 $75

HENLEY, WILLIAM ERNEST   A Book of Verses. London, 1888. Sm.8vo, original cream stiff printed wrappers (trifle dusty), 1st ed. Ximenes 47-133 1978 $40

HENLEY, WILLIAM ERNEST   A Book of Verses. London, 1888. Good in dust stained cover. Desmarais B-310 1978 $25

HENLEY, WILLIAM ERNEST   A London Garland Selected from Five Centuries of English Verse,.... London, 1895. Quarto, gilt pictorial vellum, de luxe 1st ed., spine darkened and cover soiled, text is very fine. Victoria 34-384 1978 $75

HENLEY, WILLIAM ERNEST   Lyra Heroica. London, 1892. 1 of 100 numbered copies on Dutch handmade paper, 1st ed., thick 8 vo., bds., t.e.g. uncut, good-fine. Houle 10-156 1978 $55

HENNEPIN, LOUIS   Beschryving Van Louisiana, Nieuwelijks Ontdekt Ten Zuid-Western Van Nieuw-Urankryk Door Order Van Den Koning... Amsterdam, 1688. Half morocco. Ginsberg 14-501 1978 $350

HENNEPIN, LOUIS   A New Discovery of a Vast Country in America... 1698. 1st. issue of 1st. ed., folding maps, frontispiece, plts., modern half blue morocco, t.e.g., sm. ink stain on frontispiece, tear in maps repaired, 8vo. Edwards 1012-396 1978 £850

HENNEPIN, LOUIS   A New Discovery of a Vast Country in America. Chicago, 1903. 2 vols., fold. map, illus. Hood 116-631 1978 $120

HENNEPIN, LOUIS   A New Discovery of a Vast Country in America. Chicago, 1903. Maps, illus., index, 2 vols., cloth, slight wear at top of spine of 2nd vol. Hayman 73-254 1978 $35

HENNEPIN, LOUIS   Nouvelle Decouverte d'un tres Grand Pays Situe dans L'Amerique, Entre le Nouveau Mexique, et la Mer Glaciale. Amersterdam, 1698. 14.8 x 8.2 cm., 2 maps and 2 plts. are missing, covers missing, paper crisp and lively. Wolfe 39-234 1978 $250

HENNESSY, J. POPE   Sir Walter Raleigh in Ireland. 1883. 1st & only ed., fine parchment binding, very good, scarce. Hyland 128-397 1978 £22.50

HENNIQUE, LEON   Chronique du Temps Qui Fut la Jacquerie. Paris, (1903). 8vo., contemp. full brown levant mor., uncut, orig. wr., backstrip bound in, slipcase, bound by Lortic, ltd. ed. of 500 copies prtd., numbered copy on velin d'Arches paper. Goldschmidt 110-49 1978 $300

THE HENNY Penny Picture Book. Quarto, c.1880. Fine chromolithographed plates, handsome large gilt, red and black rooster on impressed cloth, edges worn. Victoria 34-385 1978 $15

HENOT, GEORGE   The Battles of Life. The Ironmaster. London, 1884. 3 vols., orig. cloth, 1st ed. in English, red pub. cloth, very good. MacManus 238-272 1978 $75

HENRETTA, J. E.   Kane and the Upper Allegheny. Philadelphia, 1929. Illus., 8vo., ltd. to 600 copies. Morrill 241-457 1978 $30

HENRY VIII, KING OF ENGLAND   Miscellaneous Works of...., France and Ireland: In Which are Included Assertion of the Seven Sacraments; Love Letters to Anne Boleyn... (Waltham St. Lawrence): The Golden Cockerel Press, 1924. 4to., frontis. port., vellum-backed marbled bds., 1 of 365 copies, untrimmed, spine slightly soiled, fine. MacManus 238-796 1978 $60

HENRY, ALEXANDER   Travels and Adventures in Canada and the Indian Territories Between the Years 1760 and 1776. New York, 1809. Orig. full leather bind. Hood 116-632 1978 $450

HENRY, ALEXANDER   Travels and Adventures in Canada and the Indian Territories... Boston, 1901. Maps, portraits, plts., orig. cloth, 8vo, ltd. to 700 copies. Edwards 1012-432 1978 £35

HENRY, ALLAN J.   The Life of Alexis Irenee du Pont. Philadelphia, 1945. 1st ed., 2 vols., illus., orig. cloth, pub. box, ltd. to 750 copies, very fine. MacManus 239-746 1978 $45

HENRY, CALEB SPRAGUE   The Importance of Exalting the Intellectual Spirit of the Nation. Burlington, 1836. 8vo., unbound, 1st ed. Morrill 241-194 1978 $7.50

HENRY, DAVID   An Historical Account of All The Voyages Round The World Performed by English Navigators... 1773-74. 1st. ed., 4 vols., 8vo, engraved folding & other maps, plts., half calf, gilt backs. Deighton 5-184 1978 £145

HENRY, E. C.   Sea-Woman and Other Poems. Toronto, 1945. Card cover. Hood 117-808 1978 $7.50

HENRY, JAMES   A Dialogue Between a Bilious Patient and a Physician. London, 1843. Sixth ed., bds., orig. cover soiled. Rittenhouse 49-352 1976 $15

HENRY, JOHN JOSEPH   An Accurate and Interesting Account of the Hardships and Sufferings of That Band of Heroes Who Traversed The Wilderness in the Campaign Against Quebec in 1775. Lancaster, 1812. Frontis cut out. Baldwins' 51-308 1978 $20

HENRY, MARGUERITE   King of the Wind. Chicago, (1948). Illus., some in color, by Wesley Dennis, 1st ed., few sm. stains 1st few pages. Biblo 251-527 1978 $9.50

HENRY, O. PSEUD.
Please turn to
PORTER, WILLIAM SYDNEY

HENRY, PHILIP   Diaries and Letters of .... 1883. Octavo, good. Upcroft 10-78 1978 £10

HENRY, RALPH S.   First with the Most Forrest. New York, 1944. Bell Wiley's copy. Broadfoot 46-136 1978 $20

HENRY, ROBERT   The History of Great Britain..Written on a New Plan. Dublin, 1789-94. 2nd. ed., 1st. Irish ed., folding plts., folding maps, 8vo, uniform contemp. calf, gilt ruled spines, double labels, nice set. Fenning 32-155 1978 £36

HENRY, ROBERT S.   This Fascinating Railroad Business. Indianapolis, (1942). Illus., 1st ed. Biblo BL781-231 1978 $10

HENRY, ROBERT SELPH   The Story of the Confederacy. Indianapolis, 1931. Pres. copy from author to Bell Wiley. Broadfoot's 44-198 1978 $35

HENRY, MRS. S. M. I.   Frances Raymond's Investment, or the Cost of a Boy. Chicago, 1889. Bds., little worn, stain on ft. cover. Hayman 73-137 1978 $7.50

HENRY, WILLIAM   An Epitome of Chemistry in Three Parts. New York, 1808. Enlarged & illus. plts., 4to., modern buckram, some foxing, old signature on title, very good copy, 1st Amer. ed. Norman 5-142 1978 $100

HENRY, Y.   Economie agricole de l'Indochine. Hanoi, 1932. 4to, half calf, numerous large folding maps, plans, tables, 8vo, orig. covers. Van der Peet 127-109 1978 Dfl 240

HENSCHEL-ZEHDENICK, LUDWIG   Observationes Clinicae de Chloroformi in Oculorum Operationibus Usu, Adiecta Descriptione Carcinomatis Melanodis Conjunctivae Bulbi Oculi. Berolini, (1850). Litho. plt., lg. 4to., disbound. Offenbacher 30-119 1978 $75

HENSEL, WILLIAM UHLER   The Christiana Riot and Treason Trials of 1851. Lancaster, 1911. 2nd and rev'd. ed., ltd. ed., illus., 4to., scarce. MacManus 239-1492 1978 $65

HENSLER, A.   Die Altgermanische Dichtung. Berlin, 1923. 4to., cloth, colored frontis., text illus. Van der Peet H-64-469 1978 Dfl 55

HENSON, H. H.   Retrospect of an Unimportant Life. 1942-50. Plts., 3 vols., covers dull, 8vo. George's 635-1077 1978 £5.50

HENSON, JOSIAH   Father Henson's Story of His Own Life. Boston, 1858. Frontis. port., orig. cloth, foxing, but fine. MacManus 239-839 1978 $50

HENTY, GEORGE ALFRED   At Agincourt. A Tale of the White Hoods of Paris. London, 1897. Illus. by Will Paget, orig. pict. cloth, 1st Eng. ed., fine. MacManus 238-275 1978 $50

HENTY, GEORGE ALFRED   Beric the Briton. New York, 1892. 1st Amer. ed., lightly foxed, very good, illus. Victoria 34-386 1978 $22.50

HENTY, GEORGE ALFRED   Both Sides of the Border. New York, 1898. 1st Amer. ed., illus., tips rubbed, very good. Victoria 34-387 1978 $17.50

HENTY, GEORGE ALFRED   Both Sides the Border. A Tale of Hotspur and Glendower. London, 1899. Illus. by Ralph Peacock, orig. pict. cloth, 1st ed., very good. MacManus 238-277 1978 $50

HENTY, GEORGE ALFRED   In Greek Waters: A Story of the Grecian War of Independence. 1821-1827. London, 1893. Illus. by W. S. Stacey, orig. pict. cloth, 1st ed., very good. MacManus 238-273 1978 $40

HENTY, GEORGE ALFRED   In the Heart of the Rockies. New York, 1894. 1st Amer. ed., illus., almost fine. Victoria 34-388 1978 $22.50

HENTY, GEORGE ALFRED   In the Irish Brigade. New York, 1900. 1st Amer. ed., illus. tips rubbed, very good. Victoria 34-389 1978 $22.50

HENTY, GEORGE ALFRED   The Lion of St. Mark: A Tale of Venice. 1889. 1st. ed., plts. by Gordon Browne, 8vo, orig. cloth, gilt, sound & very good copy. Fenning 32-153 1978 £12.50

HENTY, GEORGE ALFRED   A March on London. Being a Story of Wat Tyler's Insurrection. London, 1898. Illus., orig. pict. cloth, 1st Eng. ed., fine. MacManus 238-276 1978 $50

HENTY, GEORGE ALFRED   Out with Garibaldi. New York, 1900. 1st Amer. ed., illus., tips rubbed, very good. Victoria 34-390 1978 $22.50

HENTY, GEORGE ALFRED   St. Bartholomew's Eve. A Tale of the Huguenot Wars. London, 1894. Illus., orig. pict. cloth, 1st Eng. ed., fine. MacManus 238-274 1978 $50

HENTY, GEORGE ALFRED   Through Three Campaigns. A Story of Chitral, Tirah, and Ashantee. London, 1904. Illus. by Will Paget, orig. pict. cloth, 1st Eng. ed., near-fine. MacManus 238-279 1978 $40

HENTY, GEORGE ALFRED   Through Three Campaigns. London, 1904. 1st ed., illus., spine lightly faded and slight cover mottling, fine copy. Victoria 34-391 1978 $25

HENTY, GEORGE ALFRED   When London Burned. New York, 1894. 1st Amer. ed., illus., "Christmas 1894" inscription, minor cover soiling, light tip rubbing, handsome gilt and color cover vignette bright, very good. Victoria 34-392 1978 $22.50

HENTY, GEORGE ALFRED   With Clive in India. London, c. 1890. Illus., by Gordon Browne, orig. cloth, nice, 8vo. K Books 244-154 1978 £5

HENTY, GEORGE ALFRED   With Cochrane the Dauntless. New York, 1896. 1st Amer. ed., illus., text very good, enpapers scribbled, covers soiled and rubbed, spine wrinkled. Victoria 34-394 1978 $12.50

HENTY, GEORGE ALFRED   With the Allies to Pekin. New York, 1903. 1st Amer. ed., illus., very good. Victoria 34-393 1978 $22.50

HENTY, GEORGE ALFRED   With the Allies to Pekin. 1903. 8vo., 1st ed., plts., map, orig. pic. cloth, fine copy. Quaritch 979-192 1978 $50

HENTY, GEORGE ALFRED   With the British Legion. A Story of the Carlist Wars. London, 1903. Illus. by Will Paget, orig. pict. cloth, 1st Eng. ed., very fine, bookplt. MacManus 238-278 1978 $50

HENTZE, C.   Chinese Tomb Figures. A Study in the Beliefs and Folklore of Ancient China. 1928. Roy. 4to., plts., cloth. Quaritch 983-17 1978 $400

HEPBURN, J. D.   Twenty Years in Khama's Country and Pioneering Among the Batauama of Lake Ngami. London, 1895. 1st. ed., 8vo, frontispiece portrait, orig. cloth, gilt, without front free endpaper, plts. Deighton 5-213 1978 £30

HEPPENSTALL, RAYNER   Apology for Dancing. London, 1936. First ed., orig. binding, very good. Rota 211-180 1978 £6

HEPWORTH, GEORGE H.   Through Armenia on Horseback. 1898. Illus., fldg. map. Austin 79-323 1978 $27.50

HEPWORTH, GEORGE H.   The Whip, Hoe, and Sword. Boston, 1864. Rebound in red cloth. Bell Wiley's copy. Broadfoot 46-137 1978 $25

HERAUD, JOHN A.   An Oration on the Death of Samuel Taylor Coleridge. 1824. 3rd. ed., orig. stabbed pamphlet, unbound as issued. Jarndyce 16-392 1978 £12.50

HERAULD, JOHN A.   Uxmal: An Antique Love Story. 1877. 1st. ed., half title, orig. brown cloth, v.g. Jarndyce 16-730 1978 £10.50

HERAUSGEGEBEN, VON FRIDA SCHOTTMULLER   Wohnungskultur Und Mobel Der Italienischen Renaissance Mit 590 Abbildungen. Stuttgart, 1921. 4to. Baldwins' 51-91 1978 $17.50

HERBART, JOHANN FRIEDRICH   Allgemeine Padagogik aus dem Zweck der Erziehung abgeleitet. Gottingen, 1806. Very rare 1st ed., half-mor., 2 library stamps on t.p. Gilhofer 75-56 1978 SFr 2,800

HERBERMANN, CHARLES GEORGE   The Sulpicians in the United States. New York, (1916). 1st ed., 8vo, orig. cloth, illus. Morrill 241-197 1978 $12.50

HERBERT, A. P.   The Water Gipsies. London, (1930). Green cloth, 1st ed., bright copy in mended dust jacket. Bradley 49-149 1978 $25

HERBERT, EDWARD HERBERT, BARON   The Autobiography of.... 1907. 2nd ed., octavo, good. Upcroft 10-79 1978 £5

HERBERT, EDWARD HERBERT, BARON   The Autobiography of Edward Lord Herbert ofCherbury. Newtown, Gregynog Press, 1928. Folio, finely prtd. on handmade paper, wood engrs., buckram, fine copy, ltd. to 300 numbered copies. Quaritch 979-183 1978 $200

HERBERT, EDWARD HERBERT, BARON   The Life and Raigne of King Henry the Eighth. London, 1649. First ed., portrait, folio, modern qtr. calf. Howes 194-58 1978 £55

HERBERT, EDWARD HERBERT, BARON   The Life and Reign of King Henry the Eighth. London, 1683. Quarto, engraved frontispiece portrait by W. Faithorne, contemp. calf, paneled spine with red leather label. Bennett 20-102 1978 $325

HERBERT, GEORGE   The Temple. 1927. 8vo., portr., fancy cloth. Quaritch 979-244 1978 $40

HERBERT, GEORGE   Works...In Prose and Verse. London, 1846. 8 vo., frontispiece, orig. cloth, 2 vols., good-fine. Houle 10-157 1978 $60

HERBERT, HENRY WILLIAM   American Game in its Seasons. New York, 1853. 1st ed., red cloth binding, illus. by author, light wear in binding, all plates. Nestler Rare 78-79 1978 $55

HERBERT, HENRY WILLIAM   The Brothers. New York, 1835. 2 vols., orig. brown cloth, 1st ed., lightly foxed, spines worn. Bradley 49-150 1978 $200

HERBERT, HENRY WILLIAM   Field Sports of the United States, And The British Providences of America. London, 1848. 1st. Eng. ed., 2 vols., sm. 8vo, half-titles in each vol., quarter calf, gilt backs. Deighton 5-42 1978 £28

HERBERT, HENRY WILLIAM   Frank Forester's Field Sports of the United States, and British Provinces of North America. New York, 1849. 3rd. ed., plts., 2 vols., headbands repaired, frontispieces & titles browned, orig. cloth, 8vo. Edwards 1012-395 1978 £55

HERBERT, HENRY WILLIAM   Frank Forester's Field Sports of the United States and British Provinces of North America. New York, 1864. Illus., 2 vols., 8vo., orig. cloth, later prtg. of 8th ed. Morrill 241-198 1978 $32.50

HERBERT, HENRY WILLIAM   The Roman Traitor: A True Tale of the Republic. A Historical Romance. New York, 1846. 2 vols. in 1, full levant, Dan'l A. Butterfield signature, floral gilt head-bands, gilt double frame border. Greene 78-52 1978 $175

HERBERT, HENRY WILLIAM   The Warwick Woodlands. Warwick, 1921. Illus., ltd to 100 copies, autographed by Smith, very good. Nestler Rare 78-78 1978 $55

HERBERT, JOHN ALEXANDER   Illuminated Manuscripts. New York, 1911. Fully illus. Baldwins' 51-92 1978 $50

HERBERT, SOLOMON   The First Principles of Heredity. 1910. 1st. ed., illus., 8vo, orig. cloth, few neat pencil notes, blind pres. stamp on half title, very good copy. Fenning 32-156 1978 £6.50

HERBERT, THOMAS   Memoirs of the Two Last Years of the Reign of that unparallel'd Prince, of ever Blessed Memory, King Charles I. 1702. 8vo., later red mor. gilt, pres. inscription by William Godwin. P. M. Hill 142-121 1978 £95

HERBERT, THOMAS   Some Yeares Travels Into Divers Parts of Asia and Afrique... 1638. 2nd. ed., engraved title, maps, folio, contemp. calf, rebacked, few minor stains & marks in text. Edwards 1012-21 1978 £150

HERBIG, R.   Vermaechtnis der Antiken Kunst. Heidelberg, 1950. Illus. Allen 234-410 1978 $10

HERBIN, J. F.   The Marshlands and the Trail of the Tide. Toronto, 1909. 3rd. ed., card cover. Hood's 115-879 1978 $12.50

HERBRUCK, EMIL P.   Early Years and Late Reflections. Cleveland, n.d. (1923). Bds., pres. copy. Hayman 73-541 1978 $8.50

HERBSTER, MME. F.   Le Souterrain ou Les Deux Soeurs. Londres, 1807. 1st ed.?, full rich green calf, few leaves pulled, very good. Victoria 34-397 1978 $35

HERCHENBACH, WILHELM   The Coiners' Cave. Dublin, 1887. lst. ed. of this translation, sm. 8vo, orig. red cloth, gilt, very good. Fenning 32-157 1978 £6.50

HERDER, JOHANN GOTTFRIED   Verstand Und Erfahrung. Frankfurt and Leipzig, 1799. 2 vols. in 1, 8vo., cortemp. bds. Salloch 348-91 1978 $150

HERE Begynneth a Good Boke of Medycynes Called the Treasure of Poore Men. (London, 1539). Sm. 8vo., woodcut, prtd. in Black letter, Riviere binding of red mor., gilt inner dentelles, fine copy, scarce. Zeitlin 245-268 1978 $2,400

HERFORD, OLIVER   This Giddy Globe. New York, (1919). lst ed., illus., fine. Victoria 34-398 1978 $12.50

HERGESHEIMER, JOSEPH   The Bright Shawl. New York, 1922. Ownership inscription, very good in chipped & soiled d.w. Desmarais B-311 1978 $7.50

HERGESHEIMER, JOSEPH   Cytherea. New York, 1922. Lg. paper ed., no. 38 of 270 copies on old Stratford laid paper, fine half lea, slip box. Baldwins' 51-445 1978 $27.50

HERGSHEIMER, JOSEPH   From an Old House. New York, 1925. Illus., 4to., lst ed., ltd. to 1,050 copies, signed by author, fine copy. MacManus 239-1493 1978 $27.50

HERGESHEIMER, JOSEPH   From an Old House. New York, 1925. Ltd. ed. signed, orig. box, very fine. Baldwins' 51-446 1978 $30

HERGESHEIMER, JOSEPH   Java Hear. New York, 1919. lst ed., 1 of 100 large paper copies, signed, scarce, orig. binding, 8vo. Americanist 101-155 1978 $65

HERGESHEIMER, JOSEPH   The Presbyterian Child. New York, 1923. lst ed. 1 of 950 copies, signed by author, orig. binding, 8vo. Americanist 101-64 1978 $30

HERGESHEIMER, JOSEPH   The Presbyterian Child. New York, 1923. Decor. bds., cloth back, slipcase, lst Amer. ed., 1 of 950 numbered copies signed by author. Dawson's 447-144 1978 $22.50

HERGESHEIMER, JOSEPH   San Cristobal De La Habana. London, 1921. Unopened, fine in worn d.w. Desmarais B-312 1978 $7.50

HERGESHEIMER, JOSEPH   Swords & Roses. New York, 1929. lst ed., 1 of 70 copies, printed on vellum, tall 8vo, orig. vellum, box, bookplate removed. Americanist 101-65 1978 $50

HERGESHEIMER, JOSEPH   Swords and Roses. New York, 1929. 8vo, brown cloth, bevelled edges, silver stamped, pr. on Borzoi rag paper, uncut, near Mint, no. 102 of 225 copies signed by author, lst ed., collector's cond. Desmarais 1-221 1978 $17.50

HERGESHEIMER, JOSEPH   Tampico. A Novel. New York, 1926. lst ed., 1 of 55 signed copies, tall 8vo, orig. vellum, repaired box, bookplate removed. Americanist 101-66 1978 $50

HERING, CONSTANTINE   Biographical Sketch. Philadelphia, 1880. Some slight wear. Rittenhouse 49-347 1976 $22.50

HERIOT, GEORGE   Travels Through the Canadas Containing a Description of the Picturesque Scenery on Some of the Rivers and Lakes. London, 1807. lst ed., 4to., extremely rare, plts. in perfect unfoxed cond., fldg. frontis., near mint cond., bound in 3/4 brown calf, marbled bds., very fine copy, scarce, perfect cond. Current 24-180 1978 $1,250

HERKOMER, HUBERT VON   My School and My Gospel. 1908. Roy. 8vo., plts., some coloured, boards, canvas back, soiled, uncut. Quaritch 983-199 1978 $20

HERMANN, BINGER   The Louisiana Purchase and Our Title West of the Rocky Mts. Washington, 1898. Maps, illus. Baldwins' 51-564 1978 $20

HERMANN, BINGER   The Louisiana Purchase, and Out Title West of the Rocky Mountains, with a Review of Annexation by the U.S. Washington, 1900. Cloth, gilt, folding maps, illus. Jenkins 116-604 1978 $15

HERMES TRISMEGISTUS   Pimandras Utraque Lingua Restitutus... Bordeaux, 1574. 4to., 1/2 calf, bottom corners chipped, bind. new. Salloch 348-152 1978 $200

HERN, GORDON   The Voice of the Shepherd... Toronto, n.d. Hood's 115-934 1978 $7.50

HERNANDEZ, DON JOSE MARIA   Scrapbook. 1900's. Nestler Rare 78-73 1978 $75

HERNDON, DALLAS T.   Letters of David O. Dodd with Biographical Sketch. N.P., n.d. circa 1920. Bell Wiley 's copy. Broadfoot 46-138 1978 $16

HERNDON, W. S.   Address of W. S. Herndon, of Tyler, Before the Literary Societies of the University of Texas. Austin, 1887. Original printed wr. Jenkins 116-605 1978 $15

HERNDON, WILLIAM H.   Herndon's Life of Lincoln... Cleveland, (1949). Cloth, spine little rubbed, illus. Hayman 72-426 1978 $7.50

HERNDON, WILLIAM H.   Herndon's Lincoln... Springfield, n.d. 3 vols., fac. of 1888 ed. MacManus 239-883 1978 $30

HERNDON, WILLIAM H.   The True Story of a Great Life. Chicago, (1889). Illus., 3 vols., 8vo., lst ed., orig. cloth. Morrill 241-675 1978 $125

HERNDON, WILLIAM H.   The True Story of a Great Life. New York, 1892. 2 vols., 8vo., orig. cloth, 3rd ed., nice. Morrill 241-199 1978 $30

HERNISZ, STANISLAS   A Guide to Conversation in the English and Chinese Languages for the Use of Americans and Chinese in California and Elsewhere. Boston, 1854. Oblong original printed wr., lst ed., half morocco slipcase. Ginsberg 14-131 1978 $750

HERO OF ALEXANDRIA   Pneumatica. Urbino, 1575. Sm. 4to., woodcuts, large crisp copy, old vellum, rebacked. Quaritch 977-101 1978 $550

HERO OF ALEXANDRIA   The Pneumatics. London, 1851. 4to., ads, frontis., text illus., orig. cloth, uncut, worn, somewhat faded, light foxing, very good copy, contemp. bkplt., lst ed. in English. Norman 5-*28 1978 $175

HERODIANUS   Historiarum Libri VIII. Oxoniae, 1704. Sm. 4to., full calf, Greek & Latin text, binding shaved, joints weak. Van der Peet H-64-348 1978 Dfl 65

HERODOTUS   Euterpe. 1888. 1 of 60 lg. paper copies, half vellum, bds. scratched. Allen 234-413 1978 $10

HERODOTUS   The History of Herodotus of Halicarnassus. London, Nonesuch Press, 1935. Wood engravings, maps, cololred plt., thick sm. folio, orig. blue vellum backed buckram, ltd. ed. of 675 numbered copies. Traylen 88-269 1978 £60

HERODOTUS   The History of Herodotus of Halicamassus. (London), 1935. Thick quarto, blue vellum with blue buckram sides, t.e.g., wood-engravings by V. Le Campion, nine new maps drawn by T. Poulton, 1 of 675 copies, fine. Duschnes 220-220 1978 $250

HERON-ALLEN, EDWARD   A Manual of Cheirosophy Being a Complete Practical Handbook of the Twin Sciences of Cheirognomy and Cheiromancy. London, 1887. 3rd ed., sm. 8vo., plts., illus., frontis., brown cloth, gilt on spine, very good, bkplt. of Dr. Alfred M. Hellman. Zeitlin 245-119 1978 $22.50

HERRERA Y TORDESILLAS, ANTONIO DE   Segunda Parte de la Historia General del Mundo,.... Valladolid, 1606. Crown quarto, full early vellum, spine shaken and somewhat soiled. Bennett 20-103 1978 $275

HERREROS DE MORA, ANGEL   The Inquisition Revived. New York, 1857. Orig. binding. Wolfe 39-120 1978 $25

HERRICK, ARNOLD   This Way to Unity. 1945. Austin 79-325 1978 $10

HERRICK, FRANCIS HOBART   The American Lobster: A Study of Its Habits and Development. Washington, 1895. Illus., plts., some in color, 4to., buckram, worn, lst ed., pres. copy. Argosy Special-51 1978 $100

HERRICK, GENEVIEVE F.   The Life of William Jennings Bryan. N.P., (1925). Cloth. Hayman 72-295 1978 $7.50

HERRICK, ROBERT 1591-1674   The Hesperides & Noble Numbers. 1891. 2 vols., portrait, sm. 8vo., half mor. gilt, gilt tops. Howes 194-932 1978 £10

HERRICK, ROBERT 1591-1674   The Poetical Works. Pickering, 1825. 2 vols., frontis, portraits, lib. stamp on title pg., 1/2 morocco ex-lib. binding, rubbed, joints weak. Eaton 45-238 1978 £12

HERRICK, ROBERT 1591-1674   The Poetical Works. London: The Cresset Press, 1928. 4 vols., 8vo., orig. bds., 1 of 750 sets on mould-made paper, pencil annotations in vol. I, spines slightly darkened, but fine. MacManus 238-785 1978 $100

HERRICK, ROBERT 1591-1674   Selections from the Poetry of... New York, (1882). First Amer. ed., 4to., drawings. Biblo 247-344 1978 $42.50

HERRICK, ROBERT 1591-1674   The Star Song. (Mt. Vernon), 1924. Bds., 1 of 750 copies. Dawson's 447-145 1978 $15

HERRICK, ROBERT 1868-1938   Chimes. New York, 1926. Green cloth, first ed., bright copy. Bradley 49-151 1978 $8

HERRINGTON, RAY D.   The Western Gateway, A Tale of the Birth Years of the Republic. New York, 1944. 1st ed., ltd. to 1,050 copies. MacManus 239-198 1978 $20

HERRINGTON, W. S.   History of the County of Lennox and Addington. Toronto, 1913. Illus., 1st ed., signed by author. Hood 116-746 1978 $75

HERRINGTON, W. S.   The War Work of the County of Lennox and Addington. Napanee, 1922. Illus. Hood 117-123 1978 $17.50

HERRIOTT, WILLIAM B.   Redwood County, Minnesota: Its Advantages To Settlers. [Redwood Falls, 1878]. Double page map, original printed wr., 1st ed. Ginsberg 14-557 1978 $85

HERRON, FRANCIS   Letters from the Argentine. New York, (1943). Biblo BL781-112 1978 $9

HERSCHEL, JOHN FREDERICK WILLIAM   Astronomy. London, 1833. Post 8vo., plts., engra. title foxed, orig. cloth, printed paper label, worn. Quaritch 977-188 1978 $40

HERSCHEL, JOHN FREDERICK WILLIAM   Essays from the Edinburgh and Quarterly Reviews. 1857. Full pink diced calf gilt, 8vo. George's 635-934 1978 £7.50

HERSCHEL, JOHN FREDERICK WILLIAM   Outlines of Astronomy. London, 1887. New ed., plts., handsome tree calf, 8vo. K Books 244-155 1978 £10

HERSCHEL, JOHN FREDERICK WILLIAM   Results of Astronomical Observations. London, 1847. Lg. 4to., frontis., plts., orig. blindstamped cloth, recased, some plts. foxed, but fine copy, 1st ed. Norman 5-143 1978 $450

HERSCHEL, JOHN FREDERICK WILLIAM   A Treatise on Astronomy. 1833. First ed., 12mo., orig. bds., bit soiled, plts. Current 24-122 1978 $135

HERSEY, A.G.   Dew-drops. Boston, 1836. 12mo, original pink printed wrappers (trifle dusty), 1st ed., foxed, very good copy. Ximenes 47-135 1978 $15

HERSEY, JOHN   Hiroshima. New York, 1946. Sm. 16mo, grey cloth, well worn d.w., inscription by Hersey, collector's cond. Desmarais 1-222 1978 $10

HERTOD A TODENFELD, JOANNES FERDINANDUS   Tartaro-Mastix Moraviae Per Quem Rariora & Admiranda a Natura in Faecundo Hujus Regionis Gremio Effusa... Viennae Austriae, 1669. Frontis., sm. 8vo., contemp. vellum, re-backed, only ed., very scarce. Offenbacher 30-67 1978 $150

HERTWIG, OSCAR   Die Actinien Anatomisch Und Histologisch Mit Besonderer Berucksichtigung Des Nervenmuskelsystems. Jena, 1879. 8vo., litho. plts., orig. green prtd. wrs., fine, unopened, uncut copy, 1st ed. Zeitlin 245-120 1978 $45

HERTWIG, OSCAR   Textbook of the Embryology of Man and Mammals. London, 1905. Ticket on spine, perforation on title. Rittenhouse 49-349 1976 $12.50

HERTZ, HEINRICH RUDOLPH   Untersuchungen Ueber Die Ausbreitung der Elek-trischen Kraft. Leipzig, 1892. 8vo., half mor., v.g., first ed. Norman 5-144 1978 $500

HERTZ, HEINRICH RUDOLF   Untersuchungen ueber die Ausbreitung der Elek-trischen Kraft. Leipzig, 1892. 8vo., contemp. half mor., worn, joints weak, first ed. Quaritch 977-102 1978 $400

HERTZLER, ARTHUR E.   Diseases of the Thyroid Gland. Presenting the Experience of More than Forty Years. New York, 1942. Rittenhouse 49-351 1976 $20

HERTZLER, ARTHUR E.   Surgical Pathology of the Diseases of Bones. Philadelphia, 1930. Rittenhouse 49-350 1976 $10

HERTZLER, ARTHUR E.   Surgical Pathology of the Gastro-Intestinal Tract. Philadelphia, Lippincott, (1936). Tall 8vo., illus., red cloth, gilt on spine, fine copy, 1st ed. Zeitlin 245-121 1978 $25

HERTZLER, ARTHUR E.   Surgical Pathology of the Mammary Gland by Arthur E. Hertzler. Philadelphia, Lippincott, (1933). Tall 8vo., illus., red cloth, gilt on spine, fine copy, 1st ed. Zeitlin 245-122 1978 $25

HERTZOG, J. CARL   The Composing Stick as a Paint Brush. Irving, n.d. Dec. wrs., 1st separate ed., fine, signed by Hertzog, ed. of 150 copies, scarce. Dykes 35-271 1978 $20

HERVEY, H.   Travels in French Indo-China. London, 1933. 2nd ed., cloth, map, plates, 8vo. Van der Peet 127-110a 1978 Dfl 45

HERVEY, JAMES   Meditations Among the Tombs. 1746. 1st. ed., 2 parts in 1, errata lf., internally good copy, contemp. calf, joints weak. Eaton 45-239 1978 £35

HERVEY, JAMES   Meditations & Contemplations. Boston, 1750. 8th ed., sm. 8vo., contemp. lea., 2 vols. in 1, little worn, very good. Americanist 103-43 1978 $50

HERVEY, JAMES   Meditations and Contemplations. 1800. 2 vols. in 1, 12mo., frontis., plts., contemp. calf. Howes 194-310 1978 £5

HERVEY, M. F. S.   The Life, Correspondence and Collections of Thomas Howard, Earl of Arundel. Cambridge, 1921. 24 plts., octavo, good. Upcroft 10-362 1978 £12.50

HERVEY, THOMAS   A Letter to William Pitt Esq. Concerning the Fifteen New Regiments Lately Voted by Parliament. 1746. 1st. ed., 8vo, disbound. Hannas 54-159 1978 £18.50

HERVEY, THOMAS K.   The Book of Christmas. 1837. 1st. ed., frontis, engraved tailpiece, illus. by Robert Seymour, full brown crushed morocco, a.e.g., fine. Jarndyce 16-731 1978 £38

HERVIEU, P.   Flirt. Paris, 1890. Lg. 4to., half mor., richly blind-tooled, engr. plts., text illus., binding shaved. Van der Peet H-64-432 1978 Dfl 95

HESELTINE, W.   A Family Scene During the Panic at the Stock Exchange, in May 1835. Canterbury, 1848. 2nd. ed., orig. purple morocco, bds., spine gilt, tall copy, fine. Jarndyce 16-732 1978 £20

HESIOD   Remains, incl. Shield of Hercules. 1815. 2nd ed., half mor. Allen 234-1526 1978 $12.50

HESIOD   Les Travaux et Les Jours. Paris, 1962. Colour etchings by Jacques Villon, one of 180 numbered copies on Rives, signed by artist, folio, unbound sheets, fine, in chemise and slip case, first ed. Rota 212-31 1978 £350

HESS, FJERIL   High Adventure. 1925. Illus. with drwgs. by author, paper, 1st ed. Austin 79-326 1978 $12.50

HESSE, HERMANN   Albert Welti: Gemalde und Radierungen. Berlin, n.d. Good, colour illus., somewhat worn wraps, first English ed. Bell Book 16-435 1978 £10

HESSE, HERMANN   Demian. New York, 1923. First U.S. ed., orig. decor. cloth, good. Bell Book 16-436 1978 £75

HESSE, HERMANN   Der Steppenwolf. Berlin, 1927. Orig. blue cloth, fine, d.w., first German ed. Bell Book 16-437 1978 £85

HESSELTINE, WILLIAM B.   Confederate Leaders in the New South. Baton Rouge, 1950. Pres. copy from author to Bell Wiley. Broadfoot's 44-200 1978 $14

HESTON, ALFRED M.   Jersey Wagon Jaunts... 1926. 2 vols., illus., fine. MacManus 239-1274 1978 $65

HEUSSER, ALBERT H.   The History of the Silk Dyeing Industry in the U.S. 1927. Illus., very good. Nestler Rare 78-80 1978 $30

HEUZEY, LEON ALEXANDRE   Catalogue Antiquities Chaldeennes. Sculpture et Gravure a la Pointe. Paris, 1902. Illus., cloth. Biblo BL781-395 1978 $17.50

HEUZEY, LEON ALEXANDRE   Les Figurines Antiques de Terre Cuite du Musee du Louvre. Paris, 1883. Imp. 4to., plts., half mor. Quaritch 983-18 1978 $85

HEVERLY, C. F.   History of Monroe Township and Borough, 1779-1885... Tonawanda, 1885. Rebound. MacManus 239-1494 1978 $40

HEWINS, CAROLINE M.   A Mid-Century Child and Her Books. 1926. Illus, first ed. Austin 82-428 1978 $12.50

HEWISON, J. K.   The Covenanters, a History of the Church in Scotland from the Reformation to the Revolution. Glasgow, 1908. Plts., 2 vols., 4to., half blue crushed mor. George's 635-679 1978 £18.50

HEWITSON, WILLIAM CHAPMAN   Coloured Illustrations of the Eggs of British Birds. 1856. Coloured plts., 2 vols., covers stained, 8vo. George's 635-1007 1978 £21

HEWITT, G. G.   Insects. Ottawa, 1922. Vol. 3. Hood's 115-59 1978 $20

HEWITT, GRAILY   The Pen and Type-Design. London, Oxford University Press, 1928. 1st ed., sm. 4to., ltd. to 250 copies, illus., bound in full gold-tooled red lea., interior near mint, scarce. Current 24-221 1978 $175

HEWITT, GRAILY   The Pen and Type-Design. London, First Edition Club, 1928. One of 250 copies, full red niger mor., very nice, first ed., signed autograph pres. inscription of A.J.A. Symons. Rota 211-181 1978 £60

HEWITT, GRAILY   The Pen and Type Design. The Treyford Type. Italics. London, 1928. 4to., orig. full mor., illus., 1st ed., 1 of 250 copies printed on Barcham hand-made paper, very nice. MacManus 238-944 1978 $125

HEWITT, H. J.   Mediaeval Cheshire. 1929. Plt. Allen 234-1298 1978 £7.50

HEWITT, J.   Ancient Armour and Weapons in Europe... Oxford, 1855. Illus. in outline, 8vo. Traylen 88-384 1978 £10

HEWITT, J. O. M.   Three Lectures on "Our Bible"...Unity Church, Oak Park, Illinois. Chicago, 1875. Orig. cl., 1st ed., auto-pres. copy. Ginsberg 16-876 1978 $15.00

HEWITT, JOHN   Malborides, Sive Bellum Britannicum. N.P., (London), 1707. 1st. ed., folio, disbound, uncut. Hannas 54-160 1978 £75

HEWLETT, ESTHER   The Cook's Complete Guide. (c. 1825). Engraved frontis., title and plts., tree calf, rubbed, 8vo. George's 635-1346 1978 £40

HEWLETT, JOSEPH THOMAS   The Parish Clerk. 1841. 1st. ed., 3 vols., green half calf, marbled bds., fine. Jarndyce 16-733 1978 £55

HEWLETT, MAURICE   The Birth of Roland. Chicago, The Alderbrink Press, 1911. 1 of 400 copies, illus., Art Nouveau decor. Battery Park 1-1 1978 $25

HEWLETT, MAURICE   Earthwork Out of Tuscany. London, 1895. 8vo, green cloth, spine sun faded, Fine, ed. limited to 500 copies, 1st ed., collector's cond. Desmarais 1-223 1978 $30

HEWLETT, MAURICE   Letters to Sanchia... 1910. Wrappers. Eaton 45-241 1978 £5

HEWLETT, MAURICE   The Little Iliad. 1915. 1st. ed., coloured frontis, 3 illus. by Sir Philip Burne-Jones, orig. cloth. Eaton 45-242 1978 £5

HEWLETT, MAURICE   A Lovers' Tale. London, 1916. 2nd ed., illus., good, red cloth, gilt, bookplate of Frances, Countess of Cassillis, inscribed & signed by author. Limestone 9-150 1978 $15

HEWLETT, MAURICE   Quattrocentisteria. 1921. 4to., vol. 1 of 300 copies prtd. on special Van Gelder handmade paper, bound in Morris paper bds., unfinished crash spine. Battery Park 1-147 1978 $75

HEWLETT, MAURICE   Rest Harrow. 1910. 1st. ed., cloth, gilt, little shaken. Eaton 45-244 1978 £5

HEWLETT, MAURICE   Songs and Meditations. Westminster, 1896. Near fine. Desmarais B-316 1978 $12.50

HEWSON, WILLIAM   The Works of... London, 1846. 8vo., frontis. portr., plts., orig. green stamped cloth, gilt lettering on spine, very good, uncut, mostly unopened copy with binders' ticket, bkplts. of Drs. James Gilpin Houseman & Alfred M. Hellman, 1st ed. Zeitlin 245-123 1978 $95

HEYER, GEORGETTE   Royal Escape. London, (1938). 1st ed., 8 vo., orig. red cloth, very good. Houle 10-158 1978 $12.50

HEYERDAHL, THOR   The Kon-Tiki Expedition: by raft across the South Seas. 1950. Plts., very good, torn d.w., first English ed. Bell Book 16-438 1978 £6.50

HEYLYN, PETTER   Ecclesia Restaurata.... 1849. 2 vols., octavo, good. Upcroft 10-80 1978 £15

HEYLYN, PETER   A Help to English History, a Succession of all the Kings of England, the English Saxons, and the Britains, the Kings and Princes of Wales, the Kings and Lords of Man, the Isle of Wight. 1680. Coats of arms, 12mo., old calf, worn. George's 635-680 1978 £7.50

HEYMANN, HANS   Property - Life Insurance. 1939. Austin 80-691 1978 $12.50

HEYSHAM, THEODORE   Norristown 1812-1912... Norristown, 1913. Illus., rear cover stained. MacManus 239-1495 1978 $15

HEYSINGER, ISAAC W.   Antietam and Maryland and Virginia Campaigns of 1862. New York, 1912. Bell Wiley 's copy. Broadfoot 46-139 1978 $20

HEYSINGER, ISAAC W.   The Organ Mountains of New Mexico. Philadelphia, 1882. Illus., map, orig. pr. wr., 1st ed. Ginsberg 14-763 1978 $150

HEYWOOD, JOHN   The Proverbs and Epigrams, 1562. 1867. Sm. 4to., orig. wrappers, reprinted from orig. ed. Howes 194-1212a 1978 £7.50

HEYWOOD, THOMAS   Gynaikeion. London, 1624. First ed., folio, orig. 17th cent. calf, expertly rebacked, raised bands, leather label. Bennett 20-104 1978 $350

HEYWOOD, WAKEFIELD   A Completed Century 1826-1926. The Story of Heywood Wakefield Company. Boston, 1926. Austin 80-692 1978 $12.50

HEYWOOD, WILLIAM SWEETZER   Westminster, Mass., History of from the Date of the Original Grant of the Township to the Present Time, 1728-1893. Lowell, 1893. Illus. with portraits, maps. Baldwins' 51-407 1978 $35

HIATT, JAMES M.   The Voter's Text Book... Indianapolis, 1868. Cloth, slight wear at extremities. Hayman 72-297 1978 $10

HIBBERD, SHIRLEY   Clever Dogs, Horses, etc. with Anecdotes of Other Animals. London, c.1871. Plates by Harrison Weir, and others; impressed cover design in gilt and blind plus inset color plate, edges rubbed, very good. Victoria 34-401 1978 $25

HIBBERD, SHIRLEY   The Seaweed Collector. London, c. 1880. Coloured plts., wood engrav., fcap. 8vo. K Books 244-156 1978 £15

HIBBERT, JULIAN   Plutarchus, and Theophrastus, on Superstition. 1828. 8vo., 19th-century half blue mor., t.e.g., others uncut, fine. P. M. Hill 142-33 1978 £48

HIBEH Papyri, Part 1. 1906. 4to., spine darkened, marginal stains. Allen 234-421 1978 $25

HIBERNICA: or, Some Ancient Pieces Relating to Ireland. Dublin, 1770. 8vo., 2 vols. in 1, new cloth, 1st ed. Morrill 241-183 1978 $25

HICKERINGILL, EDMUND   Gregory, Father Greybeard, With His Vizard Off... London, 1673. 1st. ed., sm. 8vo., orig. sheep, repaired. Traylen 88-270 1978 £75

HICKS, E. L.   Collection of Ancient Greek Inscriptions...Part 1. Attika. Oxford, 1874. Plts., demy folio, orig. bds., cloth back, rubbed and soiled. Forster 130-209 1978 £6

HICKS, EDWARD   Memoirs of the Life and Religious Labors of....., Philadelphia, 1851. 1st ed., foxed, 8vo., orig. binding. Americanist 101-7 1978 $37.50

HICKS, ELIAS   The Substance of Two Discourses...in New York, Dec. 17, 1824. New York, 1825. Uncut & unopened, prtd. wr. Butterfield 21-358 1978 $20

HICKS, IRL R.   The Rev.... Almanac, 1901. St. Louis, (1900). Pict. wrs. in color. Hayman 72-298 1978 $7.50

HICKS, JAMES E.   What the Citizen Should Know About Our Arms and Weapons. 1941. Illus. by Andre Jandot. Austin 80-131 1978 $10

HICKS, JOHN EDWARD   Adventures of a Tramp Printer, 1880-1890. Kansas City, (1950). 1st ed., d.w. Biblo BL781-276 1978 $9

HICKSON, M.   Ireland in the Seventeenth Century; or the Irish Massacres of 1641-2, Their Causes and Results... 1884. 2 vols., half calf, t.e.g., marbled bds., octavo, good. Upcroft 10-365 1978 £30

HICKSON, S. J.   The Pennatulacea of the Siboga Expedition...
1916. Folding map, plts., one is folding & coloured, text illus., lg. 4to, half
calf, worn. Edwards 1012-162 1978 £25

HIEBERT, PAUL G.   Sarah Binks. London, Toronto, 1947. 1st ed.,
drwgs. Hood 117-517 1978 $22.50

HIELSCHER, KURT   Picturesque Italy... New York, (1925). 4to.,
plts. Biblo BL781-624 1978 $10

HIELSCHER, KURT   Picturesque Spain... New York, n.d. 4to.,
plts. Biblo BL781-625 1978 $14.50

HIEROCLES OF ALEXANDRIA   De Providentia Et Fato. London, 1655. 8vo.,
contemp. calf, rebacked. Salloch 348-92 1978 $95

HIERONYMUS, SAINT   Epistolae. Rome, 1470. 2 vols., folio, Roman
letter, lg. and fine, little worming in vol. 2, green levant mor., arms of C.H. St.
John Hornby. Quaritch 978-76 1978 $12,000

HIGGINS, C. A.   Las Vegas Hot Springs and Vicinity. N.P.,
1897. Illus., orig. pict. pr. wr., 1st ed. Ginsberg 14-1111 1978 $65

HIGGINS, D. W.   The Mystic Spring and Other Tales of Western
Life. Toronto, 1904. Rebound in simulated leather, hinges cracked. Wolfe 39-
237 1978 $10

HIGGINS, FREDERICK ROBERT   Arable Holdings; poems. Dublin, Cuala Press,
1933. One of 300 numbered copies, nice, first ed., orig. binding. Rota 211-82
1978 £25

HIGGINS, G.   Anacalypsis, an Attempt to draw aside the Veil of
the Saitic Isis. 1836. 2 vols., 4to., binders cloth. George's 635-1430 1978
£50

HIGGINS, H. H.   Notes by a Field-Naturalist in the Western
Tropics... Liverpool, 1877. Map, plts., sm. 8vo, orig. cloth. Edwards 1012-
720 1978 £30

HIGGINS, JOSEPH T.   The Whale Ship Book. New York, (1927). 4to.,
good. Paine 78-66 1978 $25.00

HIGGINS, W. M.   The Mosaical and Mineral Geologies Illustrated
and Compared. London, 1833. 8vo., top of spine partly torn, 1st ed. Morrill
239-427 1978 $12.50

HIGGINS, WILLIAM   Experiments and Observations on the Atomic
Theory and Electrical Phenomena. Dublin, 1814. 1st ed., boards, 8vo. Gilhofer
75-57 1978 SFr 1,100

HIGGINSON, A. HENRY   The Hunts of the United States and Canada. Boston, 1908. 4to., crimson cloth, gilt, t.e.g., uncut, illus., one of 500 copies on
laid paper. Wolfe 39-238 1978 $60

HIGGINSON, THOMAS WENTWORTH   Army Life in a Black Regiment. Boston,
1870. Bell Wiley's copy. Broadfoot's 44-686 1978 $

HIGGINSON, THOMAS WENTWORTH   A Reader's History of American Literature. Boston, (1903). Orig. binding, clean, "Reading Circle Ed." Hayman 71-
293 1978 $7.50

HIGGINSON, THOMAS WENTWORTH   Tales of the Enchanted Islands of the
Atlantic. New York, 1898. Illus., first ed., orig. dec. cloth. Americanist 102-
58 1978 $20

HIGHET, GILBERT   Classical Tradition. 1949. Allen 234-424 1978
$11

HIGHMORE, A.   A Succinct View of the History of Mortmain...
1787. Half-title, orig. calf, brown label, v.g. Jarndyce 16-111 1978 £28

HILDENBRAND, JOHANN VALENTIN VON   Uber den Ansteckenden Typhus.
Vienna, 1810. 8vo., orig. printed wrs., slightly stained, frayed, first ed.
Quaritch 977-34 1978 $200

HILDEBRAND, M. F.   Antiquitates Romanae in compendum contractae,
et juxta ordinem alphabeti dispositae Bono Juventutis. Ultrajecti, 1713. Engraved
title, plates, 12mo., old vellum. George's 635-473 1978 £8.50

HILDEBURN, CHARLES R.   Issues of the Press in Pennsylvania, 1685-1784.
Philadelphia, 1885-86. 2 vols., 4to., ltd. to 300 sets, fine, orig. cloth, t.e.g.
MacManus 239-1496 1978 $100

HILDRETH, ARTHUR GRANT   The Lengthening Shadow of Dr. Andrew Taylor
Still. Macon, 1941. Rittenhouse 49-355 1976 $35

HILDRETH, RICHARD   Atrocious Judges. New York, 1856. Biblo
251-296 1978 $20

HILDRETH, RICHARD   Despotism in America: an Inquiry into the
Nature, Results, & Legal Basis of the Slave-Holding System in the U. S. Boston,
& Cleveland, 1854. 1st ed., 8vo., orig. cloth, very good. Americanist 103-87
1978 $30

HILDRETH, S. P.   Observations on the Bituminous Coal Deposites of
the Valley of the Ohio... N.P., n.d. (1836). Illus., map, plts., disbound.
Hayman 72-299 1978 $35

HILGARD, EUGENE W.   Preliminary Report of a Geological Reconnoissance
of Louisiana. New Orleans, 1869. Original printed wr. Ginsberg 14-502
1978 $27.50

HILGARD, EUGENE W.   Supplementary and Final Report of a Geological
Reconnoissance of the State of Louisiana...Made...In...1869. New Orleans,
1873. Original printed wr. Ginsberg 14-503 1978 $37.50

HILL, A.   Trees Have Names - A Portrait Gallery/Of Trees.
London, (1949). Faded green cloth, sm. 4to. Book Chest 17-185 1978 $17.50

HILL, A. F.   Our Boys. The Personal Experiences of a Soldier
in the Army of the Potomac. Philadelphia, 1890. 12mo., rebound. Biblo
BL781-15 1978 $12.50

HILL, ALFRED   The Violin-Makers of the Guarneri Family...
Illus., fine colour plts., photos, folio. Traylen 88-501 1978 £12

HILL, BRITTON A.   Protest of the Representatives of Don Louis
Labeaume and of Don Joseph Brazeau Against the Exercise of Jurisdiction over
the Location of Brazeau,..... Washington, 1862. Folded as issued, 1st ed.
Ginsberg 14-582 1978 $45

HILL, C.   Millinery, Theoretical and Practical. London,
1906. Text illus., cr. 8vo., orig. cloth. K Books 244-157 1978 £5

HILL, DANIEL HARVEY   Bethel to Sharpsburg. Raleigh, 1926. 2 vols.,
Bell Wiley's copy. Broadfoot's 44-574 1978 $75

HILL, EMMA   A Dangerous Crossing and What Happened on the
Other Side. Denver, 1914. Illus., original green ribbed cloth, 1st ed., signed
presentation copy from author. Ginsberg 14-391 1978 $300

HILL, FRANK PIERCE   Books, Pamphlets, and Newspapers Printed at
Newark, New Jersey 1776-1900. N.P., 1902. 8vo., orig. cloth, 1st ed., ltd.
to 300 copies. MacManus 238-991 1978 $35

HILL, FREDERICK T.   Emancipation of the Nation. New York, 1928.
Illus., 1st ed. Biblo 248-61 1978 $16.50

HILL, GEORGE BIRBECK   Harvard College by an Oxonian. New York,
1906. Illus. Biblo BL781-28 1978 $7.50

HILL, GEORGE CANNING   Amy Lee. Boston, 1856. Cloth, worn, cover
worn. Hayman 73-188 1978 $7.50

HILL, GEORGE F.   Arabic Numerals. Oxford, Clarendon Press,
1915. 8vo., orig. prtd. bds., uncut, unopened, head of spine slightly chipped,
but fine copy. Norman 5-9 1978 $50

HILL, GEORGE F.   Sources for Greek History Between the Persian &
Peloponnesian Wars. 1907. Allen 234-425 1978 $7.50

HILL, GEORGE W.   Vocabulary of the Shoshone Language. Salt
Lake City, 1877. Original printed wr., 1st ed., rare and valuable. Ginsberg
14-392 1978 $175

HILL, HARRY W.   Maryland's Colonial Charm. (Baltimore), 1938.
4to., illus., very fine, orig. cloth. MacManus 239-690 1978 $50

HILL, HENRY W.   The Champlain Tercentenary. Albany, 1911.
Orig. binding, clean. Hayman 71-492 1978 $10

HILL, JANET MC KENZIE   Salads, Sandwiches and Chafing-Dish Dainties.
Boston, 1899. 1st ed., illus., sm. 8vo., orig. cloth. Morrill 241-200 1978
$8.50

HILL, JIM DAN   Sea Dogs of the Sixties. Minneapolis, Minn.,
1935. Bell Wiley's copy. Broadfoot 46-140 1978 $16

HILL, JIM DAN   The Texas Navy. Chicago, 1937. 1st ed., mint
copy, d.j., one of 500 copies only, numbered and signed by author. Jenkins
116-633 1978 $125

HILL, JOHN   Botany Illustrated in Thirty-five Figures of Curious (
and Elegant Plants: Explaining the Sexual System; and Tending to Give Some New
Lights into the Vegetable Philosophy. 1759. Roy. folio, hand-coloured plts.,
light waterstain in lower blank margins, otherwise good, contemp. tree calf, bookplt. of George Gostling and his signature on t.p. Quaritch 983-338 1978
$5,000

HILL, JOHN   The British Herbal:.... London, 1756. 1st ed.,
folio, contemp. brown calf, neatly rebacked, orig. title label preserved, copperplates. Totteridge 29-52 1978 $250

HILL, JOHN   The Family Herbal, or an Account of All Those
English Plants, Which are Remarkable for Their Virtues, and of the Drugs Which
are Produced by Vegetables of Other Countries. Bungay, (1812). Color plts.,
8vo., 3/4 calf. Salloch 345-92 1978 $175

HILL, JOHN   The Family Herbal. Bungay, 1822. Hand-
coloured plts., very thumbed and age-marked, old style half calf, 8vo. K Books
244-158 1978 £30

HILL, JOHN A.   Stories of the Railroad. 1899. Frontis., first
ed., ex-lib. Austin 82-429 1978 $12.50

HILL, JOHN B.   History of the Town of Mason, N.H. From the
First Grant in 1749, to the Year 1858. Boston, 1858. 1st ed., illus., ports.,
plts., rebound, fine. MacManus 239-1073 1978 $45

HILL, N. N.   History of Licking County, Ohio. Newark,
1881. Facs. ed., orig. leatherette, fine. MacManus 239-1112 1978 $40

HILL, N. N.   History of Licking County, O. Newark, 1881.
Double columns, modern buckram. Hayman 73-548 1978 $60

HILL, ROWLAND 1744-1833   Village Dialogues, between Farmer Littleworth,
Thomas Newham, Mr. Lovegood and Others. 1833. Portrait, plts., 3 vols., sm.
8vo., orig. cloth-backed bds., entirely uncut. Howes 194-935 1978 £12

HILL, THOMAS   The Gardeners Labyrinth... London, 1577.
1st. ed., 2 parts in 1, black letter, woodcut on both titles, woodcuts, illus., sm.
4to., old marbled bds., new spine & corners. Traylen 88-652 1978 £950

HILL, WILLIAM B.   Experiences of a Pioneer Minister of Minnesota.
Minneapolis, 1892. Illus., original cloth, 1st ed. Ginsberg 14-558 1978 $30

HILLARD, E. B.   The Last Men of the Revolution. Hartford, 1864.
1st ed., 8vo., orig. sepia photos, 1/2 tan mor., light foxing on margins of photos,
text fine, marbilized slipcase, scarce. Current 24-83 1978 $430

HILLHOUSE, JAMES A.   Dramas, Discourses and Other Pieces. Boston,
1839. 1st ed., 2 vols., pres. copy from author. Greene 78-55 1978 $85

HILLIS, NEWELL DWIGHT   The Quest of John Chapman. 1904. First ed.
Austin 82-430 1978 $12.50

HILLS, ALFRED C.   MacPherson, The Confederate Philosopher.
New York, 1864. Cover spotted, Bell Wiley's copy. Broadfoot's 44-201 1978
$40

HILLS, GEORGE M.   History of the Church in Burlington, N.J.
Trenton, 1876. MacManus 239-1276 1978 $22.50

HILLYER, GILES M.   Address Delivered at the Third Anniversary Celebration of the Alpha Delta Phil Society of Miami University, on the Triumphs of
Mind. Cincinnati, 1839. Disbound. Hayman 72-548 1978 $10

HILLYER, ROBERT   The Death of Captain Nemo. New York, 1949.
Fine in chipped d.w. Desmarais B-318 1978 $12.50

HILPRECHT, H. V.   Explorations in Bible Lands During the 19th Century. Philadelphia, 1903. Illus., maps, back cover stained. Biblo BL781-397
1978 $22.50

HILTEBRANDT, P.   Ideen und Maechte... 1937. 4to. Allen 234-
426 1978 $10

HILTON, JAMES   Catherine Herself. London, 1920. First ed.,
orig. binding, very good, scarce. Rota 211-184 1978 £7.50

HILTON, JAMES   Random Harvest. London, 1941. Green cloth,
1st ed., fine in dust jacket. Bradley 49-152 1978 $10

HILTS, JOSEPH H.   Among the Forest Trees; or, How the Bushman
Family Got Their Homes... Toronto, 1888. Some signatures loosened. Hood's
115-437 1978 $35

HIMES, CHESTER   If He Hollers Let Him Go. New York, 1945.
First U.S. ed., very good, d.w. Bell Book 17-246 1978 £28.50

HIMES, CHESTER   Lonely Crusade. New York, 1947. First U.S.
ed., very good, slightly worn d.w. Bell Book 17-247 1978 £18.50

HIND, ARTHUR MAYGER   Giovanni Battista Piranesi. Plts., cr. 4to,
buckram. Traylen 88-502 1978 £15

HIND, C. LEWIS   Turner's Golden Vision. (1925). Paintings and
drawings in colour, cr. 4to., orig. decor. cloth, worn. George's 635-219 1978
£15

HIND, HENRY YOULE   Essay on the Insects and Diseases injurious to the
Wheat Crops. Toronto, 1857. Lacks endpapers, covers soiled and worn, 8vo.
George's 635-941 1978 £10.50

HIND, HENRY YOULE   Rapport sur L'Exploration de la Contree Situee
Entre le lac Superior et les Etablisse, emts de la Riviere Rouge... Toronto, 1858.
Folding map, illus., half mor. Ginsberg 14-393 1978 $200

HINDE, ROBERT   The Discipline of the Light-Horse. 1778. First
ed., plts., tables, contemp. calf, upper joint cracked, 8vo. Howes 194-311
1978 £35

HINDERER, ANNA   Seventeen Years in the Yoruba Country. London,
1873. 3rd. ed., folding map, 7 plts., cr. 8vo, name cut from head of title, title-
leaf backed, recased in slightly worn cloth. K Books 239-217 1978 £20

HINDLEY, CHARLES   The Old Book Collector's Miscellany:....
London, 1871-3. 3 vols., 1st ed., thick quartos, old woodcuts, spines worn, text
very good. Victoria 34-403 1978 $75

HINDLEY, CHARLES   Roxburghe Ballads. 1873-74. Woodcuts, 2 vols.,
new buckram, 8vo. George's 635-1478 1978 £35

HINE, CHARLES GILBERT   Woodside. The North End of Newark, N.J...
1909. Illus., orig. cloth, hinges weak, but very good. MacManus 239-1277
1978 $60

HINES, J.   Minstrel of the Yukon, an Alaskan Adventure.
New York, 1948. Hood 116-249 1978 $12.50

HINGESTON, F. C.   Royal and Historical Letters during the Reign of
Henry IV. Vol. 1, 1399-1404. 1860. Roy. 8vo., orig. qtr. roan, worn.
George's 635-750 1978 £7.50

HINGSTON, R.   A Naturalist in Hindustan. Boston, (c. 1922).
8vo, orig. cloth. Book Chest 17-186 1978 $35

HINKE, WILLIAM J.   A History of the Tohickon Union Church, Bed-
minster Township, Bucks County, Pa. Meadville, 1925. Illus., ltd. to 200
copies. MacManus 239-1497 1978 $30

HINKE, WILLIAM J.   Life and Letters of the Rev. John Philip Boehm
Founder of the Reformed Church in Penna. Philadelphia, 1916. Orig. cloth,
illus., scarce. MacManus 239-1498 1978 $30

HINKSON, HENRY A.   Dublin Verses by Members of Trinity College.
London & Dublin, 1895. 1st. ed., 4to, orig. cloth, gilt, binding little dull,
very good copy. Fenning 32-158 1978 £9

HINKSON, KATHERINE TYNAN   Shamrock. 1887. Good, orig. cloth, 1st
Eng. ed. Bell Book 16-1016 1978 £15

HINKSON, KATHERINE TYNAN   The Wild Harp; a Selection from Irish Poetry.
1913. Signed pres. copy from authoress to Joseph Campbell, very good, octavo
bound in cloth, reprint. Hyland 128-705 1978 £30

HINKSON, KATHERINE TYNAN   The Wild Harp; a Selection from Irish Poetry.
1913. 4to., very good, decor. by C. M. Watts, octavo bound in cloth. Hyland
128-704 1978 £17.50

HINMAN, ROYAL R.   A Historical Collection from Official Records,
Files... Hartford, 1842. Illus., orig. cloth, lacks front flyleaf. MacManus
239-560 1978 $37.50

HINMAN, ROYAL R.   Letters from the English Kings and Queens...to
the Governors of the Colony of Connecticut... Hartford, 1836. 1st ed., fine
copy, orig. cloth. MacManus 239-102 1978 $22.50

HINSDALE, B. A.   History and Civil Government of Ohio. Chicago,
(1896). Clean, orig. binding. Hayman 71-552 1978 $7.50

HINSHELWOOD, N. M.   Amidst the Laurentians, Being a Guide to Shaw-inigan Falls and Points on the Great Northern Railway of Canada.   Montreal, 1902. Many illus. Hood's 115-971 1978 $17.50

HINTON, RICHARD J.   The Hand-Book to Arizona: Its Resources, History, Towns, Mines, Ruins, and Scenery...   San F., 1878. Illus., maps, plates, original cloth, frayed and wearing, 1st ed. Ginsberg 14-13 1978 $75

HINTON, RICHARD J.   Rebel Invasion of Missouri and Kansas, and the Campaign of the Army of the Border, Against General Sterling Price, in October and November, 1864. Chicago, 1865. Illus., half morocco, 1st ed. Ginsberg 14-394 1978 $225

HINTS On Public Worship.... (Boston, n.d. c. 1816). Disbound. Hayman 71-294 1978 $7.50

HIPPISLEY, ALFRED E.   A Sketch of the history of ceramic art in China, with a catalogue of the Hippisley Collection of Chinese porcelains. N. P., 1900. Plts., boards, part of spine missing. Dawson's 449-44 1978 $45

HIPPOCRATES   Doctrina Hippocratis. Paris, 1613. 12mo., vellum. Salloch 345-93 1978 $110

HIPPOCRATES   The Genuine Works of Hippocrates Translated from the Greek with a Preliminary Discourse and Annotations by Francis Adams. London, 1849. 2 vols., 8vo., plts., orig. green stamped cloth, marginal stains, very good, uncut copy, bkplts. of Drs. James Gilpin Houseman & Alfred M. Hellman. Zeitlin 245-125 1978 $85

HIRSCH, AUGUST   Handbuch der Historisch-Geographischen Pathologie. Stuttgart, 1886. 3 vols., good, unmarked. Rittenhouse 49-356 1976 $65

HIRSCH, AUGUST   Handbook of Geographical and Historical Pathology. London, 1883-86. 8vo., 3 vols., orig. cloth, vol. I repaired. Gurney 75-54 1978 £40

HIRSCHAUER, C.   La Politique de St. Pie V en France (1566-72). 1922. 8vo. George's 635-1079 1978 £5

HIRSCHMAN, LOUIS J.   Handbook of Diseases of the Rectum. St. Louis, 1921. Rittenhouse 49-357 1976 $9

HIRSHBEIN, PERETZ   The Haunted Inn. Boston, 1921. 1st ed., very good. Austin 79-329 1978 $20

HIRTZ, LISE   "Il Etait une Petite Pie". N.P., 1928. Color prints, thin 4to., cloth-backed bds., worn, 1 of 300 numbered copies. Argosy Special-65 1978 $125

HIRTZ, LISE   Images dans le dos du Cocher. Paris, 1922. Unopened, strong paper wrappers. Eaton 45-245 1978 £5

HIS, WILHELM   Die Anatomische Nomenclature. Leipzig, 1895. 8vo., fldg. plts. in black & red, illus., half black lea., gilt, signature of former owner, very good copy, 1st separate ed. Zeitlin 245-126 1978 $75

HIS, WILHELM   Die Anatomische Nomenclatur. Leipzig, 1895. 4to., fold. plts., illus., bds., 1st ed. Gilhofer 74-93 1978 sFr 350

HISTOIRE d'Aboulhassan Ali Ebn Becar et de Schemselnihar Favorite du Calife Haroun Al-Raschid. Harlem, 1929. Lg. 8vo., fine full blue mor., gilt borders, t.e.g., fine colored illus. by M.A.J. Bauer, scarce. Van der Peet H-64-247 Dfl 250

HISTOIRE De L'Invention De L'Imprimerie par les Monuments Paris. 4to., illus., facsimiles, sm. folio, 3/4 lea., marbled paper over bds., decor. endpapers, holographic inscrip., pres. copy from publisher, from the library of Jackson Burke with his bkplt. Battery Park 1-154 1978 $125

THE HISTORIAN'S Guide. 1679. Second ed., 12mo., contemp. sprinkled calf. P. M. Hill 142-5 1978 £21

HISTORIC Nova Scotia. Halifax, n.d. Card cover, pen sketched. Hood's 115-220 1978 $12.50

HISTORIC Pulaski. N. P., (1913). Illus., 12mo., 1st ed., orig. cloth. Morrill 241-545 1978 $27.50

AN HISTORICAL Catalogue of the Old South Church (Third Church) Boston. Boston, 1883. Portrs., 8vo., orig. cloth, corners worn, 1st ed. Morrill 241-350 1978 $7.50

HISTORICAL Celebration of the Town of Brimfield, Hampden Co., Mass... Springfield, 1879. Illus., fold. map, orig. cloth, lib. marks, fine. MacManus 239-1014 1978 $35

HISTORICAL Description of the Glorious Conquest of the City of Buda. 1686. Sm. 4to., half roan, sole ed. Howes 194-22 1978 £70

HISTORICAL Records of the Queen's Own Cameron Highlanders. 1909. Coloured plts., 2 vols., imp. 8vo., orig. cloth. F. Edwards 1013-531 1978 £50

AN HISTORICAL Sketch of Los Angeles County, California:.... Los Angeles, 1876. Original printed wr. Ginsberg 14-217 1978 $125

HISTORICAL Sketches of Politics and Public Men, for the Year 1812. 1813. 8vo., tree calf. P. M. Hill 142-139 1978 £18

HISTORICAL Society of Southern California Quarterly. Los Angeles, 1884-1973. Vols. 1 through 55, unbound. Ginsberg 14-132 1978 $1100

HISTORICAL Souvenir Book. Phoenixville Home-Coming Celebration... (Phoenixville, 1910). 4to., illus., cloth, very good. MacManus 239-1651 1978 $35

THE HISTORY And Antiquities of the Parochial Church of St. Saviour Southwark. 1818. Illus. by W. G. Moss, 1st. ed., 4to, orig. half calf, marbled bds., hinges weakening, engraved plts. Jarndyce 16-1070 1978 £22

A HISTORY and Biographical Cyclopaedia of Butler County, Ohio... Cincinnati, 1882. 1st ed., folio, illus., orig. 3/4 calf, very good. MacManus 239-1105 1978 $85

HISTORY of Allegheny Co., Penna., 1753-1876. Philadelphia, 1876. Sm. folio, orig. leather-backed cloth bds., very scarce. MacManus 239-1351 1978 $225

HISTORY of Allegheny County, Pa. Chicago, 1889. 4to., illus., 2 vols., fine, orig. 1/2 leather, very scarce. MacManus 239-1352 1978 $135

HISTORY Of Allen County, Ohio. Chicago, 1885. 1/2 leather, some dampstaining, minor spine wear. Hayman 71-509 1978 $55

HISTORY of Almeda, California, Including Its Geology, Topography, Soil and Productions;.... Oakland, 1883. Illus., old cloth with leather labels, 1st ed., autograph presentation inscription from publisher. Ginsberg 14-133 1978 $175

THE HISTORY of an Irish Family. Haddington, 1822. Sm. 8vo., 1st ed., frontis., orig. wrs., uncut, from the library of Thomas Hugo with bkplt., rare. Quaritch 979-31 1978 $175

HISTORY of Beaver Co., Penna... Illus., lg. thick 4to., rebound, very scarce. MacManus 239-1367 1978 $150

HISTORY of Bedford, N.H... Boston, 1851. Fold. map, orig. cloth, lib. marks, very good. MacManus 239-1064 1978 $25

A HISTORY of Birds. Concord, 1843. Chapbook, pictorial wrappers, almost fine. Victoria 34-404 1978 $15

HISTORY of Bradford County, Penna. 1770-1878. Philadelphia, 1878. Lg. 4to., orig. leather back and cloth bds., illus., very scarce. MacManus 239-1382 1978 $135

HISTORY of Cattaraugus County, N.Y. Philadelphia, 1879. Illus., 4to., rebound, scarce. MacManus 239-1082 1978 $75

HISTORY of Cayuga County...1775 to 1908. Auburn, 1908. Sm. 4to., plts., 3/4 lea., all edges gilt, nice copy. Butterfield 21-108 1978 $35

HISTORY OF Cincinnati and Hamilton County, Ohio; Their Past and Present. Cincinnati, 1894. Morocco. Hayman 71-546 1978 $52.50

HISTORY of Cincinnati and Hamilton County, Ohio. Cincinnati, 1894. Mor. Hayman 73-537 1978 $55

HISTORY of Clermont Co., Ohio... Philadelphia, 1880. 4to., illus., half leather, recased, lib. marks, very good. MacManus 239-1106 1978 $60

HISTORY of Compton County and Sketches of the Eastern Townships... Cookshire, 1896. Illus., orig. bds., excellent cond. Hood 116-514 1978 $100

HISTORY of Crawford County, Ohio. Chicago, 1881. Double columns, mor. Hayman 73-519 1978 $60

HISTORY of Crawford County, Pennsylvania... Chicago, 1885. 1st ed., thick 4to., illus., ports., orig. half-calf and bds., hinges weak, covers worn, but good copy. MacManus 239-1427 1978 $135

HISTORY of Dearborn and Ohio Counties, Indiana. Chicago, 1885. Illus., re-bound, thick 4to., fine. MacManus 239-973 1978 $60

HISTORY of Defiance County, Ohio. Chicago, 1883. Sm. folio, illus., fine. MacManus 239-1109 1978 $95

THE HISTORY of Dublin, N.H... Boston, 1855. 1st ed., illus., ports., orig. cloth, lib. marks, fine. MacManus 239-1068 1978 $30

HISTORY of Edgar County, Illinois. Chicago, 1879. Illus., sm. 4to., old 1/2 calf, some wear, illus. MacManus 239-967 1978 $45

THE HISTORY of Edwin Judd. Philadelphia, 1829. 12mo, orig. roan-backed marbled boards, worn, woodcuts, 8vo. Americanist 101-73 1978 $20

HISTORY of Erie County, Pa. Chicago, 1884. Illus., 4to., very scarce, old 1/2 mor. MacManus 239-1447 1978 $125

HISTORY of Franklin and Cerro Gordo Counties, Iowa... Springfield, 1883. 1st ed., illus., ports., thick 4to., orig. leather, very good. MacManus 239-977 1978 $65

HISTORY of Franklin County, Pa... Chicago, 1887. Illus., 4to., old 1/2 leather, spine worn, scarce. MacManus 239-1460 1978 $95

HISTORY of Hendricks County, Indiana... Chicago, 1885. Modern cloth. Hayman 72-353 1978 $65

HISTORY of Hicking Valley, Ohio. Chicago, 1883. 1st ed., thick 4to., illus., cloth, some soiling, but very good. MacManus 239-1111 1978 $65

THE HISTORY Of Johnny Armstrong Of Westmoreland. Burlem, 1799. 12mo, wood-cuts, upper wrapper darkened and small tear on bottom edge, very scarce. Victoria 34-405 1978 $35

HISTORY of Johnson County, Iowa... Iowa City, 1883. 1st ed., 4to., illus., orig. 3/4 mor. and cloth, fine. MacManus 239-978 1978 $75

HISTORY of Julius Caesar. New York, 1865. 2 vols., 1st Amer. ed., orig. bind. Petrilla 13-50 1978 $10

HISTORY of Kennebunk, From Its Earliest Settlement to 1890. N.P., 1911. Orig. cloth, fine, ex-lib. MacManus 239-988 1978 $30

HISTORY of Luzerne, Lackawanna, and Wyoming Counties... New York, 1880. Illus., lg. thick 4to. MacManus 239-1542 1978 $75

HISTORY of Lycoming County. Philadelphia, 1876. 1st ed., folio, illus., orig. calf-backed cloth, worn at extremities, but very good copy. MacManus 239-1543 1978 $225

THE HISTORY Of New Holland, From Its First Discovery in 1616... 1787. 2nd. ed., folding engraved maps coloured in outline, modern half calf, uncut, 8vo, one map slightly foxed, other with fore-edge shaved, some slight dampstaining. Edwards 1012-334 1978 £300

THE HISTORY of New Ipwich, from its First Grant in 1736 to the Present Time, with Genealogical Notices of the Principle Families. Boston, 1852. Map, en-gravings. Biblo BL781-140 1978 $25

HISTORY of North America. Leeds, 1820. Pits., full lea. binding, excellent cond., fldg. map, restored, 2 vols. Hood 117-574 1978 $600

HISTORY of North Orange, Mass... n.d. (1924). 1st ed., oblong 4to., illus., orig. cloth, fine. MacManus 239-1043 1978 $15

HISTORY of Northampton County, Pennsylvania... Philadelphia, 1877. 1st ed., folio, illus., maps, orig. cloth, rebacked, marginal repairs, but very good copy, scarce. MacManus 239-1592 1978 $225

HISTORY of Oneida County, New York. Philadelphia, 1878. Portrs., lithos., 4to., orig. cloth, lea. back. Morrill 241-412 1978 $60

HISTORY of Otsego County. Philadelphia, 1878. Illus. & biographical sketches, 4to., frontis., litho. views & portrs., all edges gilt, orig. cloth, lea. backstrip, rubbed but sound, pencil marks on end sheets, better than average copy, scarce. Butterfield 21-344 1978 $85

THE HISTORY of Peoria County Illinois... Chicago, 1880. 4to., illus., cloth, scarce, fine. MacManus 239-969 1978 $85

HISTORY of Portage County, Ohio... Chicago, 1885. 1st ed., thick 4to., illus., orig. 3/4 calf, very good. MacManus 239-1113 1978 $85

HISTORY of Portage County, Ohio. Chicago, 1885. Mor., mod. wear. Hayman 72-564 1978 $57.50

THE HISTORY Of Prince Lee Boo. Dublin, 1822. Wood engrs., 16mo., contemp. calf, rebacked. Morrill 241-676 1978 $60

THE HISTORY of Prince Mirabel's Infancy, Rise and Disgrace;.... London, 1712. 3 vols in one, 8vo, 19th-century calf, gilt, spine gilt, (old auction sticker on front cover), 1st ed, very good copy. Ximenes 47-98 1978 $400

HISTORY of Rumson, 1665-1944. A Collection of Historical Information by the Students of Rumson H.S... (1944). Illus. Biblo BL781-151 1978 $17.50

HISTORY Of Sandusky County, Ohio, with Portraits and Biographies of Prominent Citizens and Pioneers. Cleveland, 1882. Orig. binding, clean. Hayman 71-585 1978 $25

HISTORY of Sangamon County, Illinois... Chicago, 1881. 1st ed., thick 4to., illus., orig. 3/4 calf, very good. MacManus 239-970 1978 $90

HISTORY of Schuylkill County, Pa. With Illustrations and Biographical Sketches of Some of Its Prominent Men and Pioneers. New York, 1881. 4to., illus., ports., a.e.g., orig. half-leather and cloth, recased, good copy. MacManus 239-1671 1978 $100

HISTORY of Schuylkill County, Pa., with Illustrations & Biographical Sketches of Some of its Prominent Men & Pioneers. New York, 1881. 4to, rebound, color map, portraits & views. Americanist 101-131 1978 $90

HISTORY of Seneca County, Ohio. Chicago, 1886. Mor. Hayman 73-565 1978 $60

HISTORY of Shelby County, Ohio. Philadelphia, 1883. 1st ed., folio, illus., cloth, rebound, some pgs. chipped, else nice. MacManus 239-1116 1978 $100

THE HISTORY of Singing Birds,.... Edinburgh, 1791. 12mo, contemporary calf, spine gilt, 1st ed., engraved half-title and t.p., plates, fine copy, rare. Ximenes 47-297 1978 $200

THE HISTORY of Sir Charles Grandison. London, 1754. 6 vols., 8vo., 1st octavo, lg. paper, ed., orig. calf, spines gilt, drop-back box. Quaritch 979-275 1978 $590

THE HISTORY of Sir Charles Grandison. London, 1754. 7 vols., 12mo., pol-ished calf, half brown mor. case, exceptionally fine copy with his bkplt, Edmund Gosse's copy with his bkplt. Argosy Special-76 1978 $650

HISTORY of Texas World War Heroes. Dallas, 1919. Foxed. Jenkins 116-1504 1978 $25

HISTORY of that Part of the Susquehanna and Juniata Valleys, Embraced in the Counties of Mifflin, Juniata, Perry, Union and Snyder, in the Commonwealth of Pennsylvania. Philadelphia, 1886. 1st ed., 2 vols., 4to., illus., ports., orig. cloth, recased, fine set, scarce. MacManus 239-1693 1978 $165

HISTORY of the American Field Service. Boston, 1920. Maps, plts., some in color, 3 vols., 8vo., orig. cloth. Morrill 241-10 1978 $12.50

HISTORY of the Baldwin Locomotive Works 1831-1920. (Philadelphia, c. 1920). Illus., orig. binding, 8vo. Americanist 101-81 1978 $20

THE HISTORY Of The Diocese Of Galveston: 1847-1947. Houston, 1947. Illus. Jenkins 116-482 1978 $25

HISTORY of the Excursion of the 15th Massachusetts Regiment and Its Friends to the Battlefields of Gettysburg, Antietam, Ball's Bluff and the City of Washington, D.C., September 14-20, 1900. Worcester, 1901. Tall 8vo., pencil notes in text, 1st ed. Morrill 239-509 1978 $12.50

HISTORY of the First City Troop Philadelphia City Cavalry 1774-1874. (Philadel-phia, 1875). 1st ed., nice, rebound, illus., untrimmed. MacManus 239-1618 1978 $50

HISTORY of the George Washington Bicentennial Celebration. 1932. Illus., maps, 5 vols. Nestler Rare 78-182 1978 $65

HISTORY of the Harvard Church in Charlestown, 1815-1879. Boston, 1879. Illus., 4to., new cloth, 1 of 50 quarto copies, pres. copy. Morrill 241-330 1978 $30

HISTORY of the Holy Catholic Inquisition... Philadelphia, 1835. Orig. cl. Ginsberg 16-847 1978 $10.00

THE HISTORY of the Little Old Woman Who Lived in a Shoe. New York, c.1845. Sm.8vo, hand-colored plates and text illus., later(?) marbled wrappers with color plate, very good. Victoria 34-406 1978 $30

HISTORY of the Lives and Adventures of the Most Noted Highwaymen. London, c.1805. 12mo, chapbook, modern wrappers, very good. Victoria 34-407 1978 $25

HISTORY of the Pennsylvania Hospital Unit in the Great War. New York, 1921. Rittenhouse 49-632 1976 $20

THE HISTORY of the Primitive Methodist Connexion, from Its Origin to the Conference of 1860. London, 1880. New ed., rev'd. and enlarged. Hood 116-310 1978 $10

HISTORY of the Reformed Dutch Church of Rhinebeck Flatts, N. Y. (Albany, 1931). Butterfield 21-167 1978 $10

A HISTORY of the Third Plenary Council of Baltimore, November 9-December 7, 1884. Baltimore 1885. Orig. cl., 1st ed. Ginsberg 16-848 1978 $17.50

HISTORY of Tioga, Chemung, Tomkins, and Schuyler Counties. Philadelphia, 1879. Thick tall 4to., colored frontis. map, portrs., orig. gilt cloth, lea. back, illus. & biographical sketches, good. Butterfield 21-430 1978 $65

HISTORY of Tioga, Chemung, Tomkins, and Schuyler Counties. Orig. binding, heavily scuffed, front cover & backstrip loose, plts. Butterfield 21-431 1978 $45

A HISTORY of Trenton 1679-1929. Princeton, 1929. Illus., 2 vols., ltd. to 275 sets, very nice, orig. cloth. MacManus 239-1333 1978 $75

THE HISTORY of Union County, Ohio... Chicago, 1883. 1st ed., thick 4to., illus., orig. cloth, rebacked, very good. MacManus 239-1117 1978 $90

THE HISTORY of White's, with the Betting Book from 1743-1878 and a List of Members from 1736-1892. London, (1892). 1st ed., 2 vols., lg. thick 4to., t.e.g., #222 of 500 copies, frontis, plts., illus., fine copy, 3/4 green crushed levant over marbled bds. & endpapers, sm. paint smudges at bases of spines. Current Misc. 8-48 1978 $215

THE HISTORY of Wyandot County, Ohio. Chicago, 1884. Illus., rebound. MacManus 239-1118 1978 $50

THE HISTORY of Wyandot County, Ohio... Chicago, 1844. New cloth, rebound. Hayman 72-591 1978 $60

HITCHCOCK, EDWARD   Dyspepsy Forestalled and Resisted. Amherst & Northampton, 1831. 8vo., ex-lib., worn, crudely rebacked with white tape. Morrill 239-124 1978 $10

HITCHCOCK, ENOS   Memoirs of the Bloomsgrove Family. Boston, 1790. 2 vols., 12 mo., orig. sheep, very fair, 1st ed., pres. copy. Quaritch Summer,1978-22 1978 $1,100

HITCHCOCK, ETHAN ALLEN   Fifty Years in Camp and Field. Diary of Major-Genl... New York, 1909. 1st ed., frontis. MacManus 239-1923 1978 $25

HITCHCOCK, ETHAN ALLEN   A Traveler in Indian Territory the Journal of... late Maj-Genl. in the U.S. Army. Cedar Rapids, 1930. 1st ed., illus., map, fine. MacManus 239-1924 1978 $32.50

HITCHCOCK, F. L.   History of Scranton and Its People. New York, 1914. 2 vols., illus., rebound. MacManus 239-1499 1978 $45

HITCHCOCK, P. W.   A Bill for the Relief of the Mission of Saint James. Washington, 1873. Folio. Ginsberg 14-1030 1978 $175

HITCHCOCK, ROSWELL D.   Socialism. New York, 1879. Orig. binding, clean. Hayman 71-295 1978 $10

HITCHENS, ROBERT   The Folly of Eustace & Other Stories. New York, 1896. 1st Amer. ed., red cloth, good, small tear on title page. Greene 78-223 1978 $10

HITCHENS, ROBERT   The Green Carnation. New York, 1895. 1st Amer. ed., green cloth. Greene 78-222 1978 $25

HITCHINS, FRED H.   The Colonial Land and Emigration Commission. Philadelphia, 1931. 8vo., orig. cloth, d.w., 1st ed. Morrill 241-201 1978 $10

HITLER, ADOLF   Mein Kampf, Complete and Unabridged. New York, 1939. 1st Amer. of this ed. Biblo BL781-822 1978 $12.50

HITT, J. D.   Electro-Dynamics or Electricity. The Universal Cause of Motion in Matter. Philadelphia, 1848. Looseness at upper spine. Rittenhouse 49-358 1976 $17.50

HITTELL, JOHN S.   Hittell on Gold Mines and Mining. Quebec, 1864. Half morocco, 1st ed. Ginsberg 14-134 1978 $175

HITTELL, JOHN S.   The Resources of Vallejo:.... (Vallejo, 1869). Orig. pr. wr., 1st ed. Ginsberg 14-135 1978 $175

HITTELL, THEODORE H.   The Adventures of James Capen Adams, Mountainer and Grizzly Bear Hunter of California. Boston, 1861. Illus., cloth. Ginsberg 14-2 1978 $75

HIVE: or, a Collection of Thoughts ... Hartford, 1810. Full 12mo., calf. Ginsberg 16-878 1978 $25.00

HOAR, GEORGE F.   Autobiography of Seventy Years. New York, 1903. 2 vols., ports. MacManus 239-770 1978 $15

HOARE'S Bank, a Record, 1673-1932. 1932. Illus., roy. 8vo. George's 635-333 1978 £5

HOBART, CHAUNCY   Recollections of My Life: Fifty Years of Itinerancy in the Northwest. Redwing, 1885. Illus., original cloth, 1st ed. Ginsberg 14-395 1978 $45

HOBART, WILLIAM KIRK   Medical Language of St. Luke. Dublin, 1882. Rittenhouse 49-359 1976 $35

HOBBES, THOMAS   Decameron Physiologicum. London, 1678. 8vo., panelled calf, some pages foxed & stained. Salloch 345-94 1978 $200

HOBBES, THOMAS   Elementa Philosophica de Cive.... Amsterodami, 1669. 12mo, full contemp.calf, gilt spine, very good. Bennett 20-105 1978 $50

HOBBES, THOMAS   Leviathan, or the Matter, Forme, and Power of a Commonwealth Ecclesiasticall and Civil. London, 1651. Quarto, full period calf, raised spine bands, expertly rehinged, 1st ed, 1st issue. Bennett 7-56 1978 $1,500

HOBBES, THOMAS   Mellificium Mensionis. London, 1727. 8vo., contemp. calf, portrait, plts. Gurney 75-55 1978 £60

HOBBES, THOMAS   Hobb's Tripos, in Three Discourses. London, 1684. 3rd ed., 8vo., 1/2 calf, 1st collected ed. Salloch 345-95 1978 $225

HOBBS, C. A.   Vicksburg. Chicago, 1880. Illus., 8vo., orig. cloth, 1st ed. Morrill 241-368 1978 $17.50

HOBBS, GEORGE W.   The Gasoline Automobile. New York, 1920. 2nd. ed., orig. binding, clean. Hayman 71-297 1978 $8.50

HOBBS, GEORGE W.   The Gasoline Automobile. (1919) 1920. Illus. with photos. Austin 80-694 1978 $10

HOBBS, H.   The Crayfishes of Florida. 1942. Wr., large 8vo, orig. cloth. Book Chest 17-187 1978 $22

HOBBS, SAMUEL HUNTINGTON, JR.   North Carolina: Economic and Social. Chapel Hill, 1930. Broadfoot 50-97 1978 $10

HOBBS, WILLIAM HERBERT   Characteristics of Existing Glaciers. New York, 1911. Illus., 8vo., orig. cloth, 1st ed. Morrill 241-202 1978 $15

HOBBY, A. M.   Life and Times of David G. Burnet, First President of the Republic of Texas. Galveston, 1871. Original photograph frontis, full leather, 1st ed., exceedingly rare. Ginsberg 14-64 1978 $750

HOBDAY, FREDERICK T. G.   Castration and Ovariotomy. Edinburgh, 1914. Rittenhouse 49-361 1976 $15

HOBEIKA, JOHN E.   A Tribute to the Confederate Soldier. N.P., 1930. Wrs. Bell Wiley's copy. Broadfoot 46-141 1978 $10

HOBHOUSE, JOHN CAM   Recollections of a Long Life. 1909-10. Portraits, 4 vols., orig. cloth, 8vo. Howes 194-936 1978 £18

HOBSON, GEOFFREY DUDLEY   Bindings in Cambridge Libraries. Cambridge, 1929. Ltd. to 230 copies for sale, colored plts., folio, orig. cloth, t.e.g. Forster 130-25 1978 £200

HOBSON, GEOFFREY DUDLEY   Blind-Stamped Panels in the English Book-Trade c. 1485-1555. London, 1944. Plts., fcap. 4to., orig. wrs. Forster 130-26 1978 £6

HOBSON, GEOFFREY DUDLEY   Maioli, Canevari and others. Boston, 1926. Plts., coloured, demy 4to., orig. cloth. Forster 130-24 1978 £75

HOBSON, JOHN A.   The Evolution of Modern Capitalism. 1896. Austin 80-695 1978 $12.50

HOBSON, JOHN A.   The Evolution of Modern Capitalism. 1917. New ed. Austin 80-696 1978 $10

HOBSON, JOHN A.   Poverty in Plenty. 1931. 1st Amer. ed. in dust jacket. Austin 80-697 1978 $15

HOBSON, JOHN A.   The Science of Wealth. 1911. Austin 80-698 1978 $10

HOBSON, JOHN A.   Taxation in the New State. 1920. 1st Amer. ed. Austin 80-699 1978 $15

HOBSON, JOHN A.   The War in South Africa. London, 1900. 2nd. ed., orig. cloth, 8vo, covers rather shabby. K Books 239-218 1978 £6

HOBSON, ROBERT LOCKHART   Catalogue of the Collection of English Pottery in the Department of British and Mediaeval Antiquities and Ethnography of the British Museum. 1903. 4to., plts., some in colour, buckram. Quaritch 983-107 1978 $90

HOBSON, ROBERT LOCKHART   Chinese, Korean and Japanese Potteries. Descriptive Catalogue of Loan Exhibition.... New York, 1914. 4to., coloured and plain plts., bds., cloth back, ltd. to 1,500 copies. Quaritch 983-142 1978 $300

HOCHBAUM, H.   The Canvasback on a Prairie Marsh. Washington, 1944. Scarce, ex-lib, 8vo, orig. cloth. Book Chest 17-188 1978 $60

HOCHBERG, COUNT FRITZ   An Eastern Voyage. London-New York, 1910. 2 vols., large 8vo, cloth, plts. and some in color. Van der Peet 127-112 1978 Dfl 150

HOCHSTETTER, F. VON   New Zealand, Its Physical Geography, Geology, and Natural History... Stuttgart, 1867. Folding maps, coloured plts., plain plts., wood engravings, imp. 8vo, orig. cloth, rebacked, old spine laid down, slight foxing. Edwards 1012-347 1978 £60

HOCKER, EDWARD W.   Germantown 1683-1933. Being a History of the People of Germantown, Mt. Airy and Chestnut Hill. Philadelphia, 1933. Ltd. to 500 copies, rebound. MacManus 239-1612 1978 $37.50

HOCKING, JOSEPH   "All Men Are Liars" Boston, 1895. Cloth, 1st Amer. ed., t.e.g., good. Greene 78-226 1978 $15

HODDER-WILLIAMS, RALPH   Princess Patricia's Canadian Light Infantry, 1914-1919. London, Toronto, 1923. Vol. I, fldg. maps. Hood 117-130 1978 $20

HODELL, CHARLES W.   The Old Yellow Book. Washington, 1908. Illus., quarto, 3/4 leather & bds., t.e.g, other edges, fine copy. Baldwins' 51-349 1978 $20

HODGE, DAVID   The Quest of the Gilt-Edged Girl. London, 1897. 12mo., orig. printed wrs., 1st ed., very fine. MacManus 238-190 1978 $45

HODGE, HIRAM C.   Arizona As It Is: or, The Coming Country. New York, 1877. Illus., original cloth, 1st ed. Ginsberg 14-14 1978 $75

HODGE, WILLIAM   Papers Concerning Early Navigation on the Great Lakes. Buffalo, 1883. Wrs. Hayman 73-255 1978 $12.50

HODGES, THOMAS   The Hoary Head Crowned. Oxford, 1652. 1st. ed., 4to, disbound, top edge lightly trimmed, others uncut. Hannas 54-161 1978 £8.50

HODGES, WALTER   Elihu. 1751. Old calf, joints weak, label missing, 8vo. Howes 194-312 1978 £10

HODGES, WILLIAM   Travels in India, 1780-83. 1794. 2nd. ed., folding map, engraved plts., 4to, contemp. calf, slight foxing. Edwards 1012-102 1978 £70

HODGETTS, E. A. BRAYLEY   Round About Armenia. London, 1896. 8vo., frontis., fldg. map, stains on front cover, 1st ed., orig. cloth. Morrill 241-677 1978 $30

HODGETTS, J. F.   Older England, illustrated by the Anglo-Saxon Antiquities in the British Museum. 1884. 8vo. George's 635-1176 1978 £5

HODGINS, J. B.   Report of the Historiographer of the Education Department of the Province of Ontario for the Year 1908. Toronto, 1909. Card cover. Hood 117-957 1978 $12.50

HODGKIN, FRANK E.   Pen Pictures of Representative Men of Oregon. Portland, 1882. Orig. photo frontice, orig. pr. wr. bound in half mor., 1st ed. Ginsberg 14-819 1978 $100

HODGMAN, STEPHEN A.   The Nation's Sin and Punishment... New York, 1864. 1st ed. MacManus 239-840 1978 $22.50

HODGSON, ADAM   Letters from North America, Written During a Tour of the U.S. and Canada. London, 1824. 2 vols., 1st ed., illus., library stamps, cloth, fine, fully untrimmed set. MacManus 239-200 1978 $65

HODGSON, ADAM   Remarks During a Journey Through North America in the Years 1819, 1820 and 1821, in a Series of Letters. New York, 1823. Marbled bds., lea. spine & corners, pages browned. Hood 117-575 1978 $135

HODGSON, RALPH   The Bull. 1913. Sm. 8vo., 1st ed., orig. wrs. Quaritch 979-194 1978 $15

HODGSON, RALPH   The Last Blackbird and Other Lines. London, 1907. 12mo., orig. cloth, 1st ed., 1st issue, fine, bookplt. MacManus 238-668 1978 $75

HODGSON, RALPH   The Last Blackbird. London, 1907. An immaculate, mint copy of author's 1st book still in orig. tissue wrs. Desmarais B-319 1978 $60

HODGSON, RALPH   The Muse & the Mastiff; a poem. Minerva, Ohio, 1942. 12mo., wrappers, fine, first ed. Rota 211-192 1978 £10

HODGSON, RALPH   The Mystery and Other Poems. London, 1913. 1st ed., hand-colored illus. by Fraser, wrappers, fine. Victoria 34-308 1978 $25

HODGSON, RALPH   Poems. London, 1917. Ownership inscription, cover lightly spotted, nice. Desmarais B-320 1978 $25

HODGSON, RALPH   Poems. 1917. 3rd imp., good, A.L.s. from author laid in, first English ed. Bell Book 16-440 1978 £10.50

HODGSON, RALPH   Silver Wedding and other poems. Minerva, Ohio, 1941. Second ed., wrappers, fine. Rota 211-191 1978 £5

HODGSON, RALPH   The Song of Honour. 1913. 8vo., decor. in colour, illus. wrs. Quaritch 979-195 1978 $15

HODGSON, RALPH   The Song of Honour; a poem. London, 1913. Decor. by Claud Lovat Fraser, large paper copy, uncoloured, wrappers, nice, first ed., orig. binding. Rota 211-190 1978 £10

HODGSON, MRS. WILLOUGHBY   Old English China. 1913. Roy. 4to., coloured plts., blue levant mor., gilt edges. Quaritch 983-108 1978 $190

HODIERNA, GIO. BATTISTA   Opuscoli: 1. Il Nunzio Della Terra. 2. La Nuvola Pendete. 3. L' Occhio Della Mosca. 4. Il Sole Microcosmo. Palermo, 1644. Woodcuts, 4to., half calf, gilt, very rare, fine copy. Offenbacher 30-68 1978 $800

HODSON, J. L.   British Merchantmen at War. 1945. Illus. Austin 80-132 1978 $12.50

HODSON, T.   The Cabinet of Arts. (London, 1804). Thick quarto, plates by Piranesi and others, contemporary calf, cover hinges cracked, spine crackled, very good. Victoria 34-409 1978 $65

HODSON'S Horse. Lahore, 1929. Roy. 8vo., orig. cloth, slightly worn and stained. F. Edwards 1013-578 1978 £22

HOE, ROBERT   Catalogue of the Library. New York, 1911-12. Parts 1, 2 and 4 in 6 vols., plts., med, 8vo., orig. wrs. Forster 130-28 1978 £40

HOE, ROBERT   176 Historic and Artistic book-bindings dating from the 15th century to the present time. New York, 1895. 2 vols., ltd. to 200 copies on japanese paper, colored plts., roy. 4to., half crushed levant red mor., a.e.g. Forster 130-27 1978 $300

HOECK, F. VAN   De Jezuiten te Nijmegen. den Bosch, 1921. 8vo., orig. covers. Van der Peet H-64-349 1978 Dfl 40

HOEFFDING, HARALD   Geschichte Der Neueren Philosophie. Leipzig, 1895. 2 vols., 8vo., 1/2 cloth. Salloch 348-93 1978 $30

HOEHNE, F.   Iconografia de Orchidaceas do Brasil. Sao Paulo, 1949. 4to., half leatherette, pict. bds., orig. cloth, plts., some in color. Book Chest 17-189 1978 $125

HOERNES, MORITZ   Urgeschichte der Bildenden Kunst in Europa. Von den Anfaengen bis um 500 vor Christi. Vienna, 1925. 3rd ed., illus. Biblo BL781-399 1978 $17.50

HOFF, EBBE CURTIS   A Bibliography of Aviation Medicine. Baltimore, 1942. Library markings. Rittenhouse 49-362 1976 $25

HOFFMAN, M. M.   Antique Dubuque. Dubuque, 1930. 1st ed.,
illus., orig. cloth, fine, A.L.s. from author. MacManus 239-976 1978 $30

HOFFMAN, MURRAY   Ecclesiastical Law of the State of New York.
New York, 1868. Spine torn at bottom, shaken, underscoring, ex-lib., fairly
used copy, scarce. Biblo 251-72 1978 $37.50

HOFFMAN, PAUL G.   Marketing Used Cars. 1929. Austin 80-700
1978 $15

HOFFMAN, ROBERT V.   The Olde Towne Westfield 1700-1894. Westfield, (1937). Illus., 4to. MacManus 239-1339 1978 $15

HOFFMAN'S Albany Directory and City Register, for 1847 '48. Albany, 1847.
Orig. bds., broken & loose, contents good. Butterfield 21-22A 1978 $20

HOFFMAN'S Albany Directory...for...1849 '50. Albany, 1849. Orig. bds.,
loose, backstrip gone. Butterfield 21-22B 1978 $15

HOFFMANN, E. T. A.   Nachtstucke. Munich and Leipzig, 1913.
8vo., 2 parts in 1 vol., publisher's 3/4 sheep, illus. by Alfred Kubin. Goldschmidt 110-40 1978 $90

HOFFMANN, E. T. W.   Weird Tales. New York, 1890. 2 vols., etchings by Lalauze, title page vol. I loose. Biblo 251-489 1978 $18.50

HOFFMANN, FRIEDRICH   Observationum Physico-Chymicarum Selectior-
um Libri III. Halle, 1722. 4to., cont. calf, rubbed, foxed, very good, cont.
signature, first ed. Norman 5-145 1978 $500

HOFLAND, BARBARA   Ellen, The Teacher. 1814. 2 vols., 12mo.,
orig. bds., roan backs chipped, paper largely worn away from covers, very scarce.
P. M. Hill 142-75 1978 $32

HOFLAND, BARBARA   Ellen, the Teacher. 1825. New ed., eng.
frontis, 1/4 leather. Eaton 45-248 1978 £4

HOFLAND, BARBARA   Poetical Illustrations of the Various Scenes
Represented in Mr. Linton's Sketches in Italy. 1832. 4to., bound with 24 blank
leaves, 1/2 red morocco, rubbed. Eaton 45-246 1978 £35

HOFLAND, BARBARA   Reflection. 1838. New ed., cr. 8vo, frontis,
portrait, spotted, orig. stamped cloth, corners bumped. Eaton 45-247 1978 £5

HOFLAND, BARBARA   The Sisters. Hartford, 1815. 12mo, 1st and only
ed., full calf, engraved f.p. with edge frayed, t.p. with repaired tear and bit
wrinkled, 2 leaves pulled, very good copy. Victoria 34-412 1978 $100

HOFMANN, AUGUST W.   Zur Erinnerung an Vorangegangene Freunde.
Braunschweig, 1888. 3 vols., lg. 8vo., orig. cloth, gilt, plts., very good set,
1st collected ed., inscr'd. Norman 5-146 1978 $125

HOFMANN, K.   Die Radioactiven Stoffe Nach dem Gegenwartigen Stande der Wissenschaftlichen Erkenntnis, bearfeitet von Dr. Karl Hoffmann.
Leipzig, 1903. 8vo., orig. printed wrappers, spine torn, first ed. Quaritch 977-
103 1978 $55

HOGABOAM, JAMES J.   The Bean Creek Valley. Hudson, 1876. Wrs.
Hayman 73-437 1978 $22.50

HOGAN, JAMES F.   The Irish in Australia. 1888. 3rd. ed., cr. 8vo,
orig. cloth, dull & stained, light sign of use, good & sound reading copy. Fenning
32-159 1978 £10.50

HOGAN, JOHN   Thoughts about the City of St. Louis; Her
Commerce, and Manufactures, Railroads, etc. St. Louis, 1854. Plates, disbound,
laid in cloth slipcase, 1st ed. Ginsberg 14-583 1978 $175

HOGAN, JOHN JOSEPH   On the Mission in Missouri. 1857-1868. Kansas
City, 1892. 1st ed., orig. cloth, t.p. sprung, otherwise a good copy. MacManus
239-1925 1978 $30

HOGAN, JOHN JOSEPH   On the Mission in Missouri 1857-1868. Kansas
City, 1892. Original cloth, 1st ed. Ginsberg 14-584 1978 $15

HOGAN, WILLIAM RANSOM   The Texas Republic. Norman, 1946. 1st ed.,
d.j. Jenkins 116-638 1978 $30

HOGAN, WILLIAM RANSOM   The Texas Republic: A Social and Economic
History. Norman, 1946. 1st ed., illus. Jenkins 116-639 1978 $20

HOGARTH, D. G.   The Penetration of Arabia. London, 1904.
8vo., pict. cloth, gilt stamped design, uncut, bookplate, spine dust-darkened, near
fine, 1st ed., collector's cond. Desmarais 1-224 1978 $30

HOGARTH, WILLIAM   The Analysis of Beauty... 1810. New ed.,
illus., 8vo., plts., a little foxed, fine copy in half calf gilt. Quaritch 983-200
1978 $65

HOGARTH, WILLIAM   Complete Works. c. 1865. Plts., 4to., con.
temp. half mor. Howes 194-1391 1978 £35

HOGARTH, WILLIAM   Hogarth Moralized: A Complete Edition of all the
Most Capital and Admired Works of William Hogarth. London, 1841. Calf, rubbed,
front cover loose, plts. and text fine. Biblo 247-343 1978 $75

HOGARTH, WILLIAM   Works. 1812. Plts., 2 vols., tall 8vo., contemp. polished calf, some foxing throughout. Howes 194-1390 1978 £38

HOGARTH, WILLIAM   Works. 1821. Plts., 2 vols., lge. 8vo., half
calf, rubbed. George's 635-182 1978 £20

HOGARTH, WILLIAM   Works. (c. 1845). 6 vols., sm. folio. George's
635-184 1978 £30

HOGARTH, WILLIAM   Works. (c. 1845). Steel engrav. from orig.
pictures, 4to., half mor. rubbed. George's 635-183 1978 £15

HOGARTH, WILLIAM   The Complete Works of William Hogarth in a
Series of One Hundred and Fifty Steel Engravings from the Original Pictures.
London, n.d. 4to., a.e.g., frontis., plts., rebound in blue buckram, gold lettering on spine, scuff marks to fr. bd., blue-gray endpapers, light & occas. foxing,
near fine. Current 24-222 1978 $120

HOGARTH, WILLIAM   The Works of .... London, n.d. Portraits,
plts., lg. folio, half red morocco, mottled sides, gilt edges, unusually nice copy.
Traylen 88-385 1978 £450

THE HOGARTH Letters. Hogarth Press, 1931. Cloth-backed decor. bds., very
good, first English ed. Bell Book 16-443 1978 £27.50

HOGFELDT, R.   Das Hogfeldt-Buch. Berlin, (1937). Oblong
quarto, illus., color plates, fine, dj. Victoria 34-413 1978 $17.50

HOGG, JAMES   The Brownie of Bodsbeck; and Other Tales.
Edinburgh, 1818. 2 vols, 12mo, later half calf, spines gilt, 1st ed. Ximenes
47-136 1978 $150

HOGG, JAMES   The Jacobite Relics of Scotland being the Songs,
Airs, and Legends, of the Adherents to the House of Stuart. Edinburgh, 1819-21.
2 vols., lg. 8vo., 19th-century full vellum gilt, mor. lettering pieces. P. M. Hill
142-140 1978 £75

HOGG, JAMES   The Jacobite Relics of Scotland. 1819-21. 1st.
ed., 2 vols., half title, half green morocco, gilt spines, v.g. Jarndyce 16-735
1978 £42

HOGG, JAMES   The Queen's Wake: A Legendary Poem. Edinburgh, 1814. 3rd. ed., some foxing, bookplt., contemp. 1/2 calf. Eaton 45-249
1978 £8

HOGG, JAMES   Winter Evening Tales... Edinburgh, 1820. 1st.
ed., 2 vols., fully rebound in half calf, marbled bds., fine. Jarndyce 16-736
1978 £58

HOGG, JAMES   Winter Evenings Tales Collected Among the
Cottagers in the South of Scotland. Philadelphia, 1842. 2 vols., orig. cloth,
worn spine ends, good set. Greene 78-56 1978 $30

HOGG, QUINTIN   The Case for Conservatism. Penguin Books, 1947.
1st. ed., 8vo, orig. paper wrapper, sm. fragment broken from one corner, pres.
copy to Winston Churchill. Sawyer 298-84 1978 £110

HOGUE, WAYMAN   Back Yonder. NY, 1932. Woodcuts, sketches,
Bell Wiley's copy. Broadfoot's 44-842 1978 $14.00

HOGUE, WILSON T.   History of the Free Methodist Church of North
America. Chicago, 1915. 2 vols., 1/2 lea., 2nd vol. moderately worn at extremities. Hayman 73-256 1978 $15

HOHMANN, JOHANN G.   Der Lang Verborgene Freund...Fur Menschen Und
Vieh. Demselben Ist Beigefugt Dr. G. F. Helfenstein's Vielfastig Erprobter Haus-
schatz Der Sympathie. Harrisburg, 1853. Orig. leather-backed marbled bds., a
little rubbed. Americanist 102-93 1978 $25

HOKANSON, NELS   Swedish Immigrants in Lincoln's Time. 1942.
Illus. Austin 79-332 1978 $17.50

HOKINSON, HELEN E.   So You're Going to Buy a Book. New York,
1931. 4to., 1st ed. Biblo 251-167 1978 $12.50

HOLBACH, PAUL HENRI TAIRY, BARON D' 1723-1789   Le Bons Sens Ou Idees
Naturelles Opposees Aux Idees Surnaturelles. London (Amsterdam), 1722. 8vo.,
1/2 calf. Salloch 348-94 1978 $150

HOLBACH, PAUL HENRI TAIRY, BARON D' 1723-1789   System Der Natur Von Mirabeau. Leipzig, 1841. 8vo., 1/2 cloth. Salloch 348-95 1978 $45

HOLBACH, PAUL HENRI TAIRY, BARON D' 1723-1789   Systeme Social, ou Principes Naturels de la Morale et de la Politique. London, 1773. 1st ed., octavo, contemp. half vellum over marbled bds., circular stamp of Bibliotheque Andre Mater. Bennett 20-106 1978 $225

HOLBEIN, HANS   Danse Macabre. New York, (1935). 8vo, cloth, d.j., woodcut pictures by Holbein the Younger, 1 of 155 copies, fine. Duschnes 220-143 1978 $15

HOLBEIN, HANS   Imitations of Original Drawings by...in the Collection of His Majesty, for the Portraits of Illustrious Persons in the Court of Henry VIII... 1792-1800. Atlas folio, ports., engravings mostly by Bartolozzi, handcoloured, half red mor. gilt, a little rubbed. Quaritch 983-201 1978 $4,250

HOLBEIN, HANS   Imitations of Original Drawings by... London, 1812. Quarto, cont. russia, gilt and blind tooled covers and spine, rebacked, stipple portraits printed in colours. Totteridge 29-54 1978 $600

HOLBROOK, ALFRED   Reminiscences of the Happy Life of a Teacher. Cincinnati, 1885. Orig. binding, clean. Hayman 71-553 1978 $17.50

HOLBROOK, ANN CATHERINE   The Dramatist; or, Memoirs of the Stage. Birmingham, 1809. 8vo, modern half morocco, 1st ed. Ximenes 47-137 1978 $200

HOLBROOK, JAMES   Ten Years Among the Mail Bags. Philadelphia, 1874. Illus., 8vo., orig. cloth, ex-lib. Morrill 241-203 1978 $12.50

HOLBROOK, JOHN C.   Our Country's Crisis: A Discourse Delivered... July 6, 1856... Dubuque, 1856. Original printed wr., 1st ed., rare. Ginsberg 14-411 1978 $175

HOLBROOK, STEWART H.   Ethan Allen. New York, 1946. Hood 116-250 1978 $15

HOLBROOK, STEWART H.   Little Annie Oakley and other Rugged People. New York, 1948. 1st ed. Biblo 248-258 1978 $15

HOLBROOK, STEWART H.   The Yankee Exodus. 1950. Austin 79-333 1978 $12.50

HOLCOMB, GUY R.   Texas Land Laws Annotated, With Forms. Austin, 1930. 1st ed., cloth. Jenkins 116-646 1978 $15

HOLCOMBE, ARTHUR N.   Human Rights in the Modern World. New York, 1948. Biblo BL781-823 1978 $9

HOLCROFT, THOMAS   The Road to Ruin: A Comedy. Dublin, 1792. 1st. Irish ed., 12mo, wrapper, nice copy. Fenning 32-160 1978 £10.50

HOLDEN, A. W.   Address...at the Dedication of the Hall of the Sons of Temperance...Glens Falls, Jan. 1st, 1847. Glens Falls, 1847. Disbound. Butterfield 21-462 1978 $7.50

HOLDEN, MARY ROSE   Burlington Bay, Beach and Heights, in History. Hamilton, 1898. Neatly mended. Hood's 115-816 1978 $15

HOLDEN, R.   Historical Record of the Third and Fourth Battalions of the Worcestershire Regiment. 1887. Plts., imp. 8vo., orig. cloth, joints repaired. F. Edwards 1013-504 1978 £20

HOLDER, CHARLES FREDERICK.   An Isle of Summer: Santa Catalina Island. Los Angeles, [1892]. Illus., folding map, original printed wr., 1st ed. Ginsberg 14-136 1978 $50

HOLDER, CHARLES FREDERICK   Living Lights. New York, 1887. Ex-lib. with stamp, 8vo., orig. cloth. Book Chest 17-190 1978 £20

HOLDERLIN, FRIEDRICH   Some Poems. 1943. Very good, first English ed. Bell Book 16-445 1978 £4

HOLDSWORTH, EDWARD   Remarks and Dissertations on Vergil... 1768. 1st. ed., 4to, orig. calf, 2 folding maps, v.g. Jarndyce 16-112 1978 £30

HOLDSWORTH, WILLIAM SEARLE   A History of English Law. 1903-09. 3 vols, spines faded, 8vo. George's 635-1283 1978 £10.50

HOLDT, H.   Griechenland... 19--. 4to., plt., spine frayed. Allen 234-431 1978 $7.50

HOLE, HUGH MARSHALL   The Jameson Raid. London, 1930. 2 maps, 8 plts., orig. cloth, 8vo. K Books 239-219 1978 £8

HOLE, HUGH MARHSALL   The Making of Rhodesia. London, 1926. 5 maps, 18 illus., orig. cloth, 8vo. K Books 239-220 1978 £10

HOLE, RICHARD   An Essay on the Character of Ulysses, as delineated by Homer. 1807. 8vo., 1st ed., rebound in marbled bds., from the Beckford Library with two pencil notes in his hand. Quaritch 979-24 1978 $190

HOLE, SAMUEL REYNOLDS   Our Gardens. London, 1899. No. 41 of 150 copies, full vellum, signed by author, fine copy, laid-in plate. Victoria 34-673 1978 $200

HOLFORD, MARGARET   Gresford Vale, and Other Poems. 1798. 4to., unbound, slight dampstaining, vignette. P. M. Hill 142-285 1978 £25

THE HOLFORD Collection... 1924-27. Plts., 3 vols., 4to., half vellum, gilt tops, signed by editor, ltd. to 300 no. copies. Quaritch 983-202 1978 $275

HOLINSHED, RAPHAELL   The Firste Volume of the Chronicles of England, Scotlande, and Irelande.... London, 1577. 2 vols., folio, full old calf showing wear at hinges, 1st ed. Bennett 7-57 1978 $4,500

HOLLAND, B.   The Fall of Protection, 1840-50. 1913. 8vo. George's 635-335 1978 £6.50

HOLLAND, B.   The Life of Spencer Compton, 8th Duke of Devonshire. 1911. Portraits, illus., 2 vols., 8vo. George's 635-1237 1978 £6.50

HOLLAND, HENRY   Recollections of Past Life. New York, 1872. 8vo., 1st Amer. ed. Morrill 239-125 1978 $7.50

HOLLAND, JOHN   Memoirs of the Life and Ministry of the Rev. John Summerfield. New York, 1846. Cloth. Hayman 72-303 1978 $12.50

HOLLAND, JOHN   A System of Geography. Manchester, 1798. Orig. calf, marbled bds. Jarndyce 16-113 1978 £18

HOLLAND, JOSIAH GILBERT   Arthur Bonnicastle. New York, 1873. Illus., first ed., binding faded, rubbed. Biblo 251-502 1978 $15

HOLLAND, JOSIAH GILBERT   Plain Talks on Familiar Subjects. New York, 1888. Cloth, rev. ed. from orig. ed. Hayman 73-257 1978 $7.50

HOLLAND, NORMAN   Southern Sky Trails. Montreal, 1944. Hood's 115-972 1978 $12.50

HOLLAND, RUPERT SARGENT   Historic Girlhoods. Philadelphia, (1910). Illus. Biblo 247-567 1978 $12.50

HOLLAND, RUPERT SARGENT   Pirates of the Delaware. Philadelphia, 1925. Illus. by W.H. Wolf. Baldwins' 51-225 1978 $12.50

HOLLAND, THOMAS ERSKINE   The Elements of Jurisprudence. Oxford, 1895. Inner hinges split, 7th ed. Biblo 251-341 1978 $15

HOLLANDER, EUGEN   Auferstehung. Berlin, 1923. Folio, hand-colored illuminations, full parchment binding, publisher's slipcase, fine copy, copy #4, ltd. to 1000 copies, 1st 50 prtd. on Dutch handmade paper. Zeitlin 245-127 1978 $150

HOLLANDER, EUGEN   Die Karikatur und Satire in der Medizin. Stuttgart, 1921. Lg. 8vo., cloth, colored frontis., fine colored plts., text illus., scarce, binding soiled. Van der Peet H-64-277 1978 Dfl 165

HOLLANDER, EUGEN   Die Karikatur und Satire in der Medizin. Stuttgart, 1921. Tall 8vo., color plts., frontis., guardsheets, illus., pic. beige cloth, soiled, very good copy, bkplt., 2nd ed. Zeitlin 245-128 1978 $85

HOLLANDER, JACOB HARRY   The Cincinnati Southern Railway & Memorial of Lucius S. Merriam. Baltimore, 1894. Disbound. Bell Wiley's copy. Broadfoot 46-525 1978 $10

HOLLANDER, JACOB HARRY   The Financial History of Baltimore. Baltimore, 1899. MacManus 239-1830 1978 $25

HOLLANDER, JACOB HARRY   Studies in American Trade Unionism. 1906. 8vo. George's 635-406 1978 £5.50

HOLLER, JACOB   In Aphorismos Hippocratis Commentarii Septem. Genevae, 1675. Thick 12mo., contemp. 1/2 calf, uncut, light waterstaining. Argosy Special-52 1978 $125

HOLLES, DENZIL   Memoirs, from the Year 1641 to 1648. 1699. Portrait by R. White, contemp. calf, neatly rebacked, first ed, 8vo. Howes 194-60 1978 £42

HOLLES, DENZIL   Memoirs of Denzil Lord Holles, Baron of Ifield in Sussex, From the Year 1641, to 1648. 1699. 1st. ed., 8vo, portrait, early 19th century calf, joints cracked, Ashburnham bookplt., signature on half-title of Geo. Treby. Hannas 54-162 1978 £36

HOLLEY, FRANCES CHAMBERLAIN   Once Their Home or Our Legacy from the Dahkotahs... Chicago, 1891. Illus., orig. cloth, inner hinges cracking, but a good copy. MacManus 239-1926 1978 $40

HOLLEY, GEORGE W.   The Falls of Niagara. New York, 1883. Illus. MacManus 239-341 1978 $20

HOLLEY, MARY AUSTIN   Texas: Observation, Historical, Geographical and Descriptive,.... Baltimore, 1833. Folding map, original cloth. Jenkins 116-649 1978 $1,350

HOLLEY, MARY AUSTIN   Texas. Lexington, 1836. Original cloth, original folding map, slipcased, 1st ed. Jenkins 116-1558 1978 $525

HOLLEY, O. L.   The Picturesque Tourist. New York, 1844. Maps, illus., extra engr. title page, plts., spine worn, some foxing. Hood 117-576 1978 $75

HOLLICK, FREDERICK   Male Generative Organs.... New York, 1849. Illus. Rittenhouse 49-365 1976 $10

HOLLICK, FREDERICK   The Marriage Guide or Natural History of Generations. New York, 1853. Rittenhouse 49-364 1976 $10

HOLLIDAY, CHARLES W.   The Valley of Youth. Caldwell, 1948. Dec. cloth, frontis. in color, illus., 1st ed., very good, d.w. Dykes 35-145 1978 $12.50

HOLLINGSWORTH, JOHN MC HENRY   The Journal of Lieutenant...of the First New York Volunteers (Stevenson's Regiment):.... San Francisco, 1923. Illus., original boards, limited ed. of 50 large paper copies. Ginsberg 14-533 1978 $75

HOLLINGSWORTH, S.   The Present State of Nova Scotia... Edinburgh, 1787. 2nd. ed., corrected & enlarged, 8vo, without folding map, half-title, half calf, marbled bds. Deighton 5-232 1978 £210

HOLLINGSWORTH, S.   The Present State of Nova Scotia... Edinburgh, 1787. Folding map, skilfully mounted on old paper, modern half leather, 8vo. Edwards 1012-433 1978 £120

HOLLIS, CHRISTOPHER   The Breakdown of Money. 1934. Austin 80-703 1978 $10

HOLLIS, MARGERY   Up in Arms. London, 1896. 3 vols., 12mo., orig. cloth, 1st ed., covers a bit stained and soiled, front inner hinge cracked in vol. II. MacManus 238-343 1978 $75

HOLLISTER, GIDEON HIRAM   The History of Connecticut. New Haven, 1855. 2 vols., illus., 1st ed., nice set, orig. cloth. MacManus 239-97 1978 $45

HOLLISTER, HORACE   Contributions to the History of the Lacawanna Valley. New York, 1857. 1st ed., map, orig. cloth. MacManus 239-1500 1978 $35

HOLLOWAY, EDWARD S.   American Furniture and Decoration Colonial and Federal. Philadelphia, 1928. Illus., 1st ed., nice uncut copy. MacManus 239-675 1978 $35

HOLLOWAY, LAURA C.   The Ladies of the White House. Philadelphia, (1881). Illus. MacManus 239-201 1978 $15

HOLLOWAY, WILLIAM   A General Dictionary of Provincialisms. Sussex Press, 1838. First ed., fine, orig. cloth-backed bds., 8vo. Howes 194-797 1978 £22

HOLLUNDER, CHRISTIAN FURCHTEGOTT   Die Zweckmassigste Zinkfabrikation bei Steinkohlen-Feuerung. Dresden, 1822. Fldg. copperplt., 8vo., old blue wrs., 1st ed. Offenbacher 30-69 1978 $50

HOLLWAY-CALTHROP, H. C.   Petrarch: his Life and Times. 1907. Plts., orig. cloth, 8vo. Howes 194-1093 1978 £6

HOLM, ADOLF   History of Greece From Its Commencement to the Close of the Independence of the Greek Nation. 1899-98. 4 vols., bindings slightly worn. Allen 234-432 1978 $20

HOLMAN, FREDERICK V.   Dr. John McLoughlin the Father of Oregon. Cleveland, 1907. Orig. binding, clean, scarce. Hayman 71-299 1978 $22.50

HOLME, CHARLES   The Art of the Book. London, 1914. Illus., plts., colored, demy 4to., half mor., t.e.g. Forster 130-89 1978 £45

HOLME, CHARLES   Peasant Art in Austria and Hungary. London, 1811. 816 illus., some in colour, sm. folio, binder's cloth. Traylen 88-400 1978 £15

HOLME, CHARLES   Royal Scottish Academy. London, 1907. 4to., orig. cloth, plts. in colors. Morrill 241-204 1978 $10

HOLME, CONSTANCE   Beautiful End. London, 1918. First ed., orig. binding, covers marked, very good. Rota 211-193 1978 £5

HOLME, CONSTANCE   The Things Which Belong. London, 1925. First ed., orig. binding, nice. Rota 211-194 1978 £6

HOLMES, ELEANOR   The Price of a Pearl. A Novel. London, 1894. 3 vols., orig. cloth, 1st ed., covers a bit worn, lib. labels, else very good. Mac-Manus 238-344 1978 $75

HOLMES, FLOYD J.   Indian Fights on the Texas Frontier...As Recorded by E. L. Deaton. Fort Worth, 1927. 1st ed. Jenkins 116-656 1978 $45

HOLMES, FRED L.   Badger Saints and Sinners. 1939. Illus., 1st ed., slightly frayed dust jacket. Austin 79-334 1978 $20

HOLMES, FRED L.   Old World Wisconsin. 1944. Photos. Austin 79-335 1978 $12.50

HOLMES, FRED L.   Side Roads. Excursions into Wisconsin's Past. Madison, 1949. Illus., sm. 4to. Biblo BL781-277 1978 $10

HOLMES, J. H. H.   A Treatise on the Coal Mines. London, 1816. 8vo., ads, plts., map, old bds., new calf, spine, uncut, very good copy, 1st ed.? Norman 5-147 1978 $200

HOLMES, L. SEALE   Holmes Handbook and Catalogue of Canada and British North America. (N.P., 1945). Numerous facsimiles, orig. binding. Wolfe 39-427 1978 $20

HOLMES, OLIVER WENDELL 1809-1894   Astraea: The Balance of Illusions. Boston, 1850. Cream-colored bds., dampstained, internally very fine, 1st binding. Dawson's 447-243 1978 $60

HOLMES, OLIVER WENDELL 1809-1894   The Autocrat of the Breakfast Table. Boston, 1858. Orig. cloth, 1st ed., 1st print., fine. MacManus 238-514 1978 $50

HOLMES, OLIVER WENDELL 1809-1894   The Autocrat of the Breakfast-Table. Boston, 1858. 1st ed., illus., binding somewhat worn. Nestler Rare 78-18 1978 $30

HOLMES, OLIVER WENDELL 1809-1894   The Autocrat of the Breakfast Table. Boston, 1894. 2 vols., illus. by Howard Pyle, orig. dec. cloth, 1st of this ed., fine. MacManus 238-516 1978 $35

HOLMES, OLIVER WENDELL 1809-1894   The Autocrat of the Breakfast Table. 1894. Howard Pyle Illus., first ed. Austin 82-433 1978 $47.50

HOLMES, OLIVER WENDELL 1809-1894   Boylston Prize Dissertation for 1836. Boston, 1836. 8vo., cont. brown cloth, gilt lettering on spine, foxed, good, first ed. Zeitlin 245-129 1978 $95

HOLMES, OLIVER WENDELL 1809-1894   Currents and Counter Currents. Boston, 1860. Disbound. Rittenhouse 49-367 1976 $20

HOLMES, OLIVER WENDELL 1809-1894   Currents and Countercurrents in Medical Science, with Other Addresses and Essays. Boston, 1861. 1st ed., 1st bind., excellent except for slight rubbing at foot of spine. Americanist 102-59 1978 $50

HOLMES, OLIVER WENDELL 1809-1894   Elsie Venner. 1861. Austin 82-434 1978 $27.50

HOLMES, OLIVER WENDELL 1809-1894   The Guardian Angel. Boston, 1867. First ed., cr. 8vo., orig. green cloth, very good. Howes 194-938 1978 £10

HOLMES, OLIVER WENDELL 1809-1894   The Guardian Angel. 1895. Austin 82-436 1978 $8.50

HOLMES, OLIVER WENDELL 1841-1935   His Book Notices and Uncollected Letters and Papers. New York, 1936. First ed. Biblo 251-342 1978 $18.50

HOLMES, OLIVER WENDELL 1809-1894   John Lothrop Motley. 1879. First ed., lg. paper copy. Austin 82-435 1978 $37.50

HOLMES, OLIVER WENDELL 1809-1894   Oration Delivered Before the City Authorities at Boston on the Eighty-Seventh Anniversary of the National Independence of America. Philadelphia, 1863. Wrs., Bell Wiley's copy. Broadfoot's 44-203 1978 $15

HOLMES, OLIVER WENDELL 1809-1894   Oration Delivered Before the City Authorities of Boston, on the Fourth of July, 1863. Boston, 1863. Orig. printed wrs., 1st ed., spine chipped, otherwise very good. MacManus 238-515 1978 $30

HOLMES, OLIVER WENDELL 1809-1894   Over the Teacups. Boston, 1891. 1st ed., 2nd state, fr. flyleaf missing. Biblo 251-504 1978 $37.50

HOLMES, OLIVER WENDELL 1809-1894   The Poet at the Breakfast Table. 1872. Blindstamp on title pg., rebound in cloth. Eaton 45-250 1978 £5

HOLMES, OLIVER WENDELL 1809-1894   The Poet at the Breakfast Table. 1872. Second state. Austin 82-437 1978 $12.50

HOLMES, OLIVER WENDELL 1809-1894   Puerperal Fever, as a Private Pestilence. Boston, 1855. Modern bds., wrappers not present, internally fine. Rittenhouse 49-367A 1976 $1200

HOLMES, OLIVER WENDELL 1809-1894   Works of.... Boston & New York, 1892. 13 vols., blue ribbed cloth, fine to very fine cond. Current 24-20 1978 $70

HOLMES, OLIVER WENDELL 1841-1935   The Correspondence of...and Sir Frederick Pollock, 1874-1932. Cambridge, 1941. 2 vols., illus., first ed. Biblo BL781-825 1978 $18.50

HOLMES, T. RICE   The Roman Republic and The Founder of the Empire. Oxford, 1923. Plts., 3 vols., 8vo, out of print. Traylen 88-272 1978 £25

HOLMES, TIMOTHY   Sir Benjamin Collins Brodie. Masters of Medicine. London, 1898. Rittenhouse 49-369 1976 $12.50

HOLSINGER, H. R.   Holsinger's History of the Tunkers and the Brethren Church...Including Their Origin, Doctrine, Biography and Literature. Lathrop, 1901. Cloth, scarce orig. ed. Hayman 72-306 1978 $25

HOLSTEIN, MARK   "The Unfortunate" Dr. Dodd. New York, (Harbor Press), 1934. One of 99 copies, author's penned pres., sm. 4to., wrs., reprint. Biblo 247-535 1978 $27.50

HOLSTEIN Herd Book.   Boston, 1872. Illus., tall 8vo, orig. cloth. Morrill 241-205 1978 $7.50

HOLSTENIUS, LUCAS   Lvcae Holstenii Annotationes in Geographiam Sacram Caroli a S. Pavlo.... Romae, 1666. 8vo, calf, spine gilt, very good. King 7-49 1978 £35

HOLT, ARDERN   Fancy Dresses Described. London, (1887). 5th ed., coloured plts., orig. cloth, 8vo. K Books 244-159 1978 £15

HOLT, ARDERN   Fancy Dresses Described. London, (ca. 1901). 6th ed., illus. in colours & black & white, 8vo., orig. cloth. Morrill 241-206 1978 $17.50

HOLT, HENRY   Calmire. New York, 1892. Orig. binding, clean. Hayman 71-231 1978 $15

HOLT, R. V.   The Unitarian Contribution to Social Progress in England. 1938. 8vo. George's 635-1080 1978 £6

HOLTON, I. F.   New Granada: Twenty Months in the Andes. New York, 1857. Maps, illus., orig. cloth, 8vo, cover faded, some browning in text. Edwards 1012-654 1978 £25

HOLTZAPFFEL, CHARLES   Turning and Mechanical Manipulation. London, 1866. 5 vols., 8vo., illus., rebound in cloth. Quaritch 977-230 1978 $375

HOLUB, EMIL   Sieben Jahre in Sud-Afrika. Wien, 1881. 1st ed., 2 vols., 4 folding coloured maps, 236 illus., roy. 8vo, orig. gilt-dec. pictorial cloth, fine bright copy. K Books 239-221 1978 £80

THE HOLY Land. London, 1902. Thick 8vo, orig. dec. cloth, faded. Sexton 7-8A 1978 £10

A HOLY, Sacred and Divine Book. Canterbury, 1843. 8vo., orig. bds., cloth back, spine faded, 1st ed. of part I. Morrill 241-558 1978 $15

HOLZWORTH, JOHN M.   The Wild Grizzlies of Alaska...the Grizzly & Big Brown Bears...Their Habits...& Characteristics...Notes on Mountain Sheep & Caribou, Collected...for the US Biological Survey. New York, 1930. 1st prtg., lg. 8vo., orig. decor. cloth, photos, very good. Americanist 103-133 1978 $25

HOMANS, JAMES E.   Self-Propelled Vehicles. 1902. Illus. Austin 80-704 1978 $27.50

HOMANS, JAMES E.   Self-Propelled Vehicles. 1906. Illus. Austin 80-705 1978 $27.50

HOME, CHARLES   A New Chronological Abridgement of the History of England. 1791. Contemp. half calf, joints weak, spine rubbed, first ed., some foxing, 8vo. Howes 194-313 1978 £7.50

HOME, EVERARD   Lectures on Comparative Anatomy in which are explained the Preparations in the Hunterian Collection. London, 1814-28. 4to., 4 vols., qtr. calf, vols. 5 & 6 in orig. cloth, portrait, plts. Gurney 75-56 1978 £250

HOME, FRANCIS   The Principles of Agriculture and Vegetation. Dublin, 1759. 3rd. ed., 1st. Irish ed., 8vo, orig. blue paper wrapper, uncut, spine worn, otherwise fine. Fenning 32-163 1978 £28.50

HOME, GORDON   Roman York... 1924. Plt. Allen 234-436 1978 $8.50

HOME, HENRY, LORD KAMES
Please turn to
KAMES, HENRY HOME, LORD

HOME, JOHN   Alonzo, a Tragedy in Five Acts. 1773. 2nd ed., contemp. qtr. sheep, worn, 8vo. George's 635-1407 1978 £6

HOMERUS   Clavis Homerica, sive lexicon vocabulorum omnium, quae continentur in Homeri Iliade.... 1727. Qtr. contemp. calf, 8vo. George's 635-475 1978 £8.50

HOMERUS   Homeri quae extant omnia, Illias, Odyssea, Batrachomyomachia, Hymni, Poematia aliquot, cum Latina versione. Geneva, 1606. 2 parts in 1 vol., contemp. sheep, gilt edges, occasional minor staining, 8vo., Greek & Latin text, handsome richly tooled binding. Howes 194-527 1978 £145

HOMERUS   Ilias. Venice, 1526. First ed. in modern Greek, woodcuts, few marginal repairs, some scribblings, reasonably clean and sound, sm. 4to., modern brown mor. Thomas 37-53 1978 £750

HOMERUS   Iliad. London, 1715-1720. 1st. ed., portrait mounted, maps, plts., lacks frontis to vol. 5, 6 vols. bound in 3, folio, contemp. calf, leather labels. Traylen 88-273 1978 £95

HOMERUS   The Illiad of Homer. 1720-32. 6 vols., 12mo., contemp. calf, plts., joints cracked, vol. 1 is 2nd ed., other vols. are 3rd eds. Howes 194-422 1978 £14

HOMERUS   The Iliad of Homer. 1743. 6 vols., frontis portrait, maps, text illus., orig. calf, slight dampstaining, o/w good set. Jarndyce 16-160 1978 £15

HOMERUS   Illiad and Odyssey. Oxford, 1800-01. 4 vols. in 2, thk. 8vo., finely printed in Greek letter, contemp. full mor., all edges gilt, a little foxing. Howes 194-314 1978 £45

HOMERUS   Iliad & Odyssey of Homer. 1805. 2 vols., oblong 4to., engr. plts., half mor., plts. rehinged, very foxed. Allen 234-J 1978 $55

HOMERUS   Iliad. Ca. 1860. 5th ed., 2 vols. Allen 234-440 1978 $7.50

HOMERUS   The Iliad. Nonesuch Press, 1931. Ltd. to 1,450 copies, roy. 8vo., full crushed mor. gilt. George's 635-918 1978 £50

HOMERUS   Ilias. n.d. 2 vols., "Chiswick Ed.", ltd. to 150 copies. Allen 234-438 1978 $7.50

HOMERUS   Marmor Homericum. (c. 1865). Photographs, folio, mor., gilt, rubbed. George's 635-476 1978 £7.50

HOMERUS   Odyssey. 1725-26. Some staining, engraved plates, 5 vols., 12mo., contemp. panelled calf, a little rubbed. George's 635-474 1978 £7.50

HOMERUS   The Odyssey of Homer. London, 1924. Small quarto in full leather binding by Bumpus, a.e.g., full-page plts in color after water-color-paintings by W. Russell Flint, 1 of 530 copies, heraldic bookplt, fine. Duschnes 220-97 1978 $175

HOMERUS   The Odyssey. London, 1924. Plts. in colour, edition de luxe, ltd. to 500 copies, numbered, 4to, orig. white buckram, 2 leather labels. Traylen 88-274 1978 £80

HOMERUS   Oddssey. New York, (1942). Illus. Biblo BL781-394 1978 $10

HOMERUS   Works, Printed in Greek. Venice, 1524. 2 vols., Aldus anchor on each title & last leaf, sm. 8vo, finely bound in full red morocco, gilt extra. Traylen 88-433 1978 £200

HOMES and Doorways of Old Wethersfield. 1927. Illus., 8vo., orig. leatherette, ltd. to 500 copies. Morrill 241-88 1978 $12.50

HONDERED Jaar Vrij Onderwijs. Bruxelles, 1932. 4to., cloth, illus., text in Dutch & French. Van der Peet H-64-350 1978 Dfl 65

HONE, JOSEPH M. Life of George Moore. 1936. lst ed., port., illus., very good, octavo bound in cloth. Hyland 128-152 1978 £9

HONE, JOSEPH M. The Moores of Moore Hall. 1939. lst ed., good, octavo bound in cloth. Hyland 128-153 1978 £8

HONE, JOSEPH M. W. B. Yeats, 1865-1939. 1942. lst ed., Prelim foxed, very good, octavo bound in cloth. Hyland 128-894 1978 £7

HONE, JOSEPH M. W. B. Yeats, 1865-1939. 1942. Plts., buckram, leather label, very good, d.w., first English ed. Bell Book 16-962 1978 £8.50

HONE, N. J. Manor & Manorial Records. 1906. Ex-lib., edges of spine frayed. Allen 234-1305 1978 $7.50

HONE, PHILIP The Diary of... New York, 1889. Edited by Bayard Tuckerman, 2 vols., lst ed., ex-lib., orig. cloth, some wear. MacManus 239-202 1978 $25

HONE, WILLIAM Hone's Collected Popular Political Tracts. c. 1825. Orig. woodcuts and illus., contemp. half calf, 8vo. Howes 194-941 1978 £18

HONE, WILLIAM The Queen's Matrimonial Ladder, A National Toy,.... London, 1820. 8vo, modern cloth, "Forty-third edition", caricatures by George Cruikshank, laid into copy is actual "toy" which is rarely present. Ximenes 47-138 1978 $40

HONEY Drops. Philadelphia, c.1850's. Miniature, front fly-leaf gone, cloth covers moderately worn. Victoria 34-544 1978 $10

HONEY, W. B. The Art of the Potter... London, 1946. Roy. 8vo, plts. Traylen 88-386 1978 £10

HOOD, JOHN BELL Advance and Retreat- Personal Experiences in the U.S. Confederate States Armies. New Orleans, La., 1880. Letter laid in, Bell Wiley's Copy. Broadfoot's 44-204 1978 $40.00

HOOD, THOMAS 1799-1845 Humorous Poems. London, 1893. 1 of 250 copies on large paper, illus. by Charles E. Brock, 4 to., orig. cloth, uncut, very good. Houle 10-48 1978 $15

HOOD, THOMAS 1799-1845 Miss Kilmansegg and Her Precious Leg. London, 1870. Large, thick quarto, Seccombe's lst illus. book, proof copy, text engraved, imposing blue cloth volume with gilt decorations and "Christmas 1869" impressed on silver tablet, cover tips and edges rubbed, silver tablet tarnished, very scarce. Victoria 34-718 1978 $175

HOOD, THOMAS 1799-1845 Miss Kilmansegg and Her Precious Leg, a Golden Legend. (Campden, 1904). 1 of 200 numbered copies, illus. by Reginald Savage, orig. linen-backed bds., uncut, label on spine slightly chipped, otherwise very good. Americanist 102-44 1978 $65

HOOD, THOMAS 1799-1845 Poems. London, 1848. 8vo, 2 vols., blind stamped green cloth, extremities rubbed, bol. II backstrip split horizontally, spines darkened, lst ed., collector's cond. Desmarais 1-225 1978 $60

HOOD, THOMAS 1799-1845 Whims and Oddities in Prose and Verse. 1829. Wood engrav. by the author, 2 vols., cr. 8vo., half green mor. Howes 194-943 1978 £12.50

HOOD, THOMAS 1799-1845 Works, comic and serious, in prose and verse. 1869-73. Portrait, woodcut illus., 10 vols., cr. 8vo., half navy mor., second ed. Howes 194-942 1978 £48

HOOD'S Own; Or Laughter From Year to Year. 1855. Numerous eng. in text, rebound in buckram. Eaton 45-251 1978 £8

HOOFS, Claws, & Antlers of the Rocky Mountains. Denver, 1894. lst "Edition de Luxe", ltd. to 1000 numbered copies, lg. sq. 4to, orig. pic. paper over bds., plts., very good. Americanist 103-72 1978 $95

HOOK, THEODORE Reminiscences of Michael Kelly, of the King's Theatre, and Theatre Royal Drury Lane. 1826. lst. ed., 2 vols., 8vo, portrait foxed, plts., half-titles, orig. paper bds., backstrips & labels probably renewed, uncut. Hannas 54-328 1978 £55

HOOKE, H. M. One Act Plays From Canadian History. Toronto, 1945. Hood's 115-341 1978 $7.50

HOOKE, ROBERT An Attempt to Prove the Motion of the Earth. London, 1674. 4to., fldg. copperplt., full antique calf, fine copy, lst ed. Norman 5-148 1978 $1,250

HOOKER, A. A. The International Grain Trade. 1939. Edges of covers stained, 8vo. George's 635-337 1978 £5

HOOKER, J. D. The Rhododendrons of Sikkim-Himalaya; Being an Account, Botanical and Geographical of the Rhododendrons Recently Discovered in the Mountains of Eastern Himalaya. London, 1849-1851. Tinted vignette on title-pg., hand-coloured litho. illus., lg. folio, old half vellum leather label, fine copy. Traylen 88-585 1978 £1000

HOOKER, KATHARINE Farmhouses and Small Provincial Buildings in Southern Italy. New York, (1925). 4to., photos. Biblo BL781-544 1978 $18.50

HOOKER, W. J. Journal of a Tour in Iceland in the Summer of 1809. Yarmouth, 1811. lst. ed., coloured frontis, other plts., orig. bds., rebacked, edges uncut, cover slightly soiled, waterstain affecting lower margin of few pgs., author's pres. inscription. Edwards 1012-579 1978 £185

HOOKER, WILLIAM Pomona Londinensis... London, 1818. Hand-coloured aquatint plts., lg. 4to., contemp. diced russia leather gilt, joints cracked, few captions just trimmed. Traylen 88-653 1978 £1650

HOOPER, BETT Virgins in Cellophane. New York, 1932. 4to., illus. by James Montgomery Flagg, lst ed. Biblo 251-168 1978 $17.50

HOOPER, GEORGE 1640-1727 Works. Oxford, 1757. Vignette on title, folio, orig. bds., entirely uncut, rebacked with calf, very good. Howes 194-315 1978 £32

HOOPER, JOSEPH A History of Saint Peter's Church. Albany, 1900. Plts., maps, diagrams, "letter-press ed. ltd. to 500". Butterfield 21-26 1978 $15

HOOPER, ROBERT The Anatomist's Vade-Mecum. Windsor, 1809. 12mo., contemp. calf, binding worn, 2nd Amer. ed. Morrill 239-126 1978 $17.50

HOOPER, ROBERT Examinations in Anatomy, Physiology, Practice of Physic, Surgery, Materia Medica, Chemistry, and Pharmacy. New York, 1811. 12mo., contemp. tree calf, gilt, worn, browned, good copy, signature of early owner, dated August 1812, bkplt. of Dr. Alfred M. Hellman, lst Amer. ed. Zeitlin 245-130 1978 $125

HOOPER, ROBERT Medical Dictionary. New York, 1824. Second American ed., clean. Rittenhouse 49-372 1976 $20

HOOPER, S. K. The Story of Manitou. [Denver, 1886]. Illus., original pictorial printed wr. Ginsberg 14-262 1978 $35

HOOPER, WILLIAM Rational Recreations. 1774. 4 vols., 8vo., plts., contemp. tree calf, gilt backs, a little worn. Quaritch 977-104 1978 $450

HOOPER, WILLIAM HENRY The Utah Bill: A Plea for Religious Liberty:.... Washington, 1870. Disbound, orig. wr. Ginsberg 14-656 1978 $45

HOOPER, WILLIAM HULME Ten Months Among the Tents of the Tuski, with Incidents of an Arctic Boat Expedition... London, 1853. Map, illus., plts. Hood 117-99 1978 $120

HOOPER, WILLIAM HULME Ten Months Among the Tents of the Tuski... London, 1853. lst. ed., 8vo, half-title, tinted lithograph plts., other plts., illus., folding engraved map, half calf, gilt back. Deighton 5-158 1978 £75

HOPE, ANTHONY, PSEUD.
Please turn to
HAWKINS, ANTHONY HOPE

HOPE, ARTHUR A Manual of Sorrento and Inlaid Work for Amateurs, with Original Designs. Chicago, 1876. 8vo., plts., illus., orig. cloth, lst ed. Morrill 241-207 1978 $22.50

HOPE, JOHN Thoughts, In Prose and Verse, Started in His Walks. Stockton, 1780. 8vo, contemporary half calf (covers rubbed, sound), lst ed., scattered foxing, very good copy. Ximenes 47-139 1978 $125

HOPE, LAURENCE The Garden of Kama, and other Love Lyrics from India arranged in Verse. 1914. Coloured plts. by Byam Shaw, roy. 4to., covers faded. George's 635-213 1978 £6.50

HOPE, LAURENCE Songs from the Garden of Kama. 1909. Photos, cr. 4to., orig. cloth, gilt. George's 635-1352 1978 £6.50

HOPE, THOMAS Costume of the Ancients. London, 1941. 2 vols., roy. 8vo, plts. in outline. Traylen 88-388 1978 £30

HOPE, THOMAS An Essay on the Origin and Prospects of Man. Murray, 1831. lst ed., 3 vols., 8vo, recent bds., nice copy. Fenning 32-164 1978 £32.50

HOPE, THOMAS Household Furniture and Interior Decoration. London, 1807. Engraved title, plts. in outline, lg. folio, orig. printed bds., new leather spine, some slight spotting principally in text. Traylen 88- 387 1978 £450

HOPKINS, CLAUDE C. My Life in Advertising. 1927. Austin 80-706 1978 $8.50

HOPKINS, GERARD MANLEY The Letters of G. M. Hopkins to Robert Bridges. 1935. Plts., buckram, covers faded, very good, first English ed. Bell Book 16-446 1978 £7.50

HOPKINS, GERARD MANLEY Poems of Gerard Manley Hopkins. London, 1930. First ed., fine, d.w., orig. binding. Rota 211-208 1978 £18

HOPKINS, JOHN A., JR. Economic History of the Production of Beef Cattle in Iowa. Iowa City, 1928. Cloth, gilt top, 1st ed., bookplt. removed, ex-lib?, very good. Dykes 35-158 1978 $10

HOPKINS, JOHN HENRY A Scriptural, Ecclesiastical and Historical View of Slavery... New York, (1864). Rebound. MacManus 239-841 1978 $17.50

HOPKINS, KENNETH Six Sonnets. London, 1938. One of 110 copies, wrappers, nice, author's autograph signature. Rota 211-210 1978 £10

HOPKINS, LIVINGSTON A Comic History of the United States. New York, 1876. lst ed., illus., cloth binding, good. Greene 78-325 1978 $45

HOPKINS, N. M. The Outlook for Research and Invention. 1919. Austin 80-707 1978 $12.50

HOPKINSON, M. R. Anne of England. New York, 1934. Illus. Biblo 247-728 1978 $15

HOPKINSON, R. CECIL R. Cecil Hopkinson: Memoir and Letters. 1918. Plts., cr. 8vo., orig. cloth. Howes 194-945 1978 £5

HOPLEY, CATHERINE COOPER Life in the South: From the Commencement of the War By a Blockaded British Subject. London, 1863. Rare map, catalog cards, 2 vols., Bell Wiley's copy. Broadfoot's 44-205 1978 $250

HOPLEY, GEORGE Fright. New York, (1950). First ed., fine, d.w. Biblo 247-521 1978 $13.50

HOPPE, E. O. Picturesque Great Britain. New York, (1926). 4to., photos., covers rubbed. Biblo BL781-681 1978 $36.50

HOPPE-SEYLER, ERNST FELIX Physiologische Chemie. Berlin, 1877-1881. 8vo., 4 parts in 2 vols., illus., contemp. bds., gilt on spines, light marginal browning, very good copies, lst ed. Zeitlin 245-131 1978 $285

HOPPIN, AUGUSTUS Crossing the Atlantic. Boston, 1872. Lg. oblong 4to., orig. limp lea., lst ed. Morrill 241-678 1978 $25

HOPPIN, JOSEPH CLARK A Handbook of Attic Red-Figured Vases. Cambridge, 1919. 1st ed., 2 vols., orig. cloth, ex-lib., good set. MacManus 239-676 1978 $50

HOPPUS, MARY A Great Treason. A Story of the War of Independence. London, 1883. 2 vols., 8vo., orig. cloth, lst ed., very good. MacManus 238-280 1978 $100

HOPTON, ABN'R A Dissertation on Food for Animals. St. Louis, 1863. 8vo., orig. wrs. Morrill 239-127 1978 $10

HORACE
Please turn to
HORATIUS FLACCUS, QUINTUS

HORAN, JAMES D. Desperate Men. New York, (1949). lst ed., d.w., illus. Biblo 248-260 1978 $17.50

HORATIUS FLACCUS, QUINTUS Epistola Critica.... Cantabrigae, 1723. Contemp. calf, 8vo. George's 635-478 1978 £7.50

HORATIUS FLACCUS, QUINTUS Horativs. Florence, 1503. 8vo., Italic letter, French early 19th cent. blue mor. decor. in blind and gilt, brown mor. doublures, vellum flyleaves, gilt edges, by Bozerian jeune. Quaritch 978-78 1978 $1,100

HORATIUS FLACCUS, QUINTUS Lyrics; Being the First Four Books of His Odes. Chester, (c. 1832). 2nd ed., thin 4to., quarter leather. Traylen 88-275 1978 £6

HORATIUS FLACCUS, QUINTUS The Odes, Epodes and Carmen Seculare of Horace. 1760. 2 vols., contemp. calf, frontispiece, 8vo. Howes 194-317 1978 £22

HORATIUS FLACCUS, QUINTUS Oeuvres Completes. 1823. 3 vols., half mor., one cover detached, portion of one spine missing. Allen 234-461 1978 $10

HORATIUS FLACUS, QUINTUS Opera cum quibusdam annotationnibus.... Strassburg, 1498. lst illus. ed., folio, contemp. blind-stamped calf, rebacked, clasps missing, gilt and partly gauffered edges. Gilhofer 75-58 1978 SFr 11,700

HORATIUS FLACCUS, QUINTUS Opera. Paris, 1642. Folio, frontis., cont. French mor. Gilhofer 74-132 1978 sFr 2000

HORATIUS FLACCUS, QUINTUS Opera. Ex Recensione and cum Notis atque Emendationibus R. Bentleii. Cambridge, 1711. 4to., frontispiece, half red niger mor., marbled bds., fine. Howes 194-163 1978 £75

HORATIUS FLACCUS, QUINTUS Opera. London, 1733-1737. lst issue, 2 vols., frontis., plts., octavo, calf with gilt borders, rebacked, orig. gilt paneled spines with black leather labels, inner gilt dentelles, some rubbing of covers. Bennett 20-108 1978 $550

HORATIUS FLACCUS, QUINTUS Opera. Londini, 1733-37. 2 vols. in 1, octavo, olive-brown mor., blind rules, gilt, hinges and spine rubbed, gilt edges, armorial bookplate, copperplts., lst ed., lst issue. Totteridge 29-55 1978 $300

HORATIUS FLACCUS, QUINTUS Opera, ad Fidem LXXVI Codium. Parisiis, 1770. 8vo., full old calf, shaved. Van der Peet H-64-351 1978 Dfl 55

HORATIUS FLACCUS, QUINTUS Opera. 1792-93. 2 vols., 4to., contemp. russia gilt, gilt edges, joints cracked, large paper copy. Howes 194-316 1978 £45

HORATIUS FLACCUS, QUINTUS Poemata. Londini, 1841. 8vo., half calf, notes in English. Van der Peet H-64-352 1978 Dfl 45

HORATIUS FLACCUS, QUINTUS Works. 1756. 2 vols., 18mo., contemp. half calf, Vol. 1 lacks title. George's 635-477 1978 £7.50

HORDEN, J. A Grammar of the Cree Language, as Spoken by the Cree Indians of North America. London, 1881. Orig. binding. Wolfe 39-243 1978 $60

HORETZKY, CHARLES Canada on the Pacific, Being an Account of a Journey from Edmonton to the Pacific by the Peace Rivery Valley... Montreal, 1874. Ex-lib. Hood 116-853 1978 $75

HORGAN, PAUL Look At America: The Southwest, A Handbook In Pictures, Maps and Text. Boston, 1947. Illus. Jenkins 116-662 1978 $7.50

HORGAN, PAUL The Return of the Weed. New York & London, 1936. Signed by Horgan with inscript; lithographs by Peter Hunt, rear cover stained, good, torn & soiled dw. Bernard 5-131 1978 $25

HORN, STANLEY F. The Army of Tennessee. Indianapolis, (1941). 1st ed., illus., scarce. MacManus 239-884 1978 $27.50

HORN, STANLEY F. The Hermitage. Home of Old Hickory. Richmond, 1938. 1st ed., illus., orig. pic. cloth, d.j., chipped, fine copy, inscribed by author. MacManus 239-1815 1978 $25

HORNADAY, WILLIAM TEMPLE The American Natural History. New York, 1914. Fireside ed., plts. in color, 3 vols., 8vo. Morrill 239-429 1978 $20

HORNADAY, WILLIAM TEMPLE Camp-Fires in the Canadian Rockies. New York, 1919. Illus., maps, 8vo., orig. cloth. Book Chest 17-193 1978 $23.50

HORNADAY, WILLIAM TEMPLE Taxidermy and Zoological Collecting. New York, 1892. Plts., 8vo., orig. cloth. Book Chest 17-192 1978 $30

HORNADAY, WILLIAM TEMPLE Two Years in the Jungle. 1885. First U.K. ed., maps, plts., illus., 8vo., orig. cloth, binding stained, spine defective, v.g. Fenning 32-165 1978 £16

HORNBY, C. H. Descriptive Bibliography of the Books Printed at the Ashendene Press 1895-1935. 4to., cloth, illus. Battery Park 1-169 1978 $75

HORNBY, HARRY P. Going Around. Uvalde, 1945. lst ed., illus. Jenkins 116-1412 1978 $25

HORNE, H. P.   The Binding of Books.   London, 1894. First ed.,
plts., illus., post 8vo., orig. buckram. Forster 130-31 1978 £12

HORNE, HERBERT P.   Diversi Colores. London, 1891. 12mo., gray
bds., 1st ed. Americanist 102-60 1978 $75

HORNE, JOHN   Many Days in Morocco. London, 1925.
1 of 500 copies printed on large paper by Camelot Press, signed by author,
4 to., orig. cloth over bds., illus., fine. Houle 10-160 1978 $95

HORNE, RICHARD HENGIST   Orion. London, Scholartis Press, 1928. First
ed., one of 650 copies, orig. binding, covers a little dust-marked, very good.
Rota 211-222 1978 £10

HORNE, RICHARD HENRY   A New Spirit of the Age. 1844. 2nd. ed., 2
vols., portraits, some light foxing, half red morocco, gilt, v.g. Jarndyce 16-
741 1978 £24

HORNE, THOMAS H.   Landscape Illustrations of the Bible... 1836.
Engraved title-pg., engraved plts., 2 vols., roy. 8vo, contemp. calf, gilt spines,
double labels, edges gilt, little rubbed at corners, 1 leaf misbound, nice copy.
Fenning 32-166 1978 £48.50

HORNE, THOMAS H.   Landscape Illustrations of the Bible. 1836.
Plts., 2 vols., 4to., contemp. half mor., some plts. foxed, lg. paper copy, fine.
Howes 194-1385 1978 £55

HORNOT, ANT.   Anecdotes Americaines, ou Histoire Abregee des
Principaux Evenements Arrives dans Le Nouveau Monde... Paris, 1776. Thick
sm. 8vo, contemp. calf, new label, free end-papers missing. Edwards 1012-
397 1978 £50

HORNUNG, ERNEST WILLIAM   Tiny Luttrell. London, 1893. 2 vols., orig.
cloth, 1st ed., covers very worn, lib. labels, scarce. MacManus 238-281 1978
$75

HORNUNG, W. W.   The Shadow of the Rope. 1926. Very good,
first English ed. Bell Book 17-248 1978 £8.50

HORRABIN, J. F.   An Atlas of Current Affairs. 1938. 4th ed. rev.
Austin 80-133 1978 $11

HORROCKS, JERIMIAH   Opera Posthuma...Accedunt Guilielmi Crab-
traei, Mancestriensis, Observationes Coelestis. London, 1673 (1672). Sm. 4to.,
plts., woodcuts, contemp. panelled calf, rebacked, first ed., second issue, engrav.
plts. shaved. Quaritch 977-189 1978 $850

THE HORRORS Of Negro Slavery Existing in Our West Indian Islands... 1805.
1st. ed., half-title, 8vo, modern half calf. Edwards 1012-721 1978 £45

HORRY, P.   The Life of Gen. Francis Marion. Phila., 1824.
Foxed, ink notation on title page, one page mended, new cloth, Bell Wiley's
copy. Broadfoot's 44-922 1978 $10.00

HORSFIELD, THOMAS   Zoological Researches in Java and the Neighboring Islands. 1824. 8 plain & 64 coloured plts., 4to, calf, rebacked.
Edwards 1012-163 1978 £750

HORSFORD, EBEN NORTON   The Defences of Norumbega and a Review of
the Reconnaissances of Col. T. W. Higginson, Professor Henry W. Haynes, Dr.
Justin Winsor, Dr. Francis Parkman, and Rev. Dr. Edmund F. Slafter. Boston,
1891. Illus., 4to., orig. cloth, minor cover stains, few stains in text, nice
sound copy, 1st ed. Morrill 241-208 1978 $25

HORSFORD, EBEN NORTON   The Landfall of Leif Erikson, A. D. 1000, and
the Site of His Houses in Vineland. Boston, 1892. Illus., 4to., orig. cloth,
very nice, 1st ed. Morrill 241-210 1978 $25

HORSFORD, EBEN NORTON   The Landfall of Leif Erikson A.D. 1000 and The
Site of His Houses in Vineland. Boston, 1892. Illus., maps, 4to, orig. cloth.
Edwards 1012-496 1978 £30

HORSFORD, EBEN NORTON   Leif's House in Vineland. Boston, 1893.
Map, illus., 4to., very nice, orig. cloth, 1st ed. Morrill 241-211 1978 $17.50

HORSLEY, JOHN   Britannia Romana; or the Roman Antiquities of
Britain... 1732. Folio, plts., maps, 19th century calf. Quaritch 983-19
1978 $240

HORSLEY, TERENCE   The Long Flight. 1947. Scraperboard illus. by
C. F. Tunnicliffe, roy. 8vo. George's 635-217 1978 £5

HORSTIUS, JACOBUS MERLO   The Paradise of the Soul. 1771. 12mo., contemp. calf rebacked, half-title, scarce. P. M. Hill 142-141 1978 £21

HORTEN, MAX   Die Philosophie Des Islam... Munich, 1924.
8vo., cloth. Salloch 348-96 1978 $22.50

HORTON, BYRNE J.   Dictionary of Modern Economics. Public Affairs
Press, 1948. Ex-lib. Austin 80-708 1978 $27.50

HORTON, E. J.   Directory of White Plains. (White Plains), 1891.
Plts., illus., ads, cloth covers stained, but sound. Butterfield 21-466 1978
$17.50

HORTON, R. G.   A Youth's History of the Great Civil War in the
United States from 1861 to 1865. New York, 1867. Illus., minor margin rip, almost
fine. Victoria 34-419 1978 $10

HORTUS SANITATIS   Le Jardin de Sante Translate du Latin en Francoys.... Paris, 1539. 2 parts in one vol., portrait, illus., folio, old style calf,
minor dampstaining in 1st. part, few other sm. stains, lower corner of title torn &
skilfully restored, slight marginal defects on 2 leaves not affecting text. Traylen
88-586 1978 £7500

HOSACK, DAVID   An Inaugural Discourse...Before the New York
Horticultural Society. New York, 1824. Prtd. wr., frayed, pres. copy with
inscr. from author. Butterfield 21-206 1978 $15

HOSACK, DAVID   Memoir of De Witt Clinton. New York, 1829.
4to., fine uncut copy, handsomely bound in gray bds., linen back, 1 of few on
lg. paper. Butterfield 21-128 1978 $65

HOSACK, DAVID   Observations on Febrile Contagion and on the
Means of Improving the Medical Police of the City of New York. New York, 1820.
New buckram binding. Rittenhouse 49-375 1976 $25

HOSFORD, FRANCES J.   Father Shipherd's Magna Charta. A Century of
Coeducation in Oberlin College. Boston, 1937. Cloth, d.j. Hayman 72-549
1978 $7.50

HOSKINS, NATHAN   A History of the State of Vermont, From Its
Discovery and Settlement to the Close of the Year 1830. Vergennes, 1831. 1st
ed., orig. full calf, bookplt., foxing, but very good copy, scarce in this cond.
MacManus 239-466 1978 $40

HOSMER, HEZEKIAH L.   Montana, an Address Delivered by Chief Justice...
New York, 1866. Original printed wr., 1st ed. Ginsberg 14-623 1978 $375

HOSMER, JAMES K.   The Life of Young Sir Henry Van Governor of
Massachusetts Bay... Boston, 1888. Illus. MacManus 239-824 1978 $15

HOSMER, JAMES K.   A Short History of the Mississippi Valley. Boston, 1902. Cloth. Hayman 73-254 1978 $7.50

HOSMER, RALPH S.   A Forest Working Plan for Township 40, Totten
and Crossfield Purchase, Hamilton County, New York State Forest Preserve.
Washington, 1901. Fldg. maps, plts., wr., slightly nicked. Butterfield 21-12
1978 $25

HOSSACK, B. H.   Kirkwall in the Orkneys. London, 1900. Maps,
frontis., plts., text-illus., 4to., cloth. K Books 244-160 1978 £18

HOSSCHIUS, SIDONIUS   Elegiarum Libri Sex. Antwerp, 1667. 16mo.,
Old calf, one joint cracked, stained, top of spine missing. Allen 234-1307 1978
$30

HOSTRUP, C. KOHREDIER   Sjette Udgave. Kjobenhavn, 1900. 3 vols.,
orig. pictorial cloth. Eaton 45-254 1978 £9

HOTCHKIN, JAMES H.   History of the Purchase and Settlement of Western
New York. New York, 1848. 1st ed., fine copy, orig. cloth, scarce. Mac-
Manus 239-346 1978 $50

HOTCHKIN, JAMES H.   A History of the Purchase and Settlement of Western New York, and of the...Presbyterian Church in that Section. New York,
1848. Frontis., ads, 1st ed. Butterfield 21-207 1978 $35

HOTCHKIN, SAMUEL FITCH   Rural Pennsylvania. Philadelphia, 1867. 4to,
rebacked in red lib. buckram, illus. Baldwins' 51-448 1978 $37.50

HOTCHKIN, SAMUEL FITCH   Rural Pennsylvania in the Vicinity of Philadelphia. Philadelphia, 1897. Illus., rebound, 4to., a.e.g. MacManus 239-
1501 1978 $50

HOTCHKIN, SAMUEL FITCH   The York Road, Old and New. Philadelphia,
1892. Illus., 4to., rebound, scarce. MacManus 239-1502 1978 $45

HOTCHKISS, CHANCEY C.   In Defiance of the King, a Romance of the
American Revolution. New York, 1895. Cloth. Hayman 73-139 1978 $3.50

HOTMAN, FRANCOIS　　　　Francogallia. (Geneva), 1573. Very rare 1st ed., vellum. Gilhofer 75-59 1978 SFr 2,300

HOTMAN, FRANCOIS　　　　La Vie De Messire Gaspar de Coligny.... Amsterdam, 1643. 3 parts in 1 vol., thick sm. 4to., contemp. limp vellum. F. Edwards 1013-100 1978 £150

HOTSON, LESLIE　　　　Shakespeare Versus Shallow. Nonesuch Press, 1931. Plts., octavo, good. Upcroft 10-373 1978 £12.50

HOTTEN, JOHN CAMDEN　　　　Literary Copyright. 1871. 1st. ed., half title, orig. green cloth, v.g. Jarndyce 16-742 1978 £28

HOUBRAKEN, JACOBUS　　　　The Heads of Illustrious Persons of Great Britain. 1756. Plts., folio, contemp. calf, rebacked. Howes 194-1392 1978 £120

HOUDETOT, A. D'　　　　Le Tir au Pistolet. Paris, 1850. 8vo., half calf, frontis., text illus., binding shaved. Van der Peet H-64-608 1978 Dfl 95

HOUDINI, HARRY　　　　Houdini's Paper Magic. New York, 1922. 2nd Printing, 1st publ. month, color frontispiece, illus, uncut, little used, very good or better. Limestone 9-154 1978 $22.50

HOUGH, DONALD　　　　Darling, I am Home. 1940. Austin 80-134 1978 $7.50

HOUGH, EMERSON　　　　The Covered Wagon. New York, 1922. 1st ed., 1st issue, spine sunned and slightly spotted, very good. Victoria 34-420 1978 $17.50

HOUGH, EMERSON　　　　Maw's Vacation. Saint Paul, 1921. Wrps., light dampstain on front wrapper. Hayman 71-303 1978 $7.50

HOUGH, EMERSON　　　　The Mississippi Bubble. Indianapolis, (1902). Cloth. Hayman 73-266 1978 $7.50

HOUGH, EMERSON　　　　The Mississippi Bubble. Indianapolis, (1902). Illus., olive-green cloth, 1st ed., 1st issue, spine dull. Bradley 49-154 1978 $10

HOUGH, EMERSON　　　　The Singing Mouse Stories. New York, 1895. Tall, narrow 16mo, 1st ed., 1st book, margin drawings throughout, Art Nouveau binding, gilt decorated, fine. Victoria 34-421 1978 $55

HOUGH, EMERSON　　　　The Sowing; a "Yankee's" View of England's Duty to Herself and to Canada. Winnipeg, 1909. Photos. Hood 116-633 1978 $17.50

HOUGH, EMERSON　　　　The Story of the Cowboy. New York, 1897. Decor. cloth, tan end sheets, illus., 1st ed., fine copy in slipcase, scarce. Dykes 34-27 1978 $50

HOUGH, F.　　　　Report upon Forestry (for 1877). Washington, 1878. 8vo., orig. cloth. Book Chest 17-194 1978 $12.50

HOUGH, FRANKLIN B.　　　　American Biographical Notes, Being Short Notices of Deceased Persons, Chiefly Those Not Included in Allen's or in Drake's Biographical Dictionaries... Albany, 1875. 1st ed., frontis. port., orig. cloth, ltd. to 130 copies, fine. MacManus 239-203 1978 $40

HOUGH, FRANKLIN B.　　　　American Biographical Notes. Albany, 1875. Limited to only 130 copies, good, rebound copy. Nestler Rare 78-122 1978 $45

HOUGH, FRANKLIN B.　　　　History of Duryee's Brigade...in the Summer and Autumn of 1862. Albany, 1864. Plts., half red mor. with gilt design & lettering, marbled bds., all edges gilt, some edge wear along bottom, ltd. to 300. Butterfield 21-121 1978 $60

HOUGH, FRANKLIN B.　　　　A History of Jefferson County in the State of New York... Albany, 1854. 1st ed., illus., orig. cloth, covers worn, but good. MacManus 239-1089 1978 $85

HOUGH, FRANKLIN B.　　　　History of Lewis County, New York... Albany, 1860. Old 1/2 calf, illus., very scarce. MacManus 239-1093 1978 $75

HOUGH, FRANKLIN B.　　　　A History of St. Lawrence and Franklin Counties, New York. Albany, 1853. Illus., maps, 3/4 calf, worn, some pencil markings in margins, 1st ed., fair. Biblo BL781-162 1978 $37.50

HOUGH, FRANKLIN B.　　　　Washingtoniana. Roxbury, 1865. 2 vols., tall 4to., portrs., #61 of 91 tall paper sets, initialled by Hough, total ed. 291, 3/4 lea. & bds., one cover loose. Butterfield 21-286 1978 $50

HOUGH, HORATIO GATES　　　　Diving or An Attempt to Describe Upon Hydraulic & Hydrostatic Principles,.... Hartford, 1813. Good. Nestler Rare 78-203 1978 $85

HOUGHTON, T.　　　　Rara Avis in Terris. London, 1681. 12mo., woodcut, few page numerals cut into, otherwise a very good copy, orig. sheep, second issue. Quaritch 977-231 1978 $315

HOUGHTON, WILLIAM　　　　British Fresh-Water Fishes. London, n.d. (1879). Coloured plts., folio, orig. quarter leather, lacks spine, frontis & title page foxed, "breaking" copy. Traylen 88-587 1978 £265

THE HOUGHTON Library, 1942-1967. Cambridge, 1967. Illus., sm. folio, cloth, t.e.g. Battery Park 1-327 1978 $100

HOUISON, ANDREW　　　　History of the Post Office Together With An Historical Account Of The Issue of Postage Stamps in New South Wales. Sydney, 1890. 1st ed., 4to, plts., orig. blue roan, gilt, worn, neatly repaired. Deighton 5-102 1978 £52

HOULSTON, T.　　　　Observations on Poisons.... Edinburgh, 1787. New ed., 8vo., new bds., uncut, second ed. in English. Quaritch 977-35 1978 $75

HOULT, NORAH　　　　Violet Ryder. London, 1930. 1 of 800 numbered copies, 8 vo., orig. red cloth over decorative bds., uncut, very good. Houle 10-161 1978 $60

HOURS, BOOK OF
Please turn to
CATHOLIC CHURCH. LITURGY & RITUAL. HOURS.

HOURST, LIEUT.　　　　French Enterprise in Africa. New York, 1899. 8vo, orig. cloth, folding map, 190 illus. K Books 239-223 1978 £20

HOUSE, EDWARD MANDELL　　　　The Intimate Papers of Colonel House. Boston, 1926. Chipped d.j., illus., 1st ed., 1st 2 vols. Jenkins 116-663 1978 $25

HOUSE, EDWARD MANDELL　　　　The Intimate Papers of Colonel House. Boston, 1926-28. 1st ed., 4 vols., illus., orig. calf-backed bds., pub. boxes, very fine, ltd. to 750 sets, signed by House. MacManus 239-204 1978 $75

HOUSE, EDWARD MANDELL　　　　Intimate Papers. 1926. Frontis., stains on inside front and rear cover and first and last few pages, 4 vols., 8vo. George's 635-687 1978 £5.25

HOUSE, EDWARD MANDELL　　　　Philip Dru: Administrator. New York, 1912. 1st ed., spine letters a little rubbed, laid in obituary of House, very good or better. Limestone 9-155 1978 $75

HOUSE, EDWARD MANDELL　　　　Riding for Texas: The True Adventures of Captain Bill McDonald of the Texas Rangers. New York, 1936. 1st ed., pict. cloth. Jenkins 116-1332 1978 $15

HOUSE, HOMER DOLIVER　　　　Wild Flowers of New York in Two Parts. Albany, 1918. 2 vols., folio, plts. in full color, 1st ed., attractive set. Butterfield 21-208 1978 $65

HOUSE, HOMER DOLIVER　　　　Wild Flowers of New York in Two Parts. Albany, 1921. Separate issue of loose plates only, cloth case & folder. Butterfield 21-209 1978 $15

THE HOUSE That Jack Built. Chicago, n.d. Large 8vo, linen book, color plates, very good. Victoria 34-422 1978 $7.50

HOUSMAN, ALFRED EDWARD　　　　Introductory Lecture. New York, 1937. Sma. 8vo, blue cloth, Mint in d.w., 1st ed., collector's cond. Desmarais 1-226 1978 $10

HOUSMAN, ALFRED EDWARD　　　　Manilius. London, 1903-30. 5 vols., 8 vo., orig. blue bds., linen spine, 1st ed., ltd. 400 copies, paper label to Vol. 1 is 2nd corrected state. Quaritch Summer, 1978-24 1978 $475

HOUSMAN, LAURENCE　　　　False Premises. Five One Act Plays. Oxford, 1922. Orig. vellum-backed dec. bds., 1st ed., 1 of 150 copies printed in Kelmscott hand made paper and signed by author, fine. MacManus 238-671 1978 $35

HOUSMAN, LAURENCE　　　　The Golden Sovereign. New York, (1937). 1st American ed., 1st printing, d.j., illus., very good. Houle 10-162 1978 $20

HOUSMAN, LAURENCE　　　　The Heart of Peace and other poems. London, 1918. First ed., orig. binding, very good. Rota 211-224 1978 £5

HOUSMAN, LAURENCE   The Heart of Peace. 1918. Sm. 8vo., 1st ed., cloth, fine in d.w. Quaritch 979-196 1978 $20

HOUSMAN, LAURENCE   The House of Joy. London, 1895. Orig. pict. cloth, 1st ed., very good. MacManus 238—669 1978 $60

HOUSMAN, LAURENCE   King John of Jingalo. New York, 1937. 1st Amer. ed., d.w. Biblo 251-507 1978 $15

HOUSMAN, LAURENCE   More Poems. London, 1936. 8vo, blue cloth, uncut, Fine in chipped d.w., 1st ed., collector's cond. Desmarais 1-227 1978 $15

HOUSMAN, LAURENCE   More Poems. 1936. No. 155 of 379 copies, portrait, qtr. mor., t.e.g., marbled end-papers, near fine, partly unopened copy, first English ed. Bell Book 16-450 1978 £35

HOUSMAN, LAURENCE   Odd Pairs. Lonfon, 1925. Very fine in chipped d.w. Desmarais B-325 1978 $25

HOUSMAN, LAURENCE   A Shropshire Lad. With Notes and Bibliography by Carl J. Weber. Waterville, 1946. Orig. cloth, d.j., Jubilee ed., very fine, unopened. MacManus 238-948 1978 $15

HOUSTON, ANDREW JACKSON   Texas Independence. Houston, 1938. Full mor., illus., #8 of deluxe 1st ed. of 500 copies, signed by author, fine, unopened copy. Dykes 35-247 1978 $17.50

HOUSTON, ANDREW JACKSON   Texas Independence. Houston, 1938. Maps in pocket, limited to 500 copies, full leather and signed by author. Jenkins 116-666 1978 $85

HOUSTON, SAM   Letter from Gen. Sam Houston, Giving His Reasons for Supporting Hon. Millard Fillmore for President of the United States. N.P., 1856. Jenkins 116-669 1978 $75

HOUSTON, SAM   Speech Exposing the Malfeasance and Corruption of John C. Watrous, Judge of the Federal Court in Texas. Washington, 1859. Wr. Jenkins 116-671 1978 $65

HOUSTON, SAM   Speech on the Nebraska and Kansas Bill. Washington, 1854. Jenkins 116-672 1978 $45

HOUSTON, SAM   Speeches on the Pacific Railroad Bill. Washington, 1859. Jenkins 116-673 1978 $37.50

HOUSTON, SAM   Texas Judicial District. Washington, 1859. Jenkins 116-674 1978 $15

HOUSTON, SAM   The Texas Navy. Washington, ca. 1849. Jenkins 116-675 1978 $125

HOUSTON, SAM   Warrant. Austin, 1860. Signed by Houston on verso. Jenkins 116-676 1978 $125

HOUSTON. CHARTERS   Charter of the City of Houston...As Passed by the 28th Legislature. Houston, 1903. Pr. wrs. Jenkins 116-571 1978 $25

HOUSTOUN, MATILDA   Texas and The Gulf of Mexico: or, Yachting in the New World. Philadelphia, 1845. Cloth, 1st American ed. Jenkins 116-674a 1978 $125

HOUZEAU, J. C.   Bibliographie Generale de L'Astronomie. 8vo, 3 vols., buckram gilt. Traylen 88-504 1978 £42

HOVEDEN, ROGER OF   Annales, the History of England and other Countries of Europe, 732-1201. 1853. 2 vols., ex-lib. copy, spines rubbed, cr. 8vo., orig. cloth. George's 635-557 1978 £7.50

HOVEY, HORACE C.   Hovey's Hand-Book of the Mammoth Cave of Kentucky. Louisville, 1909. Wrs. Hayman 73-364 1978 $8.50

HOW, DAVID D.   Trial of...For the Murder of Othello Church... N. P., n.d. (ca. 1824). Sewn, scarce, 8vo., orig. cloth, very good. Americanist 103-101 1978 $35

HOW Harry was Kept from the Street. (Boston, ca. 1890s). Illus., 16mo., orig. wrs. Morrill 239-421 1978 $25

HOW to Buy and Sell Money. Giant folio, pict. wrs., drwgs., fine. Battery Park 1-55 1978 $100

HOWARD, A. A.   Index Verborum C. Suetoni Tranquilli Stilique eius Proprietatum Nonnullarum. 1922. Allen 234-907 1978 $12.50

HOWARD, ALICE WOODBURY   Ching-li and the Dragons. New York, 1931. Illus. with designs and plts. by Lynd Ward, 1st ed., 1st printing, square 4 to., d.j., fine. Houle 10-359 1978 $45

HOWARD, C. F.   Howard's California Calculator,..... San Francisco, 1874. Original printed wr., 1st ed. Ginsberg 1978 $50

HOWARD, EDWARD GRANVILLE   Rattlin, The Reefer. 2nd. ed., 3 vols., lg. 12mo, 9 plts., foxed, contemp. half calf. Hannas 54-220 1978 £20

HOWARD, FRANK   Colour as a Means of Art, Being an Adaptation of the Experience of Professors to the Practise of Amateurs. 1838. 8vo., coloured lithographs, orig. cloth. Quaritch 983-203 1978 $100

HOWARD, GEORGE WILLIAM FREDERICK 7TH EARL OF CARLISLE
Please turn to
CARLISLE, GEORGE WILLIAM FREDERICK HOWARD, 7TH EARL OF

HOWARD, MRS. HENRY   The Seamen's Handbook for Shore Leave. 1942. 7th ed. rev., map. Austin 80-136 1978 $10

HOWARD, HENRY   A Course of Lectures on Painting. 1848. Lg. 12mo., 19th-century calf gilt. P. M. Hill 142-24 1978 £18

HOWARD, JAMES K.   Ten Years with the Cowboy Artists of America. Cloth, illus., some in color, 1st ed., as new. Dykes 34-193 1978 $40

HOWARD, OLIVER OTIS   Autobiography. Vol. 1. Long autograph pres. inscription by nephew. Wolfe 39-239 1978 $17.50

HOWARD, OLIVER OTIS   Nez Perce Joseph. Boston, 1881. Orig. cloth, ex-library, hinges cracked, frontis. ports., maps. Wolfe 39-244 1978 $30

HOWARD, ROBERT   A Few Words on Corn and Quakers. 1800. Fcap. 8vo., sewn. George's 635-338 1978 £5.50

HOWARD, SIDNEY   Ned McCobb's Daughter. New York, 1926. Wrs., 1st ed. Biblo BL781-997 1978 $9

HOWARD, WILEY C.   Sketch of Cobb Legion Cavalry. N.P., 1901 (?). Reprint, Bell Wiley's copy. Broadfoot's 44-447 1978 $10

HOWARD, WILLIAM A.   Kansas Affairs. (Washington, 1856). Unbound as issued, age-stained, especially on 1st. page. Hayman 71-304 1978 $7.50

HOWARD, WILLIAM F.   The Romance of Texas Money: A Story of Texas Money From Early Colonial Days To The Last Issue of the Money of the Republic. Dallas, 1946. 1st ed., wr., illus., autographed by author. Jenkins 116-675a 1978 $10

HOWARD, WILLIAM TRAVIS, JR.   Public Health Administration and the Natural History of Disease in Baltimore, Maryland 1797-1920. Washington, 1924. Clean, tight. Rittenhouse 49-376 1976 $21

HOWARD-SMITH, LOGAN   Thrilling Stories of the Great War. Toronto, 1918. Profusely illus. with photos, maps & drawings. Hood's 115-116 1978 $15

HOWAY, FREDERIC W.   The Dixon-Meares Controversy... Toronto, 1929. Ed. ltd. to 500 copies, illus. Hood 116-854 1978 $65

HOWAY, FREDERICK W.   Voyages of the "Columbia" to the Northwest Coast. 1787...1793. Massachusetts, 1941. Lg. 8vo., orig. 1/2 cloth, good. Paine 78-67 1978 $47.50

HOWDEN-SMITH, ARTHUR D.   John Jacob Astor, Landlord of New York. New York, 1929. 16 illus. Baldwins' 51-172 1978 $8.50

HOWE, C. D.   Trent (Ontario) Watershed Survey. Toronto, 1913. Maps, illus., 8vo., ex-lib., spine faded. Morrill 239-430 1978 $7.50

HOWE, DANIEL WAIT   The Puritan Republic of Massachusetts Bay in New England. Indianapolis, (1899). Cloth. Hayman 73-267 1978 $10

HOWE, E. R. J. GAMBIER   Catalogue of British and American Bookplates bequeathed to the British Museum by Sir A. W. Franks. 1903-04. Plts., 3 vols., roy. 8vo., orig. cloth, vols. 1 and 3 neatly recased. George's 635-1202 1978 £80

HOWE, ELLIC   A List of London Book-binders 1648-1815. 1950. 8vo. George's 635-1193 1978 £20

HOWE, FREDERIC C.   The Land and the Soldier. 1919. 1st ed. Austin 80-710 1978 $20

HOWE, HENRY   Memoirs of the Most Eminent American Mechanics. 1858. Engrs. Austin 80-711 1978 $27.50

HOWE, JOHN   An Abridgement of a Discourse on Self-Dedication.
Cambridge, 1785. 8vo., unbound. P. M. Hill 142-142 1978 £7

HOWE, JOHN   The Living Temple. 1702. 2 vols., portrait,
contemp. panelled calf, very good, 8vo. Howes 194-318 1978 £30

HOWE, JULIA WARD   From Sunset Ridge Poems Old and New. Boston,
1899. 8vo, boards, cloth back, gilt lettering on cover and back, ownership
inscription, lst ed., collector's cond. Desmarais 1-228 1978 $17.50

HOWE, JULIA WARD   From Sunset Ridge. Boston, 1899. Very fine.
Desmarais B-329 1978 $17.50

HOWE, MARK ANTHONY DE WOLFE   Boston. New York, 1903. Illus., 8vo.,
orig. cloth, 1st ed., pres. from author & illus'r. Morrill 241-333 1978 $10

HOWE, OCTAVIUS THORNDIKE   American Clipper Ships 1833-1858. Salem,
1926-27. 2 vols., 1st ed., lg. 8vos., orig. buckram, color fronts, illus., very
good. Americanist 103-28 1978 $75

HOWE, PAUL S.   Mayflower Pilgrim Descendants in Cape May
County, N.J. 1620-1920. (Cape May, 1921). Illus., very scarce. MacManus
239-1278 1978 $55

HOWE, R. H.   On the Birds Highway. Boston, 1899. Full page
plts. by Fuertes, ex-lib, 8vo, orig. cloth. Book Chest 17-195 1978 $20

HOWE, SONIA E.   The Drama of Madagascar. London, (1938).
8vo, orig. cloth, 2 maps, 2 plts. K Books 239-224 1978 £8

HOWE, WILLIAM F.   The Electro-Therapeutic Guide. Lima, 1902.
Sixth ed., revised and enlarged. Rittenhouse 49-377 1976 $10

HOWE, WINIFRED E.   A History of the Metropolitan Museum of Art.
New York, 1913. 1st ed., illus., orig. cloth-backed bds., ltd. to 1,000 copies,
fine. MacManus 239-691 1978 $25

HOWE, WINIFRED E.   A History of the Metropolitan Museum of Art.
New York, 1913, 1946. 2 vols., 1st eds., frontis. port., illus., 1 of 1,000
copies, orig. cloth-backed bds., fine. MacManus 239-678 1978 $35

HOWELL, ANDREW J.   Songs of Summer Nights. Wilmington, 1937.
Stiff wrs., pres. copy to Archibald Henderson with his bookplt. Broadfoot 50-101
1978 $12

HOWELL, GEORGE ROGERS   The Early History of Southampton...With Genealogies. New York, 1866. 1st ed. Butterfield 21-255 1978 $35

HOWELL, JAMES   Epistolae Ho-Elianae. The Familiar Letters.
Boston, 1907. 4 vols., orig. 1/4 cloth, uncut, frontis., 1 of 220 copies designed
by Bruce Rogers, leather bookplts. of Alex. Wyant. Americanist 102-103 1978
$35

HOWELL, JAMES   Epistolae Ho-Elianae. 1655. Engrav. frontis.,
sm. 8vo., finely bound in full levant mor., a.e.g., fine, third ed. Howes 194-
61 1978 £55

HOWELL, JAMES   Epistolae Ho-Elianae: Familiar Letters Domestick
and Foreign, Divided into Four Books. 1737. Tenth ed., frontis., contemp. calf,
rebacked, new endpapers, 8vo. Howes 194-319 1978 £16

HOWELL, JAMES   Epistolae Ho-Elianae: The Familiar Letters.
1892. Plts., 2 vols., lg. 8vo., orig. buckram backed cloth, gilt tops, backs faded.
Howes 194-947 1978 £14

HOWELL, JAMES   Instructions For Forreine Travell. 1642. 1st.
ed., engraved title, portrait, 12mo, red straight grained morocco, gilt, g. e.,
margin of portrait shaved. Edwards 1012-22 1978 £140

HOWELL, JOHN W.   History of the Incandescent Lamp. 1927. Illus.
Austin 80-712 1978 $10

HOWELL, THOMAS   Howell's Devises 1581. Oxford, 1906. Good,
octavo. Upcroft 10-89 1978 £5

HOWELL, W. H.   The De Lamar Lectures 1925-26 of the School of
Hygiene and Public Health, John Hopkins Univ. 1927. Austin 80-945 1978
$17.50

HOWELLS, JOHN M.   Lost Examples of Colonial Architecture. New
York, 1931. Lg. 4to., plts., ltd. to 1,100 copies, fine. MacManus 239-679
1978 $55

HOWELLS, MILDRED   Life in Letters of William Dean Howells. n.d. 2
vols., illus., very good. Austin 82-458 1978 $47.50

HOWELLS, WILLIAM DEAN   The Albany Depot. 1892. First ed., cover
soiled. Austin 82-439 1978 $15

HOWELLS, WILLIAM DEAN   Annie Kilburn. (1888). 1891. Austin 82-440
1978 $11

HOWELLS, WILLIAM DEAN   Certain Delightful English Towns, With Glimpses
of the Pleasant Country Between. New York, 1906. 8vo, green cloth, stamped
in red & gold, t.e.g., ownership inscription on flyleaf, lst ed., collector's cond.
Desmarais 1-229 1978 $15

HOWELLS, WILLIAM DEAN   Certain Delightful English Towns. 1906. Green
cloth, first ed. Austin 82-444 1978 $12.50

HOWELLS, WILLIAM DEAN   A Chance Acquaintance. 1873. Terra cotta
cloth, first ed., good. Austin 82-441 1978 $15

HOWELLS, WILLIAM DEAN   A Chance Acquaintance. 1884. Austin 82-442
1978 $11

HOWELLS, WILLIAM DEAN   A Chance Acquaintance. 1915. Illus. Austin
82-443 1978 $10

HOWELLS, WILLIAM DEAN   Criticism and Fiction. 1891. First ed. Austin
82-446 1978 $12.50

HOWELLS, WILLIAM DEAN   Doctor Breen's Practice. 1881. Grass green cloth,
first ed., very good. Austin 82-447 1978 $27.50

HOWELLS, WILLIAM DEAN   Evening Dress. 1893. Illus., first ed., backstrip
darkened. Austin 82-448 1978 $17.50

HOWELLS, WILLIAM DEAN   Familiar Spanish Travels. 1913. Illus., first ed.
Austin 82-449 1978 $12.50

HOWELLS, WILLIAM DEAN   The Flight of Pony Baker. New York, 1902.
1st ed., very good. Victoria 34-426 1978 $50

HOWELLS, WILLIAM DEAN   A Foregone Conclusion. 1875. Terra cotta cloth,
first ed., first printing, signed and dated by first owner. Austin 82-450 1978
$22.50

HOWELLS, WILLIAM DEAN   A Hazard of New Fortunes. 1911. Illus., Lib.
ed. Austin 82-451 1978 $15

HOWELLS, WILLIAM DEAN   The Heart of Childhood – Harper Novelettes.
(1891). 1906. Austin 82-452 1978 $7.50

HOWELLS, WILLIAM DEAN   Indian Summer. 1886. First ed., terra cotta cloth,
nice. Austin 82-454 1978 $27.50

HOWELLS, WILLIAM DEAN   Italian Journeys. 1901. Illus., first ed., half
blue leather and marbelized bds., nice. Austin 82-455 1978 $27.50

HOWELLS, WILLIAM DEAN   The Lady of the Aroostoook. 1879. Green cloth,
first ed., first printing, nice. Austin 82-456 1978 $17.50

HOWELLS, WILLIAM DEAN   Literary Friends and Acquaintances. 1900. Illus.
Austin 82-461 1978 $10

HOWELLS, WILLIAM DEAN   Literary Friends and Acquaintances. 1900. First
ed. Austin 82-459 1978 $12.50

HOWELLS, WILLIAM DEAN   Literary Friends and Acquaintances. 1911. Illus.
Austin 82-460 1978 $17.50

HOWELLS, WILLIAM DEAN   A Little Girl Among the Old Masters. 1884.
Inserted plts., olive cloth, first ed. Austin 82-462 1978 $37.50

HOWELLS, WILLIAM DEAN   London Films. New York, 1904. 8vo, green
cloth stamped in red & gold, uncut, t.e.g., lower front corner bumped, spine
slightly faded, near Fine, ownership inscription, lst ed., collector's cond. Desmarais 1-230 1978 $12.50

HOWELLS, WILLIAM DEAN   London Films. 1905. First ed., illus. Austin 82-
463 1978 $15

HOWELLS, WILLIAM DEAN   London Films. 1905. Illus. Austin 82-464 1978
$10

HOWELLS, WILLIAM DEAN   The Minster's Charge. 1887. Terra cotta cloth, first ed., first binding, signed by Howells on owner's bookplate. Austin 82-465 1978 $47.50

HOWELLS, WILLIAM DEAN   Miss Bellard's Inspiration. 1905. First ed., ex-lib. Austin 82-466 1978 $11

HOWELLS, WILLIAM DEAN   A Modern Instance. 1909. Austin 82-467 1978 $11

HOWELLS, WILLIAM DEAN   The Mouse Trap and Other Farces. 1889. First ed. Austin 82-468 1978 $12.50

HOWELLS, WILLIAM DEAN   New Leaf Mills. 1913. First ed., some cover wear. Austin 82-469 1978 $10

HOWELLS, WILLIAM DEAN   Out of the Question. Boston, 1877. First ed. Austin 82-470 1978 $22.50

HOWELLS, WILLIAM DEAN   Poems. Boston, 1873. Terra-cotta cloth, very good, illus. Dawson's 447-244 1978 $20

HOWELLS, WILLIAM DEAN   Quaint Courtships - Harper Novelettes. 1906. Austin 82-453 1978 $8.50

HOWELLS, WILLIAM DEAN   Questionable Shapes. New York, 1903. Red cloth, first ed., very good. Austin 82-471 1978 $17.50

HOWELLS, WILLIAM DEAN   The Register Farce. Boston, 1884. First ed., covers spotted. Austin 82-472 1978 $20

HOWELLS, WILLIAM DEAN   The Rise of Silas Lapham. (1884). Austin 82-474 1978 $8.50

HOWELLS, WILLIAM DEAN   The Rise of Silas Lapham. Boston, 1885. 1st ed., variant issue, 12mo., blue cloth with gilt & black decor's on spine & front cover, wear to spine extremities, else near fine, interior nearly perfect, previous owner's name on last paste-down. Current 24-21 1978 $135

HOWELLS, WILLIAM DEAN   The Rise of Silas Lapham. Boston, 1885. 8vo, blue pict. cloth, internal browning, covers somewhat worn and faded, 1st state, 1st ed., collector's cond. Desmarais 1-231 1978 $50

HOWELLS, WILLIAM DEAN   The Rise of Silas Lapham. Boston, 1885. Blue cloth, first ed., first state, good. Austin 82-473 1978 $47.50

HOWELLS, WILLIAM DEAN   The Rise of Silas Lapham. 1912. Austin 82-475 1978 $7.50

HOWELLS, WILLIAM DEAN   The Seen and the Unseen on Stratford-on-Avon. 1914. First ed. Austin 82-476 1978 $17.50

HOWELLS, WILLIAM DEAN   Seven English Cities. 1909. Illus., first ed. Austin 82-477 1978 $12.50

HOWELLS, WILLIAM DEAN   The Son of Royal Langbrith. New York, 1904. 8vo, blue cloth, uncut, t.e.g., top & bottom of spine eubbed, ownership inscription on flyleaf, near Fine, 1st ed., collector's cond. Desmarais 1-232 1978 $15

HOWELLS, WILLIAM DEAN   Their Silver Wedding Journey. 1899. 2 vols., first ed., fine, orig. silver cloth d.j. slightly frayed. Austin 82-479 1978 $37.50

HOWELLS, WILLIAM DEAN   Their Silver Wedding Journey. 1899. 2 vols., illus. ed. Austin 82-478 1978 $17.50

HOWELLS, WILLIAM DEAN   Their Silver Wedding Journey. 1900. 1 vol. ed. Austin 82-480 1978 $11

HOWELLS, WILLIAM DEAN   Their Wedding Journey. Boston, 1875. Austin 82-481 1978 $11

HOWELLS, WILLIAM DEAN   Their Wedding Journey. 1894. Illus. Austin 82-482 1978 $11

HOWELLS, WILLIAM DEAN   Their Wedding Journey. 1916. Illus. Austin 82-483 1978 $12.50

HOWELLS, WILLIAM DEAN   Through the Eye of the Needle. New York, 1907. 8vo, green cloth t.e.g., ownership inscription in pencil, Fine, 1st ed., collector's cond. Desmarais 1-234 1978 $15

HOWELLS, WILLIAM DEAN   Tuscan Cities. 1886. Illus., very good. Austin 82-484 1978 $37.50

HOWELLS, WILLIAM DEAN   The Undiscovered Country. 1880. First ed., first state. Austin 82-485 1978 $27.50

HOWELLS, WILLIAM DEAN   Venetian Life. 1892. 2 vols., illus. from orig. water colors, first trade ed., heavy d.j.'s, almost mint white cloth covers. Austin 82-487 1978 $37.50

HOWELLS, WILLIAM HOOPER   The Rescue of Desdemona & Other Verse. Philadelphia, 1908. 1 of 100 copies on toned Enfield paper, orig. cloth w/paper labels, color fronts. & illus. by Geo. Wolfe Plank, signed inscrip. by Howells, 8vo. Americanist 101-68 1978 $35

HOWES, EDITH   The Long Bright Land. Boston, 1929. 1st ed., colored and B&W plates, very fine, slightly frayed dj. Victoria 34-485 1978 $30

HOWES, WRIGHT   U. S. Iana. New York, 1962. 2nd ed., fine. Ballinger 11-42 1978 $200.00

HOWISON, JOHN   Foreign Scenes and Travelling Recreations. Edinburgh, 1825. 2 vols., 8vo, contemporary half calf, (bit rubbed, sound), 1st ed., half-titles present, very good copy. Ximenes 47-141 1978 $125

HOWISON, JOHN   Sketches of Upper Canada, Domestic, Local, and Characteristic. Edinburgh, 1822. Second ed., half calf, edges of covers worn, front cover loose. Wolfe 39-240 1978 $75

HOWITT, MARY   Our Four-Footed Friends. (1867). 4to., illus., orig. blind and gilt stamped binding with onlaid coloured illus. Quaritch 979-341 1978 $70

HOWITT, SAMUEL   A New Work of Animals: Principally Designed from the Fables of Aesop, Gay and Phaedrus. 1818. 4to., uncut, contemp. half red roan, plts. Howes 194-1393 1978 £65

HOWITT, WILLIAM   The Boy's Country Book; Being the Real Life of a Country Boy. London, 1839. Sm. 8vo, 1st. ed., illus., half dark green morocco, gilt spine. Traylen 88-277A 1978 £25

HOWITT, WILLIAM   The Desolation of Eyam: The Emigrant, A Tale of the American Woods... 1827. 1st. ed., half title, uncut, orig.blue bds., brown paper spine, hinges little rubbed, chip from paper label, otherwise v.g. Jarndyce 16-744 1978 £22

HOWITT, WILLIAM   Homes and Haunts of the Most Eminent British Poets. 1847. 2nd. ed., 2 vols., illus. by W. & G. Measom, half titles, orig. green cloth, gilt spines, v.g. Jarndyce 16-743 1978 £18.50

HOWITT, WILLIAM   The Rural Life of England. London, 1838. 2 vols., 8vo, 1st. ed., illus., half dark green morocco, gilt spine. Traylen 88-277B 1978 £20

HOWITT, WILLIAM   Visits To Remarkable Places; Old Halls, Battle Fields Etc. London, 1840-42. 2 vols., 8vo, 1st. ed., illus., half dark green morocco, gilt spine. Traylen 88-277C 1978 £30

HOWITT, WILLIAM   The Year-Book of the Country; or, The Field, The Forest and the Fireside. London, 1850. Illus. after Birket Foster, 1st. ed., half dark green morocco, gilt spine. Traylen 88-277D 1978 £18

HOWLEY, M. F.   The Old Royal Coat-of-Arms at Placentia. 1909. Illus. Hood 116-221 1978 $12.50

HOYLAND, JOHN   Historical Survey of the Customs, Habits and Present State of the Gypsies. York, 1816. Modern marbled bds., 8vo. George's 635-1353 1978 £35

HOYLE, EDMOND   Hoyle's Improved Edition of the Rules for Playing Fashionable Games. New York, 1830. 16mo., contemp.calf, fr. cover loose, back hinge cracked. Morrill 239-432 1978 $8.50

HOYNE, MORRIS   The Soldier Magician; or, the Conspirators of Washington. New York, 1886. Self wrs. Hayman 72-126 1978 $7.50

HOYNE, TEMPLE S.   Venereal and Urinary Diseases. Chicago, 1894. 2nd ed., revised & enlarged, 8vo. Morrill 239-128 1978 $10

HOYT, DERISTHE L.   The World's Painters and Their Pictures. Boston, (1893). Cloth, illus. Hayman 73-268 1978 $7.50

HOYT, R. S.   Royal Demesne in English Constitutional History: 1066-1272. 1950. Ex-lib. Allen 234-1308 1978 $7.50

HOYT, WILLIAM HENRY   The Mecklenburg Declaration of Independence.
New York, 1907. Rebound. Broadfoot 50-102 1978 $25

HOYT, WILLIAM HENRY   The Mecklenburg Declaration of Independence.
New York, 1907. Rebound. MacManus 239-205 1978 $20

HOZIER, H. M.   Hints to Captains of the Mercantile Marine.
Glasgow, 1885. Cloth bds., color. plts., good, 8vo. Paine 78-68 1978 $17.50

HOZIER, H. M.   The Seven Weeks' War... 1867. 2 vols., 8vo.,
maps, 2 colored, orig. cloth. F. Edwards 1013-335 1978 £18

HROSWITHA OF GANDERSHEIM
Please turn to
HROTSVIT, OF GANDERSHEIM

HROTSVIT, OF GANDERSHEIM   Opera Hrosuite... Nuremburg, 1501. Sm.
folio, Roman letter, woodcuts attributed to Albrecht Durer and Hans von Kulmbach,
old lib. stamp, German 18th cent. calf backed bds., bookplate of Hermann Marx,
first ed. Quaritch 978-83 1978 $10,000

HSIANG-IN LI   I Yun Tzu K'ao. Peking, (c. 1900). Sewn,
decor. chitsu case. Dawson's 449-46 1978 $20

HSIUNG, S. I.   Lady Precious Stream. 1934. Coloured plts.,
cloth gilt, t.e.g., fine, d.w., signed by author, first English ed. Bell Book 16-
451 1978 £5

HUBBACK, MRS.   The Old Vicarage. New York, 1856. 1st Am.
ed., orig. cloth binding show wear. Greene 78-57 1978 $25

HUBBARD, B. F.   Forests and Clearings. The History of Stanstead
County, Province of Quebec. Illus., orig. green cloth, orig. portrait photograph
of B. F. Hubbard with his autograph inscription, very scarce. Wolfe 39-148 1978
$250

HUBBARD, BENJAMIN   Sermo Seculaties. 1648. 4to, dedicated to
Nathanael Bacon & Francis Bacon, disbound, very good. Jarndyce 16-17 1978
£10.50

HUBBARD, C. HORACE   History of the Town of Springfield, Vermont...
Boston, 1895. 1st ed., illus., rebound, very good. MacManus 239-1127 1978
$32.50

HUBBARD, ELBERT   The City of Tagaste. No. 23 of 940 numbered
copies, signed by Elbert Hubbard, 3/4 lea., rubbed, t.e.g. Battery Park 1-!77
1978 $75

HUBBARD, ELBERT   Forbes of Harvard. Boston, 1894. 1st ed., orig.
dec. cloth, slightly soiled. Americanist 102-61 1978 $50

HUBBARD, ELBERT   Justinian and Theodora by Elbert and Alice
Hubbard. Ex-libris. Battery Park 1-175 1978 $50

HUBBARD, ELBERT   Little Journeys to the Homes of Eminent Artists.
East Aurora, 1902. 2 vols., leather-backed bds., orig. wrs. bound in. Hayman
72-309 1978 $10

HUBBARD, ELBERT   Little Journeys to the Homes of English Authors.
East Aurora, 1900. 8vo., bds., covers soiled, frontis. Battery Park 1-173 1978
$35

HUBBARD, ELBERT   Little Journeys to the Homes of Great Musicians.
East Aurora, 1901. Suede, one of 940 copies, signed by author & illuminator
Maude Baker, cover little discolored, very good copy. Hayman 71-305 1978 $10

HUBBARD, ELBERT   Little Journeys to the Homes of the Great.
East Aurora, (1916). Broken set (9 of 14 vols.), bound in decor. leather, most vols.
scuffed at spine ends & edges, inside fine. Bernard 5-134 1978 $20

HUBBARD, ELBERT   The Mintage. Being Ten Stories and One More.
East Aurora, (1910). 12mo., frontis., 1st ed., pres., signed by Hubbard, 3/4 leather, lightly rubbed. Biblo BL781-998 1978 $30

HUBBARD, EL BERT   The Philosophy of Elbert Hubbard. New York,
1930. Buckram scrapbook-style binding, large 8vol., very good in dw. Bernard
5-136 1978 $7.50

HUBBARD, ELBERT   Respectability. 1905. Orig. limp suede leather,
very good, first English ed. Bell Book 16-752 1978 £5

HUBBARD, ELBERT   Selected Writings of Elbert Hubbard. East
Aurora, (1923). Broken set (12 of 14 vols.), bound in decor. leather, most vols.
scuffed at spine ends & edges, inside fine. Bernard 5-135 1978 $25

HUBBARD, ELBERT   So Here Then Cometh Pig-Pen Pete or Some
Chums of Mine. East Aurora, (1914). Full lea., illus., very fine. Battery Park
1-!76 1978 $125

HUBBARD, ELBERT   Time and Chance. East Aurora, 1899. 1st ed.,
bound in boards with suede spines, good condition, 2 vols. Greene 78-58 1978
$65

HUBBARD, FREDERICK A.   Other Days in Greenwich... New York, 1913.
Illus., ltd. to 1,000 copies. MacManus 239-948 1978 $30

HUBBARD, G. E.   Eastern Industrialization and Its Effect on the West.
Oxford University Press, 1935. Ex-lib. Austin 80-713 1978 $12.50

HUBBARD, JOHN NILES   An Account of Sa-Go-Ye-Wat-Ha or Red Jacket
and His People, 1750-1830. Albany, 1886. Plts., inserted frontis., fine half-
lea. & red silk cloth. Butterfield 21-213 1978 $45

HUBBARD, JOHN NILES   Sketches of Border Adventures, in the Life and
Times of Major Moses Van Campen, a Surviving Soldier of the Revolution. Bath,
1842. 2nd ed., full calf, spine repaired, library bkplt. & number on spine.
Butterfield 21-375 1978 $20

HUBBARD, JOHN NILES   Sketches of the Border Adventures, in the Life
and Times of Major Moses Van Campen... Bath, 1842. Orig. cloth, very scarce.
MacManus 239-583 1978 $40

HUBBARD, R. B.   Texas: Her Area of Territory, Health and Its
Evidence, Wealth and Population, School Endowments, Products, Internal Improve-
ments, and Resources of Wealth. Austin, 1876. Later half calf, morocco label.
Jenkins 116-1559 1978 $150

HUBBARD, STEPHEN G.   Prof. Henry Bronson, M. D. (New Haven, ca.
1895). Portr., tall 8vo., 1st ed. Morrill 239-129 1978 $7.50

HUBBELL, LEVI   Trial of Impeachment of Levi Hubbell, Judge of
the Second Judicial Circuit, by the Senate of...Wisconsin, June 1853. Madison,
1853. Leather backed bds., rubbed, scarce, sm. hole in title page. Hayman 73-
767 1978 $35

HUBER, J. C. D.   German Minstrelsy: A Gathering of Choice
Flowers for English Lovers of German Poetry. 1862. Cr. 8vo, orig. cloth.
Eaton 45-256 1978 £5

HUBERMAN, LEO   America, Incorporated. 1940. Ex-lib. Austin
80-714 1978 $10

HUBERMONT, PIERRE   Thirteen Men in the Mine. New York, 1931.
Illus., 1st Amer. ed. Biblo 251-509 1978 $12.50

HUCKEL, F. F.   American Indians. Kansas City, 1920. 2nd ed.,
4to, plts. in color, orig. wrs., frayed, spine torn. Biblo 248-39 1978 $10

HUCKER, OLIVER   Parsifal. New York, Merrymount Press, 1903.
Illus., prtd. in several colors, decor. cover, gilt lettering, t.e.g. Battery Park
1-202 1978 $22.50

HUDDLESTON, SISLEY   Bohemian Literary and Social Life in Paris:
Salons, Cafes, Studios. (1928). 1st. ed., plts., illus., 8vo, orig. cloth, d.w.,
fine. Fenning 32-168 1978 £25

HUDLESTON, F. J.   Warriors in Undress. London, (1925). First ed.
Biblo 247-698 1978 $13.50

HUDSON, A. S.   The History of Concord Mass. Concord, 1904.
Illus. MacManus 239-1023 1978 $35

HUDSON, C.   On the Portion of the President's Message Relating
to the Mexican War. Washington, 1846. Jenkins 116-922 1978 $8.50

HUDSON, CHARLES   History of the Town of Lexington, Middlesex
County Massachusetts From Its First Settlement to 1868. Boston, 1913. 1st of this
ed., 2 vols., 4to., illus., orig. cloth, 1 of 300 sets, very good. MacManus
239-1033 1978 $50

HUDSON, FREDERIC   Journalism in the United States 1690-1872.
New York, 1873. 1st ed. MacManus 239-206 1978 $35

HUDSON, HENRY   Descriptio Ac Delineatio Geographica Detectionis
Freti... Amsterdam, 1612. 1st. Latin ed., maps, woodcuts, sm. 4to, old style
calf, slight waterstain affecting corner of text & maps. Edwards 1012-23 1978
£3000

HUDSON, WILLIAM C.   Random Recollections of an Old Political Reporter. New York, 1911. Cloth. Hayman 72-311 1978 $10

HUDSON, WILLIAM HENRY 1841-1922   Birds in a Village. London, 1893. Chocolate-colored buckram, 1st ed., sm. spot on front cover, spine dull. Bradley 49-155 1978 $135

HUDSON, WILLIAM HENRY   Birds in a Village. London, 1893. Orig. green cloth, 1st ed., very good. MacManus 238-283 1978 $45

HUDSON, WILLIAM HENRY   Birds in London. London, 1898. Illus., orig. cloth, 1st ed., near fine. MacManus 238-285 1978 $75

HUDSON, WILLIAM HENRY 1841-1922   Birds in London. London, 1898. 8vo., green cloth, gilt stamped cover and spine, spine badly dust darkened, uncut, unopened, t.e.g., very nice, 1st ed., collector's cond. Desmarais 1-235 1978 $40

HUDSON, WILLIAM HENRY 1841-1922   British Birds. 1895. Coloured plts. by A. Thorburn, photographs, cr. 8vo. George's 635-1008 1978 £15

HUDSON, WILLIAM HENRY 1841-1922   Far Away and Long Ago: a history of my early life. 1918. Portrait, covers little rubbed & soiled, else good, first English ed. Bell Book 17-465 1978 £5

HUDSON, WILLIAM HENRY 1841-1922   Green Mansions. New York, 1944. Coloured plts. by E. McKnight Kauffer, cloth-backed bds., very good. Bell Book 16-487 1978 £6.50

HUDSON, WILLIAM HENRY 1841-1922   A Little Boy Lost. London, 1905. Plts., illus., 1st ed., sm. 4to., picture cloth gilt, pres. copy from author. Traylen 88-279 1978 £90

HUDSON, WILLIAM HENRY 1841-1922   A Little Boy Lost. New York, 1920. Quarto, 1st ed., color & B&W plates, large gilt cover vignette signed "DPL", fine. Victoria 34-484 1978 $50

HUDSON, WILLIAM HENRY 1841-1922   El Ombu. London, 1902. Crown 8vo., orig. green cloth, first ed. Howell 5-33 1978 $50

HUDSON, WILLIAM HENRY 1841-1922   El Ombu. London, 1902. Sm. 8vo., green cloth lettered in black, unusually fine, first ed. Desmarais 1-236 1978 $65

HUDSON, WILLIAM HENRY 1841-1922   153 Letters from.... London, Nonesuch Press, 1923. 1 of 1,000 numbered copies, tall 8vo., portrait, tan buckram, uncut, unopened, good-fine. Houle 10-163 1978 $45

HUDSON, WILLIAM HENRY 1841-1922   153 Letters from W. H. Hudson. London, Nonesuch Press, 1923. 8vo., brown cloth, paper label, uncut, unopened, unusually fine, no. 707 of 1,000 copies, 1st ed., collector's cond. Desmarais 1-239 1978 $35

HUDSON, WILLIAM HENRY 1841-1922   A Shepherd's Life. London, (1910). Cloth, illus., from the Allred Collection & inscr. Dykes 34-276 1978 $25

HUDSON'S BAY COMPANY   Report From the Committee Appointed to Inquire Into the State and Condition Of The Countries Adjoining to Hudson's Bay, And of The Trade Carried On There. London, 1749. 1st. ed., folio, half calf, morocco label gilt. Deighton 5-43 1978 £765

HUEFFER, FORD MADOX
Please turn to
FORD, FORD MADOX

HUES, ROBERTO   Tractatus de Globis Coelesti et Terrestri Eorumque Usu.... Amstelodami, 1617. 1st Amsterdam ed., quarto, numerous devices, charts, diagrams, full contemp. vellum, lightly foxed. Bennett 20-109 1978 $835

HUET DE TOSTES   Ecriture Anglaise Demontree par Principes. Paris, 1821. Oblong 4to., cont. bds., eng. plts. Schumann 511-25 1978 sFr 435

HUFELAND, OTTO   A Check List of Books, Maps, Pictures and Other Printed Matter Relating to the Counties of Westchester and Bronx. White Plains, 1929. MacManus 239-335 1978 $25

HUFELAND, OTTO   Westchester County During the American Revolution 1775-1783. New York, 1926. Illus., maps, t.e.g., very fine, ltd. to 250 numbered copies. MacManus 239-609 1978 $50

HUFF, EMMA N.   Memories that Live... Springville, 1947. Fabricoid, map, illus., 1st ed., very good, scarce. Dykes 35-287 1978 $35

HUFFMAN, JAMES   Ups and Downs of a Confederate Soldier. New York, 1940. Mounted plates, Bell Wiley's copy. Broadfoot's 44-653 1978 $26

HUFFORD, D. A.   Death Valley.... Los Angeles, 1902. Plts., flexible leather. Hayman 71-306 1978 $10

HUGH of Lincoln and other Ballads. (1938). Coloured engraved frontis. and woodcuts by E. Walter, 8vo., orig. linen, spine faded. George's 635-907 1978 £5

HUGHES, A.E.   The Beginnings of Spanish Settlement in the El Paso District. Berkeley, 1914. Jenkins 116-383 1978 $65

HUGHES, E.   Studies in Administration and Finance 1558-1825. Manchester, 1934. Portrait, 8vo. George's 635-339 1978 £8.50

HUGHES, EVERETT CHERRINGTON   French Canada in Transition. Chicago, University of Chicago Press, 1943. Frontis. Austin 79-342 1978 $27.50

HUGHES, GRIFFITH   The Natural History of Barbados. London, 1750. Lg. paper copy, map, plts. all contemp. colouring, folio, calf, rebacked. Traylen 88-654 1978 £750

HUGHES, GRIFFITH   The Natural History of Barbados. London, 1750. Lg. fldg. map, plts., folio, 1/2 calf. Salloch 345-97 1978 $450

HUGHES, HENRY   First Royal Reg't. New York, 1837. Sm. 8vo., orig. wrs., 1st Amer. ed. Morrill 239-130 1978 $12.50

HUGHES, HENRY   Treatise on Sociology, Theorretical & Proctical. Phila, 1854. Spine chipped, one folding plate frayed, Bell Wiley's copy. Broadfoot's 44-711 1978 $25.00

HUGHES, J.   Controversy Between Rev. Messrs....and Breckenridge, on ... Protestant Religion... Philadelphia, 1872. Orig. cl. Ginsberg 16-879 1978 $12.50

HUGHES, JOHN   Poems on Several Occasions. 1735. 2 vols., 12mo., contemp. calf, lacking labels, neat copy, portrait, plts., first collected ed. P. M. Hill 142-286 1978 £45

HUGHES, JOHN   The Siege of Damascus. 1720. First ed., 8vo., contemp. panelled calf, rebacked, some browning of text. Howes 194-320 1978 £35

HUGHES, RICHARD   Burial and the Dark Child. 1930. 8vo., 1st ed., orig. wrs., A.L.s. loosely inserted. Quaritch 979-198 1978 $120

HUGHES, RICHARD   Ecstatic Ode on Vision. 1925. Sm. 8vo., 1st ed., orig. wrs., ltd. to only 75 copies, with T.L.s. Quaritch 979-199 1978 $120

HUGHES, RICHARD   Gipsy Night and Other Poems. Chicago, 1922. 8vo., litho. portr., bds., cloth back, ltd. to 63 copies signed by author & artist. Quaritch 979-200 1978 $150

HUGHES, RICHARD   A High Wind in Jamaica. London, 1929. 1st English ed., d.j., very good or better. Limestone 9-156 1978 $25

HUGHES, RICHARD   Lines Written Upon First Observing an Elephant Devoured by a Roc. The Golden Cockerel Press, n.d. Sm. 8vo., orig. wrs., unlettered. Quaritch 979-201 1978 $60

HUGHES, RICHARD   A Moment of Time. 1926. Worn d.w., first English ed. Bell Book 16-453 1978 £10

HUGHES, RICHARD   The Spider's Palace and other stories. London, 1931. Illus. by George Charlton, first ed., orig. binding, very good. Rota 211-231 1978 £12

HUGHES, ROBERT M.   Great Commanders....General Johnston. New York, 1893. New cloth. Bell Wiley's copy. Broadfoot 46-144 1978 $16

HUGHES, RUPERT   Why I Quit Going to Church. Free Thought Press, 1934. Austin 79-343 1978 $10

HUGHES, THOMAS   The Scouring of the White Horse; or, the Long Vacation Ramble of a London Clerk. Cambridge, 1859. Engrav. by Richard Doyle, 1st ed., orig. cloth, gilt edges, good condition. Greene 78-61 1978 $50

HUGHES, THOMAS   The Scouring of the White Horse. 1859. 1st. ed., illus. by Richard Dovle, half title, orig. blue cloth, blocked in gilt, slight rubbing of hinges, otherwise good. Jarndyce 16-746 1978 £15

HUGHES, THOMAS   The Scouring of the White Horse; or the Long Vacation Ramble of a London Clerk.   Cambridge, 1859. Illus. by Richard Doyle, orig. pict. cloth, 1st ed., fine, pencilled inscription.   MacManus 238-290 1978 $75

HUGHES, THOMAS   The Scouring of the White Horse;... London, 1859. Illus. by Richard Doyle, 1st ed., small octavo, gilt decor. blue cloth, inner hinges tender, bookplate, some foxing. Totteridge 29-56 1978 $50

HUGHES, THOMAS   Tom Brown's School Days. 1857. 4th. ed., half title, half calf, spine trifle rubbed, otherwise v.g.   Jarndyce 16-745 1978 £12.50

HUGHES, THOMAS   Tom Brown at Oxford. Boston, 1861. 1st Am. ed., 2 vols., orig. brown cloth, frayed spines, good, clean, tight copy.   Greene 78-60 1978 $50

HUGHES, WILLIAM R.   A Week's Tramp in Dickens-Land. 1891. First ed., illus., half red calf, gilt top, orig. gilt decor. binding cloth bound in, 8vo.   Howes 194-787 1978 £18

HUGNET, GEORGES   Petite Anthologie Poetique du Surrealisme. Paris, 1934. Illus., one of 2,000 copies, wrappers, nice, first ed. Rota 211-681 1978 £30

HUGO, HERMANN   Pia Desideria Emblematis, Elegiis & affectibus SS. Patrvm Illustrata,.... Antwerp, 1628. Sm. 8vo, woodcut title and full-page Barberini arms, woodcut emblems by Christopher A. Sichem after Bolswet's copperplates, 2nd Antwerp ed. Quaritch 978-84 1978 $450

HUGO, VICTOR   Hans of Iceland. London, 1825. 8vo, full blue polished calf, gilt, spine and inner dentelles gilt, t.e.g., by Zaehnsdorf, 1st ed., etched plates by George Cruikshank, orig. pr. paper spine-label, nice copy. Ximenes 47-142 1978 $80

HUGO, VICTOR   Hans of Iceland. 1825. 1st. ed., plts. by George Cruikshank, sm. waterstain on lower inner margin of plts., half green calf, label. Jarndyce 16-429 1978 £18.50

HUGO, VICTOR   Les Miserables. 1862. 2nd. ed., 3 vols., half titles, orig. purple cloth blocked in blind, gilt spines, v.g., authorized English translation. Jarndyce 16-748 1978 £18.50

HUGO, VICTOR   Les Miserables. New York, 1863. 1st(?) Amer. ed., 1 vol. ed., orig. cloth. Greene 78-227 1978 $35

HUGO, VICTOR   Le Roi S'Amuse! A Tragedy. 1843. 1st. ed., rebound in half calf, good. Jarndyce 16-747 1978 £15

HUGO, VICTOR   William Shakespeare. Paris, 1864. 1st. ed., title-pg. & several leaves with marginal damp-stain & light foxing, 1/4 calf, gilt, little scuffed. Eaton 45-257 1978 £20

A HUGUENOT Exile in Virginia. New York, 1934. Trans. from Hague ed. of 1687, illus., d.j., ltd. to 550 copies. MacManus 239-1872 1978 $17.50

HUIDEKOPER, FREDERIC LOUIS   The Military Unpreparedness of the United States. New York, 1916. Bell Wiley's copy. Broadfoot's 44-210 1978 $12

HUIE, WILLIAM BRADFORD   The Fight for Air Power. 1942. Austin 80-143 1978 $8.50

HUISH, MARCUS B.   Japan and Its Art. London, 1889. Illus., cloth, moderately browned and soiled. Dawson's 449-135 1978 $17.50

HUISH, ROBERT   The Last Voyage of Capt. Sir John Ross to the Arctic Regions, for the Discovery of a North West Passage, 1829-33. 1835. Engraved title, portrait, engraved plts., contemp. calf, gilt spine, slight stain on front cover, marginal staining, 8vo. Edwards 1012-580 1978 £65

HUISH, ROBERT   The Memoirs Private & Political of Daniel O'Connell; His Times & Contemporaries. London, 1836. 1st ed., illus., some dust marking, octavo bound in cloth. Hyland 128-217 1978 £10

HUISH, ROBERT   A Narrative Of The Voyages and Travels of Capt. Beechey to the Pacific and Behring Straits, 1825-28... 1836. 8vo, orig. cloth, engraved title, portraits, engraved plts., spine slightly faded. Edwards 1012-581 1978 £40

HULBERT, ARCHER BUTLER   Forty-niners. Boston, 1931. Illus., first ed. Biblo BL781-278 1978 $9

HULBERT, ARCHER BUTLER   The Niagara River. New York, 1908. 1st ed., illus., maps, fine. MacManus 239-207 1978 $30

HULBERT, HOMER BEZALEEL   The Passing of Korea. New York, 1906. Illus., cloth, hinges weak. Dawson's 127-222 1978 $50

HULBERT, WILLIAM D.   White Pine Days on the Taquamenon. Lansing, 1949. Cloth. Hayman 73-439 1978 $8.50

HULBERT-POWELL, C. I.   John James Wettstein, 1693-1754, an Account of his Life, Work, and some of his Contemporaries. (1938). Facs., 8vo. George's 635-1154 1978 £5.25

DIE Hulfsquellen und Vorzuge des Acterbau und Fabritwesens und de Handels-Verhaltnisse Vom Staate Minnesota.... Minneapolis, 1881. Illus., orig. pr. wr., 1st ed. Ginsberg 14-550 1978 $75

HULL, AUGUSTUS LONGSTREET   The Campaigns of the Confederate Army. Atlanta, 1901. Maps, plates, minor pencil notations, cover worn and soiled, Bell Wiley's copy. Broadfoot's 44-211 1978 $30

HULL, CORDELL   The Memoirs of... New York, 1948. 2 vols., 1st ed. Biblo BL781-205 1978 $12

HULL, E. M.   Camping in the Sahara. London, (1926). 32 plts., 8vo, orig. cloth. K Books 239-225 1978 £5

HULL, GEORGE H.   Industrial Depressions. 1911. Austin 90-717 1978 $12.50

HULL, GEORGE H.   Perpetual Prosperity. 1933. Austin 80-718 1978 $10

HULL, WILLIAM   Proceedings of the Court Martial, in the Case of William Hull, Brigadier General in the Army of the United States. N.P., (1814). 12mo., unbound, signed twice by the Adjutant General. Morrill 239-433 1978 $35

HULL, WILLIAM I.   William Penn and the Dutch Quaker Migration to Pennsylvania. Swarthmore, 1935. MacManus 239-1503 1978 $25

HULLS, JONATHAN   A Description and Draught of a New-Invented Machine for Carrying Vessels or Ships Out of or into any Habour, Port, or River Against Wind and Tide, or in a Calm. N.P., (1855). Sm. 4to., 1 of 12 numbered lg. paper copies on old paper, signed by William Gott, 1/2 red mor. with marbled bds. & endpapers, bkplt. of Institution of Naval Architects, interior spotted, generally fine, fldg. frontis. Current 24-253 1978 $185

HULME, F. E.   Familiar Wild Flowers. (c. 1900). Coloured plts., 5 vols., cr. 8vo. George's 635-956 1978 £8.50

HULOT, ETIENNE   De L'Atlantique au Pacifique a Travers le Canada et le Nord des Etats-Unis. Paris, 1888. Folding map, original wr., 1st ed. Ginsberg 14-398 1978 £37.50

HUMBER, WILLIAM   A Record of the Progress of Modern Engineering. London, 1863. Lg. orig. photo portr., diagram plts., sm. folio, ex-lib. Morrill 239-434 1978 $40

HUMBOLDT, CARL W. VON BARON   The Sphere and Duties of Government. 1854. 1st. ed. of this translation, half title, lg. 12mo, orig. brown cloth, some neat pencil notes, nice copy. Fenning 32-169 1978 £24.50

HUMBOLDT, FRIEDRICH HEINRICH ALEXANDER VON   Cosmos. 1864. 4 vols, cr. 8vo., covers worn and stained. George's 635-935 1978 £5

HUMBOLDT, FRIEDRICH HEINRICH ALEXANDER VON   Ensayo Politico Sobre La Isle De Cuba. Paris, 1827. Half leather, map, foxed, rare. Jenkins 116-266 1978 $100

HUME, DAVID   Enquiry Concerning the Principles of Morals. London, 1751. 8vo., calf. Salloch 348-97 1978 $300

HUME, DAVID   Essays and Treatises on Several Subjects. London, 1767. New ed., 2 vols., 8vo., contemp. calf, hinges weak. Salloch 348-98 1978 $125

HUME, DAVID   Essays, Literary, Moral and Political. London, n.d. 8vo., orig. cloth. K Books 244-384 1978 £5

HUME, DAVID   The History of England, from the invasion of J Julius Caesar to the Revolution in 1688. 1806. Plts., portrait, 11 vols., folio, full contemp. coarse-grained mor. Howes 194-321 1978 £300

HUME, DAVID   History of England Under the House of Stuart. 1759. 2nd. ed., 2 vols., 4to, orig. calf, spines rubbed, joints cracked. Jarndyce 16-116 1978 £11.50

HUME, DAVID   The History of England Under the House of Tudor. London, 1759. 2 vols., 1st ed., 4to, rebound in full vellum possibly 19th. century, half title in vol. 1, good. Sexton 7-232 1978 £25

HUME, DAVID   History of England Under the House of Tudor. 1759. 1st. ed., 2 vols., 4to, half-title, orig. calf, spines rubbed, joints cracked. Jarndyce 16-117 1978 £11.50

HUME, DAVID   The History of England. London, 1778. New ed., 8vols., portrait, contemp. calf, endpapers discoloured, 8vo. K Books 244-162 1978 £42

HUME, F. R.   A Digest of the Mercantile Law of Canada and Newfoundland.... Toronto, 1946. 15th. ed. Hood's 115-641 1978 $15

HUME, FERGUS   The Lonely Church. London, 1904. Orig. pict. cloth, 1st ed., very fine. MacManus 238-291 1978 $65

HUME, FERGUS   The Pagan's Cup. New York, 1902. First U.S. ed., decor. cloth, lower joint split, good. Bell Book 16-248 1978 £6

HUME, FERGUS   The Yellow Holly. New York, 1903. First U.S. ed., decor. cloth, very good. Bell Book 16-249 1978 £6.50

HUMES, THOMAS WILLIAM   The Loyal Mountaineers of Tennessee. Knoxville, 1888. Bell Wiley's copy. Broadfoot 46-379 1978 $70

HUMPHREY, LAURENCE.   The Nobels, or of Nobilitye. London, 1563. 8vo, full brown morocco, gilt, spine gilt, a.e.g., 1st ed. in English, inner margin of t.p. neatly renewed, very fine copy, very rare. Ximenes 47-143 1978 $1500

HUMPHREY, MARY A.   The Squatter Sovereign, or Kansas in the '50's. Chicago, 1883. Cloth. Hayman 73-275 1978 $15

HUMPHREYS, A. L.   The Private Library. New York, 1897. Orig. cloth. MacManus 238-949 1978 $15

HUMPHREYS, ANDREW A.   From Gettysburg to the Rapidan. New York, 1883. Fldg. maps. Bell Wiley's copy. Broadfoot 46-145 1978 $16

HUMPHREYS, ANDREW A.   The Virginia Campaign of '64 and '65. New York, 1883. Fldg. maps. Bell Wiley 's copy. Broadfoot 46-146 1978 $10

HUMPHREYS, CHARLES A.   Field, Camp, Hospital and Prison in the Civil War, 1863-1865. Boston, 1918. Bell Wiley's copy. Broadfoot's 44-524 1978 $25

HUMPHREYS, DAVID   Heroes and Spies of the Civil War. New York, 1903. Bell Wiley's copy. Broadfoot 46-147 1978 $35

HUMPHREYS, DAVID   The Life and Heroic Exploits of Israel Putnam, Major-General in the Revolutionary War. Hartford, (1833). Illus. with plts. from orig. designs, orig. cloth, minor water staining to some pages of text. Baldwins' 51-317 1978 $10

HUMPHREYS, DAVID   A Poem on the Happiness of America; Addressed to the Citizens of the United States. London, n.d. (1786). 8vo, disbound, 1st Amer. ed., very rare, occasional foxing. Ximenes 47-147 1978 $250

HUMPHREYS, F.   Humphreys' Manual. New York, (1869). 16mo., orig. wrs. Morrill 239-131 1978 $10

HUMPHREYS, HENRY NOEL   A History of the Art of Printing. London, 1868. 2nd ed., lg. 4to., 3/4 leather , joints crack., orig. decor. cloth. Ballinger 11-43 1978 $265.00

HUMPHREYS, HENRY NOEL   The Illuminated Books of the Middle Ages.... London, 1849. Orig. ed., coloured engraved title & plts., lg. folio, old half morocco gilt edges, upper cover is stained at top. Traylen 88-50 1978 £300

HUMPHREYS, HENRY NOEL   The Origin & Progress of the Art of Writing. London, 1853. Full lea. binding, rubbed, t.e.g., some in color, illus., a.e.g., binding repaired. Battery Park 1-472 1978 $100

HUMPHREYS, JENNETT   Insect Ways on Summer Days: In Garden, Forest, Field and Stream. 1888. 1st. ed., frontis, illus., 8vo, orig. blue cloth, gilt, fine. Fenning 32-170 1978 £5

HUMPHRIES, ROLFE   The Wind of Time. New York, 1949. First ed. Biblo 247-555 1978 $8.50

HUNDLEY, D. R.   Social Relations in Our Southern States. New York, 1860. Cloth. MacManus 239-1816 1978 $25

HUNEKER, JAMES   Ivory Apes and Peacocks. New York, 1916 (1915 on verso). Frontis, portrait, orig. cloth, bookplt. of Bessie Sullivan. Eaton 45-258 1978 £5

HUNEKER, JAMES   Painted Veils. New York, (1920). Blue bds., vellum spine, uncut, 1st ed., 1 of 1200 signed, worn. Bradley 49-157 1978 $25

HUNEKER, JAMES   Painted Veils. New York, 1928. 8vo, cream colored cloth, gilt stamped on cover and spine, uncut, 1 of 2,300 numbered copies, spine slightly faded, near Mint, 1st ed., collector's cond. Desmarais 1-240 1978 $12.50

HUNGERFORD, EDWARD   Daniel Willard Rides the Line. New York, 1938. Orig. binding, clean. Hayman 71-307 1978 $7.50

HUNGERFORD, EDWARD   The Romance of a Great Store. 1922. Illus. Austin 80-719 1978 $10

HUNGERFORD, EDWARD   The Story of the Baltimore and Ohio Railroad. New York, 1927. 2 vols., 1st ed., illus., maps, fine set. MacManus 239-410 1978 $47.50

HUNGERFORD, EDWARD   Wells Fargo. Advancing the American Frontier. New York, (1949). 1st ed., fine, d.w., illus., maps. Biblo 248-263 1978 $18.50

HUNNEWELL, JAMES FROTHINGHAM   Collectors. Boston, 1908. 8vo., orig. bds., lea. back, unopened, very nice, ed. ltd. to 102 copies on handmade paper. Morrill 239-435 1978 $15

HUNSICKER, CLIFTON S.   Montgomery County, Pa. A History. New York, 1923. 3 vols., 4to., illus. MacManus 239-1504 1978 $50

HUNT, FREDERICK KNIGHT   The Fourth Estate:.... London, 1850. 2 vols., 8vo, original ochre cloth, 1st ed., very scarce in this condition. Ximenes 47-145 1978 $150

HUNT, GAILLARD   Fragments of Revolutionary History... Brooklyn, 1892. Scarce. MacManus 239-584 1978 $32.50

HUNT, GAILLARD   The Life of James Madison. New York, 1902. 1st ed., frontis., orig. cloth. MacManus 239-791 1978 $25

HUNT, HENRY   Investigation of Ilchester Gaol, in the County of Somerset,.... London, 1821. 8vo, original boards (spine worn, front cover loose), 1st ed., engraved portraits by George and Robert Cruikshank. Ximenes 47-146 1978 $60

HUNT, LEIGH   The Autobiography of Leigh Hunt. London, 1850. 8vo., 3 vols., brown blind-stamped cloth, some shelf wear on spines, vol. I hinges weaken, some foxing, near Fine, 1st ed., collector's cond. Desmarais 1-241 1978 $65

HUNT, LEIGH   A Book for a Corner. London, 1849. 2 vols., 12mo., illus., orig. cloth, 1st ed., fine. MacManus 238-295 1978 $75

HUNT, LEIGH   A Book For a Corner.... 1849. 1st. ed., 2 vols., orig. half calf, green labels, v.g., wood engravings. Jarndyce 16-754 1978 £48

HUNT, LEIGH   Classic Tales, Serious and Lively: With Critical Essays on the Merits and Reputations of the Authors. London, 1807. 5 vols., 12mo, contemp. diced calf, gilt, 1st ed., sound copy. Ximenes 47-148 1978 $225

HUNT, LEIGH   The Indicator: A Miscellany for the Fields and the Fireside. New York, 1845. 2 vols. in 1, sm. 8vo., contemp. marbled bds., roan back & corners, 1st Amer. ed. Morrill 241-212 1978 $7.50

HUNT, LEIGH   A Jar of Honey from Mount Hybla. 1848. 8vo., 1st ed., 1st binding of glazed pic. bds., gilt edges, fine copy, rare, cloth wr. & mor. solander case. Quaritch 979-202 1978 $260

HUNT, LEIGH   Leigh Hunt's London Journal. London, 1834-5. 2 vols. in 1, illus., folio, orig. binder's cloth, 1st ed., bind. a bit worn, but very good, clean. MacManus 238-292 1978 $125

HUNT, LEIGH   Men, Women and Books; a Selection of Sketches, Essays, and Critical Memoirs... London, 1847. 2 vols., orig. cloth, 1st ed., bookplts., fine. MacManus 238-293 1978 $70

HUNT, LEIGH   Men, Women & Books. 1847. 1st. ed., 2 vols., orig. dark pink cloth, slight rubbing of following hinge, otherwise v.g. Jarndyce 16-752 1978 £32

HUNT, LEIGH　　　　　　　　Men, Women, and Books: A Selection of Sketches, Essays, and Critical Memoirs, From His Uncollected Prose Writings, by Leigh Hunt. London, 1847. 2 vols., octavo, orig. red publisher's cloth, elaborately blind-stamped on both covers and spine, expertly rebacked, retaining the orig. spines, lst ed. Bennett 7-58 1978 $95

HUNT, LEIGH　　　　　　　　Men, Women, and Books. London, 1857. 2 vols., orange cloth, lst ed., covers soiled. Bradley 49-158 1978 $60

HUNT, LEIGH　　　　　　　　Men, Women, and Books. Portrait, 2 vols., orig. patterned cloth, 1 spine rebacked, spines faded, hinges weak, good, first English ed. Bell Book 17-468 1978 £12

HUNT, LEIGH　　　　　　　　The Old Court Suburb... 1855. 2nd. ed., 2 vols., vignette t.p., orig. yellow patterned cloth, v.g. Jarndyce 16-758 1978 £9.50

HUNT, LEIGH　　　　　　　　Poetical Works. 1832. lst. ed., orig. calf, gilt borders & spine, brown label, v.g. Jarndyce 16-749 1978 £38

HUNT, LEIGH　　　　　　　　Poetical Works. n.d. Illus. by Corbould, rebound in marbled bds., paper spine. Eaton 45-261 1978 £6

HUNT, LEIGH　　　　　　　　The Religion of the Heart. 1853. lst. ed., half title, orig. dark green cloth, v.g. Jarndyce 16-757 1978 £18.50

HUNT, LEIGH　　　　　　　　Stories from the Italian Poets. 1846. 2 vols., sm. 8vo., lst ed., orig. blind decor. blue cloth, neatly repaired, pres. copy with inscr. written by author. Quaritch 979-203 1978 $160

HUNT, LEIGH　　　　　　　　Stories From the Italian Poets: With Lives of the Writers. 1846. lst. ed., 2 vols., half titles, inscriptions on titles, orig. dec. blue cloth, vol. I rebacked retaining orig. backstrip and endpapers, good. Jarndyce 16-751 1978 £20

HUNT, LEIGH　　　　　　　　Stories from the Italian Poets: with Lives of the Writers. London, 1846. 2 vols., orig. cloth, lst ed., bookplts., vol. I faded, but fine. MacManus 238-296 1978 $60

HUNT, LEIGH　　　　　　　　The Story of Rimini, A Poem. London, 1816. 8vo, Victorian half calf, lst ed. Ximenes 47-149 1978 $100

HUNT, LEIGH　　　　　　　　Table Talk... 1851. lst. ed., half title, Todd lib. stamp on title, orig. pale orange cloth little faded, good. Jarndyce 16-755 1978 £14.50

HUNT, LEIGH　　　　　　　　The Town; its Memorable Characters and Events. London, 1848. 2 vols., illus., orig. cloth, lst ed., near fine. MacManus 238-294 1978 $100

HUNT, LEIGH　　　　　　　　The Town: Its Memorable Characters and Events. 1848. lst. ed., 2 vols., 45 illus., half titles, orig. orange cloth little rubbed at tail of spine, o/w v.g. Jarndyce 16-753 1978 £26

HUNT, LEIGH　　　　　　　　The Wishing-Cup Papers. Boston, 1873. Sm. 8vo., orig. cloth, lst ed., signature of George William Curtis. Morrill 241-213 1978 $10

HUNT, LEIGH　　　　　　　　Works. London, 1878. 7 vols., cr. 8vo., qtr. vellum. K Books 244-163 1978 £22

HUNT, MABEL LEIGH　　　　　Michel's Island. New York, 1940. lst ed., illus. by Kate Seredy, fine, dj. Victoria 34-429 1978 $10

HUNT, R.　　　　　　　　The Poetry of Science, or Studies of the Physical Phenomena of Nature. 1859. 8vo., orig. cloth, second ed. Quaritch 977-232 1978 $70

HUNT, R. L.　　　　　　　　A History of Farmer Movements in the Southwest, 1873-1925. N.P., ca. 1927. Printed wr., scarce. Jenkins 116-683a 1978 $45

HUNT, ROBERT　　　　　　　A Popular Treatise on the Art of Photography, Including Daguerreotype, and All the New Methods of Producing Pictures by the Chemical Agency of Light. Glasgow, 1841. 8vo., frontis., half antique calf, gilt, very good copy, lst ed. Norman 5-150 1978 $750

HUNT, ROBERT　　　　　　　Researches on Light in Its Chemical Relations. London, 1854. 8vo., handcolored fldg. chart, orig. blindstamped cloth, spine repaired, sm. lib. stamp on title, but very good copy, greatly enlarged 2nd & best ed. Norman 5-151 1978 $275

HUNT, THOMAS　　　　　　　A Defence of the Charter and Municipal Rights of the City of London. n.d. (1683?). lst. ed.?, 4to, wrappers. Hannas 54-97 1978 £36

HUNT, THOMAS FREDERICK　　　Half a Dozen Hints on Picturesque Domestic Architecture in a Series of Designs for Gate Lodges, Gamekeepers' Cottages, and Other Rural Residences. 1833. 3rd ed., 4to., plts., slight marginal foxing, inked inscriptions, orig. bds. Quaritch 983-41 1978 $90

HUNT, WILLIAM　　　　　　　Political History of England. 1906-07. 12 vols., some spines a little faded, 8vo. George's 635-741 1978 £22.50

HUNT, WILLIAM MORRIS　　　Hunt's Talks on Art. Boston, 1875. 8vo., orig. wrs., lacks spine, fr. cover loose, lst ed. Morrill 239-436 1978 $15

HUNTER, ANDREW F.　　　　　History of Simcoe County. Barrie, 1948. 2 parts, bound in I vol. Hood's 115-817 1978 $10

HUNTER, DARD　　　　　　　Before Life Began. 1883-1923. Cleveland, 1941. Illus., 8vo., orig. vellum-backed patterned bds., pub. slipcase, lst ed., 1 of 219 copies designed and signed by Bruce Rogers, pres. copy from author, very fine. MacManus 238-807 1978 $350

HUNTER, DARD　　　　　　　Papermaking by Hand in America. Chillicothe, Mountain House Press, 1950. Tipped-in photo, ream wrs., orig. decor. bds. with canvas spine, near mint copy, mor.-backed fldg. case, slight damage to lea., I of 210 numbered copies signed by author. Dawson's 447-119 1978 $4,000

HUNTER, DARD　　　　　　　Papermaking by Hand in America. Chillicothe, 1950. Large folio, 18 by 13 inches, decor. paper over heavy boards, linen backstrip and corner, linen folding box in red mor. back, gilt, 1 of 200 copies signed by Hunter, printed by hand on paper made by Dard, fine. Duschnes 220-152 1978 $4,000

HUNTER, DARD　　　　　　　Papermaking in Indo-China. Chillicothe, 1947. 4to., one of only 180 numbered copies, signed by author, mor. back, vellum tips, 15 full-page swatches of paper hand-made in Indo-China. Wolfe 39-416 1978 $1200

HUNTER, DARD　　　　　　　Papermaking, the History and Technique of an Ancient Craft. New York, 1943. lst ed., T.L.s. from Dard Hunter, bkplt of Elizur Yale Smith, d.w., illus. Battery Park 1-449 1978 $225

HUNTER, DARD　　　　　　　Romance of Watermarks. A Discourse on the Origin and Motive of These Mystic Symbols Which First Appeared in Italy Near the End of the 13th Century.... Cincinnati, n.d. Orig. vellum-backed bds., 1 of 210 copies, very good. MacManus 238-950 1978 $40

HUNTER, GEORGE LELAND　　　Decorative Furniture. Philadelphia, 1923. 900 illus., 23 in color, sm. folio. Baldwins' 51-97 1978 $32.50

HUNTER, GEORGE LELAND　　　Decorative Textiles. 1918. Illus., coloured plts., 4to., covers badly stained, stitching loose. George's 635-257 1978 £45

HUNTER, GEORGE LELAND　　　Tapestries, Their Orgin, History and Renaissance. New York, 1912. 4 illus. in color, 147 halftone engravings. Baldwins' 51-98 1978 $35

HUNTER, JOHN　　　　　　　Resa Til Nya Sodra Wallis. Stockholm, 1797. lst. ed. in Swedish, sm. 8vo, contemp. half calf. Edwards 1012-335 1978 £100

HUNTER, JOHN　　　　　　　A Treatise on the Blood, Inflammation, and Gun-Shot Wounds. Philadelphia, 1817. Engr. plts., 8vo., contemp. calf, 2nd Amer. ed. Morrill 239-132 1978 $60

HUNTER, JOHN　　　　　　　A Treatise on the Venerial Disease. London, 1786. 4to., engraved plts., plts. foxed round the edges, contemp. tree calf, neatly rebacked, first ed. Quaritch 977-36 1978 $700

HUNTER, JOHN D.　　　　　　Memoirs of a Captivity Among the Indians of North America, from Childhood to the Age of Nineteen. London, 1823. New ed., portr., 3/4 lea., marbled bds., gilt tooling on spine. Hood 117-680 1978 $275

HUNTER, JOHN D.　　　　　　Memoirs of a Captivity Among the Indians of North America... 1823. New ed., portrait, contemp. half calf, 8vo, stained slightly, few ink spots on 2 pgs. Edwards 1012-554 1978 £45

HUNTER, JOHN MARVIN　　　The Story of Frontier Times Museum. Bandera, c. 1934. Printed pictorial wr. Jenkins 116-685a 1978 $12.50

HUNTER, JOHN MARVIN　　　The Trail Drivers of Texas: Interesting Sketches of Early Cowboys and Their Experiences... (San Antonio,) 1920-1923. 2 vols., lst ed., orig. cloth, illus., near mint. Jenkins 116-686a 1978 $250

HUNTER, JOHN MARVIN　　　The Trail Drivers of Texas. San Antonio, (1920). 3 vols., pic. cloth, illus., very good set, single slipcase. Dykes 34-28 1978 $200

HUNTER, WILLIAM   Biggar and the House of Fleming. Biggar, 1862.
Plts., illus., gilt cloth, 8vo., letter from author inserted, only 520 copies printed.
K Books 244-385 1978 £30

HUNTER, WILLIAM S.   Chisholm's Panoramic Guide from Niagara to
Quebec. Montreal, 1869. Very wide panoramic map, pict. ads, fine cond.
Butterfield 21-306 1978 $45

HUNTER, WILLIAM S.   Hunters Panoramic Guide From Niagara Falls
to Quebec. Boston, 1857. Fold in view frontispiece, illus. Baldwins' 51-415
1978 $50

HUNTINGTON, ANNIE OAKES   Testament of Happiness. Letters. Portland,
1947. Port., ltd. to 500 copies, penned pres., signed. Biblo BL781-999 1978
$17.50

HUNTINGTON, DAN   The Love of Jerusalem, the Prosperity of a People.
A Sermon, Preached at the Anniversary election, Hartford 12, 1814. Hartford,
1814. Sewed. Hayman 72-315 1978 $10

HUNTINGTON, DANIEL   Asher B. Durand, a Memorial Address. New
York, 1887. Frontis., wr., unopened. Butterfield 21-156 1978 $10

HUNTINGTON, E. B.   A Genealogical Memoir of the Huntington Family
in This Country. Stamford, 1863. Engrav. portraits, orig. binding, autograph
signature of Jane Huntington Bill. Wolfe 39-241 1978 $75

HUNTINGTON, GEORGE   Robber and Hero: The Story of the Raid on the
First National Bank of Northfield, Minnesota, by the James Younger Band of Robbers
in 1876... Northfield, 1895. Illus., original cloth, 1st ed. Ginsberg 14-434
1978 $45

HUNTINGTON, W. CHAPIN   The Homesick Million. Boston, 1933. Illus.
with photos. Austin 79-345 1978 $15

HUNTINGTON, WILLARD V.   Oneonta Memories and Sundry Personal Recollections of the Author. San Francisco, 1891. Frontis. portr., inner hinges cracked,
spine badly chipped. Butterfield 21-343 1978 $20

HUNTINGTON, WILLIAM 1745-1813   The History of Little Faith. 1799.
Newly rebound in bds., mor. label, 8vo. Howes 194-323 1978 £10

HUNTOON, DANIEL T. V.   History of the Town of Canton. Cambridge, 1893.
Illus., maps, lib. marks, fine. MacManus 239-1018 1978 $30

HURAULT, JACQUES   Politicke, Moral and Martial Discourses. 1595.
Sm. 4to., newly bound in half calf, woodcut initials, first English ed. Howes 194-
62 1978 £120

HURD, D. HAMILTON   History of Fairfield County, Connecticut. Philadelphia, 1881. Illus., portraits, thick 4to., cloth. MacManus 239-947 1978
$75

HURLBUTT, FRANK   Bow Porcelain. 1926. Folio, plain and coloured
plts., cloth. Quaritch 983-109 1978 $95

HURD, CHARLES   The Veterans' Program. 1946. Austin 80-144
1978 $10

HURD-MEAD, KATE CAMPBELL   History of Women in Medicine, from the Earliest Times to the Beginning of the Nineteenth Century. Haddam, 1938. 1st ed.,
illus., orig. cloth, inscribed by author, very good copy. MacManus 239-208
1978 $27.50

HURLBUTT, FRANK   Bow Porcelain. 1926. Coloured illus., sm.
folio. George's 635-230 1978 £40

HURLBUTT, FRANK   Bow Porcelain. London, 1926. Plts. 8 of which
are coloured, other in half tone, folio. Traylen 88-389 1978 £40

HURLBUTT, FRANK   Bristol Porcelain. 1938. Coloured plts., 4to.,
scarce. George's 635-231 1978 £70

HURLBUTT, FRANK   Old Derby Porcelain and Its Artist Workmen.
London, 1925. 60 plts. Baldwins' 51-99 1978 $25

HURLEY, DUNLEA   Panorama of a Century 1847-1947. N.P., 1947.
Illus. Austin 80-720 1978 $10

HURLEY, VIC   Jungle Patrol. New York, 1938. Photo. illus.,
maps, d.w., 1st ed., 8vo., orig. cloth. Morrill 241-214 1978 $17.50

HURN, ETHEL ALICE   Wisconsin Women in the War Between the
States. NP, 1911. Cover soiled, Bell Wiley's copy. Broadfoot's 44-684 1978
$16.00

HURON Silver Mining Company of Montana, Beaver Head County, Montana
Territory...Prospectus.... New York, 1866. Cloth, 1st ed. Ginsberg 14-626
1978 $125

HURRY, MRS. IVES   Moral Tales for Young People. 1807. Sm. 8vo.,
1st ed., orig. bds., uncut, fine copy, very scarce. Quaritch 979-90 1978 $315

HURST, ARTHUR F.   Essays and Addresses on Digestive and Nervous
Diseases and on Addison's Anemia and Asthma. New York, 1924. Ex-library,
tight, clean. Rittenhouse 49-379 1976 $10

HURST, C. C.   Experiments in Genetics. Cambridge, 1925.
Large 8vo., orig. cloth. Book Chest 17-196 1978 $60

HURST, FANNY   Lummox. New York, 1923. First ed., with T.L.s.
by author laid in. Biblo 247-556 1978 $27.50

HURSTHOUSE, CHARLES   New Zealand, or Zealandia, the Britain of the
South. London, 1857. 2 vols., 1st ed., 8vo., color plts., fldg. maps, maps
linen-backed, plts. with library stamps, rebound in brown cloth, text clear, very
scarce book. Current 24-181 1978 $140

HURTADO DE MENDOZA, ANTONIO   Obras Liricas, y Comicas, Divinas, y
Humanas.... Madrid, (1728). Quarto, full contemp. limp vellum, inscription,
very nice. Bennett 20-110 1978 $200

HUSBAND, JOSEPH   Americans by Adoption. 1929. Austin 79-
347 1978 $7.50

HUSE, CALEB   The Supplies for the Confederate Army: How
They Were Obtained in Europe and How Paid For. Boston, 1904. Wrs., Bell
Wiley's copy, frontis stained. Broadfoot's 44-212 1978 $16

HUSE, CHARLES F.   Sketch of the History and Resources of Santa
Barbara City and County, California. Santa Barbara, 1876. Original wrappers
bound in cloth, 1st ed. Ginsberg 14-138 1978 $97.50

HUSON, HOBART   District Judges of Refugio County. Refugio,
1941. Cloth, autographed, very scarce. Jenkins 116-1162 1978 $100

HUSSEY, J. M.   Church and Learning in the Byzantine Empire,
867-1185. 1937. Maps, 8vo. Upcroft 12-203 1978 £8.50

HUSTON, PAUL GRISWOLD   Around an Old Homestead, a Book of Memories.
Cincinnati, (1906). Orig. binding, clean. Hayman 71-555 1978 $10

HUSTON, STEWART   Rambles By Dictation. West Chester, 1937.
Illus., maps, orig. paper covers. Baldwins' 51-450 1978 $12.50

HUTCHINGS, THOMAS GIBBONS   The Medical Pilot. New York, 1855.
Sm. 8vo., lightly dampstained. Morrill 239-133 1978 $15

HUTCHINS, FRANK   Houseboating on a Colonial Waterway. Boston,
1910. Illus., photos by author, dampstained, 1st ed., orig. cloth. Morrill 241-
600 1978 $10

HUTCHINS, SILSON   The National Capital Past and Present... Washington, 1885. Illus., cloth. Hayman 72-316 1978 $10

HUTCHINS' Improved Almanac for 1846. New York, (1845). Wrps. Hayman 71-
11 1978 $7.50

HUTCHINS' Improved Family Almanac for 1847. New York, (1846). Wrps.
Hayman 71-12 1978 $7.50

HUTCHINSON, ARTHUR STUART M.   The Happy Warrior. London, 1912. First
ed., orig. binding, spine faded, v.g., author's signed autograph pres. Rota 211-
235 1978 £12.50

HUTCHINSON, ARTHUR STUART M.   This Freedom. Toronto, 1922. Some
staining on last few leaves and back cover. Hood's 116-478 1978 $10

HUTCHINSON, FRANCIS   An Historical Essay concerning Witchcraft. 1718.
8vo., contemp. panelled calf, fine, first ed., half-title. P. M. Hill 142-145
1978 £135

HUTCHINSON, FRANCIS   An Historical Essay Concerning Witchcraft,
With Observations Upon Matters of Fact.... London, 1720. Crudely rebacked,
2nd ed. Nestler Rare 78-19 1978 $85

HUTCHINSON, H. N.   Creatures of Other Days. London, 1896. New
ed., illus., author's signed pres. copy, 8vo., orig. cloth. K Books 244-164
1978 £7

HUTCHINSON, H. N.   The Story of the Hills. London, 1892. Illus.,
decor. cloth, 8vo. K Books 244-134 1978 £6

HUTCHINSON, WALTER   Hutchinson's Britain Beautiful. (c. 1933). 4 vols., 4to., maps, coloured plts., illus. George's 635-1355 1978 £7.50

HUTCHINSON, WALTER   Story of the British Nation. London, n.d. c. 1924. 4 vols., 4to, orig. pictorial cloth, illus. Sexton 7-152 1978 £20

HUTCHINSON, WALTER   Hutchinson's Story of the Nations, a Popular, Concise, Pictorial and Authoritative Account of each Nation. (c. 1925). Maps, coloured plates, illus., 3 vols., 4to. George's 635-692 1978 £7.50

HUTCHINSON, WILLIAM F.   Life on the Texan Blockade. Providence, 1883. Cloth. Jenkins 116-693 1978 $45

HUTCHINSON, WILLIAM F.   Under the Southern Cross. Providence, 1891. Illus., 8vo., orig. cloth, 1st ed. Morrill 241-216 1978 $9

HUTCHINSON'S Animals of All Countries. London, n.d.c 1924. 4 vols., 4to, orig. pictorial cloth, illus., coloured plts. Sexton 7-198 1978 £18

HUTCHISON, G. S.   Pilgrimage. London, 1936. Illus. with paintings & photos. Hood 117-131 1978 $12.50

HUTCHISON, R. J.   Reminiscences, Sketches, and Addresses During a Ministry of 45 Years in Mississippi, Louisiana, and Texas. Houston, 1874. Jenkins 116-694 1978 $85

HUTCHISON, T. S.   An American Soldier Under the Greek Flag at Bezanie. Nashville, 1913. Illus. Austin 79-349 1978 $27.50

HUTCHISON, T. W.   The Significance and Basic Postulates of Economic Theory. 1938. Ex-lib. Austin 80-721 1978 $15

HUTCHISON, WILLIAM G.   Lyra Nicotiana: Poems and Verses Concerning Tobacco. London, n.d. (c.1900). Orig. binding, clean, minor spine wear, lacks flyleaf. Hayman 71-308 1978 $7.50

HUTTON, C. A.   Greek Terracotta Statuettes. New York, 1899. Illus., 4to., cloth, front flyleaf missing. Biblo BL781-406 1978 $16.50

HUTTON, CATHERINE   The Tour of Africa. 1819. 8vo, half calf, 3 vols., folding maps. Edwards 1012-258 1978 £150

HUTTON, CHARLES   A Mathematical and Philosophical Dictionary. London, 1795. 2 vols., 4to., copperplts., woodcut text illus., contemp. tree calf, first ed. Quaritch 977-105 1978 $250

HUTTON, FREDERICK REMSON   A History of the American Societh of Mechanical Engineers from 1880 to 1915. New York, 1915. 8vo., half mor., illus., gilt top, untrimmed, 1st ed., nice. Morrill 241-218 1978 $15

HUTTON, JAMES   Theory of the Earth, with Proofs and Illustrations. Edinburgh, 1795. 2 vols., 8vo., fldg. copperplts., contemp. half calf, rebacked, occas. foxing, half title lacking to Vol. I, but very good set, only ed. Norman 5-152 1978 $3,000

HUTTON, LAURENCE   Occasional Addresses. New York, De Vinne Press, 1890. 1st ed., ltd. to 185 copies, orig. parchment wrs., uncut, fronts, 8vo., very good. Americanist 103-98 1978 $20

HUTTON, WILLIAM   A Description of Blackpool, in Lancashire; frequented for Sea Bathing. Kirkham, n.d. (1789?). 8vo, disbound, 2nd ed., very scarce. Ximenes 47-150 1978 $50

HUXLEY, ALDOUS   After Many a Summer. 1939. Very good, d.w., first English ed. Bell Book 17-469 1978 £12.50

HUXLEY, ALDOUS   Along the Road. Notes and Essays of a Tourist. London, 1925. 1st ed., d.w., bookplt. Biblo BL781-1000 1978 $25

HUXLEY, ALDOUS   Along the Road. London, 1925. Very fine in darkened d.w. Desmarais B-335 1978 $20

HUXLEY, ALDOUS   Antic Hay. 1923. Fine, worn d.w., first English ed. Bell Book 16-458 1978 £15

HUXLEY, ALDOUS   Arabia Infelix and Other Poems. New York, 1929. Orig. cloth-backed bds., 1st ed., ltd. to 692 copies signed by author, bookplt., very good. MacManus 238-675 1978 $50

HUXLEY, ALDOUS   Beyond the Mexique Bay. 1934. First ed., endpaper maps, photographs, 8vo. George's 635-1318 1978 £5

HUXLEY, ALDOUS   Brave New World. 1932. Covers somewhat soiled & rubbed, else good, first English ed. Bell Book 16-459 1978 £16.50

HUXLEY, ALDOUS   Brief Candles. Stories. London, 1930. 1st ed., covers slightly damp stained, otherwise very good, d.w. Biblo BL781-1002 1978 $22.50

HUXLEY, ALDOUS   Brief Candles. New York, 1930. 8vo, black cloth, uncut, Fine, scarce, no. 467 of 800 copies, 1st ed., collector's cond. Desmarais 1-242 1978 $75

HUXLEY, ALDOUS   Brief Candles; stories. London, 1930. First ed., orig. binding, covers a little soiled, nice. Rota 211-238 1978 £7.50

HUXLEY, ALDOUS   Brief Candles. New York, 1930. Orig. cloth, 1st ed., 1 of 842 copies signed by Huxley, fine. MacManus 238-677 1978 $75

HUXLEY, ALDOUS   Brief Candles. London, 1930. 8vo, red cloth, d.w. somewhat rubbed and repaired at top, 1st ed., collector's cond. Desmarais 1-243 1978 $20

HUXLEY, ALDOUS   Brief Candles: Stories. London, 1930. Red cloth, 1st ed., fine in dust jacket. Bradley 49-159 1978 $25

HUXLEY, ALDOUS   Brief Candles: stories. 1930. Very good, d.w., first English ed. Bell Book 17-471 1978 £15

HUXLEY, ALDOUS   The Burning Wheel. Oxford, 1916. 1st ed., orig. wrs., very good, uncut, scarce. Biblo BL781-1003 1978 $175

HUXLEY, ALDOUS   The Cicadas and Other Poems. London, 1931. Orig. cloth-backed bds., 1st ed., 1 of 160 signed copies, very good. MacManus 238-678 1978 $100

HUXLEY, ALDOUS   The Cicadas, and other poems. 1931. Fine, d.w., first English ed. Bell Book 16-461 1978 £20

HUXLEY, ALDOUS   Crome Yellow. 1921. Fine, worn d.w., first English ed. Bell Book 17-472 1978 £60

HUXLEY, ALDOUS   Crome Yellow. New York, 1922. First U.S. ed., spine spotted, good. Bell Book 16-462 1978 £8.50

HUXLEY, ALDOUS   The Defeat of Youth and Other Poems. Oxford, 1918. 1st ed., orig. bds., edges and spine rubbed, scarce. Biblo BL781-1004 1978 $47.50

HUXLEY, ALDOUS   The Discovery. London, 1924. Orig. cloth-backed bds., 1st ed., 1 0f 210 lg. paper copies. MacManus 238-672 1978 $75

HUXLEY, ALDOUS   The Discovery, a Comedy in Five Acts. London, 1924. Unopened, near mint in chipped & darkened d.w. Desmarais B-336 1978 $20

HUXLEY, ALDOUS   Do What You Will. 1929. One of 260 numbered copies signed by author, cloth-backed bds., t.e.g., good, first English ed. Bell Book 17-473 1978 £45

HUXLEY, ALDOUS   Do What You Will. London, 1929. 8vo, tan cloth, d.w. spine darkened, Fine, 1st ed., collector's cond. Desmarais 1-244 1978 $15

HUXLEY, ALDOUS   Do What You Will: Essays. London, 1929. Mustard-colored cloth, 1st trade ed., very good, repaired dust jacket. Bradley 49-160 1978 $20

HUXLEY, ALDOUS   Do What you Will: essays. 1929. Very good, d.w., first English ed. Bell Book 16-463 1978 £12.50

HUXLEY, ALDOUS   Ends and Means. London, 1937. 8vo, cloth, gilt, 1st ed., fine. Duschnes 220-157 1978 $20

HUXLEY, ALDOUS   Ends and Means. 1937. Very good, worn d.w., first English ed. Bell Book 17-474 1978 £6.50

HUXLEY, ALDOUS   Essays New and Old. London, 1926. Orig. cloth-backed marbled bds., 1st ed., 1 of 650 copies signed by author, covers worn. MacManus 238-674 1978 $45

HUXLEY, ALDOUS   Essays New and Old. Florence Press, 1926. No. 220 of 650 numbered copies, signed by author, 4to., qtr. buckram, t.e.g., covers dull, edges of bds. rubbed, good. Bell Book 16-464 1978 £28.50

HUXLEY, ALDOUS   Eyeless in Gaza. New York, 1936. 1st Amer. ed., d.w. torn. Biblo 251-510 1978 $20

HUXLEY, ALDOUS   Holy Face and Other Essays. 1929. Roy. 8vo., lst ed., drwgs. in colour, buckram, top edge gilt, slipcase, ltd. to·300 copies. Quaritch 979-204 1978 $125

HUXLEY, ALDOUS   Holy Face and Other Essays. London, 1929. Orig. cloth, 1st ed., ltd. to 300 copies, pres. copy from author, bookplts., spine slightly soiled and worn, but good. MacManus 238-676 1978 $125

HUXLEY, ALDOUS   Leda; poems. London, 1920. First ed., orig. binding, spine and covers faded and marked, internally nice. Rota 211-298 1978 £28

HUXLEY, ALDOUS   Leda. London, 1920. 1st ed. Biblo BL781-1006 1978 $17.50

HUXLEY, ALDOUS   Music at Night and Other Essays. New York, 1931. Orig. cloth-backed bds., 1st ed., 1 of 842 signed copies, very good. MacManus 238-679 1978 $85

HUXLEY, ALDOUS   Music at Night, and other essays. 1931. Very good, d.w., first English ed. Bell Book 16-465 1978 £10

HUXLEY, ALDOUS   The Olive Tree and Other Essays. London, 1936. 8vo, green cloth, spine of d.w. sun-faded, else Mint, 1st ed., collector's cond. Desmarais 1-245 1978 $20

HUXLEY, ALDOUS   Point Counter Point. London, 1928. 1st ed., very good, d.w. frayed. Biblo BL781-1007 1978 $37.50

HUXLEY, ALDOUS   Point Counter Point. London, 1928. 1st ed., ltd. to 256 numbered copies, 8vo., signed in ink by author, orig. green cloth with spine faded to brown, else very fine. Current 24-22 1978 $185

HUXLEY, ALDOUS   Point Counter Point. London, 1928. 8vo, orange cloth, d.w. chipped and somewhat rubbed, Fine, 1st ed., collector's cond. Desmarais 1-247 1978 $50

HUXLEY, ALDOUS   Proper Studies. London, 1927. 8vo, cloth, 1st ed., fine. Duschnes 220-156 1978 $15

HUXLEY, ALDOUS   Proper Studies. London, 1927. Fine in chipped & darkened d.w. Desmarais B-337 1978 $20

HUXLEY, ALDOUS   Proper Studies. London, 1927. Number 69 of 260 numbered copies signed by author, 8 vo., half cloth over marbled bds., glassine jacket, good-very good. Houle 10-165 1978 $95

HUXLEY, ALDOUS   Proper Studies. 1927. Very good, d.w., first English ed. Bell Book 16-466 1978 £12.50

HUXLEY, ALDOUS   Science, Liberty and Peace. New York, 1946. 1st Amer. ed., bind. lightly stained, d.w. Biblo BL781-1008 1978 $12

HUXLEY, ALDOUS   Selected Poems. Oxford, 1925. First ed., orig. binding, head and foot of spine worn, otherwise very nice. Rota 211-237 1978 £12

HUXLEY, ALDOUS   Selected Poems. Oxford, 1925. 8vo, orig. decor. boards, uncut, 1st ed., fine. Duschnes 220-154 1978 $50

HUXLEY, ALDOUS   Those Barren Leaves. London, 1925. 1st ed., covers damp stained, otherwise very good, d.w., bookplt. Biblo BL781-1009 1978 $17.50

HUXLEY, ALDOUS   Those Barren Leaves. New York, (1925). Orig. parchment-backed bds., d.j., pub. slipcase, lg. paper ed., ltd. to 250 copies signed by Huxley. MacManus 238-673 1978 $100

HUXLEY, ALDOUS   Those Barren Leaves. 1925. Covers little soiled, good, first English ed. Bell Book 17-477 1978 £5.50

HUXLEY, ALDOUS   Two or Three Graces and Other Stories. London, 1926. 1st ed., front cover dented, otherwise good, d.w. Biblo BL781-1010 1978 $12.50

HUXLEY, ALDOUS   Two or Three Graces, and other stories. 1926. Good, first English ed. Bell Book 16-467 1978 £8.50

HUXLEY, ALDOUS   Two or Three Graces and Other Stories. London, 1926. 8vo, cloth, gilt, 1st ed., fine. Duschnes 220-155 1978 £10

HUXLEY, ALDOUS   Vulgarity in Literature. London, 1930. 8vo, tan boards, pr. in red, near Fine, bookplate, 1st ed., collector's cond., one of the Dolphin Books. Desmarais 1-246 1978 $10

HUXLEY, ELSPETH   Murder on Safari. New York, 1938. 1st Amer. ed., d.w., frayed and mended. Biblo BL781-937 1978 $9

HUXLEY, JULIAN SORELL   Th. Huxley's Diary of the Voyage of the H. M. S. Rattlesnake. London, 1935. 8vo., cloth, tinted frontis., plts., binding poor. Van der Peet H-64-357 1978 Dfl 110

HUXLEY, LEONARD   Life and Letters of Thomas Henry Huxley. 1900. First ed., plts., 2 vols., thick 8vo., orig. cloth, nice. Howes 194-948 1978 £20

HUXLEY, LEONARD   Life and Letters of Thomas H. Huxley. 1901. 2 vols., illus., uncut, nice set. MacManus 239-209 1978 $12.50

HUXLEY, THOMAS HENRY   American Addresses with a Lecture on the Study of Biology. New York, 1890. Rittenhouse 49-389 1976 $10

HUXLEY, THOMAS HENRY   Anatomy of Invertebrated Animals. New York, 1888. Rittenhouse 49-384 1976 $9

HUXLEY, THOMAS HENRY   Anatomy of Vertebrated Animals. New York, 1888. Rittenhouse 49-383 1976 $10

HUXLEY, THOMAS HENRY   The Crayfish. London, 1880. 12mo, orig. cloth. Book Chest 17-197 1978 $30

HUXLEY, THOMAS HENRY   Critiques and Addresses. New York, 1873. Rittenhouse 49-382 1976 $10

HUXLEY, THOMAS HENRY   Evidence of Man's Place in Nature. London, 1863. Frontis., wood engrs., 8vo., cloth, 1st ed. Salloch 345-99 1978 $125

HUXLEY, THOMAS HENRY   Evidence as to Man's Place in Nature. London & Edinburgh, 1864. 8vo., frontis., illus., orig. cloth, gilt lettering, early inscr. & ex-lib., reprint of 1st ed. Zeitlin 245-132 1978 $45

HUXLEY, THOMAS HENRY   Evidence as to Man's Place in Nature. New York, 1891. Rittenhouse 49-388 1976 $9

HUXLEY, THOMAS HENRY   An Introduction to the Classification of Animals. London, 1869. 8vo., illus., blind-stamped cloth, gilt lettering on spine, good uncut copy, 1st ed., rare. Zeitlin 245-133 1978 $45

HUXLEY, THOMAS HENRY   Lay Sermons, Addresses, and Reviews. London, 1872. 4th ed., prize calf gilt. K Books 244-165 1978 £10

HUXLEY, THOMAS HENRY   Lay Sermons, Addresses, and Reviews. New York, 1890. Rittenhouse 49-381 1976 $10

HUXLEY, THOMAS HENRY   Origin of Species or Causes of the Phenomena of Organic Nature. New York, 1890. Rittenhouse 49-387 1976 $10

HUXLEY, THOMAS HENRY   Physiography. An Introduction to the Study of Nature. New York, 1890. Rittenhouse 49-386 1977 $10

HUXLEY, THOMAS HENRY   Science and Culture and Other Essays. New York, 1890. Rittenhouse 49-385 1976 $10

HUYGENS, CHRISTIAAN   The Celestial Worlds Discover'd or, Conjectures Concerning the Inhabitants, Plans and Productions of the Worlds in the Planets. London, 1698. 8vo., fldg. copperplts., contemp. panelled calf, rebacked, stains, but good copy, 1st ed. in English. Norman 5-154 1978 $450

HUYGENS, CHRISTIAAN   The Celestial Worlds Discover'd:.... London, 1698. 1st ed. in English, 1st issue, octavo, plates, full contemp. paneled calf, small marginal tears, bookplate, slightly worn. Bennett 20-112 1978 $875

HUYGENS, CHRISTIAAN   Horologium Oscillatorium.... Paris, 1673. Folio, woodcut, contemp. sheep, sometime repaired, worn, joints split, first ed. Quaritch 977-107 1978 $5,500

HUYGENS, CHRISTIAAN   Opera Varia. Leiden, 1724. 4 parts in 2 vols., 4to., fine frontis., portr., fldg. copperplts., full antique calf, gilt, very fine set, 1st ed. Norman 5-*29 1978 $750

HUYGENS, CHRISTIAAN   Traite de la Lumiere. Leiden, 1690. 4to., contemp. vellum, old signatures erased from title, occas. light browning, but fine crisp copy, 1st ed. Norman 5-153 1978 $4,000

HUYGENS, CONSTANTIN   Momenta Desultoria:.... The Hague, 1655. 8vo, contemp. Parisian red mor. gilt, gilt edges, traces of orig. Lomenie de Brienne shelf-label with later Newby Hall ownership stamp on side of upper cover, 2nd ed., presentation copy with autographed inscription from Huygens. Quaritch 978-85 1978 $1,500

HUYSHE, W.   Devorgilla, Lady of Galloway, and her Abbey of the Sweet Heart. 1913. Royal 8vo., illus. Upcroft 12-205 1978 £6.50

HUYSMANS, J. K.　　　　Against the Grain. New York, 1931. Drawings, decor. cloth, fine, d.w. Bell Book 17-478 1978 £12.50

HYAMSON, A. M.　　　　A History of the Jews in England. 1908. Maps, portraits, covers a little stained, 8vo. George's 635-694 1978 £5.25

HYATT, STANLEY PORTAL　　The Northward Trek. London, 1909. 3 maps, 14 plts., g. t., 8vo, orig. cloth. K Books 239-228 1978 £10

HYBRID Indian! Concord, n.d. (1856). 12mo, two leaves folded, ephemeral, scarce. Ximenes 46-237 1978 $30

HYDE, D.　　　　Religious Songs of Connacht. (1906). Octavo bound in cloth, reprint. Hyland 128-953 1978 £6

HYDE, EDWARD
Please turn to
CLARENDON, EDWARD HYDE

HYDE, HARTFORD MONTGOMERY　　The Trials of Oscar Wilde. 1948. First ed., d.w., v.g., octavo, cloth. Hyland 128-800 1978 £5

HYDE, SOLON　　　　A Captive of War. New York, 1900. Note by Wiley tipped in, Bell Wiley's copy. Broadfoot's 44-583 1978 $26

HYDE, W. W.　　　　Olympic Victor Monuments & Greek Athletic Art. 1921. 4to., plt., spine badly spotted & slightly worn. Allen 234-481 1978 $15

HYER, JULIEN C.　　　　The Land of Beginning Again: The Romance of the Brazos. Atlanta, 1952. 1st ed., illus., scarce in d.j. Jenkins 116-695 1978 $20

HYMA, ALBERT　　　　Albertus C. Van Raalte. Grand Rapids, 1947. Illus., 1st ed. in frayed dust jacket. Austin 79-350 1978 $27.50

HYMAN, NAT　　　　Eyes of the War. 1945. Austin 80-146 1978 $10

HYMN-Book For the Army and Navy. New York, n.d. (c.1862). Bds., worn, cover show wear but solid copy. Hayman 71-124 1978 $7.50

HYNDMAN, H. M.　　　　The Evolution of Revolution. 1920. Portrait, 8vo. George's 635-340 1978 £5.25

HYNDMAN, H. M.　　　　The Record of an Adventurous Life. 1911. 8vo., portrait. George's 635-1248 1978 £6

HYNDMAN, WILLIAM　　　　History of a Cavalry Company. Philadelphia, 1870. Orig. cloth, some chipping, otherwise nice. MacManus 239-885 1978 $45

HYPERBOREA. London, Franfrolico Press, 1928. Recased in orig. cloth, 1 of 725 numbered copies, illus. by Norman Lindsay. Battery Park 1-93 1978 $75

I

I Believe: personal philosophies. London, 1940. First English ed., nice, orig. binding, d.w. Rota 211-13 1978 £9

I HAVE Entitled This My Little Book. N.P., n.d. (circa 1888). Wrs. Hayman 73-555 1978 $7.50

IACOVLEFF, ALEXANDRE   Dessins et Peintures d'Afrique. Paris, 1927. Folio, orig. handpainted silk wr., plts. in sheets, publisher's full lea. portfolio, ltd. ed., numbered copy on Madagascar Lafuma paper, illus. with drwgs. by Iacovleff, lacks 7 plts. Goldschmidt 110-34 1978 $215

IAMBLICHUS
Please turn to
JAMBLICHUS, OF CHALCIS

IASON, A. H.   Synopsis of Hernia. New York, 1949. Rittenhouse 49-390 1976 $15

IBAR, FRANCISCO   Muerte Politica De La Republica Mexicana... Mexico, 1829. Calf spine slightly chipped. Jenkins 116-1560 1978 $550

IBRAHIM-HILMY, PRINCE   The Literature of Egypt and The Soudan. 1886-87. 2 vols., 4to, orig. cloth, covers slightly worn & repaired. Edwards 1012-220 1978 £120

IBSEN, HENRIK   Collected Works. 1906-09. Copyright ed., 11 vols., cr. 8vo, orig. cloth. Howes 194-950 1978 £40

IBSEN, HENRIK   Hedda Gabler. Kobenhavn, 1890. 1st ed., 12mo., sm. spot on upper left hand corner of title page, page edges spotted, overall fine copy, 1/2 contemp. tan mor., paneled spine with black label & gilt lettering. Current 24-23 1978 $345

ICKES, HAROLD L.   The Autobiography of a Curmudgeon. New York, (1943). Illus. Biblo BL781-206 1978 $9

ICHES, HAROLD L.   Fightin' Oil. 1943. Austin 80-147 1978 $10

ICHTHYOLOGY. Edinburgh, 1833-44. 6 vols., complete, plts., almost all coloured, 2 vols. recased, orig. cloth, first ed. K Books 244-170 1978 £100

ICONOGRAPHIE des Contemporains depuis 1789 jusqu'a 1820. Vol. I only. Paris, c. 1820. Portraits, roy. 8vo., full red mor., good. K Books 244-126 1978 £15

IDE, WILLIAM BROWN   Who Conquered California? Read the Following pages, and Then You Will Know:.... Claremont, [1880]. Original boards with cloth back strip. Ginsberg 14-141 1978 $350

IDRIESS, ION L.   The Cattle King. Sydney, 1936. 10th ed., decor. cloth, map end sheets, very good copy in d.w. Dykes 34-120 1978 $10

IGNATIUS OF LOYALO
Please turn to
LOYOLA, IGNACIO DE

IHM, M.   Palaeographia Latina, Exempla Codicum Latinorum Phototypice Expressa. Ca. 1912. Folio, limp bds., plt. in portfolio. Allen 234-485 1978 $10

ILES, FRANCIS   Malice Aforethought: the story of a commonplace crime. Mundanus, 1931. Orig. wraps, good, first English ed. Bell Book 17-249 1978 £15

ILLINOIS   Inventory of the County Archives of Illinois. No. 89, Stephenson County. Chicago, 1938. Wrps. Hayman 71-330 1978 $12.50

ILLINOIS. STATE BOARD OF HEALTH   Report of the Sanitary Investigations of the Illinois River and Its Tributaries. Springfield, 1901. Maps, tables, 8vo., ex-lib. Morrill 239-135 1978 $10

ILLUSTRATED Anderson, Indiana, U.S.A. (Anderson, 1915). Wrps. Hayman 71-333 1978 $20

ILLUSTRATED Book Of English Songs. London, n.d.(Victorian). 4th. ed., cr. 8vo, orig. cloth, front free-end-paper and half title glued together, frontis & vignette throughout, good. Sexton 7-153 1978 £5

ILLUSTRATED Catalogue of Mason & Hamlin Cabinet Organs. Boston, 1880. 4to., orig. wrs., fine, supplements & A.L.s. inserted. Morrill 239-568 1978 $37.50

THE ILLUSTRATED Exhibitor. (1851). Wood engravings, plts., roy. 8vo., half calf, worn. George's 635-28 1978 £12.50

ILLUSTRATED Family Almanac for the United States and Canadas...1853... Boston, 1853. Vol. I, No. I, sm. 8vo., orig. wrs. Morrill 239-136 1978 $7.50

ILLUSTRATED Historical Atlas of the Counties of Frontenac, Lennox and Addington, Ont. Toronto, 1878. Spine mended, few page edges stained. Hood 117-740 1978 $250

ILLUSTRATED Historical Atlas of the County of Elgin, Ont. Toronto, 1877. Reinforced spine. Hood 117-739 1978 $300

ILLUSTRATED Historical Atlas of the County of Huron, Ontario. Toronto, 1879. Reinforced spine. Hood 117-741 1978 $275

ILLUSTRATED Historical Atlas of the State of Indiana. Chicago, n.d. (1876). Clean, rebound copy. Hayman 71-345 1978 $85

THE ILLUSTRATED London Instructor. London, 1850. Frontis portrait, engraved title, illus., 8vo, orig. cloth. Traylen 88-142 1978 £10

ILLUSTRATED LONDON NEWS   British Warships. Ca. 1940. Illus., paper. Austin 80-148 1978 $12.50

THE ILLUSTRATED London News Record of the Transvaal War, 1899-1900. London, (1900). 8 photos, illus., folio, orig. coloured pic. wrappers, 8vo. K Books 239-299 1978 £10

THE ILLUSTRATED London Spelling Book. London, n.d. c.1860. New ed., profusely illus. Traylen 88-141 1978 £7

AN ILLUSTRATED Souvenir of the Exhibition of Persian Art at Burlington House, London, 1931. London, 1931. Sm. 4to., orig. bds., spine worn, upper hinge split, illus. Sexton 7-40 1978 £8

THE ILLUSTRATED Sydney News and New South Wales Agriculturalist And Grazier. (Sydney), 1876-1884. Folio, 13 numbers in 1 vol., illus., plts., few leaves loose, some tears, maroon half calf, worn. Deighton 5-106 1978 £60

ILLUSTRATIONS For the Bible. n.d. (c. 1830). Oblong 12mo., flexible marbled bds., leather back, fine. Duschnes 220-17 1978 $50

DER ILLUSTRIRTE Cincinnatier Hinkende Bote. 1888. (Cincinnati, 1887). Wrs., illus. Hayman 72-20 1978 $7.50

ILLUSTRISSIMI Principis Ducis Cornubiae et Comitis Palatini, &c., Genethliacon. Cantabrigiae, 1688. 1st. ed., 4to, contemp. limp vellum, loose in binding. Hannas 54-164 1978 £55

ILLUSTRISSIMO Doctissimoque Viro, Domino Exechieli Spanhemio... (Oxford, about 1705). 1st. ed., folio, disbound. Hannas 54-165 1978 £15

DES Imagistes: an anthology. 1914. Orig. green bds., good, first English issue. Bell Book 17-505 1978 £45

IMBART DE LA TOUR, PIERRE   Les Origines de la Reforme. 1935. Ink scored, binders buckram, 8vo. George's 635-1050 1978 £5

IMITATIO CHRISTI   L'Imitation de Jesus Christ. Paris, 1643. 8vo.,
full red mor., gilt panelled, bookplate of Edmund Engelmann, in Pierre Moreau's
printed calligraphy, eng. plts., splendid copy, mint, rare, binding signed by
Gruel. Schumann 511-62 1978 sFr 1,750

IMITATIO CHRISTI   The Imitation of Christ. New Haven, 1802.
Trans. from Latin, 12mo., contemp. calf, hinges bit cracked. Morrill 239-625
1978 $15

IMITATIO CHRISTI   Of the Imitation of Christ: In Three Books.
Stanford, 1803. Full calf. Butterfield 21-168 1978 $15

IMITATIO CHRISTI   L'Imitation de Jesus Christ. Paris, 1857. 8vo.,
half calf, t.e.g., steel engrs. Van der Peet H64-458 1978 Dfl 45

IMMELMANN, MAX   Rontgen-Atlas des Normalen Menschlichen Kor-
pers. Berlin, 1900. Plts., folio, orig. cloth-backed bds., 1st ed. Offenbacher
30-132 1978 $250

IMMS, A.   The New Naturalist Insect Natural History.
Great Britain, (1947). 8vo., orig. cloth, color plts. Book Chest 17-199 1978
$14

AN IMPARTIAL Account of the Nature and Tendency of the Late Addresses. 1681.
4to., unbound, stitched as issued, uncut. P. M. Hill 142-7 1978 £12

AN IMPARTIAL Statement of the Controversy Respecting the Decision of Canvas-
sers (in the Election of 1792). New York, 1792. Disbound, clear plastic wr.
Butterfield 21-352 1978 $75

THE IMPERIAL Journal of the Arts and Sciences. Vols. 1 and 2. London, (1852).
Illus., plts., text illus., 4to., half calf. K Books 244-166 1978 £42

IMRAY, JAMES   The British and Foreign Coaster's Guide....
1850. Maps, 8vo., orig. cloth. F. Edwards 1013-103 1978 £10

IMRAY, JAMES F.   The Lights and Tides of the World... London,
1869. Sq. 4to., orig. cloth, good. Paine 78-75 1978 $22.50

IM THURN, EVERARD FERDINAND   Among the Indians of Guiana... 1883.
Map, coloured and plain plts., woodcuts, orig. cloth, 8vo., spine faded. Edwards
1012-655 1978 £65

IN MEMORIAM. John Cox, 1795-1871. Henry Oxnard Preble, 1847-1871.
(Boston, 1871). 2 portrs., 8vo., orig. wrs., torn at backstrip with signature loose,
pres. from George H. Preble. Morrill 239-355 1978 $15

IN MEMORIAM Josephine Shaw Lowell. New York, 1906. Frontis., 8vo., 1st
ed. Morrill 239-487 1978 $10

IN MEMORY of Charles Goodrich Hammond, ... Charlotte Bradley Hammond...
Cambridge, 1887. Orig. cl., 1st ed. Ginsberg 16-873 1978 $8.50

IN Re De Chama Grant. [Washington, 1884?]. Half mor., 1st ed. Ginsberg
14-764 1978 $75

IN The Supreme Court. N.P., n.d. (c.1848). Plain wrps. Hayman 71-430
1978 $8.50

INAUGURATION of Hon. John H. Lathrop, LL. D. Chancellor of the University
of Wisconsin, at the Capitol, Madison, January 16, 1850. Milwaukee, 1850.
Wrs., back wr. & margins, stained throughout. Hayman 73-764 1978 $10

INCA, EL
Please turn to
GARCILASO DE LA VEGA

INCIDENTS and Sketches Connected with the Early History of the West. Cincinnati, [ca. 1847]. Plates, original printed pictorial wr., 1st ed. Ginsberg 14-405
1978 $75

INCIDENTS Attending the Capture, Detention, and Ransom of Charles Johnston
of Virginia. Cleveland, 1905. Frontis. map, orig. cloth, 1 of 27 copies, vellum, fine. MacManus 239-1173 1978 $37.50

INDIA and the War. 1915. Coloured frontis.; coloured plts., 8vo., orig. cloth.
F. Edwards 1013-337 1978 £12

INDIAN Records, With a Commercial View of the Relations Between The British
Government and the Nawabs Nazim of Bengal, Behar and Orissa. 1870. Sole
ed.?, portrait frontis, 8vo., orig. cloth, nice copy. Fenning 32-171 1978 £16

INDIAN Treaties Printed by Benjamin Franklin, 1736-1762. Philadelphia, 1938.
Ltd. to 500, boxed, scarce. Biblo 247-61 1978 $400

INDIANA - LAWS.   The Revised Laws of Indiana...at their 50th
Session. Indianapolis, 1831. Lea., short crack in upper joints but very good
copy. Hayman 73-322 1978 $27.50

INDUSTRIAL America. New York, 1876. Portrs., engrs., 4to., half lea., 1st
ed. Morrill 241-681 1978 $75

INDUSTRIES and Commercial Growth of Montgomery and Bucks Counties Embracing Border Towns of Adjoining Counties... Philadelphia, 1891. Illus., orig.
cloth wrs., scarce. MacManus 239-1574 1978 $30

INDUSTRIES of Maryland. A Descriptive Review of the Manufacturing and Mercantile Industries of the City of Baltimore. New York, 1882. Illus. MacManus
239-1831 1978 $25

INFANTILE Paralysis in Vermont, 1894-1922. Burlington, 1924. Illus., 8vo.,
1st ed. Morrill 239-269 1978 $10

INFANTRY in Battle. Washington, 1939. Second ed., 8vo., orig. cloth. F.
Edwards 1013-338 1978 £25

INFORMATION Concerning the Terminus of the Railroad System of the Pacific
Coast. Oakland, 1871. Orig. pr. wr., 1st ed., maps. Ginsberg 14-145 1978
$125

THE INFORMATION for His Majesty's Advocate for His Highness's Interest;....
London, 1736. 8vo, disbound, 1st ed. Ximenes 47-260 1978 $30

INGALLS, WALTER R.   Wealth and Income of the American People.
York, (1922). Biblo BL781-826 1978 $10

INGALLS, WILLIAM   A Lecture on the Subject of Phrenology Not
Opposed to the Principles of Religion. Boston, 1839. 8vo., sewn, lightly dampstained, 1st ed. Morrill 239-137 1978 $10

INGEN-HOUSZ, JAN   Experiences sur les Vegetaux. Paris, 1787-
89. 2 vols., 8vo., fldg. plts., contemp. half calf, gilt, rubbed, very good set,
bklabels. of David P. Wheatland, 1st 2-vol. French ed., 3rd ed. in French in
Vol. 1 & 1st ed. of any language of Vol. 2. Norman 5-156 1978 $450

INGEN-HOUSZ, JAN   Experiments Upon Vegetables. London, 1779.
8vo., fldg. plts., half antique calf, light foxing, but very good copy, 1st ed.
Norman 5-155 1978 $1,250

INGERSOLL, CHARLES J.   History of the Second War Between the United
States and Great Britain. Philadelphia, 1852. 2 vols., nice set, cloth, 1st
pub. in 1845, complete sets are rare. MacManus 239-474 1978 $50

INGERSOLL, ERNEST   Rand, McNally & Co.'s Illustrated Guide to the
Hudson River and Catskill Mountains. Chicago-New York, 1896. 4th ed.,
thick 16mo., folded maps tipped in, pict. wr., near fine. Butterfield 21-211
1978 $27.50

INGERSOLL, ROBERT G.   Complete Lectures of Col. R. G. Ingersoll.
n.d. Austin 79-354 1978 $10

INGERSOLL, ROBERT G.   Crimes Against Criminals. New York, 1890.
Ads, wrs., lacks back wr., 1st ed., illus. fr. wr. Hayman 73-332 1978 $10

INGERSOLL, ROBERT G.   Col. R. G. Ingersoll's Famous Speeches Complete. 1906. Austin 79-353 1978 $12.50

INGERSOLL, ROBERT G.   Ingersoll's Greatest Lectures. Free Thought
Press, 1944. Austin 79-352 1978 $11

INGERSOLL, ROBERT G.   Ingersoll's Lectures. New York, 1892. 3/4
leather & marbled bds. binding. Hayman 71-332 1978 $20

INGERSOLL, ROBERT G.   Liberty in Literature. Testimonial to Walt Whitman. New York, (1890). 12mo., orig. cloth, 1st ed., almost fine. MacManus 238-587 1978 $45

INGERSOLL, ROBERT G.   Notes on Ingersoll. 1883. Austin 79-355 1978 $11

INGHAM, G. THOMAS   Digging Gold Among the Rockies or, Exciting Adventures of Wild Camp Life in Leadville, Black Hills and the Gunnison Country... Philadelphia, 1888. Cloth. Hayman 72-341 1978 $8.50

INGLEBY, ARTHUR G.   Pioneer Days in Darkest Africa. London, c.1935. Illus., slight foxing, bookplt. on verso of title, cr. 8vo, orig. cloth. K Books 239-230 1978 £6

INGLEFIELD, EDWARD AUGUSTUS   A Summer Search For Sir John Franklin; With a Peep Into the Polar Basin. London, 1853. 1st. ed., 8vo, coloured lithograph plts., folding engraved map, laid down on linen, modern half calf, gilt back. Deighton 5-159 1978 £95

INGLEFIELD, JOHN NICHOLSON   Capt. Inglefield's Narrative, Concerning the Loss of His Majesty's Ship the Centaur, of Seventy-Four Guns:.... London, 1783. 8vo, modern marbled boards, 2nd ed., "corrected". Ximenes 47-151 1978 $55

INGLEFIELD, V. E.   The History of the Twentieth Division. 1921. Portrait frontis., plts., 8vo., orig. cloth, spine faded. F. Edwards 1013-587 1978 £10

INGLIS, HENRY D.   Scenes From the Life of Edward Lascelles, Gent. Dublin, 1837. 2 vols., 1st. & only ed., engraved frontis, engraved vignette title-pg., 2 vols. bound in 1, 8vo, recent half calf, sm. portionremoved from extreme upper blank margin of each engraved title-pg., o/w very good copy. Fenning 32-172 1978 £32

INGOLDSBY, THOMAS   Ingoldsby Legends. London, 1898. 1st ed., thick 8 vo., colour plts., drawings by Arthur Rackham, gilt stamped pictorial cloth, fine. Houle 10-273 1978 $175

INGOLDSBY, THOMAS   Ingoldsby Legends. London, 1907. 1st printing of the expanded ed., tipped-in colour plts., drawings by Arthur Rackham, thick 4 to., orig. cloth, t.e.g., uncut, clean, tight, very good. Houle 10-274 1978 $175

INGOLDSBY, THOMAS   Misadventures at Margate. London, n.d. Folio, color plates by Ernest M. Jessop, spine cracks, cover stains, fine. Victoria 34-430 1978 $30

INGOLDSBY, THOMAS   The Witches' Frolic and The Bagman's Dog. London, 1876. Quarto, 1st ed., plates, slight edge rubbing, fine. Victoria 34-177 1978 $100

INGRAHAM, PRENTISS   Land of Legendary Lore. Sketches of Romance on the Eastern Shore of the Chesapeake. Easton, 1898. Illus., map, scarce, fine. MacManus 239-1832 1978 $50

INGRAM, DALE   An Historical Account of Several Plagues That Have Appeared in the World Since the Year 1346. London, 1755. Half leather. Rittenhouse 49-392 1976 $100

INGRAM, J.   Memorials of Oxford. Oxford, 1837. 3 vols., 4to., lg. paper, plts. by John Le Keux, illus., some slight foxing, contemp. maroon mor. gilt., bookplt. of John Brooke. Quaritch 983-339 1978 $500

INGRAM, J. S.   The Centennial Exposition Described and Illustrated. Philadelphia, (1876). Illus., fine copy, orig. cloth. MacManus 239-84 1978 $32.50

INGRAM, JOHN H.   The Haunted Homes and Family Traditions of Great Britain. London, 1884. 2 vols., orig. dec. cloth, 1st eds., bind. a bit soiled, otherwise good. MacManus 238-297 1978 $60

INGRAM, JOHN K.   A History of Political Economy. 1893. Austin 80-724 1978 $12.50

INGRAM, REX   Mars in the House of Death. New York, 1939. 1st ed., author's signed pres., d.w. Biblo BL781-1014 1978 $17.50

INITIALS and Borders and Other Decorative Material. New York, 1934. Cloth, light scratch marks to cover, sm. broadside laid in, bkplt. of John Fass. Dawson's 447-75 1978 $125

INNES, A. D.   England Under the Tudors. 1918. 5th ed., binding faded. Allen 234-1316 1978 $7.50

INNES, E.   The Chersonese With the Gilding Off. 1885. 2 plts., 2 vols., sm. 8vo, orig. cloth, fine set. Edwards 1012-164 1978 £45

INNES, MICHAEL   The Daffodil Affair. 1942. Very good, d.w., first English ed. Bell Book 16-250 1978 £16.50

INNES, MICHAEL   The Journeying Boy. 1949. Covers somewhat soiled, good, d.w., first English ed. Bell Book 16-251 1978 £8.50

INNES, MICHAEL   A Night of Errors. 1948. Very good, worn d.w., first English ed. Bell Book 17-250 1978 £8.50

INNES, WILLIAM   A Letter to the Members of Parliament Who Have Presented Petitions to the Honourable House of Commons for the Abolition of the Slave Trade. London, 1792. 8vo, sewn, as issued, 1st ed., fine copy, entirely uncut. Ximenes 47-152 1978 $200

INNES, WILLIAM   The Slave-Trade Indispensable:.... London, 1790. 8vo, original pale blue wrappers, 1st ed., very fine copy, very scarce. Ximenes 47-153 1978 $225

INSH, G. P.   The Company of Scotland trading to Africa and the Indies. 1932. Illus., 8vo. George's 635-341 1978 £7.50

INSPIRATION. London, Fanfrolico Press. 1 of 725 numbered copies. Battery Park 1-96 1978 $75

INSTITUTIO Graecae Grammatices Compendiaria In Usum Regiae Scholae Westmonasteriensis. London, 1743. 12mo, orig. sheep worn, front cover loose. Traylen 88-146 1978 £5

INSTITUTIO Graecae Grammatices Compendiaria in Usum Regiae Scholae Westmonasteriensis. London, 1748. 12mo, orig. sheep, joints weak. Traylen 88-146A 1978 £5

INSTRUCTION Abregee sur les Mesures. Paris, 1794. 8vo., copperplts., orig. wrs., uncut, spine repaired, but fine copy, 1st ed. Norman 5-199 1978 $200

INSTRUCTION Generale Pour la Teinture des Laines, et Manufactures de Laine de Toutes Couleurs, & Pour la Culture des Drogues ou Ingrediens qu'on y Employe. Paris, 1671. 12mo., contemp. calf, gilt, fine copy, 1st ed. Norman 5-85 1978 $750

INSTRUCTION sur les Mesures. Paris, 1794. 8vo., fldg. copperplt., modern cloth-backed bds., fine copy, 1st ed. Norman 5-198 1978 $300

INSTRUCTIONS for the Carbine and Pistol Exercises for the Cavalry. c. 1819. Contemp. mottled calf, 8vo. Howes 194-200 1978 £15

INSTRUCTIONS For the Carbine and Pistol Exercises For the Cavalry. 1819. 8vo., contemp. tree calf. F. Edwards 1013-339 1978 £35

INSULL, SAMUEL   Public Utilities in Modern Life Selected Speeches (1914-1923). 1924. Ex-lib. Austin 80-725 1978 $27.50

INTERESTING Considerations on the Public Affairs of France prior to the Revolution. 1791. Frontispiece, contemp. speckled calf gilt, portion missing from head of spine, 8vo. Howes 194-277 1978 £14

INTERNATIONAL ASSOCIATION OF ANTIQUARIAN BOOKSELLERS   Catalogue of an Exhibition of Books, Broadsides, Proclamations, Portraits, Autographs.... London, 1912. F'scap. 4to., orig. wrappers. Forster 130-244 1978 £6

INTERNATIONAL NICKEL COMPANY OF CANADA   The Romance of Nickel. (Sudbury), n.d. Hood's 115-711 1978 $10

INTERNATIONAL PAPER CO.   After 50 Years. 1948. Illus. Austin 80-727 1978 $12.50

INTERNATIONAL Correspondence by Means of Numbers... 1874. 1st. ed., printed pres. slip from author, orig. green cloth, v.g. Jarndyce 16-806 1978 £8.50

INTERNATIONAL Railway of Canada. St. John, 1894. Narrow fldg. 8vo. leaflet, lg. map. Morrill 239-443 1978 $12.50

INTRODUCTION To Contemporary Civilization in the West. A Source Book. New York, 1946. Vol. I, 8vo., cloth. Salloch 348-99 1978 $10

AN INTRODUCTION to the Natural History of Curious and Interesting Birds. Stockton-upon-Tees, 1810. 12mo, engravings, printed wrappers. Victoria 34-432 1978 $55

INVITATION Serieuse aux Habitants des Illinois by Un Habitant des Kaskaskias. Providence, 1908. Reprinted from 1772 ed., orig. cloth bds., fine untrimmed copy, ltd. to 100 copies. MacManus 239-212 1978 $30

IOWA CITY. ORDINANCES Ordinances of Iowa City, Passed from June 15th, 1857 to June 12th, 1858, Together with a List of the Officers for 1858-59. Iowa City, 1858. Original printed wr., 1st ed. Ginsberg 14-419 1978 $100

IOWA: The Home for Immigrants Being a Treatise on the Resources of Iowa, and Giving Useful Information with Regard to the State, for the Benefit of Immigrants and Others. Des Moines, 1870. Original printed wr., 1st ed. Ginsberg 14-412 1978 $50

IRBY, C. L. Travels in Egypt, Nubia, Syria and Asia Minor, 1817-1818. 1823. Maps, illus., calf, rebacked, 8vo. Edwards 1012-70 1978 £65

IRELAND, A. The Book-Lover's Enchiridion, a Treasury of Thoughts on the Solace and Companionship of Books. 1888. Sq. 8vo., crushed mor. gilt, neatly recased and rejointed, some discolouring. George's 635-1207 1978 £18

IRELAND, JOHN Hogarth Illustrated. London, 1812. 3rd ed., 3 vols., 8vo., engravings, full blue mor., bookplts., plts. and interior fine. Current 24-223 1978 $100

IRELAND, SAMUEL Picturesque Views on the River Medway, from the Nore to the Vicinity of its Source in Sussex. 1793. First ed., frontispiece, map, sepia aquatint plts., sm. 4to., contemp. mottled calf, rebacked, mor. labels. Howes 194-1394 1978 £135

IRELAND, SAMUEL Mr. Ireland's Vindication of His Conduct,... London, 1796. 1st ed., thin octavo, quarter brown mor., gilt lettering along spine, t.p. and last leaf have been silked, Lenox Library stamp and cancel release, bookplate. Totteridge 29-57 1978 $175

IRELAND, SAMUEL Picturesque Tour Through Holland, Brabant, & Part of France, in the Autumn of 1789. London, 1790. Plts., 2 vols., 4to., mottled calf, gilt backs, 1st ed. Argosy Special-53 1978 $300

IRELAND, WILLIAM HENRY Rhapsodies. 1803. Sm. 8vo., 1st ed., contemp. calf, rebacked, signatures, nice copy, uncut. Quaritch 979-205 1978 $200

IRIBE, PAUL La Mort de Circe, ou la Revanche du Cochon. Paris, 1928. Lg. folio, orig. wr., uncut, ltd. ed. issued in 2,775 copies, one of preferred copies on Arches paper. Goldschmidt 110-35 1978 $240

IRIBE, PAUL Les Robes de Paul Poiret Raconte par Paul Iribe. Paris, 1908. 4to., orig. bds., uncut, damage to bd. repaired, ltd. ed., 250 numbered copies prtd. on Holland Van Gelder paper. Goldschmidt 110-36 1978 $325

IRIS Society Yearbook, Complete Set Vol. I, 1930 to 1975. London, 1930-1975. 48 vols., illus., roy. 8vo., orig. limp wrappers. Traylen 88-588 1978 £75

IRVINE, ALEXANDER A Fighting Parson. 1930. Austin 79-358 1978 $10

IRVINE, ALEXANDER From the Bottom Up. 1910. Illus. Austin 79-359 1978 $11

IRVINE, JOHN Mormon Protest Against Injustice. Salt Lake City, 1885. Orig. pr. front wr., 1st ed. Ginsberg 14-1105 1978 $45

IRVINE, LYN Ten Letter-Writers. Hogarth Press, 1932. First ed., d.w., orig. cloth, 8vo. Howes 194-951 1978 £5

IRVING, C. A Catechism of Roman Antiquities. London, n.d.c. 1821. Frontis, 12mo, orig. wrappers, soiled & repaired, back wrp. missing. Traylen 88-147 1978 £5

IRVING, DAVID The Elements of English Composition. Georgetown, 1825. Lacks covers, 2nd American ed., very good, rebinding copy. Biblo 247-40 1978 $27.50

IRVING, DAVID The Elements of English Composition. Edinburgh, 1828. 8th. ed., half title, lg. 12mo., orig. bds., uncut, printed paper label, binding little dull but sound, very good copy. Fenning 32-174 1978 £12

IRVING, DAVID The Lives of the Scotish Poets. 1810. 2 vols., 8vo., contemp. half russia gilt, portraits. P. M. Hill 142-146 1978 £28

IRVING, JOHN A. Psychological Aspects of the Social Credit Movement in Alberta, Part III. 1947. Hood's 115-1006 1978 $7.50

IRVING, LEIGH Santa Clara County, California. San Jose, [1912]. Illus., map, original printed colored wr. Ginsberg 14-146 1978 $20

IRVING, WASHINGTON The Alhambra: A Series of Tales and Sketches of the Moors and Spaniards. Philadelphia, 1832. 2 vols., orig. cloth-backed bds., spines faded, 1st Amer. ed., Bind. variant A in vol. II, some foxing and staining, but very good. MacManus 238-517 1978 $70

IRVING, WASHINGTON The Alhambra. A Series of Tales and Sketches of the Moors and Spaniards. Philadelphia, 1832. 2 vols., 12mo., orig. cloth-backed bds., 1st Amer. ed., covers a little soiled, some foxing throughout, otherwise good. MacManus 238-518 1978 $65

IRVING, WASHINGTON The Alhambra. New York, n.d. (1890's?). Clean, revised ed., t.e.g., former owner's inscription on front endpaper dated 1895. Hayman 71-357 1978 $7.50

IRVING, WASHINGTON Astoria, or Anecdotes of an Enterprise Beyond the Rocky Mountains. Philadelphia, 1836. Lg. fldg. map, 2 vols., purple cloth embossed with heavy dots, 1st ed., 1st state, spines faded, little foxing, signatures of two former owners, maroon buckram box. Bradley 49-161 1978 $425

IRVING, WASHINGTON Bracebridge Hall. 1822. First English ed., 2 vols., contemp. calf, gilt edges, 8vo. Howes 194-952 1978 £35

IRVING, WASHINGTON Bracebridge Hall, or the Humorists. 1822. 1st. English ed., 2 vols., lib. stamp on titles, contents soiled, diced russia, rebacked, corners repaired. Eaton 45-265 1978 £10

IRVING, WASHINGTON Bracebridge Hall Or The Humourists. New York & London, 1896. 1st ed., 2 vols., original gold-stamped covers and spine, Rackham plates, fine. Victoria 34-670 1978 $75

IRVING, WASHINGTON The Crayon Miscellany. Philadelphia, 1835. 12mo., 1st ed., cloth, paper label, bind. worn, foxed. Biblo BL781-280 1978 $22.50

IRVING, WASHINGTON A History of the Life and Voyages of Christopher Columbus. 1828. 1st. English ed., 2 folding maps, browned, 4 vols., modern half leather, red labels, 8vo. Edwards 1012-389 1978 £50

IRVING, WASHINGTON History of the Life and Voyages of Christopher Columbus. Philadelphia, 1837. 2 vols., lg. fold. map, orig. calf, foxed but good set. MacManus 239-216 1978 $20

IRVING, WASHINGTON Knickerbocker Papers, Being Rip Van Winkle and the Legend of Sleepy Hollow. London, 1914. Orig. cloth-backed bds., d.j., ltd. to 1,000 copies on hand-made Riccardi paper, fine. MacManus 238-520 1978 $35

IRVING, WASHINGTON Legend of Sleepy Hollow. San Francisco, 1930. Woodcuts, signed by printer, Charles H. Falk, ltd. to 229 copies, excellent. Nestler Rare 78-123 1978 $20

IRVING, WASHINGTON Letters of Jonathan Oldstyle. 1824. 2nd. ed., orig. brown wrappers, uncut, v.g. Jarndyce 16-766 1978 £12.50

IRVING, WASHINGTON The Life and Voyages of Christopher Columbus. New York, 1834. Abridged ed., printed boards rubbed, chipped, leather spine chipped, text foxed, scarce ed. Victoria 34-433 1978 $17.50

IRVING, WASHINGTON   Notes and Journal on Travel in Europe. 1804-1805. New York, 1921. 3 vols., illus., 12mo., orig. cloth, 1 of 257 sets printed on rag paper, very good. MacManus 238-521 1978 $60

IRVING, WASHINGTON   Rip Van Winkle. New York, (1869). 1st ed., color plates and text drawings, rear wrapper has ad, sewn, minor wrapper tears, spine chipped and offsetting. Victoria 34-566 1978 $37.50

IRVING, WASHINGTON   Rip Van Winkle. New York, 1905. 1st American ed., 4 to., green gilt stamped pictorial cloth, t.e.g., fine, illus. by Arthur Rackham. Houle 10-275 1978 $175

IRVING, WASHINGTON   Rip van Winkle. London, 1905. 1st ed., second printing, pictorial cloth with large gilt vignette, occasional foxing, mint text and plates. Victoria 34-686 1978 $175

IRVING, WASHINGTON   Rip Van Winkle. 1930. Full lea., worn, t.e.g., copy #766 of 1500 copies, signed by F. W. Goudy, newspaper clippings tipped in. Battery Park 1-128 1978 $45

IRVING, WASHINGTON   Rip Van Winkle. New York, Limited Editions Club, 1930. Full green mor., orig. cardboard slipcase soiled, handset by Bertha Goudy, in Kaatskill type designed and cut for this book by Frederic W. Goudy, ed. of 1500 copies. Wolfe 39-250 1978 $75

IRVING, WASHINGTON   The Sketch Book of Geoffrey Crayon, Gent. Parts I - IV (only). New York, 1819. One vol., 8vo., contemp. marbled bds., half calf rubbed. Wolfe 39-251 1978 $175

IRVING, WASHINGTON   Stories of the Hudson. New York, (1912). Illus., 1st of this ed., bookplt. Biblo BL781-1015 1978 $12

IRVING, WASHINGTON   Tales of a Traveller. London, 1895. 1st ed, two vols., plates by Arthur Rackham, others by various artists, colored boarders, 3/4 leather, covers loose, texts fine. Victoria 34-688 1978 $20

IRVING, WASHINGTON   A Tour on the Prairies. Philadelphia, 1835. 1st. American ed., 2nd. issue, sm. 8vo, orig. cloth, spotting on some pages. Edwards 1012-497 1978 £30

IRVING, WASHINGTON   Voyages and Discoveries of the Companions of Columbus. New York, 1929. 1 of 374 numbered copies, 4 to., cloth, t.e.g., leather label, good-fine. Houle 10-166 1978 $35

IRVING, WASHINGTON   Wolfert's Roost and Other Papers, now First Collected. 1855. First ed., second state, very good. Austin 82-490 1978 $27.50

IRWIN, EYLES   A Series of Adventures in the Course of a Voyage Up the Red-Sea... 1787. Maps, plts., 2 vols., 8vo, contemp. calf, joints slightly worn. Edwards 1012-71 1978 £60

IRWIN, WILL   Highlights of Manhattan. 1927. Illus., first ed., v.g. Austin 82-927 1978 $22.50

IRWIN, WILL   The Making of a Reporter. New York, (1942). Biblo BL781-770 1978 $8.50

ISAAC, FRANK   English and Scotish Printing Types. 1501-35. 1508-41. London, 1930. 4to., orig. cloth-backed bds., 1st ed. MacManus 238-953 1978 $40

ISABELLA. 1823. 1st. ed., 3 vols., orig. half morocco, marbled boards, good. Jarndyce 16-258 1978 £55

ISHAM, SAMUEL   History of American Painting. New York, 1936. Revised ed., 4 to., illus., d.j., very good. Houle 10-167 1978 $20

ISHERWOOD, CHRISTOPHER   Goodbye to Berlin. London, 1939. First ed., orig. binding, spine darkened, nice. Rota 211-242 1978 £22

ISHERWOOD, CHRISTOPHER   Goodbye to Berlin. 1940. Pict. bds., lower joint split, spine faded, good. Bell Book 17-506 1978 £10

ISHERWOOD, CHRISTOPHER   Lions and Shadows. Hogarth Press, 1938. 1st. ed., bds. just shade rubbed, very good copy in slight defective d.w. Jarndyce 16-1202 1978 £40

ISHERWOOD, CHRISTOPHER   Lions and Shadows. London, 1938. First ed., first binding, good ex-library, scarce. Rota 211-241 1978 £8

ISHII, HAXON   Twelve Poems. Tokyo, 1925. Wraps, fine, d.w., first English ed. Bell Book 16-099 1978 £15

THE ITALIAN Lakes. London, 1905. Thick 8vo, orig. dec. cloth, good. Sexton 7-8B 1978 £8

ITALIAN Tales. London, 1824. 8vo, full polished calf, gilt, spine and inner dentelles gilt, a.e.g. by Tout (a trifle rubbed), 1st ed., plates by George Cruikshank, very good copy. Ximenes 47-274 1978 £85

ITARD, JEAN MARIE GASPARD   Traite des Maladies de l'Oreille et de l'Audition. Paris, 1821. 2 vols., fldg. copperplts., contemp. bds., 1st ed. Offenbacher 30-70 1978 $275

IVES, BRAYTON   Catalogue of the Collections of Books and Manuscripts Belonging to Mr. Brayton Ives of New York...Early Printed Books, Americana...Missals and Books of Hours. New York, 1891. 2 vols., 4to., 1/2 mor., uncut, orig. parchment wr. bound in, 1 of 100 special copies, plts. Americanist 102-64 1978 $125

IVES, CHARLES E.   Essays Before a Sonata. 1920. First ed. Austin 82-491 1978 $27.50

IVES, E.   A Voyage From England to India, 1754... 1773. Maps, plts., 4to, half calf, rebacked, slight foxing. Edwards 1012-103 1978 £150

IVES, JOHN   Remarks upon the Garianonum of the Romans. 1773. 8vo., half calf, plts. P. M. Hill 142-147 1978 £18

IVINS, WILLIAM M.   The Artist and the Fifteenth-Century Printer. 1940. Cloth, fraying at ends of spine, 1 of 300 numbered copies. Dawson's 447-172 1978 $30

IVISON, BLAKEMAN   The New States: A Sketch of the History and Development of the States of North Dakota, South Dakota, Montana and Washington... New York, 1889. Folding colored map, original wr. bound in cloth, scarce. Ginsberg 14-430 1978 $75

IZLAR, WILLIAM VALMORE   A Sketch of the War Record of the Edisto Rifles 1861-1865, Company A, 1st Regiment, SCV Infantry Company G 25th Regiment SCV Infantry. Columbia, 1914. Cover discolored, Bell Wiley's copy. Broadfoot's 44-599 1978 $35

J

J., W.　　　　　　A Genuine Account of the Manner of Making the Best Russia Pot Ashes. London, 1753. 4to, disbound, 1st ed., half-title present (soiled), very scarce. Ximenes 47-155 1978 $65

JABOTINSKY, VLADIMIR　　　　The Story of the Jewish Legion. 1945. Illus. Austin 79-363 1978 $17.50

JACK, DAVID RUSSELL　　　　Acadiensis... (St. John), 1904. Vol. IV, card covers worn. Hood 116-224 1978 $35

JACK, DAVID RUSSELL　　　　Centennial Prize Essay on the History of the City and Country of St. John. St. John, 1883. Fold. maps, plts. Hood 116-223 1978 $65

JACK, E. M.　　　　On the Congo Frontier. London & Leipzig, 1914. Map, illus., gilt-dec. cloth, 8vo. K Books 239-231 1978 £16

JACK, ELLEN E.　　　　The Fate of a Fairy. Chicago, (1910). Clean, slight wear, orig. binding. Hayman 71-358 1978 $10

JACK, JAMES W.　　　　Daybreak in Livingstonia. Edinburgh & London, 1901. Folding map, 17 plts., dec. cloth, 8vo. K Books 239-232 1978 £6

JACK and the Bean-Stalk. Boston, (1841). Decorated wrappers, profusely illus., very good. Victoria 34-434 1978 $20

JACK the Giant Killer and Other Stories. Philadelphia, c.1895. Illus., colored pictorial cloth, lightly rubbed and soiled, very good. Victoria 34-435 1978 $12.50

JACKMAN, W. T.　　　　The Development of Transportation in Modern England. Cambridge, 1916. 2 vols., roy. 8vo. George's 635-343 1978 £15

JACKMAN, W. T.　　　　Economic Principles of Transportation. Toronto, 1935. Hood 116-352 1978 $17.50

JACKSON, A. B.　　　　Catalogue of the Trees and Shrubs in the Collection of the Late Sir George L. Holford. Oxford, 1927. 8vo., orig. cloth, collotype plts. Book Chest 17-201 1978 $90

JACKSON, A. T.　　　　Picture Writing of Texas Indians. Austin, 1912. Illus., inscribed and signed by author, fine. Jenkins 116-713 1978 $75

JACKSON, A. W.　　　　Barbariana: or, Scenery, Climate, Soils and Social Conditions of Santa Barbara City and County, California. San Francisco, 1888. Original printed wr., 1st ed. Ginsberg 14-147 1978 $100

JACKSON, ANDREW　　　　Opinions of Gen. Andrew Jackson on the Annexation of Texas. Washington, 1844. Uncut. Jenkins 116-715 1978 $150

JACKSON, CHARLES　　　　The Lost Week-End. 1945. Very good, worn d.w., first English ed. Bell Book 17-508 1978 £8.50

JACKSON, CHARLES THOMAS　　　　A Manual of Etherization. Boston, 1861. 12mo., illus., orig. blind-stamped cloth, signature of early owner & bkplt. of Dr. Carleton B. Chapman, good copy, 1st ed. Zeitlin 245-135 1978 $235

JACKSON, CHEVALIER　　　　An Autogiography. New York, 1938. D.j. Rittenhouse 49-397 1976 $25

JACKSON, CHEVALIER　　　　An Autobiography. New York, 1938. Cover lightly soiled, otherwise good. Rittenhouse 49-394 1976 $20

JACKSON, CHEVALIER　　　　Bronchoscopy and Esophagoscopy. Philadelphia and London, 1927. Second ed., illus., color plts. Rittenhouse 49-398 1976 $25

JACKSON, CHEVALIER　　　　The Nose, Throat and Ear and Their Diseases in Original Contributions by American and European Authors. Philadelphia, 1929. Rittenhouse 49-393 1976 $25

JACKSON, COATES　　　　The Nose, Throat and Ear and Their Diseases. Philadelphia, 1930. Library marks, hinges weak. Rittenhouse 49-146 1976 $12.50

JACKSON, E. S.　　　　The Inniskilling Dragoons. 1909. Thick roy. 8vo., orig. cloth, pres. copy from author, coloured plts. F. Edwards 1013-468 1978 £50

JACKSON, EMILY　　　　A History of Hand-Made Lace. London, 1900. Plts., illus., 4to., cloth. K Books 244-167 1978 £33

JACKSON, EMILY　　　　The History of Silhouettes. London, 1911. 4to., orig. cloth, illus., some plts. in color, nice copy, scarce. MacManus 239-681 1978 $45

JACKSON, EMILY　　　　Silhouette, Notes and Dictionary. 1938. Coloured plts., 4to. George's 635-29 1978 £40

JACKSON, MRS. F. NEVILL
Please turn to
JACKSON, EMILY

JACKSON, FRANCIS　　　　A History of the Early Settlement, 1639-1800. Boston, 1854. Port frontis. Baldwins' 51-401 1978 $12.50

JACKSON, FREDERICK GEORGE　　　　The Great Frozen Land (Bolshaia Zemelskija Tundra). London, 1895. 1st. ed., 8vo, frontispiece, partially coloured folding map, illus., orig. blue cloth, lib. label removed, some chafing & soiling of cover, indelible lib. stamp on maps & some leaves. Deighton 5-160 1978 £40

JACKSON, HELEN HUNT　　　　Bits of Travel at Home. Boston, 1889. Clean, orig. binding, one signature started. Hayman 71-360 1978 $7.50

JACKSON, HELEN HUNT　　　　Ramona. Boston, 1884. 1st ed., text very good, t.p. is snipped, covers moderately rubbed. Victoria 34-436 1978 $75

JACKSON, HELEN HUNT　　　　Zeph. Boston, 1885. 1st ed., spine tips frayed, front inner hinge cracked. Victoria 34-437 1978 $15

JACKSON, HENRY E.　　　　Benjamin West His Life and Work. Philadelphia, 1900. Illus., nice copy, orig. cloth, front hinge cracked. MacManus 239-682 1978 $17.50

JACKSON, HENRY ROOTES　　　　Letters to the Hon. Alex. H. Stephens. Savannah, 1860. 8vo., orig. wr., 1st ed. Morrill 241-223 1978 $17.50

JACKSON, HOLBROOK　　　　The Anatomy of Bibliomania. London, 1930. 2 vols., orig. red buckram, d.j., 1st ed., ltd. to 1,000 copies, fine. MacManus 238-954 1978 $125

JACKSON, HOLBROOK　　　　The Anatomy of Bibliomania. New York, 1931. 2 vols., orig. cloth, 1st Amer. ed., bookplts., very good. MacManus 238-955 1978 $75

JACKSON, HOLBROOK　　　　The Anatomy of Bibliomania. New York, 1931. 2 vols., t.e.g. Battery Park 1-381 1978 $100

JACKSON, HOLBROOK　　　　Bookman's Pleasure. New York, 1947. Battery Park 1-384 1978 $10

JACKSON, HOLBROOK　　　　The Eighteen-Nineties. London, 1913. 8vo, 1st ed., red cloth with rain drop marks on front cover and spine, spine faded, ownership signature on front endpaper, corners bumped, t.e.g., uncut, Good, collector's cond. Desmarais 1-248 1978 $25

JACKSON, HOLBROOK　　　　The Fear of Books. London, 1932. Orig. cloth, d.j., 1st ed., ltd., very good. MacManus 238-956 1978 $35

JACKSON, HOLBROOK　　　　The Fear of Books. One of 2000 numbered copies, t.e.g. Battery Park 1-382 1978 $50

JACKSON, HOLBROOK　　　　Of the Uses of Books. (New York. 1937). Quarto, boards and cloth, decor. by Frederic Warde, 1 of 1500 copies, fine. Duschnes 220-159 1978 $10

JACKSON, HOLBROOK　　　　The Reading of Books. London, (1946). Battery Park 1-383 1978 $10

JACKSON, HOLBROOK　　　　Town: An Essay. Westminster, 1913. 12mo., orig. pict. wrs., 1st ed., very good. MacManus 238-925 1978 $35

JACKSON, ISA G. Ballades and Bits. Toronto, 1937. Illus., card cover, ltd. ed. Hood 116-831 1978 $17.50

JACKSON, J. G. An Account of the Empire of Morocco, and the Districts of Suse and Tafilelt... 1814. Maps, plts., 4to, orig. bds., cloth back, uncut, slight foxing, extra illus. by insertion of portrait of author. Edwards 1012-239 1978 £120

JACKSON, JAMES Memoirs of James Jackson, Jr., M.D. Boston, 1835. Covers unattached, lacks cloth on spine. Rittenhouse 49-396 1976 $20

JACKSON, JAMES Memoir of James Jackson, Jr. Boston, 1835. First ed., firm, tight, clean, owner's ticket on lower spine. Rittenhouse 49-401 1976 $50

JACKSON, JAMES A Memoir of James Jackson, Jr., M.D. Boston, 1835. Cover soiled, cloth on spine much damaged, some damp staining needs a new cover. Rittenhouse 49-399 1976 $15

JACKSON, JAMES Memoir of James Jackson, Jr. Boston, 1836. 12mo., some dampstaining, 1st ed. Morrill 239-138 1978 $15

JACKSON, JAY M. Jackson's Directory of Reliable Real Estate Agents of the United States and Canada. Lorimor, 1902. Orig. binding. Wolfe 39-253 1978 $35

JACKSON, JOSEPH American Colonial Architecture. Philadelphia, (1924). Illus., orig. cloth, presentation copy from author, bookplt., very good. MacManus 239-683 1978 $15

JACKSON, JOSEPH A Bibliography of the Works of Charles Godfrey Leland. Philadelphia, 1927. 8vo., orig. cloth, 1st separate ed., ltd. to 50 copies, signed by compiler. MacManus 238-967 1978 $25

JACKSON, JOSEPH Encyclopedia of Philadelphia. Harrisburg, 1931. 4 vols., 4to., illus., very scarce. MacManus 239-1610 1978 $150

JACKSON, JOSEPH Iconography of Philadelphia. (Philadelphia, 1934). Bds., illus., very scarce. MacManus 239-1625 1978 $17.50

JACKSON, JOSEPH Literary Landmarks of Philadelphia. Philadelphia, (1939). Ltd. to 1,050 copies, illus., fine. MacManus 239-1628 1978 $22.50

JACKSON, JOSEPH Market Street Philadelphia. The Most Historic Highway in America... Philadelphia, 1918. 1st ed., ltd. to 400 copies, illus., uncut. MacManus 239-1633 1978 $37.50

JACKSON, JOSEPH HENRY Anybody's Gold. 1941. First ed., illus., former owner's inscription. Austin 82-928 1978 $27.50

JACKSON, JOSEPH HENRY Bad Company. The Story of California's Legendary and Actual Stage-robbers,.... New York, (1949). 1st ed., fine, d.w., illus. Biblo 248-264 1978 $17.50

JACKSON, JOSEPH HENRY Gold Rush Album. New York, 1949. 4to, illus., 1st ed., boxed. Biblo 248-265 1978 $32.50

JACKSON, JOSEPHINE A. Outwitting Our Nerves. New York, 1921. 8vo., 1st ed. Morrill 239-139 1978 $7.50

JACKSON, LEROY F. Rimskittle's Book. Chicago, (1926). Large quarto, colored plates and colored text illus. by Ruth Eger, small rip, fine copy, cover color plate by Milo Winter. Victoria 34-438 1978 $25

JACKSON, MRS. M. E. Botanical Lectures. London, 1804. Plts., 8vo, old bds., upper cover loose. Traylen 88-149 1978 £15

JACKSON, MARY ANNA Memoirs of Stonewall Jackson. Louisville, Ky., 1895. Bell Wiley's copy. Broadfoot 46-148 1978 $100

JACKSON, ROBERT A Systematic View of the Formation, Discipline, and Economy of Armies. 1804. First ed., 4to., contemp. bds., rebacked with cloth. Howes 194-325 1978 £45

JACKSON, ROBERT A Treatise on the Fevers of Jamaica. Philadelphia, 1795. Rebacked, fly loose, faded library stamp on title, clean. Rittenhouse 49-402 1976 $65

JACKSON, SHIRLEY The Lottery or the Adventures of James Harris. 1949. First ed., d.j., owner's bookplate, soiled around edges. Austin 82-492 1978 $20

JACKSON, STUART W. Lafayette. A Bibliography. New York, 1930. 8vo., orig. cloth, 1st ed., ltd. to 400 copies, fine, d.j. MacManus 238-965 1978 $40

JACKSON, T. G. Dalmatia, the Quarnero and Istria with Cettinge in Montenegro and the Island of Grado. 1887. 3 vols., 8vo., map, plts., orig. cloth, a little faded. Quaritch 983-340 1978 $75

JACKSON, WILFRID SCARBOROUGH Nine Points of the Law. 1903. Orig. pict. cloth, very good, first English ed. Bell Book 16-252 1978 £6.50

JACKSON, WILLIAM A. An Annotated List of the Publications of the Reverend Thomas Frognal Dibdin... Cambridge, 1965. One of 500, very scarce. Ballinger 11-29 $100.00

JACOB, GERTRUDE L. The Raja of Sarawak: An Account of Sir James Brooke...given chiefly through letters and journals. London, 1876. 2 vols., frontis., maps, cloth, a bit worn and stained. Dawson's 127-266 1978 $50

JACOB, HEINRICH EDWARD Coffee. 1935. Illus. Austin 80-728 1978 $17.50

JACOB, HILDEBRAND 1693-1739 Works. London, 1735. Mottled calf, sole collected ed., 8vo. Howes 194-326 1978 £65

JACOB, JOHN J. A Biographical Sketch of the Life of the Late Captain Michael Cresap. Cincinnati, 1866. Reprint of 1826 ed., fine, 3/4 mor., buckram bds. MacManus 239-1170 1978 $50

JACOB, NAOMI Barren Metal. 1937. Austin 79-362 1978 $12.50

JACOB, P. L. Recherches Bibliographiques sur des Livres Rares et Curieux. Paris, 1880. One of 550 copies sur papier verge, 8vo., newly rebound in 3/4 cloth, marbled paper over bds., orig. wrs. bound in. Battery Park 1-335 1978 $50

JACOB, S. S. Jeypore Enamels. London, 1886. Coloured illus., coloured plts., folio, orig. bds., new leather spine. K Books 244-386 1978 £40

JACOB, S. S. Jeypore Enamels. 1886. Folio, plts., orig. dec. printed bds., mor. back, a little scuffed. Quaritch 983-143 1978 $180

JACOBI, C. G. J. Fundamenta Nova Theoriae Functionum Ellipticarum. Konigsberg, 1829. 4to., fold. table, titlepage soiled and some spotting throughout, later bds., cloth spine, first ed. Quaritch 977-159 1978 $200

JACOBI, CHARLES THOMAS The Making and Issuing of Books. London, Chiswick Press, 1895. 12mo., 1 of 435 copies. Battery Park 1-336 1978 $50

JACOBI, CHARLES THOMAS The Printers' Handbook of Trade Recipes, Hints, and Suggestions.... London, Chiswick Press, 1887. Cr. 8vo., orig. cloth, soiled, inscription on endpaper. Forster 130-34 1978 £6

JACOBI, CHARLES THOMAS The Printers' Handbook. London, 1905. 8vo. Battery Park 1-337 1978 $50

JACOBI, CHARLES THOMAS The Printer's Vocabulary. London, Chiswick Press, 1888. Battery Park 1-40 1978 $50

JACOBS, HENRY EYSTER The German Emigration to America. Lancaster, 1898. 1st ed., illus., orig. cloth, bookplt., very good. MacManus 239-1505 1978 $40

JACOBS, WILLIAM WYMARK Dialstone Lane. 1904. Pict. cloth, illus. by Will Owen, covers somewhat soiled, good, first English ed. Bell Book 16-500 1978 £4.50

JACOBS, WILLIAM WYMARK Salthaven. London, 1908. Ownership inscription, near fine. Desmarais B-339 1978 $10

JACOBSEN, J. A. Reiser Til Nordamerikas Nordvestkyst, 1881-83. Kristiania (Oslo), 1887. Maps, plts., illus., embossed cloth, 8vo. Edwards 1012-398 1978 £45

JACOBUS DE VARAGINE   La Legende Doree. 1911. Sewn. Allen 234-1319
1978 $7.50

JACQUES, NORBERT   Dr. Mabuse: Master of Mystery. 1923. Covers
faded, good, rare, first English ed. Bell Book 17-331 1978 £18.50

JAEGER, EDMUND C.   Our Desert Neighbors. Stanford, 1950. Pic.
cloth, illus., 1st ed., fine. Dykes 35-83 1978 $12.50

JAEGER, GUSTAV   Selections from Essays on Health-Culture, and
the Sanitary Woolen System. New York, 1886. 12mo., 1st Amer. ed. Morrill
239-140 1978 $15

JAEGER, WERNER   Paideia. 1936. Vol. I only. Allen 234-489
1978 $7.50

JAEGER, WERNER   Paideia. 1939. Vol. I only. Allen 234-490
1978 $10

JAEGER, WERNER   Paideia. The Ideals of Greek Culture. New
York, 1945. 3 vols., 8vo., cloth. Salloch 348-101 1978 $36

JAHR, G. H. G.   New Homoeopathic Pharmacopoeia and Posology.
Philadelphia, 1842. 8vo., orig. bds., cloth back, 1st Amer. ed. Morrill 239-
141 1978 $42.50

JAL, AUGUSTE   La Flotte de Cesar. Paris, 1861. Sm. 8vo.,
half green calf. F. Edwards 1013-104 1978 £20

JALLABERT, JEAN   Experiences sur l'Electricite avec quelques Conjectures sur la Cause de ses Effets. Geneva, 1748. 8vo., fold plts., contemp.
marbled wrs., rare, 1st ed. Gilhofer 74-115 1978 sFr 600

JALLAND, T. G.   The Church & the Papacy. 1949. Allen 234-
1321 1978 $10

THE JAMAICA Almanack For the Year 1819. Kingston, 1819. 12mo, orig. leather,
slightly rubbed. Edwards 1012-723 1978 £50

JAMBLICHUS, OF CHALCIS   Jamblichus Chalcidensis Ex Coele-Syria in
Nicomachi Geraseni Arithmeticam Introductionem.... 1668. 4to., cloth. King
7-281 1978 £200

JAMES I, KING OF GREAT BRITAIN   Lusius Regius. 1901. Folio, parchment
backed bds., filt, plts. P.M. Hill 142-287 1978 £20

JAMES, ANNA BROWNELL   The Beauties of the Court of King Charles the
Second:.... London, 1833. 1st ed., small folio, contemp. red mor., mor. by
C. Lewis, gilt border, gilt spine, gilt edges, neat bookplt., engravings on india
paper. Totteridge 29-58 1978 $225

JAMES, BESSIE R.   Six Feet Six: The Heroic Story of Sam Houston.
Indianapolis, 1931. 1st ed., illus. woodcuts by Lowell Balcolm. Jenkins 116-681
1978 $12.50

JAMES, EDWARD   The Gardener Who Saw God. 1937. Very good,
nice d.w., first English ed. Bell Book 16-503 1978 £15

JAMES, MRS. EDWIN   Wanderings of a Beauty: A Tale of the Ideal.
New York, 1863. Cloth, frontis., 1st ed., worn spine ends & edges, interior good.
Greene 78-228 1978 $30

JAMES, EDWIN   Account of an Expedition From Pittsburgh to the
Rocky Mountains, 1819-20... 1823. Folding map, folding plts., 3 coloured, 3
vols., contemp. calf, gilt spines, 8vo. Edwards 1012-498 1978 £325

JAMES, EDWIN   Account of an Expedition from Pittsburgh to the
Rocky Mountains Performed in the Years 1819 and '20. Philadelphia, 1823. Vol.
II only, full calf. Wolfe 39-254 1978 $60

JAMES, EDWIN   A Narrative of the Captivity and Adventures of
John Tanner..... London, 1830. Portrait, half mor., tall copy, 1st ed. Ginsberg
14-941 1978 $475

JAMES, F. CYRIL   The Road to Revival. 1932. Austin 80-730
1978 $11

JAMES, F. L.   The Wild Tribes of the Soudan... New York,
(1883). Maps, plts., 8vo, orig. cloth. Edwards 1012-285 1978 £30

JAMES, GEORGE PAYNE RAINSFORD   Bernard Marsh, a Novel. 1864. 1st
ed., 2 vols. bound as 1, orig. purple cloth, one gathering sprining slightly, o/w
v.g. Jarndyce 16-768 1978 £17.50

JAMES, GEORGE PAYNE RAINSFORD   The Cavalier, An Historical Novel.
Philadelphia, (1859). 1st Amer. ed., orig. cloth, some wear. Greene 78-62
1978 $30

JAMES, GEORGE PAYNE RAINSFORD   Delaware. Edinburgh, London, 1833.
3 vols., 12mo., half calf, first ed. P.M. Hill 142-189 1978 £30

JAMES, GEORGE PAYNE RAINSFORD   Forest Days; a Romance of Old Times.
Leipzig, 1843. 1st. continental ed., sq. 8vo, contemp. quarter calf. Hannas
54-168 1978 £5

JAMES, GEORGE PAYNE RAINSFORD   The Gentleman of the Old School.
New York, 1839. Half-cloth, bds., edges rubbed, interiors good, owner's name
on title page, 1st Amer. ed., 2 vols. Greene 78-63 1978 $55

JAMES, GEORGE PAYNE RAINSFORD   Henry Masterton, or, The Adventures
of a Young Cavalier. 1851. Sm. 8vo., contemp. half calf, light spotting, very
good copy. Fenning 32-175 1978 £5.50

JAMES, GEORGE PAYNE RAINSFORD   Lives of the Most Eminent Foreign
Statesmen. 1832. Foxed, 5 vols., fcap. 8vo. George's 635-696 1978 £10

JAMES, GEORGE PAYNE RAINSFORD   The Man-At-Arms; or, Henry de Cerons.
New York, 1840. 2 vols., 12mo., orig. blue cloth, printed paper labels, 1st
Amer. ed., fine copy. Ximenes 47-157 1978 $22.50

JAMES, GEORGE PAYNE RAINSFORD   One in a Thousand; or, the Days of
Henry Quatre. Philadelphia, 1836. Half-cloth, bds., edges rubbed, interior
foxed, 1st Amer. ed., 2 vols. Greene 78-64 1978 $75

JAMES, GEORGE PAYNE RAINSFORD   Richelieu, A Tale of France. London,
1829. 3 vols., 12mo., contemp. half green calf, spines gilt, 1st ed., 2nd novel
of author, author's 1st three-decker. Ximenes 47-158 1978 $50

JAMES, GEORGE PAYNE RAINSFORD   The Robber: A Tale. 1838. 1st. ed.,
3 vols., 8vo, probably lacking half-titles, contemp. dark green half morocco.
Hannas 54-169 1978 £18

JAMES, GEORGE PAYNE RAINSFORD   The Robber. 1844. 1st ed., 3 vols.,
brown morocco, 2 title labels expertly renewed, fine. Jarndyce 16-767 1978
£45

JAMES, GEORGE WHARTON   Indian Basketry. Portland, 1902. 2nd. ed.,
revised & enlarged, illus. Baldwins' 51-100 1978 $15

JAMES, GEORGE WHARTON   Indian Basketry, and How to Make Indian and
Other Baskets. Pasadena, 1903. Illus., 3rd ed., orig. cloth, fine. MacManus
239-1171 1978 $50

JAMES, GEORGE WHARTON   Practical Basket Making. Pasadena, n.d. (c.
1920). New ed., enlgd, illus., fine. MacManus 239-1172 1978 $30

JAMES, H. E. O.   The Localisation of Sound. London, 1936.
Rittenhouse 49-404 1976 $7.50

JAMES, HENRY   The Ambassadors. A Novel. New York, 1903.
Orig. bds., 1st ed., very nice, orig. cloth pub. d.j. MacManus 238-540 1978
$100

JAMES, HENRY   The Ambassadors. 1904. Austin 82-493 1978
$12.50

JAMES, HENRY   The American. London, 1879. Orig. cloth,
first authorized Eng. ed., good. MacManus 238-524 1978 $50

JAMES, HENRY   The American Scene. New York, 1907. First
U.S. ed., spine slightly dull, very good. Bell Book 17-509 1978 £10

JAMES, HENRY   The Aspern Papers. Louisa Pallant. The Modern
Warning. London (New York), 1888. Orig. cloth, 1st Amer. ed., covers worn,
a bit soiled, else good. MacManus 238-533 1978 $45

JAMES, HENRY   The Author of Beltraffiao. London, 1884.
Tall 8vo, 2 issues, orig. pict. light green wr., complete, 1st ed., near Mint,
collector's cond. Desmarais 1-249 1978 $75

JAMES, HENRY   The Better Sort. New York, 1903. Bkplt.,
very fine. Desmarais B-340 1978 $35

JAMES, HENRY   The Bostonians. A Novel. London and New
York, 1886. Orig. cloth, 1st Amer. ed., very nice. MacManus 238-532 1978
$60

JAMES, HENRY   A Bundle of Letters. Boston, n.d. (1880). 1st
ed., 12mo., orig. printed wrs., wrs. chipped and torn. MacManus 238-526
1978 $75

JAMES, HENRY   Confidence. Boston, 1880. Sm. 8vo., 1st Amer.
ed., orig. red-brown cloth, blind stamp on brown end paper, very fine & bright
copy. Quaritch 979-355 1978 $200

JAMES, HENRY   Daisy Miller. New York, (1878). 1st ed., 32mo.,
ads, 1st issue, better than fine copy, two sm. splits at hinge at top & bottom of
spine, binding a bit askewed, but tight, scarce. Current 24-25 1978 $200

JAMES, HENRY   The Diary of a Man of Fifty and a Bundle of
Letters. New York, 1880. 1st ed., 32mo., 1st Amer. issue, better than fine copy,
fragile issue, scarce. Current 24-24 1978 $85

JAMES, HENRY   Embarrassments. London, 1896. 8vo., cloth, 1st
ed., fine copy, 1st issue. J. S. Lawrence 38-785 1978 $150

JAMES, HENRY   Embarrassments. 1896. First ed., orig. cloth,
8vo. Howes 194-955 1978 £40

JAMES, HENRY   English Hours. Cambridge, 1905. 1 of
400 numbered on large paper, illus. 8 vo., white linen cloth over green bds.,
uncut, very good-fine. Houle 10-169 1978 $115

JAMES, HENRY   Essays in London and Elsewhere. Osgood, 1893.
First ed., orig. pale salmon cloth gilt, 8vo., sole ed. Howes 194-956 1978 £20

JAMES, HENRY   The Europeans. Boston, 1879. Orig. cloth,
1st Amer. ed., extremities of spine very slightly worn, covers stained, else very
good. MacManus 238-525 1978 $40

JAMES, HENRY   French Poets and Novelists. Leipzig, 1883.
Red cloth, good. Greene 78-229 1978 $55

JAMES, HENRY   The Golden Bowl. London, 1905. First English
ed., rebound in similar style to orig. binding, lacks gilt decor., nice. Rota 211-
245 1978 £15

JAMES, HENRY   Hawthorne. 1879. Covers soiled, good, first
English ed. Bell Book 16-504 1978 £6.50

JAMES, HENRY   In the Cage. London, 1898. Orig. dec. cloth,
1st Eng.? ed., covers worn. MacManus 238-538 1978 $50

JAMES, HENRY   An International Episode. New York, 1879.
1st ed., 32mo., 1st issue, gray wrs. with red & black lettering in better than fine
cond., interior with some marginal notations in pencil, otherwise very fine, binding secure, better than fine copy, scarce. Current 24-26 1978 $185

JAMES, HENRY   Italian Hours. Boston and New York, 1909.
Color illus. by Joseph Pennell, 4to., orig. dec. cloth, 1st Amer. ed., covers
waterstained, but good, very rare d.j. in fine cond. MacManus 238-544 1978
$75

JAMES, HENRY   The Ivory Tower. 1917. First ed., portrait,
orig. cloth, 8vo., spine little faded. Howes 194-957 1978 £14

JAMES, HENRY   The Letters. 1920. First ed., portraits, 2 vols.,
orig. cloth, 8vo. Howes 194-958 1978 £24

JAMES, HENRY   Letters to A. C. Benson and Auguste Monod...
1930. 1st. ed., no. 484 of 1050 copies, unopened, near fine in glassine wrapper.
Jarndyce 16-1203

JAMES, HENRY   A Little Tour in France. 1900. Plts., text illus.
by Joseph Pennell, very good, first English ed. Bell Book 16-507 1978 £12.50

JAMES, HENRY   Notes on Novelists with Some Other Notes.
New York, 1914. Orig. cloth, 1st Amer. ed., fine. MacManus 238-546 1978
$30

JAMES, HENRY   The Outcry. London, (1911). Orig. cloth,
1st Eng.? ed., slightly faded and foxed, but near-fine. MacManus 238-545
1978 $65

JAMES, HENRY   A Passionate Pilgrim and Other Tales. 1875. First
ed., lib. copy. Austin 82-494 1978 $97.50

JAMES, HENRY   The Portrait of a Lady. 1881. 1st ed., 3 vols.,
half title, rebound expertly in correct style, half maroon morocco, marbled bds.,
E. M. Forster's copy & signed by him, fine. Jarndyce 16-769 1978 £220

JAMES, HENRY   The Portrait of a Lady. London, 1881. 3 vols.,
orig. cloth, covers stained, spine repaired on vol. I, few inner hinges cracked, 1st
ed., very good, ex-lib. MacManus 238-527 1978 $375

JAMES, HENRY   Portraits of Places. London, 1883. Orig. cloth,
1st ed., 1st issue, signature, very good. MacManus 238-529 1978 $75

JAMES, HENRY   The Reverberator. London, 1888. 2 vols.,
orig. cloth, spines worn and frayed, 1st ed., scarce, 500 copies printed. Mac-
Manus 238-534 1978 $125

JAMES, HENRY   The Reverberator. New York, 1888. 12mo.,
orig. cloth, 1st Amer. ed., fine. MacManus 238-535 1978 $50

JAMES, HENRY   The Sacred Fount. New York, 1901. 1st ed.,
nailheads not present, old rose sateen binding faded to tan, stamped in gold, t.e.g.,
stain on back cover. Greene 78-230 1978 $30

JAMES, HENRY   The Siege of London, The Pension Beauropas, The
Point of View. 1883. First ed., lending lib. copy. Austin 82-495 1978 $67.50

JAMES, HENRY   A Small Boy and Others. New York, 1913.
Ownership inscription, fine. Desmarais B-341 1978 $35

JAMES, HENRY   The Soft Side. New York, 1900. Maroon buckram, toe.g., 1st ed., blindstamped rule at top & bottom of spine, covers dull,
very good copy. Bradley 49-162 1978 $15

JAMES, HENRY   The Soft Side. 1900. Very good, first English
ed. Bell Book 16-508 1978 £12.50

JAMES, HENRY   The Spoils of Poynton. London, 1897. Orig.
cloth, 1st Colonial ed., nice. MacManus 238-537 1978 $27.50

JAMES, HENRY   Stories Revived. London, 1885. 3 vols., orig.
cloth, 1st ed., bind. A, spines repaired, lib. labels removed, sound copy, rare,
500 copies printed. MacManus 238-531 1978 $175

JAMES, HENRY   Tales of Three Cities. London, 1884. Orig.
cloth, 1st Eng. ed., fine. MacManus 238-530 1978 $75

JAMES, HENRY   Terminations. New York, 1895. Orig. cloth,
1st Amer. pub. ed., covers stained. MacManus 238-536 1978 $40

JAMES, HENRY   Theater and Friendship. New York, 1932. 8vo,
purple cloth, spine faded, torn d.w., Nice, 1st Amer. ed., collector's cond.
Desmarais 1-250 1978 $15

JAMES, HENRY   Transatlantic Sketches. Boston, 1875. Orig.
cloth, 1st ed., backstrip faded, extremities slightly worn, otherwise very good.
MacManus 238-522 1978 $85

JAMES, HENRY   Views and Reviews...Now First Collected. Boston, 1908. Orig. paper-covered bds., leather label, 1st ed., ltd. to 160 copies,
covers a bit soiled and worn. MacManus 238-543 1978 $125

JAMES, HENRY   Washington Square. The Pension Beaurespas. A
Bundle of Letters. London, 1881. 2 vols., orig. cloth, 1st Eng. ed., bind. A,
covers rather worn, spine edges torn, labels removed, inner hinges cracked, scarce.
MacManus 238-528 1978 $125

JAMES, HENRY   Watch and Ward. Boston, 1878. 12mo., orig.
cloth, 1st ed., covers worn, scarce. MacManus 238-523 1978 $75

JAMES, HENRY   What Maisie Knew. Chicago, 1897. First Amer.
ed., hinges cracked, good. Austin 82-496 1978 $47.50

JAMES, HENRY   William Wetmore Story and His Friends. From
Letters, Diaries and Recollections. Edinburgh, 1903. 2 vols., orig. cloth, 1st
Eng. ed. MacManus 238-541 1978 $35

JAMES, HENRY   The Wings of the Dove. 1902. First English ed.,
thick cr. 8vo., orig. blue cloth, very good. Howes 194-959 1978 £24

JAMES, J.   History of the Worsted Manufacture in England,
from the Earliest Times. 1857. 8vo., plts., some very lightly foxed, orig. cloth.
Quaritch 977-233 1978 $115

JAMES, JAMES A.   George Rogers Clark Papers 1771-1781. Springfield, 1912. Rebound copy, clean. Hayman 71-361 1978 $12.50

JAMES, JOHN T.   The Benders in Kansas. Wichita, (1913). Clean,
with label little shaken, former owner's name and date on title-pg., private bookplt. on front endpaper. Hayman 71-362 1978 $250

JAMES, LIONEL   High Pressure. London, (1929). 7 illus., 8vo,
orig. cloth. K Books 239-233 1978 £6

JAMES, MARQUIS   Alfred I. DuPont. 1941. Illus., 1st. ed. Baldwins' 51-226 1978 $25

JAMES, MARQUIS   Andrew Jackson, Portrait of a President. Indianapolis, (1937). Illus., 1st ed., d.w. Biblo BL781-207 1978 $9

JAMES, MARQUIS   Biography of a Business, 1792-1942. Insurance
Company of North America. Indianapolis, (1942). Illus. Biblo BL781-86 1978
$9.50

JAMES, MARQUIS   The Cherokee Strip. New York, 1945. First ed.,
d.w. Biblo 247-230 1978 $15

JAMES, MARQUIS   The Raven: A Biography of Sam Houston. London,
1929. Illus., maps., 1st English ed. Jenkins 116-682 1978 $25

JAMES, MONTAGUE RHODES   The Collected Ghost Stories of... New York,
1931. First Amer. collected ed., spine dull, else good. Biblo 251-490 1978
$17.50

JAMES, MONTAGUE RHODES   A Thin Ghost and Others. 1919. Very good.
First English ed. Bell Book 17-512 1978 £18.50

JAMES, MONTAGUE RHODES   A Warning to the Curious, and Other Ghost
Stories. 1925. Plainly rebacked, good, first English ed. Bell Book 17-513
1978 £7.50

JAMES, NORAH C.   Sleeveless Errand. Paris, 1929. 1st Paris ed.
Biblo 251-513 1978 $16.50

JAMES, REESE D.   Old Drury of Philadelphia... Philadelphia,
1932. 1st ed., illus., cloth, very good copy. MacManus 239-1506 1978
$37.50

JAMES, ROBERT   Pharmacopoeia Universalis. London, 1752.
Second ed., thick 8vo., modern buckram, half-title torn. Rittenhouse 49-405
1976 $35

JAMES, THOMAS   Bellum Papale, sive Concordia Discors Sixti
Quinti.... 1600. First ed., sm. 4to., very good, woodcut initial, contemp.
calf. Howes 194-64 1978 £80

JAMES, THOMAS   The Strange and Dangerous Voyage of Capitaine
Thomas James. 1633. 1st. ed., without 1st. blank leaf, folding map, sm. 4to,
brown morocco, top margin of text shaved, orig. cloth. Edwards 1012-434 1978
£300

JAMES, MRS. THOMAS POTTS   Memorial of Thomas Potts, Junior... Cambridge, 1874. 1st ed., illus., orig. cloth, ltd. ed., covers worn, but good, very
scarce. MacManus 239-935 1978 $55

JAMES, W. O.   The Biology of Flowers. Oxford, 1935. Illus.,
roy. 8vo. Traylen 88-589 1978 £5

JAMES, WILL   Cowboys North and South. New York, 1924.
Illus. by author, 1st ed., fine. MacManus 239-1931 1978 $25

JAMES, WILL   Lone Cowboy: My Life Story. New York, 1930.
1st ed., illus. Jenkins 116-720 1978 $8.50

JAMES, WILL   Look-See With Uncle Bill. New York,
1938. 1st ed., 8 vo., illus. by author, d.j., fine, Zane Grey's copy.
Houle 10-170 1978 $ 60

JAMES, WILL   Scorpion. New York, 1936. Illus. by author,
1st ed. Biblo 251-514 1978 $15

JAMES, WILL   The Three Mustangeers. New York, 1933.
1st ed., 8 vo., illus. by author, d.j., fine, clean & tight, Zane Grey's copy.
Houle 10-171 1978 $65

JAMES, WILLIAM   The Message of a Modern Mind. New York,
1950. Near mint in chipped d.w. Desmarais B-343 1978 $10

JAMES, WILLIAM   The Order of Release. London, 1947.
1st ed., illus. d.j., told for 1st time in their unpublished letters, very
good or better. Limestone 9-250 1978 $17.50

JAMES, WILLIAM d. 1827   A Full and Correct Account of the Chief Occur-
ences of the Late War between Great Britain and the United States of America;....
London, 1817. 1st ed., octavo, plates, 3/4 blue calf, paneled spine, sun faded.
Bennett 20-236 1978 $175

THE JAMES Fountain. New York, (1881). Orig. mounted photo, 4to., ex-lib.
Morrill 239-552 1978 $20

JAMESON, MR.   Speech of ..., of Missouri, on the Improvement of
the Western Waters. In the House...January 13, 1844. N.P., n.d. Disbound.
Hayman 72-670 1978 $8.50

JAMESON, ANNA   Characteristics of Women, Moral, Poetical and
Historical. 1836. 2 vols., 3rd. ed., corrected & enlarged, 50 vignette etchings,
contemp. sprinkled calf, rebacked, gilt lettering pieces. Eaton 45-267 1978 £40

JAMESON, ANNA   Winter Studies and Summer Rambles in Canada.
Vols. I & II (of 3). London, 1838. Contemp. marbled bds., half calf, covers
loose, backstrips bare. Wolfe 39-255 1978 $45

JAMESON, ANNA   Winter Studies and Summer Rambles in Canada.
New York, 1839. Complete in two vols., contemp. marbled bds., half calf.
Wolfe 39-256 1978 $80

JAMESON, R. P.   Montesquieu et l'Esclavage. Paris, 1911.
Author's pres. Biblo BL781-852 1978 $12

JAMESON, ROBERT   Historical Record of the Seventy-Ninth Regiment
of Foot or Cameron Highlanders. Edinburgh, 1863. Sm. 8vo., coloured frontis.,
orig. cloth. F. Edwards 1013-533 1978 £25

JAMESON, ROBERT   Historical Record of the Seventy-Ninth Regiment
of Foot or Cameron Highlanders. Edinburgh, 1863. Sm. 8vo., illus., orig. cloth.
F. Edwards 1013-534 1978 £15

JAMESTOWN and Its Surroundings. Jamestown & Portland, 1905. Side opening
wide 8vo., very good. Butterfield 21-111 1978 $12.50

JAMIESON, MRS.   The Young Travellers; or, A Visit to the Grand-
mother. London, 1822. 4th. ed., engraved frontis, 8vo, orig. bds., paper
label, edges uncut, joints broken. Traylen 88-150 1978 £12

JAMIESON, A. S.   William King, Friend and Champion of Slaves.
Toronto, 1925. 1st ed. Hood 116-251 1978 $35

JAMIESON, ALEXANDER   A Grammar of Rhetoric, and Polite Literature...
1818. 1st. ed., half title, lg. 12mo, contemp. calf backed-bds., label, nice.
Fenning 32-176 1978 £16

JAMIESON, JOHN   An Etymological Dictionary of the Scottish Language. Edinburgh, 1808. 1st. ed., 2 vols., 4to, orig. half calf, fine copy. Jarndyce 16-770 1978 £68

JAMIESON, JOHN   An Etymological Dictionary of the Scottish Language. Edinburgh, 1818. Orig. calf, black label, leading hinge weak, abridged from 4to ed. Jarndyce 16-596 1978 £15

JAMIESON, JOHN   An Etymological Dictionary of the Scottish Language. Paisley, 1879-87. Thk. 4to., 5 vols., recently rebound in half leather, buckram sides, uncut, fine paper issue. Howes 194-798 1978 £115

JAMIESON, ROBERT   The Excitement; or, A Book to Induce Young People to Read. 1840. 3rd. ed., orig. cloth. Eaton 45-268 1978 £5

JAN VAN RUYSBROECK   Die Chierheit der Gheesteliker Brulocht. Amsterdam, 1917. 8vo., full blue calf, gilt border tooled on both covers, gilt spine, t.e.g., orig. cover wrapped-up, uncut copy, very attractive binding, rare. Van der Peet H-64-383 1978 Dfl 275

JANE, FRED T.   All the World's Fighting Ships. Boston, 1898. Oblong 8vo., orig. cloth, corners and ends worn, illus. Paine 78-70 1978 $135

JANE, JOSEPH   The Image Unbroaken. N.P., Printed Anno Dom., 1651. 1st. ed., woodcut initials & ornaments, minor repairs to 3 leaves, ownership inscription on title, sm. 4to., calf-backed bds., gilt lettered spine. Traylen 88-281 1978 £80

JANE'S Fighting Ships, 1942. New York, 1943. Illus., lg. oblong 4to., back cover dampstained & buckled. Morrill 239-445 1978 $30

JANE Hudson, The American Girl; or, Exert Yourself. London, n.d.c.1850. 12mo., orig. limp cloth, frontis. Traylen 88-151 1978 £5

JANEWAY, ELIOT   The Struggle for Survival. 1950. Austin 80-154 1978 $10

JANEWAY, JAMES   A Token for Children. Boston, 1771. Original sheets, uncut and unopened. Victoria 34-439 1978 $150

JANEWAY, JAMES   A Token for Children. Luxurious crushed levant, handsome gilt dentelles, raised bands and gilt lettering. Victoria 34-440 1978 $165

JANIN, JEAN   Memoires et obvervations anatomiques,.... Lyon & Paris, 1772. 1st ed., tear in hinge, rather worn, contemp. calf, gilt back. Gilhofer 75-61 1978 SFr 450

JANIN, JULES   The American in Paris, During the Summer. New York, 1844. 8vo., unbound, foxed. Morrill 241-224 1978 $7.50

JANKUHN, H.   Haithabu, eine Germanische Stadt der Fruehzeit. 1937. 4to., plt., illus. Allen 234-1322 1978 $10

JANNIOT, ALFRED   Sculpteur Le Bas-Relief Du Musee Dea Colonies. Paris, (1931). 66 sm. folio loose plts. in folder. Baldwins' 51-101 1978 $22.50

JANOWSKY, OSCAR I.   The American Jew. 1942. Orig. ed. Austin 79-365 1978 $10

JANSE, OLOV. R. T.   The Peoples of French Indochina. 1944. Paper. Austin 80-155 1978 $8.50

JANSON, CHARLES WILLIAM   The Stranger in America 1793-1806. New York, 1935. Reprinted fron London ed. of 1807, ltd. to 750 copies. MacManus 239-219 1978 $27.50

JANSON, CHARLES WILLIAM   The Stranger in America. New York, 1935. Broadfoot 50-104 1978 $25

JANSON, FLORENCE EDITH   The Background of Swedish Immigration, 1840-1930. University of Chicago Press, 1931. 1st ed. Austin 79-366 1978 $20

JANVIER, THOMAS ALLIBONE   The Aztec Treasure-House. New York, 1890. 1st ed., original gilt cloth, illus., full-page plates by Remington, extremities shelf rubbed. Jenkins 116-1165 1978 $45

JANVIER, THOMAS ALLIBONE   Legends of the City of Mexico. New York & London, 1910. 1st ed., illus., interior fine. Limestone 9-200 1978 $25

JAPAN PAPER COMPANY   A Treatise on One of the Factors on the Advancement of the Art of Printing with Examples. 1920. Frontis. Battery Park 1-450 1978 $50

JAQUES, F. P.   Snowshoe Country. Minneapolis, 1945. Illus. by F. L. Jaques. Hood 117-897 1978 $20

JARDINE, WILLIAM   Humming Birds. Edinburgh, 1933. Coloured plts., fcap. 8vo., covers faded and worn. George's 635-1009 1978 £25

JARDINE, WILLIAM   The Naturalist's Library. Edinburgh, 1843. 12mo., 3/4 leather, marbled bds., worn, hand colored plts. Book Chest 17-202 1978 $60

JARDINE, WILLIAM   Naturgeschichtliches Cabinet Des Thierreiches. Pesth, 1836-1842. Translated into German, 10 vols., plts., some in color, 8vo., orig. dark blue bds. with paper labels, fine, uncut set. Salloch 345-100 1978 $125

JARNAC, COUNT DE   Electra: A Story of Modern Times. 1853. Illus. by Lord Gerald Fitzgerald, 1st. ed., 3 vols., orig. half calf, marbled bds., brown labels, good. Jarndyce 16-771 1978 £42

JARNIGAN, MR.S   In Senate of the U.S., Mr. Jarnagin Made the Following Report...the Committee of Private Land Claims, to Whom was Referred the Memorial of Pierre Chouteau, Jr...for the Confirmation of Their Title to a Certain Trade of Land Situated in the Territory of Iowa, and Known as the "Dubuque Claim"... Washington, 1846. Disbound. Ginsberg 14-413 1978 $10

JARRETT, FRED   B.N.A. Book. "Stamps of British North America." Toronto, (1929). Numerous facsimiles, orig. binding. Wolfe 39-428 1978 $35

JARVIS, LUCY CUSHING   Sketches of Church Life in Colonial Connecticut... New Haven, 1902. 1st ed., illus., orig. cloth, fine copy. MacManus 239-105 1978 $30

JARVIS, RUSSELL   A Biographical Notice of Com. Jesse D. Elliott; Containing a Review of the Controversy Between Him and the Late Commodore Perry... Philadelphia, 1835. 1st ed., orig. printed yellow bds., spine defective, covers worn, but good copy. MacManus 239-1759 1978 $45

JARVIS, THOMAS STINSON   Letters from East Longitudes; Sketches of Travel in Egypt, the Holy Land, Greece, and Cities of the Levant. Toronto, 1875. Signed. Hood 116-693 1978 $20

JAUFFRET, M. LOUIS-FRANCOIS   The Travels of Rolando;.... London, 1808. 4 vols., boards, spines uniformly rebound, fine. Victoria 34-442 1978 $60

JAY, JOHN   The Correspondence and Public Papers of...First Chief Justice of the U.S. New York, 1890. 4 vols., uncut, rebound, 1st ed., ltd. to 750 numbered sets, fine. MacManus 239-220 1978 $100

JAY, JOHN CLARKSON   A Catalogue of the Shells, Arranged According to the Lamarckian System. New York, 1839. Colored plts., illus., 4to., lacks backstrip, 3rd ed. Morrill 239-447 1978 $50

JAY, WILLIAM   A View of the Action of the Federal Government, in Behalf of Slavery. New York, 1839. 12mo., 1st ed., edges rubbed, some light foxing. Biblo BL781-125 1978 $32.50

JAY, WILLIAM   A View of the Action of the Federal Government in Behalf of Slavery. New York, 1839. 12mo, original dark brown cloth, 1st ed., fine copy. Ximenes 47-159 1978 $45

JAY, WILLIAM   A View of the Action of the Federal Government, in Behalf of Slavery. New York, 1839. Original cloth, extremities chipped, foxed. Jenkins 116-722 1978 $65

JAYCOCKS, T. G.   Camera Conversations, by "Jay". Toronto, 1936. Illus., inscr'd & signed by author. Hood 117-634 1978 $20

JEAFFRESON, JOHN CORDY   Annals of Oxford. 1871. 2nd. ed., 2 vols., half titles, orig. blue cloth, v.g. Jarndyce 16-772 1978 £15

JEAFFRESON, JOHN CORDY   The Real Lord Byron. 1883. 2 vols., modern 1/4 buckram, marbled bds. Eaton 45-81 1978 £15

JEAFFRESON, JOHN CORDY   A Young Squire of the Seventeenth Century. London, 1878. 2 vols., 8vo., orig. cloth. K Books 244-172 1978 £15

JEAN DE MEUN   Roman De La Rose
Please turn to
ROMAN DE LA ROSE

JEAN, ALEXANDRE   Arithmetique Au Miroir. N.P. (Paris), 1636.
8vo., old vellum, pages loose in binding.   Salloch 345-101 1978 $165

JEAN, ALEXANDRE   Arithmetique au Miroir. N.P., 1649. 12mo.,
cont. vellum. Schumann 511-26 1978 sFr 600

JEAN BAPTISTE BARTHELEMY, BARON DE   Travels in Kamtschatka, 1787-88.
1790. 2 vols., half calf, 8vo., fldg. map.   Edwards 1012-211 1978 £200

JEAN-AUBRY, G.   Joseph Conrad, Life and Letters. London,
1927. 2 vols., 1st English ed., portrait, illus., d.j., very good or better.
Limestone 9-67 1978 $45

JEANS, JAMES H.   Problems of Cosmogony and Stellar Dynamics.
Cambridge, University Press, 1919. 8vo., illus., orig. cloth, gilt, good copy,
1st ed.   Norman 5-157 1978 $75

JEANS, JAMES H.   Report on Radiation and the Quantum Theory.
1914. 8vo., orig. printed wrs.   Quaritch 977-108 1978 $70

JEAURAT, EDME SEBASTIEN   Memoire sur les Lunettes Diplantidiennes ou a
Double Image.... (Paris, 1779). 4to., bds., plts., table. Gurney 75-57 1978
£50

JEAURAT, EDME-SEBASTIEN   Traite de Perspective a l'Usage des Artistes. Paris,
1750. 4to., errata leaf, contemp. marbled calf, gilt back, fine, 1st ed. Gilhofer 74-39 1978 sFr 1,300

JEBB, J.   Practical Treatise on Strengthening and Defending
Outposts, Villages, Houses, Bridges, etc. Chatham, 1837. Part I, 2nd. ed., 15
plts. Baldwins' 51-311 1978 $35

JEDINA, L. VON   An Asiens Kusten und Furstenhofen. Wien, 1891.
4to, plts., illus., folding map, binding worn, somewhat loose, orig. covers.
Van der Peet 127-119 1978 Dfl 115

JEFFERIES, RICHARD   The Dewy Morn. A Novel. London, 1884.
2 vols., orig. cloth, a bit worn, lib. labels removed, 1st ed., inner hinges
cracked. MacManus 238-300 1978 $135

JEFFERIES, RICHARD   Field and Hedgerow. Being the Last Essays of....
London, 1889. Orig. dec. cloth, 1st ed., fine. MacManus 238-301 1978 $50

JEFFERIES, RICHARD   The Gamekeeper at Home. Sketches of Natural
History and Rural Life. London, 1878. Orig. cloth, 1st ed., very good. Mac-
Manus 238-298 1978 $75

JEFFERIES, RICHARD   The Gamekeeper at Home. 1878. Sm. 8vo., 1st
ed., orig. cloth, very good copy. Quaritch 979-206 1978 $65

JEFFERIES, RICHARD   Greene Ferne Farm. 1880. Sm. 8vo., 1st ed.,
orig. cloth, very nice copy. Quaritch 979-207 1978 $125

JEFFERIES, RICHARD   Jack Brass, Emperor of England. London, 1873.
Orig. prtd. tan wrs., uncut, 1st ed., rare, green half mor. fldg. case. Bradley
49-165 1978 $375

JEFFERIES, RICHARD   The Open Air. 1885. 1st. ed., half title, some
slight foxing, orig. cream/brown cloth, blue & gilt imprint, good. Jarndyce 16-
773 1978 £24.50

JEFFERIES, RICHARD   The Story of my Heart: my autobiography. 1912.
No. 94 of 160 copies, colour plts. by E. W. Waite, 4to., full vellum gilt, t.e.g.,
covers dust-soiled, very good, unopened, first English ed. Bell Book 17-514 1978
£27.50

JEFFERIES, RICHARD   T.T.T. Wells, 1896. One of only 100 copies,
wrappers, foxed throughout, nice, rare, first ed. Rota 212-32 1978 £85

JEFFERIES, RICHARD   Wild Life in a Southern County. London, 1879.
Orig. cloth, 1st ed., hinges cracked, covers a bit worn. MacManus 238-299
1978 $75

JEFFERIES, RICHARD   Wild Life in a Southern County. 1879. Sm. 8vo.,
1st ed., orig. cloth, bkplt., inscr., hinges cracking, good copy. Quaritch 979-
208 1978 $55

JEFFERIS, B. G.   Search Lights on Health or Light on Dark Corners.
Naperville, 1894. Second ed. Rittenhouse 49-406 1976 $10

JEFFERS, ROBINSON   Cawdor and Other Poems. New York, 1928.
Purple bds., black cloth spine, 1st trade ed., very good, soiled in dust jacket.
Bradley 49-166 1978 $40

JEFFERS, ROBINSON   Dear Judas and Other Poems. New York, 1929.
8vo, gilt stamped boards, cloth back, uncut, Fine, 1st ed., collector's cond.
Desmarais 1-253 1978 $30

JEFFERS, ROBINSON   Dear Judas and Other Poems. New York, 1929.
Tall, black bds., vellum spine, uncut, 1st ed., ltd. issue, 1 of 375 signed by
poet, pres. inscr. by Jeffers, bkplt. of Ingle Barr, uncut & unopened. Bradley
49-168 1978 $275

JEFFERS, ROBINSON   Dear Judas and Other Poems. New York, 1929.
Purple bds., black cloth spine, 1st trade ed., fine in dust jacket. Bradley 49-
167 1978 $75

JEFFERS, ROBINSON   Descent to the Dead. Poems Written in Ireland
and Great Britain. New York, 1931. 8vo., orig. parchment-backed bds., 1st
ed., 1 of 500 numbered copies, signed by author, pub. box, very fine. Mac-
Manus 238-680 1978 $125

JEFFERS, ROBINSON   Give Your Heart to the Hawks and Other Poems.
New York, 1933. 8vo., cloth, top and bottom of d.j. chipped, 1st ed., fine.
Duschnes 220-160 1978 $50

JEFFERS, ROBINSON   Give Your Heart to the Hawks and Other Poems.
New York, 1933. Cloth, signature, slightly tattered & soiled d.w. Dawson's
447-246 1978 $40

JEFFERS, ROBINSON   Poetry, Gongorism and a Thousand Years.
(Los Angeles), 1949. 1 of 200 copies, 1st ed., tall 8 vo., orig. printed
bds., fine. Houle 10-172 1978 $225

JEFFERS, ROBINSON   Solstice and Other Poems. New York, Grabhorn
Press, 1935. Cloth, bookseller's stamp. Dawson's 447-247 1978 $20

JEFFERS, ROBINSON   Solstice, and other poems. New York, 1935.
First U.S. ed., good. Bell Book 16-510 1978 £12

JEFFERS, ROBINSON   Such Counsels You Gave To Me & Other Poems.
New York, (1937). 8vo., cloth, d.j., review copy, publisher's slip laid in , 1st ed.,
fine. Duschnes 220-161 1978 $50

JEFFERS, ROBINSON   Such Counsels You Gave to Me & Other Poems.
New York, (1937). Cloth, near mint in slightly worn d.w. Dawson's 447-248
1978 $45

JEFFERS, ROBINSON   Thurso's Landing and Other Poems. New York,
(1932). Bds., cloth back, front slightly soiled. Dawson's 447-249 1978 $20

JEFFERS, ROBINSON   The Women at Point Sur. New York, (1927).
Patterned bds., white paper spine, partly unopened, 1 of 265 copies signed by
author. Dawson's 447-250 1978 $125

JEFFERS, ROBINSON   The Women at Point Sur. New York, 1927.
Good. Bernard 5-142 1978 $40

JEFFERSON, JOSEPH   The Autobiography of... New York, (1890).
Illus. Biblo 247-901 1978 $20

JEFFERSON, THOMAS   The Complete Jefferson. New York, (1943).
Illus. Biblo 251-45 1978 $12.50

JEFFERSON, THOMAS   Notes on the State of Virginia. London, 1787.
Lacks map, covers detached. Nestler Rare 78-41 1978 $125

JEFFERSON, THOMAS   Notes on the State of Virginia. Philadelphia,
1788. 1st. American ed., title pg. repaired with word "notes" missing, orig. tree
calf. Baldwins' 51-525 1978 $50

JEFFERSON, THOMAS   Notes on the State of Virginia. With an Appendix Relative to the Murder of Logan's Family. Trenton, 1803. Orig. calf,
some staining, else nice copy. MacManus 239-1876 1978 $45

JEFFREY, ALEXANDER   The History and Antiquities of Roxburghshire and
Adjacent Districts from the most Remote to the Present Time. Jedburgh, 1855-
1864. 2nd ed., 4 vols., maps, illus., half mor. K Books 244-173 1978 £40

JEFFREYS, C.   Van Dieman's Land... 1820. Half calf, 8vo.
Edwards 1012-336 1978 £300

JEFFRIES, EWEL   A Short Biography of John Leeth... Cleveland,
1904. Ltd. to 267 copies. MacManus 239-1169 1978 $22.50

JEKYL, GERTRUDE   Gardens for Small Country Homes. London, 1924.
5th ed., illus., 4to. Baldwins' 51-102 1978 $22.50

JEKYLL, W.   Jamaican Song and Story... 1907. 8vo, orig. cloth. Edwards 1012-724 1978 £20

JELLEY, SYMES M.   Shadowed to Europe. Chicago, 1885. 1st ed., orig. pict. cloth binding with outside stapling. Greene 78-231 1978 $35

JELLIFFE, SMITH ELY   Psychoanalysis and the Drama. New York, 1922. Library binding, usual marks. Rittenhouse 49-407 1976 $10

JEMMAT, CATHERINE   Miscellanies in Prose and Verse. 1766. 1st. ed., 4to, half-title, orig. bds., rebacked, uncut, single worm-hole in lower margin. Hannas 54-170 1978 £75

JEMMAT, CATHERINE   Miscellanies in Prose and Verse. 1771. 4to, half-title, contemp. sheep, gilt, joints cracking, Lord Palmerston's bookplt., slight marginal water-stains at end. Hannas 54-171 1978 £65

JENKINS, A. O.   Olive's Last Round-Up. [Loup City, n.d.] Illus., orig. pr. wr., 1st ed. Ginsberg 14-1112 1978 $125

JENKINS, MRS. C. E.   Evenings at Haddon Hall. 1846. 1st ed., tall 8vo, illus., half title, orig. cream cloth, gilt, corners stained on back bd., o/w v.g. Jarndyce 16-774 1978 £24

JENKINS, CHARLES F.   Button Gwinnett, Signer of the Delcaration of Independence. New York, 1926. Ltd. ed., illus., fine, d.j., boxed. MacManus 239-761 1978 $42.50

JENKINS, CHARLES F.   Jefferson's Germantown Letters. Together with Other. Papers Relating to His Stay in Germantown During the Month of Nov. 1793. Philadelphia, 1906. Ltd. to 500 copies, ex-lib., nice. MacManus 239-1626 1978 $12.50

JENKINS, CHARLES F.   Lafayette's Visit to Germantown, July 20, 1825. Philadelphia, 1911. Illus., uncut. MacManus 239-1509 1978 $12.50

JENKINS, CHARLES F.   Washington in Germantown... Philadelphia, 1905. Illus., ltd. to 500 copies. MacManus 239-1510 1978 $25

JENKINS, EDWARD   Lord Bantam. A Satire. NY, 1872. First Am. Ed., Author's Edition, orig. cloth binding, good cond. Greene 78-65 1978 $30.00

JENKINS, HERBERT   The Life of George Borrow. 1912. First ed., plts., orig. cloth, gilt top, 8vo. Howes 194-649 1978 £7.50

JENKINS, HOWARD M.   The Family of William Penn, Founder of Pennsylvania... Philadelphia, 1899. Illus., uncut, fine. MacManus 239-1597 1978 $40

JENKINS, HOWARD M.   Historical Collections Relating to Dwynedd, a Township of Montgomery Co.,...Settled, 1698 by Immigrants From Wales. Philadelphia, 1897. Illus., fime copy, rebound, scarce. MacManus 239-1511 1978 $60

JENKINS, HOWARD M.   Pennsylvania Colonial and Federal. A History, 1608-1903. Philadelphia, 1903. 3 vols., 4to., cloth, uncut, illus. MacManus 239-1512 1978 $30

JENKINS, J. S.   History of the War Between The United States and Mexico... Auburn, 1851. Portraits, plts., thick 8vo, orig. cloth, cover little worn. Edwards 1012-499 1978 £25

JENKINS, JEFF   The Northern Tier; or, Life Among the Homestead Settlers. Topeka, 1880. Original cloth, 1st ed. Ginsberg 14-448 1978 $125

JENKINS, JOHN   A Protestant's Appeal to the Douay Bible... Montreal, 1853. Hood's 115-935 1978 $22.50

JENKINS, JOHN A.   The Life of Silas Wright, Late Governor (and) "Cato of the American Senate". Auburn, 1847. Portr., bright copy in gilt pict. cloth. Butterfield 21-475 1978 $20

JENKINS, JOHN EDWARD   Lord Bantam. 1872. 2nd. ed., 2 vols., orig. brown cloth, diagonal black lines, gilt imprint, fine. Jarndyce 16-775 1978 £25

JENKINS, JOHN S.   James Knox Polk, and a History of His Administration. Auburn and Buffalo, (1850). Cloth, little worn at extremities. Hayman 72-372 1978 $12.50

JENKINS, JOHN S.   The Life of James Knox Polk, Late President of the United States. Auburn, 1850. 1st ed., frontis. port., orig. cloth, worn, foxing. MacManus 239-805 1978 $17.50

JENKINS, JOHN W.   James B. Duke, Master Builder. New York, 1927. Illus. Broadfoot 50-105 1978 $15

JENKINS, M.   Historical Collection Relating to Gwynedd.... Philadelphia, 1897. 1st ed., lg 8vo, spine rubbed, covers soiled, inner joint open, good, scarce work, illus., orig. binding. Americanist 101-70 1978 $40

JENKINS, OLIVER   Open Shutters a Volume of Poems. Chicago, 1922. One of 245 copies on Whatman handmade paper. Battery Park 1-225 1978 $75

JENKINS, R. S.   The Heir from New York. Toronto, 1911. Hood 116-479 1978 $10

JENKINS, STEPHEN   The Greatest Street in the World. New York, 1911. Illus., maps, 1st ed., t.e.g. MacManus 239-363 1978 $17.50

JENKINS, STEPHEN   The Greatest Street in the World. New York & London, 1911. Folded maps, 1st ed. Butterfield 21-506 1978 $15

JENKINS, STEPHEN   The Old Boston Post Road. New York, 1913. 1st ed., illus., maps. MacManus 239-227 1978 $15

JENKINS, STEPHEN   The Old Boston Post Road. New York, 1913. Illus., maps, 8vo., 1st ed., orig. cloth. Morrill 241-226 1978 $20

JENKINS, STEPHEN   The Story of the Bronx...1639 to the Present. New York & London, 1912. Illus., maps, plts., 1st ed. Butterfield 21-507 1978 $20

JENKINS, THOMAS   The Man of Alaska, Peter Trimble Rowe. New York, 1943. Illus. Hood 116-86 1978 $22.50

JENKS, BENJAMIN   Prayers and Offices of Devotion for Families and for Particular Persons. Albany, 1806. 2nd Albany ed., old lea., rubbed, but sound. Butterfield 21-27 1978 $10

JENKS, TUDOR   The Century World's Fair Book for Boys and Girls.. Harry and Philip...at the World's Columbian Exposition... New York, (1893). 1st ed., sm. sq. 4to., orig. pict. bds., excellent copy, orig. pict. d.w., somewhat worn. Americanist 102-65 1978 $30

JENKS, TUDOR   The Century World's Fair Book for Boys and Girls.. New York, (1893). Pict. bds., rubbed, little soiled, illus. Hayman 72-373 1978 $15

JENNESS, DIAMOND   The American Aborigines; Their Origin and Antiquity... Toronto, 1933. Hood 116-421 1978 $75

JENNESS, DIAMOND   The Copper Eskimos. 1913-18. Vo. XII, Parts A,B,C,D. Hood's 115-749 1978 $30

JENNESS, DIAMOND   Eskimo Folk-Lore. Ottawa, 1926. 2 parts. Hood's 115-750 1978 $35

JENNESS, DIAMOND   The Sekani Indians of British Columbia. Ottawa, 1937. Card cover, illus. Hood's 115-751 1978 $25

JENNINGS, GERTRUDE   Family Affairs: A Comedy in Three Acts. 1934. First ed., cr. 8vo., fine, d.w., orig. cloth, Richard Jenning's copy, inscribed by author to him. Howes 194-962 1978 £7.50

JENNINGS, ISAAC   Memorials of a Century. Boston, 1869. Engrav. frontis, map, orig. binding. Wolfe 39-33 1978 $40

JENNING'S Landscape Annual or Tourist in Spain for 1836. London, 1836. 8vo., full leather, engravings, frontis. lacking, pres. written in fine hand, fine, fore-edge painting. Duschnes 220-103 1978 $100

JENSEN, CARL CHRISTIAN   An American Saga. 1927. Austin 79-367 1978 $8.50

JENSEN, J. MARINUS   History of Provo, Utah. (Provo), 1924. Cloth, errata, illus., 1st ed., very good, very scarce. Dykes 35-288 1978 $40

JENSEN, WIGGO FREDERIK   The Onward Trail. n.d. ca. 1938. Frontis. Austin 79-368 1978 $27.50

JENSON, ANDREW   The Historical Record, Continuation of "Morgenstjernen." A Monthly Periodical... Salt Lake City, 1886-90. Vols. 5-9 in 1 vol., as issued, lg. thick 8vo., orig. fabrikoid cloth. Americanist 102-75 1978 $60

JENSON, NICHOLAS   The Last Will and Testament of the Late Nicholas Jenson. Chicago, 1928. Thin quarto, blind stamped cream paper boards, gilt lettering on spine, top of front cover, d. j. Totteridge 29-59 1978 $45

JENYNS, SOAME   Miscellaneous Pieces in Verse and Prose. 1770. Third ed., vignette on title, contemp. French calf-backed bds., 8vo. Howes 194-327 1978 £28

JENYNS, SOAME   A View of the Internal Evidence of the Christian Religion. 1776. 3rd. ed., half-title, sm. 8vo, contemp. calf, nice copy. Fenning 32-177 1978 £10

JEPHSON, A.   A Discourse on the Religious Observation of the Lord's Day both Doctrinal and Practical. 1760. Contemp. calf, rubbed, 8vo. George's 635-1081 1978 £7.50

JERMAIN, FRANCES D.   In the Path of the Alphabet. Fort Wayne, 1906. Illus., 8vo., ex-lib., 1st ed. Morrill 239-448 1978 $7.50

JERNINGHAM, HUBERT E. H.   Norham Castle. Edinburgh, 1883. Coloured title-vignette, 8vo., orig. cloth. K Books 244-388 1978 £7

JEROME, SAINT
Please turn to
HIERONYMUS, SAINT

JEROME, CHAUNCEY   History of the American Clock Business, for the Past Sixty Years, & Life of Chauncey Jerome, Written by Himself. New Haven, 1860. Good rebound copy. Nestler Rare 78-225 1978 $68

JEROME, JEROME K.   My First Book. London, 1897. Illus., orig. cloth. MacManus 238-957 1978 $25

JEROME, JEROME K.   Novel Notes. 1893. 1st. ed., illus., orig. cloth, very worn at head of spine, corners bumped. Jarndyce 16-1204 1978 £5

JEROME, JEROME K.   Second Thoughts of an Idle Fellow. New York, 1898. 1st Amer. ed., green cloth, good. Greene 78-233 1978 $20

JEROME, JEROME K.   Three Men in a Boat (To Say Nothing of the Dog). Bristol, 1889. 8vo., cloth, 1st ed., 1st issue, fine copy, half-mor. slipcase. J. S. Lawrence 38-825 1978 $200

JEROME, JEROME K.   Three Men in a Boat. New York, 1890. 1st Amer. ed., illus., orig. cloth, edges shelf worn, good. Greene 78-234 1978 $60

JEROME, JEROME K.   Three Men in a Boat. New York, 1890. Illus. A. Frederics, 1st Amer. ed. Biblo 251-516 1978 $17.50

JEROME, OWEN FOX   The Golf Club Murder. New York, 1929. First U.S. ed., spine dull, good. Bell Book 16-253 1978 £4

JERROLD, BLANCHARD   The Chronicles of the Crutch. 1860. 1st. ed., orig. purple pebble-grained cloth, blocked in blind, spine gilt, fine. Jarndyce 16-776 1978 £28

JERROLD, BLANCHARD   The Chronicles of the Crutch. 1860. 1st. ed., orig. purple cloth, front cover waterstained, otherwise good. Jarndyce 16-777 1978 £15

JERROLD, BLANCHARD   The Life of George Cruikshank in Two Epochs. London, 1882. 2 vols., extra illus., 1st ed., t.e.g., sm. thick 8vo., engrs. on heavy paper, fine full red French mor., near mint throughout. Current 24-225 1978 $395

JERROLD, BLANCHARD   London, A Pilgrimage. 1872. Numerous vignette & full pg. plts. by Gustave Dore, orig. blue cloth, blocked in gilt with black borders, a.e.g., fine copy except for slight wear to hinges. Jarndyce 16-829 1978 £140

JERROLD, BLANCHARD   A Pilgrimage. London, 1872. 1st. ed., lg. paper copy, folio, engraved & printed title-pg., engraved plts., red mor., panelled backs, illus. by Gustave Dore, raised bands, gilt, marbled end-papers, joints little weak. Deighton 5-119 1978 £220

JERROLD, DOUGLAS   The Barber's Chair and The Hedgehog Letters. 1874. 1st. ed., frontis portrait, orig. blue cloth, v.g. Jarndyce 16-780 1978 £8.50

JERROLD, DOUGLAS   Mrs. Caudle's Curtain Lectures... 1846. 1st. ed., frontis, bound in simple calf, good. Jarndyce 16-778 1978 £10

JERROLD, DOUGLAS   Mrs. Caudle's Curtain Lectures... 1846. 6th. ed., frontis, orig. green cloth, little faded, otherwise v.g. Jarndyce 16-779 1978 £7.50

JERROLD, WILLIAM BLANCHARD
Please turn to
JERROLD, BLANCHARD

JERVIS, HENRY JERVIS-WHITE   History of the Island of Corfu and of the Republic of the Ionian Islands. London, 1852. 1st ed., 8vo., ads, illus., orig. purple, gilt-decor. covers with some fading, fine throughout. Current 24-226 1978 $100

JESSE, EDWARD   Anecdotes of Dogs. London, 1858. Steel engrav., wood engrav., 8vo., orig. cloth. K Books 244-174 1978 £15

JESSE, F. TENNYSON   The Solange Stories. 1931. Spine faded, good, pres. inscription by author, first English ed. Bell Book 17-515 1978 £5

JESSE, F. TENNYSON   Tom Fool. London, 1926. First ed., orig. binding, upper cover stained, very good, author's initialled autograph pres. inscription. Rota 211-258 1978 £9

JESSE, JOHN HENEAGE   London & Its Celebrities. 1850. 1st. ed., 2 vols., orig. dark blue cloth, blind stamped, gilt spine lettering, v.g. Jarndyce 16-824 1978 £25

JESSE, JOHN HENEAGE   Memoirs of the Life and Reign of George III. 1867. 3 vols., covers faded, 8vo. George's 635-658 1978 £7.50

JESSE, WILLIAM   The Life of George Brummel, Esq., Commonly Called Beau Brummell. Philadelphia, 1844. 8vo., contemp. marbled bds., roan back & corners, 1st Amer. ed. Morrill 241-227 1978 $8.50

JESSE, WILLIAM   The Life of George Brummell, Commonly Called Beau Brummell. Philadelphia, 1844. 2 vols. in 1, lea.-backed bds., slightly worn. Hayman 73-342 1978 $15

JESSEN, JOHANNES   Anatomiae, Pragae, Anno M.D.C. abs se Solenniter Administratae Historia. Witebergae, 1601. 2 parts in 1 vol., woodcut portr., 8vo., half calf, 1st ed., marginal annotations & underlinings in red ink. Offenbacher 30-71 1978 $250

JESSUP, PHILIP C.   Elihu Root. New York, 1938. Illus., 2 vols., MacManus 239-810 1978 $22.50

JEUDWINE, J. W.   Tort, crime and police in mediaeval Britain; a review of some early law and custom. 1917. 8vo. Upcroft 12-213 1978 £8.50

LES JEUX des Quatre Saisons ou les Amusements du Jeune Age. Paris, 1812. 12mo, f.p., t.p. engraving, plates, original 3/4 leather and marbled boards, rubbing of spine, fine, crisp copy. Victoria 34-443 1978 $70

JEVON, THOMAS   The Devil of a Wife, or a Comical Transformation. London, 1686. 1st. ed., title-pg. repaired, little soiled throughout, 4to, new quarter dark red morocco, marbled bds., gilt lettered spine. Traylen 88-282 1978 £75

JEVONS, W. STANLEY   Money. n.d. Ca. 1895. Austin 80-735 1978 $17.50

JEVONS, W. STANLEY   Money and the Mechanism of Exchange. 20th Century Press, n.d. Austin 80-736 1978 $12.50

JEVONS, W. STANLEY   The Principles of Science. (1900) 1920. Austin 80-737 1978 $27.50

JEVONS, W. STANLEY   Studies in Deductive Logic. 1908. Austin 80-738 1978 $12.50

THE JEW. New York, 1844. Disbound, lacks wrappers. Hayman 71-365 1978 $7.50

JEWETT, CHARLES   A Forty Years' Fight With the Drink Demon.... New York, 1872. Clean, orig. binding. Hayman 71-366 1978 $15

JEWETT, CHARLES   Speeches, Poems, and Miscellaneous Writings, on Subjects Connected with Temperance and the Liquor Traffic. Boston, 1849. Cloth, moderate wear at extremities. Hayman 73-343 1978 $15

JEWETT, ISAAC APPLETON   Memorial of Samuel Appleton Ipswich, Mass. Boston, 1850. Illus., rubbed. Biblo BL781-53 1978 $35

JEWETT, SARAH ORNE   Deephaven. Boston, 1877. 12mo., orig. cloth, 1st ed., 3rd print. MacManus 238-547 1978 $32.50

JEWETT, SARAH ORNE   Play Days. A Book of Stories for Children. Boston, 1878. 12mo., orig. pict. cloth, 1st ed., scarce, near-fine. MacManus 238-548 1978 $85

JEWITT, JOHN RODGERS   Narrative of the Adventures and Sufferings of. Ithaca, 1849. Frontis, engrav., contemp. sheep. Wolfe 39-257 1978 $55

JEWITT, JOHN RODGERS   Narrative of the Adventure and Sufferings of.... Ithaca, 1851. Several illus., 1 plt., full leather binding, new leather spine & end papers, pages browned. Hood's 115-752 1978 $90

JEWITT, LLEWELLYNN   Half Hours Among the English Antiquities. 1877. 1st. ed., 300 engravings, orig. green cloth, blocked in black & gilt, prelims little browned, otherwise good. Jarndyce 16-781 1978 £7.50

JEWITT, JOHN RODGERS   Narrative of the Adventures and Sufferings of John R. Jewitt,.... Middletown, 1815. Half morocco, mended, 1st ed. Ginsberg 14-435 1978 $300

JEWITT, JOHN RODGERS   A Narrative of the Adventures and Sufferings of John R. Jewitt... Middletown, 1815. Frontis., 12mo., contemp. full calf, 2nd ed. Howell 5-34 1978 $200

JEWITT, JOHN RODGERS   Narrative of the Adventures and Suffering of... Only Survivor of the Crew of the Ship Boston... New York, 1851. Illus., plt., full lea. binding, new lea. spine & endpapers, pages browned. Hood 117-681 1978 $100

JEWSBURY, MARIA JANE   Letters to the Young. London, 1828. 1st. ed., fcap. 8vo, old half calf, worn. Traylen 88-156 1978 £12

JEYES, S. H.   Mr. Chamberlain. London, 1904. 2 vols., 31 plts., roy. 8vo, orig. cloth gilt, g.t. K Books 239-235 1978 £12

JILLSON, WILLARD ROUSE   Early Kentucky Literature. 1750-1840. Frankfort, 1932. 8vo., orig. bds., 2nd ed., rev'd. and expanded ed. ltd. to 200 copies, very good. MacManus 238-958 1978 $35

JILLSON, WILLARD ROUSE   The Geology and Mineral Resources of Kentucky. Frankfort, 1928. Cloth, photos. Hayman 73-365 1978 $15

JIMESON, M. P.   An Original Exhibition of Some of the Difficulties of Westminster Calvinism. Pittsburgh, 1845. Bds., introduction signed. Hayman 71-632 1978 $12.50

JOACHIM OF FLORIS   Vaticinia, sive Prophetiae Abbatis Ioachimi and Anselmi Episcopi Marsicani... Venice, 1589. Sm. 4to., v. f., cont. limp vellum, engravings. Schafer 19-23 1978 sFr 1200

JOANNES SECUNDUS   The Basia. Colonial Press, 1901. Portrait, text foxed, orig. bds., spine worn. George's 635-1357 1978 £6.50

JOAO VI, KING OF PORTUGAL   Edital.... Rio de Janeiro, 1808. Sm. folio, orig. cloth. Edwards 1012-656 1978 £50

JOCELIN DE BRAKELOND   Cronica Jocelini de Brakelonda de rebus gestis Samsonis Abbatis Monasterii Sancti Edmundi. 1949. Map, 8vo., parallel Latin/ English text. Upcroft 12-310a 1978 £10

JOHANN, LICHTENBERGER   Die weissagunge... Wittemberg, 1527. Sm. 4to, Gothic letter, woodcuts by Georg Lemberger, late 19th century blind-stamped brown mor. Quaritch 978-88 1978 $2,250

JOHANNES DE JANDUNO   Questiones de coelo et mundo. (Venice), 1501. Very rare 1st ed., half-mor. Gilhofer 75-62 1978 SFr 1,300

JOHANNES DE MEDIOLANO   Schola Salernitana.... 1683. Sm. 12mo., limp vellum, slightly damaged. King 7-282 1978 £60

JOHANNSDOTTIR, OLAFIA   The Waiting Shadow. Norfolk, 1927. Frontis., paper. Austin 79-373 1978 $12.50

JOHN, J.   Atlas Rostlin. Praze, 1899. Lg. 8vo., half cloth, illus., chromolith. plts., text illus. Van der Peet H-64-360 1978 Dfl 135

JOHN Jerningham's Journal. London, 1871. 8vo, original green cloth, 1st ed. Ximenes 47-249 1978 $15

JOHN MARTIN'S Big Book for Little Folk. New York, (1927). 1st ed., colored pictorial boards, very good. Victoria 34-526 1978 $17.50

JOHN Williams, or the Sailor Boy. Boston, 1827. 12mo., orig. pic. wrs., woodcuts, thread repairs on spine, covers little worn, very good. Americanist 103-46 1978 $32.50

JOHNS, C. A.   The Forest Trees of Britain. London, 1892. Illus., 8vo., orig. cloth. K Books 244-175 1978 £6

JOHNS, HENRY T.   Life with the Forty-Ninth Massachusetts Volunteers. Washington, 1890. Portr., 8vo., orig. cloth. Morrill 241-334 1978 $15

JOHNS Hopkins Hospital Reports. Vol. XIX. Fasciculus II. Baltimore, 1919. Paper covers frayed. Rittenhouse 49-409 1976 $7.50

JOHNSEN, JULIA E.   Interstate Trade Barriers. 1940. Ex-lib. Austin 80-739 1978 $11

JOHNSON, MRS.   A Narrative of the Captivity of Mrs. Johnson, Containing an Account of Her Sufferings, During Four Years, with the Indians and French. New York, 1841. Reissue of 1796 ed., orig. bds., worn, lea. spine, foxed. Hood 117-682 1978 $75

JOHNSON, A. C.   Byzantine Egypt; economic studies. Princeton, 1949. 8vo. Upcroft 12-216 1978 £10

JOHNSON, A. F.   Fruhe Basler Buchdruckerkunst. Hellerau, 1928. 8vo., bds., plts. Battery Park 1-339 1978 $45

JOHNSON, ADAM R.   The Partisan Rangers of the Confederate States Army. Louisville, 1904. Illus., front hinge reglued, front f/l creased at inner margin and chipped at outer margin, stamp on title page, Bell Wiley's copy. Broadfoot's 44-495 1978 $125

JOHNSON, ALLEN   Readings in American Constitutional History, 1776-1876. Boston, (1912). Biblo 251-347 1978 $12.50

JOHNSON, AMANDUS   The Instruction of Johan Printz, Governor of New Sweden. Philadelphia, 1930. Illus., fold. map. MacManus 239-121 1978 $27.50

JOHNSON, AMANDUS   The Swedes on the Delaware, 1638-1664. Philadelphia, 1914. 1st ed., colored frontis., illus., orig. cloth, fine. MacManus 239-228 1978 $37.50

JOHNSON, ANDREW   A Proclamation. Washington, 1866. 8vo. Jenkins 116-742 1978 $12.50

JOHNSON, ANDREW   Speech of .... On The War For the Union; delivered in the Senate, July 27, 1861. Washington, 1861. Unbound as issued. Hayman 71-367 1978 $7.50

JOHNSON, ANDREW   Trial of..., President of the U.S., Before the Senate of the U.S. on Impeachment...for High Crimes Misdemeanors. Washington, 1868. 3 vols., orig. cloth, very fine. MacManus 239-230 1978 $75

JOHNSON, BRADLEY T.   A Memoir of the Life and Public Service of Joseph E. Johnston. Baltimore, 1894. Cover stained, Bell Wiley's copy. Broadfoot's 44-214 1978 $20

JOHNSON, C.   English Court Hand A.D. 1066 to 1500...
Oxford, 1915. 2 vols., vol. I is text, vol. 2 plts., folio, good. Sexton 7-154
1978 £48

JOHNSON, C.   English Court Hand 1066-1500. Oxford, 1915.
Roy. 8vo. George's 635-697 1978 £5

JOHNSON, CECIL   A Printer's Garland. (San Francisco), Windsor
Press, (1935). Decor. bds., mint, I of 300 copies. Dawson's 447-13 1978 $25

JOHNSON, CHARLES   A General History of the Pirates. Cayme Press,
1925. Ltd. to 500 copies, 2 vols., 4to. George's 635-829 1978 £25

JOHNSON, CHARLES   History of the Lives and Bloody Exploits of the
Most Noted Pirates... Hartford, 1855. 12mo., orig. cloth, nice, plts. Paine
78-73 1978 $27.50

JOHNSON, CHARLES   The History of the Pirates, Containing the Lives
of Those Noted Pirate Captains, Misson, Bowen, Kidd... London, 1814.
12mo., contemp. calf, 1st Amer. ed. Morrill 241-228 1978 $30

JOHNSON, CHARLES   The Village Opera. 1729. 1st. ed., 8vo, half
cloth, title & last page dust-soiled, few slight stains. Hannas 54-173 1978 £25

JOHNSON, CRISFIELD   History of Cuyahoga County, Ohio. Cleveland, 1879. 4to., new cloth, 1st ed. Morrill 241-435 1978 $50

JOHNSON, CHRISTIAN ISOBEL   Scenes of Industry, Displayed in the Bee-Hive
and the Ant-Hill. London, 1830. 2nd. ed., vignette on title, illus., plts.,
8vo, orig. cloth, leather spine, trifle defective. Traylen 88-157 1978 £20

JOHNSON, D. MC I.   A Doctor Regrets...Being the First Part of "A Publisher Presents Himself." London, 1945. Illus. Hood 116-252 1978 $12.50

JOHNSON, D. W.   Battlefields of the World War, Western and Southern Fronts, a Study in Military Geography. New York, 1921. Maps, illus., plts.,
2 vols., cr. 8vo. George's 635-830 1978 £6.50

JOHNSON, E. A. J.   Predecessors of Adam Smith, the Growth of
British Economic Thought. 1937. 8vo. George's 635-344 1978 £5.25

JOHNSON, E. A. J.   Some Origins of the Modern Economic World.
1936. 1st ed. Austin 80-740 1978 $20

JOHNSON, E. C.   A Bull Fight in the City of Mexico. Portland,
(1909). Pic. wrs., punched & silk cord tie, 1st ed., autographed by author,
little dull, rare. Dykes 34-141 1978 $75

JOHNSON, F. B.   The Early Architecture of North Carolina, a Pictorial Survey. Chapel Hill, 1941. Sm. folio, 1st ed., illus., very fine, boxed.
MacManus 239-695 1978 $65

JOHNSON, FRANK   R.A.A.F. Over Europe. London, 1946. First
ed., illus., d.w. torn, 8vo., orig. cloth. K Books 244-176 1978 £5

JOHNSON, FRANK W.   A History of Texas and Texans. Chicago &
New York, 1914. 5 vols., 1st ed., illus., orig. cloth, t.e.g., very good or
better. Limestone 9-160 1978 $150

JOHNSON, FRANKLIN P.   Lysippos. Durham, 1927. 1st ed. Biblo BL781-
436 1978 $14.50

JOHNSON, GEORGE LINDSAY   Photography in Colours. London, 1914.
2nd ed., illus., sm. 8vo., orig. cloth. Morrill 241-229 1978 $12.50

JOHNSON, GEORGE WILLIAM   The British Ferns Popularly Described, and
Illustrated by Engravings of Every Species. 1857. 2nd ed., plts., lg. 12mo., orig.
green cloth, gilt, very good. Fenning 32-178 1978 £5.50

JOHNSON, GEORGE WILLIAM   A Dictionary of Modern Gardening. Philadelphia, 1847. Woodcuts, orig. cloth, very good. MacManus 239-173 1978
$35

JOHNSON, GERALD W.   Our English Heritage. 1949. Austin 79-374
1978 $10

JOHNSON, GERALD W.   Roosevelt: Dictator or Democrat? New York,
(1941). Biblo BL781-242 1978 $9

JOHNSON, GUION GRIFFIS   Ante-Bellum North Carolina, a Social History.
Chapel Hill, 1937. Broadfoot 50-108 1978 $25

JOHNSON, H. A.   The Sword of Honor. Hallowell, 1906. 12mo.,
orig. cloth, 1st ed. Morrill 241-230 1978 $15

JOHNSON, H. A.   The Sword of Honor, A Story of the Civil War.
Hallowell, 1906. Illus., inscrip. from author to another person. Broadfoot's
44-515 1978 $16

JOHNSON, H. H.   The History of a Slave. London, 1889. 47 full
page illus. Baldwins' 51-381 1978 $12.50

JOHNSON, HELEN M.   Poems. Boston, 1855. Orig. binding. Wolfe
39-149 1978 $50

JOHNSON, HENRY LEWIS   Gutenberg and the Book of Books. New York,
1932. Folio, thin, I of 750 copies, fr. cover soiled, ink stains, t.e.g. Battery
Park I-153 1978 $75

JOHNSON, HENRY LEWIS   Printing Type Specimens, Standard and Modern
Types...Their Characteristics and Uses: A Printing Guide for Printers, Advertisers
and Students of Printing. Boston, 1924. 4to., orig. bind., illus. Americanist
102-66 1978 $40

JOHNSON, JAMES WELDON   The Book of American Negro Spirituals... New
York, 1925. 1st ed., orig. bind. Americanist 102-18 1978 $20

JOHNSON, JAMES WELDON   God's Trombones. New York, 1927. Illus.,
gold bds., black cloth spine, 1st ed., very good copy, worn & dusty dust jacket,
scarce. Bradley 49-169 1978 $50

JOHNSON, JOHN   A Mathematical Question. Amherst, 1797.
12mo, papered oak cover held by leather hinge, some paper peeling, very good.
Victoria 34-447 1978 $35

JOHNSON, JOHN   The Printer. (1933). 16mo. Battery Park I-390
1978 $15

JOHNSON, JOHN A.   On the Roof of Europe Behind the Guardsman's
Rifle. Covington, 1920. Illus., thin 8vo., orig. cloth, 1st ed. Morrill 241-
231 1978 $25

JOHNSON, JOSEPH   Clever Boys of Our Time, And How They Became
Famous Men. London, n.d. (c.1869). 6th ed., plts., illuminated title pg. &
frontis, photo portrait, sm. 8vo, orig. cloth, gilt edges, little loose. Traylen 88-
159 1978 £9

JOHNSON, JOSEPH   The Interviews of Great Men; Their Influence
on Civilization. London, n.d. (c.1864). 1st. ed.?, 8vo, cloth, plts. Traylen
88-158 1978 £6

JOHNSON, JOSEPH   The Interviews of Great Men; Their Influence
on Civilization. London, n.d. (c.1875). Illuminated title pg. & frontis, plts.,
8vo, orig. cloth. Traylen 88-158A 1978 £5

JOHNSON, LIONEL   The Art of Thomas Hardy... London, 1894.
Orig. bds., 1st ed., ltd. to 150 copies on hand-made paper, frontis., head of
spine worn, but good. MacManus 238-269 1978 $150

JOHNSON, LIONEL   The Art of Thomas Hardy. 1923. Portraits, sm.
8vo., orig. cloth, best ed. Howes 194-916 1978 £8.50

JOHNSON, LIONEL   Poetical Works. 1915. First ed., portrait, 2
plts., cr. 8vo., orig. cloth, first state, rare. Howes 194-963 1978 £25

JOHNSON, LIONEL   Reviews and Critical Papers. 1921. 1st. ed.,
largely unopened, bds. slightly buckled, otherwise near fine in d.w. Jarndyce
16-1205 1978 £10

JOHNSON, MELVIN M., JR.   Automatic Weapons of the World. New York,
1945. Illus., 8vo., d.w., top edges of d.w. chipped. Morrill 239-450 1978
$22.50

JOHNSON, MERLE   You Know These Lines! A Bibliography of the
Most Quoted Verses in American Poetry. New York, 1935. 8vo., orig. cloth,
ltd. to 1,000 copies, signed by author. MacManus 238-961 1978 $32.50

JOHNSON, PAMELA HANSFORD   Thomas Wolfe, a Critical Study. 1947.
D.j. Broadfoot 50-462 1978 $15

JOHNSON, PHIL   Life on the Plains. Chicago, 1888. Cloth over
flexible bds., illus., 1st ed., rare, very good copy, slipcase. Dykes 34-29
1978 $100

JOHNSON, R.W.   A Soldier's Reminiscences in Peace and War.
Philadelphia, 1886. Inscribed by author. Jenkins 116-744 1978 $42.50

JOHNSON, RICHARD   The Blossoms of Morality. London, 1796. Woodcuts by John Bewick, 1st illus. ed., fine, contemp. calf. Victoria 34-69 1978
$300

JOHNSON, RICHARD   The Blossoms of Morality. 1806. Sm. 8vo.,
woodcuts, contemp. calf, little worn. Quaritch 979-91 1978 $75

JOHNSON, RICHARD M.   Review of a Report of the Committee, to Whom was
Referred the Several Petitions on the Subject of Mails on the Sabbath, Presented to
the Senate of the United States, January 16, 1829, by...., of Kentucky, Chairman of Said Committee. N.P., 1829. Disbound. Hayman 72-397 1978 $15

JOHNSON, ROSSITER   A History of the War of 1812-'15 Between the
United States and Great Britain. New York, (1882). Cloth. Hayman 73-344
1973 $10

JOHNSON, S. PAUL   Flying Squadrons. 1942. Illus. with photos, ex-
lib., rebound. Austin 80-158 1978 $10

JOHNSON, SAMUEL   The Adventurer. 1756. 3rd. ed., 4 vols., orig.
calf, hinges weak. Jarndyce 16-120 1978 £25

JOHNSON, SAMUEL   A Dictionary of the English Language in which the
Words are Deduced from their Originals, and Illustrated in their Different Significations by Examples from the Best Writers. London, 1755. 1st ed., folio, 2 vols.,
3/4 19th Cent. calf over marbled bds. & endpapers, rehinged & reinforced, gilt
lettering & raised bands, nice clean copies, boxed. Current Misc. 8-24 1978
$2,750

JOHNSON, SAMUEL   A Dictionary of the English Language. 1755.
First ed., some light browning, very clean and fresh, 2 vols., folio, full calf gilt,
strongly rebacked with brown levant mor. Thomas 37-41 1978 £1250

JOHNSON, SAMUEL   A Dictionary of the English Language:....
London, 1755. 2 vols., 1st ed., folio, 19th century speckled brown half calf,
rubbed, 2 pages from another copy to replace 2 torn pages. Totteridge 29-60
1978 $2,000

JOHNSON, SAMUEL   Dictionary of the English Language. 1760. 2nd.
ed., 8vo, 2 vols., orig. calf, hinges & head of spine little rubbed, spines gilt,
good set. Jarndyce 16-118 1978 £70

JOHNSON, SAMUEL   A Dictionary of the English Language. London,
1765. 2nd. ed., 2 vols., thick folio, contemp. calf, joints broken. Traylen 88-
283 1978 £400

JOHNSON, SAMUEL   A Dictionary of the English Language....
London, 1766. 2 vols., octavo, full contemp. calf, raised spine bands, gilt rules,
3rd abridged ed. Bennett 7-59 1978 $250

JOHNSON, SAMUEL   A Dictionary of the English Language. 1773.
5th. ed., 2 vols. in 1, orig. calf, rubbed hinges weakening. Jarndyce 16-72
1978 £32

JOHNSON, SAMUEL   A Dictionary of the English Language. 1784.
Folio, orig. binding, 5th. ed., 2 vols., orig. diced calf, gilt borders, spines,
fine copy, text in exceptionally fine & clean state. Jarndyce 16-119 1978 £300

JOHNSON, SAMUEL   A Dictionary of the English Language. London,
1818. Portrait, 4 vols., thick 4to, contemp diced calf, joints repaired. Traylen
88-284 1978 £65

JOHNSON, SAMUEL   Johnson's Dictionary of the English Language...
1819. New ed., orig. calf, spine worn, hinges weak, good. Jarndyce 16-784
1978 £5

JOHNSON, SAMUEL   A Dictionary of the English Language. 1827.
Frontis portrait, orig. calf, rebacked, v.g. Jarndyce 16-785 1978 £28

JOHNSON, SAMUEL   A Dictionary of the English Language. 1848.
7th. ed., frontis portrait, fully rebound in half calf, marbled bds., v.g. Jarndyce
16-786 1978 £28

JOHNSON, SAMUEL   Hurlothrumbo: or, The Super-Natural. 1729.
1st. ed., 8vo, disbound, title dust-soiled, some water-stains at end. Hannas 54-
174 1978 £17.50

JOHNSON, SAMUEL   A Journey to the Western Islands of Scotland.
London, 1775. Contemp. full calf, worn, 1st ed., 1st issue, tall copy in tan buckram box. Bradley 49-170 1978 $275

JOHNSON, SAMUEL   A Journey to the Western Islands of Scotland.
London, 1775. Octavo, contemp. mottled calf, rebacked, marbled endpapers,
1st ed., 1st issue. Bennett 7-61 1978 $150

JOHNSON, SAMUEL   A Journey to the Western Islands of Scotland.
London, 1775. 8vo., full calf, mor. label, 1st ed., 2nd issue, bookplt. Mac-
Manus 238-127 1978 $100

JOHNSON, SAMUEL   A Journey to the Western Islands of Scotland.
Edinburgh, 1792. First Edinburgh ed., sm. 8vo., contemp. calf, new label.
Howes 194-328 1978 £18

JOHNSON, SAMUEL   Letters to and from the late Samuel Johnson, LL.
D.... 1788. First ed., 2 vols., contemp. calf, rebacked, 8vo. Howes 194-329
1978 £90

JOHNSON, SAMUEL   Letters to and from the Late Samuel Johnson,
LL.D. to which are Added Some Poems Never Before Printed. London, 1788.
2 vols., 1st ed., 8vo, errata slip tipped in, uncut in orig. drab bds., spine paper
orig. with repairs, cords sound, interior fine, 1/2 brown levant slipcase, scarce.
Current 24-38 1978 $350

JOHNSON, SAMUEL   Letters To and From the Late ..., LL.D. to
Which are Added Some Poems Never Before Printed. London, 1788. 2 vols.,
8vo, contemp. calf-backed marbled bds., 1st ed, rare errata slip. MacManus
238-128 1978 $225

JOHNSON, SAMUEL   Letters to and from the Late Samuel Johnson,
LL.D Dublin, 1788. 2 vols. in 1, 8vo, contemporary tree calf, spine gilt, 1st
Dublin ed., fine copy, scarce ed. Ximenes 47-241 1978 $150

JOHNSON, SAMUEL   Letters to and From the Late.... 1788. 2 vols.,
crisp set in contemp. sprinkled calf, rebacked, gilt lettering pieces. Eaton 45-
270 1978 £40

JOHNSON, SAMUEL   Letters to and from the Late Samuel Johnson, LL.D.
to which are added some poems never before printed. 2 vols., 8vo., 1st ed.,
orig. bds., rebacked, mor.-backed box, uncut. Quaritch 979-209 1978 $525

JOHNSON, SAMUEL   The Life of Mr. Richard Savage, Son of the Earl
Rivers. 1767. Third ed., sm. 8vo., recently bound in qtr. calf, paper label.
Howes 194-330 1978 £15

JOHNSON, SAMUEL   The Lives of the English Poets; and a Criticism of
their Works. Dublin, 1779. 8vo., contemp. calf, hinge cracking, first ed. P.M.
Hill 142-149 1978 £38

JOHNSON, SAMUEL   The Lives of the English Poets; and a Criticism
On Their Works. Dublin, 1779. Vol. 1 only, lacking f.e.p., contemp. calf,
worn. Eaton 45-269 1978 £25

JOHNSON, SAMUEL   The Lives of the Most Eminent English Poets.
1781. First London ed., portrait, 4 vols., 19th cent. half buff calf, 8vo. Howes
194-331 1978 £110

JOHNSON, SAMUEL   The Lives of the Most Eminent English Poets.
Philadelphia, 1819. 3 vols., 8vo., orig. bds., all edges untrimmed, rebacked,
binding broken. Morrill 241-232 1978 $15

JOHNSON, SAMUEL   The Lives of the English Poets. 1825. 2 vols.,
red morocco, a.e.g., good. Jarndyce 16-783 1978 £36

JOHNSON, SAMUEL   Lives of the English Poets. Oxford, 1905. 3 vols.,
8vo., half red mor., gilt tops. Quaritch 979-210 1978 $120

JOHNSON, SAMUEL   London: a poem, and The Vanity of Human
Wishes. 1930. Folio, bds., covers browned & rubbed, else good, one of 450
copies, first English ed. Bell Book 17-312 1978 £18.50

JOHNSON, SAMUEL   The New London Letter Writer. Golden Cockerell
Press, 1948. Ltd. to 500 copies, wood-engravings, orig. qtr. buckram, marbled
bd. sides. George's 635-899 1978 £18

JOHNSON, SAMUEL   The New London Letter Writer Containing the Compleat Art of Corresponding with Ease, Elegance, and Perspicuity as is Now Practised by all Persons of Respectability.   Golden Cockerel, 1948. Frontis., #37 of 100 copies numbered 1-100 specially bound, signed by illus'r, marbled paper over bds., cloth spine, extremities of spine rubbed.   Battery Park 1-118 1978 $75

JOHNSON, SAMUEL   Political Tracts Containing, the False Alarm, Falkland's Islands, the Patriot and Taxation No Tyranny.   London, 1776. 1st collected ed., royal 8vo., fine contemp. tree calf, extra-gilt spine, excellent copy.   Current 24-227 1978 $385

JOHNSON, SAMUEL   The Poetical Works...   Gainsbrough, 1785. 8vo., 1st Pirated ed., contemp. calf, sound, scarce.   Quaritch 979-211 1978 $125

JOHNSON, SAMUEL   Prayers and Meditations.   1785. First ed., contemp. bds., 8vo. Howes 194-332 1978 £90

JOHNSON, SAMUEL   Prayers and Meditations.   1785. Second ed., contemp. suede calf, rubbed, joints weak, label missing, 8vo. Howes 194-333 1978 £21

JOHNSON, SAMUEL   Prayers and Meditations.   1806. New ed., half morocco, marbled bds., v.g. Jarndyce 16-782 1978 £36

JOHNSON, SAMUEL   The Prince of Abissinia. A Tale.   1783. Sixth ed., 12mo., contemp. tree calf, spine gilt, joints cracked, label missing. Howes 194-334 1978 £12

JOHNSON, SAMUEL   The Rambler.   London, 1753. 2 vols., folio, contemporary continental mottled calf, gilt (rubbed, sound), excellent condition. Ximenes 47-163 1978 $850

JOHNSON, SAMUEL   The Rambler.   London, 1751. Sm. folio, contemp. calf, 4 leaves torn with little loss of text & another poorly repaired, vol. I only, nos. 1-104. Traylen 88-285 1978 £45

JOHNSON, SAMUEL   The Rambler.   1784. Tenth ed., 4 vols., 12mo., contemp. calf, four different frontispieces. P. M. Hill 142-150 1978 £38

JOHNSON, SAMUEL   Rasselas, Prince d'Abissinie.   Londres, 1798. Sm. cr. 8vo, frontis eng. & 3 plts. from drawings by T. Stothard, plts. & title pg. browned, contemp. tree calf, joints cracked. Eaton 45-271 1978 £10

JOHNSON, SAMUEL   Thoughts on the Late Transactions Respecting Falkland Islands.   1771. 2nd. ed., half-title, old marbled bds., rubbed, new calf spine, slightly browned, 8vo. Edwards 1012-657 1978 £135

JOHNSON, SAMUEL   A Voyage to Abyssinia.   London, 1735. 1st. ed., 8vo, engraved head-pieces, contemporary polished calf, raised bands, red morocco label, gilt. Deighton 5-214 1978 £185

JOHNSON, SAMUEL   The Works of ..., LL.D.   Oxford, 1825. 11 vols., 8vo., frontis. port. to vol. III, orig. red cloth, 1st complete ed. MacManus 238-129 1978 $250

JOHNSON, SHIRLEY EVERTON   The Cult of the Purple Rose.   1902. First ed. Austin 82-498 1978 $12.50

JOHNSON, SIDDIE JOE   Texas: The Land Of The Tejas.   Dallas, 1950. Illus., d.j., 1st ed. Jenkins 116-746 1978 $10

JOHNSON, STEPHEN   "Shoot-To-Live"; the Johnson Method of Musketry Coaching, as Adopted by the Canadian Army.   Ottawa, 1945. Photos., stiff card cover. Hood 116-129 1978 $12.50

JOHNSON, T.   Novus Graecorum epigrammatum et poetatium delectus cum nova versione et notis, in usum Scholae Etonensis.   1706. Engraved frontis. of coat of arms, 12mo., contemp. calf, spine defective. George's 635-481 1978 £6.50

JOHNSON, THOMAS H.   Return to Freedom.   1944. Ex-lib. Austin 80-159 1978 $8.50

JOHNSON, TOM L.   My Story...   New York, 1911. Cloth. Hayman 72-552 1978 $10

JOHNSON, VIRGINIA W.   The Catskill Fairies.   New York, 1876. 1st ed., profusely illus. by Alfred Fredericks, gilt-illus. cloth, very good copy, cover gilt bright. Victoria 34-449. 1978 $35

JOHNSON, VIRGINIA W.   Genoa the Superb.   Boston, (1892). Illustrated. Biblo 247-699 1978 $15

JOHNSON, W. A.   The History of Anderson County from Its First Settlement.   Garnett, 1877. Original cloth, 1st ed. Ginsberg 14-449 1978 $125

JOHNSON, W. R.   Flowering Time. Color lithos., Rives & Arches paper, handsewn into a Saan cover, 1 of 150 signed & numbered. Battery Park 1-187 1978 $20

JOHNSON, W. FLETCHER   The Red Record of the Sioux.   N.P., (1891). Orig. binding, clean, little worn. Hayman 71-372 1978 $8.50

JOHNSON, WILLIAM   The Papers.   Albany, 1921-65. 14 vols., very good, several volumes new. Butterfield 21-231 1978 $225

JOHNSON, WILLIAM   The Practical Draughtsman's Book of Industrial Design.   1853. 4to., plts., 2 printed in colour, contemp. blind stamped calf. Quaritch 977-234 1978 $135

JOHNSON, WILLIAM PERCIVAL   My African Reminiscenes 1875-1895.   London, (1924). Map, 8 plts., 8vo, orig. cloth. K Books 239-237 1978 £6

JOHNSON, WILLIS F.   Col. Henry Ludington, a Memoir.   New York, 1907. Illus., 1st ed., pres. copy, signed. Biblo BL781-237 1978 $16.50

JOHNSON, WILLIS F.   Life of James G. Blaine, "The Plumed Knight."   N.P., 1892. Illus. Biblo BL781-191 1978 $9

JOHNSTON, CHARLES   Sonnets, Original and Translated.   1823. 8vo., contemp. calf gilt, portrait. P. M. Hill 142-288 1978 £20

JOHNSTON, ALEXANDER KEITH   The Physical Atlas of Natural Phenomena.   Edinburgh, 1856. Lg. folio, handcolored & chromolitho. maps on guards, orig. half calf, gilt, rebacked retaining orig. spine, occas. foxing, fine copy, 3rd & best ed. Norman 5-*30 1978 $1,250

JOHNSTON, CHARLES   Chrysal: Or The Adventures of a Guinea.   1771. 7th. ed., 4 vols., orig. calf, brown & green labels, v.g. Jarndyce 16-121 1978 £48

JOHNSTON, ELIZABETH L.   Recollections of a Georgia Loyalist. Written in 1836.   New York, 1901. Illus., 1st ed., fine. MacManus 239-1810 1978 $35

JOHNSTON, GEORGE   History of Cecil County, Md., and the Early Settlements Around the Head of the Chesapeak Bay...   Elkton, 1881. 1st ed., scarce, nice, orig. cloth. MacManus 239-999 1978 $75

JOHNSTON, GEORGE   The Poets and Poetry of Cecil County, Maryland.   Elkton, 1887. Baldwins' 51-285 1978 $15

JOHNSTON, GEORGE   The Poets and Poetry of Cecil County, Md.   Elkton, 1887. Orig. cloth. MacManus 239-1840 1978 $17.50

JOHNSTON, GEORGE   The Poets and Poetry of Chester County, Penna.   Philadelphia, 1890. Baldwins' 51-453 1978 $15

JOHNSTON, GEORGE   Poets and Poetry of Chester Co., Pa.   Philadelphia, 1890. MacManus 239-1414 1978 $15

JOHNSTON, HARRY   George Grenfell and the Congo.   London, 1908. 1st. ed., 2 vols., lg. 8vo, maps, plts., illus., orig. brown cloth, lettered in gilt on spines, neatly recased, lib. labels removed, embossed institutional stamps in margins. Deighton 5-215 1978 £85

JOHNSTON, HARRY H.   British Mammals.   1903. Sole ed., plts., come coloured, other illus., 4to, orig. cloth, gilt, t.e.g., nice. Fenning 32-179 1978 £10.50

JOHNSTON, HARRY H.   A Gallery of Heroes and Heroines.   (1915). 1st. ed., coloured portratis by Joseph Simpson, 4to, orig. cloth-backed printed paper bds., nice. Fenning 32-180 1978 £9.50

JOHNSTON, HARRY V.   My Home on the Range...   St. Paul, (1942). Pic. cloth, illus., 1st ed., fine, signed by author. Dykes 35-168 1978 $35

JOHNSTON, HENRY   Kilmallie. London, 1891. 2 vols., orig. dec. cloth, 1st ed., very good. MacManus 238-345 1978 $75

JOHNSTON, HENRY PHELPS   The Battle of Harlem Heights September 16, 1776. New York, 1897. 1st ed., fold. maps in color, orig. cloth, recased. MacManus 239-585 1978 $30

JOHNSTON, HENRY PHELPS   The Campaign of 1776 Around New York and Brooklyn. Brooklyn, 1878. Plts., maps, 1st ed., fine copy, largely unopened. Butterfield 21-376 1978 $65

JOHNSTON, HENRY PHELPS   The Campaign of 1776 Around New York and Brooklyn... Brooklyn, 1878. Illus., maps, ltd. to 1,000 copies, fine. Mac-Manus 239-586 1978 $35

JOHNSTON, HENRY PHELPS   Observations on Judge Jones' Loyalist History. New York, 1880. Wr., very good. Butterfield 21-379 1978 $17.50

JOHNSTON, HENRY PHELPS   The Storming of Stony Point on the Hudson... July 15, 1779. New York, 1900. Plts., inscr'd by author. Butterfield 21-377 1978 $27.50

JOHNSTON, HENRY PHELPS   The Yorktown Campaigns and the Surrender of Cornwallis. New York, 1881. Illus. Baldwins' 51-312 1978 $12.50

JOHNSTON, JAMES F. W.   Notes on North America: Agricultural, Econo-mical, and Social. Edinburgh, 1851. 1st ed., folding map, 2 vols., orig. cloth, 8vo. Edwards 1012-399 1978 £30

JOHNSTON, MARY   Audrey. Boston, 1902. Cloth, illus., 1st ed. Hayman 72-230 1978 $7.50

JOHNSTON, MARY   Cease Firing. Cambridge, 1912. Fine. Des-marais B-348 1978 $7.50

JOHNSTON, MARY   The Long Roll. London, 1911. First English ed., map, very good. Limestone 9-161 1978 $20

JOHNSTON, MARY   To Have and to Hold. Boston, 1900. Illus. by Howard Pyle, 1st ed., pencil inscr., partially erased on flyleaf. Biblo 251-517 1978 $15

JOHNSTON, NATHANIEL   The Execellency of Monarchical Government... London, 1686. 1st ed., title page in red & black, folio, contemp. calf, red leather label, pres. copy from author. Traylen 88-286 1978 £85

JOHNSTON, PAUL   A Bookshop Enchantment. Montreal, 1932. Hood 117-518 1978 $25

JOHNSTON, STANLEY   Queen of the Flat Tops. 1942. Illus., 1st ed. in slightly frayed dust jacket. Austin 80-161 1978 $10

JOHNSTON, STANLEY   Queen of the Flat Tops. 1942. Illus. Austin 80-162 1978 $7.50

JOHNSTON, W.   The Pioneers of Blanshard, with an Historical Sketch of the Township. Toronto, 1899. Errata sheet tipped in. Hood 117-745 1978 $50

JOHNSTON, WILLIAM P.   The Life of Gen. Albert Sidney Johnston, Em-bracing his Services in the Armies of the U.S., The Republic of Texas, and the Confederate States. New York, 1880. Original cloth, 1st and only ed. Jenkins 116-749 1978 $60

JOHNSTONE, C. L.   The Historical Families of Dumfriesshire and the Border Wars. Dumfries, c. 1890. 2nd ed., illus., cr. 8vo., orig. cloth. K Books 244-389 1978 £7

JOHNSTONE, CHEVALIER   A Dialogue in Hades. Quebec, 1887. Printed wrappers. Wolfe 39-258 1978 $15

JOHNSTONE, JOHN   Specimens of the Lyrical Descriptive and Narra-tive Poets of Great Britain... Edinburgh, 1828. 1st ed., engraved frontis & title, orig. half maroon morocco, spine gilt, fine. Jarndyce 16-787 1978 £15.50

JOINVILLE, JEAN, SIRE DE   Histoire de S. Louis, Credo, et Lettre a Louis X. 1872. Plates, some coloured, text illus., imp. 8vo., half crimson mor., rubbed. George's 635-698 1978 £10.50

JOINVILLE, JEAN, SIRE DE   The History of St. Louis. Oxford, 1938. Plts., 8vo. Upcroft 12-217 1978 £8.50

JOLINE, ADRIAN H.   The Book-Collector and Other Papers. Green-wich, 1904. One of an ed. of only 150 copies, t.e.g., binding rubbed. Battery Park 1-393 1978 $50

JOLLES, ANDRE   Architektur Und Kunstgewerbe In Alt-Holland Mit 246 Abbildwngen. Munchen, 1913. 4to, name stamp on title & few pgs. Baldwins' 51-104 1978 $12.50

JOLLY, DOUGLAS W.   Field Surgery in Total War. New York, 1941. Rittenhouse 49-411 1976 $12.50

JOLLY, THOMAS WILLIAM   Description of the New Patent Steering Machine. (1779). Plt., 4to., modern bds., orig. wrappers preserved. F. Edwards 1013-123 1978 £65

JOLY, HENRI L.   Shosankenshu. Cr. 4to. Traylen 88-505 1978 £10

JON, FRANCOIS DU
Please turn to
JUNIUS, FRANCISCUS

JONAS, NATHAN S.   Through the Years. 1940. Illus. Austin 80-743 1978 $12.50

JONES, ANSON   Letters, Relating to the History of Annexation, by the Ex-President of Texas. Galveston, 1848. Full calf, extremely rare work. Jenkins 116-751 1978 $850

JONES, ANSON   Memoranda and Official Correspondence Relating to the Republic of Texas, Its History, and Annexation. New York, 1859. Later cloth, morocco label, 1st ed. Jenkins 116-752 1978 $125

JONES, BASSETT   Horses and Apples. 1934. Austin 80-744 1978 $10

JONES, C. A.   Little Sir Nicholas. London, 1892. Plts., illus., 1st. ed., 8vo, orig. picture cloth. Traylen 88-160 1978 £6

JONES, CALEB   Orderly Book of the "Maryland Loyalists Regiment", June 18th, 1778, to October 12th, 1778. Brooklyn, 1891. 8vo., orig. wrs., ltd. to 250 copies. Morrill 241-233 1978 $15

JONES, CHARLES C.   Antiquities of the Southern Indians... New York, 1873. 1st ed., illus., ex-lib. rebound, scarce. MacManus 239-1174 1978 $50

JONES, CHARLES C.   Biographical Sketches of the Delegates from Georgia to the Continental Congress. Boston, 1891. 1st ed., uncut, orig. cloth, fine. MacManus 239-1809 1978 $35

JONES, CHARLES C.   The Evacuation of Battery Wagner, and the Battle of Ocean Pond, an Address. Augusta, 1888. Bell Wiley's copy. Broad-foot 46-150 1978 $12

JONES, CHARLES C.   The Siege of Savannah in December, 1864.... Orig. green covers, repaired & bound in green buckram, untrimmed. Baldwins' 51-204 1978 $32.50

JONES, CHARLES HENRY   Captain Gustavus Conyngham. N.P., 1903. Illus., orig. wrs., fine. MacManus 239-587 1978 $10

JONES, CHARLES HENRY   History of the Campaign for the Conquest of Can-ada in 1776. Philadelphia, 1882. Orig. cloth, illus., fine. MacManus 239-588 1978 $35

JONES, DANIEL W.   Forty Years Among the Indians. Salt Lake City, 1890. Original cloth, 1st ed. Ginsberg 14-436 1978 $65

JONES, EDWARD ALFRED   The Gold and Silver of Windsor Castle. Arden Press, Letchworth, 1911. Full page plts., folio, orig. buckram, ltd. ed. of 285 copies. Traylen 88-392 1978 £105

JONES, EDWARD ALFRED   The Loyalists of New Jersey... Newark, 1927. MacManus 239-1280 1978 $35

JONES, EDWARD ALFRED   The Old Plate of the Cambridge Colleges. Cam-bridge, 1910. Plts., stout 4to., orig. buckram, a little marked. George's 635-254 1978 £35

JONES, GEORGE   Francis Chantrey: Recollections of His Life,
Practice and Opinions. 1849. First ed., half title, orig. cloth, v.g. Jarndyce
16-384 1978 £20

JONES, GWYN   The Green Island, a Novel. Golden Cockerell
Press, 1946. Ltd. to 500 copies, wood-engravings by John Petts, orig. green and
grey buckram, t.e.g., others uncut. George's 635-900 1978 £25

JONES, H. L.   Illustrations of the Natural Scenery of the Snow-
donian Mountains: Accompanied by a Description, Topographical and Historical, of
the County of Caernarvon. 1839. Imp. 4to., frontis., plts., some very slight
offsetting onto text, contemp. russia gilt, fine. Quaritch 983-341 1978 £550

JONES, HENRY   Clifton: a Poem, in Two Cantos. Bristol, 1667
(i.e. 1767). 4to, half calf, 1st ed, few contemporary marginal notes. Ximenes
47-164 1978 £200

JONES, HENRY BENCE   Life and Letters of Michael Faraday. London,
1870. 2 vols., 8vo., frontis. portr., plts., text illus., contemp. half calf,
richly gilt spines, very light foxing, contemp. inscription, 1st ed. Norman 5-
*15 1978 $100

JONES, HENRY FESTING   Castellinaria and other Sicilian Diversions.
London, 1911. Orig. cloth, first ed., nice, author's signed autograph pres. inscription. Rota 211-269 1978 £5

JONES, HENRY FESTING   Samuel Butler, Author of Erewhon. 1920. 2
vols., plts., thick 8vo., fine, orig. cloth. Howes 194-688 1978 £8.50

JONES, HERSCHEL V.   Adventures in Americana 1492-1897. New
York, 1928. 2 vols., illus., lg. 4to., one of 200 numbered copies. Battery
1-329 1978 $250

JONES, IDWAL   Vines in the Sun. 1949. First ed., d.j. Austin
82-500 1978 $12.50

JONES, INIGO   Designs by Inigo Jones for Masques and Plays
at Court. Oxford, 1924. Illus., plts., mounted color frontispiece, Walpole
Soc. Vol. XII, very good. Limestone 9-162 1978 $75

JONES, J. B.   A Rebel War Clerk's Diary at the Confederate
States Capital. Philadelphia, Pa., 1866. 2 vols. in 1, embossed stamp on front.
Bell Wiley's copy. Broadfoot 46-151 1978 $125

JONES, J. B.   A Rebel War Clerk's Diary at the Confederate
States Capital. 2 vols., rebound by hand. Bell Wiley's copy. Broadfoot 46-
151A 1978 $125

JONES, J. B.   Wild Western Scenes. Philadelphia, 1879.
Rebound, clean. Hayman 71-374 1978 $8.50

JONES, J. D.   The Royal Prisoner; Charles I at Carisbrooke.
Maps, plts., octavo, good. Upcroft 10-383 1978 £5

JONES, J. WILLIAM   Christ in the Camp. Richmond, Va., 1887.
Bell Wiley's copy. Broadfoot 46-152 1978 $20

JONES, J. WILLIAM   The Davis Memorial Volume; or, Our Dead
President, Jefferson Davis, and the World's Tribute to His Memory. Richmond,
1890. Binding worn, inner hinges split, good. Biblo 248-19 1978 $32.50

JONES, JOHN RICHTER   The Quaker Soldier Or The British in Philadelphia. Philadelphia, (1858). Baldwins' 51-454 1978 $22.50

JONES, JONATHAN H.   Indianology: A Condensed History of the Apache
and Comanche Indian Tribes. San Antonio, 1899. Orig. cloth, extremely rare,
fine. Jenkins 116-1562 1978 $485

JONES, JOSEPH H.   The Life of Ashbel Green, V.D.M. New York,
1849. Frontis., orig. cloth, front outer hinge and top of spine worn. MacManus
239-760 1978 $25

JONES, JOSEPH SEAWELL   Defense of the Revolutionary History of North
Carolina from the Aspersions of Mr. Jefferson. Boston, 1834. 1st ed., scarce,
cloth, library stamp. MacManus 239-612 1978 $42.50

JONES, JULIA   Houston, 1836-1940. N.P., 1941. Wr. Jenkins
116-579 1978 $15

JONES, JULIA   Lee County, Historical and Descriptive. Houston,
1945. Jenkins 116-811 1978 $7.50

JONES, LESLIE WEBBER   The Script of Cologne from Hildebald to Hermann.
Cambridge, 1932. Folio, illus., plts., orig. cloth, 1st ed., fine. MacManus
238-981 1978 $35

JONES, M.   Life and Travel in Tartary, Thibet and China...
London, 1867. 1st. ed., engraved illus., fcap. 8vo, orig. cloth. Traylen 88-161
1978 £8

JONES, M.   Life and Travel in Tartary, Thibet and China...
London, 1879. Engraved illus., coloured frontis, fcap. 8vo, orig. cloth.
Traylen 88-161A 1978 £5

JONES, MARY   Miscellanies in Prose and Verse. Oxford, 1750.
1st. ed., 8vo, contemp. bds., roan spine, worn, title foxed, one leaf torn &
repaired. Hannas 54-175 1978 £50

JONES, OWEN   Fruits From the Garden and Field. 1850. 8vo,
printed in gold & colours throughout, dec. title, chromolithograph plts., little
light foxing, very good . Fenning 32-181 1978 £21.50

JONES, OWEN   The Grammar of Ornament. 1910. Illus., coloured plts., folio. George's 635-30 1978 £85

JONES, OWEN   Winged Thoughts. London, 1851. Roy. 8vo.,
illus., recased in orig. blind embossed leather. K Books 244-179 1978 £35

JONES, POMROY   Annals and Recollections of Oneida County.
Rome, 1851. Sound copy in orig. cloth. Butterfield 21-316 1978 $35

JONES, RUFUS M.   The Quakers in the American Colonies. London,
1923. Fold. maps. MacManus 239-231 1978 $27.50

JONES, RUFUS M.   The Quakers in the American Colonies. 1911.
Maps, octavo, good. Upcroft 10-384 1978 £12.50

JONES, RUFUS M.   Studies in Mystical Religion. London, 1923.
Baldwins' 51-350 1978 $12.50

JONES, SAMUEL   Opinion of Chancellor Jones, in the Case of
Forsyth vs. Clarke and Stewart. New York, 1829. Disbound. Hayman 73-349
1978 $7.50

JONES, SAMUEL   The Siege of Charleston and the Operations on
the South Atlantic Coast in the War Among the States. New York, 1911. 1st
ed., illus., frontis., port., orig. cloth, good. MacManus 239-886 1978 $40

JONES, STACY   The Medical Genius. Philadelphia, 1887. 8vo.,
1st ed. Morrill 239-142 1978 $10

JONES, STACY   The Medical Genius: A Guide to the Cure.
Philadelphia, 1894. Fourth ed. Rittenhouse 49-413 1976 $10

JONES, STEPHEN   Natural History of Birds... London, 1793. 1st.
ed., 12mo, old quarter leather, illus., plts. Traylen 88-162 1978 £10

JONES, STEPHEN   A New Biographical Dictionary. 1802. 4th. ed.,
12mo, rebound in half calf. Jarndyce 16-597 1978 £10.50

JONES, T.   The Gregynog Press, a Paper Read to the Double
Crown Club on 7 April 1954. Gregynog Press, 1954. Ltd. to 750 copies, wood-
engraved illus., orig. cloth, paper label on upper cover, fine, d.j. George's
635-905 1978 £80

JONES, T. BEDFORD   The Apostolic Rite of Confirmation. Ottawa,
1867. Pamphlet. Hood 117-354 1978 $20

JONES, THOMAS   History of New York During the Revolutionary
War and of the Leading Events in Other Colonies of that Period. 1879. Thick
4to., 2 vols., maps, illus., orig. cloth, good working copy, scarce 1st ed.
Butterfield 21-378 1978 $85

JONES, THOMAS JESSE   Education in East Africa. New York, (1925).
9 maps, 45 plts., 4to, orig. cloth, covers shabby. K Books 239-239 1978 £6

JONES, THOMAS RYMER   The Natural History of Animals (Invertebrates Only). 1845-52. 1st. collected ed., illus., 2 vols., 8vo, orig. cloth, nice. Fenning 32-182 1978 £16

JONES, THOMAS WHARTON   The Principles and Practice of Ophthalmic Medicine and Surgery. London, 1847. 1st ed., 8vo, orig. publicher's cloth, color plts. Gilhofer 75-63 1978 $SFr 300

JONES, URIAH JAMES   Early Settlement of the Juniata Valley... (Harrisburg, 1940). Illus. MacManus 239-1514 1978 $27.50

JONES, URIAH JAMES   History of the Early Settlement of the Juniata Valley: Embracing an Account of the Early Pioneers... Philadelphia, 1856. 1st. ed., illus. Baldwins' 51-455 1978 $22.50

JONES, VIRGIL CARRINGTON   Ranger Mosby. Chapel Hill, N. C., 1944. Bell Wiley's copy. Broadfoot 46-154 1978 $14

JONES, W. F.   The Experiences of a Deputy U.S. Marshal of the Indian Territory. Tulsa, 1937. Original wr., 1st ed. Ginsberg 14-437 1978 $15

JONES, MRS. WILBUR MOORE   Historic Beauvoir, Souvenir Booklet of Beauvoir-on-the-Gulf, Harrison County, Mississippi. Hattiesburg, 1921. Illus., Bell Wiley's copy. Broadfoot 46-155 1978 $10

JONES, WILLIAM   Diary of William Jones 1777-1821, Curate and Vicar of Broxbourne and the Hamlet of Hoddesdon 1781-1821. 1929. Plts., corners rubbed, 8vo. George's 635-1249 1978 £5.25

JONSON, BEN   The Best Plays. n.d. 3 vols., octavo, good. Upcroft 10-90 1978 £9.50

JONSON, BEN   The Masque of Kings. London, 1930. Plts., sm. folio, red vellum, gilt, t.e.g., others uncut, 1 of 350 copies, fine in orig. box. Bradley 49-177 1978 $85

JONSON, BEN   Songs. Eragny Press, 1906. One of 175 copies on paper, coloured woodcut frontis., orig. patterned bds., edges uncut. George's 635-888 1978 £105

JONSON, BEN   The Workes. 1640. Engrav. portrait, 2 parts in one vol., folio, very good, 19th cent. panelled calf gilt. Howes 194-65 1978 £90

JONSON, BENJAMIN   The Workes of Benjamin Jonson. London, 1640. 2nd ed., small folio, blind stamped full brown calf, bookplate of James Losh, ink signature on t.p., anecdotes written in ink on rear flyleaf, pages foxed and stained with some corners torn. Totteridge 29-61 1978 $200

JONSON, BENJAMIN   The Workes. 1640. Sm. folio, imperfect, eng. title, laid-down, several margins repaired, old calf, nicely rebacked, raised bands, lettering piece. Eaton 45-273 1978 £60

JONSON, BEN   The Works. 1716. Portrait, 6 vols., contemp. panelled calf gilt, some joints cracked, plts., first octavo ed. Howes 194-339 1978 £55

JORDAN, DAVID STARR   The Care and Culture of Men. San Francisco, 1896. 8vo., ex-lib., binding bit dust soiled, 1st ed. Morrill 239-452 1978 $12.50

JORDAN, DAVID STARR   The Voice of the Scholar. San Francisco, 1903. 8vo., ex-lib., binding slightly dust soiled, 1st ed. Morrill 239-453 1978 $12.50

JORDAN, J. A.   The Grosse-Isle Tragedy and the Monument to the Irish Fever Victims 1847. Quebec, 1909. Illus., orig. binding. Wolfe 39-259 1978 $60

JORDAN, JOHN W.   A History of Delaware County, Penna., and Its People. New York, 1914. Cloth, half leather, edges scuffed, illus., 3 vols. MacManus 239-1438 1978 $60

JORDAN, L. J.   The Philosophy of Marriage, Being Four Important Lectures on the Function and Disorders of the Nervous System and Reproductive Organs. San Francisco, (1865). Illus., 12mo., new wrs., orig. back wr. bound in, 1st ed. Morrill 239-143 1978 $25

JORDAN, LEOPOLD   Drilby Re-Versed. New York, 1895. 1st ed., paper wrs., lacks back cover, spine flaking, damp stains, illus. Greene 78-194 1978 $55

JORDAN, MARCIA B.   A Flush of June. East Aurora, 1898. 24mo., 1st ed., gilt-stamped suede, inscribed and signed by author, #67 of 500 copies. Petrilla 13-93 1978 $10

JORDAN, PHILIP D.   The National Road. Indianapolis, (1948). 1st. ed., clean, orig. binding. Hayman 71-376 1978 $10

JORDAN, THOMAS   The Campaigns of Lieut-Gen. N. B. Forrest. New Orleans, 1868. Maps, plates, new cloth, lib. stamp, Bell Wiley's copy. Broadfoot's 44-218 1978 $45

JORDAN, WILFRED   Colonial and Revolutionary Families of Pennsylvania... New York, 1932. Vol. IV, thick 4to., illus., many in color, very good. MacManus 239-1516 1978 $50

JORDAN VON QUEDLINBURG   Liber Vitasfratrum. 1943. Stiff wrs. Allen 234-1330 1978 $12.50

JORDANUS DE NEMORE   De Ponderibus Propositione XIII & Earundem Demonstrationes, Multarumque Rerum Rationes Sane Pulcherrimus Complectens... Norimbergae, 1533. 4to., half mor., 1st ed., fine copy. Offenbacher 30-73 1978 $750

JORRES, LUDWIG   De Freymaurerey, Oder Offenbarung Aller Geheimnisse,.... Pennsylvanien, 1829. Plate, orig. quarter roan with marbled boards, wear, scarce, 8vo. Americanist 101-91 1978 $35 .

JORTIN, JOHN 1698-1770   Sermons on Different Subjects. 1787. Portrait, 7 vols., contemp. calf, 8vo. Howes 194-340 1978 £18

JORTIN, JOHN 1698-1770   Tracts, Philological, Critical and Miscellaneous. 1790. First ed., portrait, 2 vols., contemp. calf, spines gilt, one joint cracked, nice, 8vo. Howes 194-341 1978 £28

JOSEPHSON, EMANUEL M.   Your Life is Their Toy. Chedney Press, 1940. Austin 80-746 1978 $12.50

JOSEPHSON, MATTHEW   Empire of the Air. 1944. Austin 80-747 1978 $10

JOSEPHSON, MATTHEW   The Politicos, 1865-1896. New York, (1938). 1st ed., good used copy. Biblo 251-82 1978 $15

JOSEPHSON, MATTHEW   The Robber Barons. New York, (1934). MacManus 239-232 1978 $8.50

JOSEPHUS, FLAVIUS   The Famous and Memorable Works of Josephus.... London, 1670. Small folio, woodcut initials, headpieces, decorations, contemp. calf, gilt-tooled paneled spine with red leather label, title page has inscription, engraved pictorial bookplate of Robert Cattle. Bennett 20-114 1978 $250

JOSEPHUS, FLAVIUS   Works. 1811. Frontis., maps, 4 vols., contemp. diced calf, 8vo. Howes 194-342 1978 £20

JOUGUET, P.   L'Imperialisme Macedonien et l'Hellenisation de l'Orient. Paris, 1926. Illus., maps, rebound. Biblo BL781-412 1978 $10

JOURDAIN, ANSELME LOUIS BERNARD BECHILLET   Traite des Maladies et des Operations Reelement Chirurgicales de la Bouche, et des Parties qui y Correspondent. Paris, 1778. 2 vols., 8vo., contemp. half calf, rubbed, copperplts., 1st ed., rare, very good set. Offenbacher 30-74 1978 $750

JOURDAIN, HENRY FRANCIS NEWDIGATE   The Connaught Rangers. 1924-28. 3 vols., roy. 8vo., orig. cloth, color plts., pres. copy. F. Edwards 1013-539 1978

JOURDAIN, HENRY FRANCIS NEWDIGATE   A History of the Mess Plate of the 88th the Connaught Rangers. Edinburgh, 1904. Plts., imp. 8vo., orig. cloth, uncut. F. Edwards 1013-538 1978 £12

JOURDAIN, MARGARET   Decoration in England from 1640-1760. 1927. 2nd ed., rev'd., sm. folio, illus., cloth, slightly soiled and faded, 1st ed printed in 1914. Quaritch 983-88 1978 $95

JOURDAIN, MARGARET   Decoration in England From 1640 to 1760. London, (1927). 2nd. ed., revised, 322 plts., sm. folio, name stamped on endpapers. Baldwins' 51-115 1978 $42.50

JOURDAIN, MARGARET   Decoration in England from 1660 to 1770. London, 1914. Lg. 4to., cloth, illus. Van der Peet H-64-163 1978 Dfl 95

JOURDAIN, MARGARET   English Decorative Plasterwork of the Renaissance. 1926. 4to., plts., illus., cloth, a little faded. Quaritch 983-42 1978 $90

JOURDAIN, MARGARET   English Decorative Plasterwork of the Renaissance. London, 1933. 4to, orig. cloth, fine, d.w., illus. Sexton 7-27 1978 £28

JOURDAIN, MARGARET   English Interior Decoration, 1500 to 1830. A Study in the Development of Design. (1950). 4to., coloured frontis., cloth, dust-wrs. Quaritch 983-85 1978 $65

JOURDAN, JEAN BAPTISTE   Memoires Pour Servir a l'Histoire de la Champagen de 1796... Paris, 1818. 1st. ed., 8vo, folding plans, contemp. half calf, very worn, uncut, slight water-stains, author's own copy with his bookplt. & pres. inscription to a Mr. Tennyson. Hannas 54-127 1978 £12

JOURNAL of a Tour in Italy, in the Year 1821. New York, 1824. Engr. plts. by author, 8vo., contemp. calf, 1st ed. Morrill 241-121 1978 $30

A JOURNAL of a Young Man of Massachusetts, Late a Surgeon on Board the American Privateer, Who Was Captured by the British in May, 1813. Boston, 1816. 12mo., contemp. calf, lacks frontis., hinges partly cracked, 2nd ed. Morrill 241-610 1978 $10

JOURNAL of an Officer in the King's German Legion. 1827. 8vo., half red calf, rebacked. F. Edwards 1013-403 1978 £70

A JOURNEY Through Part of England and Scotland Along with the Army Under the Duke of Cumberland. 1747. Third ed., sm. 8vo., 19th-century green calf, gilt back. P. M. Hill 142-148 1978 £20

JOWETT, W.   Christian Researches in Syria and the Holy Land, 1823-24. 1825. Maps, half calf, 8vo, 2 lib. stamps. Edwards 1012-72 1978 £25

JOYCE, JAMES   Anna Livia Plurabelle. 1930. Stiff wraps, covers split at spine, very good, first English ed. Bell Book 17-517 1978 £10

JOYCE, JAMES   Exiles, A Play in Three Acts. London, 1918. 1st ed., respectable copy. Ballinger 11-147 1978 $140.00

JOYCE, JAMES   Les Exiles. Paris, 1950. One of 205 numbered copies on velin, wrappers, very nice, unopened, with protective tissue. Bell Book 16-514 1978 £20

JOYCE, JAMES   Finnegan's Wake. London,1939. 1 of 425 numbered copies signed by author, 1st ed., 4 to., orig. gilt stamped red cloth, t.e.g., uncut, partly unopened, fine. Houle 10-173 1978 $1,250

JOYCE, JAMES   Finnegans Wake. New York, 1939. Very fine in damaged d.w. Desmarais B-349 1978 $75

JOYCE, JAMES   Haveth Childers Everywhere. Fragment from Work in Progress. Paris, 1930. Sm. folio, orig. wrs., tissue d.j., pub. slipcase, 1st ed., 1 of 500 copies on hand-made paper, lower spine slightly chipped, otherwise fine. MacManus 238-681 1978 $200

JOYCE, JAMES   Haveth Childers Everywhere. 1931. Stiff wraps, covers little foxed, very good, first English ed. Bell Book 17-518 1978 £10

JOYCE, JAMES   Haveth Childers Everywhere: fragment of Work in Progress. 1931. Good, wraps, first English ed. Bell Book 16-515 1978 £8.50

JOYCE, JAMES   Pastimes. (New York, 1941). 1 of 100 numbered copies, 1st ed., frontispiece portrait, sm. folio, grey bds., glassine jacket, enclosed in protective cloth folding case, fine. Houle 10-174 1978 $300

JOYCE, JAMES   Pomes Penyeach. Paris, 1927. 16mo, orig. boards, errata slip, lower portion of backstrip cracked, 1st ed., fine. Duschnes 220-164 1978 $50

JOYCE, JAMES   Ulysses. Paris, Egoist Press & London, 1922. Dark violet mor., gilt tooled, very fine, orig. wrs. bound in, slipcase, 1st English ed., 1 of 2000 numbered copies. Dawson's 447-253 1978 $450

JOYCE, JAMES   Ulysses. Paris, 1922. 1st ed., 4to., very rare, 750 copies on handmade paper, brown binder's cloth, red cloth fldg. box, rare state, unusual. Current Misc. 8-25 1978 $1,850

JOYCE, JAMES   Ulysses. Paris, 1922. 1 of 750 numbered copies on handmade paper, 1st ed., 4 to., half mor. over cloth, t.e.g., uncut, mostly unopened, fine. Houle 10-175 1978 $875

JOYCE, JAMES   Ulysses. Paris, 1925. Rebound in buckram, 7th. printing. Eaton 45-274 1978 £35

JOYCE, JAMES   Ulysses. (New York, 1934). Sixth printing, orig. binding. Wolfe 39-260 1978 $35

JOYCE, JAMES   Ulysses. New York, Limited Editions Club, 1935. Quarto, orig. brown cloth, gilt, handmade slipcase, 1 of 1500 numbered copies, signed by Matisse with illus. by him. Totteridge 29-66 1978 $1,000

JOYCE, JAMES   Ulysses. 1936. First English ed., one of 1000 numbered copies on Japon vellum, 4to., buckram, t.e.g., fine, d.w. Bell Book 17-519 1978 £200

JOYE, GEORGE   The Exposycion of Daniel the Prophete.... London, 1550. Black letter, title within woodcut border, sm. 8vo, contemp. blind stamped calf, initials R.H. on each cover, excellent copy. Traylen 88-287 1978 £205

JOYNES, AGNES   Treasure Seeking in the Store-Rooms of the Past. Toronto, 1931. Hood 117-481 1978 $7.50

JUAN, DON GEORGES   Examen Maritime.... Nantes, 1783. 2 vols., 4to., plts., contemp. mottled calf. F. Edwards 1013-125 1978 £120

JUAN Y SANTACILIA, JORGE   Voyage Historique de l'Amerique Meridionale.... Amsterdam & Leipzig, 1752. Engraved frontis, maps, plts., 2 vols., 4to., modern calf, light browning. Edwards 1012-658 1978 £300

JUAN Y SANTACILIA, JORGE   A Voyage to South America.... 1806. 4th ed., map, plts., 2 vols., contemp. calf, slightly discoloured, 8vo. Edwards 1012-659 1978 £75

JUARROS, DOMINGO   A Statistical and Commercial History of the Kingdom of Guatemala in Spanish America. 1823. Folding maps, orig. bds., rebacked, uncut, 8vo. Edwards 1012-691 1978 £240

JUBILEE Addresses on Home Missions Delivered on the Occasion of the Fiftieth Anniversary of the Board of Home Missions of the Reformed Church in the United States November 24-25, 1913. Philadelphia, 1914. Cloth. Hayman 72-656 1978 $7.50

THE JUBILEE Book of the Royal Automobile Club. London, (1947). Tall quarto, illus. Limestone 9-11 1978 $15

THE JUBILEE Book of the Royal Automobile Club. London, (1947). Tall 8 to., illus., good or better. Limestone 9-11 1978 $15

JUBILEE History of Latter-Day Saints Sunday Schools. Salt Lake City, 1900. Illus., orig. cloth, 1st ed. Ginsberg 14-657 1978 $20

JUDD, A.   The Conquest of the Poles and Modern Adventures in the World of Ice. (1924). 8vo, orig. cloth, maps, illus. Edwards 1012-582 1978 £8

JUDGE, A. W.   Modem Motor Cars, their Construction, Maintenance, Management, Care, Driving, and Running Repairs. 1924. Photographs, plans, text illus., 3 vols., roy. 8vo., covers dull. George's 635-971 1978 £10.50

JUDOVICH, BERNARD   Segmental Neuralgia in Painful Syndromes. Philadelphia, 1944. Library markings, clean, tight. Rittenhouse 49-414 1976 $10

JUDSON, A. M.   History of the Eighty-Third Regiment Pennsylvania Volunteers. Erie, 1865. New cloth, Bell Wiley's copy. Broadfoot 46-366 1978 $40

JUETTNER, OTTO   Daniel Drake and His Followers. Cincinnati, (1909). Tall 8vo., frontis. portr., illus., orig. green cloth, gilt lettering, bk-plt. & library stamps, good copy, 1st ed. Zeitlin 245-303 1978 $85

JUKES, EDWARD   On Indigestion and Costiveness. 1831. 2 colour plts. & other illus., half title, orig. patterned cloth, paper label, good. Jarndyce 16-875 1978 £8.50

JULIAN, BROTHER   Men and Deeds. 1930. Ex-lib. Austin 79-381 1978 $12.50

JUNCKER, JOHANN   Conspectus Chemiae Theoretico-Practicae. Halle, 1749-53. 3 vols., 4to., illus., old vellum, gilt, stamp of Wernigerode Library, bkplts. of Ernst Graf zu Stolberg, fine set, 1st ed. in German. Norman 5-158 1978 $500

JUNG, CARL GUSTAV   Psychologische Typen. Zurich, 1921. 8vo, orig. cloth, 1st ed. Gilhofer 75-64 1978 SFr 450

JUNIUS   The Letters of Junius. London, 1770. Sm. 8vo, contemporary half calf and marbled boards, spine gilt, unauthorized ed., early library stamp inked out on t.p. Ximenes 47-108 1978 $75

JUNIUS   The Letters of Junius. 1798. 8vo., contemp. tree sheep. P.M. Hill 142-155 1978 £10

JUNIUS   The Letters of Junius. London. One vol., new ed., 12mo., old sheep. K Books 244-391 1978 £9

JUNIUS   The Junius Tracts, No. V.   New York, 1844. Disbound. Hayman 71-643 1978 $8.50

JUNIUS, FRANCISCUS   De Pictura Veterum Libri Tres...Accedit Catalogus, Adhuc Ineditus, Architectorum, Mechanicorum, sed Praecipue Pictorum... Rotterdam, 1694. Folio, frontis., contemp. vellum, 1st augmented ed. Gilhofer 74-40 1978 sFr 1,400

JUNIUS, HADRIANIUS   The Nomenclator, or Remembrancer.... London, 1585. 1st ed. in English, octavo, contemp. calf, rebacked, preserving original spine. Bennett 20-115 1978 $450

JUNKIN, GEORGE   Two Addresses Delivered at Oxford, Ohio, on the Occasion of the Inauguration of Rev. Geo. Junkin, D. D. as President of Miami University. Cincinnati, Western Church Press, 1841. Disbound. Hayman 73-545 1978 $10

JUNKIN, PAUL S.   A Cruise Around the World. N. P., n.d. (ca. 1910). Illus., 8vo., orig. cloth. Morrill 241-236 1978 $10

JURIN, J.   Dissertationes Physico-Mathematicae, Partim Antea Editae in Actis Philosophicis Londinensibus.... London, 1732. 8vo. in 4s, engrav. plts., contemp. sprinkled calf, rebacked, first ed. Quaritch 977-37 1978 $160

JURIS et Judicii Fecialis sive Ivris Inter Gentes, et Quaestionum de codem Explicatio. Hague, 1659. 16mo., contemp. calf, nice. Morrill 241-642 1978 $35

JURY, WILFRID   The Grist Mill.   London, 1946. Card cover. Hood's 115-819 1978 $10

JUSSERAND, J. J.   The English Novel in the Time of Shakespeare. 1908. Illus., octavo, good. Upcroft 10-391 1978 £5.50

JUSTINIANIUS I, EMPEROR   Institutionum Libri Quatuor. 1761. 4to., contemp. calf, joints cracked, second ed. Howes 194-343 1978 £15

JUSTINUS, MARCUS JUNIANUS   Justini Historici Clarissimi in Trogi Pompei Historias Exordium. Venice, 1503. Folio, later bds., label on spine. Bennett 20-241 1978 $350

JUSTINUS, MARCUS JUNIANUS   The History. 1654. 12mo., contemp. calf, rebacked, crimson label, first ed. Howes 194-66 1978 £38

JUVENALIS, DECIMUS JUNIUS   Satyrae. Venice, 1481. 95 leaves of 96, folio, 18th. century calf, gilt spine. Traylen 88-434 1978 £525

JUVENALIS, DECIMUS JUNIUS   The Satyrs. 1726. 5th ed., plts., sm. 8vo., old calf, joints cracked, label missing. Howes 194-344 1978 £7.50

JUVENALIS, DECIMUS JUNIUS   Sixteen Satyrs. London, 1647. First English ed., 16mo., frontis., rebound in full calf, raised bands, gilt, interior clean, binding tight, ex-lib., fine. Current 24-228 1978 $110

THE JUVENILE. 1848. Illus. with wood engravings, orig. red cloth, gilt. Eaton 45-275 1978 £10

K

KAFKA, FRANZ   America. 1938. First English ed., cr. 8vo., covers rubbed. George's 635-1319 1978 £5

KAFKA, FRANZ   A Country Doctor. Etchings, Rives paper, 1 of 250 signed. Battery Park 1-185 1978 $50

KAFKA, FRANZ   The Trial. 1937. Fine, worn d.w., first English ed. Bell Book 16-520 1978 £30

KAGAN, SOLOMON R.   Fielding H. Garrison. A Biography. Boston, 1948. 8vo., fine, 1st ed., illus. Morrill 239-144 1978 $10

KAHLER, HEINZ   Pergamon. 1949. 4to., plts. Allen 234-497 1978 $7.50

KAHN, E. J.   The Army Life. 1942. Austin 80-163 1978 $8.50

KAHN, OTTO H.   Our Economic and Other Problems. 1920. Austin 80-748 1978 $10

KAHN, REUBEN L.   Serology with Lipid Antigen. Baltimore, 1950. D.j. almost as new. Rittenhouse 49-416 1976 $10

KAHN, REUBEN L.   Tissue Immunity. Library marks on spine and title. Rittenhouse 49-415 1976 $15

KALCKSTEIN, ANTONIUS   Notitia Philosophiae Historica in Tres Libros Divisa ubi Philosophiae Quidditas & Utilitas, Ortus & Progressus, Philosophorum Vitae & Sectae, Scientiaeque Naturales, Quoquo Modo ad Philosophiam Pertinentes, Earumque Orgines & Principia in Epitome Exhibentur. Wratislaviae, 1715. 4to., contemp. vellum, 1st ed. Offenbacher 30-75 1978 $125

KALER, SAMUEL P.   A Sketch of the Kaler Family. Columbia City, (1899). Baldwins' 51-258 1978 $15

THE KALISH Revolution. Edinburgh, 1789. 8vo., contemp. half calf, good, ?only ed. P. M. Hill 142-157 1978 £125

KALLIUS, ERICH   Sehorgan. Wiesbaden, 1898-1909. 7 parts, 8vo., illus., orange prtd. wrs., pres. inscr., good copies. Zeitlin 245-136 1978 $65

KALM, PETER   Travels into North America. Warrington & London, 1770-71. 3 vols., 1st ed. in English, 8vo., fldg. map, engr. plts., map with some soiling, linen-backed, few minor splits, scattered spotting, bound in new 3/4 brown calf, marbled bds., very scarce. Current 24-181a 1978 $1,675

KALM, PETER   Travels into North America. Warrington & London, 1770-71. Later marbled bds., mor. back, three vols., plts., map, scarce first Eng. ed. Wolfe 39-261 1978 $450

KAMES, HENRY HOME LORD Elucidations respecting the Common and Statute Law of Scotland. Edinburgh, 1777. First ed., contemp. calf, 8vo. Howes 194-351 1978 £21

KAMILOVA, S.   l'Art de la Danse en Tchecoslovaquie. Prague, 1932. 8vo., cloth, illus. Van der Peet H-64-154 1978 Dfl 35

KANAVEL, ALLEN B.   Infections of the Hand. Philadelphia, 1914. Second ed., thoroughly revised, library marks on spine. Rittenhouse 49-418 1976 $15

KANAVEL, ALLEN B.   Infections of the Hand. Philadelphia, 1925. Fifth ed., thoroughly revised. Rittenhouse 49-417 1976 $20

KANAVEL, ALLEN B.   Infections of the Hand. Philadelphia, 1939. Library marks. Rittenhouse 49-419 1976 $20

KANE, ELISHA KENT   Arctic Explorations. Philadelphia, 1856. Map, illus., 2 vols., 8vo., corners slightly rubbed, otherwise very nice, clean copy, 1st ed. Morrill 239-454 1978 $40

KANE, ELISHA KENT   Arctic Explorations: The Second Grinnell Expedition in Sear of Sir John Franklin, 1853-55. Philadelphia, 1857. Engraved title-pages, portraits, maps, 1 folding, engraved plts., illus., 2 vols., 8vo., orig. cloth, joints repaired. Edwards 1012-583 1978 £40

KANE, ELISHA KENT   The Second Grinnell Expedition in Search of Sir John Franklin... Philadelphia, 1856, 2 vols., map. MacManus 239-32 1978 $27.50

KANE, ELIZABETH D.   Twelve Mormon Homes Visited in Succession on a Journey Through Utah to Arizona. Philadelphia, 1874. Orig. cloth, 1st ed. Ginsberg 14-658 1978 $150

KANE, FRANCIS FISHER   A Further Report to the Indian Rights Association on the Proposed Removal of the Southern Utes. [Philadelphia], 1892. Orig. pr. wr., 1st ed. Ginsberb 14-1007 1978 $45

KANE, HARNETT THOMAS   The Bayous of Louisiana. New York, 1944. Illus., phots. Biblo 248-214 1978 $17.50

KANE, HARNETT THOMAS   Plantation Parade. New York, 1945. 1st ed., d.w., name in ink on t.p., illus. Biblo 248-215 1978 $17.50

KANE, JOHN   The Autobiography of Sky Hooks. Philadelphia, (1938). 4to, orig. pict. d.w., 8vo, orig. binding. Americanist 101-8 1978 $15

KANE, JOHN K.   Address on the Patent Laws, Delivered Before the Franklin Institute... Washington, 1849. Disbound, some foxing. Hayman 71-389 1978 $7.50

KANE, PAUL   Wanderings of an Artist Among the Indians of North America, from Canada to Vancouver's Island and Oregon through the Hudson's Bay Company's Territory and Back Again. Toronto, 1925. Ports., reproductions. Hood 116-187 1978 $45

KANE, R. J.   The Industrial Resources of Ireland. (1845). Octavo bound in cloth, reprint. Hyland 128-954 1978 £10

KANN, RODOLPHE   Catalogue of Rodolphe Kann Collection. 1907. Vol. 1 only, folio, limp bds., back cover soiled, hinges worn, plts. Allen 234-1334 1978 $15

KANNER, LEO   Folklore of the Teeth. New York, 1934. Rittenhouse 49-420 1976 $25

KANSAS PACIFIC RAILWAY COMPANY   By-Laws and Rules for Conducting the Business of the Kansas Pacific Railway Company... St. Louis, 1870. Half mor., first ed. Ginsberg 14-466 1978 $90

KANSAS Home Cook-Book Consisting of Recipes Contributed by the Ladies of Leavenworth and Other Cities and Towns. Leavenworth, 1874. Original cloth, flecks of paper stuck to covers, 1st ed. Ginsberg 14-450 1978 $125

KANT, IMMANUEL   Critique of Pure Reason. New York, 1915. 2nd rev'd ed., thick 8vo., cloth. Salloch 348-107 1978 $15

KANT, IMMANUEL   Critik der reinen Vernunft.... Riga, 1787. 8vo, contemp. half calf, 2nd, definitive ed. Quaritch 978-90 1978 $575

KANT, IMMANUEL   Metaphysische Anfangsgruende Der Naturwissenschaft. Riga, 1786. 8vo., bds., 1st ed., paper foxed. Salloch 348-105 1978 $225

KANT, IMMANUEL   Metaphysische Anfangsgruende Der Naturwisschaft. Frankfurt and Leipzig, 1794. 8vo., 1/2 leather. Salloch 348-106 1978 $90

KANT, IMMANUEL   Proloegomena Zu Einer Jeden Kuenftigen Metaphysik Die als Wissenschaft Wird Auftreten Koennen. Riga, 1783. 8vo., orig. marbled bds., old paper label, 1st ed., 2nd issue. Salloch 348-104 1978 $135

KANT, IMMANUEL   Religion within the Boundary of Pure Reason. Edinburgh, 1838. 1st ed. in English, royal 8vo., uncut, near mint. Current 24-230 1978 $185

KANT, IMMANUEL   Religion Within the Bounds of Pure Reason.
Edinburgh, 1838. 8vo., orig. blind-patterned cloth, uncut, first ed. in English.
P. M. Hill 142-158 1978 £65

KANTOR, MAC KINLAY   Arouse and Awake. 1936. Austin 82-503 1978
$8.50

KANTOR, MAC KINLAY   But Look, the Morn. 1947. Austin 82-504 1978
$10

KANTOR, MAC KINLAY   Diversey. New York, 1928. Orig. cloth, d.j.,
slightly worn, 1st ed., very good. MacManus 238-682 1978 $35

KANTOR, MAC KINLAY   El Goes South. 1930. Austin 82-506 1978
$8.50

KANTOR, MAC KINLAY   Glory for Me. 1945. First edition. Austin 82-
507 1978 $10

KANTOR, MAC KINLAY   Happy Land. 1942. 92 pgs. Austin 82-509
1978 $8.50

KANTOR, MAC KINLAY   Here Lies Holly Springs. (New York, 1938).
Thin quarto, patterned boards, cloth back, illus. by Donald McKay, signed by
author, special ed., fine. Duschnes 220-166 1978 $37.50

KANTOR, MAC KINLAY   The Noise of Their Wings. 1938. First edition.
Austin 82-510 1978 $10

KANTOR, MAC KINLAY   Signal Thirty-Two. 1950. First ed., cover soiled.
Austin 82-511 1978 $10

KANTOR, MAC KINLAY   Valedictory. 1939. Illus. Austin 82-514 1978
$8.50

KANTOR, MAC KINLAY   Wicked Water. 1948. First ed., d.j. Austin 82-
515 1978 $11

KAPLAN, MIOSE N.   Big Game Angler's Paradise. New York, (1937).
Baldwins' 51-545 1978 $17.50

KAPLAN, MORDECAI M.   The Future of the American Jew. 1948. 1st
ed. Austin 79-385 1978 $17.50

KAPP, K. WILLIAM   The Social Costs of Private Enterprise. 1950.
Hard cover ed. Austin 80-749 1978 $10

KAPPELMACHER, A.   Die Literatur der Romer bis zur Karolingerzeit.
Potsdam, 1934. 4to., cloth, plts., some in color, illus. Van der Peet H-64-
470 1978 Dfl 70

KARDINER, ABRAM   War Stress and Neurotic Illness. 1947. Austin
80-164 1978 $12.50

KARIG, WALTER   Battle Report. 1944. Illus. Austin 80-165 1978
$10

KARLOFF, BORIS   And the Darkness Falls. Cleveland and New
York, (1946). Very good, dw. Bernard 5-392 1978 $15

KARR, JEAN   Zane Grey Man of the West. New York, (1949).
Signed by Karr with inscription, photos, good. Bernard 5-118 1978 $15

KARSTEN, RAFAEL   The Civilization of the South American Indians,
with Special Reference to Magic and Religion. London and New York, 1926.
Cloth, scarce, worn & torn dust jacket, book is fine. Hayman 73-357 1978 $25

KARTOFFEL, BARON VON   The Germans in Cork. 1917. Wr., very good,
reprint. Hyland 128-734 1978 £5

KASSARJIAN, KEVORK   Behind the Iron Altar. Philadelphia, 1950.
Austin 79-386 1978 $20

KASTEIN, JOSEF   Eine Geschichte Der Juden. Berlin, 1931.
In German. Austin 79-387 1978 $27.50

KASTNER, ERICH   Emil and the Detectives. London, 1931. 1st
Eng. ed., illus., yellow pictorial cloth, very fine copy, text in mint condition,
very rare. Victoria 34-453 1978 $175

KATACHI: Japanese pattern and design in wood, paper, and clay. New York,
n.d. Plts in gravure and color, cloth. Dawson's 449-144 1978 $50

KATAEV, VALENTINE   The Embezzlers. London, (1929). First English
ed., orig. binding, nice. Rota 211-271 1978 £21

KATHMAN, J. C.   Information for Immigrants into the State of Louisiana. New Orleans, 1868. Original printed wr., 1st ed. Ginsberg 14-504
1978 $150

KAUFFMAN, RUTH   The Latter Day Saints. London, 1912. 1st ed.,
signed by both authors. Biblo 251-122 1978 $37.50

KAULBACK, R.   Salween. 1938. Maps, plts., 8vo, orig. cloth,
fine copy in orig. d.w. Edwards 1012-138 1978 £25

KAUTSKY, KARL   The Social Revolution. 1902. Austin 80-750
1978 $11

KAUTZ, AUGUST V.   The Company Clerk. Philadelphia, 1864. Sm.
8vo., signature of H. J. Haughton. Morrill 239-455 1978 $30

KAVAN, ANNA   Asylum Piece. New York, 1946. First Amer.
ed., nice, orig. binding, inscribed by author. Rota 211-272 1978 £21

KAVANAGH, A.   The Cruise of the R.Y.S. Eva. Dublin, 1865.
Frontispiece, tinted litho plts., slight foxing, spine repaired, 8vo, orig. cloth.
Edwards 1012-50 1978 £25

KAVANAGH, D. J.   The Holy Family Sisters of San Francisco: A
Sketch of Their First Fifty Years, 1872-1922... San Francisco, 1922. Illus.,
original cloth, 1st ed. Ginsberg 14-148 1978 $25

KAVANAGH, JULIA   Grace Lee A Tale. 1855. 1st. ed., 3 vols.,
half calf, green cloth bds., lacking front free endpaper, hinges & spines rubbed.
Jarndyce 16-791 1978 £24.50

KAVANAGH, JULIA   Grace Lee. NY, 1901. Cloth binding. Greene
78-66 1978 $10.00

KAVANAGH, JULIA   Madeleine: A Tale of Auvergne... 1848. 1st.
ed., orig. blue cloth, good. Jarndyce 16-790 1978 £18.50

KAVANAUGH, JULIA   Rachel Gray. Leipzig, 1856. 1st Tauchnitz ed.
in 1 vol., orig. half-cloth, leather. Greene 78-235 1978 $25

KAWAKAMI, KIYOSHI K.   Asia at the Door. 1914. Austin 79-390
1978 $27.50

KAY, JOHN 1742-1826   A Series of Original Portraits and Caricature
Etchings. Edinburgh, 1837-38. First ed., plts., 2 vols., 4to., late 19th cent.
full mor., raised bands, gilt edges. Howes 194-1395 1978 £135

KAY, S.   Travels and Researches in Caffraria... New
York, 1834. Folding map, plts., 12mo, cover slightly worn, some foxing, orig.
cloth. Edwards 1012-300 1978 £75

KAYE, G. W. C.   X-Rays. London, 1926. Fourth ed. Rittenhouse
49-421 1976 $15

KAYE-SMITH, SHEILA   Faithful Stranger and Other Stories. New
York, 1938. Fine in chipped d.w. Desmarais B-360 1978 $7.50

KAYE-SMITH, SHEILA   Joanna Godden. London, 1921. Green cloth,
1st ed., bkplt., scarce. Bradley 49-179 1978 $20

KAYE-SMITH, SHEILA   Joanna Godden Married and Other Stories.
London, 1926. Fine in chipped d.w. Desmarais B-361 1978 $10

KAYE-SMITH, SHEILA   Starbrace. 1909. Cloth, very good, first
English ed. Bell Book 16-522 1978 £7.50

KAYE-SMITH, SHEILA   The Tramping Methodist. 1908. Cloth gilt, good, first English ed. Bell Book 16-523 1978 £8

KAYE-SMITH, SHEILA   The Tramping Methodist. London, 1908. Dark green cloth, 1st ed., former owner's name in ink, covers worn. Bradley 49-180 1978 $50

KAYE-SMITH, SHEILA   Wedding Morn, A Story. London, 1928. 8vo, original grey boards, decorated in red, dust jacket, 1st ed., one of 530 copies numbered and signed by the author. Ximenes 47-165 1978 $22.50

KEARTON, CHERRY   The Island of Penguins. London, 1931. 1st ed., 8vo, orig. cloth. Book Chest 17-206 1978 $20

KEARTON, CHERRY   Through Central Africa From East to West. London, 1915. Folding map, coloured frontis, 8 photos, 160 illus., stout roy. 8vo, dec. cloth, covers dull. K Books 239-240A 1978 £10

KEARTON, CHERRY   Through Central Africa From East to West. New York, 1915. Folding map, coloured frontis, photos, illus., stout roy. 8vo, dec. cloth, American ed., few pages roughly opened, slightly shaken. K Books 239-240B 1978 £12

KEARTON, R.   Wild Life at Home – How to Study and Photograph it. London, 1898. Worn, faded gilt-stamped binding, scribbling inner front cover, 8vo, orig. cloth. Book Chest 17-207 1978 $15

KEATE, GEORGE   An Account of the Pelew Islands... London, 1788. 2nd. ed., 4to, engraved portrait, folding engraved map, engraved plts., contemporary tree calf, neatly rebacked, morocco label, gilt, corners worn, some foxing, offsetting, armorial bookplt. Deighton 5-103 1978 £75

KEATE, GEORGE .   An Account of the Pelew Islands... 1788. 4to, calf, spine repaired, map, plts. Edwards 1012-375 1978 £45

KEATING, J. M.   A History of the Yellow Fever. Memphis, 1879. 8vo., ex-lib., 1st ed. Morrill 239-145 1978 $47.50

KEATS, JOHN   Endymion: A Poetic Romance. 1818. First ed., second issue, excellent copy, uncut and unpressed, 8vo., modern bds. Thomas 37-42 1978 £800

KEATS, JOHN   Endymion. Elston Press, 1902. Battery Park 1-90 1978 $150

KEATS, JOHN   Endymion. London, Golden Cockerel Press, 1943-47. Ltd. ed. of 500 copies, sm. folio, orig. qtr. vellum gilt, fine. K Books 244-140 1978 £70

KEATS, JOHN   The Eve of St. Agnes and Other Poems. London, 1820. 12mo., multicolored mor., first ed., fine, uncut, lg. copy, spectacular Riviere binding. Howell 5-36 1978 $2,750

KEATS, JOHN   Lamia, Isabella, the Eve of Saint Agnes, and Other Poems. 1928. Impl. 8vo., finely prtd. on handmade paper, woodcuts, cloth, sharkskin back, fine copy, 500 copies prtd. Quaritch 979-351 1978 $300

KEATS, JOHN   The Letters of. London, 1895. Illus., 8vo., orig. cloth. Morrill 241-237 1978 $12.50

KEATS, JOHN   Life, Letters, and Literary Remains, of John Keats. London, 1848. 2 vols., octavo, orig. blind-stamped publisher's cloth, lettered in gilt, fading of spines and extremities lightly worn, 1st ed. Bennett 7-64 1978 $225

KEATS, JOHN   Odes. London, 1923. 4to, grey boards, decor. by Vivien Gribble, covers and spine darkened, near Fine, 1st ed., collector's cond. Desmarais 1-255 1978 $35

KEATS, JOHN   Poems. London & New York, 1896. Two vols., nice, first ed., orig. binding. Rota 211-47 1978 £6

KEATS, JOHN   Poems. London, 1915. 2 vols., sm. 4to, orig. vellum, gilt tops, other edges uncut, ltd. ed. of 250 copies, on hand-made paper. Traylen 88-288 1978 £25

KEATS, JOHN   Poems. 1920. Orig. cloth-backed bds., gilt tops, other edges untrimmed, bindings soiled, 2 vols., 8vo. Howes 194-977 1978 £6

KECKLEY, ELIZABETH   Behind the Scenes. New York, 1868. 1st. ed., lg. 12mo, portrait, orig. cloth, rehinged, morocco-backed slip-case, some foxing. Hannas 54-313 1978 £40

KEDDIE, HENRIETTA   Citoyenne Jacqueline. A Woman's Lot in the Great French Revolution. London, 1865. 3 vols., orig. cloth, 1st ed., signature in vol. I, very good. MacManus 238-352 1978 $85

KEEBLE, FREDERICK   Life of Planets. Oxford, 1926. Rittenhouse 49-422 1976 $7.50

KEEFER, THOMAS C.   Report on a Survey for the Railway Bridge over the St. Lawrence at Montreal. Montreal, 1853. Modern plain wrappers. Wolfe 39-469 1978 $75

KEELER, HARRY STEPHEN   The Matilda Hunter Murder. New York, (1931). 1st ed., 8 vo., orig. gilt stamped blue cloth, very good. Houle 10-176 1978 $15

KEELER, S. C.   The Murdered Maiden Student. Suncook, 1878. Portr., illus., 12mo., 1st ed. Morrill 241-391 1978 $25

KEELING, RALPH FRANKLIN   Gruesome Harvest. Chicago, 1947. Paper. Austin 79-392 1978 $15

KEEN, ARTHUR   Charing Cross Bridge. London, 1930. 4to, orig. cloth, plts., diagrams, plans, good. Sexton 7-28 1978 £5.25

KEEN, WILLIAM WILLIAMS   Selected Papers and Addresses. Philadelphia, 1922. Rittenhouse 49-423 1976 $10

KEENAN, HENRY F.   The Conflict With Spain. Philadelphia and Chicago, (1898). Rebound, clean. Hayman 71-394 1978 $7.50

KEENLEYSIDE, C. B.   God's Fellow-Workers and the House That is to be Built for Jehovah. (Toronto, 1910). Hood's 115-936 1978 $7.50

KEETON, MORRIS T.   The Philosophy of Edmund Montgomery. Dallas, 1950. Jenkins 116-963 1978 $7.50

KEGELER, CASPAR   Eyn Nutzlichs und trostlichs Regiment wider dy Pestilentz un Gifftigk Pestilentzisch Feber die Schweyssucht genant.... Leipzig, 1529. 8 vo., woodcuts, fine copy, black library half cloth. Schafer 19-52 1978 sFr. 2,200

KEHRER, H.   Die Kunst des Greco. Munchen, 1914. Sm. 4to., cloth, plts. Van der Peet H-64-49 1978 Dfl 45

KEIFER, JOSEPH W.   Slavery and Four Years of War... New York, 1900. 2 vols., illus., t.e.g., fine untrimmed set, scarce. MacManus 239-842 1978 $50

KEIFER, S. J. HARRIS   Genealogical and Biographical Sketches of the New Jersey Branch of the Harris Family in the U.S. Madison, 1888. MacManus 239-924 1978 $15

KEIGHTLEY, THOMAS   Tales and Popular Fictions. 1834. 12mo., contemp. calf, plts. P. M. Hill 142-159 1978 £12

KEILEY, A. M.   In Vinculis; or, the Prisoner of War. Petersburg, 1866. Bound in cloth, Bell Wiley's copy. Broadfoot 46-464 1978 $65

KEILL, J.   Introductio ad Veram Physicam. London, 1719. 8vo., woodcut text illus., contemp. unlettered calf, joints split. Quaritch 977-109 1978 $60

KEILL, J.   An Introduction to Natural Philosophy. London, 1745. 8vo., woodcut text illus., contemp. calf, gilt spine, fourth ed. Quaritch 977-110 1978 $85

KEILL, J.   An Introduction to the True Astronomy. London, 1733. 8vo., second ed., plts., maps, contemp. calf, rubbed. Quaritch 977-190 1978 $120

KEIR, JAMES   The First Part of a Dictionary of Chemistry. 1789. 1st. ed., 4to, half calf, marbled bds., v.g. Jarndyce 16-122 1978 $50

KEISAI, KUWAGATA   Choju Ryakugwa-Shiki (Simplified Forms of Drawings Birds and Animals). 1813. Wrs., sewn, illus. Dawson's .449-145 1978 $95

KEITH, ARTHUR B.   The Constitution of England from Queen Victoria to George VI. 1940. 2 vols., spines faded, 8vo. George's 635-346 1978 £7.50

KEITH, ARTHUR B.   The Governments of the British Empire. London, 1935. Biblo BL781-829 1978 $12

KEITH, CHARLES P.   Chronicles of Pennsylvania from the English Revolution to the Peace of Aix-La-Chapelle... Philadelphia, 1917. 2 vols., 4to. MacManus 239-1518 1978 $37.50

KEITH, ELIZABETH   Old Korea: The Land of Morning Calm. London, (1946). Illus., cloth, some fading, lacking front fly. Dawson's 127-223 1978 $35

KEITH, MELVILLE C.   What I Know About Teeth, and How to Preserve Them. Boston, 1885. 12mo., lst ed. Morrill 239-146 1978 $12.50

KEITHAHN, E. L.   Igloo Tales. Washington, D.C., (1950). Illus. by G. A. Ahgupuk, spine worn, plts. Hood 117-683 1978 $15

KELEHER, WILLIAM A.   The Fabulous Frontier... Santa Fe, (1945). Cloth, illus., lst ed., 1 of 500 copies, orig. d.w., slipcase, very scarce. Dykes 35-202 1978 $75

KELEKIAN, D.   The Kelekian Collection of Persian and Analogous Potteries 1885-1910. Paris, 1910. Folio, plts., cloth, ltd. to 100 copies, this is #6, pres. inscription from Kelekian, A.L.s. from him tipped in. Quaritch 983-144 1978 $750

KELKER, LUTHER REILY   History of Dauphin County, Pa., with Genealogical Records. New York & Chicago, 1907. lst ed., 3 vols., 4to, orig. half mor., rubbed, worn. Americanist 101-74 1978 $85

KELLAND, CLARNECE BUDINGTON   The Comic Jest. Grabhorn Press, 1949. Inscribed by author, 52 pages. Austin 82-517 1978 $27.50

KELLAR, HERBERT ANTHONY   Solon Robinson Pioneer and Agriculturist. Indianapolis, 1936. 2 vols. Bell Wiley's copy. Broadfoot 46-531 1978 $10

KELLER, A. G.   Colonization, a Study of the Founding of New Societies. Boston, 1908. 8vo. George's 635-699 1978 £5

KELLER, CHARLES FELIX   Iconographie du Costume Militaire. Paris, 1938. Plts., 8vo., half mor., ltd. to 315 copies, pres. by author, one of 15 on velin ancien de Vidalon. F. Edwards 1013-341 1978 £55

KELLER, ELIZABETH LEAVITT   Walt Whitman in Mickle Street. New York, 1921. First U.S. ed., bookplt., else very good. Bell Book 16-915 1978 £8.50

KELLER, F.   The Amazon and Madeira Rivers... 1874. Folio, woodcut illus., lst. ed. in English, orig. cloth. Edwards 1012-660 1978 £65

KELLER, ROBERT B.   Hist. of Monroe County, Pa. Stroudsburg, 1927. Illus., scarce. MacManus 239-1519 1978 $40

KELLETT, E. E.   A Book of Cambridge Verse. Cambridge, 1911. lst ed., very good or better. Limestone 9-50 1978 $15

KELLEY, FRANK   Macarthur: Man of Action. 1950. Ex-lib. Austin 80-167 1978 $10

KELLEY, HALL J.   Oregon Settlement Stock. [Boston, 1831]. Oblong 4to. Ginsberg 14-822 1978 $100

KELLEY, WILLIAM D.   Remarks of Hon. William D. Kelley...in Support of His Proposed Amendment to the Bill "to Guaranty to Certain States Whose Governments have been Usurped or Overthrown a Republican Form of Government". N.P., n.d. (Washington, 1865). Disbound. Hayman 73-358 1978 $8.50

KELLEY, WILLIAM D.   Reply to George Northrop...September 23, 1864. 1864. 8vo., sewn, complete set of 8 numbers. Morrill 241-239 1978 $37.50

KELLOGG, A. N.   Kellogg's Auxiliary Hand-Book... Chicago, 1878. Orig. binding, clean. Hayman 71-396 1978 $10

KELLOGG, EDWARD   A New Monetary System. 1861. 5th ed. Austin 80-753 1978 $12.50

KELLOGG, EDWARD L.   The Duodenum. New York, 1933. Rittenhouse 49-424 1976 $25

KELLOGG, ELIJAH   Lion Ben of Elm Island. Boston, 1869. lst. ed., virtually fine copy. Victoria 34-455 1978 $85

KELLOGG, JOHN AZOR   Capture and Escape, A Narrative of Army and Prison Life. N.P., 1908. Ltd. to 2500 copies, spine darkened, Bell Wiley's copy. Broadfoot's 44-677 1978 $20

KELLOGG, PAUL V.   British Labor and the War. 1919. Austin 80-754 1978 $12.50

KELLOGG, ROBERT H.   Life and Death in Rebel Prisons. Hartford, 1865. One page loose, Bell Wiley's copy. Broadfoot's 44-440 1978 $7

KELLOGG, V. L.   American Insects. New York, 1914. 3rd revised ed., some binding wear, 8vo, orig. cloth. Book Chest 17-208 1978 $32

KELLY, A. H.   The American Constitution. New York, (1948). 2 vols., first ed., fine, boxed. Biblo 247-74 1978 $15

KELLY, CHARLES   Salt Desert Trails:.... Salt Lake City, 1930. Illus., original soft cloth, d. j., lst ed. Ginsberg 14-467 1978 $75

KELLY, CLYDE   United States Postal Policy. 1931. Austin 80-755 1978 $11

KELLY, FANNY   Narrative of My Captivity Among the Sioux Indians. Cincinnati, 1871. Cloth, scarce lst ed., worn at ends of spine and corners, covers faded, free endpaper lacking in back. Hayman 72-388 1978 $12.50

KELLY, FELIX   Paintings by Felix Kelly. 1946. Plts., in colour, 4to., very good, repaired d.w., first English ed. Bell Book 16-488 1978 £6

KELLY, GEORGE   The Deep Mrs. Sykes... New York, 1946. lst ed., bookplt. Biblo BL781-1038 1978 $10

KELLY, HOWARD A.   Walter Reed and Yellow Fever. New York, 1906. Rittenhouse 49-425 1976 $20

KELLY, HUGH   The School for Wives, A Comedy. Dublin, 1774. lst. Irish ed., 12mo, wrapper, nice. Fenning 32-183 1978 £18.50

KELLY, HUGH   The School for Wives. Dublin, 1774. lst. Irish ed., wrapper. Jarndyce 16-123 1978 £25

KELLY, J. FREDERICK   Early Connecticut Architecture. New York, 1924. Drwgs., fldg. plts., tall 4to., bd. fldr. Argosy Special-54 1978 $75

KELLY, JOHN BERNARD   Cardinal Hayes. 1940. Illus., lst ed., inscr'd by author. Austin 79-394 1978 $12.50

KELLY, JOHN L.   Fact and Fiction! Manchester, 1853. 8vo, original blue printed wr., lst ed., fine copy. Ximenes 47-166 1978 $100

KELLY, MARY R.   Hannah Hawkins and Her Neighbor. N.P., (Groveland?), 1879. Cloth, scarce. Hayman 72-231 1978 $22.50

KELLY, R. TALBOT   Egypt. London, 1912. Frontis., plts. coloured, orig. cloth, 8vo. K Books 244-180 1978 £5

KELLY, THOMAS   1779 General Sullivan's Great War Trail. Geneseo, 1913. Butterfield 21-386 1978 $7.50

KELLY, THOMAS J.   Damage Control. 1944. Illus. Austin 80-168 1978 $17.50

KELMAN, JOHN   The Holy Land. London, 1912. Coloured plts.
by John Fulleylove, 8vo., orig. cloth. K Books 244-181 1978 £5

KELSEY, RAYNER W.   Cazenove Journal, 1794. Haverford, 1922.
Illus., map. MacManus 239-235 1978 $25

KEMBLE, EDWARD W.   Kemble's Coons. (New York), 1896. 1st ed.,
minor cover rubbing and dust-soiling, tiny margin tears, internally very fine, very
scarce. Victoria 34-456 1978 $100

KEMBLE, FRANCES ANNE   The Adventures of Mr. John Timothy Homespun
In Switzerland. London, 1889. Orig. wraps., "Harry Lee With Fanny Kembles'
Best Love" on front cover. Baldwins' 51-351 1978 $35

KEMBLE, FRANCES ANNE   Journal. Philadelphia, 1835. Two vols., orig.
binding. Wolfe 39-56 1978 $60

KEMBLE, FRANCES ANNE   Journal of a Residence on a Georgian Plantation
in 1838-9. New York, 1863. 1st ed. MacManus 239-843 1978 $30

KEMBLE, FRANCES ANNE   Journal of a Residence on a Georgian Plantation.
London, 1863. 1st. ed., sm. 8vo, half-title, orig. cloth, neatly rebacked, gilt.
Deighton 5-44 1978 £95

KEMBLE, FRANCES ANN   Record of a Girlhood; with, Records of Later
Life. 1878-82. First ed., 6 vols., cr. 8vo., half calf gilt. Howes 194-1270
1978 £45

KEMBLE, FRANCIS ANNE   Records of Later Life. London, 1882. 3 vols.,
orig. cloth, 1st ed., bookplts. removed, near fine. MacManus 238-302 1978
$85

KEMBLE, FRANCES ANNE   A Year of Consolation. New York, 1847. 2
vols. in 1, sm. 8vo., new cloth. Morrill 239-457 1978 $12.50

KEMBLE, FRANCES ANNE   A Year of Consolation. 2 vols. in 1, as issued,
clean, orig. binding. Hayman 71-75 1978 $12.50

KEMBLE, JOHN PHILLIP   Fugitive Pieces In Verse. York, 1780. 12mo,
contemp. half morocco, fine, uncut copy, evidently lacking half-title. Hannas
54-176 1978 £25

KEMMERER, EDWIN WALTER   The ABC of Inflation. 1942. Ex-lib. Austin
80-756 1978 $12.50

KEMP, DIXON   Yacht Designing. London, 1876. Plts., lg.
4to., cloth. K Books 244-182 1978 £65

KEMP, E. W.   Canonization and Authority in the Western
Church. Oxford, 1948. 8vo. Upcroft 12-228 1978 £7.50

KEMP, HARRY   Boccaccio's Untold Tale and Other One-Act
Plays. New York, (1924). Orig. cloth, d.j., 1st ed., fine. MacManus 238-
691 1978 $20

KEMP, HARRY   Chanteys and Ballads. Sea-Chanteys, Tramp-
Ballads and Other Ballads and Poems. New York, (1920). Orig. bds., 1st ed.,
pres. copy from author, good. MacManus 238-689 1978 $27.50

KEMP, HARRY   Chanteys and Ballads. Sea Chanteys, Tramp Ballads, Etc. New York, (1920). 12mo., orig. bds., 1st ed. MacManus 238-
690 1978 $15

KEMP, HARRY   The Cry of Youth. New York, 1914. Orig.
cloth, 1st ed., very good. MacManus 238-684 1978 $30

KEMP, HARRY   Judas. New York, 1913. Orig. cloth, d.j.,
a bit soiled, 1st ed., fine, rare in d.j. MacManus 238-683 1978 $40

KEMP, HARRY   More Miles. An Autobiographical Novel. New
York, (1926). Orig. cloth, d.j., 1st ed., pres. copy, inscription from author,
top of spine worn, but good. MacManus 238-692 1978 $30

KEMP, HARRY   The Passing God. Sons for Lovers. New York,
1919. Orig. bds., 1st ed., inscribed by author, outer hinges cracked, pencil
annotations. MacManus 238-687 1978 $25

KEMP, HARRY   The Thresher's Wife. New York, 1914. Orig.
bds., 1st ed., head of spine worn, else very good. MacManus 238-686 1978
$25

KEMP, JAMES F.   The Ore Deposits of the United States and Canada.
New York/London, 1900. Third ed., orig. binding. Wolfe 39-263 1978 $25

KENDAL, E. A.   Pocket Encyclopedia. 1811. Plts., 4 vols.,
12mo., spanish calf, gilt, rubbed. George's 635-1469 1978 £12.50

KENDALL, ELIZABETH   A Wayfarer in China. London, 1913. Illus.,
8vo., 1st English ed., orig. cloth. Morrill 241-682 1978 $12.50

KENDALL, GEORGE W.   Narrative of the Texan Santa Fe Expedition.
New York, 1856. 2 vols., orig. cloth, exceedingly rare, desirable 7th ed.
Jenkins 116-764 1978 $950

KENDALL, HENRY CLARENCE   Poems. 1890. Half title, orig. purple cloth,
gilt spine faded, otherwise v.g. Jarndyce 16-792 1978 £12.50

KENDALL, NANCY NOON   The New House. 1934. Mor., gilt top, #4
of 10 copies of deluxe ltd. ed. signed by author, fine, slipcase. Dykes 35-151
1978 $25

KENDO, T. A.   Treatise on Silk and Tea Culture and other Asiatic
Industries adapted to the Soil and Climate of California. San Francisco, 1870.
Cloth (faded, spine ends frayed). Dawson's 127-267 1978 $25

KENDON, FRANK   The Small Years. Cambridge, 1930. Fine in
d.w. Desmarais B-176 1978 $12.50

KENDRICK, BENJAMIN B.   The Journal of the Joint Committee of Fifteen
on Reconstruction, 39th Cong., 1865-1867. New York, 1914. Wrs., Bell Wiley's
copy. Broadfoot's 44-223 1978 $16

KENILWORTH, First Fifty Years. Kenilworth, 1947. Clean, pres. copy, private
bookplate, orig. binding. Hayman 71-316 1978 $10

KENLY, JOHN R.   Memoirs of a Maryland Volunteer. Philadelphia,
1873. 1st ed., orig. cloth, fine, scarce. MacManus 239-307 1978 $30

KENLY, JULIE CLOSSON   Little Lives. 1938. Illus., first ed., fine, d.j.
Austin 82-518 1978 $12.50

KENNAN, GEORGE   The Chicago and Alton Case. New York, (1916).
1st ed. Biblo 251-95 1978 $15

KENNAN, GEORGE   E. H. Harriman...A Biography. Boston, (1922).
2 vols. Biblo 251-94 1978 $16.50

KENNAN, GEORGE   The Tragedy of Pelee. 1902. Illus., first ed.
Austin 82-519 1978 $27.50

KENNAN, GEORGE   The Tragedy of Pelee. New York, 1902. Illus.,
1st ed. Biblo BL781-113 1978 $10

KENNARD, COLERIDGE A. FITZROY   Farewell to Eilenroc. Centaur Press,
1934. First ed., orig. buckram, d.w., 400 copies were printed, pres. inscription
from author, 8vo. Howes 194-979 1978 £5

KENNEDY, AMBROSE   Quebec to New England. Boston, 1948.
Illus. with photos, 1st ed., very good in dust jacket, inscr'd by author. Austin
79-395 1978 $37.50

KENNEDY, ANDREW   Remarks of Mr..., of Indiana, on the Motion of
Mr. Wise...as Refers to the Improvement of Western Rivers and Lakes...Delivered
in the House...December 19, 1843. Washington, 1843. Disbound. Hayman 72-
671 1978 $8.50

KENNEDY, ANDREW   Remarks of Mr..., of Indiana, on the Removal of
Obstructions in the Mississippi River and Its Tributaries. Delivered in the House...
January 16, 1844. Washington, 1844. Disbound. Hayman 72-672 1978 $8.50

KENNEDY, DONALD   Kennedy on Diseases of the Skin. Roxbury, 1871.
2nd ed., lightly colored plts., 8vo., orig. wrs. Morrill 239-148 1978 $7.50

KENNEDY, GRACE   Anna Ross, A Story for Children. Edinburgh, 1838. Plts., 12mo, orig. cloth, binding dull, otherwise nice. Fenning 32-184 1978 £12.50

KENNEDY, GRACE   Willoughby or Reformation. 1826. 1st ed., 2 vols., half calf, marbled bds., good. Jarndyce 16-793 1978 £33

KENNEDY, H. A.   Book of the West. Toronto, 1925. Illus. Hood 117-898 1978 $15

KENNEDY, H. A.   Early English Portrait Miniatures in the Collection of the Duke of Buccleuch. 1917. Plts., 12 in coloure, sm. folio, orig. cloth, gilt, t.e.g., nice copy. Fenning 32-161 1978 £18.50

KENNEDY, JAMES   A Description of the Antiquities and Curiosities in Wilton-House. Salisbury, 1769. 4to., plts., some foxing, contemp. calf, rubbed. Quaritch 983-20 1978 $90

KENNEDY, JOHN PENDLETON   The Border States: Their Power and Duty in the Present Disordered Condition of the Country. Philadelphia, 1861. 8vo., orig. cloth, 2nd prtg. Morrill 241-241 1978 $17.50

KENNEDY, JOHN PENDLETON   Quodibet: Containing Some Annal Thereof... Philadelphia, 1840. Orig. cloth, some rubbing, light foxing throughout, 1st ed., very good. MacManus 238-550 1978 $75

KENNEDY, JOHN PENDLETON   Speech of Mr...., of Baltimore, Delivered in the House of Representatives, on the 22nd and 23rd of June, 1838, in the Debate on the Sub Treasury Bill. Baltimore, 1838. Orig. wrs., first ed., sm. portion of front cover clipped, else very good. MacManus 238-549 1978 $75

KENNEDY, R. S.   The Road South. Toronto, 1947. Hood's 115-438 1978 $10

KENNEDY, R. EMMET   More Mellows. New York, 1931. 1st ed., 4to., worn d.w., very good. Americanist 103-20 1978 $22.50

KENNEDY, RANKIN   The Book of Modern Engines. (c. 1913). Plts., illus., 6 vols., roy. 8vo. George's 635-970 1978 £12.50

KENNEDY, W.   English Taxation, 1640-1799, an Essay on Policy and Opinion. 1913. 8vo. George's 635-347 1978 £6

KENNEDY, W. P. M.   The Constitution of Canada. Oxford University Press, 1922. Orig. binding. Wolfe 39-264 1978 $55

KENNEDY, W. P. M.   Theories of Law and the Constitutional Law of the British Empire... Quebec, 1929. Wrs. Hood 116-634 1978 $7.50

KENNEDY, W. R.   Sport, Travel and Adventure in Newfoundland and The West Indies. 1885. Map, coloured frontis, illus., orig. cloth, 8vo. Edwards 1012-435 1978 £25

KENNEDY, WILLIAM   A Short Narrative of the Second Voyage of The Prince Albert, in Search of Sir John Franklin. London, 1853. Orig. binding, slight foxing. Hood 117-100 1978 $140

KENNEDY, WILLIAM   Texas: The Rise, Progress, and Prospects of the Republic of Texas. Fort Worth, 1925. Reissue of 1841 rarity, folding maps. Jenkins 116-768 1978 $45

KENNEDY, WILLIAM   Texas: It Geography, Natural History, and Topography. New York, 1944. Orig. pr. wr., 1st Amer. ed. Ginsberg 14-961 1978 $175

KENNER, H. J.   The Fight for Truth in Advertising. Round Table Press, 1936. Austin 80-757 1978 $11

KENNERLEY, MITCHELL   Elements of Lettering. Forest Hills, Marchbanks Press, 1922. Folio, cloth. Battery Park 1-124 1978 $75

KENNETT, BASIL   Romae Antiquae Notitia. Philadelphia, 1822. Engrs. by R. Campbell, 8vo., contemp. calf, 1st Amer. ed. Morrill 239-459 1978 $15

KENNEY, C. E.   The Quadrant and The Quill; A Book Written in Honour of Captain Samuel Sturmy... 1947. 4to, plts., good. Upcroft 10-397 1978 £10

KENNEY, J. F.   Catalogue of Pictures, Including Paintings, Drawings, and Prints, in the Public Archives of Canada. Ottawa, 1925. Part 1, card cover, illus. Hood 116-37 1978 $17.50

KENNEY, J. F.   Catalogue of Pictures, Including Paintings, Drawings, and Prints in the Public Archives of Canada. Ottawa, 1925. Illus., signed & inscr. by editor. Hood 117-46 1978 $20

KENNINGTON, ERIC   Drawing the R.A.F. London, 1942. First ed., orig. binding, nice, torn d.w. Rota 211-275 1978 £5

KENNINGTON, ERIC   Pilots, Workers, Machines. (c.1942). Ltd. ed., monochrome reproduction of portraits, 4to, orig. printed wrappers, covers spotted, sm. stain in top margin throughout volume, inscription from author. Sawyer 299-125 1978 £38

KENNY, THOMAS MOORE   Two Graves. Baltimore, 1902. Pres. copy from author, Bell Wiley's copy. Broadfoot 46-156 1978 $9

KENT, FRANK R.   The Great Game of Politics... Garden City, 1928. Cloth. Hayman 72-389 1978 $7.50

KENT, FRANK R.   The Story of Maryland Politics. Baltimore, 1911. Baldwins' 51-287 1978 $10

KENT, JAMES TYLER   Lectures on Homeopathic Philosophy. Lancaster, 1900. Some slight marks on top cover, otherwise good. Rittenhouse 49-426 1976 $15

KENT, NATHANIEL   General View of the Agriculture of the County of Norfolk;.... Norwich, 1796. 8vo, original boards, printed paper label, 2nd ed., folding map, plates, nice copy. Ximenes 47-167 1978 $100

KENT, NATHANIEL   General View of the Agriculture of the County of Norfolk. 1796. Contemp. calf, plts., 8vo. Howes 194-125 1978 £18

KENT, ROCKWELL   The Bookplates & Marks of. New York, 1929. One of 1250 numbered, signed copies. Battery Park 1-189 1978 $100

KENT, ROCKWELL   Later Bookplates & Marks. (1937). Numbered and signed, special Japan paper. Battery Park 1-190 1978 $100

KENT, ROCKWELL   Drawings by Rockwell Kent. New York, 1924. Folio, orange paper portfolio with blue linen backstrip, signed repros. on paper made in Japan, only 30 copies, fine. Duschnes 220-171 1978 $1,500

KENT, ROCKWELL   Greenland Journal. New York, (1962). 8vo., cloth, boxed, pict. endpapers, one of 1000 numbered copies, six Kent originals, one handsigned by Kent, plts. loose in portfolio. Battery Park 1-191 1978 $100

KENT, ROCKWELL   How I Make A Wood Cut. Pasadena, 1934. 12mo, boards, paper label, illus. by author, 1 of 1000 copies printed by Ward Ritchie, front cover tender on fragile book, 1st ed., fine. Duschnes 220-172 1978 $17.50

KENT, ROCKWELL   N. By E. New York, 1930. Illus. by author, 1st ed. Biblo 251-533 1978 $17.50

KENT, ROCKWELL   Salamina. New York, 1935. Illus. by author, blue cloth, 1st ed., fine in dust jacket. Bradley 49-181 1978 $20

KENT, ROCKWELL   Wilderness...Adventure in Alaska. New York, (1927). Illus., sm. 4to. Biblo BL781-626 1978 $18.50

KENT, W. SAVILLE   A Manual of the Infusoria... London, 1880-82. Frontis, plts., 3 vols., 4to. Traylen 88-590 1978 £95

KENTISH, EDWARD   An Essay on Burns. London, Bristol, 1817. 8vo., contemp. tree calf, gilt on spine, browned, foxed, signature of early owner, good copy, 2nd ed., rare. Zeitlin 245-138 1978 $97.50

KENTON, EDNA   The Indians of North America. New York, (1927). Maps, 2 vols., scarce, fine. MacManus 239-1175 1978 $40

KENTON, EDNA   Simon Kenton His Life and Period 1755-1836. New York, 1930. 1st ed., illus. MacManus 239-1176 1978 $17.50

KENTUCKY. LAWS   Acts Passed At the First Session of the Eighth General Assembly, for the Commonwealth of Kentucky. Frankfort, 1800. Disbound, badly defective, lacking pages 215 through 226 & most of pages 193 through 206. Hayman 71-397 1978 $10

KENWORTHY, JOHN COLEMAN   The Anatomy of Misery. 1901. 1st ed. Austin 80-758 1978 $20

KENYON, F. G.   Facsimiles of Biblical Manuscripts in the B.M. London, 1900. Plts., folio, orig. cloth, text fine. Forster 130-214 1978 £30

KEOWN, ANNA GORDON   The Bright-of-Eye. London, 1925. First ed., fine, d.w., orig. binding. Rota 211-605 1978 £5

KEPHART, HORACE   The Cherokees of the Smoky Mountains. Ithaca, 1936. New cloth. Broadfoot 50-111 1978 $15

KEPLER, JOHANNES   Dioptrice seu Demonstratio Eorum Quae Visui & Visibilibus Propter Conspicilla non ita pridem inventa accidunt. Augsburg, 1611. Sm. 4to., woodcut diagrams, fine, recent limp vellum, first ed. Quaritch 977-111 1978 $5,800

KEPPEL, FREDERICK   The Gentle Art of Resenting Injuries. New York, 1904. 8vo., orig. cream pr. wr., 1st ed, presentation copy, inscribed from author, 4 page facsimile letter from author to James A. MacNeill Whistler. Ximenes 47-333 1978 $50

KEPPEL, FREDERICK   The Golden Age of Engraving. New York, 1910. Fully illus. Baldwins' 51-105 1978 $20

KEPPEL, HENRY   The Expedition to Borneo of H.M.S. Dido for Suppression of Piracy;.... London, 1847. 2 vols., plts., folding maps, cloth, spine faded, one hinge a little weak, foxing, 3rd ed. Dawson's 127-268 1978 $100

KEPPER, G. L.   Gedenkboek Koningin Wilhelmina in Haar Openbaar Leven. den Haag, 1896-1899. 4to., cloth, portr., plts., foxed. Van der Peet H-64-362 1978 Dfl 65

KER, F. I.   Press Promotion of War Finance. Toronto, 1946. Photos, war finance cartoons. Hood 117-132 1978 $15

KER, HENRY   Travels Through the Western Interior of the United States, from the Year 1808 up to the Year 1816, with a Particular Description of a Great Part of Mexico, on New Spain. Elizabethtown, 1816. Full contemp. calf, 1st ed., 1st issue. Jenkins 116-770 1978 $485

KER, W. P.   Collected Essays. 1925. Orig. ed., portrait, 2 vols., 8vo., orig. cloth. Howes 194-980 1978 £8.50

KER, W. P.   Form and Style in Poetry: Lectures and Notes. 1928. Orig. ed., orig. cloth, 8vo. Howes 194-981 1978 £4.50

KERAUDREN, P. F.   Memoire sur les Causes des Maladies des Marins... Paris, 1817. 8vo., uncut, fine. Paine 78-78 1978 $65.00

KERCHEVAL, SAMUEL   A History of the Valley of Virginia. Woodstock, 1902. Cloth. MacManus 239-1134 1978 $30

KERFOOT, J. B.   American Pewter. New York, (1924). 4to., illus. Biblo BL781-533 1978 $9.50

KEROUAC, JOHN   The Town and the City. New York, 1950. 16mo, red cloth, near Mint in d.w., 1st ed., collector's cond. Desmarais 1-256 1978 $70

KERN, G. M.   Practical Landscape Gardening, with Reference to the Improvement of Rural Residences, Giving the General Principles of the Art. Cincinnati, 1855. Illus., 8vo., orig. cloth, 1st ed. Morrill 241-242 1978 $32.50

KERN, OTTO   Inscriptiones Graecae. 1913. Folio, plts., spine worn. Allen 234-503 1978 $15

KERN, OTTO   Die Religion der Griechen. 1926. Vol. I only. Allen 234-504 1978 $12.50

KERN, VINCENZ RITTER VON   Die Steinbeschwerden der Harnblase, ihre Verwandten Ubel, und der Blasenschnitt, bei Beiden Geschlechtern. Wien, 1828. Copperplts., colored by hand, folio, contemp. gilt & decor. calf, rubbed & rebacked, gilt edges, 1st ed., fine lg. paper copy, library stamps. Offenbacher 30-76 1978 $375

KERNER VON MERILAUN, A.   The Natural History of Plants, Their Forms, Growth, Reproduction and Distribution. London, 1894. Orig. woodcut illus., plts. in colour, 2 vols., thick roy.7vo., half red morocco, trifle rubbed. Traylen 88-592 1978 £40

KERR, ALBERT BOARDMAN   Jacques Coeur, Merchant Prince of the Middle Ages. New York, 1927. Illus., spine dull, 8vo. George's 635-303 1978 £5.25

KERR, ANNIE B.   Wednesdays. The Woman's Press, 1930. Austin 79-397 1978 $12.50

KERR, HUGH   A Poetical Description of Texas, and Narrative of Many Interesting Events in that Country, Embracing a Period of Several Years.... New York, 1838. Full morocco, gilt, 1st ed. Jenkins 116-771 1978 $385

KERR, HUGH   A Poetical Description of Texas..An Appeal to Those Who Oppose the Union of Texas With the United States... 1838. Limited to 300 copies, very good. Nestler Rare 78-65 1978 $12

KERR, HUGH   A Poetical Description of Texas. Houston, 1936. Limited ed. of 300. Jenkins 116-772 1978 $10

KERR, NORMAN   Inebriety or Narcomania. New York, n.d. (ca. 1894). 3rd ed., 8vo., ex-lib. Morrill 239-3 1978 $7.50

KERR, ORPHEUS C.   The Orpheus C. Kerr Papers. 1862. First ed. Austin 82-677 1978 $20

KERR, W. C.   Report of the Geological Survey of N.C. Raleigh, 1875. Vol. I, lg. fold. map, hand-colored plts., rebound. Broadfoot 50-112 1978 $20

KERR, WILFRED B.   Bermuda and the American Revolution: 1760-1783. Princeton, 1936. Maps, orig. cloth. MacManus 239-589 1978 $20

KERR, WILFRID B.   From Scotland to Huron; a History of the Kerr Family. Ontario, 1949. Card cover. Hood's 115-26 1978 $20

KETCHUM, C. J.   Federal District Captial. Ottawa, 1939. Hood's 115-821 1978 $22.50

KETCHUM, T. C. L.   High Spots in Canadian History. St. John, 1926. Hood 116-635 1978 $20

KETCHUM, WILLIAM   An Authentic and Comprehensive History of Buffalo... Buffalo, 1864. 2 vols. bound in 1, fine, orig. cloth. MacManus 239-1081 1978 $65

KETTELL, RUSSELL HAWES   The Pine Furniture of Early New England. Garden City, 1929. Sm. folio, illus., t.e.g., ltd. to 999 copies, very fine, orig. full canvas bind. MacManus 239-684 1978 $85

KETTELL, SAMUEL   Specimens of American Poetry, with Critical and Biographical Notices. Boston, 1829. 3 vols., orig. cloth-backed bds., 1st ed., very good, untrimmed. MacManus 238-551 1978 $150

KETTELL, THOMAS PRENTICE   Constitutional Reform, in a Series of Articles Contributed to the Democratic Review... New York, 1846. New cloth, rebound. Hayman 73-372 1978 $10

KETTELL, THOMAS PRENTICE   Southern Wealth and Northern Profits, as Exhibited in Statistical Facts and Official Figures. New York, 1860. 8vo., ex-lib., lacks backstrip, 1st ed., orig. cloth. Morrill 241-683 1978 $7.50

KETTERING, CHARLES F.   The New Necessity. 1932. Austin 80-761 1978 $10

KETTLE, ROSA MACKENZIE   Over the Furze, a Novel. 1874. 1st ed., 3 vols., half titles, orig. brown cloth, blocked in black & gilt, little less than v.g., signed on t.p.s. of all vols. by George Gilfillan. Jarndyce 16-794 1978 £34

KEUFFEL & ESSER CO.   Catalog of. Hoboken, New Jersey, (1921).
36th ed., cloth, illus., very good. Houle 10- 256 1978 $20

KEY, V. O., JR.   Politics, Parties, and Pressure Groups. New
York, 1948. 2nd ed., cloth. Hayman 72-390 1978 $7.50

KEY of Solomon the King. 1909. Plts., cr. 4to., covers a little soiled.
George's 635-1431 1978 £21

KEYES, E. D.   Fifty Years' Observation of Men and Events,
Civil and Military. New York, 1884. MacManus 239-236 1978 $27.50

KEYES, FRANCES PARKINSON   Dinner at Antoine's. London, 1949.
1st English ed., drawings, very good or better. Limestone 9-165 1978
$12.50

KEYES, HERVEY   The Forest King. New York, 1878. 16mo.,
bright red pict. wr., very good. Butterfield 21-351 1978 $12.50

KEYES, ROGER   Adventures Ashore & Afloat. 1939. 1st. ed.,
photographic illus., maps, 8vo, orig. cloth, pres. copy to Winston Churchill.
Sawyer 298-88 1978 £350

KEYES, SIDNEY   The Collected Poems of Sidney Keyes. London,
1945. Fine in soiled d.w. Desmarais B-369 1978 $15

KEYNES, GEOFFREY   Blake Studies, Notes on His Life and Works.
London, 1949. Quarto, cloth, d. j., colotype plts. and black and white plts.,
fine. Duschnes 220-31a 1978 $37.50

KEYNES, GEOFFREY   The Portraiture of William Harvey. London,
1949. Rittenhouse 49-428 1976 $20

KEYNES, GEOFFREY   William Blake's Illuminated Books: A Census.
New York, 1953. 1 of 400 copies, illus., plts., fine, 4 to. Ballinger 11-17
1978 $97.50

KEYNES, J. M.   A Treatise on Money. 1930. 2 vols., covers
stained, 8vo. George's 635-348 1978 £10.50

KEYSLER, J. G.   Antiquitates Selectae Septentrionales et Celticae.
Hanover, 1720. Sm. 8vo., plts., contemp. vellum. Quaritch 983-21 1978
$130

KIBBE, PAULINE R.   Latin Americans in Texas. 1946. Illus. with
photos, 1st ed. Austin 79-399 1978 $17.50

KIBBE, PAULINE R.   Latin   Americans in Texas. Albuquerque, 1946.
1st ed., illus, d.j. Jenkins 116-773 1978 $25

KIDD, BENJAMIN   Principles of Western Civilisation. Macmillan,
1902. 1st. ed., 8vo, orig. cloth, very good. Fenning 32-186 1978 £8.50

KIDD, DUDLEY   The Essential Kafir. London, A&C Black, 1925.
2nd. ed., illus., demy. 8vo, orig. cloth, good. Sexton 7-112 1978 £12

KIDD, H. G.   "The Megantic Outlaw." Toronto, 1948.
Hood's 115-254 1978 $22.50

KIDD, H. S.   Lutherans in Berks County... (Kutztown, 1923).
Illus. MacManus 239-1522 1978 $17.50

KIDD, J. H.   Personal Recollections of a Cavalryman with
Custer's Michigan Cavalry Brigade in the Civil War. Ionia, 1908. Illus., original
cloth, 1st ed. Ginsburg 14-296 1978 $175

KIDDER, DANIEL P.   Sketches of Residence And Travels in Brazil....
London, 1845. 1st. ed., 2 vols., 8vo, engraved frontispieces, engraved plts., map,
illus., orig. blind stamped cloth, with the Imperial Arms in gilt on upper bds.,
chipping at head of backs, neatly repaired. Deighton 5-45 1978 £85

KIDSON, FRANK   Traditional Tunes. Oxford, 1891. Octavo, 3/4
brown calf over boards, t.e.g., uncut, presentation copy, signed by author.
Bennett 7-65 1978 $125

KIEFER, MONICA   American Children through their Books 1700-1835.
Philadelphia, (1948). Illus., mint, dj. Victoria 34-460 1978 $17.50

KIEFER, MONICA   American Children through Their Books. 1948.
First ed., d.j. Austin 82-520 1978 $12.50

KIEFER, OTTO   Sexual Life in Ancient Rome. New York,
1935. Illus. Biblo BL781-415 1978 $12.50

KIEHLE, D. C.   An Address...on Intelligence the Basis of Christian Civilization.... Grand Forks, 1883. Original printed wr., 1st ed. Ginsberg 14-316 1978 $75

KIEPERT, H.   Formae Urbis Romae Antiquae, acc. Nomenclator
Topographicus. 1896. 4to., plans in pocket, spine quite worn. Allen 234-506
1978 $12.50

KILDUFFE, ROBERT A.   The Blood Bank and the Technique and Therapeutics of Transfusions. St. Louis, 1942. Rittenhouse 49-432 1976 $10

KILHAM, ALEXANDER   The Life... Nottingham, (1799). 1st. ed.,
rebound in half calf, red & green labels, v.g. Jarndyce 16-124 1978 £15

KILLIKELLY, SARAH H.   The History of Pittsburg, Its Rise & Progress.
Pittsburg, 1906. 1st ed., lg 8vo, orig. decor cloth, worn, illus. Americanist
101-76 1978 $35

KILLIKELLY, SARAH H.   History of Pittsburgh. Its Rise and Progress.
Pittsburgh, 1906. 4to., ex-lib., fine copy, 3/4 mor., inscribed by author. Mac-
Manus 239-1523 1978 $35

KILMER, ANNIE KILBURN   Memories of My Son Sergeant Joyce Kilmer. New
York, (1920). Illus., 8vo, orig. cloth, 1st ed. Morrill 241-243 1978 $17.50

KILMER, JOYCE   The Circus. New York, (1921). 1st ed., edges
rubbed, portion of label on spine torn. Biblo 251-535 1978 $17.50

KIMBALL, FISKE   The Creation of the Rococo. Philadelphia,
1943. 4to. Baldwins' 51-106 1978 $75

KIMBALL, FISKE   Domestic Architecture of the American Colonies
and of the Early Republic. New York, 1922. Illus., 4to., illus, scarce. Mac-
Manus 239-685 1978 $55

KIMBALL, G. S.   The Correspondence of the Colonial Governors
of Rhode Island 1723-1775. Boston, 1902-3. 2 vols. MacManus 239-416 1978
$40

KIMBALL, G. S.   Providence in Colonial Times. Boston, 1912.
Illus., 1st ed., ltd. to 550 copies, fine untrimmed copy. MacManus 239-421
1978 $37.50

KIMBALL, MARIE   Jefferson in War and Peace 1776-1784. New
York, (1947). Illus. MacManus 239-224 1978 $10

KIMBALL, MARIE   Jefferson the Road to Glory 1743-1776. New
York, (1943). Illus. MacManus 239-225 1978 $12.50

KIMBALL, SOLOMON D.   Life of David P. Kimball and Other Sketches.
Salt Lake City, 1918. Illus., orig. cloth, 1st ed. Ginsberg 14-659 1978 $25

KIMBER, EDWARD   A Relation or Journal of a Late Expedition to the
Gates of St. Augustine on Florida. Boston, 1935. Facsimile, 8vo., orig. bds.,
cloth back, tissue d.w., fine, ltd. to 250 copies. Morrill 241-244 1978 $25

KIMBER, ISAAC   The Life of Oliver Cromwell. 1724. Frontis.,
orig. panelled calf, hinges weak and spine rubbed but sound. Jarndyce 16-63
1978 £18.50

KIMBLE, GEORGE H. T.   Canadian Military Geography. Ottawa, 1949.
Maps, cover stamped "Confidential". Hood's 115-119 1978 $35

KIMM, SILAS CONRAD   The Iroquois. Middleburgh, 1900. Orig. wr.,
bound in limp lea. Butterfield 21-214 1978 $12.50

KIMMEL, STANLEY   The Mad Booths of Maryland. New York, (1940).
1st ed., illus. MacManus 239-1797 1978 $15

KINCAID, ROBERT L.   The Wilderness Road. Indianapolis, (1947).
Fine copy in dust jacket. Hayman 73-373 1978 $3.50

KINDSLEY, GEORGE H.　　　South Sea Bubbles. NY, 1872. Imprint of Cheswick Press, red cloth binding, spine damaged, good copy w/dated inscrip., May 1872. Greene 78-67 1978 $35.00

KING, ARTHUR　　　Our Sons; How to Start Them in Life. c.1885. 2nd. ed., cr. 8vo, orig. cloth, gilt, nice. Fenning 32-187 1978 £8.50

KING, BASIL　　　The Conquest of Fear. Garden City, 1921. Hood 116-695 1978 $10

KING, BASIL　　　The Letter of the Contract. New York and London, 1914. Illus. Hood 116-480 1978 $10

KING, C. W.　　　Handbook of Engraved Gems. London, 1885. 2nd ed., plts., illus., roy. 8vo., covers shabby, otherwise good. K Books 244-392 1978 £9

KING, CHARLES　　　Cadet Days. New York, 1894. Cloth, little rubbed, 1st ed. Hayman 73-374 1978 $10

KING, CHARLES　　　Under Fire. Philadelphia, 1895. 1st. ed., cl., illus. by C.B. Cox, orig. binding. Hayman 71-406 1978 $8.50

KING, CLARENCE　　　The Helmet of Mambrino. San Francisco, 1938. 1 of 350 copies, marbled paper over bds., pres. inscrip. in ink by Carl Wheat, bkplt. of Lester Douglas. Battery Park 1-15 1978 $35

KING, CLARENCE　　　Mountaineering in the Sierra Nevada. London, 1872. 8vo, half calf, gilt back. Deighton 5-46 1978 £36

KING, D.　　　The State and Prospects of Jamaica... 1850. Cr. 8vo, contemp. calf. Edwards 1012-725 1978 £25

KING, EDWARD　　　The Great South. Hartford, 1875. 1st ed., original cloth gilt extra, illus. Jenkins 116-1564 1978 $75

KING, EDWARD　　　Munimenta Antiqua. 1799-1805. First ed., aquatint plts., 4 vols., folio, contemp. diced calf, rebacked, very good. Howes 194-352 1978 £110

KING, FRANK M.　　　Pioneer Western Empire Builders. (Pasadena, 1946). 1st ed., new buckram, deluxe ed. #315 inscribed by author, labels, orig. bind. mounted on front cover and spine, else fine. Dykes 35-52 1978 $17.50

KING, GRACE　　　Memories of a Southern Woman of Letters. New York, 1932. 1st ed., very good. Limestone 9-166 1978 $35

KING, GRACE　　　Mount Vernon on the Potomac. New York, 1929. Illus., 8vo., 1st ed. Morrill 239-639 1978 $15

KING, H.　　　Report on the Rives, Hinch, Bleeding Hill and Blanton Copper Mines, in the State of Missouri. St. Louis, 1853. Original front wr., 1st ed. Ginsberg 14-585 1978 $100

KING, HENRY　　　The English Poems of .... New Haven, 1914. Octavo, good. Upcroft 10-94 1978 £5

KING, HENRY　　　Poems, Elegies, Paradoxes and Sonnets. N.P., 1657. Sm. 8 vo., green straight-grained mor. by Kalthoeber, with his ticket, bookplates, exquisite, 1st ed. Quaritch Summer, 1978-25 1978 $3,000

KING, J. ANTHONY　　　Twenty-Four Years in the Argentine Republic.... New York, 1846. 1st. ed., orig. binding, clean, moderate wear. Hayman 71-407 1978 $50

KING, J. W.　　　The China Sea Directory. London, 1876-8. 2 vols., bds., 8vo., very good. Paine 78-79 1978 $32.50

KING, JOHN　　　The American Dispensatory. Cincinnati, 1859. Fifth ed., revised and enlarged. Rittenhouse 49-434 1976 $20

KING, JOHN H.　　　Man an Organic Community. 1893. 1st. ed., 2 vols., 8vo, orig. cloth, binding dull, but sound, nice copy. Fenning 32-188 1978 £8.50

KING, JULIUS　　　The Indian Nugget. New York, 1931. Illus. by P. Ickes. Hood 117-519 1978 $7.50

KING, MOSES　　　Handbook of New York City: An Outline History and Description of the American Metropolis. Boston, 1893. 2nd. ed., over 1000 illus., thick 8vo, orig. cloth. Edwards 1012-500 1978 £10

KING, PETER　　　An Enquiry into the Constitution, Discipline, Unity and Worship of the Primitive Church. 1713. Sm. 8vo., contemp. panelled calf, joints cracked, title and few prelim. leaves rather foxed. Howes 194-353 1978 £18

KING, R. G. S.　　　A Particular of the Howses and Famyles in London Derry, May 15, 1628. Londonderry, 1936. Lg. 8vo, good. Upcroft 10-95 1978 £6

KING, RICHARD ASHE　　　A Shadowed Life. London, 1886. 3 vols., orig. dec. cloth, 1st ed., very good, some soiling and cover wear, lib. labels. MacManus 238-346 1978 $85

KING, RICHARD ASHE　　　Swift in Ireland. 1895. 1st ed., 1/4 leather, over wr., very good. Hyland 128-610 1978 £5

KING, SPENCER BIDWELL, JR.　　　Selective Service in North Carolina in World War II. Chapel Hill, 1949. Illus. Broadfoot 50-114 1978 $7.50

KING, T. B.　　　First Annual Report of the Board of Directors of the Southern Pacific Railroad Company, Chartered by the State of Texas. New York, 1856. Half mor., 1st ed. Ginsberg 14-962 1978 $185

KING, W. R.　　　Campaigning in Kaffirland or Scenes and Adventures in the Kaffir War of 1851-51. London, 1853. 5 lithograph plts., slight age-marking, good, 8vo, slightly worn half roan. K Books 239-242 1978 £35

KING, W. L. M.　　　The Message of the Carillon, and Other Addresses. Toronto, 1927. Blank flyleaf missing. Hood 116-696 1978 $10

KING, W. L. M.　　　The Secret of Heroism. New York, 1906. Hood 17-309 1978 $17.50

KING, W. T. C.　　　History of the London Discount Market. 1936. 8vo. George's 635-349 1978 £5

KING, WILLIAM 1663-1712　　　The Art of Cookery. c.1720. 2nd. ed., frontis, orig. panelled calf, rebacked, inscribed. Jarndyce 16-125 1978 £30

KING, WILLIAM 1663-1712　　　The Art of Love. (1709). 8vo., contemp. panelled calf rebacked, very good, frontispiece, first ed. P. M. Hill 142-289 1978 £48

KING, WILLIAM 1685-1763　　　Political and Literary Anecdotes of His Own Times. 1819. Second ed., sm. 8vo., contemp. half navy calf. Howes 194-354 1978 £15

KING, WILLIAM AUGUSTUS HENRY　　　English Porcelain Figures of the 18th Century. 1925. Coloured plts., roy. 8vo. George's 635-232 1978 £16

KING, WILLIAM HENRY　　　Lessons and Practical Notes on Steam, the Steam Engine, Propellers. New York, 1863. Illus., fine copy, orig. cloth. MacManus 239-237 1978 $35

KING Alberts Book, a Tribute to the Belgian King and People from representative Men and Women throughout the World. 1914. Portrait, plts., many in colour, 4to. George's 635-189 1978 £5

THE KING and Cobler, The Entertaining History of. Nottingham, c.1790. Uncut chapbook, woodcuts, paper darkened, upper leaf loose. Victoria 34-461 1978 $35

KING Charles the First. 1737. 8vo., 1st ed., frontis., newly bound in cloth, mor. back. Quaritch 979-189 1978 $25

THE KING'S Regulations and Orders for the Canadian Militia, 1939. Ottawa, 1939. Hard-cover binder. Hood's 115-120 1978 $22.50

KINGDOM, FRANK　　　"That Man in the White House." You and Your President. New York, (1944). Illus., 1st ed. Biblo BL781-243 1978 $9

KINGDOM, JOHN   Redeemed Slaves. Bristol, (c. 1755). Fcap. 8vo., new buckram. George's 635-1358 1978 £7.50

KINGSFORD, CHARLES LETHBRIDGE   English Historical Literature in the 15th Century. Oxford, 1913. 8vo. Upcroft 12-234 1978 £12.50

KINGSFORD, CHARLES LETHBRIDGE   The Stonor Letters and Papers 1290-1483. Plts., map, 2 vols., 8vo. Upcroft 12-235 1978 £10

KINGSFORD, CHARLES LETHBRIDGE   The Story of the Duke of Cambridge's Own Middlesex Regiment. (1916). Illus., 8vo., orig. cloth, spine faded, plts. F. Edwards 1013-521 1978 £15

KINGSFORD, CHARLES LETHBRIDGE   The Story of the Royal Warwickshire Regiment. (c.1925). Color frontis., maps, plts., illus. George's 635-831 1978 £12.50

KINGSLEY, CHARLES   Alexandria and Her Schools. Four Lectures Delivered at the Philosophical Institution. Edinburgh, 1854. Orig. cloth, 1st ed., spine faded, inscription from author. MacManus 238-304 1978 $40

KINGSLEY, CHARLES   At Last: A Christmas in the West Indies. London, New York, 1871. 1st Amer. ed., illus., scarce, very good. Victoria 34-463 1978 $17.50

KINGSLEY, CHARLES   At Last. A Christmas in the West Indies. London, 1871. Illus., 2 vols., orig. cloth, 1st ed., covers slightly worn, but good. MacManus 238-307 1978 $125

KINGSLEY, CHARLES   Glaucus; or, The Wonders of the Shore. Cambridge, 1859. 4th. ed., coloured plts. by W. Dickes, sm. 8vo, cloth gilt, gilt edges. Traylen 88-163 1978 £20

KINGSLEY, CHARLES   Hereward the Wake, "Last of the English." London, 1866. 2 vols., orig. cloth, 1st ed., covers a bit spotted, outer hinges split, cloth fold. boxes. MacManus 238-306 1978 $150

KINGSLEY, CHARLES   The Heroes: or, Greek Fairy Tales for My Children. 1856. 1st. ed., half title, rebound in half dark green calf, label, v.g. Jarndyce 16-795 1978 £25

KINGSLEY, CHARLES   The Heroes; or, Greek Fairy Tales. Cambridge, 1856. 1st ed., illus., spine sunned, very good. Victoria 34-462 1978 $25

KINGSLEY, CHARLES   The Heroes or Greek Fairy Tales for my Children. Riccardi Press, 1912. 4to., illus. in colour, limp vellum, fine copy, slipcase, ltd. to 500 copies. Quaritch 979-274 1978 $185

KINGSLEY, CHARLES   The Heroes or, Greek Fairy Tales for My Children. New York, (1928). Color plts. by Squire and Mars, handsome large gilt pict. cover design, covers faded and rough. Victoria 34-754 1978 $10

KINGSLEY, CHARLES   Hypatia: or, New Foes with an Old Face. London, 1853. 2 vols., orig. cloth, 1st ed., spines chipped and frayed, otherwise good. MacManus 238-303 1978 $125

KINGSLEY, CHARLES   Two Years Ago. London, 1857. 3 vols., orig. cloth, 1st ed., vol. I worn. MacManus 238-305 1978 $50

KINGSLEY, CHARLES   The Water-Babies. London, 1885. Illus. by Linley Sambourne, sm. 4to., full red calf gilt extra, fine. K Books 244-183 1978 £15

KINGSLEY, CHARLES   Westward Ho! New York: The Limited Editions Club, 1947. Lg. 8vo., 2 vols., illus. by Edward A. Wilson, orig. cloth-backed bds., pub. box, 1 of 1,500 copies, signed by illustrator, fine. MacManus 238-825 1978 $27.50

KINGSLEY, FLORENCE MORSE   Henry Fowle Durant...Founder of Wellesley College. New York, (1924). Illus., spine dull. Biblo BL781-26 1978 $10

KINGSLEY, GEORGE H.   South Sea Bubbles. New York, 1872. 1st Am. ed., red cloth, good. Greene 78-68 1978 $30

KINGSLEY, HENRY   Austin Elliott. London, 1875. New Ed., pict. glazed boards, "yellow-back" format, good condition. Greene 78-69 1978 $40.00

KINGSLEY, HENRY   Leighton Court. A Country House Story. London, (c.1875). Pict. glazed boards, "yellow-back" format, spine worn, hinges weak, interior good, 2 vols. Greene 78-70 1978 $25

KINGSLEY, HENRY   Ravenshoe. 1862. 1st. ed., 3 vols., purple cloth, maroon roan spines, sound. Jarndyce 16-796 1978 £32

KINGSLEY, MARY H.   Travels in West Africa. London, 1897. 5th. thousand, frontis, 2 plts., 44 full page & smaller illus., few pencil notes, 8vo, orig. cloth, covers dull. K Books 239-245 1978 £18

KINGSLEY, MARY H.   West African Studies. London, 1899. 1st. ed., folding map, frontis, 27 plts.,8vo, orig. cloth, few pencil notes, covers slightly dull. K Books 239-246 1978 £20

KINGSLEY, NELSON   Diary of...a California Argonaut of 1849. Berkeley, 1914. Wrs. Biblo BL781-284 1978 $12

KINGSLEY, SIDNEY   Dead End. New York, (1936). 1st ed., author's signed pres., bind. faded, edges rubbed. Biblo BL781-1039 1978 $12.50

KINGSMILL, HUGH   Blondel. 1927. Very good, first English ed. Bell Book 17-527 1978 £6.50

KINGSMILL, HUGH   The Progress of a Biographer. 1949. Very good, first English ed. Bell Book 17-528 1978 £5.50

KINGSMILL, HUGH   Talking of Dick Whittington. 1947. Drawings, covers little faded & marked, good, first English ed. Bell Book 17-529 1978 £5

KINGSMILL, HUGH   This Blessed Plt. 1942. Drawings, very good, first English ed. Bell Book 17-530 1978 £5

KINGSTON, G. A.   Legendary Lyrics. 1938. Privately printed, signed by author. Hood's 115-881 1978 $10

KINGSTON, WILLIAM HENRY GILES   The African Trader. London & Edinburgh, n.d. First ed., color frontis., good. Victoria 34-466 1978 $10

KINGSTON, WILLIAM HENRY GILES   In the Rocky Mountains. 1886. Plts., sm. 8vo., dec. cloth. Edwards 1012-501 1978 £12

KINGSTON, WILLIAM HENRY GILES   The Log House by the Lake. n.d. Illus., some water stains on covers. Austin 82-522 1978 $12.50

KINGSTON, WILLIAM HENRY GILES   Peter the Whaler. London, n.d. Color plts. Hood's 117-520 1978 $17.50

KINLOCH, A. A. A.   Large Game Shooting in Thibet, the Himalayas, and Northern India. Calcutta, 1885. Folding map, photogravure plts., 4to, orig. cloth, pres. copy. Edwards 1012-139 1978 £35

KINLOCH, CHARLES WALKER   De Zieke Reiziger; or, Rambles in Java and the Straits, in 1852. London, 1853. Color plts., maps, cloth, gilt, light foxing, very good. Dawson's 127-269 1978 $265

KINSMAN, FREDERICK JOSEPH   Salve Mater. 1920. Austin 79-401 1978 $8.50

KINSTON, Whitehall and Goldsboro Expedition, December, 1862. New York, 1890. 12mo., 1st ed., orig. cloth. Morrill 241-430 1978 $17.50

KINNEY, MRS. HANNAH   A Review of the Principal Events of the Last Ten Years in the Life of Mrs. Kinney. Boston, 1841. Orig. binding. Wolfe 39-268 1978 $25

KIP, FREDERICK ELLSWORTH   History of Kip Family in America. Montclair, 1928. Baldwins' 51-259 1978 $30

KIP, JAMES   Nouveau Theatre de la Grande Bretagne.... A Londres, 1708. 1st. ed., folio, engraved arms on title-pg., sl. ageing of paper, o/w fine set, contemporary mottled calf, gilt, raised bands, marbled edges. Deighton 5-129 1978 £1,350

KIPLING, RUDYARD   Abaft the Funnel. New York, 1909. 1st issue, pirated ed., blue cloth, lettered in gold, very good. Greene 78-237 1978 $50

KIPLING, RUDYARD   The Absent-Minded Beggar. 1899. Portrait, illus., sm. folio, orig. cloth. Howes 194-984 1978 £12.50

KIPLING, RUDYARD   An Almanac of Twelve Sports. London, (1897). 1st ed., colored boards, very good. Victoria 34-583 1978 $115

KIPLING, RUDYARD   The Budget.... New York, 1899. 12mo., illus., ltd. to 500 copies, covers slightly soiled, bookplt. Biblo BL781-1040 1978 $24.50

KIPLING, RUDYARD   'Captains Courageous' A Story of the Grand Banks. 1897. 1st. ed., illus., half titles, orig. dark blue cloth, gilt imprint, a.e.g., v.g. Jarndyce 16-799 1978 £25

KIPLING, RUDYARD   Captains Courageous. 1897. Illus. by I. W. Taber, orig. pict. cloth gilt, a.e.g., very good, first English ed. Bell Book 17-532 1978 £17.50

KIPLING, RUDYARD   Captains Courageous. London, 1897. Orig. pict. cloth, a.e.g., 1st ed., some minor foxing, very fine, slipcase. MacManus 238-310 1978 $110

KIPLING, RUDYARD   Captains Courageous. London, 1897. 1st ed., illus., bright copy, some dulling of spine, light foxing, text very fine. Victoria 34-468 1978 $75

KIPLING, RUDYARD   The City of Dreadful Night. London, 1891. 15mo, orig. green paper wr. soiled and worn, some fading of t.p. and last page, 1st English ed., slipcase, collector's cond. Desmarais 1-257 1978 $120

KIPLING, RUDYARD   Collectanea. Being certain reprinted verses.... New York, 1898. Ltd. to 500 copies, bound in yellow cloth. Greene 78-238 1978 $30

KIPLING, RUDYARD   Collected Dog Stories. London, 1934. First collected ed., text illus. by G. L. Stampa, d.w., 8vo, orig. cloth. K Books 244-184 1978 £6

KIPLING, RUDYARD   The Collected Works. Vols. 1-26 (of 31). 1913-27. 26 vols., roy. 8vo., orig. linen backed bds., printed labels, vol. 1 signed by author, ltd. ed., fine. Howes 194-983 1978 £130

KIPLING, RUDYARD   The Complete Stalky & Co. 1929. Drawings, pict. cloth, t.e.g., spine faded, good, first English ed. Bell Book 16-526 1978 £12.50

KIPLING, RUDYARD   The Courting of Dinah Shadd and Other Stories... New York, 1890. 2 vols., orig. blue wrs., 1st and 2nd eds., both fine, half mor. slipcase. MacManus 238-308 1978 $250

KIPLING, RUDYARD   The Day's Work. 1898. First English ed., orig. cloth, 8vo. Howes 194-985 1978 £8.50

KIPLING, RUDYARD   The Day's Work. London, 1898. First English ed., orig. binding, nice. Rota 211-277 1978 £8

KIPLING, RUDYARD   The Dead King. London, 1910. 4to, purple cloth, gilt stamped, illus. by W. Heath Robinson, spine sun-faded, bookplate, near Fine, 1st ed., collector's cond. Desmarais 1-258 1978 $25

KIPLING, RUDYARD   Departmental Ditties, Barrack-Room Ballads and Other Verses. New York, (1890). 12mo., cloth, 1st ed. in book form, excessively scarce, near mint copy, half-mor. slipcase, 1st issue. J. S. Lawrence 38-868 1978 $350

KIPLING, RUDYARD   The Five Nations. London, 1903. 8vo, red cloth, t.e.g., uncut, spine slightly faded, very Fine, 1st ed., collector's cond. Desmarais 1-259 1978 $15

KIPLING, RUDYARD   A Fleet in Being. 1898. Blue paper covers, illus. by N. Wilkinson. Eaton 45-276 1978 £10

KIPLING, RUDYARD   A Fleet in Being. London, 1898. Blue cloth, nice. Desmarais B-371 1978 $10

KIPLING, RUDYARD   La France en Guerre. Paris & Nancy, 1915. First French ed., plts., orig. wrappers, pres. copy from the author, inscribed from author, 8vo. Howes 194-986 1978 £36

KIPLING, RUDYARD   From Sea to Sea. New York, 1899. 2 vols., 1st ed., covers worn, some minor stains at upper margins otherwise a good set. Biblo 251-536 1978 $27.50

KIPLING, RUDYARD   From Sea to Sea. New York, 1899. 8vo, 2 vols., green cloth, bookplates, boards lightly shelf worn, Fine, 1st ed., collector's cond. Desmarais 1-260 1978 $25

KIPLING, RUDYARD   From Sea to Sea. Letters of Travel. New York, 1899. 2 vols., orig. cloth, 1st ed., 1st issue, very fine, half mor. slipcases. MacManus 238-311 1978 $85

KIPLING, RUDYARD   The Holy War. London, n.d. Heavy paper folded once, Mint, slight darkening, 1st ed., collector's cond. Desmarais 1-261 1978 $15

KIPLING, RUDYARD   In Black and White. London, n.d. (1890). 1st Eng. ed., orig. grey-green wrs., cover frayed & spine flaking, good. Greene 78-239 1978 $85

KIPLING, RUDYARD   The Incarnation of Krishna Mulvaney. New York, 1896. 1st separate ed. published in America. Biblo 251-537 1978 $27.50

KIPLING, RUDYARD   The Irish Guards in the Great War. London, 1923. 8vo, 2 vols., red cloth, gilt stamped, t.e.g., boards somewhat warped on vol. 2, fine, 1st ed., collector's cond. Desmarais 1-262 1978 $35

KIPLING, RUDYARD   The Irish Guards in the Great War. 1923. 2 vols., maps, 8vo. George's 635-832 1978 £15

KIPLING, RUDYARD   The Jungle Book. The Second Jungle Book. London, 1894, 1895. 2 vols., orig. pict. cloth, 1st eds., very slightly worn, but nice. MacManus 238-309 1978 $275

KIPLING, RUDYARD   The Jungle Book; The Second Jungle Book. London, 1894-5. 1st. ed., illus. by J.L. Kipling, W.H. Drake & P. Frenzeny, 2 vols., sm. 8vo, orig. blue dec. cloth gilt, gilt edges, fine. Traylen 88-164 1978 £110

KIPLING, RUDYARD   The Jungle Book. London, 1908. 1st book ed., octavo, plates laid in loose, contents very fine, very scarce. Victoria 34-240 1978 $85

KIPLING, RUDYARD   Just So Stories for Little Children. New York, 1902. Illus., 1st Amer. ed., bind. soiled, name on flyleaf, edges rubbed. Biblo BL781-1028 1978 $18.50

KIPLING, RUDYARD   Just So Stories. For Little Children. London, 1902. Orig. pict. cloth, 1st ed., very nice. MacManus 238-313 1978 $125

KIPLING, RUDYARD   Just So Stories, for Little Children. London, 1902. 1st ed., illus. by Kipling, spine sunned, very good. Victoria 34-464 1978 $85

KIPLING, RUDYARD   Just So Stories. London, 1910. Orig. wrs., 25 copies, wrs. slightly faded at edges, fine copy, excessively rare. Victoria 34-467 1978 $550

KIPLING, RUDYARD   Kim. 1901. Plts., very good, first English ed. Bell Book 16-527 1978 £12.50

KIPLING, RUDYARD   Kim. London, 1901. Orig. cloth, 1st Eng. ed. MacManus 238-312 1978 $25

KIPLING, RUDYARD   Land and Sea Tales for Scouts and Guides. London, 1923. 1st. ed., sm. 4to, fine copy in d.w. Traylen 88-165 1978 £20

KIPLING, RUDYARD   Letters of Marque. Allahabad, 1891. 1st ed., 8vo., 1 of only 1000 copies, orig. red & blue cloth with gilt lettering on fr. bd. & spine, very little wear, bds. slightly soiled, one inner hinge cracked, very good copy, fragile, encased in fldg. 1/2 mor. slipcase with scuff marks, exceedingly rare. Current 24-28 1978 $265

KIPLING, RUDYARD   Limits and Renewals. London, 1932. Near mint in chipped d.w. Desmarais B-372 1978 $15

KIPLING, RUDYARD   The Naulahka: a story of west and east. 1892. Covers faded, good, first English ed. Bell Book 16-530 1978 £8.50

KIPLING, RUDYARD   The Naulahka. A Story of West and East.
NY, 1892. Orig. brown cloth binding, good condition. Greene 78-240 1978
$40.00

KIPLING, RUDYARD   The Phantom Rickshaw & Other Tales. London,
n.d. (1890). 1st Eng. ed., orig. grey-green wrs. Greene 78-241 1978 $125

KIPLING, RUDYARD   Poems. 1886-1929. New York, 1930. Quarto,
Japan vellum boards, red label lettered in gold on spine, handmade deckle-edged
paper, d.j., t.e.g., ltd. to 537 sets, 1st vol. of each set signed by Kipling, 3
vols., 1st American ed., fine. Duschnes 220-175 1978 $250

KIPLING, RUDYARD   Puck of Pook's Hill. New York, 1906. 8vo,
green pict. cloth, top and bottom of spine worn, bookplate, shaken, title page
started, t.e.g., uncut, very Good, 1st ed., collector's cond. Desmarais 1-347
1978 $60

KIPLING, RUDYARD   Sea Warfare. 1916. First ed., fine, d.w., orig.
cloth, 8vo. Howes 194-987 1978 £5

KIPLING, RUDYARD   The Second Jungle Book. 1895. Drawings by
J. Lockwood Kipling, orig. pict. cloth gilt, a.e.g., very good, first English ed.
Bell Book 17-533 1978 £15

KIPLING, RUDYARD   A Song of the English. (1909). Ltd. to 500
copies signed by the artist, coloured plts. by W. Heath Robinson, roy. 4to., orig.
vellum gilt, coloured design on front cover, lacks silk ties. George's 635-1536
1978 £150

KIPLING, RUDYARD   Songs of the Sea from Rudyard Kipling's Verse.
1927. Lg. 4to., lg. paper, coloured plts., illus., bds., parchment back, spec.
ed. ltd. to 500 copies on spec. paper, signed by Kipling. Quaritch 979-215
1978 $110

KIPLING, RUDYARD   Stalky & Co. London, 1899. 8vo, red cloth,
gilt stamped, 1st Eng. ed, unusually Fine, 1st ed., collector's cond. Desmarais
1-263 1978 $20

KIPLING, RUDYARD   Stalky & Co. 1899. Orig. red cloth, gilt,
1st. English ed. Eaton 45-277 1978 £7

KIPLING, RUDYARD   The Story of the Gadsby. London, n.d. (1890).
1st Eng. ed., orig. grey-green wrs., lacks back cover, name stamped on front
cover, good. Greene 78-243 1978 $75

KIPLING, RUDYARD   The Story of the Gadsby and Under the Deodars.
New York, (1891). 1st Amer. authorized ed., bears pr. letter from Kipling, maroon cloth, t.e.g., good. Greene 78-244 1978 $75

KIPLING, RUDYARD   "They". London, 1905. Color plts., decor.
white cloth, 1st separate ed., 1st issue, covers dust-soiled. Bradley 49-183 1978
$15

KIPLING, RUDYARD   Traffics and Discoveries. 1904. Good, signed
by author, first English ed. Bell Book 17-534 1978 £45

KIPLING, RUDYARD   Traffics and Discoveries. New York, 1904. First
American ed., ink writing on fly. Biblo 247-577 1978 $17.50

KIPLING, RUDYARD   Traffics and Discoveries. 1904. Red. decorated
cloth, spine faded. Eaton 45-278 1978 £8

KIPLING, RUDYARD   Twenty Poems. London, 1918. Wrs., fine.
Desmarais B-373 1978 $12.50

KIPLING, RUDYARD   Under the Deodars. London, (1890). 1st Eng.
ed., text very good, some foxing, pictorial wrs. chipped at edges and spine.
Victoria 34-465 1978 $25

KIPLING, RUDYARD   Rudyard Kipling's Verse. 1919. 3 vols., buckram, very good, first English ed. Bell Book 16-528 1978 £12.50

KIPLING, RUDYARD   Complete Works in Prose and Verse. 1937-39.
35 vols., lg. 8vo., Sussex ed., finely prtd. on handmade paper, niger mor.,
gilt tops, very fine set, only 500 sets prtd., 1st vol. signed by Kipling. Quaritch 979-369 1978 $3,250

KIPLING, RUDYARD   The Years Between. London, 1919. 8vo, red
cloth, bookplate, 1st ed., collector's cond. Desmarais 1-264 1978 $15

KIPPINGIUS, JOHAN WOLFGANG   Historiae Eivsqve Nominis Abvsv Commentatio evm Sylloge Exemplorvm Historiae Eivsque Nominis Absionem in Ivre cvm....
1745. 4to., marbled bds., woodcut vignette. King 7-359 1978 £25

KIPPIS, ANDREW   A Narrative of the Voyages Round the World,
Preformed by Capt. James Cook... 1880. Mounted photographic reproductions,
orig. cloth gilt, g.e., spine little faded, 8vo. Edwards 1012-363 1978 £35

KIRBY, WILLIAM   Annals of Niagara. Toronto, 1927. Illus.
Hood 116-753 1978 $40

KIRBY, WILLIAM   The Golden Dog. Boston, 1897. Illus., first ed.
Austin 82-523 1978 $12.50

KIRBY, WILLIAM B.   A Souvenir of Bridgeton, N.J.... Bridgeton,
1895. Illus., 4to., rebacked. MacManus 239-1282 1978 $35

KIRCHER, ATHANASIUS   China Monumentis qua Sacris qua Profanis,....
(Amsterdam), 1667. 1st ed., folio, engraved full-page plates, folding maps,
pictorial t.p., portrait of Kircher, contemp. mottled calf, rubbed, paneled spine,
leather label, remnants of gilt, lengthy inscriptions. Bennett 20-237 1978
$950

KIRCHER, ATHANASIUS   Scrutinium Physico-Medicum Contagiosae Luis
Quae Pestis Dicitur. Romae, 1658. 4to., contemp. vellum, 1st ed., fine copy.
Offenbacher 30-77 1978 $1,200

KIRCHER, ATHANASIUS   Scrutinium Pestis Physico-Medicum, Publico Com-
modo Recusum Per Urbanum Madcho, S.J. Graecii, 1740. 8vo., contemp. Baroque gold-paper with flowers. Salloch 345-104 1978 $250

KIREEFF, O.   Russia & England from 1876-1880... 1880.
2nd. ed., frontis portrait, 2 folding maps, half title, orig. dark olive cloth, gilt,
v.g. Jarndyce 16-800 1978 £9.50

KIRKBRIDE, SHERMAN A.   A Brief History of the Kirkbride Family with Special Reference to the Descendants of David Kirkbride 1775-1830. (Alliance), 1913.
Cloth. Hayman 72-263 1978 $10

KIRKBRIDGE, JOSEPH   The ABC of Camping. Kineo, 1898. Wr.,
private distribution, good, scarce. Nestler Rare 78-20 1978 $10

KIRKBY, JOHN   The Capacity and Extent of the Human Understanding;.... Dublin, 1746. 12mo, contemporary calf, 1st Irish ed., very good
copy, rare. Ximenes 47-170 1978 $200

KIRKCONNELL, WATSON   The Flying Bull, and Other Tales. Toronto,
1940. Drawings by J. W. McLaren. Hood's 115-882 1978 $17.50

KIRKCONNELL, WATSON   Liberal Education in the Canadian Democracy.
Hamilton, 1948. Card cover, illus. Hood 116-372 1978 $7.50

KIRKE, HENRY   The First English Conquest of Canada, with Some
Account of the Earliest Settlements in Nova Scotia and Newfoundland. London,
1908. 2nd ed., enlarged and rev'd. Hood 116-225 1978 $40

KIRKE, HENRY   Twenty-Five Years in British Guiana. 1898.
8vo, coloured folding map, portrait, illus., modern half blue leather, tear in map
repaired, slight spotting in text. Edwards 1012-661 1978 £15

KIRKLAND, F.   Letters on the American Revolution in Library
at "Karolfred". Philadelphia, 1941. Illus., ltd. to 200 copies, vol. 2 in 1952,
ltd. to 500 copies, very good set. Nestler Rare 78-167 1978 $45

KIRKLAND, JOHN THORNTON   A Discourse Occasioned by the Death of
General George Washington. Boston, 1800. Disbound. Hayman 71-758 1978
$12.50

KIRKLAND, THOMAS   Herrn Thomas Kirklands Wundarztes Bemerkungen Uber Hrn. Potts Allgemeine Ammerkungen Von Den Beinbruchen U. S. W....
Aus Dem Englischen Ubersetzt. Altenburg, 1771. 1st German ed., orig. rubbed
bds., 8vo., very good. Americanist 103-58 1978 $25

KIRKMAN, F. B.   The British Bird Book. 1910. Coloured drawings, photographs, 12 vols., roy. 4to., orig. bds., spines worn. George's 635-1004 1978 £?.?

KIRKMAN, F. B.   British Birds. London, 1932. Sm. 4to., orig. cloth, color plts. Book Chest 17-210 1978 $30

KIRKPATRICK, ELLIS L.   The English River Congregation of the Church of the Brethren. Iowa City, 1930. Orig wrps., 1st ed. Ginsberg 16-880 1978 $12.50

KIRN, LEON   L'Alimentation Du Soldat. Paris, 1885. 8vo., half mor., gilt on spine, foxed, very good copy, newspaper article tipped in, 1st ed. Zeitlin 245-139 1978 $37.50

KIRTON, JOHN WILLIAM   The Gin Shop. n.d., (1869). 1st. ed., 8vo, disbound. Hannas 54-177 1978 £6

KIRWIN, J. M.   History of the Diocese of Galveston and St. Mary's Cathedral, 1847-1922. Galveston, 1922. Very scarce. Jenkins 116-1550 1978 $45

KISCH, GUIDO   In Search of Freedom. London, 1949. Illus. Austin 79-402 1978 $27.50

KITCHIN, WILLIAM C.   A Wonderland of the East...the Lake and Mountain Region of New England and Eastern New York. Boston, 1920. Illus., maps, good. Biblo BL781-136 1978 $10

KITCHINER, WILLIAM   The Cook's Oracle, and Housekeeper's Manual... New York, 1832. Contemp. calf, rubbed, weak joint, illus. Americanist 102-33 1978 $37.50

KITE, ELIZABETH S.   Beaumarchais and the War of American Independence. Boston, (1918). 2 vols., illus. MacManus 239-591 1978 $35

KITTLE, SAMUEL   A Concise History of the Colony and Natives of New South Wales. Edinburgh, (1814). Engraved plts., thick sm. 8vo, binders' cloth. Edwards 1012-337 1978 £175

KITTLE, SAMUEL   A Concise History of the Cossacks:.... Edinburgh, 1814. 12mo, disbound, 1st ed. Ximenes 47-171 1978 $60

KITTO, F. H.   The North West Territories. Ottawa, 1930. Card cover. Hood's 115-52 1978 $20

KITTO, JOHN   Cyclopaedia of Biblical Literature. Edinburgh, 1852. 2 vols., illus., maps, roy. 8vo., half calf. K Books 244-185 1978 £12

KITTON, FREDERIC G.   The Novels...of Dickens. Battery Park 1-262 1978 $35

KITTRELL, NORMAN G.   Governors Who Have Been, and Other Public Men from Texas. Houston, 1921. Near-mint copy, 1st ed. Jenkins 116-779 1978 $60

KLAPROTH, J.   Atlas de l'Ouvrage. (Paris, 1824). Atlas-vol. only, folio, half calf (rubbed), rare. Van der Peet 127-304 1978 Dfl 250

KLEBERG, ROBERT J.   The Santa Gertrudis Breed of Beef Cattle. Kingsville, n.d. Wrs., illus., 1st ed., very good copy. Dykes 34-109 1978 $7.50

KLEES, FREDRIC   The Pennsylvania Dutch. New York, 1950. Illus, first ed., fine, d.w. Biblo 247-120 1978 $16.50

KLEFFEL, WALTHER   Die Zeppelin-Fahrt. Berlin, (1928). Illus., 12mo., orig. wrs. Morrill 241-32 1978 $12.50

KLEIN, A. M.   The Hitlerlad. (New York, 1944). Orig. binding, d.j. Wolfe 39-269 1978 $15

KLEIN, ERNEST L.   How to Stay Rich. 1950. Austin 80-765 1978 $7.50

KLEIN, F. S.   Lancaster County 1841-1941. Lancaster, (1941). Illus. MacManus 239-1525 1978 $15

KLEIN, F. S.   Lancaster County Pennsylvania, a History. New York, 1924. 4 vols., illus., 4tos., 1/2 leather. MacManus 239-1526 1978 $85

KLEIN, H. M. J.   A Century of Education at Mercersburg 1836-1936. (Lancaster), 1936. Orig. binding, clean, light spotting on cover. Hayman 71-628 1978 $7.50

KLEIN, WALTER C.   Johann Conrad Beissell, Mystic and Martinet... Philadelphia, 1942. MacManus 239-1369 1978 $15

DIE KLEINE Lieder Sammlung. Psalterspiel de Kinder Zions. Ephrata, 1827. 24mo, one leaf lacking, shaken, very good. Victoria 34-469 1978 $50

KLEINSCHMIDT, B.   Die Basilika San Francesco in Assisi. Berlin, 1915-1926. 2 vols., thick lg. folio, 8vo., cloth, illus., colored plts. Van der Peet H-64-155 1978 Dfl 450

KLEISER, GRENVILLE   Training for Power and Leadership. Garden City, 1923. Austin 80-766 1978 $10

KLEMPERER, V.   Die Romanische Literaturen von der Renaissance bis zur Franzosischer Revolution. Potsdam, 1924. 4to., cloth, plts., some in color, text illus. Van der Peet H-64-471 1978 Dfl 85

KLEUTGEN, S. J.   La Philosophie Scolastique Exposee et Defendue. Paris, 1870. 4 vols., 8vo., wrs. Salloch 348-109 1978 $20

KLEYNTJENS, J.   Documenten Over Den Beeldenstorm van 1566 in de Bourgondische Monarchie. Tilburg, n.d. 8vo., orig. covers. Van der Peet H-64-363 1978 Dfl 55

KLINCK, CARL F.   Wilfred Campbell. Toronto, 1942. Austin 82-524 1978 $12.50

KLINEBERG, OTTO   Race Differences. 1935. Austin 79-403 1978 $12.50

KLINGBERG, FRANK J.   An Appraisal of the Negro in Colonial South Carolina... Washington, 1941. Scarce. MacManus 239-1858 1978 $25

KLINOV, I.   Israel Reborn. 1949. Illus., in Hebrew & English, photos. Austin 79-404 1978 $12.50

KLONDIKE, The Chicago Record's Book for Gold Seekers. Chicago, 1897. Orig. binding, scarce 1st. ed. Hayman 71-6 1978 $20

KLOPSTOCK, FREDERIC GOTTLIEB 1724-1803   The Messiah. c. 1810. Roy. 8vo., plts., contemp. diced calf, slight foxing. Howes 194-355 1978 £10

KLUCKHORN, CLYDE   The Navaho. Cambridge, 1946. 1st ed., illus., d.j., scarce. MacManus 239-1177 1978 $22.50

KLUSSMANN, R.   Bibliotheca Scriptorum Classicorum et Graecorum et Latinorum. 1909-13. 2 vols. in 4, buckram. Allen 234-512 1978 $100

KNAPP, CHARLES M.   New Jersey Politics During the Period of the Civil War and Reconstruction. Geneva, 1924. 1st ed., frontis., orig. cloth, fine. MacManus 239-1283 1978 $30

KNAPP, F.   Chemical Technology. 1851. Vol. 3 only, engraved plts., some coloured, woodcuts, covers faded and worn. George's 635-968 1978 £5

KNAPP, H. S.   History of the Maumee Valley Commencing with Its Occupation by the French in 1680. Toledo, 1872. Lea., sm. chip top of spine, very good copy, orig. full lea. binding, 1st ed. Hayman 73-546 1978 $60

KNAPP, JOHN LEONARD   The Journal of a Naturalist. 1829. Engraved frontis. and plts., cr. 8vo., full green diced calf, somewhat worn. George's 635-998 1978 £25

KNAPP, JOHN LEONARD   Journal of a Naturalist. London, 1830. 3rd. ed., 11 plts. full brown calf, neatly rebacked. Baldwins' 51-352 1978 $17.50

KNATCHBULL-HUGESSEN, E. H.   Queer Folk, Seven Stories. London, 1874. 1st ed., illus., author's inscription, covers slightly bubled and rubbed, inner hinges cracked, gilt covers bright. Victoria 34-471 1978 $20

KNAUSS, JAMES O.   Territorial Florida Journalism. Deland, 1926. Bds., cloth back, ports., ltd. to 360 copies. MacManus 239-1805 1978 $35

KNEIPP, SEBASTIAN   Ma Cure D'Eau pour La Guerison des Maladies. Paris, Bruxelles, Strasbourg, n.d. Edition populaire, half leather, marbled bds. and endpapers. Rittenhouse 49-437 1976 $10

KNEIPP, SEBASTIAN   Thus Shalt Thou Live. Bavaria, 1897. Rittenhouse 49-435 1976 $10

KNIGHT, C. R. B.   Historical Records of the Buffs East Kent Regiment. 1935. 2 vols., 8vo, orig. cloth, frontis., plts., fine, orig. d.j. F. Edwards 1013-483 1978 £20

KNIGHT, C. W. R.   Knight in Africa. London, 1937. 60 illus., 4to, orig. cloth. K Books 239-247 1978 £5

KNIGHT, CHARLES   The Land We Live In.... n.d. (1840). 4 vols., 4to, engraved title & frontis., full page engravings & vignettes, half dark green calf, maroon labels, spine gilt, very fine. Jarndyce 16-801 1978 £50

KNIGHT, CHARLES   The Old Printer and the Modern Press. London, 1854. Frontis., newly rebound. Battery Park 1-394 1978 $45

KNIGHT, CHARLES   Once Upon a Time. 1854. 2 vols., orig. cloth, soiled. Eaton 45-279 1978 £10

KNIGHT, CHARLES   Once Upon A Time. 1854. 1st. ed., orig. blue cloth, v.g. Jarndyce 16-802 1978 £18.50

KNIGHT, CHARLES   Shadows of the Old Booksellers. 1865. 8vo., orig. cloth, uncut, fresh. P. M. Hill 142-160 1978 £25

KNIGHT, ELLIS CORNELIA 1757-1837   Dinarbas: a Tale. 1790. Sm. 8vo., contemp. tree calf gilt, joints cracked, label missing. Howes 194-356 1978 £50

KNIGHT, GEORGE W.   History and Management of Land Grants for Education in the Northwest Territory.... New York & London, 1885. Orig. binding, clean. Hayman 71-408 1978 $15

KNIGHT, HENRY GALLY   Ilderim: a Syrian Tale. London, 1816. 8vo, disbound, 1st ed. Ximenes 47-172 1978 $25

KNIGHT, HENRY GALLY   Phrosyne: a Grecian Tale;.... London, 1817. 8vo, disbound, 1st ed. Ximenes 47-173 1978 $30

KNIGHT, LAURA   A Book of Drawings. 1923. Ltd. ed., signed by author, plts., 4to. George's 635-190 1978 £30

KNIGHT, R. P.   The Symbolical Language of Ancient Art and Mythology. New York, 1876. New ed. Biblo BL781-417 1978 $32.50

KNIGHT, SAMUEL   The Life of Dr. John Colet. Oxford, 1823. Plts., calf, lacking label, good. Upcroft 10-400 1978 £7.50

KNIGHT, THOMAS ANDREW   Pomona Herefordiensis... London, 1811. 4to, coloured plts., 19th. century polished brown calf, leather label, superb copy. Traylen 88-655 1978 £750

KNIGHT, W. S. M.   The History of the Great European War, its Causes and Effects. 1914-18. Maps, coloured and other illus., 10 vols., roy. 8vo. George's 635-834 1978 £8.50

KNIGHT, WILLIAM HENRY   Diary of a Pedestrian in Cashmere and Thibet. London, 1863. 1st ed., 8vo., plts., rebound in new red buckram, plts. with mild waterstain, interior otherwise better than fine, scarce. Current 24-182 1978 $110

KNIGHTON, WILLIAM   The Private Life of an Eastern King. 1856. New ed., illus., half title, orig. blue cloth, gilt spine & imprint v.g. Jarndyce 16-803 1978 £5.50

KNOBLAUCH, AUGUST   Klinik und Atlas Der Chronischen Krankheiten des Zentrainervensystems. Berlin, 1909. Rittenhouse 49-438 1976 $20

KNOBLOCK, EDWARD   Round the Room; autobiography. London, 1939. First ed., orig. binding, nice. Rota 211-285 1978 £5

KNOTT, JOHN F.   War Cartoons. N.P., 1918. Folio, 1st ed., comers bumped, mint copy, very scarce book. Jenkins 116-289 1978 $35

KNOTTS, MINNIE P.   Nebraska Territorial Pioneer's Association:..... Lincoln, 1917. Illus., orig. pr. pict. wr., 1st ed. Ginsberg 14-718 1978 $15

KNOW, DUDLEY W.   The Naval Genius of George Washington. Boston, 1932. Illus., maps, ltd. to 550 copies, fine, inscribed by author. MacManus 239-1761 1978 $30

KNOWER, DANIEL   The Adventures of a Forty-Niner. Albany, 1894. Cloth, 1st ed., some spotting on spine, otherwise very good copy. Hayman 73-76 1978 $15

KNOWER, DANIEL   Adventures of a Forty-Niner... Albany, 1894. 12mo., pic. cloth, 1st ed. MacManus 239-1936 1978 $20

KNOWLES, J. A.   Essays in the History of the York School of Glass-Painting. 1936. Sm. 4to., coloured and plain plts., cloth. Quaritch 983-111 1978 $85

KNOWLES, JAMES SHERIDAN   The Love Chase. 1837. 1st. ed., 1/2 calf, gilt, little scuffed. Eaton 45-280 1978 £8

KNOWLES, JOSEPH   Alone in the Wilderness. 1913. Illus., first ed. Austin 82-525 1978 $27.50

KNOWLES, R. E.   St. Cuthbert's; a Novel. Toronto, 1933. Hood 116-481 1978 $7.50

KNOWN Signatures. 1932. Very good, d.w., first English ed. Bell Book 16-677 1978 £7.50

KNOX, ELLEN M.   Girl of the New Day. Toronto, 1919. Hood 117-521 1978 $10

KNOX, RONALD ARBUTHNOTT   Caliban in Grub Street. 1930. Very good, worn d.w., first Eng. ed. Bell Book 17-538 1978 £7.50

KNOX, RONALD ARBUTHNOTT   Essays in Satire. 1928. Cloth backed bds., v.g., first Eng. ed. Bell Book 17-807 1978 £10

KNOX, RONALD ARBUTHNOTT   The Miracles of King Henry VI. Cambridge, 1923. Latin and English text, 8vo. Upcroft 12-239 1978 £9

KNOX, THOMAS WALLACE   Boy Travellers in Ceylon and India. 1882. Illus. Austin 82-526 1978 $17.50

KNOX, THOMAS WALLACE   Boy Travellers in Egypt and the Holy Land. 1882. Illus. Austin 82-527 1978 $17.50

KNOX, THOMAS WALLACE   Boy Travellers in Great Britain and Ireland. 1891. Illus. Austin 82-528 1978 $12.50

KNOX, THOMAS WALLACE   Boy Travellers in Japan and China. 1879. Illus. Austin 82-529 1978 $17.50

KNOX, THOMAS WALLACE   Boy Travellers in Mexico. 1890. Illus. Austin 82-530 1978 $17.50

KNOX, THOMAS WALLACE   Boy Travellers in Siam and Java. 1881. Illus., colored frontis. Austin 82-532 1978 $17.50

KNOX, THOMAS WALLACE   Boy Travellers in the Russian Empire. 1887. Illus, colored frontis. Austin 82-531 1978 $17.50

KNOX, THOMAS WALLACE   Camp-Fire and Cotton-Field: Southern Adventure in Time of War Life with the Armies, and Residence on a Louisiana Plantation. NY, 1865. Illus, pres copy from author, spine badly chipped, taped. Broadfoot's 44-234 1978 $25.00

KNOX, THOMAS WALLACE   How to Travel. New York, 1881. 16mo., orig. cloth, first ed. Morrill 241-245 1978 $12.50

KNOX, THOMAS WALLACE   Life and Work of Henry Ward Beecher.   Hartford, 1887. Cloth. Hayman 72-408 1978 $7.50

KNOX, VICESIMUS   Essays, Moral and Literary.   1793. 3 vols., contemp. tree calf gilt, 8vo. Howes 194-357 1978 £20

KNOX, VICESIUMUS   Winter Evenings: or, Lucubrations on Life and Letters. 1790. 2nd. ed., 2 vols., orig. tree calf, red & green labels, v.g. Jarndyce 16-126 1978 £27

KNUTSEN, R. M.   Japanese Polearms. Illus., cr. 4to, buckram, gilt. Traylen 88-506 1978 £10

KNYVETT, THOMAS   The Knyvett Letters (1620-1644). 1949. Roy. 8vo, plts., good. Upcroft 10-97 1978 £8.50

KOBBE, GUSTAV   The Central Railroad of New Jersey...   New York, 1891. 12mo., illus., plts., lg. colored fold. map, orig. limp cloth, good. MacManus 239-1284 1978 $25

KOBBE, GUSTAV   The Hudson Fulton Celebration. 1909. Illus., hand made paper, limited to only 122 copies. Nestler Rare 78-124 1978 $25

KOBBE, GUSTAV   The New Jersey Coast and Pines. An Illustrated Guide Book, with Road-maps. Short Hills, 1889. 12mo., author's pres. Biblo BL781-152 1978 $16.50

KOCH, ADRIENNE   Jefferson and Madison...The Great Collaboration. New York, 1950. First ed., fine, d.w. Biblo 247-72 1978 $15

KOCH, AUGUSTUS.   Bird's Eye View of the City of San Antonio, Bexar County, Texas. 1873. San Antonio, n.d. Large repro. of map. Jenkins 116-108 1978 $7.50

KOCHO, UEDA   Kocho Gwafu. Osaka, (1833). Illus., wrs., sewn, somewhat soiled and worn, signed by Kocho. Dawson's 449-150 1978 $275

KOCK, CHARLES PAUL DE   Memoirs of... 1899. Half title, orig. blue cloth, v.g. Jarndyce 16-457 1978 £8.50

KOCK, CHARLES PAUL DE   The Modern Cymon, from the "Jean". Philadelphia, 1833. 2 vols., 8vo., orig. bds., cloth backs, untrimmed, 1st Amer. ed. Morrill 241-246 1978 $10

KOCK, CHARLES PAUL DE   The Works of Charles Paul De Kock.   London, 1902-02. 25 vols., 8vo., t.e.g., ltd. to 1000 copies, illus., engr. plts., photogravures, 3/4 brown levant with marbled bds. & endpapers, raised bands on spine with gilt decor's & lettering, better than fine. Current 24-29 1978 $265

KOCH, FREDERICK H.   American Folk Plays. New York, 1939. Ex-lib. Broadfoot 50-115 1978 $10

KOCH, FREDERICK H.   Carolina Folk-Plays. New York, 1922. Broadfoot 50-116a 1978 $20

KOCH, FREDERICK H.   Carolina Folk-Plays. New York, 1926. 2nd series. Broadfoot 50-116b 1978 $50

KOCH, ROBERT   The Aetiology of Tuberculosis. New York, 1932. Library marks. Rittenhouse 49-441 1976 $15

KOCHER, A. E.   Reconnoissance Soil Survey of South-Central Texas. Washington, 1915. Folding map, pr. wr. Jenkins 116-783 1978 $12.50

KOCHER, P. H.   Christopher Marlowe; A Study of His Thought, Learning and Character. Chapel Hill, 1946. Octavo, good. Upcroft 10-402 1978 £7.50

KODDIGE en Ernstige Opschriften op Luifels, Wagens, Glazen, Uithangborden en Andere Tafereelen. Amsterdam, 1830. 2 parts in 1, orig. bds., soiled copy, 8vo., somewhat loose. Van der Peet H-64-151 1978 Dfl 65

KOEHLER, FRANCIS C.   Three Hundred Years. The Story of the Hackensack Valley... Chester, (1940). 1st ed., frontis., illus., orig. cloth, very good, inscribed by author. MacManus 239-1285 1978 $25

KOEHLER, GEORGE   Nick Putzel or Arthur Gurney's Ruin. 1881. Illus, first ed. Austin 82-533 1978 $20

KOELLIKER, ALBERT   Die Bildung der Samenfaden in Blaschen als allgemeines Entwicklungsgesetz. (Neusenburg, 1846). 4to., lithographed plts., 1st ed., modern half cloth. Schafer 19-54 1978 sFr. 500

KOELLIKER, ALBERT   Die Selbstandigkeit und Abhangigkeit des sympathischen Nervensystems,.... Zurich, 1844 (1845). 1st ed., 4to., orig. pr. wr., uncut. Gilhofer 75-65 1978 SFr 600

KOELLIKER, RUDOLF ALBERT VON
Please turn to
KOELLIKER, ALBERT

KOEPPE, C. E.   The Canadian Climate. Bloomington, 1931. Hood 116-38 1978 $25

KOESTLER, ARTHUR   Darkness at Noon. New York, 1941. First Amer. ed. Biblo 247-578 1978 $7.50

KOESTLER, ARTHUR   Darkness at Noon. New York, 1941. First U.S. ed., very good, worn d.w. Bell Book 16-535 1978 £12.50

KOESTLER, ARTHUR   The Yogi and the Commissar and Other Essays. New York, 1945. 1st ed. Biblo 251-538 1978 $12.50

KOETTERITZ, JOHN B.   Andrew Finck, Major in the Revolutionary Wars. Utica, 1897. Orig. pr. wr., pres. copy, very good or better. Limestone 9-170 1978 $8.50

KOHL, JOHANN GEORG   Kitchi-Gami. London, 1860. 1st ed., 8vo., pen & ink textual sketches, rebound in blue marbled bds., brown calf spine. Current 24-183 1978 $210

KOHL, JOHANN GEORG   Russia and The Russians, In 1842. London, 1842. 1st. ed., 2 vols., sm. 8vo, plts., half calf, gilt backs. Deighton 5-130 1978 £28

KOHL, JOHANN GEORG   Russia and the Russians in 1842. 1842. 2 vols., lg. 12mo., half roan, marbled sides, frontispieces, plts. P. M. Hill 142-210 1978 £20

KOIZUMI, G.   Lacquer Work... 1923. 4to., plts., cloth. Quaritch 983-86 1978 $90

KOIZUMI, G.   Lacquer Work. London, 1923. Sm. 4to, orig. gilt dec. cloth, good, illus. by half tone & collotype plts. Sexton 7-29 1978 £22

KOK, J.   Vaderlandsch Woordenboek. Amsterdam, 1746-1785. 38 vols., 8vo., clothbound, illus. with engr. plts., portrs., colored maps, rare complete set. Van der Peet H-64-364 1978 Dfl 750

KOKAN, SHIBA   Seiyu Ryotan. (Edo, 1803). 5 vols., illus., wrs., sewn, chitsu case. Dawson's 449-152 1978 $500

KOLB, E. L.   Through the Grand Canyon from Wyoming to Mexico... New York, 1946. New ed., illus., cloth. Hayman 72-410 1978 $7.50

KOLB, PETER   The Present State of the Cape of Good-Hope: Or, A Particular Account of the Several Nations of the Hottentots. London, 1731. 1st. ed in English, 2 vols., frontispieces, folding map, engraved plts., occasional age-marking throughout, smudged lib. stamp repeated several times, old calf, worn, preserved in cloth slip-case, 8vo. K Books 239-248 1978 £400

KOLBEN, PETER
Please turn to
KOLB, PETER

KOLFF, D. H.   Voyages of the Dutch Brig of War Dourga... 1840. Maps, binders' cloth, slight foxing, 8vo. Edwards 1012-167 1978 £75

KOMROFF, MANUEL   Juggler's Kiss. 1927. First ed. Austin 82-534 1978 $11

KOMROFF, MANUEL   The March of the Hundred. 1939. First ed.,
d.j. Austin 82-535 1978 $11

KOMROFF, MANUEL   A New York Tempest. 1932. First ed. Austin
82-536 1978 $11

KOMROFF, MANUEL   A New York Tempest. 1932. Austin 82-537
1978 $8.50

KONEWKA, PAUL   Illustrations to Goethe's Faust. Boston, 1871.
1st ed., quarto, illus., inscription, covers faded, fine. Victoria 34-472 1978
$30

KONKLE, BURTON ALVA   Benjamin Chew, 1722-1810. Head of the Pennsylvania Judiciary System Under Colony and Commonwealth. Philadelphia, 1932.
Illus. MacManus 239-1527 1978 $22.50

KONKLE, BURTON ALVA   John Motley Morehead and the Development of
N.C. 1796-1866. Philadelphia, 1922. Uncut. Broadfoot 50-117 1978 $15

KONKLE, BURTON ALVA   The Life and Speeches of Thomas Williams.
Philadelphia, 1905. 1st ed., 2 vols., illus., orig. cloth, presentation copy from
author, hinges cracking, scarce. MacManus 239-830 1978 $37.50

KONKLE, BURTON ALVA   The Life and Times of Thomas Smith, 1745-1809,
a Pennsylvania Member of the Continental Congress. Philadelphia, 1904. Illus.,
maps. MacManus 239-1683 1978 $22.50

KONKLE, BURTON ALVA   The Life of Andrew Hamilton... Philadelphia,
1941. Illus. MacManus 239-763 1978 $17.50

KONKLE, BURTON ALVA   The Life of Chief Justice Ellis Lewis, 1798-1871,
of the First Elective Supreme Court of Pennsylvania. Philadelphia, 1907. Illus.,
8vo., 1st ed. Morrill 239-579 1978 $12.50

KOONTZ, LOUIS K.   Robert Dinwiddie, His Career in American Colonial Government and Westward Expansion. Glendale, 1941. 1st ed., illus.,
fine uncut copy. MacManus 239-240 1978 $37.50

KOPP, HERMANN   Beitrage zur Geschichte der Chemie. Braunschweig, 1869-75. 3 parts in 1 vol., 8vo., fldg. plt., modern buckram, some foxing, very good copy, 1st ed. Norman 5-160 1978 $85

KOPP, HERMANN   Die Entwickelung der Chemie in der Neueren
Zeit. Munich, 1873. 8vo., contemp. cloth-backed bds., fine copy, stamp of
Wernigerode Library on title, 1st ed. Norman 5-161 1978 $75

KOPP, HERMANN   Geschichte der Chemie. Braunschweig, 1843-
47. 4 vols., 8vo., portrs., old half mor., rubbed, hinges cracked, rather foxed,
but good set, 1st ed. Norman 5-159 1978 $150

KORAN   The Koran, Commonly Called the Alcoran of
Mohomet. Springfield, 1806. 1st Amer. ed., somewhat worn. Nestler Rare 78-
237 1978 $25

KORTRIGHT, FRANCIS H.   The Ducks, Geese and Swans of North America.
Washington, 1942. Artifical leather, illus. by T.M. Shortt, color plts. Hayman
71-409 1978 $7.50

KOSTER, HENRY   Travels in Brazil. London, 1817. 2nd. ed.,
2 vols., 8vo, folding engraved map, neatly repaired, sepia aquatint plts., labels
removed from title-pg. of each vol., polished half calf, marbled bds., gilt panelled
backs, little worn. Deighton 5-47 1978 £155

KOSTER, S.   Serenade. Amsterdam, 1924. Sm. 8vo., orig.
covers, plts., ltd. ed. of 100 numbered copies only, wrs. soiled, edges slightly
worn. Van der Peet H-64-377 1978 Dfl 35

KOTZEBUE, AUGUST FRIEDRICH VON   Lovers' Vows. Boston, 1799. 12mo.,
unbound, first Amer. ed. Morrill 239-468 1978 $22.50

KOTZEBUE, AUGUST FRIEDRICH VON   The Wild Goose Chace. New York,
1800. Portraits, 8vo., cont. calf, first ed. Morrill 241-684 1978 $50

KOTZEBUE, OTTO VON   Entdeckungs-Reise In die Sud-See und Nach Der
Berings-Strasse Zur Erforschung Einer Nordostlichen Durchfahrt. Weimar, 1821.
1st. ed., 3 vols. in 1, 4to, 15 coloured aquatine plts., maroon straight-grained
half morocco, matching bds. Deighton 5-Cover 1978 £1350

KOTZEBUE, OTTO VON   A Voyage of Discovery into the South Sea and
Beering's Straits for the Purpose of Exploring a North West Passage Undertaken in
the Years 1815-1818...in the Ship Rurick. London, 1821. 3 vols., 1st English ed.,
8vo., colored plts., maps & charts, orig. polished calf, gilt decor. spines, light
foxing on charts, rare. Current 24-184 1978 $1,285

KOVEN, MRS. REGINALD DE   The Life and Letters of John Paul Jones. New
York, 1913. 1st ed., 2 vols., illus., maps, orig. cloth, bookplts., very good
set. MacManus 239-1760 1978 $20

KRAMER, SIDNEY   A History of Stone and Kimball and Herbert S.
Stone and Co. With a Bibliography of Their Publications. 1893-1905. Chicago,
(1940). Orig. cloth, d.j., chipped, 1st trade ed. MacManus 238-1061 1978
$50

KRAMER, SIDNEY   A History of Stone and Kimball and Herbert S.
Stone and Co., 1893-1905. Chicago, 1940. Orig. cloth, pub. box, 1st ed.,
1 of 500 copies signed by author, fine. MacManus 238-1059 1978 $75

KRAMER, JOHN E.   First Decennial Supplement to the "First Century
of the Philadelphia College of Pharmacy," 1921-1931. Philadelphia, 1934.
Rittenhouse 49-447 1976 $10

KRAFT, JENSEN   Mechanica Latine reddita et aucta a Joanne
Nicolao Tetens. Buetzow & Wismar, 1773. Fldg. engr. plts., 4to., contemp.
tree calf., 1st ed. in Latin, signature of Carl Ferdinand Degen. Argosy Special-
55 1978 $125

KRAFFT-EBING, R. VON   Die transitorischen Storungen des Selbstbewusst-
seins. Erlangen, 1868. 8vo., cloth, first ed. Gurney 75-58 1978 £25

KRAFFT-EBING, CHADDOCK   Psychopathia Sexualis with Expecial Reference to
Contrary Sexual Instinct. Philadelphia, 1925. Rittenhouse 49-446 1976 $10

KRAFFT, HERMAN F.   Sea Power in American History... New York,
1920. Cloth. Hayman 72-411 1978 $10

KRACHENNIKOW, S. P.   Histoire Et Description Du Kamtchatka...
Amsterdam, 1770. Lg. folding maps, plts., 2 vols., thick sm. 8vo., contemp.
calf. Edwards 1012-209 1978 £270

KRACAUER, SIEGFRIED   From Caligari to Hitler: A Psychological History
of the German Film. 1947. Illus., very good, first English ed. Bell Book 17-
165 1978 £15

KOWALCGYH, GEORG   Selected by...., Decorative Sculpture. New
York, 1927. Illus., sm. folio, name stamp on title and few pgs., top of spine torn.
Baldwins' 51-107 1978 $22.50

KRAMER, SIDNEY   A History of...1893-1905. 1931. One of 500
copies, signed. Battery Park 1-487 1978 $50

KRANZLIN, F.   Orchidacearum Sibiriae Enumeratic. Berlin,
1931. 8vo., wrs. Book Chest 17-213 1978 $30

KRATZ, JOHN VALENTINE   A Brief History of and a Complete Genealogical
Family Regs. Elkhart, 1892. Covers shabby, contents complete. Baldwins' 51-
261 1978 $25

KREDEL, FRITZ   Glass Flowers. New York, (1940). 8vo,
pictorial paper over boards, color plts. by Fritz Kredel. Duschnes 220-177 1978
$20

KREHBIEL, H. P.   The History of the General Conference of the
Mennonites of North America. N.P., 1898. Errata, cloth, back inner hinges
cracking, very scarce. Hayman 72-412 1978 $25

KREIDER, HARRY JULIUS   Lutheranism in Colonial New York. New York,
1942. Butterfield 21-135 1978 $7.50

KREPS, THEODORE J.   The Economics of the Sulfuric Acid Industry.
Stanford, 1938. 8vo. George's 635-350 1978 £6

KRISTELLER, PAUL   Andrea Mantegna. 1901. Plts., text illus.,
sm. folio. George's 635-192 1978 £10.50

KRISTELLER, PAUL   Early Florentine Woodcuts. Cr. 4to, ltd. to
500 copies. Traylen 88-507 1978 £15

KROHN, HENRY   Foetus extra Uterum Historia. London, 1791.
Folio, orig. marbled bds., coloured plts., in 2 parts with text in Latin and English.
Gurney 75-59 1978 £75

KROM, N. J.   De Tempels van Angkor. Amsterdam, n.d.
(c.1930). Large 8vo, half cloth, plts., map. Van der Peet 127-306 1978 Dfl 30

KRONFELD, R.   On Gliding and Soaring, the Theory of Motorless
Flight. (1932). Diagrams, illus., 8vo. George's 635-835 1978 £22.50

KROPOTKIN, PETER   The Conquest of Bread. Vanguard Press, 1926.
Austin 80-769 1978 $8.50

KROUPA, B.   An Artist's Tour: Gleanings and Impressions of
Travels in North and Central America and The Sandwich Islands. 1890. 8vo,
orig. cloth, plts. Edwards 1012-376 1978 £30

KRUEGER, MAX   Pioneer Life in Texas: An Autobiography. San
Antonio, 1930. 1st ed., rare, presentation copy from Krueger's son Carl, to
William R. Simpson. Jenkins 116-785 1978 $125

KRUMBACHER, K.   Geschichte der Byzantinischen Literatur von
Justinian bis zum Ende des Ostroemischen Reiches (527-1453). 1891. New buckram. Allen 234-1341 1978 $17.50

KRUSE, GERTRUDE   Notes by.... Philadelphia, 1932. Drawings
by Albert Kruse. Baldwins' 51-227 1978 $7.50

KRUSENSTERN, ADAM JOHANN VON   Resa Omkring Jorden, Forrattad Aren
1803, 1804, 1805 och 1806. Orebro, 1811-12. 3 vols., calf and marbled bds.,
mor. labels, spine of vol. 2 slightly darkened. Dawson's 127-270 1978 $600

KRUSENSTERN, ADAM JOHANN VON   Voyage Round the World, 1803-06.
1813. 2 vols., map, coloured aquatint plts., thick 4to., cont. half calf, joints
repaired. Edwards 1012-26 1978 £1,650

KRUSENSTERN, ADAM JOHANN VON   Voyage Around the World, in the Years
1803, 1804, 1805, & 1806.... London, 1813. 1st English ed., in 1, quarto,
colored aquatints, folding map, contemp. calf, rebacked, preserving original
gilt paneled spine with red leather label, marbled edges, later endpapers, occasional
light foxing. Bennett 20-116 1978 $2,750

KRYSKILL, WILLIAM   The Story of Hyeholde. Philadelphia, (1940).
Illus., author's signed pres. Biblo BL781-87 1978 $10

KU Klux Kismet March. Aransas Pass, 1924. Folio. Jenkins 116-787 1978
$17.50

KUCK, LORAINE E.   Hawaiian Flowers. Honolulu, 1943. 1st ed.,
color plts., tall 8vo, orig. cloth. Book Chest 17-215 1978 $18

KUENEN, A.   The Religion of Israel to the Fall of the Jewish
State. London, 1882-1883. 3 vols., 8vo., ex-lib. Morrill 239-467 1978
$15

KULISCHER, EUGENE M.   Europe on the Move. War and Population Changes,
1917-47. New York, 1948. Maps. Biblo BL781-830 1978 $8

KUMM, H. K. W.   Khout-Hon-Nofer. London, 1910. Folding map,
plts., some foxing, backstrip dull, orig. cloth, 8vo. K Books 239-250 1978 £9

KUMM, H. K. W.   Khout-Hon-Nofer. London, 1910. Folding map,
plts., some foxing, orig. cloth, 8vo, covers slightly worn. K Books 239-250A
1978 £7

KUNSTSAMMLUNGEN Des Herrn Geheimrats Dr. J. Von Hefner-Alteneck, Munchen. Munchen, 1904. 4to., plts., orig. covers. Van der Peet H-64-112 1978
Dfl 38

KUNTZ, ALBERT   Autonomic Nervous System. Philadelphia, 1934.
Second ed., library copy. Rittenhouse 49-449 1976 $15

KUNTZE, J. E.   Excurse Ueber Roemisches Recht... 1880.
Allen 234-517 1978 $12.50

KUNZ, GEORGE FREDERICK   The Book of the Pearl. New York, 1908. Illus.,
full pg. plts., quarto, gilt, decorated cloth, t.e.g., other edges uncut, fine copy.
Baldwins' 51-109 1978 $125

KUNZ, GEORGE FREDERICK   The Book of the Pearl. New York, 1908. Illus.,
some in color, lg. thick 4to., scarce. MacManus 239-668 1978 $75

KUNZ, GEORGE FREDERICK   The Book of the Pearl. The History, Art, Science
and Industry of the Queen of Gems. 1908. Imp. 8vo., maps, plain and coloured
plts., buckram, gilt, gilt top. Quaritch 983-Addenda j 1978 $250

KUNZ, GEORGE FREDERICK   The Curious Lore of Precious Stones. Philadelphia, (1913). Color illus., scarce. MacManus 239-686 1978 $50

KUNZ, GEORGE FREDERICK   The Magic of Jewels and Charms. Philadelphia,
& London, 1915. Illus., 8 color plts., thick 8vo, backstrip faded. Baldwins' 51-
110 1978 $60

KUNZ, GEORGE FREDERICK   Rings for the Fingers. Philadelphia, & London,
1917. Illus., 3 color plts., thick 8vo, uncut. Baldwins' 51-111 1978 $75

KUO, HELENA   I've Come a Long Way. 1942. 1st ed., very
good in dust jacket, inscr'd by author in English & Chinese. Austin 79-415 1978
$15

KUPPER, WINIFRED   The Golden Hoof. New York, 1945. 1st ed.,
cloth, yellow end sheets, frontis., fine copy, prtd. on yellow paper. Dykes 34-
61 1978 $15

KUPRIN, ALEXANDRE   Gambrinus and Other Stories. New York,
1925. 1st Amer. ed. Biblo 251-539 1978 $12.50

KURTH, JULIUS   Die Wandmosaiken von Ravenna. Munich, 1912.
4to., plts., some in color. Biblo BL781-644 1978 $22.50

KURTZ, CHARLES M.   Illustrations from the Art Gallery of the World's
Columbian Exposition. Philadelphia, (1893). 336 engrs., 1st ed., cloth, soiled
& little worn, cover somewhat soiled, little worn. Hayman 73-160 1973 $10

KURTZ, ELMA S.   Civil War Diary of Cornelius R. Hanleiter.
Atlanta, n.d. New cloth, Bell Wiley's copy. Broadfoot's 44-446 1978 $18

KURZ, HERMAN   Falstaff und seine Gesellen. Strassburg, c.1871.
Ornate binding, deeply impressed designs, overall gilt decor., very good. Victoria
34-473 1978 $27.50

KURZE Anmerkungen Ueber das Betragen des Meinisters in Portugall in Denen Han-
deln der Jesuiten. Franckfurt-Leipzig, 1761. 2 parts in 1 vol., sm. 4to., orig.
covers as issued, rare. Van der Peet H-64-365 1978 Dfl 60

KUSHIN, NATHAN   Memoirs of a New American. 1949. Austin
79-416 1978 $15

KUSSMAUL, ADOLF   Die Storungen der Sprache. Leipzig, 1877.
8vo., half mor., first ed., very rare. Gurney 75-60 1978 £135

KVIST, ANTON   Den Gamle Pioner Fortaeller. 1935. Illus.
with photos, paper, in Danish. Austin 79-417 1978 $37.50

KYNE, PETER B.   The Parson of Panamint and Other Stories. New
York, 1929. 1st ed., d.w. Biblo BL781-1042 1978 $10

KYNER, JAMES H.   End of Track. Caldwell, 1937. Cloth, illus.,
1st ed., fine, d.w. Dykes 35-146 1978 $17.50

L

LABAT, R. B.   Voyages aux Isles de L'Amerique 1693-1705.
Paris, (1931). 2 vols., illus., orig. paper wrs., good set. MacManus 239-241
1978 $25

LABILLARDIERE, JACQUES JULIEN HOUTON DE   Voyage in Search of La
Perouse, 1791-94. 1800. Fldg. chart, plts., 2 vols., calf, titles browned &
some foxing, 8vo. Edwards 1012-27 1978 £150

LA BOESSIERE, TEXIER DE   Traite de l'art des armes. Paris, 1818. Plts.,
first ed., 8vo., half calf, repaired. F. Edwards 1013-343 1978 £95

LABORDE, A. DE   Descriptions des Nouveaux Jardins de la France
et de ses Anciens Chateaux Melee d'Observations sur la Vie de la Campagne et la
Composition des Jardins. 1808. Folio, text in French, German and English,
plts., contemp. bds., worn, uncut. Quaritch 983-43 1978 $2,250

LABORS in the Vineyard. Salt Lake City, 1884. Orig. cloth, lst ed. Ginsberg
14-660 1978 $15

LABOULAYE, EDWARD RENE LEFEBRE   Abdallah, or the Four-Leaved Shamrock.
Lond., 1868. Fir. Eng. Ed., red cloth binding, edges gilt. Greene 78-245
1978 $45.00

LABRIE, JACQUES   Les Premiers Rudimens de la Constitution Britannique; Traduits de l'Anglais de M. Brooke.... Montreal, 1827. Orig. paper cover,
erratum. Hood 116-636 1978 $135

LABRIOLA, ANTONIO   Essays on the Materialistic Conception of History.
1908. Austin 80-773 1978 $20

LABRUNIE, GERARD
Please turn to
GERARD DE NERVAL

LA BRUYERE, JEAN DE   Characters. 1709. Fifth ed., engrav. frontispiece, contemp. panelled calf, joints cracked, label missing, 8vo. Howes 194-
358 1978 £18

LABUS, GIOVANNI   Antichi Monumenti. Scoperti in Brescia.
Brescia, 1823. 4to., plts., wrs. Biblo BL781-419 1978 $27.50

LAC, FRANCOIS MARIE PERRIN DE
Please turn to
PERRIN DU LAC, FRANCOIS MARIE

LACAILLE, NICOLAS LOUIS DE   The Elements of Astronomy. London, 1750.
8vo., cont. half calf, plts., first Eng. ed. Gurney 75-61 1978 £50

LA CEPEDE, BERNARD GERMAIN ETIENNE DE LA VILLE SUR ILLON, COMTE DE
Histoire Naturelle de l'Homme. Paris, 1827. 8vo., old quarter calf, portrait,
plts., first ed. Gurney 75-62 1978 £25

LA CEPEDE, BERNARD GERMAIN ETIENNE DE LA VILLE SUR ILLON, COMTE DE
Physique Generale et Particuliere... Paris, 1782, 1784. First ed., 2 vols.,
12mo., plts., cont. quarter calf over later bds. Bennett 20-117 1978 $400

LA CHAUME, DE, DOCTEUR EN MEDECINE   Traite de Medecine Contenant la
Parfaite Connoissance de l'Homme, la Sanguification au Coeur, la Circulation du
Sang... Auxerre, 1679. 12mo., contemp. calf, back gilt, lst ed., very scarce.
Offenbacher 30-78 1978 $150

LACKINGTON, JAMES   Memoirs of the First Forty-Five Years of Life of
James Lackington... London, 1792. Rebound in cloth. Ballinger 11-48 1978
$75.00

LACLOS, PIERRE AMBROSE FRANCOIS CHODERLOS DE   Les Liaisons Danger-
euses... 1782. 4 vols. in 2, 12mo., dark blue mor., first ed. Quaritch 978-91
1978 $750

LACLOS, PIERRE AMBROSE FRANCOIS CHODERLOS DE   Les Liaisons Danger-
euses. Paris, Black Sun Press, 1929. 4to., orig. wrs., 1 of 1000 copies on
Moirans paper, illus., very good. Americanist 103-3 1978 $85

LACOMBE OF QUERCY, SIEUR JEAN DE   A Compendium of the East... Golden
Cockerel Press, 1937. Sm. folio, end-paper map, plts., orig. cloth, one of 300
numbered copies. Edwards 1012-210 1978 £100

LACOUTRE, C.   Repertoire Chromatique. Solution Raisonee et
Pratique des Problems les Plus Usuels dans l'Etude et l'Emploi des Couleurs. Paris,
1890. 4to., coloured frontis., plts., bds., mor. spine. Quaritch 983-206 1978
$180

LACRETELLE, PIERRE LOUIS   Memoire a Consulter et Consultation Pour les
Negocians Faisant le Commerce des Marchandises des Indes. Paris, 1786. 4to.,
modern wrappers. Wolfe 39-106 1978 $200

LA CROIX, JEAN FRANCOIS DE   Anecdotes Italiennes, Depuis la Destruction
de l'Empire Romain en Occident Jusqu'a nos Jours. Paris, 1769. 2 vols. in 1,
8vo., half calf. Van der Peet H64-301 1978 Dfl 55

LACROIX, PAUL   Catalogue de Cent Reliures d'Art executees sur
des Editions de Grand Luxe. Paris, 1902. 2 vols. in 1, plts., demy 4to., marbled bds., crushed levant mor. back. Forster 130-39 1978 £40

LACROIX, PAUL   Moeurs, Usages et Costumes au Moyen Age et a
l'Epoque de la Renaissance. 1871. 4to., colored plts., illus., buckram, ex-lib.
Allen 234-1343 1978 $15

LACROIX, SYLVESTRE FRANCOIS   Complement des Elemens d'Algebre a l'Use-
age de l'Ecole Centrale des Quatre-Nations. Paris, 1825. Half calf, 8vo.,
5th ed. K Books 244-394 1978 £7

LACROIX, SYLVESTRE FRANCOIS   Elements of Algebra. Cambridge, 1818.
8vo., orig. bds., all edges uncut, lst Amer. ed. Morrill 241-247 1978 $15

LACROIX, SYLVESTRE FRANCOIS   Traite Elementaire de Calcul Differentiel
er de Calcul Integral. Paris, 1828. Plts., half calf, 8vo. K Books 244-393
1978 £12

LACTANTIUS, LUCIUS FIRMIANUS   Divinarum Institutionum Libri Septem.
Venice, 1515. lst Aldine ed., sm. 8vo., 18th Cent. calf, full gilt spine, red
edges. Traylen 88-435 1978 £150

LADD, PARISH B.   Appendix to Hebrew and Christian Mythology.
New York, (1898). Wrs. Hayman 73-373 1978 $8.50

LADENBURG, ALBERT   Vortrage Uber Die Entwicklungsgeschichte der
Chemie von Lavoisier bis zur Gegenwart. Braunschweig, 1907. 8vo., modern
cloth, very good copy, 4th ed., revised & explanded. Norman 5-162 1978 $60

LADIES' Indispensable Assistant. New York, 1851. Bds., some wear on spine &
corners. Hayman 73-375 1978 $15

LADIES' Manual of Fancy Work. New York, 1884. Illus., 4to., orig. wrs., wrs.
slightly torn. Morrill 239-469 1978 $12.50

THE LADIES Physical Directory. London, 1736. 8vo, half morocco, 6th ed.,
some foxing, sound copy. Ximenes 47-206 1978 $125

THE LADIES' Wreath. Boston, n.d. (circa 1850). Illus., gilt-stamped & decor.
roan, lacks spine, internally dampstained, pres. plt., plts. engr. by Oliver Pel-
ton. Hayman 73-377 1978 $7.50

LAENNEC, RENE THEOPHILE HYACINTHE   Propositions Sur La Doctrine
D'Hippocrate. Paris, (1804). 4to., facsimile reprint, quarter brown lea., gilt,
fine copy, no. 241, notes in author's hand. Zeitlin 245-141 1978 $95

LAENNEC, RENE THEOPHILE HYACINTHE   A Treatise on the Diseases of the
Chest... Philadelphia, 1823. Rebacked. Rittenhouse 49-450 1978 $300

LA FARGE, CHRISTOPHER   Each to the Other. New York, 1939. 1st ed.,
d.w. Biblo 251-540 1978 $12.50

LA FARGE, JOHN   Reminiscences of the South Seas. New York,
1912. First ed., plts., mostly in color, lg. 8vo. Biblo 247-350 1978 $37.50

LAFARGE, OLIVER   The Eagle in the Egg. Boston, 1949. First ed.
Austin 82-538 1978 $22.50

LA FEUILLE, DANIEL DE   Livre Nouveau et Utile pour Toutes Sortes d'Artistes
... Amsterdam, 1691. Sm. 4to., full green mor. Janssenist binding, eng. plts.,
first ed., rare, splendid copy. Schumann 511-29 1978 sFr 1750

LAFFAN, R. G. D.   Select Documents of European History, 800-1492.
New York, (ca. 1929). Biblo 251-271 1978 $9.50

LAFITAU, JOSEPH FRANCOIS   Moeurs des Sauvages Ameriquains,.... Paris,
1824. 2 vols., 4to, frontis., map and plates, occasional light browning, contemp.
vellum, 1st ed. Quaritch 978-92 1978 $1,400

LA FOLLIE, LOUIS GUILLAUME DE   Le Philosophe Sans Pretention ou l'Homme
Rare. Paris, 1775. 8vo., engr. frontis., engr. vignette, contemp. half calf,
gilt, very good copy, 1st ed. Norman 5-163 1978 $375

LA FOND, GABRIEL   Fragmens de Voyages Autour du Monde:....
Paris, 1861. Plts, 9 colored, half mor., 1st ed. Ginsberg 14-469 1978 $150

LA FONTAINE, G. H.   Dictionary of Terms Used in the Paper, Printing
and Allied Industries. Toronto, 1949. Card cover. Hood's 115-28 1978 $25

LA FONTAINE, JEAN DE   Les Amours de Psiche et de Cupidon. Paris,
1669. 8 vo., light brown mor. gilt, gilt edges, by Trautz-Bauzonnet, 1st ed.
Quaritch Summer, 1978-26 1978 $3,250

LA FONTAINE, JEAN DE   Fables. Paris, 1836. Rebound in cloth, 5 eng.
by Johannot. Eaton 45-282 1978 £6

LA FONTAINE, JEAN DE   Fables. 1931. 2 vols., 8vo., engrs. on copper,
vellum, ltd. to 525 copies signed by translator & artist. Quaritch 979-145 1978
$150

LA FONTAINE, JEAN DE   Fables. London, Heinemann, New York, 1931.
Engravings by Stephen Gooden, 2 vols., 8vo., full vellum, ltd. to 525 copies,
signed by illustrator, fine, unopened, uncut. Howell 5-40 1978 $200

LA FONTAINE, JEAN DE   La Fontaine Fables Choisies pour les Enfants.
Paris, n.d. Spine worn, dust soiled, text very good. Victoria 34-233 1978
$22.50

LA FONTAINE, JEAN DE   The Fables of Jean De La Fontaine. London,
1931. 2 vols., tall octavo, cream vellum, engravings on copper by Stephen Gooden,
1 of 525 numbered copies, signed by trans. and illus. Totteridge 29-62 1978
$200

LA FONTAINE, JEAN DE   The Fables of... London, 1933. 8vo., brown
cloth, reproductions from engravings by Stephen Gooden, bookplate, ownership
inscription, very nice, first ed. Desmarais 1-299 1978 $20

LA FONTAINE, JEAN DE   Masterpieces of La Fontaine. Oxford, 1916.
Illus., 8vo., orig. pic. bds., cloth back, ex-lib. Morrill 241-248 1978 $10

LA FONTAINE, SIEUR DE   The Military Duties of the Officers of Cavalry.
1678. Plts., sm. 8vo., modern mor. F. Edwards 1013-344 1978 £175

LA FRENTZ, FERDINAND WILLIAM   Cowboy Stuff. New York, 1927.
Vellum & bds., portr. as frontis., plts., 1st ed., rare, #46 of 500 numbered
copies signed by author, illus'r & publisher, minor wear, fine copy, slipcase.
Dykes 34-30 1978 $200

LAFRENTZ, FERDINAND WILLIAM   Cowboy Stuff. New York, 1927. Illus.,
full page plts., orig. bds., 1 of 500 numbered copies, signed by author, publisher
& artist. Ginsberg 14-470 1978 $150

LAGERLOF, SELMA   Invisible Links. Boston, 1899. 1st Amer. ed.,
almost mint copy. Victoria 34-474 1978 $12.50

LAGESTROM, HUGO   Svensk Bokkonst. Stockholm, 1920. Sm. folio,
newly bound in cloth, orig. wr. bound in, very fine. Battery Park 1-474 1978
$75

LAGG, JARED   Crimes of Jared Flagg. New York, 1920. 8th
ed., of part 1, 2nd ed. of part 2. Limestone 9-106 1978 $15

LA GRANGE, HELEN   Clipper Ships of America and Great Britain...
New York, (1936). 1st ed., 4to., illus., orig. cloth-backed bds., fine, ltd. to
300 signed copies. MacManus 239-1762 1978 $100

LAGRANGE, JOSEPH LOUIS   De la Resolution des Equations Numeriques de tous
les Degrees. Paris, (1798). 4to., mod. half-calf, orig. blue wrs. bound in, fine
uncut copy, some light spots, 1st ed. Gilhofer 74-116 1978 sFr 400

LA GRANGE, JOSEPH LOUIS   Mechanique Analytique. Paris, 1788. 4to.,
old wrs., uncut, cloth case, 1st ed., uncut copy. Offenbacher 30-80 1978
$950

LAGRILLIERE-BEAUCLERC, E.   Voyages pittoresques a travers le Monde: De
Marseille aux Frontieres de Chine. Paris, 1900. 4to, cloth, plts., illus. Van
der Peet 127-307 1978 Dfl 55

LA GUARDIA, FIORELLO H.   The Making of an Insurgent. 1948. Frontis.,
1st ed. Austin 79-418 1978 $12.50

LA GUARDIA, FIORELLO H.   The Making of an Insurgent. 1948. Austin
79-419 1978 $10

LA GUARDIA, FIORELLO H.   The Making of an Insurgent. An Autobiography:
1882-1919. Philadelphia, (1948). Port., 1st ed. Biblo BL781-212 1978 $7.50

LAHONTAN, LOUIS ARMAND DE LEON D'ARCE, BARON   Dialogues Curieux
entre L'auteur et un Sauvage de bon Sens Qui a Voyage et Memoirs de L'Amerique
Septentrionale. Baltimore, 1931. Ltd. to 1,000 numbered copies, fine, scarce.
MacManus 239-243 1978 $25

LAHONTAN, LOUIS ARMAND DE LEON D'ARCE, BARON   Memoires de L'
Amerique Septentrionale, au la Suite des Voyages de Mr. Le Baron de La Hontan...
Amsterdam, 1741. Second ed., fold. map, plts., orig. binding. Wolfe 39-274
1978 $100

LAHONTAN, LOUIS ARMAND DE LEON D'ARCE, BARON   New Voyages to
North America. Chicago, 1905. Reprinted from Eng. ed. of 1703, 2 vols., uncut,
illus., spine tops worn, else good, scarce. MacManus 239-244 1978 $40

LAHONTAN, LOUIS ARMAND DE LEON D'ARCE, BARON   Suite des Voyages
du Baron de la Hontan dans L'Amerique Septentrionale, qui Contiennent une Relation
des Differens Peuples qui y Habitent.... Amsterdam, 1741. Marbled bds., calf
back, fold. map, plts., second ed. Wolfe 39-273 1978 $75

LAIDLER, HARRY W.   Boycotts. 1914. 1st ed., signed by author. Austin 80-774 1978 $27.50

LAIDLER, HARRY W.   The Road Ahead. 1932. Illus., 1st ed. in dust
jacket. Austin 80-775 1978 $12.50

LAING, A. M.   Prayers and Graces. 1944. Illus. by Mervyn
Peake, 16mo. George's 635-197 1978 £5

LAING, DAVID   Early Popular Poetry of Scotland and the Northern
Border. London, 1895. 2 vols., cr. 8vo., fine, orig. cloth. K Books 244-186
1978 £9

LAIRD, DONALD A.   Psychology and Profits. 1929. Austin 80-776
1978 $10

LAIRD, MAC GREGOR   Narrative of An Expedition Into the Interior of
Africa, by the River Niger in The Steam-Vessels Quorra and Alburkah in 1832
1833, and 1834. London, 1837. 1st. ed., 2 vols., 8vo, engraved plts. by Westall,
half calf, gilt backs. Deighton 5-17 1978 £75

LAIRD, MARY   The Eggplant Skin Pants and Poems. Pen & ink
drwgs. by author, 4to., one of 175 or less individually numbered copies, #48,
Japanese handmade paper, signed by author, pict. cloth. Battery Park 1-224
1978 $200

LAKE, STUART N.   Wyatt Earp, Frontier Marshal. Boston, (1931).
Cloth, fine, d.j. Hayman 72-414 1978 $7.50

LAKE, WILLIAM   The Parnassian Pilgrim,.... Hudson, 1807.
1st ed., old full calf, scuffed & worn, old sign on t.p., 8vo. Americanist
101-77 1978 $75

LAKES, Ponds and Streams on the C&M. (Boston), 1892. Pict. wrappers, illus. Wolfe 39-9 1978 $50

LAKING, GUY FRANCIS   The Furniture of Windsor Castle. 1905. Plts., roy. 4to., orig. qtr. mor., a little rubbed, sides a little soiled. George's 635-246 1978 £60

LAKING, GUY FRANCIS   Sevres Porcelain of Buckingham Palace and Windsor Castle. 1907. Folio, coloured plts., cloth, pigskin back, a little rubbed. Quaritch 983-Addenda k 1978 $300

LALANDE, JOSEPH DE   The Art of Papermaking. Kilmurry, 1976. Folio, bound by hand in half leather, one of 405 numbered copies. Wolfe 39-418 1978 $125

LALANDE, JOSEPH DE   The Art of Papermaking. Kilmurry, Ashling Press, 1976. 1st ed. in English, sm. folio, ed. ltd. to 405 numbered copies signed by paper-maker, plts. on blue decor. handmade paper, prtd. on all rag mouldmade paper, handmade marbled endpapers, 3/4 brown calf with brown hopsackcovered bds. Current 24-235 1978 $125

LALANDE, JOSEPH DE   Ladies' Astronomy. Paris, 1815. 12mo., plts., some spotting, new calf backed bds. Quaritch 977-191 1978 $45

LA LOUBERE, SIMON DE   A New Historical Relation of the Kingdom of Siam. London, 1693. 1st. ed. in English, sm. folio, engraved maps, engraved plts., contemporary panelled calf, raised bands, morocco label gilt, joints weak, back sl. defective, worn, without endpapers. Deighton 5-78 1978 £255

LAMA, GIUSEPPE DE   Elogio Storico del Conte Cesare Ventura Marchese di Gallinella Parmigiano. Parma, 1818. 4to., wrappers, very wide margins, very good uncut copy. King 7-162 1978 £30

LAMAR, JOSEPH R.   The Private Soldier of the Confederacy. NY, 1902. Wraps detached & chipped, Bell Wiley's copy. Broadfoot's 44-236 1978 $35.00

LAMAR, LUCIUS QUINTUS CINCINNATUS   Report Texas Boundary Commission. Washington, 1887. Cloth, leather label. Jenkins 116-790 1978 $125

LAMAR, LUCIUS QUINTUS CINCINNATUS   Texas and Pacific Railroad. Washington, 1877. Jenkins 116-791 1978 $15

LAMAR, LUCIUS QUINTUS CINCINNATUS   The Texas and Pacific Railroad. Washington, 1878. Pr. wrs. Jenkins 116-792 1978 $35

LAMARTINE, ALPHONSE DE   Graziella. Nonesuch Press, 1929. Illus. by Jacquier, sm. 8vo., orig. decor. buckram, in slipcase, ed. ltd. and numbered. Howes 194-1072 1978 £8.50

LAMARTINE, ALPHONSE DE   Graziella. London, Nonesuch Press, 1929. 8vo., cloth, t.e.g., colored frontis., text illus., ltd. ed. of 1600 numbered copies, uncut. Van der Peet H-64-398 1978 Dfl 45

LAMARTINE, ALPHONSE DE   History of the Girondists. Bohn, 1847. 3 vols., frontis., cr. 8vo. George's 635-701 1978 £5

LAMARTINE, ALPHONSE DE   A Pilgrimage to the Holy Land... 1835. Sm. 8vo, half calf, portrait, 3 vols. Edwards 1012-73 1978 £60

LAMARTINE, ALPHONSE DE   Portraits-Vignettes Pour l'Histoire des Girondins. Paris, 1848. 1st. ed., 8vo, lg. paper, 40 plts., 1 loose, contemp. half calf, front wrapper bound in. Hannas 54-129 1978 £7.50

LAMARTINE, GRAZIELLE   l'Image Litteraire. Nice, 1947. 4to., bds., slipcase, plts. by P. Leroy, ltd. ed. of 450 numbered copies only. Van der Peet H-64-433 1978 Dfl 95

LAMB, CHARLES   Beauty and the Beast. London, n.d. (c.1890). Engraved plts., sm. 4to, orig. printed bds. Traylen 88-166 1978 £5

LAMB, CHARLES   A Book Explaining the Ranks and Diginities of British Society. London, 1809. Engraved plts., coloured by hand, 2nd. ed., fcap. 8vo, contemp. quarter calf, little worn. Traylen 88-167 1978 £50

LAMB, CHARLES   A Dissertation Upon Roast Pig. (Concord: Will Bradley, n.d.). 12mo., illus., frontis. and tail pieces by Bradley, orig. bds., paper label, very fine unopened copy. MacManus 238-780 1978 $50

LAMB, CHARLES   Elia. 1836. 1st. complete authorized ed., 2 vol., 12mo, orig. cloth, faded, vol. 2 loose, split joints. Hannas 54-179 1978 £25

LAMB, CHARLES   Elia and the Last Essays of Elia. Gregynog Press, 1929. Wood engravings adapted from contemp. prints, 2 vols., roy. 8vo, orig. buckram, ltd. ed. of 285 copies. Traylen 88-261 1978 £110

LAMB, CHARLES   Eliana: Being the Hitherto Uncollected Writings. 1864. 1st. ed., calf, rebacked retaining orig. label, v.g. Jarndyce 16-804 1978 £14.50

LAMB, CHARLES   Great Stories From Shakespeare. London, n.d. Black & white plts. by Arthur Rackham, sm. 8vo, spine faded. Traylen 88-407 1978 £8

LAMB, CHARLES   John Woodvil. 1802. Sm. 8vo., 1st ed., orig. pink bds., entirely uncut, blue mor. case, very fine pres. copy, very scarce. Quaritch 979-217 1978 $1,575

LAMB, CHARLES   The Letters of ... 1837-48. 1st. ed., 4 vols., lg. 12mo, portraits, half-titles, half green morocco, gilt, t.e.g., others uncut, fine set. Hannas 54-180 1978 £35

LAMB, CHARLES   The Letters of Charles Lamb. 1935. 3 vols., 8vo., portrs., cloth with d.ws., 1st complete ed. Quaritch 979-216 1978 $125

LAMB, CHARLES   Letters, to Which are Added Those of His Sister. London, 1935. Frontis., 3 vols., 8vo., out of print & scarce. Traylen 88-291 1978 £30

LAMB, CHARLES   The Letters of Charles Lamb. 1935. Portrait, thick 8vo., orig. buckram, very good, d.w. Howes 194-990 1978 £30

LAMB, CHARLES   Mrs.' Leicester's School... London, 1809. 1st. issue of 1st. ed., engraved frontis. by J. Hopwood, 8vo, contemp. tree calf, excellent copy. Traylen 88-169 1978 £250

LAMB, CHARLES   Poetry for Children. 1872. Sm. 8vo, half-title, final blank leaf, comtemp. green half morocco, t.e.g. Hannas 54-181 1978 £15

LAMB, CHARLES   Prince Dorus. London, 1889. Colour plts., sm. 4to, half vellum, reprint ltd. ed. of 500 proof copies numbered & signed by publisher. Traylen 88-168 1978 £10

LAMB, CHARLES   Prince Dorus. London, 1889. Hand-colored plates, limited to 500 copies, proof copy, numbered and signed by publisher, internally fine, 3/4 vellum boards moderately soiled. Victoria 34-475 1978 $30

LAMB, CHARLES   Prince Dorus. Leadenhall Press, 1890-91. First English ed., coloured plts., 12mo., wraps, very good. Bell Book 16-550 1978 £7.50

LAMB, CHARLES   Rosamund Gray; Recollections of Christ's Hospital, etc. 1835. Contemp. 1/2 calf. Eaton 45-283 1978 £20

LAMB, CHARLES   A Tale of Rosamund Gray and Old Blind Margaret. London, 1928. 1 of 500 copies, sm. 8vo., orig. vellum-backed bds., uncut, frontis. Americanist 102-52 1978 $22.50

LAMB, CHARLES   A Tale of Rosamund Gray and Old Blind Margaret. Golden Cockerel, 1928. Frontis., 16mo., bds., #21 of 500 copies. Battery Park 1-117 1978 $35

LAMB, CHARLES   Tales From Shakespear. London, 1807. 1st. ed., engraved plts. by William Mulready, 2 vols., sm. 8vo, contemp. sheep, joints repaired, fine copy. Traylen 88-170 1978 £300

LAMB, CHARLES   The Works. 1903-05. 7 vols., plts., orig. red cloth, printed labels, gilt tops, good, 8vo. Howes 194-989 1978 £75

LAMB, JOSEPH   A Voyage to the Gardens of the Hesperides. (New York, n.d. (1899?). 4to., orig. 1/2 lea., 1 of 100 numbered copies, plts., very good. Americanist 103-13 1978 $85

LAMB, MARTHA J.   History of the City of New-York. New York & Chicago, 1877-1880. Thick 4to., 2 vols., plts., rebound set, excellent cond. Butterfield 21-513 1978 $45

LAMB, MARTHA J.   History of the City of New York: Its Origin, Rise and Progress. New York, (1896). Illus., 3 vols., fine set, orig. cloth. MacManus 239-366 1978 $45

LAMB, MARY MONTGOMERIE   The Story of Helen Davenant.   London, 1889.
New ed., author inscrip. signed, orig. cloth, edges rubbwd, inner hinges repaired.
Greene 78-199 1978 $40

LAMBERT, A.   L'Isle St. Louis. Une douzaine de Croquis Avec
une Preface Illustree... Paris, 1920. Oblong 4to., plts., mor., 1 of 10 copies
on Japan, of an ed. of 290. Quaritch 983-207 1978 $480

LAMBERT, CONSTANT   Music Ho! London, 1934. First ed., orig.
binding, nice, inscribed by author. Rota 211-289 1978 £25

LAMBERT, EDWARD R.   History of the Colony of New Haven, Before and
After the Union with Connecticut. New Haven, 1838. 1st ed., illus., maps,
orig. cloth, nice copy. MacManus 239-98 1978 $50

LAMBERT, GEORGE C.   Treasures in Heaven. Salt Lake City, 1914.
Cloth. Ginsberg 14-661 1978 $15

LAMBERT, J. F.   A History of Catasauqua in Lehigh Co., Pa.
Allentown, 1914. 4to., illus. MacManus 239-1528 1978 $40

LAMBERT, J. M.   Two Thousand Years of Gild Life... 1891.
Plts., octavo, good. Upcroft 10-404 1978 £20

LAMBERT, JOHANN HEINRICH   Cosmologische Briefe uber die Einrichtung des
Weltbaues. Augsburg, 1761. Very rare 1st ed., 8vo, contemp. boards, lightly
rubbed. Gilhofer 75-66 1978 SFr 1,800

LAMBERT, JOHN   Travels Through Lower Canada, and the United
States of North America in the Years 1806, 1807, and 1808 to which are added...
Anecdotes of some of the Leading Characters... London, 1810. 1st ed., 3 vols.,
8vo., lg. fldg. frontis map, plts., rebound full brown calf, fine. Current Misc.
8-28 1978 $1,375

LAMBERT, MARCUS BACHMAN   A Dictionary of the Non-English Words of the
Penna-German Dialect. Lancaster, (1924). Baldwins' 51-457 1978 $20

LAMBERT, R. S.   Grand Tour: A Journey in the Tracks of the Age
of Aristocracy. 1935. Advance proof copy, good, dusty & slightly torn publisher's
wraps. Bell Book 17-018 1978 £5

LAMBERT, SAMUEL W.   Medical Leaders from Hippocrates to Osler.
Indianapolis, 1929. Rittenhouse 49-452 1976 $12.50

LAMBORN, R.   Dragon Flies vs. Mosquitoes. New York, 1890.
Good, worn brown binding, ex-lib., 8vo, plts, fronts. Book Chest 17-218 1978
$32.50

LAMBROPOULOS, NICK   Reverends and Priests. 1935. Paper, in Greek.
Austin 79-420 1978 $47.50

LAMEY, M.   Le Chene-Liege en Algerie. Algeria, 1879.
French text, full scarlet leather, waterstained, slim 4to. Book Chest 17-219
1978 $30

LAMMER, E. G.   Jungborn, bergfahtten und hohengedanken eines
ein samen Psadsuchers. Munchen, (c. 1933). Portrait, map, photographs, orig.
linen, 8vo. George's 635-1515 1978 £5.25

LAMOIGNON, C. F. DE   Agones Mathematici ad Arcem Copernicani Sys-
tematis. Paris, 1663. 4to., bds., evidently very rare. Gurney 75-27 1978
£95

LAMON, WARD HILL   The Life of Abraham Lincoln. Boston, 1872.
1st ed., illus., later cloth. MacManus 239-887 1978 $37.50

LA MORLIER, CH. J. LA ROCHETTE   Angola, histoire indienne, ouvrage sans
vraisemblance. (Paris) 1748. 2 vol., 12mo., lev. morocco, fine. Paine 78-
100 1978 $165.00

LAMOTHE, H. DE   Cinq Mois Chez les Francais D'Amerique. Paris,
1879. Wolfe 39-277 1978 $25

LA MOTTE, A.   Voyage Dans Le Nord De L'Europe... A Londres, 1813. 1st. ed., 4to, half-title, lg. folding engraved map, engraved plts.,
orig. bds., rebacked with buckram, upper corners strengthened, inside joints
strengthened, morocco label gilt, uncut edges, pres. inscription. Deighton 5-131
1978 £245

LA MOTTE FOUQUE, FRIEDRICH DE   Undine. London, 1909. Quarto, full
classic leather binding by Zcehnsdorf, silk doublures and endleaves, illus. by
Arthur Rackham, 1 of 1000 copies signed by artist, fine. Duschnes 220-248 1978
$350

LA MOTTE FOUQUE, FRIEDRICH DE   Undine. 1919. Coloured plts. by Arthur
Rackham, roy. 8vo., covers a little marked. George's 635-201 1978 £25

LA MOTTE FOUQUE, FRIEDRICH DE   Undine. London, 1920. Pict. bds.,
tipped-in color plts., spine dulled, fine. Victoria 34-689 1978 $50

LAMPADIUS, JACOBUS   De Republica Romano-Germanica Liber Vnvs....
Helmestadt, 1671. 4to., cloth, lettering piece gilt. King 7-283 1978 £30

LAMPELL, MILLARD   The Hero. 1949. 1st ed. Austin 79-421
1978 $20

LAMPMAN, ARCHIBALD   The Poems of... Toronto, 1900. 2nd ed.
Hood 117-810 1978 $37.50

LAMURE, FRANCOIS BOURGUIGNON DE BUSSIERE DE   Recherches sur la
Cause de la Pulsation des Arteres, et sur les Mouvemens du Cerveau Dans l'Homme
et les Animaux Trepanes, sur la Coene du Sang. Montpellier, 1769. 8vo., contemp. calf, back gilt, 1st collected ed. Offenbacher 30-81 1978 $185

LAMY, BERNARD   Traitex de Mechanique de L'Equilibre des Solides
et des Liqueurs. Paris, 1679. 12mo., woodcut text illus., contemp. sprinkled
calf, gilt spine. Quaritch 977-112 1978 $200

LANCASTER, BRUCE   Bright to the Wanderer. Boston, 1942. Hood
117-523 1978 $15

LANCASTER, JOSEPH   Improvements in Education, as it respects the In-
dustrious Classes of the Community. 1803. 2nd ed., wrappers. George's 635-
1297 1978 £20

LANCASTER, OSBERT   Classical Landscape with Figures. 1947. 4to.,
coloured plts., drawings by author, very good, worn d.w., first English ed. Bell
Book 16-537 1978 £4.50

LANCASTER, OSBERT   Progress at Pelvis Bay. 1936. Drawings by the
author, cloth-backed bds., spine faded, good, first English ed. Bell Book 16-538
1978 £6.50

LANCASTER, ROBERT A.   Historic Virginia Homes and Churches. Philadelphia, 1915. 4to., illus., plts., ltd. ed., orig. pic. cloth, nice, very scarce.
MacManus 239-1128 1978 $65

LANCELEY, E. B.   The Devil of Names; and Other Lectures and
Sermons by the Late Rev.... Toronto, 1900. Hood's 115-937 1978 $10

LANCIANI, RODOLFO AMEDEO   Wanderings in the Roman Campagna. London,
1909. Map, illus., plts., roy. 8vo., d.w. Traylen 88-18 1978 £8

LANCTOT, G.   Francois Xavier Garneau... Toronto, n.d. Hood
116-698 1978 $7.50

THE LAND of Milk and Honey. Junction City, 1878. Illus., disbound, 1st ed.
Ginsberg 14-452 1978 $95

LANDE, LAWRENCE M.   The Lawrence Lande Collection of Canadiana in
the Redpath Library of McGill University. Montreal, 1966. Folio, superbly bound
in coarse cloth, natural niger mor. back, printed letterpress on imported mould-made
paper, illus., one of 950 numbered copies, signed by Dr. Lande. Wolfe 39-281
1978 $165

LANDE, LAWRENCE M.   Old Lamps Aglow. Montreal, 1957. Signed,
ltd. ed., illus., orig. binding. Wolfe 39-280 1978 $100

LANDELLS, E.   The Boy's Own Toy-Maker... London, 1860.
3rd. ed., engravings, sq. cr. 8vo, orig. cloth, little loose. Traylen 88-172
1978 £12

LANDELLS, E.   The Boy's Own Toy-Maker... London, 1862.
5th. ed., engravings, sq. cr. 8vo, cloth, little faded. Traylen 88-171 1978 £7

LANDER, HARRY   Lucky Bargee. New York, 1898. Cloth, front cover initialed, vignette, good. Greene 78-247 1978 $15

LANDER, RICHARD   Explorations & Adventures on the Niger: A Voyage Down the Dark River. London, n.d. 2 vols. in l, sm. stout 8vo, no plts., cloth, paper label. K Books 239-253 1978 £30

LANDER, RICHARD   Records of Captain Clapperton's Last Expedition to Africa. London, 1830. 2 vols. in l, portrait frontis, little foxed, agemarked throughout, good in functional modern quarter calf, 8vo. K Books 239-253 1978 £30

LANDER, RICHARD   Records of Captain Clapperton's Last Expedition to Africa... 1830. lst. ed., 2 vols., 8vo, engraved portrait, other illus., some soiling, calf, gilt backs. Deighton 5-18 1978 £65

LANDIS, HENRY G.   How to Use the Forceps. New York, 1880. Some foxing. Rittenhouse 49-453 1976 $25

LANDIS, JOHN B.   A Short History of Molly Pitcher... Carlisle, 1905. Illus., orig. cloth, nice. MacManus 239-592 1978 $15

LANDIS, SIMON MOHLER   A Strictly Private Book for Married Persons, on the Secrets of Generation! Philadelphia, 1866. 16mo., orig. cloth wrs., lst ed. Morrill 239-149 1978 $12.50

THE LANDLORDS Law. (London), M DCC XXVII. 16mo., lea., raised bands, Van Rensselaer's copy, fine engr. bkplt. & dated signature of Van Rensselaer, 18th Cent. binding, simple blind-tooled border on both covers. Butterfield 21-249 1978 $250

LANDON, ALFRED M.   Official Reports of the Proceedings of the 21st Republican National Convention, Cleveland...1936. New York, (1936). Illus., cloth. Biblo BL781-213 1978 $10

LANDON, C. P.   Numismatique du Voyage du Jeune Anacharsis ou Medailles des Beaux Temps de la Grece. Paris, 1818. 2 vols. in l, illus., covers rubbed. Biblo BL781-421 1978 $37.50

LANDON, FRED   Lake Huron. Indianapolis, 1944. Illus. Hood's 115-975 1978 $25

LANDON, FRED   Lake Huron. Indianapolis, (1944). Signed by Milo M. Quaife, cloth. Hayman 73-373 1973 $8.50

LANDON, FRED   Western Ontario and the American Frontier... New Haven, Toronto, London, 1941. 1st ed. Hood 116-755 1978 $45

LANDON, FRED   When Laurier Met Ontario in 1888. 1941. Hood's 115-823 1978 $7.50

LANDOR, A. HENRY SAVAGE   The Gems of the East... 1904. Map, illus., 2 vols., 8vo., orig. cloth. Edwards 1012-168 1978 £20

LANDOR, A. HENRY SAVAGE   In the Forbidden Land. 1899. Folding map, illus., 8vo, orig. cloth, very good. Fenning 32-190 1978 £12.50

LANDOR, ROBERT EYRES 1781-1869   The Fountain of Arethusa. 1848. First ed., 2 vols., cr. 8vo., contemp. full calf, rebacked, orig. spines preserved, rare. Howes 194-991 1978 £38

LANDOR, WALTER SAVAGE   Andrew of Hungary, and Giovanna of Naples. 1839. Full contemp. tree calf, good, first English ed. Bell Book 16-539 1978 £15

LANDOR, WALTER SAVAGE   Citation and Examination of William Shakespeare. 1834. 8vo., lst ed., orig. bds., linen spine, nice copy, slipcase. Quaritch 979-218 1978 $125

LANDOR, WALTER SAVAGE   Garibaldi and the President of the Sicilian Senate. London, 1917. One of only 30 copies, 4to., wrappers, unsewn, very nice. Rota 212-33 1978 £30

LANDOR, WALTER SAVAGE   Imaginary Conversations of Literary Men and Statesmen. 1824. First ed., 2 vols., new half calf, rare. 8vo. Howes 194-992 1978 £55

LANDOR, WALTER SAVAGE   The Last Fruit Off an Old Tree. 1853. Nice copy, rebound in l/4 calf, gilt spine. Eaton 45-284 1978 £20

LANDOR, WALTER SAVAGE   The Last Fruit Off an Old Tree. London, 1853. Orig. cloth, lst ed., covers faded, otherwise fine. MacManus 238-314 1978 $85

LANDOR, WALTER SAVAGE   Poems from the Arabic and Persian. Warwick, 1800. 4to., lst ed., modern bds. Quaritch 979-219 1978 $180

LANDOR, WALTER SAVAGE   Selections From the Writings of... 1902. Sm. cr. 8vo, full green morocco, gilt, one joint rubbed. Eaton 45-285 1978 £4

LANDOR, WALTER SAVAGE   Works. London, 1853. lst. collected ed., 2 vols., roy. 8vo. Traylen 88-292 1978 £15

LANDOR, WALTER SAVAGE   Works. London, 1891-93. 10 vols., orig. green cloth, uncut, 8vo., very good. Americanist 103-49 1978 $50

LANDRUM, J. B. O.   History of Spartanburg County. Atlanta, 1900. 1st ed., lib. marks removed, illus., fine, orig. cloth. MacManus 239-1123 1978 $75

THE LANDSCAPE Alphabet. (c. 1840). Lithographs, sm. 4to., silk cloth, worn. George's 635-31 1978 £10.50

LANDSEER, EDWIN   Works. London, n.d. Steel engraved plts., woodcuts, l vol. bound in 2, folio, half morocco, gilt edges. Traylen 88-393 1978 £40

LANDT, J. L.   Coke as a Household Fuel in Central Canada. Ottawa, 1925. Bound, many illus., fldg. plans. Hood's 115-692 1978 $12.50

LANE, CARL D.   What the Citizen Should Know About the Merchant Marine. 1941. Illus. Austin 80-173 1978 $8.50

LANE, F. VAN Z.   Motor Truck Transportation. 1921. Illus. Austin 80-777 1978 $17.50

LANE, J. J.   History of the University of Texas. Austin, 1891. lst ed., original cloth, some outer wear. Jenkins 116-1380 1978 $65

LANE, SAMUEL A.   Fifty Years and Over of Akron and Summit County. Akron, 1892. Orig. binding, clean, back cover dampstained, o/w very good copy. Hayman 71-591 1978 $50

LANE, SAMUEL A.   Fifty Years and Over of Akron and Summit County...Pioneer Incidents, Interesting Events,.... Akron, 1892. Illus., original cloth, lst ed. Ginsberg 14-472 1978 $75

LANE, WHEATON J.   From Indian Trail to Iron Horse... Princeton, 1939. 1st ed., scarce, illus. MacManus 239-1286 1978 $40

LANEHAM, ROBERT   Laneham's Letter Describing the Magnificient Pageants presented before Queen Elizabeth at Kenilworth Castle in 1575.... London, 1821. Octavo, quarter calf, original boards, hinges weak, rare. Bennett 7-67 1978 $35

LANESSAN, J. L. DE   La Colonisation Francaise en Indo-Chine. Paris, 1895. Half cloth, folding map, 8vo. Van der Peet 127-125 1978 Dfl 65

LANFREY, PIERRE   History of Napoleon I. 1886. 4 vols., cr. 8vo. George's 635-725 1978 £5

LANG, ANDREW   Ballads and Lyrics of Old France. Portland, Mosher Press, 1898. Ltd. ed., wrs., 12mo. Biblo 247-604 1978 $12.50

LANG, ANDREW   Ban and Arrier Ban. A Rally of Fugitive Rhymes. London, 1894. lst ed., errata slip and f.p. by H. J. Ford, fine. Victoria 34-477 1978 $20

LANG, ANDREW   Ban and Arriere Ban. 1894. Frontis by H. J. Ford, blind-stamp on title pg., orig. cloth, slightly soiled. Eaton 45-287 1978 £5

LANG, ANDREW   The Grey Fairy Book. 1900. First ed., illus., plts., cr. 8vo., orig. grey cloth, all edges gilt, nice. Howes 194-994 1978 £20

LANG, ANDREW   Letters to Dead Authors. London, 1892. New ed., lg. paper ed., ltd. to 113 copies only, orig. bds., uncut, 8vo. K Books 244-187 1978 £16

LANG, ANDREW   The Library. London, 1892. 2nd ed. Battery
Park 1-395 1978 $15

LANG, ANDREW   Life and Letters of John Gibson Lockhart. 1897.
2 vols., portraits, sm. blind-stamp on title-pgs., cloth, gilt. Eaton 45-288 1978
£15

LANG, ANDREW   A Monk of Fife. 1896. Wood engravings by
Selwyn Image, reprinted, good. Bell Book 17-491 1978 £6

LANG, ANDREW   Oxford. London, 1905. New ed., frontispiece, illus., upper hinge pulling, very good or better. Limestone 9-171
1978 $15

LANG, ANDREW   Oxford. London, 1916. Large 4to, brown cloth,
illus. in color by George F. Carline, hand-made paper, ex-lib, covers dust stained,
no. 121 of 355 copies, 1st ed., collector's cond. Desmarais 1-265 1978 $20

LANG, ANDREW   Rhymes a La Mode. London, 1885. 1st ed.,
frontispiece, uncut, orig. green cloth, very good or better. Limestone 9-172
1978 $25

LANG, ANDREW   The True Story Book. London, 1893. Illus.,
orig. pict. cloth, 1st ed., bookplt., signature, otherwise fine. MacManus 238-
315 1978 $50

LANG, ANDREW   XXII Ballades in Blue China. London, 1880.
1st ed., 12mo, very rare, orig. soft vellum wrs. lettered & decor. in blue, library stamps, very fine to mint copy, lightly soiled covers. Current Misc. 8-53
1978 $100

LANG, ANDREW   The Violet Fairy Book. 1901. First ed., colored
plts., cr. 8vo., orig. violet cloth, all edges gilt, binding little stained. Howes
194-995 1978 £20

LANG, MRS. E. H.   Handy Guide to the Laws of Ontario. Toronto,
1918. Hood's 115-647 1978 $10

LANG, JOHN   Robinson Crusoe. London, n.d. 12mo, color
plates by Robinson, fine. Victoria 34-703 1978 $7.50

LANG, JOHN DUNMORE   An Historical and Statistical Account of New
South Wales. London, 1834. 2 vols., good, orig. cloth, paper labels, 8vo.
K Books 244-395 1978 £90

LANG, WILLIAM B.   History of Seneca Co., From the Close of the
Revolutionary War to July, 1880. Springfield, 1880. Illus., orig. cloth, very
good, scarce. MacManus 239-1115 1978 $60

LANG, WILLIAM R.   The Origanization, Administration and Equip-
ment of His Majesty's Land Forces in Peace and War. Toronto, 1916. 1st. ed.
Hood's 115-121 1978 $15

LANGDON, EMMA F.   The Cripple Creek Strike, 1903-1904. [Colorado
City?], 1904. Illus., original cloth, rare 1st ed. Ginsberg 14-265 1978 $75

LANGDON, JOHN E.   Canadian Silversmiths, 1700-1900. Toronto,
1966. 4to., illus., as new in d.j., orig. binding. Wolfe 39-282 1978 $150

LANGDON-DAVIES, JOHN   Invasion in the Snow. 1941. Illus. with photos.
Austin 80-177 1978 $12.50

LANGE, FRANCIS D.   A Refutation of the Wage-Fund Theory 1866.
Lord Baltimore Press, 1904. Austin 80-779 1978 $12.50

LANGEVIN, HECTOR L.   Le Canada, ses Institutions, Ressources, Produits,
Manufactures.... Quebec, 1855. Wolfe 39-284 1978 $25

LANGFELD, WILLIAM R.   The Young Men's Hebrew Association of Philadelphia: A Fifty Year Chronicle. 1928. Illus. with photos. Austin 79-422
1978 $27.50

LANGFORD, R. J. S.   Corporal to Field Officer, a Ready Reference.
Toronto, (1940). 4th ed. Hood 117-134 1978 $7.50

LANGHORNE, JOHN   Solyman and Almena with "Hymn to Eternal
Providence". London, 1799. 1st Amer. ed., new cloth. Greene 78-246 1978
$85

LANGLAND, WILLIAM   The Vision of William Concerning Piers, the
Plowman. Elston Press, 1901. Folio, 1 of 210 copies, woodcut illus. Battery
Park 1-87 1978 $150

LANGLEY, BATTY   The Builder's Director, or Bench-Mate:....
London, n.d. (ca. 1750). 12mo, contemporary calf, rebacked, very good copy.
Ximenes 47-176 1978 $150

LANGLEY, BATTY   Pomona. London, 1729. Plts., folio, cont. calf,
fine lg. copy, from the Evelyn lib. Traylen 88-594 1978 £550

LANGLEY, SAMUEL P.   Experiments in Aerodynamics. Washington,
D.C., 1891. Folio, plts., orig. cloth, gilt, fine copy, 1st ed. Norman 5-*31
1978 $175

LANGSDORFF, GEORG HENRICH VON   Bemerkingen auf Einer Reise um Die
Welt, 1803-1807. Frankfort, 1813. 2 vols., orig. bds. Ginsberg 14-473 1978
$225

LANGSDORFF, GEORG HEINRICH VON   Narrative of the Rezanov Voyage to
Nueva California in 1806. San Francisco, 1927. Frontis., 8vo., linen backed
blue paper bds., ltd. to 260 copies, fine, uncut. Howell 5-41 1978 $75

LANGSTROTH, L. L.   Langstroth on the Hive and the Honey-Bee.
1914. Illus., sm. 8vo., orig. cloth. Morrill 241-275 1978 $10

LANGTON, H. H.   A Gentlewoman in Upper Canada, the Journal
of Anne Langton. Toronto, 1950. Illus. Hood 117-748 1978 $50

LANGTON, ROBERT   The Children & Youth of Charles Dickens. 1891.
4to, handmade paper uncut india proofs, ltd. to 300 copies, half title, orig. slate
brown cloth, gilt, v.g., unnumbered pres. copy. Jarndyce 16-589 1978 £23

LANGTON, ROBERT   The Pilgrimage of Robert Langton, Transcribed
with an Intro & Notes by E. M. Blackie. Cambridge, Harvard University Press,
1924. 1 of 755 copies, woodcut illus., tall 8vo., orig. linen-backed bds., unopened copy, very good. Americanist 103-139 1978 $27.50

LANGTRY, JOHN   A Struggle for Life; Higher Criticism Criticised.
Toronto, 1905. Hood's 115-938 1978 $7.50

LANGUET, HUBERT   Vinciciae contra Tyrannos:.... Edinburgh,
1579. Rare 1st ed., small 8vo, old calf, hinges a bit worn, gilt back. Gilhofer
75-67 1978 SFr 2,200

LANGWORTHY, LUCIUS HART   Dubuque: Its History, Mines, Indian Legends,
Etc., ... Dubuque, 1855. 1st ed. Ginsberg 14-415 1978 $200

LANIER, HENRY WYSHAM   A. B. Frost. New York, Darrydale Press,
1933. Good, rebound, illus., ltd. to 950 copies. Nestler Rare 78-251 1978
$120

LANIER, SYDNEY   The Boy's Froissart. New York, 1879. Illus.
by Kappes, 1st ed., 1st issue, rubbed, inner hinges cracked. Victoria 34-478
1978 $15

LANKESTER, E.   Extinct Animals. New York, 1905. Ex-lib,
worn binding, some markings, 8vo, orig. cloth. Book Chest 17-220 1978 $25

LANMAN, CHARLES   Adventures in the Wilds of the United States and
British American Provinces. Philadelphia, 1856. Illus. by author and Oscar Bessau,
orig. cloth, 2 vols. Wolfe 39-10 1978 $100

LANMAN, CHARLES   The Private Life of Daniel Webster. New York,
1852. Cloth. Hayman 73-379 1978 $12.50

LANSDOWNE, GEORGE GRANVILLE, VISCOUNT   Poems Upon Several
Occasions. 1726. 4th ed., orig. calf, little worn, v.g. text. Jarndyce 16-100
1978 £14.50

LANTIER, ETINNE FRANCOIS DE 1734-1826   The Travels of Antenor in Greece
and Asia. 1799. First English ed., 3 vols., contemp. half calf, 8vo. Howes
194-359 1978 £35

LANUX, PIERRE DE   Sud. Paris, 1932. Illus., wrs., Bell Wiley's
copy. Broadfoot 46-158 1978 $8

LANZA, A. J.   Silicosis and Asbestosis. New York, 1938. Ex-
library. Rittenhouse 49-454 1976 $15

LANZA, CLARA   Scarabaeus. New York, (1900). Wrps. Hayman 71-232 1978 $7.50

LANZI, LUIGI   Storia Pittorica dell'Italia dal Risorgimento delle
Belle Arti fino Presso Alla Fine Del Secolo XVIII.   Milano, 1831. 12 vols. in 4,
12mo., half-cloth, fine.   Gilhofer 74-41 1978 sFr 700

LA PALME, ROBERT   Les 20 Premieres Annees du Caricaturiste Canadien. Montreal, (1950). 4to., illus. Wolfe 39-285 1978 $85

LA PEYRERE, ISAAC DE   An Account of Greenland.... (1704). Sm.
folio, map, engravings, binders' cloth. Edwards 1012-585 1978 £20

LA PEYRERE, ISAAC DE   An Account of Iceland... (1704). Sm. folio,
binders' cloth. Edwards 1012-584 1978 £15

LAPHAM, A. G.   The Old Planters of Beverly in Massachusetts...
Cambridge, 1930. Illus., maps. MacManus 239-1011 1978 $17.50

LAPHAM, WILLIAM B.   History of Rumford, Oxford Co., Maine from Its
First Settlement in 1779 to the Present Time. Augusta, 1890. Illus., fine, orig.
cloth. MacManus 239-991 1978 $55

LA PLACA, PIETRO   La Reggia in Trionfo per l'Acclamazione,....
Palermo, 1736. 1st ed., folio, contemp. calf, rubbed, light marginal stains,
tear in two plates. Gilhofer 75-68 1978 SFr 2,700

LAPLACE, PIERRE-SIMON DE   Exposition du Systeme du Monde. Paris, (1796).
2 vols., 8vo., mid-19th Cent. half mor., gilt, little foxing, but fine set, 1st ed.
Norman 5-164 1978 $650

LAPLACE, PIERRE SIMON DE   Exposition du Systeme du Monde. Paris, 1799.
2nd ed., 4to., mottled calf, good. King 7-360 1978 £35

LAPLACE, PIERRE SIMON DE   Mecanique Celeste. Boston, 1829-39. 4 vols.,
4to., engrav. portraits, portraits and some text foxed, orig. cloth, rebacked, one
bd. recovered, uncut, first ed., ltd. to 250 copies. Quaritch 977-192 1978
$1,500

LAPLACE, PIERRE-SIMON DE   The System of the World. London, 1809.
Trans. from French, 2 vols., 8vo., half antique calf, gilt, fine set in handsome
period-style binding, 1st ed. in English. Norman 5-165 1978 $350

LAPTHORNE, RICHARD   The Porledge Papers... 1928. Plts., octavo,
good. Upcroft 10-98 1978 £6

LA RAMEE, LOUISE DE
Please turn to
DE LA RAMEE, LOUISE

LA RAMEE, PIERRE DE   Dialectica... Cologne, 1577. 8vo., contemp.
stamped & dated pigskin bind., 1577, lacks two leaves. Salloch 348-216 1978
$100

LA RAMEE, PIERRE DE   Scholae in Tres Primas Libera.es Artes. Frankfurt, 1595. Thick 8vo., vellum. Salloch 348-218 1978 $250

LARCHEY, LOREDAN   History of Bayard, the good Chevalier sans peur
et sans reproche. 1883. Illus., roy. 8vo. George's 635-1359 1978 £8.50

LARCOM, LUCY   Lays of the Emigrants, as Sung by the Parties for
Kanzas, on the Days of Their Departure from Boston, During the Spring of 1855.
Boston, 1855. Disbound, 1st ed. Ginsberg 14-453 1978 $100

LARDEN, WALTER   Inscriptions from Swiss Chalets...Found Outside
and Inside Swiss Chalets, Storehouses and Sheds. Oxford, 1913. Illus., orig.
cloth, 8vo. Howes 194-996 1978 £6.50

LARDNER, DIONYSIUS   Handbook of Natural Philosophy. London, 1865.
Cr. 8vo, orig. cloth, illus., good. Sexton 7-200 1978 £6

LARDNER, DIONYSIUS   Steam Communication With India by the Red
Sea... 1837. 1st. & only ed., maps, 8vo, orig. cloth-backed paper wrapper,
light damp staining, very good copy. Fenning 32-191 1978 £8.50

LARDNER, RING   Best Stories. Garden City, 1938. Austin 82-542
1978 $11

LARDNER, RING   The Big Town. 1925. Austin 82-543 1978
$8.50

LARDNER, RING   How to Write Short Stories with Samples. 1924.
Austin 82-544 1978 $8.50

LARDNER, RING   Round Up. 1929. 467 pages. Austin 82-546
1978 $7.50

LARDNER, RING   The Story of a Wonder Man. 1927. Illus. Austin
82-547 1978 $10

LARDNER, RING   What of It? 1925. 220 pages. Austin 82-548
1978 $7.50

LARENAUDIERE, M. DE   Mexique et Guatemala. Paris, 1843. 8vo.,
bds., maps, plts., text in double columns. King 7-361 1978 £40

LARIMER, A. V.   Argument of...on the Union Pacific Railroad
Terminus and Bridge. [Council Bluffs, 1873]. Orig. pr. wr., 1st ed. Ginsberg
14-991 1978 $85

LARIMER, WILLIAM H. H.   Reminiscences of General...And His Son...Two
of the Founders of Denver City... Lancaster, 1918. Facs., plates, limp black
calf, 1st ed. Ginsberg 14-474 1978 $300

LARISUN, C. W.   Solomon'z Son. Ringos, 1887. Sm. 8vo., orig.
cloth, 1st ed. Morrill 241-276 1978 $9

LARKIN, OLIVER W.   Art and Life in America. New York, (1949).
4to., illus., 1st ed. Biblo BL781-646 1978 $17.50

LARKIN, PHILIP   A Girl in Winter. 1947. First English ed., covers little rubbed, good, scarce. Bell Book 17-542 1978 £27.50

LARKIN, PHILIP   Jill. Fortune Press, 1946. Very good, scarce,
first English ed. Bell Book 16-991 1978 £28.50

LARNER, E. T.   Practical Television. 1928. Illus., 1st Amer.
ed., bottom edge waterstained, otherwise good. Austin 80-780 1978 $27.50

LA ROCHE-GUILHEM, MLLE. DE   The History of Female Favourites. 1772.
8vo., recent half calf, marbled sides. P. M. Hill 142-304 1978 £145

LA ROCHEFOUCAULD, FRANCOIS DE   Maxims and Moral Reflections by the
Duke de la Rochefoucauld. London, 1775. New ed., 8vo., full cont. red mor.,
gilt, dedication copy with bookplate of David Garrick, v.f. Ximenes 47-69 1978
$450

LA ROCHEFOUCAULD, FRANCOIS DE   Maxims and Moral Reflections...
London, 1775. 8vo., contemp. red mor., gilt line border on sides, gilt panelled
spine, green mor. label, gilt edges, dedication copy with bkplt. of David Garrick.
Quaritch 978-94 1978 $265

LA ROCHEFOUCAULD, FRANCOIS DE   Moral Maxims and Reflections. Philadelphia, 1778. Copperplt. portr., 12mo., full red mor., 1st Amer. ed. Argosy
Special-56 1978 $250

LA ROCHEFOUCAULD LIANCOURT, FRANCOIS ALEXANDRE FREDERIC   Travels
through the United States of Nort'. America...1795, 1796 and 1797... London,
1799. First ed. in Eng., 2 vols., quarto, orig. bds., exquisite set, unopened.
Bennett 20-175 1978 $1,200

LAROCHEJAQUELEIN, MARIE LOUISE   Memoirs of the Marchioness de Laroache-
jaquelein. Edinburgh, 1816. 1st. English ed., 8vo, folding map, contemp. half
calf, joint cracked. Hannas 54-295 1978 £8.50

LAROQUE, FRANCOIS A.   Journal de Larocque de la Riviere Assiniboine
Jusqu'a la Riviere "Aux Roches Jaunes" 1805. Ottawa, 1911. Orig. wr. Ginsberg 14-475 1978 $30

LARREY, D. J.   Observations of Wounds, and Their Complications
by Erysipelas, Gangrene and Tetanus. Philadelphia, 1832. Rittenhouse 49-455
1976 $30

LARSEN, A. J.   Minnesota Under Four Flags. Saint Paul, 1946.
Maps, wrs. Hood 116-856 1978 $10

LARSON, L. M.   Canute the Great and the rise of Danish imperialism during the Viking Age. 1912. Illus., 8vo. Upcroft 12-250 1978 £6

LAS CASAS, BARTOLOME DE
Please turn to
CASAS, BARTOLOME DE LAS

LAS CASAS, LUCAS DE   El Verbo Divino Fuego Brasa En La Encarnation Y
Llama En El Sacramento Eucharistico De Alter:.... Mexico, 1742. Full polished
Mexican calf, brilliant, unfoxed copy. Jenkins 116-800 1978 $1,500

LA SERRE, JEAN PUGET DE   Le Secretaire a la mode par le Sr. De La Serre.
Amsterdam, 1663. Sm. 12mo., marbled bds., calf spine, woodcut initials, a few
ink spots in lower margin, very good. King 7-284 1978 £15

LASKI, HAROLD J.   The American Presidency, an Interpretation.
New York, (1940). First ed. Biblo 247-133 1978 $15

LASPEE, H. DE   Prospectus. London, 1860. 8vo., unbound.
Quaritch 977-38 1978 $45

LASSALLE, FERDINAND   Herr Bastiat-Schulze von Delitzsch,.... Berlin,
1864. 1st ed., 8vo, orig. blind-stamped cloth. Gilhofer 75-69 1978 SFr 400

THE LAST Days of Dr. Johnson. (?c. 1850). Sm. 8vo., unbound. P. M. Hill
142-152 1978 £5

LASTON, MADELINE   From the Heart of the Veld. London, 1916.
Cr. 8vo, orig. cloth, age-browned reading copy. K Books 239-256 1978 £7

THE LATEST and Best Views of the Pan-American Exposition. Buffalo, 1901.
Side opening 4to., plts., wr. Butterfield 21-80 1978 $10

LATHAM, J. D.   Saracen Archery; An Edited Version of a Medieval Work on Archery. 16 plts., cr. 4to. Traylen 88-519 1978 £10

LATHAM, PETER MERE   The Collected Works of... London, 1876-1878.
2 vols., 8vo., brown stamped cloth, gilt lettering on spines, worn, bkplt.,
library stamps of former owners, good copy, 1st collected ed. Zeitlin 245-142
1978 $65

LATHAM, W.   The States of the River Plate... 1866. 1st. ed.,
orig. cloth, 8vo, spine faded. Edwards 1012-662 1978 £25

LATHROP, BARNES F.   Migration into East Texas, 1835-1860. Austin,
1949. Charts, maps. Jenkins 116-805 1978 $12.50

LATHROP, ELSIE   Early American Inns and Taverns. New York,
1935. Illus. Baldwins' 51-112 1978 $10

LATHROP, GEORGE   Memoirs of a Pioneer. Lusk, [1929]. Illus., orig.
pr. wr. Ginsberg 14-1079 1978 $45

LATHROP, HENRY WARREN   The Life and Times of Samuel J. Kirkwood.
Iowa City, 1893. Hinges cracked, ex libris, Bell Wiley's copy. Broadfoot's
44-238 1978 $10.00

LATHROP, VIRGINIA TERRELL   Educate a Woman. Chapel Hill, 1942. Illus.
Broadfoot 50-118 1978 $10

LATIMER, HUGH   A notable Sermon...preached in ye Shrouds
at paules churche in London, in the xviii daye of January, 1548. N.P., (1548).
Sm. 8 vo., black leather, mor. gilt. Quaritch Summer, 1978-27 1978 $2,500

LATINI, BRUNETTO   L'Ethica D'Aristotile Ridotta in Compendio.
Lyons, 1568. Folio, vellum with label. Salloch 348-113 1978 $900

LATINI, BRUNETTO   Il Trattato delle Virtu morali di Roberto Re di
Gerusalemme.... Torino, 1750. 8vo., bds., calf spine, very good. King 7-
179 1978 £35

LATOURETTE, KENNETH SCOTT   A History of the Expansion of Christianity.
1944. 7 vols., 8vo. George's 635-1087 1978 £20

LATROBE, FERDINAND C.   Iron Men and Their Dogs. 1941. Illus. Austin
80-778 1978 $20

LAUCK, W. JETT   The Causes of the Panic of 1893. Boston and
New York, 1907. Orig. binding, clean, some annotations in pencil. Hayman
71-414 1978 $8.50

LAUD, WILLIAM   The Daily Office of a Christian. 1705. Engraved
portrait, 12mo., contemp. panelled calf. George's 635-1088 1978 £10.50

LAUDE, G. A.   Kansas Shorthorns: A History of the Breed in
the State from 1857 to 1920. Iola, 1920. Illus., original cloth, 1st ed. Ginsberg 14-454 1978 $17.50

LAUDER, THOMAS DICK   The Wolfe of Badenoch; a Historical Romance of
the Fourteenth Century. Edinburgh, 1827. 1st. ed., 3 vols., sm. 8vo, contemp.
half calf, joints repaired. Traylen 88-293 1978 £30

LAUFER, BERTHOLD   Notes on Turquois in the East. Chicago, 1913.
Wrs., worn and some foxing. Dawson's 127-308 1978 $12.50

LAUGHTON, LEONARD GEORGE CARR   Old Ship Figure-Heads and Sterns...
London, 1925. 1st ed., folio, illus., plts., some in color, orig. cloth, dust jacket, chipped, very good, ltd. to 1500 copies. MacManus 239-1763 1978 $65

LAUNAY, A.   Histoire generale de la Societe des Missions
etrangere. Paris, 1894. 3 vols., full red mor., gilt, red mor. binding, gold
tooling, edges gilt, 8vo. Van der Peet 127-309 1978 Dfl 300

LAUNAY, A.   Histoire Generale de la Societe des Missions Etran-
geres. Paris, 1894. 3 vols., full red mor., a.e.g., excellent bound copy.
Van der Peet H-64-479 1978 Dfl 300

LAUNER, JAY   The Enemies Fighting Ships. 1944. Illus. Austin 80-178 1978 $10

LAUNOY, JEAN DE   De Varia Aristotelis in Academia Parisiensi
Fortuna, and De Victorino Episcopo Et Martyre Dissertatio. Paris, 1653. 8vo.,
vellum, 1st ed. Salloch 348-114 1978 $200

LAURAND, L.   Manuel des Etudes Grecques et Latines. 1935-38.
3 vols., sewn, browned. Allen 234-525 1978 $10

LAURENCE, EDWARD   The Duty of a Steward to his Lord. 1727. First
ed., map, contemp. panelled calf, joints cracked, very good, 4to. Howes 194-
126 1978 £80

LAURENCE, JOHN 1668-1732   The Clergy-Man's Recreation. 1716. First ed.,
frontis., plts., 2 parts in 1 vol., rebound in cloth-backed bds., 8vo. Howes 194-
127 1978 £40

LAURENT, AUGUSTE   Chemical Method, Notation, Classification &
Nomenclature. (London), 1855. 8vo., orig. cloth, gilt, slightly worn, but fine
copy, 1st ed. in English. Norman 5-167 1978 $125

LAURENT, AUGUSTE   Methode de Chimie. Paris, 1854. 8vo., new
half mor., orig. wrs. bound in, occas. very light foxing, but fine copy, 1st ed.
Norman 5-166 1978 $350

LAURIER, WILFRID   Life and Letters. Toronto, 1921. Illus., two
vols., orig. binding. Wolfe 39-286 1978 $35

LAURISTON, VICTOR   Lambton's Hundred Years 1849-1949. Sarnia,
1949. Illus. Hood 117-749 1978 $45

LAUT, AGNES C.   The Conquest of the Great North-West. Toronto, 1918. 2 vols. in one. Hood 117-901 1978 $30

LAUT, AGNES C.   Lords of the North. 1900. First ed. Austin 82-
549 1978 $27.50

LAUT, AGNES C.   Pathfinders of the West. New York, (1907).
Cloth. Hayman 73-330 1978 $7.50

LAUT, AGNES C.   The Quenchless Light. Toronto, 1924. Hood's
115-439 1978 $15

LAVALLEE, J.   Voyage Pittoresque Et Historique de l'Istrie et de la Dalmatie... Paris, 1802. Engraved title, frontispiece, maps, plts., some folding, large folio, early 19th. century straight-grained red morocco, gilt, blind borders on sides g.e. Edwards 1012-51 1978 £1500

LA VARENNE, FRANCOIS PIERRE DE   Il Cuoco Francese Ove e Insegnata La maniera di condire ogni forti di Viuande.... Bologna, 1693. 1st Italian ed., 12mo, old calf, floral gilt spine panels. Bennett 20-119 1978 $250

LAVATER, JOHN CASPAR   Essays on Physiognomy, Designed to Promote the Knowledge and the Love of Mankind. London, 1789-98. 1st ed. in English, lg. 4to., in 5, engrs., 1st issue, portrs., bokplt. of the Earl of Charlemont, full contemp. diced calf, internally fine copy, orig. tissue guards. Current Misc. 8-29 1978 $800

LAVATER, JOHN CASPAR   Essays on Physiognomy. London, 1792. Illus. by more than 800 engravings, 3 vols. bound in 5, quarto, contemp. full dark blue straight-grained mor., 3 vols. rebacked with old spine over the new. Totteridge 29-63 1978 $300

LAVATER, JOHN CASPAR   Essays on Physiognomy for the Promotion of the Knowledge and the Love of Mankind. Boston, (1794). First Amer. ed., orig. bds., title strip missing, usual wear. Rittenhouse 49-456 1976 $65

LAVATER, JOHANN CASPAR   Essays on Physiognomy. London, Jan. 7, 1806. 12mo., engr. plts., contemp. tree calf, gilt, browning, good copy from the library of Dr. Alfred M. Hellman, 2nd abridged ed. Zeitlin 245-143 1978 $45

LAVATER, JOHANN CASPAR   Essays on Physiognomy. 1810. 3 vols. in 5, folio, contemp. marbled bds., new calf backs and corners, plts. Howes 194-1396 1978 £225

LAVATER, JOHANN CASPAR   Physiognomische Fragmente, Zur Befoer de rung der Menschenkenntnis und Menschenliebe. Leipzig & Winterthur, 1775-1778. Engrs., 4 vols., plts., folio, contemp. marbled calf, spine gilt with lea. labels, fine set, orig. bindings. Salloch 345-105 1978 $900

LAVATER, JOHN CASPAR   The Whole Works of Lavater on Physiognomy. London, n.d. (ca. 1798). 4 vols., 8vo., engr. frontis., marbled bds., red 1/2 calf with gold ornamen. on spine, lightly foxed throughout, text & plts. near fine, contemp. bindings bit scuffed & soiled, very firm. Current 24-123 1978 $145

LAVEDAN, P.   Dictionnaire Illustre de la Mythologie et des Anti-quites Grecques et Romaines. 1931. 4to., illus., 1 joint cracked, spine worn. Allen 234-528 1978 $15

LA VEGA, GARCILASO DE
Please turn to
GARCILASO DE LA VEGA

LAVENDER, THEOPHILUS   The Travels of Foure English Men and a Preacher Into Africa, Asia, Troy, Bythinia, Thracia, and to the Blacke Sea. London, 1612. 4to., vellum, 2nd ed. Salloch 345-25 1978 $900

LAVER, JAMES   The Circle of Chalk. 1929. Signed pres. copy, 8vo. George's 635-1360 1978 £10.50

LAVOISIER, ANTOINE-LAURENT   Elements of Chemistry. Edinburgh, 1793. Trans. from French, 8vo., fldg. copperplts., engr. after origs., fldg. tables, full antique calf, gilt, fine copy, 2nd ed. in English. Norman 5-168 1978 $375

LAVOISIER, ANTOINE-LAURENT   Elements of Chemistry. Philadelphia, 1799. Trans. from French, 8vo., copperplts. after origs., tables, full antique calf, gilt, light foxing, some offsetting on plts., but very good copy, signature of Washington Lemuel Atlee on title, 1st Amer. ed. Norman 5-169 1978 $350

LAVOISIER, ANTOINE-LAURENT   Opuscules Physiques et Chymiques. Paris, 1774. 8vo., fldg. plts., contemp. red & green mottled calf, richly gilt spine, rubbed, but fine copy, contemp. signature on title, 1st ed. Norman 5-168a 1978 $1,250

LAVOISIER, ANTOINE-LAURENT   Opuscules Physiques et Chimiques. Paris, 1801. 8vo., fldg. plts., contemp. tree calf, gilt, rubbed, but very good copy, 2nd ed., 2nd issue. Norman 5-170 1978 $150

LAVOISIER, ANTOINE-LAURENT   Oeuvres. Paris, 1862-93. 6 vols., 4to., frontis. portr., fldg. tables, plts., old cloth, occas. light foxing, but very good set, best collected ed. Norman 5-173 1978 $450

LAVOISNE, C. V.   A Complete Genealogical, Historical, Chrono-logical, & Geographical Atlas.... Philadelphia, 1820. 2nd Amer. ed., tall folio, contemp. half leather, rebacked w/orig. spine retained, signed by Dr. David Hosack, maps & charts, 8vo. Americanist 101-13 1978 $250

LAW, T. P.   Report of the Trials of A. M. Sullivan and R. Pigott for Seditious Libels on the Government. 1868. First ed., orig. bds. shaky, clean. Hyland 128-587 1978 £22.50

LA WALL, CHARLES HERBERT   Four Thousand Years of Pharmacy. Philadelphia, 1927. Third ed., shaken, top hinge wear. Rittenhouse 49-459 1978 $12.50

LAWDAHL, NELS SORENSEN   De Danske Baptisters Historie I Amerika. 1909. Illus., in Danish. Austin 79-423 1978 $47.50

LAWLOR, P. A.   The Mystery of Maata: a Katherine Mansfield novel. Wellington, 1946. No. 223 of 250 copies signed by author, plts., very good, d.w. Bell Book 16-624 1978 £15

LAWRENCE, A. W.   Later Greek Sculpture and Its Influence on East and West. New York, 1927. Sm. 4to., illus., spine faded, edges rubbed. Biblo BL781-423 1978 $17.50

LAWRENCE, ADA   Young Lorenzo: early life of D. H. Lawrence. Florence, 1931. One of 740 copies, unnumbered, photographs, paintings, orig. full vellum, edges untrimmed, fine, unopened, slightly worn d.w. Bell Book 17-550 1978 $27.50

LAWRENCE, ADA   Young Lorenzo: Early Life of D.H. Lawrence Containing Hitherto Unpublished Letters, Articles and Reproductions of Pictures. Florence, (1931). 8vo., printed parchment, d.j., 1st ed., ltd. and no., d.j. chipped. J.S. Lawrence 38-L147 1978 $50

LAWRENCE, ADA   Young Lorenzo: Early Life of D.H. Lawrence Containing Hitherto Unpublished Letters, Articles and Reproductions of Pictures. Florence, (1931). 8vo., printed parchment, d.j., 1st ed., ltd., very fine. J.S. Lawrence 38-L146 1978 $65

LAWRENCE, B. F.   History of Jay, Franklin Co., Maine. Boston, 1912. Illus., fold. map. MacManus 239-987 1978 $17.50

LAWRENCE, CHARLES   History of the Philadelphia Almshouses and Hos-pitals from the Beginning of the 18th Century to the Close of the 19th... N.P., 1905. Illus. MacManus 239-1533 1978 $30

LAWRENCE, DAVID HERBERT   L'Amante di Lady Chatterley Illutrazioni di I. Cremona. (1946). Folio, pict. bds., torn d.w., plts., tissue guards, very good, no. 515 of ed. of 1096 copies. King 7-180 1978 £20

LAWRENCE, DAVID HERBERT   Aaron's Rod. New York, 1922. 8vo., blue-grey cloth pr. in black, fine, 1st ed., collector's cond. Desmarais 1-266 1978 $25

LAWRENCE, DAVID HERBERT   Aaron's Rod. New York, 1922. 8vo., cloth, 1st ed., fine. J.S. Lawrence 38-L1 1978 $75

LAWRENCE, DAVID HERBERT   Amores: Poems. London, n.d. (1916). Sm. 8vo., cloth, 1st ed., 1st issue, pub. stamp on t.p., very fine. J.S. Lawrence 38-L2 1978 $450

LAWRENCE, DAVID HERBERT   Amores. New York, 1916. Cloth, fine, 1st Amer. ed. Dawson's 447-254 1978 $17.50

LAWRENCE, DAVID HERBERT   Apocalypse. Florence, 1931. 8vo., bds., d.j., 1st ed., ltd., numbered, d.j. browned and lightly chipped, fine. J.S. Lawrence 38-L3 1978 $200

LAWRENCE, DAVID HERBERT   Apocalypse. Florence, 1931. One of 750 numbered copies on Binda paper, first ed., frontis., 3/4 dark blue mor., t.e.g., uncut, fine. Houle 10-182 1978 $175

LAWRENCE, DAVID HERBERT   Apocalypse. London, (1932). 8vo., cloth over bevelled bds., 1st Eng. ed., bookplt., spine foxed. J.S. Lawrence 38-L4 1978 $20

LAWRENCE, DAVID HERBERT   Apocalypse. 1932. First ed., portrait, ex-libris copy, covers soiled, 8vo. George's 635-1321 1978 £6.50

LAWRENCE, DAVID HERBERT   Apocalypse. 1932. Portrait, buckram, near fine, first English ed. Bell Book 17-544 1978 £10

LAWRENCE, DAVID HERBERT   Apocalypse. London, (1932). Port. frontis., 8vo, cloth, 1st Trade ed., back faded, fine. Duschnes 220-181 1978 $12.50

LAWRENCE, DAVID HERBERT   Assorted Articles. London, 1930. 8vo, red cloth, gilt lettering on spine and cover, uncut, very fine, 1st ed., collector's cond. Desmarais 1-267 1978 $20

LAWRENCE, DAVID HERBERT   Assorted Articles. London, 1930. 8vo, cloth, 1st ed., name in ink. J.S. Lawrence 38-L8 1978 $20

LAWRENCE, DAVID HERBERT   Assorted Articles. London, 1930. 8vo, cloth, 1st ed., fine. J.S. Lawrence 38-L7 1978 $25

LAWRENCE, DAVID HERBERT   Assorted Articles. 1930. First ed., 8vo. George's 635-1322 1978 £7.50

LAWRENCE, DAVID HERBERT   Bay: A Book of Poems. (Beaumont Press: Westminster, 1919). Sm. 8vo, buckram-backed dec. bds., 1st ed., 1 of 50 no. copies, illus. by Anne Estelle Rice, corners of bds. lightly rubbed. J.S. Lawrence 38-L9 1978 $650

LAWRENCE, DAVID HERBERT   Birds, Beasts and Flowers. 1923. First English ed., orig. cloth-backed bds., 8vo. Howes 194-997 1978 £15

LAWRENCE, DAVID HERBERT   Birds, Beasts and Flowers. London, 1923. 8vo, cloth, 1st English ed., fine. Duschnes 220-179 1978 $35

LAWRENCE, DAVID HERBERT   Birds, Beasts and Flowers. New York, 1923. 8vo, cloth, d.j., 1st ed., d.j., very fine. J.S. Lawrence 38-L10 1978 $350

LAWRENCE, DAVID HERBERT   Birds, Beasts and Flowers. London, 1930. Folio, vellum-backed bds., 1st illus. ed., ltd. to 530 copies, 1 of 500 no. copies, illus. J.S. Lawrence 38-L11 1978 $250

LAWRENCE, DAVID HERBERT   The Boy in the Bush. New York, 1924. 8vo, cloth, 1st Amer. ed., bookplt. J.S. Lawrence 38-L13 1978 $15

LAWRENCE, DAVID HERBERT   The Boy in the Bush. New York, 1924. First American ed., orig. binding, exceptionally nice. Rota 211-296 1978 £25

LAWRENCE, DAVID HERBERT   The Boy in the Bush. London, (1924). 8vo, cloth, 1st ed., spine a bit browned. J.S. Lawrence 38-L12 1978 $35

LAWRENCE, DAVID HERBERT   The Collected Poems of....: Rhyming Poems and Unrhyming Poems. London, 1928. 2 vols., 8vo, cloth, 1st ed., trade issue, sm. bookplt., else fine. J.S. Lawrence 38-L16 1978 $100

LAWRENCE, DAVID HERBERT   A Collier's Friday Night. London, 1934. Sm. 8vo, cloth, 1st ed. J.S. Lawrence 38-L17 1978 $40

LAWRENCE, DAVID HERBERT   A Collier's Friday Night. London, 1934. Orig. cloth, d.j., paper label, 1st ed., fine. MacManus 238-696 1978 $30

LAWRENCE, DAVID HERBERT   David: A Play. London, (1926). 8vo, cloth, 1st ed., ltd. to 500 copies. J.S. Lawrence 38-L20 1978 $50

LAWRENCE, DAVID HERBERT   England, My England and Other Stories. New York, 1922. 8vo, cloth, 1st ed., spine dulled. J.S. Lawrence 38-L23 1978 $100

LAWRENCE, DAVID HERBERT   England My England and Other Stories. New York, 1922. 1st ed., covers dull. Biblo BL781-1043 1978 $25

LAWRENCE, DAVID HERBERT   England, My England. 1924. Very good, 1st Eng. ed. Bell Book 17-545 1978 £8.50

LAWRENCE, DAVID HERBERT   England, My England. London, (1924). Orig. cloth, d.j., 1st Eng. ed., few leaves lightly foxed, else fine. MacManus 238-694 1978 $65

LAWRENCE, DAVID HERBERT   England my England. London, (1924). First English ed., 8vo., orig. cloth. K Books 244-188 1978 £9

LAWRENCE, DAVID HERBERT   The Escaped Cock. Paris: Black Sun Press, 1929. 8vo, printed French wrs., orig. glassine, slipcase, 1st ed., ltd. to 500 copies, 1 of 450 no. copies on Holland Van Gelder, color illus. by author, very fine. J.S. Lawrence 38-L24 1978 $350

LAWRENCE, DAVID HERBERT   Etruscan Places. 1932. First ed., illus., ex-libris, copy, covers soiled, 8vo. George's 635-1323 1978 £5.25

LAWRENCE, DAVID HERBERT   Etruscan Places. London, 1932. Tall 8vo., cloth over bevelled bds., 1st ed., illus., spine tanned. J.S. Lawrence 38-L25 1978 $125

LAWRENCE, DAVID HERBERT   Fantasia of the Unconscious. New York, 1922. 8vo, cloth, 1st ed., spine browned. J.S. Lawrence 38-L26 1978 $100

LAWRENCE, DAVID HERBERT   Fire and Other Poems. N.P., (San Francisco), 1940. Lg. 8vo., natural linen, 1st ed., ltd. to 300 copies, fine. J.S. Lawrence 38-L27 1978 $200

LAWRENCE, DAVID HERBERT   The First Lady Chatterley. New York, (1944). 8vo., cloth, 1st ed. J.S. Lawrence 38-L28 1978 $10

LAWRENCE, DAVID HERBERT   Glad Ghosts. London, 1926. 12mo., printed wrs., 1st ed., ltd. to 500 copies, faint stains front and back. J.S. Lawrence 38-L30 1978 $85

LAWRENCE, DAVID HERBERT   Glad Ghosts. London, 1926. 12mo., printed wrs., 1st ed., ltd. to 500 copies, fine. J.S. Lawrence 38-L29 1978 $125

LAWRENCE, DAVID HERBERT   Kangaroo. London, (1923). 8vo., cloth, 1st ed., hinges lightly rubbed. J.S. Lawrence 38-L34 1978 $30

LAWRENCE, DAVID HERBERT   Kangaroo. London, (1923). 8vo., cloth, 1st ed. J.S. Lawrence 38-L33 1978 $45

LAWRENCE, DAVID HERBERT   The Ladybird: The Fox: The Captain's Doll. London, (1923). 8vo., dark brown cloth, 1st ed. J.S. Lawrence 38-L35 1978 $65

LAWRENCE, DAVID HERBERT   The Ladybird: The Fox: The Captain's Doll. London, (1923). 8vo., chocolate brown cloth, 1st ed., front and back flyleaves discolored, sev. pgs. roughly opened. J.S. Lawrence 38-L36 1978 $25

LAWRENCE, DAVID HERBERT   Lady Chatterley's Lover. (Florence), 1928. Lg. 8vo., bds., 1st ed., ltd., no. and signed by author, lower corners lightly rubbed, else very fine, unopened. J.S. Lawrence 38-L38 1978 $550

LAWRENCE, DAVID HERBERT   Lady Chatterley's Lover. (Florence), 1928. Lg. 8vo., bds., orig. plain d.j., 1st ed., ltd., no. and signed by author, very fine, unopened. J.S. Lawrence 38-L37 1978 $850

LAWRENCE, DAVID HERBERT   Lady Chatterley's Lover, Including My Skirmish with Jolly Roger... N.P. (Paris), 1929. 8vo., wrs., 1st Paris popular ed., fine. J.S. Lawrence 38-L39 1978 $150

LAWRENCE, DAVID HERBERT   Lady Chatterley's Lover. Secker, 1932. Very good, first English ed. Bell Book 16-542 1978 £6.50

LAWRENCE, DAVID HERBERT   Last Poems. Florence, 1932. 1 of 750 copies, roy. 8vo., bds., fine largely unopened copy, torn d.w. Bell Book 16-543 1978 £28.50

LAWRENCE, DAVID HERBERT   Last Poems. Florence, 1932. Lg. 8vo., bds., 1st ed., ltd., numbered, spine extremities lightly rubbed, else very fine. J.S. Lawrence 38-L42 1978 $150

LAWRENCE, DAVID HERBERT   Last Poems. 1933. Cloth-backed bds., very good, first English ed. Bell Book 17-546 1978 £15

LAWRENCE, DAVID HERBERT   Letters from...to Martin Secker, 1911-1930. N.P. (Bridgefoor Iver, Buckingham). Tall 8vo., cloth over bevelled bds., d.j., 1st ed., ltd. to 500 no. copies, fine. J.S. Lawrence 38-L47 1978 $50

LAWRENCE, DAVID HERBERT   The Letters of... London, (1932). 8vo., parchment over bds., 1st ed., ltd. to 525 no. copies, bookplt., else fine. J.S. Lawrence 38-L45 1978 $150

LAWRENCE, DAVID HERBERT   The Letters of D. H. Lawrence. London, 1932. First ed., orig. binding, nice, frayed d.w. Rota 211-192 1978 £10

LAWRENCE, DAVID HERBERT   The Letters of... London, 1932. 8vo., cloth, 1st ed., trade issue, lacks front free endpaper, front hinge broken. J.S. Lawrence 38-L46 1978 $20

LAWRENCE, DAVID HERBERT   The Letters of... London, (1932). Lg. 8vo., parchment bds., orig. glassine, slipcase, 1st ed., ltd. to 525 no. copies, very fine. J.S. Lawrence 38-L44 1978 $200

LAWRENCE, DAVID HERBERT   D.H. Lawrence's Letters to Bertrand Russel. New York, (1948). Tall 8vo., cloth, 1st ed., ltd., fine. J.S. Lawrence 38-L21 1978 $65

LAWRENCE, DAVID HERBERT   Look! We Have Come Through! London, 1917. 8vo., cloth, 1st ed., spine sunned a bit. J.S. Lawrence 38-L50 1978 $250

LAWRENCE, DAVID HERBERT   The Lost Girl. London, (1920). 8vo., cloth, 1st ed., 1st issue, very scarce. J.S. Lawrence 38-L51 1978 $300

LAWRENCE, DAVID HERBERT   Love Among the Haystacks and Other Pieces. The Nonesuch Press: London, 1930. Tall 8vo., burlap-backed buckram, 1st ed., ltd., numbered, bookplt. removed. J.S. Lawrence 38-L52 1978 $65

LAWRENCE, DAVID HERBERT   Love Poems and Others. London, 1913. 8vo., gilt-stamped cloth, 1st ed., smooth blue buckram, fine. J.S. Lawrence 38-L55 1978 $300

LAWRENCE, DAVID HERBERT   Love Poems and Others. London, 1913. 8vo., gilt-stamped cloth, d.j., 1st ed., coarse dark blue buckram, d.j. shelf-rubbed. J.S. Lawrence 38-L54 1978 $350

LAWRENCE, DAVID HERBERT   The Lovely Lady. London, (1932; 1933). 8vo., cloth, 1st ed., fine. J.S. Lawrence 38-L53 1978 $25

LAWRENCE, DAVID HERBERT   The Man Who Died. London, (1931). Sm. 8vo., brown cloth, bookplt. J.S. Lawrence 38-L56 1978 $10

LAWRENCE, DAVID HERBERT   The Man Who Died. London, 1931. 8vo, green cloth, gilt stamped, uncut, unopened, t.e.g., spine sun-faded, Fine, 1st English ed., limited to 2,000 copies, collector's cond. Desmarais 1-268 1978 $40

LAWRENCE, DAVID HERBERT   The Man Who Died. 1931. One of 2000 copies, roy. 8vo., buckram gilt, t.e.g., near fine, first English ed. Bell Book 17-547 1978 £21

LAWRENCE, DAVID HERBERT   The Man Who Died. London, 1935. Quarto, marbled boards, cloth backstrip, gilt, illus drawn and engraved on wood by John Farleigh, small rust stain on endpapers and t.p., fine. Duschnes 220-182 1978 $65

LAWRENCE, DAVID HERBERT   A Modern Lover. New York, 1934. 8vo., cloth, d.j., 1st Amer. ed., jacket chipped along edges. J.S. Lawrence 38-L63 1978 $25

LAWRENCE, DAVID HERBERT   A Modern Lover. London, (1934). 8vo., cloth, 1st ed., fine. J.S. Lawrence 38-L62 1978 $25

LAWRENCE, DAVID HERBERT   Mornings in Mexico. London, 1927. 8vo., cloth, 1st ed. J.S. Lawrence 38-L65 1978 $35

LAWRENCE, DAVID HERBERT   Mornings in Mexico. London, 1927. 8vo., cloth, 1st ed., very fine. J.S. Lawrence 38-L64 1978 $45

LAWRENCE, DAVID HERBERT   Movements in European History. 1925. First illus. ed., maps, cr. 8vo., orig. dark blue cloth, lg. paper copy. Howes 194-998 1978 £18

LAWRENCE, DAVID HERBERT   My Skirmish with Jolly Roger. New York, 1929. Thin 8vo., bds., 1st ed., 1 of 700 copies, scarce. J.S. Lawrence 38-L67 1978 $150

LAWRENCE, DAVID HERBERT   Nettles. London, (1930). 8vo., printed French wrs., 1st ed., wrs. issue, fine. J.S. Lawrence 38-L69 1978 $25

LAWRENCE, DAVID HERBERT   New Poems. London, 1918. 8vo., printed wrs., 1st ed., 1 of 500 copies, fine, cloth fold. case. J.S. Lawrence 38-L70 1978 $250

LAWRENCE, DAVID HERBERT   New Poems. New York, 1920. 8vo., bds., 1st Amer. ed., spine extremities chipped. J.S. Lawrence 38-L71 1978 $65

LAWRENCE, DAVID HERBERT   An Original Poem. (Cheswick), 1934. 8vo., sewn wrs., 1st separate ed., 1 of 150 copies, very fine, cloth fold. case. J.S. Lawrence 38-L72 1978 $250

LAWRENCE, DAVID HERBERT   The Paintings of... London, n.d. (1929). Folio, green stamped cloth, leather backstrip and corners, spine lettered gilt, t.e.g., 1st ed., 1 of 500 copies, edge of rear cover lightly discolored, else fine. J.S. Lawrence 38-73 1978 $500

LAWRENCE, DAVID HERBERT   Pansies: Poems. N.P. (London), 1929. Tall 8vo., printed French wrs., orig. glassine, 1st definitive ed., ordinary issue, ltd. to 500 no. copies, signed by author, glassine browned, else very fine. J.S. Lawrence 38-L76 1978 $250

LAWRENCE, DAVID HERBERT   Pansies; poems. London, 1929. One of 250 numbered copies, signed by author, first ed., orig. binding, very nice. Rota 211-291 1978 £75

LAWRENCE, DAVID HERBERT   Pansies: Poems. London, (1929). 8vo., cloth-backed dec. bds., 1st ed., trade issue, light wear at foot of spine. J.S. Lawrence 38-L77 1978 $75

LAWRENCE, DAVID HERBERT   Pansies: Poems. London, (1929). Tall 8vo., parchment-backed dec. bds., d.j., 1st ed., special copy, ltd. to 250 no. copies, signed by author, fine, frayed d.j. J.S. Lawrence 38-L75 1978 $375

LAWRENCE, DAVID HERBERT   Phoenix: The Posthumous Papers of.... London, (1936). Lg. 8vo., cloth, 1st Eng. ed., fine. J.S. Lawrence 38-L78 1978 $45

LAWRENCE, DAVID HERBERT   The Plumed Serpent. London, (1926). 8vo., cloth, 1st ed., fine. J.S. Lawrence 38-L80 1978 $65

LAWRENCE, DAVID HERBERT   The Plumed Serpent. London, (1926). 8vo., cloth, 1st ed., bind. a little dull. J.S. Lawrence 38-L81 1978 $50

LAWRENCE, DAVID HERBERT   Pornography and Obscenity. London, (1929). 8vo., printed French wrs., 1st ed., wrs. issue, faint stains front and back, else fine. J.S. Lawrence 38-L83 1978 $15

LAWRENCE, DAVID HERBERT   Pornography and Obscenity. 1929. Very good, wraps, first English ed. Bell Book 16-544 1978 £4

LAWRENCE, DAVID HERBERT   A Prelude. Surrey, 1949. 8vo., leather-backed cloth, 1st ed., ltd. to 160 no. copies. J.S. Lawrence 38-L85 1978 $125

LAWRENCE, DAVID HERBERT   A Propos of Lady Chatterley's Lover. London, 1930. Sm. 8vo., cloth, 1st rev'd. ed., spine sunned. J.S. Lawrence 38-L6 1978 $25

LAWRENCE, DAVID HERBERT   A Propos of Lady Chatterley's Lover. London, 1930. Sm. 8vo., cloth, 1st rev'd. ed. J.S. Lawrence 38-L5 1978 $35

LAWRENCE, DAVID HERBERT   The Prussian Officer and Other Stories. London, 1914. Orig. cloth, 1st ed., 1st issue, near-fine. MacManus 238-693 1978 $100

LAWRENCE, DAVID HERBERT   The Prussian Officer, and other stories. 1914. Good, first English ed. Bell Book 16-545 1978 £20

LAWRENCE, DAVID HERBERT   The Prussian Officer and Other Stories. London, (1914). 8vo., gilt-stamped cloth, 1st ed., very fine, half-mor. slipcase. J.S. Lawrence 38-L86 1978 $350

LAWRENCE, DAVID HERBERT   The Prussian Officer and Other Stories. London, (1914). 8vo., gilt-stamped cloth, 1st ed., spine lightly browned, else fine. J.S. Lawrence 38-L87 1978 $150

LAWRENCE, DAVID HERBERT   Psychoanalysis and the Unconscious. New York, 1921. Sm. 8vo., bds., 1st ed., fine. J.S. Lawrence 38-L88 1978 $100

LAWRENCE, DAVID HERBERT   The Rainbow. London, (1915). 8vo., cloth, d.j., 1st ed., scarce, very fine, half-mor. slipcase. J.S. Lawrence 38-L89 1978 $2,500

LAWRENCE, DAVID HERBERT   Rawdon's Roof. London, 1928. Thin 8vo., bds., d.j., 1st ed., ltd. to 530 no. copies, signed by author, d.j. unevenly browned. J.S. Lawrence 38-L90 1978 $165

LAWRENCE, DAVID HERBERT   Rawdon's Roof. London, 1929. Thin 8vo., dec. bds., d.j., 1st ed., ltd. to 530 no. copies, signed by author, d.j. lightly chipped and frayed. J.S. Lawrence 38-L91 1978 $150

LAWRENCE, DAVID HERBERT   Reflections on the Death of a Porcupine and Other Essays. Philadelphia, 1925. 8vo., linen-backed marbled bds., 1st ed., ltd., no. J.S. Lawrence 38-L92 1978 $50

LAWRENCE, DAVID HERBERT   St. Mawr. Together with the Princess. London, (1925). Orig. cloth, 1st ed., fine, very slightly soiled d.j. MacManus 238-695 1978 $50

LAWRENCE, DAVID HERBERT   St. Mawr: Together with: The Princess.   London, (1925). 8vo., cloth, 1st ed., fine. J.S. Lawrence 38-L94 1978 $50

LAWRENCE, DAVID HERBERT   Sea and Sardinia.   New York, 1921. Lg. 8vo., cloth-backed bds., 1st ed., color illus., spine extremities browned, very good. J.S. Lawrence 38-L95 1978 $50

LAWRENCE, DAVID HERBERT   Sex Locked Out.   London, 1929. 8vo., sewn without wrs., orig. glassine, as issued, 1st ed., very fine, cloth. fold. slipcase. J.S. Lawrence 38-L96 1978 $350

LAWRENCE, DAVID HERBERT   The Ship of Death and other poems.   London, 1941. First ed., fine, orig. binding, d.w. Rota 211-293 1978 £6

LAWRENCE, DAVID HERBERT   Sons and Lovers.   London, 1913. 8vo., gilt-stamped cloth, d.j., 1st ed., very fine, half-mor. slipcase. J.S. Lawrence 38-L97 1978 $1,100

LAWRENCE, DAVID HERBERT   The Story of Doctor Manente, Being the Tenth and Last Story from the Suppers of A.F. Grazzini called II Lasca. Florence (1929). 8vo., parchment over bds., d.j., 1st ed., ordinary issue, ltd., no. tear in d.j., otherwise fine, unopened. J.S. Lawrence 38-L99 1978 $65

LAWRENCE, DAVID HERBERT   The Story of Doctor Manente, Being the Tenth and Last Story from the Suppers of A.F. Grazzini called II Lacas. Florence, (1929). 8vo., parchment over bds., d.j., 1st ed., ordinary issue, ltd., no., covers bent, d.j. browned. J.S. Lawrence 38-L100 1978 $35

LAWRENCE, DAVID HERBERT   Studies in Classic American Literature.   New York, 1923. Lg. 8vo., cloth, 1st ed., gilt and spine dulled. J.S. Lawrence 38-L101 1978 $75

LAWRENCE, DAVID HERBERT   Sun.   London, 1926. Sm. 4to., dec. wrs., 1st ed., ltd. to 100 no. copies, wrs. browned at edges, fine, cloth fold. slipcase. J.S. Lawrence 38-L102 1978 $750

LAWRENCE, DAVID HERBERT   Sun.   Paris: The Black Sun Press, 1928. Tall 8vo., printed French wrs., orig. glassine, 1st unexpurgated ed., ordinary issue, 1 of 150 copies on Holland Van Gelder, frontis., very fine. J.S. Lawrence 38-L103 1978 $450

LAWRENCE, DAVID HERBERT   The Tales of D. H. Lawrence.   1934. Covers somewhat rubbed & dull, hinges sprung, else good, first English ed. Bell Book 17-548 1978 £7.50

LAWRENCE, DAVID HERBERT   Tortoises.   New York, 1921. 8vo., pict. bds., spine label, orig. glassine, 1st ed., glassine chipped, else almost mint, perfect bds. J.S. Lawrence 38-L104 1978 $125

LAWRENCE, DAVID HERBERT   Touch and Go: A Play in Three Acts.   London, 1920. 8vo., flexible bds., paper labels, d.j., 1st ed., unopened, fine. J.S. Lawrence 38-L105 1978 $200

LAWRENCE, DAVID HERBERT   Touch and Go: A Play in Three Acts.   London, 1920. Sm. 8vo., flexible bds., paper labels, 1st ed., covers warped, else fine. J.S. Lawrence 38-L106 1978 $75

LAWRENCE, DAVID HERBERT   The Trespasser.   London, 1912. 8vo., gilt-stamped blue cloth, 1st ed., stamp., very fine, fold. cloth slipcase. J.S. Lawrence 38-L107 1978 $650

LAWRENCE, DAVID HERBERT   The Trespasser.   1912. Good, first English ed. Bell Book 16-546 1978 £65

LAWRENCE, DAVID HERBERT   The Triumph of the Machine.   London, 1930 (1931). Thin 8vo., gilt-stamped bds., lg. paper ed., ltd. to 400 no. copies, illus. by Althea Willoughby, #28 of Ariel Poems series, spine extremities lightly nicked. J.S. Lawrence 38-L108 1978 $100

LAWRENCE, DAVID HERBERT   Twilight in Italy.   London, (1916). 8vo., cloth, 1st ed., spine browned, but fine. J.S. Lawrence 38-L109 1978 1978 $300

LAWRENCE, DAVID HERBERT   D.H. Lawrence's Unpublished Foreword to "Women in Love", 1919. San Francisco, 1936. Lg. 8vo., bds., 1st ed., ltd. to 100 copies, top of spine chipped. J.S. Lawrence 38-L22 1978 $250

LAWRENCE, DAVID HERBERT   The Virgin and the Gipsy.   New York, 1930. Bookplate, very good, dust wrapper faded at spine. Bernard 5-160 1978 $30

LAWRENCE, DAVID HERBERT   The Virgin and the Gipsy.   London, 1930. 8vo., brown cloth, gilt lettering on spine, d.w. chipped and with 2-inch tear at top of spine, unusual in d.w., very nice, 1st ed., collector's cond. Desmarais 1-269 1978 $45

LAWRENCE, DAVID HERBERT   The Virgin and the Gipsy.   1930. Very good, first English ed. Bell Book 16-547 1978 £8.50

LAWRENCE, DAVID HERBERT   The Virgin and the Gypsy.   Florence, 1930. 8vo., pict. bds., d.j., 1st ed., ltd., no., spine of d.j. browned. J.S. Lawrence 38-L111 1978 $175

LAWRENCE, DAVID HERBERT   The Virgin and the Gypsy.   Florence, 1930. 8vo., pict. bds., d.j., slipcase, 1st ed., 1 of 810 copies, slipcase worn a bit, spine of d.j. browned, book very fine. J.S. Lawrence 38-L110 1978 $200

LAWRENCE, DAVID HERBERT   We Need Each Other.   New York, 1933. Narrow 8vo., cloth, 1st separate ed., illus. J.S. Lawrence 38-L112 1978 $35

LAWRENCE, DAVID HERBERT   The White Peacock.   New York, 1911. 8vo., pict. cloth, 1st ed., 1st issue, fine, cloth slipcase. J.S. Lawrence 38-L113 1978 $9,500

LAWRENCE, DAVID HERBERT   The Widowing of Mrs. Holroyd: A Drama in Three Acts.   New York, 1914. Sm. 8vo., cloth, 1st ed., bookplt., else fine. J.S. Lawrence 38-L115 1978 $75

LAWRENCE, DAVID HERBERT   The Widowing of Mrs. Holroyd: A Drama in Three Acts.   New York, 1914. Sm. 8vo., cloth, d.j., 1st ed., 500 copies printed, fine, scarce d.j. J.S. Lawrence 38-L114 1978 $250

LAWRENCE, DAVID HERBERT   The Widowing of Mrs. Holroyd: A Drama in Three Acts.   New York, 1914. Sm. 8vo., cloth, 1st ed., spine lightly rubbed at extremities. J.S. Lawrence 38-L116 1978 $45

LAWRENCE, DAVID HERBERT   The Woman Who Rode Away and Other Stories.   New York, 1928. 8vo., cloth, d.j., 1st Amer. ed., fine. J.S. Lawrence 38-L119 1978 $100

LAWRENCE, DAVID HERBERT   The Woman Who Rode Away and Other Stories.   London, (1928). 8vo., cloth, 1st ed., scarce. J.S. Lawrence 38-L118 1978 $125

LAWRENCE, DAVID HERBERT   Women in Love.   New York, 1920. Lg. 8vo., cloth, 1st ed., ltd., this copy no., fine. J.S. Lawrence 38-L117 1978 $250

LAWRENCE, FRIEDA   Not I, But the Wind...   Santa Fe, (1934). Lg. 8vo., linen-backed bds., 1st ed., ltd., no. and signed, pres. copy, inscribed by author, bookplt., bds., rubbed, spine spotted. J.S. Lawrence 38-L150 1978 $50

LAWRENCE, FRIEDA   Not I, But the Wind...   Santa Fe, (1934). Lg. 8vo., linen-backed bds., d.j., 1st ed., ltd., no., signed by author, d.j. browned on spine. J.S. Lawrence 38-L149 1978 $75

LAWRENCE, FRIEDA   Not I, But the Wind.   Santa Fe, (1934). 1 of 1,000 copies, 1st ed., 8 vo., illus., plts., cloth over bds., uncut, d.j., very good. Houle 10-184 1978 $95

LAWRENCE, FRIEDA   "Not I, But the Wind..."   New York, 1934. 1st ed., very good. Ballinger 11-149 1978 $20.00

LAWRENCE, GEORGE ALFRED   Border and Bastille.   New York, n.d. circa 1863. Bell Wiley's copy. Broadfoot 46-160 1978 $14

LAWRENCE, GEORGE ALFRED   Sword and Gown.   London, 1859. 1st ed., crimson quarter calf, marbled bds., lea. label, very good, obit. of author tipped in. Greene 78-248 1978 $55

LAWRENCE, GEORGE ALFRED   Sword and Gown.   Boston, 1859. Orig. cloth, 1st Am. ed., very good condition. Greene 78-72 1978 $25

LAWRENCE, H. W.   French Line Engravings of the late 18th Century.   1910. Plts., roy. 4to. George's 635-32 1978 £50

LAWRENCE, JAMES COOPER   The Year of Regeneration.   1932. Austin 80-781 1978 $11

LAWRENCE, JOHN   A Philosophical & Practical Treatise on Horses, and on the Moral Duties of Man towards the Brute Creation. London, 1796, 98. 2 vols., 1st ed variant, orig. marbled boards, crudely taped on spine and corners, 8vo. Book Chest 17-222 1978 $225

LAWRENCE, JOSEPH S.   Banking Concentration in the United States. New York, (1930). Biblo BL781-833 1978 $9.50

LAWRENCE, JOSEPH STAGG   Stabilization of Prices. 1928. Austin 80-782 1978 $17.50

LAWRENCE, JOSEPH STAGG   Wall Street and Washington. Princeton, 1920. Good. Biblo BL781-834 1978 $10

LAWRENCE, JOSEPH WILSON   Foot-Prints, or Incidents in the Early History of New Brunswick. St. John, 1883. Illus. Hood 117-256 1978 $30

LAWRENCE, MARY   A Collection of Roses From Nature. London, 1799(i.e. 1796-1810). Engraved title, frontis, plts., hand-coloured etchings by author, folio, 487 by 373mm., modern half red morocco, inner hinge of title repaired, slight traces of foxing, mottled bds. Traylen 88-656 1978 £8000

LAWRENCE, R. DE T.   History of Bill Yopp. N.P., 1920? Wrs., illus., Bell Wiley's copy. Broadfoot 46-161 1978 $14

LAWRENCE, ROBERT F.   The New Hampshire Churches. Claremont, 1856. Frontis., 8vo., 1st ed. Morrill 239-539 1978 $25

LAWRENCE, ROBERT MEANS   Primitive Psycho-Therapy and Quackery. Boston, 1910. 8vo., 1st ed., pres. copy. Morrill 239-150 1978 $17.50

LAWRENCE, ROBERT MEANS   The Site of Saint Paul's Cathedral, Boston, and Its Neighborhood. Boston, 1916. Illus., 8vo., inner hinges cracked, 1st ed. Morrill 241-335 1978 $7.50

LAWRENCE, THOMAS   Franci Nichollsii, M.D. London, 1780. 4to., contemp. half calf, corners worn, rebacked, plts., very ltd. ed. Gurney 75-79 1978 £50

LAWRENCE, THOMAS EDWARD   Crusader Castles. Vol. I, The Thesis. Vol. II, The Letters. (London), Golden Cockerel Press, 1936. Quarto, publisher's 3/4 red mor., t.e.g., portraits, repros. of photos, diagrams & facsimiles and maps drawn by author laid in a loose pocket, 1 of 1,000 copies, 2 vols., only ed., fine. Duschnes 220-183 1978 $550

LAWRENCE, THOMAS EDWARD   Crusader Castles. Golden Cockerel Press, 1936. Ltd. to 1,000 copies, maps, 2 vols., cr. 4to., orig. half mor., t.e.g., others uncut. George's 635-901 1978 £325

LAWRENCE, THOMAS EDWARD   Letters. 1938. Second impression, plts., maps, lg. 8vo., orig. cloth. Howes 194-1003 1978 £5

LAWRENCE, THOMAS EDWARD   Oriental Assembly. 1939. First ed., plts., orig. buckram, 8vo. Howes 194-1005 1978 £7.50

LAWRENCE, THOMAS EDWARD   Revolt in the Desert. London, 1927. 4th impression, plts., roy. 8vo. K Books 244-397 1978 £6

LAWRENCE, THOMAS EDWARD   Revolt in the Desert. New York, 1927. 1st printing, 1st American ed., illus., portraits, map, fine, scarce multi-colored d.j. Houle 10-185 1978 $30

LAWRENCE, THOMAS EDWARD   Secret Despatches from Arabia. London, Golden Cockerel Press, (1939). Quarto, cloth, mor. back, t.e.g., bound by Sangorski and Sutcliffe, frontis., one of 1000 copies, only ed., fine. Duschnes 220-184 1978 $250

LAWRENCE, THOMAS EDWARD   Secret Despatches from Arabia. Golden Cockerel Press, (1939). Ltd. to 1,000 copies, portrait, cr. 4to., orig. qtr. black mor., t.e.g., others uncut. George's 635-902 1978 £150

LAWRENCE, THOMAS EDWARD   Seven Pillars of Wisdom. New York, 1935. 8vo., grey cloth, gilt stamped, near mint, d.w., 1st ed., collector's cond. Desmarais 1-272 1978 $35

LAWRENCE, THOMAS EDWARD   Shaw-Ede: T. E. Lawrence's Letters to H. S. Ede 1927-1935. London, Golden Cockerel Press, 1942. One of 500 numbered copies, qtr. dk. blue mor., very nice, first ed. Rota 211-297 1978 £80

LAWRENCE, W. H.   Report as to Grant County... Silver City, 1881. Orig. pr. front wr., 1st ed. Ginsberg 14-766 1978 $185

LAWRENCE, WILLIAM   Memories of a Happy Life. Boston, (1926). Clean, 2nd. impression. Hayman 71-415 1978 $7.50

LAWRENCE, WILLIAM   Report of the Select Committee on Alleged New York Election Frauds. Washington, 1869. Butterfield 21-550f 1978 $20

LAWLESS, EMILY   Maelcho. New York, 1894. 1st Am. ed., orig. cloth, spine ends frayed, good copy. Greene 78-71 1978 $25

LAWSON, HENRY   The Romance of the Swag. Sydney, Australian Limitee Editions Society, 1940. Illus. with woodcuts by Lionel Lindsay, extra set of plts. bound in, prtd. on Japanese vellum. Battery Park 1-6 1978 $75

LAWSON, J. H.   Processional. New York, 1925. Illus., 1st ed. Biblo 251-544 1978 $17.50

LAWSON, JOHN   The History of Carolina. Raleigh, 1860. Rebound, ex-lib. Broadfoot 50-119 1978 $50

LAWSON, JOHN   The History of Carolina. Charlotte, 1903. Lg. fold. map, front hinge cracked. Broadfoot 50-120 1978 $30

LAWSON, JOHN HOWARD   Loud Speaker. New York, (1927). Illus., 1st ed. Biblo 251-543 1978 $15

LAWSON, MARIE A.   The Sea is Blue. New York, 1946. 1st ed., color illus., very fine, dust jacket. Victoria 34-487 1978 $12.50

LAWSON, THOMAS W.   Frenzied Finance. Vol. I - The Crime of Amalgamated. New York, 1905. Biblo BL781-835 1978 $9.50

LAWSON, THOMAS W.   Friday, the Thirteenth. 1907. Frontis. in color, first ed. Austin 82-550 1978 $12.50

LAWSON, THOMAS W.   The Lawson History of the America's Cup. Boston, 1902. Lg. 8vo., canvas, fine internally, inside hinges cracked, water stain, plts. Paine 78-80 1978 $65

LAWSON, WILLIAM   A New Orchard & Garden.... London, 1927. Illus., sm. 4to, bds., parchment spine, ltd. ed. of 650 copies. Traylen 88-595 1978 £18

LAWSON, WILLIAM   A New Orchard and Garden: or, the Best Way for Planting, Grafting, and to Make Any Ground Good for a Rich Orchard:.... London: The Cresset Press, 1927. 8vo., illus., orig. vellum-backed bds., ltd. to 650 copies, t.e.g., fine. MacManus 238-786 1978 $40

LAWTON, EBA ANDERSON   Major Robert Anderson and Fort Sumter, 1861. New York, 1911. Portr., facsimiles, 8vo., orig. bds., 1st ed. Morrill 241-278 1978 $7.50

LAXNESS, HALLDOR   Independent People, an Epic. New York, 1946. Hood 117-524 1978 $15

LAY, WILLIAM   A Narrative of the Mutiny, on board the Ship Globe, of Nantucket,.... New-London, 1828. 12mo, some light browning and dampstaining, contemp. sheep, rebacked, 1st ed. Quaritch 978-61 1978 $600

LAY of the Nibelung Men. Cambridge, 1911. Sq. 8vo. George's 635-1361 1978 £5

THE LAY of the Scottish Fiddle. New York, 1813. 16mo., contemp. calf, hinges slightly cracked, 1st ed., very scarce. Morrill 241-451 1978 $65

LAYE, ELIZABETH P. RAMSAY   Social Life and Manners in Australia. 1861. Sm. 8vo, engraved plts., foxed, orig. cloth. Edwards 1012-338 1978 £60

LAYMAN, WILLIAM   Outline of a Plan for the Better Cultivation, Security, and Defence of the British West Indies... 1807. 8vo, modern half calf. Edwards 1012-730 1978 £70

LAZAREFF, PIERRE   Deadline. 1942. Austin 80-175 1978 $10

LAZESIO, FRANCESCO FELICIANO DA
Please turn to
FELICIANO DA LAZESIO, FRANCESCO

LEA, ELIZABETH   Domestic Cookery. Baltimore, 1846. 2nd. ed., foxed. Baldwins' 51-353 1978 $22.50

LEA, HENRY CHARLES   History of Auricular Confession & Indulgences in the Latin Church. 1896. 3 vols. Allen 234-1329a 1978 $42.50

LEA, HENRY CHARLES   A History of the Inquisition of Spain. 1906. 4 vols., 1st ed., good bright set, slight wear. Austin 79-425 1978 $47.50

LEA, HENRY CHARLES   Indulgences. 1896. Vol. 3 only. Allen 234-1330a 1978 $7.50

LEA, J. HENRY   The Ancestry of Abraham Lincoln. Boston, Riverside Press, 1909. 1st ed., 4to., t.e.g., engr. plts., fldg. genealogical table, facsimile signatures, bound in full green levant, gilt paneled spine, raised bands, brown satin endpapers, near mint, ribbon bookmark, rubbed brown mor. box with library stamp. Current 24-86 1978 $365

LEA, TOM.   The Brave Bulls. Boston, 1949. Very fine in somewhat damaged d.w. Desmarais B-391 1978 $7.50

LEA, TOM   Pelein Landing. El Paso, 1945. Original boards, spine starting to crack, illus., inscribed and signed by Lea. Jenkins 116-1568 1978 $450

LEACH, BERNARD   A Potter's Book. London, 1940. 1st. ed., plts., illus., 8vo. Traylen 88-394 1978 £18

LEACOCK, STEPHEN   Arcadian Adventures with the Idle Rich. New York, London, 1917. Hood 117-525 1978 $15

LEACOCK, STEPHEN   Baldwin, Lafontaine, Hincks; Responsible Government... Toronto, 1910. Hood 116-255 1978 $17.50

LEACOCK, STEPHEN   Canada's War at Sea. Montreal, 1944. Two vols. in one, folio, illus., orig. binding. Wolfe 39-303 1978 $30

LEACOCK, STEPHEN   College Days. Toronto, 1923. Hood 117-482 1978 $17.50

LEACOCK, STEPHEN   The Garden of Folly, a Picture of the World We Live in. London, 1924. Ads. Hood 117-483 1978 $17.50

LEACOCK, STEPHEN   Happy Stories, Just to Laugh At. New York, 1943. 1st Amer. ed., rubber stamp on tail. Biblo 251-545 1978 $12.50

LEACOCK, STEPHEN   The Hohenzollerns in America. New York, 1919. Orig. binding. Wolfe 39-299 1978 $9.50

LEACOCK, STEPHEN   How to Write. New York, 1943. Orig. binding, d.j. Wolfe 39-301 1978 $10

LEACOCK, STEPHEN   How to Write. New York, 1946. Hood 117-484 1978 $30

LEACOCK, STEPHEN   The Iron Man and the Tin Woman, with Other Such Futurities. New York, 1929. 1st ed. Hood 116-482 1978 $30

LEACOCK, STEPHEN   The Leacock Roundabout; a Treasury of the Best Works of.... New York, 1947. Hood 116-483 1978 $7.50

LEACOCK, STEPHEN   Literary Lapses. Montreal, 1910. 1st ed. Hood 117-485 1978 $55

LEACOCK, STEPHEN   Model Memoirs and Other Sketches from Simple to Serious. New York, 1938. 1st ed. Hood 117-486 1978 $30

LEACOCK, STEPHEN B.   Moonbeams From the Larger Lunacy. Toronto, 1915. 1st. ed., free endpaper missing, hinge mended. Hood's 115-440 1978 $12.50

LEACOCK, STEPHEN   Nonsense Novels. 1921. First illus. ed., colour plts. by John Kettelwell, 4to., bds., good, first English ed. Bell Book 16-549 1978 £5

LEACOCK, STEPHEN   Over the Footlights. Toronto, 1923. Hood 117-487 1978 $15

LEACOCK, STEPHEN   Short Circuits. New York, 1928. Hood's 115-344 1978 $20

LEACOCK, STEPHEN   Sunshine Sketches of a Little Town. Toronto, 1943. Illus. by Grant Macdonald. Hood 117-526 1978 $35

LEACOCK, STEPHEN   The Unsolved Riddle of Social Justice. London/New York, 1920. Orig. binding. Wolfe 39-300 1978 $10

LEAKE, ISAAC Q.   Memoir of the Life and Times of General John Lamb. Albany, 1857. Portr., maps in fine cond., 2nd prtg. Butterfield 21-380 1978 $35

LEAMING, AARON   The Grants, Concessions, and Original Constitutions of the Province of New Jersey... Philadelphia, (1881). 2nd ed., orig. cloth, very good. MacManus 239-1287 1978 $25

LEAMING, THOMAS   A Philadelphia Lawyer in the London Courts. New York, 1911. Illus., bind. stained. Biblo BL781-836 1978 $8.50

LEAMY, EDMUND   Moods and Memories. New York, 1920. 1st ed., author's signed pres., d.w. Biblo 251-546 1978 $15

LEAR, EDWARD   The Book of Nonsense. 1893. 29th ed., orig. cloth, oblong 4to., drawings by author. Howes 194-1007 1978 £14

LEAR, EDWARD   Illustrated Excursions in Italy. London, 1846. Tinted lithographs & engravings, two vols., lg. 4to., orig. cloth, rebacked, plts., good, scarce, pres. inscription by author. Rota 212-34 1978 £1,500

LEAR, EDWARD   Journals of a Landscape Painter in Southern Calabria. London, 1842. 1st. ed., roy. 8vo., half-title, tinted lithograph plts., lithograph maps, rebound cloth, gilt back. Deighton 5-132 1978 £185

LEAR, EDWARD   Nonsense Botany and Nonsense Alphabets.... London, 1889. 5th ed., illus., decor. cloth, new endpapers, 8vo. K Books 244-189 1978 £18

LEARNED, MARION D.   Abraham Lincoln, an American Migration Family English not German. Philadelphia, 1909. 1st ed., orig. cloth, recased, spine repaired, illus., ltd. to 500 copies, nice. MacManus 239-888 1978 $25

LEARNED, MARION D.   The Life of Francis Daniel Pastorius, the Founder of Germantown, Pa. Philadelphia, 1908. Illus., fine. MacManus 239-799 1978 $30

LEARY, FREDERICK   The Earl of Chester's Regiment of Yeomanry Cavalry Its Formation and Services 1797 to 1897. Edinburgh, 1898. Portrait frontis., plts., imp. 8vo., orig. cloth, spine faded. F. Edwards 1013-558 1978 £30

LEARY, LEWIS GASTON   Problems of Protestantism. 1933. Austin 79-427 1978 $12.50

LEASK, J. C.   The Regimental Records of the Royal Scots. Dublin, 1915. Thick imp. 8vo., illus., coloured plts., port. frontis., orig. calf, spine faded, uncut. F. Edwards 1013-481 1978 £135

LEATHAM, EDWARD A.   Charmione, a Tale of the Great Athenian Revolution. 1858. 1st. ed., 2 vols., half titles, contemp. full red morocco binding, panelled & diced blind, gilt gauffered edges marbled endpapers, v.g. Jarndyce 16-807 1978 £48

LEATHERNECK ASSOC.   Guidebook for Marines. 1947. Photos, illus., paper. Austin 80-176 1978 $12.50

LEAVES. 1816. 1st. ed., 8vo, evidently lacking half-title, mid 19th. century half calf, foxed at beginning & end. Hannas 54-202 1978 £17.50

LEAVIS, F. B.   D. H. Lawrence. Cambridge, Minority Press, 1930. First ed., cr. 8vo., orig. wrappers. Howes 194-1000 1978 £5

LEAVITT, LYDIA   Bohemian Society. Brockville, n.d. (1885). Hood 116-699 1978 $12.50

LEAVITT, R. K.   Prologue to Tomorrow. 1950. Austin 80-783 1978 $10

LE BAS, PHILIPPE   Suede et Norwege. Paris, 1838. 8vo., bds., plts., map, text in double column, good. King 7-362 1978 £30

LE BEAU, C.   Aventures Ou Voyage Curieux Et Nouveau Parmi Les Sauvages De L'Amerique Septentrionale. Amsterdam, 1738. Engr. fldg. plts., map, sm. 8vo., marbled calf with labels. Salloch 345-105 1978 $600

LEBEDEV, VLADIMIR.   The Lion and the Ox. New York, 1932. 1st Amer. ed., almost fine. Victoria 34-489 1978 $35

LEBEN Und Thaten Des Beruchtigen Raubers Johannes Buckler, Genannt Schinder-hannes.... Philadelphia, 1818. 1st US ed., portr., orig. calf-backed boards, rubbed, good sound copy, 8vo. Americanist 101-129 1978 $40

LEBESON, ANITA LIBMAN   Pilgrim People. 1950. Illus. Austin 79-428 1978 $12.50

LEBLANC, LOUIS   Nouvelle Methode d'Operer les Hernies. Paris, 1768. Engr. fldg. plts., 8vo., contemp. mottled calf. Argosy Special-57 1978 $125

LE BLOND, GUILLAUME   Elemens de Fortification, Contenant la Construction, Raisonnee des Ouvrages de la Fortification; les Systems des Ingenieurs les Plus Celebres... Paris, 1786. Huitieme ed., 8vo., plts., contemp. mottled calf. Quaritch 983-44 1978 $130

LEBOURDAIS, D. M.   Northward on the New Frontier. Ottawa, 1931. Illus., inscr. & signed by author. Hood 117-101 1978 $25

LE CAT, CLAUDE NICHOLAS   Traite des sens.... Amsterdam, 1744. Nouvelle ed., 8vo., engrav. plts., fine, contemp. sprinkled calf, gilt spine, second ed. Quaritch 977-39 1978 $120

LECHFORD, THOMAS   Plain Dealing... London, 1642. Sm. 4to., first ed., very rare, Royal Arms, 19th cent. half calf. Quaritch 978-95 1978 $1400

LECHLER, J.   Vom Hakenkreuz. Leipzig, 1921. 8vo., orig. covers, illus., plts. out of text. Van der Peet H-64-481 1978 Dfl 50

LECKY, WILLIAM E. H.   History of European Morals from Augustus to Charlemagne. 1919. 3rd ed., 2 vols., spine slightly frayed. Allen 234-530 1978 $15

LECLERC, CHARLES   Bibliothecana Americana. Paris, 1878. Thick lg. 8vo., cloth scuffed. Battery Park 1-331 1978 $150

LE CLERC, JEAN   A Funeral Oration upon the Death of Mr. Philip Limborch. 1713. 8vo., unbound. P. M. Hill 142-161 1978 £8

LECLERC, JUSTA   Au Coin du Feu. Montreal, 1931. Card cover, illus. Hood's 117-532 1978 $17.50

LECLERC, JUSTA   En Veillant. Montreal, 1931. Inscribed and signed by author, card cover, illus. Hood's 117-533 1978 $20

LECLERC, MARC   La Passion de Notre Frere le Poilu. Paris, 1918. 8vo., fine half brown mor., gilt tooled title on spine, fine colored fold-out plt., fine illus. in colors by L. Lebegue, orig. cover wrapped up. Van der Peet H-64-482 1978 Dfl 100

LECLERC, MAX   Choses D'Amerique: Les Crises Economique et Religieuse... Paris, 1891. Orig. wrps., 1st ed. Ginsberg 16-890 1978 $35.00

LE CLERC, S.   Principles of Design. 1794. Sm. 8vo., plts., coloured title, last plt. soiled, mod. bds. Quaritch 983-208 1978 $300

LE CLERCQ, CHRESTIEN   Nouvelle Relation de la Gaspesie, qui Contient les Moeurs & la Religion des Sauvages Gaspesiens Porte-Croix.... Paris, 1691. Full later mor. gilt, fine binding, t.e.g., one third of upper portion of dedication leaf torn away and replaced with matching plain paper, extremely fine. Wolfe 39-304 1978 $700

LE CLERT, LOUIS   Le Papier. Paris, 1927. One of 675 sets, folio, 2 vols., very fine, illus. Battery Park 1-459 1978 $325

L'ECLUSE, CHARLES DE   Rariorum aliquot stirpium per Hispanias observatarum Historia,.... Antwerp, 1576. 8vo, full page woodcuts, contemp. vellum. Quaritch 978-35 1978 $1,750

LECOMTE, H.   Costumes Civils et Militaires de la Monarchie Francais Depuis 1200 Jusqu'a 1820. 1820. 2 vols., folio, hand-coloured plts., marginal soiling, 1/2 blue niger mor., bd. slipcase, bookplts., fine copy. Quaritch 983-65 1978 $2,150

LECORNU, JOSEPH   La Navigation Aerienne. Paris, 1903. 8vo., woodcuts, photographs, fine pict. cloth binding, a little worn. Quaritch 977-235 1978 $275

LE COUTEUR, J. D.   English Mediaeval Painted Glass. 1926. Plts., illus., 8vo. Upcroft 12-254 1978 £7.50

LECUIRE, PIERRE   Consul Constant. Paris, 1958. 4to., in sheets, uncut, orig. wr. in orig. limp lea. cover, ltd. ed., only 75 copies prtd., numbered copy signed by author and illus'r on papier d'Auvergne, 1 orig. illus. books by Alain de La Boubdonnaye, fine copy. Goldschmidt 110-41 1978 $290

LEDERMUELLER, MARTIN FROBEN   Mikroskopischer Gemuetsund Augenergoet-zung Erstes Fuenfzig... Nuernberg, 1760. Engr. frontis., handcolored plts., 4to., contemp. 1/2 calf, spine gilt with label, 1st vol. of a 3-vol. set. Salloch 345-107 1978 $350

LEDESEMA, ENRIQUE FERNANDEZ   Historia Critica de la Tipografia en La Ciudad De Mexico. 1934-35. Illus., newly bound in cloth, orig. wrs. bound in. Battery Park 1-397 1978 $75

LEDYARD, JOHN   A Journal of Captain Cook's Last Voyage to the Pacific Ocean, and in Quest of a North-West Passage, between Asia & America. Hartford, 1783. Chart not present, modern full sheep, page is 17.4 x 11 cm. Wolfe 39-305 1978 $1500

LEE, BOURKE   Death Valley Men. New York, 1932. Illus., 1st ed. Biblo BL781-283 1973 $12.50

LEE, CHARLES   North, East, South, West. 1945. First ed. Austin 82-551 1978 $12.50

LEE, EDMUND J.   Lee of Virginia. Philadelphia, 1895. 4to., extremely scarce. MacManus 239-931 1978 $85

LEE, FITZHUGH   General Lee. New York, 1894. Fldg. map, Bell Wiley's copy. Broadfoot 46-162 1978 $16

LEE, FRANCIS B.   History of Trenton, N.J... 1895. Lg. 4to. MacManus 239-1288 1978 $60

LEE, FRANCIS B.   New Jersey as a Colony and as a State. New York, 1902. 4 vols., illus., orig. cloth. MacManus 239-1289 1978 $55

LEE, G.   King Edward VII, a Biography. 1925. Illus., 2 vols. George's 635-628 1978 £5.25

LEE, GEORGE J.   The Voice. London & Dublin, 1870. 2nd ed., illus., 8vo., ex-lib. Morrill 239-151 1978 $10

LEE, HENRY 1756-1818   Memoirs of the War in the Southern Department of the United States. Philadelphia, 1812. 2 vols., 1st ed., illus., portraits. MacManus 239-593 1978 $55

LEE, HENRY 1765-1836   Poetic Impressions. London, 1817. 1st. ed., sm. 8vo, orig. bds., spine & label slightly defective, uncut. Hannas 54-203 1978 £15

LEE, HENRY 1782-1867   Exposition of Facts and Arguments in Support of a Memorial to the Legislature of Massachusetts, by Citizens of Boston and Vicinity... Boston, 183.6. Disbound, inscribed on title-page by author. Hayman 71-445 1978 $7.50

LEE, JAMES   An Introduction to Botany: Containing an Explanation of the Theory of that Science from the Works of Dr. Linnaeus. London, 1788. Orig. boards, 4th ed., plates, 8vo. Book Chest 17-223 1978 $100

LEE, JOHN EDWARD   Note-Book of an Amateur Geologist. London, 1881. First ed., woodbury type frontis., plts., 8vo., orig. cloth. K Books 244-135 1978 £16

LEE, LAURIE   We Made a Film in Cypress. 1947. Plts., very good, d.w., first English ed. Bell Book 16-554 1978 £15

LEE, ROBERT   Steer By A Star. La Porte, 1946. Wood engr. by Lee from orig. blocks, d.w. Bernard 5-161 1978 $8.50

LEE, ROBERT C. Steer By A Star. La Porte, 1946. Wood engr. by Lee from orig. blocks, d.w. Bernard 5-161 1978 $8.50

LEE, ROBERT E. Difficulties between the People of Texas and Mexico. Washington, 1860. Jenkins 116-813 1978 $45

LEE, ROBERT E. Recollections and Letters of General Robert E. Lee...By His Son. New York, 1904. First ed., illus. Biblo 247-21 1978 $18.50

LEE, RUTH WEBB American Glass Cup Plates. Northborough, (1948). 131 plts. Baldwins' 51-114 1978 $20

LEE, S. A Grammar and Vocabulary of the Language of New Zealand. 1820. Sm. 8vo, orig. bds., rebacked. Edwards 1012-349 1978 £150

LEE, SIDNEY The French Renaissance in England; An Account of the Literary Relations of England and France in the 16th Century. Oxford, 1910. Octavo, good. Upcroft 10-412 1978 £10

LEE, VERNON PSEUD.
Please turn to
PAGET, VIOLET

LEE, W. L. MELVILLE A History of Police in England. London, 1901. 8vo., orig. cloth, 1st ed. Morrill 241-280 1978 $9

LEE, WILLIAM Daniel Defoe: His Life, and Recently Discovered Writings, Extending from 1716 to 1729. London, 1869. 3 vols., illus., orig. cloth, 1st ed., extremities of spines worn, but nice, bookplt. MacManus 238-112 1978 $50

LEECHMAN, DOUGLAS Indian Summer. Toronto, 1949. Ex-lib., worn. Hood 117-685 1978 $10

LEEDER, S. H. The Desert Gateway, Biskra and Thereabouts. London, 1910. Frontis., illus., decor. cover, 8vo. K Books 244-190 1978 £7

LEEDES, EDWARD Animadversions Upon the First Part of Mr. Richard Johnson's Grammatical Commentaries. 1706. 1st. ed., 8vo, disbound, some ink stains in margins. Hannas 54-191 1978 £12.50

LEEDS, LEWIS W. Lectures on Ventilation. New York, 1868. Tinted plts., text cuts, ex-lib., 1st ed. Morrill 239-152 1978 $10

LEEDS, VIRGINIA NILES The Honor of a Gentleman. 1899. First ed., inscribed. Austin 82-552 1978 $27.50

LEEPER, A. W. A. History of Medieval Austria. 1941. 8vo. George's 635-702 1978 £8

LEEPER, DAVID ROHRER The Argonauts of 'Forty-Nine. South Bend, 1894. Cloth, fine in dust jacket. Hayman 73-383 1978 $10

LEERING, C. Manifesto al Presidente de Los Estados Unidos de America. El Paso, 1912. Jenkins 116-1432 1978 $45

LEERS, JOHANN VON Juden Sehen Dich An. Berlin, n.d. (ca. 1932). Illus., paper, in German, photos. Austin 79-431 1978 $27.50

LEES, JOHN Journal of J. L. of Quebec. Detroit, 1911. Fold. map, orig. binding. Wolfe 39-307 1978 $40

LE FANU, JOSEPH SHERIDAN In a Glass Darkly. 1929. Fine, drawings by Edward Ardizzone, 1st Eng. ed. Bell Book 16-475 1978 £40

LE FANU, JOSEPH SHERIDAN In a Glass Darkly. 1929. Drawings by Edward Ardizzone, fine, d.w., 1st Eng. ed., later issue in orange cloth. Bell Book 17-481 1978 £25

LEFEVRE, E. Un Voyage au Laos. Paris, 1898. Map, plts., 8vo, orig. covers. Van der Peet 127-128 1978 Dfl 45

LEFEVERE, EDWIN The Making of a Stockbroker. 1925. Austin 80-784 1978 $7.50

LEFEVRE, EDWIN Sampson Rock of Wall Street. New York, 1907. Cloth, lacks free endpaper on fr., 1st ed. Hayman 73-170 1978 $7.50

LEFEVRE, RALPH History of New Paltz, New York and Its Old Families, 1678-1820.... Albany, 1903. Illus., 1st ed., covers rubbed, soiled. Biblo BL781-163 1978 $34.50

LEFEVRE GALLERIES Primitive African Sculpture (Exhibition Catalogue). London, 1933. Map, tipped-in illus., 4to, orig. printed wrappers. K Books 239-260 1978 £15

LEFFERTS, CHARLES M. Uniforms of the American, British, French and German Armies in the War of the American Revolution 1775-1783. New York, 1926. 1st ed., ltd. to 500 numbered copies, 4to., plts. in full color painted by author, orig. brown buckram with blue spine, near mint. Current 24-85 1978 $365

LEFFINGWELL, ALBERT An Ethical Problem, or Sidelights Upon Scientific Experimentation on Man and Animals. London, 1914. 8vo., 1st English ed., pres. from author. Morrill 239-153 1978 $12.50

LEFROY, JOHN HENRY Magnetical and Meterological Observations at Lake Athabasca and Fort Simpson... 1855. Folding plts., orig. cloth, 8vo, headband slightly worn, front end-paper missing. Edwards 1012-436 1978 £35

LEFT to their Own Devices. 1937. Cloth, mint in unevenly browned but very fine d.w., mint slipcase, 1 of 190 numbered copies. Dawson's 447-173 1978 $180

LE GALLIENNE, RICHARD The Book-Bills of Narcissus. London, 1895. 8vo, blue cloth, gilt lettering on spine, ownership inscription, frontis. by Robert Fowler, some shelf wear, Nice, 1st ed., collector's cond. Desmarais 1-274 1978 $10

LE GALLIENNE, RICHARD English Poems. London and New York, 1892. Orig. bds., soiled, ltd. ed. of 800 copies. Eaton 45-289 1978 £10

LE GALLIENNE, RICHARD Limited Editions. London, 1893. Wrappers, first ed., nice, author's signed autograph pres. inscription. Rota 211-300 1978 £25

LEGALLIENNE, RICHARD The Philosophy of Limited Editions. Wr., 8vo., thin, prtd on Linweave Japan paper, one of 2000 copies. Battery Park 1-403 1978 $22.50

LE GALLIENNE, RICHARD Robert Louis Stevenson, An Elegy, and Other Poems, Mainly Personal. London, 1895. 8vo, blue cloth, gilt lettering on spine, uncut, front cover slightly bubbled, Fine, 1 of 500 copies, 1st ed., collector's cond. Desmarais 1-275 1978 $25

LE GALLIENNE, RICHARD The Romance of Perfume. New York, 1928. Illus. in color, fine, boxed. Biblo 247-580 1978 $27.50

LE GALLIENNE, RICHARD The Silk-Hat Soldier and Other Poems. London, New York & Toronto, 1915. 1st ed., laid paper, uncut, pictorial wr., protective wr., very good or better, Review Copy with John Lane's Compliments. Limestone 9-174 1978 $35

LEGALLOIS, JULIEN JEAN CESAR Experiences sur le Principe de la vie, No-tamment sur Celui des Mouvemens du Coeur, et sur le Siege de ce Principe. Paris, 1812. Fldg. copperplt., 8vo., contemp. half calf, 1st ed. Offenbacher 30-82 1978 $500

LEGENDRE, ADRIEN MARIE Essai sur la Theorie des Nombres. Paris, (1798). 4to., contemp. marbled calf, gilt back, a bit worn, 1st ed. Gilhofer 74-117 1978 sFr 800

LEGGE, A. O. The Unpopular King, the Life and Times of Richard III. 1885. Plates, stained, 2 vols., 8vo. George's 635-747 1978 £7.50

LEGGE, CHARLES A Glance at the Victoria Bridge, and the Men Who Built It. Montreal, 1860. Paper cover. Hood 117-579 1978 $35

LEGGE, M. D. Anglo-Norman and the Cloisters; the influence of the Orders upon Anglo-Norman Literature. 1950. 8vo. Upcroft 12-259 1978 £6

LEGGETT, WILLIAM A Collection of the Political Writings of. New York, 1840. 2 vols., port., orig. cloth, nice. MacManus 239-250 1978 $35

LEGGI Nuove Della Republica Di Genova,.... Genoa, 1584. 1st ed., small 8vo, full contemp. limp vellum, a bit worn at edges, Andrew Fletcher copy. Bennett 20-120 1978 $250

LEGH, E. C.   Lyme Letters 1660-1760. 1925. Plts., octavo, good. Upcroft 10-414 1978 £8.50

LEGLER, HENRY E.   Of Much Love and Some Knowledge of Books. Chicago, 1912. Thin 8vo, bds., parchment spine. Traylen 88-51 1978 £20

LEGOFF, L.   Katolik Deneya'tiye Dittlisse... Montreal, 1890. Black cloth, orig. wrs. Hood 116-423 1978 $75

LE GRAND, AUGUSTIN   Etude Graphique De La Terre. c. 1892. Sm. folio, hand-coloured lithograph title-pg., hand-coloured lithograph plts., coloured folding maps, some soiling & penciling, red cloth, orig. red roan back-strip, gilt, defective. Deighton 5-186 1978 £95

LE GRAND, J. B.   Partenopex de Blois, Romance in Four Cantos. London, 1807. 4to, 3 plts., engraved, foxing throughout, contemp. red morocco, gilt, rebacked. Eaton 45-290 1978 £40

LEGRAND, P. E.   New Greek Comedy. 1917. Binding spotted. Allen 234-532 1978 $12.50

LE GRAND D'AUSSY, P. J. B.   Fabliaux, or Tales, Abridged from French Manuscripts of the XIIth and XIIIth Centuries by M. Le Grand. 1815. 3 vols., sm. 8vo., contemp. diced calf, gilt panelled backs, repaired. Quaritch 979-221 1978 $95

LE GRANT Herbier En Francoys... Paris, n.d. (1540?). Woodcuts, 4to., full levant mor., gilt edges, mor. & marbled endleaves, slipcase, extremely rare ed. of the French "Grand Herbal", ed. undated. Salloch 345-82 1978 $6,000

LE HAIN, G. M.   Historic Montreal. Past and Present. Montreal, n.d. (c. 1905-10). Folio, lithos and color plts. Biblo 251-23 1978 $27.50

LEHMANN, ALFRED   Die Hauptgesetze Des Menschlichen Gefuhlslebens. Leipzig, 1892. 8vo., fldg. photolitho. plts., 3/4 mor., gilt on spine, ex-lib., very good copy. Zeitlin 245-144 1978 $125

LEHMANN, JOHN   Folios of New Writing. London, 1941. Nice, first ed., orig. binding, d.w. Rota 211-12 1978 £5

LEHMANN, ROSAMOND   A Letter to a Sister. 1931. Wraps, very good, first English ed. Bell Book 16-556 1978 £6.50

LEHMANN, ROSAMOND   The Weather in the Streets. 1936. Near fine, worn d.w., first English ed. Bell Book 17-563 1978 £10

LEIBER, FRITZ   Night's Black Agents. Sauk City, 1947. Black cloth, 1st ed., fine in dust jacket. Bradley 49-185 1978 $60

LEICHHARDT, LUDWIG   Journal of An Overland Expedition in Australia... 1847. 1st. ed., roy.8vo, folding engraved plt., illus., half calf, gilt back. Deighton 5-104 1978 £80

LEIDING, HARRIETTE KERSHAW   Charleston Historic and Romantic. Philadelphia, 1931. 80 illus. Baldwins' 51-526 1978 $12.50

LEIDING, HARRIETTE KERSHAW   Historic Houses of South Carolina. Philadelphia, 1921. Ltd. ed., 100 illus. Baldwins' 51-527 1978 $35

LEIGH, CHARLES 1662-1701   The Natural History of Lancashire, Cheshire, and the Peak, in Derbyshire. Oxford, 1700. Portrait, plts., folio, contemp. panelled calf, good, first ed. Howes 194-67 1978 £95

LEIGH, FLORENCE   Discontented Susan. London, n.d. Illus. in color, inner hinges split, covers rubbed and soiled. Biblo BL781-1029 1978 $10

LEIGH, FLORENCE   Greedy Frederick. London, n.d. 4to., illus. in color, covers rubbed and soiled. Biblo BL781-1030 1978 $10

LEIGH, MABEL CONSTANCE   Love Songs and Verses. 1913. First ed., sm. 4to., plts., orig. cloth gilt, gilt top, pres. copy inscribed by author. Howes 194-1008 1978 £10

LEIGH, W. R.   Frontiers of Achievement. New York, 1938. 8vo, orig. cloth, illus. K Books 239-261 1978 £7

LEIGH, W. R.   Frontiers of Enchantment. New York, 1938. 8vo, orig. cloth. Book Chest 17-226 1978 $22

LEIGHTON, CLARE   Sometime-Never. New York, 1939. Near mint in d.w. Desmarais B-397 1978 $10

LEIGHTON, CLARE   Southern Harvest. 1943. Engrav. by authoress, roy. 8vo., covers faded. George's 635-191 1978 £5.25

LEIGHTON, J.   Suggestions in Design. Being a Comprehensive Series of Original Sketches in Various Styles of Ornament... (1880). Roy. 4to., frontis., plts., fine, clean copy in half mor. Quaritch 983-87 1978 $130

LEIGHTON, JOHN M.   History of the County of Fife. Glasgow, 1840. Plts., 3 vols., 4to., good, half blue calf gilt. K Books 244-398 1978 £50

LEISERSON, WILLIAM M.   Adjusting Immigrant and Industry. 1924. Austin 79-432 1978 $11

LEITCH, GORDON B.   Chinese Rugs. New York, (1935). 43 illus., d.j. Baldwins' 51-116 1978 $25

LEITHEAD, WILLIAM   Electricity. London, 1837. Illus., 12mo., contemp. calf, ex-lib., crudely rebacked with white tape, 1st ed. Morrill 241-282 1978 $12.50

LELAND, CHARLES G.   The Union Pacific Railway, Eastern Division, or, Three Thousand Miles in a Railway Car. Philadelphia, 1867. Half morocco, 1st ed. Ginsberg 14-478 1978 $75

LELAND, THOMAS   History of Ireland... 1773. 1st. ed., 3 vols., 4to, half-titles, orig. calf, red & green labels, spines gilt. Jarndyce 16-127 1978 £45

LELAND, THOMAS   The History of the Life and Reign of Philip King of Macedon. 1758. First ed., frontispieces, map, 2 vols., 4to., contemp. half calf, joints cracked. Howes 194-360 1978 £21

LELY, GILBERT   Ma Civilization. Pairs, 1947. Etchings by Lucien Coutaud, one of 200 numbered copies on Marais, 4to., unbound sheets, in portfolio, fine, in pict. chemise and slipcase, first ed. Rota 212-35 1978 £95

LE MAIR, W. WILLEBEEK.   Little Stories of Long Ago. London, (1912). Color plates, fine. Victoria 34-493 1978 $65

LE MAIR, H. WILLEBEEK   Nursie's Little Rhyme Book. Philadelphia, n.d. Oblong 12mo, miniature ed., color plates, colored pictorial boards worn at edges, text very good, scarce. Victoria 34-495 1978 $22.50

LE MAIR, H. WILLEBEEK   Old Dutch Nursery Rhymes. London-New York, (1917). Oblong quarto, color plates, cover color plate, about fine. Victoria 34-494 1978 $45

LEMELIN, ROGER   Au Pied de la Pente Douce. Montreal, 1944. Card cover. Hood 116-484 1978 $10

LEMERCIER, H. L.   Chants Heroiques Des Montagnards et Matelots Grecs... 1825. 2 vols. in 1, half calf, one joint cracked. Allen 234-646 1978 $10

LEMERY, LOUIS   Traite des Aliments, ou L'On Trouve par Ordre, et Separement. Paris, 1705. Seconde ed., 8vo., contemp. mottled bds., uncut. Quaritch 977-41 1978 $125

LEMERY, LOUIS   A Treatise of Foods in General. London, 1704. Written in French, 8vo., ads, old blind-tooled calf, gilt, rubbed, very good copy, old signature on title, 1st ed. in English. Norman 5-175 1978 $350

LEMERY, WINSLOW   A Collection of 22 Memoirs by a Group of French Scientists... 4to., engr. plts., disbound. Zeitlin 245-145 1978 $175

LEMNIUS, LEVINUS   De Habitv Et Constitvtione Corporis. Antverpiae, 1561. Sm. 8vo., rare 1st ed., modern 3/4 black mor., gilt lettered, browned, signatures of former owners, good copy from library of Dr. Alfred M. Hellman. Zeitlin 245-146 1978 $450

LEMNIUS, LEVINUS   The Touchstone of Complexions. London, 1576. Sm. 8vo. (14.5 x 9.4cm), largely black letter, nineteenth century calf, gilt edges, first ed. in English. Quaritch 977-42 1978 $900

LEMOINE, HENRY   Present State of Printing and Bookselling in America (1796). 1929. Narrow 12mo., cloth spine, one of 160 copies, prtd. on Rives paper. Battery Park 1-405 1978 $45

LEMON, GEORGE WILLIAM   English Etymology. 1783. 4to., later half calf, 19th-century marbled sides and endpapers. P. M. Hill 142-301 1978 £75

LEMON, MARK   The Jest Book. London, 1864. 1st ed., orig. cloth, very good. Greene 78-326 1978 $70

LEMON, R.   Catalogue of a Collection of Printed Broadsides in the possession of the Society of Antiquaries of London. London, 1866. Illus., roy. 8vo., cloth. Forster 130-245 1978 £30

LEMONNIER, CAMILLE   Felicien Rops, L'Homme et l'Artiste. Paris, 1908. Portrait, plts., illus., 4to, binder's buckram. Traylen 88-412 1978 £20

LEMORE, CLARA   Penhala: A Wayside Wizard. 1895. 1st. ed., 3 vols., half titles, orig. olive cloth, blocked in green & gilt, v.g. Jarndyce 16-808 1978 £43

LE MORMONISME: Histoire et Doctrines des Mormons. Paris, 1855. Orig. wr. bound in boards, 1st ed. Ginsberg 14-666 1978 $75

LE MOUEL, E.   Le Nain Gosmon. Paris, 1889. Sm. 4to., pict. cloth, plts. in color by author. Van der Peet H-64-439 1978 Dfl 55

LE MOYNE, PETER   The Gallery of Heroick Women. London, 1652. Tall folio, full early calf, expertly rebacked, gilt spine, bookplates, 1st ed., engravings, very good, the William Hogarth copy. Bennett 7-69 1978 $750

LEMPERLY, PAUL   Among My Books. Cleveland, The Rowfant Club, 1929. 12mo., illus., #138 of 190 numbered copies. Battery Park 1-398a 1978 $75

LEMPERLY, PAUL   Books and I. Cleveland, The Rowfant Club, 1938. Boxed, #3 of 200 copies. Battery Park 1-399 1978 $75

LEMPRIERE, J.   A Classical Dictionary... London, 1831. 8vo., old bds., newly rebacked in calf, good. Sexton 7-78 1978 £12

LEMPRIERE, WILLIAM   A Tour From Gibraltar to Tangier, Sallee, Mogodore, Santa Cruz, Tarudant... London, 1791. 1st. ed., folding map, contemp. calf gilt, fully gilt spine, covers little rubbed, internally crisp & fresh, 8vo. K Books 239-263 1978 £40

LENDUM, JOHN   A History of the Rise of Methodism in America, Containing Sketches of Methodist Itinerant Preachers. Philadelphia, 1859. Name stamp on title pg. Baldwins' 51-12 1978 $22.50

LENDY, CAPT.   A Practical Course of Military Surveying including the Principles of Topographical Drawing. 1864. Plates, imp. 8vo. George's 635-836 1978 £15

LENGYEL, EMIL   Americans From Hungary. 1948. Austin 79-433 1978 $12.50

LENIN, VLADIMIR ILYICH   Letters from Afar. 1932. Paper. Austin 80-785 1978 $7.50

LENIN, VLADIMIR ILYICH   Selected Works, Vols. 1-5, 7-12 (ex 12). 1936. 11 vols., 8vo. George's 635-352 1978 £18

LENIN, VLADIMIR ILYICH   Staat und Revolution. Berlin, 1918. 8vo., orig. printed wrs., 1st German ed. Gilhofer 74-16 1978 sFr 200

LENIN, VLADIMIR ILYICH   The Threatening Catastrophe and How to Fight It. 1932. Paper. Austin 80-786 1978 $7.50

LENIN, VLADIMIR ILYICH   Die Wahlen zur Konstituierenden Versammlung und Die Diktatur des Proletariats. (Hamburg), 1920. 8vo., orig. printed wrs., lightly stained, 1st German ed. Gilhofer 74-17 1978 sFr 100

LENIN, VLADIMIR ILYICH   The Young Generation. 1940. Paper. Austin 80-787 1978 $7.50

LENK, TORSTEN   The Flintlock, Its Origin and Development. Illus. with 134 plts., line illus., med. 4to, buckram. Traylen 88-508 1978 £12

LENNEP, J. VAN   Klaasje Zevenster. Leiden, n.d. (ab. 1930). 4to., gilt tooled cloth, gilt spine, a.e.g., plts., orig. drwg. signed by de Famars Testes. Van der Peet H-64-378 1978 Dfl 300

LENNOX, WILLIAM G.   Science and Seizures. New York/London, 1946. Rittenhouse 49-463 1976 $10

LENORMANT, FR.   Monnaies et Medailles. Paris, n.d. (ab. 1920). 8vo., half calf, text illus., corners broken. Van der Peet H-64-484 1978 Dfl 45

LENOTRE, G.   The Flight of Marie Antoinette. Philadelphia, 1906. Illus. Biblo 247-713 1978 $17.50

LENOX, EDWARD H.   Overland to Oregon in the Tracks of Lewis and Clarke. Oakland, 1904. Plates, map, orig. pict. cloth, 1st ed., autographed by author. Ginsberg 14-823 1978 $75

LENS, ARNOLDUS DE   In Geometrica Elementa Eisagoge. Antwerp, 1565. 8vo., wrappers, woodcut diagrams, rather sm. copy. Gurney 75-65 1978 £50

LENSKI, LOIS   A-Going to the Westward. New York, 1937. 1st ed., very fine, excellent illus. dust jacket. Victoria 34-496 1978 $25

LENT, EDWARD B.   Being Done Good. Brooklyn, 1904. 8vo., 1st ed. Morrill 239-154 1978 $10

LENTZ, HAROLD   The "Pop-Up" Pinocchio. New York, (1932). 1st ed., colored pop-ups in good state, very fine, colored d.j. Victoria 34-498 1978 $37.50

LENYGON, FRANCIS PSEUD.
Please turn to
JOURDAIN, MARGARET

LEO, H.   Treatise on the Local Nomenclature of the Anglo-Saxons. 1852. Orig. bds., spine strengthened, 8vo. Upcroft 12-262 1978 £9

LEO-WOLF, GEORG   Tractatus Anatomico-Pathologicus Sistens Duas Observationes. Heidelbergae et Lipsiae, 1832. 4to., litho. plts., orig. pink prtd. wrs., browned, light foxing, good copy, 1st ed. Zeitlin 245-148 1978 $45

LEOB, HANAU W.   Operative Surgery of the Nose, Throat, and Ear. St. Louis, 1917. Two volumes. Rittenhouse 49-487 1976 $25

LEON, L.   Diary of a Tar Heel Confederate Soldier. Charlotte, 1913. Pictorial cover, spine lightly spotted, rare, Bell Wiley's copy. Broadfoot's 44-566 1978 $75

LEON & BROTHER   Catalogue of First Editions of American Authors. New York, 1885. Pict. wrs., uncut. Wolfe 39-310a 1978 $45

LEON & BROTHER   Catalogue of First Editions of American Authors. New York, 1885. 8vo., orig. pict. wrs., nice. Morrill 241-685 1978 $17.50

LEON & BROTHER   First Editions of American Authors. Pict. wrs., newly bound in 3/4 leather and marbled paper over bds., orig. wrs. bound in. Battery 1-332 1978 $125

LEONARD, C. HENRI   The Hair. Detroit, 1880. Engrs., 8vo., 1st ed. Morrill 239-155 1978 $30

LEONARD, C. HENRI   The Multum in Parvo Dose Book. New York, 1875. Rittenhouse 49-464 1976 $10

LEONARD, DANIEL   Massachusettensis. Boston printed, London reprinted, 1776. Later half mor. Wolfe 39-308 1978 $200

LEONARD, JACOB CALVIN   Centennial History of Davidson County, N.C. Raleigh, 1927. Illus., fine copy, d.j. Broadfoot 50-124 1978 $25

LEONARD, JOHN W.   The Gold Fields of the Klondike. Chicago, 1897. 12mo, original pictorial wr., (spine restored, front wr. surface partly scraped) 1st ed., owner's stamp on several places, decent copy. Ximenes 47-177 1978 $35

LEONARD, JOSEPH A.   History of Olmsted Co., Minn. Chicago, 1910. Thick 4to., illus., 1/2 leather. MacManus 239-1060 1978 $60

LEONARD, LEVI W.   The History of Dublin, N.H. 1920. Illus.,
fine. MacManus 239-1067 1978 $30

LEONARD, THOMAS H.   From Indian Trail to Electric Rail... Atlantic
Highlands, 1923. Illus., very scarce. MacManus 239-1290 1978 $60

LEONARD, WILLIAM ELLERY   A Son of Earth: Collected Poems. New York,
1928. Portr., signed in ink by poet, full parchment bds., t.e.g., others uncut,
lst ed., I of 350, fine. Bradley 49-186 1978 $40

LEONARD, WILLIAM ELLERY   A Son of Earth: Collected Poems. Blue cloth,
trade ed., errata slip tipped in, fine. Bradley 49-187 1978 $15

LEONARDO DA VINCI   Il Codice Atlantico. Milan, 1894-1904. Plts.,
contemp. half mor. fldrs., gilt, rubbed, very good set, 1st full ed., 4 portfolios of
text & 4 portfolios of plts. Norman 5-L10 1978 $4,500

LEONARDO DA VINCI   Il Codice Atlantico. Florence & New York,
1973-1977. 12 vols., lg. folio, plts. in treu color facsimile, full lea., gilt, the
definitive ed., ltd. to 998 numbered sets. Norman 5-L10a 1978 $10,000

LEONARDO DA VINCI   Il Codice Trivulziano Trascritto Per Cura di
Nando de Toni. Milan, 1939. 8vo., orig. prtd. wrs. Norman 5-L28 1978 $15

LEONARDO DA VINCI   Documenti e Memorie Riguardanti la Vita e le
Opere di Leonardo. Milan, 1919. 8vo., frontis. portr., orig. prtd. wrs., uncut,
very good copy, ltd. to 600 copies. Norman 5-L17 1978 $45

LEONARDO DA VINCI   Malerbuch. Berlin, 1919. 8vo., illus., orig.
printed bds. Norman 5-L18 1978 $30

LEONARDO DA VINCI   I Manoscritti e i Disegni. Rome, 1934. 3
vols., lg. folio, fascicules I-III, color plts., parchment, richly gilt, little rubbed,
some hinges repaired, but fine set, handsomely bound, ltd. to 500 copies. Norman 5-L26 1978 $1,250

LEONARDO DA VINCI   I Manoscritti e i Disegni. Rome, 1941. Vol.
V, lg. folio, orig. wrs., uncut, fine copy, ltd. to 300 copies on special paper.
Norman 5-L29 1978 $450

LEONARDO DA VINCI   I Manoscritti e i Disegni. Rome, 1941. 2 parts,
lg. folio, mounted color plts., text in orig. wrs., uncut, plts. loose in portfolio,
text spine repaired, but fine set, ltd. to 500 copies on special paper, map. Norman 5-L30 1978 $750

LEONARDO DA VINCI   Notes Et Dessins Sur Le Coeur Et Sa Constitution
Anatomique Avec Quelques Details De L'Appareil Respiratoire... Paris, 1901.
Folio, facsimile reproduc. on blue paper tipped in, orig. prtd. bds., backed in
grey linen, slightly dust-soiled, fine copy, ltd. to 100 copies. Zeitlin 245-307
1978 $200

LEONARDO DA VINCI   Le Opere Scientifiche. Naples, 1885. 8vo.,
orig. prtd. wrs., uncut, pres. copy. Norman 5-L6 1978 $35

LEONARDO DA VINCI   Raccolta Vinciana. Milan, 1905-39. Fasicules
1-16 in 12 vols., illus., orig. prtd. wrs., very good set. Norman 5-L12 1978
$150

LEONARDO DA VINCI   Traite de la Peinture. Paris, 1716. 8vo., ads,
frontis., plts., contemp. calf, gilt, rubbed, very good copy, 2nd French ed.
Norman 5-L1 1978 $125

LEONARDO DA VINCI   Traite de la Peinture. Paris, (c. 1910). Lg.
8vo., illus., orig. prtd. wrs., uncut, very good copy. Norman 5-L15 1978
$45

LEONARDO DA VINCI   Traite du Paysage Traduit. Paris, (c. 1910).
Lg. 8vo., illus., orig. prtd. wrs., uncut, very good copy. Norman 5-L16 1978
$45

LEONARDO DA VINCI   Trattato Della Pittura. Florence, 1792. 4to.,
etchings after drawings by Stefano Della Bella, orig. limp bds., uncut, very fine
copy, 1st Della Bella ed. Norman 5-L3 1978 $450

LEONARDO DA VINCI   Trattato Della Pittura. Milan, 1804. 8vo.,
plts., half antique calf, gilt, uncut, very light dampstaining in edge of outer margin of first few leaves, but fine copy. Norman 5-L4 1978 $300

LEONARDO DA VINCI   Tratto Della Pittura. Milan, 1859. 8vo.,
frontis., plts., contemp. half mor., gilt, slightly rubbed, but fine copy. Norman
5-L5 1978 $175

LEONARDO DA VINCI   A Treatise of Painting. London, 1721. 8vo.,
ads, frontis. portr., copperplts., contemp. calf, gilt, rebacked, little rubbed, fine
copy, 1st ed., in English. Norman 5-L2 1978 $475

LEONARDO DA VINCI   La Vita di Giorgio Vasari Nuovamente Commen-
tata. Florence, 1919. Folio, illus., orig. bds., uncut, very good copy, ltd. to
500 numbered copies. Norman 5-L21 1978 $50

LEONARDUS MATTHAEI DE UTINO   Amina Fidelis. Paris, 1507. 8vo., 1/2
calf over marbled bds., label, binding new. Salloch 348-115 1978 $175

LEONG, Y. S.   Silver. 1933. Ex-lib. Austin 80-788 1978
$12.50

LEONI, J.   Leone Leoni, Sculpteur de Charles--Quint et
Pompeo Leoni, Sculpteur de Phillippe II... 1887. Sm. folio, plts., facs. letters,
fine copy, half red mor., gilt spine. Quaritch 983-209 1978 $75

LEONORA. 1745. 2 vols., 12mo., old qtr. calf, backs repaired, orig. marbled
sides, title and two next leaves of Vol. I, and title of Vol. II, browned and age-
soiled, rare. P. M. Hill 142-190 1978 £70

LE PAGE DU PRATZ, M.   Historie De La Louisane:.... Paris, 1758. 3
vols., folding maps and plates, contemp. mottled calf, gilt, morocco label, 1st ed.
Jenkins 116-818 1978 $475

L'EPEE, CHARLES MICHEL DE   La Veritable Maniere d'Instruire les Sourds et
Muets, Conf rmee par une Longue Experience. Paris, 1784. Fldg. table, 12mo.,
contemp. calf, worn, hinges split. Offenbacher 30-83 1978 $175

LE PRINCE DE BEAUMONT, JEANNE MARIE   Lettres de Madame Du Montier....
Lyon, 1780. Half-titles, 2 vols., lg. 12mo, contemp. calf, gilt, binding worn,
sound, very good copy. Fenning 32-194 1978 £12.50

LEPROHON, ROSANNA ELEANOR   Antoinette de Mirecourt. Montreal, 1864.
Orig. buckram soiled. Wolfe 39-311 1978 $75

LEPSIUS, R.   Discoveries in Egypt, Ethiopia, and the Peninsula of Sinai, 1842-54... 1852. Map, tinted litho. frontis., orig. cloth, 8vo.
Edwards 1012-221 1978 £30

LE QUEUX, WILLIAM   The Broken Thread. London, 1916. 1st
ed., frontispiece, very good or better. Limestone 9-175 1978 $20

LE QUEUX, WILLIAM   Her Majesty's Minister. 1901. Plts., pict.
cloth, very good, first English ed. Bell Book 16-557 1978 £8.50

LE QUEUX, WILLIAM   The Hunchback of Westminster. 1904. Pict.
cloth, good, first English ed. Bell Book 16-558 1978 £8.50

LERNER, ABBA P.   The Economics of Control. 1944. Austin 80-
789 1978 $11

LERNER, MAX   Public Journal. 1945. Austin 80-180 1978
$10

LEROND D'ALEMBERT, JEAN
Please turn to
ALEMBERT, JEAN LEROND D'

LE ROSSIGNOL, J. E.   Little Stories of Quebec. Cincinnati, 1908.
Illus. Hood 116-485 1978 $12.50

LEROUX, GABRIEL   Les Origines de l'Edifice Hypostyle en Grece, en
Orient et Chez les Romains. Paris, 1913. Illus., wrs., unopened. Biblo BL781-
425 1978 $17.50

LEROUX, JOSEPH   Collector's Vade Mecum. Montreal, 1885.
Orig. binding. Wolfe 39-401 1978 $25

LEROUX, JOSEPH   Supplement to the Canadian Coin Cabinet.   Montreal, (1890). Printed wrappers.   Wolfe 39-400 1978 $30

LEROY, ALFRED   Evolution de l'Art Antique. Egypte-Asie-Occidentale--Grece et Rome.   Paris, (1945). Illus., wrs.   Biblo BL781-426 1978 $10

LE ROY, JULIEN DAVID   Les Navires Des Anciens.   Paris, 1883. 8vo., half calf. F. Edwards 1013-133 1978 £65

LEROY, LOUIS   De La Vicissitude Et Variete Des Choses En L'Univers...   Paris, 1584. Thick 8vo., vellum.   Salloch 348-116 1978 $550

LE ROY, LOYS   Les Politiques d'Aristote, Esquelles est monstree la science de gouvernor le genre humain en toutes especes d'estats publique. Paris, 1576. Folio , very fine copy, orig. contemp. gilt calf binding (hinges repaired).   Schafer 19-24 1978 sFr. 1,100

LE SAGE, ALAIN RENE   Les Avantures de Gil Blas de Santillane.   Londres, 1749. 4 vols., 12mo, 32 eng. plts., 1/2 leather, w.a.f., nouvelle ed.   Eaton 45-293 1978 £10

LE SAGE, ALAIN RENE   The Adventures of Gil Blas of Santillane. London, 1774. 2 vols., 21 eng. plts., generally browned, 1/2 calf, rebacked, preserving orig. spines, red lettering pieces.   Eaton 45-294 1978 £10

LE SAGE, ALAIN RENE   Gil Blas Von Santillana.   Berlin, 1798. 2 vols., 4 eng., contemp calf, rubbed, spines gilt.   Eaton 45-292 1978 £10

LE SAGE, ALAIN RENE   Adventuras de Gil Blas de Santillana. 1809. Thk. 12mo., 4 vols. in 1, contemp. half calf.   Howes 194-361 1978 £12.50

LE SAGE, ALAIN RENE   The Adventures of Gil Blas de Santillane. 1819. Coloured engravings, 3 vols., calf, rubbed, neatly rebacked, 8vo.   George's 635-1363 1978 £37.50

LE SAGE, ALAIN RENE   The Adventures of Gil Blas de Santillane.   Edinburgh, 1886. Illus., 3 vols., roy. 8vo.   George's 635-1364 1978 £8.50

LE SAGE, ALAIN RENE   The Bachelor of Salamanca. 1737. Plts., sm. 8vo., contemp. calf.   Howes 194-362 1978 £12

LE SAGE, ALAIN RENE   The Devil upon Two Sticks. 1772. 12mo., contemp. sheep, hinge worn, frontispiece.   P. M. Hill 142-191 1978 £15

LE SAGE, ALAIN RENE   Le Diable Boiteaux... 1708. Frontis, engraving, contemp. panelled calf, later rebacked, 1st. English ed.   Eaton 45-296 1978 £75

LE SAGE, ALAIN RENE   Le Diable Boiteux. 1741. Seventh ed., plts., 2 vols., 12mo., contemp. calf gilt.   Howes 194-363 1978 £15

LE SAGE, ALAIN RENE   Le Diable boiteux. 1751. Engraved plts., 2 vols. in 1, 18mo., old sheep.   George's 635-1362 1978 £7.50

LESAGE, L. E.   Paris au XIX eme Siecle et a la Fin du XVIIIeme... Costumes, Scenes et Elegances Parisiennes.   Paris, 1907. Elephant folio, plts., portfolio.   Quaritch 983-66 1978 $3,500

LESCARBOT, MARC   Nova Francia, a Description of Acadia, 1606. New York and London, 1928.   Hood 116-226 1978 $50

LESEBUCH, oder Sammlung von Leseubungen fur die Untern Klassen der Deutschen Schulen. Cincinnati, 1848. Bds.   Hayman 72-382 1978 $15

LESLIE, C.   A New History of Jamaica... 1740. 1st. ed., folding maps, old style panelled calf, 8vo., text slightly browned.   Edwards 1012-726 1978 £150

LESLIE, ELIZA   Pencil Sketches, or Outlines of Character & Manners. Philadelphia, 1833. 1st ed., rubbed, inner joints weak, orig. binding, 8vo.   Americanist 101-78 1978 $30

LESLIE, ELIZA   Seventy-Five Receipts for Pastry, Cakes, & Sweetmeats. By a Lady of Philadelphia. Boston, 1829. Orig. cloth, worn, moderate stains in text, complete copy, 8vo.   Americanist 101-79 1978 $40

LESLIE, FRANK   On the Road. New York, 1893. Illus., 2 vols. in 1, 8vo., tall 8vo., orig. wrs., wrs. slightly torn.   Morrill 239-471 1978 $10

LESLIE, FRANK   There's a Spot in My Heart. 1947. Illus., first ed., d.j., inscribed by author. Austin 82-553 1978 $12.50

LESLIE, FRANK   There's a Spot in My Heart. New York, 1947. Illus., 12mo., 1st ed., author's signed pres., very good, d.w. Biblo BL781-1046 1978 $10

LESLIE, JOHN   A Short Account of Experiments and Instruments, depending on the relations of Air to Heat and Moisture. Edinburgh, 1813. 8vo., orig. bds., rebacked, uncut, plt., first ed. Gurney 75-67 1978 £40

LESLIE, K. H.   Historical Records of the Family of Leslie from 1067 to 1868-9. Edinburgh, 1869. 3 vols., spines faded, orig. cloth, 8vo. K Books 244-191 1978 £30

LESLIE, JOHN RANDOLPH SHANE   The Cantab. 1926. 1st ed., cr. 8vo., spine dull. George's 635-1324 1978 £5

LESLIE, JOHN RANDOLPH SHANE   Jutland, a Fragment of Epic. 1930. 1st ed., 8vo., orig. pale blue cloth, spine faded, pres. copy to Winston Churchill. Sawyer 298-90 1978 £85

LESLIE, JOHN RANDOLPH SHANE   The Skull of Swift: An Extempore Exhumation. Indianapolis, 1928. 1st ed., plts., orig. cloth-backed bds., pres. copy with unsigned holograph inscr. by author, 8vo. Howes 194-1241 1978 £7.50

LESLIE, ROBERT C.   A Sea Painter's Log. London, 1886. 8vo., orig. cloth, fine, uncut, illus. Paine 78-82 1978 $45

LESLIE, ROBERT C.   A Waterbiography. London, 1894. 8vo., orig. cloth, good, plts. Paine 78-83 1978 $27.50

LESPINASSE, P.   Le Miniature en France au XVIIIe Siecle. Paris and Brussels, 1929. 4to., plts., buckram. Quaritch 983-210 1978 $150

LESSING, DORIS   The Grass is Singing. 1950. Very good, d.w., first English ed. Bell Book 17-564 1978 £20

LESSIUS, LEONARDUS   Hygiasticon. 1742. 8vo., contemp. half calf, decor. Dutch-paper sides. P. M. Hill 142-170 1978 £38

LESSNER, ERWIN   Blitzkrieg and Bluff. 1943. Austin 80-181 1978 $10

LESTER, CHARLES EDWARDS   Life and Public Services of Charles Sumner. New York, 1874. Illus., 8vo., orig. cloth, 1st ed., nice. Morrill 241-283 1978 $10

LESTER, CHARLES EDWARDS   The Life of Sam Houston. New York, 1855. 1st ed., illus., maps, some wear to spine and corners. Jenkins 116-683 1978 $25

LESTER, CHARLES EDWARDS   The Life of Sam Houston. Philadelphia, 1867. Illus. Jenkins 116-684 1978 $35

LESTER, CHARLES EDWARDS   Sam Houston and His Republic. New York, 1846. Engraved frontis., protrait of Houston, half calf, 1st ed. Jenkins 116-1581 1978 $250

LESTER, PAUL   The True Story of the Galveston Flood as Told by Survivors... Philadelphia, 1900. 1st ed., illus., gilt edges, extremely fine. Jenkins 116-484 1978 $25

L'ESTRANGE, HAMON 1605-60   The Reign of King Charles. 1655. First ed., portrait vignette, sm. folio, contemp. calf, neatly rebacked, orig. label preserved, some light dampstaining. Howes 194-28 1978 £55

L'ESTRANGE, ROGER   Seneca's Morals by Way of Abstracts. 1775. Plts., 12mo., contemp. calf, joints weak. Howes 194-451 1978 £12.50

LE SUEUR, PHILLIP   Tables Showing the Interest at 6, 7 & 8 per cent, on any Sum from 1 to 10,000 Dollars in a Comprehensive Series of Days, Months and Years. Quebec, 1857. Orig. binding, joint cracked, backstrip chipped. Wolfe 39-312 1978 $45

LETAROUILLY, PAUL MARIE Edifices de Rome Moderne, ou Recueil des Palais, Maisons, Eglises, Couvents...de la Ville de Rome. Washington, n.d. 4to., 3 vols, plts., 1840 reprint, binding worn, hinges sprung. Biblo BL781-545 1978 $75

LETCHER, OWEN Big Game Hunting in North-Eastern Rhodesia. London, 1911. Map, portrait, 52 illus., 8vo, orig. cloth, slightly shaken, spine faded. K Books 239-264 1978 £20

LETHABY, W. R. Londinium. Architecture and the Crafts. New York, 1924. Illus. Biblo BL781-427 1978 $12.50

LETHERIDGE, MELVIN W. Montgomery County, N. Y. Marriage Records Performed by Rev. Elijah Herrick...Rev. Calvin Herrick...Rev. John Calvin Toll. 1930-35. Index, wrs., very good. Butterfield 21-277e 1978 $8

LETI, GREGORIO Il Cardinalismo della Santa Chiesa. (Geneva), 1668. 3 vols., 12mo., shell patterned bds., cloth spine gilt, very good, first ed., rare. King 7-55 1978 £65

L'ETRURIA Pittrice, ovvero Storia della Pittura Toscana, Dedotta dai Suoi Monumenti... Flroence, 1791-1795. Folio, 2 vols., frontis., contemp. half calf, lightly rubbed, 1st ed. Gilhofer 74-37 1978 sFr 2,400

LETT, LEWIS Papua, Its People and Its Promise--Past and Future. Melbourne, 1944. Illus., cloth in d.w., bit worn, paper yellowed, signed presentation of Evan R. Gill. Dawson's 127-272 1978 $10

A LETTER Concerning the Disabling Clauses Lately Offered to the House of Commons, for regulating Corporations. 1690. 4to., unbound, very good. P. M. Hill 142-9 1978 £38

A LETTER From the Lady Creswell to Madam C. The Midwife, on the Publishing Her Late Vindication. N.P., n.d. (1680). First ed., folio, disbound. Hannas 54-47b 1978 £18

LETTER on the Use and Abuse of Incorporations, Addressed to the Delegation of the City of New-York, in the State Legislature, by One of Their Constituents. New York, 1827. Uncut, orig. prtd. wr., very good. Butterfield 21-514 1978 $12.50

A LETTER signed A. L. from a French Lawyer to an English Gentleman, Upon the Present Revolution. 1689. Sm. 4to., disbound. Howes 194-53 1978 £20

A LETTER to a Member of Parliament, concerning Guards and Garisons. 1699. 4to., unbound. P. M. Hill 142-10 1978 £15

A LETTER to an Honourable Brigadier General, Commander in Chief of His Majesty's Forces in Canada. London, 1760. Errata. Hood 116-132 1978 $250

A LETTER To His Majesty's Ministers on the Cause of the Present Distress of the Country With Proposed Remedies by a Merchant. 1830. 1st. ed., orig. grey wrappers, fine. Jarndyce 16-261 1978 £14.50

A LETTER to William Paley from a poor Labourer, in answer to his Reason for Contentment.... 1793. 8vo., unbound, scarce. P.M. Hill 142-201 1978 £45

A LETTER to Wm. Smith in Answer to His Address to the People of I. Dublin, 1799. 1st ed., plain wrs. Hyland 128-290 1978 £8

LETTERE Sopra A. Cornelio Celso al Celebre Abate Girolamo Tiraboschi. Roma, 1779. 8vo., decor. bds., soiled, vellum spine wormed, tall uncut copy. King 7-181 1978 £20

LETTERS from America 1776-1779. Boston, 1924. 1st ed., ltd. to 450 copies, cloth. MacManus 239-594 1978 $35

LETTERS From Golden Latitudes. (St. Paul, 1885). Wrps., narrow strip cut from bottom of both front & back wrapper, not affecting printing. Hayman 71-416 1978 $25

LETTERS Intercepted on Board the Admiral Aplin, Captured by the French, and Inserted by the French Government in the Moniteur.... 1804. New buckram, edges uncut. George's 635-695 1978 £10.50

LETTERS of Charlotte, during her Connection with Werter. 1813. Engraved frontis., fcap. 8vo., orig. bds. George's 635-1365 1978 £5

LETTERS, Poems, and Tales: Amorous, Satirical and Gallant, Which Passed between Several Persons of Distinction. 1718. 8vo., unbound, some browning and staines. P. M. Hill 142-291 1978 £160

LETTERS to a Young Nobleman. 1762. 8vo., contemp. calf, fine, errata leat at end, first ed. P. M. Hill 142-163 1978 £48

LETTRES Au R. P. Parrenin, Jesuite, Missionnaire a Pekin... Paris, 1770. Contemp. calf, uncut, cover worn, some worming, 8vo. Edwards 1012-194 1978 £35

LETTS, C. HUBERT The Hundred Best Pictures. London, 1901. Half mor. gilt, tipped-in sepia plts., folio. K Books 244-192 1978 £5

LEURET, FRANCOIS Du Traitement Moral de la Folie. Paris, 1840. 8vo., old qtr. shagreen, signed pres. copy, first ed. Gurney 75-68 1978 £45

LE VAILLANT, FRANCOIS Travels Into The Interior Parts of Africa... 1790. 2 vols., 1st. English ed., engraved plts., contemp. half calf, rebacked, some foxing, sm. hole in text of one pg., 8vo. Edwards 1012-301 1978 £150

LE VAILLANT, FRANCOIS Travels Into The Interior Parts of Africa... Perth, 1791. 2 vols. in 1, folding frontispieces, engraved plts., 12mo, contemp. calf gilt, one plt. repaired, some shaved. Edwards 1012-302 1978 £45

LEVATI, AMBROGIO Viaggi di Francesco Petrarca in Francia in Germania ed in Italia. Milano, 1820. 5 vols., 8vo., paper wrappers, uncut, first ed. King 7-182 1978 £25

LEVEN, MAURICE America's Capacity to Consume. 1934. Austin 80-790 1978 $10

LEVEQUE, CHARLES DE ST. Savinien. Montpellier, 1853. Disbound, 8vo. Paine 78-84 1978 $18.50

LEVER, CHARLES Barrington. 1863. 1st. ed., frontis, 24 plts. by H.K. Browne, some slight spotting, 1/2 morocco, edges rubbed. Eaton 45-299 1978 £9

LEVER, CHARLES Charles O'Malley, Harry Lorrequer, Arthur O'Leary, Jack Hinton, and Tom Burke of "Ours". Boston, 1891-92. Uniformly bound set of 9 vols., 8vo., t.e.g., engr. frontis., tissue guards, bound in 3/4 crushed green levant faded to brown at spines with marbled bds. & endpapers, raised bands & gilt decor's, near mint set, no sign of wear. Current 24-30 1978 $100

LEVER, CHARLES Davenport Dunn, A Man of Our Day. Philadelphia, 1859. Orig. paper wrs., with statement on front cover "From Advance Sheets Purchased from Author", illus. by Phiz, edges worn, interior damp staining, good. Greene 78-73 1978 $85

LEVER, CHARLES Davenport Dunn. A Man of Our Day. London, 1859. Illus. by Phiz, thick 8vo., orig. cloth, 1st ed., spine faded, very nice. MacManus 238-317 1978 $75

LEVER, CHARLES Diary & Notes of Horace Templeton Esq. 1849. 2nd. ed., 2 vols., half titles, orig. green cloth, blocked in blind, very fine. Jarndyce 16-812 1978 £22

LEVER, CHARLES The Dodd Family Abroad. London, Chapman & Hall, 1872. 8vo, orig. cloth, illus. by H. K. Browne, good. Sexton 7-155 1978 £5

LEVER, CHARLES The Fortunes of Glencore. London, 1857. 3 vols., orig. cloth, 1st ed., covers a bit soiled, otherwise very good. MacManus 238-316 1978 $100

LEVER, CHARLES Jack Hinton The Guardsman. Dublin, 1843. 1st ed., frontis., plates by Phiz, all plates present but oxidized, bound in full contemp. claf lacks one inch off top of spine, hinge starting. Greene 78-250 1978 $20

LEVER, CHARLES Luttrell of Arran. 1865. 1st. ed., illus. by Phiz, half calf, marbled bds., fine. Jarndyce 16-813 1978 £34

LEVER, CHARLES Our Mess. Dublin, 1843-4. 1st. ed., 3 vols., frontis portrait & illus. by Phiz, half green morocco, little rubbed. Jarndyce 16-809 1978 £25

LEVER, CHARLES Roland Cashel. 1850. Plt., very good, half leather, first English ed. Bell Book 16-560 1978 £10

LEVER, CHARLES Roland Cashel. London, 1858. Plum ripple grain cloth, blocked in blind front & back, lettered in gold on spine, 38 plates by Phiz, damaged spine. Greene 78-74 1978 $30

LEVER, CHARLES   St. Patrick's Eve. 1845. 1st. ed., illus. by Phiz, orig. green cloth, little dulled, some foxing to plts. Jarndyce 16-811 1978 £18

LEVER, CHARLES   Tales of the Trains... Dublin, 1845. 1st. ed., illus. by Phiz, green morocco, spine gilt, fine. Jarndyce 16-810 1978 £45

LEVER, CHARLES JAMES   Charles O'Malley, the Irish Dragoon. n.d., (1840s). 2 vols., 8vo, illus. by Phiz, engraved titles, plts., many foxed, binder's cloth, inscribed by author. Hannas 54-204 1978 £20

LEVER, CHARLES JAMES   The Confessions of Harry Lorrequer. Dublin, 1839. 1st. ed., 8vo, frontispiece, additional engraved title, plts., illus. by Phiz, little spotted, orig. green cloth, joints splitting loose, uncut. Hannas 54-205 1978 £30

LEVER, DARCY   The Young Officer's Sheet Anchor... Boston, 1930. 4to., illus., ltd. to 500 copies, reprint of 1819 ed., orig. cloth, some staining. MacManus 239-1764 1978 $25

LEVER, DARCY   The Young Sea Officer's Sheet Anchor... Boston, 1938. 4to., orig. cloth, good. Paine 78-85 1978 $35.00

LEVER, HARRY   Wartime Racketeers. 1945. Austin 80-182 1978 $10

LEVERING, JOSEPH M.   A History of Bethlehem, Panna, 1741-1802. With Some Account of Its Founders... Bethlehem, 1903. Illus., 4to., maps, scarce. MacManus 239-1534 1978 $75

LEVESON GOWER, ELIZABETH   Views in Orkney and on the North Eastern Coast of Scotland. N.P., (1807?). Lg. paper, etchings, folio, contemp. grained green calf, blind-embossed cathedral style. K Books 244-193 1978 £48

LEVESQUE, PIERRE CHARLES   Pensees Morales De Divers Auteurs Chinois... Dresden, 1786. 8vo., contemp. marbled bds., paper label. Salloch 348-33 1978 $50

LEVI BEN GERSON, RALBAG-GERSONIDES   Peirush Al Ha 'Torah. Venice, 1547. Second ed., title soiled and detached, some waterstaining, folio, contemp. blind-stamped calf over wooden bds., binding very worn, one cover detached, the other defective. Thomas 37-23 1978 £475

LEVIN, PETER R.   Seven by Chance. New York, 1948. Biblo 251-85 1978 $15

LEVINGE, R. G. A.   Historical Records of the Forty-Third Regiment.... 1868. Roy. 8vo., orig. cloth, repaired, coloured frontis. F. Edwards 1013-515 1978 £40

LEVINGTON, JOHN   The Law of Thought. Dayton, 1872. Cloth. Hayman 73-384 1973 $7.50

LEVINS, PETER   Manipulus Vocabulorum... 1937. Octavo, good. Upcroft 10-102 1978 £7.50

LEVIS, HOWARD C.   A Descriptive Bibliography....Relating to The Art and History of Engraving and the Collecting of Prints. London, 1913 and 1912. Thick 4to., fine. Battery 1-476 1978 $275

LEVY, H.   Monopolies, Cartels and Trusts in British Industries. 1927. 8vo. George's 635-353 1978 £5

LEVY, S. J.   Chester, N.Y. a History. Chester, 1947. Newspaper clipping & postcard laid in. Butterfield 21-333 1978 $10

LEW, IRVING   Auction Record of the Limited Editions Club Publications. New York, 1949. Wr. Battery Park 1-400 1978 $12.50

LEW, IRVING   A Catalogue of Books & Pamphlets & Ephemera Relating to Bookplates in English, French, Swedish, Italian, Polish, Japanese, Spanish, German, etc. Very fine. Battery Park 1-297 1978 $10

LEWINSOHN, RICHARD   Barney Barnato. London, 1937. 8 plts., 8vo, orig. cloth, covers shabby. K Books 239-266 1978 £5

LEWIS, A. VIRGIL   History of the Battle of Point Pleasant Fought Between White Men and Indians at the Mouth of the Great Kanawha River. Charlestown, 1909. Illus. MacManus 239-595 1978 $20

LEWIS, ALFRED HENRY   A Wolfville Thanksgiving. New York, 1897. 1st ed., very good or better. Limestone 9-176 1978 $15

LEWIS, BERNARD   Land of Enchanters. London, (1948). Illus. Biblo 247-925 1978 $12.50

LEWIS, BRANSFORD   Cystoscopy and Urethroscopy for General Practitioners. Philadelphia, 1915. Rittenhouse 49-469 1976 $10

LEWIS, BRANSFORD   History of Urology. Volume I and Volume II. Baltimore, 1933. Rittenhouse 49-467 1976 $75

LEWIS, BRANSFORD   History of Urology. Volume I and II. Baltimore, 1933. Library marks. Rittenhouse 49-468 1976 $65

LEWIS, C. S.   That Hideous Strength. 1945. Good, first English ed. Bell Book 16-561 1978 £6.50

LEWIS, CECIL DAY   Please turn to DAY-LEWIS, CECIL

LEWIS, DIO   Talks About People's Stomachs. Boston, 1870. 8vo., 1st ed. Morrill 239-156 1978 $17.50

LEWIS, DOMINIC BEVAN WYNDHAM   Four Favourites. New York, 1949. 1st Amer. ed. Biblo 247-705 1978 $12.50

LEWIS, DOMINIC BEVAN WYNDHAM   I Couldn't Help Laughing! London, 1941. 1st ed., illus., very good or better. Limestone 9-177 1978 $17.50

LEWIS, EDWARD R.   A History of American Political Thought from the Civil War to the World War. New York, 1937. Cloth, 1st ed. Hayman 73-385 1973 $7.50

LEWIS, ESTELLE ANNA   Records of the Heart, and Other Poems. London, New York, 1866. Special gilt edged ed., illus., excellent. Nestler Rare 78-42 1978 $20

LEWIS, GEORGE CORNEWALL   An Essay on the Government of Dependencies. London, 1841. 8vo, original green cloth, printed paper label, 1st ed., author's own copy, signed and annotated throughout, six-page A.l.s. from Lewis laid-in. Ximenes 47-179 1978 $200

LEWIS, GEORGE GRIFFIN   The Practical Book of Oriental Rugs. Philadelphia, 1913. Coloured plts., illus., new ed., sq. 8vo. George's 635-258 1978 £18

LEWIS, GEORGE HENRY   Problems of Life and Mind. 1874-5-7. Vol. 1 3rd ed., vol. 2- 1st. ed., vol. 3 - 1st. ed., orig. brown cloth, little rubbed, good. Jarndyce 16-815 1978 £24

LEWIS, GEORGE M.   An Introduction to Medical Mycology. Chicago, 1939. D.j. Rittenhouse 49-470 1976 $20

LEWIS, H. A.   Hidden Treasures. Cleveland, 1892. Cloth, slight wear. Hayman 73-387 1973 $8.50

LEWIS, H. C.   Bazilwlogia. Chiswick Press, 1913. Facsimiles, 8vo., engr. English Royal portrs., 1 of 300 copies prtd. on Japan vellum, bound in buff bds. Battery Park 1-145 1978 $100

LEWIS, JANE   Narrative of the Captivity and Providential Escape of Mrs. Jane Lewis, Who, With a Son and Daughter and an Infant Babe,.... New York, 1833. Woodcut plate, original pictorial printed wr., 1st ed. Ginsberg 14-479 1978 $300

LEWIS, JOHN L.   The Miners Fight for American Standard, by Pres. of the United Mine Workers of America. 1925. Port., good. Nestler Rare 78-43 1978 $15

LEWIS, JOSEPH   The Bible Unmasked. 1926. Austin 79-435 1978 $8.50

LEWIS, LLOYD   Captain Sam Grant. Boston, 1950. 1st ed., fine, d.w. Biblo 248-21 1978 $16.50

LEWIS, LLOYD   It Takes All Kinds. 1947. First ed., d.j. Austin 82-555 1978 $11

LEWIS, LLOYD   Letters from...Showing Steps in the Research for his Biography of U. S. Grant. Boston, 1950. First ed. Biblo 247-22 1978 $16.50

LEWIS, MATTHEW GREGORY   The Castle Spectre. Boston, (1798). 12mo., unbound, orig. cloth, lst Amer. ed. Morrill 241-284 1978 $20

LEWIS, MATTHEW GREGORY   The Castle Spectre: A Drama. Dublin, 1798. lst. Irish ed., 12mo, wrapper, few catchwords touched, nice copy. Fenning 32-195 1978 £10.50

LEWIS, MATTHEW GREGORY   Journal of a Residence Among the Negroes in the West Indies, 1815-17. 1845. Sm. 8vo, contemp. half leather, rebacked. Edwards 1012-727 1978 £18

LEWIS, MATTHEW GREGORY   The Monk. 1796. 3 vols., sm. 8vo, one gathering sprung, lib. stamp on titles, tree calf rebacked in tan morocco, lib. crest at foot of spine. Eaton 45-302 1978 £30

LEWIS, MATTHEW GREGORY   The Monk: A Romance. London, 1797. 3 vols., full calf, leather labels, a.e.g., 3rd ed., 3rd issue, spines faded, slightly worn along edges, otherwise very good. MacManus 238-130 1978 $125

LEWIS, MATTHEW GREGORY   Tales of Wonder. Dublin, 1805. Half red morocco, marbled bds., good. Jarndyce 16-816 1978 £36

LEWIS, MERIWETHER   Travels in the Interior Parts of America... 1807. Modern half calf, slight spotting on few pages, folding table, 8vo. Edwards 1012-502 1978 £60

LEWIS, ORLANDO FAULKLAND   The Development of American Prisons and Prison Customs 1776-1845. (Albany, 1922). Butterfield 21-356 1978 $27.50

LEWIS, OSCAR   The Big Four. New York, 1938. Cloth, signed by author, shabby dust jacket. Hayman 73-385 1973 $7.50

LEWIS, OSCAR   Sea Routes to the Gold Fields... New York, 1949. Illus., fold. map, 1st ed. MacManus 239-1937 1978 $12.50

LEWIS, OSCAR   Sea Routes to the Gold Fields. New York, (1949). Map, illus., first ed., d.w. Biblo 247-237 1978 $16.50

LEWIS, PERCY WYNDHAM
Please turn to
LEWIS, WYNDHAM

LEWIS, SINCLAIR   Babbitt. 1922. Illus. Austin 82-557 1978 $10

LEWIS, SINCLAIR   Bethel Merriday. New York, 1940. 1st ed. Biblo BL781-1048 1978 $7.50

LEWIS, SINCLAIR   Cass Timberlane. 1945. Austin 82-558 1978 $7.50

LEWIS, SINCLAIR   Dodsworth. Toronto, 1929. First Canadian ed. Austin 82-1173 1978 $17.50

LEWIS, SINCLAIR   Free Air. 1919. First ed. Austin 82-559 1978 $27.50

LEWIS, SINCLAIR   Gideon Planish. 1943. First ed., d.j. Austin 82-561 1978 $12.50

LEWIS, SINCLAIR   Gideon Planish. 1943. First ed. Austin 82-562 1978 $10

LEWIS, SINCLAIR   The God Seeker. 1949. First ed. Austin 82-563 1978 $8.50

LEWIS, SINCLAIR   The God Seeker. 1949. Blue-green cloth, first ed., d.j. Austin 82-564 1978 $12.50

LEWIS, SINCLAIR   It Can't Happen Here. 1935. Dust jacket. Austin 82-566 1978 $10

LEWIS, SINCLAIR   Jayhawker. 1935. First ed., backstrip faded. Austin 82-586 1978 $17.50

LEWIS, SINCLAIR   The Job. 1917. 326 pages. Austin 82-568 1978 $27.50

LEWIS, SINCLAIR   Main Street. 1920. First ed., wear to extremities. Austin 82-570 1978 $25

LEWIS, SINCLAIR   Main Street. 1920. Frontis., movie ed., illus. Austin 82-571 1978 $12.50

LEWIS, SINCLAIR   Main Street. Chicago: for The Limited Editions Club, 1937. 4to., illus. by Grant Wood, orig. limp cloth, pub. box, 1 of 1,500 copies signed by illustrator, fine. MacManus 238-826 1978 $90

LEWIS, SINCLAIR   The Man Who Knew Coolidge. London, 1928. Austin 82-572 1978 $17.50

LEWIS, SINCLAIR   Martin Arrowsmith. London, 1925. Austin 82-573 1978 $10

LEWIS, SINCLAIR   Our Mr. Wrenn. 1914. Austin 82-574 1978 $22.50

LEWIS, SINCLAIR   Our Mr. Wrenn. The Romantic Adventures of a Gentle Man. New York, 1914. Orig. cloth, 1st ed., very nice. MacManus 238-697 1978 $75

LEWIS, SINCLAIR   The Prodigal Parents. 1938. First ed., d.j., very good. Austin 82-575 1978 $15

LEWIS, SINCLAIR   The Prodigal Parents. Garden City, 1938. Very good in chipped and worn dw. Bernard 5-164 1978 $8

LEWIS, SINCLAIR   The Prodigal Parents. 1938. Red cloth, first ed. Austin 82-576 1978 $11

LEWIS, SINCLAIR   Sam Dodsworth. Berlin, 1930. In German, first German ed., covers rubbed. Austin 82-579 1978 $27.50

LEWIS, SINCLAIR   Selected Short Stories of Sinclair Lewis. 1935. First ed., d.j., very good. no cover fading. Austin 82-580 1978 $37.50

LEWIS, SINCLAIR   Work of Art. 1934. First ed., d.j. Austin 82-581 1978 $12.50

LEWIS, SINCLAIR   Work of Art. 1934. First ed. Austin 82-582 1978 $8.50

LEWIS, THADDEUS   Autobiography of Thaddeus Lewis, a Minister of the Methodist Episcopal Church in Canada. Picton, 1865. Orig. purple cloth, frontis. port. Wolfe 39-316 1978 $150

LEWIS, THOMAS   Clinical Disorders of the Heart Beat. Chicago, 1925. Sixth ed. Rittenhouse 49-473 1976 $20

LEWIS, THOMAS   Clinical Electrocardiography. London, 1913. Rittenhouse 49-478 1976 $10

LEWIS, THOMAS   Diseases of the Heart. London, 1933. Fresh, clean. Rittenhouse 49-475 1976 $25

LEWIS, THOMAS   Diseases of the Heart, Described for Practitioners and Students. London, 1943. Third ed. Rittenhouse 49-476 1976 $15

LEWIS, THOMAS   Lectures on the Heart, Clinical Disorders of the Heart Beat.... London, 1913. Rittenhouse 49-477 1976 $15

LEWIS, THOMAS   The Mechanism and Graphic Registration of the Heart Beat. New York, 1921. 4to., illus., plts., some in color, orig. red cloth, very good copy, bkplts. of Drs. Emmet Field Horine & Carleton B. Chapman, lst Amer. ed. Zeitlin 245-149 1978 $85

LEWIS, THOMAS   Der Mechanismus Der Herzaktion Und Seine Klini-sche Pathologie. Wien und Leipzig, 1912. 4to., plts., plain wrs., frayed, very good, uncut copy, bkplts. of Drs. Emmet Field Horine & Carleton B. Chapman, lst German ed. Zeitlin 245-150 1978 $75

LEWIS, THOMAS   Pain. New York, 1941. Library markings. Rittenhouse 49-471 1976 $15

LEWIS, THOMAS   A Retrospect of the Moral and Religious State of Islington, During the Last 40 Years. 1842. Frontis, orig. maroon cloth, good. Jarndyce 16-822 1978 £7.50

LEWIS, THOMAS   These Seventy Years. London, c. 1923. Maps, illus., 8vo, orig. cloth. K Books 239-270 1978 £8

LEWIS, THOMAS   Vascular Disorders of the Limbs. New York, 1936. Rittenhouse 49-474 1976 $15

LEWIS, TRAV.   The NYA Resident Project at San Marcos, Texas. Austin, 1938. Wr. Jenkins 116-595 1978 $9.50

LEWIS, VIRGIL A.   History of the Battle of Point Pleasant Fought Between White Men and Indians at the Mouth of the Great Kanawha River... October 10th, 1774. Charleston, 1909. Cloth, covers little rubbed, minor spotting on fr. cover, pencil notes on back endpapers. Hayman 73-739 1978 $10

LEWIS, WILMARTH S.   Three Tours Through London in the Years 1748, 1776, 1797. 1941. First ed., plts., endpaper maps, 8vo, orig. cloth. Howes 194-1010 1978 £5.50

LEWIS, WYNDHAM   American and Cosmic Man. London, 1948. Mint in slightly rubbed d.w. Desmarais B-401 1978 $30

LEWIS, WYNDHAM   Beginnings. 1935. Very good, worn d.w., first English ed. Bell Book 17-567 1978 £10

LEWIS, WYNDHAM   The Childermass. Section I. London, 1928. Orig. cloth, d.j., 1st ed., fine. MacManus 238-698 1978 $60

LEWIS, WYNDHAM   The Enemy; Nos. 1-3. 1927-29. Coloured & b/w plts. by author, 3 vols., roy. 8vo, orig. pict. wraps, upper cover detached in Vol. I, internally very good, first English ed. Bell Book 17-568 1978 £65

LEWIS, WYNDHAM   Filibusters in Barbary. New York, 1932. First U.S. ed., plts., map, very good, worn d.w. Bell Book 17-569 1978 £42.50

LEWIS, WYNDHAM   Left Wings over Europe. 1936. Very good, first English ed. Bell Book 16-563 1978 £25

LEWIS, WYNDHAM   Men Without Art. 1934. Near fine, d.w., first English ed. Bell Book 16-564 1978 £42.50

LEWIS, WYNDHAM   Paleface. 1929. Spine soiled, good, first English ed. Bell Book 16-565 1978 £17.50

LEWIS, WYNDHAM   Tarr. 1918. Half-inch tear at head of spine, very good, signed by author, first English ed. Bell Book 16-566 1978 £85

LEWISOHN, LUDWIG   The Case of Mr. Crump. Paris, 1926. 4to., orig. printed wrs., somewhat soiled and worn, 1st ed., ltd. to 500 numbered copies, signed by author, very good. MacManus 238-699 1978 $40

LEYBOLD, E.   Nachfolger. Coln, n.d. (1904). Fine wood engrs., sm. folio, orig. prtd. cloth, 16-page pamphlet laid in, fine copy. Offenbacher 30-84 1978 $125

LEYCESTERS Commonwealth: Conceived, Spoken, and Published With Most Earnest Protestation of all Dutiful Good Will and Affection Towards this Realme. N.P., (London), 1641. 2 parts in I, sm. 8vo, portrait, old half roan, margin of I leaf burned, just touching side-note. Hannas 54-207 1978 £55

LEYCESTERS Common-wealth: Conceived, Spoken, and Published With Most Earnest Protestation of all Dutifull Good Will and Affection Towards this Realme. N.P., (London), 1641. 2 parts in I, sm. 8vo, lacking portrait, 19th century half morocco, titles rubricated, minor tears in 2 leaves. Hannas 54-208 1978 £28

LEYMARIE, J.   La Peinture Francaise. Geneve, n.d. Lg. 4to., cloth, slipcase, plts. in color. Van der Peet H-64-56 1978 Dfl 115

LEZIUS, MARTIN   Das Ehrenkleid des Soldaten. Berlin, 1936. Coloured plts., 4to., orig. cloth, repaired. F. Edwards 1013-347 1978 £55

LHOMME, G.   A travers le Tonkin: de Lang-Son a Cao-Bang. Rochefort, 1899. Plans, maps, 8vo, orig. covers. Van der Peet 127-132 1978 Dfl 45

L'HOSPITAL, GUILLAUME FRANCOIS ANTOINE, MARQUIS DE   The Method of Fluxions Both Direct and Inverse. London, 1730. 8vo., fold. tables, fine, contemp. tree calf, gilt borders & spine. Quaritch 977-160 1978 $200

LHUYD, E.   Archaeologia Britannica, I: Glossography. (1707). Reprint, octavo bound in cloth. Hyland 128-956 1978 £20

LI, PO   The Works of... New York, 1928. Biblo 251-9 1978 $12.50

LIBAVIUS, ANDREAS   Alchymia Triumphans. Frankfurt, 1607. 16mo., 17th cent. or 18th cent. vellum, v.g., first ed. Norman 5178 1978 $600

LIBAVIUS, ANDREAS   Antigramania. Frankfurt, 1595. 16mo., woodcut, 17th or 18th Cent. limp vellum, browned due to poor quality paper, old stamp, worming throughout, partially repaired, good copy, 1st ed. Norman 5-176 1978 $375

LIBAVIUS, ANDREAS   Defensio et Declaratio Perspicua Alchymiae Transmutatoriae... Ursellis, 1604. 16mo., 17th or 18th cent. vellum, browned, little worming, v.g., first ed. Norman 5-177 1978 $450

DE LIBERTAT: A Historical and Genealogical Review Comprising an Account of the Submission of the City of Marseilles in 1596 to the Authority of Henry of Navarre.... London, 1888. 4to, orig. cloth, ed. ltd. to 250 copies, engravings, 2 folding, good. Sexton 7-241 1978 £25

THE LIBERTY Bell, By Friends of Freedom. Boston, 1858. Engraved frontis, sm. 8vo, orig. cloth. Edwards 1012-503 1978 £15

LIBRETTO of the Beautiful Biblical Cantata of Queen Esther, Which Will be Presented at Mercantile Library Hall...Nov. 12 and 13 by the Esther Choral Society. St. Louis, 1880. 8vo., orig. wrs. Morrill 239-472 1978 $7.50

LICETI, FORTUNIO   De Luna Subobscura Luce Prope Coniunctiones, and in Eclipsibus Observata Libros Tres... Udine, 1642. 8vo., port. of author, contemp. limp vellum, lightly stained, 1st ed. Gilhofer 74-6 1978 sFr 1,250

LICHTENBERG, GEORG CHRISTOPH   Gesammelte Werke. Frankfurt, 1949. 2 vols., 8vo., cloth. Salloch 348-117 1978 $50

LICHTERVELDE, COMTE LOUIS DE   Leopold of the Belgians. London, (1928). Frontis, folding map, shaken, 8vo, orig. cloth, endpapers marked. K Books 239-271 1978 £6

LICHTMAN, S. S.   Diseases of the Liver, Gallbladder and Bile Ducts. Philadelphia, 1949. Rittenhouse 49-479 1976 $15

LICKLEY, I. D.   The Nervous System. London, 1931. New ed. Rittenhouse 49-480 1976 $15

LIDDELL HART, BASIL HENRY   The British Way in Warfare. 1932. 1st ed., 8vo., orig. cloth, spine faded, pres. copy to Winston Churchill. Sawyer 298-80 1978 £140

LIDDELL-HART, BASIL HENRY   The British Way in Warfare. 1933. Ex-lib., top & bottom of backstrip worn. Austin 80-183 1978 $10

LIDDELL-HART, BASIL HENRY   The Defense of Britain. 1939. Austin 80-184 1978 $17.50

LIDDELL-HART, BASIL HENRY   The Defence of Britain. 1939. 1st ed., 8vo., orig. cloth, pres. copy to Winston churchill. Sawyer 298-81 1978 £85

LIDDELL HART, BASIL HENRY   The Defence of Britain. 1939. First ed., 8vo., orig. cloth. F. Edwards 1013-328 1978 £15

LIDDELL HART, BASIL HENRY   Sherman. Soldier--Realist--American. New York, 1930. Illus., maps, orig. cloth, d.j., fine. MacManus 239-905 1978 $17.50

LIDDELL HART, BASIL HENRY   T. E. Lawrence, In Arabic and After. 1934. Portrait frontis., plts., maps, 8vo., orig. cloth, first ed. F. Edwards 1013-329 1978 £30

LIDDIARD, WILLIAM   Mont St. Jean, A Poem, by William Liddiard.
London, 1816. 8vo, disbound, 1st ed. Ximenes 47-180 1978 $30

LIE, SOPHUS   Vorlesungen uber Differentialgleichungen mit
bekannten Infinitesimalen Transofrmationen. Leipzig, 1891. 8vo., half-calf, 1st
ed. Gilhofer 74-118 1978 sFr 200

LIEBER, FRANCIS   Instructions for the Government of Armies of
the United States in the Field. NY, 1863. Wraps, Bell Wiley's copy. Broadfoot's
44-243 1978 $15.00

LIEBER, FRANCIS   No Party Now, But All for Our Country. Philadelphia, 1863. Orig. dec. wrs. Americanist 102-67a 1978 $8.50

LIEBER, FRANCIS   The Stranger in America... London, (1835).
2 vols. in 1, 1st Eng. ed., orig. cloth, top of spine worn. MacManus 239-256
1978 $40

LIEBERMANN, F.   The National Assembly in the Anglo-Saxon Period.
Halle, 1913. 8vo., wrs. Upcroft 12-267 1978 £4

LIEBIG, JUSTUS VON   Animal Chemistry, or Organic Chemistry in
Its Applications to Physiology and Pathology. London, 1842. 8vo., ads, orig.
cloth, uncut, slightly worn, but fine copy, 1st ed. in English. Norman 5-180
1978 $275

LIEBIG, JUSTUS VON   Chemische Briefe. Heidelberg, 1844. 8vo.,
orig. green cloth, lightly rubbed, 1st German ed., some light browning, otherwise
good. Gilhofer 74-119 1978 sFr 550

LIEBIG, JUSTUS VON   Der Chemische Process der Ernahrung der Vegeta-
bilien-Die Naturgesetze des Feldbaures. Brunswick, 1862. 2 vols., 8vo., orig.
cloth, spines faded, seventh German ed. Quaritch 977-113 1978 $225

LIEBIG, JUSTUS VON   Die Chemische Untersuchung Uber das Fleisch.
Heidelberg, 1847. 8vo., buckram, orig. wrs. bound in, very good copy, 1st ed.
Norman 5-181 1978 $125

LIEBIG, JUSTUS VON   Chimie Organique Appliquee a La Physiologie
Animale et a La Pathologie. Paris, 1842. 8vo., half black cloth, gilt lettering
on spine, light foxing, very good copy, 1st ed. in French. Zeitlin 245-151 1978
$175

LIEBIG, JUSTUS VON   Organic Chemisty in its Application to Agriculture and Physiology. London, 1840. 1st ed. in English, octavo, original cloth.
Bennett 20-121 1978 $250

LIEBIG, JUSTUS VON   Die Organische Chemie in Ihrer Anwendung auf
Agricultur und Physiologie. Braunschweig, 1840. 8vo., contemp. half calf,
gilt, little rubbed, sm. library stamp, but fine copy, 1st ed. Norman 5-179 1978
$850

LIEBIG, JUSTUS VON   Die Organische Chemise in ihre Anwendung auf
Physiologie und Pathologie. Brunswick, 1842. 8vo., blind stamp on title, waterstained at end, contemp. half roan, first ed. Quaritch 977-43 1978 $850

LIEBMANN, JOSHUA LOTH   Peace of Mind. New York, 1948. 8vo.,
cloth. Salloch 348-119 1978 $7.50

LIEUTAUD, JOSEPH   Essais Anatomiques, Contenant L'Histoire Exacte
de Toutes Les Parties qui Composent le corps de L'Homme.... Paris, 1742. 8vo.,
folding plts., few minor stains, contemp. calf, gilt, worn, first ed. Quaritch
977-44 1978 $450

LIFE MAGAZINE   Picture History of World War II. 1950. Austin
80-186 1978 $15

THE LIFE And Adventures of Martin Chuzzlewit. 1844. 1st. ed., illus. by Phiz,
half calf, spine gilt, blue label, fine. Jarndyce 16-510 1978 £60

THE LIFE and Enterprises of Robert William Elliston, Comedian. London, 1857.
Illus. by George Cruikshank and "Phiz." London, 1857. 12mo., orig. pict.
cloth, 1st ed., 2 vols., spine a little torn, but very good. MacManus 238-188
1978 $40

THE LIFE And Explorations of David Livingstone. London, c.1875. Coloured
frontis, title & 10 coloured plts., 4to, orig. dec. cloth, g.e., covers little dull,
new calf spine. K Books 239-279 1978 £7

THE LIFE And Explorations of David Livingstone Carefully Complied From Reliable
Sources. London, n.d.c. 1900. 4to, orig. leather backed bds., binding worn &
rubbed, sepia plts. Sexton 7-114 1978 £20

LIFE and Letters of Wilder Dwight. Boston, 1868. Bell Wiley's copy. Broadfoot
46-339 1978 $12

THE LIFE, Trial, Confession and Execution of Albert W. Hicks, the Pirate...
New York, 1860. 8vo., pr. wrs. bound in later bds., good, plts. Paine 78-65
1978 $32.50

THE LIFE History of the United States, Covers Years Prehistory-1917.   5 vols.
Bell Wiley's copy. Broadfoot 46-532 1978 $25

LIFE in a Man-of-War or Scenes in "Old Ironsides" During Her Cruise in the Pacific. Boston, 1927. 1st of this ed., illus., 4to., fine unopened copy, ltd. to
785 copies. MacManus 239-1794 1978 $45

LIFE In The Mofussil; or, the Civilian in Lower Bengal. Kegan Paul, c.1878.
Sole ed., 8vo, orig. cloth, few neat pencil notes, short tear in headband, inside
joints weak, very good copy. Fenning 32-196 1978 £14

THE LIFE Of David Hoggart, The Murderer Alias M'c Colgan, Alias Daniel O'Brian..
(1821). Folding coloured frontispiece, new bds., v.g. Jarndyce 16-257 1978 £18

LIFE of Joseph Green Cogswell as Sketched in His Letters. Cambridge, Riverside
Press, 1874. Frontis., 1 of 222 numbered copies, cloth. Battery Park 1-348 1978
$100

THE LIFE of Merlin, Sirnamed Ambrosivs. London, 1641. 1st ed., sm. 4to., 1st
issue, engr. frontis, early 19th Cent. pigskin, contemp. spine laid down, very
good. Current Misc. 8-23 1978 $600

LIFE of Michael Powers, Now Under Sentence of Death, for the Murder of Timothy
Kennedy. Boston, 1820. 8vo., sewn, outer leaves dust soiled, sm. dampstain,
1st ed., lacks plt. Morrill 239-473 1978 $7.50

THE LIFE of Saint David. Newtown, Gregynog Press, 1927. 4to., finely prtd.
in red, blue & black on handmade paper, coloured vellum, wood engrs., slipcase,
fine copy, 175 copies prtd. Quaritch 979-182 1978 $400

THE LIFE of Sir Walter Raleigh, From His Birth to His Death on the Scaffold. London, 1740. Rebound. Broadfoot 50-183 1978 $120

THE LIFE of Solitude of Francis Petrarch. Urbana, 1924. Tall 8vo., 1/2 cloth,
uncut. Salloch 348-191 1978 $35

THE LIFE of the Late Dr. Benjamin Franklin, Written by Himself. Middletown,
1823. Contemp. calf, worn and soiled. MacManus 239-147 1978 $20

LIFE Of The Late Thomas Coutts, Esq. n.d. (1822). 8vo, disbound, title dust-
soiled. Hannas 54-329 1978 £8

LIGHT, R.   Focus on Africa. New York, 1944. Large 8vo,
orig. cloth. Book Chest 17-230 1978 $25

LIGHTFOOT, JOHN   Flora Scotica. London, 1792. 2nd ed., 2 vols.
newly bound in 2-tone leatherette, plates, small hole in vol 1, 8vo. Book Chest
17-231 1978 $225

LIGHTHALL, W. D.   The False Chevalier. Montreal, 1898. Hood
117-527 1978 $12.50

LIGHTON, WILLIAM B.   Narrative of the Life and Suffering of a Young
British Captive;.... Concord, 1836. Rev'd. ed., engravings, orig. marbled
covers. Hood 116-133 1978 $75

LIGHTON, WILLIAM B.   Narrative of the Life and Sufferings of... Troy,
1846. Steel engrs., 12mo., orig. cloth. Morrill 241-285 1978 $7.50

LIGNAC, JOSEPH-ADRIEN LE LARGE   Lettres a Un Ameriquain Sur L'Histoire
Naturelle, Generale et Particuliere de Monsieur De Buffon.   Hamburg, 1751.
1st. ed., woodcut initials, 3 parts in o vol., sm. 8vo, contemp. calf, gilt spine.
Edwards 1012-384 1978 £85

LILIENTHAL, OTTO   Birdflight as the Basis of Aviation. London,
1911. 8vo., ads, frontis. portr., litho. fldg. tables, text illus., orig. green
cloth, lib. stamp, little soiled, but very good copy, 1st ed. in English, 1st issue.
Norman 5-**18 1978 $275

LILIENTHAL, OTTO   Der Vogelflug als Grundlage der Fliegekunst.
Berlin, 1889. 8vo., frontispiece, illus., plts., orig. cloth gilt, first ed. Quaritch
977-236 1978 $1,750

LILIUS, ZACHARIAS   Breve Descrittione del Mondo tradotta per M.
Francesco Baldelli.   Venice, 1551. 1st trans. into modern European language,
octavo, full-page plate, full vellum, tooled and lettered in gilt on spine.
Bennett 20-122 1978 $240

LILLARD, JOHN F. B.   The Medical Muse Grave and Gay.   New York,
1895. Sm. 8vo., 1st ed. Morrill 239-157 1978 $10

LILLE, M. L'ABBE DE   Le Malheur et La Pitie, Poeme en Quatre Chants.
Londres, 1803. Ex-lib. copy, russia, worn, rebacked later in morocco, gilt spine.
Eaton 45-303 1978 £8

LILLINGSTON, LUKE   Reflections on Mr. Burchet's Memoirs.   London,
1704. 8vo, contemporary panelled calf, spine gilt, 1st ed., paste-on errata slip,
very good copy, very scarce. Ximenes 47-181 1978 $275

LIMBORCH, PHILIP   The History of the Inquisition....   London, 1731.
1st ed. in English, 2 vols., quarto, woodcut devices, engraved vignettes, plates,
early-style calf, rebacked, spines gilt. Bennett 20-123 1978 $375

LIMITED EDITIONS CLUB   Ten Years and William Shakespeare: A Survey of
the Publishing Activities of the Limited Editions Club from October 1929 to
October 1940. Limited Editions Club, 1940. Good, illus., first Eng. ed. Bell
Book 16-571 1978 £10

LINCKLAEN, JOHN   Travels...1791 & 1792 In Penna., N. Y. &
Vermont.   New York, 1897. 1st ed., ltd. to 500 copies, maps, plts., uncut,
bkplt. of the "Butler Place", 8vo., orig. cloth, very good. Americanist 103-50
1978 $45

LINCOLN, ABRAHAM   Address in Indication of the Policy of the Framers
of the Constitution and the Principles of the Republican Party, Delivered at Cooper
Institute, February 27th, 1860. New York, 1860. 8vo., full calf binding, 1st
ed. Morrill 239-474 1978 $50

LINCOLN, ABRAHAM   An Autobiography of Abraham Lincoln.   Indianapolis, (1926). Cloth. Hayman 73-391 1978 $7.50

LINCOLN, ABRAHAM   Political Debates Between Hon. Abraham Lincoln and
Hon. Stephen A. Douglas, in the Celebrated Campaign of 1858, in Illinois.
Columbus, 1860. Cloth, 3rd ed., 4th state, endpapers & prelim. leaves foxed.
Hayman 73-390 1978 $15

LINCOLN, ABRAHAM   The Literary Works of...   Menasha: The Limited
Editions Club, 1942. Sm. 4to., illus. by John Steuart Curry, orig. cloth, mor.
label, pub. box, 1 of 1,500 copies, signed by illustrator, fine. MacManus 238-
827 1978 $27.50

LINCOLN, ABRAHAM   Political Debates Between Hon...and Hon. Stephen A. Douglas in the Celebrated Campaign of 1858, in Illinois...   Columbus,
1860. Cloth, 3rd state of 3rd ed. Hayman 72-430 1978 $15

LINCOLN, ABRAHAM   The Writings of Abraham Lincoln.   New York,
1905. 8 vols., Bell Wiley's copy. Broadfoot 46-159 1978 $20

LINCOLN, CHARLES H.   Correspondence of William Shirley Governor of
Mass. and Military Commander in America.   New York, 1912. 2 vols. Mac-
Manus 239-440 1978 $35

LINCOLN, JAMES F.   Lincoln's Incentive System.   1946. Austin 80-
792 1978 $10

LINCOLN, JOSEPH C.   The Aristocratic Miss Brewster.   New York, 1927.
1st ed., d.w. Biblo BL781-1049 1978 $10

LINCOLN, JOSEPH C.   Blair's Attic.   New York, 1929. 1st ed., pictorial
endpapers by Wyeth in color, very good. Victoria 34-886 1978 $7.50

LINCOLN, JOSEPH C.   Blair's Attic.   New York, 1929. 1st ed., signed
by both authors. Biblo BL781-1054 1978 $12.50

LINCOLN, JOSEPH C.   Cape Cod Yesterdays.   Boston, 1935. Orig.
binding, as new in d.j., pictures. Wolfe 39-81 1978 $15

LINCOLN, JOSEPH C.   Christmas Days.   New York, 1938. 1st ed.,
colored pictorial endpapers, illus., d.j., signed by author, good-fine.
Houle 10-188 1978 $30

LINCOLN, JOSEPH C.   The Depot Master.   New York, 1910. Illus., 1st
ed. Biblo BL781-1050 1978 $9.50

LINCOLN, JOSEPH C.   Kent Knowles: Quahang.   New York, 1914.
Illus., 1st ed., rear cover spotted. Biblo BL781-1051 1978 $8.50

LINCOLN, JOSEPH C.   The Postmaster.   New York, 1912. Illus., 1st
ed., bookplt. Biblo BL781-1052 1978 $9.50

LINCOLN, JOSEPH C.   Storm Signals.   New York, 1935. 1st ed., auth-
or's signed pres. Biblo BL781-1053 1978 $10

LINCOLN, LEVI   Speech of His Excellency Levi Lincoln, Delivered
to the Two Branches of the Legislature, May 25, 1831. Boston, 1831. Disbound.
Hayman 71-444 1978 $7.50

LINCOLN, WALDO   Genealogy of the Waldo Family.   Worcester, 1902.
Vol. 1 only, illus., signed pres. from compiler. Biblo 247-51 1978 $52.50

LINCOLN, WILLIAM S.   Alton Trials: Of Winthrop S. Gilman Who Was
Indicted...for the Crime of Riot...While Engaged in Defending a Printing Press.
New York, 1838. Frontis., 12mo., orig. cloth, some foxing, light binding
stains, 1st ed. Morrill 241-219 1978 $45

LIND, JAMES   A Treatise of the Scurvy.   Edinburgh, 1753. 8vo.,
contemp. gilt-ruled calf, worn, sm. stain, few tiny holes, very good copy preserved in half blue mor. box, 1st ed., rare. Zeitlin 245-152 1978 $7,750

LIND-AF-HAGEBY, L.   August Strindberg: the spirit of revolt.   1913.
Plts., very good, first English ed. Bell Book 16-804 1978 £4.50

LINDAL, W. J.   Two Ways to Life.   Toronto, 1940. Hood 117-
488 1978 $10

LINDBERGH, ANNE MORROW   Listen! the Wind!   New York, (1938). Map
drwgs., 8vo., d.w., orig. cloth, 1st ed. Morrill 241-33 1978 $7.50

LINDBERGH, ANNE MORROW   Listen! the Wind.   New York, 1933. Near
mint in chipped d.w. Desmara's B-403 1978 $7.50

LINDBERGH, CHARLES A.   "We".   New York, 1927. First ed., illus. Biblo
247-654 1978 $10

LINDBLOM, CHARLES E.   Unions and Capitalism.   Yale University Press,
1949. Austin 80-793 1978 $12.50

LINDERMAN, FRANK B.   Indian Why Stories: Sparks from War Eagle's
Lodge-Fire.   New York, 1915. Illus., illus. by Russell, original pictorial cloth,
spine faded, 1st ed. Ginsberg 14-482 1978 $30

LINDESTROM, PETER   Geographia Americae with an Account of the
Delaware Indians.   Philadelphia, 1925. Illus., fold. map, t.e.g., orig. dec.
cloth, very fine. MacManus 239-1178 1978 $60

LINDGREN, WALDEMAR   Mineral Deposits.   New York, 1913. 8vo.,
illus., ex-lib., 1st ed. Morrill 239-476 1978 $10

LINDHOLM, RICHARD W.   Introduction to Fiscal Policy.   1948. Austin 80-
794 1978 $12.50

LINDL, IGNAZ   Der Kern des Christenthums, nebst einer Abhandlung uber die Sunde wider den Heiligen Geist, in Predigten Vorgetragen. Harrisburg, 1830. 2 vols. in 1, 16mo., contemp. calf. Morrill 241-286 1978 $7.50

LINDLAHR, HENRY   The Practice of Nature Cure.   New York, 1931.
Spine cloth missing in places. Rittenhouse 49-481 1976 $7.50

LINDLEY, DOCTOR   Illustrations of Fossil Plants....   Newcastle
Upon Tyne, 1877. Portrait, plts., roy. 8vo., orig. wrappers, loose, nice copy.
Traylen 88-597 1978 £1150

LINDLEY, AUGUSTUS F.   Adamantia.   London, 1873. Coloured frontispiece, 8 maps, orig. gilt-lettered cloth, 8vo. K Books 239-272 1978 £60

LINDLEY, BETTY   A New Deal for Youth. The Story of the National
Youth Adminstration.   New York, 1938. Illus., pres., signed by Charles W. Taussig. Biblo BL781-839 1978 $10

LINDLEY, JOHN   Medical and Oeconomical Botany.   London,
1869. Wood-engravings, full prize calf gilt, 8vo. K Books 244-194 1978 £9

LINDLEY, JOHN   Rosarum Monographia...   London, 1820. Roy.
8vo, coloured engraved plts., quarter morocco, edges uncut. Traylen 88-658
1978 £350

LINDSAY, COUTTS   Boadicea: A Tragedy. 1857. lst. ed., lg. 8vo, orig. cloth, pres. copy. Hannas 54-209 1978 £12.50

LINDSAY, DAVID   A Voyage to Arcturus. 1920. Very good, rare, first English ed. Bell Book 17-570 1978 £185

LINDSAY, JACK   The London Aphrodite. London, 1928-1929. 8vo., blue cloth, t.e.g., tight near fine, 1st ed., collector's cond. Desmarais 1-277 1978 $50

LINDSAY, MAURICE   Modern Scottish Poetry, an Anthology 1920-1945. London, 1946. Very nice, d.w., first ed., orig. binding. Rota 211-15 1978 £5

LINDSAY, MAURICE   Modern Scottish Poetry. London, 1946. 1st ed., d.j., very good or better. Limestone 9-206 1978 $12.50

LINDSAY, PHILIP   Here Comes the King. 1933. lst. ed., author's signed, pres. copy, orig. cloth, soiled. Eaton 45-304 1978 £8

LINDSAY, ROBERT   An Essay on Malaria and Its Consequences. London, 1895. Rittenhouse 49-482 1976 $10

LINDSAY, VACHEL   Collected Poems. New York, 1923. Bds., cloth back, 1 of 400 numbered copies signed by author. Dawson's 447-256 1978 $50

LINDSAY, W. M.   Early Latin Verse. 1922. Allen 234-539 1978 $7.50

LINDSEY, T. J.   Ohio at Shiloh. Report of the Commission. (Cincinnati, 1903). Fold. maps, cloth. Hayman 72-130 1978 $10

LINDSLEY, JOHN BERRIEN   The Military Annals of Tennessee, Confederate, First Series. Nashville, 1886. Steel Engr., rubber stamp on about half of engravings, title page backed, rebound, Bell Wiley's copy. Broadfoot's 44-627 1978 $60.00

LINGARD, JOHN   The Antiquities of the Anglo-Saxon Church. Newcastle, 1806. 2 vols., 8vo., contemp. blind-tooled purple calf, gilt backs faded, woodcuts. P. M. Hill 142-164 1978 £40

LINGARD, JOHN   History of England from the First Invasion by the Romans to 1688. 1855. Portrait, 10 vols., cr. 8vo. George's 635-705 1978 £5.25

LINGBERG, MAJA   Karl's Jouney to the Moon. New York, c.1930. 1st Amer. ed., color plates, very good, scarce. Victoria 34-500 1978 $15

LINGEL, R. J. C.   A Bibliographical Checklist of the Writings of Richard LeGallienne. Metuchen, 1926. 8vo., orig. bds., 1st ed., ltd. to 151 copies, pres. copy from author. MacManus 238-966 1978 $50

LINK, SAMUEL ALBERT   Pioneers of Southern Literature. Nashville & Dallas, 1899. 2 vols., 1st ed., good, sound copies. Limestone 9-232 1978 $25

LINK, WILLIAM F.   The Hudson by Daylight. New York, (1883). Long fldg. map, wrs., some wear, tear in back wr. repaired. Hayman 73-477 1978 $12.50

LINKLATER, ERIC   Sealskin Trousers and Other Stories. London, (1947). Wood engravings, 1st ed., d.w. Biblo BL781-1057 1978 $9

LINKLATER, ERIC   Sealskin Trousers and Other Stories. London, 1947. 1st ed., finely bound in black mor., colored mor. onlays, blind & gilt dark blue art paper endpapers, blue slipcase, woodengravings, excellent copy, impeccable cond., bkplt. of J. R. Abbey. Van der Peet H-64-399 1978 Dfl 650

LINN, BETHINA   Flea Circus. 1936. First ed., d.j. Austin 82-588 1978 $12.50

LINN, JOHN BLAIR   Annals of Buffalo Valley, Pa... Harrisburg, 1877. Illus., rebound, scarce. MacManus 239-1535 1978 $50

LINN, JOHN BLAIR   Charter to Wm. Penn & Laws of the Province of Penna.... Harrisburg, 1879. 1st ed., lg. 8vo, orig. quarter mor., complete with facsimile & other illus. Americanist 101-80 1978 $22.50

LINN, JOHN BLAIR   Papers Relating to the Colonies on the Delaware 1614-1682. Harrisburg, 1890. Maps, rebound in cloth. MacManus 239-122 1978 $20

LINN, JOHN BLAIR   Pennsylvania in the War of the Revolution, Battalions and Line. Harrisburg, 1895. 2 vols., cloth, illus., maps. MacManus 239-596 1978 $50

LINN, JOHN J.   Reminiscences of Fifty Years in Texas. Austin, 1935. Facsimile reissue of rare 1883 ed. Jenkins 116-827 1978 $22.50

LINN, LEWIS FIELDS   Report of the...Committee on the Occupation of Oregon Territory. Washington, 1838. Maps, full leather, lst ed. Ginsberg 14-824 1978 $100

LINNE, CARL VON   Amoenitates Academicae seu Dissertationes Variae Physicae.... Erlangen, 1787-90. 10 vols., 8vo., engrav. plts., contemp. mottled calf, very slightly worn, good set, first ed. in 10 vols. Quaritch 977-45 1978 $1,700

LINNE, CARL VON   Philosophia Botanica in Qua Explicantur Fundamenta Botanica. Vienna, 1763. Engr. fold-out plts., 8vo., contemp. bds. Salloch 345-108 1978 $150

LINNE, CARL VON   Systema Naturae in quo Proponuntur Naturae Regna Tria Secundum Classes, Ordines, Genera & Species. Paris, 1744. 8vo., contemp. mottled calf, gilt panels on spine, very nice, fourth ed. Quaritch 977-46 1978 $700

LINNE, CARL VON   Systema Naturae Per Regna Tria Naturae, Secundum Classes.... Stockholm, 1766-68. 3 vols. in 4, engrav. plts., some browning in text, contemp. half calf, marbled bds. Quaritch 977-48 1978 $1,500

LINNE, CARL VON   Systema Naturae Sistens Regna Tria Naturae.... Leipzig, 1748. 8vo., engrav. portrait, engrav. plts., 19th century half mor, seventh ed. Quaritch 977-47 1978 $450

LINT, JAN GERARD DE   Rembrandt. The Hague, n.d. Illus., 8vo., cloth. Salloch 345-56 1978 $12.50

LINTON, RALPH   Arts of the South Seas. New York, (1946). First ed., d.w., color illus., sm. 4to. Biblo 247-403 1978 $17.50

LIONBERGER, I. H.   The Annals of St. Louis and a Brief Account of Its Foundation and Progress 1764-1928. [N.P.], 1929. Wr. Ginsberg 14-586 1978 $7.50

LIPMAN, JEAN   American Primitive Painting. New York, 1942. Illus. in color & b/w, 4to., binding partly stained, lst ed. Morrill 239-477 1978 $12.50

LIPPINCOTT, HORACE MATHER   Early Philadelphia, Its People, Life and Progress. Philadelphia, 1917. Illus., uncut. MacManus 239-1609 1978 $20

LIPPINCOTT, HORACE MATHER   A Narrative of Chestnut Hill. Philadelphia, 1948. Baldwins' 51-459 1978 $12.50

LIPPINCOTT, HORACE MATHER   A Narrative of Chestnut Hill, Philadelphia With Some Account of Springfield, Whitemarsh and Cheltenham Townships in Montgomery Co., Pa. (1948). Illus. MacManus 239-1536 1978 $15

LIPPINCOTT, HORACE MATHER   The University of Pennsylvania, Franklin's College. Philadelphia, 1919. Illus., ltd. ed. MacManus 239-1649 1978 $12.50

LIPPMAN, EDMOND O. VON   Entstehung und Ausbreitung der Alchemie. Berlin, 1919. 8vo., orig. cloth, fine copy, lst ed. Norman 5-183 1978 $75

LIPPMANN, EDMUND O. VON   Entstehung und Ausbreitung Der Alchemie. Berlin, 1919. Thick 4to., wrs., with appendix. Salloch 345-109 1978 $65

LIPS, EVA   Rebirth of Liberty. 1942. Austin 79-442 1978 $10

LIPSCOMBE, G.   Historical Record of 180 Coy. Royal Army Service Corps Mechanical Transport. Aldershot, 1919. Plts., cr. 8vo., orig. cloth. K Books 244-195 1978 £6

LIPSCOMBE, G.   The Peregrinations of the 34th Divisional Coy.
during the Great War of 1914-19. Aldershot, 1920. Plts., cr. 8vo., orig. cloth.
K Books 244-196 1978 £6

LIPSON, E.   The History of the Woollen and Worsted Industries.
1921. Map, folding frontis., 8vo. George's 635-354 1978 £6

LISIANSKY, UREY   A Voyage Round the World, 1803-06... 1814.
Portrait, coloured map, plts., 2 coloured, 4to., bds., rebacked, uncut, some offsets. Edwards 1012-29 1978 £1400

LISITZKY, GENE   Thomas Jefferson. Chicago, (1933). Biblo
BL781-209 1978 $9

A LIST of Books Printed in Cambridge at the University Press 1521-1800. Cambridge, 1935. Demy 8vo., orig. bds., 1 corner cracked, linen back. Forster
130-317 1978 £4

LIST of Lands to be Sold April, 1830, for Arrears of Taxes. Albany, 1829. Self-
wr., title page supplied in Xerox copy. Butterfield 21-244 1978 $15

LIST of Lands to be Sold in May, 1839, for Arrears in Taxes. Albany, 1838.
Index, self-wr., good. Butterfield 21-245 1978 $20

LIST of Lands to be Sold in June, 1843, for Arrears of Taxes. Albany, 1843.
Prtd. green wr. Butterfield 21-246 1978 $25

LIST of Publications, Exhibition Catalogues and Other Items Issued by the Grolier
Club, 1884-1948. Grolier Club, 1948. 8vo., wrs. Battery Park 1-151 1978
$10

A LIST of the Colonels, Lieutenant Colonels, Majors, Captains, Lieutenants, and
Ensigns of His Majesty's Forces on the British Establishment.... (1740). Sm. folio,
contemp. calf. F. Edwards 1013-237 1978 £100

A LIST of the Flag Officers and other Commissioned Officers of His Majesty's Fleet.
1820. 8vo., new half calf. F. Edwards 1013-159 1978 £20

A LIST of the Flag Officers and other Commissioned Officers of His Majesty's Fleet.
1821. 8vo., contemp. straight grained mor, spine faded. F. Edwards 1013-160
1978 £20

A LIST of the Flag Officers and other Commissioned Officers of His Majesty's Fleet.
1827. 8vo., contemp. straight grained mor. F. Edwards 1013-161 1978 £25

A LIST of the Flag Officers and other Commissioned Officers of His Majesty's Fleet.
1842. 8vo., contemp. half calf, rebacked. F. Edwards 1013-162 1978 £20

LISTER, JEREMY   Concord Fight... Cambridge, 1931. 12mo,
orig. cloth, nice. MacManus 239-597 1978 $12.50

LISTER, JOSEPH   The Autobiography of .... 1842. Orig. limp
cloth, octavo, good. Upcroft 10-103 1978 £7

LISTER, MARTIN   A Journey to Paris in the Year 1698. London,
1699. 8vo., plts., contemp. calf, very good copy from the library of Dr. Alfred
M. Hellman, rare 2nd issue of 1st ed. Zeitlin 245-153 1978 $225

LISTER, THOMAS HENRY   Granby, a Novel. 1826. 3 vols., 12mo., half
blue calf, gilt backs, very good, tall copy, first ed. P. M. Hill 142-192 1978
£65

LITCHFIELD, FREDERICK   Pottery and Porcelain. New York, 1925. 4th
ed., revised & corrected. Baldwins' 51-117 1978 $17.50

LITCHFIELD, W. F.   Diphtheria in Practice. London, 1908. Slight
foxing. Rittenhouse 49-483 1976 $15

LITERARY and Historical Activities in North Carolina 1900-1905. Raleigh, 1907.
Vol. I, new cloth. Broadfoot 50-352 1978 $20

LITERARY and Historical Activities in North Carolina 1900-1905. Raleigh, 1907.
Vol. 1, Bell Wiley's copy. Broadfoot's 44-575 1978 $16

LITERARY AND HISTORICAL SOCIETY OF QUEBEC   Catalogue of Books. Quebec, 1873. Orig. printed wrappers. Wolfe 39-482a 1978 $75

LITERARY & HISTORICAL SOCIETY OF QUEBEC   Catalogue of Books in the
Literary and Historical Society of Quebec. Quebec, 1873. Paper cover,
appendix, index. Hood 117-24 1978 $30

LITERARY AND HISTORICAL SOCIETY OF QUEBEC   List of Transactions and
Historical Documents. Quebec, (1887). Orig. binding. Wolfe 39-462 1978
$15

LITERARY AND HISTORICAL SOCIETY OF QUEBEC   Transactions. Volume I.
Quebec, 1829. Orig. printed bds., loose, plts., some folded, some printed in
colour. Wolfe 39-453 1978 $150

LITERARY AND HISTORICAL SOCIETY OF QUEBEC   Transactions. Vol. V. Part
I. Quebec, 1862. Printed front wrapper. Wolfe 39-454 1978 $45

LITTLE, A. G.   Essays in Medieval History Presented to T. F.
Tout. 1925. Lg. 8vo. Upcroft 12-268 1978 £15

LITTLE, FRANCES   Early American Textiles. New York, (1931).
1st ed., illus., orig. cloth, ex-lib., very good. MacManus 239-687 1978
$22.50

LITTLE, FRANCES   The Lady and Sada San. 1912. first ed., color
frontis. Austin 82-589 1978 $12.50

LITTLE, FRANCES   The Lady of the Decoration. 1906. Austin 82-590
1978 $8.50

LITTLE, GEORGE   A History of Lumsden's Battery C. S. A. Tuscaloosa, 1905. Wrs., Bell Wiley's copy. Broadfoot 46-310 1978 $40

LITTLE, JAMES A.   From Kirtland to Salt Lake City... Salt Lake
City, 1890. Illus., orig. full gold stamped leather, 1st ed. Ginsberg 14-1008
1978 $125

LITTLE, SHELBY   George Washington. New York, 1929. Ltd.
to 140 numbered copies, signed, covers slightly stained. Biblo 248-219 1978
$37.50

LITTLE, W. J. KNOS   Sketches and Studies in South Africa. London,
1899. Roy. 8vo., orig. cloth. K Books 239-274 1978 £7

LITTLE Child's Home ABC Book. New York, (1886). Spine and inner margins
taped, colored wrappers with small tears. Victoria 34-501 1978 $10

LITTLE Lasses and Lads. London, 1869. Coloured title-pg., coloured plts. by
Oscar Pletsch, 4to, cloth, little loose. Traylen 88-174 1978 £5

LITTLE Orphan Annie and Her Junior Commandos. Racine, (1943). Good or better.
Bernard 5-345 1978 $7.50

LITTLEDALE, RICHARD F.   Plain Reasons Against Joining the Church of Rome.
London, 1892. Rev'd. and enlarged, cloth. Hayman 72-433 1978 $7.50

LITTLEFIELD, GEORGE EMERY   Catalogue of the Valuable Private Library of the
Late George Emery Littlefield. Boston, 1915. 2 vols., 8vo., orig. wrs., portr.
Morrill 241-24 1978 $10

LITTLEFIELD, GEORGE EMERY   Early Schools and School-Books of New England.
Boston, 1904. 1st ed., "must" book, light rubbing, text very fine, scarce.
Victoria 34-502 1978 $150

LITTLEFIELD, LYMAN O.   The Martyrs:.... Salt Lake City, 1882. Illus.,
orig. cloth, 1st ed. Ginsberg 14-662 1978 $35

LITTLEHALES, H.   The Prymer. 1891-2. 2 vols., royal 8vo.
Upcroft 12-269 1978 £10

LITTLETON, ADAM   Linguae Latinae Liber Dictionarius. 1715. Thk.
8vo., fourth ed., contemp. reversed calf. Howes 194-243 1978 £24

LITTLETON, EDWARD   The Groans of the Plantations:.... London,
1698. 1st ed., sm. 4to., modern half mor. Quaritch 978-157 1978 $575

LIVERMORE, ABIEL ABBOT   The War with Mexico Reviewed. Boston, 1850.
1st ed., fine copy, old library stamp. MacManus 239-311 1978 $17.50

LIVERMORE, ABIEL ABBOT   The War With Mexico Reviewed. Boston, 1850.
Ist ed. Jenkins 116-923 1978 $17.50

LIVERMORE, SAMUEL TRUESDALE   A Condensed History of Cooperstown, with a
Biographical Sketch of J. Fenimore Cooper. Albany, 1862. First ed., orig. cloth.
MacManus 239-336 1978 $37.50

LIVERMORE, SAMUEL TRUESDALE   A Condensed History of Cooperstown, with a
Biographical Sketch of J. Fenimore Cooper. Albany, 1862. First ed. Butterfield
21-346 1978 $22.50

LIVERMORE, SAMUEL TRUESDALE   A History of Block Island from Its Discovery
in 1514 to 1876. Hartford, 1877. Ist ed., very scarce, fine, orig. cloth. Mac-
Manus 239-1078 1978 $60

LIVERMORE, THOMAS L.   Days and Events 1860-1866. Boston, 1920.
One folding plate, front hinge cracked, Bell Wiley's copy. Broadfoot's 44-548
1978 $20

LIVES and Bloody Exploits of the Most Noted Pirates, Their Trials and Executions
... Hartford, 1836. Woodcut plts., 8vo, contemp. calf, ex-lib. Morrill 239-
478 1978 $17.50

LIVINGOOD, J. W.   The Philadelphia Baltimore Trade Rivalry...
Harrisburg, 1947. Maps. MacManus 239-1537 1978 $17.50

LIVINGSTON, MRS.   Love Each Other or Strive to Be Good. 1854.
Illus. Austin 82-591 1978 $15

LIVINGSTON, EDWARD   Address to the People of the United States,....
New Orleans, 1808. Half calf, complete work. Ginsberg 14-505 1978 $1,750

LIVINGSTON, EDWARD M.   Clinical Study of the Abdominal Cavity and Peri-
toneum. New York, 1932. Rittenhouse 49-484 1976 $20

LIVINGSTON, LUTHER S.   A Bibliography of the First Editions in Book Form
of the Writings of James Russell Lowell Compiled Largely from the Collection Formed
by the Late Jacob Chester Chamberlain... New York, 1914. Frontis. port., orig.
bds., d.j., pub. box, 1st ed., 1 of 50 copies on Van Gelder paper, mint. Mac-
Manus 238-972 1978 $50

LIVINGSTON, PHILIP   The Third Part of Modern Reports, Being a Collection of Several Special Cases, in the Court of Kings-Bench.... 1725. Light
dampstains on some latter pages, original leather covers detached, signed on title
page by Livingston. Nestler Rare 78-168 1978 $110

LIVINGSTON, ROBERT R.   Essay on Sheep. Concord, 1813. Lea. & marbled
bds., 1st ed., bds. worn & faded, some moisture stains & foxing, rare, slipcase.
Dykes 34-279 1978 $50

LIVINGSTONE, DAVID   The Last Journals of ...., In Central Africa,
From 1865 to His Death... 1874. Maps, plts., illus., 2 vols., 8vo, orig. cloth.
Edwards 1012-305 1978 $90

LIVINGSTONE, DAVID   Missionary Travels and Researches in South Africa.
1857. Ist. ed., Ist. issue, coloured frontis, coloured plts., maps, other illus., 8
vo, orig. cloth, inscribed by author to Sir Titus Salt with his bookplt., preserved
in red buckram box, good. Sawyer 299-126 1978 £375

LIVINGSTONE, DAVID   Missionary Travels and Researches in South Africa.
London, 1857. Ist. ed., inscribed & signed pres. copy, folding maps, folding
chart, folding frontispiece, portrait, plts., text-illus., lib. stamp on title recto
and verso, modern half morocco, 8vo. K Books 239-277 1978 £200

LIVINGSTONE, DAVID   Missionary Travels and Researches in South Africa.
London, 1857. First ed., frontispiece, portrait, maps, plts., good, neatly recased
in orig. cloth. K Books 244-197 1978 £45

LIVINGSTONE, DAVID   Missionary Travels and Researches in South Africa.
London, 1857. Ist. ed., maps, folding frontis, plts., text-illus., 8vo, nice fresh
copy, neatly recased in orig. cloth. K Books 239-276 1978 £50

LIVINGSTONE, DAVID   Missionary Travels and Researches in South
Africa... 1857. Ist. ed., 2nd. issue, folding maps, folding frontispiece, portrait,
plts., illus., thick 8vo, orig. cloth, spine repaired. Edwards 1012-303 1978
£45

LIVINGSTONE, DAVID   Missionary Travels and Researches in South Africa.
London, 1857. Ist. ed., 8vo, newly rebound in buckram, folding maps, good.
Sexton 7-113 1978 £20

LIVINGSTONE, DAVID   Narrative of An Expedition to the Zambesi and
Its Tributaries... 1865. Ist. ed., folding map, frontis, plts., illus., thick 8vo,
orig. cloth, spine faded. Edwards 1012-306 1978 £90

LIVINGSTONE, DAVID   A Popular Account of Dr. Livingstone's Expedition
to the Zambesi and Its Tributaries... London, 1875. Folding map, frontispiece,
plts., text-illus., cr. 8vo, gilt cloth. K Books 239-278 1978 £9

LIVINGSTONE, R. W.   The Legacy of Greece. Oxford, (1928). Illus.
Biblo BL781-430 1978 $7.50

LIVINGSTONE, W. P.   Christina Forsyth of Fingoland. London, 1918.
Map, 9 plts., cr. 8vo, orig. cloth. K Books 239-280 1978 £6

LIVIUS, TITUS   Ab Urbe Condita Libri. 1921. 4 vols. Allen
234-941 1978 $40

LIVIUS, TITUS   The First Five Books of the Roman History. Edinburgh, 1822. Cr. 4to., contemp. mor., woodcut initials. Howes 194-622
1978 £28

LIVIUS, TITUS   Historiarum Quod Exstat, cum Integris J. Frein-
shemii Supplementis. 1710. 10 vols., vellum, maps, ex-lib. Allen 234-1535
1978 $35

LIVIUS, TITUS   History of Rome. 1823. Ist Amer. ed., 6 vols.,
full calf, worn, one joint partly cracked. Allen 234-542 1978 $30

LIVIUS, TITUS   Opera. 1722. Engrav. frontispiece, 6 vols.,
12mo., contemp. mottled calf, spines fully gilt. Howes 194-364 1978 £55

LIVIUS, TITUS   Titi Livii Patavini Romanae Historiae Principis....
London, 1589. Ist English ed., small thick octavo, woodcut initials, contemp.
calf, rebacked with paneled spine, numerous neat underscorings and marginal notations in early hand. Bennett 20-124 1978 $450

LIVRE de Diverses Sortes d'Escritures les plus Usites en la Chrestiente. N.P., n.d.
(France, c. 1600). Oblong 4to., cont. vellum, some soiling and wear. Schumann
511-30 1978 sFr 2250

LIVRES de Liturgie Imprimes aux XVth et XVIth Siecles. Paris, 1932. Illus.,
tall 8vo., orig. wrs. Morrill 241-27 1978 $10

LIZARS, JOHN   A System of Anatomical Plates of the Human Body.
Edinburgh, (1822-1826?). Ist ed., folio atlas, engr. plts., wood engrs., rebound
in half red mor. & marbled bds., very fine, scarce. Current Misc. 8-30 1978
$640

LIZARS, JOHN   A System of Anatomical Plates. Edinburgh, 1822-
1826. Thick 8vo., orig. cloth, binding partly faded, lacks plts. Morrill 239-153
1978 $17.50

LIZARS, K. M.   The Valley of the Humber, 1615-1913. Toronto,
1913. Hood 116-757 1978 $45

LIZARS, R.   In The Days of the Canada Company... Toronto,
1896. Ist. ed., portraits, illus. Hood's 115-825 1978 $90

LLEWELLYN, RICHARD   None But the Lonely Heart. London, 1943. 8vo,
cloth, leather label, 1 of 250 copies signed by author, Ist ed., fine. Duschnes
220-190 1978 $30

LLOYD, C. F.   Sunlight and Shadow. Toronto, 1923. Inscr'd
& signed by author. Hood 117-439 1978 $10

LLOYD, DAVID   Economy of Agriculture. Germantown, 1832.
Contemp. calf, rebacked, bookplt., good copy. MacManus 239-14 1978 $40

LLOYD, DAVID   State-Worthies... 1766. 2 vols., orig. speckled
calf, gilt borders, sm. repair to title of vol. 2, elaborate gilt spines, orig. marbled
endpapers, fine set. Jarndyce 16-128 1978 £48

LLOYD, GEORGE   Travels at Home, and Voyages by the Fire-Side,
for the Instruction and Entertainment of Young Persons. Philadelphia, 1816. Vol.
I of II, leather, worn, spine chipped, scarce. Hayman 72-434 1978 $7.50

LLOYD GEORGE, D.   War Memoirs. 1938. Illus., complete ed. in
2 vols., 8vo. George's 635-706 1978 £5.25

LLOYD, J.   Thesaurus Ecclesiasticus. 1796. Contemp. tree
calf, rubbed, 8vo. George's 635-1090 1978 £8.50

LLOYD, J. E.   Owen Glendower. Oxford, 1931. Ex-library copy, cloth rubbed at extremities, 8vo. Upcroft 12-270 1978 £8.50

LLOYD, JOHN URI   Stringtown on the Pike. New York, 1900. 8vo, cloth, illus., 1st ed., fine. Duschnes 220-191 1978 $15

LLOYD, ROBER B.   The Stricken Lute: An Account of the Life of Peter Abelard. 1932. Orig. ed., orig. buckram, fine, d.w., 8vo. Howes 194-585 1978 £7.50

LLOYD, WYNDHAM E. B.   A Hundred Years of Medicine. London, 1936. Rittenhouse 49-486 1976 $15

LOAN Exhibition of Drinking Vessels. 1933. Plts., roy. 8vo., orig. wrappers. George's 635-71 1978 £6

LOBEIRA, JOAO VASCO DE   Amadis of Gaul. London, 1803. 4vols., 12mo, uniformly bound in elegant 19th-century blond calf, spines profusely gilt, bookplate, 1st Southey translation, fine. Bennett 7-70 1978 $250

LOBO, JEROME   A Voyage to Abyssinia. 1735. Contemp. calf, rebacked, very good, first ed., 8vo. Howes 194-335 1978 £225

LOCATELLI, LODOVICO   Theatro d'Arcani..., nel Quale si Tratta dell'Arte Chimica, and dei suoi Arcani con gli Afforismi d'Ippocrate Commentati da Paracelso. Milano, 1644. 8vo., engraved title, contemp. vellum lightly worn, rare, 1st ed. Gilhofer 74-120 1978 sFr 700

LOCHER, JACOB   Opuscula. Nurnberg, 1506. Woodcuts, sm. 4 to., very fine, unwashed copy, 1st ed., modern vellum over bds. Schafer 19-25 1978 sFr. 8,000

LOCKE, DAVID R.   Nasby in Exile: or, Six Months of Travel in England, Ireland, Scotland, France, Germany, Switzerland & Belgium. Toledo, 1882. Illus., 1st ed., lg. 8vo., orig. pic. cloth stamped in black & gold, binding A, 1st prtg., very good. Americanist 103-51 1978 $25

LOCKE, EMMA P. BOYLSTON   Colonial Amherst. (Milford), 1916. Illus., 8vo., 1st ed., orig. cloth. Morrill 241-392 1978 $15

LOCKE, JOHN   Essai Philosophique Concernant L'Entendement Humain... Amsterdam, 1742. Port., thick 4to., old mor. Salloch 347-121 1978 $90

LOCKE, JOHN   An Essay Concerning Humane Understanding. London, 1694. 2nd ed., folio, calf. Salloch 348-120 1978 $200

LOCKE, JOHN   An Essay Concerning Humane Understanding. 1706. Folio, fifth ed., contemp. half calf, rebacked. Howes 194-366 1978 £70

LOCKE, JOHN   An Essay Concerning Humane Understanding. 1710. Sixth ed., portrait frontispiece, 2 vols., contemp. calf, rebacked, first ed. to be published in octavo. Howes 194-367 1978 £36

LOCKE, JOHN   An Essay Concerning Human Understanding. 1812. 22nd. ed., folding table, 2 vols., 8vo, contemp.mottled calf, gilt spines, nice copy. Fenning 32-197 1978 £16

LOCKE, JOHN   Some Thoughts concerning Education. N.P., 4695. 8 vo., contemp. calf, 3rd (actually 2nd) enlarged ed. Quaritch Summer, 1978-28 1978 $600

LOCKE, JOHN   Some Thoughts Concerning Education. 1705. 5th. ed., lacking free end-paper, orig. panelled calf, rubbed at head & corners v.g. Jarndyce 16-129 1978 £24

LOCKE, JOHN   The Works. 1727. Third ed., 3 vols., folio, contemp. calf, portrait. Howes 194-365 1978 £105

LOCKE, JOHN   The Works. London, 1727. Third ed., 3 vols., portrait, plt., woodcut ornaments, folio, nice, old style calf. K Books 244-198 1978 £80

LOCKE, JOHN L.   Sketches of the History of the Town of Camden, Maine. Hallowell, 1859. 1st ed., errata leaf, orig. cloth, lib. marks, fine. MacManus 239-985 1978 $35

LOCKER-LAMPSON, FREDERICK   Lyra Eligantiarum. 1867. Orig. cloth, gilt. Eaton 45-305 1978 £8

LOCKER-LAMPSON, FREDERICK   Poems by... 1868. Half title, orig. half binding, only 100 copies printed, frontis. Jarndyce 16-441 1978 £58

LOCKHART, CAROLINE   The Man From the Bitter Roots. Philadelphia, and London, 1915. Illus. in colour by Gayle Hoskins, 3 colour plts., red cloth blocked in white & gold, mint, author's own ex-libris stamp lightly gummed in. Eaton 45-306 1978 £5

LOCKHART, JOHN GIBSON   The Ballantyne-Humbug Handled, in A Letter to Sir Adam Fergusson. 1839. 1st. ed., lg. 12mo, half title, uncut, orig. wrappers, as issued, v.g. Jarndyce 16-1020 1978 £38

LOCKHART, JOHN GIBSON   The Ballantyne-Humbug Handled, in a Letter to Sir Adam Fergusson. Edinburgh, 1839. 1st. ed., lg. 12mo, contemp. gray paper wrappers, stabbed, uncut as issued. Hannas 54-296 1978 £20

LOCKHART, JOHN GIBSON   Memoirs of the Life of Sir Walter Scott. Edinburgh, 1837-38. First ed., portrait, 7 vols., half dark gr. levant mor., uncut, fine. Howes 194-1169 1978 £45

LOCKHART, JOHN GIBSON   Memoirs of the Life of Sir Walter Scott. Paris, 1838. 4 vols., half green mor., 8vo. K Books 244-199 1978 £20

LOCKHART, JOHN GIBSON   Memoirs of the Life of Sir Walter Scott. Edinburgh, 1839. 2nd. ed., 10 vols., engraved frontis & vignette tailpieces in all vols., orig. cloth, fine. Jarndyce 16-1021 1978 £35

LOCKHART, JOHN GIBSON   Memoirs of the Life of Sir Walter Scott. Edinburgh, 1851. 10 vols., sm. 8vo., frontis., half green mor., gilt panelled back, gilt tops. Quaritch 979-288 1978 $100

LOCKHART, JOHN GIBSON   Peter's Letters to his Kinsfolk. Edinburgh, London, 1819. Portraits, vignettes, 3 vols., half mor., gilt tops, other edges untrimmed. Howes 194-368 1978 £25

LOCKHART, JOHN GIBSON   Peter's Letters to His Kinsfold. 1819. 1st. ed., 3 vols., frontis portrait, vignette tailpieces, orig. red calf, spines gilt, black labels, fine. Jarndyce 16-817 1978 £50

LOCKHART, JOHN GIBSON   Peter's Letters to his Kinsfolk. Edinburgh, London, Glasgow, 1819. 3 vols., lg. 8vo., later full red mor. gilt, uncut, fine, portraits, vignettes. P. M. Hill 142-165 1978 £75

LOCKLEY, FRED   Across the Plains by Prairie Schooner. Personal Narrative of B.F. Bonney of his Trip to Sutter's Fort, Calif. in 1846... Eugene, n.d. Wrs. Biblo BL781-286 1973 $13.50

LOCKLEY, FRED   Across the Plains by Prairie Schooner:.... Eugene, [n.d.]. Original wr. Ginsberg 14-486 1978 $10

LOCKMAN, JOHN   Travels of the Jesuits into Various Parts of the World... 1762. 2nd. ed., 5 folding maps, folding plt., 2 vols., old style modern calf, slight defects in few pgs., 8vo. Edwards 1012-25 1978 £150

LOCKRIDGE, ROSS   Raintree County. Boston, 1948. 1st ed. Biblo BL781-1058 1978 $7.50

LOCKRIDGE, ROSS   Raintree County. 1948. First ed., frayed d.j. Austin 82-592 1978 $12.50

LOCKRIDGE, ROSS   Raintree County. Boston, (1948). Signed copy with suppressed d.w., jacket torn & frayed, bkplt. Biblo 251-552 1978 $17.50

LOCKWOOD, FRANK C.   Arizona Characters. Los Angeles, 1928. Illus., original cloth, 1st ed., inscribed presentation copy from author. Ginsberg 14-18 1978 $40

LOCKWOOD, FRANK C.   The Life of E. E. Ayer. Chicago, 1929. Illus., 8vo, orig. cloth. Book Chest 17-232 1978 $35

LOCKWOOD, GEORGE B.   The New Harmony Movement. New York, 1905. 1st ed., illus. MacManus 239-257 1978 $27.50

LOCKWOOD, LUKE V.   Colonial Furniture in America. New York, 1901. Illus. MacManus 239-688 1978 $30

LOCKWOOD, MARY S.   Art Embroidery. 1878. 19 coloured plts., lg. 4to., illus., orig. cloth, gilt, spine little worn, very good copy. Fenning 32-198 1978 £24.50

LOCKYER, JOSEPH NORMAN   The Chemistry of the Sun. London, 1887. 8vo., ads, text illus., orig. cloth, gilt, very good copy, 1st ed. Norman 5-184 1978 $50

LOCKYER, JOSEPH NORMAN   The Sun's Place in Nature. London, 1897. 8vo, illus., orig. cloth, gilt, uncut, v.g., first ed. Norman 5-**19 1978 $85

LODGE, GEORGE E.   Memoirs of an Artist Naturalist. London, 1946. Plts., some coloured, 4to., d.w., orig. cloth. K Books 244-200 1978 £12

LODGE, HENRY CABOT   Address Delivered Before a Joint Convention of the Senate and House...of Massachusetts on Friday, February 12, 1909...on the Occasion of the One-hundredth Anniversary of the Birth of Abraham Lincoln... Boston, 1909. Cloth. Hayman 72-429 1978 $7.50

LODGE, HENRY CABOT   The Works of Alexander Hamilton. New York, 1904. 12 vols., very fine, untrimmed, t.e.g., ltd. to 600 sets. MacManus 239-189 1978 $175

LODGE, OLIVER   Electrons or the Nature and Properties of Negative Electricity. London, 1906. 8vo., ads, illus., orig. cloth, gilt, back cover stained, good copy, 1st ed. Norman 5-185 1978 $30

LODGE, R. C.   Manitoba Essays... Toronto, 1937. Hood's 115-397 1978 $25

LOEB, HAROLD   Full Production Without War. 1946. Austin 80-797 1978 $20

LOEB, JAMES   Festschrift Fuer...Zum Sechzigsten Geburtstag Gewidmet von Seinen Archaeologischen Freunden in Deutschland un Amerika. Munich, 1930. 4to., illus., color plts. Biblo BL781-431 1978 $47.50

LOFTIE, W. J.   Lessons in the Art of Illuminating. London, n.d. (1885). Orig. 4 parts, tipped-in plts. in gold and colours, illus., post 4to., orig. wrappers. Forster 130-215 1978 £25

LOFTIE, W. J.   Orient-Pacific Line Guide. London, (ca. 1902). 6th ed., numerous maps, illus., ads, 8vo. Morrill 239-479 1978 $12.50

LOFTING, HUGH   Doctor Dolittle in the Moon. 1928. Illus., first ed. Austin 82-593 1978 $20

LOGAN, DEBORAH NORRIS   Memoir of Dr. George Logan of Stenton. Philadelphia, 1899. Illus., 4to., uncut, ltd. to 250 copies. MacManus 239-784 1978 $25

LOGAN, H.   Orchids Are Easy to Grow. New York & Chicago, 1949-1960. 8vo, orig. cloth. Book Chest 17-234 1978 $15

LOGAN, JAMES   The Scottish Gael. London, 1831. 2 vols., hand-coloured plts., roy. 8vo., neatly recased in orig. cloth. K Books 244-201 1978 £33

LOGAN, MRS. JOHN A.   Reminiscences of a Soldier's Wife. New York, 1913. Bell Wiley's copy. Broadfoot 46-165 1978 $18

LOGAN, OLIVE   Before the Footlights and Behind the Scenes.... Philadelphia, 1870. Little worn at extremities, light internal dampstains on some pages, illus., clean, orig. binding. Hayman 71-425 1978 $15

LOGAN, SAMUEL C.   A City's Danger & Defense, or, Issues & Results of the Strikes of 1877,.... Scranton, 1887. 1st ed., illus., rare, photo of author pasted to end paper, orig. binding, 8vo. Americanist 101-83 1978 $40

LOGAN, SAMUEL C.   A City's Danger and Defense, or, Issues and Results of the Strikes of 1877. Scranton, 1877. Illus., very scarce. MacManus 239-1538 1978 $40

LOGAN, SAMUEL C.   The Life of Thomas Dickson. Scranton, 1888. Illus., 8vo., orig. cloth, 1st ed. Morrill 241-287 1978 $10

LOGGAN, DAVID   Oxonia Illustrata. Oxoniae: e Theatro Sheldoniano, MDCLXXV. Oxford, 1675. Folio, plts., few marginal tears repaired, old calf. Quaritch 983-342 1978 $1,625

LOLME, JEAN LOUIS DE   The Constitution of England. 1784. Fourth ed., portrait, contemp. calf, 8vo. Howes 194-369 1978 £18

LOMAX, JOHN A.   American Ballads & Folk Songs. New York, 1949. Bell Wiley's copy. Broadfoot 46-536 1978 $12

LOMAX, JOHN A.   Cowboy Songs and Other Frontier Ballads. New York, 1910. Pic. cloth, 1st ed., covers dull, fine copy, scarce, slipcase. Dykes 34-31 1978 $65

LOMAX, JOHN A.   Songs of the Cattle Trail and Cow Camp. London, (1920). 1st British ed., decor. cloth, covers dull & worn, very good, scarce. Dykes 34-212 1978 $7.50

LOMAX, JOHN A.   Songs of the Cattle Trail and Cow Camp. New York, (1950). Fine, d.w., illus. Biblo 247-238 1978 $15

LOMAX, LOUISE   San Antonio's River. San Antonio, 1948. 1st ed., illus., maps, signed by author. Jenkins 116-1519 1978 $12.50

LONCHAMP, F. C.   Manuel du Bibliophile Francais 1470-1920. Paris, 1927. 2 vols. in 4, ltd. to 1000 copies on "velin simili couche", illus., roy. 8vo., orig. wrs., unopened. Forster 130-44 1978 £55

LONDON, HANNAH R.   Shades of My Forefathers. Springfield, 1941. Illus., ltd. to 500 copies, signed by author. Austin 79-445 1978 $47.50

LONDON, JACK   The Abysmal Brute. Toronto, 1913. Olive-green cloth, 1st Canadian ed., fine in chipped dust jacket. Bradley 49-191 1978 $225

LONDON, JACK   The Abysmal Brute. New York, 1913. Olive-green cloth, 1st ed., 1st issue, genuine 1st binding, stamped in yellow & dark green, very good. Bradley 49-190 1978 $125

LONDON, JACK   The Apostate. Chicago, n.d. (not before 1912). 12mo., orig. wrs., reprint of 1906 ed., almost fine. MacManus 238-700 1978 $45

LONDON, JACK   Before Adam. New York, 1907. 1st. ed., orig. binding, clean. Hayman 71-427 1978 $20

LONDON, JACK   Best Short Stories of Jack London. New York, (c. 1945). 1st Armed Services ed., No. 1011, oblong 16 mo., pictorial printed wrappers, good-fine. Houle 10-191 1978 $45

LONDON, JACK   Burning Daylight. New York, 1910. Cloth, slightly worn d.w. Dawson's 447-257 1978 $60

LONDON, JACK   Burning Daylight. New York, 1910. Pic. blue cloth, 1st ed., name on end paper. Bradley 49-192 1978 $25

LONDON, JACK   The Call of the Wild. New York, 1903. Illus., orig. pict. cloth, 1st ed., very nice, inscription on flyleaf. MacManus 238-556 1978 $125

LONDON, J.   The Cruise of the Snark. New York, 1911. 8vo, orig. cloth. Book Chest 17-236 1978 $45

LONDON, JACK   A Daughter of the Snows. Philadelphia, 1902. Illus., orig. pict. cloth, 1st ed., fine. MacManus 238-555 1978 $125

LONDON, JACK   The Game. New York, 1905. Illus., green cloth, t.e.g., 1st ed., covers worn & soiled. Bradley 49-193 1978 $20

LONDON, JACK   The Game. 1st ed., flyleaf inscr., worn & soiled. Bradley 49-194 1978 $30

LONDON, JACK   The God of His Fathers and Other Stories. New York, 1901. Orig. cloth, 1st ed., scarce, bind. worn, inner hinges cracked. MacManus 238-554 1978 $65

LONDON, JACK   The House of Pride. New York, 1912. 1st ed., very bright. Ballinger 11-151 1978 $20.00

LONDON, JACK   The Iron Heel. New York, 1908. 1st ed., binding shows wear, name in ink on title page otherwise good copy. Biblo 251-553 1978 $22.50

LONDON, JACK   John Barleycorn. New York, 1913. Cloth. Dawson's 447-259 1978 $40

LONDON, JACK   Michael, Brother of Jerry. New York, 1917. 1st ed., frontis. in color, pic. red cloth, sm. spot. Bradley 49-195 1978 $25

LONDON, JACK   The Night-Born. New York, 1913. Orig. cloth, 1st ed., 1st print., very good. MacManus 238-558 1978 $75

LONDON, JACK   The Sea-Wolf. New York, 1904. Orig. binding, clean, some cracking of back inner hinges, book not loose. Hayman 71-428 1978 $7.50

LONDON, JACK   The Son of the Wolf. Tales of the Far North. New York, 1900. Orig. cloth, stamped in silver, very slightly rubbed, 1st ed., 3rd print., about fine. MacManus 238-553 1978 $110

LONDON, JACK   When God Laughs and Other Stories. New York, 1911. Illus., orig. dec. cloth, 1st ed., very good, scarce. MacManus 238-557 1978 $85

LONDON, KURT   The Seven Soviet Arts. 1937. Plts., covers little marked, very good, first English ed. Bell Book 17-585 1978 £5.50

LONDON & Londonery; Transactions of Three Centuries Consodered from a Historical & Legal Standpoint. 1890. Wr., good, reprint. Hyland 128-735 1978 £10

THE LONDON Directory of 1677. 1677, 1878. Sm. 8vo., printed bds., cloth back, reprint. P.M. Hill 142-166 1978 £15

LONDON Kalendar and Court and City Register for England, Scotland, Ireland and the Colonies 1793. 1793. Coats of arms, 12mo., sheep, worn. George's 635-707 1978 £7.50

LONDON Kalendar and Court and City Register for England, Scotland, Ireland and the Colonies 1808. 1808. Coats of arms, lg. 12mo., sheep badly worn. George's 635-708 1978 £7.50

THE LONDON Minstrel:... London, 1821. 12mo, orig. pr. boards, minor foxing, uncut. Totteridge 29-67 1978 $75

LONDON Oddities; or, the Theatrical Cabinet:.... London, n.d. (1822-3). Twelve numbers in 1 vol., 8vo, full polished calf, gilt, spine and inner dentelles gilt, by Wallis, each number has hand-colored frontispiece signed by Robert Cruikshank, rare fine copy from Albert M. Cohn collection. Ximenes 47-307 1978 $300

LONDONIO, F. A.S.E.   Milord d'Exeter Pari d'Ingilterra Dedica Questi Suoi Pensieri da Esso lui Incisi in Attestato di Profonda Stima... 1764. Oblong 4to., engravings, contemp. calf. Quaritch 983-213 1978 $2,150

LONE, EMMA MIRIAM   Some Noteworthy Firsts in Europe During the Fifteenth Century. New York, 1930. Illus., orig. cloth, pub. box, 1st ed., fine. MacManus 238-969 1978 $40

LONE, EMMA MIRIAM   Some Noteworthy Firsts in Europe During the Fifteenth Century. New York, 1930. One of 425 numbered copies, illus., 8vo., cloth. Battery Park 1-402 1978 $50

LONFAT, G.   Les Colonies Agricoles De La Republique Argentine.... Lausanne, 1879. Sm. 8vo, orig. wrapper bound in, illus., leather, text slightly browned. Edwards 1012-663 1978 £15

LONG, BASIL   British Miniaturists 1520-1860. Illus. with 32 pages in half tone, med. 4to, buckram. Traylen 88-509 1978 £15

LONG, BRECKINRIDGE   Genesis of the Constitution of the United States of America. New York, 1926. 8vo., 1st ed., orig. cloth. Morrill 241-288 1978 $7.50

LONG, CATHERINE   Sir Roland Ashton, Tale of the Times. 1844. 1st. ed., 2 vols. in 1, half titles, orig. cloth, v.g. Jarndyce 16-835 1978 £40

LONG, CRAWFORD W.   Anesthetics: An Account of the first Use of Sulphuric Ether by Inhalation as an Anesthetic Agent in Surgical Operations. Philadelphia, 1850. Bound in bds., binding much decayed. Rittenhouse 49-489 1976 $100

LONG, EDWARD   The History of Jamaica... 1774. Maps, plts., lacking frontis to vol. 1, 3 vols., 4to, modern half calf, tear in 1 pg. repaired, marginal stain affecting few leaves in vol. 2. Edwards 1012-728 1978 £300

LONG, JOHN   Voyages and Travels of an Indian Interpreter and Trader... 1791. 1st. ed., folding map, 4to, contemp. calf, rebacked. Edwards 1012-438 1978 £600

LONG, JOHN   Voyages Chez Differentes Nations Sauvages de L'Amerique Septentrionale. Paris, 1794. Contemp. bds. Wolfe 39-318 1978 $75

LONG, JOHN D.   At the Fireside. Hingham, The Village Press, 1905. One of 200 copies, 12mo., bds., one of only few books prtd. at Hingham. Battery Park 1-121 1978 $125

LONG, MARGARET   The Shadow of the Arrow. Caldwell, 1941. First ed., d.w., illus., maps. Biblo 247-200 1978 $15

LONG, MARY ALVES   High Time to Tell It. Durham, 1950. Illus. Broadfoot 50-127 1978 $14

LONG, STEPHEN H.   Voyage in a Six-Oared Skiff to the Falls of Saint Anthony in 1817. Philadelphia, 1860. 1st ed., half morocco. Ginsberg 14-488 1978 $100

LONG, WILLIAM J.   School of the Woods. Boston, 1902. Illus., plts., gilt-decor. cover, 8vo. K Books 244-204 1978 £9

LONG ISLAND HISTORICAL SOCIETY   Catalogue of the Library of the...1863-1893. Brooklyn, 1893. Thick 8vo., orig. cloth, ex-lib. MacManus 238-970 1978 $20

LONG ISLAND HISTORICAL SOCIETY   Catalogue of the Library of the Long Island Historical Society, 1863-1893. Brooklyn, 1893. Tall 8vo., ex-lib., nice. Morrill 239-548 1978 $12.50

LONGFELLOW, HENRY WADSWORTH   The Courtship of Miles Standish, and Other Poems. Boston, 1858. Orig. cloth, 1st ed., 1st print., very nice, mor.-backed slipcase. MacManus 238-560 1978 $60

LONGFELLOW, HENRY WADSWORTH   The Courtship of Miles Standish, and Other Poems. Boston, 1859. 12mo., later ed. Biblo BL781-1059 1978 $10

LONGFELLOW, HENRY WADSWORTH   Evangeline: A Tale of Acadie. Boston, 1850. Illus., full red blindstamped mor., a.e.g., 1st Amer. illus. ed., hinges and extremities rubbed. MacManus 238-559 1978 $35

LONGFELLOW, HENRY WADSWORTH   The Hanging of the Crane. Boston, 1907. Illus. in color by Arthur I. Keller, 1st illus. ed. Biblo 251-554 1978 $27.50

LONGFELLOW, HENRY WADSWORTH   Kavanagh, a Tale. Boston, 1849. 1st ed., later issue, spinal extremities nicked, edges rubbed, bkplt., good copy. Biblo 251-555 1978 $15

LONGFELLOW, HENRY WADSWORTH   Kavanagh.... Boston, 1849. 12mo., 1st ed., later state. Biblo BL781-1060 1978 $14.50

LONGFELLOW, HENRY WADSWORTH   The New-England Tragedies. Boston, 1868. 12mo., 1st ed., covers stained. Biblo BL781-1061 1978 $17.50

LONGFELLOW, HENRY WADSWORTH   The New-England Tragedies. Boston, 1868. 12mo., 1st trade ed. Biblo 251-556 1978 $10

LONGFELLOW, HENRY WADSWORTH   Prose Works. London, 1863. Engs., cr. 8vo., half calf. K Books 244-205 1978 £6

LONGFELLOW, HENRY WADSWORTH   The Song of Hiawatha. Boston, 1855. Gilt-decor. red cloth, all edges gilt, 1st Amer. ed., 1st prtg., scarce, cover soiling, very good copy. Bradley 49-196 1978 $75

LONGFELLOW, HENRY WADSWORTH   Song of Hiawatha. Boston, 1855. First ed., 3rd printing, 8vo., orig. red cloth, extra deluxe ed., v.g. Houle 10-192 1978 $175

LONGFELLOW, HENRY WADSWORTH   Tales of a Wayside Inn. Boston, 1863. Orig. cloth, 1st Amer. ed., 1st print., nice. MacManus 238-561 1978 $30

LONGFELLOW, SAMUEL   Life of Henry Wadsworth Longfellow. 1886. First English ed., portraits, 2 vols., orig. cloth, spines faded, 8vo. Howes 194-1013 1978 £15

LONGFIELD, A. K.   Anglo-Irish Trade in the 16th Century. 1929. Frontis., roy. 8vo. George's 635-355 1978 £7.50

LONGHURST, M. H.   English Ivories. 1926. 4to., plts., some coloured, buckram. Quaritch 983-89 1978 $100

LONGINUS, DIONYSIUS   On the Sublime... London, 1739. 8vo., contemp. calf, rebacked, frontis. MacManus 238-131 1978 $25

LONGINUS, DIONYSIUS   On the Sublime. 1770. Engraved frontis., contemp. sheep, worn, 8vo. George's 635-484 1978 £5

LONGINUS, DIONYSIUS   Trattato del Sublime di Dionisio Longino Tradotto
dal Greco.... Firenze, 1737. 8vo., new half calf, second ed. King 7-183
1978 £25

LONGLEY, ELIAS   American Manual of Phonography... Cincinnati,
1854. Cloth, some wear, back flyleaf lacking. Hayman 72-438 1978 $15

LONGLEY, ELIAS   American Manual of Phonography... Cincinnati,
1858. Cloth, worn at extremities, lacks free endpaper in front. Hayman 72-439
1978 $12.50

LONGLEY, J. W.   Love. Toronto, 1898. Hood's 115-345
1978 $15

LONGMAN, WILLIAM   History of Life & Times of Edward III. 1869.
3 vols., nick in one spine. Allen 234-1217 1978 $17.50

LONGMORE, T.   A Treatise on Gunshot Wounds. Philadelphia,
1862. Rittenhouse 49-491 1976 $15

LONGSTREET, JAMES   From Manassas to Appomattox. Philadelphia,
1896. Bell Wiley's copy. Broadfoot 46-166 1978 $65

LONGSTRETH, THOMAS MORRIS   The Adirondacks. New York, 1917. Illus.,
first ed., nice, orig. pict. cloth. MacManus 239-332 1978 $17.50

LONGSTRETH, THOMAS MORRIS   In Scarlet and Plain Clothes. New York,
1940. Hood's 115-652 1978 $20

LONGSTRETH, THOMAS MORRIS   Murder at Belly Butte and Other Mysteries
from the Records of the Mounted Police. New York, 1931. Illus., Hood's 115-
653 1978 $25

LONGSTRETH, THOMAS MORRIS   The Silent Force. New York, London, 1928.
3/4 leather, marbled bds., map. Hood's 116-858 1978 $40

LONGSTRETH, THOMAS MORRIS   To Nova Scotia, the Sunrise Province. New
York, 1938. Illus., maps, Hood's 117-258 1978 $17.50

LONGSWORTH, BASIL NELSON   Diary of...March 15, 1853 to January 22,
1854:.... Denver, 1927. Original wr. Ginsberg 14-490 1978 $40

LONGUEIL, CHRISTOPHE DE   De suis infortunis epistola.... Bourges, 1533.
Extremely rare, small 8vo, brown mor. Gilhofer 75-70 1978 SFr 3,900

LONGUERUE, LOUISE DU FOUR DE   Longueruana, ou Recueil de Pensee, de
Discours et de Conversations... Berlin, 1754. 2 parts in 1, old calf, joints
rubbed, lacking part of lettering piece, book label of Roger Senhouse with his notes.
Eaton 45-308 1978 £10

LONGUEVILLE, ANNE GENEVIEVE DE BOURDON   Lettres Inedites De Madame
De Longueville... Paris, 1844. Red mor., marbled bds., gilt spine and rules,
1st ed., very fine. Petrilla 13-15 1978 $67.50

LONGUEVILLE, PETER   The English Hermit. London, 1816. Orig. bds.,
printed label, calf back. Wolfe 39-320 1978 $30

LONGUEVILLE, PETER   The Hermit. London, 1768. Fourth ed., frontispiece, map, contemp. sheep, front cover loose. Wolfe 39-319 1978 $30

LONGUEVILLE, T.   Falklands. 1897. 7 vols. (ex 8), illus., 8vo.
George's 635-1240 1978 £5

LONGUEVILLE, T.   The Life of Sir Kenelm Digby. 1896. Plts.,
good, octavo. Upcroft 10-423 1978 £5

LONGUS   Les Amours Pastorales de Daphnis et de Chloe
Traduit du Grec de Longus par Amyot. Paris, 1800. Sm. 8vo., fine polished
calf, tall clean copy. King 7-363 1978 £30

LONGUS   Daphnis and Chloe. Golden Cockerell Press,
1923. Ltd. to 450 copies, engravings, imp. 8vo., orig. baize buckram, discoloured
George's 635-903 1978 £35

LONGUS   Les Amours Pastorales de Daphnis et Chloe. 1933
(1934). 4to., prtd. on handmade paper, woodcuts, half vellum, slipcase, fine
copy, ltd. to 290 copies. Quaritch 979-10 1978 $600

LONGUS   Pastorals, Literally and Completely Translated
from the Greek. Athens, 1896. Ltd. ed., bookplate, rebound, illus. Biblo
247-473 1978 $22.50

LONGWAY, A. HUGE   Much Darker Days. London, 1884. Half-
leather and cloth, ends worn, interior good. Greene 78-163 1978 $55.00

LONGWORTH DE CHAMBRUN, CLARA   An Explanatory Introduction to Thorpe's
Edition of Shakespeare's Sonnets 1609. Aldington, Kent, Hand and Flower Press,
1950. Folio, orig. vellum backed buckram, gilt top, ltd. and numbered ed., printed
on hand-made paper. Howes 194-909 1978 £30

LONICER, JOH. ADAM   Stand und Orden der H. Romischen Catholischen
Kirchen, darinn aller Geistlichen Personen, H. Ritter und dero verwandten
Herkommen... Frankfurt on the Main, 1585. Sm. 4 to., woodcuts by Jost
Amman, old half vellum, very good copy, First German ed.. Schafer 19-2
1978 sFr. 1,600

LONN, ELLA   Reconstruction in Louisiana After 1868. New
York, 1918. Hinges cracked, autographed by author, Bell Wiley's copy. Broadfoot's 44-509 1978 $30

LONSDALE, HENRY   The Life of John Heysham, M. D. and His Correspondence with Mr. Joshua Milne Relative to the Carlisle Bills of Mortality.
London, 1870. 4to., frontis. portr., orig. stamped cloth, gilt stamped on upper
cover & spine, light foxing, good copy from the library of Dr. Alfred M. Hellman,
1st ed. Zeitlin 245-124 1978 $95

LONSDALE, JOHN JAMES   Songs and Ballads. London, Edinburgh &
Carlisle, 1867. 1st ed., orig. green cloth, very good or better. Limestone
9-180 1978 $21

LOOMIS, CHARLES BATTELL   Cheerful Americans. New York, 1903.
1st ed., illus., very good or better. Limestone 9-181 1978 $20

LOOMIS, CHARLES BATTELL   I've Been Thinking. New York, 1905. First ed.
Austin 82-595 1978 $12.50

LOOMIS. CHARLES BATTELL   More Cheerful Americans. 1904. Illus., first ed.
Austin 82-596 1978 $15

LOOMIS, J. L.   Leadville, Colorado. Colorado Springs, 1879.
Original printed wr., 1st ed. Ginsberg 14-266 1978 $350

LOOS, ANITA   "Gentlemen Prefer Blondes." New York, 1925.
Illus. by Ralph Barton, 8vo., 1st issue. Morrill 239-481 1978 $25

A LOOSE Rein. London, 1887. Color illus., nos. I-II, color pic. wrs.,
bound in 3/4 brown mor., fine, rare. Argosy Special-58 1978 $150

LORAND, ARNOLD   Defective Memory, Absentmindedness and Their
Treatment. Philadelphia, 1927. Rittenhouse 49-493 1976 $10

LORANGER, T. J. J.   Report of the Committee Appointed to Enquire into
the Transactions of the Montreal and Bytown Railway Company. (Toronto, 1856).
Printed wrappers. Wolfe 39-470a 1978 $75

LORANT, STEFAN   The New World. New York, (1946). First ed.,
boxed, illus., 4to. Biblo 247-30 1978 $35

LORANT, STEFAN   The New World. New York, (1946). 4to.,
plts. in color & b/w, 1st ed. Biblo 251-35 1978 $18.50

LORD, JOSEPH L.   Dr. Charles T. Jackson's Claims to the Discovery
of Etherization. Boston, 1848. Paper covers frayed. Rittenhouse 49-494 1976
$75

LORD, LINDSAY   Naval Architecture of Planing Hulls. Cornell
Maritime Press, 1946. Illus. Austin 80-187 1978 $12.50

LORD, W. B.   Shifts and Expedients of Camp Life, Travel and
Exploration. London, 1876. 1st. ed., thick 8vo, plts., illus., orig. green cloth,
gilt, inside front joint weak. Deighton 5-216 1978 £58

LORENTZ, HENDRIK ANTOON   Das Relativitatsprinzip. Leipzig & Berlin,
1914. 8vo., orig. prtd. wrs., uncut, very good copy. Norman 5-188 1978 $75

LORENTZ, HENDRIK ANTOON   Les Theories Statistiques en Thermo-dynami-
que. Leipzig & Berlin, 1916. 8vo., orig. prtd. wrs., uncut, chipped & soiled
but very good copy, 1st ed., pres. copy. Norman 5-189 1978 $85

LORENTZ, HENDRIK ANTOON   The Theory of Electrons and Its Applications
to the Phenomena of Light and Radiant Heat. Leipzig, 1909. 8vo., ads, orig.
cloth, gilt, worn but very good copy, 1st ed. Norman 5-187 1978 $75

LORENTZ, HENDRIK ANTOON   Versuch Einer Theorie der Electrischen und
Optischen Erscheinungen in Bewegten Korpern. Leiden, 1895. 8vo., contemp.
cloth-backed bds., endpapers renewed, fine copy, 1st ed. Norman 5-186 1978
$650

LORENZINI, CARLO   Le Avventure di Pinocchio. Firenze, c.1920. Illus. by Attilio Mussino, quarto, 3rd ed., color plates and illus., spine sunned, very good, excessively rare. Victoria 34-171 1978 $150

LORENZINI, CARLO   Pinocchio. New York, (1932). 1st ed., color plates, t.p., and cover inset, cover plate rubbed, rear cover spotted. Victoria 34-614 1978 $12.50

LORIA, ACHILLE   The Economic Foundations of Society. 1899. 1st ed., front fly loose. Austin 80-798 1978 $27.50

LORIA, ACHILLE   The Economic Synthesis. 1914. 1st ed. Austin 80-799 1978 $37.50

LORIMER, NORMA   Mirry-Ann A Manx Story. NY, 1900. Fir. Am. Ed., cloth binding, good cond. Greene 78-251 1978 $15.00

LORING, DR.   Agriculture. Omaha, 1883. Orig. pr. wr., 1st ed. Ginsberg 14-719 1978 $50

LORING, AMASA   A History of Shapleigh. Portland, 1854. 1st ed., 3/4 calf, lib. makrs, very good. MacManus 239-994 1978 $50

LORING, CHARLES G.   Neutral Relations of England and the United States. Boston, 1863. Wrs., Bell Wiley's copy. Broadfoot 46-298 1978 $12

LORITI, HEINRICH GLAREANUS
Please turn to
GLAREANUS, HENRICUS

LORNE, MARQUIS OF
Please turn to
ARGYLL, JOHN GEORGE CAMPBELL, 9TH DUKE OF

LORRIS, GUILLAUME DE   Roman De La Rose
Please turn to
ROMAN DE LA ROSE

LORRY, ANNE CHARLES DE   Tractatus de Morbis Cutaneis. Paris, 1777. 4to., mod. calf, 1st ed., fine copy. Gilhofer 74-95 1978 sFr 1,000

LORWIN, LEWIS L.   Economic Consequences of the Second World War. 1941. Ex-lib. Austin 80-189 1978 $10

LOS ALAMOS SCIENTIFIC LABORATORY   The Effects of Atomic Weapons. Combat Forces Press, 1950. Illus. Austin 80-190 1978 $12.50

LOS ANGELES As a Summer Resort. Los Angeles, n.d.(1902?). Wrps. Hayman 71-76 1978 $8.50

LOS ANGELES: City and County: Resources, Climate, Progress and Outlook. Los Angeles, 1884. Map, orig. pr. wr., 1st ed. Ginsberg 14-150 1978 $75

LOS ANGELES County: Resources and General Characteristics of Soil and Climate. Los Angeles, 1890. Illus., map, tables, original printed wr., 1st ed. Ginsberg 14-151 1978 $85

LOSKIEL, GEORGE HENRY   History of the Mission of the United Brethren Among the Indians in North America. London, 1794. 1st ed. in English, cloth, lacks map, but nice copy. MacManus 239-1540 1978 $65

LOSSADA, LUDOVICO DE   Institutiones Dialecticae Vulgo Summulae,.... Salamanca, 1721. 1st ed., quarto, full contemp. vellum, woodcut diagrams. Bennett 20-125 1978 $150

LOSSING, BENSON JOHN   The Empire State: A Compendious History of the Commonwealth of New York. Hartford, 1888. 1st ed., 4to, illus., orig. cloth, ex-lib., fine. MacManus 239-340 1978 $30

LOSSING, BENSON JOHN   The Hudson, from the Wilderness to the Sea. Troy, (1866). Illus. MacManus 239-259 1978 $45

LOSSING, BENSON JOHN   The Pictorial Field-Book of the Revolution.... New York, 1851. 2 vols., royal 8vo, nice set, 1st. ed., frontis in color in vol. 1. Baldwins' 51-313 1978 $65

LOSSING, BENSON JOHN   The Pictorial Field-Book of the Revolution... New York, 1860. 2 vols., illus., later cloth, fine. MacManus 239-598 1978 $60

LOSSING, BENSON JOHN   The Two Spies, Nathan Hale and John Andre. New York, 1886. Illus. Butterfield 21-52 1978 $15

LOSSIUS, CASPAR FRIEDRICH   Gumal and Lina. 1828. Third ed., 12mo., contemp. half blue calf, gilt, plts. P. M. Hill 142-76 1978 £12

LOSSIUS, LUCAS   Historia Passionis, Mortis Sepulturae et Ressurectionis Iesu Christi, Interrogationibus and Obiectionibus Explicata: and Iconibus Artificiosae Expressa. (Frankfurt, 1551). 8vo., woodcuts, rare, bds. Gilhofer 74-134 1978 sFr 1,000

LOSTELNEAU, LE SIEUR DE   Le Mareschal de Bataille. Paris, 1647. Folio, cont. calf, rebacked, engravings, pencil signature of John Fortescue. F. Edwards 1013-343 1978 £1,250

LOTH, A.   Saint Vincent de Paul et sa Mission Sociale. Paris, 1880. 4to., half red calf, gilt spine, colored frontis., plts., text illus. Van der Peet H-64-488 1978 Dfl 45

LOTI, PIERRE   Un Pelerin d'Angkor. Paris, 1930. 4to., full blue polished calf, uncut, orig. wr., backstrip bound in slipcase, bound by Bayard, Lyon, ltd. ed. issued in 225 numbered copies, all on velin de Lana paper, illus. by Paul Jouve, very fine. Goldschmidt 110-37 1978 $900

LOTZE, HERMANN
Please turn to
LOTZE, RUDOLPH HERMANN

LOTZE, RUDOLPH HERMANN   Allegemeine Physiologie des Korperlichen Lebens. Leipzig, 1851. 8vo., half-calf, 1st ed. Gilhofer 74-96 1978 sFr 600

LOTZE, RUDOLPH HERMANN   Microcosmus... Edinburgh, n.d. 4th ed., 2 vols. in 1, very thick 8vo., Salloch 348-122 1978 $40

LOUBAT, JOSEPH FLORIMOND DUC DE   The Medallic History of the United States...1776-1876. New York, 1878. 2 vols., folio, etchings by Jules Jacquemart, covers soiled, spines torn at extremities, contents of text & plts. fine, scarce. Biblo 251-229 1978 $150

LOUBAT, JOSEPH FLORIMOND, DUC DE   Narrative of the Mission to Russia, in 1866, of the Hon. Gustavus Vasa Fox, Assistant Secretary of the Navy. New York, 1873. Lg. 8vo., first ed., pres. from Loubat. Morrill 239-482 1978 $30

LOUCKS, ALBERT C.   Black River and Northern New York Conference Memorial... Sandy Creek, 1923. 3rd vol., illus., cloth. Biblo BL781-164 1978 $12

LOUD, JEREMY   Gabriel Vane. 1856. First ed. Austin 82-597 1978 $22.50

LOUDON, ARCHIBALD   A Selection, of some of the Most Interesting Narratives,.... Carlisle, reprint (1888). 100 numbered copies only, signed by William H. Egle, 2 vols., half mor. with marbled boards, t.e.g., very good set, 8vo. Americanist 101-84 1978 $250

LOUDON, JOHN CLAUDIUS   An Encyclopaedia of Agriculture... 1831. 2nd. ed., woodcut illus. by Branston, thick 8vo, light signs of use, very good, contemp. calf. Fenning 32-199 1978 £28.50

LOUDON, JOHN CLAUDIUS   An Encyclopaedia of Cottage, Farm and Villa Architecture and Furniture. 1837. Lithographs and wood engravings, incomplete, only 560 pages, ex 1122, binders buckram. George's 635-83 1978 £7.50

LOUHI, E. A.   The Delaware Finns... New York, (1925). MacManus 239-118 1978 $25

LOUIS, PIERRE CHARLES ALEXANDRE   Anatomical, Pathological and Therapeutic Researches on the Yellow Fever of Gibraltar of 1828. Boston, 1839. 8vo., partly unopened, 1st Amer. ed. Morrill 239-159 1978 $47.50

LOUIS, PIERRE CHARLES ALEXANDRE   Recherches... Paris, 1829. Two vols., Some spine cloth missing, hinges weak. Rittenhouse 49-495 1976 $130

LOUIS, PIERRE CHARLES ALEXANDRE   Researches on Phthisis. London, 1844. 8vo., 2nd ed., orig. green stamped cloth, gilt emblem on covers, very good copy from Library of Dr. Alfred M. Hellman. Zeitlin 245-155 1978 $65

LOUIS, PIERRE CHARLES ALEXANDRE   Pathological Researches on Phthisis. Washington, 1836. Modern bds. Rittenhouse 49-496 1976 $65

LOUIS, TRACY   The Final War. A Story of the Great Betrayal. London, 1896. Fir. Ed., illus. by Sherie, orig. cloth binding, shelf wear w/Smith Library blind-stamp, good. Greene 78-277 1978 $30.00

LOUIS Bond, The Merchant's Son. Troy, c.1840. Chapbook, woodcuts, 2 wood-cuts signed by Anderson, wrappers and stitching gone. Victoria 34-506 1978 $10

LOUISE, ELLEN   The Book of the Boudoir; or, Memento of Friend-ship. Boston, 1853. 6 plts., full leather, gilt, worn. Eaton 45-311 1978 £10

LOUISIANA. LAWS.   Acts Passed by the Fourth Legislature of the State of Louisiana, at Their Session Held and Begun in the Town of Baton Rouge, on the 19th of January, 1852. New Orleans, 1852. Full calf, 1st ed. Ginsberg 14-492 1978 $75

LOUKOMSKI, G. K.   Art Etrusque. Paris, (1930). 4to., plts., wrs. Biblo BL781-432 1978 $17.50

LOUNSBERRY, A.   Gardens Near the Sea. New York, 1910. 8vo, orig. cloth. Book Chest 17-238 1978 $25

LOUNSBERRY, CLEMENT A.   Early History of North Dakota: Essential Out-lines of American History. Washington, 1919. Illus., original gold stamped cloth, 1st ed. Ginsberg 14-317 1978 $50

LOUTHERBOURG, PHILIPPE JACQUES DE   The Romantic and Picturesque Scenery of England and Wales. 1805. Roy. 8vo., coloured plts., descriptions in English & French, contemp. half red mor., fine copy. Quaritch 983-343 1978 $1,735

LOUTTIT, GEORGE W.   The Eddyite. Fort Wayne, 1908. 8vo., orig. cloth, 1st ed. Morrill 241-289 1978 $12.50

LOUYS, PIERRE   The Adventures of King Pausole. Fortune Press, 1929. No. 95 of 1125 copies on handmade paper, buckram-backed marbled bds., fine, first English ed. Bell Book 16-589 1978 £12.50

LOUYS, PIERRE   The Adventures of King Pausole. New York, 1933. Coloured plts. by Beresford Egan, covers little faded, very good. Bell Book 17-487 1978 £8.50

LOUYS, PIERRE   The Adventures of King Pausole. N.P., n.d. Ltd. ed., edges rubbed. Biblo BL781-1063 1978 $12

LOUYS, PIERRE   Aphrodite. Fortune Press, 1928. No. 185 of 1075 copies on handmade paper, roy. 8vo., cloth-backed marbled bds., fine, first English ed. Bell Book 16-590 1978 £12.50

LOUYS, PIERRE   Aphrodite, a Novel of Ancient Morals. London, Fortune Press, n.d. Roy. 8vo, bds., buckram spine, corners trifle worn, ltd. ed. of 1075 copies. Traylen 88-295 1978 £10

LOUYS, PIERRE   Cyprian Masques. Fortune Press, n.d. No. 112 of 1200 copies on Kelmscott handmade paper, drawings by Beresford Egan, buckram backed marbled bds., fine, first English ed. Bell Book 16-591 1978 £20

LOUYS, PIERRE   Dialogue sur le Danse. Paris, (1949). Tall quarto, loose in sheets as issued, watercolor drawings by Marie Laurencin, engraved by Louis Maccard, 1 of 130 copies, board wrs. with slipcase to match, fine. Duschnes 220-178 1978 $150

LOUYS, PIERRE   Mimes des Courtisanes. Paris, 1935. Illus., one of 20 lettered copies, 4to., sewn into orig. wrappers, fine, first ed. Rota 212-37 1978 £200

LOUYS, PIERRE   The Songs of Bilitis. London, New York, 1904. Tall octavo, full light brown levant, red and green floral onlays on both covers and spine, moire silk free endpapers, 1 of 3 copies on Jap. vellum, initial letters hand colored. Totteridge 29-68 1978 $250

LOUYS, PIERRE   The Songs of Bilitis. Fortune Press, n.d. No. 102 of 925 copies on Kelmscott handmade paper, buckram, fine, first English ed. Bell Book 16-592 1978 £12.50

LOUYS, PIERRE   The Twilight of the Nymphs. Fortune Press, 1928. No. 192 of 1200 copies on handmade paper, plts., buckram,roy. 8vo., fine, first English ed. Bell Book 16-593 1978 £20

LOVE, PHILIP H.   Andrew W. Mellon, the Man and His Work. Bal-timore, 1929. Illus., inner hinges split. Biblo BL781-217 1978 $9

LOVE, WILLIAM DE LOSS   The Colonial History of Hartford. Hartford, 1935. 2nd ed., cloth, ltd. to 500 copies, fold. maps. MacManus 239-93 1978 $30

LOVE and Death in a Barn. Philadelphia, (1875). Pict. wrs., minor chipping around edges. Hayman 73-171 1973 $20

LOVE & Madness: A Story Too True, in a Series of Letters. London, 1780. 8vo., polished 3/4 calf, 1st ed., rare. Argosy Special-30 1978 $150

THE LOVE of an Unknown Soldier; Found in a Dug Out. Toronot, 1918. Hood 116-134 1978 $15

LOVE'S Pilgrimage: a Story Founded on Facts. Philadelphia, 1799. 1st Amer. ed., contemp. calf, worn, 8vo., very good. Americanist 103-126 1978 $60

LOVECRAFT, H. P.   Something About Cats and Other Pieces. Sauk City, 1949. Frontis., black cloth, 1st ed., fine in dust jacket. Bradley 49-197 1978 $75

LOVELACE, RICHARD   Poems. Oxford, 1925. 1 of 400 copies on large paper, 4 to., frontispiece portrait, illus., half cloth, uncut, 2 vols., very good. Houle 10-193 1978 $65

LOVELASS, PETER   The Law's Disposal of a Person's Estate Who Dies Without Will or Testament... 1787. 12mo, contemp. calf, nice. Fenning 32-200 1978 £16.50

LOVER, SAMUEL   Handy Andy: A Tale of Irish Life. London, 1896. Illus., orig. bind. Petrilla 13-16 1978 $7.50

LOVERING, MARTIN   History of the Town of Holland, Mass. Rutland, 1915. 1st ed., thick 8vo., illus., ports., orig. cloth, very good. MacManus 239-1030 1978 $35

LOVETT, RICHARD 1692-1780   Philosophical Essays, in Three Parts. Worcester, 1766. 8vo., contemp. calf, spine gilt, 1st ed., fldg. frontis. & plts., half title present, fine copy. Ximenes 47-184 1978 $250

LOVETT, RICHARD 1851-1904   The History of the London Missionary Society, 1795-1899. 1899. Maps, portraits, 2 vols., 8vo. George's 635-1091 1978 £10.50

LOVETT, RICHARD 1851-1904   Pictures from Holland. London, 1887. Lg. 8vo, gilt pict. cloth, plts., illus., binding worn and discolored, shaved, scarce. Van der Peet H64-489 1978 Dfl 95

LOVETT, ROBERT W.   The Treatment of Infantile Paralysis. Philadel-phia, 1916. Ex-library. Rittenhouse 49-497 1976 $10

LOVING, BRADY ANTOINE   Thornton Kelly Tyson: Pioneer Home Missionary. Kansas City, 1915. Illus., orig. cloth, 1st ed. Ginsberg 14-988 1978 $50

LOW, CHARLES R.   Maritime Discovery: A History of Nautical Exploration From the Earliest Times. 1881. Sole ed., 2 vols., 8vo, orig.cloth, nice copy. Fenning 32-201 1978 £18.50

LOW, NATHANIEL   An Astronomical Diary: or Almanack, for...1801. Boston, (1800). Sewed. Hayman 72-6 1978 $12.50

LOW, DAVID   The Best of Low. 1930. 4to., cloth-backed bds., good, first English ed. Bell Book 17-588 1978 $7.50

LOW, DAVID   Lions and Lambs. 1928. Roy. 8vo., signed pres. copy to H. G. Wells by artist, orig. drawing on flyleaf, drawings. George's 635-123 1978 £20

LOW, DAVID   Low Again: a pageant of politics. Cresset Press, n.d. (1938). Oblong 4to., cloth-backed pict. bds., somewhat soiled & rubbed covers, else good, first English ed. Bell Book 17-590 1978 £6.50

LOW, DAVID   Low's War Cartoons. Cresset Press, (1941). Sm. oblong 4to., cloth-backed bds., covers somewhat rubbed & soiled, good, first Eng-lish ed. Bell Book 17-592 1978 £5

LOW, DAVID   Sketches from the New Statesman. 1926. Sm. folio, drawings, no text, loose in portfolio as issued. George's 635-124 1978 £5.25

LOW, DAIVD   Ye Madde Designer. 1935. Spine dull, 4to., good, first English ed. Bell Book 17-593 1978 £8.50

LOW, DAVID   Years of Wrath. 1949. Drawings, 4to. George's 635-125 1978 £10.50

LOW, HUGH   Sarawak, Its Inhabitants and Productions:.... London, 1848. Illus., cloth, rebacked, corners worn. Dawson's 127-273 1978 $45

LOW, JULIET   How Girls Can Help Their Country. New York, 1916. Illus. flexible cloth bubbled, lightly stained, very good. Victoria 34-335 1978 $10

LOW, NATHANIEL   An Astronomical Diary; or, Almanack for 1777. Boston, 1777. Dampstain on bottom of pp. edges, very rare. Nestler Rare 78-91 1978 $145

LOW, SIDNEY   Egypt in Transition. New York, 1914. 8vo, orig. cloth, portraits, g.t. K Books 239-282 1978 £7

LOWDERMILK, WILL H.   History of Cumberland, Maryland, from the Time of the Indian Town, Caiuctucuc, in 1728, Up to the Present Day... Washington, D.C., 1878. 1st ed., illus., cloth, very scarce, very fine. MacManus 239-1001 1978 $90

LOWE, E. J.   Beautiful Leaved Plants. London, 1868. Ex-lib, respined, colored plts., 8vo., orig. binding. Book Chest 17-239 1978 $95

LOWE, E. J.   Beautiful Leaved Plants. London, 1868. Coloured plts., wood-engravings, roy. 8vo., nice, half hard-grain mor. gilt. K Books 244-206 1978 £45

LOWE, ROBERT   General View of the Agriculture of the County of Nottingham. 1798. Hand-coloured map, contemp. half calf, 8vo. Howes 194-128 1978 £28

LOWELL, A. LAWRENCE   Final Report of The Commission on Medical Education. New York, 1932. Rittenhouse 49-498 1976 $15

LOWELL, AMY   Can Grande's Castle. New York, 1918. 8vo, boards, cloth back, paper labels, near Fine, 1st ed., collector's cond. Desmarais 1-278 1978 $15

LOWELL, AMY   East Wind. Boston, 1926. 8vo, boards, cloth back, paper labels chipped, light wear to covers, ownership inscription, Nice, 1st ed., collector's cond. Desmarais 1-279 1978 $12.50

LOWELL, AMY   John Keats. Boston, 1925. 8vo, 2 vols., red cloth, gilt lettering on spine, near Mint set, 1st ed., collector's cond. Desmarais 1-280 1978 $40

LOWELL, AMY   What's O'Clock. Boston, 1925. 8vo, grey-blue boards, cloth back, paper labels, bookplate, small hole in t.p., nice, 1st ed., collector's cond. Desmarais 1-281 1978 $15

LOWELL, EDWARD J.   The Hessians and Other German Auxilliaries of Great Britain in the Revolutionary War. New York, 1884. Maps, plans, orig. binding. Wolfe 39-322 1978 $15

LOWELL, JAMES RUSSELL   Converstaion on Some of the Old Poets. 1845. 1/2 calf. Eaton 45-312 1978 £5

LOWELL, JAMES RUSSELL   Latest Literary Essays and Addresses. Cambridge, 1891. Ltd. to 300 copies, stain on back cover. Biblo 247-594 1978 $25

LOWELL, JAMES RUSSELL   My Study Windows. 1871. 1/2 green morocco, ex-lib. binding, gilt, spine, t.e.g. Eaton 45-313 1978 £10

LOWELL, JAMES RUSSELL   Political Essays. Boston, 1888. 1st ed., untrimmed, 75 copies prepared. Americanist 102-68 1978 $25

LOWELL, JAMES RUSSELL   The Present Crisis. N. P., John Henry Nash Fine Arts Press, 1941. 8vo., lg. folio, orig. real vellum wrs. lettered in gold, #105 of ltd. ed., portr., excellent copy. Americanist 103-52 1978 $35

LOWELL, JAMES RUSSELL   Under the Willows and Other Poems. Boston, 1869. 8vo, green cloth, gilt stamped cover and spine, bevelled edges, 1st printing, t.e.g., near Fine, 1st ed., collector's cond. Desmarais 1-282 1978 $35

LOWELL, MARIA   Poems. Cambridge, 1907. 1 of 330 copies designed by Bruce Rogers, tall thin 8vo, orig. bds., uncut, boxed, excellent copy, slightly worn box. Americanist 102-104 1978 $40

LOWELL, ROBERT   Near the Ocean. New York, (1871). Wrs., 1st Noonday paperback ed. Biblo 251-557 1978 $7.50

LOWENTHAL, MARVIN   The Jews of Germany. New York, 1936. Spine faded, top rubbed. Biblo 251-698 1978 $15

LOWMAN, MOSES   A Paraphrase and Notes on the Revelation of St. John. London, 1737. Blind tooled original leather binding with spine label, very good, somewhat worn & loose. Nestler Rare 78-243 1978 $25

LOWNDES, BELLOC   Lizzie Borden. New York, 1939. 8vo., orig. cloth, 1st ed., remains of scotch tape inside front cover. Morrill 241-290 1978 $10

LOWNDES, WILLIAM THOMAS   The Bibliographer's Manual of English Literature. 1858. New ed., 6 vols., 1/2 leather, some covers loose. Eaton 45-315 1978 £40

LOWNE, B. T.   The Anatomy & Physiology of the Blow-Fly. London, 1870. Scarce, inner hinge cracking, worn binding, 8vo., plts., some in color. Book Chest 17-240 1978 $70

LOWRIE, HENRY BERRY   The Lowrie History. Lumberton, 1909. Wrs., illus. Broadfoot 50-129 1978 $50

LOWRY, MALCOLM   Under the Volcano. New York, (1947). 1st ed., author's 1st book, top of spine chipped, otherwise good copy. Biblo 251-559 1978 $17.50

LOWRY, MALCOLM   Under the Volcano. 1947. First ed. Austin 82-1174 1978 $22.50

LOWRY, MALCOLM   Under the Volcano. New York, 1947. First US ed., very good. Bell Book 17-597 1978 $37.50

LOWRY, ROBERT   Casualty. New York, (1946). 12mo., 1st ed., good, d.w. clipped & repaired. Biblo 251-558 1978 $12.50

LOWTH, ROBERT   The Life of William of Wykeham, Bishop of Winchester. Oxford, 1777. Third ed., half calf, vignette, rebacked, plts., 8vo. Howes 194-520 1978 £25

LOWTH, ROBERT   A Short Introduction to English Grammar. 1791. New ed., sm. 8vo., contemp. sheep. Howes 194-298 1978 £12.50

LOYOLA, IGNACIO DE   Exercitia spiritualia. Rome, 1576. Very rare early ed., old half-calf, lightly rubbed. Gilhofer 75-60 1978 SFr 1,500

LOZANO, P.   A True and Particular Relation of the Dreadful Earthquake Which Happen'd at Lima.... London, 1748. 2nd. ed., map, plts., contemp. calf, rebacked, 8vo. Edwards 1012-664 1978 £120

LUARD, JOHN   A History of the Dress of the British Soldier, From the Earliest Period to the Present Time. 1852. Roy. 8vo., plts., cloth, covers dampmarked. Quaritch 983-67 1978 $130

LUARD, JOHN   A History of the Dress of the British Soldier. 1852. Frontis., plts., roy. 8vo., orig. cloth, spine repaired. F. Edwards 1013-350 1978 £30

LUBBOCK, BASIL   Sail, the Romance of the Clipper Ships. 1927-29. Plates by J. Spurling, sm. labels removed from titles, 2 vols., lg. 4to., Vol. 1 orig. dark green buckram, Vol. 2 orig. blue buckram. George's 635-839 1978 £120

LUBBOCK, F. R.   Report of the Treasurer of the State of Texas. Austin, 1880. Printed wr., charts. Jenkins 116-840 1978 $12.50

LUBITSCH, ERNEST   An Index to the Films of Ernst Lubitsch. (London), 1947. Orig. binding. Wolfe 39-325 1978 $10

LUBKE, WILHELM   Die Kunst des Altertums. Fuenfzehnte Auflage. Esslingen, 1921. Illus., color plts. Biblo BL781-433 1978 $15

LUBKER, F.   Reallexikon des Classischen Alterthums fuer Gymnasien. 1877. Allen 234-552 1978 $10

LUCANUS, MARCUS ANNAEUS   Belli Civilis Libri X Editorum in Usum ed. A. E. Housman. 1950. Allen 234-553 1978 $7.50

LUCANUS, MARCUS ANNAEUS   Pharsalia. Venetiis, 1515. Octavo, full contemp. limp vellum, very sound, contemp. ink interlineation. Bennett 20-126 1978 $300

LUCANUS, MARCUS ANNAEUS   Pharsalia, sive de bello civili inter Caesarem et Pompeum, libri decem. 1719. Engr. frontis., 12mo., contemp. panelled calf, rubbed. George's 635-485 1978 £7.50

LUCANUS, MARCUS ANNAEUS   Pharsalia, cum Scholiaste Hucusque Inedito, et Notis Integris H. Glareani, J. Micylli, et al., cur. F. Oudendorp. 1728. 4to., old calf, covers detached, fldg. map. Allen 234-554 1978 $15

LUCANUS, MARCUS ANNAEUS   Pharsaliae. Rotterodami, 1805. Sm. 8vo., half calf, uncut, corners broken. Van der Peet H-64-490 1978 Dfl 65

LUCAS, C.   Les eglises circulaires d'Angleterre. Paris, 1882. Second ed., folio, plts., cloth. Upcroft 12-274 1978 £8

LUCAS, C. P.   The Beginnings of English Overseas Enterprise, a Prelude to the Empire. Oxford, 1917. Covers stained, 8vo. George's 635-357 1978 £5

LUCAS, C. P.   Lord Durhams's Report on the Affairs of British North America. Oxford, 1912. 3 vols. Hood 116-639 1978 $125

LUCAS, CHARLES   The Complaints of the City of Dublin.... (Dublin?), 1749. Engraved frontis, 8vo, orig. marbled paper wrapper, uncut, fine. Fenning 32-202 1978 £18.50

LUCAS, E. V.   Mixed Vintages. London, 1919. 1st ed., very good or better. Limestone 9-182 1978 $9.50

LUCAS, E. V.   Roving East and Roving West. London, 1921. 1st ed., very good or better. Limestone 9-183 1978 $8.50

LUCAS, E. V.   A Swan and her Friends. 1907. Illus., 8vo. George's 635-1263 1978 £5.25

LUCAS, E. V.   A Wanderer in Holland. London, 1909. 9th ed., illus., frontispiece, endpaper map, unread copy, very good or better. Limestone 9-184 1978 $15

LUCAS, THOMAS J.   The Zulus and the British Frontiers. London, 1879. Dec. cloth, little dis coloured & marked, boxed, 8vo. K·Books 239-283 1978 £45

LUCE, ROBERT   Legislative Assemblies. Boston, 1924. Biblo BL781-840 1978 $10

LUCIAN US SAMOSATENSIS   Les Oeuvres de Lucian de Samosate Philosophe excellent,.... Paris, 1581. Folio, Roman letter, woodcut illus., 17th-century sprinkled calf, backstrip panelled in gilt, unrecorded, 1st ed. Quaritch 978-97 1978 $1,950

LUCIAN US SAMOSATENSIS   Opera omnia. Paris, 1615. Folio, text in Greek & Latin, contemp. calf, Ben Jonson's copy with his signature and motto on the title. Quaritch Summer, 1978-29 1978 $2,400

LUCIANUS SAMOSATENSIS   Opera. 1896. 3 vols., half calf. Allen 234-944 1978 $20

LUCILLUS, CAIUS   Satyrographorum Principiis, Eq. Romani.... Patavii, 1735. 8vo., marbled bds., calf spine, very good. King 7-184 1978 £25

LUCK, J. VERNON   Bone and Joint Diseases. Springfield, 1950. First ed. Rittenhouse 49-499 1976 $20

LUCKE, JEROME B.   History of the New Haven Grays, from Sept. 13, 1816, to Sept. 13, 1876. New Haven, 1876. Portrs., 8vo., portion of text dampstained, 1st ed. Morrill 239-349 1978 $17.50

LUCKHARDT, C. A.   Report on the "Green Nick" Mine, of Nevada. [New York, 1880]. Orig. green wr., 1st ed. Ginsberg 14-733 1978 $75

LUCRETIUS CARUS, TITUS   Tito Lucrezio Caro: Della Natura Delle Cose. Milan, 1813. 8vo., vellum, fine, spine label missing. Salloch 348-124 1978 $65

LUCRETIUS CARUS, TITUS   De la Natura Delle Cose, Libri Sei, Trad. da A. Marchetti. 1804. 2 vols., half calf. Allen 234-586 1978 $7.50

LUCRETIUS CARUS, TITUS   The Nature of Things. 1813. 2 vols., 4to., contemp. half russia, very good, first ed. Howes 194-370 1978 £45

LUCRETIUS CARUS, TITUS   The Nature of Things, a Didascalic Poem... 1813. 2 vols. in 1, folio, old calf, joints broken. Allen 234-574 1978 $25

LUCRETIUS CARUS, TITUS   De la Nature. 1924-28. 5 vols., sewn, vol. 2 of text is bound. Allen 234-567 1978 $25

LUCRETIUS CARUS, TITUS   De Rerum Natura Buch III. 1897. Sewn, tear in margin of title. Allen 234-570 1978 $7.50

LUCRETIUS CARUS, TITUS   Titi Lucretii Cari De Rerum Natura Libri Sex. Paris, 1563. 4to., Italic and Roman letter, 19th century half vellum, red edges, 1st ed. Quaritch 978-98 1978 $575

LUCRETIUS CARUS, TITUS   De Rerum Natura Libri Sex. 1659. Buckram. Allen 234-564 1978 $17.50

LUCRETIUS CARUS, TITUS   De Rerum Natura Libri Sex. Cambridge, 1675. Vellum, 1st ed. of the Latin text. Allen 234-565 1978 $60

LUCRETIUS CARUS, TITUS   De Rerum Natura Libri Sex. Oxford, 1695. Vellum. Allen 234-566 1978 $25

LUCRETIUS CARUS, TITUS   De Rerum Natura Libri Sex.... London, 1712. Engraved title, copperplates, printed by Jacob Tonson, rebound in modern green leather, 4to. Book Chest 17-241 1978 $125

LUCRETIUS CARUS, TITUS   De Rerum Natura. Birminghamae, Baskerville Press, 1772. First Baskerville ed., 4to., contemp. calf, joints cracked. Howes 194-153 1978 $60

LUCRETIUS CARUS, TITUS   De Rerum Natura Libri Sex. Birmingham, 1772. Folio, contemp. calf, rehinged, spine gilt with label. Salloch 345-110 1978 $150

LUCRETIUS CARUS, TITUS   De Rerum Natura Libri Sex. Birmingham, Baskerville, 1773. Sm. 8vo., calf with label. Salloch 348-123 1978 $60

LUCRETIUS CARUS, TITUS   De Rerum Natura Libri Sex. 1832. 4to., full contemp. russia gilt, all edges gilt, rebacked, orig. backstrip laid down. Howes 194-1015 1978 £25

LUCRETIUS CARUS, TITUS   De Rerum Natura. On the Nature of Things. Cambridge, 1891. 4th ed., rev'd., 8vo., contemp. cloth. Salloch 348-125 1978 $20

LUCRETIUS CARUS, TITUS   De Rerum Natura Libri Vi. 1907. Flyleaves written on, some notes in ink. Allen 234-569 1978 $7.50

LUCRETIUS CARUS, TITUS   His Six Books, De Natura Rerum Done Into English Verse with Notes. 1683. 3rd ed., old calf, covers detached. Allen 234-572 1978 $12.50

LUCRETIUS CARUS, TITUS   Traduction Nouvelle, Avec Des Notes: Par M. Lagrange. 1798. 2 vols. in 1, new buckram. Allen 234-583 1978 $10

LUCY, HENRY W.   The Balfourian Parliament, 1900-1905. 1906. 1st. ed., illus., 8vo, orig. cloth, spine darkened, covers faded along foreedge, pres. inscription to Winston Churchill. Sawyer 298-91 1978 £60

LUDLOW, LOUIS   From Cornfield to Press Gallery. 1924. Illus., first ed. Austin 82-599 1978 $12.50

LUDLOW, W. R.   Zululand and Cetawayo... London & Birmingham, 1882. Portrait, illus., map, plts., cr. 8vo, dec. cloth, joints little worn, boxed. K Books 239-284 1978 £45

LUDOLF, HIOB   Lexicon Aethiopico-Latinum. London, 1661. 1st. ed., 3 parts in one vol., 4to, slight worming throughout, contemp. vellum. K Books 239-285 1978 £250

LUDWIG, CHRISTIAN FRIEDRICH   Scriptores Neurologici Minores Selecti Sive Opera Minora ad Anatomiam Physiologicam et Pathologiam Nervorum Spectantia. Lipsiae, 1791-1795. 4 parts in 2 vols., fldg. copperplts., 4to., contemp. vellum, very fine.   Offenbacher 30-86 1978 $750

LUDWIG, EMIL   Goethe: The History of a Man. 1928. Plts., 2 vols., orig. cloth, 8vo.   Howes 194-894 1978 £6

LUDWIG, EMIL   Lincoln. Boston, 1930. Illus., woodcuts, orig. cloth, 1 of 775 copies, signed by author, fine.   MacManus 239-892 1978 $17.50

LUDWIG, EMIL   The Nile. New York, 1937. First ed., illus., maps.   Biblo 247-926 1978 $12.50

LUDWIG, EMIL   The Nile: Life Story of a River. New York, 1937. Photos, maps, orig. bind., 1st ed. in English.   Petrilla 13-17 1978 $8.50

LUGARD, F. D.   The Dual Mandate in British Tropical Africa. Edinburgh, 1923. 2nd. ed., little age-browned, binders buckram, 8vo.   K Books 239-286 1978 £14

LUGLI, G.   Classical Monuments of Rome & Its Vicinity. 1929. Vol. I, plt.   Allen 234-828 1978 $10

LUHAN, MABEL DODGE   Lorenzo in Taos. New York, 1932. 8vo., cloth, spine lettered in gilt, 1st ed.   J.S. Lawrence 38-L152 1978 $25

LUHAN, MABEL DODGE   Lorenzo in Taos. 1933. Plts., 2 1/2 inch split in upper joint, crack in upper cover, else good, first English ed.   Bell Book 16-548 1978 £6.50

LUHAN, MABEL DODGE   Lorenzo in Taos. New York, (1935). 8vo., cloth, 1st ed., 4th printing, pres. copy, inscribed, and signed by Luhan, bookplts. J.S. Lawrence 38-L153 1978 $25

LUIS DE LEON   La Perfecta Casada. Valencia, 1773. 12mo., calf.   Salloch 348-126 1978 $50

LUKE, L. D.   Journey from the Atlantic to the Pacific Coast by Way of Salt Lake City, Returning by Way of the Southern Route, Describing the Natural and Artificial Scenes of Both Lines. Utica, 1884. Original printed wr., 1st ed.   Ginsberg 14-519 1978 $125

LUKINICH, E.   Im Memoriam Sancti Stephani Hungariae Apostoloci Protoregis, 997-1038. Budapest, 1938. Lg. 8vo., plts., map. Upcroft 12-275 1978 £10

LULL, CLIFFORD B.   Control of Pain in Childbirth. Philadelphia, 1944. D.j., signed by author.   Rittenhouse 49-501 1976 $15

LULL, RAMON   Blanquerna, a Thirteenth Century Romance. (c. 1925). 8vo.   George's 635-1388 1978 £6

LULLIN DE CHATEAUVIEUX, FREDERIC   Le Manuscrit Vendu de Ste. Helene, d'une Maniere Inconnue. Montreal, 1818. Marbled bds., half calf. Wolfe 39-326 1978 $250

THE LUMIERE. New York, 1831. Contemp. bds., uncut, woodcut views.   Wolfe 39-327 1978 $150

LUMMIS, CHARLES F.   The Enchanted Burro. 1897. Illus., first ed., illuminated tan cloth.   Austin 82-598 1978 $47.50

LUMMIS, CHARLES F.   The King of the Broncos. 1897. First ed., pres. copy.   Austin 82-1175 1978 $47.50

LUMMIS, CHARLES F.   Some Strange Corners of Our Country: The Wonderland of the Southwest. New York, 1892. Illus., many engravings.   Jenkins 116-842 1978 $20

LUMPKIN, KATHARINE DU PRE   The Making of a Southerner. New York, 1947. 1st ed., edges rubbed, covers faded, spine dull.   Biblo 251-111 1978 $8.50

LUMSDEN, ANDREW   Remarks on the Antiquities of Rome and its Environs.... London, 1812. Second ed., 4to., half calf, new spine, wide margins, very good.   King 7-364 1978 £50

LUNAN, A.   The Office of the Holy Communion. Edinburgh, 1711. Engraved frontis., some staining, 16mo., old calf, worn.   George's 635-1093 1978 £7.50

LUNDBERG, FERDINAND   America's 60 Families. 1937. Austin 90-800 1978 $7.50

LUNDIN, LEONARD   Cockpit of the Revolution. The War for Independence in New Jersey. Princeton, 1940. 1st ed., fine, illus., maps.   MacManus 239-1293 1978 $30

LUNDSGAARD, CHRISTEN   Cyanosis. Baltimore, 1923.   Rittenhouse 49-503 1976 $15

LUNDY, BENJAMIN   The War in Texas: A Review of Facts and Circumstances. Philadelphia, 1837. Enlarge ed.   Jenkins 116-843 1978 $185

LUNET DE LA JONQUIERE, E.   Inventaire descriptif des Monuments du Cambodge. Paris, 1902. Large 8vo., cloth, folding maps, plts.   Van der Peet 127-138 1978 Dfl 195

LUNT, DOLLY SUMMER   A Woman's Wartime Journal An Account of the Passage Over a Georgia Plantation of Sherman's Army.... New York, 1918. Pres. copy from author's grand-daughter, 12 page biography of author laid in, bright copy, Bell Wiley's copy.   Broadfoot's 44-251 1978 $45

LUNT, GEORGE   The Origin of the Late War. New York, 1866. Bell Wiley's copy.   Broadfoot 46-167 1978 $20

LUPTON, J. H.   A Life of John Colet, D.D. 1909. 2nd. ed., octavo, good.   Upcroft 10-427 1978 £7.50

LUPUS, SERVATIUS   Epistolarum liber, nunc primum in lucem aeditus Papirji Masoni... opera. Paris, 1588. 8 vo., 1st ed., very fine copy, orig. contemp. limp vellum binding with ties.   Schafer 19-26 1978 sFr. 1,200

LUSH, CHARLES K.   The Federal Judge. Boston, 1897. Cloth.   Hayman 73-192 1978 $10

THE LUSITANIA Case. New York, 1915. 8vo., orig. wrs., 1st ed.   Morrill 241-291 1978 $10

LUSITANO, FRANCISCO MANUEL   Carta de Guia de Casados y Avisos para Palacio,.... Madrid, 1724. 1st ed., octavo, full contemp. vellum, ties, floral devices, initials throughout, armorial woodcut device.   Bennett 20-127 1978 $185

LUSK, WILLIAM T.   War Letters of William Thompson Lusk- Captain, Assistant Adjutant-General U.S. Vols. 1861-1863. NY, 1911. Pres card from Lusk's children, Bell Wiley's copy.   Broadfoot's 44-253 1978 $20.00

LUSKA, SIDNEY   As It Was Written. 1885. Austin 79-447 1978 $20

LUSSAC, JOSEPH LOUIS GAY
Please turn to
GAY-LUSSAC, JOSEPH LOUIS

LUSSE, CHARLES DE   Recueil of Romances, Historique, Tendres et Burlesques, Tant Anciennes que Modernes, Avec les Air Notes. 1767 & 1774. 2 vols., 8vo, f.p. and t.p. by Eisen, 2nd t.p. by Gravelot, full tree calf, gold ruled, spines expertly and handsomely rebacked, fine, crisp.   Victoria 34-232 1978 $125

LUSVERGH, DOMENICO   Di Galileo Galilei il Compasso Geometrico Adulto per Opera di Giacomo Lusuergh. Roma, 1698. 12mo., contemp. vellum, 1st ed.   Offenbacher 30-49 1978 $375

LUTHER, MARTIN   Das diese wort Christi (Das ist mein leib etce) noch fest stehen widder die Schwermgeister. Wittenberg, 1527. Sm. 4to, Gothic letter, woodcut title border by Lucas Cranach the Elder, modern blind-stamped calf, 1st ed.   Quaritch 978-99 1978 $1,100

LUTHER, MARTIN   Enchiridion piarum predicationum,.... Wittenberg, 1543. 8vo, contemp. blind-stamped pigskin, very rare ed., woodcuts, very fine.   Gilhofer 75-71 1978 SFr 2,500

LUTHER, MARTIN   Ein Nutzlich Und Fast Trostlich Predig oder Underrichtung, wie sich ein Christen Mensch mit Freuden Bereyten sol zu Sterben. Basle, 1520. 4to., woodcuts, mod. bds., 1st illus. ed.   Gilhofer 74-135 1978 sFr 4,000

LUTHER, MARTIN   XII Predig D. Martin Luthers, uff entliche unser Frauwen, und der Heyligen Fest. N.P., n.d. (Wittenberg, 1524?). 4to., wrs.   Argosy Special-59 1978 $200

LUTTRELL, HENRY   Advice to Julia. 1820. First ed., 12mo., contemp. calf gilt, joints cracked.   Howes 194-371 1978 £12.50

LUTZ, GRACE LIVINGSTON HILL   The Man of the Desert. New York, (1914). 1st ed., scarce, illus., orig. decor. cloth, 8vo. Americanist 101-156 1978 $35

LUTZ, SAMUEL   Die Paradisische Aloe de Jungfraulichen Keuschheit Welche Gott Giebet Allen.... Germantown, 1770. 1st Amer. ed., sm. 8vo, orig. leather ruled in blind, rubbed & worn, clasps gone, upper port. of leaves browned. Americanist 101-85 1978 $75

LUXEMBURG, ROSA   Die Akkumulation des Kapitals. Ein Beitrag zur okonomischen Erklarung des Imperialismus. Berlin, 1913. 8vo., contemp. half-cloth, fine., 1st ed. Gilhofer 74-18 1978 sFr 450

LUXMORE, CHARLES F. C.   English Saltglazed Earthenware. Numerous illus., ltd. ed. of 750 copies. Traylen 88-510 1978 £15

LUYS, JULES BERNARD   Recherches sur le systeme nerveux cerebro-spinal, sa structure,.... Paris, 1865. 8vo, 2 vols., contemp. brown half-mor., corners bit worn, gilt back, 1st ed. Gilhofer 75-72 1978 SFr 1,200

LYALL, ARCHIBALD   Black and White Make Brown. London, (1938). Maps, illus., orig. cloth, 8vo. K Books 239-287 1978 £6

LYAUTEY, LOUIS HUBERT GONZALVE   Lettres du Tonkin. Paris, 1928. 2 vols, 4to., plts. in color, ltd. ed., deluxe, loose colored plts., rare. Van der Peet 127-139 1978 dfl 250

LYAUTEY, LOUIS HUBERT GONZALVE   Lettres du Tonkin et de Madagascar 1894-1899. Paris, 1933. 3rd ed., orig. covers, 8vo., Van der Peet 127-140b 1978 Dfl 55

LYAUTEY, LOUIS HUBERT GONZALVE   Lettres du Tonkin et de Madagascar 1894-1899. Paris, 1946. 5th ed., illus., colored maps, 8vo., orig. covers. Van der Peet 127-140a 1978 Dfl 60

LYCOPHRON   Cassandra. Cambridge, 1804. Folio, illus., half title, orig. polished calf, spine gilt, green label, inscribed pres. copy from author to Dr. Parr, fine. Jarndyce 16-981 1978 £50

LYDEKKAR, RICHARD   Royal Natural History. London, 1893-4. Coloured plts., engravings by W. Kuhnert, P.J. Smith, A.T. Elwes, Q. Wolf & others, 6 vols., roy. 8vo., gilt extra, exceptionally fine set. Traylen 88-622 1978 £30

LYDEKKER, JOHN WOLFE   The Faithful Mohawks. Cambridge, 1938. Illus., fold. map. Hood 116-425 1978 $35

LYDEKKER, JOHN WOLFE   The Life and Letters of Charles Inglis. London, (1936). Folding map, clean, tiny piece torn from d.j., nice copy, orig. binding. Hayman 71-431 1978 $7.50

LYDELSKER, R.   Royal Natural History. 1893-94. Coloured plts., engravings, 6 vols., roy. 8vo. George's 635-1000 1978 £27.50

LYDSTON, G. FRANK   Panama and the Sierras. Chicago, 1900. Illus., photos, inscribed copy. Baldwins' 51-354 1978 $17.50

LYE, LEN   No Trouble. Deya, The Seizin Press, 1930. 4to., one of 200 numbered copies, handmade paper signed by author, cover is by author. Battery Park 1-227 1978 $200

LYELL, CHARLES   Elements of Geology. London, 1865. Sixth ed., illus., woodcuts, prize calf gilt, 8vo. K Books 244-207 1978 £16

LYELL, CHARLES   The Geological Evidences of the Antiquity of Man with Remarks on Theories of the Origin of Species by Variation. London, 1863. 1st ed., lg. 8vo., ads, near fine cond., orig. green cloth, gilt decor's on fr. bd., lettering on spine, pencil notations, no foxing, binding firm. Current 24-124 1978 $170

LYELL, CHARLES   The Geological Evidences of the Antiquity of Man, with Remarks on Theories of the Origin of Species by Variation. Philadelphia, 1863. Illus., woodcuts, 1st U.S. ed., tall 8vo., orig. dec. cloth. Americanist 102-69 1978 $40

LYELL, CHARLES   The Principles of Geology. London, 1830-1833. 3 vols., 8vo., orig. red cloth, rebacked, editor's back labels preserved, uncut set, 1st ed. Gilhofer 75-73 1978 SFr 3,200

LYELL, CHARLES   Principles of Geology. 1872. 11th ed., maps, plates, woodcuts, 2 vols., Vol. 1 neatly rebound, old spine replaced. George's 635-981 1978 £7.50

LYELL, CHARLES   Principles of Geology. New York, 1872. 11th entirely revised ed., maps, illus., plts., woodcuts, 4to., publisher's cloth, two vols., good. Wolfe 39-328 1978 $45

LYELL, CHARLES   A Second Visit to the United States of North America. 1849. 1st. ed., illus., 2 vols., half maroon calf, gilt spines, coloured labels, 8vo. Edwards 1012-504 1978 £65

LYELL, CHARLES   The Student's Elements of Geology. London, 1871. First ed., illus., cr. 8vo., recased in orig. cloth. K Books 244-136 1978 £9

LYELL, CHARLES   Travels in North America; with Geological Observations on the United States, Canada, and Nova Scotia. London, 1845. 2 vols, first ed., bindings broken, spine missing on vol. 1, text, map and plts. very good, scarce. Biblo 247-43 1978 $82.50

LYLE, EUGENE P., JR.   The Lone Star. New York, 1907. Illus., 1st ed. Biblo BL781-287 1978 $9

LYMAN, BENJAMIN SMITH   Topography of the Punjab Oil Region (India). Philadelphia, 1872. Map, 4to., orig. wrs. Morrill 239-488 1978 $7.50

LYMAN, GEORGE D.   John Marsh, Pioneer. The Life Story of a Trailblazer on Six Frontiers. Chautauqua, 1931. Cloth. Hayman 72-442 1978 $7.50

LYMAN, GEORGE D.   Ralston's Ring. New York, 1937. Cloth, fine bright copy of 1st ed., no dust jacket. Hayman 73-393 1978 $8.50

LYMAN, HENRY M.   Insomnia and other Disorders of Sleep. Chicago, 1885. Damp stain upper right top cover, otherwise good. Rittenhouse 49-504 1976 $15

LYMAN, THEODORE   Meade's Headquarters, 1863-1865. Boston, 1922. Portrs., 8vo., orig. bds., cloth back, 1st ed. Morrill 239-489 1978 $15

LYMINGTON, LORD   Spring Song of Iscariot. Paris, Black Sun Press, 1929. 1 of 25 numbered copies, Japan vellum, signed by author, 1st ed., orig. gold & silver foil box, fine copy, orig. wrappers, glassine jacket, cloth case. Houle 10-34 1978 $250

LYNCH, B.   Decorations and Absurdities. London, 1923. 8vo., cloth, caricatural plts. Van der Peet H-64-278 1978 Dfl 40

LYNCH, B.   A Guide to Health Through the Various Stages of Life. London, 1744. 8vo., contemp. calf, rebacked. Quaritch 977-49 1978 $75

LYNCH, DENIS TILDEN   An Epoch and a Man. Martin Van Buren and His Times. New York, 1929. 1st ed., illus., orig. cloth, d.j., very good. MacManus 239-832 1978 $20

LYNCH, DENIS TILDEN   Grover Cleveland, a Man Four-Square. New York, (1932). Illus. Biblo BL781-195 1978 $10

LYNCH, DENIS TILDEN   The Wild Seventies. New York, 1941. 1st ed., illus., d.j., fine. MacManus 239-262 1978 $12.50

LYNCH, JAMES D.   Kemper County Vindicated- and a Peep at Radical Rule in Mississippi. NY, 1879. Spine worn, Bell Wiley's copy. Broadfoot's 44-895 1978 $25.00

LYNCH, WILLIAM FRANCIS   Official Report of the United States' Expedition to Explore the Dead Sea and the River Jordan. Baltimore, 1852. 1st. complete ed., 4to, lg. folding engraved map, torn in margins, lithograph plts., half calf, marbled sides & endpapers, gilt, cover trifle rubbed, text heavily foxed. Deighton 5-79 1978 £75

LYND, ROBERT   In Defence of Pink. London, 1937. Illus., first ed., hole in cloth of upper cover, otherwise nice, orig. binding, author's autograph signature. Rota 211-329 1978 £6

LYNDE, HUMPHREY 1579-1636   Via Devia: The By-Way. 1630. Thk. 12mo., 19th century calf, good, first ed., second issue. Howes 194-68 1978 £55

LYNDE, JAMES P.   Infantile Mortality. Boston, 1882. 8vo., orig. wrs., 1st ed. Morrill 239-160 1978 $7.50

LYNE, CHARLES   New Guinea: An Account of the establishment of the British Protectorate over the southern shores of New Guinea. London, 1885. Illus., cloth, a bit soiled, unopened. Dawson's 127-274 1978 $40

LYNN, THOMAS   An Improved System of Telegraphic Communication. 1818. Second ed., plts., coloured illus., sm. 8vo., contemp. half calf. F. Edwards 1013-138 1978 £70

LYON, C. J.   History of St. Andrews. Edinburgh, 1843. 2 vols., plts., calf somewhat rubbed, labels defective, good, 8vo. K Books 244-401 1978 £24

LYON, E. WILSON   Louisiana in French Diplomacy 1759-1804. Norman, 1934. D.j. MacManus 239-1819 1978 $12.50

LYON, GEORGE FRANCIS   A Brief Narrative of an Unsuccessful Attempt to reach Repulse Bay. London, 1825. Plts., generally age-marked and thumbed, title dust-stained, binders cloth, 8vo. K Books 244-402 1978 £50

LYON, GEORGE FRANCIS   The Private Journal of .... 1824. 1st. ed., map, plts., modern half leather, 8vo. Edwards 1012-587 1978 £75

LYON, JOHN   Harp of Zion:... Liverpool, 1853. Orig. cloth, 1st ed. Ginsberg 16-928 1978 $60.00

LYON, JOHN   Harp of Zion; A Collection of Poems, Etc. Liverpool, 1853. Port., orig. cloth, 1st ed. Ginsberg 14-663 1978 $60

LYON, MARGUERITE   Take to the Hills. A Chronicle of the Ozarks. Indianapolis, (1941). Illus. Biblo BL781-253 1978 $9

LYON, PATRICK   Observations on the Barrenness of Fruit Trees, and the Means of Prevention and Cure. Edinburgh, 1813. 8vo, contemporary half calf, 1st ed., frontispiece (foxed), half-title present, fine copy. Ximenes 47-185 1978 $80

LYON, SIDNEY S.   Report on the Physical, Topographical, Geological and Mineralogical Condition of the Pah-Ranagat Silver Mining District. New York, 1866. Orig. pr. wr. Ginsberg 14-734 1978 $75

LYSONS, DANIEL   The Environs of London.... London, 1792-1811. 1st. ed., 6 vols., vignette title-pgs., engraved plts., some hand-coloured, bound in early 19th century full russia, gilt tooled border on sides, double morocco labels, some foxing, sl. bumping of corners, o/w fine set. Deighton 5-133 1978 £225

LYSONS, DANIEL   Magna Britannia... London, 1806-22. 1st. ed., 6 vols., 4to, engraved plts. of maps, some hand-coloured, bound in half calf, raised bands, double green morocco labels, gilt, very sl. chafing of covers, some foxing & offsetting. Deighton 5-134 1978 £400

LYONS, I.   A Treatise of Fluxions. 1758. 8vo., large paper, fold. plts., contemp. half calf, gilt. Quaritch 977-162 1978 £65

LYSONS, SAMUEL   An Account of Roman Antiquities Discovered at Woodchester in the County of Gloucester. 1797. Roy. folio, plain and hand-coloured plts., foxing of text and plain plts., half mor. Quaritch 983-22 1978 $1,250

LYONS, WILLIAM R.   Atlas of Peripheral Nerve Injuries. Philadelphia, 1949. Library marks. Rittenhouse 49-505 1976 $25

LYSONS, SAMUEL   The Model Merchant of the Middle Ages. 1860. 8vo., cloth, covers a little stained, frontispiece, illus. P. M. Hill 142-167 1978 £35

LYTE, H.C. MAXWELL   A History of Eton College 1440-1884. Lond., 1889. New Ed., orig. cloth binding, stain on front cover, good copy, uncut. Greene 78-254 1978 $25.00

LYTLE, MILTON S.   History of Huntingdon County in the State of Pennsylvania, From the Earliest Times to the Centennial Anniversary of American Independence, July 4, 1876. Lancaster, 1876. Illus., scarce. MacManus 239-1544 1978 $75

LYTTELTON, GEORGE LYTTELTON, 1ST BARON   Further Considerations on the Present State of Affairs at Home and Abroad. 1739. 2nd ed., rebound in half brown cloth, marbled bds., v.g. Jarndyce 16-132 1978 £10

LYTTELTON, GEORGE LYTTELTON, 1ST BARON   History of Life of King Henry II, and of the Age in Which He Lived. 1769. 3rd ed., 4 vols., new buckram. Allen 234-1288 1978 $45

LYTTLETON, GEORGE LYTTELTON, 1ST BARON   Letters from a Persian in England, to His Friend at Ispahan. 1735. First ed., sm. 8vo., cont. calf gilt, sewing and joints weak, contents dust soiled. Howes 194-373 1978 £12.50

LYTTELTON, GEORGE LYTTELTON, 1ST BARON   The Progress of Love. 1732. 2nd ed., folio, limp bds., uncut. Hannas 54-211 1978 £55

LYTTELTON, GEORGE LYTTELTON, 1ST BARON   The Works of... 1775. 2nd ed., 4to., portrait, foxed, cont. calf, spine rubbed, monogram of Duke of Buccleuch on covers. Hannas 54-212 1978 £12.50

LYTTON, CONSTANCE G. B.   Prisons & Prisoners. 1914. 1st. ed., portraits, cr. 8vo, orig. cloth, good sound copy. Fenning 32-204 1978 £14

LYTTON, EDWARD GEORGE EARLE LYTTON BULWER-LYTTON, 1ST BARON 1803-1873   The Caxtons: A Family Picture. New York, n.d. (circa 1849). Double columns, modern cloth. Hayman 73-193 1978 $7.50

LYTTON, EDWARD GEORGE EARLE LYTTON BULWER-LYTTON, 1ST BARON 1803-1873   Novels. Boston, c. 1900. Plts., 25 vols., half olive mor., very nice, illus. cabinet ed. Howes 194-1016 1978 £110

LYTTON, EDWARD GEORGE EARLE LYTTON BULWER-LYTTON, 1ST BARON 1803-1873   Pelham; or, the Adventures of a Gentleman. New York, 1829. 1st Amer. ed., 2 vols., orig. half cloth, bds. with yellow paper labels, foxed. Greene 78-15 1978 $75

LYTTON, EDWARD GEORGE EARLE LYTTON BULWER-LYTTON, 1ST BARON 1803-1873   The Pilgrims of the Rhine. 1891. Plts., roy. 8vo., orig. cloth, prtd. label, ed. deluxe, ltd. to 500 copies. Howes 194-1017 1978 £15

LYTTON, EDWARD GEORGE EARLE LYTTON BULWER-LYTTON, 1ST BARON 1803-1873   Reinzi, the Last of the Tribunes. London, 1835. 3 vols., orig. bds., printed paper labels, 1st ed., very good, cloth fold. box. MacManus 238-175 1978 $250

LYTTON, EDWARD GEORGE EARLE LYTTON BULWER-LYTTON, 1ST BARON 1803-1873   Rienzi, the Last of the Tribunes. Philadelphia, 1836. Contemp. bds., cloth back, loose in case, uncut, 2 vols. in 1, 1st Amer. ed. Wolfe 39-51 1978 $45

LYTTON SPRINGS The Ideal Resort For Health and Pleasure. N.P., n.d. (c.1903). Wrps. Hayman 71-78 1978 $8.50

M

MC ADAM, J. T.   Canada; the Country, its People, Religion, Politics, Rulers and its Apparent Future.   Montreal, 1882. Cloth dampstained, illus., internally very good. Wolfe 39-329 1978 $25

MC ADAM, JOHN LOUDON   Observations on the Management of Trusts for the Care of Turnpike Roads. London, 1825. 8vo., fine, orig. bds., paper label, uncut, first ed. Quaritch 977-238 1978 $225

MC ADAM, JOHN LOUDON   Remarks on the Present System of Road Making... 1821. 4th. ed., 8vo, orig. bds., uncut, printed paper label, fresh almost fine. Fenning 32-205 1978 £48

MC ADAM, JOHN LOUDON   Remarks on the Present System of Roadmaking. London, 1822. Sixth ed., carefully revised, 8vo., orig. bds., uncut. Quaritch 977-237 1978 $125

MC ADOO, WILLIAM   Crowded Years. The Reminiscneces of. Boston, 1931. 1st ed., illus., orig. cloth-backed bds., ltd. to 650 copies signed by author, very good. MacManus 239-264 1978 $35

MC ADOO, WILLIAM   Crowded Years. Reminiscences... Boston, (1931). Illus. Biblo BL781-215 1978 $10

MC ALLISTER, ANNA   Ellen Ewing, Wife of General Sherman. New York, 1936. Rebound, ex-libris, Bell Wiley's copy. Broadfoot 46-168 1978 $9

MC ALLISTER, ETHEL M.   Amos Eaton. Scientist and Educator. Philadelphia, 1941. 1st ed., illus., orig. cloth, fine. MacManus 239-747 1978 $22.50

MC ALLISTER, J. GRAY   Sketch of Captain Thompson McAllister, Citizen, Soldier, Christian. Petersburg, 1896. Wrs., Bell Wiley's copy. Broadfoot 46-390 1978 $30

MAC ALLISTER, WARD   Society as I Have Found It. New York, Cassell, (1890). 1st. ed., portrait, 8vo, orig. cloth, gilt, t.e.g., very good copy. Fenning 32-206 1978 £12

MAC ALPINE, AVERY   A Man's Conscience. NY, 1891. Fir. Am. Ed., illus., orig. cloth binding, good cond. Greene 78-256 1978 $10.00

M'ALPINE, D.   The Botanical Atlas Vol. II Only: Cryptogams. Edinburgh, 1883. Plates, sm. folio, worn binding, 8vo. Book Chest 17-248 1978 $22.50

MAC ARTHUR, CHARLES   War Bugs. New York, 1929. 1st ed. Biblo 251-560 1978 $10

M'ARTHUR, JOHN   Financial and Political Facts of the Eighteenth Century... London, 1801 3rd ed., cloth, foxed. MacManus 239-263 1978 $30

MC ATEE, W.   Effectiveness in Nature of the So-Called Protective Adaptations in the Animal Kingdom. Washington, 1932. Wraps, 8vo. Book Chest 17-242 1978 $12.50

MC AULEY, JEREMIAH   Jerry McAuley, His Life and Work. New York, (1885). Cloth, spine faded. Hayman 73-417 1973 $10

MAC BAIN, A.   Celtic Mythology and Religion. Stirling, 1917. Illus., good, octavo, cloth, first ed. Hyland 128-1 1978 £14

MAC BETH, R. G.   The Romance of Western Canada. Toronto, 1918. 1st ed. Hood 117-902 1978 $15

MAC BRIDE, MAUD GONNE   A Servant of the Queen. 1950. Very good, octavo bound in cloth, reprints. Hyland 128-3 1978 £5

MC CABE, JAMES DABNEY   The Grayjackets. Richmond, 1867. Orig. cloth laid over rebinding, Bell Wiley's copy. Broadfoot 46-169 1978 $90

MC CABE, JAMES DABNEY   History of the War Between Germany and France. (Philadelphia, 1871). Fine engrs., maps, 1st ed., orig. cloth. Morrill 241-686 1978 $10

MC CABE, JAMES DABNEY   The Life and Public Services of Horatio Seymour. New York, 1868. Cloth. Hayman 73-418 1978 $12.50

MC CABE, W. B.   Bertha; or the Pope & the Emperor. Duffy, 1856. F.p. & vignette t.p., very good, octavo bound in cloth, reprint. Hyland 128-4 1978 £4

MC CAFFREY, JOHN   Oration Delivered at the Commemoration of the Landing of the Pilgrims of Maryland... Gettysburg, 1842. Disbound. Hayman 71-442 1978 $10

MC CALEB, WALTER F.   The Aaron Burr Conspiracy. New York, 1936. Illus. MacManus 239-599 1978 $22.50

MC CALL, GEORGE A.   Letters from the Frontiers, Written during a Period of 30 Years' Service in the Army of the U.S. Philadelphia, 1868. 1st ed, bookplate and inscription of descendant, very rare. Jenkins 116-846 1978 $200

MC CALL, JOHN D.   Report of the Comptroller of Public Accounts of the State of Texas. Austin, 1890. Wr. Jenkins 116-847 1978 $12.50

MC CALLA, WILLIAM L.   Adventures in Texas, Chiefly in the Spring and Summer of 1840. Philadelphia, 1841. Original cloth, gilt, 1st ed. Jenkins 116-848 1978 $750

MAC CALLUM, D. C.   Addresses. Montreal, 1901. 8vo., 1st ed., pres. from author. Morrill 239-161 1978 $17.50

MC CALLUM, HUGH   An Original Collection of the Poems of Ossian, Orrann, Ulin and Other Bards, Who Flourished in the Same Age. Montrose, 1816. 8vo, orig. bds., uncut, new paper spine. Traylen 88-297 1978 £12

MC CALLUM, JAMES   A Brief Sketch of the Settlement and Early History of Giles Co., Tenn. N.P., 1876. Reprinted in 1928. MacManus 239-1124 1978 $22.50

MC CALLUM, JAMES   A Brief Sketch of the Settlement and Early History of Giles County, Tennessee. Pulaski, 1928. Bell Wiley's copy. Broadfoot's 44-961 1978 $16

MC CALLUM, JAMES D.   Eleazar Wheelock Founder of Dartmouth College. Hanover, 1939. Port., fine, d.j. MacManus 239-827 1978 $12.50

MC CANN, A.   God - Or Gorilla. New York, (1922). 8vo, orig. worn binding. Book Chest 17-243 1978 $17.50

MC CANTS, E. C.   History, Stories and Legends of South Carolina. Dallas, (1927). Illus., fine. MacManus 239-1862 1978 $15

MC CARTAN, H. A.   The Glamour of Belfast. 1921. D.w., very good, 1st ed., octavo bound in cloth. Hyland 128-18 1978 £5

MC CARTER, J. M.   Historical and Biographical Encyclopaedia of Delaware. Wilmington, 1882. 4to, orig. full lea, recased. Baldwins' 51-228 1978 $100

MC CARTHY, CARLETON   Detailed Minutiae of Soldier Life in the Army of Northern Virginia 1861-1865. Richmond, 1882. Illus., Bell Wiley's copy. Broadfoot 46-388 1978 $20

MC CARTHY, D. A.   The Harp of Life. Boston, 1929. 1st ed., very good, octavo bound in cloth. Hyland 128-7 1978 £5

MC CARTHY, D. G.   History of Palo Alto County, Iowa. Cedar Rapids, 1910. Illus. MacManus 239-981 1978 $35

MC CARTHY, DENIS FLORENCE   Poems. Dublin, 1882. 1st ed., 8vo., orig. cloth, gilt, very good copy. Fenning 32-207 1978 £8.50

MC CARTHY, DENIS FLORENCE   Poems. Dublin, 1882. 1st. ed., half title, orig. light blue cloth, trifle rubbed. Jarndyce 16-836 1978 £15

MC CARTHY, EUGENE   Familiar Fish. New York, 1900. Illus., sm. 8vo., 1st ed. Morrill 239-490 1978 $20

MAC CARTHY, J. G.   A Plea for the Home Government of Ireland. London, 1871. 1st ed., very good, octavo bound in cloth. Hyland 128-11 1978 £8.50

MC CARTHY, J. G.   A Plea for the Home Government of Ireland. Dublin, 1872. 2nd ed., 16mo, stiff linen wr., very good. Hyland 128-12 1978 £5

MAC CARTHY, J. G.   A Plea for the Home Government of Ireland. Dublin, 1872. 3rd ed., 16mo, stiff linen wr., very good. Hyland 128-13 1978 £5

MC CARTHY, JUSTIN   A History of Our Own Times. 1912. New ed., illus., 7 vols., 8vo. George's 635-711 1978 £5.25

MC CARTHY, JUSTIN   A History of the Four Georges. 1884. 4 vols., 8vo. George's 635-710 1978 £5.25

MC CARTHY, JUSTIN   Miss Misanthrope. 1878. 1st. ed., 2 vols., 12 illus. by Arthur Hopkins, half titles, half red calf, blue & olive labels, good. Jarndyce 16-872 1978 £24

MC CARTHY, JUSTIN HUNTLY   The Case For Home Rule. 1887. 1st. ed., half title, orig. olive cloth, v.g. Jarndyce 16-764 1978 £5.50

MC CARTHY, JUSTIN HUNTLY   The White Carnation and Other Pieces. N.P., n.d. 8vo, tan paper covers, uncut, unopened, covers and pages slightly dust-darkened, spine worn, Nice, rare, inscription from author, 1st ed., collector's cond. Desmarais 1-285 1978 $45

MAC CATHMHAOIL, SEOSAMH   The Rush-Light; poems. Dublin, 1906. First ed., orig. binding, spine and covers marked, very good. Rota 211-338 1978 £6

MC CAUSLAND, ELIZABETH   The Life & Work of Edward Lamson Henry, N. A. 1841-1919. 1945. Wr., port., illus., good. Nestler Rare 78-126 1978 $25

MC CHEANE, W. H.   Flowers and Fruits of the Bible. (c. 1860). 4to., colour printed throughout, some foxing. George's 635-34 1978 £30

MC CLELLAN, CARSWELL   Notes on the Personal Memoirs of P. H. Sheridan. St. Paul, 1889. Maps, orig. front wr., 1st ed., autograph slip to Gen. Crook tipped in. Ginsberg 14-918 1978 $45

MAC CLELLAN, ELIZABETH   Historic Dress in America 1607-1800. Philadelphia, 1904-1910. 1st. ed., over 700 illus. in color, pen & ink by Sophie B. Steel, orig. garments, quarto, 2 vols. Baldwins' 51-125 1978 $45

MC CLELLAN, GEORGE B.   Letter of the Secretary of War, Transmitting Report on the Organization of the Army of the Potomac, and of Its Campaigns in Virginia and Maryland, Under the Command of Maj. Gen. George B. McClellan. Washington, 1864. 8vo., orig. cloth. Morrill 241-687 1978 $12.50

MC CLELLAN, GEORGE B.   The Life, Campaigns, and Public Services of General McClellan. Philadelphia, 1864. Bell Wiley's copy. Broadfoot 46-170 1978 $14

MC CLELLAN, GEORGE B.   Manual of Bayonet Exercise Prepared for the Use of the Army of the United States. Philadelphia, 1852. 24 plts., cut signature of McClellan tipped in. Baldwins' 51-314 1978 $27.50

MC CLELLAN, GEORGE B.   Manual of Bayonet Exercise. Philadelphia, 1862. Plts., ex libris and signed by Lt.-Col. B. Hancock, perforation stamp, marginal stains, spine taped, Bell Wiley's copy. Broadfoot's 44-256 1978 $14

MC CLELLAN, GEORGE B.   Report on the Organization of the Army of the Potomac... New York, 1864. Maps, 1st ed., very fine, orig. cloth. Mac-Manus 239-894 1978 $35

MC CLELLAND, JAMES   Journal of a Visit to India and the Far East. Glasgow, 1877. 8vo, original blue cloth, 1st ed., presentation copy, inscribed to A. F. Stevenson, presentation slip tipped-in, very fine copy. Ximenes 47-192 1978 $35

MC CLELLAND, R.   Speech of Mr..., of Michigan, on the Bill Making Appropriations for Certain Rivers and Harbors: Delivered in the House...April 17, 1844. Washington, 1844. Disbound. Hayman 72-673 1978 $7.50

MC CLEOD, LYONS   Madagascar and Its People. London, 1865. 1st. ed., 8vo, engraved map, orig. cloth, neatly repaired, back faded, gilt. Deighton 5-19 1978 £38

MC CLINTOCK, FRANCIS LEOPOLD   The Voyage of the "Fox" in the Arctic Seas.... 1859. 1st ed., maps, illus., orig. cloth, 8vo., label removed from front cover. Edwards 1012-588 1978 £40

MC CLINTOCK, GILBERT S.   Valley Views of Northeastern Pennsylvania. Wilkes-Barre, 1948. 4to., illus., scarce. MacManus 239-1545 1978 $42.50

MC CLINTOCK, J. C.   Hand Book of the First Presbyterian Church, Burlington Iowa. Burlington, 1877. Front wr., 1st ed. Ginsberg 14-417 1978 $17.50

MC CLINTOCK, JAMES H.   Mormon Settlement in Arizona. Phoenix, 1921. Illus., 1st ed. Biblo BL781-288 1978 $28.50

MC CLINTOCK, JAMES H.   Mormon Settlement in Arizona: A Record of Peaceful Conquest of the Desert. Phoenix, 1921. Illus., plates, folding map, orig. cloth, 1st ed. Ginsberg 14-664 1978 $35

MC CLINTOCK, WALTER   Old Indian Trails. Boston, 1923. 1st ed., illus., fine, orig. pic. cloth. MacManus 239-1179 1978 $27.50

M'CLUNE, JAMES   History of the Presbyterian Church in the Forks of Brandywine, Chester Co., Pa. From A.D. 1735 to A.D. 1885. Philadelphia, 1885. Baldwins' 51-465 1978 $22.50

MC CLUNG, L. S.   The Anaerobic Bacteria and Their Activities in Nature and Disease. Berkeley, 1941. Ex-library. Rittenhouse 49-531 1976 $15

MC CLUNG, NELLIE L.   In Times Like These. Toronto, 1915. Fly leaf missing. Hood's 115-444 1978 $7.50

MC CLUNG, NELLIE L.   The Next of Kin; Those Who Wait and Wonder. Toronto, 1917. Hood's 115-445 1978 $7.50

MC CLUNG, NELLIE L.   The Second Chance. Toronto, 1910. 1st. ed. Hood's 115-446 1978 $7.50

MC CLUNG, NELLIE L.   Sowing Seeds in Danny. Toronto, 1912. Hood's 115-447 1978 $7.50

MC CLUNG, NELLIE L.   The Stream Runs Fast; My Own Story. Toronto, 1945. Hood's 115-255 1978 $12.50

MC CLURE, ALEXANDER K.   Old Time Notes of Pennsylvania... Philadelphia, 1905. 1st ed., 2 vols., autograph ed., ltd. to 1,000 signed sets, illus., uncut. MacManus 239-1546 1978 $35

MC CLURE, DAVID   Memoirs of the Rev. Eleazar Wheelock, D.D. Founder and President of Dartmouth College and Moor's Charity School. Newburyport, 1811. 1st ed., old 1/2 leather. MacManus 239-1180 1978 $30

MC CLURE, ALEXANDER K.   Old Time Notes of Pennsylvania. Philadelphia, 1905. 1st ed., the ltd. autograph ed., signed, illus., 2 vols. Baldwins' 51-466 1978 $25

MC CONNELL, H. H.   Five Years a Cavalryman; or, Sketches of Regular Army Life on the Texas Frontier. Jacksboro, 1889. Cloth, 1st ed., scarce, covers a little rubbed else fine. Dykes 35-238 1978 $50

MC CONNELL, H. H.   Five Years A Calvaryman:.... Texas, 1889. Original cloth, 1st ed. Jenkins 116-849 1978 $125

MC CONNELL, S. D.   History of the American Episcopal Church...
New York, 1894. Orig. cloth, fine copy. MacManus 239-137 1978 $20

MC CONNELL, STANLEY   Now Take Canada. Toronto, 1939. Hood 116-
702 1978 $10

MC CONNOCHIE, A. I.   Deerstalking in Scotland. London, 1924. 8vo.,
frontis., plts., orig. cloth. K Books 244-211 1978 £6

MAC CORKLE, S. A. .   Texas Government. New York, 1949. Biblo
BL781-289 1978 $9

MC CORMICK, CALVIN   Memoir of Miss Eliza McCoy. Dallas, 1892.
Illus., original cloth, 1st ed. Ginsberg 14-520 1978 $75

MC CORMICK, RICHARD C.   Arizona: Its Resources and Prospects. New
York, 1865. Folding map, original wr., 1st ed. Ginsberg 14-19 1978 $75

MC CORMICK, THOMAS J. JR.   A Study of Church Architecture in Syracuse.
Illus., blue buckram. Butterfield 21-323 1978 $15

MC COY, ELIZABETH   The Anaerobic Bacteria and Their Activities in
Nature and Disease. Berkeley, 1939. Ex-library. Rittenhouse 49-532 1976
$25

MC COY, ISAAC   The Annual Register of Indian Affairs within the
Indian (or Western) Territory. Shawanoe Baptist Mission, 1837. Wr., 1st ed.
Ginsberg 14-521 1978 $450

MC COY, ISAAC   Remarks on the Practicability of Indian Reform,
Embracing Their Colonization. Boston, 1827. Half morocco, 1st ed. Ginsberg
14-522 1978 $400

MC COY, JOSEPH   The Frontier Maid; or, a Tale of Wyoming:....
Wilkesbarre, 1819. 12mo, original yellow boards (spine a bit worn), 1st ed., fine
copy, rare. Ximenes 47-187 1978 $175

MC COY, SAMUEL   This Man Adams. New York, 1928. Illus., first
ed. Biblo 247-3 1978 $15

MC COY, SAMUEL   Nor Death Dismay. 1944. Austin 80-191 1978
$10

MC CRADY, EDWARD   The History of South Carolina Under the Proprietary Government. 1670-1719. New York, 1897. 1st ed., lg. fold. map, orig.
cloth, front cover faded, but very good copy. MacManus 239-1861 1978 $35

MC CRAE, JOHN   In Flanders Field and Other Poems. New York,
London, The Knickerbocker Press, 1919. 8vo, dark blue cloth, t.e.g., minimal
water staining, 1st ed., collector's cond., Fine. Desmarais 1-286 1978 $20

MC CRAE, JOHN   In Flanders Fields and Other Poems. Toronto,
1919. Illus. Hood 117-811 1978 $20

MC CRARY, GEORGE W.   Letter from the Sec. of War Communicating
Information in Relation to the Establishment of a Military in the Vicinity of El Paso,
Texas. Washington, 1879. Jenkins 116-388 1978 $8.50

MC CRARY, JOHN RAYMOND, SR.   Thoughts About Things I Love.
Cleveland, 1941. Autographed by author. Broadfoot 50-130 1978 $14

MC CRAW, WILLIAM   Professional Politicians. Washington, 1940. 1st
ed. Jenkins 116-851 1978 $15

MC CREA, R. B.   Lost Amid the Fogs... 1869. Coloured frontis,
orig. cloth, 8vo. Edwards 1012-439 1978 £60

M'CREADY, C. T.   Dublin Street Names Dated and Explained.
1892. 1st ed, good, octavo bound in cloth. Hyland 128-20 1978 £12

MC CUE, JAMES W.   Joe Lincoln of Cape Cod. Silver Lake, 1949.
1st ed. Biblo BL781-1054 1978 $9.50

MC CULLAGH, W. T.   The Industrial History of Free Nations, considered
in relation to their Domestic Institutions and Extreme Policy. 1846. 2 vols., 8vo.
George's 635-358 1978 $7.50

MC CULLERS, CARSON   The Member of the Wedding. Cresset Press,
1946. Very good, worn d.w., first English ed. Bell Book 16-601 1978 £6.50

MC CULLOCH, DEREK   Uncle Mac. 1928. Drawings, sm. 4to., cloth-
backed pict. bds., very good, first English ed. Bell Book 17-876 1978 £6.50

MC CULLOCH, J. H.   A Million Miles in Sail. Toronto, 1933. Illus.
Hood 116-257 1978 $45

MC CULLOCH, JOHN RAMSAY   A Dictionary, Practical, Theoretical, and
Historical of Commerce and Commercial Navigation. 1832. Folding maps, half
calf, rubbed, tops of joints cracked, 8vo. George's 635-359 1978 £18

MC CULLOCH, JOHN RAMSAY   A Dictionary Practical, Theoretical & Historical of Commerce and Commercial Navigation. 1835. 2nd ed., 6 lg. folding
maps, full reverse calf, 1 vol. bound as 2, brown & black labels, v.g. Jarndyce
16-873 1978 £42

MC CURDY, E. A.   Views of the Neilgherries... (1840). Oblong
folio, vignette on title, litho plts., orig. wrapper, worn, title & vignette repeated
on front cover. Edwards 1012-104 1978 £45

MC CURDY, EDWARD   Leonardo Da Vinci's Note-Books. New York,
1923. Orig. bind., plts. Petrilla 13-20 1978 $7.50

MAC CURDY, EDWARD   The Mind of Leonardo. New York, 1928.
8vo., illus., orig. cloth, gilt, uncut. Norman 5-L25 1978 $30

MC CUSKEY, DOROTHY   Bronson Alcott, Teacher. New York, 1940.
Cloth, 1st printing. Hayman 72-452 1978 $7.50

MC CUTCHEON, GEORGE BARR   Castle Craneycrow. Chicago, 1902. 8vo.,
pict. cloth, t.e.g., 1st ed., fine. Duschnes 220-200 1978 $15

MC CUTCHEON, J. FORREST   J. Frank Dobie: Texan, an Appreciation.
Roanoke, 1932. Wr., limited to 250 numbered copies. Jenkins 116-351 1978
$7.50

MC CUTCHEON, JOHN T.   In Africa. Indianapolis, (1910). Illus. with
photos & cartoons by author, lg. 8vo., inner hinges slightly cracked, 1st ed.
Morrill 239-491 1978 $22.50

MC DANIEL, H. F.   The Coming Empire: or, Two Thousand Miles in
Texas on Horseback. New York, 1877. Original decorated cloth, gilt, near-
mint copy. Jenkins 116-853 1978 $100

MC DANIEL, RUEL   Vinegarroon: The Saga of Judge Roy Bean, "The
Law West of the Pecos". Kingsport, 1936. 1st ed. Jenkins 116-84 1978 $7.50

MAC DERMOT, E. T.   History of the Great Western Railway. 1927-31.
2 vols. in 3, 8vo., portraits, maps, illus., orig. cloth, first ed. Quaritch 977-
239 1978 $95

MAC DERMOT, F.   Theobald Wolfe Tone. 1939. 1st ed., illus.,
good. Hyland 128-655 1978 £7

MAC DERMOT, H. E.   Sir Thomas Roddick, his Work in Medicine and
Public Life. Toronto, 1938. Errata page pasted onto inside cover. Hood 117-316
1978 $15

MC DERMOTT, JOHN F.   Private Libraries in Creole Saint Louis. Baltimore, 1938. Original cloth, 1st ed. Ginsberg 14-587 1978 $25

MC DERMOTT, P. L.   British East Africa or Ibea. London, 1895.
New ed., folding map, frontis, gilt cloth, 8vo, slightly shaken, cover little
spotted. K Books 239-290 1978 £30

MAC DIARMID, HUGH PSEUD.
Please turn to
GRIEVE, CHRISTOPHER MURRAY

MAC DONAGH, DONAGH   Veterans and other poems. Dublin, Cuala Press,
1941. First ed., orig. binding, one of 270 numbered copies, edges of covers worn,
nice. Rota 211-341 1978 £18

MAC DONAGH, M.   The Irish at the Front. 1916. 1st ed., cover dull,
good, octavo bound in cloth. Hyland 128-22 1978 £4

MAC DONAGH, M.   Irish Life & Character. 1905. Very good, octavo bound in cloth, reprint. Hyland 128-21 1978 £7

MAC DONAGH, M.   The Viceroy's Post-Bag. 1904. 1st ed., good, octavo bound in cloth. Hyland 128-23 1978 £7.50

MAC DONAGH, T.   Lyrical Poems. 1913. 1st ed. ltd. 500 copies, very good, octavo bound in cloth. Hyland 128-25 1978 £20

MAC DONALD, ALEXANDER   Western Oregon. London, 1875. Half 24mo. mor., 1st ed. Ginsberg 14-825 1978 $100

MAC DONALD, CARLOS F.   The Infliction of the Death Penalty by Means of Electricity. New York, 1892. Frontis., 8vo., orig. wrs., 1st separate ed. Morrill 241-294 1978 $25

MC DONALD, CORNELIA   A Diary with Reminiscences of the War & Refugee Life in the Shenandoah Valley 1860-1865. Nashville, 1934. Illus., fldg. map, Bell Wiley's copy. Broadfoot 46-172 1978 $35

MAC DONALD, D. B.   Sunday Evenings at St. Andrew's College. Toronto, 1946. Hood's 115-939 1978 $10

MC DONALD, EDWARD D.   A Bibliography of the Writings of D. H. Lawrence. Philadelphia, 1925. 12mo, blue boards and cloth, paper labels, port. frontis., six-line inscription by McDonald to David Jester, Jr., 1 of 500 copies, fine. Duschnes 220-180 1978 $45

MC DONALD, EDWARD D.   A Bibliography of the Writings of Norman Douglas. Philadelphia, 1927. 12mo., orig. cloth, 1st ed. MacManus 238-907 1978 $12.50

MC DONALD, EDWARD D.   A Bibliography of the Writings of Theodore Dreiser. Philadelphia, 1928. 12mo., orig. cloth, paper label, 1st ed., 1 of 350 copies, pres. copy. MacManus 238-909 1978 $22.50

MAC DONALD, FREDERIKA   Jean Jacques Rousseau: A New Criticism. 1906. Plts., 2 vols., thick 8vo., orig. buckram, spines faded. Howes 194-1135 1978 £8.50

MAC DONALD, GEORGE   Annals of a Quiet Neighbourhood. London, 1867. 3 vols., orig. cloth, 1st ed., cover a bit soiled, labels removed, scarce. MacManus 238-319 1978 $125

MAC DONALD, GEORGE   Annals of a Quiet Neighborhood. London, 1877. Orig. blue cloth, very good or better. Limestone 9-186 1978 $30

MAC DONALD, GEORGE   David Elginbrod. 1863. 1st. ed., 3 vols., later half morocco, inscribed pres. copy from Greville MacDonald with an ALS, good. Jarndyce 16-837 1978 £55

MAC DONALD, GEORGE   David Elginbord. Boston, n.d. (1863). Orig. green cloth binding lettered in gold, 1st Am. ed.?, 3 vols. in 1, lib. bookplate, good. Greene 78-75 1978 $25

MAC DONALD, GEORGE   The Disciple and Other Poems. London, 1868. 2nd ed., orig. maroon cloth, upper hinge pulling, very good or better. Limestone 9-187 1978 $18.50

MAC DONALD, GEORGE   The Elect Lady. London, 189-?. New ed., 2nd English ed., very good or better. Limestone 9-188 1978 $18.50

MAC DONALD, GEORGE   Paul Faber, Surgeon. Philadelphia, 1879. Orig. cloth, some wear, 1st Am. ed., 3 vols. in 1. Greene 78-76 1978 $30

MAC DONALD, GEORGE   Phantastes: A Faerie Romance for Men and Women. London, 1858. 1st ed., spine lightly faded, minor tip rubbing, inner joints cracked, scarce. Victoria 34-509 1978 $140

MAC DONALD, GEORGE   Phantastes. A Faerie Romance for Men and Women. New York, n.d. Binding worn, good. Biblo BL781-963 1978 $12

MAC DONALD, GEORGE   Ronald Bannerman's Boyhood. London, n.d. New ed., illus. Biblo BL781-1031 1978 $12.50

MAC DONALD, GEORGE   The Vicar's Daughter. An Autobiographical Story. London, 1872. 3 vols., orig. cloth, 1st ed., back covers on 2 vols. very stained, lib. stamps, very rare. MacManus 238-320 1978 $350

MAC DONALD, GOODRIDGE   Recent Poems. Toronto, 1945. Card cover. Hood 117-812 1978 $7.50

MAC DONALD, HUGH   Rambles round Glasgow, Descriptive, Historical, and Traditional. Glasgow, 1854. 1st ed., sm. 8vo., good, orig. cloth. K Books 244-404 1978 £7

MC DONALD, J. G.   Rhodes. London, (1929). Maps, illus., 3 facsimile letters, 8vo, orig. cloth. K Books 239-291 1978 £6

MC DONALD, J. G.   Rhodes. London, (1934). 4th. ed., maps, illus., facsimile letters, 8vo, orig. cloth. K Books 239-292 1978 £6

MAC DONALD, N.   The Orchid Hunters. New York, (1939), London, 1942. Illus., 8vo, orig. cloth. Book Chest 17-245 1978 $27.50

MAC DONALD, R. J.   The History of the Dress of the Royal Regiment of Artillery 1625-1897. 1899. Coloured frontis., coloured plts., illus., 4to., orig. half buckram, corners damaged, only 1,500 copies were issued. F. Edwards 1013-354 1978 £50

MC DONALD, W.   Spiritualism Identical With Ancient Sorcery, New Testament Demonology and Modern Witchcraft.... New York and Cincinnati, n.d. (1890's?). Orig. binding, clean. Hayman 71-452 1978 $10

MAC DONALDS Irish Directory & Gazetter with Which is Incorporated "The Business Directory of Ireland". 1938 ed., map & town plans, very good, octavo bound in cloth, reprint. Hyland 128-26 1978 £10

MAC DONELL, A. G.   Autobiography of a Cad. 1938. Fine, worn d.w., first English ed. Bell Book 16-605 1978 £5.50

MAC DONNELL, E.   Catholic Question: Practical Views of the Principles & Conduct of the Catholic Clergy & Laity of Ireland. 1827. Signed, plain wrs., octavo bound in cloth, reprint. Hyland 128-28 1978 £12

MC DONNELL, E.   Vindication of the House of Lords...in a Series of Letters to the Editor of the Times. c. 1835. Stitched as issued, very good, octavo bound in cloth, reprint. Hyland 128-27 1978 £7

MC DONNELL, H.H.G.   Chartae et Statuta T.C.D. 1844. Complete ed., good, reprint, octavo bound in cloth. Hyland 128-699 1978 £5

MC DONNELL, M.F.J.   Ireland & The Home Rule Movement. 1908. 2nd ed., wr. good, octavo bound in cloth. Hyland 128-30 1978 £4.50

MC DONNELL, M.F.J.   Ireland & The Home Rule Movement. 1908. 1st ed., wrs. good, octavo bound in cloth. Hyland 128-29 1978 £4

MC DOUGALL, JOHN   Pathfinding on Plain and Prairie. Toronto, 1898. First ed. Austin 82-602 1978 $27.50

MC DOUGALL, WILLIAM   Outline of Psychology. New York, 1926. Slight tear top of spine. Rittenhouse 49-533 1976 $25

MC EACHREN, JUSTIN WALLACE   From an Old Fogey's Inglenook. Chicago, (1930). Orig. binding. Wolfe 39-331 1978 $15

MAC ELREE, WILMER W.   Along the Western Brandywine. (West Chester), 1912. Illus., maps, 4to., very fine copy, orig. cloth, recased. MacManus 239-1550 1978 $75

MAC ELREE, WILMER W.   Around the Boundaries of Chester County. West Chester, 1934. 1st ed., large 8vo, many photos & maps, orig. binding. Americanist 101-87 1978 $57.50

MAC ELREE, WILMER W.   Around the Boundaries of Chester County. West Chester, 1934. Maps, illus., signed by author, fine. MacManus 239-1551 1978 $70

MAC ELREE, WILMER W.   Along the Western Brandywine. West Chester, 1912. 2nd. ed., illus., autographed, 4to, orig. green cloth. Baldwins' 51-460 1978 $65

MAC ELREE, WILMER W.   Around the Boundaries of Chester County.   West
Chester, 1934. 1st. book with Andrew Wyeth illus., 4 pen & ink drawings. Baldwins' 51-461 1978 $87.50

MAC ELREE, WILMER W.   Down the Eastern and Up the Black Brandywine.
West Chester, 1906. Illus., 2nd. ed., green cloth. Baldwins' 51-462 1978
$65

MAC ELREE, WILMER W.   Down the Eastern & Up the Black Brandywine.
West Chester, 1906. 1st ed., 4to, orig. limp morocco, spines & corners rubbed,
photos. Americanist 101-67 1978 $75

MAC ELREE, WILMER W.   Down the Eastern and Up the Black Brandywine.
N.P., 1912. Illus., orig. cloth, recased, scarce. MacManus 239-1552 1978
$75

MAC ELREE, WILMER W.   Shadow-Shapes.   West Chester, 1904. Baldwins'
51-463 1978 $22.50

MC ELROY, JOHN   Andersonville: A Story of Rebel Military Prisons,
Fifteen Months a Guest of the So-Called Southern Confederacy... Toledo, 1879.
Illus., 8vo., orig. cloth, 1st ed., ex-lib. Morrill 241-295 1978 $15

MC ELROY, JOSEPH C.   The Battle of Chickamauga Historical Map and
Guide Book. Chattanooga, n.d. circa 1900. Lg. fldg. map in color, wrs., Bell
Wiley's copy. Broadfoot 46-173 1978 $15

MC ELROY, JOSEPH C.   The Battle of Chickamauga.   N.P., n.d. Wrs.,
lg. folding map, cover speckled, Bell Wiley's copy. Broadfoot's 44-694 1978
$30

MC ELROY, JOSEPH C.   Chickamauga.   Cincinnati, 1896. Orig. binding,
folding map in pocket, clean. Hayman 71-132 1978 $8.50

MC ELROY, ROBERT   Grover Cleveland...The Man and the Statesman.
New York, 1923. 2 vols. Biblo 248-93 1978 $22.50

MC ELROY, ROBERT   Grover Cleveland, the Man and the Statesman.
New York, 1923. 2 vols., ports. MacManus 239-739 1978 $12.50

MC ELROY, ROBERT   Jefferson Davis.   The Real and the Unreal.
New York, 1937. Illus., 2 vols., 1st ed. MacManus 239-895 1978 $25

MC ELROY, ROBERT   The Winning of the Far West...1829-1867. New
York, 1914. 1st ed., illus., folding maps. Jenkins 116-856 1978 $25

MAC ELWEE, ROY S.   Economic Aspects of the Great Lakes-St. Lawrence Ship Channel. New York, 1921. Card cover, maps, charts. Hood's 115-
979 1978 $15

MC FALL, FRANCES ELIZABETH The Heavenly Twins. New York, (1893). 1st
Am. ed., orig. cloth, lacks last end paper with inscription dated Aug 9/93, 3 vols.
in 1. Greene 78-47 1978 $25

MAC FALL, HALDANE   Henrik Ibsen, The Man, His Art and His Significance. New York, 1907. First ed., illus. Biblo 247-829 1978 $17.50

MAC FALL, HALDANE   A History of Painting.   (1911). Coloured plts.,
8 vols., 4to., spines faded, corners rubbed. George's 635-35 1978 £15

MAC FALL, HALDANE   The Splendid Wayfaring.   1913. 4to., illus.,
orig. silken cloth, very good, first English ed. Bell Book 16-489 1978 £21

MAC FALL, HALDANE   The Wooings of Jezebel Pettyfer. 1898. Yellow
cloth with pictorial upper cover by author, 1st. ed. Eaton 45-317 1978 £20

MAC FARLANE, CHARLES   A History of British India... 1854. 2nd. ed.,
illus. by George Routledge, frontis, engraved title & plts., half title, orig. red
cloth, blocked in gilt, good. Jarndyce 16-760 1978 £9.50

MAC FARLANE, CHARLES   The Romance of History: Italy. 1832. First
ed., 3 vols., cr. 8vo., contemp. half calf. Howes 194-1021 1978 £30

MAC FARLANE, J. D.   Herbie! Toronto, n.d. Hood's 115-184 1978
$17.50

MAC FARLANE, JAMES J.   History of Early Chestnut Hill. Philadelphia,
1927. Enlarged and rev'd, illus., map, ltd. to 500 copies. MacManus 239-
1617 1978 $25

MAC FARLANE, JOHN J.   Manufacturing in Philadelphia 1683-1912.
Philadelphia, 1912. Illus. MacManus 239-1632 1978 $17.50

MC FEE, WILLIAM   Aliens. London, 1914. 8vo, blue decor. cloth,
near Mint, Edward Newton's copy with bookplate, 1st ed., collector's cond.
Desmarais 1-287 1978 $15

MC FEE, WILLIAM   Captain Macedoine's Daughter.   Garden City,
1920. 8vo, cloth, 1st state of binding, yellow stamping on cover and decor.
spine, 1st ed., fine. Duschnes 220-202 1978 $12.50

MC FEE, WILLIAM   The Harbourmaster.   New York, 1932. Bkplt.,
minimally spotted covers, d.w. chipped. Desmarais B-417 1978 $10

MC FEE, WILLIAM   In the First Watch. New York, 1946. Bkplt.,
nice, d.w. slightly stained & chipped. Desmarais B-416 1978 $7.50

MC FEE, WILLIAM   Letters from an Ocean Tramp. 1908. Coloured
frontis., good, one 2-page and one 1-page A.L.s. from author laid in, 1-page
T.L.s. from author's mother laid in, first English ed. Bell Book 17-614 1978 £40

MC FEE, WILLIAM   Life of Sir Martin Frobisher. 1928. Plt. Allen
234-1248 1978 $7.50

MC FEE, WILLIAM   North of Suez. New York, 1930. Very good
in bright, chipped d.w. Desmarais B-418 1978 $7.50

MAC FIE, J. W. S.   An Ethiopian Diary. Liverpool & London, 1936.
Orig. cloth, 8vo, map, plts. K Books 239-293 1978 £5

MC GAVRAN, S. B.   A Brief History of Harrison County, Ohio.
Cadiz, 1894. Wrps., scarce. Hayman 71-550 1978 $15

MC GEE, THOMAS D'ARCY   A History of the Irish Settlers in North America. Boston, 1851. 1st ed. Austin 79-448 1978 $47.50

MC GEENEY, P. S.   El Diablo Cojo. The Limping Devil. San
Antonio, (1936). Pic. cloth, 1st ed., very good, scarce. Dykes 35-239 1978
$22.50

MAC GEORGE, ANDREW   Old Glasgow: the Place and the People from the
Roman Occupation to the Eighteenth Century. Glasgow, 1880. Plts., illus., 4to.,
good, orig. cloth. K Books 244-406 1978 £10

MC GEORGE, THOMAS E.   Humboldt County, California. Eureka, [ca. 1889]
Original printed wr., 1st ed. Ginsberg 14-152 1978 $95

MAC GIBBON, DAVID   The Architecture of Provence and the Riviera.
Edinburgh, 1888. Illus., 8vo., 1st ed., orig. cloth, ex-lib. Morrill 241-296
1978 $10

MC GIFFERT, J. N.   History of the Presbyterian Church of Ashtabula,
Ohio. Ashtabula, 1876. Wrs. Hayman 73-490 1978 $10

MC GILLICUDDY, T. D. M.   Proceedings of the Annual and Semi-Annual
Encampments of the Department of Ohio Grand Army of the Republic.... Columbus, 1912. Clean, orig. binding. Hayman 71-133 1978 $8.50

MAC GILLIVRAY, WILLIAM   The Life, Travels and Researches of Baron Humboldt. London, 1860. Map, illus., fine, 8vo., orig. cloth. K Books 244-213
1978 £8

MAC GILLIVRAY, WILLIAM   A Memorial Tribute to William Macgillivray.
Edinburgh, 1901. Frontis., plts., 4to., orig. cloth. K Books 244-214 1978
£12

MC GLASHAN, CHARLES FAYETTE   History of the Donner Party. San Francisco,
1880. Binding worn, scarce, second ed., illus. Biblo 247-252 1978 $75

MC GOUN, A.   A Federal Parliament of the British People. Toronto, Montreal, 1890. Card cover. Hood 116-640 1978 $15

MC GOWAN, EDWARD   Narrative of Edward Mc Gowan, Including a Full Account of the Authors Adventures and Perils While Persecuted by the San Francisco Vigilance Committee of 1856. San Francisco, 1857. Illus., bound copy, 1st ed., 3/4 leather binding rubbed. Nestler Rare 78-66 1978 $185

MC GRATH, FRANCIS SIMS   Pillars of Maryland. Richmond, (1950). Illus., first ed., d.w. Biblo 247-156 1978 $47.50

MC GRATH, PATRICK THOMAS   Newfoundland in 1911... 1911. Orig. cloth, 8vo, illus. Edwards 1012-440 1978 £18

MC GRATH, SISTER PAUL   Political Nativism in Texas, 1825-1860. Washington, 1930. Charts, very scarce. Jenkins 116-858 1978 $35

MC GREEVY, T.   Jack B. Yeats. 1945. 1st ed., d.w., illus., very good, octavo bound in cloth. Hyland 128-841 1978 £14

MC GREGOR, DUNCAN   A Narrative of the Loss of the Kent East Indiaman, by Fire in the Bay of Biscay, on the 1st. March, 1825. Edinburgh, 1825. 2nd. ed., half calf, marbled bds., v.g. Jarndyce 16-874 1978 £10.50

MAC GREGOR, J. G.   On the Utility of Knowledge-Making as Means of Liberal Training. Halifax, 1899. Card cover, cover worn, inscribed by author. Hood 116-374 1978 $10

MC GREGOR, JOHN   British America. Edinburgh, 1833. 2nd. ed., maps, 2 vols., contemp calf, rebacked, no half-titles. Edwards 1012-442 1978 £50

MAC GREGOR, JOHN   The Commercial and Financial Legislation of Europe and America. London, 1841. Modern cloth. Wolfe 39-332 1978 $75

MC GREGOR, JOHN C.   Southwestern Archaeology. New York, 1941. Illus. Salloch 345-111 1978 $10

MAC GREGOR, MARY   The Story of Greece. (c. 1910). Coloured plts. by Walter Crane, sq. 8vo. George's 635-132 1978 £5

MC GUIRE, C. E.   Catholic Builders of the Nation. Boston, Continental Press, 1923. 5 vols. Austin 79-449 1978 $67.50

MC GUIRE, HUNTER   The Confederate Cause and Conduct in the War Between the States. Richmond, 1907. Bell Wiley's copy. Broadfoot 46-175 1978 $30

MC GUIRE, JUDITH W.   Diary of a Southern Refugee, During the War, by a Lady of Virginia. New York, 1867. New cloth, Bell Wiley's copy. Broadfoot's 44-258 1978 $25

MC HALE, FRANCIS   The Life and Public Services of William Howard Taft. Philadelphia, (1931). Edges rubbed, covers faded. Biblo 248-102 1978 $16.50

MAC HUGH, HUGH   Get Next. 1905. Illus. Austin 82-605 1978 $11

MAC HUGH, HUGH   I'm From Missouri. 1904. Illus. Austin 82-606 1978 $11

MAC HUGH, HUGH   Out for the Coin. 1903. Illus. Austin 82-607 1978 $11

MAC HUGH, HUGH   You Can Search Me. 1905. Illus. Austin 82-608 1978 $10

MC HUGH, M. F.   Thalassa, A Story of Childhood by the Western Wave. 1931. 1st ed., d.w., very good, octavo bound in cloth. Hyland 128-42 1978 £4.50

MC HUGH, VINCENT   The Blue Hen's Chickens. New York, (1947). 1st ed., d.w. Biblo 251-564 1978 $15

MC ILWAIN, C. H.   The High Court of Parliament and its supremacy. New Haven, 1910. Spine dull, 8vo. Upcroft 12-279 1978 £12.50

MC ILWAINE, RICHARD   Memories of Three Score Years and Ten. New York, 1908. 1st ed., illus., ports., orig. cloth, very good. MacManus 239-896 1978 $25

MC ILWRAITH, JEAN N.   Sir Frederick Haldimand. Toronto, 1904. Ed. de luxe, spine darkened. Hood 117-318 1978 $17.50

MAC INNES, C. M.   The Early English Tobacco Trade. 1926. Plts., good, octavo. Upcroft 10-430 1978 £8.50

MAC INNES, C. M.   In the Shadow of the Rockies. London, 1930. Illus., fold. maps. Hood 116-862 1978 $70

MAC INNES, COLIN   To the Victors the Spoils. 1950. Very good, first English ed. Bell Book 16-610 1978 £8.50

MAC INNES, COLIN   To the Victor the Spoils. 1950. Very good, slightly worn d.w., first English ed. Bell Book 17-620 1978 £10

MC INNES, GRAHAM   A Short History of Canadian Art. Toronto, 1939. Illus. dust jacket, colored frontis., plts. Hood 117-214 1978 $30

MAC INNES, TOM   The Teaching of the Old Boy. Toronto, 1927. Hood 116-302 1978 $12.50

MC INNIS, EDGAR   Canada, a Political and Social History. New York, Toronto, 1947. Illus. Hood 117-580 1978 $20

MC INNIS, EDGAR   The War, Sixth Year. Toronto, 1946. Maps. Hood 117-136 1978 $12.50

M'INTIRE, JAMES   A New Treatise on the Use of the Globes, With Notes and Observations...Problems.... Baltimore, 1823. Very good. Nestler Rare 78-220 1978 $30

MC INTOSH, JOHN   The Discovery of America by Christopher Columbus. Toronto, 1836. Orig. binding. Hood 117-688 1978 $130

MC INTOSH, JOHN   The Discovery of America by Christopher Columbus; and the Origin of the North American Indians. Toronto, 1836. Probably orig. binding, list of subscribers at the end. Hood's 115-754 1978 $120

MAC INTOSH, M. T.   Joseph Wright Taylor. Founder of Bryn Mawr College. Haverford, 1936. Illus., pres. Biblo BL781-24 1978 $12.50

MC INTOSH, MARIA J.   Charms and Counter Charms. 1849. Austin 82-609 1978 $12.50

MC INTOSH, WILLIAM DENNES   The Archko Volume. Michigan, 1929. Frontis. Austin 79-450 1978 $12.50

MAC INTYRE, IRWIN   History of Thomas County Georgia from the Time of DeSoto to the Civil War. Thomasville, 1923. Bell Wiley's copy. Broadfoot's 44-857 1978 $12

MC INTYRE, O. O.   White Light Nights. 1924. Ltd. to 600 signed by author. Austin 82-610 1978 $12.50

MC KAGUE, W. A.   Investment. Toronto, 1931. Hood 117-429 1978 $20

MAC KANESS, GEORGE   The Life of William Bligh, Vice-Admiral. New York, n.d. Illus., maps, 2 vols in 1. Baldwins' 51-502 1978 $10

MAC KAY, ALEX   The Western World. London, 1849. 1st ed., 3 vols., 8vo., fldg. map frontis., interiors of all vols. fine, orig. brown cloth, few spots, very excellent cond. Current 24-185 1978 $250

M'KAY, ARCHIBALD   The History of Kilmarnock. Kilmarnock, 1880. Portrait frontis., 4th ed., plt., orig. cloth, 8vo. K Books 244-407 1978 £15

MAC KAY, CHARLES   Fisher's Drawing Room Scrap-Book, 1852. London, (1851). Engr. plts., 4to., orig. cloth, text nice. Morrill 241-297 1978 $27.50

MAC KAY, CHARLES   Memoirs of Extraordinary Popular Delusions and The Madness of Crowds. 1852. 2nd. ed., 2 vols., frontis., orig. brown cloth, gilt spines, good. Jarndyce 16-838 1978 £12.50

MAC KAY, CHARLES   The Mormons; or, Latter-Day Saints: A Contemporary History. London, [1851]. Illus., orig. cloth, lst ed. Ginsberg 14-665 1978 $30

MAC KAY, CHARLES   The Salamandrine. 1853. lst. ed., 4to, illus. by John Gilbert, engraved by Brothers Dalziel, orig. green cloth, spine & bds. gilt, pres. copy from The Brothers Dalziel, fine copy. Jarndyce 16-839 1978 £25

MAC KAY, CONSTANCE D'ARCY   The Little Theatre in the United States. New York, 1917. Illus., 8vo., bottom margin lightly dampstained, lst ed. Morrill 239-493 1978 $12.50

MAC KAY, DOUGLAS   The Honourable Company. Toronto, 1936. Maps by R. R. H. Macaulay, lst ed. Hood 117-905 1978 $45

MAC KAY, DOUGLAS   The Honourable Company. Indianapolis. Maps, illus. MacManus 239-268 1978 $17.50

MC KAY, GEORGE L.   A Bibliography of Robert Bridges. New York, 1933. Orig. cloth-backed bds., lst ed., ltd. to 550 copies. MacManus 238-878 1978 $40

MAC KAY, ISABEL E.   Blencarrow. Toronto, 1926. Hood 116-486 1978 $10

MAC KAY, ISABEL E.   Complete Poems. Toronto, 1930. Ltd. no. ed. Hood's 115-889 1978 $30

MAC KAY, ISABEL E.   Up the Hill and Over. Toronto, 1917. lst ed. Hood 117-529 1978 $15

MAC KAY, J.   The Ten Islands & Ireland. 1919. lst ed., illus., spine faded, very good, octavo bound in cloth. Hyland 128-43 1978 £7

MAC KAY, J.   The Ten Islands & Ireland. 1919. Very good, octavo bound in cloth, reprint. Hyland 128-44 1978 £8.50

MC KAY, RICHARD C.   Some Famous Sailing Ships and Their Builder, Donald McKay. New York, 1931. Illus., some in color, very fine copy, d.j. MacManus 239-1766 1978 $27.50

MC KAY, RICHARD C.   South Street. New York, (1934). Nice copy, lst ed. in dust jacket. Butterfield 21-516 1978 $20

MAC KAY, ROBERT WILLIAM   The Progress of the Intellect... London, 1850. 2 vols., tall 8vo., contemp. embossed cloth, 1st ed. Salloch 348-130 1978 $75

MAC KAY, WILLIAM   Narrative of the Shipwreck of the Juno, on the Coast of Aracan, in the Year MDCCXCV. Edinburgh, 1831. New ed., 12mo, new bds. K Books 239-294 1978 £20

MAC KAY, WILLIAM   Urquhart and Glenmoriston. Inverness, 1893. Frontis., plts., full calf, good, 8vo. K Books 244-217 1978 £12

MAC KAYE, PERCY   Dogtown Common. New York, 1921. 1st ed. Biblo 251-568 1978 $15

MC KAYE, PERCY   The Life of Steele MacKaye, Genius of the Theatre in Relation to His Times and Contemporaries. New York, (1927). 8vo., 2 vols., illus., lst ed., orig. cloth. Morrill 241-688 1978 $20

MC KECHNIE, SAMUEL   Popular Entertainments Through the Ages. London, (1931). Illus., 8vo., orig. cloth. Morrill 241-298 1978 $10

MC KECHNIE, W. E.   Magna Carta; a commentary on the Great Charter of King John with an historical introduction. 1914. 2nd ed., 8vo. Upcroft 12-280 1978 £15

MAC KEE, GEORGE M.   Cutaneous Cancer and Pre-cancer. New York, 1937. Rittenhouse 49-506 1976 $15

MC KENDRICK, JOHN GRAY   Hermann Ludwig Ferdinand von Helmholtz. Masters of Medicine. London, 1899. Rittenhouse 49-538 1976 $15

MC KENNA, MARTHE   I Was A Spy! 1932. lst. ed., plts., 8vo, orig. cloth, d.w., partly unopened, fine copy. Sawyer 298-37 1978 $25

MC KENNEY, RUTH   Jake Home. 1943. First ed., review copy. Austin 82-612 1978 $12.50

MC KENNEY, RUTH   The Loud Red Patrick. 1947. Austin 82-613 1978 $8.50

MC KENNEY, RUTH   Love Story. 1950. first ed., d.j. Austin 82-614 1978 $12.50

MC KENNEY, RUTH   The McKenney's Carry On. 1939. First ed. Austin 82-615 1978 $11

MAC KENZIE, AGNES MURE   The Rise of the Stewarts. London, 1935. Map, tables, frontis., 8vo., orig. cloth. K Books 244-218 1978 £5

MAC KENZIE, AIMEE L.   The George Sand -- Gustave Flaubert Letters. New York, (1921). 1st ed., ltd. to 1,500 copies, orig. bind. Petrilla 13-23 1978 $8.50

MAC KENZIE, ALEXANDER   History of the Clan Mackenzie. Inverness, 1879. New binders cloth, 8vo. K Books 244-219 1978 £9

MAC KENZIE, ALEXANDER   Voyages from Montreal, on the River St. Laurence, Through the Continent of North America to the Frozen and Pacific Oceans; in the Years 1789 and 1793... New York, 1802. Illus., map, 1st Amer ed., 3/4 leather, marbled bds., gilt tooled spine, excellent cond. Hood 116-584 1978 $450

MAC KENZIE, ALEXANDER   Voyages from Montreal on the River St. Laurence through the Continent of North America to the Frozen and Pacific Oceans in the Years 1789 and 1793. Toronto, 1927. Illus. Hood 117-581 1978 $50

MAC KENZIE, ALEXANDER SIDELL   Commodore Oliver Hazard Perry. Akron, (1910). Cloth. Hayman 73-400 1978 $7.50

MAC KENZIE, ANNA MARIA   Burton-Wood. Dublin, 1783. 1st. ed., 2 vols. in 1, lacks free endpapers, orig. calf, red label. Jarndyce 16-133 1978 £125

MAC KENZIE, COLIN   Sailors of Fortune. Austin 80-194 1978 $10

MAC KENZIE, COMPTON   Poems. Oxford, 1907. 8vo, original pale blue printed wr., lst ed., author's lst book, bookplate, very good copy. Ximenes 47-189 1978 $65

MAC KENZIE, COMPTON   Whisky Galore. 1947. Very good, worn d.w., first English ed. Bell Book 16-611 1978 £4.50

MAC KENZIE, DONALD A.   Egyptian Myth and Legend. London, Gresham Publishing, 1913. 8vo, orig. cloth, 7 coloured & 33 b/w plts., good. Sexton 7-90 1978 £6

MAC KENZIE, DONALD A.   Egyptian Myth and Legend. London, 1913. Plts., dec. cloth, 8vo, few pencil notes, g.t. K Books 239-295 1978 £5

MAC KENZIE, FAITH COMPTON   Mandolinata: Fourteen Stories. 1931. First ed., cr. 4to., orig. buckram, special lg. paper ed., ltd. to 330 copies signed by the author. Howes 194-1023 1978 £12

MC KENZIE, FREDERICK ARTHUR   Canada's Day of Glory. Toronto, 1918. Hood 117-137 1978 $12.50

MAC KENZIE, FREDERICK ARTHUR   Paul Kruger: His Life Story. London, 1899. 16 illus., cr. 8vo., orig. cloth, covers dull. K Books 239-296 1978 £6

MAC KENZIE, GEORGE   Observations on the Acts of Parliament,.... Edinburgh, 1686. 1st ed., folio, full period calf, blindstamped, untrimmed copy, top hinge tender, fine. Bennett 20-131 1978 $250

MAC KENZIE, HENRY 1745-1831   An Account of the Life and Writings of John Home. Edinburgh, 1822. First ed., portrait, orig. bds., printed label, entirely uncut, fine, 8vo. Howes 194-940 1978 £35

MAC KENZIE, HENRY 1745-1831   The Anecdotes and Egotisms. 1927. Plts., orig. cloth, 8vo. Howes 194-1024 1978 £6.50

MAC KENZIE, JAMES 1680?-1761　The History of Health, and the Art of Preserving It.... Edinburgh, 1759. 2nd ed., contemp. calf, 8vo., wanting blank fly-leaves & with some light signs of use, very good copy. Fenning 32-208 1978 £26

MAC KENZIE, JAMES 1680?-1761　The History of Health, and the Art of Preserving It. Edinburgh, 1760. 3rd ed., 8vo., contemp. calf, hinges partly broken, pieces torn from spine. Morrill 239-162 1978 $22.50

MAC KENZIE, JAMES 1853-1925　Principles of Diagnosis & Treatment in Heart Affections. London, 1916. Rittenhouse 49-507 1976 $35

MAC KENZIE, JAMES STUART FRASER　British Orchids, how to tell One from Another. (1911). Coloured plts. by C. E. T. Ponsonby, 4to., loose in case. George's 635-957 1978 £10.50

MAC KENZIE, JOHN　The Beauties of Gaelic Poetry and the Lives of the Highland bards. Edinburgh, 1907. 8vo., orig. cloth. K Books 244-220 1978 £11

MAC KENZIE, JOHN　Ten Years of the Orange River. Edinburgh, 1871. Folding map, 8 litho plts., few text illus., orig. cloth slightly rubbed, 8vo. K Books 239-297 1978 £65

MAC KENZIE, KATHLEEN CUFFE　Number 4 Canadian Hospital. Toronto, 1933. Hood 117-138 1978 $15

MAC KENZIE, MARY JANE　Geraldine; or Modes of Faith and Practice. 1821. 2nd. ed., 3 vols., orig. half calf, v.g. Jarndyce 16-841 1978 £38

MAC KENZIE, MARY JANE　Private Life. 1830. 2 vols., 2nd. ed., orig. cloth, good. Jarndyce 16-842 1978 £32

MAC KENZIE, MORELL　Case of Emperor Frederick III, Full Official Reports. New York, 1888. First complete ed., sm. stamp on title. Rittenhouse 49-508 1976 $35

MAC KENZIE, MURDOCH　A Treatise of Maritim Surveying, in Two Parts. 1774. 4to., contemp. qtr. calf, rebacked, old marbled sides, endpapers new, plts., scarce. P. M. Hill 142-180 1978 £120

MAC KENZIE, T. A.　Historical Records of the 79th Queen's Own Cameron Highlanders. Devonport, 1887. 8vo., orig. cloth, port. frontis., coloured plts. F. Edwards 1013-535 1978 £35

MAC KENZIE, W. C.　The Life and Times of John Maitland, Duke of Lauderdale (1616-1682). 1923. Orig. cloth, recased, octavo, good. Upcroft 10-431 1978 £7.50

MAC KENZIE, W. L.　Mackenzie's Own Narrative of the Rebellion with Notes Critical and Explanatory Exhibiting the Only True Account of What Took Place at the Memorable Siege of Toronto in the Monthe of December, 1837. Toronto, 1937. Hood 116-758 1978 $70

MC KERROW, R. B.　John Weever's Epigrammes in the Oldest Cut and Newest Fashion, 1599. 1911. Sm. 4to., full salmon calf, fine, reprinted from orig. ed. Howes 194-1026 1978 £18

MAC KEURTAN, GRAHAM　The Cradle Days of Natal (1497-1845). London, 1930. Illus., 8vo, orig. cloth, good. Sexton 7-115 1978 £12

MAC KEURTAN, GRAHAM　The Cradle Days of Natal (1497-1845). London, 1930. 8vo, orig. cloth, 24 plts. K Books 239-298 1978 £8

MC KIM, RANDOLPH H.　A Soldier's Recollections. New York, 1910. Bell Wiley's copy. Broadfoot 46-176 1978 $60

MAC KINDER, H. J.　The Rhine. New York, 1908. Color plates, maps, t.e.g., bookplate, very good to fine. Bernard 5-173 1978 $40

MC KINLEY, ANDREW　Agricultural, Manufacturing, Commercial and Geographical Center of the Mississippi Valley, Missouri, the Imperial State, Its Wealth and Resources. [St. Louis], 1880. Large folding map, original printed wr., 1st ed. Ginsberg 14-588 1978 $125

MC KINLEY, CARLYLE　An Appeal to Pharaoh. Columbia, 1907. 3rd ed., nice, orig. cloth. MacManus 239-844 1978 $15

MC KINLEY, S. B.　Old Rough and Ready: The Life and Times of Zachary Taylor. New York, [1946]. Cloth, d.j., 1st ed. Ginsberg 14-945 1978 $12.50

MC KINLEY, WILLIAM　Liberty and Labor. N.P., n.d. Stapled, sm. piece torn from bottom of final leaf, not affecting printing. Hayman 71-656 1978 $7.50

MC KINLEY, WILLIAM　Speeches and Addresses of.... From March 1, 1897 to May 30, 1900. New York, 1900. Cloth. Hayman 72-647 1978 $10

MC KINNEY, LAURENCE　Garden Clubs and Spades. New York, 1941. 12mo., author's signed pres., pictures. Biblo 247-595 1978 $9.50

MAC KINNON, JAMES　The Social and Industrial History of Scotland from the Union to the Present Time. 1921. 8vo. George's 635-360 1978 £5

MAC KINNON, L. B.　Some Account of the Falkland Islands... 1840. Folding map, including half-title, orig. limp cloth, 8vo. Edwards 1012-665 1978 £125

MAC KINNONG, J. Y.　The Protestant Doctrine of Revelation. Toronto, 1946. Hood's 115-940 1978 $7.50

MAC KINTOSH, H. B.　The Grant, Strathspey or First Highland Fencible Regiment 1793-1799. Elgin, 1934. Imp. 8vo., coloured plts., orig. cloth, partly unopened, faded, coloured frontis. F. Edwards 1013-560 1978 £15

MAC KINTOSH, H. B.　The Inverness Shire Highlanders. Elgin, 1926. Plts., imp. 8vo., orig. cloth. F. Edwards 1013-550 1978 £15

MAC KINTOSH, JOHN　A Treatise on the Disease Termed Puerperal Fever. London, 1822. Top cover detached. Rittenhouse 49-509 1976 $25

MAC KINTOSH, MARGARET　An Outline of Trade Union History in Great Britain, the United States and Canada... Ottawa, 1938. Multilithed. Hood's 115-309 1978 $10

MAC KINTOSH, W. A.　Economic Problems of the Prairie Provinces. Toronto, 1935. Hood 117-906 1978 $55

MAC KINTOSH, W. A.　The Economic Background of Dominion-Provincial Relations, a Study... Ottawa, 1939. Card cover, tables, graphs. Hood 117-948 1978 $35

M'KNIGHT, J.　The Ulster Tenant's Claim of Right; or Landlordship a State Trust. 1848. Disbound, reprint, octavo bound in cloth. Hyland 128-48 1978 £20

MAC KNIGHT, T.　Ulster as It Is, or 28 Years Experience as an Irish Editor. 1896. 1st ed., 2 vols., very good, octavo bound in cloth. Hyland 128-49 1978 £17

MC KNIGHT, W. J.　A Pioneer History of, 1755 - 1844, and My First Recollections of Brookville, Penna. Philadelphia, 1898. Illus., lib. marks, very scarce. MacManus 239-1507 1978 $85

MC KNIGHT, W. J.　A Pioneer Outline History of Northwestern Pennsylvania... Philadelphia, 1905. Illus., maps, 4to., scarce. MacManus 239-1547 1978 $50

MAC KOWSKY, H.　Michelagniolo. Berlin, 1908. Thick 8vo., bds., frontis., plts. Van der Peet H-64-166 1978 Dfl 40

MC LACHLAN, R. W.　Fleury Mesplet, the First Printer at Montreal. 1907. Modern cloth, second series. Wolfe 39-372 1978 $95

MC LACHLAN, R. W.　The Money of Canada from the Historical Standpoint. Presidential Address. (1915). Plts., reproductions of coins, bound. Hood 117-639 1978 $20

MC LAREN, M.　The House of Neill, 1749-1949. Edinburgh, 1949. Illus., roy. 8vo. George's 635-370 1978 £6

MC LAUCHLAN, DAVID   An Essay Upon Improving and Adding to the Strength of Great Britain and Ireland, by Fornication, Justifying the Same from Scripture and Reason. 1735. 4to., 1st ed., modern decor. books, very rare. Quaritch 979-223 1978 $500

MC LAUGHLIN, ANDREW C.   Lewis Cass. Boston & New York, (1899). Fine copy. Hayman 73-442 1978 $7.50

MAC LAURIN, COLIN   Geometrica Organica. London, 1720. 4to., old vellum, plts., first ed. Gurney 75-70 1978 £60

MAC LAURIN, COLIN   A Treatise of Algebra, in three parts. London, 1748. 8vo., plts., contemp. sheep, joints split, head and foot of spine chipped, first ed. Quaritch 977-163 1978 $110

MAC LEAN, DONALD   Remarks on the Facility which Steam Navigation affords for invading Great Britain and Ireland. 1824. 8vo., bd., uncut. F. Edwards 1013-139 1978 £60

MAC LEAN, DONALD   Typographia Scoto-Gadelica. (1915). Reprint, octavo bound in cloth. Hyland 128-958 1978 £10

MC LEAN, DUNCAN   Description of the Largest Ship in the World, the New Clipper Great Republic, of Boston, Designed, Built & Owned by Donald Mc-Kay.... Boston, 1853. Detailed folding plates. Nestler Rare 78-209 1978 $115

MAC LEAN, JOHN   Canadian Savage Folk; The Native Tribes of Canada. Toronto, 1896. Illus., ex-lib., cover scuffed. Hood's 115-756 1978 $30

MAC LEAN, JOHN   History of the College of New Jersey, From Its Origin in 1746 to the Commencement of 1854. Philadelphia, 1877. 1st ed., 2 vols., 3/4 calf, marbled bds., rubbed, but very good, scarce. MacManus 239-1295 1978 $50

MAC LEAN, JOHN PATTERSON   A Critical Examination of the Evidences Adduced to Establish the Theory of the Norse Discovery of America. Chicago, 1892. Ltd. ed., bound. Biblo BL781-46 1978 $22.50

MAC LEAN, JOHN PATTERSON   An Historical Account of the Settlements of Scotch Highlanders in America. 1900. Illus. Austin 79-451 1978 $47.50

MAC LEAN, JOHN PATTERSON   Mastodon, Mammoth and Man. Cincinnati, 1880. 2nd ed., illus., sm. 8vo., orig. cloth. Morrill 241-299 1978 $12.50

MAC LEAN, LACHLAN   An Inquiry into the Nature, Causes and Cure of Hydrothorax. Hartford, 1818. First Amer. ed., covers detached but present. Rittenhouse 49-510 1976 $45

MAC LEAN, N. N.   Life at a Northern University. Aberdeen, 1914. 3rd ed., portraits, plts., 8vo. George's 635-1298 1978 £5.25

MAC LEISH, ARCHIBALD   Air Raid. A Verse Play for Radio. New York, 1938. Near mint in slightly faded d.w. Desmarais B-422 1978 $12.50

MAC LEISH, ARCHIBALD   Conquistador. 1933. First English ed., d.w., orig. cloth, 8vo., ed. ltd. to 1,000 copies. Howes 194-1028 1978 £15

MAC LEISH, ARCHIBALD   Einstein. Paris, Black Sun Press, 1939. Wr., drwg. of author by Paul Emile Becat, 1 of 100 numbered copies on Holland Van Gelder Zonen paper, thin 4to. Battery Park 1-11 1978 $125

MAC LEISH, ARCHIBALD   The Fall of the City. A Verse Play for Radio. New York, (1937). Orig. printed bds., somewhat soiled and rubbed, 1st ed., signed by author. MacManus 238-702 1978 $30

MAC LEISH, ARCHIBALD   The Irresponsibles: A Declaration. New York, 1940. 8vo, maroom cloth, stated 1st ed., d.w. spotted on front cover, else Mint. Desmarais 1-288 1978 $15

MAC LEISH, ARCHIBALD   Nobodaddy. Cambridge, 1926. 8vo, black pr. cloth, uncut, partially unopened, unusually Fine, inscribed to Hugh Palmer, 1st ed., collector's cond. Desmarais 1-290 1978 $20

MAC LEISH, ARCHIBALD   The Pot of Earth. Boston, 1925. Orig. cloth-backed bds., 12mo., 1st ed., 1 of 100 lg. paper copies, fine. Mac Manus 238-701 1978 $60

MAC LEISH, ARCHIBALD   A Time to Speak. Boston, (1940). 1st ed., binding stained. Biblo 251-565 1978 $15

MC LENDON, S. G.   History of the Public Domain of Georgia. Atlanta, 1924. Bell Wiley's copy. Broadfoot's 44-858 1978 $12

MAC LENNAN, HUGH   The Precipice. Toronto, 1948. 1st ed., blank flyleaf missing. Hood 116-487 1978 $10

MAC LENNAN, HUGH   Two Solitudes. Toronto, 1945. 1st ed. Hood 117-530 1978 $10

MC LEOD, A. W.   Arrows in the Heart of the King's Enemies; or, Atheistic Errors of the Day Refuted... Toronto, (1881). Hood 116-303 1978 $10

MC LEOD, CHRISTIAN   The Heart of the Stranger. 1908. Illus. with photos, 1st ed., signed by author. Austin 79-452 1978 $17.50

MAC LEOD, JOHN J. R.   Diabetes: Its Pathological Physiology. London, 1913. Rittenhouse 49-511 1976 $20

MAC LEOD, JOHN J. R.   Insulin, Its Use in the Treatment of Diabetes. Baltimore, 1925. Rittenhouse 49-512 1976 $35

MAC LEOD, NORMAN   Caraid Na n Gaidheal; The Friend of the Gael. 1910. Very good, octavo bound in cloth, reprint. Hyland 128-50 1978 £9

MC LEOD, NORMAN   The Oid Lieutenant & His Son. 1862. 1st. ed., 2 vols., half titles, orig. green cloth, good. Jarndyce 16-882 1978 £34

MC LEOD, ROBERT R.   Markland, or Nova Scotia: Its History, Natural Resources and Native Beauties. Toronto, 1902. Portrait, map, illus., roy. 8vo, orig. cloth. Edwards 1012-443 1978 £40

MAC LEOD, WILLIAM C.   The American Indian Frontier. New York, 1928. Cloth, in worn dust jacket. Hayman 73-401 1978 $20

MC LOUGHLIN, JOHN   The Elves of the Fairy Forest. New York, c.1850. 12mo, hand-colored pictorial wrapper, sewn, almost fine copy. Victoria 34-512 1978 $30

MC LOUGHLIN, JOHN   Letters of Dr...., Written at Fort Vancouver, 1829-1832. Portland, 1948. Hood 116-566 1978 $60

MAC LYSAGHT, E.   The Surnames of Ireland. Reprint, octavo bound in cloth. Hyland 128-959 1978 £5

MAC MANUS, M. J.   Irish Cavalcade, 1550-1850. 1939. 1st ed., d.w., very good, octavo bound in cloth. Hyland 128-58 1978 £14

MAC MANUS, SEUMAS   Donegal Fairy Tales. New York, 1916. Illus. Biblo 247-569 1978 $9.50

MAC MANUS, SEUMAS   Ireland's Case. 1919. Austin 79-454 1978 $11

MAC MANUS, SEUMAS   The Story of the Irish Race. New York, 1921. Very good, octavo bound in cloth, reprint. Hyland 128-60 1978 £5

MC MASTER, GUY H.   History of the Settlement of Steuben County. Bath, 1853. Orig. cloth, light wear on spine, sound copy, minimal foxing. Butterfield 21-424 1978 $75

MC MASTER, GUY H.   History of the Settlement of Steuben County, New York... Bath, 1853. 1st ed., illus., very scarce, orig. calf, spine repaired. MacManus 239-1101 1978 $45

MC MASTER, JOHN BACH   A History of the People of the United States During Lincoln's Administration. New York, 1927. 1st ed., maps, orig. cloth, fine. MacManus 239-266 1978 $25

MC MASTER, JOHN BACH   The Life and Times of Stephan Girard. Philadelphia, 1918. 1st. ed., illus., color frontispieces, 2 vols., fine. Baldwins' 51-439 1978 $20

MC MASTER, JOHN BACH   The Life and Times of Stephen Girard. Philadelphia, 1918. 2 vols., illus. MacManus 239-756 1978 $35

MC MASTER, JOHN BACH   Pennsylvania and the Federal Constitution... N.P., 1888. Illus., uncut, 4to., scarce. MacManus 239-1548 1978 $45

MAC MECHAN, ARCHIBALD   Old Province Tales. Toronto, 1924. End-paper maps. Hood 117-260 1978 $25

MAC MECHAN, ARCHIBALD   There Go the Ships. Toronto, 1928. Ex-lib. Hood 116-227 1978 $10

MC MECHEN, EDGAR CARLISLE   The Moffat Tunnel of Colorado: An Epic of Empire. Denver, 1927. 2 vols., illus., original cloth, 1st ed. Ginsberg 14-267 1978 $75

MAC MEEKEN, J. W.   History of the Scottish Metrical Psalms. Glasgow, 1872. 4to., plts., good, orig. cloth. K Books 244-408 1978 £9

MC MEEKIN, CLARK   City of Flags. 1950. First ed., d.j., very good. Austin 82-616 1978 $12.50

M'MICHAEL, ARCHIBALD C.   Notes by the Way. Ayr, c. 1880. Sm. 8vo., good, orig. cloth. K Books 244-409 1978 £6

MAC MICHAEL, MORTON,   A Landlubber's Log of a Voyage Round the "Horn" Being a Journal Kept by...... [Philadelphia, 1879]. Illus., original cloth, author's ed. Ginsberg 14-525 1978 $100

MAC MICHAEL, WILLIAM   The Gold-headed Cane. 1884. 8vo., inscribed pres. from Munk to George Shaw with Shaw's bookplt., orig. cloth, gilt. Quaritch 977-50 1978 $65

MAC MILLAN, DONALD BAXTER   Etah and Beyond; or, Life Within Twelve Degrees of the Pole. Boston, New York, 1927. Photos, ex-lib. Hood's 115-63 1978 $20

MAC MILLAN, HUGH   The Riviera. London, 1902. Third ed., map, frontis., plts., 4to., gilt-decor. cover. K Books 244-222 1978 £10

MAC MILLAN, MIRIAM   Green Seas and White Ice. Far North with Captain Mac. New York, 1948. Photos. Hood 116-91 1978 $15

MAC MILLIAN, CYRUS   Canadian Fairy Tales. London, 1922. Illus. by Marcia L. Foster, 1st ed., colour plts., sm. quarto. Hood 116-488 1978 $75

MC MINN, EDWIN   A German Hero of the Colonial Times of Pennsylvania... Moorestown, 1886. Illus., 1st ed., fine, scarce. MacManus 239-1549 1978 $45

MC MORRIES, EDWARD YOUNG   History of the First Regiment Alabama Volunteer Infantry C.S.A. Montgomery, 1904. Wrs., Bell Wiley's copy. Broadfoot 46-311 1978 $40

MAC MULLAN, MARY ANN   The Naiad's Wreath. London, 1816. 8vo, disbound, 1st ed., half-title present, uncommon. Ximenes 47-193 1978 $40

MAC MULLEN, JOHN   The History of Canada, From Its Discovery to the Present Time. Brockville, 1868. Orig. cloth, 8vo, several leaves browned. Edwards 1012-444 1978 £10

MC MURTRIE, DOUGLAS C.   A Bibliography of Books and Pamphlets Printed at Ithaca, N.Y. 1820-1850. Buffalo, 1937. Printed wrappers. Wolfe 39-333 1978 $20

MC MURTRIE, DOUGLAS C.   A Bibliography of Chicago Imprints 1835-1850. Chicago, 1944. Cloth, only 200 copies. Hayman 73-50 1978 $25

MC MURTRIE, DOUGLAS C.   A Bibliography of Chicago Imprints. 1835-1850. Chicago, 1944. Illus., orig. cloth, 1st ed., ltd. to 200 copies, very fine. MacManus 238-889 1978 $35

MC MURTRIE, DOUGLAS C.   The Book. The Story of Printing and Bookmaking. London, (1943). Orig. cloth, 3rd rev'd. ed. MacManus 238-975 1978 $30

MC MURTRIE, DOUGLAS C.   Early Printing in Tennessee. With a Bibliography of the Issues of the Tennessee Press. 1793-1830. Chicago, 1933. Illus., orig. cloth, 1st ed., 1 of 900 copies, fine. MacManus 238-1064 1978 $35

MC MURTRIE, DOUGLAS C.   Early Printing in Wisconsin... Seattle, 1931. Folio, illus., orig. cloth, 1st ed., ltd. to 300 copies, fine. MacManus 238-1077 1978 $75

MC MURTRIE, DOUGLAS C.   Early Printing in Wisconsin. Seattle, Dogwood Press, 1931. 1 of 300 copies, 4to., cloth, water mark stains on spine & endpapers. Battery Park 1-71 1978 $75

MC MURTRIE, DOUGLAS C.   The Golden Book. 1927. Illus., 8vo., 3/4 lea., marbled paper over bds., t.e.g., one of 220 copies on special binding, signed by author, 3 extra illus., binding repaired. Battery Park 1-404 1978 $100

MC MURTRIE, DOUGLAS C.   Jotham Meeker. Pioneer Printed of Kansas... Chicago, 1930. 8vo., orig. cloth, 1st ed., 1 of 650 no. copies, pres. copy from McMurtrie, fine. MacManus 238-983 1978 $37.50

MC MURTRIE, DOUGLAS C.   A Note on P. Joseph Forster, Pioneer Alabama Printer. Hattiesburg, 1943. Orig. binding. Wolfe 39-335 1978 $9.50

MC MURTRIE, DOUGLAS C.   Oregon Imprints, 1847-1870. Oregon, 1950. Orig. cloth, fine. MacManus 238-976 1978 $30

MC MURTRIE, DOUGLAS C.   Pioneer Printing in North Carolina. Springfield, 1932. Wrs., facs. illus., ltd. ed. of 200 copies. Broadfoot 50-133 1978 $15

MC MURTRIE, DOUGLAS C.   The Royalist Printers at Shelburne, Nova Scotia. Chicago, 1933. Printed wrappers. Wolfe 39-334 1978 $17.50

MC MURTRIE, FRANCIS E.   Jane's Fighting Ships. London, 1938. Oblong 8vo., orig. cloth, corners worn, illus. Paine 78-71 1978 $35

MAC NAIR, PETER   History of the Geological Society of Glasgow, 1858-1908. Glasgow, 1908. Plts., 8vo., orig. cloth. K Books 244-410 1978 £7

MAC NAMARA, CHARLES M.   A Manual of the Diseases of the Eye. London, 1868. 1st ed., chromolithographed plates, 8vo, orig. publisher's cloth. Gilhofer 75-75 1978 SFr 200

MAC NAMARA, M. H.   The Irish Ninth in Bivouac & Battle; or, Virginia & Maryland Campaign. Boston, 1867. 1st ed., illus., hinges strained, good, octavo bound in cloth. Hyland 128-63 1978 £22.50

MC NAMEE, EDWARD   Breaking the Soul Barrier. N. P., n.d. Author's signed pres. Biblo 251-566 1978 $7.50

MC NAUGHTON, JAMES   An Enquiry into the Present System of Medical Education, in the State of New-York, Respectfully Submitted to the Consideration of the Members of the Legislature... Albany, 1830. Disbound. Hayman 72-453 1978 $12.50

MAC NAUGHTON, S.   My Canadian Memories. London, 1920. Hood 116-260 1978 $17.50

MAC NEICE, LOUIS   Autumn Journal. 1939. Very good, first English ed. Bell Book 17-622 1978 £12.50

MAC NEICE, LOUIS   Blind Fireworks. London, 1929. 8vo, tan cloth, 1st ed., Fine, 1st binding, signed by author, collector's cond. Desmarais 1-292 1978 $350

MAC NEICE, LOUIS   Blind Fireworks. 1929. Very good, rare, first English ed. Bell Book 16-613 1978 £70

MAC NEICE, LOUIS   The Earth Compels. 1938. Very good, scarce, first English ed. Bell Book 17-623 1978 £16.50

MAC NEICE, LOUIS   Gardener Melancholy & Adonis. Cambridge, 1928. Very good, wraps, first English ed. Bell Book 17-624 1978 £15

MAC NEICE, LOUIS   I Crossed the Minch. London, (1938). Illus., orig. cloth, d.j., 1st ed., very good. MacManus 238-703 1978 $50

MAC NEICE, LOUIS   Modern Poetry: a personal essay. 1938. Covers faded, somewhat soiled, good, first English ed. Bell Book 17-625 1978 £14

MAC NEICE, LOUIS   Plant and Phantom. 1941. Fine, unopened, d.w., first English ed. Bell Book 16-615 1978 £25

MAC NEICE, LOUIS   Plant and Phantom. 1941. Very good, first English ed. Bell Book 17-627 1978 £10

MAC NEICE, LOUIS   Poems. New York, 1937. First U.S. ed., very good, repaired d.w. Bell Book 17-628 1978 £38.50

MAC NEICE, LOUIS   Poems, 1925-40. New York, 1940. First U.S. ed., fine, slightly worn d.w. Bell Book 17-629 1978 £27.50

MAC NEICE, LOUIS   Springboard. New York, (1945). Green cloth, 1st ed., fine in dust jacket. Bradley 49-210 1978 $20

MC NEILE, HERMAN CYRIL   The Finger of Fate. 1930. Good, 1st Eng. ed. Bell Book 16-763 1978 £4.50

M'NEILE, HUGH   A Lecture on the Life of Dr. Franklin.... Philadelphia, c.1841. Amer. ed., disbound, orig. printed wrs., libr. blindstamps, fdg. facsimile, 8vo. Americanist 101-53 1978 $20

MC NEILE, R. F.   Christianity in Southern Fenland. 1948. Map, plts., 8vo. Upcroft 12-281 1978 £4.50

MAC NEILL, E.   St. Patrick, Apostle of Ireland. 1934. 1st ed., d.w., very good, octavo bound in cloth. Hyland 128-65 1978 £4.50

MAC NEILL, J.G.S.   What I have Seen and Heard. 1925. 1st ed., illus., good, octavo bound in cloth. Hyland 128-66 1978 £4.50

MC NEILL, WARREN A.   Cabellian Harmonics. New York, 1928. Quarto, tan buckram, 1 of 1500 copies printed by Richard W. Ellis, fine. Duschnes 220-56 1978 $15

MAC NISH, ROBERT   The Philosophy of Sleep. Glasgow, 1830. 12mo., orig. green bds., signature of early owner dated 1831, very good uncut copy, rare 1st ed. Zeitlin 245-156 1978 $95

MAC ORLAN, PIERRE   La Maison du Retour Ecoeurant. Paris, 1929. Sm. 8vo., contemp. 3/4 tan mor., uncut, gilt back, orig. wr. bound in, ltd. ed. prtd. in 1050 copies, numbered on velin teinte paper, woodcuts. Goldschmidt 110-7 1978 $70

MAC PACKE, JOSE   Oikidiaia, or Nutshells: Being Ichnographic Distributions for Small Villas: Chiefly Upon Oeconomical Principles. 1785. 8vo., plts., contemp. calf. Quaritch 983-46 1978 $175

MAC PHAIL, J. G.   St. Andrew's Church, Ottawa. Ottawa, 1931. Pits. Hood 17-336 1978 $20

MC PHERREN, IDA   Imprints on Pioneer Trails. Boston, (1950). First ed., d.w. Biblo 248-274 1978 $24.50

MAC PHERSON, BYRON   Picturesque Washington. Seattle, 1945. Orig. drwgs., 4to., 1st ed. Biblo 251-121 1978 $18.50

MC PHERSON, EDWARD   The Political History of the United States of America During the Period of Reconstruction. Washington, 1880. Bell Wiley's copy. Broadfoot's 44-260 1978 $20

MAC PHERSON, H. A.   The Birds of Cumberland. Carlisle, 1886. Map, coloured frontispiece by Keulemans, 8vo., orig. cloth. K Books 244-223 1978 £10

MAC PHERSON, JAMES 1736-96   An Introduction to the History of Great Britain and Ireland. 1771. First ed., 4to., 19th cent. half red roan, little age-staining. Howes 194-375 1978 £14

MC QUEEN, J.   The West India Colonies... 1825. 8vo, 2nd. ed., no half-title, contemp. half calf. Edwards 1012-731 1978 £150

MAC QUOID, KATHARINE S. At the Red Glove. A Novel. London, 1885. 3 vols., orig. dec. cloth, somewhat soiled, 1st ed. MacManus 238-321 1978 $50

MAC QUOID, PERCY   A History of English Furniture. London, (1938). 4 vols., sm. folio, fully illus. many in color, few pgs. repaired with scotch tape, sound set. Baldwins' 51-118 1978 $125

MAC READY, N.   Annals of an Active Life. (c. 1925). 2 vols., spine of vol. I torn, ex lib, good, octavo bound in cloth, reprint. Hyland 128-69 1978 £4.50

MC REYNOLDS, ROBERT   Thirty Years on the Frontier. Colorado Springs, 1906. Pic. cloth, illus., 1st ed., very good copy inscr. by McReynolds, slipcase. Dykes 34-155 1978 $75

MAC SARCASM, ARCHIBALD   The Life of Hannah More, With a Critical Review of Her Writings. 1802. 1st. ed., uncut in orig. bds., worn, text fine. Jarndyce 16-892 1978 £38

MC SORLEY, JOSEPH   Italian Confessions. Paulist Press, 1916. Austin 79-457 1978 $27.50

MAC SWINEY, T.   Principles of Freedom. Dublin, 1921. Cover dull, text good, reprint, octavo bound in cloth. Hyland 128-71 1978 £4

MAC SWINEY, T.   Principles of Freedom. Dublin, 1921. 1st Irish ed., good, octavo bound in cloth. Hyland 128-70 1978 £4.50

MAC TAGGART, JOHN   Three Years in Canada.... London, 1829. 1st ed., 2 vols., 8vo., half calf, gilt backs. Deighton 5-48 1978 £75

MC TAGGART, M. F.   Mount and Man. London, 1925. Frontis., plts., 4to., cover slightly stained. K Books 244-224 1978 £6

MC TAVISH, NEWTON   Thrown in. Toronto, 1923. Autograph pres. inscription, signed by author, orig. binding. Wolfe 39-336 1978 $40

MC TYEIRE, HOLLAND N.   A History of Methodism, Vol. I. Nashville, 1914. Bell Wiley's copy. Broadfoot 46-541 1978 $10

MC VOY, LIZZIE CARTER   Louisiana in the Short Story. 1940. Cloth, 1st ed., very good, scarce. Dykes 35-166 1978 $15

MAC WETHY, LOU D.   The Book of Names Especially Relating to the Early Palatines and the First Settlers in the Mohawk Valley. St. Johnsville, 1933. Inscr'd by MacWethy, dated 1933, full index. Butterfield 21-276 1978 $25

MC WHORTER, LUCULLUS V.   The Border Settlers of Northwestern Virginia from 1768 to 1795, Embracing Life of Jesse Hughes and Other Noted Scouts.... 1915. Illus., very scarce. Nestler Rare 78-44 1978 $65

MC WILLIAMS, CAREY   Louis Adamic: Shadow – America. Los Angeles, 1935. Austin 79-458 1978 $27.50

MC WILLIAMS, CAREY   A Mask for Privilege. 1948. Austin 79-459 1978 $7.50

MAANDBLAD Voor Beeldende Kunsten. Amsterdam, 1924. Thick lg. 8vo., half cloth, plts., illus., advertism, binding poor, sm. wormholes in first pages. Van der Peet H-64-165 1978 Dfl 50

MAARTENS, MARTIN   The Sin of Joost Avelingh. London, 1914. Green cloth, plts., pres. copy from author, signed with author's initials, bkplt. of Sir James M. Barrie. Bradley 49-12 1978 $10

MABELAN, D.   Home Rule & Imperial Unity. 1886. Good, octavo bound in cloth, reprint. Hyland 128-75 1978 £5.50

MABEY, CHARLES RENDELL   The Pony Express... Salt Lake City, 1940. Dec. cloth, illus., 1st ed., fine, signed by author. Dykes 35-289 1978 $15

MABIE, HAMILTON W.   A Child of Nature. New York, 1901. Illus., 1st ed. Biblo BL781-1065 1978 $9

MABILLON, JEAN   De Re Diplomatica Libri VI. 1681-1704. 1st ed., folding plates, 2 vols., folio, dust soiled, contemp. calf rubbed, rebacked. Quaritch 978-100 1978 $1,150

MACARTNEY, C. E.   The Bonapartes in America.   Philadelphia,
(1939).   Illus., inscribed.   MacManus 239-267 1978 $12.50

MACAULAY, JAMES   Grey Hawk: Life and Adventures Among the Red
Indians.   Philadelphia, 1883.   Orig. binding, clean.   Hayman 71-432 1978
$17.50

MACAULAY, ROSE   A Casual Commentary.   London, 1925.   First
ed., orig. binding, nice.   Rota 211-331 1978 £6

MACAULAY, ROSE   Catchwords and Claptrap.   Hogarth Press, 1926.
Sm. 8vo, 1st. ed., orig. dec. bds., fragile paper spine defective at tail, sunned
otherwise v.g.   Jarndyce 16-1206 1978 £5.50

MACAULAY, ROSE   I Would be Private.   1937.   About fine, trifle
chipped d.w., first U.S. ed.   Bell Book 17-599 1978 £10

MACAULAY, ROSE   Life Among the English.   London, 1942.   First
ed., orig. binding, illus., fine, d.w.   Rota 211-333 1978 £5

MACAULAY, ROSE   Potterism.   New York, 1920.   First American
ed., orig. binding, spine and covers severely worn and marked, internally nice.
Rota 211-330 1978 £9

MACAULAY, ROSE   They Were Defeated.   1932.   Spine faded, some
foxing, else good, first English ed.   Bell Book 17-603 1978 £5

MACAULAY, ROSE   Told by an Idiot.   1923.   Covers a little faded,
nice, chipped d.w., first U.S. ed.   Bell Book 17-604 1978 £12.50

MACAULAY, ROSE   The Two Blind Countries.   1914.   Fine, partly
unopened, first English ed.   Bell Book 17-606 1978 £15

MACAULAY, ROSE   Views and Vagabonds.   1912.   Some slight foxing,
very good, scarce, first English ed.   Bell Book 17-607 1978 £16.50

MACAULAY, THOMAS BABBINGTON   Critical and Historical Essays Contributed
to the Edinburgh Review.   1860.   Full diced calf, 3 vols., 8vo.   Howes 194-
1020 1978 £20

MACAULAY, THOMAS BABBINGTON   Critical and Historical Essays Contributed to the Edinburgh Review.   (Edinburgh), 1865.   Full prize tree calf gilt, 8vo.
K Books 244-208 1978 £8

MACAULAY, THOMAS BABBINGTON   The History of England from the Accession of James II.   1849.   4 vols., polished calf, spines gilt, a little rubbed, some
lettering pieces worn, 8vo.   George's 635-709 1978 £15

MACAULAY, THOMAS BABBINGTON   Lays of Ancient Rome.   London, 1842.
Small octavo, orig. brown publisher's cloth, stamped in blind with arabesques upon
both covers, previous owner's signature, 1st ed., fine.   Bennett 7-71 1978 $175

MACAULAY, THOMAS BABBINGTON   Lays of Ancient Rome.   London, 1904.
Illus., full prize tree calf, 8vo.   K Books 244-209 1978 #7

MACAULAY, THOMAS BABBINGTON   Miscellaneous Works.   New York,
1880.   3/4 mor., mottled bds., 5 vols.   Biblo 247-711 1978 $57.50

MACAULAY, THOMAS BABBINGTON   Complete Works.   1875.   Portrait, 8
vols., demy 8vo., full prize mor., fine.   Howes 194-1019 1978 £65

MACAULAY, ZACHARY   A Letter to William Whitmore, Esq. M.P.
London, 1823.   8vo, sewn, as issued, 1st ed., very fine uncut copy.   Ximenes
47-186 1978 $85

MACCARANI, FR. D.   Vita di S. Antonino, Arcivescovo di Firenze et
dell' ordine de Predicatori.   Venezia, 1709.   Woodcut portrait on title, sm. 8vo.,
old vellum.   George's 635-1023 1978 £6.50

MACCIONI, MIGLIOROTTO   Osservazioni e Dissertazioni varie sopra Il Dir-
itto....   1764.   4to., vellum, spine gilt, vignette.   King 7-185 1978 £30

MACE, A. C.   The Tomb of Senebtisi at Lisht.   New York,
1916.   Plain & coloured plts., illus., folio, orig. bds., leather spine.   Edwards
1012-223 1978 £35

MACE, RICHARD   The First Families.   New York, 1897.   Cloth,
free endpaper missing in back.   Hayman 73-194 1978 $7.50

THE MACEDONIAL Silver Ledge Company, California [Prospectus]...   Buffalo,
1865.   Original printed wr., 1st ed.   Ginsberg 14-154 1978 $125

MACHEN, ARTHUR   The Angels of Mons: The Bowmen and Other Legends of the War.   London, 1915.   Stiff wrs., slightly stained.   Dawson's 447-
260 1978 $10

MACHEN, ARTHUR   The Bowmen and other Legends of the War.   1915.
12mo., pict. bds., good, orig. wraparound band laid in, first English ed.   Bell
Book 16-606 1978 £4

MACHEN, ARTHUR   Dog and duck.   1924.   One of 900 copies, unnumbered & marked 'Presentation', bds., fine, unopened, d.w., first English ed.
Bell Book 17-615 1978 £15

MACHEN, ARTHUR   Fantastic Tales or the Way to Attain: a Book Full
Pantagruelism Now for the First Time done into English.   Carbonnek, 1923.   Bds.,
white paper spine, fine in slightly worn & torn d.w., partly unopened, 1 of 1050
numbered copies signed by author.   Dawson's 447-261 1978 $60

MACHEN, ARTHUR   The Great Return.   London, 1915.   First ed.,
orig. binding, very nice.   Rota 211-355 1978 £5

MACHEN, ARTHUR   The Hill of Dreams.   1907.   Buckram, t.e.g.,
good, first English ed.   Bell Book 16-607 1978 £17.50

MACHEN, ARTHUR   The House of Souls.   1906.   Fine, scarce, first
English ed.   Bell Book 16-993 1978 £27.50

MACHEN, ARTHUR   The London Adventure.   London, (1924).   1st
ed.   Biblo 251-567 1978 $20

MACHEN, ARTHUR   The London Adventure...   London, (1924).   1st
ed., name on flyleaf, covers faded.   Biblo BL781-1067 1978 $12

MACHEN, ARTHUR   The Shining Pyramid.   1925.   Bookplts., very
good, first English ed.   Bell Book 17-616 1978 £16.50

MACHIAVELLI, NICCOLO   The Florentine History in VIII books.   1674.
Portrait, 8 parts in 1 vol., sm. 8vo., contemp. calf, first ed. of this translation.
Howes 194-70 1978 £70

MACHIAVELLI, NICCOLO   Tutte Le Opere.   Geneva, 1550.   Port., 4to.,
vellum.   Salloch 348-127 1978 $250

MACHIAVELLI, NICCOLO   The Works...   1675.   Folio, calf with label,
1st Eng. ed., damp stain on 1st few leaves otherwise fine.   Salloch 348-128 1978
$300

MACHIAVELLI, NICCOLO   The Works of the Famous Nicolas Machiavel.
1695.   Folio, contemp. calf, newly rebacked.   Howes 194-69 1978 £115

MACHIAVELLI, NICCOLO   The Works.   1775.   Illus., second ed., 4 vols.,
contemp. calf, gilt panelled backs, 8vo.   Howes 194-374 1978 £40

MACHIAVELLI, NICCOLO   Works.   1905.   2 vols., orig. buckram-backed
bds., 8vo.   Howes 194-1297 1978 £12.50

MACHUCA, DON BERNARDO DE VARGAS   Teorico y Exercicios de la Gineta....
Madrid, 1619.   1st ed., plts. and illus., rare work, modern leather spine, marbled
boards, light foxing, fine.   Victoria 34-510 1978 $400

MACK, ROBERT C.   Exercises on the 150th Anniversary of the Settlement of Old Nuffield.   Manchester, 1870.   1st ed., illus., ports., rebound, lib.
marks, 1 of 60 copies.   MacManus 239-1074 1978 $35

MACK, ROBERT ELLICE   All-Round the Clock.   New York, n.d.   Color
plates, illus. text, very good.   Victoria 34-511 1978 $22.50

MACKAIL, JOHN WILLIAM   Homer: An Address Delivered on Behalf of the
Independent Labour Party.   1905.   First ed., full vellum, 8vo.   Howes 194-1022
1978 £28

MACKAIL, JOHN WILLIAM   Homer, an Address delivered on behalf of the In-dependant Labour Party. Chiswick Press, 1905. Orig. qtr. parchment, 8vo. George's 635-911 1978 £10

MACKAIL, JOHN WILLIAM   Homer. Chiswick Press, 1905. Battery Park 1-38 1978 $35

MACKAIL, JOHN WILLIAM   The Parting of the Ways. Chiswick Press, 1903. Qtr. vellum, very good, first English ed. Bell Book 16-653 1978 £10

MACKAIL, JOHN WILLIAM   The Parting of the Ways. Hammersmith, Chis-wick Press, 1903. Battery Park 1-37 1978 $35

MACKAIL, JOHN WILLIAM   The Parting of the Ways, an Address. Chiswick Press, 1903. Orig. qtr. parchment, 8vo. George's 635-912 1978 £10

MACKAIL, JOHN WILLIAM   Socialism and Politics, an Essay and a Programme. Chiswick Press, 1903. Orig. parchment, 8vo. George's 635-913 1978 £10

MACKAIL, JOHN WILLIAM   William Morris. Hammersmith, 1902. 8vo., orig. bds., vellum back, unnumbered pages, sm. stain on fr. cover, otherwise nice. Morrill 239-492 1978 $17.50

MACKALL, LAWTON   Scrambled Eggs. 1920. Illus., ex-lib., signed by author. Austin 82-618 1978 $15

MACKEY, JOHN   A Method of Finding a Cube, Double of a Cube, Founded on the Principles of Elementary Geometry. Dublin, 1824. 8vo, disbound, 1st ed.; plate. Ximenes 47-190 1978 $20

MACKIE, PAULINE BRADFORD   Mademoiselle De Berny. 1897. Austin 82-619 1978 $12.50

MACKIE, SAMUEL J.   A Handbook for Folkestone, For Visitors. Folkestone, 1860. Folding maps, plts., 12mo, orig. yellow glazed printed paper wrapper, little wear to spine & tear in frontis, otherwise nice. Fenning 32-209 1978 £12.50

MACKINAC. History and Guide Book. Lansing, 1899. Map, fourth ed., printed wrappers, illus. Wolfe 39-337 1978 $17.50

MACKLIN, HERBERT W.   The Brasses of England. London, (1928). Scarce, 4th ed., illus. Biblo 247-319 1978 $52.50

MACLAY, EDGAR STANTON   A History of the United States Navy. From 1775-1893. New York, 1894. 2 vols., illus., orig. pic. cloth, t.p. of vol. I de-tached, otherwise a good set. MacManus 239-1767 1978 $17.50

MACLAY, WILLIAM   Journal of. New York, 1927. MacManus 239-1553 1978 $12.50

MACON, NATHANIEL   Letters to Charles O'Conor. N. P., n.d. (ca. 1862). 8vo., orig. wr., 2nd prtg. Morrill 241-300 1978 $12.50

MACOUN, J.   Catalogue of Canadian Birds. Ottawa, 1909. Clothbound. Hood 116-41 1978 $35

MACROBIUS, AMBROSIUS AURELIUS THEODOSIUS   In Somnium Scipionis ex Ciceronis Vi. Venice, Aldus, 1528. Diagrams, map, generally v.g. within, old calf somewhat worn, pres. copy from Joseph Scaliger. Thomas 37-47 1978 £250

MACROSTY, H. W.   The Trust Movement in British Industry, a Study of Business Organisation. 1907. 8vo. George's 635-361 1978 £6

MACY, OBED   The History of Nantucket...1835 to 1885. Mans-field, 1880. 2nd ed., 8vo., orig. cloth, good. Paine 78-89 1978 $65.00

MACY, WILLIAM F.   The Story of Old Nantucket. Boston, 1928. 2nd ed., revised & enlarged, illus., 12mo., d.w., part of d.w. & covers water-stained, pres. copy. Morrill 239-511 1978 $10

MADAGASCAR: Its Missions and Its Martyrs. 1863. Map, illus., sm. 8vo, orig. cloth. Edwards 1012-318 1978 £18

MADAGASCAR, Past And Present, With Considerations as to the Political and Commercial Interests of Great Britain and France... 1847. 8vo, orig. cloth. Edwards 1012-319 1978 £45

MADAN, MARTIN   Thelyphthora; or, A Treatise on Female Ruin... 1781. 2 vols., fully rebound in 19th. century calf, red labels, good. Jarndyce 16-134 1978 £45

MADDEN, D. H.   The Diary of Master William Silence: A Study of Shakespeare and of Elizabethan Sport. 1897. Orig. buckram, gilt top, 8vo. Howes 194-1181 1978 £7.50

MADDEN, JEROME   The Lands of the Southern Pacific Railroad Com-pany of California:.... San Francisco, [ca. 1877]. Original printed wr., 1st ed. Ginsberg 14-155 1978 $100

MADDEN, RICHARD ROBERT   The Infirmities of Genius Illustrated by Refer-ring the Anomalies in the Literary Character to the Habits & Constitutional Pecu-liarities of Men of Genius. London, 1833. 2 vols., 1st ed., old full calf, 8vo., very good. Americanist 103-53 1978 $35

MADDEN, SAMUEL   Memoir of the Life of the Late Rev. Peter Roe, A.M., Rector of Odogh, and Minister of St. Mary's, Kilkenny. Dublin, 1842. 1st. ed., frontis, lightly foxed, 8vo, orig. cloth, very good copy. Fenning 32-211 1978 £7.50

MADDEN, SAMUEL   Themistocles, the Lover of his Country. 1729. Sm. 8vo., 1st ed., newly bound in bds., calf back. Quaritch 979-224 1978 $30

MADISON, JAMES   Letters and Other Writings. Philadelphia, 1865. 1st ed., 4 vols., illus., orig. cloth, spine of vol. II worn, else very fine. Mac-Manus 239-270 1978 $100

MADISON, JAMES   The Papers of..., Purchased by Order of Congress. Washington, 1840. 3 vols., 1st ed., lg. 8vos, fine, cloth. MacManus 239-271 1978 $60

MAETERLINCK, MAURICE   Hours of Gladness. 1912. Separately-mounted plts. by E. J. Detmold, 4to., pict. white cloth, very good, first English ed. Bell Book 17-486 1978 £28.50

MAETERLINCK, MAURICE   The Life of the Bee. New York, 1904-1917. 8vo, orig. cloth. Book Chest 17-247 1978 $10

MAETERLINCK, MAURICE   Mary Magdalene... New York, 1910. 1st Amer. ed. Biblo BL781-1068 1978 $8.50

MAFFEI, RAFFAELE   Commentariorum Urbanorum Raphaelis Volaterrani, Octo & Triginto Libri,.... Basileae, 1530. 1st ed., folio, quarter old calf, marbled boards, rather rubbed, woodcut device on title, woodcut initials, neatly re-hinged. Bennett 20-132 1978 $500

MAFFEI, SCIPIONE   Teatro...cioe La Tragedia La Comedia e II Drama non piu stampato. Verona, 1730. 8vo., Italian calf, vignettes, first ed. King 7-186 1978 £35

MAGALOTTI, LORENZO
Please see also
ACCADEMIA DEL CIMENTO

MAGEE'S Illustrated Guide of Philadelphia and the Centennial Exhibition... Philadelphia, 1876. Cloth, illus., fold. maps, nice. MacManus 239-1631 1978 $17.50

MAGENDIE, FRANCOIS   An Elementary Compendium or Physiology for the Use of Students. Philadelphia, 1824. Modern bds. Rittenhouse 49-514 1976 $35

MAGENDIE, FRANCOIS   Recherches Physiologiques et Cliniques sur l'Emploi de l'Acide Prussique. Paris, 1819. 8vo., modern wrs., light foxing but fine copy, 1st separate ed. Norman 5-191 1978 $200

MAGENIS, LOUISA   The Challenge of Barletta. 1880. 1st. ed., 2 vols., orig. green cloth, good. Jarndyce 16-844 1978 £15

MAGGIO, PIETRO   Le Guerre Festive. Palermo, 1680. Folio, frontis., folding plts., excellent copy, contemp. vellum, only ed., rare. Quaritch Summer, 1978-30 1978 $2,500

MAGGS BROS.   Catalogue 491: Australia and the South Seas. London, 1927. Lg. 8vo., cloth, orig. wrs. bound in, illus., plts. Battery 1-333 1978 $50

MAGGS BROS.   Catalog 495: Books Printed in Spain and Spanish Books in Other Countries. London, 1927. Illus., lg. 8vo., orig. wrs., wrs. dust-soiled. Morrill 239-495 1978 $10

MAGGS BROS.   Booksellers 500th Catalogue. London, 1928. Orig. wrps. Baldwins' 51-193 1978 $50

MAGGS BROS.   Catalog 520: Manuscripts and Books on Medicine, Alchemy, Astrology & Natural Sciences. London, 1929. Portrs., autographs, illus., lg. 8vo., orig. wrs. Morrill 239-163 1978 $12.50

MAGGS BROS.   Catalog 542: The Art of Writing, 2800 B.C. to 1930 A.D. London, 1930. Lg. 8vo., illus. wrs. Schumann 511-31 1978 sFr 150

MAGGS BROS.   Catalog 550: English Literature and History from the 15th to the 18th Century. London, 1931. Illus., thick 8vo., orig. wrs. Morrill 239-496 1978 $10

MAGIC, Pretended Miracles and Remarkable Natural Phenomena. London, c.1858. 12mo, faded, very good. Victoria 34-517 1978 $85

MAGIL, A. B.   The Truth About Father Coughlin. 1935. Austin 79-171 1978 $12.50

MAGINN, J. D.   Fitzgerald The Fenian, a Novel. 1889. 1st. ed., 2 vols., half titles, lib. labels inside front covers, orig. dark green cloth, good. Jarndyce 16-845 1978 £25

MAGINN, WILLIAM   The O'Doherty Papers. New York, 1855. 1st ed., 2 vols., orig. brown cloth, very fine condition. Greene 78-77 1978 $100

MAGINNIS, ARTHUR J.   The Atlantic Ferry, Its Ships, Men and Working. London, 1892. Illus., orig. vellum, 1 of 150 lg. paper copies. MacManus 239-1768 1978 $25

MAGIRUS, TOBIAS   Eponymologium Criticum ex Principum Sacrorum, Secularum, Virorum. Frankfort, 1644. Quarto, original boards, engraved printer's device of Pegasus on t.p., engraved dedicatory plate, sound, rare, only ed. known. Bennett 20-134 1978 $185

MAGISTRIS, J. DE   Status, ecclesiae, Civitatis Neapol. Neapoli, 1671. Folio, old vellum, stained. George's 635-1094 1978 £18

THE MAGNETIC Fish Pond. England, c.1890's. Pictorial bos, cheaper version to the original. Victoria 34-322 1978 $20

MAGNUS, LAURIE   A Dictionary of European Literature. 1926. Orig. ed., thick roy. 8vo., orig. buckram, scarce. Howes 194-1030 1978 £8.50

MAGNUS, MAURICE   Memoirs of the Foreign Legion. London, 1924. 8vo., cloth, d.j., 1st ed., very fine. J.S. Lawrence 38-L58 1978 $175

MAGNUS, MAURICE   Memoirs of the Foreign Legion. London, 1924. 8vo., cloth, 1st ed. J.S. Lawrence 38-L59 1978 $65

MAGNUS, MAURICE   Memoirs of the Foreign Legion. London, 1924. One of 2000 copies, fine, frayed d.w., first ed., orig. binding. Rota 211-294 1978 £10

MAGNUS, MAURICE   Memoirs of the Foreign Legion. New York, 1925. 8vo., two-toned cloth, 1st Amer. ed., bookplt. J.S. Lawrence 38-L60 1978 $25

MAGOON, E. L.   The Eloquence of the Colonial and Revolutionary Times. Cincinnati, 1847. Cloth. Hayman 73-506 1978 $12.50

MAGUIRE, CHARLES H. J.   Maguire's Code of Ciphers. Quebec, 1880. 8vo., part of fr. cover faded, 1st ed. Morrill 239-497 1978 $15

MAGUIRE, JAMES ROCHFORT   Cecil Rhodes. London, 1897. Folding map, portraits, cr. 8vo, orig. cloth, inferior paper age-browned, covers shabby. K Books 239-299 1978 £8

MAGUIRE, JOHN FRANCIS   The Industrial Movement of Ireland as Illustrated by the National Exhibition of 1852. Cork, 1853. 1st ed., Bellew Cloth binding, spine damaged, text firm, good. Hyland 128-77 1978 £20

MAHAFFY, JOHN PENTLAND   An Epoch in Irish History, Trinity College, Dublin, 1591-1660. 1906. 2nd ed., signed presentation copy, very good, octavo bound in cloth. Hyland 128-78 1978 £12.50

MAHAFFY, JOHN PENTLAND   Sketches from a Tour Through Holland & Germany. London, 1889. Illus., 8vo., 1st ed., orig. cloth. Morrill 241-301 1978 $10

MAHAFFY, JOHN PENTLAND   Social Life in Greece. London, 1894. Biblo 247-474 1978 $15

MAHAN, ALFRED THAYER   The Gulf and Inland Waters. New York, 1883. Fldg. map, Bell Wiley's copy. Broadfoot 46-177 1978 $10

MAHAN, ALFRED THAYER   Retrospect and Prospect. Boston, 1902. Map, 8vo., 1st ed. Morrill 239-493 1978 $12.50

MAHAN, ALFRED THAYER   Retrospect and Prospect. Studies in International Relations Naval and Political. Boston, 1902. Cloth. Hayman 72-443 1978 $12.50

MAHAN, ALFRED THAYER   Sea Power in Its Relations to the War of 1812. London, 1905. 2 vols., 1st ed., illus., fold. maps, nice set. MacManus 239-1769 1978 $32.50

MAHON, R. H.   Life of General the Hon. James Murray, a Builder of Canada. London, 1921. Illus., spine marked. Hood 117-320 1978 $15

MAHONEY, ELLA V.   Sketches of Tudor Hall and the Booth Family. Belair, 1925. Illus. MacManus 239-1822 1978 $8.50

MAHONY, M. F.   A Chronicle of the Fermors: Horace Walpole in Love. London, 1873. 2 vols., frontis. port., orig. cloth, 1st ed., very good, corners bumped. MacManus 238-153 1978 $75

MAHONY, P.   Letter to Sir John Romilly..on the Encumbered Estates Bill, Ireland. 1848. Disbound, very good, reprint, octavo bound in cloth. Hyland 128-82 1978 £12

MAHOOD, H. A.   Maiden's Fury. London, 1935. 1 of 285 numbered & signed copies, d.j., nice. Houle 10-198 1978 $60

THE MAID'S Metamorphosis 1600. 1908. Facsimile, parchment backed bds. Eaton 45-514 1978 £5

MAILE, JOHN L.   "Prison Life in Andersonville" With Special Reference to the Opening of Providence Spring. Los Angeles, (1912). Clean, Orig. binding, one of 500 numbered & signed copies. Hayman 71-130 1978 $25

MAILER, NORMAN   The Naked and the Dead. 1948. First ed., frayed d.j. Austin 82-620a 1978 $25

MAILER, NORMAN   The Naked and the Dead. New York, 1948. Black paper-covered bds., 1st ed., 1st prtg., exceptionally scarce, mint copy, perfect dust jacket. Bradley 49-211 1978 $200

MAILLOL, ARSTIDE   The Woodcuts of... New York, (1943). Fine, d.w., illus. Biblo 247-362 1978 $97.50

MAILLOUX, AL.   L'Lvrognerie est L'Oeuvre du Demon Mais la Sainte Temperance de la Croix est L'Oeuvre de Dieu. Quebec, 1867. Wolfe 39-338 1978 $25

MAILLY, H.   Le Pilori. Paris, n.d. (ab. 1930). 8vo., orig. covers, rare. Van der Peet H-64-279 1978 Dfl 65

MAIMBOURG, LOUIS   Histoire de la Ligue. Paris, 1684. Sm. 12mo., very good. King 7-287 1978 £15

MAIMBOURG, LOUIS   Histoire du Pontificat de S. Gregoire le Grand. Paris, 1686. 12mo., bds., calf spine gilt, in sm. roman, good. King 7-288 1978 £20

MAIMBOURG, LOUIS   The History of the Crusade... 1685. 1st. English ed., folio, contemp. calf, worn, repaired, new end-papers, marginal water-stains, 1 leaf torn, just touching letters. Hannas 54-214 1978 £23

MAIMBOURG, LOUIS   The History of the League. London, 1684. Octavo, contemp. calf, rebacked, preserving original spine, 1st English trans. Bennett 7-72 1978 $195

MAIMBOURG, LOUIS   The History of the League. London, 1684. 1st English ed., octavo, engraved frontispiece portrait, contemp. calf, rebacked, preserving original spine label, very minor damp-staining. Bennett 20-238 1978 $195

MAIMBOURG, LOUIS   The History of the League. 1684. 1st. English ed., 8vo, frontispiece, contemp. calf, slightly worn, single worm-hole in lower margin. Hannas 54-215 1978 £25

MAIMIEUX, JOSEPH DE   Pasigraphie et Pasilalie. Paris, (1801). 4to., leather, plate. Schumann 511-32 1978 sFr 420

MAIMONIDES
Please turn to
MOSES BEN MAIMON, 1135-1204

MAINE, G. F.   The Wind in the Pines, a Celtic Miscellany. 1922. 4to, 1st ed., illus., 1/4 cl., very good, octavo bound in cloth. Hyland 128-83 1978 £12

MAINE, HENRY SUMNER   Popular Government. New York, 1886. 1st Amer. ed. Biblo BL781-844 1978 $9.50

MAINE FEDERATION OF WOMEN'S CLUBS   The Trail of the Maine Pioneer. Lewiston, 1916. 1st ed., illus., orig. cloth, fine, ltd. to 2000 copies. Mac-Manus 239-275 1978 $25

MAIR, JOHN   The Tyro's Dictionary, Latin and English. Edinburgh, 1808. Seventh ed., 12mo., orig. sheep. K Books 244-411 1978 £6

MAIRET, FRANCOIS AMBROISE   Notice sur la Lithographie,.... Dijon, 1818. Small 8vo, contemp. half-calf, half-mor. slipcase, very rare 1st ed. Gilhofer 75-76 1978 SFr 3,400

MAIS, S. P. B.   Breaking Covert; a romance of the hunting field. London, 1921. First ed., orig. binding, fine, author's signed autograph pres. inscription. Rota 211-356 1978 £7.50

MAISSIAT, JACQUES HENRI   Des Lois Du Mouvement Des Liquides Dans Les Canaux, et de leurs applications a la circulation des etres organises en general. Paris, 1839. 4to., sewn into plain green wrs., light foxing, good copy on lg. paper, 1st ed. Zeitlin 245-157 1978 $67.50

MAISTRE, XAVIER DE   Voyage autour de ma chambre. Turin, 1794. 12 mo., light brown mor. gilt, 1st ed., rare. Quaritch Summer, 1978-31 1978 $1,800

MAITLAND, CHARLES   The Church in the Catacombs.... 1846. Sole ed.?, folding plt., other illus., 8vo, orig. cloth, binding little worn & dull, sound & very good copy. Fenning 32-212 1978 £14.50

MAITLAND, E.   Anna Kingsford, her Life, Letters, Diary and Work. 1913. 3rd ed., portraits, 2 vols., 8vo. George's 635-1432 1978 £6.50

MAITLAND, F. W.   Roman canon law in the Church of England. 1898. Lg. 8vo. Upcroft 12-282 1978 £8.50

MAITLAND, F. W.   Selected Essays. Cambridge, 1936. 8vo. Upcroft 12-284 1978 £7.50

MAITLAND, FRANCIS HEREWARD   Hussar of the Line. 1951. 8vo, orig. black cloth, pres. copy to Winston Churchill, illus. with photos & drawings by John Board. Sawyer 298-92 1978 £260

MAITLAND, S. R.   The Dark Ages. 1844. 8vo. George's 635-712 1978 £5.25

MAJOR, H.   In Search of Gold or Our Adventures in Mata-beleland. London, 1900. Illus. from drawings & photos, cr. 8vo, g.e., orig. cloth. K Books 239-300 1978 £10

MAJOR, HOWARD   The Domestic Architecture of the Early American Republic. Philadelphia, 1926. 1st ed., 4to., illus., plts., orig. cloth, d.j., fine. MacManus 239-689 1978 $65

MAJOR, RALPH H.   Classic Descriptions of Disease. Springfield, 1932. Rittenhouse 49-515 1976 $15

MAJOR, RALPH H.   Classic Descriptions of Disease. Springfield, 1932. Trifle worn. Rittenhouse 49-515A 1976 $12.50

MAKOWER, STANLEY V.   Richard Savage: A Mystery in Biography. 1935. Plts., orig. cloth, 8vo, spine faded. Howes 194-1152 1978 £5.50

MALCOLM, JOHN   The Life of Robert, Lord Clive... 1836. 3 vols., folding map, portraits, 8vo, half calf. Edwards 1012-94 1978 £35

MALCOLM, JOHN   A Memoir of Central India... 1823. Maps, 2 vols., calf, 8vo, joints repaired. Edwards 1012-105 1978 £60

MALCOLM, JOHN   A Memoir of Central India... 1824. 2nd. ed., lg. folding engraved maps, 2 vols., 8vo, contemp. diced calf, gilt, gilt spines, nice copy. Fenning 32-213 1978 £38.50

MALCOLM, JOHN   Sketches of Persia. 1845. Sm. 8vo, half calf. Edwards 1012-75 1978 £15

MALCOLM, ROBERT   The Life of Oliver Goldsmith. (London, n.d.) (1895?). 1st. separate ed., 8vo, portrait, plt., extra-illus., polished calf, gilt, head-band snagged, no. 46 of 50 copies printed. Hannas 54-149 1978 £10

MALDONATI, JOANNES   Commentarii in Quatour Evangelistas.... Paris, 1621. Folio, 3/4 early style calf over marbled boards, title on red morocco spine label and spine panel devices, gilt. Bennett 20-129 1978 $235

MALE, EMILE   Religious Art in France, XIII Century; a study in mediaeval iconography and its sources of inspiration. 1913. 4to., illus. Upcroft 12-286 1978 £20

MALE, EMILE   Religous Art. New York, (1949). Plts. Biblo 251-226 1978 $17.50

MALEBRANCHE, N.   Treatise concerning the Search after Truth. Oxford, 1694. Folio, contemp. calf, woodcut diagrams, first English ed. Gurney 75-71 1978 £75

MALET, REV. WILLIAM WYNDHAM   An Errand to the South in the Summer of 1862. London, 1863. Wraps, Bell Wiley's copy. Broadfoot's 44-264 1978 $12.00

MALLESON, CONSTANCE   After Ten Years. 1931. Pres. copy inscribed from author, portrait, map, orig. linen, very good, worn d.w., first English ed. Bell Book 16-617 1978 £6.50

MALLET, DAVID   The Life of Francis Bacon Lord Chancellor of England. 1740. 8vo., recent half calf, marbled sides, nice. P. M. Hill 142-29 1978 £38

MALLET, DAVID   The Life of Francis Bacon, Lord Chancellor of England. London, 1740. Octavo, full early calf, neatly rebacked, gilt panels and red mor. labels, circular bookplate of William Allen, notation in neat contemp. hand on front free endpaper, 1st ed. Bennett 7-73 1978 $125

MALLET, DAVID   Memoirs of the Life and Ministerial Conduct...of the Late Lord Visc. Bolingbroke. 1752. First ed., contemp. calf, spine rubbed, label missing, 8vo. Howes 194-180 1978 £25

MALLET, EDME   Essai Sur L'Etude Des Belles Lettres. Paris, 1747. 8vo., contemp. marbled calf, spine gilt, with label. Salloch 348-131 1978 $75

MALLET, PAUL HENRI   Northern Antiquities. 1770. First English ed., 2 vols., contemp. calf, rebacked, 8vo. Howes 194-277 1978 £68

MALLET, THIERRY   Glimpses of the Barren Lands. New York, 1930. Illus. Hood 117-103 1978 $22.50

MALLET, THIERRY   Plain Tales of the North. New York, 1925.
Illus. Hood 116-92 1978 $30

MALLETT, W. E.   An Introduction to Old English Furniture.
(c. 1910). Illus. by H. M. Brock, sm. folio, half mor. George's 635-247 1978
£10

MALLOCK, WILLIAM HURRELL   Property and Progress, or a Brief Inquiry Into
Contemporary Social Agitation in England. New York, 1884. 1st American ed.,
8vo., orig. cloth, printed paper label, label rubbed, otherwise nice copy.
Fenning 32-214 1978 £10.50

MALLOCK, WILLIAM HURRELL   A Romance of the Nineteenth Century. 1881.
2nd ed., 2 vols., new preface, half titles, orig. dull olive cloth, star & moon
pattern, good. Jarndyce 16-846 1978 £12.50

MALONE, DESMOND   The Last Landfall. 1936. D.w., (torn), very
good, octavo bound in cloth, reprint. Hyland 128-85 1978 £4

MALONE, DICK   Missing from the Record. Toronto, 1946. Hood
116-135 1978 $10

MALONE, DUMAS   Edwin A. Alderman. New York, 1940. Broadfoot 50-135 1978 $10

MALONE, DUMAS   Jefferson the Virginian. Boston, 1948. First ed.,
d.w. Biblo 247-71 1978 $16.50

MALONE, DUMAS   Jefferson the Virginian. Boston, 1948. Illus.
Biblo 251-46 1978 $8.50

MALONE, R. F.   The Witcheens; A Tale of Maynooth & London.
1928. 1st ed., very good, octavo bound in cloth. Hyland 128-87 1978 £5

MALONE, THOMAS H.   Memoir of Thomas H. Malone. Nashville, 1928.
Bell Wiley's copy. Broadfoot's 44-616 1978 $150

MALONEY, JOHN   Let There By Mercy. 1941. Illus. Austin 80-
195 1978 $10

MALONEY, TOM   U.S. Camera Annual...1951. American International. New York, (1950). 4to., illus., some in color, 1st ed., bind. rubbed.
Biblo BL781-698 1978 $9.50

MALORY, THOMAS   Arthur Pendragon of Britain. New York,
(1943). 1st ed., fine d.w., illus. by Andrew Wyeth. Biblo 251-222 1978 $42.50

MALORY, THOMAS   The Birth Life and Acts of King Arthur of His
Noble Knights of the Round Table.... London, 1893-4. 2 vols., large octavo,
orig. beige cloth, gilt, some edges uncut, very good, ltd. to 1,500 copies, illus.
by Beardsley. Totteridge 29-9 1978 $450

MALORY, THOMAS   The Birth Life and Acts of King Arthur of His
Noble Knights.... New York, 1927. 3rd ed., large octavo, orig. black cloth
with gilt, t.e.g., edges uncut, bookplate removed, illus. by Beardsley, ltd. to
1,600 copies. Totteridge 29-10 1978 $200

MALORY, THOMAS   Le Morte Darthur. 1908. 2 vols., orig. red
cloth, 8vo. Howes 194-1032 1978 £7.50

MALORY, THOMAS   Le Morte Darthur. London, 1923. Coloured
plts. by W. Russell Flint, 2 vols., roy. 8vo., orig. buckram gilt, gilt tops, spines
little faded. Traylen 88-298 1978 £40

MALPIGHI, MARCELLO   Consulationum Medicinalium centuria prima,....
Patavia, 1713. 1st ed., quarto, full contemp limp vellum. Bennett 20-135 $250

MALPIGHI, MARCELLO   Consultationum Medicinalium Centuria Prima,....
Patavii, 1713. 4to., limp vellum, sm. defect on spine, first ed. King 7-189
1978 £100

MALRAUX, ANDRE   Days of Wrath. New York, 1936. First American
ed., d.w. Biblo 247-597 1978 $15

MALRAUX, ANDRE   Days of Wrath. New York, 1936. Fine in
chipped d.w. Desmarais B-434 1978 $15

MALRAUX, ANDRE   Saturne. Essay sur Goya. Montrouge, (1950).
4to., illus., color plts., ltd. ed. Biblo BL781-600 1978 $42.50

MALTBY, ISAAC   The Elements of War. Boston, 1813. 2nd ed.,
plates, hinges lightly cracked, rubbed. Victoria 34-518 1978 $15

MALTBY, WILLIAM JEFF   Captain Jeff or Frontier Life in Texas with the
Texas Rangers... Colorado, 1908. Illus., orig. red pict. wrs., 2nd print.,
covers loose, paper bind., lacking on spine. Biblo BL781-290 1978 $18.50

MALTE-BRUN, M. V. A.   La Sonora et ses Mines. Paris, 1864. Folding
colored map, original printed wr., 1st ed. Ginsberg 14-20 1978 $100

MALTHUS, THOMAS ROBERT   An Essay on the Principle of Population.
Georgetown, 1809. 2 vols., 8vo., contemp. bds., roan backs, vols. dampstained,
very heavy & dark in spots, 1st Amer. ed. Morrill 239-164 1978 $150

MALTZ, ALBERT   The Journey of Simon McKeever. 1949. First ed.
Austin 82-623 1978 $11

MALVEZZI, VIRGILIO   Discourses Upon Cornelius Tacitus. 1642.
Folio, old calf, one joint broken. Allen 234-923 1978 $100

MALVEZZI, VIRGILIO   Opere Historiche e Politiche Nuovamente raccolte insieme. Geneva, 1656. 2 vols., sm. 8vo., marbled bds., calf spine gilt.
King 7-58 1978 £25

MALVEZZI, VIRGILIO   Romulus and Tarquin First Written in Italian by
the Marques Virgilio Malvezzi.... London, 1637. 1st English ed., 12mo, full
period style pressed vellum, gilt rules, handsomely bound, last leaf strengthened
with Japan paper, fine. Bennett 20-136 1978 $285

MALVEZZI, VIRGILIO   Il Romvlo. Geneva, 1647. 12mo., calf, worn,
spine defective. King 7-57 1978 £25

MAMMALIA. Edinburgh, 1833-44. 12 vols., (of 13, lacks the vol. on Horses),
plts., almost all coloured, orig. cloth, first ed. K Books 244-171 1978 £200

MANAGEMENT Of The Tongue. 1706. Cr. 8vo, contemp. blind-panelled calf,
worn. Eaton 45-320 1978 £50

MANCEAU, MME.   Traits Historiques. Paris, c.1832. Engraved
plates and t.p. vignette, gilt-decor. leather, cover hinges cracked, small spine
chips. Victoria 34-519 1978 $20

MANCO-CAPAC PSEUD.
Please turn to
MAURY, MATTHEW FONTAINE

MANDEVILLE, BERNARD   The Fable of the Bees: or, Private Vices, Publick Benefits. London, 1723. 2nd ed., enlarged, 8vo., 3/4 calf. Salloch 348-
132 1978 $110

MANDEVILLE, BERNARD   The Fable of the Bees. 1723. Second ed.,
contemp. panelled calf, joints little cracked, 8vo. Howes 194-378 1978 £35

MANDEVILLE, BERNARD   Free Thoughts on Religion, the Church and
National Happiness. 1729. Second ed., fcap. 8vo., contemp. calf, upper joint
cracked, label missing, binding rubbed. Howes 194-379 1978 £18

MANDRAKE the Magician and the Flame Pearls. Racine, (1946). Very good or
better. Bemard 5-346 1978 $7.50

MANGIN, A.   Voyages et Decouvertes Outre-Mer au XIX
Siecle. Rours, 1880. Illus. by Durand-Brager, 3rd ed., 4to, cloth, illus.
Van der Peet 127-312 1978 Dfl 75

MANGIN, EDWARD   A View of the Pleasures Arising from a Love of
Books. 1814. Sm. 8vo., later bds., uncut, first ed. P. M. Hill 142-168 1978
£38

MANHATTAN, Riley County, Kansas. [Waterville, 1888]. Ginsberg 14-455
1978 $35

MANHOOD, H.A.   Little Peter the Great. London, 1931. 8vo, yellow cloth, gilt lettering on cover and spine, t.e.g., pr. at Chiswick Press, near Mint, no. 145 of 550 copies signed by author, 1st ed. Desmarais 1-294 1978 $15

MANHOOD, H. A.   Little Peter the Great. 1931. 1 of 550 copies numbered and signed by author, roy. 8vo., buckram, t.e.g., very good, first English ed. Bell Book 16-618 1978 £4

MANHOOD, H.A.   Three Nails. White Owl Press, 1933. Very good, bds., first English ed. Bell Book 16-619 1978 £5.50

MANIFESTACION que Hace al Manuel Gandara,.... Mexico, 1857. Half morocco, 1st ed. Ginsberg 14-21 1978 $450

MANILIUS, MARCUS   Astronomicon. Nurembert, (1473-4). Sm. 4to., roman letter, fine woodcut initials, good, 19th century olive mor., gilt edges. Quaritch 977-193 1978 $7,000

MANLEY, A. STEWART   Hit and Miss or the Mystery of Nellie Clare. Chicago, 1889. Cloth, dampstained, little worn. Hayman 72-233 1978 $7.50

MANLEY, MARY DE LA RIVIERE   Memoirs of Europe. 1710. 8vo., contemp. panelled calf, rebacked, first ed. P. M. Hill 142-193 1978 £45

MANLEY, MARY DE LA RIVIERE   Secret Memoirs and Manners of Several Persons of Quality of Both Sexes. London, 1709. 2 vols., full contemp. blind-stamped calf, rebacked later, damp staining, 2nd ed., very nice. Bennett 20-137 1978 $125

MANN, EDWIN JOHN   The Deaf and Dumb:.... Boston, 1836. 1st ed., plates, cloth with handsomely rebacked leather spine, very good. Victoria 34-520 1978 $25

MANN, MARY E.   Mrs. Peter Howard. 1886. 1st. ed., 2 vols., lib. label removed fron front endpaper, orig. maroon cloth, good. Jarndyce 16-847 1978 £24

MANN, ROBERT JAMES   The Colony Of Natal. London, (1859). 8vo, errata slip, neatly recased in orig. cloth. K Books 239-301 1978 £45

MANN, S. A.   Governor's Message to the Legislative Assembly of the Territory of Utah. Salt Lake City, 1870. Sewn, 1st ed. Ginsberg 14-1009 1978 $125

MANN, THOMAS   The Beloved Returns: Lotte in Weimar. New York, 1940. Mint in d.w. Desmarais B-436 1978 $10

MANN, THOMAS   Buddenbrooks. Berlin, 1930. Cloth, d.w. Eaton 45-321 1978 £5

MANN, THOMAS   A Christmas Poem. Equinox, 1932. First U.S. ed., very good, wraps. Bell Book 16-621 1978 £8.50

MANN, THOMAS   The Magic Mountain. London, 1927. First English ed., two vols., fine, d.w., slipcase, orig. binding, scarce. Rota 211-359 1978 £15

MANN, THOMAS   This Peace. New York, 1938. Fine in lightly damaged d.w. Desmarais B-437 1978 $12.50

MANNE, LOUIS-FRANCOIS   Observation de Chirurgie, au Sujet d'une Playe a la Tete Avec Fracas, et une Piece d'os Implantee Dans le Cerveau Pendant un Mois Sans Aucum Simptome... Avignon, 1729. Copperplt., 12mo., contemp. calf, rubbed, back gilt, 1st ed., very good copy. Offenbacher 30-88 1978 $150

MANNERING, MAY   The Little Spaniard; or, Old Jose's Grandson. Boston, 1869. Orig. binding, clean, cover faded & little worn, some internal dampstains. Hayman 71-384 1978 $7.50

MANNERS, LADY   Poems. 1794. 1st. ed., half-title, later cloth, good. Jarndyce 16-136 1978 £18

MANNERS, LADY   Poems. 1794. 1st. ed., uncut, unopened orig. blue bds., cream paper spine, mint. Jarndyce 16-135 1978 £36

MANNERS and Social Usages. New York, (1907). Rev'd. and corrected, illus. Biblo BL781-800 1978 $8

MANNING, ANNE   The Household of Sir Thomas More. London, 1906. Color illus. by Charles E. Brock, 8 vo., gilt stamped decorative green cloth, t.e.g., uncut, good. Houle 10-49 1978 $15

MANNING, ANNE   The Maiden & Married Life of Mary Powell afterwards Mistress Milton. New York, (1849). 1st Amer. ed., cloth binding with date 1643 stamped in gilt antique frame on front cover, edges bevelled, page edges stained red, good. Greene 78-259 1978 $125

MANNING, ANNE   Town & Forest. 1860. 1st. ed., frontis, half calf, red labels, spine rubbed, Royal Artillery Regimental Lib. label on inside front cover, good. Jarndyce 16-849 1978 £12.50

MANNING, ANNE   The Year Nine. 1858. 1st. ed., frontis, orig. green cloth, good. Jarndyce 16-848 1978 £12.50

MANNING, CLARENCE A.   Soldier of Liberty. 1945. Austin 79-464 1978 $12.50

MANNING, FREDERIC   The Middle Parts of Fortune. Somme and Ancre, 1916. 1929. 2 vols., orig. cloth, marbled end-papers, 1st in pub. box ed., 1 of 520 copies on hand-made paper, fine. MacManus 238-706 1978 $100

MANSEL, HENRY LONGUEVILLE   The Philosophy of the Conditioned. London and New York, 1866. 8vo, original brown cloth, 1st ed., fine copy. Ximenes 47-195 1978 $40

MANSEL, ROBERT   Free Thoughts Upon Methodists, Actors and the Influence of the Stage. 1814. 1st. ed., 12mo, modern half calf, uncut, partly unopened. Hannas 54-330 1978 £90

MANSFIELD, EDWARD D.   The Mexican War: a History of Its Origin, and a Detailed Account of the Victories. New York, 1848. Illus., maps, 1st ed. MacManus 239-308 1978 $37.50

MANSFIELD, KATHERINE   The Aloe. New York, 1930. Green bds., 1st Amer. ed., 1 of 975 copies, bkplt., nice copy, uncut & unopened. Bradley 49-215 1978 $30

MANSFIELD, KATHERINE   The Aloe. New York, 1930. 8vo, boards, paper label, d.j., slipcase as issued, 1 of 975 copies, 1st Amer. ed., fine. Duschnes 220-195 1978 $40

MANSFIELD, KATHERINE   The Aloe. New York, 1930. 8vo, grey-green boards, paper label, uncut, unopened, near Mint in chipped d.w., 1st Amer. ed., limited to 975 copies, this is no. 560, pr. by Plimpton Press. Desmarais 1-295 1978 $25

MANSFIELD, KATHERINE   Bliss and Other Stories. London, (1920). Orig. cloth, 1st ed., 1st issue, bookplts., very good, half-mor. case. MacManus 238-707 1978 $125

MANSFIELD, KATHERINE   The Doves' Nest, and other stories. 1923. Very good, d.w., first English ed. Bell Book 16-622 1978 £17.50

MANSFIELD, KATHARINE   The Garden Party and Other Stories. 1922. Very good, first English ed. Bell Book 17-637 1978 £12.50

MANSFIELD, KATHERINE   Novels and Novelists. 1930. Some foxing, near fine, d.w., first English ed. Bell Book 17-638 1978 £22.50

MANSFIELD, KATHERINE   Novels and Novelists. New York, 1930. 1st Amer. ed. Biblo BL781-1071 1978 $10

MANSFIELD, KATHERINE   Poems. 1923. 1st. ed., linen backed bds. with leather label. Eaton 45-322 1978 £20

MANSFIELD, KATHERINE   Something Childish, and other stories. 1924. Good, spine dull, first English ed. Bell Book 16-623 1978 £35

MANSFIELD, KATHERINE   Something Childish and Other Stories. London, 1924. 8vo, grey cloth stamped in black, 2nd issue, ownership inscription, light foxing, very Nice, 1st ed., collector's cond. Desmarais 1-296 1978 $20

MANSFIELD, KATHERINE   Something Childish, and other stories. 1924. Very good, worn d.w., first English ed. Bell Book 16-996 1978 £15

MANSFIELD, KATHERINE   Stories by Katherine Mansfield. New York, (1930). 1st Amer. ed., brown cloth, very good. Bradley 49-216 1978 $15

MANSION, L.   Lettres sur la Miniature. Paris, c. 1820. 12mo, 5 leaves worm-holed, boards, upper hinge cracked, fine, lithographed by Engelmann. Victoria 34-521 1978 $35

MANSON, JACQUES CHARLES DE   Traite du fer et de l'Acier. Paris, (1804). 4to., very fine lg. fldg. copperplts., half antique calf, gilt, very fine, uncut copy, 1st ed. Norman 5-192 1978 $275

MANSON, PATRICK   Lectures on Tropical Diseases Being the Lane Lectures for 1905 Delivered at Cooper Medical College, San Francisco U.S.A. August 1905. London, 1905. 8vo., illus., lib. stamps, binders cloth. Quaritch 977-51 1978 $55

MANTEGAZZA, PAOLO   Anthropological Studies of Sexual Relations of Mankind. New York, (1932). Illus., #102 of 1,500 copies, orig. bind. Petrilla 13-26 1978 $15

MANTELL, GIDEON ALGERNON   A Pictorial Atlas of Fossil Remains. London, 1850. Frontispiece, hand-coloured plts., 4to., new binders cloth, orig. gilt-titling preserved, scarce. K Books 244-412 1978 £80

MANTICA, FRANCISCO   De Coniecturis Ultimarum Voluntatum Libri Duodecim. Frankfort, 1580. 1st ed. to contain all twelve books, folio, full cont contemp. limp vellum, title in contemp. hand, engraved pict. devices, very fine. Bennett 20-138 1978 $475

MANTUANUS, BAPTISTA   De Calamitatibus Temporu. (Paris), 1502. Heavily annotated in a contemp. hand, sm. 4to., vellum, rebacked. Thomas 37-56 1978 £300

A MANUAL of Communities Served by Corporations Operated by the Henry L. Doherty Organization. 1920. Austin 80-552 1978 $27.50

MANUAL of Heraldry. London, n.d. (ca. late 19th Century). Colored frontis., illus. on wood, 12mo., orig. cloth. Morrill 241-196 1978 $12.50

MANUAL of the Lancasterian System, of Teaching, Reading, Writing, Arithmetic, and Needle-Work, as Practised in the Schools of the Free-School Society. New York, 1820. Folded plts., uncut, orig. bds., loose, old library stamp on one plt. Butterfield 21-498 1978 $15

MANUEL des Habitans de Saint-Domingue, Contenant un Precis de L'Histoire de Cette Ile, Depuis sa Decouverte. Paris, 1803. Contemp. bds., half calf, map dampstained. Wolfe 39-496 1978 $100

MANUFACTURE De Sevres Epoque Empire. Paris, n.d. 40 folio plts. in folder. Baldwins' 51-119 1978 $27.50

MANWOOD, JOHN   A Treatise and Discovrse of the Lawes of the Forrest.... London, 1598. 1st. ed., woodcut initials, printed mostly in black letter, sm. 4to, brown morocco gilt, panelled in blind & gilt, gilt lettered spine, g.e., fine copy. Traylen 88-468 1978 £350

MANWOOD, JOHN   A Treatise of the Laws of the Forest, Wherein is declared not onely those Laws, as they are now in force, but also the Original and beginning of Forests:.... London, 1665. Quarto, full early style calf, worn at extremities, bookplate, 3rd ed. Bennett 7-74 1978 $325

MANZANED Y ENCINAS, DIEGO MIGUEL BRINGAS DE
Please turn to
BRINGAS DE MANZANED Y ENCINAS, DIEGO MIGUEL

MANZINI, CARLO ANTONIO   L'Occhiale all' Occhio. Bologna, 1660. Woodcut vignette, fine engr. portr., 4to., contemp. limp vellum, 1st ed., very fine copy. Offenbacher 30-89 1978 $600

MAP Of The Transvaal...and Surrounding Counties. London, 1899. 3 folding coloured maps, little used & soiled, 8vo, orig. cloth. K Books 239-238 1978 £12

MAPES, JOHN JAY   Inaugural Address...Jan. 7, 1845, Before the Mechanics' Institute of the City of New-York. New York, 1845. Prtd. wr., little dusty, very good. Butterfield 21-519 1978 $17.50

MAPLETT, JOHN   A Greene Forest... 1930. Reprint, 4to, good. Upcroft 10-113 1978 £20

MARAT, JEAN PAUL   Polish Letters. Boston, 1905. 4to, 2 vols., boards, Italian handmade paper, uncut, slipcase, dust darkening, 1st ed., collector's cond. Desmarais 1-42 1978 $25

MARAT, JEAN PAUL   Recherches Physiques sur l'Electricite. Paris, 1782. 8vo., fold. plts., contemp. calf, gilt back, rubbed, rare, 1st ed. Gilhofer 74-122 1978 sFr 600

MARAT, JEAN PAUL   Recherches Physiques sur le Feu. Paris, 1780. Fldg. copperplts., 8vo., contemp. light blue wrs., uncut, in red half mor. solander case, 1st ed., excellent cond., Marat's copy with his autograph notes. Offenbacher 30-90 1978 $3,600

MARBERRY, M. M.   The Golden Voice. New York, 1947. 8vo., d.w., 1st ed. Morrill 239-501 1978 $8.50

MARBLE'S Specialties for Sportsmen. (Chicago), 1908-9. Illus., 12mo., orig. wrs. Morrill 241-137 1978 $15

MARBOT, BARON DE   The Memoirs of Baron de Marbot, Late Lieutenant-General in the French Army. 1892. 2 vols., 8vo., contemp. half calf, maps, frontis. portraits. F. Edwards 1013-355 1978 £60

MARCELLO, BENEDETTO   Il Toscanismo e La Crusca, osia Il Cruscante Impazzito.... Venezia, 1739. 8vo, marbled bds., calf spine, good, first ed. King 7-191 1978 £35

MARCET, JANE   Conversations on Natural Philosophy. London, 1820. 2nd. ed., engraved plts., sm. 8vo, contemp. calf, joints neatly repaired. Traylen 88-175 1978 £30

MARCET, JANE   Conversations on Natural Philosophy. 1820. 12mo., contemp. diced calf, spine gilt. Howes 194-380 1978 £10

MARCET, JANE   Conversations on Political Economy. 1819. 12mo., contemp. diced calf, gilt spine. Howes 194-381 1978 £12

MARCH, ALDEN   A Lecture on the Expediency of Establishing a Medical College and Hospital in the City of Albany: Delivered January 11th, 1830... Albany, 1830. Disbound. Hayman 72-445 1978 $12.50

MARCH, FRANCIS A.   History of the World War. 1918. Illus. Austin 80-196 1978 $10

MARCH, LEONARD   The Apocatastasis. Burlington, 1854. Orig. binding. Wolfe 39-340 1978 $30

MARCH, RICHARD   T. S. Eliot: a symposium. 1948. Plts., worn d.w, very good, first English ed. Bell Book 16-315 1978 £6

MARCH to Quebec; Journals of the Members of Arnold's Expedition. Garden City, 1947. Hood 116-138 1978 $30

MARCHAL, COLONEL   La Bataille de Verdun Expliquee Sur Le Terrain. Verdun, n.d. 8vo, red cloth with green morocco lettering piece, orig. wrappers bound in at back, t.e.g., sm. mark on upper cover, pres. copy to Winston Churchill, good copy. Sawyer 298-93 1978 £60

MARCHAL, S.   Costumes et parures khmers, d'apres les Devata d'Angkor-Vat. Paris-Bruxelles, 1927. Illus., plts., rare, 8vo, orig. covers. Van der Peet 127-142 1978 Dfl 85

MARCHANT, BESSIE   A Countess from Canada, a Story of Life in the Backwoods. Boston, n.d. Illus. by Cyrus Cuneo. Hood 117-531 1978 $17.50

MARCHELLI, LUIGI   Memoria Sull' Inoculazione Dell Vaccina. Genova, 1801. Disbound. Rittenhouse 49-517 1976 $35

MARCOLINI, FRANCESCO   Di Francesco Marcolino Da Forli, Intitolate Giardino di Pensieri all IIIvstrissimo Signore Hercole Estense Dvca di Ferrara. Vencie, 1540. First ed., woodcuts, some browning and soiling, sm. folio, 17th cent. mottled calf, rebacked. Thomas 37-57 1978 £1250

MARCONI, GUGLIELMO   Sulla Propagazione di Micro-Onde a Notevole Distanza. Rome, 1933-XI. Offprint, 8vo., ads, orig. prtd. wrs., fine copy, lst ed. Norman 5-193 1978 $100

MARCONI, GUISEPPE LORETO   Ragguaglio della Vita del Servo di Dio Benedetto Guiseppe Labre, Francese. Rome, 1783. Contemp. vellum, 8vo., slight damp-stain affecting leaves at end. Howes 194-558 1978 £22

MARCOSSON, ISAAC F.   The Black Golconda...Petroleum. New York, 1924. Illus., 1st ed. Biblo BL781-845 1978 $9.50

MARCOU, JULES   American Geology: Letter on Some Points of the Geology of Texas, New Mexico, Kansas and Nebraska. Surich, 1858. Jenkins 116-1573 1978 $85

MARCOU, JULES   La Dyas au Nebraska. Paris, 1867. Folding plan, orig. wr., inscribed presentation copy from Marcou to Gen. G. K. Warren. Ginsberg 14-720 1978 $50

MARCUS AURELIUS
Please turn to
AURELIUS ANTONINUS, MARCUS

MARCY, E. E.   Homoeopathy and Allopathy. New York, 1852. 12mo., foxed, ends of spine worn, lst ed. Morrill 239-165 1978 $20

MARCY, HENRY D.   Hernia. The Anatomy and Surgical Treatment. New York, 1892. Half leather dried, cracking at hinges, chipped on spine. Rittenhouse 49-518 1976 $25

MARCY, HENRY ORLANDO   The Anatomy and Surgical Treatment of Hernia. New York, 1892. Tall 4to., heliotype & litho. plts., woodcuts, orig. half sha-green, worn, internally fine copy, lst ed. Zeitlin 245-158 1978 $85

MARCY, HENRY ORLANDO   The Recent Advances of Sanitary Science. Philadelphia, 1883. 8vo., orig. wrs., autographed. Morrill 239-166 1978 $7.50

MARCY, MARY E.   Rhymes of Early Jungle Folk. Chicago, (1922). Woodcut plates and illus. by Wharton E. Esherick, original work, fine. Victoria 34-522 1978 $20

MARCY, WILLIAM L.   Report of...Transmitting...Documents in Relation to the Difficulties which Took Place at the Payment of the Sac and Fox Annuities Last Fall. Washington, 1848. Disbound, 1st ed. Ginsberg 14-906 1978 $25

MAREY, ETIENNE JULES   La Circulation du Sang a l'Etat Physiologique et Dans les Maladies. Paris, 1881. 8vo., contemp. half shagreen, back gilt, lst ed., fine copy. Offenbacher 30-91 1978 $150

MAREY, ETIENNE JULES   La Circulation du sang a L'Etat Physiologique et Dans Les Maladies. Paris, 1881. 8vo., woodcuts, orig. wrappers. Quaritch 977-53 1978 $275

MAREY, ETIENNE JULES   Du mouvement dans les fonctions de la vie. Paris, 1868. 8 vo., 1st ed., fine copy, wood-engraved figures, contemp. half leather. Schafer 19-55 1978 sFr. 750

MAREY, ETIENNE JULES   Physiologie Medicale de la Circulation du sang Basee sur L'Etude Graphique des Movements.... Paris, 1863. 8vo., woodcuts, contemp. quarter mor., first ed. Quaritch 977-52 1978 $400

MARGARETE OF NAVARRE
Please turn to
MARGUERITE D'ANGOULEME

MARGOLIOUTH, G.   Descriptive List of Syriac and Karshuni MSS... acquired since 1873. London, 1899. Roy. 8vo., orig. cloth. Forster 130-217 1978 £5

MARGRY, PIERRE   Decouvertes et Establissements de Francais Dans L'ouest et dan le Sud de L'Amerique Septentrionale (1614-1754).... Paris, 1876-1886. 6 vols., illus., ports and maps, orig. wr., 1st ed. Ginsberg 14-527 1978 $300

MARGRY, PIERRE   Decouvertes et Etablissements des Francais dans L-Quest et dans Le Sud de L'Amerique Septentrionale 1614-1698. Paris, 1879-1888. 6 vols., lg. 8vo., illus., ports., maps. MacManus 239-276 1978 $300

MARGUERITE D'ANGOULEME   The Heptameron. 1894. Ltd. to 312 sets on handmade paper, engraved plts., 5 vols., orig. buckram. George's 635-914 1978 £15

MARGUERITE, VICTOR   L'Or. Paris, 1910. 12mo, edges untrimmed, inscribed on half-title by author, 1/2 leather with orig. wrappers bound in, one of 15 copies on Holland paper, no. 8. Eaton 45-323 1978 £20

MARGUERITE Kirmse's Dogs. New York, The Derrydale Press, 1930. 1st ed. ltd. to 750 copies, 4to., 75 numbered plts., engr. frontis. signed by artist in pencil, illus., near mint in orig. gray-blue bds. backed in buckram. Current 24-211 1978 $145

MARIANUS, SCOTUS   Chronica...Adiecimus Martini Poloni...Eiusdem Argumenti Historiam.... Basle, 1559. First ed., 2 parts in 1 vol., excellent condition, Astle Library stamp, folio, late 17th cent. sprinkled calf, rebacked and recornered, rare. Thomas 37-29 1978 £300

MARIE LOUISE, PRINCESS   Letters From the Gold Coast. London, 1926. 75 illus., foxed, covers slightly marked, 8vo., orig. cloth. K Books 239-303 1978 £7

MARIET, JANE   Conversations on Political Economy... 1816. 1st. ed., half title, orig. blue bds., paper label, uncut, v.g. Jarndyce 16-850 1978 £36

MARINE Hospital at Chelsea. Washington, 1854. 8vo., unbound. Morrill 239-170 1978 $7.50

MARINIS, TAMMARO DE   La Legatura Artistica in Italia nei secoli XV & XVI, notizie ed elenchi. Firenze, 1960. 3 vols., ltd. to 500 copies, plts., colored, roy. 4to., orig. cloth, mor. backs, t.e.g., in slipcases, fine. Forster 130-51 1978 £300

MARINONI, AUGUSTO   Gli Appunti Grammaticali e Lessicali di Leonardo. Milan, 1944-52. 2 vols., sm. folio, illus., orig. prtd. wrs., uncut, fine set, ltd. to 700 numbered copies. Norman 5-L33 1978 $60

MARINONI, PIETRO   Horticello di Parnasso Plantato di Varij Essemplari de Caratteri e Mansione di Lettere. Padua, 1675. Oblong 8vo., vellum, engravings. Schumann 511-34 1978 sFr 6,300

MARIOTTE, EDME   Essays de Phisique ou Memoires Pour Servir a la Science des Choses Naturelles. Paris, 1679-1681. 4 parts in 2 vols., copperplts., 12mo., contemp. calf, backs gilt, lst ed. Offenbacher 30-92 1978 $1,800

MARIOTTE, EDME   The Motion of Water, and Other Fluids, Being a Treatise of Hydrostaticks. London, 1718. 8vo., fold. engrav. plts., contemp. calf, gilt spine, sm. piece chipped from top of spine. Quaritch 977-114 1978 $250

MARIOTTI, L.   The Blackgown Papers. 1846. 1st. ed., 2 vols., frontis, half titles, some marking of leading free endpaper, orig. black cloth, little rubbed, pres. inscriptions from author in both vols. Jarndyce 16-851 1978 £24

MARITAL, MARCUS VALERIUS   Epigrammata Paucis admodum vel reiectis,.... Rome, 1558. 8vo, cancelled library rubber-stamps and owner's signatures on title, marginal waterstaining, 18th-century vellum, green edges. Quaritch 978-87 1978 $550

MARITI, ABBE   Travels Through Cyprus, Syria, and Palestine: With a General History of the Levant. London, 1791. 1st. English ed., 3 vols., 8vo, half-titles, modern half calf, gilt backs. Deighton 5-187 1978 £43

MARIZ, PEDRO DE   Dialogos de Varia Historia, em que Sumariamente se Referem Muytas Couzas Antiguas de Hespanha... Coimbra, 1594. 8vo., contemp. vellum, lower part of spine repaired, lightly browned, but fine, rare, 1st ed. Gilhofer 74-69 1978 sFr 3,800

MARJOLAINE, PSEUD.
Please turn to
LECLERC, JUSTA

MARJORAM, J., PSEUD.
Please turn to
MOTTRAM, RALPH HALE

MARJORIBANKS, ALEXANDER   Travels in South and North America. 1853.
Coloured frontispiece, orig. cloth, 8vo, cover slightly soiled, few pages badly
opened. Edwards 1012-401 1978 £18

MARKENS, ISAAC   The Hebrews in America. 1888. Austin 79-
466 1978 $27.50

MARKEY, MORRIS   Well Done! 1945. Austin 80-197 1978 $10

MARKHAM, C. A.   The History of the Northamptonshire and Rutland
Militia. 1924. Portrait frontis., coloured plt., roy. 8vo., orig. cloth. F. Edwards 1013-569 1978 £25

MARKHAM, C. A.   The New Pewter Marks and Old Pewter Ware
Domestic and Ecclesiastical. London, 1928. 2nd. ed.   Baldwins' 51-120 1978
$75

MARKHAM, CLEMENTS R.   Cuzco: A Journey to the Ancient Capital of
Peru... 1856. Map, tinted litho. plts., 8vo, orig. cloth, some slight spotting.
Edwards 1012-666 1978 £70

MARKHAM, CLEMENTS R.   A Life of John Davis, the Navigator, 1550-1605;
Discoverer of Davis Straits. London, 1889. Spine scuffed. Hood 116-261 1978
$20

MARKHAM, CLEMENTS R.   Narrative of the Mission of George Bogle to
Tibet, 1774... 1876. Portrait, maps, plts., illus., spine slightly faded, 8vo,
orig. cloth.   Edwards 1012-140 1978 £80

MARKHAM, CLEMENTS R.   Travels in Peru and India.... 1862. 1st. ed.,
roy. 8vo, half-title plts., illus., folding maps, orig. green cloth, gilt, ex-lib.
copy, light lib. stamps throughout, o/w good, clean copy. Deighton 5-49 1978
£48

MARKHAM, EDWIN   The Man with the Hoe and Other Poems. New
York, 1899. First New York ed., later issue, good. Biblo 247-599 1978 $15

MARKHAM, FRED   Shooting in the Himalayas... 1854. Folding
map, tinted litho plts., woodcuts, 8vo, orig. cloth, cover slightly faded, little
foxing.   Edwards 1012-141 1978 £45

MARKHAM, GERVASE   A Way to get Wealth. 1657. Sm. 4to., woodcuts, well rebound in half calf, old style. Howes 194-72 1978 £210

MARKHAM, RICHARD   Fireside Yarns...Stories for Young Patriots...
New York, (1881). Illus., orig. bind. Petrilla 13-28 1978 $7.50

MARKS, ELIAS   Hippocrates, The Aphorisms. New York, 1817.
Rittenhouse 49-519 1976 $65

MARKS, JEANNETTE   Through Welsh Doorways. 1909. First ed. Austin
82-624 1978 $12.50

MARKS, M. A. M.   England and America 1763-1783 the History of a
Reaction. New York, 1907. 2 vols., very scarce. MacManus 239-600 1978
$50

MARKS, RICHARD   The Village Observer. 1818. 4th. ed., 12mo,
half-title, orig. roan-backed bds., spine worn. Fenning 32-215 1978 £10.50

MARLES, M. DE   Histoire generale de l'Inde Ancienne et Moderne,
depuis l'an 2000 avant J.C., jusqu'a nos jours. Paris, 1828. 6 vols., orig.
covers, folding engraved maps, 8vo. Van der Peet 127-313 1978 Dfl 250

MARLIANO, AMBROGIO   Theatrum Politicum, in Quo Quid Agendum
Sit a Principe and Quid Cavendum, Accurate Prescribitur. Rome, 1631. Sm. 4to.,
full contemp. red mor., back and edges gilt. Salloch 348-136 1978 $550

MARLOTH, R.   The Flora of South Africa... Cape Town, 1913-
1932. Map, plts. of portraits, 180 coloured & 96 plain plts., 4 vols. in 6, sm.
folio, orig. buckram. Traylen 88-603 1978 £650

MARLOWE, CHRISTOPHER   Hero and Leander. London, 1894. 8vo, full
vellum, some leaves foxed, 1 of 220 copies, fine. Duschnes 220-261a 1978 $150

MARLOWE, GEORGE FRANCIS   Coaching Roads of Old New England. New York,
1945. Illus. Biblo 247-106 1978 $15

MARMADUKE Multiply. Boston, 1845. Sq. 12mo, decorated wrappers, rare, spine
is mostly gone, slight cover tears in margins, very good. Victoria 34-523 1978
$110

MARMER, H. A.   The Tide. New York, 1926. 8vo., dust wrapper,
1st ed. Morrill 241-310 1978 $15

MARMONTEL, JEAN FRANCOIS   Belisarius. Edinburgh, 1767. Sm. 8vo.,
contemp. sheep, marginal defect in one leaf, first Edinburgh ed. Howes 194-382
1978 £25

MARMONTEL, JEAN FRANCOIS   The Incas or, the Destruction of Peru. Dublin, 1777. 2 vols., half title in vol. 2, orig. half calf, marbled bds. Jarndyce
16-137 1978 £24

MAROLLES, L. DE   An Essay on Providence. 1790. Contemp.
mottled calf, unlettered, rubbed, 8vo. George's 635-1096 1978 £5.25

MARQUAND, JOHN P.   Do Tell Me, Doctor Johnson. Cleveland, 1928.
Gray wr., 1 of 160 numbered copies, Mint, 1st ed., collector's cond. Desmarais
1-297 1978 $90

MARQUAND, JOHN P.   Point of No Return. Boston, 1949. Near mint
in chipped d.w. Desmarais B-438 1978 $12.50

MARQUET, J.   De la Riviere a la Montagne. Paris, 1920.
8vo, orig. covers. Van der Peet 127-144 1978 Dfl 30

MARQUETTE, PERE JACQUES   Ontdekking Van Eenige Landen en Volkeren...
(Leyden, 1707). Sm. 8vo, unbound, folding map, folding plt., sm. tear at fold,
slight marginal staining, orig. cloth. Edwards 1012-505 1978 £55

MARQUIS, DON   Archy and Mehitabel. Garden City, 1927.
First ed., very good or better. Limestone 9-189 1978 $25

MARQUIS, DON   Archys Life of Mehitabel. Garden City, 1933.
Envelope pasted to front with typed letter signed by Marquis, very good. Bernard
5-182 1978 $30

MARQUIS, DON   Out of the Sea. Garden City, 1927.
1st ed., 8 vo., 1/2 cloth over illus. bds., uncut, glassine jacket, very good.
Houle 10-201 1978 $15

MARQUIS, DON   When the Turtle Sings. Garden City, 1928.
first ed., 8vo., orig. red cloth, good. Houle 10-202 1978 $15

MARQUIS, T. G.   The Cathedral and Other Poems. Toronto, 1936.
Hood 116-836 1978 $12.50

MARQUIS, T. G.   The Jesuit Missions, a Chronicle of the Cross in
the Wilderness. Toronto, 1916. Leather, mint. Hood 116-305 1978 $7.50

MARQUIS, T. G.   Stories From Canadian History, Based Upon
"Stories of New France." Toronto, 1893. Stiff card cover. Hood's 115-604
1978 $7.50

MARRIOTT, J. A. R.   The Crisis of English Liberty; A History of the
Stuart Monarchy and the Puritan Revolution. Oxford, 1930. Octavo, good.
Upcroft 10-439 1978 £7.50

MARRIOTT, J. A. R.   The Life and Times of Lucius Cary, Viscount Falkland. 1908. 2nd. ed., plts., octavo, good. Upcroft 10-438 1978 £10

MARRIOTT, J. A. R.   The Life of John Colet. 1933. Octavo, good.
Upcroft 10-440 1978 £6.50

MARRIOTT, J. W.   One-Act Plays of To-Day. Dunsany, 1931.
(1st eds.), 1st, 2nd & 3rd series, very good, octavo bound in cloth. Hyland
128-908 1978 £12

MARROT, H. V.   A Bibliography of the Works of John Galsworthy.
London, 1928. 8vo., orig. full buckram, d.j., top of spine chipped, 1st ed., 1
of 200 copies, sm. damp-stained on front cover, otherwise very fine. MacManus
238-927 1978 $45

MARROT, H. V.   The Life and Letters of John Galsworthy. 1936.
Illus., thick 8vo., orig. cloth. Howes 194-878 1978 £6.50

MARRYAT, FLORENCE   A Scarlet Sin. New York, (1889). Orig.
cloth, coated end papers, good. Greene 78-79 1978 $30

MARRYAT, FRANCIS SAMUEL   Borneo and the Indian Archipelago. 1848.
Litho. plts., & title, 4to, orig. red cloth, rebacked. Edwards 1012-169 1978
£150

MARRYAT, FREDERICK   The Children of the New Forest. London, n.d.
(1847). 1st. ed., plts., little foxed, 2 vols., fcap. 8vo, orig. cloth, little loose.
Traylen 88-177 1978 £70

MARRYAT, FREDERICK   Diary of a Blase. Philadelphia, 1836. 1st.
ed., half title, orig. half cloth, grey bds., uncut, very slight dampmarking at top
of one or two leaves, otherwise fine in orig. condition. Jarndyce 16-852 1978
£54

MARRYAT, FREDERICK   Jacob Faithful. 1834. 2nd. ed., 3 vols., lg.
12mo, contemp. grey calf, blind-tooled & gilt, some brown-stains. Hannas 54-
216 1978 £25

MARRYAT, FREDERICK   The King's Own. 1836. 2nd. ed., 3 vols.,
lg. 12mo, lacks half-titles, contemp. half calf, some brown-stains throughout.
Hannas 54-217 1978 £17.50

MARRYAT, FREDERICK   The Little Savage. London, 1849. 2 parts in
1 vol., part 1-2nd. ed., part 2-1st. ed., titles in blue & red, thick cr. 8vo, contemp. half calf. Traylen 88-178 1978 £15

MARRYAT, FREDERICK   Masterman Ready. 1841. 3 vols., sm. 8vo., 1st
ed., illus. by author, orig. cloth, fine copy. Quaritch 979-225 1978 $230

MARRYAT, FREDERICK   Masterman Ready; or, The Wreck of the Pacific.
London, 1841. 1st. ed., illus., 3 vols., sm. 8vo, orig. cloth, vol. 1 little worn.
Traylen 88-176 1978 £60

MARRYAT, FREDERICK   The Mission: Or Scenes in Africa, Writeen For
Young People. 1845. 2 vols., engraved plts., map, sm. 8vo, half morocco.
Edwards 1012-307 1978 £25

MARRYAT, FREDERICK   Narrative of the Travels and Adventures of
Monsieur Violet in California, Sonora, and Western Texas. New York, 1843.
1st Amer. ed. Jenkins 116-887 1978 $135

MARRYAT, FREDERICK   Captain Marryat's Novels and Tales. London,
n.d. 9 vols., thick 8vo., bound in blue cloth with black decor's., illus., frontis.,
tissue guards, shelf wear to extremities, fine reading set. Current 24-31 1978
$50

MARRYAT, FREDERICK   The Pacha of Many Tales. 1835. 1st. ed., 3
vols., lg. 12mo, contemp. binder's cloth, little worn, few stains. Hannas 54-218
1978 £32

MARRYAT, FREDERICK   Peter Simple. Philadelphia, 1833-34. 1st ed.,
3 vols., half-cloth & boards, paper labels. Greene 78-80 1978 $150

MARRYAT, FREDERICK   The Phantom Ship. 1839. 1st. ed., 3 vols., lg.
12mo, lacks half-titles, contemp. paper bds., cloth spines faded, occasional slight
foxing. Hannas 54-219 1978 £35

MARRYAT, FREDERICK   The Phantom Ship. 1847. Engraved frontis.,
orig. cloth, good. Jarndyce 16-853 1978 £6

MARRYAT, FREDERICK   The Pirate & Three Cutters. 1836. 1st. ed.,
tall 8vo, engraved title & other splendid engravings, half title, good, clean unfoxed
copy, full red morocco, gilt dec. & spine, a.e.g., black label, little rubbing to
hinges else v.g. Jarndyce 16-854 1978 £18.50

MARRYAT, FREDERICK   Poor Jack. London, 1840. 8vo, marbled boards,
1/2 calf with raised bands, gilt decor. on spine, Fine, 1st ed., collector's cond.
Desmarais 1-298 1978 $50

MARRYAT, FREDERICK   Poor Jack. 1840. Tall 8vo, illus. by Clarkson
Stanfield, few leaves affected by light spotting, 1/2 tan morocco. Eaton 45-324
1978 £15

MARRYAT, JOSEPH   A History of Pottery and Porcelain, Mediaeval
and Modern. 1857. 2nd ed., rev'd. and augmented, 8vo., plts., woodcuts,
fine copy, contemp. purple mor. gilt, a little rubbed. Quaritch 983-113 1978
$100

MARRYAT, JOSEPH   More Thoughts still on the State of the West-India
Colonies,.... London, 1818. 8vo, disbound, 1st ed. Ximenes 47-196 1978
$80

MARRYAT, JOSEPH   A Reply to the Arguments Contained in Various
Publications,.... London, 1823. 8vo, disbound, 1st ed. Ximenes 47-197
1978 $70

MARRYAT, JOSEPH   The Substance of a Speech Delivered by Joseph
Marryat, Esq. in the House of Commons, on Thursday, July 25th, 1822,....
London, 1823. 8vo, disbound, 1st ed., half-title present. Ximenes 47-198
1978 $60

MARRYAT, T.   Therapeutics. Bristol, 1798. Fcap. 8vo., orig.
bds., spine worn. George's 635-992 1978 £8.50

MARSH, ANNE   Tales of Woods and Fields. New York, 1836.
1st Am. ed., 3 vols. in 1, orig. cloth. Greene 78-78 1978 $50

MARSH, CHARLES   Review of Some Important Passages in the Late
Administration of Sir G.H. Barlow, Bart. of Madras... 1813. 2nd. ed., 8vo,
orig. bds., uncut, printed paper label, spine worn, sound, nice copy. Fenning
32-218 1978 £18.50

MARSH, GEORGE P.   Speech of Mr. Marsh, of Vermont, on the Bill
for Establishing the Smithsonian Institution.... Washington, 1846. Unbound
as issued. Hayman 71-439 1978 $7.50

MARSH, J. B. T.   The Story of the Jubilee Singers. Cleveland,
1892. Cloth, new ed. Hayman 73-405 1978 $7.50

MARSH, M. P.   Overland From Southampton to Queensland.
1867. 1st. ed., frontis map & folding map, half title, orig. green cloth, v.g.
Jarndyce 16-278 1978 £18.50

MARSH, NGAIO   Colour Scheme. 1943. Very good, worn d.w.,
first English ed. Bell Book 17-257 1978 £10

MARSH, NGAIO   Death in Ecstasy. 1936. Bds., good, first English ed. Bell Book 17-258 1978 £12.50

MARSH, NGAIO   Final Curtain. 1947. Covers little faded,
good, first English ed. Bell Book 16-254 1978 £4.50

MARSH, NGAIO   The Nursing Home Murder. New York, (1941).
First American ed., frayed d.w. Biblo 247-526 1978 $15

MARSH, REIGNETTE   Scotch Plains. The Story of an Old Community.
(New Brunswick), 1936. 1st ed., illus., orig. cloth, fine. MacManus 239-
1296 1978 $20

MARSH, WILLIAM J. JR.   Our President Herbert Hoover. New Milford,
1930. 1st ed., illus., very good, d.j. Victoria 34-525 1978 $15

MARSH-CALDWELL, ANNE   Emilia Wyndham. 1846. 1st. ed., 3 vols., orig.
half calf, rubbed but sound. Jarndyce 16-855 1978 £28

MARSHALL, MRS. A. B.   Cookery Book. London, c. 1900. Frontis.,
illus., 8vo., orig. cloth. K Books 244-225 1978 £7

MARSHALL, MRS. A. B.   Larger Cookery Book of Extra Recipes. 1894.
Text-illus., roy. 8vo., cover stained. K Books 244-226 1978 £20

MARSHALL, ALFRED   Industry and Trade, a Study of Industrial Technique and Business Organisation; and of their Influences on the Conditions of various
Classes and Nations. 1932. 8vo. George's 635-363 1978 £5.25

MARSHALL, ARCHIBALD   The Clinton Twins and Other Stories. New York,
1923. First American ed. Biblo 247-600 1978 $10

MARSHALL, C.   The Canadian Dominion. London, 1871. 3/4
leather, illus. Hood 116-641 1978 $50

MARSHALL, C. K.   Texas Pacific Railway--Senate Committee.
Washington, c.1878. Sewn. Jenkins 116-888 1978 $65

MARSHALL, DOROTHY   The English Poor in the 18th Century, a Study in
Social and Administrative History. 1926. Illus., 8vo. George's 635-364 1978
£8.50

MARSHALL, DUNCAN   Les Champs et la Ferme. 1930. Card cover,
illus. Hood 117-431 1978 $7.50

MARSHALL, E. H.   History of Obion County. Union, City, 1941.
Illus. MacManus 239-1125 1978 $25

MARSHALL, EDISON   Dian of the Lost Land. 1935. First ed., review
copy. Austin 82-625 1978 $20

MARSHALL, EDISON   The Land of Forgotten Men. 1923. Frontis., first
ed. Austin 82-626 1978 $17.50

MARSHALL, GEORGE C.   General Marshall's Report. Sept. 1, 1945.
Illus., maps, paper. Austin 80-198 1978 $12.50

MARSHALL, H. E.   An Island Story. New York, n.d. Illus. in color.
Biblo 247-570 1978 $10

MARSHALL, JAMES   A Winter with Robert Burns. Edinburgh, 1846.
Sm. 8vo., cloth, uncut, frontispiece. P. M. Hill 142-56 1978 £18

MARSHALL, JOHN   The Life of George Washington, Commander in
Chief of the American Forces, During the War which Established the Independence
of His Country, and First President of the United States. Philadelphia, 1804/05/
07. 1st ed., 5 vols., 8vo., rare, maps bound in text, mild foxing, orig. old calf,
gilt decor. spines. Current 24-89 1978 $395

MARSHALL, JOHN   The Life of George Washington... London,
1807. 1st English ed., 5 vols., 4to., fldg. maps, frontis, bound in 3/4 red mor.,
marbled bds. & endpapers, t.e.g., some foxing, bindings firm. Current 24-90
1978 $365

MARSHALL, JOHN   The Life of George Washington, Commander in
Chief of the American Forces. New York, 1930. 3ds., 2 vols., attractive set.
Hayman 73-406 1978 $10

MARSHALL, JOHN   Opinion of the Supreme Court of the United
States, Delivered by Mr. Chief Justice.... [N.P., 1829]. Sewn as issued,
1st ed. Ginsberg 14-506 1978 $75

MARSHALL, JOHN SAYRE   Injuries and Surgical Diseases of the Face, Mouth,
and Jaws. Philadelphia, 1902. Second ed., revised and enlarged, upper hinge
detached. Rittenhouse 49-521 1976 $15

MARSHALL, NINA LOVERING The Mushroom Book. New York, 1902, 4, 14.
Plates, 8vo., orig. cloth. Book Chest 17-249 1978 $20

MARSHALL, ROBERT   Arctic Village. New York, 1933. Photos,
spine faded. Hood's 115-65 1978 $12.50

MARSHALL, S. L. A.   Island Victory. 1945. Photos, illus. Austin
80-199 1978 $27.50

MARSHALL, STEPHEN   A Sacred Record to be Made of Gods Mercies to
Zion. 1645. Good. Jarndyce 16-5 1978 £10.50

MARSHALL, T. H.   James Watt. London, (1925). 8vo., frontis.,
orig. cloth, gilt. Norman 5-298 1978 $20

MARSHALL, THOMAS MAITLAND Early Records of Gilpin County, Colorado
1859-1861. Boulder, 1920. Folding map, orig. cloth, some discoloration.
Ginsberg 14-268 1978 $15

MARSHALL, WILLIAM ADOLF LUDWIG   Die Tiere der Erde. Stuttgart und
Leipzig, n.d. (ca. early 1900s). Illus., few in color, 3 vols., 4to., orig. pic.
front covers, ex-lib., embossed stamp on colored plts., very nice. Morrill 241-
311 1978 $35

MARSHALL, WILLIAM BARRETT   A Personal Narrative of Two Visits to New Zealand, In His Majesty's Ship Alligator, A.D. 1834. 1836. 1st. ed., engraved
frontis, half-title, post 8vo, orig. cloth, spine faded, otherwise nice copy.
Fenning 32-219 1978 £95

MARSHALL, WILLIAM GORE   Through America. London, 1882. Illus., orig.
binding. Wolfe 39-341 1978 $27.50

MARSHALL, WILLIAM I.   Acquisition of Oregon and the Long Suppressed
Evidence about Marcus Whitman. Seattle, 1911. 2 vols, illus., orig. cloth, 1st
ed. Ginsberg 14-827 1978 $100

MARSHALL, WILLIAM I.   The Hudson's Bay Co.'s Archives Furnish No
Support to the Whitman Saved Oregon Story. Chicago, 1905. Orig. pr. wr., 1st
ed. Ginsberg 14-828 1978 $15

MARSHALL Newell. Boston, 1898. Plts., 8vo., full lea., ends of spine worn.
Morrill 239-536 1978 $12.50

MARSHMAN, JOHN CLARK   Memoirs of Major General Sir Henry Havelock.
1861. Second ed., frontis., coloured maps, 8vo., contemp. mor. F. Edwards
1013-332 1978 £15

MARTENS, OTTO   The African Handbook. London, 1938. 2nd.
ed., 6 folding maps, other plans & maps, sm. 8vo, orig. cloth, covers slightly
soiled. K Books 239-305 1978 £6

MARTHA, J.   l'Art Etrusque. Paris, 1889. Lg. thick 8vo.,
half calf, colored frontis., colored plts., illus., corners damaged, loose in binding. Van der Peet H-64-168 1978 Dfl 185

MARTIALIS, MARCUS VALERIUS   Select Epigrams. 1755. Old calf, one cover
detached, other joint cracked. Allen 234-1537 1978 $10

MARTIN, MISS   The Changeling. 1848. 1st. ed., 3 vols.,
half titles, recently rebound in half calf, hand-marbled bds., good. Jarndyce
16-857 1978 £25

MARTIN, MRS.   Reparation, Or The Savoyards. 1823. Gilt
spines, inscription in ink on title from W. Martin, modern 1/4 grey calf, marbled
bds. Eaton 45-325 1978 £30

MARTIN, ANNIE   Home Life on an Ostrich Farm. New York, 1891.
1st. American ed., 8vo, orig. cloth. K Books 239-309 1978 £9

MARTIN, ANNIE   Home Life on An Ostrich Farm. London &
Liverpool, 1891. 2nd. ed., 8vo, orig. cloth. K Books 239-307 1978 £8

MARTIN, ANNIE   Home Life on An Ostrich Farm. London &
Liverpool, 1891. 1st. ed., inner hinges frayed, rubber-stamped "Specimen copy",
8vo, orig. cloth. K Books 239-306 1978 £12

MARTIN, ANNIE   Home Life On An Ostrich Farm. London &
Liverpool, 1892. 3rd. ed., 8vo, orig. cloth, shaken. K Books 239-308 1978
£6

MARTIN, BEN   John Black's Body. New York, (1939). 1st ed.
Biblo 251-172 1978 $12.50

MARTIN, BENJAMIN   Institutions of Language;.... London, 1748.
8vo, disbound, 1st ed., scarce. Ximenes 47-199 1978 $45

MARTIN, BENJAMIN   Thermometrum Magnum. London, 1772. 8vo.,
sewn, 1st ed. Morrill 239-503 1978 $12.50

MARTIN, BESSIE   Desertion of Alabama Troops from the Confederate Army. NY, 1932. Bell Wiley's copy. Broadfoot's 44-420 1978 $40.00

MARTIN, CHESTER   Prophets of the Commonwealth. Ottawa, 1927.
Hood 116-643 1978 $12.50

MARTIN, E. S.   Among the Pimas or the Mission to the Marocpi Indians. Albany, 1893. Illus. MacManus 239-1182 1978 $20

MARTIN, EDWARD WINSLOW, PSEUD.
Please turn to
MC CABE, JAMES DABNEY

MARTIN, F. R.   The Miniature Paintings and Painters of Persia, India and Turkey. 5 beautiful plts. in orig. tissue, ltd. ed. of 500 copies. Traylen 88-511 1978 £60

MARTIN, FRANCOIS-XAVIER   The History of North Carolina, From the Earliest Period. New Orleans, 1829. 2 vols. in 1, spine rebacked in leather. Broadfoot 50-137 1978 $500

MARTIN, GEORGE CASTOR   The Shark River District, Monmouth County, New Jersey... Asbury Park, 1914. 1st ed., very good. MacManus 239-1297 1978 $35

MARTIN, GEORGE W.   The First Two Years of Kansas; or,.... Topeka, 1907. Original wr., 1st ed. Ginsberg 14-456 1978 $15

MARTIN, HELEN M.   "Ne-saw-je-won" as the Ottawas say: A Tale of the Waters That Run Down From Lake Superior to the Sea. Cleveland, 1939. Illus., maps, signed by author. Hood's 115-980 1978 $30

MARTIN, I. T.   A Voice From the West. St. Louis, 1908. Cl., orig. binding. Hayman 71-440 1978 $7.50

MARTIN, ISAAC   A Journal of the Life, Travels, Labours, and Religious Exercises of Isaac Martin, Late of Rahway in East Jersey. Philadelphia, 1834. Orig. calf. MacManus 239-1298 1978 $30

MARTIN, J. L.   Native Bards; A Satirical Effusion; with Other Occasional Pieces. Philadelphia, 1831. 1st ed., orig. pr. boards, uncut, slightly soiled, 8vo. Americanist 101-90 1978 $45

MARTIN, JOHN   John Martin's Annual. Garden City, 1917. Thick quarto, vellum-like paper, very fine, d.j. Victoria 34-527 1978 $22.50

MARTIN, JOHN Fl. 1794   An Account of the Natives of the Tonga Islands, in the South Pacific Ocean. Edinburgh, 1827. 2 vols., cloth worn, 3rd ed., folding map and music sheet. Dawson's 127-275 1978 $85

MARTIN, JOHN HILL   Historical Sketch of Bethlehem in Pennsylvania... Philadelphia, 1872. Illus., frontis., ltd. to 150 copies, signed. MacManus 239-1555 1978 $40

MARTIN, LUTHER   Modern Gratitude, in Five Numbers:.... N.P. (Baltimore), n.d. (1801-2). 8vo, original plain wr. (somewhat worn), 1st ed., privately printed and scarce. Ximenes 47-200 1978 $60

MARTIN, M.   A Description of the Western Isles of Scotland. 1703. 1st. ed., lg. folding map, orig. panelled calf, label, leading hinge weakening, o/w v.g. Jarndyce 16-138 1978 £110

MARTIN, M.   The History, Antiquities, Topography, and Statistics of Eastern India... 1838. 3 vols., 8vo., plts., orig. cloth. Quaritch 983-145 1978 $130

MARTIN, M. J.   Practical Electro-Therapeutics and X-Ray Therapy with Chapters on Phototherapy.... St. Louis, 1912. Rittenhouse 49-522 1976 $20

MARTIN, MARY EMMA   A Girl's Past. A Novel. London, 1893. 3 vols., orig. cloth, 1st ed., signature, inner hinges cracked, but good. MacManus 238-349 1978 $75

MARTIN, MARY EMMA   Many a Year Ago. London, 1892. 2 vols., orig. cloth, 1st ed., pres. copy, inscribed by author, very good. MacManus 238-348 1978 $100

MARTIN, P. S.   Indians Before Columbus: 20,000 Years of North American History. Chicago, 1949. 1/2 morocco. Jenkins 116-890 1978 $35

MARTIN, PERCY F.   The Sudan in Evolution. London, 1921. 8vo, orig. cloth, lg. folding map in pocket, covers faded. K Books 239-310 1978 £10

MARTIN, ROBERT MONTGOMERY   The British Colonies; Their History, Extent, Condition and Resources. London and New York, 1851-57? 6 vols. in 3, 3/4 leather and cloth, frontispieces, portraits, 21 plts., 36 tinted double maps, sm. quarto. Hood's 115-603 1978 $350

MARTIN, ROBERT MONTGOMERY   History of Nova Scotia, Cape Breton, the Sable Is., New Brunswick, P. E. I., the Bermudas, Newfoundland, etc. London, 1837. Hood 117-263 1978 $40

MARTIN, ROBERT MONTGOMERY   History, Statistics, and Geography of Upper and Lower Canada. London, 1838. 2nd ed., maps, frontis., cloth. Hood 116-644 1978 $60

MARTIN, ROBERT MONTGOMERY   Ireland, Before & After the Union with Great Britain. 1843. 1st ed., signed presentation inscription, leather (rubbed), very good, octavo bound in cloth. Hyland 128-106 1978 £20

MARTIN, ROBERT MONTGOMERY   Ireland, Before & After the Union with Great Britain. 1843. 1st ed., repaired, spine repaired, cover frayed, map, text good, octavo bound in cloth. Hyland 128-105 1978 £10

MARTIN, ROBERT MONTGOMERY   Ireland, Before & After the Union with Great Britain. 1848. 3rd ed., 1/2 leather (rubbed), good, octavo bound in cloth. Hyland 128-103 1978 £10

MARTIN, ROBERT MONTGOMERY   Ireland, Before & After the Union with Great Britain. Cover stained, very good, octavo bound in cloth, pres. copy from author. Hyland 128-104 1978 £15

MARTIN, ROBERT MONTGOMERY   The Political, Commercial & Financial Condition of the Anglo-Eastern Empire, in 1832.... London, 1832. 8vo., orig. bds., uncut, spine little defective. Traylen 88-78 1978 £20

MARTIN, SELINA   A Sister's Stories. 1833. 1st. ed., woodcuts, half title, orig. black cloth, little worn, paper label rubbed, frontis, good. Jarndyce 16-856 1978 £6.50

MARTIN, WILLIAM   Fireside Philosophy; or Home Science. London, n.d. c.1842. Litho. plts.,16mo, binders' cloth. Traylen 88-180 1978 £15

MARTIN, WILLIAM   The Parlour Book. London, n.d. (c.1840). Plts., illus., 16mo, orig. picture bds., lacks spine. Traylen 88-179 1978 £9

MARTIN-LEAKE, S.   An Historical Account of English Money, from the Conquest to the Present Time.... 1745. Second ed., contemp. calf, a little rubbed, 8vo. George's 635-365 1978 £30

MARTINDALE, JOSEPH C.   History of the Townships of Byberry and Moreland in Phila., Pa. Philadelphia, 1867. Baldwins' 51-464 1978 $27.50

MARTINDALE, JOSEPH C.   A History of the Townships of Byberry and Moreland in Phila. 1867. Worn. MacManus 239-1622 1978 $25

MARTINDALE, THOMAS   With Gun and Guide. Philadelphia, (1910). 1st ed., illus., orig. pic. cloth. MacManus 239-25 1978 $12.50

MARTINE, GEORGE   Essays of the Construction and Graduation of Thermometers, and on the Heating and Cooling of Bodies. Edinburgh, 1792. 12mo., contemp. polished calf, gilt on spine, lightly browned, dampstains, signature of former owner, very good copy, 4th ed. Zeitlin 245-159 1978 $225

MARTINEAU, HARRIET   British Rule in India; a Historical Sketch. 1857. 1st. ed., half title, orig. blue cloth, v.g. Jarndyce 16-866 1978 £12.50

MARTINEAU, HARRIET   Dawn Island, A Tale. Manchester, 1845. 1st. ed., frontis & engraved title, orig. blind & gilt stamped blue cloth, a.e.g., fine copy of rare book. Jarndyce 16-864 1978 £42

MARTINEAU, HARRIET   Feats on the Fjord. London, 1899. 1st ed., Rackham illus., flexible leather covers worn, small tear in covers, text very good. Victoria 34-674 1978 $15

MARTINEAU, HARRIET   Illustrations of Political Economy; No. IX, Ireland a Tale. 1832-33. Orig. grey wrappers, sm. yellow Galignani label on upper cover, double titles, front wrapper is printed 2nd. ed., not the titles, fine. Jarndyce 16-859 1978 £8.50

MARTINEAU, HARRIET   Illustrations of Political Economy; No. XII, French Wines and Politics. 1833. 1st. ed., orig. grey wrappers, sm. yellow Galignani label on upper cover, double titles, fine.   Jarndyce 16-860 1978 £10

MARTINEAU, HARRIET   Illustrations of Political Economy; No. XIV, Berkeley the Banker, Part I. 1833. 1st. ed., orig. grey wrappers, sm. yellow Galignani label on upper cover, double titles, fine.   Jarndyce 16-861 1978 £9.50

MARTINEAU, HARRIET   Illustrations of Political Economy; No. XV, Berkeley the Banker, Part II. 1833. 1st. ed., orig. grey wrappers, sm. yellow Galignani label on upper cover, double titles, fine.   Jarndyce 16-862 1978 £9.50

MARTINEAU, HARRIET   Life in the Sick-Room. Boston, 1845. 12mo., 2nd Amer. ed.   Morrill 239-167 1978 $12.50

MARTINEAU, HARRIET   Life in the Sick-Room. 1849. 3rd. ed., half title, orig. green cloth, v.g.   Jarndyce 16-865 1978 £14.50

MARTINEAU, HARRIET   Retrospect of Western Travel. London, 1838. 1st ed., 1st issue, 3 vols., 8vo., orig. tan bds., some soiling, very occas. spotting on interior, bindings tight, interior mostly clean, fine cond.   Current 24-186 1978 $395

MARTINEAU, HARRIET   Retrospect of Western Travel. (New York, 1942). 2 vols., fine set, fasc. of the 1838 ed. MacManus 239-277 1978 $22.50

MARTINEAU, HARRIET   Traditions of Palestine. 1843. 2nd. ed., front free endpaper laid down, otherwise good in orig. black cloth. Jarndyce 16-863 1978 £6.50

MARTINEAU, J.   Essays, Reviews and Addresses. 1890. 4 vols., cr. 8vo. George's 635-1454 1978 £7.50

MARTINELLI, FIORAVANTE   Carbognano Illustrato. Roma, 1694. Sm. 8vo., vellum. King 7-61 1978 £25

MARTINENGO-CESARESCO, EVELYN   Essays in the Study of Folk-Songs. 1886. Orig. cloth, spine soiled, 8vo. Howes 194-1035 1978 £5

MARTINET, LOUIS   Manual of Pathology. London, 1835. 4th ed., sm. 8vo., orig. cloth. K Books 244-413 1978 £10

MARTINEZ, M.   Los Pinos Mexicanos. Mexico, 1948. Wide 8vo, orig. cloth. Book Chest 17-250 1978 $30

MARTINIUS, MARTIN   Sinicae Historiae. Munich, 1658. 4to., vellum with label. Salloch 345-117 1978 $300

MARTRIN-DONOS, CH. DE   Les Belges Dans L'Afrique Centrale... Brussels, 1886. 3 vols., illus., 4to, covers repaired, orig. cloth. Edwards 1012-259 1978 £50

MARTYN, BENJAMIN   Timoleon. 1730. 1st. ed., 8vo, half-title, loose, leaf containing the 2nd. epilogue missing, disbound. Hannas 54-221 1978 £12.50

MARTYN, CARLOS   Wendell Phillips, the Agitator. New York, (1890). Rev. ed. Biblo 247-95 1978 $10

MARTYN, CHARLES R.   The Life of Artemas Ward the First Commander-in-Chief of the American Revolution. New York, 1921. Cloth. Hayman 72-447 1978 $8.50

MARTYN, W. CARLOS   A History of the Huguenots. 1866. Austin 79-470 1978 $17.50

MARTYR, JUSTIN   A Reply to the Rev. Dr. George Junkin's Treatise Entitled "Sabbatismos". Philadelphia, 1867. Cloth. Hayman 73-408 1978 $10

MARVELL, ANDREW   S'too Him Bayes; Or Some Observations Upon the Humour of Writing Rehearsal's Transpros'd. Oxon, 1673. 1st. ed., sm. 8vo, orig. sheep, sm. piece torn from blank f/l, fine copy. Traylen 88-299 1978 £140

MARVIN, ABIJAH P.   The Life and Times of Cotton Mather. Boston and Chicago, 1890. 1st ed., illus., orig. cloth, bookplt., very good. MacManus 239-794 1978 $35

MARVIN, E. M.   A Series of Lectures on Transubstantiation and Other Errors of the Papacy. St. Louis, 1873. 2nd ed., cloth, slight wear. Hayman 73-409 1978 $8.50

MARVIN, WINTHROP L.   The American Merchant Marine. Its History and Romance from 1620 to 1902. New York, 1902. MacManus 239-1770 1978 $15

MARX, KARL   Das Kapital. Hamburg, 1867, 1885, 1894. 3 vols., 8 vo., modern tan mor., slipcases, 1st ed. Quaritch Summer, 1978-32 1978 $18,000

MARX, KARL   Selected Works. Moscow, 1935-36. 2 vols., 8vo., cloth. Salloch 348-139 1978 $60

MARY Of The Incarnation, Foundress of the Ursuline Monastery, Quebec. Quebec, 1939. Card cover, illus. Hood's 115-258 1978 $10

MARZIALS, FRANK T.   Life of Charles Dickens. 1887. 1st. ed., half title, orig. blue cloth, v.g. Jarndyce 16-557 1978 £5

MARZIALS, FRANK T.   Life of Charles Dickens. London, 1887. 1st ed., very good or better. Limestone 9-86 1978 $12.50

MASAOKA, NAOICHI   Japan to America. 1914. Austin 79-471 1978 $22.50

MASCAGNI, PAOLO   Anatomia per Uso Degli Studiosi di Scultura e Pittura. Firenze, 1816. Copperplts., partly prtd. in color, partly colored by hand, lg. folio, contemp. half vellum, 1st & only ed., very rare, fine copy, bkplt. Offenbacher 30-93 1978 $2,750

MASCARDI, AGOSTINO   Dell' Arte Historica...Trattati Cinque. Roma, 1636. 4to., mottled calf, spine gilt, first ed. King 7-63 1978 £40

MASCARDI, AGOSTINO   La Congivra del Conte Gio. Anuersa, 1629. 4to., orig. soft bds., slightly damaged, rare. King 7-62 1978 £50

MASEFIELD, JOHN   Ballads and Poems. 1910. 1st. ed., orig. cloth. Eaton 45-326 1978 £8

MASEFIELD, JOHN   The Bird of Dawning. London, 1933. 8vo, blue cloth, gilt lettering, near Mint, d.w., 1st ed., collector's cond. Desmarais 1-300 1978 $15

MASEFIELD, JOHN   The Bird of Dawning. London, 1933. First ed., orig. binding, very good, inscribed by author. Rota 211-366 1978 £18

MASEFIELD, JOHN   The Conway. London, 1933. Illus., advance proof copy, wrappers marked and worn, nice. Rota 211-367 1978 £12

MASEFIELD, JOHN   The Dream. London, (1922). Illus., woodcuts, No. 107 of ltd. ed., signed by author & illus. by Judith Masefield, unopened, buckram backed orig. bds., very good or better. Limestone 9-190 1978 $22

MASEFIELD, JOHN   Easter; a play. London, (1929). One of 375 numbered copies, signed by author, fine, d.w., first ed., orig. binding. Rota 211-365 1978 £10

MASEFIELD, JOHN   End and Beginning. London, 1933. 8vo, blue cloth, gilt lettering, cover slightly spotted, near Mint, slipcase, uncommon, no. 234 of 275 signed copies by Masefield, 1st ed. Desmarais 1-301 1978 $30

MASEFIELD, JOHN   Esther, A Tragedy. London, 1922. 8vo, grey boards stamped in black, offset inside covers, near Fine, 1st ed., orig. tissue wr., collector's cond. Desmarais 1-302 1978 $10

MASEFIELD, JOHN   A Generation Risen. New York, 1943. 1st Amer. ed., library marks, light dust-soiling, fine, d.j. Victoria 34-528 1978 $10

MASEFIELD, JOHN   In the Mill.   New York, 1941. 1st Amer. ed.
Biblo BL781-1073 1978 $9

MASEFIELD, JOHN   A Letter From Pontius & Other Verse.   London,
1936. 8vo, blue cloth, gilt stamped, near Mint, d.w., 1st ed.   Desmarais 1-303
1978 $15

MASEFIELD, JOHN   A Macbeth Production.   London, 1945. Fine
in lightly soiled & chipped d.w.   Desmarais B-441 1978 $15

MASEFIELD, JOHN   Minnie Maylow's Story and Other Tales and
Scenes.   New York, 1931. 1st trade ed., laid paper, uncut, blue cloth,
very good or better.   Limestone 9-191 1978 $10

MASEFIELD, JOHN   Odtaa.   London, 1926. Fine, foxed fore-edge,
lightly soiled d.w.   Desmarais B-442 1978 $15

MASEFIELD, JOHN   Poetry.   1931. Sm. 8vo., ed. de luxe, prtd. on
fine paper, buckram, soiled, ltd. to 275 numbered copies signed by author.   Quaritch 979-227 1978 $25

MASEFIELD, JOHN   Reynard the Fox.   London, 1921. Illus. by G.
D. Armour, plts., 4 in colour, text illus., roy. 8vo., d.w., orig. cloth.   K Books
244-227 1978 £19

MASEFIELD, JOHN   Reynard the Fox.   1931. One of 25 copies only,
hand-made paper, numbered & signed by author, watercolour decor. by author, roy.
8vo., full blue calf, t.e.g., spine discoloured, very nice, fleece-lined buckram
slip-case, first English ed.   Bell Book 17-640 1978 £165

MASEFIELD, JOHN   Right Royal.   London, 1922. Illus. by Cecil
Aldin, coloured plts., text illus., roy. 8vo., backboard stained.   K Books 244-
228 1978 £5

MASEFIELD, JOHN   Salt Water Ballads.   London, 1902. 1st ed., 1st
issue, 12mo., fewer than 50 copies, top edges gilt, bottom edges & fore edges uncut, very fine cond., fading of spine, rare, fldg. blue-green cloth box with lea.
spine label.   Current 24-32 1978 $675

MASEFIELD, JOHN   Salt Water Ballads.   New York, 1913. Cloth,
former owner's name & date, 1st Amer. ed.   Dawson's 447-262 1978 $30

MASEFIELD, JOHN   Sonnets and Poems.   1916. Cloth, clean copy.
Eaton 45-327 1978 £8

MASEFIELD, JOHN   The Square Peg or the Gunfella.   London, 1937.
Fine in chipped d.w.   Desmarais B-443 1978 $15

MASEFIELD, JOHN   The Wanderer of Liverpool.   1930. 4to., ed. de
luxe, plans, coloured frontis., illus., photos, drwgs., buckram, fine, ltd. to
525 copies signed by author.   Quaritch 979-228 1978 $85

MASERES, FRANCIS   The Canadian Freeholder.   London, 1777, 1779.
Vols. I & II (of three), autograph pres. by author, orig. grey bds., separated at
joints, backstrips bare, uncut.   Wolfe 39-342 1978 $300

MASERES, FRANCIS   Occasional Essays on Various Subjects.   1809.
8vo., contemp. calf, upper hinge cracked.   P. M. Hill 142-169 1978 £70

MASERES, FRANCIS   Scriptores Logarithmici.   London, 1796. Vol.
III (of 6), folio, covers badly worn & loose, internally very good.   Wolfe 39-343
1978 $50

MASON, MRS.   Ellegiac Poems, Sacred to Friendship.   N.P.
(Greenwich), n.d. (1803). 12mo, stitched, as issued, 1st ed., fine copy.
Ximenes 47-201 1978 $75

MASON, ALFRED EDWARD WOODLEY   At the Villa Rose.   London, 1910.
1st ed., 2nd issue, red cloth, good-fine.   Houle 10-204 1978 $175

MASON, ALFRED EDWARD WOODLEY   Clementina.   1901. Plts., cloth, very
good, 1st Eng. ed.   Bell Book 16-625 1978 £6

MASON, ALFRED EDWARD WOODLEY   Dean's Elbow.   London, 1930. 1st
ed., blue cloth, very good-fine.   Houle 10-205 1978 $25

MASON, ALFRED EDWARD WOODLEY   Dilemas.   London, 1934. 1st ed.,
blue cloth, good.   Houle 10-206 1978 $25

MASON, ALFRED EDWARD WOODLEY   The Drum.   London, 1937. 1st ed.,
illus., dust jacket, very good or better.   Limestone 9-192 1978 $12.50

MASON, ALFRED EDWARD WOODLEY   Four Feathers.   London, 1902. 1st ed.,
blue cloth, good-very good.   Houle 10-208 1978 $70

MASON, ALFRED EDWARD WOODLEY   The Four Corners of the World.   London, (1917). 1st ed., blue cloth, fine, inscr'd by Ellery Queen.   Houle 10-207
1978 $90

MASON, ALFRED EDWARD WOODLEY   House of the Arrow.   New York,
(1924). 1st Amer. ed., tan cloth stamped in green, fine, Vincent Starrett's copy
with his signature, Sherlock Holmes bkplt.   Houle 10-209 1978 $60

MASON, ALFRED EDWARD WOODLEY   The House in Lordship Lane.   1946.
Fine, signed by author, d.w., 1st Eng. ed.   Bell Book 16-626 1978 £10

MASON, ALFRED EDWARD WOODLEY   No Other Tiger.   London, n.d.   Blue
cloth, good.   Houle 10-210 1978 $20

MASON, ALFRED EDWARD WOODLEY   The A. E. W. Mason Omnibus.   London, (1931). 1st ed., thick 8vo., dust jacket, very good-fine.   Houle 10-203
1978 $50

MASON, ALFRED EDWARD WOODLEY   The Philanderers.   London, 1897.
Orig. green cloth, uncut, very good.   Houle 10-211 1978 $20

MASON, ALFRED EDWARD WOODLEY   The Prisoner in the Opal.   (1928).
Good, 1st Eng. ed., scarce.   Bell Book 17-261 1978 £15

MASON, ALFRED EDWARD WOODLEY   Prisoners in the Opal.   London, n.d.
1st ed., blue cloth, very good.   Houle 10-212 1978 $37.50

MASON, ALFRED EDWARD WOODLEY   A Romance of Wastdale.   London,
1895. Orig. cloth, 1st ed., covers a bit soiled.   MacManus 238-708 1978
$45

MASON, ALFRED EDWARD WOODLEY   Running Water.   London, 1907. 1st
ed., blue cloth, good.   Houle 10-213 1978 $25

MASON, ALFRED EDWARD WOODLEY   The Sapphire.   London, 1933. 1st ed.,
blue cloth, very good.   Houle 10-214 1978 $30

MASON, ALFRED EDWARD WOODLEY   The Summons.   London, n.d. 1st ed.,
blue cloth, dust jacket, very good.   Houle 10-216 1978 $50

MASON, ALFRED EDWARD WOODLEY   The Summons.   London, n.d. 1st ed.,
blue cloth, good.   Houle 10-215 1978 $15

MASON, ALFRED EDWARD WOODLEY   Witness for the Defense.   London,
(1913). 1st ed., blue cloth, very good.   Houle 10-218 1978 $40

MASON, ALFRED EDWARD WOODLEY   They Wouldn't Be Chessmen.   London,
1935. 1st ed., orig. binding, fine.   Rota 211-371 1978 £5

MASON, ALFRED EDWARD WOODLEY   The Turnstile.   London, (1912). 1st ed.,
blue cloth, good.   Houle 10-217 1978 $25

MASON, ALFRED EDWARD WOODLEY   The Turnstile.   London, 1912. 1st ed.,
orig. binding, covers soiled, very good.   Rota 211-369 1978 £6

MASON, ALFRED EDWARD WOODLEY   The Witness for the Defence.   London,
1913. 1st ed., orig. binding, very good, torn d.w., rare.   Rota 211-370 1978
£6

MASON, ARTHUR JAMES   Memoir of George Howard Wilkinson.   1909.
Illus., 2 vols., 8vo.   George's 635-1156 1978 £5

MASON, ARTHUR JAMES   The Mission of St. Augustine to England according to the original documents.   Cambridge, 1897. Maps, parallel Latin/English
text, 8vo.   Upcroft 12-288 1978 £8.50

MASON, C. H.   Message of the Governor of the Territory of Washington;...   Olympia, 1855. Stitched, laid in half mor. slipcase.   Ginsberg
14-1033 1978 $350

MASON, EUGENE   Considered Writers, Old & New.   1925. 1st ed.,
signed, d.w., very good, octavo bound in cloth.   Hyland 128-107 1978 £5.50

MASON, FRANCIS VAN WYCK   Valley Forge: 24 December 1777.   New
York, 1950. 1st ed., d.w.   Biblo BL781-1074 1978 $7.50

MASON, SHAW   Reports from the Commissioners Appointed to Execute the Measures Recommended Respecting the Public Records of Ireland with Supplements & Appendices. 1810-1820. 2 vols., reports 1-10, plts., 1/2 leather, very good. Hyland 128-405 1978 £65

MASON, JOHN MITCHELL   Hope For the Heathen. New York, 1797. 8vo, orig. cloth, wrappers. Edwards 1012-506 1978 £30

MASON, JOHN 1706-1763   Self-Knowledge, a Treatise. 1824. Fscp. 8vo., contemp. divinity calf, gilt edges. Howes 194-1037 1978 £5

MASON, JOHN 1706-1763   Self-Knowledge... London, 1778. Frontis., 10th ed., sm. 8vo., calf. Salloch 348-141 1978 $40

MASON, J. Y.   Report of the Secretary of the Navy Communicating Copies of Commodore Stockton's Despatches, ... Washington, 1849. Disbound. Ginsberg 14-156 1978 $15

MASON, J. S.   Forty Years After. Class of 1898 Yale College. 1940. Illus. Biblo 247-168 1978 $15

MASON, GEORGE CHAMPLIN   Newport Illustrated. Newport, (1854). Printed wrappers. Wolfe 39-389 1978 $45

MASON, GEORGE CHAMPLIN   The Life and Works of Gilbert Stuart. New York, 1879. Illus., 4to. Baldwins' 51-121 1978 $50

MASON, GEORGE CHAMPLIN   Life and Works of Gilbert Stuart. New York, 1879. Illus., lg. 4to., fine, scarce. MacManus 239-707 1978 $45

MASON, GEORGE CHAMPLIN   The Life and Works of Gilbert Stuart. New York, 1879. 1st ed., 4to., photogravure, portrs., very fine copy, lg. paper bound in 3/4 crushed red levant over marbled bds. Current Misc. 8-32 1978 $85

MASON, GEORGE CARRINGTON   Colonial Churches of Tidewater, Virginia. Richmond, 1945. Illus., maps. MacManus 239-1866 1978 $17.50

MASON, SHAW   Reports from the Commissioners Appointed to Execute the Measures Recommended Respecting the Public Records of Ireland with Supplements & Appendices. (1815). Original boards (shaky), text very good. Hyland 128-406 1978 £50

MASON, SHAW   Reports from the Commissioners Appointed to Execute the Measures Recommended Respecting the Public Records of Ireland with Supplements & Appendices. (1815). 1/2 leather (shaky), text good, reprint. Hyland 128-404 1978 £20

MASON, W. S.   Bibliotheca Hibernicana. (1823). De Luxe binding, slip-case, reprint. Hyland 128-962 1978 £15

MASON, W. S.   Bibliotheca Hibernicana. (1823). Octavo bound in cloth, reprint. Hyland 128-961 1978 £5.25

MASON, WILLIAM   The Dean and the 'Squire: A Political Eclogue. London, 1782. 4to, half morocco, 1st ed., very good copy. Ximenes 47-202 1978 $125

MASON, WILLIAM   The English Garden: a Poem. 1772. 2nd. ed., 4to, lacking half-title, disbound, loose, in folder, sm. tear in title. Hannas 54-222 1978 £6

MASON, WILLIAM   The English Garden: A Poem Book the Fourth. York, 1781. 1st. ed., 4to, disbound. Jarndyce 16-140 1978 £10.50

MASON, WILLIAM   An Heroic Epistle to Sir William Chambers, Knight, Comptroller General of His Majesty's Works,.... London, 1773. 4to, disbound, 6th ed. Ximenes 47-203 1978 $25

MASON, WILLIAM   An Heroic Postscript to the Public, Occasioned by Their Favourable Reception of a Late Heroic Epistle to Sir William Chambers, Knt., etc. London, 1774. 4to, modern boards, 1st ed., scarce. Ximenes 47-204 1978 $125

MASON, WILLIAM   Poems. 1764. 1st. ed., vignette t.p., orig. calf, hinges weak, lacks label, good. Jarndyce 16-139 1978 £17.50

MASON, WILLIAM   Poems. Glasgow, Foulis Press, 1777. 2 vols., 12mo., contemp. sheep. Howes 194-271 1978 £7.50

MASON, WILLIAM MONCK   Hibernia Antiqua et Hodierna. Dublin, 1819. 1st. ed., engraved plts., portrait, 4to, contemp. half morocco, rubbed at corners, sound & very good copy. Fenning 32-220 1978 £48.50

MASON-MANHEIM, MADELINE   Hill Fragments. London, (1925). Drwgs. by Kahlil Gibran, 1st ed., spine creased. Biblo 251-571 1978 $12.50

MASPERO, G.   Etudes de Mythologie et d'Archeologie. Egyptiennes. Tome Cinquieme. Paris, 1911. Illus., rebound. Biblo BL781-438 1978 $18.50

MASPERO, G.   l'Indochine. Paris-Bruxelles, 1929-1930. 2 vols. 4to, orig. boards, plts., folding maps. Van der Peet 127-146 1978 Dfl 350

MASPERO, G.   Le Royaume de Champa. Paris-Bruxelles, 1928. 4to, plts, orig. covers. Van der Peet 127-145 1978 Dfl 145

THE MASQUERADE... Southampton, 1818. Orig. wrappers, torn. Eaton 45-328 1978 £5

MASSA, ANTONIO   Contra l'Uso del Duello. Venice, 1555. Sm. 8vo., contemp. vellum, second ed., vignette on title. F. Edwards 1013-360 1978 £55

MASSA, ANTONIO   De Origine et rebus Faliscorum liber. Rome, 1562 Very rare 2nd ed., 4to, half-vellum. Gilhofer 75-78 1978 SFr 850

MASSACHUSETTS. BOARD OF RAILROAD COMMISSIONS   Special Report by the Massachusetts Board of Railroad Commissions...in Relation to the Disaster on... March 14, 1887, on the Dedham Branch of the Boston & Providence Railroad, at the Bridge Commonly Known as Bussey Bridge...in that Part of Boston Called West Roxbury. Boston, 1887. Plts., heliotypes, inner fr. hinge cracked, 1st ed., orig. cloth. Morrill 241-352 1978 $22.50

MASSACHUSETTS. SECRETARY OF THE COMMONWEALTH   Massachusetts Soldiers and Sailors of the Revolutionary War. Boston, 1896. 1st ed., 17 vols., thick 4to, orig. cloth, very good. MacManus 239-602 1978 $250

MASSACHUSETTS MEDICAL SOCIETY   Acts of Incorporation and Acts Regulating the Practice of Physick and Surgery, with the By-Laws and Orders, of the Massachusetts Medical Society. Boston, 1822. 8vo., orig. wrs. Morrill 239-168 1978 $15

MASSACHUSETTS MEDICAL SOCIETY   Acts of Incorporation and Acts Regulating the Practice of Physic and Surgery, with the By-Laws and Orders of the Massachusetts Medical Society. Boston, Steam Power Press, 1832. 8vo., sewn, upper wr. only, light foxing, dust-soiled, good copy. Zeitlin 245-161 1978 $75

MASSACHUSETTS Register, and United States Calendar; for the Year of our Lord 1824. Boston, (n.d.). Orig. binding. Wolfe 39-344 1978 $17.50

MASSE, H.J.L.J.   Pewter Plate. London, 1904. Illus., 4to, water stained, good working copy. Baldwins' 51-122 1978 $22.50

MASSENGILL, SAMUEL EVANS   A Sketch of Medicine and Pharmacy and a View of Its Progress by the Massengill Family from the Fifteenth to the Twentieth Century. Bristol, 1943. Rittenhouse 49-525 1976 $17.50

MASSEY, GERALD   Ancient Egypt, The Light of the World... 1907. Roy. 8vo, illus., 2 vols., orig. cloth, ltd. to 500 copies. Edwards 1012-224 1978 £45

MASSEY, GERALD   Craigcrook Castle, A Poem. 1856. 1st. ed., orig. blind-stamped green cloth, v.g. Jarndyce 16-868 1978 £12.50

MASSEY, VINCENT   Good Neighbourhood and Other Addresses in the United States. Toronto, 1930. Autograph pres. inscription signed by Massey, orig. binding. Wolfe 39-345 1978 $35

MASSEY, VINCENT   On Being a Canadian. Toronto, 1948. Signed by the author. Hood's 115-350 1978 $17.50

MASSEY, VINCENT   The Sword of Lionheart, and Other Wartime Speeches. Toronto, 1942. Hood's 115-349 1978 $12.50

MASSEY, W. T.   How Jerusalem was Won, Record of Allenby's Campaign in Palestine. 1919. Maps, illus., 8vo. George's 635-842 1978 £5

MASSIE, SUSANNE WILLIAMS   Homes and Gardens in Old Virginia. Richmond, 1932. Illus., 8vo., 2nd prtg. Morrill 239-521 1978 $10

MASSINGER, PHILIP   The Best Plays. 1889. 2 vols., octavo, good. Upcroft 10-115 1978 £6.50

MASSINGHAM, H. W.   H.W.M. A Selection from the Writings of H. W. Massingham. London, 1925. Very fine in slightly soiled & chipped d.w. Desmarais B-444 1978 $10

MASSINGHAM, J. D.   The Church of Ireland Defended. 1868. Disbound, very good, octavo bound in cloth, reprint. Hyland 128-108 1978 £12

MASSON, C.   Narrative of Various Journeys in Balochistan,
Afghanistan, and the Panjab... 1842. Litho. plts., text illus., 3 vols., half
calf, lib. stamp on titles, slight staining & foxing, 8vo.   Edwards 1012-119
1978 £100

MASSON, DAVID   MacMillan's Magazine. 1859-1886. 50 vols.,
half calf, mor. lables, 8vo. Howes 194-1029 1978 £220

MASSON, JOHN   Lucretius, Epicurean & Poet. 1907. Vol. I
rebacked, 2 vols. Allen 234-591 1978 $17.50

MASSON, MADELEINE   Lady Anne Barnard. London, (1949). 12 plts.,
8vo, orig. cloth. K Books 239-311 1978 £5

MASSON, ROSALINE   The Life of Robert Louis Stevenson. London,
1923. First ed., orig. binding, photographs, nice. Rota 211-666 1978 £8

MASSON, THOMAS   Tom Masson's Annual. Garden City, 1925.
1st ed., illus., fine, d.j., cloth slipcase. Houle 10-318 1978 $45

MAST, C. Z.   Annals of the Conestoga Valley in Lancaster,
Berks, and Chester Counties, Pennsylvania. (Scottdale), 1942. 1st ed., illus.,
orig. cloth, d.j., worn, fine, very scarce. MacManus 239-1556 1978 $110

MASTAI. Classified Directory of American Art and Antique Dealers. 1950.
Biblo BL781-714 1978 $10

MASTER Johann Dietz, Surgeon in the Army of the Great Elector, and Barber to
the Royal Court. London, 1923. Plts., illus., thick 8vo., 1/2 cloth, 1st English
ed. Salloch 345-54 1978 $25

THE MASTERPIECE Library of Short Stories, Vol. XI. c. 1920. Ports., very
good, octavo bound in cloth. Hyland 128-907 1978 £7

MASTERPIECES of Engraving and Etching. New York, 1936. Tall 8vo., orig.
bds., illus. Morrill 241-29 1978 $8.50

MASTERPIECES of French Modern Bindings. New York. Illus. cover, newly
bound in cloth, orig. wrs. bound in. Battery Park 1-278 1978 $35

MASTERS, EDGAR LEE   Children of the Market Place. New York, 1922.
16mo, blue cloth, d.w. soiled and chipped, near Fine, 1st ed. Desmarais 1-304
1978 $10

MASTERS, EDGAR LEE   Kit O'Brien. (New York), 1927. Orig. pict.
cloth, d.j., very minor wear at extremities, 1st ed., very fine, inscribed by
author. MacManus 238-710 1978 $37.50

MASTERS, EDGAR LEE   Lincoln the Man. New York, 1931. Illus.,
orig. vellum-backed cloth, 1st ed., ltd. to 150 signed copies, fine, slipcase.
MacManus 238-711 1978 $50

MASTERS, EDGAR LEE   Mitch Miller. New York, 1920. 8vo, blue
cloth, gilt stamped, 1st state, uncut, unopened, d.w. somewhat soiled and chipped,
Fine, 1st ed. Desmarais 1-305 1978 $25

MASTERS, EDGAR LEE   The New Spoon River. New York, 1924. Orig.
parchment-backed bds., 1st ed., ltd. to 360 signed copies, spine slightly worn,
otherwise very good. MacManus 238-709 1978 $50

MASTERS, EDGAR LEE   Poems of People. New York, 1936. 8vo, blue
cloth, uncut, Mint in d.w., 1st ed. Desmarais 1-306 1978 $12.50

MASTER, EDGAR LEE   The Serpent in the Wilderness. New York,
(1933). Quarto, boards and cloth, gilt, 1 of 400 copies signed by author, 1st ed.,
fine. Duschnes 220-196 1978 $35

MASTERS, EDGAR LEE   Spoon River Anthology. New York, 1915. 8vo,
pict. cloth, spine very slightly faded, near Fine, 1st ed. Desmarais 1-307 1978
$45

MASTERS, EDGAR LEE   The Tale of Chicago. New York, 1933. 1st ed.,
orig. cloth, d.j., chipped, very good copy. MacManus 239-213 1978 $12.50

MATEROT, LUCAS   Les Oeuvres... N.P., n.d. (Avignon, 1608).
Eng. portrait, oblong 4to., half leather, first ed., of great rarity. Schumann
511-35 1978 sFr 11,000

MATHER, CHARLES E.   Master of Radnor: Diary of Chas. E. Mather,
M.F.H. 1887-1901. N.P., 1947. 1st ed., 1 of 750 copies, map-end papers,
illus., orig. binding, 8vo. Americanist 101-135 1978 $35

MATHER, COTTON   The Life and Death of the Reverend Mr. John
Eliot, Who Was The First Preacher of the Gospel to the Indians in America.
London, 1694. 12mo, contemp. mottled calf, 2nd London ed. Ximenes 47-205
1978 $425

MATHER, COTTON   The Life of Sir William Phips. New York, 1929.
Ltd. to 500 copies, fine, vellum-backed bds. MacManus 239-300 1978 $22.50

MATHER, COTTON   Magnalia Christi Americana. London, 1702.
1st ed., folio, a.e.g., map, bound in full mottled calf, gilt decor. paneled spine,
bds. pockmarked, occas. foxing & waterstaining, generally fine. Current 24-91
1978 $2,250

MATHER, FRED   Men I Have Fished With. New York, 1897.
Portraits, orig. binding. Wolfe 39-11 1978 $20

MATHER, GILBERT   Diary of Charles E. Mather, M.F.H., 1887-
1901. 1947. Ltd. to 700 copies, no. 367, fine. Baldwins' 51-546 1978 $20

MATHER, INCREASE   A Brief History of the Warr with the Indians in
Nevv-England... Boston, 1676. 1st ed. of both parts, sm. 4to., scarce, 1st
vol. bound in 1/4 brown mor. with marbled bds., occas. foxing, 2nd vol. bound
in full green levant, marbled endpapers, enclosed in single solander slipcase of
full green crushed levant, raised bands. Current 24-92 1978 $3,500

MATHER, MARSHALL   Life and Teaching of John Ruskin. London, n.d.
(1883). Orig. green cloth, v.g. Jarndyce 16-984 1978 £6

MATHER, MRS. R. C.   The Storm Swept Coast of South Carolina.
Woonsocket, 1894. Orig. wraps., illus. Baldwins' 51-528 1978 $17.50

MATHERS, E. POWYS   Red Wise. 1926. Ltd. ed. of 500 copies,
wood-engravings by Robert Gibbings, 8vo, orig. buckram backed bds., corners
little worn, good copy, inscribed by author. Sawyer 299-128 1978 £75

MATHESON, R. E.   Varieties & Synonymes of Surnames & Christian
Names in Ireland. 1901. 1/4 cl., very good, octavo bound in cloth, reprint.
Hyland 128-109 1978 £15

MATHEW, A. H.   The Life of Sir Tobie Mathew. 1907. Plts.,
good, octavo. Upcroft 10-442 1978 £8.50

MATHEWS, ALFRED   History of the Counties of Lehigh and Carbon.
Philadelphia, 1884. 4to., illus., maps, rebound, very scarce. MacManus 239-
1557 1978 $110

MATHEWS, C. E.   The Earlier and Less-known Poems of Alfred
Tennyson, Poet-Laureate. Birmingham, (1883). Blue paper covers, front present
but severed at spine, darkening of pages, very Nice, very scarce, 1st ed., collector's cond. Desmarais 1-399 1978 $40

MATHEWS, CHARLES   The Theatrical Olio; or Actor's Ways and Means.
n.d., (1818?). 12mo, coloured frontispiece, half calf, orig. wrappers bound in,
uncut. Hannas 54-332 1978 £15

MATHEWS, MRS. E. K.   Lessons Of Truth. York, 1806. Wood engraved
frontis & cuts by Bewick, 12mo, orig. bds., loose & some staining, lacks pgs. 97-
100. Traylen 88-181 1978 £10

MATHEWS, F. SCHUYLER   The Writing Table of the Twentieth Century.
New York, 1900. Illus., 8vo., white cloth partly dust-soiled, 1st ed. Morrill
241-359 1978 $10

MATHEWS, F. SCHUYLER   The Writing Table of the 20th Century. Illus.
by author. Battery Park 1-407 1978 $45

MATHEWS, G. M.   A Century. Dayton, 1901. Cloth. Hayman
73-416 1978 $8.50

MATHEWS, JOSEPH J.   The Capture and Wonderful Escape of General
John H. Morgan. Atlanta, 1947. Wraps, Bell Wiley's copy. Broadfoot's 44-265
1978 $10.00

MATHEWSON, CHRISTIE   Won in the Ninth. New York, 1916. Illus.
Austin 82-627 1978 $12.50

MATHIAS, THOMAS JAMES   The Pursuits of Literature: a Satirical Poem.
1797. New ed. revised & corrected, orig. diced calf, gilt borders & spine, black
label, v.g. Jarndyce 16-141 1978 £20

MATHIAS, THOMAS JAMES   The Pursuits of Literature. Dublin, 1798. 8vo,
half-titles, contemp. calf, gilt spine, nice. Fenning 32-221 1978 £16.50

MATHIAS, THOMAS JAMES   The Pursuits of Literature. 1801. Eleventh ed.,
contemp. calf, 8vo. Howes 194-384 1978 £22

MATHIAS, THOMAS JAMES   Runic Odes Imitated from the Norse Tongue in the Manner of Mr. Gray. London, 1781. 4to., new cloth, 1st ed., fine. MacManus 238-133 1978 $100

MATHIEZ, A.   The French Revolution. (1928). 8vo. George's 635-716 1978 £5.25

MATHIS, C.   Recherches de Parasitologie et de Pathologie Humaine et Animales au Tonkin. Paris, 1911. Color plts., cloth, 8vo., orig. covers. Van der Peet 127-147 1978 Dfl 75

MATON, WILLIAM GEORGE   Observations relative chiefly to the Natural History, picturesque Scenery.... Salisbury, 1797. 2 vols., map, plts., full russia gilt, 8vo. K Books 244-414 1978 £70

MATSCHAT, C. H.   Suwannee River. New York, (1938). Illus. by Alexander Key. Biblo 251-104 1978 $13.50

MATTER, J.   Ueber Den Einfluss Der Sitten Auf Die Gesetze Und Der Gesetze Auf Die Sitten. Freiburg, 1833. Tall 8vo., contemp. marbled bds. with label. Salloch 348-142 1978 $35

MATTHEW OF PARIS
Please turn to
PARIS, MATTHEW

MATTHEW OF WESTMINSTER   Flowers of History, especially such as relate to the Affairs of Britain, to 1307. 1853. 2 vols., cr. 8vo., orig. cloth. George's 635-555 1978 £10.50

MATTHEW, G. F.   The Geological Age of the Little River Group. Illus., card cover. Hood 117-952 1973 $7.50

MATTHEWMAN, LISLE DE VAUX   Crankisms. Philadelphia, 1901. Illus., sq. 12mo., 1st ed., orig. cloth. Morrill 241-360 1978 $12.50

MATTHEWS, BRANDER   Bookbindings Old and New. 1895. Illus., 8vo., geometric full lea. binding, all edges gilt. Battery Park 1-406 1978 $100

MATTHEWS, BRANDER   Moliere, his Life and Works. 1910. Orig. ed., portrait, orig. cloth, 8vo. Howes 194-1056 1978 £6.50

MATTHEWS, BRANDER   A Study of the Drama. Boston, (1910). Illus. Biblo 247-904 1978 $15

MATTHEWS, FREDERICK C.   American Merchant Ships 1850-1900. Salem, 1930. Sm. 4to., illus., fine. MacManus 239-1771 1978 $35

MATTHEWS, FREDERICK C.   American Merchant Ships 1850-1900. Salem, 1930-31. 2 vols., 1st eds., lg. 8vos., orig. buckram, illus., very good. Americanist 103-82 1978 $95

MATTHEWS, HAROLD J.   Candle by Night:.... Boston, 1942. 1st ed. Jenkins 116-313 1978 $25

MATTHEWS, HAROLD J.   Candle by Night. Boston, (1942). Cloth, very good copy in dust jacket. Hayman 73-696 1978 $7.50

MATTHEWS, HERBERT L.   The Education of a Correspondent. 1946. Austin 80-201 1978 $7.50

MATTHEWS, JOHN   Voyage a la Riviere de Sierra-Leone, sur la Cote d'Afrique. Paris, (1797). 12mo., polished calf, very good, first French translation. King 7-365 1978 £25

MATTHEWS, WASHINGTON   Ethnography and Philology of the Hidatsa Indians. Washington, 1877. 8vo, orig. cloth. Edwards 1012-556 1978 £12

MATTHEWS, WILLIAM   American Diaries: An Annotated Bibliography of American Dairies Written Prior to the Year 1861. Berkeley & Los Angeles, 1945. Wrappers, mended, passable copy, 8 vo. Ballinger 11-2 1978 $25

MATTHEWS, WILLIAM   American Diaries. An Annotated Bibliography of American Diaries Written Prior to the Year 1861... Berkeley, 1945. Orig. cloth, 1st ed., sm. bookplt., very good. MacManus 238-978 1978 $25

MATTHEWS, WILLIAM   Canadian Diaries and Autobiographies. Berkeley, 1950. Orig. cloth, d.j., 1st ed., very good. MacManus 238-883 1978 $22.50

MATTHEWS, WILLIAM   Canadian Diaries and Autobiographies. Los Angeles, 1950. Hood 117-58 1978 $40

MATTHIAS, JOHN   The "J.B. Gough" Series of Temperance Dialogues for Social Gatherings and Home Use. London, n.d. Hood 116-705 1978 $10

MATTHIESSEN, F. O.   Henry James; the major phase. London, 1946. First English ed., orig. binding, very nice. Rota 211-250 1978 £5

MATTHIESSEN, F. O.   The James Family. New York, 1947. 16mo., black cloth, d.w., front cover bumped, very Nice, 1st ed., collector's cond. Desmarais 1-252 1978 $15

MATTHIESSEN, F. O.   Translation; An Elizabethan Art. Cambridge, 1931. Octavo, good. Upcroft 10-447 1978 £7.50

MATTHIEU, PIERRE   Unhappy Prosperitie Expressed in the Histories of Aelius Seianus and Phillipa the Catanian Written in French by P. Matthieu and Translated into Englus by Sir Th. Hawkins. N.P. (London), 1632. 1st ed., quarto, full contemp. vellum, contemp. notations on front free endpaper, very fine and very rare. Bennett 20-139 1978 $295

MATTIOLI, PIETRO ANDREA   Opusculum de Simplicium Medicamentorum Facultatibus Secundum Locos and Genera. Venice, 1569. 16mo., woodcuts, first sep. ed., rare, fine, cont. limp. vellum. Schafer 19-56 1978 sFr 850

MATTISON, H.   Spirit Rapping Unveiled! New York, 1853. Vignette wood engrs. by Nathaniel Orr, pict. cloth, worn but sound. Butterfield 21-393 1978 $45

MATURIN, CHARLES ROBERT   Melmoth, the Wanderer. 1892. 3 vols., new ed., very good, octavo bound in cloth. Hyland 128-111 1978 £35

MATZ, B. W.   The Inns & Taverns of "Pickwick". London, 1921. 1st ed., frontispiece, plts., drawings, edges a bit foxed, else very good or better. Limestone 9-87 1978 $20

MATZ, FR.   Le Monde Egeen. Paris, 1950. 8vo., cloth, illus., map. Van der Peet H-64-169 1978 Dfl 45

MAUCLAIR, C.   Gustave Richard, 1823-1873. (c. 1880). Thin 4to., plts., half purple mor., gilt top, orig. wrs. bound in. Quaritch 983-245 1978 $45

MAUCLAIR, CAMILLE   Le Charme de Versailles. Paris, (1931). Illus. in color, wrs. Biblo 247-351 1978 $17.50

MAUDE, JOHN   Visit to the Falls of Niagara in 1800. London, 1826. Pres. copy signed by author, leather, plts., errata slip. Hood 116-760 1978 $600

MAUDE, JOHN EDWARD   The Foundation of Ethics. New York, 1887. Sm. 8vo., 1st ed. Morrill 239-445 1978 $7.50

MAUDSLAY, A.   Roland, a Masque. 1856. 1st. ed., half title, orig. green cloth, fine. Jarndyce 16-869 1978 £10.50

MAUDSLEY, HENRY   Body and Mind. New York, 1871. Some wear. Rittenhouse 49-527 1976 $17.50

MAUDSLEY, HENRY   Heredity, Variation and Genius, With Essay on Shakespeare, ...and address on Medicine; Present and Prospective. London, 1908. Rittenhouse 49-526 1976 $20

MAUGHAM, WILLIAM SOMERSET   Books and You. 1940. 1st. ed., d.w. Eaton 45-332 1978 £4

MAUGHAM, WILLIAM SOMERSET   Cakes and Ale, or, the Skeleton in the Cupboard. London, (1930). Blue cloth, 1st ed., 1st issue, very good in chipped dust jacket. Bradley 49-217 1978 $15

MAUGHAM, WILLIAM SOMERSET   Cakes and Ale. London, (1930). 8vo., cloth, d.j., 1st ed., fine. Duschnes 220-197 1978 $50

MAUGHAM, WILLIAM SOMERSET   Cakes and Ale, or, the Skeleton in the Cupboard. 1st ed., fine in chipped dust jacket. Bradley 49-218 1978 $10

MAUGHAM, WILLIAM SOMERSET   Cakes and Ale. London, (1930). Orig. cloth, d.j., 1st ed., fine, very good d.j. MacManus 238-712 1978 $40

MAUGHAM, WILLIAM SOMERSET   Cakes and Ale. (1954). Portrait, orig. calf, gilt top, other edges untrimmed, unopened mint copy, orig. cellophane wrapper, slipcase, signed by author, ltd. to 1000 numbered copies, 8vo. Howes 194-1039 1978 £85

MAUGHAM, WILLIAM SOMERSET   Christmas Holiday. London, (1939). Blue cloth, 1st ed., fine in chipped jacket. Bradley 49-219 1978 $15

MAUGHAM, WILLIAM SOMERSET   The Circle. New York, (1921). First Amer. ed. Biblo 247-601 1978 $17.50

MAUGHAM, WILLIAM SOMERSET   The Judgement Seat. London, 1934. 8vo., black cloth, t.e.g., slightly chipped glassine jacket, wood engraving by Ulica Hyde, mint, no. 86 only 150 numbered copies, signed by Maugham and Hyde, 1st ed. Desmarais 1-308 1978 $10

MAUGHAM, WILLIAM SOMERSET   Liza of Lambeth. London, 1897. 8vo., decor. cloth, 1st ed., pres. copy. Argosy Special-61 1978 $500

MAUGHAM, WILLIAM SOMERSET   Of Human Bondage. (New York), Yale University Press, 1938. 2 vols., cloth, 1 of 1500 signed by Joan Sloan, slipcase. Bradley 49-220 1978 $195

MAUGHAM, WILLIAM SOMERSET   Of Human Bondage. (1946). Ltd. ed., signed by author, bds., slightly soiled, signature of Lady K. Sansom on endpaper. Eaton 45-330 1978 £20

MAUGHAM, WILLIAM SOMERSET   Orientations. 1899. 1st. ed., orig. cloth, worn. Eaton 45-331 1978 £5

MAUGHAM, WILLIAM SOMERSET   The Painted Veil. 1925. Very good, 2nd issue, first state, first English ed. Bell Book 16-627 1978 £12.50

MAUGHAM, WILLIAM SOMERSET   The Razor's Edge. London, 1944. First English ed., orig. binding, nice. Rota 211-377 1978 £6

MAUGHAM, WILLIAM SOMERSET   The Razor's Edge. London, (1944). 8vo., cloth, gilt, d.j., 1st ed., fine. Duschnes 220-198 1978 $17.50

MAUGHAM, WILLIAM SOMERSET   The Tenth Man: A Tragic Comedy in Three Acts. London, 1913. 1st ed., very good or better. Limestone 9-193 1978 $18

MAUGHAM, WILLIAM SOMERSET   Theatre: a novel. 1937. Good, first English ed. Bell Book 17-645 1978 £5

MAUGHAM, WILLIAM SOMERSET   A Writer's Notebook. Garden City, 1949. 1st Amer. ed., tall octavo, red buckram, gilt top, publisher's slipcase, 1 of 1000 copies signed by Maugham. Totteridge 29-69 1978 $85

MAUGHAM, WILLIAM SOMERSET   A Writer's Notebook. New York, 1949. Very fine copy, d.w. clean but repaired in several spots. Desmarais B-448 1978 $15

MAUGHAM, WILLIAM SOMERSET   A Writer's Notebook. GC, 1949. Frontis. port., spine rubbed, d.j. worn, 1st trade ed. Petrilla 13-30 1978 $8.50

MAULDE LA CLAVIERE, R. DE   Women of the Renaissance. 1901. Allen 234-1355 1978 $10

MAULL, BALDWIN   John Maull of Lewes, Delaware. New York, 1941. MacManus 239-932 1978 $25

MAUNDER, SAMUEL   The Treasury of Natural History or, a Popular Dictionary of Zoology. England, 1862. 6th ed., revised & corrected, worn, 8vo., orig. cloth. Book Chest 17-251 1978 $17.50

MAUPASSANT, HENRY RENE ALBERT, GUY DE   The Life Work of Henry Rene Guy de Maupassant. Akron, 1903. 17 vols., Academie Ed., ltd. to 750 sets, 8vo., uncut, unopened, landco,ored frontis's, illus. from orig. drwgs., 3/4 green crushed levant with green linen covered bds. & marbled endpapers, spines faded brown, mint, no wear, no cracking. Current 24-33 1978 $385

MAUPASSANT, HENRY RENE ALBERT, GUY DE   Complete Works. New York, 1910. Plts., illus., 17 vols., half navy mor., ltd. ed., 8vo. Howes 194-1040 1978 $75

MAUPERTUIS, PIERRE LOUIS MOREAU DE   Astronomie Nautique: ou Elemens D'astronomie, Tant Pour un Observatoire Fixe, Que Pour un Observatoire Mobile. Paris, 1745. 8vo., illus., old quarter vellum, 1st ed. Gilhofer 74-7 1978 sFr 300

MAUPERTUIS, PIERRE LOUIS MOREAU DE   Discours Sur Les Differentes Figures Des Astres. Paris, 1742. Engr. frontis. in color, 2nd enlarged ed., 8vo., contemp. calf, back gilt. Salloch 345-119 1978 $135

MAUPERTUIS, PIERRE LOUIS MOREAU DE   Lettre sur la Comete. (Paris, 1742). 12mo., old bds., calf rebacked, frontis. Gurney 75-72 1978 £50

MAUQUEST DE LA MOTTE, GUILLAUME   Traite Complet Des Accouchemens Naturels, non Naturels, et Contre Nature, Explique dans un grand nombre d'Observations & Reflexions sur l'Art d'accoucher. Paris, 1721. Thick 4to., modern cloth, gilt on spine, browned, dampstained, good copy from the library of Dr. Alfred M. Hellman, scarce. Zeitlin 245-162 1978 $125

MAURIAC, FRANCOIS   A Kiss for the Leper. London, 1950. First ed., orig. binding, nice. Rota 211-382 1978 £5

MAURICE, ARTHUR BARTLETT   The New York of the Novelists. 1916. Illus., first ed. Austin 82-628 1978 $27.50

MAURICE, F.   The History of the Scots Guards from the Creation of the Regiment to the Eve of the Great War. 1934. Coloured plts. and frontis., 2 vols., roy. 8vo., orig. cloth. F. Edwards 1013-478 1978 £40

MAURICE, THOMAS   Poems, Epistolary, Lyric and Elegiacal in Three Parts. 1800. 1st. ed., orig. half calf, marbled bds., black label, v.g. Jarndyce 16-870 1978 £35

MAURICEAU, FRANCOIS   Observations Sur La Grossesse Et L'Accouchement Des Femmes, et sur leurs maladies, & celles des Enfans nouveau-nez. Paris, 1715. 4to., contemp. mottled calf, gilt decor. spine, gilt dentelles, worn, crisp copy on lg. paper, bkplt. of Dr. Alfred M. Hellman. Zeitlin 245-163 1978 $150

MAUROIS, ANDRE   Byron. Paris, 1931. Coloured frontispieces and vignettes by Hermine David, one of 200 numbered copies on velin, 2 vols., wraps, fine, largely unopened. Bell Book 17-485 1978 £15

MAUROIS, ANDRE   Chateaubriand. 1938. First English ed., table, plts., 8vo., orig. cloth. Howes 194-718 1978 £4

MAUROIS, ANDRE   Un Essai sur Dickens. Paris, 1927. First French ed., one of 19 numbered copies, very fine, wrappers, slipcase. Bell Book 16-267 1978 £12.50

MAUROIS, ANDRE   Les Silences du Colonel Bramble. (1930). Black/pink paper bds., wrappers bound in, author's signed pres. copy. Eaton 45-334 1978 £10

MAUROLICO, FRANCESCO   Cosmographia, in tres dialogos distincta:.... Venice, 1543. Extremely rare 1st ed., old vellum, 4to. Gilhofer 75-79 1978 SFr 3,600

MAURY, ANNE FONTAINE   Intimate Virginiana. A Century of Maury Travels by Land and Sea. Richmond, 1941. 1st ed., illus., orig. cloth-backed bds., d.j., very fine. MacManus 239-1843 1978 $20

MAURY, L. F. ALFRED   La Magie et L'Astrologie dans Antiquite et au Moyen.... Paris, 1860. Half calf, mottled end papers and edges, sound. Rittenhouse 49-528 1976 $60

MAURY, MATTHEW FONTAINE   The Physical Geography of the Sea. New York, 1855. 12 plts., 1st. ed., very good sound copy. Baldwins' 51-509 1978 $275

MAUTHNER, FRITZ   Woerterbuch Der Philosophie. Munich, 1910. 2 vols., thick 4to., cloth. Salloch 348-143 1978 $45

MAVCH, J. M.   The Architectural Orders of the Greeks and Romans. New York, (1930). 100 loose plts. in folder. Baldwins' 51-124 1978 $22.50

MAVELOT, CHARLES   Livre de Differens Cartouches for Recherchez... N.P., n.d. (Paris, 1685). Sm. 8vo., eng. plts., Janssenist binding of full blue mor., inner gilt dentelles, beautiful copy. Schumann 511-36 1978 sFr 2,600

MAVELOT, CHARLES   Nouveaux Desseins pour la Pratique de l'Art Heraldique. N.P., (Paris), 1696. Frontis., 4to., eng. plts., Janssenist binding in full red mor., inner gilt dentelles, splendid lg. copy, mint, of utmost rarity. Schumann 511-38 1978 sFr 2,950

MAVELOT, CHARLES   Nouveau Livre de Chiffres... N.P., n.d. (Paris, 1680). Engravings, 4to., Janssenist binding of full red mor., gilt inner dentelles, by Cuzin, rare, magnificent and complete copy. Schumann 511-37 1978 sFr 2,950

MAVELOT, CHARLES   Nouveau Livre de Differens Cartouches, Couronnes, Casques... N.P., n.d. (Paris, 1685). Oblong 8vo., Janssenist binding of full red mor., inner gilt dentelles, by Cuzin, eng. designs, splendid and complete copy. Schumann 511-39 1978 sFr 2,350

MAVERICK, MARY A.   Memoirs of Mary A. Maverick. San Antonio, 1921. 1st ed., stiff printed wr., illus. Jenkins 116-1520 1978 $45

MAVOR, WILLIAM   The British Nepos. 1798. First ed., sm. 8vo., contemp. calf, spine and joints worn. Howes 194-348 1978 £15

MAVOR, WILLIAM   The British Nepos; or, Mirror of Youth.... London, 1800. 2nd ed., plates, mottled calf, fine, crisp copy. Victoria 34-530 1978 $50

MAVOR, WILLIAM   The English Spelling-Book. London, 1806. 30th. ed., frontis, illus., sm. 8vo, orig. calf, spine trifle defective. Traylen 88-182 1978 £18

MAVOR, WILLIAM   Miscellanies, In Two Parts: Prose; Verse. Oxford, (1829). Frontis portrait, green calf, spine gilt, red label, good. Jarndyce 16-871 1978 £32

MAWE, JOHN   Familiar Lessons on Mineralogy and Geology. London, 1825. 7th ed., hand-coloured plts., 12mo., half calf. K Books 244-229 1978 £30

MAWE, JOHN   A Treatise on Diamonds and Precious Stones.... 1815. 2nd. ed., coloured plts., 8vo, orig. bds., uncut, spine little worn & label rubbed, some light foxing, very good copy. Fenning 32-222 1978 £24

MAXEY, SAMUEL B.   University Address by Gen. S. B. Maxey, of Paris, Texas. Austin, 1889. Printed wr. Jenkins 116-899 1978 $35

MAXFIELD, ALBERT   Roster and Statistical Record of Company D, Eleventh Regiment Maine Infantry Volunteers, with a Sketch of Its Services in the War of the Rebellion. New York, 1890. 8vo., orig. wrs., nice. Morrill 241-305 1978 $10

MAXIMUS, PACIFICUS   Elegiae non nullae icosae & festivae. Camerino, 1523. 4to, boards. Gilhofer 75-80 1978 SFr 1,300

MAXSE, F. I.   Seymour Vandeleur, Lieutenant-Colonel, Scots Guards & Irish Guards. London, 1906. 9 maps, roy. 8vo, orig. cloth, g. t. K Books 239-312 1978 £9

MAXTON, JAMES   Lenin. 1932. 1st. ed., portrait frontis, 8vo, orig. cloth, pres. copy to Winston Churchill. Sawyer 298-94 1978 £95

MAXWELL, CAROLINE   The History of the Holy Bible. London, 1827. 1st. ed., plts., illus., 8vo, orig. printed bds., leather spine. Traylen 88-183 1978 £20

MAXWELL, H.   British Fresh Water Fishes. London, 1904. Color plts., illus., 4to, orig. cloth. Book Chest 17-252 1978 $60

MAXWELL, H. E.   The Early Chronicles Relating to Scotland. 1912. 8vo. Upcroft 12-291 1978 £10.50

MAXWELL, HERBERT   The Lowland Scots Regiments. Glasgow, 1918. Coloured frontis., coloured plts., thick imp. 8vo., orig. cloth, uncut. F. Edwards 1013-361 1978 £35

MAXWELL, HERBERT   The Life of Wellington. Boston, 1899. 2 vols., illus., maps. Biblo 247-757 1978 $37.50

MAXWELL, HU   History of Hampshire County, West Virginia. Morgantown, 1897. Cloth. Hayman 73-740 1978 $20

MAXWELL, JAMES CLERK   An Elementary Treatise on Electricity. Oxford, Clarendon Press, 1881. 8vo, ads, plts., text illus., orig. cloth, uncut, worn, but very good copy, signature crossed out on title, 1st ed. Norman 5-**22 1978 $100

MAXWELL, MARY ELIZABETH (BRADDON)   Eleanor's Victory. 1863. 1st ed., 3 vols., half titles, orig. green diagonal grain cloth, spines little rubbed. Jarndyce 16-305 1978 £45

MAXWELL, MARY ELIZABETH (BRADDON)   The Golden Calf. n.d. (1906). Orig. decor. cloth. Eaton 45-60 1978 £5

MAXWELL, MARY ELIZABETH (BRADDON)   Mount Royal. A Novel. London, 1882. 3 vols., orig. cloth, 1st ed., covers stained, slightly worn. MacManus 238-170 1978 $250

MAXWELL, MARY ELIZABETH (BRADDON)   One Life, One Love. 1890. 3 vols., 8vo., 1st ed., orig. green cloth, fine & fresh. Quaritch 979-57 1978 $260

MAXWELL, MARY ELIZABETH (BRADDON)   The Venetians. New York, 1892. 1st Amer. ed., 3 vols. in 1, cloth, contemp. inscr. Greene 78-11 1978 $20

MAXWELL, W.   Wild Sports of the West. 1832. Aquatint plts., woodcuts in text, 2 vols., modern blue mor., 8vo. George's 635-1510 1978 £80

MAY, E.   A Most Certaine and True Relation of a Strange Monster or Serpent Found in the Left Ventricle of the Heart of John Pennant.... London, 1639. Sm. 4to., woodcuts, modern half red mor. Quaritch 977-54 1978 $2,000

MAY, JOHN BICHARD   The Hawks of North America. New York, 1935. Illus. by Allan Brooks & Roger Tory Peterson. Baldwins' 51-547 1978 $22.50

MAY, JOSEPH   Nicholas Danforth of Framingham, England and Cambridge N.E., (1589-1638) and William Danforth of Newbury, Mass., (1640-1721). Boston, 1902. Binding broken loose. Baldwins' 51-248 1978 $65

MAY, PHIL   Fun, Frolic & Fancy. 1894. Illus. by author, sm. 4to., orig. wraps, backstrip worn, good, first English ed. Bell Book 16-490 1978 £5

MAY, PHIL   Gutter-Snipes. 1896. Proofs on fine paper, ltd. to 1050 copies, orig. sketches in pen and ink, 4to., orig. cloth a little stained. George's 635-127 1978 £21

MAY, SAMUEL J.   Some Recollections of the Anti-Slavery Conflict. Boston, 1869. 1st ed., orig. cloth, fine. MacManus 239-846 1978 $25

MAY, SOPHIE   Dotty Dimple. Boston, 1865. 1st ed., split in lower spine edge and tips rubbed, text foxed, completely firm. Victoria 34-164 1978 $55

MAY, SOPHIE   Little Prudy. Boston, 1865. 1st ed., fly-leaves lacking and cover fading. Victoria 34-165 1978 $40

MAY, THOMAS   The History of the Parliament of England Which Began Nov. 3, 1640... Oxford, 1854. Spine dull, octavo, good. Upcroft 10-116 1978 £15

MAYER, ALFRED M.   Sport With Gun and Rod in American Woods and Waters. Edinburgh, 1884. 2 vols., imp. 8vo, bds., leather spines, covers slightly rubbed, plts., illus. Edwards 1012-402 1978 £60

MAYER, BRANTZ   Captain Canot; or, Twenty Years of an African Slaver... New York, 1854. 1st. ed., illus., 8vo, orig. cloth, rather foxed, age-marked & shaken, good reading copy. K Books 239-84 1978 £25

MAYER, BRANTZ   Mexico As It Was and As It Is. New York, 1844. 1st. ed., woodcut on title, plts., orig. cloth, 8vo, spine slightly worn, spotting in text. Edwards 1012-692 1978 £30

MAYER, JOHANN CHRISTOPH ANDREAS   Anatomisch-Physiologische Abhandlung von Gehirn, Ruckenmark, und Ursprung der Nerven. Berlin und Leipzig, 1779. 4to., half calf, copperplts., 1st ed., fine copy. Offenbacher 30-94 1978 $350

MAYER, L.   Interesting View in Turkey... 1819. Coloured plts., 4to, orig. cloth, spine repaired, bland margin to 2 plts. slightly defective. Edwards 1012-52 1978 £120

MAYES, EDWARD   Lucius Q. C. Lamar: His Life, Times and Speeches 1825-1893. Nashville, 1896. Illus., front hinge cracked, cover speckled, Bell Wiley's copy. Broadfoot's 44-896 1978 $25.00

MAYGRIER, JACQUES PIERRE Midwifery Illustrated. New York, 1834. 3rd ed., plts., 4to., ex-lib., covers loose, plts. foxed. Morrill 239-173 1978 $10

MAYHAM, ALBERT CHAMPLIN   The Anti-Rent War on Blenheim Hill. Jefferson, 1906. Illus., plts., very scarce. Butterfield 21-58 1978 $75

MAYHEW, EDWARD   The Horse's Mouth showing the Age by the Teeth. London, c. 1852. 2nd ed., coloured plts., woodcuts, orig. cloth, 8vo. K Books 244-230 1978 £12

MAYNARD, THEODORE   Humanist as Hero, Life of Sir Thomas More. 1947. Allen 234-1370 1978 $7.50

MAYNE, R.   The Turn of the Road. Maunsel, 1907. 1st ed., wr., very good, octavo bound in cloth. Hyland 128-112 1978 £9

MAYNE, R. C.   Four Years in British Columbia and Vancouver Island... 1862. 8vo, orig. cloth, vignette on title, woodcut plts. Edwards 1012-445 1978 £90

MAYNE, R. C.   Four Years in British Columbia and Vancouver Island. London, 1862. Map, illus., orig. bds., new endpapers. Hood 117-208 1978 $225

MAYNO DE MAYNERI, SUPPOSED AUTHOR Regimen Sanitatis
Please turn to
REGIMEN SANITATIS SALERNITANUM

MAYO, JOSEPH   Woodbourne: a Novel of the Revolutionary Period in Virginia and Maryland. Philadelphia, (1884). Two parts, cloth. Hayman 73-196 1978 $10

MAYO, LAWRENCE SHAW   John Endecott. Cambridge, 1936. 1st ed., frontis. port., illus., t.e.g., uncut, orig. cloth, fine. MacManus 239-750 1978 $17.50

MAYO, LAWRENCE SHAW   The Winthrop Family in America. Boston, 1948. 1st ed., 4to., illus., ports., orig. cloth, fine. MacManus 239-944 1978 $25

MAYO, ROBERT   The Affidavit of Andrew Jackson, Taken by the Defendants in the Suit of Robert Mayo vs. Blair and Rives for a Libel, Analysed and Refuted. Washington, 1840. Half morocco, 1st ed. Ginsberg 14-431 1978 $350

MAYO, ROBERT   Political Sketches... Baltimore, 1839. 1st ed., nice copy, rebound, scarce. MacManus 239-301 1978 $50

MAYO, ROBERT   Political Sketches of Eight Years in Washington. Baltimore, 1839. 1st ed. Jenkins 116-898 1978 $110

MAYO-SMITH, RICHMOND   Emmigration and Immigration. (1890). Ex-lib. Austin 79-474 1978 $12.50

MAYOL, LURLINE BOWLES   Jiji Lou. Akron, (1925). Color plates by Fern Bissel Peat, fine. Victoria 34-605 1978 $30

MAZER, CHARLES   Diagnosis and Treatment of Menstrual Disorders and Sterility. New York, 1947. Second ed., d.j. Rittenhouse 49-529 1976 $20

MAZOIS, F.   Le Palais de Scaurus. Paris, 1869. Quatrieme ed., illus. Biblo BL781-439 1978 $16.50

MAZZANOVICH, ANTON   Trailing Geronimo...Some Hitherto Unrecorded Incidents Bearing upon the Outbreak of the White Mountain Apaches and Geronimo's Band in Arizona and New Mexico... Hollywood, 1931. Illus., original cloth, 3rd ed., revised. Ginsberg 14-363 1978 $20

MAZZINI, JOSEPH   The Duties of Man. Addressed to Workingmen... New York, 1892. Wrs. Hayman 72-451 1978 $10

MAZZUCHELLI, GIOVANNI MARIA   Notizie Istoriche e Critiche Intorno alla Vita,.... Brescia, 1737. 1st ed., quarto, engraved vignette, engraved initial letters, folding copperplates, contemp. vellum, gilt title on spine, bookplate of Landau and Galletti libraries. Bennett 20-140 1978 $325

MEAD, JAMES   Tell the Folks Back Home. 1944. Austin 80-204 1978 $8.50

MEAD, MARGARET   The Changing Culture of an Indian Tribe. New York, 1932. 1st ed. MacManus 239-1183 1978 $12.50

MEAD, MARGARET   Coming of Age in Samoa. New York, (c. 1944). First Armed Services ed., no. 826, oblong 16mo., pict. wrs., v.g. Houle 10-220 1978 $15

MEAD, RICHARD   A Mechanical Account of Poisons in Several Essays. London, 1702. Sm. 8vo., fldg. plt., orig. calf, rebacked, new endpapers, lightly browned, foxed, very good copy, 1st ed. Zeitlin 245-164 1978 $200

MEAD, RICHARD   A Mechanical Account of Poisons in several Essays. London, 1702. 8vo., contemp. calf, plt., pirated ed. Gurney 75-73 1978 £50

MEAD, RICHARD   A Mechanical Account of Poisons in several Essays. Dublin, 1729. Third ed., 8vo., contemp. calf, rebacked, rather sm. copy. Gurney 75-74 1978 £30

MEAD, W. E.   The English Medieval Feast. 1931. Plates, 8vo. George's 635-717 1978 £5

MEADE, GEORGE   The Life and Letters of George Gordon Meade. New York, 1913. 1st ed., 2 vols., illus., fold. maps, orig. cloth, fine. Mac-Manus 239-897 1978 $40

MEADE, ROBERT   Judah P. Benjamin, Confederate Statesman. New York, 1943. Illus., Bell Wiley's copy. Broadfoot 46-178 1978 $14

MEADER, J. W.   The Merrimack River; Its Source and Its Tribu-taries... Boston, 1869. 1st ed., fold. map laid in. MacManus 239-302 1978 $25

MEADOWS, ROBERT   A Private Anthropological Cabinet of 500 Authen-tic Racial-Esoteric Photographs and Illustrations... New York, (1934). #509 of 1,500 copies, orig. bind. Petrilla 13-32 1978 $20

MEANS, JAMES   The Aeronautical Annual. Boston, 1895-97, 1910. 4 vols., 8vo., plts., numbers 1-3, orig. linen-mounted sky-blue prtd. wrs., 3 vols. in mint cond., 1 very good, in cloth case, only ed. Norman 5-195 1978 $750

MEANS, PHILIP A.   The Spanish Main, Focus of Envy, 1492-1700. New York, 1935. 1st ed., illus., maps. MacManus 239-1772 1978 $12.50

MEARNS, HUGHES   Creative Power. 1930. Austin 82-631 1978 $11

MEAUTIS, G.   Les Chefs-d'Oeuvres de la Peinture Grecque. Paris, (1939). Illus., orig. wrs. Biblo BL781-440 1978 $12

MECHAM, CLIFFORD HENRY   Sketches and Incidents of the Siege of Lucknow... 1858. Vignette on title, litho plts., all coloured by hand, folio, title browned, blank corner of one plt. repaired, orig. cloth. Edwards 1012-107 1978 £160

MECHI, JOHN J.   An Appeal on Behalf of the Royal Agricultural Benevolent College.... (1859). Sm. 8vo, unbound sewn as issued, fine. Fenning 32-223 1978 £10.50

MECHNIKOV, IL'IA IL'ICH   Essais Optimistes. Paris, 1907. 8vo., 1st ed., very fine copy, green half mor., gilt back with red title-labels. Schafer 19-59 1978 sFr. 400

MECHNIKOV, IL'IA IL'ICH   Lecons sur la Pathologie Comparee de l'Inflam-mation Faites a l'Institut Pasteur en Avril et Mai 1891. Paris, 1892. Colored plts., figures, partly colored, 8vo., library cloth, orig. prtd. fr. wr. bound in, library stamps, pres. copy from author. Offenbacher 30-99 1978 $475

MECKEL, JOHANN FRIEDRICH   Nova Experimenta et Observationes de Fini-bus Venarum ac Vasorum Lymphaticorum in Ductus Visceraque Excretoria Corporis Humani, Ejusdemque Structurae Utilitate. Lugduni Batavorum, 1772. 8vo., marbled bds., paper slightly discolored. Offenbacher 30-95 1978 $225

MEDBERY, R. B.   Memoir of Mrs. Sarah Emily York, Formerly Miss S. E. Waldo. Boston, 1853. Portr., 8vo., orig. cloth, foxed, 1st ed. Morrill 241-361 1978 $10

MEDHURST, W. H.   China: Its State and Prospects... 1838. Half calf, map, coloured frontis, vignette title & plts. by G. Baxter, 8vo. Edwards 1012-191 1978 $50

MEDHURST, W. H.   China: Its State and Prospects... 1838. 8vo, engraved vignette title-pg., folding aquatint frontispiece, folding engraved map, engraved plts., half calf, gilt back. Deighton 5-80 1978 £43

MEDICAL and Agricultural Register, for the Years 1806 and 1807. Boston, 1806-7. Vols. I, Nos. 1-24, 8vo., contemp. marbled bds., calf back. Morrill 239-174 1978 $25

MEDICAL Botany; or History of Plants in the Materia Medica of the London, Edin-burgh, and Dublin Pharmacopoeias, arranged according to the Linnaean System. 1821. 2 vols., 8vo., portrait, hand-coloured engrav. plts., contemp. half green mor., rubbed. Quaritch 977-56 1978 $500

MEDICAL Coloradoana. Denver, 1922. 4to., ex-lib. Morrill 239-49 1978 $12.50

THE MEDICAL Recorder of Original Papers and Intelligence in Medicine and Sur-gery. Philadelphia, 1826-27. Vols. 9, 10, 11 & 12, very good, half leather, marbled bds., leather a little dry. Rittenhouse 49-541 1976 $35

MEDICI, LORENZO DE   Poesie del Magnifico Lorenzo de Medici Tratte da testi a penna Dalla Libreria.... Liverpool, 1791. 8vo., red straight-grained mor., a.e.g., text in fine italic, first ed., one of only 12 copies printed. King 7-190 1978 £100

MEDICO, GIUSEPPE DEL   Anatomia per uso dei Pittori e Scultori. Roma, 1811. Folio, plts., contemp. half-vellum, marginal stains on sev. leaves, very fine, 1st ed. Gilhofer 74-97 1978 sFr 1,500

MEDLYCOTT, A. E.   India and the Apostle Thomas. 1905. Map, plts., covers marked, 8vo. George's 635-1098 1978 £5.25

MEDWIN, THOMAS   The Angler in Wales. 1834. First ed., frontis., 2 vols., orig. bds., entirely uncut, 8vo. Howes 194-1437 1978 £30

MEDWIN, THOMAS   Conversations of Lord Byron... 1824. 2nd. ed., folding frontis, orig. half calf, green label, v.g. Jarndyce 16-348 1978 £20

MEDWIN, THOMAS   Journal of the Converstaions of Lord Byron Noted During a Residence with his Lordship at Pisa in the Years 1821 & 1822. 1824. 1st. ed., 4to, lacks folding frontis, half title, uncut, edges little dusted, rebound in half calf, hand marbled bds. Jarndyce 16-347 1978 £12.50

MEEHAN, C. P.   The Fate and Fortune of Hugh O'Neill, Earl of Tyrone, and Rory O'Donel, Earl of Tyrconnel; Their Flight From Ireland and Death in Exile. 1886. 3rd. ed., octavo, good. Upcroft 10-450 1978 £12

MEEKER, EZRA   Washington Territory West of the Cascade Mountains,... Olympia, 1870. Orig. pr. wr., 1st ed. Ginsberg 14-1034 1978 $350

MEEK'REN, JOB VAN   Heel- en Geneeskonstige Aanmerkingen. Amsterdam, 1668. Engr. frontis., few sm. woodcuts, 8vo., contemp. vellum, 1st ed., rare. Offenbacher 30-96 1978 $750

MEGARO, GAUDENS   Mussolini in the Making. Boston, 1938, 1st ed., portrait, illus, very good, d.j. Limestone 9-217 1978 $20

MEGAW, W. R.   Carragloon; Tales of Our Townland. Belfast, 1935. D.w., good, octavo bound in cloth, reprint. Hyland 128-115 1978 £4

MEGGLE, A.   l'Indochine. Paris, 1931. Illus., portrs., 8vo, orig. covers. Van der Peet 127-152 1978 Dfl 25

MEGINESS, JOHN FRANKLIN   Otzinachson; or, a History of the West Branch Valley of the Susquehanna. Philadelphia, 1857. Illus., rebound, scarce. MacManus 239-1558 1978 $55

MEIER-GRAEFE, JULIUS   Vincent. Munich, (1921). 2 vols., 4to., plts., text in German. Biblo BL781-752 1978 $34.50

MEIER-GRAEFE, JULIUS   Vincent van Gogh, a Bibliographical Study. 1922. Illus., 2 vols., 4to., orig. cloth-backed bds., corners rubbed. George's 635-221 1978 £35

MEIGS, ARTHUR VINCENT   The Origin of Disease. Philadelphia, London, 1897. 8vo., plts., orig. red cloth, gilt on spine, very good copy, 1st ed. Zeitlin 245-165 1978 $55

MEIGS, ARTHUR VINCENT   A Study of the Human Blood-Vessels in Health and Disease. A Supplement to the Origin of Disease. Philadelphia, 1907. Rittenhouse 49-545 1976 $25

MEIGS, CORNELIA   The Wonderful Locomotive. New York, 1928. 1st ed., illus. by Berta and Elmer Hader, large cover stain. Victoria 34-531 1978 $10

MEIGS, J. AITKEN   Catalogue of Human Crania in the Collection of the Academy of Natural Sciences of Philadelphia. Philadelphia, 1857. Printed wrappers in board binder. Rittenhouse 49-546 1976 $35

MEIGS, JOHN FORSYTH   A History of the First Quarter of the Second Century of the Pennsylvania Hospital. Philadelphia, 1877. Plts. MacManus 239-1559 1978 $20

MEIGS, JOHN FORSYTH   The Story of the Seaman. Being an Account of the Ways and Appliances of Seafarers and of Ships... Philadelphia, 1924. 2 vols., illus. MacManus 239-1773 1978 $37.50

MEIGS, JOHN FORSYTH   The Story of the Seamen. Philadelphia, 1924. 2 vols., illus. Baldwins' 51-510 1978 $30

MEIGS, JOSIAH   Memorial for an Act of Incorporation of a National Vaccine Institution for the U.S.A. Washington, 1820. Browning. Rittenhouse 49-547 1976 $15

MEINE, FRANKLIN, J.   John McCutcheon's Book. Chicago, 1948. Quarto, cloth, ed. of 1000 copies, fine. Duschnes 220-63a 1978 $65

MEINHOLD, WILHELM   Sidonia the Sorceress. 1894. First trade ed., 2 vols., orig. cloth, 8vo. Howes 194-1333 1978 £25

MEINHOLD, WILHELM   Sidonia the Sorceress. 1926. Ltd. to 225 copies, illus. by Thomas Lowinsky, 4to. George's 635-915 1978 £45

MEININGER, ERNEST   Histoire de Mulhouse Depuis Ses Origines Jusqu'a Nos Jours. Mulhouse, 1923. 8vo., illus., orig. wrs., partly unopened, fine, 1st ed. Morrill 239-522 1978 $17.50

MEISSNER Rechtsbuch. (Saxonia, c. 1375-1385). Folio, orig. contemp. bagbinding over wooden boards in doeskin, one clasp missing. Gilhofer 75-117 1978 S Fr 33,000

MEJER, WOLFGANG   Bibliographie der Buchbinderei Literatur. Leipzig, 1925. Post 4to., orig. cloth. Forster 130-52 1978 £20

MELA, POMPONIUS   Cosmographia, Parvo Quodam Compendio Joannis Coclei, Norici adaucta, quo Geographiae Principia Generaliter Comprehenduntur. (Nuremberg, 1512). 4to., woodcut, old wrs., fine, rare ed. Gilhofer 74-70 1978 sFr 3,400

MELANCHTHON, PHILIP   Epistolae Selectiores Aliquot. Wittenberg, 1565. Thick 8vo., contemp. stamped pigskin. Salloch 348-147 1978 $400

MELANCHTHON, PHILIP   Initia Doctrinae Physicae. Wittenberg, 1555. 8vo., bds. Salloch 345-123 1978 $110

MELANCHTHON, PHILIP   Liber De Anima. Wittenberg, 1558. 8vo., 1/2 vellum over dec. paper. Salloch 348-146 1978 $225

MELANCON, ARTHUR   Memoires Touchant la Mort et la Vertue des Peres Isaac Jogues, Anne de Noue, Anthoine Daniel, Jean de Brebeuf, Gabriel Lallement, Charles Garnier, Noel Chanbanel, Rene Goupil. Montreal, n.d. Bound copy. Hood 117-585 1978 $65

THE MELANGE OF Humour; a Series of Fifty Coloured Engravings, Comprising a Great Variety of Comic Subjects, by the Most Popular Artists of the Present Day. 1821-24. Folio, hand-coloured plts., contemp. half roan. Quaritch 983-216 1978 $1,500

MELETIUS, MONK   De Natura Structuraque Hominis Opus... Venice, 1552. Sm. 4to., woodcut, old vellum, fine, rare, 1st ed. Gilhofer 74-98 1978 sFr 1,300

MELISH, JOHN   A Geographical Description of the United States, With the Contiguous British & Spanish Possessions,.... Philadelphia, 1816. 1st ed., orig. half roan, rubbed, joints weak, maps, 8vo. Americanist 101-96 1978 $125

MELISH, JOHN   A Geographical Description of the World,.... Philadelphia, 1818. 1st ed., orig. half roan with marbled boards, rubbed, worn, maps, 8vo. Americanist 101-97 1978 $90

MELISH, JOHN   Travels in the United States of America, in the Years 1806, and 1807, and 1809, 1810, & 1811. Philadelphia, 1812. Maps, 2 vols., orig. bds., uncut, 1st ed., slight foxing, minor stains, very good set. Salloch 345-124 1978 $375

MELISS, JOHN CHARLES   St. Helena: A Physical, Historical, and Topographical Description of the Island... London, 1875. 1st. ed., thick roy. 8vo, coloured lithograph plts., maps outlined in colour, illus., orig. brown cloth, gilt back, neatly rebacked, retaining orig. backstrip. Deighton 5-217 1978 £245

MELLAND, FRANK H.   In Witch-Bound Africa. London, 1923. 3 maps, 47 illus., 8vo, orig. cloth. K Books 239-317 1978 £12

MELLERIO, ANDRE   L'Exposition de 1900 et l'Impressionisme. Paris, 1900. 12mo., orig. pict. wr., uncut, 1st ed. Goldschmidt 110-55A 1978 $95

MELLING, A. I.   Voyage Pittoresque de Constantinople et des Rives du Bosphore...Publie par Mm. Treuttel et Wurtz. Paris, 1819. 2 vols., imp. folio, port., contemp. russia gilt, occasional spotting, otherwise excellent. Quaritch 983-344 1978 $15,000

MELLOR, F. H.   Sword & Spear. London, (1934). 16 plts., 8vo, orig. cloth. K Books 239-318 1978 £6

MELLOR, WILLIAM B.   Sank Same. 1944. Illus. with photos. Austin 80-205 1978 $7.50

MELLQUIST, JEROME   Les Caricatures de Jacques Villon ou la Marge de l'Indulgence. Geneva, 1960. Sq. 12mo., orig. pict. wr., 170 numbered deluxe copies issued, orig. etching signed by Villon & numbered. Goldschmid-110-78 1978 $300

MELNIKOVA, N.   Putovani za Lidovym Umenim (Volkskunst). Prague, 1941. 4to., colored frontis., illus. Van der Peet H-64-172 1978 Dfl 55

MELONEY, WILLIAM BROWN   Rush to the Sun. 1937. First ed., backstrip faded. Austin 82-632 1978 $12.50

MELVILL, ANDREW   Memoirs of .... 1918. Maps, illus., octavo, good. Upcroft 10-117 1978 £7.50

MELVILLE, MRS.   A Residence at Sierra Leone. London, 1861. Cr. 8vo, some foxing, rebacked. K Books 239-319 1978 £35

MELVILLE, E. W. M. BALFOUR-   James I, King of Scots, 1406-1437. 1936. 8vo. Upcroft 12-294 1978 £8.50

MELVILLE, GEORGE W.   In The Lena Delta. Boston, (1884). 1st. American ed., 8vo, portrait, plts., maps, orig. decorative cloth, gilt back, good copy. Deighton 5-161 1978 £40

MELVILLE, HERMAN   Benito Cereno. Nonesuch Press, 1926. Illus., vignettes in colour, folio, buckram, d.w., ed. ltd. and numbered. Howes 194-1073 1978 £18

MELVILLE, HERMAN   Benito Cereno. London, 1926. Folio, with pictures in color by E. McKnight Kauffer, ltd. ed. Biblo 251-588 1978 $42.50

MELVILLE, HERMAN   Benito Cereno. Wood engrs., boxed, bound in quarter lea., ltd. ed. Battery Park 1-178 1978 $35

MELVILLE, HERMAN   Israel Potter: His Fifty Years of Exile. New York, 1855. Orig. cloth, spine ends worn, some rubbing, 1st ed., 2nd print., good. MacManus 238-563 1978 $110

MELVILLE, HERMAN   Israel Potter: His Fifty Years of Exile. New York, 1885. 12mo, 1st ed., purple stamped cloth with some water marks, fading and somewhat rubbed, spine faded, corners bumped, foxing, generally Good. Desmarais 1-309 1978 $175

MELVILLE, HERMAN   Moby Dick. 1925. Illus. Austin 82-633 1978 $12.50

MELVILLE, HERMAN   Moby Dick or the Whale. New York, 1930. Illus. by Rockwell Kent, 1st trade ed., thick 8vo., pict. cloth, bright copy. Americanist 102-73 1978 $25

MELVILLE, HERMAN   Moby Dick or the Whale. Chicago, The Lakeside Press, 1930. Ed. ltd. to 1000 sets, 3 vols., 4to., very fine set, slightly damaged glassine d.j.'s, orig. black cloth with silver lettering & decor., boxed in publisher's orig. aluminum slipcase. Current Misc. 8-56 1978 $750

MELVILLE, HERMAN   Moby Dick or the Whale. Chicago, The Lakeside Press, 1930. Ed. ltd. to 1000 sets, 3 vols., 4to., signed & dated by Rockwell Kent in pencil, illus., orig. black cloth with silver lettering & decor's generally very fine, boxed in publisher's orig. aluminum slipcase. Current 24-34 1978 $650

MELVILLE, HERMAN   Narrative of a Four Month's Residence Among the Natives of a Valley of the Marquesas Islands. 1846. Newly rebound in full crimson crushed grain mor., very handsome, first English ed. Bell Book 16-628 1978 £175

MELVILLE, HERMAN   Omoo: A Narrative of Adventures in the South Seas. New York, 1847. 1st Amer. ed., 12mo., orig. brown cloth blindstamped with gilt decor's, lettering on spine, covers lightly spotted, text partially foxed, marbled endpapers, binding firm, good copy, duplicate signature bound in. Current 24-35 1978 $315

MELVILLE, HERMAN   Omoo: A Narrative of Adventures in the South Seas. New York, London, 1847. Page size 18 x 12 cm., frontis. map, illus., marbled bds. badly worn, loose. Wolfe 39-368 1978 $100

MELVILLE, HERMAN   Redburn: His First Voyage. Being the Sailor-Boy Confessions and Reminiscences of the Son-of-a-Gentleman, in the Merchant Service. New York, 1849. Orig. cloth, 1st Amer ed., foxed, spine faded, but good. MacManus 238-562 1978 $350

MELVILLE, HERMAN   Romances of Herman Melville. 1931. Good ed., illus. Austin 82-634 1978 $27.50

MELVILLE, HERMAN   Typee. 1848. Rev. ed. Austin 82-635 1978 $27.50

MELVILLE, HERMAN   Typee: a Peep at Polynesian Life, During a Four Months' Residence at a Valley of the Marquesas. New York & London, 1849. Revised ed., map, 8vo., orig. embossed cloth, 1st ed. Salloch 345-125 1978 $90

MELVILLE, HERMAN   Typee. Boston, 1902. Illus. Austin 82-636 1978 $12.50

MELVILLE, HERMAN   Typee. A Romance of the South Seas. New York: The Limited Editions Club, 1935. 8vo., illus. by Miguel Covarrubias, orig. patterned bds., pub. box, 1 of 1,500 copies, signed by illustrator, bookplt., nice. MacManus 238-829 1978 $35

MELVILLE, HERMAN   White-Jacket: or the World in a Man-of-War. New York, 1850. Foxing, 1st Amer. ed., 2nd printing, orig. bind. Petrilla 13-34 1978 $85

MELVILLE, LEWIS   The Life and Letters of William Cobbett in England and America. London, 1913. Illus., 2 vols., uncut, scarce. MacManus 239-741 1978 $35

THE MELVIN Memorial- Sleepy Hollow Cemetery, Concord, Mass. Cambridge, 1910. Plates, note by Wiley inside front cover, ex libris, Bell Wiley's copy. Broadfoot's 44-520 1978 $20

MEMOIR Of Capt. M. M. Hammond, Rifle Brigade. London, 1858. 5th. ed. Hood's 115-123 1978 $35

MEMOIRES d'une Contemporaine, ou, Souvenirs d'une femme sur les principaux personnage de la republique.... 1828. Engraved portrait, 8 vois. in 4, contemp. calf gilt. George's 635-720 1978 £21

MEMOIRES sur le Canada, dupis 1749 jusqu'a 1760. Quebec, 1838. Marbled bds., half calf, covers loose. Wolfe 39-456 1978 $75

MEMOIRS & Auto-Biography of Some of the Wealthy Citizens of Philadelphia, with a Fair Estimate of Their Estates...& Accounts of the Lives of Stephen Girard, Jacob Ridgway, & Obed Coleman...By a Merchant of Phila. Philadelphia, 1846. 1st ed., orig. prtd. wrs., 8vo., very good. Americanist 103-69 1978 $37.50

MEMOIRS of Myles Byrne. (1863). Reprint, octavo bound in cloth. Hyland 128-932 1978 £12

MEMOIRS OF Richard Lovell Edgeworth. (1820). 2 vols., reprint, octavo bound in cloth. Hyland 128-944 1978 £8.40

MEMOIRS Of The Danby Family... 1799. Lg. 12mo, half title, orig. calf, little rubbed, good. Jarndyce 16-33 1978 £35

MEMOIRS Of the Verney Family During the Civil War, During the Commonwealth, and From the Restoration to the Revolution. London, 1892-1899. Portraits, illus., 4 vols., 8vo, half dark green levant morocco, spines mellowed to lighter shade, very fine set. Traylen 88-351 1978 £60

MEMORANDUM Relative to The General Officers Appointed by the President in the Armies of the Confederate States 1861-1865. Washington, 1905. New cloth, Bell Wiley's Copy. Broadfoot's 44-163 1978 $16.00

MEMORIAL Addresses on the Life and Character of Andrew Johnson.... (Washington), 1876. Orig. binding, clean, some soiling of covers, little worn at extremities. Hayman 71-368 1978 $7.50

A MEMORIAL for Rev. Moses Merrill and His Wife, Eliza Wilcox Merrill, Missionaries...to the Otoes, in Indian Territory, Now Nebraska...from 1883 to 1840. (Rochester, 1888). Orig. wrs. Americanist 102-5 1978 $30

MEMORIAL of Sundry Inhabitants of Murfreesborough, North Carolina. Washington, 1828. Wrs. Broadfoot 50-140 1978 $20

MEMORIAL of the Citizens of St. Louis, Missouri, to the Congress of the United States, Praying an Appropriation for Removing the Obstruction to the Navigation of the Western Rivers... St. Louis, 1844. Orig. pr. wr., 1st ed. Ginsberg 14-589 1978 $100

MEMORIAL of the City Council of Charleston, Praying that the South Carolina Canal and Railroad Company be Authorized to Import... Washington, 1828. 8vo., 1st ed., orig. cloth. Morrill 241-546 1978 $10

MEMORIAL of the Curators of the University of the State of Missouri, Relative to the Location of the College of Agriculture and Mechanic Arts. St. Louis, 1869. Wrs. Hayman 73-454 1978 $7.50

MEMORIAL Of The English and French Commissaries Concerning St. Lucia... London, 1755. No half-titles, contemp. calf, rebacked, cover & text waterstained in lower margin, 8vo. Edwards 1012-740 1978 £120

MEMORIAL of the Excursion from New York to Montreal, Given by the Delaware and Hudson...Upon the Opening of the New York and Canada Railway November ...1875. New York, 1876. Tipped in map, wr. chipped & stained, text & map good. Butterfield 21-152C 1978 $15

MEMORIAL of the International Exhibition at Philadelphia. 1876. Sm. oblong 8vo., orig. cloth. K Books 244-257 1978 £7

MEMORIAL of the Legislative Committee of Oregon for the Establishment of a Territorial Government Under the Protection of the United States. Washington, 1845. Disbound, 1st ed. Ginsberg 14-830 1978 $7.50

MEMORIAL Of The Manufacturers of Salt, In The County of Kenhawa, Virginia, Against the Repeal of the Duty on Imported Salt. (Washington, 1830). Disbound. Hayman 71-772 1978 $20

MEMORIAL of the Union Merchant's Exchange of Saint Louis, to the Forty Third Congress of the United States. St. Louis, 1874. Illus., orig. pr. front wr., 1st ed. Ginsberg 14-590 1978 $125

A MEMORIAL to Congress to Secure an Adequate Appropriation for a Prompt and Thorough Improvement of the Mississippi River with an Apendix by Sylvester Waterhouse. St. Louis, 1877. Original wr. Ginsberg 14-579 1978 $25

MEMORIALS Concerning Deceased Friends. Philadelphia, 1821. Lea., moderate wear, joints starting to crack. Hayman 73-638 1978 $12.50

MEMORIALS Of The Empire of Japan in the XVI and XVII Centuries. 1850. Illus., folding map, 8vo, orig. cloth. Edwards 1012-206 1978 £25

MEMORIALS Presented to the Commissioners, Under the Treaty of July 1, 1863 between Great Britain and the U.S., for the Final Settlement of the Claims of the Hudson's Bay and Puget's Sound Agricultural Companies.... Washington, 1846. Disbound. Ginsberg 14-815 1978 $25

MEMORIE Istoriche di piu Illustri Pisani. Pisa, 1790-1792. 4 vols., 4to., plts., contemp. half-calf, lightly rubbed, some browning, 1st ed. Gilhofer 74-46 1978 sFr 1,200

MEN of Mark. London, 1876-78. 3 vols., 4to., mounted Woodburytype portrs., each with biography leaf, orig. richly gilt green cloth, little worn, but very good set, handsomely bound. Norman 5-220 1978 $600

MENABONI, ATHOS   Menaboni's Birds. New York, (1950). Plates, 4to., orig. cloth. Book Chest 17-253 1978 $30

MENAGIO, EGIDIO   Mescolanze. Venezia, 1737. 8vo., marbled bds., half calf, spine gilt, very clean crisp copy. King 7-193 1978 £25

MENAI, HUW   The Passing of Guto and other Poems. Hogarth Press, 1929. Orig. bds., very good, first English ed. Bell Book 17-456 1978 £7.50

MENARD, R.   La Vie Privee des Anciens (Greeks and Romans). Paris, 1880-1884. 4 vols., large thick 8vo., half calf bound, text illus. Van der Peet H-64-493 1978 Dfl 450

MENCHACA, ANTONIO   Memoirs. San Antonio, 1937. Limited to 500 numbered copies. Jenkins 116-905 1978 $12.50

MENCKEN, HENRY LOUIS   The American Language. (1923). 1930. Third ed. Austin 82-637 1978 $12.50

MENCKEN, HENRY LOUIS   The American Language. 1937. 4th ed. Austin 82-638 1978 $10

MENCKEN, HENRY LOUIS   The American Language. New York, 1945. Thick quarto, cloth, gilt, d.j., fine. Duschnes 220-206 1978 $12.50

MENCKEN, HENRY LOUIS   The American Language. 1948. First ed., very good, d.j. Austin 82-640 1978 $27.50

MENCKEN, HENRY LOUIS   The American Language. 1948. Very good, d.j. Austin 82-639 1978 $15

MENCKEN, HENRY LOUIS   Americana 1925. London, 1925. 1st English ed., very good or better. Limestone 9-196 1978 $25

MENCKEN, HENRY LOUIS   Christmas Story. New York, 1946. 1st ed., sq. 12mo, illus. in color by Bill Crawford, very fine, d.j. Victoria 34-534 1978 $10

MENCKEN, HENRY LOUIS   George Bernard Shaw. His Plays. Boston, 1905. Orig. cloth, paper label, 1st ed., fine. MacManus 238-713 1978 $135

MENCKEN, HENRY LOUIS   The Gist of Nietzche. Boston, 1910. 1st ed., very good, scarce. Ballinger 11-152 1978 $35.00

MENCKEN, HENRY LOUIS   The Gist of Nietzsche. Boston, 1910. First ed. Austin 82-655 1978 $20

MENCKEN, HENRY LOUIS   Heliogabalus. A Buffoonery in Three Acts. New York, 1920. 8vo, cloth, gilt, 1 of 2000 copies, 1st ed., fine. Duschnes 220-204 1978 $60

MENCKEN, HENRY LOUIS   James Branch Cabell. New York, 1927. 12mo, dark green wrs., portrait frontis., 1st ed., fine. Duschnes 220-55 1978 $15

MENCKEN, HENRY LOUIS   Menckeniana. A Schimpflexicon. New York, 1928. 8vo., orig. red-stained vellum, edges trimmed, 1st ed., 1 of 80 no. copies on Japan vellum, signed by Mencken, pub. box. MacManus 238-719 1978 $190

MENCKEN, HENRY LOUIS   Menckeniana. A Schimpflexicon. New York, 1928. Orig. cloth-backed bds., 1st ed., 1 of 230 copies signed by Mencken, mint, slipcase. MacManus 238-718 1978 $85

MENCKEN, HENRY LOUIS   Notes on Democracy. New York, (1926). Orig. cloth-backed bds., spine slightly faded, paper label, 1st ed., 1 of 235 no. copies, signed by author, boxed, about fine. MacManus 238-715 1978 $100

MENCKEN, HENRY LOUIS   Prejudices, Fourth Series. New York, 1924. 8vo., orig. cloth-backed bds., paper label, 1st ed., 1 of 110 numbered copies signed by author, fine. MacManus 238-714 1978 $135

MENCKEN, HENRY LOUIS   Prejudices: Fifth Series. New York, (1926). 8vo, patterned bds., cloth back, first ed., fine. Duschnes 220-205 1978 $15

MENCKEN, HENRY LOUIS   Prejudices. Fifth Series. New York, (1926). Orig. cloth-backed bds., later label, 1st ed., 1 of 200 no. copies, signed by author, fine. MacManus 238-716 1978 $125

MENCKEN, HENRY LOUIS   Prejudices, Sixth Series. New York, 1927. Orig. cloth-backed bds., 1st ed., 1 of 140 signed copies, very fine, pub. box. MacManus 238-717 1978 $150

MENCKEN, HENRY LOUIS   Treatise on the Gods. New York, 1930. Orig. blue vellum, 1st ed., 1 of 375 no. copies, signed by author, boxed, fine. MacManus 238-720 1978 $95

MENDE, ELSIE PORTER   An American Soldier and Diplomat Horace Porter. New York, 1927. Cloth.   Hayman 72-456 1978 $8.50

MENDELEEV, DMITRY IVANOVITCH   The Principles of Chemistry.   London, 1891. Trans. from Russian, 5th ed., 2 vols., 8vo., ads, fldg. table, text illus., tables, orig. cloth, uncut, recased retaining orig. endpapers, blindstamp on titles, ink stamp on title of vol. I, but fine set, 1st ed. in English.   Norman 5-197 1978 $275

MENDELL, MISS   Notes of Travel and Life.   New York, 1854. 1st ed., orig. cloth, foxed, good copy.   MacManus 239-303 1978 $35

MENDELSSOHN, MOSES   Phaedon, Oder Ueber Die Unsterblichkeit Der Seele.   Berlin and Stettin, 1769. Frontis., 3rd ed., 8vo., contemp. calf.   Salloch 348-148 1978 $55

MENDELSSOHN, MOSES   Philosophische Schriften.   Troppau, 1784. 2 vols., 8vo., contemp. calf with labels.   Salloch 348-149 1978 $125

MENDELSSOHN, SIDNEY   The Jews of Africa.   London, 1920. Frontis., 1st ed.   Austin 79-480 1978 $27.50

MENDES DA COSTA, EMMANUEL   A Natural History of Fossils.   London, 1757. Engr. frontis., 4to., cloth-backed bds., uncut.   Salloch 345-126 1978 $145

MENDO, ANDREA   Il Principe E Ministri Adattati.   Rome, 1816. Folio, gilt-tooled tree calf.   Salloch 348-150 1978 $225

MENDOCA, HIERONYMO DE   Jornada De Africa.   Lisbon, 1785. Sm. 8vo, contemp. calf.   Edwards 1012-240 1978 £75

MENDOZA, DIEGO HURTADO DE   Vie de Lazarille de Tormes.   Paris, 1886. Lg. 8vo., full tobacco brown mor., uncut edges, orig. wr. & backstrip bound in, bound by Chambolle-Duru, ltd. ed., lg. paper issue on Japan paper, 106 numbered copies, etchings & vignettes by Maurice Leloir, fine.   Goldschmidt 110-43 1978 $215

MENESTRIER, CLAUDE-FRANCOIS   Philosophia Imaginum id est Sylloge Symbolorum Amplissima....   Amsterdam & Danzig, 1695. 8vo, engraved frontis., contemp. panelled calf, some wear to head and tail of spine.   Quaritch 978-103 1978 $500

MENGER, RUDOLPH   Texas Nature Observations and Reminiscences. San Antonio, 1913. 1st ed., illus., scarce.   Jenkins 116-906 1978 $45

MENKIN, ADAH ISAACS   Infelicia.   London, Paris & New York, 1869. 3rd English ed., portrait, illus., green cloth, very good or better.   Limestone 9-198 1978 $18

MENSCHING, JOHANN HEINRICH   De Aeris Fixi ac Dephlogisticati in Medicina Usu.   Goettingae, (1787). 8vo., bds.   Offenbacher 30-97 1978 $115

MENTZER, B.   Sceleton Geographicum, in quo Methodo Brevi, Facili et Necessaria ex Coaevis et Antiquis....   Giessen and Hamburg, (c.1695). Sm. 8vo., engrav. frontispiece, engrav. plts., contemp. vellum, scarce.   Quaritch 977-194 1978 $225

MENZINI, BENEDETTO   Opere.   Firenze, 1731-1732. 4 vols., 4to., vellum, vignette, uncut.   King 7-194 1978 £70

MERCER, A. S.   The Banditti of the Plains;....   San Francisco, 1935. Illus., orig. cloth.   Ginsberg 14-1080 1978 $60

MERCER, HENRY C.   The Lenape Stone of the Indian and the Mammoth.   New York, 1885. 1st ed., illus., fine, scarce.   MacManus 239-1183a 1978 $32.50

MERCER, HENRY C.   The Lenape Stone Or The Indian & The Mammoth.   New York, 1885. 1st ed., orig. pict. cloth, illus., 8vo.   Americanist 101-98 1978 $22.50

MERCER, HENRY C.   November Night Tales.   New York, (1928). 1st ed., orig. bind.   Petrilla 13-35 1978 $16.50

MERCER, W. H.   The Colonial Office List 1905.   London, (1905). 8vo, orig. cloth, folding maps, rather dusty & shaken, working copy.   K Books 239-99 1978 £10

MERCIER, LOUIS SEBSTIEN   Eloges Et Discours Philosophiques...   Amsterdam, 1776. Woodcut title, 8vo., marbled calf, gilt, armorial bind., bookplt., fine.   Salloch 348-151 1978 $300

MERCURIUS TRISMEGISTES
Please turn to
HERMES TRISMEGISTUS

THE MERCURY Book.   1926. Illus., 4to., covers little soiled, good, first English ed.   Bell Book 16-013 1978 $5

MEREDITH, MRS. CHARLES
Please turn to
MEREDITH, MRS. LOUISA ANNE (TWANLEY)

MEREDITH, GEORGE   The Amazing Marriage.   1895. 2 vols., sm. 8vo., 1st ed., orig. cloth backs faded, neat signatures.   Quaritch 979-232 1978 $75

MEREDITH, GEORGE   Beauchamp's Career.   London, 1876. 1st ed., bound in grass-green diagonal fine ribbed cloth, good condition, 3 vols.   Greene 78-81 1978 $75

MEREDITH, GEORGE   Beauchamp's Career.   London, 1876. 3 vols., orig. cloth, 1st ed., some inner hinges cracked, labels removed.   MacManus 238-324 1978 $75

MEREDITH, GEORGE   Catalogue of the Altschul Collection of George Meredith in the Yale University Library.   (Boston), 1931. 4to., orig. cloth backed marbled bds., d.j., first ed., ltd. to 500 copies printed at Merrymount Press, v.f.   MacManus 238-985 1978 $50

MEREDITH, GEORGE   Diana of the Crossways.   London, 1885. 3 vols., 8vo., orig. smooth brown cloth, 1st ed., spine slightly rubbed, very nice.   MacManus 238-326 1978 $75

MEREDITH, GEORGE   The Egoist, A Comedy in Narrative.   1879. 1st. ed., 3 vols., orig. olive cloth, black borders, lib. labels removed, marking of back bd., vol. 2, slight damage to spine vol. 3, acceptable copy.   Jarndyce 16-877 1978 £52

MEREDITH, GEORGE   The Egoist.   1879. 3 vols., 8vo., 1st ed., orig. greenish-ochre cloth, uncut, bindings somewhat worn.   Quaritch 979-233 1978 $135

MEREDITH, GEORGE   The Egoist. A Comedy in Narrative.   London, 1879. 3 vols., orig. cloth, 1st ed., lib. labels removed, bind. slightly faded, few inner hinges cracked, better than average copy, half mor. case.   MacManus 238-325 1978 $210

MEREDITH, GEORGE   Emilia in England.   London, 1864. 3 vols., cloth, 1st ed., poor copy, ex-lib.   MacManus 238-323 1978 $50

MEREDITH, GEORGE   Evan Harrington; or, He Would be a Gentleman.   New York, 1860. 12mo, original black cloth (tips of spine renewed), 1st ed., very good copy, scarce.   Ximenes 47-207 1978 $85

MEREDITH, GEORGE   Evan Harrington.   London, 1861. 3 vols., 1st English ed., marbled boards, library labels on inside of front covers, spines heavily rubbed and small chips, texts very good.   Victoria 34-533 1978 $30

MEREDITH, GEORGE   Jump-to-Glory Jane.   1889. Sm. 8vo., prtd. wrs., uncut, 50 copies prtd.   Quaritch 979-234 1978 $40

MEREDITH, GEORGE   Last Poems.   London, 1909. 8vo, brown buckram, uncut, bookplate, ownership inscription, very Nice, 1st ed.   Desmarais 1-310 1978 $15

MEREDITH, GEORGE   Last Poems.   London, 1909. 1st ed., uncut, very good or better.   Limestone 9-199 1978 $25

MEREDITH, GEORGE   Letters of George Meredith to Alice Meynell.   London, Nonesuch Press, 1923. 1 of 850 copies, 1 of 70 for presentation, signed inscription from Everard Meynell, 4 to., cloth over bds., uncut, d.j., fine.   Houle 10-222 1978 $45

MEREDITH, GEORGE   Letters to Algernon Charles Swinburne and Theodore Watts-Dunton.   1922. Ltd. ed. of 30 copies, 8vo., orig. wrappers, pres. copy to Meredith's son by Publisher, scarce.   Sawyer 299-129 1978 £120

MEREDITH, GEORGE   Letters to Various Correspondents. 1924. Ltd. ed. of 30 copies, 8vo, orig. blue wrappers, fine copy, inscribed by publisher. Sawyer 299-130 1978 £120

MEREDITH, GEORGE   Lord Ormont and His Aminta. London, 1894. 1st ed., 3 vols., olive green morocco cloth, good condition. Greene 78-82 1978 $85

MEREDITH, GEORGE   Lord Ormont and His Aminta. A Novel. London, 1894. 3 vols., orig. cloth, 1st ed., slightly worn, but good. MacManus 238-328 1978 $60

MEREDITH, GEORGE   Modern Love and Poems of the English Roadside. London, 1862. 8vo, green cloth with wavy grain, spine dust-darkened, small corner torn from top margin of page, Fine, scarce, 1st ed. Desmarais 1-311 1978 $70

MEREDITH, GEORGE   Odes in Contribution to the Song of French History. London, 1898. 8vo, brown buckram, very Nice, 1st ed., collector's cond. Desmarais 1-312 1978 $20

MEREDITH, GEORGE   One of Our Conquerors. London, 1891. 1st ed., 3 vols., royal-blue coarse morocco cloth with decor. in black & spine lettering in gilt. Greene 78-83 1978 $75

MEREDITH, GEORGE   One Of Our Conquerors. 1891. 1st. ed., 3 vols., orig. blue cloth, v.g. Jarndyce 16-878 1978 £28

MEREDITH, GEORGE   One of Our Conquerors. London, 1891. 3 vols., orig. cloth, 1st ed., slightly worn, front inner hinge cracked in vol. I, otherwise good. MacManus 238-327 1978 $50

MEREDITH, GEORGE   A Reading of Earth. London, 1888. 8vo, blue cloth, feather-patterned end papers, interior sign. beginning to loosen, Fine, 1st ed. Desmarais 1-313 1978 $30

MEREDITH, GEORGE   The Shaving of Shagpat. An Arabian Entertainment. London, 1856(1855). Orig. cloth, 1st ed., lib. label removed. MacManus 238-322 1978 $175

MEREDITH, GEORGE   Tales of Chloe- The House on the Beach- The Case of General Ople & Lady Camper. London, 1894. 1st Eng. ed., smooth very dark olive-green cloth, gold lettered spine, very fine copy. Greene 78-84 1978 $75

MEREDITH, GEORGE   The Tragic Comedians. London, 1880. 1st ed., 2 vols., dark sage-green diagonal-fine ribbed cloth, black end papers, very good. Greene 78-85 1978 $70

MEREDITH, LOUISA ANNE (TWAMLEY)   The Romance of Nature. 1836. 2nd ed., illus., handcolored plts., orig. coarse-grained mor., 8vo. Howes 194-1414 1978 £65

MEREDITH, LOUISA ANNE (TWAMLEY)   The Romance of Nature. London, 1836. Handcolored plts., nice, neatly recased in orig. gilt-decor. green mor., 8vo. K Books 244-452 1978 £65

MEREDITH, ROY   Mr. Lincoln's Camera Man, Mathew B. Brady. NY, 1946. Illus., Bell Wiley's copy. Broadfoot's 44-268 1978 $20.00

MEREJCOVSKI, DMITRI   The Romance of Leonardo Da Vinci. New York, (1938). Illus., many in color, Heritage Reprints Ed. Biblo 251-246 1978 $9.50

MERIAM, LEWIS   The Problem of Indian Administration. Baltimore, 1928. Thick 8vo., binding faded, rubbed, good used copy. Biblo 251-44 1978 $18.50

MERIMEE, PROSPER   An Authors Love. London, 1889. 2 vols., 8vo, orig. cloth, little worn. Sexton 7-161 1978 £6

MERIMEE, PROSPER   Chronique du Regne de Charles IX. Paris, 1945. 4to., bds., bds. slipcase, chromolithos by J. Lechantre, ltd. ed. of 450 numbered copies only. Van der Peet H-64-434 1978 Dfl 95

MERIMEE, PROSPER   Colomba. Grenoble, 1946. Bds. in slipcase, orig. engr. in color by P. Humbert, ltd. ed. of 650 copies only, 8vo., copy of P. Humbert. Van der Peet H-64-435 1978 Dfl 125

MERIMEE, PROSPER   Writings. New York, 1905. 8 vols., lg. 8vo., lg. paper ed., frontis., coloured & uncoloured, illus. prtd. on Japanese vellum, half dark blue mor., gilt panelled backs, gilt top, other edges uncut, fine set. Quaritch 979-370 1978 $325

MERINGTON, MARGUERITE   The Life and Intimate Letters of General George A. Custer and His Wife Elizabeth. New York, 1950. First ed., fine, d.w., illus. Biblo 247-198 1978 $17.50

MERITON, GEORGE 1634-1711   The Praise of York-Shire Ale. 1697. Third ed., 2 parts in 1 vol., 12mo., full polished mottled calf, fine. Howes 194-73 1978 £140

MERIVALE, C.   History of the Romans under the Empire. 1896. Folding map, 8 vols., cr. 8vo. George's 635-486 1978 £5.50

MERIVALE, HERMAN   Life of W. M. Thackeray. London, 1891. 1st ed., uncut in orig. cloth, very good or better. Limestone 9-298 1978 $13.50

MERIVALE, LEWIS   The Thackeray Country. London, 1905. Portrait, illus., folding map, 1st ed., orig. cloth, gilt cover design, A.L.s from Sir Sidney Lee to author, laid in, very good or better. Limestone 9-297 1978 $30

MERKEL, ANDREW   Tallahassee. Halifax, 1945. Hood 117-814 1978 $15

MERKEN, L. W. VAN   Germanicus in Zestien Boeken. Amsterdam, 1779. 8vo., half calf, engr. frontis. Van der Peet H-64-380 1978 Dfl 85

MERKEN, L. W. VAN   Het nut der Tegenspoeden. Amsterdam, 1768. 8vo., half calf, frontis. Van der Peet H-64-379 1978 Dfl 85

MERRIAM, CHARLES   Machete: "It Happened in Mexico". Dallas, 1932. 1st ed., illus., pictorial d.j., unusually nice. Jenkins 116-908 1978 $10

MERRIAM, GEORGE S.   The Life and Times of Samuel Bowles. New York, 1885. 1st ed., fine set, orig. cloth. MacManus 239-725 1978 $25

MERRIAM, ROBERT E.   Dark December. 1947. Austin 80-206 1978 $8.50

MERRICK, LEONARD   Cynthia. A Daughter of the Philistines. London, 1896. 2 vols., orig. cloth, 1st ed., hinges cracked, front flyleaf loose in vol. II, lib. labels removed. MacManus 238-329 1978 $75

MERRICK, LEONARD   This Stage of Fools. New York, 1913. 1st ed. Biblo BL781-1076 1978 $9

MERRICK, M. M.   Thomas Percy; Seventh Earl. 1948. Illus., octavo, good. Upcroft 10-452 1978 £5.50

MERRILD, KNUD   A Poet and Two Painters: A Memoir of D. H. Lawrence. 1938. First ed., illus., 8vo., orig. cloth. Howes 194-1001 1978 £6

MERRILL, GEORGE P.   Handbook and Descriptive Catalogue of the Meteorite Collections in the United States National Museum. Washington, 1916. Wrps. Hayman 71-457 1978 $7.50

MERTON, ARTHUR   The Book of Life. Philadelphia, 1876. Illus., 12mo., 1st ed., pres. copy. Morrill 239-175 1978 $12.50

MERWIN, SAMUEL   The Road to Frontenac, a Romance of Early Canada. New York, 1901. Illus. by E. Blumenschein, mended. Hood 117-534 1978 $15

MESERVE, FREDERICK HILL   The Photographs of Abraham Lincoln. New York, (1944). Illus., 8vo., d.w., book fine, 1st ed. Morrill 241-361A 1978 $37.50

MESNIL DU BUISSON, COMTE DU   La Technique des Fouilles Archeologiques. Les Principes Generaux. Paris, 1934. Illus., wrs. BL781-441 1978 $12.50

MESPLET, FLEURY   Officium in Honorem Nostri J. C. Summi Sacerdotis et Omnium Sanctorum ac Levitarum. 1777. Sewn. Wolfe 39-371 1978 $350

MESPLET, FLEURY Reglement de la Confrerie de L'Adoration Perpetuelle du S. Sacrement, et de la Bonne Mort. Montreal, 1776. 24mo., orig. wallpaper-covered bds. Wolfe 39-370 1978 $500

MESSAHALA Libri Tres De Revolutione Annorum Mundi...De Significatione Planetarum in Nativitatibus...De Receptione. Nuernberg, 1549. Woodcuts, 4to., 1/2 calf. Salloch 345-127 1978 $425

MESSITER, CHARLES ALSTON Sport and Adventures among the North-American Indians. London, 1890. Orig. illus. by Charles Whymper, plts., orig. cloth, 8vo. K Books 244-231 1978 £22

MESSITER, CHARLES ALSTON Sport and Adventures Among the North-American Indians. London, 1890. Orig. illus. by Charles Whymper, covers wanting. Wolfe 39-374 1978 $60

MESSLER, ABRAHAM Centennial History of Somerset County. Somerville, 1878. Orig. cloth, very scarce. MacManus 239-1299 1978 $60

MESSLER, ABRAHAM First Things in Old Somerset,... Somerville, 1899. Scarce. MacManus 239-1300 1978 $37.50

METABOLISM and Function. New York, 1950. Tall 8vo., portr., illus., blue cloth, gilt lettered, shaken, ex-lib., good copy, lst ed. Zeitlin 245-166 1978 $25

METCALF, SAMUEL L. A Collection of Some of the Most Interesting Narratives of Indian Warfare in the West.... Lexington, 1821. Leather. Hayman 71-402 1978 $400

METCALFE, RICHARD L. The Real Bryan. Des Moines, 1908. Orig. binding, clean. Hayman 71-658 1978 $7.50

METCHNIKOFF, ELIAS
Please turn to
MECHNIKOV, IL'IA IL'ICH

METCHNIKOFF, ELIE
Please turn to
MECHNIKOV, IL'IA IL'ICH

METHUEN, HENRY M. Life in the Wilderness; or Wanderings in South Africa. London, 1848. 2nd. ed., 18 illus., cr. 8vo, orig. cloth, rebacked. K Books 239-320 1978 £55

METZ, H. W. A National Labor Policy. Washington, D.C., 1947. Biblo BL781-850 1978 $8.50

METZLER, NORBERT Illustrated Halifax, Its Civil, Military and Naval History. Montreal, (1891). Illus., oblong sm. 8vo, orig. cloth-backed printed bds., little worn at corners, sound, light traces of use, very good. Fenning 32-224 1978 £14

MEUNG, JEAN DE Roman De La Rose
Please turn to
ROMAN DE LA ROSE

MEUNIER, C. Cent Planches de Reliures d'Art. Paris, 1897-1902. 3 vols., ltd. to 100 signed copies, plts., demy 4to., half cloth, marbled bds., orig. wrs. bound in, vol. 2 has pres. inscription by the author. Forster 130-53 1978 £40

MEURMAN, OTTO Svenskt och Ryskt Lexikon. Helsingfors, 1846-47. lst. ed., 2 vols. in 1, 8vo, contemp. half morocco. Hannas 54-192 1978 £10

MEUSEL, H. Lexicon Caesarianum. 1887-93. 2 vols. in 3, 4to., half calf. Allen 234-153 1978 $75

MEW, CHARLOTTE The Farmer's Bride. 1916. First ed., lg. 8vo., orig. printed wrappers, fine, rare. Howes 194-1042 1978 £25

MEW, CHARLOTTE The Farmer's Bride. 1921. New ed., orig. printed bds., fine, 8vo. Howes 194-1043 1978 £12

MEW, CHARLOTTE The Rambling Sailor. 1929. First ed., portrait, orig. bds., fine, d.w., 8vo. Howes 194-1044 1978 £15

MEW, CHARLOTTE The Rambling Sailor. London, 1929. Fine copy, d.w. lightly torn. Desmarais B-450 1973 $15

MEYER, AGNES E. Chinese Painting as Reflected in the Thought and Art of Li Lung-Mien 1070-1106. New York, 1923. Plts in gravure, boards, spine chipped. Dawson's 449-61 1978 $75

MEYER, EDUARD Caesars Monarchie und das Principat des Pomejus. 1922. Allen 234-633 1978 $12.50

MEYER, ERNST VON Geschichte der Chemie von den Altesten Zeiten bis zur Gegenwart. Leipzig, 1905. 8vo., cloth, fine copy, 3rd ed., revised & expanded. Norman 5-200 1978 $45

MEYER, JOSEPH E. The Herbalist and Herb Doctor. Hammond, (1932). Illus., colored plts., narrow 12mo. Morrill 239-176 1978 $10

MEYER, LUDWIG Philosophia S. Scripturae Interpres. Eleutheropolis (Amsterdam), 1666. 4to., calf. Salloch 348-153 1978 $285

MEYER, OSKAR EMIL Die kinetische Theorie der Gase. Breslau, 1877. 8 vo., old half cloth, lst edition. Schafer 19-57 1978 sFr. 450

MEYER, RICHARD EMIL Vorlesungen Uber Die Geschichte der Chemie. Leipzig, 1922. 8vo., contemp. cloth-backed bds., very good copy, lst ed. Norman 5-201 1978 $40

MEYER, ROLAND Saramani Danseuse Khmer. Saigon, 1919. Plts., 4to, orig. calf-backed bds. Edwards 1012-153 1978 £20

MEYER, THEODOSIUS St. Francis and Franciscans in New Mexico. Santa Fe, 1926. Orig. pict. wr., lst ed. Ginsberg 14-767 1978 $30

MEYERS, AUGUSTUS Ten Years in the Ranks: U. S. Army. New York, 1914. Original cloth, lst ed., presentation copy signed by author. Ginsberg 14-540 1978 $85

MEYERS, WILLIAM H. Naval Sketches of the War in California. New York, 1939. Illus., colored plates, original boards with leather backstrip, quarto, limited ed. to 1,000 copies. Ginsberg 14-541 1978 $125

MEYNELL, ALICE Ceres' Runaway & Other Essays. 1910. Cloth, faded, inscribed from author. Eaton 45-338 1978 £10

MEYNELL, ALICE Essays of To-Day and Yesterday. 1926. Very good, wraps, pres. copy inscribed by the author's husband with author's signature attached to title, first English ed. Bell Book 16-629 1978 £6.50

MEYNELL, ALICE Poems. 1893. 1 of 550 copies, buckram, good, covers somewhat marked & dull, first English ed. Bell Book 16-630 1978 £8.50

MEYNELL, ALICE Poems. 1913. lst. ed., frontis, portraits, orig. cloth, gilt, signatures of Wilfried Meynell & Viola Meynell. Eaton 45-337 1978 £10

MEYNELL, FRANCIS English Printed Books. London, 1948. Plts. in color, illus. in black & white, d.w., very fine. Battery Park 1-409 1978 $10

MEYNELL, WILFRID The New Young: Rhymes Made for a Few of Them by a Grandfather... (London), 1927. Orig. vellum wrs., signed by Meynell. Americanist 102-74 1978 $27.50

MEYNEN, EMIL Bibliography on German Settlements in Colonial North America... Leipzig, 1937. 4to. MacManus 239-1561 1978 $40

MEYRICK, SAMUEL RUSH The Costume of Original Inhabitants of the British Islands, From the Earliest Period to the 6th Century. 1815. Folio, frontis. and plts., hand-coloured by R. Havell, lg. clean copy, orig. calf, rebacked. Quaritch 983-68 1978 $500

MICALI, G. Antichi Monumenti Per Servire all'Opera Intitolata L'Italia Avanti il Dominio dei Romani. Florence, 1810. Roy. folio, without 8vo text, maps, plts., half rough calf. Quaritch 983-23 1978 $115

MICARD, G. Fleurs de Jasmin; Inde-Ceylan-Birmanie, 1906-1907. Paris, 1930. Limited ed., 1 of 500 numbered copies only, 8vo, orig. covers. Van der Peet 127-155 1978 Dfl 35

MICHAEL SCOTUS
Please turn to
SCOTT, MICHAEL

MICHAEL Freebern Gavin. A Biography. Cambridge, 1915. Illus., 8vo., 1st ed. Morrill 239-94 1978 $10

MICHAELIS, JOHANN DAVID   Receuil de Questions... Amsterdam, 1774. 4to, lg. paper, 19th. century quarter calf, corners worn, top edge trimmed, others uncut, title slightly dust-soiled. Hannas 54-224 1978 £35

MICHAUX, R. R.   Sketches of Life in North Carolina. Culler, 1894. Slightly worn. Broadfoot 50-142 1978 $100

MICHEL, E.   Gerard Terburg (ter Borch) et sa Famille. Paris, n.d. 2 vols., 8vo., orig. covers, plts. Van der Peet H-64-63 1978 Dfl 95

MICHEL, E.   Rembrandt: His Life, His Work, and His Time. 1895. 2 vols., 4to., plts., some foxing, half mor., gilt spines, a little rubbed. Quaritch 983-243 1978 $50

MICHEL, F.   Anglo-Norman Poem on the Conquest of Ireland by Henry II. 1837. 1st ed., scarce, good, octavo bound in cloth. Hyland 128-826 1978 £15

MICHEL, MARIUS   La Reliure Francaise Depuis L'Invention De L'Imprimerie jusqua La Fin Du XVIII Siecle. Paris, 1880. 4to., newly rebound preserving most of orig. binding, frontis., plts., illus., t.e.g. Battery Park 1-281 1978 $200

MICHEL, MARIUS   La Reliure Francaise depuis l'invention de l'imprimerie jusqu'a la fin du XVIIIe siecle. Paris, 1880-1. 2 vols., plts. colored, illus., med. 4to., 3/4 mor., t.e.g., others uncut, fine. Forster 130-55 1978 £175

MICHEL, MARIUS   La Reliure Francaise commerciale et industrielle depuis l'invention de l'imprimerie jusqu'a nos jours. Paris, 1881. One of a few copies on jap vellum, colored plts., illus., med. 4to., orig. wrappers, spine split. Forster 130-56 1978 £50

MICHELANGELO
Please turn to
BUONARROTI, MICHEL ANGELO

MICHELET, J.   The Bird. London, 1869. Faded binding, 8vo, orig. cloth. Book Chest 17-255 1978 $30

MICHELET, J.   The Insect. London, 1875. Gold-stamped cloth, inner front hinge cracking, 8vo., engravings by Giacomelli. Book Chest 17-256 1978 $32.50

MICHELL, H.   The Place of Silver in Monetary Reconstruction. New York, 1944. Card cover. Hood 117-432 1978 $7.50

MICHELSON, ALBERT A.   Light Waves and Their Uses. Chicago, University Press, 1903. 8vo., chromolitho. plts., text illus., orig. cloth, gilt, little worn, but fine copy, 1st ed. Norman 5-*33 1978 $125

MICHENER, EZRA   Early Quakerism... Philadelphia, 1860. Rebound in cloth. MacManus 239-312 1978 $22.50

MICHIE, ALLAN A.   Retreat to Victory. 1942. Austin 80-207 1978 $8.50

MICHIE, CHRISTOPHER Y.   The Practice of Forestry. Edinburgh, 1888. Text illus., gilt decor. cover, 8vo. K Books 244-232 1978 £6

MICHIGAN. LAWS.   Acts of the Legislature of the State of Michigan, Passed at the Annual Session of 1844. Detroit, 1844. Appendix, cloth-backed bds. Hayman 73-440 1978 $17.50

MICHIGAN MINING SCHOOL   Catalogue of the Michigan Mining School. Houghton, 1891. Sm. 8vo., orig. wrs. Morrill 241-362 1978 $7.50

MICHON, L. M.   Les Reliures Mosaiquees du XVIIIe Siecle. Paris, 1956. Ltd. to 500 copies, colored plts., cr. 4to., crushed levant mor. gilt, a.e.g. Forster 130-57 1978 £60

MICKLE, ISAAC   Reminiscences of Old Gloucester... Philadelphia, 1845. Illus., cloth, very scarce. MacManus 239-1301 1978 $75

MIDDLEBROOK, LOUIS F.   History of Maritime Connecticut During the American Revolution 1775-83. Salem, 1925. 2 vols., illus., fine set, d.js. MacManus 239-1774 1978 $25

MIDDLETON, CLARA   Green Fields Afar; Memories of Alberta. Toronto, 1947. Drawings. Hood 116-866 1978 $12.50

MIDDLETON, CONVERS   Life of Cicero. London, 1741. 2 vols., 4to., full calf, backstrips torn, one label split, covers worn and age-marked, corners frayed, text good. K Books 244-233 1978 £12

MIDDLETON, GEORGE   That was Balzac... New York, (1936). 1st ed., author's signed pres. Biblo BL781-1077 1978 $10

MIDDLETON, J. E.   The Province of Ontario, a History, 1615-1927. Toronto, 1927 (1928). 5 vols., indices, not a matched set, Vols. 1, 2, 3 & 5 in 3/4 lea., Vol. 4 has marbled bds. Hood 117-754 1978 $200

MIDDLETON, J. E.   Toronto's 100 Years. Toronto, 1934. Illus., bound. Hood 117-753 1978 $30

MIDDLETON, JOHN HENRY   Ancient Rome in 1885. 1885. Maps, tips of spine slightly worn. Allen 234-829 1978 $10

MIDDLETON, JOHN HENRY   The Remains of Ancient Rome. London, 1892. 2 vols., illus., maps. Biblo BL781-442 1978 $14.50

MIDDLETON, JOHN IZARD   Grecian Remains in Italy, a Description of Cyclopian Walls and of Roman Antiquities... 1812. Folio, plain and coloured plts., contemp. mor., gilt spine, rubbed. Quaritch 983-24 1978 $1,300

MIDDLETON, M.   Flowers of Bermuda. England, (1927). Color plates, stiff pictorial wr., 8vo. Book Chest 17-257 1978 $20

MIDDLETON, RICHARD   Monologues. 1913. Cloth gilt, bright, first English ed. Bell Book 16-631 1978 £4

MIDDLETON, RICHARD   The Pantomime Man. 1933. Portrait, spine faded, good, first English ed. Bell Book 16-632 1978 £4

MIDDLETON, THOMAS   The Best Plays. 1890. 2 vols., octavo, good. Upcroft 10-118 1978 £6.50

MIDDLETON, THOMAS   A Game at Chesse. Cambridge, 1929. Plts., Octavo, good. Upcroft 10-119 1978 £8.50

MIDDLETON, THOMAS   Sir Robert Sherley, Sent Ambassadour In The Name Of The King Of Persia,.... London, 1609. Sm. 4to, inoffensive staining, cloth folder and half mor. case, contemp. signature on title and inscription, 1st ed. Quaritch 978-123 1978 $2,500

MIDDLETON, THOMAS C.   Historical Sketch of the Augustinian Monastery, College, and Mission of St. Thomas of Villanova, Delaware County, Pa... 1893. 1st ed., illus., orig. cloth, t.e.g., lib. marks. MacManus 239-1706 1978 $20

MIDGLEY, MARGARET   Ministers' Accounts of Earldom of Cornwall, 1296-97. 1942-45. 2 vols. Allen 234-1157 1978 $12.50

THE MIDNIGHT Court. 1945. 1st ed., d.w., very good, octavo bound in cloth. Hyland 128-223 1978 £9

MIDOLLE, JEAN   Oeuvres.... Strassburg, 1834-36. 3 vols. in 1, oblong folio, 120 coloured lithograph plates, old leather-backed boards, armorial bookplate of A. Brolemann, complete set. Quaritch 978-109 1978 $1,650

MIDON, FRANCIS   The History of the Rise and Fall of Masaniello, the Fisherman of Naples, Containing an Exact and Impartial Relation of the Tumults and Popular Insurrections, that Happened in that Kingdom, in the Year 1647... London, 1729. Full contemp. calf, 1st ed. MacManus 238-132 1978 $60

MIDON, FRANCIS   A History of the Rise and Fall of Masaniello. London, 1729. 8vo., calf, first ed., portrait. King 7-366 1978 £50

MIDSUMMER Holidays at Briar's Hall; or, Summer Mornings Improved. London, 1828. Plts., 1st. ed., sm. 8vo, orig. bds., leather spine. Traylen 88-184 1978 £25

MIERS, EARL SCHENCK   Bookmaking and Kindred Amenities... New Brunswick, 1942. 4to., orig. cloth, d.j., soiled, ltd. to 1,500 copies, very good. MacManus 238-986 1978 $25

MIERS, EARL SCHENCK   Composing Sticks & Mortar Boards. New Brunswick, 1941. D.w., as new. Battery Park 1-410 1978 $22.50

MIKKELSEN, C.   Canada Som Fremtidsland. Aschehoug, 1927. Illus., paper, in Danish. Austin 79-483 1978 $37.50

MILES, G. I.   A Glance at the Baptists. West Chester, 1836. 12mo., disbound. MacManus 239-43 1978 $15

MILES, J. S.   Historical Sketch of Roxborough, Manayunk, Wissahickon... N.P., (1940). Lg. 4to., illus., fold. map. MacManus 239-1562 1978 $35

MILES, M. F.   Dr. Carl Brown. St. Louis, 1888. Cloth, fine bright copy. Hayman 73-197 1978 $15

MILES, W.   The Horse's Foot and how to keep it Sound. London, 1863. 9th ed., faded binding, 8vo, orig. cloth. Book Chest 17-258 1978 $70

MILHAM, WILLIS I.   Time and Timekeepers Inc. History, Construction, Care and Accuracy of Clocks and Watches. New York, 1941. Illus. Baldwins' 51-126 1978 $20

THE MILITARY and Naval Situation and the Glorious Achievements of Our Soldiers and Sailors. Washington, 1864. Disbound. Hayman 72-633 1978 $8.50

MILITARY Medical Manual. 1942. Illus., tables, charts, 5th ed. Austin 80-209 1978 $27.50

MILL, JOHN STUART   Autobiography. 1873. Orig. cloth, good, first English ed. Bell Book 17-648 1978 £25

MILL, JOHN STUART   Autobiography. New York, 1924. 8vo., cloth. Salloch 348-156 1978 $10

MILL, JOHN STUART   Nature, The Utility of Religion & Theism. 1874. 2nd. ed., half title, orig. pebble-grained green cloth, fine. Jarndyce 16-881 1978 £7.50

MILL, JOHN STUART   The Subjection of Women. New York, 1869. 8vo., cloth. Salloch 348-155 1978 $75

MILL, JOHN STUART   A System of Logic. 1851. 3rd. ed., 2 vols., new preface, orig. dark green cloth, paper labels, v.g. Jarndyce 16-879 1978 £30

MILLAIS, JOHN GUILLE   British Diving Ducks. London, 1913. 2 vols., imp. 4to, ltd. ed., orig. buckram, 35 monochrome & 39 colour plts. by Thorburn. Traylen 88-605 1978 £650

MILLAIS, JOHN GUILLE   Far Away Up The Nile. London, 1924. Roy. 8vo, map, plts. minor foxing, orig. cloth. K Books 239-322 1978 £20

MILLAIS, JOHN GUILLE   The Life and Letters of Sir John Everett Millais, President of the Royal Academy by His Son... 1899. 2 vols., roy. 8vo., illus., some foxing cloth gilt, pres. copy from author. Quaritch 983-218 1978 $125

MILLAIS, JOHN GUILLE   Life and Letters of John Everett Millais. London, 1899. Illus., photogravures, 2 vols., roy. 8vo, little loose in case, pres. copy from author. Traylen 88-395 1978 £40

MILLAIS, JOHN GUILLE   The Mammals of Great Britain and Ireland. London, 1904-1906. 3 vols., thick roy. 4to, many coloured & other plts., ltd. ed. of 1025 copies. Traylen 88-606 1978 £225

MILLAIS, JOHN GUILLE   The Natural History of the British Surface-Feeding Ducks. London, 1902. Photogravure plts. & coloured plts. by A. Thornburn, illus., ltd. ed. of 600 copies, lg. 4to. Traylen 88-607 1978 £300

MILLAIS, JOHN GUILLE   Newfoundland and Its Untrodden Ways. 1907. Roy. 8vo, maps, plts. 6 in colour, cloth gilt, back cover faded. Edwards 1012-446 1978 £45

MILLAIS, JOHN GUILLE   Rhododendrons.... London, 1917. 1st. series only, coloured & other plts., folio, cloth. Traylen 88-609 1978 £150

MILLAIS, JOHN GUILLE   Rhododendrons.... London, 1917-1924. 2 vols., folio, coloured & other plts., covers little worn but sound copy, ltd. ed. of 550 copies. Traylen 88-608 1978 £250

MILLAR, E.G.   A Thirteenth Century Bestiary in the Library of Alnwich Castle. Oxford, 1958. Plts., 4to, quarter blue morocco, 40 copies printed for members. Traylen 88-325 1978 £290

MILLAR, R.   More Stirabout from An Ulster Pot. 1934. 1st ed. d.w., very good, octavo bound in cloth. Hyland 128-119 1978 £5

MILLAR, WILLIAM   The Fair Minstrel, and Other Poems. 1822. 1st. ed., sm. 8vo, orig. bds., new cloth spine, with orig. label remounted, uncut. Hannas 54-225 1978 £20

MILLAR, WILLIAM   Plastering Plain and Decorative. London, 1905. 3rd. ed., revised & enlarged, 4to, top of spine torn, name stamped on several pgs. Baldwins' 51-127 1978 $75

MILLARD, DAVID   The True Messiah, in Scripture Light...Proper Sonship of Jesus Christ, Affirmed and Defended. Union Mills, 1837. 2nd ed. with additions, 18mo., orig. cloth. Butterfield 21-281 1978 $17.50

MILLARD, JOHN   The Gentleman's Guide in his Tour through France. 1788. Tenth ed., map, sm. 8vo., rebound in half calf, lettering piece, entirely uncut, 8vo. Howes 194-391 1978 £18

MILLAY, EDNA ST. VINCENT   Aria Da Capo. A Play in One Act. London, 1920. Orig. pict. wrs., 1st ed., near fine. MacManus 238-723 1978 $45

MILLAY, EDNA ST. VINCENT   The Ballad of the Harp-Weaver. New York, 1922. 1st ed., d.w. well preserved, Fine, tan stiff wr. in orig. orange, collector's cond. Desmarais 1-315 1978 $75

MILLAY, EDNA ST. VINCENT   Collected Sonnets. New York, 1941. 1st ed., very good, boxed. Biblo 251-574 1978 $17.50

MILLAY, EDNA ST. VINCENT   Conversations at Midnight. New York & London, 1937. Name, very good, d.w. Bernard 5-522 1978 $12.50

MILLAY, EDNA ST. VINCENT   The King's Henchman. New York, 1927. Woodcut frontis., blue bds., black cloth spine, 1st ed., very good in chipped dust jacket. Bradley 49-224 1978 $8

MILLAY, EDNA ST. VINCENT   The King's Henchman. New York, 1927. 1st ed. Biblo BL781-1078 1978 $10

MILLAY, EDNA ST. VINCENT   Poems Selected for Young People. New York and London, 1929. Illus., orig. cloth-backed bds., paper label, chipped, 1st ed., ltd. fine. MacManus 238-724 1978 $25

MILLAY, EDNA ST. VINCENT   Renascence and Other Poems. New York, 1917. Orig. cloth, 1st regular ed., 1st issue, extremities of spine and covers a bit worn, but nice, scarce. MacManus 238-722 1978 $200

MILLAY, EDNA ST. VINCENT   Three Plays. New York, 1926. Frontis., blue bds., black cloth spine, 1st ed., fine in very good d.j. Bradley 49-225 1978 $8.50

MILLAY, EDNA ST. VINCENT   Wine from These Grapes. New York, 1934. Blue-green bds., black cloth spine, 1st ed., very good in dust jacket. Bradley 49-226 1978 $10

MILLAY, EDNA ST. VINCENT   Wine from These Grapes. New York, 1934. 1st ed., covers faded, name on flyleaf. Biblo BL781-1079 1978 $7.50

MILLER, A. E.   Military Drawings and Paintings in the Collection of Her Majesty the Queen. 1969. 2nd ed., 2 vols., 4to., coloured plts., illus., half red mor. Quaritch 983-220 1978 $190

MILLER, ARTHUR   Focus. 1949. Very good, d.w., first English ed. Bell Book 16-633 1978 £10

MILLER, C. W.   Points of Controversy. St. Louis, 1871. Orig. cloth, 1st ed. Ginsberg 16-908 1978 $15.00

MILLER, C. W.   Selections from the Brief Mention of Basil Lanneau Gildersleeve. 1930. Austin 82-395 1978 $27.50

MILLER, CINCINNATUS HINER   The Destruction of Gotham. New York & London, 1886. 1st ed., orig. half cloth, 8vo., very good. Americanist 103-59 1978 $20

MILLER, CINCINNATUS HINER   Memorie and Rime. New York, 1884. 1st ed., wrs. Hayman 73-449 1978 $7.50

MILLER, DOROTHY C.   The Sculpture of John B. Flannagan. New York, (1942). Wrs., sm. 4to., plts. Biblo 247-422 1978 $12.50

MILLER, DUNCAN   Interior Decorating. London, 1944. 4to, orig. bds., tipped in photo illus., good. Sexton 7-32 1978 £8

MILLER, EDGAR G., JR.   American Antique Furniture, a Book for Amateurs. New York, (1937). 1st ed., 4tos., illus., orig. bind. Americanist 102-9 1978 $50

MILLER, EDMUND T.   A Financial History of Texas. Austin, 1916. Printed wr. Jenkins 116-947 1978 $37.50

MILLER, EDMUND T.   A Financial History of Texas. Austin, 1916. Orig. pr. wr., 1st ed. Ginsberg 14-964 1978 $20

MILLER, ELLEN   Wild Flowers of the North-Eastern States. New York, 1898. Illus., 1 in color, 4to., d.w., boxed, fine, few tears in d.w., box partly broken. Morrill 239-525 1978 $10

MILLER, FRANCIS T.   History of World War II. 1945. Illus. Austin 80-215 1978 $20

MILLER, GEORGE   Latter Struggles in the Journey of Life. Edinburgh, 1833. 8vo., old cloth, rather soiled, head of spine and one hinge worn, uncut. P. M. Hill 142-175 1978 £30

MILLER, HENRY   The Air-Conditioned Nightmare. 1945. Very good, defective d.w., first English ed. Bell Book 16-634 1978 £15

MILLER, HENRY   The Amazing and Invariable Beauford DeLaney. Yonkers, 1945. Thin 8vo, pict. wrs., 1 of 750 copies, very faint waterstain at bottom of pages throughout, 1st ed., fine. Duschnes 220-210 1978 $17.50

MILLER, HENRY   Black Spring. Paris, 1936. 16mo, pict. pr. wr., ownership inscription, wr. lightly rubbed and chipped, Fine copy, 1st ed., collector's cond. Desmarais 1-317 1978 $350

MILLER, HENRY   The Colossus of Maroussi. San Francisco, Colt Press, 1941. First U.S. ed., pres. copy with contemp. inscription by author, very good. Bell Book 17-649 1978 £85

MILLER, HENRY   The Colossus of Maroussi. 1942. Good, spine faded, first English ed. Bell Book 16-636 1978 £6.50

MILLER, HENRY   The Cosmological Eye. Norfolk, 1939. 16mo, tan buckram pr. in brown with picture on front cover, 1st ed., collector's cond. Desmarais 1-318 1978 $20

MILLER, HENRY   Insomnia or the Devil at Large. Albuquerque, Loujon Press, 1970. 1 of 385 copies, signed by author, water colours, 4to., very good, orig. wooden box. Bell Book 16-637 1978 £95

MILLER, HENRY   Max and the White Phagocytes. Paris, (1938). 8vo, decor. wrs., lage light blue panel, 1st ed., fine. Duschnes 220-209 1978 $150

MILLER, HENRY   Murder the Murderer. Fordingbridge, Delphic Press, 1946. First English ed., wrappers, nice, scarce. Rota 211-389 1978 £9

MILLER, HENRY   Murder the Murderer. The Delphic Press, 1946. Some underlining in pencil, near fine, wraps, first English ed. Bell Book 17-650 1978 £25

MILLER, HENRY   A Night with Jupiter & Dream of Mobile. New York, 1945. First U.S. ed., illus., very good, scarce. Bell Book 17-651 1978 £27.50

MILLER, HENRY   Order and Chaos. (Tuscon, 1966). 1 of 99 copies signed by author, blue oasis leather ed., sm. 4 to., d.j., as new, in publisher's box. Houle 10-227 1978 $125

MILLER, HENRY   Remember to Remember. (Norfolk or New York, 1947). Portr. frontis., plts., red cloth, 1st ed., very good. Bradley 49-230 1978 $8.50

MILLER, HENRY   Tropic of Cancer. Blue bds. & cloth, 1st ed., review copy with dated slip from publisher laid in, fine in dust jacket. Bradley 49-231 1978 $8.50

MILLER, HENRY   The Wisdom of the Heart. New York, 1941. Fine in torn & damaged d.w. Desmarais B-456 1978 $25

MILLER, HENRY   The Wisdom of the Heart. London, 1947. Very good, worn d.w., first English ed. Bell Book 17-653 1978 £6.50

MILLER, HENRY   The World of Sex. N.P., n.d. 8vo, red cloth, gilt lettering on spine, limited ed. to 1000 copies, 1st ed., collector's cond. Desmarais 1-321 1978 $35

MILLER, HENRY RUSSELL   The Ambition of Mark Truitt. Indianapolis, 1913 First ed. Austin 82-657 1978 $17.50

MILLER, HERBERT ADOLPHUS   Races, Nations and Classes. 1924. Ex-lib. Austin 79-485 1978 $12.50

MILLER, HUGH   The Old Red Sandstone. Edinburgh, 1857. Sixth ed., map, plts., fcap. 8vo., orig. cloth faded. K Books 244-137 1978 £7

MILLER, HUGH   The Testimony of the Rocks. Edinburgh, 1857. 8vo., orig. cloth, plts., woodcuts, first ed. Gurney 75-76 1978 £25

MILLER, JAMES   The Amethyst. Philadelphia, n.d. (1860's?). Cloth, minor spotting on cover. Hayman 73-447 1978 $7.50

MILLER, JAMES   The History of Dunbar. Dunbar, 1859. Frontis., plts., cr. 8vo., half roan. K Books 244-415 1978 £9

MILLER, JAMES M.   The Genesis of Western Culture. Columbus, 1938. Fine copy, cloth. Hayman 73-448 1978 $12.50

MILLER, JOAQUIN
Please turn to
MILLER, CINCINNATUS HINER

MILLER, JOE   Joe Miller's Jests. (c. 1796). New ed., 8vo., portr. frontis., modern bds. Quaritch 979-235 1978 $80

MILLER, JOHN   Guadalcanal: The First Offensive. 1949. Fldg. map. Austin 80-211 1978 $47.50

MILLER, JOHN   New York Considered and Improved, 1695. Cleveland, 1903. Orig. bds., ltd. to 400 numbered copies. MacManus 239-354 1978 $40

MILLER, JOHN A.   Men and Volts at War. 1947. Illus. Austin 80-213 1978 $8.50

MILLER, JOHN G.   The Black Patch War. Chapel Hill, 1936. Cloth. Hayman 72-401 1978 $10

MILLER, JOSEPH   Botanicum Officinale. London, 1722. 8vo., contemp. panelled calf, spine rebacked. Quaritch 977-57 1978 $200

MILLER, KELLY   Kelly Miller's History of the World War for Human Rights...the Important Part Taken by the Negro in the Tragic Defeat of Germany... N.P., (1919). Cloth, minor discoloration on back cover. Hayman 72-471 1978 $17.50

MILLER, LEE G.   The Story of Ernie Pyle. 1950. Austin 80-214 1978 $7.50

MILLER, LEWIS B.   A Crooked Trail. Pittsburgh, (1908). Wrps., 1st. ed., rare. Hayman 71-473 1978 $125

MILLER, LEWIS B.   Saddles and Lariats:.... Boston, [1912]. Illus., original pictorial cloth, 1st ed. Ginsberg 14-542 1978 $100

MILLER, MAX   The Great Trek. Garden City, 1935. Illus. Hood 117-104 1978 $22.50

MILLER, NATHANIEL   A Dissertation, Read Before the Massachusetts Medical Society, on the Importance and Manner of Detecting Deep Seated Matter. Boston, 1827. 8vo., orig. wrs., ex-lib., resewn, 1st ed. Morrill 239-178 1978 $20

MILLER, OLIVE BEAUPRE   Heroes of the Bible. Chicago, (1940). Thick 8vo, signed by author on t.p., cover color plate, fine. Victoria 34-537 1978 $17.50

MILLER, OLIVE BEAUPRE   My Book House. 1925. 12 vols. Austin 82-659 1978 $97.50

MILLER, OLIVE BEAUPRE   A Picturesque Tale of Progress. 1933. 8 vols., illus. Austin 82-660 1978 $67.50

MILLER, PATRICK   The Elevation, Section, Plan and Views of a Triple Vessel and of Wheels. Edinburgh, 1787. Folio, contemp. tree calf, all corners worn. F. Edwards 1013-150 1978 £300

MILLER, PATRICK   Woman in Detail. Golden Cockerel Press, 1947. Lg. 8vo., spec. ed., prtd. on spec. paper, illus., bds., mor. back, slipcase, ltd. to 100 copies signed by author & artist. Quaritch 979-168 1978 $100

MILLER, PHILIP   The Abridgement of the Gardener's Dictionary. 1763. 5th. ed., 4to, engraved frontis, folding plts., 2 leaves pinned in to text, orig. calf, hinges weak, slightly rubbed. Jarndyce 16-143 1978 £20

MILLER, PHILLIP   The Gardener's and Botanist's Dictionary. 1807. Plts., 2 vols. in 4, folio, contemp. half russia. Howes 194-129 1978 £85

MILLER, S.   A Sermon Delivered Before the New York Missionary Society... New York, 1802. 8vo, orig. cloth, wrappers, some spotting. Edwards 1012-507 1978 £30

MILLER, T.   History of Education in West Virginia. Charleston, 1904. Illus., nice copy, bit loose in bind. MacManus 239-1888 1978 $17.50

MILLER, THOMAS   Common Wayside Flowers. London, c. 1880. Illus. by Birket Foster, coloured frontis., coloured illus., decor. cover, neatly recased, 8vo. K Books 244-234 1978 £18

MILLER, THOMAS   The Poetical Language of Flowers, or the Pilgrimage of Love. 1847. 1st. ed., coloured litho. plts., half-title, cr. 8vo, orig. publisher's full red morocco, gilt, lg. pictorial centre-piece on each cover, edges gilt, handsome copy. Fenning 32-225 1978 £85

MILLER, THOMAS   The Poetical Language of Flowers.... London, 1847. 1st. ed., coloured plts. by James Andrews, sm. 8vo, orig. morocco, gilt extra, gilt edges, binding little worn. Traylen 88-610 1978 £30

MILLER, W.   A Centenary Bibliography of the Pickwick Papers. London, 1936. 8vo., orig. cloth, 1st ed. MacManus 238-904 1978 $30

MILLER, W. T.   Birds at Home. Cape Town, (1947). Frontis, 50 full-pg. illus., 4to, orig. cloth. K Books 239-323 1978 £5

MILLER, WALTER   Yesterday and To-morrow in Northern Nigeria. London, (1938). Illus., cr. 8vo, orig. cloth. K Books 239-324 1978 £6

MILLER, WEBB   I Found No Peace. 1938. Austin 80-216 1978 $7.50

MILLER, WILLIAM   Evidence...of the Second Coming of Christ, About the Year 1843. Boston, 1842. 16mo., fldg. chart, fine cond., later prtg., orig. cloth, sound copy, minimum foxing. Butterfield 21-271 1978 $65

MILLER, WILLIAM   View of the Prophecies & Prophetic Chronology, by...With a Memoir of His Life by Joshua V. Himes. Boston 1842. Folding chart, binding worn. Nestler Rare 78-130 1978 $75

MILLERS New York as It is... New York, 1862. 12mo, illus., plts., 1st ed., fine. MacManus 239-369 1978 $37.50

THE MILLERITE Humbug. Boston, 1845. 12mo., orig. wrs., 1st ed., scarce. Morrill 241-365 1978 $50

MILLET, JOSHUA   A History of the Baptists in Maine... Portland, 1845. 1st ed., orig. cloth, spine chipped, but very good copy. MacManus 239-272 1978 $27

MILLET, SAMUEL   A Whaling Voyage in the Bark "Willis". 1849-1850. The Journal Kept by... Boston, 1924. 1st ed., illus., orig. cloth, lacks free endpaper, fine copy, ltd. to 475 copies on Amer. vellum. MacManus 239-1775 1978 $37.50

MILLETT, MRS. EDWARD   An Australian Parsonage.... London, 1872. 1st. ed., 8vo, half-title, engraved frontispiece, lt. lib. stamps, half calf, gilt back. Deighton 5-105 1978 £43

MILLEVOYE, C. H.   Oeuvres completes. 1822. Portrait, 4 vols, half russia, gilt, 8vo. George's 635-1391 1978 £25

MILLIKEN, J.   Verbum Sapienti or A Few Reasoning for Thinking That It Is Imprudent to Oppose & Difficult to Prevent the Projected Union. Dublin, 1799. 2nd ed., plain wrs. Hyland 128-730 1978 £7

MILLIN, SARAH GERTRUDE   General Smuts. London, 1936. 2nd. imp., 2 vols., 23 illus., 8vo, orig. cloth. K Books 239-325 1978 £10

MILLIS, WALTER   The Last Phase. 1946. Illus. Austin 80-217 1978 $10

MILLISON, JOHN R.   The New Practical Window Gardener. 1889. 8vo., orig. pict. cloth, illus., coloured lithograph frontispiece, plt., scarce. P. M. Hill 142-117 1978 £12

MILLOT, CLAUDE F. -X.   Elements of General History. 1778-79. First English ed., 5 vols., fine, full contemp. polished tree calf, 8vo. Howes 194-392 1978 £30

MILLS, ALFRED   Pictures of Grecian History in Miniature, With Description. London, n.d. c.1812. Plts., 48mo, cloth. Traylen 88-186 1978 £20

MILLS, ALFRED   Pictures of Roman History in Miniature. London, n.d. 48mo, orig. cloth, many plts. Traylen 88-185 1978 £20

MILLS, BILL   Twenty-Five Years Behind Prison Bars. Emory, 1939. Printed wr., very rare. Jenkins 116-951 1978 $75

MILLS, CHARLES   The Travels of Theodore Ducas, in Various Countries in Europe, at the Revival of Letters and Art. 1822. 2 vols., contemp. roan-backed bds., unlettered, worn, 8vo. George's 635-1392 1978 £15

MILLS, CHARLES K.   Physiology, Hygiene and Narcotics. Philadelphia, 1883. Top hinge weak. Rittenhouse 49-553 1976 $10

MILLS, JOHN   Our Country..In Three Volumes. 1850. 1st. & only ed., 3 vols., bound in 1, 8vo, orig. blindstamped cloth, nice copy. Fenning 32-226 1978 $32.50

MILLS, PETER   The Survey of Building Sites in the City of London After the Great Fire of 1666... 1946 and 1956. 2 vols., plans, diagrams, octavo, good. Upcroft 10-120 1978 £6.50

MILLS, ROGER Q.   Speech on the Tariff. Washington, 1888.
Jenkins 116-949 1978 $15

MILLS, WEGMER JAY   Caroline of Courtlandt Street. 1905. First ed.,
illus. Austin 82-663 1978 $20

MILLS, WEYMER JAY   Historic Houses of New Jersey. Philadelphia,
1902. Illus., orig. pic. cloth, scarce. MacManus 239-1302 1978 $50

MILMAN, HENRY HART   Poetical Works. 1840. 3 vols., eng. frontis,
title vignettes, rebound in marbled bds., paper spines & labels. Eaton 45-339
1978 £14

MILNE, A. H.   Sir Alfred Lewis Jones K.C.M.G. Liverpool,
1914. 8vo, orig. cloth, plts. K Books 239-326 1978 £6

MILNE, ALAN ALEXANDER   A Complete Set of the Large Paper Signed Editions
of His Famous "Pooh" Stories. London,1924, 1926, 1927, 1928. Illus. by E. H.
Shepard, 4to, orig. bds., linen spines in frayed d.w., ltd. eds., all signed by
author. Traylen 88-187 1978 £1000

MILNE, ALAN ALEXANDER   Fourteen Songs from "When We Were Very
Young". New York, (1925). 1st US ed., tall thin 4to, orig. cloth-backed
bds., very good. Americanist 103-135 1978 $30

MILNE, ALAN ALEXANDER   A Gallery of Children. London, (1925). Color
plts., folio, gilt pic. white buckram, t.e.g., others uncut, 1 of 500 copies on
lg. paper signed by author. Bradley 49-232 1978 $650

MILNE, ALAN ALEXANDER   The House at Pooh Corner. London, (1928). 1st
ed., illus. by Ernest H. Shepard, covers faded, text very fine. Victoria 34-539
1978 $22.50

MILNE, ALAN ALEXANDER   The House at Pooh Corner. London, 1928. Sm.
4to, illus., edition de luxe, bds., buckram, spine in orig. d.w., little worn, ltd.
ed. of 350 copies signed by author & artist. Traylen 88-188 1978 £150

MILNE, ALAN ALEXANDER   Michael & Mary. London, 1930. 8vo, green
buckram, t.e.g., 1 of 260 copies signed by author, 1st ed., fine. Duschnes
220-211 1978 $45

MILNE, ALAN ALEXANDER   Michael and Mary. London, 1930. Cloth,
very good, 1 of 260 numbered copies signed by author. Dawson's 447-263 1978
$50

MILNE, ALAN ALEXANDER   Now We are Six. 1927. Sm. 8vo., 1st ed.,
illus., orig. cloth, gilt top, fine with d.w. Quaritch 979-236 1978 $150

MILNE, ALAN ALEXANDER   Now We Are Six. London, (1927). Illus. by
Ernest H. Shepard, 1st ed., bears signature of Marcia vanDresser, covers moderately
darkened, gilt vignettes and text fine. Victoria 34-540 1978 $30

MILNE, ALAN ALEXANDER   Now we are Six. 1927. Orig. pict. cloth gilt,
t.e.g., spine faded, good, first English ed. Bell Book 17-655 1978 £18.50

MILNE, ALAN ALEXANDER   The Red House Mystery. 1922. Very good,
first English ed. Bell Book 16-255 1978 £28.50

MILNE, ALAN ALEXANDER   Two People. London, (1931). Tan buckram,
1st ed., fine in dust jacket. Bradley 49-234 1978 $20

MILNE, ALAN ALEXANDER   When We Were Very Young. London, 1926.
Very good copy. Victoria 34-542 1978 $50

MILNE, ALAN ALEXANDER   "When We Were Very Young". Complete set,
all 1st ed., almost fine, very good and bright. Victoria 34-538 1978 $400

MILNE, ALAN ALEXANDER   Winnie-the-Pooh. New York, (1926). Limited
to 200 copies, signed by Milne and Ernest H. Shepard, bound in pink illus. boards,
light blue cloth spine with pictorial label, Amer. ed., scarce, very fine condition,
perfect d.j. Victoria 34-541 1978 $300

MILNE, ALAN ALEXANDER   Winnie-the-Pooh. 1926. Drawings, pict. cloth,
t.e.g., very good, first English ed. Bell Book 16-640 1978 £25

MILNE, JAMES   The Romance of a Pro-Consul:.... London,
1899. Cloth, spine faded, preliminaries foxed. Dawson's 127-276 1978 $15

MILNE, L.   Living Plants of the World. New York. 4to,
orig. cloth. Book Chest 17-260 1978 $15

MILNE, L.   The Phoenix Forest. New York, n.d. Illus.,
8vo, orig. cloth. Book Chest 17-261 1978 $10

MILNE, R.   The Blackfriars of Perth... 1893. 4to, map,
facsimiles, ltd. to 250 copies, good. Upcroft 10-121 1978 £25

MILNE EDWARDS, HENRI   A Manual of Zoology. London, 1863. 2nd
English ed., text illus., sm. 8vo., covers dull. K Books 244-235 1978 £6

MILNER, ALFRED   England in Egypt. London, 1892. 8vo, orig.
cloth, rather shabby ex-lib. K Books 239-327 1978 £6

MILNER, EDITH   Life in Ober Ammergau. York, 1910. Illus. by
Lucia Lang, frontis., coloured plts., 4to, orig. cloth. K Books 244-236 1978
£25

MILNER, GEORGE   Speech on the Probable Fate of Lord Byron's
Poetical Works,.... Derby, n.d. (1824). 8vo, disbound, 2nd ed., rare.
Ximenes 47-209 1978 $60

MILNER, JOHN   The End of Religious Controversy, in a Friendly
Correspondence Between a Religious Society of Protestants and a Catholic Devine...
Baltimore, n.d. (c. 1860?). Cloth. Hayman 72-472 1978 $12.50

MILNOR, WILLIAM   A History of the Schuylkill Fishing Company...
1732-1888. Philadelphia, 1889. Thick 4to, half morocco with marbled boards,
tips rubbed, rebacked in matching cloth with added end papers, orig. spine over
new spine, orig. printed front wrapper, illus. Americanist 101-136 1978 $45

MILTON, VISCOUNT   The North-West Passage by Land. London, 1865.
8vo., cloth, frontis., plts., map. Van der Peet H-64-496 1978 Dfl 165

MILTON, CHARLES J.   Landmarks of Old Wheeling and Surrounding
Country. Wheeling, 1943. Cloth, very good copy, slightly worn dust jacket.
Hayman 73-741 1978 $15

MILTON, GEORGE FORT   The Eve of Conflict- Stephen A. Douglas and
the Needless War. Boston, 1934. Bell Wiley's copy. Broadfoot's 44-1934
1978 $12.00

MILTON, JOHN   Milton's L'Allegro and Il Penseroso. London,
1855. Illus. by Birket Foster, 1st Foster ed., 4to., orig. pub. full mor., edges
rubbed, some wear. Americanist 102-49 1978 $75

MILTON, JOHN   Ioannis Miltoni Angli Pro Populo Anglicano
Defensio... 1651. 12mo, orig. vellum, fine. Jarndyce 16-18 1978 £65

MILTON, JOHN   Areopagitica. 1903. 4to., woodcut border, bds.,
ltd. to 200 copies. Quaritch 979-135 1978 $945

MILTON, JOHN   A Complete Collection of the Historical, Political
and Miscellaneous Works of ... London, 1738. 2 vols., folio, frontis portrait,
orig. calf, hinges weak & bds. rubbed, sm. Abergavenny Lib. stamp on each title,
containing several orig. papers, clean, sound copy. Jarndyce 16-144 1978 £78

MILTON, JOHN   Comus. New York, 1903. Ltd. 520
copies, very good or better. Limestone 9-204 1978 $25

MILTON, JOHN   Comus. Elston Press. 1 of 160 copies prtd. from
orig. ed. Battery Park 1-89 1978 $100

MILTON, JOHN   Literae Pseudo-Senatus Anglicani,.... N.P.,
1676. 12mo, full early pressed vellum, tight and crisp. Bennett 20-141 1978
$125

MILTON, JOHN   Paradise Lost. London, 1688. Folio, plts.,
portrait, full old calf, extremities worn, 1st Illus. ed. Bennett 7-75 1978 $550

MILTON, JOHN   Paradise Lost. 1793. Second ed., 12mo., contemp. cheep. Howes 194-393 1978 £10

MILTON, JOHN   Paradise Lost, a Poem in Twelve Books. 1821.
Contemp. green calf, sm. 8vo. Howes 194-1052 1978 £5

MILTON, JOHN   Il Paradiso Perduto Tradotto in verso italiano da Felice Mariottini. Roma, 1813-1814. 3 vols., 8vo., marbled bds., uncut and unopened. King 7-196 1978 £15

MILTON, JOHN   Paradise Lost. N.P., 1825-27. Illus. designed & engraved by author, orig. 12 parts, imperial 4 to., steel plts., orig. grey pr. wr., uncut, fold-down cloth box with leather label, splendid. Quaritch Summer, 1978-33 1978 $4,250

MILTON, JOHN   The Paradise Lost of Milton. London, 1825-7. Mezzotints engraved on steel by John Martin, 2 vols., 1st ed., large quarto, contemp. red mor., panelled gilt covers, extremely good copy of this lg. proof copy, plts fine and marked proof. Totteridge 29-72 1978 $1,250

MILTON, JOHN   Paradise Lost. (c. 1865). Illus. by G. Dore, lacks endpaper, folio, covers worn. George's 635-136 1978 £10.50

MILTON, JOHN   Paradise Lost and Paradise Regain'd. San Francisco: The Limited Editions Club, 1936. Sm. folio, illus. by Carlotta Petrina, orig. cloth-backed marbled bds., paper label, 1 of 1,500 copies, signed by illustrator, fine. MacManus 238-830 1978 $30

MILTON, JOHN   Poetical Works. London, 1835. 6 vols., 12mo., illus., 1st ed., covers rubbed, some marginal stains of few pgs. of vol. I. Biblo BL781-1081 1978 $30

MILTON, JOHN   Poetical Works. 1841. 2 vols. in 1, engrav. frontispiece, fscp. 8vo., contemp. calf, label missing. Howes 194-1048 1978 £5

MILTON, JOHN   The Poetical Works. London, 1891. Globe ed., cr. 8vo., prize calf gilt, attractive. K Books 244-237 1978 £5

MILTON, JOHN   Poetical Works. 1900. Orig. cloth, 8vo. Howes 194-1049 1978 £5

MILTON, JOHN   Milton--Private Correspondence and Academic Exercises... Cambridge 1932. Octavo, good, cloth spotted. Upcroft 10-122 1978 £6.50

MILTON, JOHN   Samson Agonistes: a Dramatic Poem. (Florence, 1930/31). Bds., bit soiled, 1 of 103 copies. Dawson's 447-160 1978 $175

MILTON, WILLIAM FITZWILLIAM, VISCOUNT 1839-1877 The North-West Passage by Land.... (1865). Maps, plts., half calf, slightly worn, some spotting in text, 8vo., 2nd ed. Edwards 1012-447 1978 £35

MILTON, WILLIAM FITZWILLIAM, VISCOUNT 1839-1877 The North-west Passage by Land. Being the Narrative of an Expedition from the Atlantic to the Pacific.... London, 1865. 3rd ed., 3/4 leather, plts., fold. maps. Hood 116-867 1978 $50

MILWARD, EDWARD   A Circular Invitatory Letter to All Orders of Learned Men, but More Especially to the Professors of Physick and Surgery, in Great Britain. London, 1740. 8vo., modern bds., only ed. Offenbacher 30-100 1978 $125

MINCHIN, H. C.   The Legion Book. London, (1929). Quarto cloth, illus., 1st ed., fine. Duschnes 220-185 1978 $125

MINER, CHARLES   History of Wyoming, in a Series of Letters from Charles Miner to His Son, William Penn Miner. Philadelphia, 1845. Maps, re-bound, fold. map. MacManus 239-1564 1978 $40

MINER, HORACE   St. Denis, a French-Canadian Parish. Chicago, (1939). Orig. binding. Wolfe 39-375 1978 $30

MINISTERE Des Colonies De Belgique... Londres, 1919. 4to., orig. printed wrps. K Books 239-328 1978 £30

MINKOWSKI, H.   Zwei Abhandlung uber die Grundgleihungen der Elektrodynamik. Leipzig and Berlin, 1910. 8vo., orig. wrappers, cloth folder. Quaritch 977-115 1978 $200

MINNIGERODE, MEADE   Black Forest. 1937. First ed. Austin 82-664 1978 $12.50

MINNIGERODE, MEADE   The Fabulous Forties 1840-1850. New York, 1924. Illus. MacManus 239-316 1978 $10

MINNEGERODE, MEADE   The Fabulous Forties, 1840-1850. New York, 1924. Illus. Baldwins' 51-13 1978 $10

MINNIGERODE, MEADE   Jefferson Friend of France 1793. The Career of Edmond Charles Genet. New York, 1928. Illus. MacManus 239-177 1978 $15

MINNIGERODE, MEADE   Jefferson, Friend of France. New York, 1928. Illus., 1st ed. Biblo 248-50 1978 $17.50

MINNIGERODE, MEADE   Jefferson, Friend of France 1793. New York, 1928. Cloth, with facsimile reproductions of documents. Hayman 73-452 1978 $10

MINNIGERODE, MEADE   The Magnificent Comedy. 1931. Illus., first ed., from Sinclair Lewis' Library. Austin 82-665 1978 $20

MINNIGERODE, MEADE   Oh Susanna! 1922. First ed. Austin 82-666 1978 $12.50

MINNESOTA Guide:.... St. Paul, 1869. Small folding map, woodcuts, original printed wr., 1st ed. Ginsberg 14-560 1978 $150

MINNESOTA History. St. Paul, 1918-1974. Vols. 1-45, few numbers in Xerox. Ginsberg 14-561 1978 $650

MINNESOTA in the Civil and Indian Wars. St. Paul, 1891. 2nd ed., 2 vols., 4to., cloth, ex-lib. MacManus 239-899 1978 $20

MINNESOTA: Its Advantages to Settlers. St. Paul, 1867. 6th. ed., wrps. Hayman 71-475 1978 $10

MINNESOTA, The Empire State of the New North-West:.... St. Paul, 1878. Original printed wr., 1st ed. Ginsberg 14-562 1978 $75

A MINOR Poet Sings. (Kensington, 1907). Laid paper, uncut, some leaves unopened, ltd. 300 copies, 6 not for sale, on vellum, very good or better. Limestone 9-205 1978 $20

MINOT, CHARLES S.   The Problem of Age, Growth, and Death. New York, 1908. 8vo., ex-lib., 1st ed., illus. Morrill 239-179 1978 $15

MINTO, MR.   The Speech of Lord Minto in the House of Peers, April 11th, 1799...Respecting an Union Between Great Britain & Ireland. 1799. 1st ed., modern bds., very good. Hyland 128-121 1978 £9.50

MINTON, BRUCE   The Fat Years and the Lean. New York, (1940). Biblo BL781-851 1978 $8.50

MINUCIUS FELIX, MARCUS   Octavius, et Caecilii Cypriani De Vanitate Idolorum, a C. Cellario. 1748. Vellum, fore-edge of binding & several pages of text mouse-eaten. Allen 234-635 1978 $7.50

MIOT, J.   Memoires Pour Servir a l'Histoire Des Expeditions En Egypte et en Syrie. Paris, 1814. 8vo, wrapper, uncut, deuxienne ed. Edwards 1012-76 1978 £35

MIRABEAU, HONORE GABRIEL RIQUETI   Errotika Biblion. Rome, 1783. 1st ed., small octavo, contemp. half calf over marbled bds., rebacked, preserving orig. spine label. Bennett 20-142 1978 $175

MIRABEAU, HONORE GABRIEL RIQUETI   Gallery of Portraits of the National Assembly... 1790. 1st. English ed., 2 vols., 8vo, lacks half-titles, early 19th century half calf, 2 gatherings misbound. Hannas 54-130 1978 £15

MIRANDOLA, PICO DELLA   A Platonic Discourse Upon Love. Merrymount Press, 1907. Prtd. in red & black. Battery Park 1-204 1978 $75

MIRCHOND, MOHAMMEDIS VULGO   Mohammedis filii Chavendschahi.... Goettingae, 1808. 4to., bds., good, first ed. King 7-367 1978 £40

MIRE, GEORGES DE   The Treasures of Delphi
Please turn to
FROTIER DE LA COSTE-MESSELIERE, PIERRE

MISCELLANEA Curiosa Sive Ephemeridum. Nurnberg, 1689. Thick octavo, orig. sheep, crack at top edge, otherwise good to very good. Rittenhouse 49-554 1976 $100

MISCELLANEOUS Poems, by Several Hands. London, 1726. 8vo, contemporary calf (spine worn, later label), 1st ed. Ximenes 47-244 1978 $200

MISCELLANEOUS Translations from Oriental Languages. 1831-1834. 2 vols. in 1, full calf, ex-lib. binding, nicely rebacked. Eaton 45-377 1978 £20

MISCELLANEOUS Writings on Henry the Eighth. 1924. Frontis., 1 of 365 numbered copies. Battery Park 1-111 1978 $75

MISODOLUS, H. S. The Young-Man's Counsellor. 1724. Third ed., 12mo., neat 19th-century calf gilt, marbled endpapers, woodcut frontispiece, rare. P. M. Hill 142-131 1978 £125

MISSAL
Please turn to
CATHOLIC CHURCH. LITURGY & RITUAL. MISSAL.

THE MISSING Gutenburg Wood Blocks. New York, 1940. 8vo, boards and cloth, fine. Duschnes 220-246 1978 $50

MISSION a l'Expostion de Hanoi, et en Extreme-Orient. (1903). 4to, tables, orig. covers. Van der Peet 127-158 1978 Dfl 55

MISSIRINI, MELCHIOR Del Tempio Eretto in Possagno da Antonio Canova. Venice, 1833. Folio, contemp. red mor., plts., gilt inside dentelles, gilt back and panels, 1 of 150 copies, 1st ed. Gilhofer 74-42 1978 sFr 2,200

MISSISQUOI COUNTY HISTORICAL SOCIETY Annual Reports. First to Fifth Report (inclusive). St. Johns, 1906-1909. Bound together in one half calf vol., front wrapper of each report preserved. Wolfe 39-151 1978 $175

MISSISSIPPI Historical Society, Publications of Vol. IX. 1906. Bell Wiley's copy. Broadfoot 46-343a 1978 $25

MISSISSIPPI Historical Society, Publications of Vol. VII. Oxford, 1903. Bell Wiley's copy. Broadfoot 46-343 1978 $25

MISSOURI. UNIVERSITY. BOARD OF CURATORS Report by the...to the Governor, Containing Catalogue, Announcements and Other Matter Pertaining to the University. Year Ending June 24, 1874. St. Louis, 1874. Wrs. Hayman 72-475 1978 $7.50

MISSOURI. UNIVERSITY. BOARD OF CURATORS Report of...to the Twenty-Fourth General Assembly, January, 1868. Jefferson City, 1868. Wrs. little worn. Hayman 72-473 1978 $7.50

MISSOURI Historical Review. Columbia, 1906/7-1972. Bound in cloth, vols. 1-67. Ginsberg 14-592 1978 $750

MRS. Figg's Grand Ball. London, n.d. 10 coloured illus., sq. cr. 8vo, orig. wrappers. Traylen 88-191 1978 £20

MR. Miles Prance's Answer to Mrs. Cellier's Libel and Divers Other False Aspersions Cast Upon Him.... 1680. 1st. ed., folio, disbound. Hannas 54-47E 1978 £15

MITCHEL, J. History of Ireland. Dublin, n.d. 2 vols., very good, reprint, octavo bound in cloth. Hyland 128-125 1978 £6

MITCHELL, ARNOLD GENTHE The Book of the Dance. Kennerley, (1916). 4to., cloth, covers faded. Battery Park 1-131 1978 $150

MITCHELL, D. W. Ten Years in the United States... 1862. 8vo, orig. cloth, spine repaired, age browning in text. Edwards 1012-508 1978 £20

MITCHELL, DONALD GRANT American Lands and Letters. 1897. Illus., first ed. Austin 82-667 1978 $12.50

MITCHELL, DONALD GRANT American Lands and Letters. 1899. Illus., first ed. Austin 82-668 1978 $12.50

MITCHELL, DONALD GRANT English Lands, Letters and Kings. 1889. Austin 82-669 1978 $11

MITCHELL, DONALD GRANT Fudge Doings: Being Tony Fudge's Record of the Same. New York, 1855. 2 vols., 1st ed., orig. cloth worn, t.e.g., end papers stained. Greene 78-327 1978 $75

MITCHELL, DONALD GRANT Reveries of a Bachelor.... New York, 1852. 1st Darley ed., illus., tented plts., lg. sq. 8vo., orig. grained blue cloth, book-plt. of Henry Dexter. Americanist 102-40 1978 $35

MITCHELL, EDWARD Sketches after Anty. Van-Dyck. (Leith and Edinburgh), 1815. Plts., folio, orig. half roan gilt, with ties. K Books 244-238 1978 £22

MITCHELL, EDWIN VALENTINE Morocco Bound: Adrift Among Books. New York. 1st ed., illus. Battery Park 1-411 1978 $22.50

MITCHELL, ELISHA A Memoir Plus Addresses by Otey and Swain. Chapel Hill, 1858. New cloth. Broadfoot 50-143 1978 $16

MITCHELL, JOHN A Guide to the Principles and Practice of the Con-gregational Churches of New England. Northampton, 1838. 12mo., 1st ed., orig. cloth. Morrill 241-368A 1978 $15

MITCHELL, JOHN AMES Dr. Thorne's Idea, Originally Published as "Gloria Victis." New York, 1910. Illus. by Balfour Ker, 1st of this rev'd. ed. Americanist 102-47 1978 $20

MITCHELL, JOSEPH Old Mr. Flood. New York, (1948). Very good, dw. Bernard 5-187 1978 $15

MITCHELL, JUSTIN The Sword of O'Malley. c. 1930. F.p., good, reprint, octavo bound in cloth. Hyland 128-128 1978 £4

MITCHELL, LEWIS The Life of the Rt. Hon. Cecil John Rhodes. London, 1910. 2 vols., 7 plts., 8vo, orig. cloth. K Books 239-321 1978 £12

MITCHELL, LUCY M. History of Ancient Sculpture. 1883. 4to., illus., colored plts., binding scratched, one hinge shaken, corners of spine worn. Allen 234-637 1978 $10

MITCHELL, LUCY M. Selections from Ancient Sculpture, Representing 36 Masterpieces of Antiquity. 1883. Folio, plts., portfolio. Allen 234-638 1978 $10

MITCHELL, SAMUEL AUGUSTUS An Accompaniment to Mitchell's Reference and Distance Map of the United States... Philadelphia, 1835. 1st. ed., 8vo, orig. half leather, some slight spotting, name on title. Edwards 1012-509 1978 $25

MITCHELL, SAMUEL LATHAM
Please turn to
MITCHILL, SAMUEL LATHAM

MITCHELL, SILAS WEIR Doctor and Patient. London, 1888. Sm. 8vo., orig. brown cloth, gilt lettering, lightly browned, very good copy, 1st ed. Zeitlin 245-168 1978 $50

MITCHELL, SILAS WEIR Doctor and Patient. Philadelphia, 1888. Rittenhouse 49-557 1976 $17.50

MITCHELL, SILAS WEIR Little Stories. New York, 1903. Sm. 8vo., nice, 1st ed. Morrill 239-526 1978 $8.50

MITCHELL, SILAS WEIR Mr. Kris Kringle. A Christmas Tale. Philadelphia, (1904). Color plts. by Clyde O. DeLand, 1st ed., decorated binding in color, very good. Victoria 34-548 1978 $15

MITCHELL, SILAS WEIR Prince Little Boy and Other Tales Out of Fairy-Land. Philadelphia, 1888. Illus., 8vo., orig. pic. cloth, 1st ed., inscr'd from Weir Mitchell. Morrill 241-369 1978 $50

MITCHELL, SILAS WEIR The Red City. 1908. First U.S. ed., plts. by Arthur I. Keller, pict. cloth, good. Bell Book 17-658 1978 £6.50

MITCHELL, SUSAN L. Aids to the Immortality of Certain Persons in Ireland. 1913. 2nd ed., revised, b./parchment spine, very good, octavo bound in cloth. Hyland 128-130 1978 £6

MITCHELL, MRS. T.   Gleanings From Travels in England, Ireland and Through Italy... Belfast, c.1840. Sole ed.?, 2 vols., lg. 12mo, orig. cloth, printed paper label, bindings lightly stained, but very good copy. Fenning 32-227 1978 £21.50

MITCHELL, THOMAS D.   The Pains and Pleasures of a Medical Life. Lexington, 1839. Disbound. Rittenhouse 49-555 1976 $65

MITCHELL, THOMAS D.   Valedictory to the Graduating Class of the Philadelphia College of Medicine, February 28, 1852. Philadelphia, 1852. Disbound. Rittenhouse 49-556 1976 $10

MITCHELL, W. H.   Geographical and Statistical Sketch of the Past and Present of Wabasha County, Together with a General View of the State of Minnesota. Rochester, 1870. Original printed wr., 1st ed. Ginsberg 14-564 1978 $150

MITCHELL, WILLIAM A.   Linn County, Kansas. Kansas City, (1928). Orig. binding, clean. Hayman 71-391 1978 $20

MITCHELL, WILMOT B.   Elijah Kellogg, the Man and His Work... 1903. Port., illus., good. Nestler Rare 78-23 1978 $12

MITCHELL'S New General Atlas...Countries of the World...Cities Embraced in 47 Quarto Maps, Forming a Series of 76 Maps and Plans...and Valuable Statistical Tables. Philadelphia, 1861. Folio, orig. cloth sides, new spine and tips. Americanist 102-12 1978 $185

MITCHILL, SAMUEL LATHAM   A Discourse on the Life and Character of Thomas Addis Emmet. New York, 1828. 8vo., woodcut tailpiece, foxed, disbound, good copy, 1st ed. Zeitlin 245-71 1978 $45

MITELLI, GIUSEPPE MARIA   Alfabeto in Sogno. N.P., (Bologna), 1683. Folio, 18th cent. bds., leather spine, eng. plts., first ed., fine. Schumann 511-40 1978 sFr 6,475

MITFORD, MARY RUSSELL   Christina, The Maid of the South Seas; A Poem. London, 1811. 8vo, contemporary half red morocco, gilt, spine gilt, 1st ed., extensive notes, revised and arranged by Capt. Burney, attractive and rare. Ximenes 47-210 1978 $150

MITFORD, MARY RUSSELL   Our Village. London, 1910. Thick, large 8vo, color plates by Alfred Rawlings, text drawings by Thomson, spine sunned, very good. Victoria 34-792 1978 $35

MITFORD, NANCY   Christmas Pudding. 1932. Very good, drawings, orig. linen, rear hinge sprung, first English ed. Bell Book 16-641 1978 £15

MITFORD, NANCY   The Pursuit of Love. London, 1945. First ed., orig. binding, nice, frayed d.w. Rota 211-394 1978 £6

MITFORD, NANCY   Wigs on the Green. 1935. Scarce, very good, first English ed. Bell Book 16-643 1978 £22.50

MITFORD, WILLIAM   The History of Greece. 1808. 4 vols., 4to., contemp. diced calf. Howes 194-394 1978 £30

MITTELBERGER, GOTTLIEB   Journey to Pennsylvania in the Year 1750 and Return to Germany in the Year 1754... Philadelphia, 1898. Illus., contemp. 3/4 calf and marbled bds., bookplt., very good copy, 1 of 26 copies printed on fine paper, inscribed by Jos. Y. Jeanes. MacManus 239-1565 1978 $50

MIVART, ST. GEORGE   Birds - The Elements of Ornithology. London, (1892). Ex-lib with blind stamp, 8vo, orig. cloth. Book Chest 17-262 1978 $25

MIX, DAVID E. E.   Catalogue of Maps and Surveys in the Offices of the Secretary of State, State Engineer and Surveyor, and Controller, and the... State Library. Albany, 1859. Orig. calf, worn & chipped, one cover loose, good working copy, full index, out of print. Butterfield 21-243 1978 $75

MIXER, KNOWLTON   Old Houses of New England. New York, 1927. Illus. Baldwins' 51-400 1978 $12.50

MIZAULD, ANTOINE   Harmonia Superioris Naturae Mundi Et Inferioris. Paris, 1577. 8vo., bds. Salloch 345-128 1978 $175

MIZAULD, ANTOINE   Meteororologia Sive Perspicua Declaratio Rerum Quae in Aere Fiunt, id est Pluviae, Grandinis, Tonitrui & id Genus Aliorum Causas, Generationem, Naturam, Differentias et Effectus Exhibens. Paris, 1587. 8vo., marbled 1/2 calf over decor. bds., 2nd ed. Salloch 345-129 1978 $275

MIZAULD, ANTOINE   Antonii Mizaldi Monsluciani Cometographia crinitarum Stellarum quas Mundus Nunquam Impune vidit.... Paris, 1549. 1st ed., quarto, early boards, rebacked in calf, morocco spine label, gilt, tear in title page repaired, water staining, rare. Bennett 20-143 1978 $400

MIZWA, STEPHEN P.   Nicholas Copernicus, 1543-1945. New York, 1943. Illus., roy. 8vo., half calf. George's 635-932 1978 £12.50

MOAT, T.   The Short-Hand Standard Attempted by an Analysis of Circles as an introductory Foundation of a new System of Stenography. 1833. Plts., foxed, recently rebound, old sides replaced, 8vo. George's 635-1393 1978 £10.50

MOATS, ALICE LEONE   Blind Date with Mars. 1943. Austin 80-219 1978 $7.50

MOBERLY, F. J.   The Campaign in Mesopotamia 1914-1918. 1923-27. Coloured maps, plts., 4 vols., 8vo., orig. cloth, fine. F. Edwards 1013-393 1978 £60

MOCHS, TETA E.   Gregorius V, 996-999. 1922. Allen 234-1270 1978 $12.50

MOCKLER-FERRYMAN, A. F.   British Nigeria. London, c. 1902. Folding map, illus., inscription roughly erased from head of titlepage, otherwise good, 8vo, orig. cloth. K Books 239-329 1978 £12

MODDER, M. F.   The Jew in the Literature of England. Philadelphia, 1939. Biblo 251-699 1978 $10

MODERN Language Instruction in Canada. Toronto, 1928. 2 vols. Hood's 115-400 1978 $22.50

MODESTY Triumphing Over Impudence. 1680. First ed., folio, disbound. Hannas 54-47c 1978 £18

MODIUS, FRANCISCUS   Pandectae Triumphales, sive, Pomparvm... Frankfurt, 1586. Rare first ed., folio, 2 parts in 1 vol., plate, illus., cont. vellum, lacking ties., woodcut illus. by Jost Amman. Quaritch 978-114 1978 $2750

MOEBIUS, AUGUST FERDINAND   Der Barycentrische Calcul. Leipzig, 1827. 8vo., fold plts., contemp. half-cloth, fine copy, rare, 1st ed. Gilhofer 74-123 1978 sFr 500

MOES, E. W.   Frans Hals. Brussel, 1909. Lg. 8vo., nice plts., orig. covers. Van der Peet H-64-66 1978 Dfl 55

MOES, E. W.   Nederlandsche Kasteelen en hun Historie. Amsterdam, 1912-1915. 3 vols., 4to., cloth, frontis's, fldg. plts., text illus., genealogical tables, scarce. Van der Peet H-64-499 1978 Dfl 850

MOFFATT, C. B.   Life and Letters of Alexander Goodman More. Dublin, 1898. 1st ed., portrait, map, 8vo., orig. cloth, gilt, t.e.g., lightly stained, very good. Fenning 32-233 1978 £12.50

MOFFAT, ROBERT   A Life's Labours in South Africa... London, 1871. Photo portrait frontis, cr. 8vo, cloth gilt. K Books 239-331 1978 £15

MOFFAT, ROBERT   Missionary Labours and Scenes in Southern Africa. New York, 1844. Frontis, 5 plts., sm. 8vo, slight foxing, orig. gilt-dec. cloth, 6th. ed., g.e., backstrip slightly snicked at head. K Books 239-330 1978 £18

MOFFETT, J. W.   The Second Coming of Our Lord:.... Abilene, 1925. Printed wr., scarce. Jenkins 116-956 1978 $15

MOFFIT, ALEXANDER   A Check-list of Iowa Imprints, 1837-1860. Iowa City, 1902. Original wr., 1st ed. Ginsberg 14-418 1978 $12.50

MOHR, E.   To The Victoria Falls Of The Zambesi. 1876. Maps, portrait, woodcuts, chromo-lithographs, half roan, 8vo. Edwards 1012-308 1978 £120

MOHR, MARIE HELENE   A Bibliography of Westmoreland County, Pa....
Harrisburg, 1949. 8vo, orig. binding. Americanist 101-148 1978 $7.50

MOHRMANN, K.   Germanische Fruehkunst. 1905-07. 2 vols.,
folio, plts. loose in portfolio, spines torn. Allen 234-1363 1978 $50

MOIR, FRED L.   After Livingstone. London, c. 1922. Map,
plts., 8vo, orig. cloth. K Books 239-332 1978 £7

MOISTER, WILLIAM   Memorials of Missionary Labours in Western Africa,
the West Indies, and the Cape of Good Hope. London, 1866. 3rd. ed., revised &
enlarged, portrait, cr. 8vo, little age-marked, neatly recased in orig. cloth.
K Books 239-333 1978 £25

MOISTER, WILLIAM   The West Indies Enslaved and Free. London,
1883. Illus., map. Baldwins' 51-382 1978 $12.50

MOIVRE, ABRAHAM DE   The Doctrine of Chances. London, 1718. 4to.,
vignette, contemp. mottled calf, new leather label, very rubbed, first ed. Quaritch 977-164 1978 $700

MOLANUS, JOANNES   Medicorum Ecclesiasticum Diarium. Lovanii,
1595. Sm. 8vo., old calf, back gilt, 1st ed. Offenbacher 30-101 1978 $135

MOLBECH, O. C.   Den Gule By. Copenhagen, 1905. Paper,
in Danish. Austin 79-491 1978 $37.50

MOLESWORTH, MRS.   The Story of a Year. 1910. Plts., cloth, rear
hinge sprung, good, first English ed. Bell Book 16-644 1978 £4

MOLIERE, JEAN BAPTISTE POQUELIN   Le Bourgeois Gentilhomme. Bois Originaux de F. Simeon. Paris, 1922. Ltd. ed., bds., leather back, rubbed. Biblo
BL781-1082 1978 $17.50

MOLIERE, JEAN BAPTISTE POQUELIN   Oeuvres Completes. Paris, 1885.
Roy. 8vo., portraits, printed in colours, half red mor., gilt spine, 1st few leaves
stained in lower margin. Traylen 88-437 1978 £15

MOLIERE, JEAN BAPTISTE POQUELIN   Oeuvres. Paris, 1954. 8 vols., 8vo.,
bds., slipcases, plts. by Dubout each vol., fine set. Van der Peet H-64-437
1978 Dfl 600

MOLIERE, JEAN BAPTISTE POQUELIN   Plays In French. Edinburgh, 1926.
8 vols., portraits, cloth, t.e.g., mint. Eaton 45-340 1978 £15

MOLINA, ANTONIO DE   Exercicios Espiritvales Primera y Segvnda Parte.
Caragoca, 1630. 4to., limp vellum, ties missing. King 7-279 1978 £20

MOLINA, JUAN IGNACIO   The Geographical, Natural, and Civil History of
Chili. London, 1809. 2 vols., 8vo., 3/4 red calf, gilt tooled, gilt spine over
decor. paper. Salloch 345-130 1978 $225

MOLISCH, HANS   Mikrochemie der Pflanze. Jena, 1923. 8vo.,
illus., orig. cloth, very good copy, 3rd ed., revised. Norman 5-202 1978 $20

MOLISI, GIOVANNI BATTISTA DI NOLA   Cronica dell'Antichissima, e Nob-
ilissima Citta di Crotone, e della magna Grecia. 1649. 4to., marbled bds., calf
spine, first ed. King 7-66 1978 £70

MOLL, ALBERT   Perversions of the Sex Instinct: A Study of Sexual Inversion, Based on Clinical Data and Official Documents. Newark, 1931.
Spine lightly rubbed, 1st ed. in English, orig. bind. Petrilla 13-40 1978 $15

MOLLER, LEVIN   Mouveau Dictionaire Francois-Svedois et Svedois-
Francois. Stockholm and Uppsala, 1745. 1st. ed., 4to, frontispiece, contemp.
calf, gilt spine, minor damage, slight marginal worming. Hannas 54-194 1978
£20

MOLLHAUSEN, BALDWIN   Diary of a Journey from the Mississippi to the
Coasts of the Pacific with a United States Government Expedition... London,
1858. 2 vols., 1st ed. in English, 8vo., colored chromolitho. plts., woodcuts,
fldg. colored map, embossed library stamps, neatly rebacked, otherwise a sound
tight copy. Current 24-187 1978 $275

MOLLIEN, G.   Travels in the Republic of Colombia. 1824.
Folding map, plt., browned, contemp. leather, 8vo, badly soiled. Edwards
1012-668 1978 $50

MOLSON, JOHN, SR.   Montreal Capitalist, Founder of Numerous Commercial Enterprises. London, 1823. Vol. 1, orig. bds., loose, backstrip chipped,
autograph signature by author. Wolfe 39-380 1978 $50

MOLYNEAUX, PETER   The Romantic Story of Texas. New York, 1936.
Jenkins 116-953 1978 $15

MOLYNEUX, NELLIE Z. R.   History, Genealogical and Biographical of the
Eaton Families. Syracuse, 1911. Illus., bind. poor, contents good. Biblo
BL781-57 1978 $18.50

MOMBERT, J. I.   An Authentic History of Lancaster Co., Pa.
Lancaster, 1869. Illus., maps, rebound, very scarce. MacManus 239-1566
1978 $75

MOMBERT, J. I.   A History of Charles the Great. 1888. 8vo.
Upcroft 12-301 1978 £8.50

MOMMSEN, THEODOR   Das Weltreich der Caesaren. Wien-Leipzig, 1933.
8vo., cloth, illus., maps. Van der Peet H-64-500 1978 Dfl 35

MONAGHAN, FRANK   John Jay...Defender of Liberty. New York,
1935. 1st ed., covers faded, illus. Biblo 248-98 1978 $17.50

MONAGHAN, FRANK   This was New York. Garden City, 1943. Plts.,
1st ed., dust jacket. Butterfield 21-522 1978 $8.50

MONAGHAN, JAY   The Overland Trail. Indianapolis, (1947). 1st
ed., illus. Biblo BL781-292 1978 $10

MONAHAN, MICHAEL   Heinrich Heine. The Village Press, 1911. 8vo.,
bds., prtd. on fine paper, extremities of spine worn. Battery Park 1-122 1978
$25

MONCKTON, JAMES H.   The National Stair-Builder... New York,
(1873). Lg. 4to., lacks front flyleaf, illus. MacManus 239-692 1978 $75

MONCREIFF, JOHN   Appius: A Tragedy. 1755. Sm. 8vo., half
mor., sole ed. Howes 194-395 1978 £20

MONCRIEFF, A. R. HOPE   Bonnie Scotland. London, 1912. Coloured plts.,
roy. 8vo., decor. cloth. K Books 244-417 1978 £5

MONCRIEFF, WILLIAM T.   Paris & London. New York, 1828. 18mo., orig.
wrs., nice. Morrill 241-370 1978 $30

MONET, P.   Annamites, au travail! – Annam, Tinh Day !
Saigon, 1926. Rare, 8vo, orig. covers. Van der Peet 127-159 1978 Dfl 55

MONETTE, JOHN W.   History of the Discovery and Settlement of the
Valley of the Mississippi.... New York, 1846. 2 vols., maps. Jenkins 116-959
1978 $225

MONEY, JAMES WILLIAM B.   Java: Or, How to Manage a Colony... 1861.
2 vols., 8vo, orig. cloth, covers slightly soiled. Edwards 1012-171 1978 $35

MONEY, W.   A Vade-Mecum of Morbid Anatomy, Medical
and Chirurgical. London, 1831. Plts., drwgs., 8vo., ex-lib., worn, back
cover loose, 2nd ed. Morrill 239-180 1978 $12.50

MONEY, W.   A Vade-Mecum of Morbid Anatomy, Medical
and Chirurgical... London, 1831. 8vo, orig. cloth bds., worn, illus. by
drawings on plts., good. Sexton 7-201 1978 £20

MONFREID, HENRY DE   Vers Les Terres Hostiles de L'Ethiopie. Paris,
(1933). 69 illus., cr. 8vo., wrappers. K Books 239-334 1978 £5

MONGEZ, A.   Memoire sur les Cygnes qui chantent. Paris,
1783. 8vo., new parchment. King 7-368 1978 £30

THE MONKS of Kublai Khan;.... London, (1928). Cloth, foxed, a little worn.
Dawson's 449-62 1978 $35

MONKSHOOD, G. F.   Rudyard Kipling. London, 1899. 1st ed.,
portrait, laid paper, t.e.g., very good or better. Limestone 9-169 1978
$12.50

MONNET, ANTOINE-GRIMOALD   Nouvelle Hydrologie, ou Nouvelle Exposition de la Nature et de la Qualite des Eaux.... London, 1772. 1st ed., 12mo, full contemp. calf, gilt-panelled spine, rubbed, bookplate of Monnet family.   Bennett 20-144 1978 $100

MONODY on the Victims and Sufferers by the Late Conflagration in the City of Richmond, Virginia. Boston, 1812. 8vo., unbound, foxed, 1st ed.   Morrill 241-599 1978 $25

A MONOGRAPH on the Epidemic of Poliomyelitis.   New York, 1917. Maps, illus., charts, 8vo., buckram, 1st ed.   Morrill 239-211 1978 $15

MONRO, DANA C.   Crusades & Other Historical Essays, Presented to Him by His Former Students. 1928. Allen 234-1376 1978 $10

MONRO, HAROLD   Strange Meetings. London, 1917. 4to, decor. grey paper covers, spine chipped and front cover severed from backstrip, illus. by Lovat Fraser, Good, 1st ed. Desmarais 1-322 1978 $22.50

MONROE, J.   The Company Drill of the Infantry of the Line. NY, 1862. Ex libris, front f/1 taped, pages & cover stained, Bell Wiley's copy. Broadfoot's 44-276 1978 $25.00

MONROE, J. ALBERT   Battery D., First Rhode Island Light Artillery, at the Second Battle of Bull Run. Providence, 1890. Wrs., Bell Wiley's copy. Broadfoot 46-368 1978 $12

MONROE, JOHN D.   Chapters in the History of Delaware County. N. P., 1949. Butterfield 21-150 1978 $15

MONROE, JOEL HENRY   Schenectady, Ancient and Modern...1661 to 1914. (Geneva), 1914. Plts. Butterfield 21-402 1978 $12.50

MONROE, NELSON   The Grand Army Button. Boston, 1899. 2nd ed., portrs., 8vo., orig. wrs. Morrill 241-371 1978 $10

MONSTERRAT - Warhafftige und Grundliche Historia, Vom Ursprung, auch Zunemung, des Hochheiligen Spannischen Gotteshauf Montis Serrati... Munchen, 1588. Sm. 4to., fine, rare, mod. half vellum. Schafer 19-28 1978 sFr 1,400

MONSTRELET, ENGUERRAND DE   Chroniques Contenans les Cruelles Guerres Civilles Entre Les Maisons d'Orleans & de Bourgongne... Paris, 1572. 3 vols. in 2, folio, 3 blank leaves, contemp. calf, gilt spines, very worn, slight marginal worming & browning. Hannas 54-227 1978 £75

MONSTRELET, ENGUERRAND DE   Chronicles. 1840. 2 vols., new buckram. Allen 234-1366 1978 $25

MONTAGU, EDWIN S.   A Tribute. n.d. Portraits, sm. folio, orig. cloth, lower cover stained. Sawyer 298-95 1978 £21

MONTAGU, EDWARD WORTLEY   Reflections on the Rise and Fall of the Antient Republicks. 1759. 8vo., contemp. calf, fine, first ed. P. M. Hill 142-176 1978 £50

MONTAGU, WALTER   Miscellanae Spiritualia. 1648. First ed., sm. 4to., contemp. sheep. Howes 194-74 1978 £55

MONTAGUE, CHARLES EDWARD   Right Off the Map. London, 1927. Nice in chipped & worn d.w. Desmarais B-459 1978 $10

MONTAGUE, CHARLES EDWARD   A Writer's Notes on his Trade. London, 1930. 8vo., cloth and decor. bds., t.e.g., d.j., 1 of 750 copies signed by H. M. Tomlinson, 1st ed., fine. Duschnes 220-212 1978 $37.50

MONTAGUE, CHARLES EDWARD   A Writer's Notes on His Trade. London, 1930. Orig. cloth-backed patterned bds., d.j., a little soiled, 1st ed., ltd. to 750 copies signed by H. M. Tomlinson, very good. MacManus 238-726 1978 $50

MONTAGUE, CHARLES EDWARD   A Writer's Notes on His Trade. London, 1930. 8vo., brown patterned bds. rumpled from water damage, lower edge of spine creased, t.e.g., uncut, 1 of 700 numbered copies signed by H. M. Tomlinson, 1st ed., collector's con. Desmarais 1-323 1978 $25

MONTAGUE, EDWARD WORTLEY   Reflections on the Rise and Fall of the Antient Republicks. 1759. First ed., cont. calf, very good, 8vo. Howes 194-396 1978 £25

MONTAGUE, EDWARD WORTLEY   Reflections on the Rise and Fall of Antient Republicks, Adapted to the Present State of Great Britain. 1759. Cont. calf, 8vo. George's 635-722 1978 £7.50

MONTAGUE, MRS. ELY   An Essay on the Writing & Genius of Shakespear, Compared with the Greek and French Dramatic Poets. 1772. 3rd. ed., contemp. calf, rebacked. Eaton 45-341 1978 £20

MONTAIGNE, MICHEL DE   Essais.... Bourdeaux, 1580. Rare 1st ed., 2 vols., 8vo, minor repairs to outer blank margins, few headings just shaved, calf antique. Quaritch 978-111 1978 $2,500

MONTAIGNE, MICHEL DE   Livre des essais. Lyons, 1593. 2 vols. in 1, 8 vo., excellent copy, French near-contemp. mottled calf gilt, 5th ed. Quaritch Summer, 1978-34 1978 $3,000

MONTAIGNE, MICHEL DE   Les Essays. Paris, 1595. Ed. nouvelle, folio, full levant mor., gilt edges, very fine. Salloch 348-157 1978 $2.750

MONTAIGNE, MICHEL DE   Essais. Leydon, 1602. Full contemp. vellum, thick 8 vo., free endpaper missing, else very good, portraits. Houle 10-228 1978 $225

MONTAIGNE, MICHEL DE   Essays. 1685-86-85. Engrav. portrait in each vol., 3 vols., cr. 8vo., contemp. calf, good. Howes 194-75 1978 £110

MONTAIGNE, MICHEL DE   Essays in Three Books. London, 1700. 3 vols., octavo, exquisitely bound by Root, full early polished calf, gilt borders on both covers, inner gilt dentelles, gilt spines, fine , 3rd and best ed. Bennett 7-77 1978 $225

MONTAIGNE, MICHEL DE   Essays of... 1892-93. 3 vols., sm. 4to., half red mor., panelled backs, gilt edges. Quaritch 979-322 1978 $85

MONTAIGNE, MICHEL DE   Essays. 1923. Portraits, 5 vols., orig. white buckram, gilt tops, 8vo. Howes 194-1060 1978 £20

MONTAIGNE, MICHAEL DE   Montaigne's Essays. London: The Nonesuch Press, 1931. 2 vols., full leather, pub. box, ltd. to 900 copies, very good. MacManus 238-838 1978 $75

MONTAIGNE, MICHEL DE   The Works of...with Notes, Life and Letters. New York, 1910. 10 vols., illus., ltd. ed., cloth, linen backs, very nice. Biblo BL781-1083 1978 $57.50

MONTALVO, GARCI ORDONEZ   Le Prodezze di Splandiano, che Seguona a i Quattro Libri di Amadis di Guala Suo Padre. [Venice, 1550]. 8vo, contemp. limp vellum, 1st Italian ed. Ginsberg 14-158 1978 $3,500

MONTANA. LEGISLATURE.   House Journal. Second Session. Helena, 1867. Orig. pr. wr., 1st ed. Ginsberg 14-624 1978 $125

MONTANUS, J. B.   In Libros Galeni de Arte Curandi ad Glauconem Explanationes. 1554. Sm. 8vo., italic letter, contemp. blindstamped pigskin, spine repaired. Quaritch 977-58 1978 $250

MONTANYA, H. DE LA   The Pacific Railroad: A Defense Against Its Enemies,.... N.P., 1864. Orig. pr. wr., 1st ed. Ginsberg 14-1089 1978 $175

MONTBARD, G.   The Case of John Bull in Egypt, The Transvaal, Venezuela, and Elsewhere. London, c. 1900. Text-illus., sm. 8vo, orig. cloth, little dusty. K Books 239-335 1978 £10

MONTCALM-GOZON, LOUIS JOSEPH DE, MARQUIS DE SAINT-VERAN Letters from the Marquis de Montcalm, Governor-General of Canada. London, 1777. 8vo., new half mor., untrimmed, text lightly dampstained, 1st ed. Morrill 241-372 1978 $125

MONTECUCULI, RAIMONDO, COUNT OF   Memoirs. Amsterdam & Leipzig, 1770. Plts., contemp. calf, spines gilt, maps, 3 vols., 8vo. Howes 194-397 1978 £40

MONTEIRO, JOACHIM JOHN   Angola and The River Congo. 1875. Sm. 8vo, folding map, engraved plts., 2 vols. Edwards 1012-260 1978 £90

MONTEIRO, JOACHIM JOHN   Angola and the River Congo. London, 1875.
2 vols., folding map, 16 plts., cr. 8vo, orig. cloth. K Books 239-336 1978
£60

MONTEMAGNO, BUONACORSO   Rime. Bologna, 1709. 12mo., bds.,
calf spine, very good. King 7-197 1978 £20

MONTES DE OCA   Jose Maria. Mexico City, 1801. Sm. 4to., eng.
plts., uncut, bound with binder's blanks in mod. calf, first issue. Quaritch 978-
107 1978 $850

MONTESINO, FRAY AMBROSIO   Coplas sobre diversas devociones y misterios
de nuestra santa fe catolica. London, 1936. Med. 8vo., orig. buckram. Forster
130-218 1978 £5

MONTESQUIEU, CHARLES LOUIS DE SECONDAT 1689-1755   Oeuvres De
Monsieru.... London (Paris), 1767. Vols. I and II of III, 4to., marbled bds.
Salloch 348-158 1978 $80

MONTESQUIEU, CHARLES LOUIS DE SECONDAT 1689-1755   The Spirit of
Laws. 1793. Contemp. calf, sixth ed., nice, 8vo. Howes 194-398 1978 £25

MONTESQUIEU, CHARLES LOUIS DE SECONDAT 1689-1755   The Spirit of
Laws. London, 1794. 2 vols., orig. bds., uncut, front bd. of vol. I detached.
Petrilla 13-41 1978 $45

MONTESSORI, MARIA   Pedagogical Anthropology. London, 1913.
Demy. 8vo, orig. cloth, binding rather badly worn & spine damaged, illus.,
good copy internally. Sexton 7-202 1978 £10

MONTFORT, GUILLAUME   Pieces d'Ecriture Anglaise. Paris, n.d. (c. 1795).
Eng. plts., folio, cont. paper wrs., uncut, rare. Schumann 511-41 1978 sFr 1100

MONTGAILLARD, ABBE DE   Histoire de France depuis la fin du regne de Louis
XVI jusqua 1825. 1828. Portrait, 9 vols., contemp. calf gilt, spines a trifle
rubbed. George's 635-723 1978 £27.50

MONTGOMERY, A.   The Story of the Fourth Army, August 8th-Nov.
11th 1918. 1919. Photographs, some loose, maps in separate vol., 2 vols., 4to.,
covers badly stained and worn. George's 635-843 1978 £6.50

MONTGOMERY, BERNARD L.   Ten Chapters 1942 to 1945. 1945. 1st. ed.,
oblong 8vo, orig. leatherette, name on fly-leaf, fine copy. Sawyer 298-131
1978 £12

MONTGOMERY, ELIZABETH   Reminiscences of Wilmington in Familiar Village
Tales Ancient and New. Philadelphia, 1851. 1st. ed., illus., rebacked in cloth.
Baldwins' 51-231 1978 $50

MONTGOMERY, ELIZABETH   Reminiscences of Wilmington, in Familiar Village Tales, Ancient and New. Wilmington, 1872. 2nd ed., illus., scarce.
MacManus 239-965 1978 $35

MONTGOMERY, H.   The Life of Major-General William H. Harrison,
Ninth President of the United States. Cleveland, 1852. 1st ed., illus., front
inner hinge cracking, otherwise a nice copy, scarce. MacManus 239-765 1978
$20

MONTGOMERY, H.   The Life of Major-General Zachary Taylor,
12th President of the U. S. Philadelphia, n.d. Illus., worn, good used copy.
Biblo 251-112 1978 $12.50

MONTGOMERY, H. B.   The Empire of the East. Chicago, 1909. Illus.
Biblo 251-11 1978 $15

MONTGOMERY, J. E.   Our Admiral's Flag Abroad: The Cruise of Admiral D. G. Farragut... New York, 1869. Photo portrait, illus., imp. 8vo, contemp. morocco, raised bands, sides & back tooled in blind, pres. inscription from
Farragut. Edwards 1012-31 1978 £75

MONTGOMERY, JAMES   Journal of Voyages and Travels by the Rev. Daniel
Tyerman and George Bennet. 1831. 2 vols., portraits, engraved plts., half blue
calf, 8vo, spines slightly faded, slight dampstains on few plts., some foxing.
Edwards 1012-377 1978 £150

MONTGOMERY, JAMES   Poems on the Abolition of the Slave Trade.
1809. 1st. ed., 4to, additional engraved title, foxed, 12 plts., half calf. Hannas
54-314 1978 £65

MONTGOMERY, JAMES   The Poetical Works... 1851. 4to, engraved
frontis & title, full maroon morocco, gilt borders & spine, a.e.g., slight rubbing,
handsome copy. Jarndyce 16-885 1978 £10.50

MONTGOMERY, JAMES   A Poet's Portfolio; or, Minor Poems: In Three
Books. 1836. 2nd. ed., half title, orig. brown cloth, a.e.g., good. Jarndyce
16-883 1978 £10.50

MONTGOMERY, JAMES   The West Indies and Other Poems. 1810. 2nd.
ed., 12mo, contemp. calf, rebacked, some slight browning in text, with author's
signature. Edwards 1012-732 1978 £25

MONTGOMERY, JAMES   The West Indies and Other Poems. 1814. 4th.
ed., half titles, orig. diced calf, good. Jarndyce 16-884 1978 £7

MONTGOMERY, JEMINA   The Initials. New York, n.d. (c.1900). 2 vols.
reprint, cloth binding, t.e.g., good. Greene 78-113 1978 $20

MONTGOMERY, JEMINA   Quits. Philadelphia, 1883. 3 vols. in 1, cloth,
good. Greene 78-114 1978 $15

MONTGOMERY, L. M.   Emily of New Moon. Toronto, 1923. 1st ed.
Hood 117-535 1978 $25

MONTGOMERY, L. M.   Kilmeny of the Orchard. London, 1940. Hood
116-489 1978 $12.50

MONTGOMERY, M. W.   History of Jay County, Indiana. Chicago,
(1864). Clean, folding map, rebound. Hayman 71-346 1978 $50

MONTGOMERY, MORTON L.   History of Berks County, in Pennsylvania.
Philadelphia, 1886. 1st ed., illus., lg. thick 4to., rebound. MacManus 239-
1567 1978 $125

MONTGOMERY, MORTON L.   History of Berks County, Pa., in the Revolution from 1774 to 1783. Reading, 1894. Illus., fine. MacManus 239-1568
1978 $40

MONTGOMERY, MORTON L.   History of Berks County, Pa, In The Revolution.... Reading, 1894. 1st ed., spine rubbed, illus., orig. binding, 8vo.
Americanist 101-99 1978 $40

MONTGOMERY, MORTON L.   History of Reading, Pa., 1748-1898. Reading, 1898. Illus., map. MacManus 239-1569 1978 $22.50

MONTGOMERY, R. G.   "Pechuck"; Lorne Knight's Adventures in the
Arctic. Caldwell, 1948. Illus. Hood 116-93 1978 $20

MONTGOMERY, THOMAS H.   A History of the University of Pennsylvania from
Its Foundation to 1770. Philadelphia, 1900. Ltd. to 750 copies. MacManus
239-1623 1978 $17.50

MONTGOMERY, THOMAS LYNCH   Report of the Commission To Locate The
Site of the Frontier Forts of Penna. Harrisburg, 1916. 2nd. ed., maps & views, 2
vols., new red lib. buckram. Baldwins' 51-316 1978 $60

MONTGOMERY, W. H.   Jesus Was Not a Jew. Poughkeepsie, 1935.
Austin 79-493 1978 $12.50

MONTHERLANT, HENRY DE   Oeuvres Romanesque. Paris, 1963-64. 8 vols.,
lg. 8vo., half calf, gilt tooled spines, slipcases, plts. by Clairin, ltd. ed. of
400 copies, fine. Van der Peet H64-438 1978 Dfl 800

MONTIFAUD, MARC DE   Les Joyeuses Nouvelles de Marc de Montifaud.
Paris, 1883. Frontis, 1/2 cloth, marbled bds. Eaton 45-342 1978 £5

MONTIGNY, LOUVIGNY DE   Antoine Gerin-Lajoie. Toronto, n.d.(c.1925).
Hood 116-706 1978 $7.50

MONTIJN, A. M. M.   Gedenkboek der Nieuwe of Litteraire Societeit te 's-Gravenhage ter Gelegenheid van haar Honderjarig Bestaan. den Haag, 1902. Sm. 4to., orig. covers, plts. Van der Peet H-64-501 1978 Dfl 75

MONTISIANUS, MARCUS ANTONIUS   De Sanguinis Missione in Morbo Laterali Conclusiones. Florentiae, (1556). 8vo., contemp. limp vellum, 1st ed., very rare. Offenbacher 30-102 1978 $160

MONTLUC, BLAISE DE LASSARAN-MASSENCOME   The Commentaries. 1674. First English ed., folio, early 19th cent. half calf, short splits in joints. Howes 194-560 1978 £75

MONTPENSIER, ANTOINE PHILLIPPE D'ORLEANS   Relation de la Captivite de S.A.S. Mgr. le Duc de Montpensier pendant, les Annees 1793, 1794, 1795, 1796. 1816. 1st. ed., 8vo., orig. bds., spine defective, label intact. Hannas 54-131 1978 £20

MONTREAL General Hospital Reports. Montreal, 1880. 8vo., plts., illus., orig. cloth, lightly dust-oiled, light waterstain, former owner's signature, very good copy. Zeitlin 245-180 1978 $200

MONTRESOR, F.E.   Into Highways and Hedges. NY, 1895. Fir. Am. Ed., quarter calf, marbled boards, good cond. Greene 78-260 1978 $15.00

MONTULE, EDOUARD DE   A Voyage to North America and the West Indies in 1817. London, 1821. 1st ed. in English, 8vo., illus., plts., wrs. not contemp., foxing on 1 plt., else fine. Current 24-188 1978 $125

MONTVERT, RAOUL, DU   Sesuit Les Fleurs & Secretz De Medecine Lequel Traicte De Plusieurs Remedes Receptes Et Conseruatoires Pour Le Corps Humain Contre Toutes Maladies Come De Peste Fiebures Pleureries. (Paris, N.P., n.d.) (ca. 1530). Sm. 8vo., woodcuts, illus., contemp. blind-stamped calf, bkplt. & ownership inscr's, good copy, rare. Zeitlin 245-170 1978 $350

MONUMENT and Cementary Review, Sept., 1916 to Aug., 1917. New York, 1916-17. Illus., 4to., 1 vol., bind. poor, very good. Biblo BL781-660 1978 $27.50

THE MONUMENT to Robert Gould Shaw...1865-1897. Boston, 1897. 1st ed., 4to., orig. buckram, uncut, spine and edges rubbed. Americanist 102-105 1978 $50

MONVEL, LOUIS MAURICE BOUTET DE
Please turn to
BOUTET DE MONVEL, LOUIS MAURICE

MOODIE, DUNCAN CAMPBELL FRANCIS   The History of the Battles and Adventures of the British, The Boers, and the Zulus... Cape Town, 1888. 2 vols., 2 folding maps, 21 plts., cr. 8vo., orig. cloth, very scarce. K Books 239-337 1978 £80

MOODIE, JOHN WEDDERBURN DUNBAR   Ten Years in South Africa.... London, 1835. 2 vols., litho frontispieces, foxed, slight age-browning throughout, half roan, gilt spine, 8vo. K Books 239-338 1978 £140

MOODIE, SUSANNA   Roughing it in The Bush; or, Life in Canada. New York, 1852. 2 vols. in 1, sm. 8vo, half calf, slight stain affecting 5 leaves, vignette on titles. Edwards 1012-448 1978 £35

MOODY, E. A.   The Logic of William of Ockham. 1935. 8vo., rebound, cloth. Upcroft 12-303 1978 £6

MOODY, IRENE H.   Lava. Toronto, 1940. Hood 117-815 1978 $20

MOODY, WILLIAM V.   Poems. Boston, 1901. 1st ed., bind. slightly rubbed. Biblo BL781-1084 1978 $12

MOON, A.R.   Leaders & Pages. 1939. 1st ed., f.p., very good, octavo bound in cloth. Hyland 128-138 1978 £4

MOON, R. C.   Paralysis of Accommodation with Illustrative Cases, Treated by the Calabar Bean. 1864. 8vo., disbound. Quaritch 977-59 1978 $55

MOON, WILLIAM   Light For the Blind... 1873. 1st. ed., portrait, frontis, 8vo., orig. blue cloth, gilt, gilt edges, nice copy. Fenning 32-228 1978 £85

MOONEY, GEORGE S.   Co-operatives Today and Tomorrow. Montreal, 1938. Printed wrappers. Wolfe 39-379 1978 $15

MOORE, LADY   De La More; or, Scenes in Many Lands (a tale)! Cork, 1857. Sole ed.?, 8vo., orig. cloth, very good copy. Fenning 32-229 1978 £12.50

MOORE, ADDISON W.   Creative Intelligence. 1917. 1st ed., slightly rubbed. Austin 80-990 1978 $20

MOORE, ALAN   Last Days of Mast and Sail, an Essay in Nautical Comparative Anatomy. Oxford, 1925. Illus. by R. Morton Nance, 8vo. George's 635-844 1978 £7.50

MOORE, ALAN   Sailing Ships of War 1800-60, including the Transition to Steam. 1926. Illus., some coloured, 4to. George's 635-845 1978 £45

MOORE, BENJAMIN   A Sermon, Preached Before the Bible and Common Prayer Book Society of New-York, in Trinity Church. New York, 1810. Sewn uncut, unopened, John Pintard's copy. Butterfield 21-523 1978 $10

MOORE, CHARLES   Washington Past and Present. 1929. Illus., first ed., v.g. Austin 82-929 1978 $17.50

MOORE, CLARENCE B.   Aboriginal Sites on Tennessee River. Philadelphia, 1915. Thick folio, illus., plts., some color, very fine. MacManus 239-1185 1978 $50

MOORE, CLARENCE B.   Antiquities of the St. Francis, White, and Black Rivers, Arkansas. Philadelphia, 1910. Lg. 4to., illus., some in color, scarce. MacManus 239-1187 1978 $40

MOORE, CLARENCE B.   Certain Aboriginal Mounds of the Florida Central West-Coast. Philadelphia, 1903. Illus., folio, ex-lib., nice. MacManus 239-1189 1978 $35

MOORE, CLARENCE B.   Certain Aboriginal Mounds of the Florida Central West-Coast. Philadelphia, 1903. Thin folio, illus., orig. cloth, fine. MacManus 239-1188 1978 $40

MOORE, CLARENCE B.   Certain Aboriginal Remains of the Alabama River. Philadelphia, 1899. Thin folio, illus., map, orig. cloth, very good. MacManus 239-1190 1978 $30

MOORE, CLARENCE B.   Certain Aboriginal Remains of the Black Warrior River. Philadelphia, 1905. Thick folio, illus., orig. cloth, very fine. MacManus 239-1191 1978 $40

MOORE, CLARENCE B.   Certain Mounds of Arkansas and of Mississippi. Philadelphia, 1908. Thin folio, illus., plts., some in color, orig. cloth. MacManus 239-1192 1978 $40

MOORE, CLARENCE B.   Certain River Mounds of Duval County, Florida. Philadelphia, 1895. Thin folio, frontis., illus., orig. cloth, pres. copy, very fine. MacManus 239-1193 1978 $45

MOORE, CLARENCE B.   Certain Sand Mounds of the St. John's River Florida. Philadelphia, 1894. 2 vols., thin folio, colored crontis., illus., orig. cloth, pres. copies, very fine. MacManus 239-1194 1978 $75

MOORE, CLARENCE B.   Moundville Revisited. Philadelphia, 1907. Thin folio, illus., orig. cloth, very fine. MacManus 239-1195 1978 $40

MOORE, CLARENCE B.   The Northwestern Florida Coast Revisited. Philadelphia, 1918. Thin folio, illus., colored plts., orig. cloth, very fine. MacManus 239-1197 1978 $35

MOORE, CLARENCE B.   Some Aboriginal Sites in Louisiana and in Arkansas. Philadelphia, 1913. Thin folio, illus., orig. cloth, inscribed by Moore, very fine. MacManus 239-1198 1978 $35

MOORE, CLARENCE B.   Some Aboriginal Sites on Green River, Kentucky.
Philadelphia, 1916. Thin folio, illus., orig. cloth, very fine. MacManus 239-
1199 1978 $40

MOORE, CLARENCE B.   Some Aboriginal Sites on Mississippi River.
Philadelphia, 1911. Thin folio, illus., orig. cloth, very fine. MacManus 239-
1200 1978 $40

MOORE, CLARENCE B.   Some Aboriginal Sites on the Red River. Philadelphia, 1912. Thick folio, illus., plts., some in color, very fine. MacManus
239-1201 1978 $45

MOORE, CLEMENT   The Night Before Christmas. Philadelphia, 1942.
1st ed., full color, very good. Victoria 34-731 1978 $20

MOORE, DECIMA   We Two in West Africa. London, 1909. 2 maps,
illus., neatly recased in orig. gilt-dec. cloth, g.t., covers slightly marked, 8vo.
K Books 239-339 1978 £12

MOORE, E. S.   The Mineral Resources of Canada. Toronto,
1933. Maps. Hood's 115-717 1978 $12.50

MOORE, EDWARD   Fables for the Female Sex. London, 1744. Octavo, full contemp. calf, rebacked, 1st ed., engravings, very nice. Bennett 7-78
1978 $95

MOORE, EDWARD   The Gamester, A Tragedy. 1753. 1st. ed.,
8vo, wrapper, fine. Fenning 32-230 1978 £16.50

MOORE, EDWARD   The Gamester. 1792. Early ed., uncut in orig.
bds., biro marking on upper cover. Jarndyce 16-145 1978 £6.50

MOORE, EDWARD A.   The Story of a Cannoneer Under Stonewall
Jackson. Lynchburg, 1910. Small paice of dj stuck to upper spine, Bell Wiley's
copy. Broadfoot's 44-646 1978 $25

MOORE, F. F.   The Conscience of Coralie. 1900. 1st ed.,
illus. by F. H. Townsend, very good, octavo bound in cloth. Hyland 128-143
1978 £5

MOORE, F. F.   A Nest of Linnets. 1901. 1st ed., illus., good,
octavo bound in cloth. Hyland 128-144 1978 £4

MOORE, FRANCIS   Map and Description of Texas, Containing Sketches of Its History. Philadelphia & New York, 1840. Neatly rebacked. Baldwins'
51-565 1978 $250

MOORE, FRANCIS   Travels Into The Inland Parts of Africa... 1738.
Map, plts., calf, 8vo, rebacked. Edwards 1012-261 1978 £150

MOORE, FRANK   The Civil War in Song and Story. 1860-1865.
(New York), 1889. Worn, cover dull, cloth. Hayman 72-128 1978 $8.50

MOORE, FRANK   Diary of the American Revolution. New York,
1860. 2 vols., illus., fold. maps. MacManus 239-603 1978 $55

MOORE, FRANK   Record of the Year 1876. New York, 1876.
Portrs., 2 vols., tall 8vo., half mor., marbled bd. sides, 1st ed. Morrill 241-
373 1978 $30

MOORE, FRANK   Speeches of Andrew Johnson... Boston, 1865.
1st ed., port. MacManus 239-229 1978 $20

MOORE, FREDERICK H.   Dorothy Drake. London, 1885. 2 vols., orig.
cloth, 1st ed., covers soiled, lib. labels, else good. MacManus 238-350 1978
$75

MOORE, GEORGE   An Anthology of Pure Poetry. New York,
1924. 1st ed. of 1,000 numbered & signed copies, No. 614, laid paper, uncut, very good or better. Limestone 9-207 1978 $25

MOORE, GEORGE   Aphrodite and Aulis. London, 1930. 8vo,
full vellum, uncut, Mint, no.1344 of 1825 copies numbered and signed, 1st ed.
Desmarais 1-324 1978 $30

MOORE, GEORGE   The Apostle: A Drama in Three Acts. Dublin,
1911. Purple cloth, edges water stained. Eaton 45-343 1978 £5

MOORE, GEORGE   The Brook Kerith. 1929. Roy. 8vo., prtd. on
handmade paper, engrs., vellum, fine with slipcase, ltd. to 375 copies signed by
author & artist. Quaritch 979-237 1978 $75

MOORE, GEORGE   The Brook Kerith. New York, 1929. Engravings
by Stephen Gooden, 1st Amer. illus. ed., octavo, black paper boards with vellum
spine, gilt, gilt top, uncut, one of 500 numbered copies, signed by author and
artist. Totteridge 29-70 1978 $75

MOORE, GEORGE   Celibates. 1895. 1st ed., very good, octavo
bound in cloth. Hyland 128-145 1978 £10

MOORE, GEORGE   Celibates. 1895. 1st. ed., half title, orig.
red cloth, v.g. Jarndyce 16-890 1978 £10.50

MOORE, GEORGE   Celibates. 1895. 1st ed., orig. red cloth,
gilt, t.e.g., good copy. Eaton 45-344 1978 £10

MOORE, GEORGE   Celibates. London, 1895. 1st ed., bookplt.,
1/2 mor. slipcase. Biblo BL781-1085 1978 $24.50

MOORE, GEORGE   Celibates. 1895. 1st ed., d.w., near fine,
octavo bound in cloth. Hyland 128-146 1978 £12.50

MOORE, GEORGE   Celibate Lives. 1927. 1st ed., 1/4 cl., very
good, octavo bound in cloth. Hyland 128-150 1978 £6.50

MOORE, GEORGE   Esther Waters. 1894. Cloth gilt, t.e.g., lower
cover stained, good, first English ed. Bell Book 16-646 1978 £25

MOORE, GEORGE   Evelyn Innes. 1898. 1st ed., lacks fly, cover
shaky, good, octavo bound in cloth. Hyland 128-147 1978 £6.50

MOORE, GEORGE   Evelyn Innes. n.d. Blind-stamp on title, new
red cloth. Eaton 45-345 1978 £5

MOORE, GEORGE   Heloise and Abelard. London, 1921. 8vo, 2
vols., boards, vellum backed, paper label, d.w. slightly soiled, Mint, no. 953
of 1500 copies, numbered and signed, 1st ed. Desmarais 1-325 1978 $30

MOORE, GEORGE   Impressions and Opinoins. 1891. 1st. ed.,
half-title, orig. cloth, gilt border. Eaton 45-346 1978 £10

MOORE, GEORGE   In Single Strictness. London, 1922. 8vo, boards,
vellum back, paper label, d.w. faded, spine shelf-rubbed, Nice, no. 538 of ed.
limited to 1,030 copies, pr. on hand-made paper from hand-set type, signed by
Moore, 1st ed., collector's cond. Desmarais 1-327 1978 $25

MOORE, GEORGE   The Making of an Immortal. New York, 1927.
8vo, boards, decor. by Claire Bruce, 1 of 1240 copies signed by author, fine.
Duschnes 220-213 1978 $17.50

MOORE, GEORGE   The Making of an Immortal. New York, 1927.
No. 490 of 1240 copies, signed by author, 1st. ed., top & tail of spine slightly
bumped otherwise v.g. in glassine wrapper. Jarndyce 16-1208 1978 £8.50

MOORE, GEORGE   Memoirs of My Dead Life. 1921. 1 of 1030
numbered copies signed by the author, bds., good, first English ed. Bell Book 16-
647 1978 £12.50

MOORE, GEORGE   The Passing of the Essenes. London, 1930.
4to, boards, vellum back, uncut Mint, ed. limited 775 copies, this is no. 555,
signed by Moore, 1st ed., collector's cond. Desmarais 1-326 1978 $25

MOORE, GEORGE   Peronnik the Fool. (New York), 1926. 8vo,
decor. boards, 1 of 785 copies, printed in red and black, fine. Duschnes 220-270
1978 $30

MOORE, GEORGE   Peronnik the Fool. London, 1933. Engrs., full vellum, fine in worn slipcase, 1 of 525 numbered copies signed by author and artist. Dawson's 447-264 1978 $95

MOORE, GEORGE   Peronnik the Fool. London, 1933. Engravings by Stephen Gooden, octavo, orig. cream vellum, gilt top, slip-case, one of 525 numbered copies, signed by artist & author, fine. Totteridge 29-71 1978 $65

MOORE, GEORGE   Sister Teresa. 1901. 1st ed., very good, port., octavo bound in cloth. Hyland 128-148 1978 £7.50

MOORE, GEORGE   A Story-Tellers Holiday. New York, 1918. Ltd. to 1250 copies, very good, octavo bound in cloth, reprint. Hyland 128-149 1978 £10

MOORE, H.   Heads, Figures and Ideas... 1959. Folio, il-lus., bds., linen back, d.w. Quaritch 983-345 1978 $220

MOORE, HENRY   The Life of Mrs. Mary Fletcher. 1817. 1st. ed., 2 vols., half title, frontis portrait, orig. half calf, marbled bds., beautiful set, fine. Jarndyce 16-665 1978 £25

MOORE, J. S.   The Pictorial Book of Ballads, Traditional and Romantic... 1849. Wood engravings, contemp. 1/2 green calf, scuffed. Eaton 45-348 1978 £8

MOORE, JAMES   The History and Practice of Vaccination. Lon-don, 1817. 8vo., orig. half cloth, paper label, cover detached. Rittenhouse 49-561 1976 $29

MOORE, JAMES   Kilpatrick and Our Cavalry. New York, (1800's?). Nice copy in orig. cloth. Hayman 73-113 1978 $7.50

MOORE, JAMES   Kilpatrick and Our Cavalry. New York, 1865. New cloth, 1st ed., rebound copy, considerable foxing. Hayman 73-112 1978 $12.50

MOORE, JAMES   Kilpatrick and Our Cavalry. New York, 1865. Illus., sm. 8vo., orig. cloth, 1st ed. Morrill 241-374 1978 $15

MOORE, JAMES   A Narrative of the Campaign of the British Army in Spain, commanded by His Excellency Lieut.-General Sir John Moore. 1809. Fifth ed., portrait frontis., plt., 4to., orig. cloth backed bds., spine repaired, maps. F. Edwards 1013-373 1978 £35

MOORE, JANE ELIZABETH   Miscellaneous Poems. Dublin, 1797. 2nd. ed., folding frontis, edges uncut, rebound in paper bds., spine labelled. Eaton 45-347 1978 £20

MOORE, JOHN   A Mappe of Mans Mortalitie. London, 1617. Sm. 4to, library stamp, lower margins cut close, light stain in outer margins, early vellum, scarce issue of 1st ed. Quaritch 978-112 1978 $200

MOORE, JOHN   Medical Sketches, in two parts. Providence, 1794. First Amer. ed., hinges weak, chipped top and bottom of spine. Rittenhouse 49-562 1976 $65

MOORE, JOHN HAMILTON   Sailing Directions...North Sea. London, 1798. 12mo., wrps., stitched, back wrp. miss. Paine 78-98 1978 $47.50

MOORE, JOHN W.   History of North Carolina. Raleigh, 1880. 2 vols., good set, slight spine wear. Broadfoot 50-144a 1978 $140

MOORE, JOHN W.   History of North Carolina. Raleigh, 1880. 2 vols., rebound. Broadfoot 50-144b 1978 $70

MOORE, JOHN W.   School History of North Carolina, From 1584 to the Present Time. Raleigh, 1884. Cover worn. Broadfoot 50-145 1978 $8

MOORE, JOSEPH SHERIDAN   The Ethics of the Irish Under the Pentarchy.... Sydney, 1872. 1st ed., 8vo, half calf, fine. Fenning 32-231 1978 £32

MOORE, JOSEPH WEST   Picturesque Washington... Providence, 1886. 4to., illus., very fine. MacManus 239-125 1978 $20

MOORE, M. H.   Sketches of the Pioneers of Methodism in North Carolina and Va. Nashville, 1884. Lib. marks, nice copy, scarce. MacManus 239-1850 1978 $25

MOORE, MARIANNE   Observations. New York, Dial Press, 1924. First U.S. ed., half cloth, very good, rare. Bell Book 17-662 1978 £50

MOORE, MARIANNE   Poems. London, 1921. Orig. sewn pr. paper wr., Mint, author's inscription on fly leaf, and author's hand corrections in Acknowledgement, table of contents, and text, 1st ed., collector's cond. Desmarais 1-329 1978 $600

MOORE, N. HUDSON   Old Glass, European and American. New York, 1924. Illus., 8vo., orig. cloth, nice, 2nd prtg. Morrill 241-375 1978 $7.50

MOORE, THOMAS 1779-1852   A Canadian Boat Song. London, (1815). Folio, paper watermarked, orig. binding. Wolfe 39-75a 1978 $100

MOORE, THOMAS 1779-1852   Epistles, Odes and Other Poems. 1806. 1st. ed., 4to, half title, orig. blue bds., uncut, lacking the paper spine otherwise v.g. in orig. condition. Jarndyce 16-886 1978 £48

MOORE, THOMAS 1779-1852   Irish Melodies... London, 1821. 1st. London ed., illus., sm. 8vo, new calf spine, old bd. sides, sm. piece missing from blank margin of 1st. 3 leaves. Traylen 88-302 1978 £25

MOORE, THOMAS 1779-1852   Lalla Rookh. An Oriental Romance. London, 1853. 8vo, green polished mor., gilt tooling, red leather label, marbled end-leaves, all edges marbled, pict. t.p., felt lined slipcase. Duschnes 220-104 1978 $175

MOORE, THOMAS 1779-1852   Lalla Rookh, an Oriental Romance. 1854. Sm. 8vo., full mor., vignette on title, gilt edges, fully gilt back. Howes 194-1061 1978 £7.50

MOORE, THOMAS 1779-1852   Lalla Rookh, an Oriental Romance. New York, (c.1880s). Plts., full grained mor. over bevelled bds., stamped. Petrilla 13-42 1978 $8.50

MOORE, THOMAS 1779-1852   Lalla Rookh. New York and Nurnberg, n.d. 2 21/2 x 5", early 19th century, full leather, gilt spine, scuffed, Campe's Ed. Eaton 45-350 1978 £5

MOORE, THOMAS 1779-1852   The Loves of the Angels, a Poem. Philadelphia, 1823. 1st US ed., boards (shaky), lacks fly, good, octavo bound in cloth. Hyland 128-154 1978 £5

MOORE, THOMAS 1779-1852   The Loves of the Angels. 1823. 1st ed., orig. bds., spine gone. Eaton 45-351 1978 £10

MOORE, THOMAS 1779-1852   M.P. or The Blue Stocking--A Comic Opera in 3 Acts. 1811. Some staining throughout, modern 1/2 calf, gilt spine. Eaton 45-349 1978 £50

MOORE, THOMAS 1779-1852   Marriage Customs and Ceremonies and Modes of Courtship of the Various Nations of the Universe. New York, 1827. 12mo, frontis, orig. mottled calf, spine gilt, black label, good. Jarndyce 16-889 1978 £14.50

MOORE, THOMAS 1779-1852   Melodies by ... Philadelphia, 1821. 1st. U.S. ed., lacking front endpaper, 1/2 calf, worn. Eaton 45-353 1978 £10

MOORE, THOMAS 1779-1852   Memoirs of the Life of Richard Brinsley Sheridan. 1825. 1st ed., 4to., orig. 1/4 cloth, good. Hyland 128-519 1978 £30

MOORE, THOMAS 1779-1852   The Poetical Works Collected by Himself. 1840-1. 1st. ed., 10 vols., frontis & vignette titles, orig. green ribbed cloth, spines lettered in gilt, mint set. Jarndyce 16-887 1978 £48

MOORE, THOMAS 1779-1852   The Poetical Works of Thomas Moore. London, 1849. 10 vols., 12mo., a.e.g., engr. frontis, foxed, bound in full green calf with heavy gilt ornamentation on spines, raised bands, better than fine cond. Current 24-36 1978 $55

MOORE, THOMAS 1779-1852   Poetical Works, With a Life of the Author. 1859. Cr. 8vo, illus. by Thomas Corbould, contemp. morocco blocked elaborately in black bds., title gilt on spine, embossed edges, gilt. Eaton 45-352 1978 £8

MOORE, THOMAS 1779-1852   Songs, Ballads & Sacred Songs. 1849. 1st. ed., attractive half calf, spine gilt, black labels, v.g. Jarndyce 16-888 1978 £9.50

MOORE, THOMAS 1779-1852   Travels of an Irish Gentleman in Search of a Religion. n.d. Good, octavo bound in cloth, reprint. Hyland 128-155 1978 £4

MOORE, THOMAS 1821-1887   The Nature Printed British Ferns. London, 1859-60. Octavo ed., 2 vol., colour plts., fine, half red mor. K Books 244-239 1978 £240

MOORE, THOMAS STURGE   A Brief Account of the Origin of the Eragny Press and a Note on the Relations of the Printed Book as a Work of Art to Life. Eragny Press, 1903. One of 235 copies on paper, woodcuts, orig. patterned bds., tissue guards between each leaf, edges uncut. George's 635-889 1978 £325

MOORE, THOMAS STURGE   The Sea is Kind. New York, 1914. First U.S. ed., very good. Bell Book 16-650 1978 £5

MOORE, WILLIAM HENRY   The Commandments of Men. Toronto, 1925. Hood 116-307 1978 $7.50

MOORE, WILLIAM HENRY   Underneath it All. Pickering, 1942. Hood 117-433 1978 $15

MOORE'S Almanack for 1846. Dublin. Disbound, octavo bound in cloth, reprint. Hyland 128-139 1978 £10

MOORE-WILSON, MINNIE   The Seminoles of Florida. Philadelphia, 1896. 1st ed., illus., orig. cloth, very good. MacManus 239-1202 1978 $35

MOOREHEAD, ALAN   Mediterranean Front. New York, (1942). Maps. Biblo 247-788 1978 $12.50

MOOREHEARD, WARREN K.   The Stone Age in North America. New York, 1910. 2 vols., spine worn top & bottom, Archibald Crozier's copy. Baldwins' 51-128 1978 $127.50

MOOREHEAD, WARREN K.   Stone Ornaments Used by Indians in the United States and Canada. Andover, 1917. 1st ed., 4to., illus., color plts., good, orig. cloth, bit soiled. MacManus 239-1203 1978 $25

MOORMAN, F. W.   Robert Herrick; A Biographical and Critical Study. 1910. Octavo, good. Upcroft 10-454 1978 £5

MOORMAN, J. J.   The Mineral Waters of the United States and Canada, with a Map and Plates, and General Directions for Reaching Mineral Springs. Baltimore, 1867. Sm. 8vo., spine partly torn, 1st ed. Morrill 239-181 1978 $20

MORA, ANGEL HERREROS DE
Please turn to
HERREROS DE MORA, ANGEL

MORA, JO   Trail Dust and Saddle Leather. New York, 1946. Illus. by drawings by author, 1st ed., name in ink on flyleaf, d.w. Biblo 248-278 1978 $20

MORAIS, HENRY S.   The Jews of Philadelphia. Their History from the Earliest Settlements to the Present Time. Philadelphia, 1894. Very scarce. MacManus 239-1627 1978 $75

MORAL Amusement,.... Hallowell, 1808. 12mo, 1st Hallowel ed., orig. material by unknown author, paper over oak, very good. Victoria 34-549 1978 $55

MORALES, J.B.   Esposicion...La Guerra Contra Tejas Y Los Estados Unidos De America. Guanajuato, 1845. Original printed wr., near mint, woodcut. Jenkins 116-963 1978 $225

THE MORALS of Odd-Fellowship. Auburn, 1854. 24mo., gilt cloth. Butterfield 21-103 1978 $7.50

MORAN, CHARLES   The Sea of Memories...Mediterranean Strife. New York, 1942. Plts., 1st ed., orig. bind. Petrilla 13-43 1978 $7.50

MORAN, FRANK E.   Bastiles of the Confederacy, a Reply to Jefferson Davis. Baltimore, Md., 1890. Bell Wiley's copy. Broadfoot 46-183 1978 $10

MORAN, P. F.   Irish Saints in G. B. 1903. New England ed., good, octavo bound in cloth. Hyland 128-159 1978 £6

MORAN, P.F.   Occasional Papers. Dublin, 1890. 1st ed., 1/2 leather, very good. Hyland 128-160 1978 £5

MORAN, P.F.   Occasional Papers. Dublin, 1899. 1/2 leather, very good, reprint. Hyland 128-161 1978 £4.50

MORAND, PAUL   Open all Night. 1923. Ltd. to 275 copies, signed by author, sq. 8vo. George's 635-917 1978 £6.50

MORANGE, WILLIAM   A Poem Delivered...on the Occasion of the Opening of Tweddle Hall, June 28th, 1860. Albany, 1860. Disbound. Butterfield 21-47 1978 $12.50

MORANT, GEORGE C.   Chile and the River Plate in 1891. London, 1891. Illus. Biblo BL781-115 1978 $10

MORAVIA, ALBERTO   Due Cortigiane e Serata di Don Giovanni. Rome, 1945. Orig. paper wrappers, loose, spine torn. Eaton 45-356 1978 £5

MORAVIA, ALBERTO   L'Epidemia. Roma, 1944. Wrappers. Eaton 45-355 1978 £5

MORAZZONI, GIUSEPPE   La Rilegatura Piemonese nel '700. Milano, 1929. Ltd. to 300 copies, plts., demy 4to., orig. wrappers. Forster 130-59 1978 £30

MORCAY, R.   Saint Antonin; Archeveque de Florence 1389-1459. Tours and Paris, 1914. Plts., recent buckram, 8vo. Upcroft 12-304 1978 £10

MORDAUNT, ELINOR   The Tales of Elinor Mordaunt. London, 1934. First ed., orig. binding, very nice. Rota 211-409 1978 £5

MORDAUNT, ELIZABETH   Anecdotes, &c. of .... 1810. 1st. & only ed., 12mo, contemp. half red calf, gilt, large copy. Fenning 32-232 1978 £14.50

MORDAUNT, JOHN, VISCOUNT   Letterbook, 1658-60. 1945. Allen 234-1159 1978 $7.50

MORDECAI, SAMUEL   Richmond in By-Gone Days. 1946. Good. Nestler Rare 78-45 1978 $10

MORDECAI, SAMUEL   Virginia, Especially Richmond, in By-Gone Days; with a Glance at the Present... Richmond, 1860. 2nd ed., orig. cloth, worn along spine, but nice. MacManus 239-1883 1978 $35

MORDEN, ROBERT   An Introduction to Astronomy, Geography, Navigation, and Other Mathematical Sciences.... London, 1702. 8vo., plts., map, contemp. panelled calf, joints weak, first (and only?) ed. Quaritch 977-195 1978 $300

MORE, HANNAH   Coelebs in Search of a Wife. 1809. 5th. ed., 2 vols., spotted, contemp. cloth. Eaton 45-358 1978 £8

MORE, HANNAH   Hints towards Forming the Character of a Young Princess. 1809. 2 vols., contemp. binding of full panelled calf, all edges gilt, nice, 8vo. Howes 194-399 1978 £40

MORE, HANNAH   Ode to Dragon, Mr. Garrick's House-Dog, at Hampton. London, 1777. 4to, disbound, 1st ed. Ximenes 47-211 1978 $150

MORE, HANNAH   Sacred Dramas. 1782. 2nd. ed., orig. calf, red label, leading hinge weak otherwise v.g. Jarndyce 16-146 1978 £21

MORE, HANNAH   Sacred Dramas; Chiefly Intended for Young
Persons: The Subjects Taken From the Bible. Dublin, 1784. 1st. Irish ed.,
half-title, 12mo, recent bds., light browning, very good copy. Fenning 32-234
1978 £24

MORE, HANNAH   Strictures on the Modern System of Female
Education. London, 1799. 2 vols., 8vo, contemporary half red morocco, spines
gilt, 2nd ed., corrected, half-title in 1st vol., fine copy. Ximenes 47-212
1978 $125

MORE, HANNAH   Strictures on the Modern System of Female
Education. Dublin, 1800. 5th. ed., portrait, lg. 12mo, contemp. calf, little
dusty, very good copy. Fenning 32-235 1978 £8.50

MORE, HANNAH   Works. 1830. New ed., 11 vols., portrait,
full blue calf, spines gilt, 8vo. George's 635-1394 1978 £105

MORE, HENRY   Discourses on Several Texts of Scripture. 1692.
Contemp. panelled calf, first ed, 8vo. Howes 194-76 1978 £45

MORE, HENRY   Enchiridium Ethicum. Amsterdam, 1679.
12mo., wrs. Salloch 348-160 1978 $65

MORE, HENRY   Enchiridium Ethicum. London, 1711. 4th
ed., 8vo., calf. Salloch 348-159 1978 $125

MORE, HENRY   Enchiridium Metaphysicum, Sive de Rebus In-
corporeis Succincta and Luculenta Dissertatio. London, 1671. 4to., contemp.
calf, armorial bind., 1st ed., fine. Salloch 348-161 1978 $150

MORE, HENRY   Historia Missionis Anglicanae Societatis Iesu,....
St. Omer, 1660. 1st ed., folio, engraved t.p., bookplates, full contemp. calf,
hinges cracked, fine. Bennett 20-145 1978 $450

MORE, HENRY   A Modest Enquiry into the Mystery of Iniquity.
1664. Folio, first ed., contemp. full mor., very good. Howes 194-77 1978
£125

MORE, THOMAS   The English Works of ... 1931. 2 vols., roy.
8vo, buckram. Eaton 45-359 1978 £30

MORE, THOMAS   Lucubrationes...Utopia. Progymnasmata.
Epigrammata. Ex Luciano Conversa Quaedam Declamatio...Epistolae. Basle,
Episcopius, 1563. Thick 8vo., full calf. Salloch 348-163 1978 $650

MORE, THOMAS   La Republique d'Utopie, par Thomas Maure,
Chancelier d'Angleterre. Lyons, 1559. Sm. 8 vo., nice copy, 18th century
calf, gilt back (small repair on spine). Schafer 19-31 1978 sFr. 1,200

MORE, THOMAS   Utopia: Containing an Excellent, Learned,
Wittie, and Pleasant Discourse of the Best State of a Publike Weale... London,
1624. Sm. 4to., new calf, back gilt, 4th ed. of Eng. version. Salloch 348-164
1978 $300

MORE, THOMAS   Utopia. 1685. 8vo, lacks initial & final blank
leaves, 18th. century bds., calf spine, title slightly worn, light worming. Hannas
54-39 1978 £35

MORE, THOMAS   Idee D'Une Republique Heureuse: ou L'Utopie
De Thomas Morus... Amsterdam, 1730. Plts., 8vo., old mor. Salloch 348-
165 1978 $70

MORE, THOMAS   Utopia in Latin. 1903. 4to., tear at base of
spine, ltd. to 210 copies. Allen 234-1368 1978 $25

MORE, THOMAS   Utopia. (Chelsea, 1906). Small folio, blue
holland boards with linen back, 1 of 100 copies (only 80 for sale), large initials
designed by Eric Gill, fine. Duschnes 220-6a 1978 $1050

MORE, THOMAS   Utopia. 1906. Folio, bds., linen back, fine
copy, ltd. to only 100 copies on paper. Quaritch 979-11 1978 $1,250

MOREAU, B.-A.   Fondateur de la Congregation de Sainte-Croix
(1799-1873). Montreal, 1923. Quarto. Hood 117-357 1978 $15

MOREAU, F. FREDERIC   Aux Etats-Unis Notes de Voyage. Paris, 1888.
Original pr. wr., 1st ed. Ginsberg 14-635 1978 $50

MOREAU, FRANCOIS JOSEPH Traite pratique des accouchemens. Paris, 1837-
1841. 1st ed., 2 vols. in contemp. half-calf, 8vo, folio, atlas in half-cloth, rebacked. Gilhofer 75-81 1978 SFr 1,200

MOREAU-VAULTIER, CHARLES Les Portraits de l'enfant. (c. 1890). Plts.,
illus., folio, new binders buckram. George's 635-38 1978 £21

MOREL, A. M. T.   Traite Pratique des Feux d'Artifice pour le Spectacle et pour la Guerre. Paris, 1800. Plts., 8vo., calf-backed bds. F. Edwards
1013-376 1978 £45

MORELAND, ARTHUR   Dickens Landmarks In London. London, 1931.
1st ed., illus. by author, imperial 8 vo., orig. pictorial bds., line drawings,
very good or better. Limestone 9-88 1978 $20

MORES, EDWARD ROWE   A Dissertation Upon English Typographical
Founders & Founderies. New York, Merrymount Press, 1924. 1 of 250 copies,
orig. marbled cloth, portr., 8vo., very good. Americanist 103-132 1978 $85

MORET, ALEXANDRE   The Nile and Egyptian Civilization. London,
1927. 3 maps, 24 plts., text-illus., 8vo, orig. cloth. K Books 239-341 1978
£7

MORFI, JUAN AGUSTIN   History of Texas, 1673-1779. Albuquerque,
1935. 2 vols., limited to 500 copies, signed presentation inscription from
Castaneda to Frederick C. Chabot, fine. Jenkins 116-971 1978 $285

MORFIT, HENRY M.   Condition of Texas: The Political, Military,
and Civil Conditions of Texas. Washington, 1836. Boards with leather label.
Jenkins 116-972 1978 $85

MORFORD, HENRY   The Days of Shoddy. Philadelphia, 1863.
1st ed., portrait, orig. cloth, good. Limestone 9-208 1978 $25

MORGAN, ALBERT TALMON Yazoo, or On the Picket Line of Freedom in
the South. Washington, 1884. Rear hinge cracked, spine worn, bookplate
removed from inside, Bell Wiley's copy. Broadfoot's 44-543 1978 $40.00

MORGAN, C. P.   The Jolly Boat or Perils & Disasters Illustrating
Courage, Endurance, & Heroism... 1865. 1st. ed., 2 vols., orig. dark green
cloth, half titles, v.g. Jarndyce 16-8● 1978 £10.50

MORGAN, CHARLES   The Gun Room. 1919. 1st. ed., inscription on
fly leaf from author, cr. 8vo, one joint defective. Traylen 88-303B 1978 £30

MORGAN, CHARLES   The Judges Story. 1947. 1st. ed. in d.w., cr.
8vo, inscription on fly leaf from author. Traylen 88-303C 1978 £8

MORGAN, CHARLES   The Judge's Story. 1947. Pres. copy inscribed
by author, good, first English ed. Bell Book 16-651 1978 £6.50

MORGAN, CHARLES   The River Line. 1949. 1st. ed., frayed d.w.,
cr. 8vo, inscription on fly leaf from author. Traylen 88-303D 1978 £5

MORGAN, CHARLES   Sparkenbroke. London, 1936. 1st ed. Biblo
BL781-1088 1978 $9.50

MORGAN, CHARLES   Sparkenbroke. 1936. 1st. ed., cr. 8vo,
inscription on fly leaf from author. Traylen 88-303E 1978 £8

MORGAN, E. R.   Essays Catholic and Missionary. London, 1928.
8vo, orig. cloth. K Books 239-342 1978 £6

MORGAN, ELIZABETH   A Descriptive Catalogue of an Exhibition of
the Works of William Blake. Philadelphia, 1939. Frontispiece, plts., orig.
wr., cover plate, scarce, very good or better. Limestone 9-26 1978 $85

MORGAN, FREDERICK   Overture to Overlord. 1950. Austin 80-221
1978 $10

MORGAN, GEORGE H.   Annals, Comprising Memoirs, Incidents and
Statistics of Harrisburg From the Period of Its First Settlement. Harrisburg, 1858.
MacManus 239-1575 1978 $30

MORGAN, GEORGE H.   Annals of Harrisburg.... N.P., 1906. Index, enlarged & best ed., orig. binding, 8vo. Americanist 101-101 1978 $25

MORGAN, HENRY   Boston Inside Out! Sins of a Great City!... Boston, 1880. Cloth, bookplt. Hayman 72-234 1978 $15

MORGAN, HENRY JAMES   Sketches of Celebrated Canadians and Persons Connected with Canada, from the Earliest Period in the History of the Province, Down to the Present Time. Quebec, 1862. Hood 116-44 1978 $65

MORGAN, HENRY JAMES   The Tour of H. R. H. the Prince of Wales Through British America and the United States. Montreal, 1860. Hood 117-585 1978 $30

MORGAN, J. DE   Fouilles A Dahchour, Mars-Juin 1894... Vienna, 1895. 4to, plts., illus., orig. cloth, rebacked, t.e.g.   Edwards 1012-225 1978 £20

MORGAN, JAMES   Stock Certificate in the Town of Swartwout, Texas, 1838, signed by Morgan as owner. Swartwout, 1838. Jenkins 116-973 1978 $75.

MORGAN, JAMES M.   Recollections of a Rebel Reefer. Boston, 1917. 1st ed. MacManus 239-900 1978 $35

MORGAN, JOHN ED.   University Oars. London, 1873. Sm. 8vo., half calf, marbled bd. sides, ex-lib., top third of spine lacking, 1st ed.   Morrill 239-182 1978 $12.50

MORGAN, JOHN HARTMAN   The New Irish Constitution. (1912). Ex lib, good, octavo bound in cloth, reprint. Hyland 128-162 1978 £4.50

MORGAN, JOHN HILL   The Life Portraits of Washington and Their Replicas. Philadelphia, (1931). 1st ed., thick sm. folio, illus., colored frontis., uncut, orig. cloth, very fine, d.j., pub. box, ltd. to 900 copies. MacManus 239-693 1978 $110

MORGAN, JOHN HILL   Life Portraits of George Washington. Philadelphia, (1931). 4to, fine copy in slip box. Baldwins' 51-129 1978 $75

MORGAN, JOHN HILL   A Sketch of Life of John Ramage, Miniature Painter. 1930. Illus., ltd. to 300 copies. Nestler Rare 78-200 1978 $20

MORGAN, JOHN HUNT   The Great Indiana-Ohio Raid. Louisville, Ky., n.d. Illus., Bell Wiley's copy. Broadfoot 46-184 1978 $8

MORGAN, JOHN PIERPONT   Pictures in the Collection of...at Prince's Gate and Dover House, London.... 1907. 3 parts in 1 vol., 8vo., half levant mor. extra, gilt panelled spine. Quaritch 983-223 1978 $35

MORGAN, JOSEPH   Phoenix Britannicus. 1732. 6 vols., 4to., contemp. calf. P. M. Hill 142-177 1978 £45

MORGAN, SYDNEY OWENSON, LADY   The Missionary. 1811. Second ed., 3 vols. in 1, 12mo., 19th century half calf, portrait, good. P. M. Hill 142-194 1978 £48

MORGAN, SYDNEY OWENSON, LADY   The O'Briens and the O'Flahertys. A Natural Tale.... London, 1827. 4 vols., contemp. binders cloth, 1st ed., covers very slightly worn, fine. MacManus 238-357 1978 $110

MORGAN, SYDNEY OWENSON, LADY   O'Donnell. A National Tale. London, 1814. 3 vols., later 3/4 calf, 1st ed., very good, lacking half-titles in vos vols. 2 and 3. MacManus 238-356 1978 $90

MORGAN, T. R.   Californian Sketches. 1898. Orig. cloth, good. Jarndyce 16-894 1978 £5

MORGAN, THOMAS J.   The Present Phase of the Indian Question.... Boston, 1891. Orig. pr. wr., chipped, 1st ed. Ginsberg 14-636 1978 $45

MORGAN, WILLIAM HENRY   Personal Reminiscences of the War of 1861-5. Lynchburg, 1911. Front hinge reglued and wrinkled, stamp on front f/l, Bell Wiley's copy. Broadfoot's 44-654 1978 $36

MORGAN, WILLIAM THOMAS   Queen Anne's Canadian Expedition of 1711. Kingston, 1928. Card cover. Hood's 115-124 1978 $12.50

MORGANN, MAURICE 1726-1802   An Essay on the Dramatic Character of Sir John Falstaff. 1820. Contemp. calf, rebacked, second ed., 8vo. Howes 194-457 1978 £28

MORGENSTERN, GEORGE   Pearl Harbor. 1947. Austin 80-222 1978 $12.50

MORGENSTERN, GEORGE   Pearl Harbor, The Story of the Secret War. New York, 1947. Biblo 247-789 1978 $13.50

MORGENTHAU, HENRY   Ambassador Morgenthau's Story. 1918. Illus. Austin 79-496 1978 $7.50

MORIARTY, G. P.   Dean Swift & His Writings. 1893. 1st ed., very good, octavo bound in cloth. Hyland 128-609 1978 £5

MORICE, A. G.   Thawing Out the Eskimo. Boston, 1943. Hood 117-692 1978 $30

MORIER, JAMES   Abel Allnut. London, 1837. 3 vols., contemp. 3/4 calf, 1st ed., covers worn, lib. labels and stamp, some staining in vol. 1. MacManus 238-360 1978 $75

MORIER, JAMES   The Adventures of Hajji Baba of Ispahan. London, 1824. 3 vols., 12mo., contemp. 3/4 calf, leather labels, two lacking, 2nd ed. MacManus 238-358 1978 $75

MORIER, JAMES   The Adventures of Hajji Baba of Ispahan, in England. London, 1828. 2 vols., 12mo., contemp. 3/4 mor., somewhat rubbed, 1st ed. MacManus 238-359 1978 $85

MORIER, JAMES   Adventures of Hajji Baba of Ispahan in England. London, Edinburgh, & Dublin, 1835. Revised, corrected, illus., with notes by author, 2nd English ed., 1st 1 vol. ed., uncut, orig. cloth, top of upper hinge pulled, very good or better. Limestone 9-209 1978 $40

MORIER, JAMES   Hajji Baba of Ispahan. New York, 1937. Illus. in color, 1st ed., bookplt. Biblo BL781-611 1978 $8.50

MORIER, JAMES   The Adventures of Hajji Baba of Ispahan. New York: The Limited Editions Club, 1947. 8vo., 2 vols., illus., orig. half-mor. and floral bds., pub. box, 1 of 1,500 copies, spines a bit rubbed. MacManus 238-831 1978 $15

MORIER, JAMES   A Journey Through Persia, Armenia and Asia Minor to Constantinople, 1808-09. 1812. Folding maps, engraved plts., 4to, contemp. half diced calf, slightly worn. Edwards 1012-77 1978 £250

MORIER, JAMES   A Second Journey Through Persia, Armenia, and Asia Minor, to Constantinople, Between the Years 1810 and 1816... 1818. 4to., maps, plts., some in colour, some foxing, little light offsetting, old calf. Quaritch 983-346 1978 $875

MORIN, H.   Numismatique Feodale du Dauphine. 1854. 4to., half calf, worn, plts. Allen 234-694 1978 $50

MORIN, VICTOR   Les Medailles Decernees aux Indiens. Ottawa, 1916. Printed wrappers, numerous illus. Wolfe 39-402 1978 $35

MORINUS, JOANNES BAPTISTUS   Longitudinem Terrestrium Necnon Coelestium, Nova et Hactenus Optata Scientia. Parisiis, 1634. Woodcut diagrams, 4to., contemp. limp vellum, 1st ed. Offenbacher 30-103 1978 $475

MORISON, J. COTTER   Macaulay. London, 1889. New ed., cover dusty, very good or better. Limestone 9-185 1978 $7.50

MORISON, J. L.   British Supremacy and Canadian Autonomy. Kingston, 1913. Card cover. Hood 116-645 1978 $10

MORISON, J. L.   The Canadian People in the British Commonwealth; a Study in Sane Nationality. Newcastle upon Tyne, 1941. Card cover, inscribed by author. Hood 116-646 1978 $10

MORISON, SAMUEL ELIOT   Admiral of the Ocean Sea; A Life of Christopher Columbus. Boston, 1942. Maps by E. Raisz, drawings by B. Greene. Hood's 115-260 1978 $17.50

MORISON, SAMUEL ELIOT   The Battle of the Atlantic. 1947. Austin 80-223 1978 $10

MORISON, SAMUEL ELIOT   Builders of the Bay Colony. Boston, 1930. Illus., uncut, 1st ed., fine. MacManus 239-284 1978 $10

MORISON, SAMUEL ELIOT   Christopher Columbus, Admiral of the Ocean Sea. Boston, 1942. 2 vols., 1st ed., fine, illus., scarce. MacManus 239-317 1978 $55

MORISON, SAMUEL ELIOT   The Development of Harvard Univ. Since the Inauguration of President Eliot 1869-1929. Cambridge, 1930. Illus. MacManus 239-196 1978 $10

MORISON, STANLEY   An Account of Calligraphy & Printing in the 16th Century from Dialogues Attributed to Christopher Plantin. Cambridge, Merrymount Press, 1940. French & Flemish text, 12mo., 1 of 250 copies, bkplt. removed. Battery Park 1-415 1978 $50

MORISON, STANLEY   The Art of the Printer. London, 1925. 4to., cloth, spine darkened. Battery Park 1-412 1978 $100

MORISON, STANLEY   The Art of the Printer. London, 1925. Binding worn & rubbed. Baldwins' 51-194 1978 $37.50

MORISON, STANLEY   Fra Luca de Pacioli of Borgo S. Sepolcro. New York, Grolier Club, 1933. Decor. bds., vellum spine, near mint, worn slipcase, 1 of 397 copies. Dawson's 447-147 1978 $360

MORISON, STANLEY   German Incunabula in the B.M. London, 1928. Ltd. to 398 copies, folio, orig. cloth, d.w. defective. Forster 130-219 1978 £135

MORISON, STANLEY   Modern Fine Printing. London, 1925. No. 516 of ed. printed in English, folio, near to fine condition. Baldwins' 51-195 1978 $85

MORISON, STANLEY   The Typographic Arts. Cambridge, 1950. Illus., d.w. Battery Park 1-414 1978 $25

MORISSET, GERARD   Evolution d'une Piece d'Argenterie. Quebec, 1943. Card cover, plts. Hood 117-217 1978 $35

MORISSET, GERARD   Philippe Liebert. Quebec, 1943. Card cover, plts. Hood 117-218 1978 $35

MORITZ, KARL PHILIP   Gutter lehre oder Mythologische Dichtungen der Alten. Berlin, 1825. 6th ed., plates, original 3/4 leather, very good. Victoria 34-552 1978 $25

MORLAND, SAMUEL   Elevation des Eaux par toute sorte de Machines reduite a la Mesure, au Poids, a la Balance, par le moyen.... Pairs, 1685. 4to., contemp. calf, plts., orig. and only ed. Gurney 75-77 1978 £150

MORLAND, WILLIAM WALLACE   Diseases of the Urinary Organs. Philadelphia, 1859. Illus., 8vo., 1st ed., pres. from author. Morrill 239-183 1978 $15

MORLEY, CHRISTOPHER   The Blue & the Gray or War is Hell. New York, 1930. Mint in d.w. Desmarais B-469 1978 $10

MORLEY, CHRISTOPHER   The Bowling Green. New York, 1924. 12mo., 1st ed., d.w. torn & fr. flyleaf missing. Biblo 251-578 1978 $17.50

MORLEY, CHRISTOPHER   The Goldfish Under the Ice. London, 1929. 1 of 530 numbered copies, signed by author, d.j., nice. Houle 10-231 1978 $45

MORLEY, CHRISTOPHER   The Goldfish Under the Ice. London, 1929. 4to, pr. boards, no. 14 of Woburn Books, Mint in d.w., ed. limited to 500 copies, this is no. 400, signed by Morley, 1st ed., collector's cond. Desmarais 1-332 1978 $30

MORLEY, CHRISTOPHER   Hostages to Fortune. Haverford, 1925. 8vo, blue-orange decor. boards, blue cloth spine, endpapers browned with some foxing, ownership sign. on front free endpaper, inscription and sign. of author on flyleaf, very Good, 1st ed., collector's cond. Desmarais 1-333 1978 $10

MORLEY, CHRISTOPHER   John Mistletoe. New York, 1931. 1st ed. Biblo BL781-1089 1978 $7.50

MORLEY, CHRISTOPHER   Thorofare. New York, 1942. Near mint in chipped d.w. Desmarais B-470 1978 $15

MORLEY, CHRISTOPHER   The Trojan Horse. London, 1938. First English ed., orig. binding, very nice, d.w. Rota 211-415 1978 £5

MORLEY, CHRISTOPHER   Where the Blue Begins. London and New York, (1922). Tall 8vo, light blue cloth, gilt, pictorial endpapers, illus., 1st Amer. ed., fine. Duschnes 220-250 1978 $60

MORLEY, CHRISTOPHER   Where the Blue Begins. Garden City, 1922. 1st ed., cloth over pictorial bds., very good or better. Limestone 9-211 1978 $15

MORLEY, CHRISTOPHER   Where the Blue Begins. New York, 1923 (1922 on verso). Pictorial bds., cloth spine. Eaton 45-360 1978 £6

MORLEY, HENRY   Ireland under Elizabeth & James 1st. 1890. Good, octavo bound in cloth, reprint. Hyland 128-164 1978 £7.50

MORLEY, HENRY   Memoirs of Bartholomew Fair With Facsimile Drawings Engraved Upon Wood. London, Frederick Warne, n.d. Cr. 8vo, orig. cloth, binding damp-stained, good. Sexton 7-171 1978 £5

MORLEY, HENRY   Palissy the Potter. London, 1852. 2 vols., 8vo., decor. cloth. Salloch 345-141 1978 $65

MORLEY, HENRY   Shorter English Poems. Cassell, c. 1880. Woodcuts, roy. 8vo., half roan gilt, a little scuffed but good. K Books 244-418 1978 £8

MORLEY, JOHN   Life of William Ewart Gladstone. 1903. Illus., 3 vols., 8vo. George's 635-661 1978 £5.25

MORLEY, MARGARET W.   The Carolina Mountains. Boston, (1913). Illus., 1st ed., Homespun bind., paper label torn. Biblo BL781-254 1978 $10

MORLEY, MARGARET W.   The Carolina Mountains. Boston, (1913). Illus. MacManus 239-1844 1978 $12.50

MORLEY, MARGARET W.   The Carolina Mountains. Boston, 1913. Ex-lib. Broadfoot 50-147 1978 $12

MORMONISM Not Christianity as Proved in a Discussion Between a Mormon Elder and a Defender of Evangelical Christianity;.... [Norwich, c.1850]. Disbound. Ginsberg 14-637 1978 $50

THE MORMONS: Or Latter-Day Saints With Memoirs of Joseph Smith "The American Mahomet". 1852. 3rd. ed., 40 engravings, fine, bright, copy, stamped in blind, spine gilt. Jarndyce 16-897 1978 £28

MORNEWECK, EVELYN FOSTER   Chronicles of Stephen Foster's Family. Pittsburgh, 1944. 2 vols., illus. MacManus 239-753 1978 $15

MORNING Conversations of a Governess and Her Pupils... London, 1830. Frontis, fcap. 8vo, orig. quarter leather. Traylen 88-189 1978 £25

MORO, GAETANO   Abstract of a Report on the Practicability of Forming a Communcation between the Atlantic and Pacific Oceans,.... (London), n.d.(ca. 1845). 8vo, original tan printed wr., 1st ed., map, fine copy, scarce. Ximenes 47-213 1978 $80

MORRELL, W. WILBERFORCE   The History and Antiquities of Selby,.... Selby, 1867. 8vo, contemporary full green morocco, gilt, spine gilt, a.e.g., 1st ed., mounted photographs by W. Monkhouse, errata slip, fine copy. Ximenes 47-214 1978 $125

MORRELL, WILLIAM   New England or a Brief Enarration of the Ayre, Earth, Water, Fish and Fowles of that Country... Boston, 1895. 1 of 100 no. copies, nice copy, orig. leather-backed bds., untrimmed, orig. pub. in 1625. MacManus 239-318 1978 $35

MORRELL, WILLIAM PARKER   British Colonial Policy in the Age of Peel and Russell. London, 1930. Hood 116-647 1978 $65

MORRELL, WILLIAM PARKER   The Gold Rushes. London, 1940. Maps. Hood 116-648 1978 $15

MORREN, CHARLES FRANCOIS ANTOINE   Responsio Ad Quaestionem Ab Ordine Disciplinarum Mathematicarum Et Physicarum In Academia Gandaviensi Anno 1825 Propositam. (1829?). 4to., engr. plts., contemp. marbled bds., backed in lea., worn, some browning & foxing, good uncut, lg. paper copy from library of Dr. Charles Atwood Kofoid, bkplt., 1st ed., rare. Zeitlin 245-321 1978 $125

MORREY, LEWIS   The Great Historical, Geographical and Poetical Dictionary... 1694. 1st. ed., folio, licence leaf orig. panelled calf, hinges worn, lacking free end-papers, bookplt. of Earl Fitzwilliam. Jarndyce 16-19 1978 £85

MORRICE, DAVID   Mentor; or the Moral Conductor of Youth From The Academy to Manhood. London, 1801. 1st ed., 8vo, old half calf, worn. Traylen 88-190 1978 £20

MORRILL, E. N.   History and Statistics of Brown County, Kansas, From Its Earliest Settlement to the Present Time Embracing Incidents and Hardships of Pioneer Life... Hiawatha, 1876. Original printed wr., piece missing, 1st ed. Ginsberg 14-458 1978 $115

MORRILL, FRANK L.   Southern California:.... Los Angeles, 1886. Illus., original pictorial [map] printed wr., 1st ed. Ginsberg 14-159 1978 $100

MORRILL, JUSTIN S.   State of the Union. Speech of Hon..., of Vermont, in the House...February 18, 1861. (Washington, 1861). Unbound as issued. Hayman 72-483 1978 $7.50

MORRIS, ANTHONY P.   The Mountain Cannoneer... New York, 1889. Self wrps. Hayman 71-131 1978 $7.50

MORRIS, CHARLES EVANS   Modern Rejuvenation Methods. New York, 1926. Rittenhouse 49-565 1976 $7.50

MORRIS, CLAVER   The Diary of a West Country Physician. 1934. Plts., cloth spotted, octavo, good. Upcroft 10-124 1978 £5

MORRIS, D. B.   The Stirling Merchant Gild, and Life of John Cowane. Stirling, 1919. 8vo. George's 635-366 1978 £6

MORRIS, EDWARD   A Short Enquiry into the Nature of Monopoly and Forestalling. 1796. Second ed., 8vo., contemp. russia, rather coarsely mor. rebacked. P. M. Hill 142-178 1978 £30

MORRIS, FELIX   Reminiscences. New York, (1892). 12mo., illus, author's signed pres. Biblo 247-905 1978 $17.50

MORRIS, FRANCIS ORPEN   Anecdotes of Natural History. London, n.d. "1875" inscription, plates by Harrison Weir, impressed gilt and black binding, light hinge cracking and cup mark on lower cover. Victoria 34-553 1978 $25

MORRIS, FRANCIS ORPEN   A History of British Birds. London, 1891. Third ed., newly revised, 6 vols., coloured plts., roy. 8vo., good, modern half calf. K Books 2440241 1978 £250

MORRIS, FRANCIS ORPEN   A Natural History of the Nests and Eggs of British Birds. 1875. Coloured plts., 3 vols., roy. 8vo., covers rubbed. George's 635-1010 1978 £30

MORRIS, FRANCIS ORPEN   A Series of Picturesque Views of Seats of Noblemen and Gentlemen of Great Britain and Ireland. London, n.d. 6 vols., coloured plts., 4to., orig. gilt-decor. cloth. K Books 244-242 1978 £65

MORRIS, FRANK   Our Wild Orchids, Trails and Portraits. New York, 1929. 1st ed., orig. d.w., plts., some in color, orig. bind. Americanist 102-76 1978 $25

MORRIS, GEORGE S.   The Bottlers' Formulary. Kansas City, (1910). Sm. 8vo. Morrill 239-528 1978 $12.50

MORRIS, GOUVERNEUR   The Diary and Letters of. New York, 1888. 2 vols., portrs., 1st ed., fine, scarce. MacManus 239-319 1978 $45

MORRIS, H. R.   History of the Principal Transactions of the Irish Parliament from the Year 1634 to 1666. (1792). 2 vols., reprint, octavo bound in cloth. Hyland 128-963 1978 £20

MORRIS, HERMAN C.   War II in Pictures. 1942. Vol. I & Vol. 2, illus. Austin 80-225 1978 $27.50

MORRIS, I. N.   Speech of Hon. I. N. Morris, of Illinois, on Executive Abuses, and the Duty of the Democratic Party. (Washington, 1859?). Unbound as issued. Hayman 73-296 1973 $7.50

MORRIS, J. H.   Description of the Nagpur (Ambajhari) Water-Works... Bombay, 1872. 1st. ed., folio, photographs, red morocco, gilt, little rubbed & worn. Deighton 5-81 1978 £275

MORRIS, LEWIS   Songs Unsung. London, 1883. 1st ed., gilt cloth, very good or better. Limestone 9-212 1978 $15

MORRIS, LLOYD   The Rebellious Puritan: Portrait of Mr. Hawthorne. New York, 1927. Illus., stains on front cover. Biblo 247-826 1978 $15

MORRIS, M. C. F.   Yorkshire Folk Talk... London, 1892. Cr. 8vo, orig. cloth, good. Sexton 7-106 1978 £7.50

MORRIS, M. O'CONNOR   Memini or a Mingled Yarn. 1892. 1st ed., very good, octavo bound in cloth. Hyland 128-167 1978 £6

MORRIS, MAY   William Morris: artist, writer, socialist. Oxford, 1936. 1 of 750 copies, plts., 2 vols., linen-backed bds., very good, largely unopened, first English ed. Bell Book 16-654 1978 £110

MORRIS, R. K.   Catalogue for an Exhibition of Brass Rubbings, Including Hints on How to Rub a Brass. Card cover, illus. Hood 117-645 1978 $10

MORRIS, T. A.   Miscellany: Consisting of Essays, Biographical Sketches, and Notes on Travel. Cincinnati, 1854. Jenkins 116-975 1978 $225

MORRIS, W. A.   The Constitutional History of England to 1216. New York, 1930. 8vo. Upcroft 12-307 1978 £7.50

MORRIS, W. A.   The Frankpledge System. 1910. 8vo. Upcroft 12-306 1978 £10

MORRIS, WILLIAM   An Address Delivered...at the Distribution of Prizes to Students of the Birmingham Municipal School of Art of Feb. 21, 1894. London, Chiswick Press, 1898. Battery Park 1-39 1978 $50

MORRIS, WILLIAM   The Defence of Guenevere and Other Poems. (Hammersmith: The Kelmscott Press, 1892). 8vo., orig. limp vellum, 1st ed., 1 of 300 copies, covers slightly soiled, otherwise very nice. MacManus 238-810 1978 $400

MORRIS, WILLIAM   A Dream of John Ball and a King's Lesson. (Hammersmith, Kelmscott Press, 1892). 1 of 300 copies printed on handmade paper, orig. full limp vellum, blue silk ties, woodcut, fine, Edward Robeson Taylor's copy with his bookplate. Houle 10-177 1978 $625

MORRIS, WILLIAM   The Earthy Paradise. 1896-97. 8 vols., 8vo., vellum, bkplts., fine set, 225 copies prtd. Quaritch 979-214 1978 $1,000

MORRIS, WILLIAM   Gothic Architecture: A Lecture for the Arts and Crafts Exhibition Society. (Hammersmith, Kelmscott Press...London, 1893). Sm. 8vo., orig. linen-backed bds., slight foxing on front cover, orig. donor's inscription, 1 of 1,500 copies, 1st printing. Americanist 102-67 1978 $115

MORRIS, WILLIAM   Guenevere. London, (1930). 1 of 450 numbered copies on Barcham Green vellum, 4 to., cloth over bds., t.e.g., uncut, good-fine. Houle 10-232 1978 $ 45

MORRIS, WILLIAM   The Life and Death of Jason. London, 1867. Octavo, original cloth, paper label, hinges weakening, label stained, scarce, only 500 copies, Walter Pater's early signature on inside front cover, pencilled memoranda on last fly-leaf, great rarity. Bennett 20-146 1978 $200

MORRIS, WILLIAM   News from Nowhere. 1891. Lower cover soiled, bookplt., good, first English ed. Bell Book 16-652 1978 £15

MORRIS, WILLIAM   Of the Friendship of Amis and Amile... Upper Mall, Hammersmith: Kelmscott Press, 1894. 16mo., orig. canvas-backed blue-grey bds., 1st ed., 1 of 500 copies, fine. MacManus 238-811 1978 $125

MORRIS, WILLIAM   Sir Galahad: A Christmas Mystery. (Chicago), The Blue Sky Press, (1904). Tipped in frontis., decor. greenish-gray paper over green cloth bds., top edges trimmed, others uncut, 1 of 500 copies on paper. Bradley 49-24 1978 $65

MORRIS, WILLIAM   The Tale of the Emperor Coustans and of Over Sea. 1894. 16mo., bds., 525 copies prtd. Quaritch 979-357 1978 $180

MORRISON, ARTHUR   The Hole in the Wall. 1902. Covers little marked, some foxing, very good, first English ed. Bell Book 16-655 1978 £10

MORRISON, ARTHUR   The Painters of Japan. London, 1911. 2 vols., tipped-in plts., cloth, near fine, 1 of 150 signed and numbered sets. Dawson's 449-162 1978 $350

MORRISON, JOHN H.   History of American Steam Navigation. New York, 1903. 1st ed., lg. 8vo., cover little soiled, illus., scarce, orig. cloth, very good. Americanist 103-83 1978 $80

MORRISON, JOHN S.   History of American Steam Navigation. New York, 1903. Illus., 1st ed., scarce. MacManus 239-1776 1978 $50

MORRISON, RICHARD JAMES   Zadkiel's Legacy... London, 1842. 1st. ed., cr. 8vo, orig. cloth. Sexton 7-67 1978 £15

MORRISON & Fourmy's General Directory of the City of Austin, 1893-94. Austin, 1893. Jenkins 116-1383 1978 $100

MORROW, HONORE WILLSIE   Mary Todd Lincoln. New York, 1928. Illus., first ed. Biblo 248-65 1978 $16.50

MORROW, MAUDE E.   Recollections of the Civil War, from a Child's Point of View. Lockland, 1901. Bell Wiley's copy. Broadfoot's 44-544 1978 $15.00

MORROW, PRINCE A.   Social Diseases and Marriage. Philadelphia, (1904). 8vo., 1st ed. Morrill 239-184 1978 $10

MORROW, R. A. H.   Story of the Springhill Disaster... St. John, (1891). 2nd.ed., fully illus. Hood's 115-227 1978 $25

MORSE, A. REYNOLDS   The Works of M. P. Shiel: ... Los Angeles, 1948. Ltd., fine, d.j. Ballinger 11-81 1978 $25.00

MORSE, ANSON D.   Parties and Party Leaders. Boston, 1923. Cloth. Hayman 73-459 1978 $7.50

MORSE, CHARLES S.   Rules for the Courts of Texas, Adopted by Order of the Supreme Court. Austin, 1890. Full orig. calf, scarce. Jenkins 116-978 1978 $60

MORSE, EDWARD LINN   Samuel F. B. Morse His Letters and Journals. Boston, 1914. 2 vols., fine set, orig. cloth, illus., inscribed by the editor. MacManus 239-320 1978 $50

MORSE, H. B.   In the Days of the Taipings, Being the Recollections of Ting Kienchang...Captain in the Ever-Victorious Army and Interpreter-in-Chief to General Ward and Gen. Gordon... Salem, 1927. 1st ed., illus., orig. bind. Americanist 102-28 1978 $30

MORSE, JEDIDIAH   The American Gazetteer. Boston, 1797. 1st ed., thick 8vo, all maps present and fine, rebound in full calf, matching original, fine copy. Victoria 34-554 1978 $85

MORSE, JEDIDIAH   The American Geography... 1792. 2nd. ed., folding map, orig. bds., uncut, spine slightly cracked, 8vo. Edwards 1012-403 1978 £175

MORSE, JEDIDIAH   Annals of the American Revolution. Hartford, 1824. 1st ed., 8vo., copperplts., contemp. tree calf, rubbed, gilt decor's on spine, hinges reinforced, some foxing throughout most of text, good firm copy. Current 24-67 1978 $135

MORSE, JEDIDIAH   A Compendious History of New England. Charlestown, 1820. Third ed., contemp. calf. Wolfe 39-381 1978 $30

MORSE, JEDIDIAH   A New Gazetteer of the Eastern Continent Designed as a Second Volume to the American Gazetteer. Charlestown, 1802. 1st ed., all maps present, full calf. Victoria 34-555 1978 $125

MORSE, JOHN F.   Illustrated Historical Sketches of California,.... Sacramento, 1854. Illus., original pictorial printed wr. bound in half morocco. Ginsberg 14-160 1978 $450

MORSE, JOHN T.   Abraham Lincoln. Cambridge, Riverside Press, 1893. Portrs., fldg. map, 2 vols., 8vo., orig. bds., cloth backs, untrimmed, slightly dust soiled but nice, ed. ltd. to 250 copies, publisher's copy. Morrill 239-529 1978 $17.50

MORSE, JOHN T.   Abraham Lincoln. Cambridge, 1893. 1st ed., orig. cloth-backed bds., soiled, ports., ltd. to 250 numbered sets, 2 vols. MacManus 239-890 1978 $32.50

MORSE, JOHN T.   Abraham Lincoln. Cambridge, The Riverside Press, 1893. 1st ed., 8vo., 2 vols., t.e.g., lg. paper ed., ltd. to 250 copies, extra-illus., frontis portrs., full red crushed levant, gilt lettering & raised bands on spine, unusual. Current Misc. 8-33 1978 $135

MORSE, JOHN T.   Life and Letters of Oliver Wendell Holmes. 1896. Portraits, plts., 2 vols., cr. 8vo., orig. buckram. Howes 194-939 1978 £7.50

MORSE, JOHN T.   The Life of Alexander Hamilton. Boston, 1876. 2 vols., 1st ed., nice set, orig. cloth. MacManus 239-762 1978 $20

MORSE, LUCY GIBBONS   Breezes. New York, 1921. Sole ed., cloth over pictorial bds., mostly unopened, very good or better. Limestone 9-214 1978 $25

MORSE, SIDNEY   Household Discoveries. Petersburg, 1914. Illus., fine copy. Baldwins' 51-358 1978 $22.50

MORSE, SIDNEY E.   An Atlas of the U.S. on an Improved Plan,.... New Haven, 1823. Maps, binding worn. Nestler Rare 78-2 1978 $95

MORSE, WILLIAM INGLIS   Acadiensia Nova 1598-1779. London, 1935. 2 vols., illus., 1 of 375 copies, fold. maps, errata slip, mint. Hood 116-229 1978 $150

MORSE, WILLIAM INGLIS   Gravestones of Acadie... 1929. Pres. copy, inscribed by author, ltd. ed. of 500 copies, illus., roy. 8vo, full brown crushed morocco, spine gilt, t.e.g., others uncut, fine. Sawyer 299-131 1978 £185

MORSE, WILLIAM INGLIS   Gravestones of Acadie, and Other Essays on Local History, Genealogy and Parish Records of Annapolis County, Nova Scotia. London, 1929. Photos, one of 500 copies, mint. Hood's 115-228 1978 $75

MORSELLI, ENRICO   Suicide, an Essay on Comparative Moral Statistics. 1881. 1st. ed. in English, folding maps, sm. 8vo, recent bds., very good copy. Fenning 32-236 1978 £10.50

MORSELS For Merry and Melancholy Mortals. Ipswich, 1815. Coloured frontis, uncut, orig. grey bds., respined at some date, v.g. Jarndyce 16-255 1978 £25

MORTENSEN, WILLIAM   Print Finishing. San Francisco, (1943). Illus., sm. 4to. Biblo 247-399 1978 $9.50

MORTIMER, ALFRED S. Marks Church Philadelphia and Its Lady Chapel With Account of Its History and Treasures. New York. Ltd. 400, full blue morocco, some rubbing and hinge wear. Baldwins' 51-468 1978 $50

MORTIMER, JOHN Answer Yes or No. 1950. Very good, d.w., first English ed. Bell Book 16-998 1978 £4

MORTON, A. S. Sir George Simpson, Overseas Governor of the Hudson's Bay Company. Toronto, 1944. 1st ed., ex-lib., pen picture. Hood's 115-261 1978 $55

MORTON, ARTHUR The Ducal Coronet... New York, n.d. (185-?). Pict. wrps., sketches. Hayman 71-233 1978 $45

MORTON, ELEANOR Josiah White. Prince of Pioneers. New York, (1946). D.j. MacManus 239-828 1978 $8.50

MORTON, H. V. In Search of Ireland. 1932. 1st US ed., very good, octavo bound in cloth. Hyland 128-169 1978 £4

MORTON, J. B. Penny Royal. 1921. 12mo., decor. cloth, lower cover damp-stained, very good, first English ed. Bell Book 16-656 1978 £5

MORTON, NATHANIEL The New England's Memorial. Plymouth, 1826. 12mo., contemp. calf, ex-lib., lacks spine. Morrill 241-377 1978 $7.50

MORTON, NATHANIEL New England's Memorial... Boston, 1826. 8vo, orig. bds., rebacked, uncut, browning in text, folding reproduction of map. Edwards 1012-510 1978 £20

MORTON, OREN F. A History of Pendleton County West Virginia. Franklin, 1910. Fold. map, illus., very scarce, fine. MacManus 239-1137 1978 $60

MORTON, OREN F. A History of Rickbridge County, Virginia. Staunton, 1920. 4to., illus. MacManus 239-1131 1978 $45

MORTON, ROSALIE SLAUGHTER A Woman Surgeon. New York, 1937. Some wear. Rittenhouse 49-564 1976 $7.50

MORTON, THOMAS A Catholike Appeale for Protestants, out of the Romane Doctors. 1610. Folio, contemp. calf, rebacked and repaired. Howes 194-78 1978 £75

MORTON, THOMAS The School of Reform, or How to Rule a Husband. (1805). Cloth. Eaton 45-361 1978 £5

MORVILLO, ANTHONY A Dictionary of the Numpipu or Nez Perce Language, by a Missionary of the Society of Jesus, in the Rocky Mountains. St. Ignatius Mission, 1895. Half morocco, 1st ed. Ginsberg 14-627 1978 $175

MORYSON, FYNES An Itinerary. London, 1617. Woodcuts, folio, gilt-tooled red mor., few margins stained, very attractive, fine copy. Salloch 345-132 1978 $750

MOSBY, JOHN S. Mosby's War Reminiscences and Stuart's Cavalry Campaigns. Boston, 1887. Lacks one plate, cover badly stained & worn, front hinge cracked, Bell Wiley's copy. Broadfoot's 44-650 1978 $10

MOSCHCOWITZ, ELI Biology of Disease. New York, 1948. Rittenhouse 49-567 1976 $15

MOSCOW, WARREN Politics in the Empire State. New York, 1948. 1st ed., d.w. Biblo BL781-168 1978 .$10

MOSELEY, J. A. R. The Presbyterian Church in Jefferson. Austin, 1946. Limited ed of 675 copies printed by Carl Hertzog. Jenkins 116-979 1978 $18.50

MOSELEY, NICHOLAS Teacher's Manual. Cornell Maritime Press, 1943. Austin 80-230 1978 $10

MOSENTHAL, J. DE Ostriches and Ostrich Farming. London, 1877. 1st ed., ex-lib with pencil markings, spine letters, scattered foxing. 8vo, orig. cloth. Book Chest 17-263 1978 $75

MOSER, JEFFERSON The Salmon and Salmon Fisheries of Alaska. Washington, 1899. Illus., 4to, maps. Baldwins' 51-359 1978 $20

MOSES BEN MAIMON 1135-1204 Milloth ha-higgayon (in Hebrew). (Venice, 1550). Extremely rare editio princeps, woodcut, half vellum. Gilhofer 75-75 1978 SFr 3,700

MOSES, HENRY A Collection of Antique Vases, Altars, Paterae, Tripods, Candelaba, Sarcophagi... (London), (1814). 1st ed., 4to., illus., orig. cloth, fine. MacManus 239-694 1978 $50

MOSES, HENRY A Collection of Antique Vases, Altars, Paterae, Tripods, Candelabra, Sarcophagi Etc...from Various Museums...with Historical Essays. London, (1814). Plts., full leather, covers rubbed. Biblo BL781-444 1978 $57.50

MOSHER, ROBERT B. Executive Register of the United States, 1789-1902. Washington, 1905. 1st ed., ltd. to 1,500 copies, orig. bind. Petrilla 13-44 1978 $8.50

MOSHER, THOMAS B. The Germ. Portland, 1898. 8vo., no. 9 of only 25 numbered copies prtd. on Japan vellum, orig. plain protective wr. over cover, slip laid in, unusually fine. Battery Park 1-209 1978 $250

MOSS, FRANK The American Metropolis from Knickerbocker Days to the Present. New York, 1897. 3 vols., 1st ed., illus., orig. cloth, re-cased. MacManus 239-359 1978 $45

MOSSO, ANGELO Fatigue. New York, London, 1904. Sm. 8vo., illus., green cloth, gilt decor. & lettering, shaken, embossed stamp & bkplt. of former owner, bkplt. of Carleton B. Chapman, M. D., good copy. Zeitlin 245-173 1978 $45

THE MOST Ancient and Famous History of the Renowned Prince Arthur King of Britaine... London, 1634. 3 parts in 1 vol., printed in black letter, frontis., thick sm. 4to., full sprinkled calf, good. Traylen 88-98 1978 £480

MOTHER GOOSE Histories or Tales of Past Times told by Mother Goose with Morals. 1925. Hand coloured plts., 12mo., orig. gilt marbled bds., buckram sides, ltd. and numbered ed. Howes 194-1074 1978 £8

MOTHER GOOSE Mother Goose; or, National Nursery Rhymes and Nursery Songs. New York, 1872. 4to., wood eng. plts., orig. bright blue cloth, bright copy, scarce work. Houle 10-98 1978 $95

MOTHER GOOSE Mother Goose Jingles. London, n.d. (c. 1900). Pict. cloth, edges rubbed, shaken, pictures in color. Biblo 247-571 1978 $15

MOTHER GOOSE The Original Mother Goose Melodies. Boston, (1877). Very good. Victoria 34-338 1978 $20

THE MOTHER'S Gift. New York, c.1836. Chapbook, woodcuts, woodcuts on both wrappers, very good. Victoria 34-556 1978 $17.50

MOTHERWELL, MAIBEN C. A Memoir of the Late Albert Blest.... Dublin, 1843. Sole ed.?, portrait, sm. 8vo, orig. cloth, some light signs of use, very good. Fenning 32-237 1978 £6.50

MOTLEY, JOHN LOTHROP The Causes of the American Civil War. New York, 1861. 8vo., unbound. Morrill 241-378 1978 $8.50

MOTLEY, JOHN LOTHROP Merry-Mount: A Romance of the Massachusetts Colony. Boston, 1849. 1st edl, 2 vols., purple cloth, contemp. inscriptions, very good. Greene 78-86 1978 $90

MOTOR'S Factory Shop Manual for 1941. New York, 1940. Quarto, inner hinges cracked, scarce. Petrilla 13-45 1978 $27.50

MOTRAYE, AUBRY DE LA   Travels Through Europe, Asia and Into Part of Africa... 1732. Maps, 5 folding, plts., 3 vols., folio, contemp. calf, rebacked, few leaves slightly browned. Edwards 1012-32 1978 £500

MOTTLEY, JOHN   The History of the Life of Peter I. 1739. First ed., map, portraits, plts., 3 vols., contemp. calf gilt, rebacked, 8vo. Howes 194-414 1978 £50

MOTTRAM, RALPH HALE   Castle Island. London, 1931. Near mint in d.w. Desmarais B-472 1978 $15

MOTTRAM, RALPH HALE   Europa's Beast. London, 1930. First ed., one of 358 numbered copies, signed by author, very nice, orig. binding. Rota 211-422 1978 £6

MOTTRAM, RALPH HALE   Europa's Beast. London, 1930. Near mint in d.w. Desmarais B-473 1978 $15

MOTTRAM, RALPH HALE   Poems New and Old. London, 1930. 8vo, tan buckram, gilt lettering on spine, uncut, unopened, spine of d.w. lightly browned, very fine, 1 of 215 copies, signed by Mottram, 1st ed., collector's cond. Desmarais 1-334 1978 $30

MOTTRAM, RALPH HALE   Repose and other verses. London, 1907. First ed., wrappers, nice, signed autograph pres. inscription of Edward Thomas. Rota 211-704 1978 £50

MOTTRAM, RALPH HALE   Through Five Generations, the History of the Butterley Company. 1950. Map, illus., 8vo. George's 635-295 1978 £5

MOUBRAY, BONINGTON   A Practical Treatise on Breeding, Rearing, and Fattening All Kinds of Domestic Poultry. 1816. 2nd. ed., orig. blue bds., uncut, paper label, fine. Jarndyce 16-897 1978 £28

MOUHOUT, H.   Travels in the Central Parts of Indo-China (Siam), Cambodia and Laos 1858-60. 1864. 2 vols., folding & other plts., illus., orig. green cloth, lib. stamps on titles & flyleaves, 8vo. Edwards 1012-154 1978 £75

MOULE, THOMAS   Bibliotheca Heraldica Magnae Britannkae an Analytical Catalogue of Books on Genealogy,.... London, 1822. Large octavo, calf and marbled boards, rebacked preserving the orig. gilt-tooled spine, marbled endpapers, t.e.g., 1st ed. Bennett 7-79 1978 $125

MOULIN, PETER DU 1601-84   A Vindication of the Sincerity of the Protestant Religion in the Point of Obedience to Sovereignes. 1664. First ed., sm. 4to., contemp. calf. Howes 194-79 1978 £40

MOULTON, HAROLD G.   The Control of Germany & Japan. 1944. Austin 80-232 1978 $8.50

MOULTON, HAROLD G.   Controlling Factors in Economic Development. Washington, D.C., 1949. Biblo BL781-854 1978 $9

MOULTON, R. G.   Ancient Classical Drama. 1898. 2nd ed., corners of spine slightly worn. Allen 234-662 1978 $8

MOULTON-BARRETT, HARRY PEYTON   Cat. of the Papers. Sotheby, 1937. Plts., illus., med. 8vo., orig. wrappers. Forster 130-262 1978 £4

MOUNT Vernon, Va. (Washington, 1912). Wrps., little soiled, both externally and internally, photographic views. Hayman 71-750 1978 $7.50

MOUNT Vista Gold and Silver Mining Company.... New York, [1864]. Disbound, 1st ed. Ginsberg 14-735 1978 $75

MOUNTAIN, G. J.   Sermons. London, 1865. Cover scuffed. Hood 116-308 1978 $35

MOUNTAIN, G. J.   Visit to the Gaspe Coast. Quebec, 1943. Card cover, ltd. ed. Hood 117-358 1978 $15

MOUNTAIN, Moor and Loch. London, 1895. Plts., text-illus., one leaf loose, 8vo., cover slightly stained. K Books 244-243 1978 £6

MOUNTAINE, WILLIAM   A Description of the Lines Drawn on Gunter's Scale, as Improved by Mr. John Robertson, late Librarian to the Royal Society... London, 1778. Fldg. copperplts., 8vo., bds., 1st ed. Offenbacher 30-104 1978 $125

MOUNTEVANS, ADMIRAL LORD   Adventurous Life. (1946). 1st. ed., 8vo, orig. cloth, pres. copy to Winston Churchill. Sawyer 298-98 1978 £120

MOUNTFORD, J. F.   Index Rerum et Nominum in Scholiis Servii et Aelii Donati Tractatorum. 1930. Allen 234-663 1978 $10

MOUSSINOT, ABBE   Memoire sur la Ville Souterraine decouverie au pied du Mont Vesuve. Paris, 1748. 8vo., new half calf, very rare. King 7-347 1978 £100

MOVING, J. H.   Volks and Vaterlandslieder. Leipzig, c.1840. 12mo., 3/4 leather, front hinge cracked, some foxing, very good. Victoria 34-557 1978 $17.50

MOWAT, OLIVER   Christianity and Some of Its Evidences. Toronto, 1890. Card cover. Hood's 115-942 1978 $15

MOWRER, PAUL SCOTT   The House of Europe. 1945. Austin 80-233 1978 $7.50

MOWRIS, JAMES A.   A History of the One Hundred and Seventeenth Regiment NY Volunteers. Hartford, 1866. New cloth, Bell Wiley's copy. Broadfoot 46-346 1978 $25

MOWRIS, JAMES A.   A History of the One Hundred and Seventeenth Regiment, N. Y. Volunteers, Fourth Oneida, from...August, 1862 till...June 1865. Hartford, 1866. Butterfield 21-122 1978 $25

MOXON, JOSEPH   A Tutor to Astronomie and Geographie: or An Easie and speedy way to know the use of both the globes, coelestial and terrestrial. London, 1659. Calf, rebacked and somewhat worn. Dawson's 127-277 1978 $300

MOXON, JOSEPH   A Tutor to Astronomy and Geography. London, 1674. 4to., text illus., contemp. calf, rubbed, but fine copy, endpapers renewed, bkplt., 3rd ed., enlarged. Norman 5-204 1978 $250

MOYER, WILLARD   The Witchery of Sleep. New York, 1903. 8vo., 1st ed., pres. copy. Morrill 239-185 1978 $10

MOYLE, SETH   My Friend O. Henry. New York, 1914. Stiff printed wr., frontis photo of Porter, scarce work. Jenkins 116-1099 1978 $17.50

MUCH Instruction from Little Reading or,.... New York, 1827. 1st ed., 5 vols., 8vo, tree calf, leather labels, gilt rules and numbers, remarkably fine, light chewing on front edge of cover, rubbed spots. Victoria 34-559 1978 $85

MUCKERSY, JOHN   M. Gener. 1815. Fourth ed., 3 vols., contemp. half calf, 8vo. Howes 194-400 1978 £12.50

MUDD, JOSEPH A.   With Porter in North Missouri, A Chapter in the History of the War Between the States. Washington, 1909. Some marginal stains, front hinge cracked, cover lightly stained, Bell Wiley's copy. Broadfoot's 44-545 1978 $35

MUDDOCK, JOYCE EMERSON PRESTON   From Clue to Capture. A Series of Thrilling Detective Stories. London, n.d. (c.1893). Illus., pict. glazed boards, "yellow-back" format, front cover detached, spine scuffed. Greene 78-190 1978 $25

MUDGE, I. G.   A Thackeray Dictionary. 1910. Orig. cloth, 8vo. Howes 194-1258 1978 £5.50

MUDIE, ROBERT   The Air. 1835. Frontis. and vignette on title by G. Baxter, fcap, 8vo. George's 635-937 1978 £5

MUDIE, ROBERT   The Feathered Tribes of the British Islands. 1834. Coloured engraved frontispieces, coloured vignettes, coloured plts., 2 vols., post 8vo., covers faded and spotted. George's 635-1011 1978 £65

MUDIE, ROBERT   The Feathered Tribes of the British Islands. 1834.
Coloured plts., frontispieces, and vignettes, 2 vols., post 8vo., covers repaired
with selotape, Vol. 1 only lacks 5 plts. George's 635-1012 1978 £8.50

MUDIE, ROBERT   Spring, Summer, Autumn, Winter. London, 1837.
4 vols., each with Baxter frontis, sm. 8vo. Traylen 88- 611 1978 £30

MUELLER, HANS ALEXANDER   Woodcuts & Wood Engravings: How I Make
Them. New York, 1939. Cloth, illus. Dawson's 447-96 1978 $50

MUELLER, HENRY B.   The Whig Party in Pennsylvania. New York,
1922. Maps, orig. wrs. MacManus 239-1576 1978 $17.50

MUGGE, THEODORE   Afraia, A Norwegian & Lapland Tale; or, Life
and Love in Norway. Phil., 1854. Fir. Am. Ed., red cloth & gilt binding
damaged, contents good, scarce title. Greene 78-261 1978 $45.00

MUHLENBERG, D. HENRICO   Descripto Uberio Graminum Et Plantarum
Calamariarum Americae Septentrionalis Indigenarum Et Cicurum. Philadelphia,
1817. 1st ed., scarce work, contemp. calf, scuffed, joint weak, 8vo. Americanist
101-102 1978 $95

MUHLENBERG, WILLIAM AUGUSTUS   The Rebuke of the Lord. Jamaica,
1835. 8vo., new bds., 1st ed. Morrill 241-414 1978 $25

MUIR, EDWIN   Poor Tom. 1932. 1st. ed., bookseller's stamp
on f.e.p., cloth, faded and marked. Eaton 45-363 1978 £10

MUIR, EDWIN   Scottish Journey. 1935. Very good, d.w.,
first English ed. Bell Book 16-660 1978 £12.50

MUIR, EDWIN   The Three Brothers. 1931. Near fine, first
English ed. Bell Book 17-668 1978 £18.50

MUIR, JOHN   The Cruise of the Corwin. Boston & New York,
1917. Hand-colored frontis, plts., bds., cloth back, very fine, partly unopened,
worn d.w., slipcase, 1 of 550 numbered lg. paper copies. Dawson's 447-265
1978 $125

MUIR, JOHN   Our National Parks. Boston, 1901. 1st ed.,
illus., orig. decorated cloth, bookplt., very good. MacManus 239-321 1978
$50

MUIR, JOHN   A Thousand-Mile Walk to the Gulf. Boston,
1916. Trade ed., 8vo., orig. cloth. Book Chest 17-265 1978 $14

MUIR, JOHN   Travels in Alaska. Boston, 1915. 8vo, orig.
cloth, coloured illus., plts., some slight browning. Edwards 1012-511 1978 £15

MUIR, PERCIVAL HORACE   Book-Collecting as a Hobby. In a Series of Letters
to Everyman. London, n.d. Illus., orig. wrs. MacManus 238-988 1978 $10

MUIR, PERCIVAL HORACE   Talks on Book-Collecting. D.w. Battery Park
1-419 1978 $25

MUIR, THOMAS   The Telegraph... N.P., n.d. (1796). 1st. ed.,
4to., names inserted in a contemp. hand, rebound in brown bds., good. Jarndyce
16-147 1978 £60

MUIR, WILLA   Mrs. Ritchie. (1933). Very good, first English
ed. Bell Book 16-661 1978 £4.50

MUIRHEAD, JAMES PATRICK   The Life of James Watt, with Selections from His
Correspondence. London, 1858. Frontis., plts., text illus., 8vo., orig. cloth,
uncut, gilt, spine faded, hinges cracked, but very good copy, 1st ed. Norman
5-297 1978 $75

MULDER, ARNOLD   The Outbound Road. Boston, 1919. 1st ed.
Austin 79-498 1978 $20

MULERIUS, NICOLAUS   Tabulae Frisicae Lunae-Solares Quadruplices e
Fontibus Cl. Ptolemaei, Regis Alphonsi, Nic. Copernici et Tychonis Brahe recens
Constructae.... Alkmaer, 1611. 4to., engraved title, woodcut, contemp. vel-
lum, 1st ed., autograph signature of author. Gilhofer 74-9 1978 sFr 1,600

MULFORD, PRENTICE   Prentice Mulford's Story: Life by Land and Sea.
New York, 1889. Orig. cloth, 1st ed. Ginsberg 14-700 1978 $35

MULFORD, WILLIAM C.   Historical Tales of Cumberland County, N.J.
Bridgeton, 1941. Illus., maps, scarce, fine, d.j. MacManus 239-1303 1978
$37.50

MULGAN, ALAN   Home: a New Zealander's Adventure. 1927.
Woodcuts by Clare Leighton, cloth-backed bds., very good, first English ed. Bell
Book 17-493 1978 £5

MULGRAVE, JOHN SHEFFIELD, 3RD EARL OF
Please turn to
BUCKINGHAM, JOHN SHEFFIELD, DUKE OF

MULHERN, JAMES   A History of Secondary Education in Pennsylvania.
Philadelphia, 1933. 1st ed., illus., orig. cloth, very fine. MacManus 239-
1578 1978 $15

MULHOLLAND, ROSA   The Late Miss Hollingford. 1887. 1st. separate
English ed., plts., 8vo, orig. cloth, gilt, illus., nice copy. Fenning 32-238
1978 £6.50

MULLBACH, LOUISA   Historical Romances. New York, 1898. Frontispieces, ltd. to 1000 sets, 20 vols., spines faded, 8vo. George's 635-1396
1978 £20

MULLEN, B.   Life is My Adventure. 1937. 1st ed., very
good, ocatvo bound in cloth. Hyland 128-173 1978 £6

MULLER, ERNST   History of Jewish Mysticism. Oxford, 1946.
Austin 79-499 1978 $12.50

MULLER, G.   Deutsche Dichtung von der Renaissance bis zum
Ausgang des Barock. Potsdam, 1927. 4to., cloth, plts., mostly in color, text
illus. Van der Peet H-64-472 1978 Dfl 75

MULLER, HERBERT J.   Thomas Wolfe. 1947. D.j. Broadfoot 50-466
1978 $16

MULLER, JOHANNES   Handbuch der Physiologie des Menschen.
Coblenz, 1833-1840. 5 parts in 2 vols., large 8 vo., 1st ed., wood engraved
figures, plate, contemp. half-calf vol. 1, corresponding modern binding vol. 2.
Schafer 19-60 1978 sFr. 3,400

MULLER, JOHN   A Treatise Containing the Elementary Part of
Fortification. 1756. 8vo., claf, spine gilt, mor. label, copper plts. F. Edwards
1013-592 1978 £90

MULLER, MAX   Lectures on the Science of Language. 1862-64.
2 vols., pink diced calf gilt, rubbed, one spine faded, 8vo. George's 635-1370
1978 £12.50

MULLER, MAX   On the Stratification of Language. 1868. 1st.
ed., pamphlet as issued, inscribed pres. copy from author. Jarndyce 16-898
1978 £15

MULLER, P. L.   Geschiedenis van Onzen Tijd Sedert 1848. Haarlem, 1903-1913. 3 vols., thick 8vo., half calf. Van der Peet H-64-502 1978
Dfl 50

MULLER, PIERRE   New York-San Francisco: Voyage D'un Vagabond A Travers Les Etats-Unis D'Amerique. [Paris, 1944]. Illus., orig. printed
wr., 1st ed. Ginsberg 14-701 1978 $15

MULLER, SOPHUS   L'Europe Prehistorique. n.d. 4to., several
colored plts., illus. Allen 234-664 1978 $7.50

MULLIN, L.   Lands of the Moon & Other Poems. 1907. 1st
ed., signed, pres. copy, very good, octavo bound in cloth. Hyland 128-174
1978 £5

MULLOOLY, JOSEPH   Saint Clement, Pope and Martyr, and His Basilica in Rome. Rome, 1869. 1st. ed., plts., 10 actual mounted photos, roy. 8vo,
contemp. vellum, vellum on lower cover defective, binding strong & sound, fine
internally. Fenning 32-239 1978 £14.50

MULOCK, MISS
Please turn to
CRAIK, DINAH MARIA (MULOCK)

MULTER, JACOB J.   The Farmers' Law Book and Town Officers' Guide.
Albany, 1853. Orig. calf, 3rd ed., very good. Butterfield 21-288 1978 $15

MULVANEY, CHARLES P.   The History of the North-West Rebellion of 1885.
Toronto, 1885. Illus. with portrs., maps, diagrs. & engrs., blank flyleaf missing.
Hood 117-909 1978 $50

MUMEY, NOLIE   Creede: The History of a Colorado Silver Mining
Town. Denver, 1949. Illus., maps, folding map, orig. cloth, d.j., 1st ed.,
ltd. to 500 numbered copies signed by author. Ginsberg 14-269 1978 $60

MUMEY, NOLIE   The Life of Jim Baker 1818-1898... Denver,
1931. One of 250 copies, signed by Mumey, fine, illus. Biblo 247-169 1978
$47.50

MUMEY, NOLIE   A Study of Rare Books...with Special Reference to
Colophons, Press Devices and Title Pages of Interest to the Bibliophile and the Student of Literature. Denver, 1930. 4to., orig. cloth-backed bds., 1st ed., ltd.
to 100 copies signed by author. MacManus 238-989 1978 $100

MUMFORD, A. A.   Hugh Oldham 1452 (?)-1519; Bishop of Exeter etc.
1936. Plts., octavo, good. Upcroft 10-457 1978 £5.50

MUMFORD, ETHEL W.   The Complete Cynic's Calendar of Revised Wisdom 1906. San Francisco, (1905). 1st ed., illus., 12mo. Biblo 251-580 1978
$15

MUMFORD, JOHN KIMBERLY   Oriental Rugs. New York, 1905. Illus. mostly
in color, 4to. Baldwins' 51-131 1978 $50

MUMFORD, JOHN KIMBERLY   Oriental Rugs. New York, 1915. Plts., 16
in color, photo-engrs., lg. 8vo. Morrill 239-530 1978 $25

MUMFORD, S. K.   Oriental Rugs. 1902. Maps, coloured plts.,
illus., roy. 8vo., covers faded. George's 635-259 1978 £18

MUNCHAUSEN   The Travels and Surprising Adventures of....
London, 1877. Illus., engravings, woodcuts by G. Cruikshank, half brown calf,
gilt top, orig. cloth covers bound in black. Baldwins' 51-360 1978 $27.50

MUNDY, FRANCIS NOEL CLARK   Poems. Oxford, 1768. 4to., 1st ed.,
disbound. Quaritch 979-238 1978 $50

MUNDY, R. G.   English Delft Pottery. 1928. Plts., 2 plts. detached and frayed, inscription on title, 4to., covers faded and soiled. George's
635-233 1978 £25

MUNDY, RODNEY   Narrative of Events in Borneo and Celebes, Down
to the Occupation of Labun... 1848. 1st. ed., 2 vols., 8vo, portrait frontispiece,
tinted lithograph plts., woodcut plts., some neat repairs, half calf, gilt backs.
Deighton 5-82 1978 $60

MUNFORD, BEVERLY B.   Virginia's Attitude Toward Slavery and Secession.
Richmond, (1915). MacManus 239-847 1978 $15

MUNFORD, BEVERLY B.   Virginia's Attitude Toward Slavery and Secession
Richmond, 1915. Cover rubbed, Bell Wiley's copy. Broadfoot's 44-667a 1978
$14.00

MUNFORD, GEORGE WYTHE   The Two Parsons; Cupid's Sports; the Dream; and
the Jewells of Virginia. Richmond, 1884. 1st ed., tall 8vo., inner joints open,
orig. bind. Americanist 102-118 1978 $35

MUNFORD, WILLIAM   Poems and Compositions in Prose on Several
Occasions. Richmond, 1798. 8vo., calf-backed bds., 1st ed. Argosy Special-
66 1978 $150

MUNICH Crisis of 1938. Amalgamated Press, 1938-39. Illus., 12 parts, very
good, orig. wraps, scarce. Bell Book 17-669 1978 £10

MUNOZ, LUYS.   Vida y Virtudes del venerable varon el P.
Maestro Juan de Avila Predicador Apostolico. Madrid, 1635. 1st ed., quarto,
engraved t.p., full-page engraved portrait, full contemp. vellum. Bennett
20-147 1978 $125

MUNRO, C. K.   At Mrs. Beam's; a comedy. London, 1923. First
ed., orig. binding, spine discoloured, nice. Rota 211-423 1978 £6

MUNRO, H. A. J.   Criticisms & Elucidations of Catullus. 1938.
Allen 234-1513 1978 $7.50

MUNRO, HECTOR HUGH   Beasts and Super Beasts. London, (1914). 1st
ed., 8vo., gilt stamped black cloth, fine, enclosed in 1/2 mor. box. Houle 10-
234 1978 $90

MUNRO, HECTOR HUGH   Reginald. 1904. Fscp. 8vo., very good, first
English ed. Bell Book 17-787 1978 £45

MUNRO, HECTOR HUGH   Short Stories of.... New York, 1932. 2nd
printing, d.j., very good. Houle 10-235 1978 $8.50

MUNRO, HECTOR HUGH   The Toys of Peace. 1919. Portrait, very good,
worn d.w., first English ed. Bell Book 17-788 1978 £32.50

MUNRO, HECTOR HUGH   The Westminster Alice. (1902). Drawings by
F. Carruthers Gould, very good, pict. wraps, first English ed. Bell Book 17-789
1978 £32.50

MUNRO, R.   The Lake Dwellings of Europe... London, 1890.
Roy. 8vo, maps, plts., illus. Traylen 88-20 1978 £15

MUNRO, WILLIAM BENNETT   Crusaders of New France. New Haven, 1918.
Orig. binding. Wolfe 39-382 1978 $15

MUNRO, WILLIAM BENNETT   Personality in Politics, Reformers, Bosses, and
Leaders. What They do and How They do It. New York, 1925. Cloth, some underlining. Hayman 72-482 1978 $7.50

MUNROE, DAVID HOADLEY   The Grand National, 1839-1930. (1931).
Illus., new, 4to. Baldwins' 51-548 1978 $15

MUNROE, KIRK   Wakulla. New York, 1886. 1st ed., illus.,
Munroe's 1st book, very good. Victoria 34-560 1978 $17.50

MUNSELL, A. H.   A Grammer of Color Arrangements of Strathmore
Papers in A Variety of Printed Colored Combinations.... Mittineague, 1921. Sm.
folio, mint copy. Baldwins' 51-196 1978 $27.50

MUNSEY, FRANK A.   A Tragedy of Errors. New York, 1889.
1st ed., frontispiece, illus., orig. cloth, very good or better. Limestone
9-215 1978 $15

MUNSON, EDWARD LYMAN   Leadership. 1944. Paper. Austin 80-234
1978 $10

MUNSON, GORHAM   Aladdin's Lamp. The Wealth of the American People. New York, (1945). Biblo BL781-856 1978 $9.50

MUNSON, GORHAM   Style and Form in American Prose. 1929. First
ed. Austin 82-674 1978 $12.50

MUNSON, JAMES E.   The Complete Phonographer, and Reporter's
Guide. New York, 1881. Rev. ed., cloth. Hayman 73-461 1978 $7.50

MUNSON, JOHN W.   Reminiscences of a Mosby Guerilla. New York,
1906. Bell Wiley's copy. Broadfoot 46-389 1978 $45

MUNSTERBERG, HUGO   American Problems. 1910 (1912). Austin 79-
501 1978 $10

MUNSTERBERG, HUGO   American Traits. Boston, (1901). Biblo 251-
358 1978 $7.50

MUNSTERBERG, HUGO   The Americans. 1904. Austin 79-500 1978
$10

MUNSTERBERG, HUGO   The War and America. 1914. Austin 79-
502 1978 $12.50

MUNTZ, EUGENE   A Short History of Tapestry. London, 1885.
Illus., 8vo., inner hinges slightly cracked. Morrill 239-531 1978 $10

MURALT, L. VON   Die Zeitalter der Entdeckungen, der Renaissance
und der Glaubenskaempfe. 1941. 4to., plt. Allen 234-1378 1978 $12.50

MURASAKI, LADY   The Sacred Tree. Boston, 1926. Biblo 251-12
1978 $15

MURAT, JEAN-ARNAUD   Topographie Medicale de la Ville De Montpellier,.... Montpellier, 1810. 1st ed., 8vo, plates, some folding, half green
calf over marbled boards, spine gilt. Bennett 20-148 1978 $125

MURATORI, LUDOVICO ANTONIO   Della perfetta Poesia Italiana spiegata....
Venezia, 1770. 2 vols., 4to., half calf, good. King 7-198 1978 £25

MURCHIE, R. W.   Agricultural Progress on the Prairie Frontier.
Toronto, 1936. Illus., 1st ed. Hood 117-911 1978 $55

MURCHISON, RODERICK IMPEY   The Silurian System. London, 1839. 2 vols.
in one, 4to., coloured map in separate slipcase, numerous woodcuts, plts., contemp. calf gilt, marbled end-leaves and edges, first ed. Quaritch 977-116 1978
$850

MURCHISON, RODERICK IMPEY   Siluria. London, 1867. Coloured frontis.,
4th ed., plts., wood-engrav., orig. cloth, roy. 8vo. K Books 244-419 1978 £8

MURDOCH, W. G. BURN
Please turn to
BURN-MURDOCH, WILLIAM GORDON

MURDOCK, CHARLES A.   A Backward Glance at Eighty. San Francisco,
1921. Bds., ltd. ed., signed by author, slight repair to edge of backstrip, good
solid copy. Hayman 73-462 1978 $10

MURDOCK, GEORGE PETER   Our Primitive Contemporaries. New York,
(1934). Illus., orig. binding. Wolfe 39-247 1978 $20

MURDOCK, HAROLD   Bunker Hill. Boston, 1927. Illus., 4to, ltd.
to 525 copies, uncut. MacManus 239-604 1978 $32.50

MURDOCK, HAROLD   Earl Percy Dines Abroad. Boston, 1924. Tall
8vo., illus., boxed, uncut, unopened, fine, ltd. to 550 copies, orig. cloth.
Morrill 241-501 1978 $15

MURDOCK, HAROLD   Earl Percy Dines Abroad. Boston, 1924. Illus.,
tall 8vo., 1 of 550 copies. Morrill 239-591 1978 $12.50

MURDOCK, HAROLD   Earl Percy's Dinner-Table. Boston, 1907. Tall
8vo., 1 of 550 copies. Morrill 239-590 1978 $12.50

MURDOCK, KENNETH B.   Increase Mather the Foremost American Puritan.
Cambridge, 1925. 1st ed., illus., uncut, fine. MacManus 239-795 1978
$17.50

MURDOCK, KENNETH B.   The Portraits of Increase Mather. Cleveland,
Harvard University Press, 1924. 1st ed., ltd. to 250 numbered copies, 4to., T.L.s.
by William G. Mather included, bkplt. of Frank C. Deering, John Singer Sargent's
copy, plts. with colored frontis., green marbled bds., faded green mor. spine, very
fine cond. in publisher's box. Current 24-93 1978 $235

MURET, MARC-ANTOINE   M. Antonii Muretti I. C. et Civis Romani
Orationum Volumina Duo.... Leiden, 1606. Octavo, full contemp. vellum,
spine label in early 18th century hand, Andrew Fletcher copy with signature on
both t.p. Bennett 2-140 1978 $175

MURFREE, MARY NOAILLES   The Champion. Boston, 1902. Cloth, spine
slightly discolored along one edge, first ed. Hayman 73-199 1978 $8.50

MURFREE, MARY NOAILLES   Down the Ravine. Boston, 1885. Cloth,
slightly worn. Hayman 72-235 1978 $7.50

MURFREE, MARY NOAILLES   In the "Stranger People's" Country. New York,
1891. Cloth. Hayman 73-198 1978 $7.50

MURPHEE, JOEL   Autobiography and Civil War Letters of Joel
Murphee of Troy, Alabama 1864-1865. Disbound, cardboard wrs., Bell Wiley's
copy. Broadfoot's 44-415 1978 $7

MURPHY, ARTHUR   The Life of David Garrick. 1801. 1st. ed., 2
vols., frontis portrait, half title, orig. tree calf, red labels, good. Jarndyce
16-676 1978 £45

MURPHY, B. S.   English and Scottish Wrought Ironwork. 1904.
Imp. folio, plts., buckram. Quaritch 983-128 1978 $90

MURPHY, D.   Cromwell in Ireland.... Dublin, 1883. Plans,
illus., octavo, good. Upcroft 10-458 1978 £15

MURPHY, EDMUND R.   Henry De Tonty: Fur Trader of the Mississippi.
Baltimore, 1941. Illus., orig. cloth, 1st ed. Ginsberg 14-986 1978 $30

MURPHY, EMILY   The Black Candle. Toronto, 1922. Hood's
115-659 1978 $15

MURPHY, HENRY C.   Anthology of New Netherland or Translations
from the Early Dutch Poets of New York with Memoirs of Their Lives. New York,
1865. 4to., 3/4 lea., rubbed, front inner hinge tender, #4 in Bradford Club
Series, 75 copies prtd., subscriber's copy #13. Butterfield 21-293 1978 $75

MURPHY, J.   The Shan Van Vocht, A Story of the United
Irishmen. n.d. Stain on cover, good, reprint, octavo bound in cloth. Hyland
128-179 1978 £4

MURPHY, J.N.   Terra Incognita or the Convents of the United
Kingdom. 1873. 1st ed., cover poor, text very good, octavo bound in cloth.
Hyland 128-181 1978 £5

MURPHY, K.M.   Poems. 1932. 1st ed., d.w., signed, very
good, octavo bound in cloth. Hyland 128-182 1978 £4

MURPHY, MARY E.   The British War Economy. Prof. & Tech. Press,
1943. Austin 80-235 1978 $20

MURRAY, A. S.   Handbook of Greek Archaeology. Vases, Bronzes, Gems, Sculpture, Terra-Cottas, Etc. New York, 1892. Illus. Biblo BL781-
446 1978 $10

MURRAY, ADOLPHUS   A Description of the Arteries of the Human Body,
reduced into the Form of Tables. London, 1801. 8vo., wrappers, some minor
stains. Gurney 75-78 1978 £20

MURRAY, ALAN E.   Shoes and Feet to Boot. The Truth about Original
Sin and Shoemaking. Chapel Hill, 1950. Rittenhouse 49-570 1976 $7.50

MURRAY, ALICE EFFIE   A History of the Commercial and Financial Relations between England and Ireland from the Restoration. 1903. 8vo. George's
635-367 1978 £6

MURRAY, ARCHIBALD K.   History of the Scottish Regiments in the British
Army. Glasgow, 1862. Coloured frontis., coloured portraits & plts., thick sq.
8vo., contemp. mor. F. Edwards 1013-377 1978 £100

MURRAY, CHARLES AUGUSTUS   The Prairie-Bird. 1844. 1st. ed., 3 vols.,
fully rebound in half red morocco, marbled bds., good. Jarndyce 16-900 1978
£42

MURRAY, CHARLES AUGUSTUS   The Prairie-bird. London, 1858. New ed., flexible cloth binding, some wear, interior good. Greene 78-87 1978 $35

MURRAY, CHARLES AUGUSTUS   Travels in North America During the Years 1834, 1835, and 1836. New York, 1839. 1st Amer. ed., 2 vols., cloth, foxing and staining. MacManus 239-1204 1978 $65

MURRAY, DAVID   History of Education in New Jersey. Washington, 1899. 1st ed., frontis., port., illus., orig. wrs., worn. MacManus 239-1304 1978 $35

MURRAY, E. C. GRENVILLE   The Social Zoo, Satirical, Social and Humorous Sketches of Our Gilded Youth.... 1884. Engravings, imp. 8vo. George's 635-1397 1978 £5.25

MURRAY, GILBERT   Aeschylus, Creator of Tragedy. 1940. Allen 234-12 1978 $7.50

MURRAY, HUGH   Historical Account of Discoveries and Travels in Africa... Edinburgh, 1818. 2 vols., engraved maps, contemp. calf, rebacked, 8vo, slight foxing & offsetting. Edwards 1012-262 1978 £120

MURRAY, HUGH   An Historical and Descriptive Account of British America... New York, 1840. 1st U.S. ed., 2 vols., 12mo, orig. cloth, very good set. MacManus 239-322 1978 $45

MURRAY, HUGH   Historical and Descriptive Account of British India...Narrative of the Early Voyages... Edinburgh, (1843). 3 vols., 16mo., fold. map, half leather and dec. cloth, bookplts. Petrilla 13-47 1978 $35

MURRAY, J. A. H.   Oxford English Dictionary. Oxford, 1888-1933. 13 vols., thick 4to., orig. half maroon mor., gilt tops, orig. ed., complete with bibliography & supplement. Howes 194-801 1978 £245

MURRAY, J. OGDEN   Three Stories in One. N. P., 1915. Pres. copy from author, Bell Wiley's copy. Broadfoot 46-185 1978 $20

MURRAY, JAMES   Antartic Days. London, 1913. 1 of 230 numbered deluxe copies signed by all 3 authors, 4 to., cloth, t.e.g., uncut, very good, illus. with colored plts. House 10-387 1978 $165

MURRAY, JAMES   Kilmacolm. Paisley, 1907. Map, plts., orig. cloth, 8vo. K Books 244-420 1978 £10

MURRAY, K. M. E.   The Constitutional History of the Cinque Ports. Manchester University, 1935. 1st. ed., map frontis, 8vo, orig. black cloth, very slightly worn, good copy, pres. copy to Winston Churchill. Sawyer 298-99 1978 £52

MURRAY, LINDLEY   English Exercises, Adapted to Murray's English Grammar. York, 1825. 33rd. ed., 12mo, contemp. sheep, spine worn but sound, very good copy. Fenning 32-240 1978 £6

MURRAY, LINDLEY   Murray's Spelling Book, with Reading Lessons, Adapted to...Children... New York, 1819. 1st U.S. ed., improved, 12mo., orig. calf-backed bds., spine worn, woodcuts. Americanist 102-77 1978 $25

MURRAY, LOUISE W.   Notes from the Craft Collection...on the Sullivan Expedition of 1779. Athens, 1929. Illus., maps, orig. cloth bds. MacManus 239-626 1978 $25

MURRAY, NICHOLAS   Notes, Historical and Biographical, Concerning Elizabethtown... Elizabeth-Town, 1844. 1st ed., frontis., orig. calf-backed bds., outer hinges weak, otherwise good. MacManus 239-1306 1978 $85

MURRAY, RHAYNEL   Gerald's Ordeal A Novel. Dublin, 1872. 1st. ed., 3 vols., half titles, orig. green cloth, vol. I nicely recased, retaining endpapers, good. Jarndyce 16-901 1978 £25.50

MURRAY, SEAN   The Irish Case for Communism. New York, 1934. Austin 79-504 1978 $12.50

MURRAY, T. C.   Maurice Harte. 1912. 1st ed., wr., very good. Hyland 128-186 1978 £8

MURRAY, W. W.   Five Nines and Whiz Bangs by "The Orderly Sergeant". Ottawa, 1937. Inscr. & signed by author, spine faded. Hood 117-141 1978 $12.50

MURRAY, WILLIAM HENRY HARRISON   Daylight Land. Boston, 1888. Illus. with designs in color. Hood 117-910 1978 $35

MURRAY, WILLIAM HENRY HARRISON   The Doom of Mamelons, a Legend of the Saguenay. Quebec, 1888. Tourist ed., printed wrappers. Wolfe 39-383 1978 $20

MURRAY, WILLIAM HENRY HARRISON   How John Norton Kept His Christmas. 1883. Good. Nestler Rare 78-131 1978 $35

MURRAYS Handbook for Travellers in Ireland. 1902. Maps, very good, octavo bound in cloth, reprint. Hyland 128-185 1978 £9

MURRY, JOHN MIDDLETON   Fyodor Dostoevsky. London, 1916. First ed., orig. binding, very good. Rota 211-425 1978 £16

MURRY, JOHN MIDDLETON   Reminiscences of D. H. Lawrence. New York, (1933). 8vo., cloth, 1st ed., name on endpaper. J. S. Lawrence 38-L156 1978 $25

MURRY, JOHN MIDDLETON   Reminiscences of D. H. Lawrence. New York, (1933). First American ed., spine dull, covers rubbed. Biblo 247-836 1978 $15

MURSELL, JAMES L.   A Personal Philosophy for War Time. 1942. Austin 80-236 1978 $7.50

MUSAE Cantabrigienses. 1810. Full gilt-tooled mor., slightly rubbed, painting. Allen 234-K 1978 $125

MUSANTIUS, JOANNES DOMINICUS   Fax Chronologica ad Ominigenam Historium,.... Rome, 1701. Small octavo, contemp. flecked calf, gilt back with morocco label, gilt, a.e.r. Bennett 20-150 1978 $125

MUSEE Retrospectif de la Classe 34 Aerostation a L'Exposition Universelle International de 1900. Paris, 1900. 8vo., plts., half title and one leaf of text foxed, contemp. cloth backed bds., a little worn. Quaritch 977-204 1978 $150

MUSGRAVE, R.   Memoirs of the Different Rebellions in Ireland. 1802. 3rd ed., 2 vols., plts., 1/2 leather, worm traces to p. 15 vol.2 only, good. Hyland 128-187 1978 £26.50

MUSSCHENBROEK, PIERRE VAN   Essai de Physique. Leyden, 1739. Fine engr. portr., fldg. copperplts., 4to., contemp. calf, rubbed, backs gilt, fine & complete copy. Offenbacher 30-105 1978 $450

MUSSET, ALFRED DE   Illustrations Pour Les Oeuvres de A. de Musset. Paris, 1883. 4to., orig. covers, ltd. ed. on "Velin". Van der Peet H-64-441 1978 Dfl 200

MUSSET, ALFRED DE   Premieres Poesies 1828-1833, Poesies Nouvelles 1833-1952. Paris, 1922-23. 2 vols., curious white calf bindings, gilt stamped on both sides, slipcase, t.e.g., illus. by E. Nourigat. Van der Peet H-64-440 1978 Dfl 150

MUSSET, PAUL EDME DE   Mr. Wind and Madam Rain. New York, 1904. Illus., fine. Victoria 34-235 1978 $15

MUSSEY, BARROWS   Yankee Life by Those Who Lived It. New York, 1947. Illus., 1st of this Ed., fine, d.w. Biblo 248-76 1978 $15

MUSSEY, BARROWS   We Were New England. New York, (1937). Illus. Biblo 247-108 1978 $15

MUSSO, CORNELIO   Delle Prediche Quadragesimali. Venice, 1592. 1st ed., 2 vols., octavo, full contemp. limp vellum, title in contemp. MS hand, engraved portrait of Musso by Giacomo Franco, numerous headpieces, initials, and devices, Andrew Fletcher copy with signature on t.p. Bennett 20-151 1978 $350

MUSSON, PIERRE   Tragoediae sev Diversarvm Gentivm et Imperiorvm Magni Principes. La Fleche, 1621. 1st ed., 8vo, engraved title by Picart, contemp. limp vellum, stitching a little strained. Quaritch 978-113 1978 $300

MUSSON'S Improved Ready Reckoner, Form and Log Book. Toronto, 1904. Stiff card cover. Hood 117-253 1978 $10

MUTHER, RICHARD   The History of Painting from 4th to the early 19th century. 1907. 2 vols., illus. George's 635-39 1978 £10.50

MUTSCHMANN, H.   The Place-Names of Nottinghamshire; their origin and development. Cambridge, 1913. 8vo. Upcroft 12-308 1978 £8.50

MUZIK, H.   Kunst und Leben im Altertum. 1909. Oblong 4to., one joint cracked, back cover stained, illus. Allen 234-666 1978 $10

MUZZEY, A. B.   Reminiscences of the Men of the Revolution and Their Families. Boston, 1883. Illus., scarce. MacManus 239-605 1978 $15

MUZZEY, DAVID S.   J. G. Blaine, a Political Idol of Other Days. New York, 1934. Illus., 1st ed., d.w. Biblo BL781-192 1978 $12

MY FLOWER Pot. Concord, c.1840. Chapbook, well-printed cuts, wrapper, very fine. Victoria 34-562 1978 $15

MY LITTLE Book. New York, 1848. Well-illus. chapbook. Victoria 34-563 1978 $12.50

MY New Home. New York, 1866. Cloth, frontis., plts., one signed by Herrick. Hayman 73-352 1978 $7.50

MY PRETTY Story Book.... London, n.d. c. 1866. Coloured plts., black & white illus., sm. 4to, orig. cloth. Traylen 88-192 1978 £20

MY Son's Book. New York, 1839. 1st ed., engr. t.p. & fronts, 8vo., orig. cloth, very good. Americanist 103-47 1978 $25

MY TEACHER'S Gem. Boston, (1863). Sm. 16mo, woodcuts, impressed cloth, light text foxing, very good. Victoria 34-564 1978 $7.50

MYERS, ALBERT COOK   The Boy George Washington, Aged 16, His Own Account of an Iroquois Indian Dance, 1748. Philadelphia, 1932. Illus. MacManus 239-1579 1978 $12.50

MYERS, ALBERT COOK   Hanna Logan's Courtship. A True Narrative of the Wooing of the Daughter of James Logan, Colonial Governor of Pennsylvania... Philadelphia, (1904). Illus. MacManus 239-1580 1978 $20

MYERS, ALBERT COOK   Hannah Logan's Courtship. Philadelphia, (1904). Illus. Baldwins' 51-469 1978 $17.50

MYERS, ALBERT COOK   Immigration of the Irish Quakers Into Pennsylvania... Swarthmore, 1902. Illus., scarce. MacManus 239-1581 1978 $65

MYERS, ALBERT COOK   Immigration of the Irish Quakers into Penna., 1682-1750. Swarthmore, 1902. Orig. ed. Baldwins' 51-262 1978 $25

MYERS, ALBERT COOK   Narratives of Early Pennsylvania, West New Jersey and Delaware, 1630-1707. New York, 1912. Maps, good copy, cracked hinges, lacking free endpaper, 1st ed., orig. bind. Petrilla 13-49 1978 $15

MYERS, ALBERT COOK   Sally Wister's Journal. Philadelphia, (1902). 1st ed., illus. MacManus 239-606 1978 $25

MYERS, ELIZABETH   The Basilisk of St. James's: a romance. 1945. Bookplt., very good, first English ed. Bell Book 17-674 1978 £5.50

MYERS, ELIZABETH   Good Beds - Men Only. 1948. Covers dull, bookplt., good, d.w., first English ed. Bell Book 16-1000 1978 £5

MYERS, ELIZABETH LEHMAN   A Century of Moravian Sisters, A Record of Christian Community Life. New York, 1918. 1st ed., color illus., orig. binding, 8vo. Americanist 101-100 1978 $20

MYERS, GRACE WHITING   History of the Massachusetts General Hospital, June, 1872, to December, 1900. (Boston, 1900). Illus., 8vo., front cover lightly spotted, 1st ed. Morrill 239-186 1978 $17.50

MYERS, GUSTAVUS   A History of Canadian Wealth. Vol. 1. Chicago, 1914. Orig. binding. Wolfe 39-384 1978 $45

MYERS, GUSTAVUS   History of the Great American Fortunes. Chicago, (1909). 3 vols. MacManus 239-324 1978 $37.50

MYERS, JOHN MYERS   The Alamo. New York, 1948. Maps, first ed., d.w. Biblo 247-245 1978 $17.50

MYERS, JOHN MYERS   The Last Chance. Tombstone's Early Years. New York, 1950. 1st ed., illus., maps. MacManus 239-1896 1978 $10

MYERS, JOHN MYERS   The Last Chance. New York, 1950. Illus., 1st ed., fine, d.w. Biblo 248-280 1978 $17.50

MYERS, MINNIE WALTER   Romance and Realism of the Southern Gulf Coast. Cincinnati, 1898. Illus., 8vo., binding partly faded, 1st ed. Morrill 239-533 1978 $10

MYERS, WILLIAM S.   The Hoover Administration. New York, 1936. First ed. Biblo 247-132 1978 $13.50

MYSINGER, JOACHIM   Apotelesma Hoc Est Scholiorum ad Institutiones Justinian eas Pertinentium Corpus. Basle, 1584. Printer's device on title & last pages, folio, contemp. calf, new leather labels, 1st. & last few leaves frayed at edges. Traylen 88-437A 1978 £55

MYSTERE des Actes des Apostres. Paris, 1541. 3 parts in 1 vol., folio, good copy, late 18th century russia, repaired, 3rd and definitive ed. Quaritch Summer, 1978-35 1978 $7,000

THE MYSTERIES of Ireland, Giving..An Account of Irish Secret Societies & Their Plots from 1798 to 1883.... n.d. Very good, octavo bound in cloth, reprint. Hyland 128-169 1978 £7.50

N

NABOKOV, VLADIMIR   The Real Life of Sebastian Knight. Norfolk, 1941. First U.S. ed., orig. hessian binding, very good, 1500 copies printed. Bell Book 17-677 1978 $28.50

NABOKOV, VLADIMIR   The Real Life of Sebastian Knight. London, (1945). Purplish brown cloth, 1st English ed., worn but complete dust jacket. Bradley 49-243 1978 $25

NADAR, G. F. T.   The Right to Fly. (1866). Sm. 8vo., contemp. cloth. Quaritch 977-241 1978 $75

NADASI, JOHANNES   Annuae Litterae Societatis Iesu Anni MDCL. Dillingen, 1658. 1st ed., small 8vo, contemp. vellum. Gilhofer 75-82 1978 SFr 600

NAFTEL, M.   Flowers and How to Paint Them. 1891. Oblong 8vo., orig. cloth gilt, slightly stained. Quaritch 983-224 1978 $25

NAIL, OLIN W.   Texas Methodist Yearbook:.... Elgin, 1934. 1st ed., illus. Jenkins 116-988 1978 $45

NAILER Tom's Diary Otherwise the Journal of Thomas B. Hazard of Kingstown, Rhode Island 1778-1840. Boston, 1930. 1st ed., lg. 4to, ltd. to 400 copies. MacManus 239-419 1978 $45

NAISMITH, JOHN   Elements of Agriculture. 1807. First ed., nice, contemp. half calf, 8vo. Howes 194-130 1978 £35

NAISMITH, JOHN   General View of the Agriculture of the County of Clydesdale. 1806. Hand-coloured map, contemp. mottled calf, 8vo. Howes 194-131 1978 £30

NAISMITH, ROBERT   Stonehouse: Historical and Traditional. Glasgow, 1885. Frontis., map, plts., good, orig. cloth, 8vo. K Books 244-421 1978 £10

NAKAMURA, KOYA   Admiral Togo: A Memoir... Tokyo, 1937. Dec. cloth, illus. Dawson's 449-200 1978 $75

THE NAKED and Undisguised Truth. 1721. Second ed., 8vo., unbound, stitched as issued, uncut. P. M. Hill 142-179 1978 £12

NALSON, JOHN   An Impartial Collection of the Great Affairs of State... 1682-83. 1st. ed., engraved frontis., engraved portrait, 2 vols., folio, uniform contemp. calf, contemp. manuscript paper spine labels, very good copy. Fenning 32-241 1978 £65

NAMES and Places of Abode of the Members of the Common Council, and of the Officers Who Hold Appointments Under Them. New York, 1837. Stiff prtd. wr. Butterfield 21-524 1978 $12.50

NANCE, R. MORTON   Sailing-Ship Models. London, 1924. Plts., some American, 4to., orig. cloth, ltd. to 1750 copies. Morrill 241-379 1978 $40

NANNINI, REMIGIO   Considerationi Civili, Sopra l'Historia Di M. Francesco Guicciardini, e d'altri Historici. Venice, 1582. 1st ed., octavo, full contemp. vellum, lightly foxed, Fletcher of Saltoun copy with signature on t.p. Bennett 20-152 1978 $370

NANSEN, FRIDTJOF   "Farthest North".... New York, London, 1897. 2 vols., illus., folding maps, 3/4 leather, marbled bds., gilt topped, coloured plts. Hood's 115-70 1978 $100

NANSEN, FRIDTJOF   Farthest North: The Record of a Voyage of Exploration of the Ship Fram, 1893-96... 1898. 2nd. London ed., map, coloured plt., portraits, illus., 2 vols., orig. dec. cloth, headbands slightly worn, 8vo. Edwards 1012-590 1978 £20

NANSEN, FRIDTJOF   Fram Over Polhavet: Den Norske Polarfærd, 1893-1896.... Kristiania, 1897. 1st. ed., maps, illus. some in colour, 2 vols., cloth gilt, one spine repaired, 8vo. Edwards 1012-589 1978 £60

NANSEN, FRIDTJOF   In Northern Mists. London, 1911. 1st. ed., 2 vols., 4to, mounted coloured plts., illus., orig. blue cloth, gilt, lib. labels removed, embossed lib. stamps on upper margin, cover somewhat soiled, internally very good. Deighton 5-162 1978 £70

NANSEN, FRIDTJOF   In Northern Mists: Artic Exploration in Early Times. 1911. 2 coloured plts., maps, illus., 2 vols., roy. 8vo, orig. cloth. Edwards 1012-591 1978 £100

NANSEN, FRIDTJOF   Through Siberia. London, 1914. 1st. ed., roy. 8vo, portrait, plts., maps, orig. blue cloth, gilt. Deighton 5-163 1978 £43

NANTEUIL, MME. DE   Le Secret de la Greve. Paris, 1893. Wood-engravings, roy. 8vo., cloth. K Books 244-244 1978 £8

NAPIER, A. S.   The Old English version of the enlarged rule of Chrodegang. 1916. Cloth dull, 8vo. Upcroft 12-309 1978 £4.50

NAPIER, J.   De Arte Logistica Johannis Naperi Merchistonii Baronis Libri qui Supersunt. Edinburgh, 1839. 4to., large paper, portrait, contemp. half calf, rebacked, uncut, one of twelve copies on large paper. Quaritch 977-165 1978 $200

NAPIER, M.   Memorials and Letters Illustrative of the Life and Times of John Graham of Claverhouse, Viscount Dundee, 1643-1689. 1859-1862. 3 vols., portraits, plts., octavo, good. Upcroft 10-460 1978 £25

NAPIER, M.   Memoirs of the Marquis of Montrose. 1856. 2 vols., portraits, vol. I rebacked with some loss of lettering, octavo, good. Upcroft 10-459 1978 £12.50

NAPIER, WILLIAM FRANCIS PATRICK   Colonel Napier's Justification of His Third Volume.... 1833. 1st ed., 8vo., wrapper, nice copy. Fenning 32-242 1978 £15

NAPIER, WILLIAM FRANCIS PATRICK   History of the War in the Peninsula and in the South of France... 1862. New ed., maps, 6 vols., sm. 8vo., orig. cloth. F. Edwards 1013-379 1978 £45

NAPIER, WILLIAM FRANCIS PATRICK   A Reply to Various Opponents.... 1832. 1st ed., 8vo., wrapper, nice copy. Fenning 32-243 1978 £16

NAPOLEON I, EMPEROR OF THE FRENCH   Letters to Marie Louise. New York, (1935). Illus., first American ed. Biblo 247-716 1978 $13.50

NARBOROUGH, JOHN   An Account of Several and Late Voyages and Discoveries to the South and North Towards the Streights of Magellan, the South Seas, the Vast Tracts of Land Beyond Hollandia Novia, etc.... London, 1694. 1st ed., sm. 8vo., copperplts., fldg. maps, plts. very fine, fine lg. fldg. copperplt., old bds. & spine rubbed, well worn, rare & fine book. Current 24-189 1978 $545

NARCOTIA. 1857. 8vo., half calf, gilt, orig. printed wrappers bound in. P. M. Hill 142-298 1978 £45

NARDI, JACOPO   Istorie della Citta di Firenze. Firenze, 1842. 2 vols., 8vo., half vellum, very good. King 7-199 1978 £25

NARES, EDWARD   Think's-I-to-Myself. London, 1811. 2 vols., 12mo, contemporary half calf, spines gilt, 1st ed. Ximenes 47-215 1978 $100

NARES, EDWARD   Thinks-I-To Myself. A Serio-Ludicro, Tragico Comico Tale. Exeter, 1836. Early Amer. ed., 2 vols. in 1, disbound. Greene 78-264 1978 $45

NARES, EDWARD   Thinks-I-to-Myself, a Serio-Ludicro, Tragieo-Comico Tale. 1826. Engraved frontis., post 8vo., calf, rubbed. George's 635-1420 1978 £7.50

NARES, GEORGE S.   Un Voyage a La Mer Polaire Sur Les Navires de S.M.B. L'Alerte et la Decouverie, 1875-6... Paris, 1880. Maps, engravings, roy. 8vo, calf, gilt spine, institute stamp in gilt on front cover. Edwards 1012-592 1978 £25

NARES, ROBERT   A Glossary or Collection of Words, Phrases, Names and Allusions to Customs, Proverbs... 1822. 4to, green buckram. Eaton 45-365 1978 £30

NARES, ROBERT   A Glossary or Collection of Words, Phrases, Names, Proverbs...in the Works of English Authors.... 1888. New ed., 2 vols., orig. cloth, printed labels, 8vo. Howes 194-800 1978 £12

NARRATION Authenique De L'Echange Des Prisonniers Faits Aux Cedres Pendant la Guerre Americaine de 1775. Montreal, 1873. Privately bound. Hood's 115-125 1978 $40

A NARRATION of the Lives of the 13 Compilers of the Liturgy of the Church of England. (1774). Engraved frontis., contemp. calf, rubbed, joints cracking, 8vo. George's 635-1099 1978 £7.50

NARRATIVE of Johann Carl Buettner in the American Revolution. New York, n.d. (c. 1914). Ltd. to 320 copies, unopened copy, orig. bds. MacManus 239-555 1978 $20

NARRATIVE of Nicholas "Cheyenne" Dawson. San Francisco, Grabhorn Press, 1933. Cloth & colored pic. bds., illus. in color, #7, fine copy in d.w. Dykes 34-149 1978 $75

THE NARRATIVE of the Captivity and Restoration of Mrs. Mary Rowlandson. Lancaster, 1903. 1st printed in 1682, 4to., orig. 3/4 cloth, ltd. to 250 copies. MacManus 239-1214 1978 $40

A NARRATIVE Of The Incidents Attending the Capture, Detention, and Ransom of Charles Johnston, of Botetourt County, Virginia.... New York, 1827. Leather, joints cracked, copy belonged to B.M. Ambler. Hayman 71-369 1978 $85

A NARRATIVE Or The Official Conduct of Valentine Morris, Late Captain General, Governor in Chief of the Island of St. Vincent. 1787. Contemp. calf, rebacked, 8vo. Edwards 1012-741 1978 £95

NARRATIVE Of The Shipwreck of the Antelope, East-India, On the Pelew Islands... Perth, 1888. 12mo, orig. wrappers, slightly defective, uncut, engraved frontis. Edwards 1012-378 1978 £60

NASH, E. B. Leaders in Homeopathic Therapeutics. Philadelphia, 1913. Fourth ed., hinges weak, library marks. Rittenhouse 49-572 1976 $25

NASH, FREDERICK 1782-1856 Picturesque Views of the City of Paris and its Environs. 1820-23. Plts., 2 vols. in 1, folio, contemp. half mor., rebacked, lg. paper copy. Howes 194-1398 1978 £135

NASH, JOHN English Garden Flowers. 1948. Coloured plts., roy. 8vo. George's 635-958 1978 £5.25

NASH, JOHN HENRY Stevenson's Baby Book. 1922. 8vo., frontis., Etruria paper, bound in paper bds., blue cloth spine, one of 500 numbered copies. Battery Park 1-212 1978 $45

NASH, JOHN HENRY The Vintage Festival. No. 139 of 500 numbered copies, 12mo., bds., thin, frontis., inscr. pres. copy. Battery Park 1-211 1978 $35

NASH, JOSEPH Interiors of Old English Mansions. New York, n.d. Reproduced in colours after orig. coloured drwgs., folio, 8vo., half cloth, portfolio with coloured plts. Van der Peet H-64-179 1978 Dfl 70

NASH, JOSEPH The Mansions of England in the Olden Time. 1839-49. Imp. folio, frontis., plts., cloth, mor. spine, gilt top, worn, bookplt. of A.S. Beazley, facs. reprint c. 1900. Quaritch 983-45 1978 $135

NASH, OGDEN Good Intentions. Boston, 1942. First ed., d.w. Biblo 247-606 1978 $15

NASH, OGDEN Good Intentions. Boston, 1942. Fine in lightly soiled d.w. Desmarais B-479 1978 $20

NASH, OGDEN Hard Lines. New York, 1931. Illus., 1st ed., stain on front cover, name on flyleaf. Biblo BL781-1091 1978 $12.50

NASMITH, GEORGE C. On the Fringe of the Great Fight. Toronto, 1917. Hood 116-137 1978 $12.50

NASON, E. H. Old Hallowell on the Henneber. Augusta, 1909. Illus. MacManus 239-986 1978 $30

NASON, ELIAS A Gazetteer of the State of Massachusetts. Boston, 1874. Map, illus., 8vo., binding faded, 1st ed., orig. cloth. Morrill 241-694 1978 $12.50

NASON, ELIAS A Gazetteer of the State of Massachusetts... Boston, 1874. Illus., lg. colored fold. map, orig. 3/4 calf and bds., very good. MacManus 239-287 1978 $30

NATALI, GIULIO Storia Dell'Arte. Tornio, 1909. 3rd ed., 3 vols., illus., rebound. Biblo BL781-665 1978 $16.50

NATALIBUS, PETRUS DE Catalogus Sanctorum et Gestorum Eorum ex Diversis Voluminibus Collectus. Vicenza, 1493. 331 leaves of 332, title printed in red & black, woodcut device on verso of R8, folio, 17th century calf, old rebacking, binding worn. Traylen 88-438 1978 £750

NATHAN, GEORGE JEAN Bottoms Up. New York, 1917. 1st ed., nice, scarce. Ballinger 11-156 1978 $20.00

NATHAN, I. Fugitive Pieces and Reminiscences of Lord Byron. Illus., autograph of Lord Byron, sm. 8vo., 1st ed., facsimiles, contemp. half calf. Quaritch 979-75 1978 $120

NATHAN, MAUD Once Upon a Time and Today. New York, 1933. Illus., 1st ed., signed. Biblo 251-359 1978 $15

NATHAN BEN YECHIEL OF ROME Hebrew-Aramaic Dictionary. Pesaro, 1517. Second ed., woodcut border, some worming and marginal staining, good margins, folio, full goatskin, blind-tooled border, decor. panel on sides, raised bands, binding by Bernard Middleton. Thomas 37-62 1978 £1850

NATIONAL ASSOCIATION OF RAILWAY SURGEONS Official Report of 6th Annual Meeting in Omaha. Chicago, 1893. Chip on spine, cover stained. Rittenhouse 49-573 1976 $12.50

NATIONAL CATHOLIC ALUMNI FEDERATION Catholic Thought and National Reconstruction. Chicago, 1935. Austin 79-508 1978 $12.50

NATIONAL COMMITTEE ON IMMIGRATION POLICY Economic Aspects of Immigration. (1947). Austin 79-509 1978 $12.50

NATIONAL CONFERENCE ON THE CHRISTIAN WAY OF LIFE And Who Is My Neighbor? Association Press, 1924. Austin 79-510 1978 $12.50

NATIONAL COUNCIL OF JEWISH WOMEN Proceedings of the First Convention of the National Council of Jewish Women New York, 1896. Philadelphia, 1897. Orig. cloth, 1st ed. Ginsberg 16-884 1978 $15

NATIONAL EDUCATION ASSOC. Americans All. 1942. Austin 79-511 1978 $12.50

NATIONAL MEDICAL COLLEGE Annual Circular of the Session of 1851-52. Washington, 1851. Disbound. Rittenhouse 49-574 1976 $10

NATIONAL STEEPLECHASE AND HUNT ASSOCIATION By-Laws, Rules of Racing. New York, 1900. Illus., 12mo., plts., 1st ed., orig. cloth. Morrill 241-381 1978 $7.50

THE NATIONAL Cook Book By a Lady of Philadelphia. Philadelphia, 1863. 9th ed. Baldwins' 51-337 1978 $15

NATIONAL History and Views of London. London, 1832. Frontispiece, plts., somewhat age-browned, worn later binding, upper cover detached, 8vo. K Books 244-202 1978 £45

NATIONAL Treasures of Japan, Series II. N.P., n.d. Unpaged, plts., boards, little soiled and worn. Dawson's 449-164 1978 $17.50

NATORP, PAUL Die logischen Grundlagen der exacten Wissenschaften. Leipzig, 1910. 1st ed., 8vo, orig. publisher's cloth. Gilhofer 75-83 1978 SFr 150

NATTES, J. C. Scotia Depicta; or the Antiquities, Castles, Public Buildings...and Picturesque Scenery of Scotland. 1804. Folio, frontis., some foxing, contemp. calf, rubbed, joints cracked. Quaritch 983-347 1978 $335

NATURAL History of Animals; Containing an Account of Remarkable Beasts, Birds, Fishes and Insects. Dublin, 1822. Woodcuts, 12mo, orig. sheep, worn, joints weak. Traylen 88-193 1978 £18

NATURAL History of Domestic Animals Containing an Account of Their Habits and Instincts... Dublin, 1821. Woodcut frontis, woodcut plts., vignettes, 12mo, orig. sheep, lacks upper cover. Traylen 88-195 1978 £15

A NATURAL History of Reptiles, Serpents, and Insects. Alnwick, c.1815. Woodcuts by Bewick, pictorial wrappers taped, fine. Victoria 34-569 1978 $35

NATURAL History of Remarkable Beasts. Dublin, 1820. Woodcuts illus., 12mo, orig. sheep, worn. Traylen 88-194 1978 £15

NATURAL History of Remarkable Birds, With Their Habits and Instincts. Dublin, 1821. Woodcut frontis, woodcuts, 12mo, orig. sheep, worn. Traylen 88-196 1978 £20

NATURAL History of Remarkable Trees, Shrubs and Plants. London, n.d. (1823). Plts., 12mo, old tree calf, one joint weak. Traylen 88-197 1978 £25

NATURAL History of Reptiles and Serpents... Dublin, 1821. Wood engraved frontis, vignette, illus., 12mo, orig. sheep, lacks upper cover. Traylen 88-198 1978 £15

NATURAL Science: A Monthly Review of Scientific Progress. Vols. 1-8. London, 1892-6. Illus., roy. 8vo., half dark blue calf, gilt spines. K Books 244-423 1978 £30

NATURALIST'S Poetical Companion With Notes. London, 1833. 12mo, half green calf, spine faded, half title, good. Sexton 7-203 1978 £25

NAUNTON, ROBERT   Fragmenta Regalia, or Observations on the Late Queen Elizabeth, Her Times and Favoits. [London], 1641. Quarto, half 19th-century grained calf over marbled boards, 1st ed. Bennett 7-80 1978 £185

NAUNTON, ROBERT   Fragmenta Regalia, Memoirs of Elizabeth, her Court and Favourites. 1824. New ed., engraved portrait, post 8vo., cloth. George's 635-630 1978 £10.50

NAUSEA, FRIDERICUS   Fredericus Navseae Blanciacampiani,.... Cologne, 1532. Sm. 4to, Roman letter, spirited woodcuts by Anton Woensam of Worms, 19th-century marbled boards, mottled calf back, rare. Quaritch 978-115 1978 $550

THE NAVAL And Military Sketch Book and History of Adventure by Flood and Fiels. (1845). Illus. by Landells, 8vo, contemp. half green calf, nice copy. Fenning 32-244 1978 £24

NAVAL Intelligence Handbook, French Equatorial Africa & Cameroons. London, 1942. 2 maps in pocket, 170 plts., illus., 8vo, orig. cloth. K Books 239-344 1978 £8

NAVAL Intelligence Handbook--French West Africa. London, 1943-44. 2 vols., maps, plts., illus., 8vo, orig. cloth. K Books 239-345 1978 £10

NAVARRE, O.   Essai sur la Rhetorique Grecque Avant Aristote. 1900. half mor. Allen 234-672 1978 $12.50

NAVARRO Y NORIEGA, FERNANDO   Memoria Sobre La Poblacion Del Reino De Nueva Espana. Mexico, 1820. Folding table, plain paper wr., small worm hole. Jenkins 116-990 1978 $400

NAVILLE, EDOUARD   The Route of the Exodus. 1891. Fldg. colored map, "author's copy", signed by Naville. Austin 79-512 1978 $47.50

NEAL, JOSEPH CLAY   In Town & About, or Pencillings & Pennings. Philadelphia, (1843). Illus., lg. oblong 4to, orig. pale yellow plain wrs., top right corner of fr. cover & next few leaves dampstained, 1st ed., very scarce. Morrill 239-535 1978 $75

NEALE, ADAM   Letters from Portugal and Spain. 1809. Plts., 4to., contemp. tree calf, rebacked, single wormhole through entire book, affecting letters and in some cases words, as well as plts. F. Edwards 1013-386 1978 £40

NEALE, C. M.   An Index to Pickwick. 1st. ed., orig. half green cloth, green paper bds., v.g. Jarndyce 16-486 1978 £12.50

NEALE, F. A.   Narrative of a Residence at the Capital of the Kingdom of Siam... 1852. Map, illus., sm. 8vo, orig. cloth. Edwards 1012-155 1978 £25

NEALE, JOHN MASON   Good King Wenceslas. Birmingham, 1895. Roy. 8vo., pictured by A. J. Gaskin, orig. bds. George's 635-152 1978 £18

NEALE, W. JOHNSON   The Priors of Prague. Philadelphia, 1836. Two vols., orig. bds., uncut. Wolfe 39-385 1978 $45

NEANDER, MICHAEL   Opus Aureum Et Scholasticum.... Leipzig, 1577. 3 parts in 2 vols., 4to., contemp. maroon mor., gilt tooled with labels. Salloch 348-167 1978 $400

NEASE, LILLA   In Music's Thrall. Toronto, 1903. Hood 116-492 1978 $15

NECESSITY of an Incorporate Union Between Great Britain and Ireland... Dublin, 1799. First ed., plain wrs. Hyland 128-171 1978 £10

THE NECESSITY of Augmenting of our Land-Forces, during the Present Unsettled State of the Affairs of Europe. 1734. Dampstained, 8vo., unbound. F. Edwards 1013-387 1978 £10

THE NECESSITY of Lowering Interest and Continuing Taxes, Demonstrated. London, 1750. 8vo, disbound, 1st ed., very good. Ximenes 47-90 1978 $45

NECKER, JACQUES   Compte rendu au Roi... Au mois de Janvier 1781. Paris, 1781. 4 to., folding table, engraved & colored folding maps, 1st ed., fine copy, complete with 2 often missing maps, contemp. calf. Schafer 19-61 1978 sFr. 1,600

NEDDO, EDWARD   The Horse and His Diseases. South Bend, 1880. Ads, 1/2 lea., worn along one edge of spine. Hayman 73-327 1978 $12.50

NEEDELL, MRS. J. H.   The Vengeance of Vansittart. NY, 1895. Fir. Am. Ed., quarter calf, marbled boards, good cond. Greene 78-265 1978 $15.00

NEEDHAM, JOHN TURBERVILLE   New Microscopical Discoveries Containing Observations... London, 1745. Fldg. copperplts., 8vo., contemp. calf, worn, 1st ed. Offenbacher 30-106 1978 $250

NEEDHAM, WALTER   Disquisitio Anatomica de Formato Foetu. Londini, 1667. Fldg. copperplts., 8vo., contemp. calf, sides & back gilt, 1st ed., very fine copy. Offenbacher 30-107 1978 $750

NEEDLER, GEORGE HENRY   Goethe and Scott. Toronto, 1950. Signed by the Author. Hood's 115-353 1978 $17.50

NEEDLER, GEORGE HENRY   The Jameson Medal. Toronto, 1939. Paper cover, illus. Hood 116-377 1978 $7.50

NEEDLER, GEORGE HENRY   Moore and His Canadian Boat Song. Toronto, 1950. Design by Thoreau Mac Donald, card cover. Hood's 115-355 1978 $15

NEEDLES, EDWARD   An Historical Memoir of the Pennsylvania Society for Promoting the Abolition of Slavery. Philadelphia, 1848. Disbound. Biblo 247-90 1978 $22.50

NEESER, ROBERT W.   Letters and Papers Relating to the Cruises of Gustavus Conyngham, a Captain of the Continental Navy. New York, 1915. Bds., vellum back, illus., uncut, boxed, ltd. to 600 copies. MacManus 239-607 1978 $27.50

NEFF, BOSS   Some Experiences of Boss Neff in the Texas and Oklahoma Panhandle. Amarillo, 1941. 5to, "Limited to 200 copies...mighty scarce..." Jenkins 116-991 1978 $75

NEFF, PAT M.   The Battles of Peace. Ft. Worth, 1925. 1st ed., illus., autographed by author, faded. Jenkins 116-992 1978 $15

THE NEGOCIATIONS for a Treaty of Peace, in 1709. 1711. 2 parts, 8vo., 1st ed., disbound, 2nd ed. Quaritch 979-188 1978 $20

THE NEGRO'S Friend, or, The Sheffield Anti-Slavery Album. Sheffield, 1826. Engraved plts., browned, one guarded in, woodcuts, 12mo, orig. cloth. Edwards 1012-733 1978 £20

NEIDECK, P.   Mit der Buchse in Funf Weltteilen. Berlin, 1922. 8vo., cloth, portr., illus., map. Van der Peet H-64-507 1978 Dfl 40

NEIHARD, CHARLES   Diphtheria, as It Prevailed in the United States from 1860 to 1866... New York, 1867. 8vo., top part of spine lacking, 1st ed. Morrill 239-187 1978 $17.50

NEIHARDT, JOHN G.   Black Elk Speaks. New York, 1932. First ed., author's signed pres., fine, d.w. Biblo 247-62 1978 $82.50

NEILL, EDWARD D.   A Hand Book for the Presbyterian Church in Minnesota... Philadelphia, 1856. Original 12mo cloth, 1st ed. Ginsberg 14-565 1978 $22.50

NEILL, EDWARD D.   The History of Minnesota: From the Earliest French Explorations to the Present Time. Philadelphia, 1858. 1st ed., 4to, illus., plts., 1 of 100 lg. paper copies, rebound, fine. MacManus 239-314 1978 $75

NEILL, H.   A Report Upon Deafness When Resulting from Diseases of the Eustachian Passages. Liverpool, 1840. 8vo., lithograph plt., some light staining, new cloth. Quaritch 977-60 1978 $75

NEILL, J. G. S.   Historical Record of the Honourable East India Company's First Madras European Regiment. 1843. 8vo., plts., portrait, orig. cloth. F. Edwards 1013-551 1978 £25

NEILSON, CHARLES   An Original, Compiled and Corrected Account of Burgoyne's Campaign... Albany, 1844. 1st ed., nice copy, orig. cloth, fold. map. MacManus 239-608 1978 $37.50

NEILSON, G.R. The Book of Bulls: Being a Very Complete & Entertaining Essay. (c. 1890). Lacks fly, very good, reprint, octavo bound in cloth. Hyland 128-173 1978 £6.50

NEILSON, J. L. H. Facsimile of Pere Marquette's Illinois Prayer Book. Quebec, 1908. 300 copies issued, facs. of orig. hand-written pages, plts. Hood's 115-759 1978 $35

NELL-BREUNING, OSWALD VON Reorganization of Social Economy. 1936-37. Austin 79-515 1978 $27.50

NELSON, A. H. The Battles of Chancellorsville and Gettysburg. Minneapolis, 1899. Bell Wiley's copy. Broadfoot 46-363 1978 $16

NELSON, ARVID Y. S. K. V. Jas-Liiton 50-Vuotishistoria. 1937. In Finnish. Austin 79-244 1978 $47.50

NELSON, AVEN The Red Desert of Wyoming and Its Forage Resources. Washington, D. C., 1898. Wrs., illus., plts., 1st ed., wrs. fraying, from the Allred Collection, rare. Dykes 34-255 1978 $25

NELSON, CHARLES A. Waltham, Past and Present. Cambridge, 1882. 8vo., ex-lib., ends of spine worn, inner hinges cracked, 1st ed., orig. cloth. Morrill 241-338 1978 $12.50

NELSON, DONALD M. Arsenal of Democracy. The Story of American War Production. New York, (1946). Biblo BL781-857 1978 $8.50

NELSON, JOHN An Extract of John Nelson's Journal. Leeds, 1773. Bds., two sm. stains on cover. Hayman 73-466 1978 $20

NELSON, RAPHAEL Cries and Criers of Old London. Quarto, 1st ed., linocut plates in black on yellow backgrounds, fine, d.j. Victoria 34-570 1978 $30

NELSON, ROBERT An Address to Persons of Quality and Estate. 1715. 8vo., contemp. panelled calf, portrait, only ed. P. M. Hill 142-181 1978 £30

NELSON, ROBERT A Companion for the Festivals and Fasts of the Church of England. 1720. Plts., thk. 8vo., nice, contemp. polished calf, with lettering piece. Howes 194-401 1978 £18

NELSON, WILLIAM The New Jersey Coast in Three Centuries... 3 vols., illus., orig. 1/2 leather, hinges weak. MacManus 239-1307 1978 $100

NEPOS, CORNELIUS Vitae Excellentium Imperatorum, Observationibus & Notis Commentatorum Omnium. 1707. New cloth, text stained, engr. illus. Allen 234-674 1978 $15

NERI, ANTONIO De Arte Vitraria Libri Septem. Amsterdam, 1669. Thick 12mo., fldg. plts., wallet-edged vellum. Salloch 345-133 1978 $275

NERVAL, GERARD DE Please turn to GERARD DE NERVAL

NESBIT, E. The Story of the Treasure Seekers. 1899. Plts., covers rubbed, good, scarce, first English ed. Bell Book 17-682 1978 £18.50

NESBITT, L. M. Desert and Forest. London, (1937). 6 plts., 8vo, orig. cloth, index leaves torn without loss. K Books 239-347 1978 £6

NETHERLANDS East Indies. 1944. Maps, some folding, plts., illus., 2 vols., 8vo, orig. cloth, covers soiled. Edwards 1012-172 1978 £35

NETON, A. l'Indo-Chine, et son avenir economique. Paris, 1904. Half cloth, tables, 8vo. Van der Peet 127-167 1978 Dfl 60

NETTANCOURT-VAUBECOURT, J. DE En Zigzag de Singapour A Moscou. Paris, 1905. Sm. 8vo., orig. covers. Van der Peet H-64-506 1978 Dfl 35

NETTLE, RICHARD The Salmon Fisheries of the St. Lawrence and its Tributaries. Montreal, 1857. Contemp. bds., half mor. Wolfe 39-386 1978 $60

NETTLEFOLD, F. J. The Collection of Bronzes and Castings in Brass and Ormolu Formed by... 1934. Folio, plts., cloth, gilt top. Quaritch 983-129 1978 $80

NETTLEFOLD & SONS LTD. Illustrated Catalogue of General and Builders' Ironmongery, issued by .... London, 1911. Illus., 4to. Traylen 88-86 1978 £20

NETTLESHIP, HENRY Lectures & Essays on Subjects Connected with Latin Literature & Scholarship. 1885. Allen 234-678a 1978 $8.50

NETTLESHIP, R. L. Lectures on the Republic of Plato. London, 1898. 8vo., cloth. Salloch 348-169 1978 $12.50

NETTLESHIP, R. L. Lectures on the Republic of Plato. London, 1929. 8vo., cloth. Salloch 348-168 1978 $15

NETZHAMMER, RAYMOND Theophrastus Paracelsus. Einsiedeln, 1901. Portr., fldg. plts., woodcuts, 8vo., cloth, orig. prtd. wrs. bound in. Salloch 345-146 1978 $20

NEUBURGER, MAX Geschichte Der Medizin. Stuttgart, 1906-1911. 2 vols., tall 8vo., plts., orig. yellow prtd. wrs., fine copy, unopened, uncut, 1st ed. Zeitlin 245-174 1978 $45

NEUBERGER, RICHARD L. An Army of the Aged... 1936. Dec. cloth, frontis., 1st ed., review copy, fine. Dykes 35-152 1978 $10

NEUBERGER, RICHARD L. An Army of the Aged. Caldwell, 1936. Biblo 251-360 1978 $15

NEUE, F. Formenlehre der Lateinischen Sprache. 1877-75. 2 vols. Allen 234-679 1978 $15

NEUGEBAUER, KARL A. Antike Bronzestatuetten. Berlin, 1921. Illus., covers slightly soiled. Biblo BL781-448 1978 $15

NEUHUSIUS, REINERUS Suada Alcmariana sive Tyrocinium Eloquentiae. Amsterdam, 1656. 12mo., vellum. Salloch 348-170 1978 $45

NEUMAN, A. M. Economic Organization of the British Coal Industry. 1934. 8vo. George's 635-371 1978 £5

NEUMANN, CARL Rembrandt. Munchen, 1922. 2 vols., sm. 4to., half cloth, 3rd rev. ed., plts. Van der Peet H-64-70 1978 Dfl 125

NEUMANN, CASPAR The Chemical Works of Caspar Neumann Abridged and Methodized. London, 1759. 4to., rebound in calf, first English ed. Quaritch 977-117 1978 $300

NEUMANN, CHRISTIAN ERNST Plan zur Erfindung und Befertigung Derjenigen Maschine. Lubeck, 1767. Sm. 4to., half calf, plt. F. Edwards 1013-165 1978 £70

NEUMANN, K. J. Der Roemische Staat und die Allgemeine Kirche bis auf Diocletian. 1890. Vol. I only, sewn, broken, stitching loose. Allen 234-680 1978 $7.50

NEUNZIG, K. Fremdlandisch e Stubenvogel. Magdeburg, 1921. Colored plts., 8vo., orig. cloth. Book Chest 17-269 1978 $100

NEUNZIG, K. Praxis der Vogelpflege und-Zuchtung. Magdeburg, 1927. Orig. green cloth, colored plate, 8vo. Book Chest 17-268 1978 $42.50

NEVADA SILVER MINING COMPANY. Prospectus. New York, 1864. Orig. pr. wr., 1st ed. Ginsberg 14-736 1978 $125

NEVILL, RALPH Old French Line Engravings. 1924. 4to., plts., full padded calf, gilt top, a little rubbed, uncut, ed. de-luxe, ltd. to 100 copies. Quaritch 983-226 1978 $125

NEVILLE, A. W. The Red River Valley, Then and Now. Paris, 1948. Cloth, map, illus., 1st ed., fine, d.w. Dykes 35-260 1978 $50

NEVILLE, A. W. The Red River Valley. Then and Now. Paris, 1948. Illus., 1st ed., d.w., pres., signed by Carl Hertzog, ltd. ed. Biblo BL781-295 1978 $32.50

NEVILLE, C. The Justice & Expediency of Tenant Right Legislation Considered. 1848. Disbound, very good, reprint. Hyland 128-174 1978 £10

NEVILLE, SYLAS Diary, 1767-88. 1950. Plts., 8vo. George's 635-1251 1978 £5.25

NEVILLE, WILLIAM B. On Insanity: Its Nature, Causes, and Cure. London, 1836. Fldg. plan, litho. plts., 8vo., orig. bds., prospectus, fr. cover loose, stain on fr. cover, 1st ed. Morrill 239-188 1978 $30

NEVINS, ALLAN American Social History. New York, 1923. Nice copy. MacManus 239-326 1978 $20

NEVINS, ALLAN A Century of Political Cartoons. New York, 1944. 1st ed., 4to., 100 cartoons. Biblo 251-175 1978 $20

NEVINS, ALLAN   A Century of Political Cartoons: Caricature in the U.S. from 1800 to 1900. With 100 Reproductions of Cartoons. New York, 1944. 1st printing, orig. pict. d.w., sm. 4to. Americanist 102-78 1978 $20

NEVINS, ALLAN   Grover Cleveland, A Study in Courage. New York, 1933. Illus. Baldwins' 51-176 1978 $10

NEVINS, ALLAN   Hamilton Fish... New York, 1936. Illus. MacManus 239-325 1978 $17.50

NEVINS, ALLAN   Hamilton Fish, the Inner History of the Grant Administration. New York, 1937. Bell Wiley's copy. Broadfoot 46-546 1978 $9

NEVINS, ALLAN   John D. Rockefeller. New York, 1940. 2 vols., in slipcase. Bell Wiley's copy. Broadfoot 46-548 1978 $14

NEVINS, ALLAN   Ordeal of the Union. New York, 1947. 2 vols., Bell Wiley's copy. Broadfoot 46-187 1978 $16

NEVINS, ALLAN   Polk: the Diary of a President. London, 1929. Bell Wiley's copy. Broadfoot's 44-713 1978 $12.00

NEVINS, ALLAN   This is England Today. 1941. Austin 80-239 1978 $8.50

NEVINS, ALLAN   The War for the Union. 4 vols., 1st ed., with letter from Nevins laid in, Bell Wiley's copy. Broadfoot's 44-281 1978 $40

NEVINS, J. B.   A Narrative in Two Voyages to Hudson's Bay... 1847. 1st. ed., sm. 8vo, 4 plts., illus., orig. decorative blind-stamped brown cloth, gilt back. Deighton 5-50 1978 £95

NEVINSON, HENRY W.   Neighbours of Ours. Bristol and London, n.d. Author's autograph pasted on to f/1, margins dust soiled, cloth. Eaton 45-366 1978 £5

NEVINSON, HENRY W.   Pictures of Classic Greek Landscape and Architecture. 1897. Plates by J. Fulleylove, roy. 4to. George's 635-487 1978 £18

NEW, CHESTER W.   Lord Durham, a Biography of John George Lambton, First Earl of Durham. Oxford, 1929. Hood 116-262 1978 $50

NEW and Nonofficial Remedies, 1917. Chicago, 1917. 8vo., 1st ed. Morrill 239-189 1978 $12.50

A NEW and True History of the Wandering Jew. (c. 1800). Sm. 8vo., unbound, crude woodcut. P. M. Hill 142-71 1978 £13

THE NEW Deal. 1937. Ex-lib., some underling, library binding. Austin 80-572 1978 $10

NEW-ENGLAND TRACT SOCIETY   The Publications of the New England Tract Society. Andover, 1820. 4vols., fine set, orig. sheepskin. Victoria 34-572 1978 $150

NEW England Historic Genealogical Society, Rolls of Membership of, 1844-1891. Boston, 1892. 8vo., orig. wrs., unopened. Morrill 241-385 1978 $7.50

THE NEW England Mercantile Union Business Directory...1849. New York, 1849. Maps, orig. cloth, fine. MacManus 239-327 1978 $30

NEW England Primer. Newark, 1824. Finely printed, illus. wrappers, spine paper lacking, wrappers soiled, text fine. Victoria 34-571 1978 $25

NEW England's First Fruits. (London, 1643). 4to., bds. & lea., #22 of 50 lg. paper copies initialled by Joseph Sabin, total prtg. 250. Butterfield 21-289 1978 $125

NEW HAMPSHIRE MEDICAL SOCIETY   Records of the... Concord, 1911. 8vo., first ed. Morrill 239-191 1978 $15

A NEW History of England,.... London, 1812. Part I only, 12mo, large copper-plate engravings, two lower corners torn, very good condition. Victoria 34-573 1978 $45

NEW JERSEY   Correspondence of the Executive of New Jersey 1776 to 1786. Newark, 1848. MacManus 239-1316 1978 $17.50

NEW JERSEY   Inventory of the County Archives of New Jersey. Bergen County. Hackensack, 1939. MacManus 239-1241 1978 $20

NEW JERSEY. DEPT. OF LABOR   Industrial Directory of New Jersey... Paterson, 1918. Lg. fold. colored map, orig. cloth, fine. MacManus 239-1279 1978 $15

NEW MEXICO MINING COMPANY. Preliminary Report for the Use of the Stockholders. New York, 1864. Orig. pr. wr., 1st ed. Ginsberg 14-771 1978 $125

NEW Mexico College of Agriculture and Mechanic Arts...1892/93. [Las Cruces], 1893. Illus., plate, orig. pr. wr., 1st ed. Ginsberg 14-768 1978 $35

NEW Mexico-Convention of Delegates. Washington, 1850. Disbound, 1st ed. Ginsberg 14-769 1978 $25

NEW Mexico Historical Review. Santa Fe, 1928-1972. Vols. 3-47, unbound, lacks 3 vols. Ginsberg 14-770 1978 $525

THE NEW Quarrel in China. 1859. 8vo, unbound, sewn as issued, nice copy. Fenning 32-245 1978 £10.50

THE NEW Republic, a Journal of Opinion, Vol. 1, Nos. 1-12. New York, 1914-15. Folio, orig. cloth. George's 635-372 1978 £5.25

A NEW System of Fortification.... London, 1770. 8vo., folding plate, half blue mor., 1st ed. Quaritch 978-159 1978 $250

THE NEW Tory Guide. 1819. First ed., sm. 8vo., orig. bds., entirely uncut, very good, in orig. state. Howes 194-403 1978 £25

NEW Universal Atlas..of the World, With a Special Map of Each of the United States...117 Maps, Plans and Sections. Philadelphia, 1847. Plates are good, binding worn, colored maps. Nestler Rare 78-54 1978 $425

NEW Writing & Daylight 1945. 1945. Very good, repaired d.w., first English ed. Bell Book 16-970 1978 £4

NEW YORK   Communication from the Governor, Transmitting Certain Proceedings of the Seneca Nation of Indians for a New Form of Government. Albany, 1849. 8vo., unbound. Morrill 241-220 1978 $7.50

NEW YORK. BOARD OF COMMISSIONERS   Report of the... Representing the State of New York at the Cotton States and International Exposition Held at Atlanta, Georgia, 1895. Albany, 1896. Cloth, front inner hinges cracked but not loose. Hayman 72-659 1978 $10

NEW YORK. BOARD OF RAILROAD COMMISSIONERS   Seventh Annual Report of... Albany, 1890. 2 vols., orig. bind. Petrilla 13-105 1978 $17.50

NEW YORK. FOREST COMMISSION   Fifth Annual Report of the New York Forest Commission...Dec. 31, 1890. Albany, 1891. Lg. fldg. map, fldg. chart. Butterfield 21-4 1978 $20

NEW YORK. METROPOLITAN MUSEUM OF ART   Catalogue of European Court Swords and Hunting Swords Including the Ellis, De Dino, Riggs, and Reubell Collections. New York, 1922. 4to., frontis., half blue mor., ltd. to 900 copies. Quaritch 983-Addenda f 1978 $500

NEW YORK. SENATE   Report of the Senate Committee...on the Bill to Provide for the Enlargement of the Erie, Oswego and Champlain Canals, so as to Admit the Passage of Gunboats and Vessels of War. Albany, 1862. Very lg. fldg. map, fine cond, wr., partly loose. Butterfield 21-95 1978 $20

NEW YORK. STATE LIBRARY   Catalog of the New York State Library. 1856. Maps, engravings, some wear on binding. Nestler Rare 78-100 1978 $20

NEW YORK (CITY)   Manual of the Corporation of the City of New York, for 1852. (New York, 1852). Fldg. maps, illus., fine copy, orig. cloth. MacManus 239-367 1978 $35

NEW YORK (CITY)   Manual of the Corporation of the City of New York for 1858. (New York, 1858). Thick 8vo., illus., litho. plts., orig. cloth, good copy. MacManus 239-368 1978 $35

NEW YORK ATHENAEUM   Prospectus, Constitution and By-Laws, Scheme of Lectures for 1825, etc. (New York, 1824). Orig. wr., very good. Butterfield 21-525 1978 $7.50

THE NEW YORK JEWELER   Illustrated Catalogue with Wholesale List Prices. New York, 1903. 4to., covers stained, orig. cloth. Morrill 241-427 1978 $30

NEW YORK STATE HISTORICAL ASSOCIATION   Proceedings...Vol. I. (Albany), 1901. Frontis. portr., out of print. Butterfield 21-300 1978 $15

NEW York Advancing. (New York), 1939. World's Fair ed., color plts., photo. illus., stiff wr. Butterfield 21-512 1978 $10

NEW York Directory for 1786... New York, (1905). Illus., 12mo., ltd. ed. Biblo BL781-169 1978 $32.50

NEW York Styles. New York, 1920. Illus., 4to., orig. wrs. Morrill 241-626 1978 $15

THE NEW-YORK Submarine Company, Office, 61 William Street, New-York. New York, 1867. 8vo, original green printed wr., 1st ed., laid in lithograph, large folding plate, very good condition, very rare and very unusual. Ximenes 47-277 1978 $225

NEW Yorker. New York, 1929. 2nd album, 4to., 1st ed. Biblo 251-176 1978 $15

NEW Yorker. New York, 1931. 4th album, 4to., 1st ed. Biblo 251-177 1978 $12.50

NEW Yorker Album. 1942. New York, (1941). 4to., cartoons, d.w. BL781-567 1978 $9.50

NEW Yorker War Album. New York, (1942). 4to., cartoons, d.w. Biblo BL781-568 1978 $12

NEWBERY, DR. J. S. The U.S. Sanitary Commission in the Valley of the Mississippi 1861-1866. Cleveland, 1871. Pres. copy from author, spine frayed. Broadfoot's 44-696 1978 $35

NEWBOLD, H. B. House and Cottage Construction. (c. 1925). Photographs, 3 vols., roy. 8vo. George's 635-84 1978 £5.25

NEWBOLT, FRANCIS The History of the Royal Society of Painter-Etchers and Engravers. 1880-1930. 1930. 4to., frontis., plts., cloth. Quaritch 983-227 1978 $45

NEWBOLT, HENRY Collected Poems, 1897-1907. London, (1910). Sole ed., frontispiece portrait, orig. cloth, t.e.g., scarce, very good or better. Limestone 9-218 1978 $12.50

NEWBY, P. H. Agents and Witnesses. 1947. Very good, d.w., first English ed. Bell Book 16-670 1978 £4.50

NEWBY, P. H. Maria Edgeworth. London, 1950. First ed., orig. binding, very nice, d.w. Rota 211-435 1978 £6

NEWCOMB, PEARSON The Alamo City. San Antonio, 1926. 1st ed., illus., autographed by author. Jenkins 116-110 1978 $25

NEWCOMB, PEARSON The Alamo City. San Antonio, (1926). Orig. binding, clean. Hayman 71-727 1978 $7.50

NEWDIGATE, BERNARD The Art of the Book. London, (1938). Cloth, tattered d.w., fine. Dawson's 447-9 1978 $30

NEWELL, C. History of the Revolution in Texas, Particularly the War of 1835 & 36:.... New York, 1838. Folding map, original cloth, gilt, covers virtually mint, some browning internally, 1st ed. Jenkins 116-997 1978 $275

NEWELL, PETER Pictures and Thymes. New York, 1900. 2nd ed., written and illus. by Newell, shaken, very good. Victoria 34-579 1978 $10

NEWELL, PETER The Slant Book. New York, (1910). Binding cut on slant, edges rubbed, very good. Victoria 34-580 1978 $32.50

NEWELL, ROBERT H. The Orpheus C. Kerr Papers. New York, 1863. 1st and 2nd series, 2 vols., spine ends chipped, 1st ed., 1st state, pub. cloth. Petrilla 13-52 1978 $10

NEWHALL, C. The Leaf-Collector's Hand-book & Herbarium. New York, 1892. 8vo, orig. cloth. Book Chest 17-270 1978 $14

NEWKIRK, NEWTON Back to Nature. New York, 1911. Illus. by author, 12mo., 1st ed., bds., rubbed. Biblo 251-585 1978 $12.50

NEWLAND, HENRY The Life and Contemporaneous Church History of Antonio de Dominis, Archbishop of Spalatro... 1859. Octavo, good, spine rubbed. Upcroft 10-461 1978 £6.50

NEWLANDS, JAMES The Carpenter and Joiner's Assistant. (c. 1865). Plts., cuts in text, folio, half calf, worn. George's 635-248 1978 £25

NEWLANDS, JOHN A. R. On the Discovery of the Periodic Law, and on Relations Among the Atomic Weights. London, 1884. 8vo., fldg. tables, orig. cloth, fine copy, 1st ed. in book form. Norman 5-208 1978 $150

A NEWLY-Discovered Broadside Specimen of Fell Type Printed at Oxford About 1685. Cambridge, 1940. 4to., orig. wrs., 1 of 210 no. copies, slipcase. MacManus 238-918 1978 $25

NEWMAN, ANGIE F. McKinley Carnations of Memory. (New York, 1903). Cloth. Hayman 73-469 1978 $7.50

NEWMAN, C. On the Importance of a Mutual Arrangement between the Landlord & Tenant. 1848. Disbound, reprint, octavo bound in cloth. Hyland 128-177 1978 £10

NEWMAN, EDWARD An Illustrated Natural History of British Butterflies and Moths. (c. 1890). Figures drawn by G. Willis, engraved by T. Kirchner, roy. 8vo. George's 635-975 1978 £15

NEWMAN, EUGENE WILLIAM Essays on Men, Things and Events... New York, 1904. Ports., binding faded, rubbed and stained, margins damp-stained. Biblo BL781-247 1978 $12

NEWMAN, EUGENE WILLIAM Essays on Men, Things and Events. New York and Washington, 1904. 8vo., first ed. Morrill 239-597 1978 $9.50

NEWMAN, GEORGE Bacteria, Especially as They Are Related to the Economy of Nature to Industrial Processes and to the Public Health. New York, 1908. Library marks. Rittenhouse 49-577 1976 $12.50

NEWMAN, HARRY W. Charles County Gentry. Washington, 1940. Frontis., ltd. to 150 copies. MacManus 239-1000 1978 $55

NEWMAN, HENRY STANLEY Memories of Stanley Pumphrey. New York, 1883. Portr., 8vo., 1st ed. Morrill 239-537 1978 $15

NEWMAN, JOHN HENRY Apologia Pro Vita Sua. London, 1864. 1st book ed., 8vo., rebound in 1/2 calf, slight shelf wear & rubbing, interior very fine, nice copy. Current 24-233 1978 $165

NEWMAN, JOHN HENRY Apologia Pro Vita Sua... London, 1864. 1st. ed., 8vo, modern half calf, sm. rubber stamp on title-page. Traylen 88-307 1978 £21

NEWMAN, JOHN HENRY Apologia Pro Vita Sua: being a Reply to a Pamphlet.... 1864. First ed., contemp. half vellum, 8vo. Howes 194-1067 1978 £35

NEWMAN, JOHN HENRY The Dream of Gerontius. Yellow Springs, 1927. Ltd. to 600 copies. Biblo 251-586 1978 $8.50

NEWMAN, JOHN HENRY A Letter Addressed to His Grace the Duke of Norfolk on Occasion of Mr. Gladstone's Recent Expostulations. London, 1875. 8vo, original light blue printed wr., 1st ed., nice copy. Ximenes 47-216 1978 $50

NEWMAN, SAMUEL P. Address Delivered Before the Benevolent Society of Bowdoin College...Sept. 5, 1826. Portland, 1826. 8vo., orig. wrs., 1st ed. Morrill 241-306 1978 $12.50

NEWMAN AND CO. London. Twenty-Four Views of Ramsgate. c.1870. Oblong 8vo., plts., fine copy, orig. limp green cloth. Quaritch 983-348 1978 $90

NEWMARCH, C. H. Recollections of Rugby by an Old Rugbean. London, 1848. 12mo, orig. cloth, worn. Sexton 7-172 1978 £5

NEWMAYER, S. W. Medical and Sanitary Inspection of Schools, for the Health Officer, the Physician, the Nurse and the Teacher. Philadelphia, 1913. Rittenhouse 49-578 1976 $10

NEWNHAM-DAVIS, LIEUT. COL. The Transvaal Under the Queen. London, 1900. 4to, dec. cloth, illus. K Books 239-348 1978 £13

NEWNOM, CLYDE L. Michigan's Thirty-Seven Million Acres of Diamonds. Detroit, 1927. Artificial leather. Hayman 72-463 1978 $8.50

NEWSOME, ALBERT RAY The Presidential Election of 1824 in North Carolina. Chapel Hill, 1939. New cloth. Broadfoot 50-151 1978 $10

NEWTON, A. P. Travel and Travellers of the Middle Ages. 1930. Plts., 8vo. Upcroft 12-311 1978 £5

NEWTON, ALEXANDER H. Out of the Briars, an Autobiography, and Sketch of the 29th Regt. Connecticut Volunteers. (Philadelphia, 1910). 1st ed., covers soiled, errata slip, port., illus. Americanist 102-15 1978 $35

NEWTON, ALFRED EDWARD Amenities of Book-Collecting and Kindred Affections. Boston, 1918. Illus., orig. cloth-backed bds., paper label, pres. copy from author, bookplt., good. MacManus 238-994 1978 $40

NEWTON, ALFRED EDWARD The Amenities of Book-Collecting. Boston, 1918. 8vo., orig. cloth-backed bds., 1st ed., erratum slip, very good. MacManus 238-993 1978 $20

NEWTON, ALFRED EDWARD   The Amenities of Book-Collecting. Boston, (1924). 3/4 mor., slightly rubbed, illus. MacManus 238-992 1978 $12.50

NEWTON, ALFRED EDWARD   Amenities of Book Collecting. Boston, (1924). 5th printing, 3/4 mor., t.e.g., illus., very good. Houle 10-238 1978 $37.50

NEWTON, ALFRED EDWARD   Bibliography and Pseudo-Bibliography. Philadelphia, 1936. Orig. cloth, d.j., 1st ed., inscribed by author, fine. MacManus 238-996 1978 $25

NEWTON, ALFRED EDWARD   Bibliography and Pseudo-Bibliography. Philadelphia, 1936. 8vo., orig. cloth-backed bds., d.j., 1st ed. MacManus 238-997 1978 $10

NEWTON, ALFRED EDWARD   Bibliography & Pseudo-Bibliography. 1936. 2nd prtg. Battery Park 1-425 1978 $15

NEWTON, ALFRED EDWARD   Derby Day and Other Adventures. Boston, 1934. 8vo., orig. cloth-backed bds., 1st ltd. ed., 1 of 1,129 no. copies, signed by author, boxed, fine. MacManus 238-1001 1978 $35

NEWTON, ALFRED EDWARD   Derby Day and Other Adventures. Boston, 1934. 8vo., orig. cloth, 1st ed., fine, d.j. MacManus 238-1000 1978 $10

NEWTON, ALFRED EDWARD   Derby Day. Boston, 1934. 1st ed., limited, signed, 4 to., half cloth, illus., fine, almost mint. Houle 10-239 1978 $85

NEWTON, ALFRED EDWARD   Doctor Johnson. A Play. Boston, 1923. Orig. cloth-backed bds., 1st ed., signed and inscribed by author, fine. MacManus 238-1003 1978 $30

NEWTON, ALFRED EDWARD   Doctor Johnson. A Play. Boston, 1923. Illus., orig. cloth-backed bds., 1st ed., 1 of 585 copies signed by author, fine. MacManus 238-1002 1978 $35

NEWTON, ALFRED EDWARD   End Papers. Literary Recreations. Boston, 1933. Illus., orig. cloth, d.j., worn, 1st ed. MacManus 238-1005 1978 $12.50

NEWTON, ALFRED EDWARD   End Papers. 1933. 1st., d.w., illus. Battery Park 1-424 1978 $22.50

NEWTON, ALFRED EDWARD   The Greatest Book in the World. Boston, (1925). 8vo., orig. cloth-backed bds., 1st ltd. ed., 1 of 470 no. copies, signed by author, bookplt., very good. MacManus 238-1007 1978 $45

NEWTON, ALFRED EDWARD   The Greatest Book in the World. Boston, (1925). 1 of 475 numbered & signed copies on large paper, 4 to., cloth over bd., t.e.g., uncut, illus., fine, almost mint. Houle 10-240 1978 $95

NEWTON, ALFRED EDWARD   The Greatest Book in the World. Boston, 1925. Orig. bds., 1st ed., signed and inscribed by author. MacManus 238-1006 1978 $35

NEWTON, ALFRED EDWARD   The Greatest Book in the World. Boston, 1925. Orig. cloth-backed bds. MacManus 238-1008 1978 $10

NEWTON, ALFRED EDWARD   The Homes of the Poets Illustrated with Etchings.... Philadelphia, (actually c. 1891). 2nd rev. ed., etchings, oblong 4to, orig. pict. wrs., front wr. soiled. Americanist 101-105 1978 $300

NEWTON, ALFRED EDWARD   A Magnificent Farce. Boston, (1921). Illus., orig. cloth-backed bds., 1st ed., very good. MacManus 238-1009 1978 $10

NEWTON, ALFRED EDWARD   A Magnificent Farce. Boston, (1921). Illus., orig. bds., signed inscription from Newton. MacManus 238-1010 1978 $35

NEWTON, ALFRED EDWARD   Newton on Blackstone. Philadelphia, 1937. Orig. cloth, d.j., faded spine, 1st ed., ltd. to 2,000 copies, signed by author, bookplt., fine. MacManus 238-1011 1978 $25

NEWTON, ALFRED EDWARD   On Books and Business. N.P., 1930. Orig. bds., 1st ed., ltd. to 325 signed copies. MacManus 238-1012 1978 $35

NEWTON, ALFRED EDWARD   Pope, Poetry, & Portrait. Privately Printed, Not To Be Sold. Daylesford, 1936. Illus., orig. blue wrs., 8vo. Americanist 101-106a 1978 $20

NEWTON, ALFRED EDWARD   This Book-Collecting Game. Boston, 1928. 8vo., orig. cloth-backed bds., t.e.g., 1st trade ed. MacManus 238-1013 1978 $10

NEWTON, ALFRED EDWARD   This Book-Collecting Game. Boston, 1928. Illus., 1st trade ed., d.w. Biblo BL781-772 1978 $12.50

NEWTON, ALFRED EDWARD   This Book-Collecting Game. Boston, 1928. 1st. Battery Park 1-422 1978 $25

NEWTON, ALFRED EDWARD   Thomas Hardy Novelist or Poet. 1929. 4to., 1 of 950 copies, illus. Battery Park 1-423 1978 $35

NEWTON, ALFRED EDWARD   A Tourist in Spite of Himself. Boston, 1930. 8vo., orig. cloth-backed bds., 1st ltd. ed., ltd. to 500 no. copies, boxed. MacManus 238-1015 1978 $40

NEWTON, ALFRED EDWARD   A Tourist in Spite of Himself. Boston, 1930. 8vo., orig. cloth, 1st ed. MacManus 238-1014 1978 $10

NEWTON, C. J.   Essays on Art and Archaeology. 1880. Folding plts. of inscriptions, 8vo. George's 635-1178 1978 £6.50

NEWTON, CHARLES THOMAS   Essays on Art and Archaeology. London, 1880. Plts., 1st ed. BL781-449 1978 $16.50

NEWTON, CHARLES THOMAS   Travels and Discoveries in the Levant. 1865. 1st. ed., 2 vols., roy. 8vo, folding lithograph maps, lithograph plts., woodcuts, orig. embossed green cloth, gilt, some chafing of covers. Deighton 5-135 1978 £155

NEWTON, CHARLES THOMAS   Travels and Discoveries in the Levant. 1865. Folding maps, plts., 2 vols., roy. 8vo, covers soiled, margins of one map repaired, orig. cloth. Edwards 1012-53 1978 £120

NEWTON, ISAAC   An Account of Sir Isaac Newton's Philosophical Discoveries. London, 1748. 4to., fldg. plts., contemp. tree calf, richly gilt spine, little rubbed, spine repaired, but fine copy, 1st ed. Norman 5-209 1978 $275

NEWTON, ISAAC   Berhardi Vareni Geographia Generalis. Cambridge, 1672. 8vo., fldg. plts., contemp. calf, rubbed, dampstaining in lower right corner, but very good copy, 1st ed. Norman 5-*35 1978 $450

NEWTON, ISAAC   The Chronology of Ancient Kingdoms Amended. 1728. First ed., very good, plts., 4to., contemp. polished calf. Howes 194-402 1978 £80

NEWTON, ISAAC   The Chronology of Antient Kingdoms Amended. Dublin, 1728. 1st ed., 8vo, full original calf, rebacked, t.p. dust soiled, text fine. Victoria 34-582 1978 $125

NEWTON, ISAAC   The Method of Fluxions and Infinite Series. London, 1736. 4to., frontis. & text diagrs., contemp. blind-tooled calf, rubbed, rebacked, dampstaining in outer margin of some leaves & frontis., browned but very good copy, 1st ed. Norman 5-*37 1978 $1,500

NEWTON, ISAAC   Il Newtonianismo per le dame ovvero dialoghi sopra la luce e i colori. Naples, 1737. Sm. 4to., fine contemp. mottled calf, gilt back, first ed. Quaritch 977-123 1978 $300

NEWTON, ISAAC   Opticks. London, 1704. 4to., fold. engrav. plts., fine, contemp. panelled calf, rebacked with orig. gilt spine laid down, first ed., first issue. Quaritch 977-118 1978 $3,000

NEWTON, ISAAC   Opticks... London, 1721. 3rd ed., fldg. plts., 8vo., calf, rehinged. Salloch 345-134 1978 $250

NEWTON, ISAAC   Philosophiae Naturalis Principia Mathematica. Cambridge, 1713. 4to., fldg. plt., text diagrs., contemp. blind-tooled & gilt calf, rubbed, rebacked, but fine, crisp copy, bklabel of Edward Neville da Costa Andrade, 2nd ed., 1 of 750 copies. Norman 5-*36 1978 $1,250

NEWTON, ISAAC   Philosophiae Naturalis Principia Mathematica. Cambridge, 1713. 4to., fine, mid nineteenth century full russet mor., gilt, gilt edges, second ed. Quaritch 977-119 1978 $1,850

NEWTON, ISAAC   Philosophiae Naturalis Principia Mathematica. London, 1726. 4to., portrait, contemp. calf, gilt spine, joints repaired, 750 copies printed. Quaritch 977-120 1978 $800

NEWTON, ISAAC   Principes Mathematiques de la Philosophie Naturelle. 1759. 2 vols., 4to., engrav. plts., several gatherings browned, a few rust spots, contemp. French mottled calf, gilt spines, joints weak, one corner bumped, only French ed. Quaritch 977-121 1978 $1,600

NEWTON, ISAAC   A View of Sir Isaac Newton's Philosophy. 1728. 4to., plts., contemp. sprinkled calf, rebacked, Earl of Harington's copy with bookplt., first ed. Quaritch 977-124 1978 $300

NEWTON, J. H.   History of the Pan-Handle; Being Historical Collections of the Counties of Ohio, Brooke, Marshall and Hancock, West Virginia. Wheeling, 1879. 1/2 leather, professionally rebacked, 2 maps, 22 plts. Hayman 71-773 1978 $125

NEWTON, J. R.   The Modern Bethesda.   New York, (1879).
Portr., 8vo., 1st ed.   Morrill 239-192 1978 $25

NEWTON, JOHN   The Christian Correspondent; or A Series of
Religious Letters...   1790. Orig. calf, rubbed, hinges weak. Jarndyce 16-
115 1978 £9.50

NEWTON, LEWIS W.   A Social and Political History of Texas. Dallas,
(1932). Illus. Biblo 247-246 1978 $15

NEWTON, LEWIS W.   A Social and Political History of Texas. Dallas,
1935. Cover speckled, Bell Wiley's copy. Broadfoot's 44-969 1978 $12

NEWTON, LEWIS W.   A Social and Political History of Texas. Dallas,
1935. Revised, illus., maps. Jenkins 116-1000 1978 $15

NEWTON, M. B.   Anecdotes of Omaha. Omaha, 1891. Half
calf, 1st ed. Ginsberg 14-722 1978 $25

NEWTON, VIRGINIUS   The Confederate States Ram Merrimac or
Virginia. Richmond, 1906. Wraps, reprinted, Bell Wiley's copy. Broadfoot's
44-285 1978 $16.00

NEWTON, W.   A Familiar Introduction to the Science of Astronomy and the Use of the Globes. London, 1832. Frontis., 12mo., orig. cloth,
rather soiled, inner hinge weak. K Books 244-245 1978 £9

NEWTON-ROBINSON, CHARLES   The Viol of Love and Other Poems. London,
1895. Orig. dec. cloth, 1st ed., covers designed by Laurence Housman, pres.
copy, spine a bit rubbed, else very good. MacManus 238-670 1978 $65

NEXO, MARTIN ANDERSEN   Die Passagiere der Leeren Platze. Berlin, 1921.
Royal 8vo., half cloth, very clean. Goldschmidt 110-32 1978 $60

NEXO, MARTIN ANDERSEN   Die Passagaiere de leeren Platze. Berlin, (1921).
8vo., boards and cloth, illus. by George Grosz, 1st ed., fine. Duschnes 220-134
1978 $90

NIAGARA in Summer & Winter. (Philadelphia, 1904). Oblong 4to., pict. wrappers. Wolfe 39-394 1978 $10

NIAGARA in Summer and Winter. N.P., n.d.(about 1910). Album of 20 views
of the Falls. Hood 117-757 1978 $17.50

THE NIBELUNGENLIED. London, 1874. 2nd ed., 8vo., orig. cloth. Morrill
241-428 1978 $12.50

NICHOLAS, JOHN L.   Narrative of a Voyage to New Zealand, Performed
in the Years 1814 and 1815 in Company with Rev. Samuel Marsden. London, 1817.
1st ed., 2 vols., plts., maps, rare, orig. marbled bds., interior fine. Current
24-190 1978 $285

NICHOLL, EDITH M.   Observations of a Ranchwoman in New Mexico.
Cincinnati, 1901. Original cloth, 1st Amer. ed., autograph presentation copy
from "author". Ginsberg 14-772 1978 $125

NICHOLLS, JOHN   Recollections & Reflections, Personal & Political,
As Connected With Public Affairs During the Reign of George III. 1820. 1st ed.,
rebound in half calf, hand-marbled bds., v.g. Jarndyce 16-903 1978 £12.50

NICHOLS, BEVERLEY   A Thatched Roof. London, 1933. Illus. by Rex
Whistler, first ed., orig. binding, nice. Rota 211-776 1978 £5

NICHOLS, CHARLES L.   Bibliography of Worcester. Worcester, 1899.
Ltd. to 225 copies, fine untrimmed copy. MacManus 239-279 1978 $35

NICHOLS, EFFINGHAM H.   The Nature and Extent of the Obligations of the
Pacific Companies to the Government in Reference to Bonds Issued by the United
States,.... Washington, 1871. Orig. pr. wr., 1st ed. Ginsberg 14-786 1978
$65

NICHOLS, G. H. F.   The 18th Divsion in the Great War. 1922. Portrait frontis., plts., orig. cloth, thick 8vo. F. Edwards 1013-586 1978 £15

NICHOLS, GEORGE WARD   The Story of the Great March from the Diary of
a Staff Officer. New York, 1865. 1st. ed., map, illus. Baldwins' 51-205 1978
$12.50

NICHOLS, ISAAC T.   Historic Days in Cumberland County, N.J.,
1855-1865... N.P., 1907. Illus., 4to. MacManus 239-1309 1978 $40

NICHOLS, JEANNETTE PADDOCK   James Styles of Kingston, New York, and
George Stuart, of Schoolcraft, Michigan. Swarthmore, 1936. Illus., 8vo., ex-
lib., nice, 1st ed. Morrill 239-562 1978 $10

NICHOLS, JOHN   Biographical and Literary Anecdotes of William
Bowyer, Printer, F.S.A. and of many of his learned friends. London, 1782. Demy
4to., port., half mor., fine. Forster 130-146 1978 £75

NICHOLS, JOHN   A Collection of all the Wills Not Known to be
Extant, of the Kings and Queens of England... 1780. 1st. ed., 4to, contemp.
gilt polished calf. Hannas 54-229 1978 £45

NICHOLS, JOHN   Collection of All the Wills, Now Known to be
Extant, of the Kings & Queens of England, Princes & Princesses of Wales, etc.,
from William the Conqueror to Henry VII. 1780. Buckram, ex-lib. Allen 234-
1381 1978 $25

NICHOLS, ROBERT   Fisbo. 1934. 1st. ed., no. 369 of 1000 copies,
signed by author, unopened, v.g., slightly worn d.w., bookplt. Jarndyce 16-
1209 1978 £8.50

NICHOLS, ROBERT   Fisbo. 1934. First ed., ltd. to 1000 signed
copies, 8vo. George's 635-1327 1978 £5

NICHOLS, ROSE STANDISH   English Pleasure Gardens. New York, 1902.
Plans, reproductions of photos & drwgs., 8vo., 1st ed. Morrill 241-429 1978
$12.50

NICHOLS, ROSE STANDISH   Italian Pleasure Gardens, the best & most typical
examples. London, 1929. 8vo., orig. cloth. Book Chest 17-271 1978 $22.50

NICHOLSON, A.   Cimabue, a Critical Study. 1932. 4to., plt.,
new buckram. Allen 234-1180 1978 $17.50

NICHOLSON, H.   The Ancient Life-History of the Earth. New
York, 1896. 1/2 leather, 8vo., orig. cloth. Book Chest 17-272 1978 $25

NICHOLSON, H.   The Desire to Please. 1942. 1st ed., very good,
octavo bound in cloth. Hyland 128-182 1978 £5

NICHOLSON, H. A.   Report Upon the Palaeontology of the Province of
Ontario. Toronto, 1875. Illus., plts. Hood 116-764 1978 $25

NICHOLSON, J. S.   A Project of Empire, a Critical Study of the
Economics of Imperialism with special reference to Adam Smith. 1909. 8vo.
George's 635-373 1978 £5

NICHOLSON, JOHN   The Operative Mechanic, and British Machinist.
London, 1825. 8vo., fldg. frontis., plts., contemp. half mor., rubbed, some
foxing, but very good copy, 2nd ed. Norman 5-210 1978 $100

NICHOLSON, JOHN   The Operative Mechanic, and British Machinist.
London, 1830. Third ed., 8vo., frontispiece, plts., some plt. foxed, orig. cloth
backed bds., printed paper label, uncut. Quaritch 977-242 1978 $85

NICHOLSON, MEREDITH   A Hoosier Chronicle. Boston, 1912. Illus., first
ed. Austin 82-678 1978 $20

NICHOLSON, NORMAN   H. G. Wells. Denver, 1950. Very fine in
rubbed d.w. Desmarais B-651 1978 $10

NICHOLSON, PETER   The Carpenter's New Guide... Philadelphia,
1827. 9th ed., 4to, contemp. full calf, scuffed, worn, text foxed, plates, 8vo.
Americanist 101-6 1978 $125

NICHOLSON, PETER   The New and Improved Practical Builder, and
Workman's Companion. (c. 1850). Plts., 3 vols. in 1, 4to., half calf, rubbed.
George's 635-86 1978 $35

NICHOLSON, PETER   New Practical Builder, and Workman's Companion
in Carpentry.... (1823). Engraved plts., lacks frontis., some foxing, 4to., new
qtr. calf. George's 635-85 1978 $25

NICHOLSON, THOMAS   Visions of the Muse; A Series of Poems... 1828.
1st. ed., uncut, orig. marbled bds., paper label, bds. detached. Jarndyce 16-
904 1978 £12.50

NICHOLSON, WILLIAM   The British Encyclopedia. London, 1809. 6
vols., engrav. plts., contemp. half calf, a trifle rubbed. Quaritch 977-125 1978
$225

NICHOLSON, WILLIAM   A Dictionary of Chemistry. London, 1795. First
ed., 4to., engrav. plts., one plt. cropped, title soiled, some marginal soiling in
text, contemp. tree calf, rebacked. Quaritch 977-126 1978 $250

NICHOLSON, WILLIAM   An Introduction to Natural Philosophy. London,
1805. Fifth ed., 2 vols., plts., uncut, orig. bds., neatly respined, 8vo. K Books
244-246 1978 £25

NICHOLSON, WILLIAM   London Types. New York, 1898. Quatorzains by W. E. Henley, chipped, cloth spine chipped, coloured woodcuts. Totteridge 29-73 1978 $100

NICIUS, JANUS   Iani Nicii Erythraei Exempla Virtvtvm et Vitiorvm. 1645. Sm. 8vo., marbled bds., calf spine, very good. King 7-292 1978 £15

NICKERSON, HOFFMAN   The Turning Point of the Revolution... Boston, 1928. 1st ed., illus., maps, nice copy, scarce. MacManus 239-610 1978 $35

NICKERSON, W. SEARS   Land Ho! 1620. A Seaman's Story of the May-flower... Boston, 1931. 1st ed., illus., cloth bds. MacManus 239-1777 1978 $30

NICKERSON, W. SEARS   Land Ho! - 1620. 1931 Maps, good. Nestler Rare 78-24 1978 $18

NICKLES, JOHN M.   Bibliography of North American Geology 1919-1923. Washington, 1931. Cloth. Hayman 73-51 1978 $10

NICKLIN, PHILIP H.   Remarks on Literary Property. Philadelphia, 1838. 12mo, disbound, 1st ed. Ximenes 47-217 1978 $50

NICOL, ERIC   The Roving '. Toronto, 1950. Hood 117-493 1978 $10

NICOLAI, ERNST ANTON   Gedancken Von Der Erzeugung Der Misgeburten Und Mondkaelber. Halle, 1749. Engr. plts., wrs. Salloch 345-135 1978 $35

NICOLAS, NICHOLAS HARRIS   History of the Orders of Knighthood of the British Empire. London, 1842. 1st ed., lg. quarto, green half mor., pebbled cloth covers, gilt edges, some foxing, color plts., frontis. is orig. drwg. by George Baxter. Totteridge 29-74 1978 $325

NICOLAS, P.   Notices sur l'Indo-Chine. (Paris), 1900. Plts., illus., 8vo., orig. covers. Van der Peet 127-172 1978 Dfl 65

NICOLAY, CHARLES G.   The Oregon Territory:.... London, 1846. Plates, folding map, orig. pr. pict. wr., 1st ed. Ginsberg 14-834 1978 $75

NICOLAY, CHARLES G.   The Oregon Territory... 1846. 1st. ed., 8vo, frontis, maps, orig. cloth blind-stamped. Edwards 1012-512 1978 £35

NICOLAY, JOHN G.   The Outbreak of Rebellion. New York, 1881. Bell Wiley's copy. Broadfoot 46-190 1978 $10

NICOLL, W. ROBERTSON   A Bookman's Letters. London, 1913. 1st ed., very good or better. Limestone 9-220 1978 $13.50

NICOLLET County, Minnesota, as an Agricultural and Dairying Section and St. Peter as a Manufacturing Center. St. Peter, 1884. Illus., original pictorial printed wr., 1st ed. Ginsberg 14-567 1978 $75

NICOLSON, HAROLD   Diplomacy. New York, (1939). 1st Amer. ed. Biblo BL781-858 1978 $9.50

NICOLSON, HAROLD   Friday Mornings, 1941-44. London, (1944). First ed. Biblo 247-610 1978 $15

NICOLSON, HAROLD   Paul Verlaine. London, (1921). Good, first ed., orig. binding. Rota 212-40 1978 £40

NICOLSON, HAROLD   Some People. 1927. First ed., cr. 8vo., fine, d.w., orig. cloth, pres. copy inscribed by the author. Howes 194-1068 1978 £8.50

NICOLSON, WILLIAM   The English, Scotch and Irish Historical Libraries. London, 1776. Quarto, newer marbled boards and calf spine with red mor. label, bookplate, very nice copy, 2nd Collected ed. Bennett 7-81 1978 $250

NIEBUHR, CARSTEN   Beschreibung Von Arabien aus Eigenen Boebach-tungen und im Lande Selbst Gesammleten Nachrichten. Kopenhagen, 1772. 1st. ed., 4to, engraved plts., 2 hand coloured, maps, engraved vignette title-pg., rebound in modern quarter calf, raised bands, marbled sides, fine copy. Deighton 5-83 1978 £450

NIEBUHR, REINHOLD   The Children of Light and the Children of Dark-ness. 1944. Austin 82-679 1978 $12.50

NIELSEN, KAY   East of the Sun and West of the Moon. New York, 1930. Large 8vo, all color plates present, cover lettering and large vignette in blue on orange cloth, very good. Victoria 34-586 1978 $85

NIELSEN, KAY   East of the Sun and West of the Moon. (London). Signed, limited ed, in full vellum, decor. in gilt and blue, tipped-in color plates, laid-in brochure of exhibition of orig. water-colors for book, boards lightly warped, very fine copy, ties present, very rare, magnificent. Victoria 34-585 1978 $1,500

NIESE, B.   Grundriss der Roemischen Geschichte nebst Quel-lenkunde. 1910. Allen 234-686 1978 $12.50

NIETO, ABRAHAM H.   Nieto's Jewish Almanac for 100 Years...1902 to 2002... New York, 1902. Cloth, 1st ed. Ginsberg 16-883 1978 $15.00

NIETZSCHE, FRIEDRICH   Also Sprach Zarathustra. Leipzig, 1927. 8vo., cloth, India paper. Salloch 348-172 1978 $12.50

NIETZSCHE, FRIEDRICH   Ecce Homo. Leipzig, 1908. Sm. 4to., publ. gray suede, uncut, half lea. case, first ed., ltd. issue of 1250 copies, one of 150 copies on Jap. paper, perfect state. Goldschmidt 110-73 1978 $1,400

NIETZSCHE, FRIEDRICH   Ecce Homo. Leipzig, 1908. Sm. 4to., pub-lisher's half vellum, uncut, regular numbered copy on Holland Van Gelder paper, excellent. Goldschmidt 110-73A 1978 $245

NIETZSCHE, FRIEDRICH   Werke. Ausgewaehlt von A. Messer. Leip-zig, 1930. 2 vols., 8vo., full mor., gilt top. Salloch 348-171 1978 $30

NIEUWENHUIS, G. M.   De Stad aan het Spaarne in Zeven Eeuwen. Am-sterdam, 1946. Illus. cloth, 8vo., colored frontis., plts., illus. Van der Peet H-64-508 1978 Dfl 30

NIEUWENTYT, BERNARD 1654-1718   The Religious Philosopher. 1721-20-21. 3 vols., plts., contemp. panelled calf, 8vo. Howes 194-404 1978 £35

NIFO, AUGUSTINUS   De Falsa Dilvvii Prognosticatione Quae Ex Conuen-tu Omnium Planetarium Qui in Piscibus Contiget Anno 1524 Diuulgata Est. Libri tres. Sm. 4to., half calf, red marbled bds., dust-soiled, very good copy from library of Dr. Alfred M. Hellman, scarce Augsburg ed. Zeitlin 245-176 1978 $175

THE NIGERIA Handbook Containing Statistical and General Information Respecting the Colony and Protectorate. Lagos, 1927. 8th. ed., maps, illus., covers dull, 8vo, orig. cloth. K Books 239-349 1978 £8

THE NIGERIA Handbook Containing Statistical and General Information Respecting The Colony and Protectorate. Lagos, 1929. 9th. ed., maps, illus., orig. cloth, 8vo. K Books 239-350 1978 £8

THE NIGERIA Handbook Containing Statistical and General Information Respecting the Colony and Protectorate. Lagos, 1933. 10th. ed., maps, illus., orig. cloth, roy. 8vo. K Books 239-351 1978 £7

NIGHTINGALE, FLORENCE   Notes on Nursing. Harrison, (1860). 1st. ed., orig. black cloth wrappers, mint. Jarndyce 16-907 1978 £45

NIGHTINGALE, FLORENCE   Notes on Nursing. New York, 1860. Sm. 8vo., orig. wrs., 1st Amer. ed., uncommon in wrs. Morrill 239-194 1978 $25

NIGHTINGALE, FLORENCE   Notes on Nursing: What Is, and What is Not. New York, 1860. 1st Amer. ed., orig. cloth. MacManus 239-376 1978 $35

NIGHTINGALE, J.   Memoirs of the Public and Private Life of Caroline Queen of Gt. Britain. 1820. Engraved title, frontis. and plates, foxed, half calf, worn. George's 635-589 1978 £5.25

NILES, GRACE GREYLOCK   The Hoosac Valley. New York, 1912. 1st ed., illus., very fine. MacManus 239-348 1978 $37.50

NILES, H.   Principles and Acts of the American Revolution. Baltimore, 1882. 1st ed., rebound. MacManus 239-611 1978 $27.50

NILES, JOHN J.   Singing Soldiers. New York, 1927. Bell Wiley's copy. Broadfoot 46-550 1978 $10

NILES, M. A. H.   Address Before the Society of Alumni of Hanover College, at Their First Anniversary, Sept. 25th, 1836. Hanover, 1836. 2nd ed., disbound. Hayman 73-320 1978 $12.50

NILSEN, ALFRED   The Story of the Amoy. Brooklyn, n.d. (c. 1924) 12mo., wrps., good. Paine 78-101 1978 $12.50

NIMMO, A.   Songs and Ballads of Clydesdale. Edinburgh & Glasgow, 1882. Cr. 8vo., orig. cloth. K Books 244-425 1978 £8

NIMMO, JOSEPH   Report on the Internal Commerce of the U.S., 1882. Washington, 1884. Large folding plates, original cloth, near mint. Jenkins 116-1002 1978 $15

"NIMROD" PSEUD.
Please turn to
APPERLY, CHARLES JAMES

NIN, ANAIS   Children of the Albatross. New York, 1947.
First U.S. ed., very good, d.w. Bell Book 16-673 1978 £8.50

NIN, ANAIS   D. H. Lawrence. An Unprofessional Study.
Paris, 1932. Orig. cloth, d. j., soiled, 1st ed., 1 of 550 copies, very good.
MacManus 238-728 1978 $100

NIN, ANAIS   Nuances. (Cambridge, 1970). 1 of only
99 numbered copies signed by author, finely printed on Hayle paper in Palatino
type, 1st ed., 4 to., full Indian raw silk cloth, as new. Houle 10-242
1978 $150

NIN, ANAIS   Under a Glass Bell. 1947. Spine faded, good,
first English ed. Bell Book 16-675 1978 £5.50

NIPHUS, AUGUSTINUS
Please turn to
NIFO, AUGUSTINUS

NIPOTISME DI ROMA, IL   O vero relatione della raggioti che muouno i
Pontefic iall' aggrandiment de Nipoti.... Roma, 1667. 2 vols. in 1, 12mo.,
old calf, worn. George's 635-728 1978 £6

NISENWURZEL, PAUL ARTHUR AMADEUS   Doomsday Books. Sm. folio, 1 of
only 150 copies, thin, erratum slip tipped in. Battery Park 1-134 1978 $75

NISHI, KIICHI   The Monthly Calendar of Floral Japan. (Yoko-
hama, 1936). Color illus., tipped-in plts., decor. boards. Dawson's 449-168
1978 $27.50

NIVERNOIS, LOUIS-JULES MANCINI   Fables by the Duke of Nivernois. Edinburgh, 1799. 1st. English ed., 8vo, contemp. tree calf, gilt, head-band worn,
French & English text. Hannas 54-230 1978 £25

NIXON, HERMAN CLARENCE   Forty Acres and Steel Mules. 1938. Bell Wiley's
copy. Broadfoot's 44-716 1978 $10.00

NIXON, J. A.   Freemasonry and the Secrets of Nature and Sciences. Bristol, 1932. 4to., binders cloth. George's 635-1433 1978 £5

NIXON, JOHN   The Complete Story of the Transvaal From the
'Great Trek' to the Convention of London. London, 1885. Folding map, somewhat
foxed throughout, half calf, gilt spine, 8vo. K Books 239-353 1978 £35

NIXON, LARRY   When War Comes. 1939. Austin 80-242 1978
$10

NIXON, OLIVER W.   How Marcus Whitman Saved Oregon. Chicago,
1895. 2nd ed., cloth, lib. numeral on spine, solid copy. Hayman 73-485 1978
$7.50

NIXON, PAT IRELAND   The Medical Story of Early Texas, 1528-1853.
San Antonio, 1946. Near mint copy, 1st ed. Jenkins 116-1003 1978 $85

NIXON, RAYMOND B.   Henry W. Grady. New York, 1943. Illus.,
pres. copy from author to Bell Wiley. Broadfoot's 44-717 1978 $12

NOAILLES, AMBLARD RAYMOND   Souvenirs D'Amerique et D;Orient. Paris,
[1920]. Orig. pr. wr., 1st ed. Ginsberg 14-787 1978 $25

NOBILI, LEOPOLDO   Nuovo Trattato d'Ottica o sia la Scienza Della
Luce Dimostrata Coi Puri Principi di Meccanica. Milano, 1820. Fldg. copperplts., 8vo., half vellum, uncut, 1st ed., fine. Offenbacher 30-III 1978 $150

NOBLE, FREDERIC PERRY   The Redemption of Africa. Chicago, 1899.
2 vols., maps, plts., good ex-lib., 8vo, orig. cloth. K Books 239-354 1978 £15

NOBLE, JOHN W.   Letter from the Secretary of the Interior....
Washington, 1893. Cloth, 1st ed. Ginsberg 14-798 1978 $75

NOBLE, MARGARET E.   Myths and Legends of Hindus and Buddhists.
Boston, n.d. Illus. in color. Biblo 251-134 1978 $17.50

NOBLE, MARK   Memoirs of the Protectoral-House of Cromwell.
1787. Portraits, plts., 2 vols., calf-backed bds., neatly rebacked, third ed.,
8vo. Howes 194-232 1978 £28

NODIER, CHARLES   The Luck of the Bean-Rows. London, n.d.
Trans. from French, illus. in color by Claud Lovat Fraser, 8vo., pattern paper
in several colors over bd., cloth spine. Battery Park 1-101 1978 $35

NODIER, CHARLES   The Woodcutter's Dog. Curwen Press, 1922.
8vo., trans. from French, illus. in color by Fraser, pattern paper over bds.
Battery Park 1-102 1978 $25

NOE, M. LE COMTE DE   Memoirs Relatifs a l'Expedition Anglaise. Paris,
1826. Fine coloured lithograph plts., 8vo., orig. wrs., worn, in cloth box, pres.
copy inscribed by author. F. Edwards 1013-389 1978 £125

NOE, SYDNEY P.   A Bibliography of Greek Coin Hoards. New
York, 1937. 2nd ed., wrs., 12mo., author's signed pres. Biblo BL781-450 1978
$12.50

NOLAN, EDWARD H.   The History of the British Empire in India and
the East. London, n.d. (c. 1870). 8 vols., steel engrs., color maps, plts., some
foxing, tissue guards, orig. red gilt-decor. cloth, light rubbing. Current 24-
234 1973 $55

NOLAN, EDWARD H.   The Illustrated history of the British Empire in
India and the East, from the earliest times to the suppression of the Sepoy munity
in 1859. London, n.d., (c. 1880). 3 vols., large 8vo, half calf, ports., maps.
Van der Peet 127-317 1978 Dfl 250

NOLAN, EDWARD H.   The Illustrated History of the War Against
Russia. (1855-57). 2 vols., engraved title-pg., engraved portraits, plts.,maps,
orig. 8 parts, roy. 8vo., orig. red cloth, gilt, nice set. Fenning 32-246 1978
£25

NOLAN, EDWARD H.   The Illustrated History of the War Against Russia.
London, (1857). 2 vols., 8vo., mor. binding, a.e.g., plts., very good. King
7-369 1978 £50

NOLAN, J. BENNETT   Early Narratives of Berks County. (Reading,
1927). Plts., 1st ed., orig. bind. Petrilla 13-53 1978 $20

NOLAN, J. BENNETT   Printer Strahan's Book Account, a Colonial Controversy. Reading, 1939. Sm. quarto, illus., bookplt. withdrawn, 1st ed.
Petrilla 13-54 1978 $30

NOLAN, J. BENNETT   Southeastern Pennsylvania, A History Of The
Counties Of Berks, Bucks, Chester,.... Philadelphia, (1943). 3 vols., 4tos,
illus., portraits, color plates, &c. indices, orig. binding. Americanist 101-108
1978 $75

NOLAN, J. BENNETT   Southeastern Pennsylvania. A History of the
Counties of Berks, Bucks, Chester, Delaware, Montgomery, Philadelphia and
Schuylkill. Philadelphia, (1943). 3 vols., 4to., illus. MacManus 239-1591
1978 $85

NOLHAC, P. DE   La Reine Marie-Antoinette. Paris, 1890. Lg.
4to., half calf, colored frontis., plts., portrs. out of text, binding shaved, front
joint cracked, but firm. Van der Peet H-64-509 1978 Dfl 125

NOLL, ARTHUR HOWARD   Doctor Quintard, Chaplain, C.S.A. and Second
Bishop of Tennessee. Sewanee, 1905. Ex libris, Bell Wiley's copy. Broadfoot's
44-618 1978 $60

NOLL, ARTHUR HOWARD   A Short History of Mexico. Chicago, 1890.
Jenkins 116-1005 1978 $17.50

NOLL, JOHN F.   Father Smith Instructs Jackson. "Our Sunday
Visitor Press", n.d. ca. 1940. Paper. Austin 79-517 1978 $7.50

NOLTE, VINCENT   Fifty Years in Both Hemispheres... New York,
1854. 1st ed. in English. MacManus 239-377 1978 $27.50

NONA, FRANCIS   The Fall of the Alamo: An Historical Drama....
New Yor, 1879. 1st ed. Jenkins 116-111 1978 $20

NORD, SVERRE   A Logger's Odyssey. Caldwell, 1943. Austin 79-518 1978 $17.50

NORDENSKIOLD, NILS ADOLF ERIK   The Voyage of the Vega Round Asia and
Europe. London, 1881. 1st English ed., 2 vols., 8vo., portraits, fold. lithograph maps, some coloured, wood engrav. plts. & illus., orig. green cloth, ruled
& lettered in gilt, recased, lib. labels removed, covers soiled. Deighton 5-164
1978 £85

NORDENSKIOLD, NILS ADOLF ERIK   The Voyage of the "Vega" Round Asia
and Europe.... 1881. 2 vols., map, portraits, woodcut illus., 8vo., orig.
cloth. Edwards 1012-593 1978 £45

NORDHOFF, CHARLES   California for Immigrants. London, [1883].
Folding map, original printed wr., 1st ed. Ginsberg 14-161 1978 $125

NORDHOFF, CHARLES   Notes on the Off-Shore Fishing of the Society
Islands. 1930. Illus., wrs., marginal damage at front, spine browned, reprint.
Dawson's 127-281 1978 $40

NORDHOFF, CHARLES   Stories of the Island World. New York, 1857.
Illus., cloth, spine a little worn. Dawson's 127-280 1978 $65

NORDHOFF, CHARLES   Whaling and Fishing. Cincinnati, 1856. Very
good copy. Baldwins' 51-511 1978 $75

NORDYKE, LEWIS   The Truth about Texas. New York, 1947.
Signed. Jenkins 116-1006 1978 $15

NORFLEET, FILLMORE   Saint-Memin in Virginia. Richmond, 1942.
First ed., engravings, 4to. Biblo 247-377 1978 $67.50

NORGATE, G. LE GRYS   The Life of Sir Walter Scott. 1906. Plts., 8vo.,
orig. cloth, illus. Howes 194-1170 1978 £5.50

NORMANBY, CONSTANTIN HENRY PHIPPS, MARQUIS OF   The English in
Italy. 1825. First ed., 3 vols., rebound in half green mor., hand marbled bds.
v.g. Jarndyce 16-934 1978 £68

NORRIS, EDWIN M.   The Story of Princeton. Boston, 1917. Illus.
MacManus 239-1310 1978 $12.50

NORRIS, FRANK   McTeague: a Story of San Francisco. New York,
1899. Cloth, bkplt., ink signature, very bright copy. Dawson's 447-266 1978
$90

NORRIS, FRANK   McTeague. 1950. First ed. of this ed., beautifully rebound in blue leather and marbelized bds. Austin 82-681 1978 $27.50

NORRIS, FRANK   Moran of the Lady Letty. A Story of Adventure
off the California Coast. New York, 1898. Orig. dec. cloth, 1st ed., rare,
near-fine. MacManus 238-565 1978 $85

NORRIS, FRANK   The Octopus. New York, 1901. 1st ed., inner
hinges split, name in ink dated May, 1901 on flyleaf. Biblo 251-589 1978 $25

NORRIS, FRANK   The Pit. New York, 1903. 1st ed.,
red cloth, interior sound. Limestone 9-221 1978 $15

NORRIS, FRANK   The Pit. 1903. First ed., third printing. Austin
82-682 1978 $12.50

NORRIS, FRANK   The Pit. New York, 1903. 1st trade ed.
Biblo 251-590 1978 $15

NORRIS, FRANK   The Pit. (1903). 1904. Austin 82-683 1978
$11

NORRIS, GEORGE W.   Fighting Liberal. Autobiography. New York,
1945. 1st ed. Biblo BL781-221 1978 $9

NORRIS, GEORGE WILLIAM   The Early History of Medicine in Philadelphia.
Philadelphia, 1886. 1st ed., 4to., illus., old lib. stamp, bookplt., nice copy,
ltd. to 125 no. copies, letter from author tipped in, very scarce. MacManus
239-1608 1978 $150

NORRIS, GEORGE WILLIAM   The Early History of Medicine in Philadelphia.
Philadelphia, 1886. 4to., portrs., orig. blue cloth, gilt lettering, bkplt. &
library stamps, very good copy, #110 of ltd. ed. of 125 copies. Zeitlin 245-308
1978 $175

NORRIS, HENRY   Poems on Various Subjects. Taunton, 1774. 8vo,
original pale blue boards, white paper spine, 1st ed., very fine copy. Ximenes
47-218 1978 $175

NORRIS, JOHN   Spiritual Counsel; or, The Father's Advice to His
Children. London, 1694. 1st. ed., 12mo, contemp. calf, joints repaired.
Traylen 88-199 1978 £85

NORRIS, THADEUS   The American-Angler's Book. Philadelphia,
(copyright 1865). New ed. with supplement, engravings on wood, orig. binding.
Wolfe 39-13 1978 $45

NORRIS, W.   The Dancer in Yellow. New York, 1896. 1st
Am. ed., bound in yellow cloth. Greene 78-88 1978 $15

NORRIS, WALTER B.   Annapolis, Its Colonial and Naval Story. New
York, (1925). Illus. Baldwins' 51-289 1978 $7.50

NORRY, C.   Relation De L'Expedition D'Egypte. Paris,
(1799). Engraved plts., sm. 8vo, wrapper, edges uncut. Edwards 1012-222
1978 £20

NORTH, ELISHA   A Treatise on a Malignant Epidemic, Commonly
Called Spotted Fever... New York, 1811. 8vo., contemp. bds., worn, uncut,
1st ed., some foxing & discoloring. Offenbacher 30-112 1978 $200

NORTH, F.   The Compleat Clerk. 1777. Edges of title and
early leaves frayed, lg. 8vo., old calf, worn, crudely rebacked. George's 635-
1284 1978 £7.50

NORTH, ROBERT CARVER   Bob North Starts Exploring... New York, London,
1927. Illus. Hood 116-96 1978 $17.50

NORTH, ROGER   The Life of the Rt. Hon Francis North...
1808. 2nd. ed., 2 vols., frontis portraits, orig. tree calf, gilt spines, v.g.
Jarndyce 16-908 1978 £16.50

NORTH, SAFFORD E.   Our County and Its People. Boston, 1899.
Thick 4to., illus., cloth, fine. MacManus 239-1085 1978 $75

NORTH, STERLING   Night Outlasts the Whippoorwill. 1936. First
ed., d.j., ex-lib. Austin 82-685 1978 $12.50

NORTH, BEN SLAEVIN   Mexico as Described in Personal Correspondence
Between Mr. Ben Slaevin North and His Friend Mr. Seymour South. (Chicago,
n.d., 1905?). Wrps. Hayman 71-460 1978 $7.50

NORTH BROS. MFG. CO.   Catalogue of "Yankee" Tools Manufactured by...
N.P., 1905. Wrps. Hayman 71-98 1978 $7.50

NORTH America, Nos. 1-12, Parliamentary Papers, Being Diplomatic Correspondence
with the United States During 1861-62. 1862. 12 parts, 1 part 8vo, 11 parts sm.
folio, bound in 1 vol., buckram, slightly rubbed. Edwards 1012-546 1978 £200

THE NORTH American Almanac for...1847. Philadelphia, (1846). Sewn. Hayman 73-16 1978 $10

THE NORTH American and West Indian Gazetteer... London, 1776. 4to.,
fold. maps, half-calf, 1st ed. Gilhofer 74-72 1978 sFr 1,600

THE NORTH Atlantic Telegraph via the Faeroe Isles, Iceland and Greenland. 1861.
8vo., folding map, text illus., printed wrappers, spine repaired. Quaritch 977-
243 1978 $30

NORTH CAROLINA   North Carolina-Executive and Legislative Documents Session of 1864-65, Doc. No. 6, Report to the Public Treasurer. Raleigh,
1864. Disbound, Bell Wiley's copy. Broadfoot 46-448 1978 $25

NORTH CAROLINA   North Carolina-Executive and Legislative
Documents, Session of 1864-65, Doc. No. 7, Report of the Comptroller of Public
Accounts, for the Fiscal Year Ending Sept. 30, 1863. Raleigh, 1864. Disbound,
Bell Wiley's copy. Broadfoot 46-449 1978 $25

NORTH CAROLINA   North Carolina-Executive and Legislative Documents, Adjourned Session 1864 Doc. No. 8, Report of the State Commissioner on
Cherokee Bonds. Raleigh, 1864. Disbound, Bell Wiley's copy. Broadfoot 46-
447 1978 $30

NORTH Carolina-A Guide to the Old North State, American Guide Series.
Chapel Hill, 1939. Lacks map. Broadfoot 50-155 1978 $15

NORTH Carolina and Its Resources. Winston, 1896. Illus., 8vo., orig. cloth.
Morrill 241-431 1978 $10

NORTH Carolina, the Land of Opportunity. Raleigh, 1923. Illus., new cloth,
stamp on t.p. Broadfoot 50-158 1978 $12

NORTH Central Michigan Year Book. Cadillac, n.d. (1907). Wrs. Hayman 73-
444 1978 $7.50

NORTH Dakota Historical Society Collections. Bismarck, 1906-1925. Partly
bound, complete file, vols. 1-7. Ginsberg 14-320 1978 $125

NORTH Dakota History. Bismarck, n.d. Orig. pr. wr. Ginsberg 14-321 1978
$425

THE NORTH Shore and Part of Middlesex County, Mass. Boston, 1893. Lg.
fldg. map, orig. narrow 8vo. wrs. Morrill 241-341 1978 $10

THE NORTH-WESTERN Journal of Homoeopathia. Chicago, October, 1848-
Sept. 1850. 2 vols. in 1, 8vo., contemp. bds., lea. back & corners, rare. Morrill 239-195 1978 $150

NORTHALL, G.F.   English Folk-Rhymes. London, 1892. Buckram,
8vo. K Books 244-247 1978 $10

NORTHUMBERLAND, HENRY PERCY, 9TH EARL OF   Advice to His Son. 1930. Portrait, plts., octavo, good. Upcroft 10-136 1978 £5.50

THE NORTHCLIFFE Collection. Oitawa, 1926. Card Cover, illus. Hood's 115-32 1978 $15

NORTHCOTE, JAMES   One Hundred Fables, Original and Selected, by... R.A. 1828-33. 1st and 2nd series, 2 vols., roy. 8vo., 1st eds., lg. paper, engravings by William Harvey, half mor., gilt tops, tall copy. Quaritch 983-349 1978 $315

NORTHCOTE, JAMES   One Hundred Fables, Original and Selected, by James Northcote, R.A. 1828-33. 2 vols., roy. 8vo., lst eds., lg. paper, engrs., half mor., gilt tops, tall copy. Quaritch 979-247 1978 $250

NORTHCOTE, JOHN   Note-Book of .... 1877. Octavo, good. Upcroft 10-129 1978 £8

NORTHROP, HENRY D.   Indian Horrors, or Massacres by the Red Men. Philadelphia, 1891. Illus., decor. cover. Hood 117-694 1978 $35

NORTHROP, JOHN WORRELL   Chronicles from the Diary of a War Prisoner in Andersonville and Other Military Prisons of the South in 1864. Wichita, 1904. Bell Wiley's copy. Broadfoot's 44-554 1978 $18

NORTHRUP, EDWIN F.   Zero to Eighty. Being My Lifetime Doings.... Princeton, 1937. Illus., 1st ed. Biblo BL781-964 1978 $12

NORTHRUP, SOLOMON   Twelve Years a Slave. Auburn, 1854. Illus., fine. MacManus 239-848 1978 $22.50

NORTON, CAROLINE (SHERIDAN)   Old Sir Douglas. 1868. 1st ed., 3 vols., half titles, orig. green cloth, spines little rubbed, otherwise v.g. Jarndyce 16-909 1978 £38

NORTON, CHARLES ELIOT   Historical Studies of Church-Building in the Middle Ages. New York, 1880. Edges rubbed. Biblo 247-476 1978 $32.50

NORTON, CHARLES ELIOT   Letters... 1913. 2 vols., first ed. Austin 82-686 1978 $27.50

NORTON, CLARENCE CLIFFORD   The Democratic Party in Ante-Bellum North Carolina 1835-1861. Chapel Hill, 1930. Vol. 21, new cloth. Broadfoot 50-160 1978 $10

NORWOOD, GILBERT   Greek Comedy. 1931. Allen 234-688 1978 $7.50

NORWOOD, HAYDEN   The Marble Man's Wife. Thomas Wolfe's Mother. New York, 1947. D.j. Broadfoot 50-467 1978 $16

A NOTE by William Morris on his Aims in Founding the Kelmscott Press. Kelmscott Press, 1898. 1st ed., 8vo., ed. ltd. to 525 copies, woodcut frontis, very fine copy, orig. blue-gray paper covered bds., last book prtd. at William Morris' famous Kelmscott Press. Current Misc. 8-26 1978 $350

NOTENSTEIN, LUCY L.   Wooster of the Middle West. New Haven, 1937. Orig. binding, clean, fine, d.j. Hayman 71-570 1978 $7.50

NOTES And Queries: A Medium of Inter-Communication for Literary Men, Artists, Antiquaries, Genealogists, etc. 1849/1850. Vol. first, 1/2 calf, badly scuffed. Eaton 45-368 1978 £8

NOTES on Two Reports from the Committee of the Honourable House of Assembly of Jamaica,.... London, 1789. 8vo, sewn, 1st ed., very fine, entirely uncut, unopened. Ximenes 47-156 1978 $275

NOTICES of Sullivan's Campaign in Western New-York. Rochester, 1842. 16mo., old lea., rubbed, black label, sound copy, minimum foxing, scarce. Butterfield 21-387 1978 $75

NOTICES of Sullivan's Campaign, or the Revolutionary Warfare in Western New York. Rochester, 1842. 12mo., foxed, 1st ed., lacks portr., orig. cloth. Morrill 241-415 1978 $27.50

NOTMAN, W.   Portraits of British Americans.... Montreal, 1865. Card cover repaired, plts. Hood 116-45 1978 $20

NOTOVITCH, N.   L'Empereur Alexandre III et son entourage. 1893. Half mor., 8vo. George's 635-527 1978 £5.25

NOTT, ELIPHALET   A Sermon Preached Before the General Assembly of the Presbyterian Church in the United States of America... Philadelphia, 1806. 8vo, orig. cloth, wrappers. Edwards 1012-514 1978 £12

NOTT, ELIPHALET   A Sermon Preached Before the General Assembly of the Presbyterian Church in the United States of America... Philadelphia, 1806. Disbound. Hayman 71-503 1978 $10

NOTT, MANFROD A.   Across the Plains in '54:.... San Francisco, [ca. 1910]. Orig. pict. wr. Ginsberg 14-792 1978 $75

NOTT, SAMUEL, JR.   Sermons for Children. New York, 1823. 16mo., leather-backed bds., gilt. Petrilla 13-55 1978 $15

NOVA Britannia. New York, 1867. Limited to 250 copies, lacks part of backstrip. Nestler Rare 78-50 1978 $25

NOVA SCOTIA   Journal and Proceedings of the Legislative Council of the Province of Nova Scotia. Session 1914, Part II. Halifax, 1914. Rebound in fab. Hood's 115-566 1978 $45

NOVA SCOTIA   Journals of the Legislative Assembly, From January 2, 1908, to February 26, 1908, Being the First Session of the Twelfth Legislature. Winnipeg, 1908. Bound, leather spine. Hood's 115-553 1978 $25

NOVA SCOTIA, DEPT. OF MINES   Geology of Nova Scotia; The Mineral Province of Eastern Canada... Halifax, n.d. Folding map dated 1949, wrappers. Hood's 115-721 1978 $7.50

NOVUS Orbis. Id est, Navigationes Primae in Americam. Thick 8vo., 3/4 calf. Salloch 345-98 1978 $500

NOYES, ALFRED   Beyond the Desert. New York, (1920). Bds. Hayman 71-504 1978 $7.50

NOYES, ALFRED   The Book of the Earth. New York, 1925. Cloth, pictorial upper cover, author's signed pres. copy. Eaton 45-369 1978 £5

NOYES, ALFRED   Poems. 1904. First ed., 8vo. George's 635-1328 1978 £5.25

NOYES, ALFRED   The Torch Bearers. A Trilogy. London, 1937. Nice in soiled & mended d.w. Desmarais B-432 1978 $10

NOYES, ALFRED   William Morris. London, 1921. Cr. 8vo., half green prize calf. K Books 244-248 1978 £6

NOYES, GEORGE W.   Religious Experience of John Humphrey Noyes, Founder of the Oneida Community. 1923. Illus., good. Nestler Rare 78-134 1978 $25

NOYES, JOHN P.   The Canadian Loyalists and Early Settlers in the District of Bedford. St. Johns, 1900. Printed wrs., autograph pres. inscription by author, scarce. Wolfe 39-157 1978 $60

NUNBERG, RALPH   The Fighting Jew. 1945. Austin 79-521 1978 $12.50

NUOVO Dizionario Italiano-Inglese-Francese, Di Stefano Egidio Petronj.... 1828. 2 vols., contemp. stamped calf, leather labels. Eaton 45-266 1978 £8

NURSING the Sick. Practical Information by a Trained Nurse. Montreal, 1897. Picture of Royal Victoria Hospital on cover, commercial ads. Rittenhouse 49-21 1976 $37.50

NUTT, A.   Cuchulainn, The Irish Achilles. 1900. 1st ed., wr., very good. Hyland 128-187 1978 £7

NUTT, FREDERICK   The Complete Confectioner. London, 1819. Frontis., 8vo., 3/4 tan calf antique, marbled bds., 8th ed., eng. plts., fine. Howell 5-48 1978 $70

NUTTALL, T.   A Manual of the Ornithology of the U.S. and of Canada. Boston, 1834, 1832. Respined, 3/4 leather, 8vo., woodcuts. Book Chest 17-273 1978 $150

NUTTING, WALLACE   The Clock Book, Being a Description of Foreign and American Clocks. Framingham, (1924). Profusely illus., 1st. ed. Baldwins' 51-133 1978 $27.50

NUTTING, WALLACE   The Clock Book...Antique Clocks, List of Their Makers. 1935. Good. Nestler Rare 78-219 1978 $25

NUTTING, WALLACE   Connecticut Beautiful. New York. Sm. 4to., illus. Biblo BL781-143 1978 $9

NUTTING, WALLACE   Ireland Beautiful. Massachusetts, 1925. 1st ed., very good. Hyland 128-188 1978 £6

NUTTING, WALLACE   Ireland Beautiful. Framingham, (1925). Illus.
Biblo 247-722 1978 $15

NYE, EDGAR WILSON   Remarks by Bill Nye. Chicago, (1891). Orig.
binding, clean. Hayman 71-506 1978 $7.50

NYROP, KR.   Grammaire historique de la langue francaise.
Copenhague, 1904. 2 vols., orig. wrappers, worn, 8vo. George's 635-1371
1978 £5.25

O

OAKELEY, HILDA D.   Greek Ethical Thought from Homer to the Stoics. London, 1925. 8vo., cloth. Salloch 348-78 1978 $10

OAKESHOTT, GEORGE J.   Detail and Ornament of the Italian Renaissance Drawn by George J. Oakeshott Architect. London, 1888. Folio, cloth gilt, plts., very good. King 7-370 1978 £20

OAKLEY, THOMAS POLLOCK   English Penitential Discipline and Anglo-Saxon Law in Their Joint Influence. New York, 1923. Wrs. Biblo 247-478 1978 $12.50

OAKLEY, VIOLET   Samuel F. B. Morse. Philadelphia, (1939). Orig. bds., ltd. to 500 copies, signed. MacManus 239-797 1978 $12.50

OATES, JOHN A.   The Story of Fayetteville. Fayetteville, 1950. Illus., signed by author. Broadfoot 50-161 1978 $40

OATES, W. J.   Stoic & Epicurean Philosophers. n.d. Modern Library ed. Allen 234-698 1978 $7.50

OBER, CAROLYN FAVILLE   Manhattan Historic and Artistic. New York, (1892). Maps, ads, illus., prtd. yellow wr. Butterfield 21-517 1978 $20

OBERBECK, GRACE J.   History of La Crescenta-La Canada Valleys. Montrose, 1938. Fabricoid, map end sheets, #152 of ltd. ed. of 200 copies signed by author, very good copy, scarce. Dykes 34-238 1978 $25

OBERHOLSER, HARRY C.   The Bird Life of Louisiana. New Orleans, 1938. Cloth, illus. title label, plts., some in color, 1st ed., fine, scarce. Dykes 35-167 1978 $25

OBERHOLTZER, ELLIS PAXSON   Jay Cooke, Financier of the Civil War. Philadelphia, (1907). Illus., 2 vols., 8vo., ex-lib., 1st ed., orig. cloth. Morrill 241-432 1978 $17.50

OBERHOLTZER, ELLIS PAXSON   Jay Cooke, Financier of the Civil War. Philadelphia, (1907). 1st ed., 2 vols., illus., fine, very scarce. MacManus 239-901 1978 $45

OBERHOLTZER, ELLIS PAXSON   The Literary History of Philadelphia. Philadelphia, 1906. 1st ed., 1 of 1000 copies, orig. smooth buckram, uncut, illus., 8vo. Americanist 101-109 1978 $15

OBERLEITNER, CHARLES   Album de Fac-Simile des Regents, Capitaines et Hommes d-Etat Depuis l'An 1500 Jusqu'en 1576. Vienna, 1862. Plts., 4to., old cloth, lea. back and corners, fr. cover & text waterstained. Morrill 239-563 1978 $10

OBERMANN, J.   Der Philosophische Und Religioese Subjektivismus Ghazalis. Vienna, 1921. Tall 8vo., wrs. Salloch 348-178 1978 $45

OBERMANN, KARL   Joseph Wey Demeyer. 1947. Austin 79-522 1978 $8.50

OBITUARY Addresses Delivered on the Occasion of the Death of Zachary Taylor, President of the United States, in the Senate and House...July 10, 1850... Washington, 1850. Wrs., some wear. Hayman 72-741 1978 $8.50

OBITUARY Notice of Charles Stewart Richards. Honolulu, 1845. Wrs. Dawson's 127-284 1978 $75

OBJECT Lesson A-B-C. Chicago, (c.1890s). Sm. quarto, illus., color-pict. bds., cloth back, some wear to bind. Petrilla 13-57 1978 $12.50

O'BRIEN, A. H.   Haliburton ("Sam Slick"), A Sketch and Bibliography. 1909. 2 plts. Hood's 115-229 1978 $12.50

O'BRIEN, ANDREW LEARY   The Journal of Andrew Leary O'Brien. Athens, 1946. Bell Wiley's copy. Broadfoot's 44-860 1978 $10

O'BRIEN, C.   A Series of Fifteen Views in Ceylon Illustrative of Sir J. E. Tennent's Work, From Sketches Made on The Spot. London, 1864. 1st ed., folio, tinted lithograph vignette title-pg., tinted lithograph plts., some staining in margins, some repairs, orig. cloth, title in gilt, neatly rebacked. Deighton 5-84 1978 £225

O'BRIEN, E. J.   The Best Stories of 1922: I: English. London, 1923. First English ed., orig. binding, spine darkened, very good. Rota 211-7 1978 £5

O'BRIEN, EDWARD J.   The Best Short Stories of 1915. Austin 82-131 1978 $7.50

O'BRIEN, EDWARD J.   The Best Short Stories of 1916. Austin 82-132 1978 $7.50

O'BRIEN, EDWARD J.   The Best Short Stories of 1917. Austin 82-133 1978 $7.50

O'BRIEN, EDWARD J.   The Best Short Stories of 1918. Austin 82-134 1978 $7.50

O'BRIEN, EDWARD J.   The Best Short Stories of 1919. Austin 82-135 1978 $7.50

O'BRIEN, EDWARD J.   The Best Short Stories of 1920. Austin 82-136 1978 $7.50

O'BRIEN, EDWARD J.   The Best Short Stories of 1921. Austin 82-137 1978 $7.50

O'BRIEN, EDWARD J.   The Best Short Stories of 1922. Austin 82-138 1978 $7.50

O'BRIEN, EDWARD J.   The Best Short Stories of 1923. Austin 82-139 1978 $7.50

O'BRIEN, EDWARD J.   The Best Short Stories of 1924. Austin 82-140 1978 $7.50

O'BRIEN, EDWARD J.   The Best Short Stories of 1925. Austin 82-141 1978 $7.50

O'BRIEN, EDWARD J.   The Best Short Stories of 1926. Austin 82-142 1978 $7.50

O'BRIEN, EDWARD J.   The Best Short Stories of 1927. Austin 82-143 1978 $7.50

O'BRIEN, EDWARD J.   The Best Short Stories of 1928. Austin 82-144 1978 $7.50

O'BRIEN, EDWARD J.   The Best Short Stories of 1929. Austin 82-145 1978 $7.50

O'BRIEN, EDWARD J.   The Best Short Stories of 1930. Austin 82-146 1978 $8.50

O'BRIEN, EDWARD J.   The Best Short Stories of 1931. Austin 82-147 1978 $7.50

O'BRIEN, EDWARD J.   The Best Short Stories of 1932. Austin 82-148 1978 $7.50

O'BRIEN, EDWARD J.   The Best Short Stories of 1933. Austin 82-149 1978 $12.50

O'BRIEN, EDWARD J.   The Best Short Stories of 1934. Austin 82-150 1978 $12.50

O'BRIEN, EDWARD J.   The Best Short Stories of 1935. Austin 82-151 1978 $15

O'BRIEN, EDWARD J.   The Best Short Stories of 1936. Austin 82-152 1978 $10

O'BRIEN, EDWARD J.   The Best Short Stories of 1937. First ed., slightly frayed d.j. repaired. Austin 82-153 1978 $15

O'BRIEN, EDWARD J.   The Best Short Stories of 1937. Austin 82-154 1978 $8.50

O'BRIEN, EDWARD J.   The Best Short Stories of 1938. Austin 82-155 1978 $12.50

O'BRIEN, EDWARD J.   The Best Short Stories of 1939. Austin 82-156 1978 $15

O'BRIEN, EDWARD J.   The Best Short Stories of 1940. Austin 82-157
1978 $12.50

O'BRIEN, EDWARD J.   The Best Short Stories of 1941. Austin 82-158
1978 $12.50

O'BRIEN, FRANK M.   The Story of "The Sun". New York, 1918-1933.
Half leather worn, inscribed by author. Austin 82-688 1978 $17.50

O'BRIEN, G.   The Economic History of Ireland in the 17th Century. 1919. 8vo. George's 635-374 1978 £5.25

O'BRIEN, G.   An Essay on Mediaeval Economic Teaching.
1920. 8vo. George's 635-376 1978 £5

O'BRIEN, G.   An Essay on the Economic Effects of the Reformation. 1923. 8vo. George's 635-375 1978 £5

O'BRIEN, HARRIET E.   Paul Revere's Own Story. Boston, 1929. 4to,
illus., uncut, ltd. ed. MacManus 239-614 1978 $25

O'BRIEN, HOWARD V.   All Things Considered. Indianapolis, (1948).
Cloth, 1st ed. Hayman 73-293 1978 $7.50

O'BRIEN, J. T.   The Case of the Established Church in Ireland.
1867. Disbound, very good, octavo bound in cloth. Hyland 128-194 1978
£12

O'BRIEN, JOHN G.   O'Brien's City and Country Merchants' Pocket
Directory, to the Principal Mercantile Houses, Extensive Manufacturing Establishments, and Most Eminent Artists in Various Branches of Business in the City of
Philadelphia, for the Year 1841. Philadelphia, 1841. 12mo., contemp. calf,
front cover detached. MacManus 239-1635 1978 $40

O'BRIEN, MICHAEL J.   Irish Pioneers in Kentucky. n.d. ca. 1912.
Paper. Austin 79-523 1978 $22.50

O'BRIEN, MICHAEL J.   Pioneer Irish in New England. 1937. Austin 79-524 1978 $20

O'BRIEN, PAT   Outwitting the Hun. New York, (1918). Illus.
Biblo 247-657 1978 $10

O'BRIEN, RICHARD BARRY   Two Centuries of Irish History, 1691-1870. 1907.
Very good, octavo bound in cloth, reprint. Hyland 128-197 1978 £7.50

O'BRIEN, W.   Recollections. 1905. 1st ed., illus., very
good, octavo bound in cloth. Hyland 128-199 1978 £5

O'BRIEN, W. P.   The Great Famine in Ireland. 1896. 8vo.
George's 635-729 1978 £6

OBSERVATIONS And Remarks on the Two Accounts Lately Published, of the Behaviour of William Late Earl of Kilmarnock and of Arthur Late Lord Ba'merino...
1746. 1st. ed., 8vo, half-title, disbound. Hannas 54-231 1978 £15

OBSERVATIONS of an Illinois Boy in Battle, Camp and Prisons 1861-1865. Mendota,
1910. Bell Wiley's copy. Broadfoot's 44-464 1978 $20

OBSERVATIONS of the Provisional Directors of the Mullingar, Athlone & Longford
Railway, of the Report of the Board of Trade on Railways Proposed to be Made in
Ireland, Westward from Dublin. 1845. Photocopy, map in cloth binding, very
good, reprint. Hyland 128-176 1978 £11

OBSERVATIONS on a Pamphlet, Intitled an Answer to one Part of a late Infamous
Libel... 1731. 8vo., newly bound in cloth, mor. back, uncut. Quaritch 979-
5 1978 $40

OBSERVATIONS on a Pamphlet..Entitled Arguments for & Against an Union.
Dublin, 1799. 1st ed., plain wrs. Hyland 128-582 1978 £9

OBSERVATIONS on Rail-Roads,.... Cincinnati, 1850. Orig. front pr. wr.,
half mor. Ginsberg 14-862 1978 $125

OBSERVATIONS on Round Towers in Ireland & Scotland. 1779. Plts., 4to,
1/4 leather, good, reprint. Hyland 128-459 1978 £10

OBSERVATIONS on the Evils Resulting to Ireland from the Insecurity of Title &
the Existing Laws of Real Property; With Some Suggestions Towards a Remedy.
1847. Disbound, very good, octavo bound in cloth, reprint. Hyland 128-203
1978 £15

OBSERVATIONS Upon Certain Evils Arising Out of the Present State of the Laws
of Real Property in Ireland & Suggestions for Remedying the Same. 1847. 1st ed.,
disbound, very good, octavo bound in cloth. Hyland 128-204 1978 £15

O'BYRNE, C.   The Grey Feet of the Wind. 1917. 1st ed., port.,
1/4 cloth, very good. Hyland 128-205 1978 £5

O'BYRNE, JOHN   "Pikes Peak or Bust" and Historical Sketches of
the Wild West. Colorado Springs, 1922. Illus. Biblo 247-254 1978 $13.50

O'CALLAGHAN, EDMUND BAILEY   The Documentary History of the State of
New York. Albany, 1849-51. Thick 8vo, 4 vols., good set, orig. black cloth,
maps, plts., binding faded, sound, excellent working copy. Butterfield 21-153
1978 $45

O'CALLAGHAN, EDMUND BAILEY   History of New Netherland. New York,
1855. 2 vols., "second edition", inscr'd by author, nice copy, orig. cloth.
Butterfield 21-162 1978 $35

O'CALLAGHAN, EDMUND BAILEY   Papers Relating to the French Seigniories
on Lake Champlain. (Albany, 1849). Modern Buckram. Wolfe 39-275 1978
$25

O'CALLAGHAN, J. C.   History of the Irish Brigades in the Service of
France. 1870. Shaky, clean, octavo bound in cloth, reprint. Hyland 128-208
1978 £15

O'CALLAGHAN, J. C.   History of the Irish Brigades in the Service of
France. (1870). Reprint, octavo bound in cloth. Hyland 128-964 1978 £12

O'CASEY, SEAN   The Flying Wasp. 1937. Pres. copy inscribed
by author, light damp-stain throughout, good, worn d.w., first English ed. Bell
Book 16-680 1978 $45

O'CASEY, SEAN   Oak Leaves and Lavender. London, 1946.
Ownership inscription, nice in faded & chipped d.w. Desmarais B-487 1978
$12.50

O'CASEY, SEAN   The Story of the Irish Citizen Army. Dublin,
1919. 8vo, grey paper wr. pr. in black, near Mint, 1st ed., collector's cond.
Desmarais 1-336 1978 $85

OCCUPATION of the Columbia River. [Washington], 1821. Folio, half mor.
Ginsberg 14-835 1978 $75

OCKLEY, SIMON   The Conquest of Syria, Persia and Aegypt, by the
Saracens... 1708. 8vo, contemp. calf, rebacked. Edwards 1012-78 1978 £75

OCKLEY, SIMON   The History of the Saracens. Cambridge, 1757.
Third ed., 2 vols., plt., very good, orig. calf-backed bds., 8vo. Howes 194-
405 1978 £32

O'CONNELL, DANIEL   A Memoir on Ireland, Native & Saxon. 1869.
Very good, reprint, octavo bound in cloth. Hyland 128-214 1978 £5

O'CONNELL, DANIEL   Observations on the Corn Laws, on Political
Pravity & Ingratitude & on Clerical & Personal Slander, in the Shape of a Meek
& Modest Reply to the Second Letter of the Earl of Shrewsbury &c. 1842. 1st ed.,
unusual, octavo bound in cloth. Hyland 128-215 1978 £22.50

O'CONNELL, DANIEL   A Special Report of the Proceedings in the
Case of the Queen Against Daniel O'Connell... Dublin, 1844. Roy. 8vo,
orig. red cloth, signed on both covers by W. Boland, nice copy. Fenning 32-
248 1978 £16

O'CONNELL, MRS. M.J.   The Last Colonel of the Irish Brigade...
(1892). 2 vols., reprint, octavo bound in cloth. Hyland 128-924 1978 £12

O'CONNER, G.B.   Stuart Ireland, Catholic & Protestant. 1910.
1st ed., very good, (scarce), octavo bound in cloth. Hyland 128-232 1978 £15

O'CONNOR, ANTO   The Little Company. 1925. 1st ed., wr., signed,
very good, octavo bound in cloth. Hyland 128-220 1978 £4

O'CONNOR, ARTHUR   Letter to Lord Castlereagh Written From Kilmain-
ham Prison January 4th 1799. (1799). Uncut pamphlet, slight damage to bottom
margin of last 3 pages, rebound in half calf. Jarndyce 16-148 1978   £28

O'CONNOR, FRANK   Crab Apple Jelly. Stories and Tales. New
York, 1944. Very fine in chipped d.w. Desmarais B-438 1978 $15

O'CONNOR, FRANK   Dutch Interior. 1940. Very good, scarce, first
English ed. Bell Book 16-681 1978 £17.50

O'CONNOR, FRANK   Irish Miles. 1947. Plts., very good, worn d.w.,
first English ed. Bell Book 16-682 1978 £6.50

O'CONNOR, J.   A Plea for Home Rule. 1909. 1st ed., wr.,
very good, octavo bound in cloth. Hyland 128-233 1978 £4

O'CONNOR, N. J.   Godes Peace and the Queenes; Vicissitudes of
a House, 1539-1615. Oxford, 1934. Illus., octavo, good. Upcroft 10-465 1978
£7.50

O'CONNOR, N. J.   A Servant of the Crown, in England and North
America, 1756-1761..Papers of John Appy, Secretary and Judge Advocate of His
Majesty's Forces. New York, 1938. 1st ed., illus., d.j., scarce. MacManus
239-167 1978 $20

O'CONNOR, T.P.   The Parnell Movement with a Sketch of Irish
Parties from 1843. 1886. 1st ed., very good, octavo bound in cloth. Hyland
128-322 1978 £12.50

O'CONNOR, T.P.   The Parnell Movement with a Sketch of Irish
Parties from 1843. 1886. Very good, octavo bound in cloth, reprint. Hyland
128-323 1978 £11

O'CONNOR, V. C. S.   Mandalay: And Other Cities of the Past in Burma.
1907. Maps, 8 coloured plts., other illus., roy. 8vo, orig. cloth. Edwards
1012-156 1978 £20

O'CONNOR, W. D.   Mr. Donnelly's Reviewers. 1889. 1st ed., pres.
copy, very good, octavo bound in cloth. Hyland 128-240 1978 £4.50

O'CONOR, C.   Rerum Hibernicarum Scriptores Veteres.
Buckingham, 1814-26. 4 vols., modern buckram, fine condition. Hyland 128-241
1978 £110

O'CONOR, W. A.   History of the Irish People. 1886. 2nd. ed.,
orig. green cloth, gilt, good. Jarndyce 16-763 1978 £7.50

O'CURRY, E.   Manners & Customs of the Ancient Irish. 1873.
1st ed., vol. I & II only in superb condition, octavo bound in cloth. Hyland
128-243 1978 £50

O'DANIEL, VICTOR F.   The Dominican Province of Saint Joseph. New
York, (1942). Cloth, little worn dust jacket. Hayman 73-487 1978 $12.50

ODDI, MUZIO   Della Squado. Milano, 1625. 1st ed., quarto,
half-vellum over marbled boards, woodcuts, fine laid paper, rare work. Bennett
20-154 1978 $225

ODDO DEGLI ODDI   De Coenae Et Prandii Portione Libri II. (Venice,
1532). 16mo., woodcut, old paper wrs., browned, stained, good copy, 1st ed.,
ver rare. Zeitlin 245-177 1978 $175

ODELEBEN, ERNST OTTO VON   Relation Circonstanciee de la Campagne de
1813 en Saxe. Paris, 1817. 2 vols., contemp. half calf, 8vo. Howes 194-561
1978 £18

ODGERS, MERLE M.   Alexander Dallas Bache, Scientist and Educator,
1806-1867. Philadelphia, 1947. Port., d.j. MacManus 239-1361 1978 $10

O'DONNELL, E.   The Irish Abroad. 1915. 1st ed., illus., good,
octavo bound in cloth. Hyland 128-246 1978 £6

O'DONNELL, F. H.   A History of the Irish Parliamentary Party. 1910.
2 vols., 1st ed., very good, octavo bound in cloth. Hyland 128-247 1978 £18

O'DONNELL, H.   Historical Records of the 14th Regiment....
Devonport, (1893). Coloured plts., illus., 8vo., orig. cloth. F. Edwards 1013-
492 1978 £70

O'DONNELL, THOMAS C.   Snubbing Post. Boonville, 1949. Plts., 1st ed.,
signed by author. Butterfield 21-310 1978 $15

O'DONOGHUE, D. J.   Catalogue of the Musical Loan Exhibition in the
National Library. Feis Ceoil, 1899. Wr., good, octavo bound in cloth, reprint.
Hyland 128-248 1978 £10

O'DONOVAN, JOHN   The Banquet of Dun na n-Gedh and the Battle of
Magh Rath, An Acient Historical Tale. Dublin, 1842. 4to, orig. cloth, nice.
Fenning 32-250 1978 £32

O'DONOVAN, JOHN   Grammar of the Irish Language for the..Senior
Classes of the College of St. Columba. 1845. 1st ed., good, octavo bound in
cloth. Hyland 128-249 1978 £25

O'DONOVAN, JOHN   The Tribes & Customs of Hy-Many. (1843).
Reprint, octavo bound in cloth. Hyland 128-926 1978 £9

O'DONOVAN, P.   Imperfectly Proper. Toronto, 1920. Hood's
115-358 1978 $10

O'DUFFY, E.   The Bird Cage, A Mystery Novel. 1932.
1st ed., cover dull, text good, octavo bound in cloth. Hyland 128-252 1978
£6

ODUM, HOWARD W.   Southern Pioneers in Social Interpretation •
1925. Bell Wiley's copy. Broadfoot's 44-718 1978 $12.00

ODUM, HOWARD W.   Southern Regions of the United States • 1936 •
Bell Wiley's copy. Broadfoot's 44-719 1978 $16.00

OECHSNER, F.   This is the Enemy. Germany, 1942. Austin 80-
243 1978 $8.50

THE OECONOMY Of Human Life. 1751. 1st. ed., 2 parts in 1, 8vo, frontis,
engraving, contemp. 1/2 calf, gilt spine with red leather label, crisp copy.
Eaton 45-370 1978 £40

OELLACHER, JOSEF   Beitrage Zur Entwicklungsgeschichte Der Knochen-
fische Nach Beobachtungen Am Bachforelleneie. Leipzig, 1872. 8vo., litho.
fldg. plts., half maroon mor. over marbled bds., gilt on spine, orig. prtd. wrs.
bound in, browning & foxing, good copy. Zeitlin 245-178 1978 $37.50

OEMLER, MARIE CONWAY   The Holy Lover. 1927. First ed., illus. endpapers
Austin 82-687 1978 $17.50

O'FAOLAIN, E.   The Shadowy Man. 1949. 1st ed., d.w., lacks
fly, very good, octavo bound in cloth. Hyland 128-253 1978 £4

O'FAOLAIN, S.   The Story of Ireland. 1943. 1st ed., d.w., 4to,
illus., fine. Hyland 128-258 1978 £4.50

OFFICIAL Catalogue of the Second Annual Exhibit of Horses Given by the Pittsburgh Horse Show Association Held at Duquesne Garden, Pittsburgh, Pa. N.P.,
1907. Wrps. Hayman 71 629 1978 $10

OFFICIAL Chinatown Guidebook. New York, 1939. Illus., paper. Austin
79-135 1978 $12.50

OFFICIAL Programme and Souvenir Handbook, Eleventh International Sunday
School Convention. Toronto, 1905. Photos, ads, biographical sketches. Hood
117-359 1978 $20

OFFICIAL Records of the Union and Confederate Armies- The War of the Rebellion,
Index to Battles, Campaigns, etc. Series I. Washington, 1899. New cloth,
wraps bound, front wrap backed, Bell Wiley's copy. Broadfoot's 44-290 1978
$10.00

OFFICIAL RECORDS of the Union and Confederate Navies in the War of the
Rebellion • 29 vols., lacks vol. 8 & Index for compl. set, spines badly water
stained, some hinges cracked, Bell Wiley's copy • Broadfoot's 44-697 1978
$250.00

OFFICIAL Register of Rhode Island Officers and Soldiers Who Served in the United
States Army and Navy, from 1861 to 1866. 1866. 4to., illus., cloth. Mac-
Manus 239-904 1978 $45

OFFICIAL Report of the Proceedings and Debates of the Convention Assembled at
Alt Lake City on the Fourth of March, 1895,.... Salt Lake City, 1898. 2 vols.,
thick 8vo, full calf, 1st ed. Ginsberg 14-1010 1978 $125

OFFICIAL Views of the Pan-American Exposition. Buffalo, 1901. Side opening
16mo., pocket-size, plts. Butterfield 21-81 1978 $7.50

OFFICIAL Views of Pan-American Exposition. Buffalo, (1901). Wrs., leaves
prtd. on one side only, minor wear. Hayman 73-162 1978 $3.50

THE OFFICE of the Holy Week according to the Roman Missal and Breviary. 1796.
Vignette on title, sm. 8vo., spanish calf, rubbed. George's 635-1105 1978 £5

THE OFFICERS' Guide. Pennsylvania, 1942. Illus., 7th ed. Austin 80-210
1978 $10

THE OFFICINA Bodoni: the Operation of a Hand-Press During the First Six Years of its Work. Paris & New York, 1929. Cloth in d.w., d.w. spine reinforced, 1 of 500 numbered copies. Dawson's 447-114 1978 $200

OFFUTT, T. S.   Patriotic Maryland and the Maryland Society Sons of American Revolution. Baltimore, 1930. Baldwins' 51-290 1978 $15

O'FLAHERTY, LIAM   The Ecstasy of Agnus. London, 1931. Quarto, green buckram, gilt, t.e.g., 1 of 365 copies signed by author, orig. prospectus laid in, fine. Duschnes 220-223 1978 $37.50

O'FLAHERTY, LIAM   The Ecstasy of Angus. London, 1931. One of 365 numbered copies, signed by author, 4to., very nice, first ed., orig. binding, author's signed autograph pres. inscription. Rota 211-457 1978 £30

O'FLAHERTY, LIAM   The Fairy Goose and Two Other Stories. New York & London, 1927. Sq. 12mo., bds., linen back, d.w., signed by author, ltd. ed. Quaritch 979-251 1978 $45

O'FLAHERTY, LIAM   The Fairy Goose and Two Other Stories. New York, 1927. Orig. cloth-backed bds., 1st ed., ltd. and signed by author, fine. MacManus 238-729 1978 $40

O'FLAHERTY, LIAM   The Fairy Goose and Two Other Stories. New York, 1927. 4to, decor. boards, cloth spine with paper label, uncut, signed by author, d.w. chipped and rubbed on edges of spine, near Mint, 1st ed., collector's cond. Desmarais 1-337 1978 $45

O'FLAHERTY, LIAM   Famine. London, 1937. Nice in soiled & worn d.w. Desmarais B-489 1978 $25

O'FLAHERTY, LIAM   Famine. London, 1937. First ed., orig. binding, good, d.w. Rota 211-458 1978 £10

O'FLAHERTY, LIAM   Land. 1946. Very good, d.w., first English ed. Bell Book 16-684 1978 $4.50

O'FLAHERTY, LIAM   The Mountain Tavern and Other Stories. London, (1929). 1st ed., bind. faded. Biblo BL781-1096 1978 $12

O'FLAHERTY, LIAM   Red Barbara and other stories. New York and London, 1928. Illus. by Cecil Salkeld, one of 600 copies, signed by author, nice, first ed., orig. binding. Rota 211-456 1978 £20

O'FLAHERTY, LIAM   Return of the Brute. Mandrake Press, 1929. First ed., cr. 8vo., nice, signed by the author, orig. cloth. Howes 194-1077 1978 £7.50

O'FLAHERTY, LIAM   The Tent. 1926. 1st ed., very good, octavo bound in cloth. Hyland 128-260 1978 £7

O'FLAHERTY, LIAM   A Tourist's Guide to Ireland. (1929). First ed., 12mo., orig. cloth backed gilt bds., d.w., signed by the author. Howes 194-1078 1978 £7.50

OGDEN, C. A.   Into the Light. Boston, 1869. 8vo., inner fr. hinge bit cracked, 1st ed. Morrill 239-564 1978 $12.50

OGDEN, GEORGE W.   Letters from the West, Comprising a Tour through the Western Country, and a Residence of Two Summers in the States of Ohio and Kentucky. New Bedford, 1823. Sm. 8vo., old bds., all edges untrimmed, front cover joined with stitching, 1st ed., very scarce. Morrill 241-434 1978 $250

OGDEN, LEW J. G.   New Century Atlas of Counties of the State of New York. New York-Philadelphia, 1912. Very tall folio, maps, prtd. in color on thick paper, very good cond., backstrip gone, cloth covers held together by orig. broad tapes. Butterfield 21-63 1978 $75

OGG, D.   England in the Reign of Charles II. Oxford, 1934. 2 vols., maps, octavo, good. Upcroft 10-466 1978 £8.50

OGG, FREDERICK AUSTIN   The Opening of the Mississippi. New York, 1904. 1st ed., illus., maps, orig. cloth, d.j., chipped, very fine. MacManus 239-378 1978 $37.50

OGIER GHISLAIN DE BUSBECQ
Please turn to
BUSBECQ, OGIER GHISLAIN DE

OGILVIE, WILL H.   Over the Grass. London, 1925. Illus. by Lionel Edwards, coloured tipped-in plts., sm. 4to., cover slightly stained. K Books 244-249 1978 £6

OGILVIE, WILL H.   Over The Grass. London, 1927. Illus. by Lionel Edwards, with tipped-in color plts. Baldwins' 51-549 1978 $12.50

OGILVY, GAVIN   An Edinburgh Eleven. London, 1889. 12mo., orig. printed wrs., 1st ed., 1st issue, near-fine, bookplt. of Morris Parrish, cloth fold. case. MacManus 238-164 1978 $50

OGLE, A.   Tragedy of the Lollards' Tower. 1949. Plt. Allen 234-1384 1978 $8.50

OGLE, NATHANIEL   The Life of Addison. 1826. Orig. bds., worn, inscribed from the author, bookplt. of Holland House, notes by Roger Senhouse, one of 50 copies printed separately. Eaton 45-371 1978 £35

OGLE, NATHANIEL   Memoirs of Monkeys. 1825. 1st. ed., sm. 8vo, half-title, contemp. half calf. Hannas 54-233 1978 £15

OGRADY, STANDISH   Selected Essays and Passages. Dublin, n.d. Frontis, portraits, cloth. Eaton 45-372 1978 £5

O'HAGAN, H.O.   Leaves from My Life. 1st ed., 2 vols., f.p., very good, octavo bound in cloth. Hyland 128-262 1978 £4

O'HAGAN, THOMAS   Songs of the Settlement and Other Poems. Toronto, 1899. Inscribed & signed. Hood's 115-892 1978 $15

O'HAGAN, THOMAS   With Staff and Scrip. Toronto, 1924. Photos. Hood 116-707 1978 $7.50

O'HALLORAN, S.   A General History of Ireland..to the Close of the 12th Century..from the Most Authentic Records. 1778. 2 vols., 4to, large paper full leather, (front hinge weak), text very good, reprint. Hyland 128-264 1978 £30

O'HANLON, JOHN CANON   Irish-American History of the United States. 1907. Austin 79-525 1978 $37.50

O'HARA, JOHN   Appointment in Samarra. New York, 1934. First U.S. ed., covers stained, good, scarce. Bell Book 17-690 1978 £38.50

O'HARA, JOHN   Butterfield 8. New York, 1935. First U.S. ed., very good, worn d.w., scarce, d.w. Bell Book 17-691 1978 £40

O'HARA, JOHN   Pipe Night. 1946. Very good, worn d.w., first English ed. Bell Book 16-1002 1978 £6.50

O'HARA, JOSEPH M.   Chester's Century of Catholicism. Philadelphia, (1942). Frontis. MacManus 239-1594 1978 $12.50

O'HARA, MARY   My Friend Flicka. Philadelphia, New York, (1941). Colored f.p., plates, very good. Victoria 34-206 1978 $25

O'HART, J.   The Irish & Anglo-Irish Landed Gentry When Cromwell Came to Ireland. (1870). Octavo bound in cloth, reprint. Hyland 128-965 1978 £10

OHIO   Inventory of the County Archives of Ohio. Columbus, 1939. Wrps. Hayman 71-512 1978 $15

OHIO. BOARD OF AGRICULTURE   Twelfth Annual Report of the Ohio State Board of Agriculture... Columbus, 1858. Orig. binding, clean, minor wear, some soiling of covers. Hayman 71-599 1978 $8.50

OHIO. LAWS.   Statutes of the State of Ohio, of a General Nature, in Force, December 7, 1840. Columbus, 1841. Lea., little worn, internal stains. Hayman 73-547 1978 $12.50

OHIO Short-Horn Breeders' Record... Columbus, 1878. Vol. 1, clean, orig. binding. Hayman 71-572 1978 $10

OHIO Short-Horn Breeders' Record. Columbus, 1880. Vol. 2, 1/2 leather, little worn at bottom corner. Hayman 71-573 1978 $10

OHIO. CONSTITUTION   Constitution of the State of Ohio.   Columbus, 1874. Wrps., dust soiled. Hayman 71-529 1978 $7.50

OKALAUTSIT Attoraksat Kattimajunut Sontagine, Piluartomik Kattimavingmit Apsimanerme. Stolpen, 1870, 1871. 2 vols., black plain bind.   Hood 116-430 1978 $200

O'KANE, T. C.   Jasper and Gold: A Choice Collection of Song-Gems for Sunday-Schools, Social Meetings, and Time of Freshing.   Cincinnati, (1877). Printed bds.   Hayman 71-606 1978 $7.50

O'KANE, WALTER COLLINS   Sin in the Sky.   Norman, 1950. Illus., 1st ed., fine, d.w.   Biblo 248-40 1978 $10

O'KANE, WALTER COLLINS   Trails and Summits of the Green Mountains. Boston, 1926. Maps, illus., 12mo., 1st ed., orig. cloth.   Morrill 241-593 1978 $10

O'KELLY, J. J.   Ireland, Elements of Her Early Story.   1921. Illus., good, octavo bound in cloth, reprint.   Hyland 128-267 1978 £5

O'KELLY, PAT   Killarney, A Descriptive Poem.   1791. 1st ed., modern 1/2 leather, very good.   Hyland 128-270 1978 £80

O'KELLY, SEUMAS   Waysiders.   Dublin and London, 1917. Frontis, cloth, illus., pict. upper cover.   Eaton 45-373 1978 £8

OKELY, W. SEBASTIAN   Development of Christian Architecture in Italy. London, 1860. Lg. in 8vo., orig. cloth, good, plts.   King 7-371 1978 £20

OKEN, LORENZ   Isis, oder Encyclopaedische Zeitung.   Leipzig, 1819. Engraved plts., 4to., bound in library cloth.   Salloch 348-100 1978 $40

OKIE, A. HOWARD   Bonninghausen's Therapeutic Pocket-Book for Homoeopathists.   Boston, 1847. 12mo., some binding wear, 1st Amer. ed.   Morrill 239-196 1978 $17.50

OKIE, HOWARD PITCHER   Old Silver and Old Sheffield Plate.   New York, 1944. Spine dull, illus., edges rubbed.   Biblo 247-303 1978 $15

OLAFSEN, E.   Travels in Iceland...   Phillips, 1805. Map, plts., lib. stamped & slightly browned, modern half calf, 8vo.   Edwards 1012-594 1978 £45

OLCOTT, CHARLES S.   The Life of William McKinley.   Boston, 1916. 1st ed., 2 vols., illus., orig. cloth, fine set, ltd. to 285 copies.   MacManus 239-786 1978 $45

OLD English Carols.   London, c.1875. Large quarto, plates in style of 13th century miniatures, covers in gilt and blind-stamped, worn at edges, cover mottling, text and plates fine.   Victoria 34-588 1978 $50

OLD French Court Memoirs, the Correspondence of Mde. Princesse Palatine of Marie-Adelaide de Savoie and Marie de Maintenon.   New York, 1899. 12 vols., illus., cr. 8vo., spines a little faded and rubbed.   George's 635-732 1978 £7.50

OLD Gardens In and About Philadelphia and Those Who Made Them.   Indianapolis, (1932). Illus.   MacManus 239-1636 1978 $10

THE OLD Palatine Church.   1930-35. Wrs., very good.   Butterfield 21-277c 1978 $7.50

OLD Sudbury.   Boston, (1929). Reproductions of pencil sketches, 8vo., orig. bds., boxed, 1st ed.   Morrill 241-342 1978 $7.50

OLDCASTLE   Remarks on the History of England.   1742. Orig. calf, leading bd. only loosely attached.   Jarndyce 16-149 1978 £7

OLDE Tayles Newlye Relayted.   London, Leadenhall Press, (1883). Woodcuts by Joseph Crawhall, large octavo, orig. decor. cloth binding, edges and corners rubbed.   Totteridge 29-64 1978 $100

OLDENBOURG, R.   Der Heilige Bezirk von Delphi.   n.d. Rolled map, upper portion stained, slightly torn.   Allen 234-700 1978 $10

OLDER, MRS. FREMONT   William Randolph Hearst...American.   New York, 1936. Illus., 1st ed.   Biblo BL781-768 1978 $12

OLDHAM, J. B.   Shrewsbury School Library Bindings.   Oxford, 1943. Ltd. to 200 copies, colored plts., roy. 4to., orig. buckram.   Forster 130-67 1978 £120

OLDHAM, W. S.   A Digest of the General Statute Laws of the State of Texas,....   Austin, 1859. Later cloth.   Jenkins 116-1025 1978 $45

OLDHAM, W. S.   Speech on the Subject of the Finances. Richmond, 1863. Sewn, poor copy, chewed, E. W. Winkler's copy.   Jenkins 116-1024 1978 $35

OLDMIXON, JOHN   The Critical History of England, Ecclesiastical and Civil.   1726. Second ed., nice, full contemp. russia, 2 vols., 8vo.   Howes 194-406 1978 £30

OLDROYD, OSBORN H.   The Assassination of Abraham Lincoln, Flight, Pursuit, Capture and Punishment of the Conspirators.   Washington, 1917. Bell Wiley's copy.   Broadfoot's 44-292 1978 $12.00

OLDROYD, OSBORN H.   A Soldier's Story of the Siege of Vicksburg... Springfield, 1885. Portrs., engrs., Bell Wiley's copy.   Broadfoot 46-354 1978 $65

OLDS, CHAUNCEY N.   A Valedictory Address to the Graduates of the Union Literary Society of Miami University, Delivered August 7th, 1839.   Oxford, 1839. Disbound, foxed.   Hayman 73-554 1978 $12.50

OLDS, EDSON B.   Arbitrary Arrests. Speech of Hon..., for Which He was Arrested, and His Reception Speeches on His Return from the Bastile... N.P., n.d. (1863?). Sewed as issued.   Hayman 72-131 1978 $20

O'LEARY, A.   Miscellaneous Tracts...   London, 1782. 3rd ed., Enlarged & Corrected, contemp. calf, front loose, text very good.   Hyland 128-273 1978 £6

O'LEARY A.   Miscellaneous Tracts.   Dublin, 1816. Leather worn, some worm traces, reprint.   Hyland 128-274 1978 £5

O'LEARY, IRIS (PROUTY)   Department Store Occupations.   1916. Austin 80-840 1978 $8.50

O'LEARY, J.   The Most Ancient Lives of St. Patrick Including the Life by Jocelin.   New York, c.1900. Illus., ex lib., good, octavo bound in cloth.   Hyland 128-277 1978 £4.50

O'LEARY, J.   Recollections of Fenians & Fenianism.   (1896). Octavo bound in cloth, reprint.   Hyland 128-966 1978 £9

O'LEARY, PETER   Travels and Experiences in Canada, the Red River Territory and the United States.   London, [1876]. Orig. cloth, 1st ed.   Ginsberg 14-803 1978 $85

OLINDEE, THOMAS   Poems.   1854. Author's pres. inscpt., full panelled morocco, gilt spine, bds., a.e.g., slightly scuffed.   Eaton 45-374 1978 £5

OLIPHANT, LAURENCE   Altiora Peto.   1883. 1st. ed., 2 vols., pictorial titles and frontis, 3/4 blue calf, little faded, edges rubbed.   Eaton 45-375 1978 £15

OLIPHANT, LAURENCE   The Land of Khemi Up and Down the Middle Nile. 1882. 1st. separate ed., 8vo, half-title, tinted plts., half calf, neatly rebacked, gilt, marbled bds.   Deighton 5-20 1978 £38

OLIPHANT, LAURENCE   Narrative of the Earl of Elgin's Mission to China and Japan, 1857-59.   1859. Folding maps, 20 coloured & tinted litho. plts., text illus., 2 vols., 8vo. orig. cloth.   Edwards 1012-193 1978 £90

OLIPHANT, LAURENCE   The Russian Shores Of The Black Sea In the Autumn of 1852.   Edinburgh and London, 1854. 3rd. ed., revised & enlarged, 8vo, half-title, tinted lithograph frontispiece, map, illus., half calf, gilt.   Deighton 5-136 1978 £35

OLIPHANT, LAURENCE   Sympneumata or Evolutionary Forces Now Active In Man.   1885. Half title, fine half brown morocco, good.   Jarndyce 16-910 1978 £38

OLIPHANT, MARGARET   Chronicles of Carlingford. Salem Chapel.   Edinburgh, 1863. 2 vols., orig. cloth, 1st ed., covers slightly soiled, but very good. MacManus 238-363 1978 $150

OLIPHANT, MARGARET   Memoirs and Resolutions of Adam Fraeme of Mossgray. 1859. 1st. one-vol. ed., frontis, 8vo, orig. cloth, gilt, binding stained & endpapers foxed, good sound copy. Fenning 32-249 1978 £7.50

OLIPHANT, MARGARET   The Victorian Age in English Literature. New York, (1892). 1st Amer. ed., 2 vols., red cloth, t.e.g., engrav. illus. with tissue guards. Greene 78-266 1978 $40

OLIPHANT, T. L. K.   The New English. London, 1886. 2 vols., crown 8vo, orig. cloth, little worn. Sexton 7-173 1978 £10

OLIVER, DAVID D.   The Society for the Propagation of the Gospel in the Province of North Carolina and Correspondence of John Rust Eaton. Chapel Hill, 1909. Vol. 9, no. 1, new cloth. Broadfoot 50-162 1978 $10

OLIVER, FREDERICK SCOTT   Alexander Hamilton...an Essay on American Union. New York, 1911. Illus. Biblo 248-96 1978 $17.50

OLIVER, FREDERICK SCOTT   Alexander Hamilton, an Essay on American Union. New York, 1928. New ed., frontis., map. Biblo BL781-203 1978 $9

OLIVER, GEORGE   The Antiquities of Free-Masonry. London, 1823. First ed., plts., maps, binders buckram. K Books 244-250 1978 £20

OLIVER, PETER   The Puritan Commonwealth. Boston, 1856. 1st. ed., covers faded. Baldwins' 51-402 1978 $15

OLIVER, SAMUEL PASSFIELD   Fortification Plates, R.M.A. 1857-58. Orig. drawings, folio, half roan, repaired. F. Edwards 1013-395 1978 £30

OLIVER, SAMUEL PASFIELD   Madagascar and the Malagasy... (1863). Map, tinted litho. plts., roy. 8vo, orig. cloth, cover repaired. Edwards 1012-320 1978 £50

OLIVIER, EDITH   Night Thoughts of a Country Landlady. 1943. Coloured frontis., plts. by author, very good, d.w., first English ed. Bell Book 16-908 1978 £8.50

OLIVIER, JULES   Anselme De Cantobery d'apres ses Meditations. Toulouse, 1890. 8vo., pamphlet bind., orig. wrs. bound in. Salloch 348-3 1978 $10

OLLIER, EDMUND   Cassell's History of the United States. London, n.d. 3 vols., sm. 4to., illus., 3/4 leather, bindings rubbed. Biblo BL781-182 1978 $42.50

OLMSTEAD, FREDERICK LAW   A Journey in the Back Country. New York, 1860. 1st ed., orig. cloth, soiled. MacManus 239-1851 1978 $37.50

OLMSTED, FREDERICK LAW   A Journey in the Back Country. New York, 1907. 2 vols., marginal stains, vol. I in poor cond., Bell Wiley's copy. Broadfoot's 44-722 1978 $16

OLMSTED, FREDERICK LAW   A Journey Through Texas: or, A Saddle-Trip on the South-western Frontier. New York, 1857. Ex libris, 3/4 leather, scuffed, Bell Wiley's copy. Broadfoot's 44-970 1978 $25

OLMSTEAD, JOHN   A Trip to California in 1868. New York, 1880. Orig. cloth, near mint. Ginsberg 14-804 1978 $100

OLSCHKI, L.   Die Romanischen Literaturen des Mittelalter. Potsdam, 1928. 4to., orig. cover, plts., some in color, illus. Van der Peet H-64-473 1978 Dfl 50

OLSON, CHARLES   The Maximus Poems. n.d. 4to., very good, first English ed. Bell Book 17-693 1978 £6.50

THE OMAHA Fire Insurance Company of Omaha, Nebraska. Omaha, [c. 1885]. 12mo, folder. Ginsberg 14-723 1978 $25

O'MAHONY, J.   Poetry & Legendary Ballads of the South of Ireland. 1894. 1st ed., 1/2 leather, very good. Hyland 128-282 1978 £27.50

O'MAHONY, J.   The Sunny Side of Ireland. 1902. 2nd ed., very good, octavo bound in cloth. Hyland 128-280 1978 £7

O'MAHONY, J.   The Sunny Side of Ireland. 1902. Illus., very good, octavo bound in cloth. Hyland 128-281 1978 £7.50

OMAN, C.   The Great Revolt of 1381. Oxford, 1906. Maps, 8vo. Upcroft 12-319 1978 £7.50

OMAN, C.   A History of the Art of War in the Sixteenth Century. 1937. Mps., plts., octavo, good. Upcroft 10-471 1978 £20

OMAR KHAYYAM   The Quatrains of. (Worchester, Mass.), 1906. Cloth, uncut, translated by Eben Francis Thompson. 1 of 435 signed by Thompson, pres. copy inscribed by Thompson, A.L.s. from Thompson laid in, very good. Houle 10-245 1978 $95

OMAR KHAYYAM   The Rubaiyat of Omar Khayyam, the Astronomer-Poet of Persia. London, 1872. Sm. sq. quarto, Roxburgh binding of dark red cloth, brown lea. spine, gilt, cover spotting & fading, 3rd ed., rare. Bradley 49-120 1978 $250

OMAR KHAYYAM   Rubaiyat of Omar Khayyam. New York, Wayside Press, 1897. 1 of 1250 numbered copies prtd., bound in full blue mor., gilt ruled borders on covers, spine gilt lettered, t.e.g., others uncut, signed by Richard Le Gallienne, very fine. Battery Park 1-17 1978 $250

OMAR KHAYYAM   Rubaiyat of. London, 1897. 8 vo., full gilt stamped white vellum, uncut, fine. Houle 10-246 1978 $30

OMAR KHAYYAM   Rubaiyat of Omar Khayyam. New York, Bodley Head, 1897. Orig. bds., signed by Richard Le Gallienne. Battery Park 1-18 1978 $125

OMAR KHAYYAM   The Rubaiyat of Omar Khayyam. New York, (1905). 1st ed., 4to., illus. by Adelaid Hanscom. Biblo 251-219 1978 $16.50

OMAR KHAYYAM   Rubaiyat of Omar Khayyam. London, (1910). Illus. with tipped in color plts. by Edmund Dulac, 4to., orig. gilt stamped white cloth, little soiled, else very good, bookplate. Houle 10-95 1978 $175

OMAR KHAYYAM   Rubiyat of Omar Khayyam. London, (c.1914). Color plts., 8 vo., full gilt stamped brown mor., very good. Houle 10-47 1978 $45

OMAR KHAYYAM   Rubaiayat. London, 1939. Sm. 8vo., full blue mor. binding, richly gilt tooling on both covers, plts., colored by W. Poyang, excellent binding, minor scratches. Van der Peet H-64-511 1978 Dfl 250

O'MEARA, BARRY EDWARD   Napoleon at St. Helena. 1888. Coloured plts., illus., 2 vols., 8vo., orig. cloth. F. Edwards 1013-384 1978 £18

OMMANEY, F. D.   South Latitude. London, 1938. 8vo., orig. cloth, good. Paine 78-102 1978 $15.00

OMOND, W. T.   Belgium. London, 1908. Thick 8vo, orig. dec. cloth, good. Sexton 7-8D 1978 £6

OMWAKE, JOHN   The Conestoga Six-horse Bell Teams of Eastern Pennsylvania. Cincinnati, 1930. 4to, illus., orig. binding. Americanist 101-157 1978 $75

OMWAKE, JOHN   The Conestoga Six-Horse Bell Teams of Eastern Pennsylvania. 1930. Illus., 2nd ed., illus. Nestler Rare 78-187 1978 $45

ON Going to Sleep. London, 1868. Sm. 8vo., orig. maroon stamped cloth, gilt on upper cover, worn, good copy, 1st ed., rare. Zeitlin 245-171 1978 $67.50

ONDENDONK, JAMES   Idaho: Facts and Statistics Concerning Its Mining, Farming, Stock Rising, Lumbering and Other Resources,.... San Francisco, 1885. Original printed wr., 1st ed. Ginsberg 14-404 1978 $125

ONDERDONK, BENJAMIN T.   The Proceedings of the Court...in the... Trial of the Right Rev. Benjamin T. Onderdonk, D.D. Bishop of New-York. New York and Philadelphia, 1845. Bound with 3 related pamphlets. Butterfield 21-528 1978 $35

ONE Hundred & One Ballades. London, (1931). 1st ed., 8 vo., orig. yellow cloth, illus. by John Nash, very good. Houle 10-62 1978 $20

ONE Hundred Views of the Pan American Exposition, Buffalo and Niagara Falls. Buffalo, 1901. Oblong 8vo., orig. wrs. Morrill 239-570 1978 $8.50

O'NEIL, GEORGE   The White Rooster and Other Poems. New York,
1927. 1st ed., bind. faded, spine dull. Biblo BL781-1098 1978 $8.50

O'NEILL, EUGENE   Ah, Wilderness! New York, (1933). Blue cloth,
1st ed., back cover lightly stained, good, repaired dust jacket. Bradley 49-254
1978 $10

O'NEILL, EUGENE   All God's Chillun Got Wings and Welded. New
York, (1924). Tan bds., tan cloth spine, 1st ed., covers soiled, scarce. Bradley 49-255 1978 $15

O'NEILL, EUGENE   All God's Chillun Got Wings and Welded. New
York, (1924). 12mo, boards and cloth, chipped d.j., 1st ed., fine. Duschnes
220-228 1978 $45

O'NEILL, EUGENE   All God's Chillun Got Wings and Welded. New
York, (1924). Orig. cloth-backed bds., 1st ed., signed by O'Neill, very good.
MacManus 238-731 1978 $100

O'NEILL, EUGENE   Anna Christie. New York, 1930. Illus. by
Alexander King, orig. cloth-backed bds., 1 of 750 signed copies, extremities
slightly worn, covers partially faded, otherwise very good. MacManus 238-735
1978 $100

O'NEILL, EUGENE   Beyond the Horizon. New York, (1920). Brown
bds., tan cloth spine, 1st ed., covers soiled & worn, light dampstaining, scarce.
Bradley 49-256 1978 $25

O'NEILL, EUGENE   Days Without End. New York, (1934). Blue
cloth, 1st ed., back cover spotted, good. Bradley 49-257 1978 $10

O'NEILL, EUGENE   Day's Without End. New York, 1934. Very
fine, d.w. soiled & damaged. Desmarais B-494 1978 $20

O'NEILL, EUGENE   Days Without End. New York, (1934). 8vo,
cloth, d.j., 1st ed., fine. Duschnes 220-235 1978 $25

O'NEILL, EUGENE   Dynamo. New York, 1929. Green cloth, 1st
ed., fine in dust jacket. Bradley 49-258 1978 $15

O'NEILL, EUGENE   Dynamo. New York, 1929. 1st Trade ed., d.j.,
fine. Duschnes 220-233 1978 $25

O'NEILL, EUGENE   Dynamo. Dust jacket less fine, spine of book
lightened. Bradley 49-259 1978 $10

O'NEILL, EUGENE   The Emperor Jones: Diff'rent: The Straw. New
York, (1921). Plain tan bds., tan cloth spine, 1st ed., 1st issue, covers worn &
soiled, writing on end papers. Bradley 49-260 1978 $15

O'NEIL, EUGENE   The Emperor Jones. New York, (1921). 12mo,
bds. & cloth back, 1st ed., 1st issue, fine. Duschnes 220-224 1978 $50

O'NEILL, EUGENE   The Emperor Jones. New York, 1928. Illus. by
Alexander King, orig. cloth-backed bds., 1st illus. ed., 1 of 775 no. copies,
signed by author, fine, browned d.j., boxed. MacManus 238-733 1978 $100

O'NEILL, EUGENE   The Hairy Ape. Anna Christie. The First Man.
New York, (1922). 12mo, boards, cloth back, 1st ed., 1st issue, fine. Duschnes
220-225 1978 $50

O'NEILL, EUGENE   The Hairy Ape, Anna Christie, the First Man.
New York, (1922). Tan bds., tan cloth spine, 1st ed., dampstaining, covers
& spine worn. Bradley 49-261 1978 $15

O'NEILL, EUGENE   The Hairy Ape. New York, 1929. Illus. by
Alexander King, 4to, orig. dec. bds., 1st separate and illus. ed., 1 of 775 no.
copies, signed by author, d.j., fine, boxed. MacManus 238-734 1978 $100

O'NEILL, EUGENE   The Iceman Cometh. New York, 1946. Near
mint in torn d.w. Desmarais B-495 1978 $30

O'NEILL, EUGENE   The Iceman Cometh. New York, (1946). 1st
ed. Biblo BL781-1097 1978 $16.50

O'NEILL, EUGENE   The Iceman Cometh. New York, (1946). Chipped d.j., 1st ed., orig. bind. Petrilla 13-59 1978 $15

O'NEILL, EUGENE   The Iceman Cometh. New York, (1946). 8vo.,
d.w., sm. tears on d.w., 1st ed. Morrill 239-566 1978 $20

O'NEILL, EUGENE   Lazarus Laughed. New York, 1927. 8vo,
patterned boards, jap vellum spine, 1 of 775 copies signed by author, 1st ed., fine.
Duschnes 220-230 1978 $50

O'NEILL, EUGENE   Lazarus Laughed and Dynamo. 1929. Very
good, browned d.w., first English ed. Bell Book 16-685 1978 £8.50

O'NEILL, EUGENE   Marco Millions. New York, 1927. 8vo, patterned boards, jap vellum spine, darkened, 1 of 450 copies signed by author, 1st ed.,
fine. Duschnes 220-229 1978 $50

O'NEILL, EUGENE   Marco Millions. New York, 1927. Orig. bds.,
1st ed., 1 of 450 signed copies, spine very slightly darkened, else fine, pub. slipcase. MacManus 238-732 1978 $100

O'NEILL, EUGENE   Mourning Becomes Electra. New York, 1931.
Green cloth, gilt, 1st ed., spine worn, good, chipped dust jacket. Bradley 49-
262 1978 $15

O'NEILL, EUGENE   Mourning Becomes Electra. New York, 1931.
8vo, decorative cloth, pict. endpapers, d.j., 1st ed., fine. Duschnes 220-234
1978 $40

O'NEILL, EUGENE   Mourning Becomes Electra. A Trilogy. New
York, (1931). Orig. full vellum with mor. label, pub. box, 1st ed., ltd. to 500
copies signed by author, very good. MacManus 238-736 1978 $100

O'NEILL, EUGENE   Plays. New York, (1934). 1 of 775 sets
signed by author, 1st ed., orig. cloth, t.e.g., uncut, bookplates, 12 vol.,
fine. Houle 10-249 1978 $600

O'NEILL, EUGENE   Strange Interlude: a play. New York, 1928.
First U.S. ed., front hinge weak, very good, d.w. Bell Book 17-694 1978 £30

O'NEILL, EUGENE   Strange Interlude. New York, 1928. Quarto,
full vellum bds., gilt, ltd. ed., 1 of 775 signed, fine copy. Bradley 49-263
1978 $85

O'NEILL, EUGENE   Strange Interlude. New York, 1928. 1st Trade
ed., d.j., fine. Duschnes 220-232 1978 $25

O'NEILL, EUGENE   Thirst and Other One-Act Plays. Boston, Gorham
Press, (1914). Bds., cloth back. Dawson's 447-267 1978 $125

O'NEILL, EUGENE   Thirst and Other One-Act Plays. Boston, (1914).
Orig. bds., 1st ed., very good, 1,000 copies printed. MacManus 238-730 1978
$175

O'NEILL, EUGENE   The Complete Works. New York, 1924. Thick
8vo, boards with cloth back, gilt, 1 of 1200 copies signed by author, 2 vols.,
front hinge weak on vol. 1, bookplt., fine. Duschnes 220-226 1978 $125

O'NEILL, J.   Wind from the North. 1934. 1st ed., cover dull,
text very good, octavo bound in cloth. Hyland 128-286 1978 £4

ONIONS, OLIVER   The Debit Account. 1913. Some foxing, else
near fine, first English ed. Bell Book 17-696 1978 £7.50

ONIONS, OLIVER   In Accordance with the Evidence. 1912. First
ed., T.L.s. from the author tipped in, orig. cloth, 8vo. Howes 194-1080 1978
£8.50

ONIONS, OLIVER   In Accordance with the Evidence. 1912. Very
good, first English ed. Bell Book 17-697 1978 £7.50

ONIONS, OLIVER   Poor Man's Tapestry. 1946. Very good, worn
d.w., first English ed. Bell Book 17-699 1978 £6

ONIONS, OLIVER   Tales of a Far Riding. 1902. Fine, scarce, first
English ed. Bell Book 17-700 1978 £20

ONIS, LUIS DE   Memoir upon the Negotiations Between Spain
and the United States of America, Which Led to the Treaty of 1819, with a
Stitistical Notice of that Country. Washington, 1821. Half morocco, 1st ed. in
English. Jenkins 116-1030 1978 $950

ONTARIO. BUR. OF ARCHIVES   Fourth Report, 1906. Toronto, 1907. Bound.
Hood's 115-557 1978 $15

ONTARIO. DEPT. OF EDUCATION   Catalogue of Books in the Departments of
Art, Music, Commerce, Manual Training, Household Science and Farming for
Public and High School Teachers and Libraries. Toronto, 1912. Wrs. Hood 117-
61 1978 $12.50

ONTARIO. DEPT. OF EDUCATION   Report on the Schools Attended by French-
Speaking Pupils, 1932-33. Toronto, 1933. Card cover. Hood 116-379 1978
$7.50

ONTARIO. DEPT. OF MINES   Ontario Gold Deposits, Their Character, Distribution and Productiveness. Toronto, 1922. Card cover, illus., folding map. Hood's 115-561 1978 $7.50

ONTARIO. LAWS   Acts Relating to the Education Department. Toronto, 1901. Few water spots on cover. Hood 117-955 1978 $15

ONTARIO AND ST. LAWRENCE STEAMBOAT COMPANY, Handbook For Travelers.. Buffalo, 1854. Folding map, illus., numerous engravings. Hood's 115-832 1978 $75

ONTARIO INSTITUTION FOR THE EDUCATION OF THE BLIND   By-Laws of the...Brantford. Toronto, 1872. Wrs. Hood 116-364 1978 $12.50

ONTARIO MEDICAL ASSOCIATION   The Canadian Medical Week, Hamilton, May 27-June 1, 1918. Toronto, 1918. Hood's 115-662 1978 $10

ONTARIO Historical Society, Annual Reports, 1901-1906.   Bound in 1 vols. Hood's 115-830 1978 $35

ONTARIO Library Association: An Historical Sketch 1900-1925. Toronto, 1926. Lib. bookplt. Hood's 115-831 1978 $25

ONTYD, C. G.   De Morte et Varia Moriende Ratione. Leyden, 1797. Rittenhouse 49-583 1976 $65

OORDT, A. VAN   Warhold. Bussum, 1912. 2 vols. in 1, fine full light brown calf, ribbed gilt tooled spine, bds. case. Van der Peet H-64-381 1978 D.fl 50

VAN OOSTEN, HENRIK
Please turn to
OOSTEN, HENRIK VAN

OPPE, ADOLF PAUL   The Drawings of Paul and Thomas Sandby in the Collection of His Majesty at Windsor Castle. 1947. Reproductions, some coloured, 4to. George's 635-209 1978 $15

OPPE, ADOLF PAUL   The Drawings of Paul and Thomas Sandby in the Collection of His Majesty the King at Windsor Castle. Phaidon, 1947. Sm. folio, orig. cloth, plts., some coloured, good. Sexton 7-37 1978 £10

OPPE, ADOLF PAUL   The Drawings of William Hogarth. New York, 1948. Illus., 4to., name in ink on title page. Biblo 251-214 1978 $37.50

OPPE, ADOLF PAUL   Thomas Rowlandson, His Drawings and Water-Colours. London, 1923. 1st ed., 4to., illus., some plts. in color, orig. parchment-backed bds., covers dust-soiled, but very good. MacManus 239-700 1978 $85

OPPE, ADOLF PAUL   The Water-Colours of John Sell Cotman. 1923. Coloured plts., imp. 8vo., orig. wrappers. George's 635-131 1978 £10

OPPELN, ALEXANDER AUGUST FERDINAND BRONIKOWSKI VON
Please turn to
BRONIKOWSKI, ALEXANDER AUGUST FERDINAND VON OPPELN

OPPELN-BRONIKOWSKI, F. VON   Archaeologische Entdeckungen im 20. Jahrhundert. Berlin, 1931. Illus., bottom of spine torn. BL781-452 1978 $13.50

OPPENHEIM, HERMANN   Lehrbuch der Nervenkrankheiten fur Arzte und Studirende. Volumes I and II. Berlin, 1908. Fifth ed., ex-library, some wear. Rittenhouse 49-584 1976 $35

OPPENHEIMER, CARL   Die Fermente und ihre Wirkungen. Leipzig, 1900. 8vo., orig. cloth, gilt, good copy, 1st ed. Norman 5-213 1978 $30

OPENING Ceremonies of the New York and Brooklyn Bridge May 24, 1883. Brooklyn, 1883. Frontis., orig. cloth, inner hinges cracking, all edges gilt, inscr'd pres. copy. Butterfield 21-484 1978 $12.50

OPIE, AMELIA   Illustrations of Lying in All Its Branches. 1825. 1st. ed., 2 vols., full calf, spines & bds. gilt dec., black labels, fine. Jarndyce 16-915 1978 £40

OPIE, AMELIA   Lays for the Dead. 1834. 1st. ed., frontis, litho, 1/2 calf, raised bands, gilt. Eaton 45-376 1978 £10

OPIE, AMELIA   Lays for the Dead. 1834. 12mo., orig. bds. uncut, frontispiece, first ed., author's inscribed pres. copy. P. M. Hill 142-290 1978 £48

OPIE, AMELIA   Madeline, A Tale. 1822. 1st. ed., 2 vols., full calf, spines & bds. gilt dec., black labels, fine. Jarndyce 16-919 1978 £45

OPIE, AMELIA   Tales of the Heart. 1820. 2nd. ed., 4 vols., half titles, some slight foxing, half brown calf, v.g. Jarndyce 16-914 1978 £30

OPIE, AMELIA   Tales of the Heart. 1820. 2nd. ed., 4 vols., full calf, spines & bds. gilt dec. black labels, fine. Jarndyce 16-916 1978 £36

OPIE, AMELIA   Temper, Or Domestic Scenes: A Tale. 1812. 2nd. ed., 3 vols., half titles, orig. half calf, slight damage to head of spine vol. 2, otherwise v.g. Jarndyce 16-913 1978 £24

OPIE, AMELIA   Temper, or Domestic Scences. 1813. 3rd. ed., 3 vols., full calf, spines & bds. gilt dec., black labels, fine. Jarndyce 16-918 1978 £36

OPIE, AMELIA   Valentine's Eve. 1816. 2nd. ed., 3 vols., full calf, spines & bds. gilt dec.,black labels, fine. Jarndyce 16-917 1978 £36

THE Opinions of the Judge and the Colonel as to the Vast Resources of Colorado.... N.P., 1896. Illus., original pictorial printed wr. Ginsberg 14-270 1978 $65

OPINION of Twelve of the Most Eminent Advocates of Paris, Touching the Right of the Seminary of Montreal, in Canada, to Certain Property. Montreal, 1940. Pamphlet, excellent cond. Hood 117-360 1978 $55

OPPEL, KARL   Das Alte Wunderland der Pyramiden. Leipzig, 1906. 5th ed., illus., color plts. Biblo BL781-451 1978 $14.50

OPPENHEIM, E. PHILLIPS   Great Prince Shan. Boston, 1922. 1st ed., very good. Houle 10-251 1978 $12.50

OPPENHEIM, E. PHILLIPS   Jeremiah and the Princess. Boston, 1933. 1st Amer. ed. Biblo 251-595 1978 $12.50

OPPENHEIM, SAMUEL   The Early History of the Jews in New York, 1654-1664. New York, 1909. Wr., inscr'd by author. Butterfield 21-232 1978 $12.50

OPPERT, ERNEST   A Forbidden Land: Voyages to the Corea.... New York, 1880. Illus., folding maps, orig. cloth with leather spine and tips added later, withdrawal stamps on t.p. Dawson's 127-233 1978 $75

OPUSCULES D'Un Freethinker. N.P., 1781. 8vo., orig. wrs., stitched, uncut. Salloch 348-179 1978 $55

ORARIUM Seu Libellus Precationum Per Regiam Maiestaten & Cleru Latine Aeditus. London, 1546. Woodcut title-pg., other woodcuts, many leaves printed in red & black, sm. 8vo, blue morocco, gilt edges, joints repaired. Traylen 88-315 1978 £450

ORBELIANI, SULKHAM-SABA   The Book of Wisdom and Lies, A Georgian Storybook of the Eighteenth Century. Upper Mall, Hammersmith: Kelmscott Press, 1894. 8vo., orig. vellum, 1st ed., 1 of 250 copies, bookplt., very nice. MacManus 238-812 1978 $350

ORCUTT, SAMUEL   A History of the Old Town of Stratford and the City of Bridgeport, Conn. 1886. 2 vols., old 1/2 leather, illus., maps. MacManus 239-956 1978 $75

ORCUTT, SAMUEL   History of Torrington, Conn., from Its First Settlement in 1737... Albany, 1878. Rebound, some staining, else fine. MacManus 239-957 1978 $40

ORCUTT, WILLIAM DANA   The Book in Italy During the Fifteenth and Sixteenth Centuries... New York, 1928. 4to., orig. cloth-backed bds., illus., ltd. to 750 copies, very fine, orig. pub. box. MacManus 238-1017 1978 $60

ORCUTT, WILLIAM DANA   The Book in Italy During the Fifteenth and Sixteenth Century. New York, 1928. One of 750 copies, lg. paper ed. Battery Park 1-435 1978 $125

ORCUTT, WILLIAM DANA   Celebrities Off Parade. 1925. Pen & ink portrs., 1 of 300 copies, copy #51, signed by Orcutt, 1/2 lea. Battery Park 1-431 1978 $50

ORCUTT, WILLIAM DANA   In Quest of the Perfect Book. Boston, 1926. 8vo., orig. 3/4 vellum, pub. box, 1 of 365 copies signed by author, near-fine, bookplt. MacManus 238-1018 1978 $45

ORCUTT, WILLIAM DANA   In Quest of the Perfect Book. Reminiscences and Reflections of a Bookman. Boston, 1926. Coloured frontis., d.j., 1st ed. MacManus 238-1019 1978 $15

ORCUTT, WILLIAM DANA   The Kingdom of Books. Boston, 1927. Illus., orig. vellum backed bds., 1st ed., ltd. to 475 signed copies, fine, pub. box. MacManus 238-1020 1978 $40

ORCUTT, WILLIAM DANA   In Quest of the Perfect Book. Boston, 1926. Lg. paper copy, one of 365, copy #N, signed by Orcutt. Battery Park 1-433 1978 $100

ORCUTT, WILLIAM DANA   The Magic of the Book. 1st trade ed., t.e.g., illus. Battery Park 1-430 1978 $22.50

ORCUTT, WILLIAM DANA   The Manual of Linotype Typography. Brooklyn, (1923). 4to. Battery Park 1-429 1978 $75

ORCZY, BARONESS   The Emperor's Candlesticks. New York, (1908). 1st Amer. ed. Biblo 251-596 1978 $15

ORD, JOHN   The Story of the Barony of Gorbals. Paisley, 1919. Plts., cr. 8vo., orig. cloth. K Books 244-426 1978 £5

ORDER Book Kept by Peter Kinnan July 7-September 4, 1776. Princeton, 1931. Illus. MacManus 239-590 1978 $15

ORDINAIRE, C. N.   The Natural History of Volcanoes. 1801. Half calf, worn, some foxing, 8vo. George's 635-982 1978 £18

OREGON. Philadelphia, 1846. Half mor., 1st ed. Ginsberg 14-836 1978 $100

OREGON: Facts Regarding Its Climate, Soil, Mineral and Agricultural Resources, Means of Communication, Commerce and Industry, Laws, etc. for the Use of Immigrants. Boston, 1876. Orig. pr. wrs. Ginsberg 14-837 1978 $60

OREGON Historical Quarterly. Salem, 1900-1973. Orig. pr. wr., vols. 1-74. Ginsberg 14-838 1978 $950

O'REILLY, E.   A Chronological Account of Nearly 400 Irish Writers. (1820). Octavo bound in cloth, reprint. Hyland 128-967 1978 £7.35

O'REILLY, E.   Irish-English Dictionary. 1817. 1st ed., shaky, octavo bound in cloth. Hyland 128-301 1978 £8

O'REILLY, E.   Irish-English Dictionary. 1864. 1st ed., Amateur rebacking, good. Hyland 128-300 1978 £10

O'REILLY, E.   Irish-English Dictionary. 1864. Needs rebinding, reprint. Hyland 128-302 1978 £5

O'REILLY, JOHN   The Placenta, the Organic Nervous System, the Blood, the Oxygen, and the Animal Nervous System, Physiologically Examined. New York, 1861. Plts., 8vo., 1st ed. Morrill 239-197 1978 $12.50

O'REILLY, R.   Essai sur le Blanchiment, avec la Description de la Nouvelle Methode de Blanchir par la Vapeur, d'apres le Procede du Citoyen Chaptal. Paris, (1801). 8vo., fldg. copperplts. after drwgs. by author, contemp. half vellum with prtd. paper label on spine, very fine copy, 1st ed. Norman 5-214 1978 $275

O'RELL, MAX   A Frenchman in America. N.P., n.d. (ca. 1889). Pages browned. Hood 117-494 1978 $10

O'RELL, MAX   A Frenchman in America. New York, (1891). Illus., 8vo., 1st ed. Morrill 239-567 1978 $15

O'RELL, MAX   A Frenchman in America; Recollections of Men and Things. New York, 1891. Illus., wrs. Hood 116-708 1978 $17.50

ORFILA, M. P.   A General System of Toxology. 1816-17. 4 parts in 2 vols., some dampstaining, half calf, rebacked. Quaritch 977-61 1978 $95

ORFORD, HORACE WALPOLE, EARL OF
Please turn to
WALPOLE, HORACE, EARL OF ORFORD 1717-1797

ORGEL, S.   Inigo Jones: The Theatre of the Stuart Court, Including the Complete Designs for Productions at Court for the Most Part in the Collection of the Duke of Devonshire... 1973. 2 vols., folio, colour plts., illus., cloth, d.js., cloth slip-case, ltd. to 2,000 no. copies. Quaritch 983-84 1978 $165

THE ORIENTAL Navigator   London, 1801 2nd ed., 4to., orig. calf rebacked, very nice. Paine 78-103 1978 $92.50

ORIGINAL Land Titles in Delaware Commonly Known as the Duke of York Record. Wilmington, n.d. Wrs. MacManus 239-961 1978 $20

L'ORIGINE del Danubio, con lin omi antichi, e moderni di tutti li Fiumi,.... Venice, 1685. 12mo, 2 parts in 1 vol., plates, contemp. vellum over boards, very fine. Gilhofer 75-2 1978 SFr 1,800

ORIGO, IRIS   Allegra. Hogarth Press, 1935. Very good, first English ed. Bell Book 16-686 1978 £5

ORIGO, IRIS   War in Val d'Orcia: a diary. 1947. Near fine, d.w., first English ed. Bell Book 16-687 1978 £5

O'RIORDAN, C.   In London. 1922. 1st ed., signed pres. copy from author to J.D. Beresford, very good, octavo bound in cloth. Hyland 128-304 1978 £15

ORLANDINI, NICOLA   Annuae litterae Societatis Iesu Anni. Rome, 1586. 1st ed., 8vo, vellum, waterstained throughout. Gilhofer 75-84 1978 SFr 750

ORLEANS, E.   Interlude and Other Essays. Toronto, 1934. Hood 117-495 1978 $7.50

ORLEANS, ELIZABETH-CHARLOTTE   Memoires Sur La Code de Louis XIV et de la Regence. Paris, 1823. 8vo, contemp. marbled bds., uncut, from Beckford library. Traylen 88-440 1978 £150

ORLEANS, HENRI D'   Autour du Tonkin. Paris, 1894. 1st ed., plts., 8vo, orig. covers. Van der Peet 127-176 1978 Dfl 75

ORLEANS, HENRI D'   Autour du Tonkin. Paris, 1896. 4th ed., half calf, orig. covers. Van der Peet 127-177 1978 Dfl 55

ORLEANS, HENRI D'   Du Tonkin aux Indes, Janvier 1895 - Janvier 1896. Paris, 1898. 4to, half red mor., maps, illus., plts., orig. French ed. Van der Peet 127-174 1978 Dfl 145

ORLEANS, HENRI D'   Du Tonkin to India, by the sources of the Irawadi, Jan. 1895-Jan. 1896. London, 1898. Large 8vo, cloth, map in color, illus., rare English ed. Van der Peet 127-175 1978 Dfl 145

ORLEANS, LOUIS PHILLIPPE   Extrait de Mon Journal de Mois de Mars, 1815. 1816. 1st. ed., 8vo, orig. wrappers, printed label. Hannas 54-133 1978 £20

ORLEY, ALEXANDER   Neuroradiology. Springfield, 1949. First ed., ex-library. Rittenhouse 49-586 1976 $15

ORME, EDWARD   An Essay on Transparent Prints, and on Transparencies in General. 1807. 4to., text in French and English, frontis., plain and hand-coloured plts., contemp. Russia gilt, joints weak, scarce. Quaritch 983-228 1978 $1,200

ORME, EDWARD   Historic, Military and Naval Anecdotes, of Personal Valour, Bravery and particular Incidents. 1819. Finely coloured aquatint plts., folio, contemp. straight grained mor., lg. paper copy. F. Edwards 1013-399 1978 £600

ORNITZ, SAMUEL   Haunch, Paunch and Jowl. 1923. Austin 79-529 1978 $7.50

ORNITZ, SAMUEL   A Yankee Passional. 1927. Austin 79-530 1978 $11

OROSIUS, PAULUS   Tradotto Di Latino In Volgare Per Giovanni Guerini Da Lanciza Novamente Stampato. Toscolano, c. 1520. 1st ed. in Italian, 8vo, Italic letter, recased in contemp. Italian Black mor., blind-stamped frame, little worn. Quaritch 978-118 1978 $225

ORPEN, WILLIAM   An Onlooker in France 1917-1919. London, 1921. 1st ed., signed pres. copy, full-page pen & ink drawing by author, envelope with author A.L.s, with charcoal sketch, very good or better. Limestone 9-222 1978 $85

ORR, DOROTHY   A History of Education in Georgia. 1950. Bell Wiley's copy. Broadfoot's 44-861 1978 $12.00

ORR, G.   Here Come the Elephants. Idaho, 1943. 8vo,
orig. cloth. Book Chest 17-275 1978 $13.50

ORR, H. WINNETT   Modern Orthopedic Surgery. Springfield, 1949.
D.j., almost mint. Rittenhouse 49-587 1976 $15

ORR, J. W.   Pictorial Guide to the Falls of Niagara... Buffalo, 1842. Illus., orig. cloth, fine. MacManus 239-375 1978 $45

ORR, R.   A Review of the Speech of the Rt. Hon. Wm.
Pitt.. on 31st Ja., 1799. Dublin, 1799. Plain wrs, reprint. Hyland 128-362
1978 £12

ORR, MRS. SUTHERLAND   Life and Letters of Robert Browning. Boston,
1891. 2 vols. Biblo 247-805 1978 $12.50

ORSINI, L.   Trattato del Radio Latino. Rome, 1586. Sm.
8vo., woodcuts, contemp. vellum, second ed. Quaritch 977-166 1978 $175

ORTEGA, LUIS B.   California Stock Horse. 1949. 1st ed., pic.
fabricoid, pic. end sheets, illus., fine copy, autographed by author, scarce.
Dykes 34-62 1978 $35

ORTEGAT, PAUL, S. J.   Philosophie De La Religion. Louvain and
Paris, 1948. 2 vols., tall 8vo., wrs. Salloch 348-182 1978 $20

ORTH, SAMUEL P.   A History of Cleveland, Ohio. Chicago-Cleve-
land, 1910. 1st ed., 2 vols., thick 4to., illus., cloth, fine. MacManus 239-
1107 1978 $75

ORTHODOXY and Charity United. 1745. Contemp. sheep, a little rubbed, 8vo.
George's 635-1108 1978 £7.50

ORTON, C. W. PREVITE-   The Early History of the House of Savoy, 1000-
1233. Cambridge, 1912. Maps in pocket, fore-edge of cloth marked, 8vo. Upcroft 12-322 1978 £12

ORTON, EDWARD   Report of the Geological Survey of Ohio. Columbus, 1888. Orig. binding, clean, covers little spotted, Vol. VI. Hayman
71-574 1978 $7.50

ORTON, HELEN FULLER   The Secret of the Rosewood Box. New York,
1937. First ed., illus. Biblo 247-572 1978 $12.50

ORTON, VREST   Goudy, Master of Letters. Chicago, Black
Cat Press, 1939. 1st ed., ltd. to 500 copies, illus., 8vo., orig. cloth, very
good. Americanist 103-39 1978 $35

ORVALE, P. D'.   Essay sur les Feux D'Artifice Pour le Spectacle
et Pour la Guerre. Paris, 1745. 8vo., plts., marginal wormhole in first 6 leaves,
contemp. calf, gilt spine. Quaritch 977-244 1978 $150

ORWELL, GEORGE   Animal Farm. New York, (1946). Orig. binding, frayed d.j. Wolfe 39-403 1978 $15

ORWELL, GEORGE   Critical Essays. 1946. Very good, worn d.w.,
first English ed. Bell Book 16-688 1978 £30

ORWELL, GEORGE   Dickens, Dali & Others. New York, 1946.
First U.S. ed., very good, worn d.w. Bell Book 16-689 1978 £15

ORWELL, GEORGE   Down and Out in Paris and London. New York,
1933. First U.S. ed., very good, rare. Bell Book 17-703 1978 £85

ORWELL, GEORGE   The English People. 1947. Coloured plts.,
text illus., bds., fine, d.w., first English ed. Bell Book 16-690 1978 £10

ORWELL, GEORGE   The English People. 1947. 1st. ed., sm. 4to,
sm. string mark on one bd. otherwise v.g., d.w. Jarndyce 16-1210 1978 £10.50

ORWELL, GEORGE   Inside the Whale, and other essays. 1940.
Covers dull, good, very scarce, first English ed. Bell Book 16-692 1978 £38.50

ORWELL, GEORGE   Nineteen Eighty-Four. 1949. Fine, d.w.,
first English ed. Bell Book 16-693 1978 £60

ORWELL, GEORGE   Nineteen Eighty-Four. 1949. Very good, worn
d.w., first English ed. Bell Book 17-704 1978 £55

ORWELL, GEORGE   The Road to Wigan Pier. 1937. Plts., very good,
d.w., first English ed., blue cloth, very scarce. Bell Book 17-705 1978 £95

ORWELL, GEORGE   The Road to Wigan Pier. London, 1937. Orange
wrs., 1st ed., worn & soiled. Bradley 49-264 1978 $12.50

ORWELL, GEORGE   The Road to Wigan Pier. London, 1937. 1st.
ed., plts., 8vo, orig. orange limp cloth. Traylen 88-309 1978 £15

ORWELL, GEORGE   Road to Wigan Pier. London, 1937.
1st ed., soiled orange wr., very good or better. Limestone 9-223 1978
$48

ORWELL, GEORGE   The Road to Wigan Pier. 1937. Plts., orig.
limp cloth, very good, first English ed. Bell Book 16-694 1978 £15

ORWELL, GEORGE   Shooting an Elephant and Other Essays. London,
1950. 1st ed. Biblo 251-597 1978 $17.50

ORWELL, GEORGE   Shooting an Elephant and other essays. London,
1950. First ed., orig. binding, spine faded, very nice, portion of d.w. neatly
tipped-in. Rota 211-464 1978 £12

ORWIG, JOSEPH R.   History of the 131st Penn. Volunteers. Williamsport, 1902. Bell Wiley's copy. Broadfoot 46-367 1978 $14

OSBORN, A. W.   Sir Philip Sidney en France. Paris, 1932. Orig.
wraps., octavo, good. Upcroft 10-473 1978 £6.50

OSBORN, GEORGE COLEMAN   John Sharp Williams. Baton Rouge, 1943.
Copy of letter from author, Bell Wiley's copy. Broadfoot's 44-897 1978 $12.00

OSBORN, HENRY FAIRFIELD   The Earth Speaks to Bryan. New York, 1925.
1st ed., orig. cloth, fine. MacManus 239-69 1978 $15

OSBORN, HENRY FAIRFIELD   Men of the Old Stone Age. New York, 1923.
3rd ed., 8vo., sm. cover stains. Morrill 239-569 1978 $10

OSBORN, ROBERT   The Vulgarians. Greenwich, n.d. Oblong
4to, pictures in color. Biblo 251-178 1978 $12.50

OSBORN, SHERARD   Japanese Fragments... London, 1861. 1st. ed.,
cr. 8vo, 6 hand-coloured plts., illus., orig. purple embossed cloth, gilt, neatly
rebacked, retaining orig. backstrip, lib. label removed. Deighton 5-85 1978 £35

OSBORN, SHERARD   The Polar Regions. New York, 1854. Pages
slightly waterstained. Hood 117-106 1978 $50

OSBORN, SHERARD   Quedah; Or, Stray Leaves From a Journal in
Malayan Waters. London, 1857. 1st. ed., 8vo, folding engraved map coloured
in outline, tinted lithograph plts., orig. red cloth, blind stamped design on bds.,
gilt back. Deighton 5-86 1978 £52

OSBORNE, DUFFIELD   Engraved Gems. New York, 1912. Sm. quarto,
32 full-pg. plts. Baldwins' 51-135 1978 $30

OSBORNE, E. ALLEN   In Letters of Red. 1938. Covers little marked,
spine faded, good, first English ed. Bell Book 16-015 1978 £10

OSBORNE, FRANCIS   Politicall Reflections Upon the Government of
the Turks. London, 1656. 1st. ed., 12mo, orig. sheep. Traylen 88-310 1978
£65

OSBORNE, JOSEPH ALEXANDER   Williamsburg in Colonial Times. Richmond,
1936. Signed by author, Bell Wiley's copy. Broadfoot's 44-982 1978 $12

OSBOURNE, KATHARINE D.   Robert Lou's Stevenson in California. Chicago,
1911. Nice, slightly shaken. Desmarais B-603 1978 $35

OSGOOD, HERBERT LEVI   The American Colonies in the 17th Century.
New York, 1904-26. 3 vols., vol. 3 ex-lib. MacManus 239-383 1978 $37.50

O'SHEA, K.   Charles Stewart Parnell; His Love Story & Political
Life. 1914. 1 vols., 1st ed., illus., very good, octavo bound in cloth. Hyland
128-332 1978 £10

O'SHEA, K.   Charles Stewart Parnell; His Love Story and
Political Life. 1914. Ex-lib., good, octavo bound in cloth, reprint. Hyland
128-333 1978 £8

OSLAND, BIRGER   A Long Pull Form Stavanger. 1945. Austin
79-531 1978 $12.50

OSLER, WILLIAM   Aequanimitas. London, 1904. Orig. binding,
printed slip "With the author's compliments" tipped in. Wolfe 39-351 1978 $40

OSLER, WILLIAM   Aequanimitas. London, 1928. Second ed.,
eighth impression, orig. binding. Wolfe 39-352 1978 $40

OSLER, WILLIAM   An Alabama Student and Other Biographical
Essays. Toronto/London, 1908. Frontis. port., orig. binding. Wolfe 39-353
1978 $40

OSLER, WILLIAM   Brief Tributes to his Personality, Influence and
Public Service. Montreal, 1920. Illus., orig. binding. Wolfe 39-349 1978
$50

OSLER, WILLIAM   Diagnosis of Abdominal Tumors. New York,
1897. Rittenhouse 49-592 1976 $30

OSLER, WILLIAM   The Diagnosis of Typhoid Fever. New York,
(1900). 8vo., very good copy in orig. brown cloth, gilt on spine. Zeitlin 245-
179 1978 $25

OSLER, WILLIAM   An Investigation Into the Parasites in the Pork
Supply of Montreal. Montreal, 1883. First ed., inscribed "From the Authors."
Rittenhouse 49-589 1976 $75

OSLER, WILLIAM   Lectures on the Diagnosis of Abdominal Tumors.
New York, 1895. Rittenhouse 49-591 1976 $30

OSLER, WILLIAM   Lectures on the Diagnosis of Abdominal Tumors.
New York, 1899. Orig. binding. Wolfe 39-348 1978 $40

OSLER, WILLIAM   Memorial Number, Appreciations and Reminiscences. Montreal, 1926. No. 906, one of 1500 numbered copies, cover somewhat
worn. Rittenhouse 49-593 1976 $15

OSLER, WILLIAM   Memorial Number, Appreciations and Reminiscences. Montreal, 1926. No. 1347, one of 1500 numbered copies, cover somewhat worn. Rittenhouse 49-594 1976 $25

OSLER, WILLIAM   The Principles and Practice of Medicine. New
York, 1904. Fifth ed., half leather binding worn, chipped top and bottom of spine.
Rittenhouse 49-595 1976 $20

OSLER, WILLIAM   The Principles and Practice of Medicine. New
York/London, 1907. Sixth ed., orig. binding. Wolfe 39-350 1978 $25

OSLER, WILLIAM   The Principles and Practice of Medicine. New
York/London, 1912. Eighth ed., shaken. Rittenhouse 49-596 1976 $10

OSLER, WILLIAM   Science and Immortality. Boston/New York,
1904. Orig. binding. Wolfe 39-354 1978 $25

OSLER, WILLIAM   A Way of Life: an Address Delivered to Yale Students on the Evening of Sunday, April 20th, 1913... New York, (1937). Bds.
Hayman 72-593 1978 $7.50

OSLER, WILLIAM   A Way of Life; an Address Delivered to Yale Students, April 20, 1913. New York, 1937. Hood 116-709 1978 $12.50

OSMASTON, F. P. B.   The Paradise of Tintoretto: an essay. Bognor,
Pear Tree Press, 1910. Plts., cloth-backed bds., covers soiled, good. Bell Book
17-727 1978 £15

OSMOND, J.   History of the Presbytery of Luzerne. State of
Penna. (Wilkes-Barre, 1897). MacManus 239-1595 1978 $15

OSPOVAT, HENRY   The Work of... London, 1911. 4to, orig. cloth,
3 coloured & 60 black/white plts., good. Sexton 7-38 1978 £18

OSSENDOWSKI, FERDINAND The Fire of Desert Folk. London, (1926). Illus.,
8vo, orig. cloth. K Books 239-357 1978 £6

OSSIAN   The Poems of Ossian... Edinburgh, 1805. 1st.
ed., 2 vols., 8vo, contemp. calf, gilt, gully gilt spines, with labels, fine.
Fenning 32-210 1978 £28.50

OSTERVALD, J. F.   Treatise concerning the Causes of the Present
Corruption of Christians, and the Remedies thereof. 1711. 3rd ed., 2 pts. in 1
vol. as issued, contemp. panelled calf, unlettered. George's 635-1109 1978
£8.50

OSTERWEIS, ROLLIN G.   Rebecca Gratz, a Study in Charm. New York,
1935. Illus. MacManus 239-758 1978 $15

OSTRANDER, STEPHEN M.   A History of the City of Brooklyn and Kings
County. Brooklyn, 1894. 2 vols., illus., maps. MacManus 239-1079 1978
$65

O'SULLIVAN, D.   The Irish Free State & Its Senate. 1940. 1st ed.,
proof copy in wr., very good. Hyland 128-311 1978 £7

O'SULLIVAN, SEUMAS PSEUD.
Please turn to
STARKEY, JAMES

OSWALD, F. L.   Zoological Sketches. London, n.d. (ab. 1890).
Sm. 8vo., cloth, frontis., text illus. Van der Peet H-64-513 1978 Dfl 45

OSWALD, FELIX   Alone in Sleeping-Sickness Country. London,
1923. Folding map, plts., 2nd. impression, 8vo, orig. cloth. K Books 239-358
1978 £10

OSWALD, JOHN C.   Benjamin Franklin Printer. 1917. 1st ed.,
frontis. MacManus 239-155 1978 $22.50

OSWALD, JOHN CLYDE   Printing in the Americas. New York, (1937).
Illus., orig. cloth, 1st ed., inscribed by author, fine. MacManus 238-1021
1978 $50

OSWALD, JOHN CLYDE   Printing in the Americas. New York, (1937).
Illus., facsimiles, ex-library, very good, orig. binding. Wolfe 39-403a 1978
$35

OSWEGO. BOARD OF TRADE   Proceedings of the Oswego Board of Trade and
Its Special Committee...on the...Transportation Routes from the West to the Seaboard. Oswego, 1873. Lg. fldg. map on thin paper, excellent cond., sewn,
never bound, front cover lacking. Butterfield 21-93 1978 $45

OTERO, JESUS   A Schoolmaster's Son. Azteca Press, 1947.
Austin 79-531 1978 $12.50

OTIS, FESSENDEN NOTT   Illustrated History of the Panama Railroad...
New York, 1862. Maps, illus., sm. 8vo, orig. cloth, cover slightly faded, 2nd.
ed. Edwards 1012-693 1978 £35

OTIS, HARRISON GRAY   Otis' Letters in Defence of the Hartford Convention, and the People of Massachusetts. Boston, 1824. 8vo., sewn, signature
of J. T. Gilman. Morrill 241-441 1978 $35

OTIS, HARRISON GRAY   Speech of Mr..., on the Restriction of Slavery in
Missouri. Delivered in the Senate...January 25, 1830. N.P., n.d. (Washington? 1820?). Disbound. Hayman 72-711 1978 $27.50

OTIS, JAMES   Toby Tyler or Ten Weeks with a Circus. New
York, (1881). Sq. 16mo., illus., bind. rubbed, 2nd print., orig. bind. Petrilla
13-61 1978 $10

OTTER, W. D.   The Guide: A Manual for the Canadian Militia
(Infantry) Embracing the Interior Economy. Toronto, 1906. 6th. ed. rev. Hood's
115-127 1978 $12.50

OTTER, WILLIAM   The Life and Remains of Edward Daniel Clarke.
1825. Portrait, 2 vols., half calf, 8vo. Howes 194-734 1978 £18

OTTLEY, W. Y.   Engravings of the Marquis of Stafford's Collection
of Pictures in London. 1818. 4 vols., plts., lg. folio, qtr. linen, unlettered.
George's 635-60 1978 £40

OTWAY, THOMAS   The Atheist: Or, the Second Part of the Souldiers
Fortune... London, 1684. 4to., later 3/4 calf and cloth, 1st ed., spine and
corners slightly rubbed, but very good, bookplt. MacManus 238-136 1978
$250

OTWAY, THOMAS   The Complete Works of... Bloomsbury: The
Nonesuch Press, 1926. 3 vols., 4to., buckram-backed bds., paper labels, 1 of
1,250 sets, unnumbered, bds. a bit soiled, uncut, fine. MacManus 238-839
1978 $100

OUDE En Tegenwoordige Staat en Geschiedenis van de Godsdienstplichten, Kerk-
zeden en Gewoontes van alle Volkeren der Waereld, van de Schepping af tot op
Heden, in een Kort Bestek Bijeen Gebracht. Amsterdam, 1787. 2 vols., 8vo.,
orig. bds., engr. plts., spines damaged. Van der Peet H-64-515 1978 Dfl 55

OUIMET, ADOLPHE   Les Contemporains Canadiens. Trois Rivieres,
1858. 24mo., cloth vol., orig. pict. wrappers, caricature frontis. of each subject.
Wolfe 39-403b 1978 $100

OULTON, A.N.   Index to the Statutes at Present in Force In, or
Affecting Ireland, 1310-1838. 1839. Cover stained, text very good, octavo
bound in cloth, reprint. Hyland 128-314 1978 £7

OUR County and Its People. A Descriptive and Biographical Record of Bristol
County, Mass. Boston, 1899. 1st ed., thick 4to., illus., ports., orig. half-
calf, very good. MacManus 239-1015 1978 $45

OUR Flying Navy New York, 1944. 80 color repro., 4to, very good in ragged,
wall-worn dw. Bernard 5-312 1978 $17.50

OUR LIVING and Our Dead. Raleigh, 1874-1876. Vols. 1-3. 3/4 leather, scuffed. Broadfoot 50-357 1978 $225

OUR Memories. Oxford, Daniel Press, 1893. 4to., blue levant mor., gilt panelled back, pres. in gilt on upper cover, little dull, 100 copies prtd. of some numbers. Quaritch 979-107 1978 $115

OUR Merchant Marine. N. P., 1888. 12mo., orig. wrs. Morrill 241-439 1978 $7.50

OUR Native Land. London, 1879. Mounted coloured plts., 4to., black hard-grain mor. gilt, red edges, inner joints strengthened. K Books 244-427 1978 £10

OUR Navy. N. P., n.d. (ca. 1900). 12mo., orig. wrs. Morrill 241-440 1978 $10

OUR Own Country. Cassell, c. 1880. 6 vols., frontispieces, wood-engravings, 4to., half maroon calf, gilt spines. K Books 244-428 1978 £10

OUR Pacific Possessions. Washington, 1861. Orig. pr. wr., 1st ed. Ginsberg 14-863 1978 $100

OURSLER, FULTON   Poor Little Fool. 1928. Austin 82-691 1978 $8.50

OURSLER, FULTON   The Precious Secret. 1947. First ed., d.j. Austin 82-692 1978 $12.50

OURSLER, FULTON   Sandalwood. 1925. Ex-lib. Austin 82-693 1978 $12.50

OURSLER, FULTON   Stepchild of the Moon. 1926. First ed., ex-lib. Austin 82-694 1978 $12.50

OURSLER, WILL   Murder Memo to the Commissioner, the Carl Houston Case. New York, (1950). 4to., illus., orig. wrs., scarce. Biblo 251-451 1978 $17.50

OUTRAM, WILLIAM   De Sacrificiis Libri Duo... Londini, 1677. 1st. ed., 4to, contemp. calf, gilt spine, fine copy. Fenning 32-251 1978 £24.50

OVERBECK, J.   Geschichte der Griechischen Plastik. 1881-82. 4to., new buckram, 2 vols. Allen 234-703 1978 $17.50

OVERBECK, J.   Geschichte der Griechischen Plastik. Leipzig, 1881. 3rd rev'd. ed., 2 vols. in 1, illus., rebound. Biblo BL781-453 1978 $37.50

OVERBROOK PRESS   A Specimen Book of Types, Ornaments and Mis-cellany. Stamford, 1948. Decor. bds., very good, 1 of 50 copies. Dawson's 447-117 1978 $200

OVERBROOK PRESS   The Types, Borders, Rules & Devices of the Press Arranged as a Keepsake. (Stamford), 1934. Marbled bds., fine with bkplt. of T. M. Cleland, 1 of 150 copies. Dawson's 447-118 1978 $85

OVERDYKE, W. DARRELL   The Know-Nothing Party in the South. Baton Rouge, 1950. Bell Wiley's copy. Broadfoot's 44-724 1978 $12.00

OVERS, JOHN   Evenings of a Working Man. 1844. 1st. ed., half title, orig. pink cloth, slightly worn at base of spine, otherwise v.g. Jarndyce 16-509 1978 £32

OVERSTREET, H. A.   The Mature Mind. New York, 1949. 8vo., cloth. Salloch 348-183 1978 $7.50

OVERTON, GRANT   Cargoes For Crusoes. New York & Boston, 1924. 1st printing, illus., portraits, partly unopened, very good or better. Limestone 9-224 1978 $20

OVIATT, EDWIN   The Beginnings of Yale. New Haven, 1916. Illus., orig. cloth, fine. MacManus 239-540 1978 $15

OVIDIUS NASO, PUBLIUS   Ovid's Art of Love; Together with His Remedy of Love. 1776. Plts., 12mo., contemp. sheep, joints cracked. Howes 194-408 1978 £12.50

OVIDIUS NASO, PUBLIUS   Epistles with his Amours. 1719. Engraved frontis. stuck down inside front cover, corner torn from title, 12mo., contemp. calf, rubbed. George's 635-488 1978 $7.50

OVIDIUS NASO, PUBLIUS   Opera Omnia. Amsterdam, 1702. 3 vols., contemp. panelled calf, frontispiece, 8vo. Howes 194-562 1978 £21

OVIDIUS NASO, PUBLIUS   Operum. Amstelodami, 1702. 8vo., full red calf, gilt tooling, chiselled edges, library stamp, ink notes in margins, binding shaved. Van der Peet H-64-516 1978 Dfl 50

OVIDIUS NASO, PUBLIUS   Opera. 1922-24. Vols. 1 & 3 only in 3 vols., some scorings & notes. Allen 234-948 1978 $12.50

OVIEDO Y BANOS, JOSE DE   Historia de la Conquista Y Poblacion de la Provincia de Venezuela. New York, 1940. Illus., 1st print., orig. bind., facs. of rare 1st ed. of 1723. Petrilla 13-63 1978 $12

OVITT, S. W.   The Balloon Section of the American Expeditionary Forces. New Haven, 1919. Portraits, plts., oblong 8vo., orig. cloth, extremely rare. F. Edwards 1013-400 1978 £160

OWEN, CHARLES   The Justice of the Mexican War:.... New York, 1908. 1st ed. Jenkins 116-924 1978 $35

OWEN, DAVID DALE   Report of a Geological Survey of Wisconsin, Iowa, and Minnesota and Incidentally of a Portion of Nebraska Territory. Philadelphia, 1852. Thick 4to, illus., plts., maps, one coloured, some staining, orig. blind stamped green cloth, gilt back. Deighton 5-51 1978 £75

OWEN, DAVID DALE   Second Report of a Geological Reconnoissance of the Middle and Southern Counties of Arkansas, made During 1859 and 1860. Philadelphia, 1860. Engraved & tinted litho. plts., roy. 8vo., orig. cloth, head & tail bands repaired. Edwards 1012-515 1978 £65

OWEN, HENRY   The Modes of Quotation Used by the Evangelical Writers Explained and Vindicated. 1789. 1st. ed., 4to, orig. tree calf, red label, v.g. Jarndyce 16-150 1978 £12.50

OWEN, HUGH J.   Merioneth Volunteers and Local Militia during the Napoleonic Wars, 1795-1816. Dolgelly, (1934). Coloured frontis., plts., 8vo., orig. cloth. F. Edwards 1013-568 1978 £10

OWEN, JOHN   An Humble Testimony Unto the Goodness and Severity of God in His Dealing With Sinful Churches and Nations Etc. 1681. 1st. ed., orig. calf, rebacked, good. Jarndyce 16-20 1978 £15

OWEN, JOHN   Travels Into Different Parts of Europe, In the Years 1791 and 1792. London, 1796. 1st. ed., 2 vols., 8vo, half-titles, one torn, half calf, gilt backs. Deighton 5-138 1978 £45

OWEN, MARY ALICIA   Voodoo Tales as Told among the Negroes of the Southwest. New York, 1893. 1st Amer. ed., 8vo, intro. by Charles Godfrey Leland, Illus. by Juliette A. Owen and Louis Wain, fine copy, scarce. Victoria 34-593 1978 $35

OWEN, W. F. W.   Narrative of Voyages to Explore the Shores of Africa, Arabia and Madagascar... 1833. Woodcuts, plts., 2 vols., half calf, 8vo. Edwards 1012-33 1978 £200

OWEN, WILFRED   Poems. 1920. First ed., portrait frontis., sq. 8vo., orig. cloth, printed label, torn d.w., rare. Howes 194-1082 1978 £75

OWEN, WILFRED   Poems. London, 1920. Nice, d.w., first ed., orig. binding. Rota 212-43 1978 £85

OWEN, WILFRED   Poems. 1931. Portrait, new ed., fine, d.w., orig. cloth, 8vo. Howes 194-1083 1978 £20

OWEN-MADDEN, D.   Revelations of Ireland in the Past Generation. Dublin, 1848. 1st. ed., half titles, orig. brown cloth, slightly rubbed, good. Jarndyce 16-762 1978 £14.50

OWENS, HARRY J.   Doctor Faust. Woodcuts, prtd. on fine paper, 1 of 350 copies, 8vo., pattern paper over bds., cloth spine, t.e.g. Battery Park 1-160 1978 $75

OWENS, JOHN ALGERNON   Sword and Pen. Philadelphia, 1880. 8vo., illus., 1st ed., orig. cloth. Morrill 241-442 1978 $12.50

OWENS, WILLIAM A.   Texas Folk Songs. Austin, 1950. 1st ed., very good in d.j. Jenkins 116-1036 1978 $25

OWENSON, SYDNEY   The Wild Irish Girl; a National Tale. Philadelphia, 1807. Old sprinkled calf, gilt label, spine mended, endpapers lacking, good copy, grained mor. and bds., 1st Amer. ed. Petrilla 13-64 1978 $65

OWGAN, HENRY   The Long Run, A Novel. 1860. 1st. ed., orig. red cloth, good. Jarndyce 16-922 1978 £24

OWSLEY, FRANK LAWRENCE   King Cotton Diplomacy. Foreign Relations of the Confederate States of America. Chicago, (1931). 1st ed. MacManus 239-1852 1978 $12.50

OWSLEY, FRANK LAWRENCE   Plain Folk of the Old South. Baton Rouge, 1949. Long presentation from author to Bell Wiley. Broadfoot's 44-726 1978 $16

OXBERRY, WILLIAM   Oxberry's Anecdotes of the Stage.   1827. 8vo.,
orig. printed bds., uncut, portrait. P. M. Hill 142-225 1978 £28

OXFORD And Cambridge Miscellany Poems.   London, (1708). Allegorical engraved
frontis, 8vo, old panelled calf, rebacked, good copy, sm. hole on page 119.
Traylen 88-311 1978 £80

OXFORD History of Music.   Oxford, 1901-05. 6 vols., one cover stained, 8vo.,
musical settings in text. George's 635-1411 1978 £17.50

OXFORD Poetry, 1914-1916.   Oxford, 1917. 1st ed. Biblo 251-599 1978 $15

OXFORD UNIVERISTY   Illustrated Catalogue of a Loan Exhibition of
Portraits of English Historical Personages Who Died Between 1625 and 1714 Exhibited
in the Examination Schools. Oxford, 1905. 4to, plts., buckram-backed bds.,
rubbed in places, sm. stain in margin of few leaves.   Upcroft 10-475 1978 £7

OXFORD UNIVERSITY. INSTITUTE OF STATISTICS   The Economics of Full Employment. Oxford, 1944. Biblo BL781-863 1978 $8

OXYRHYNCHUS Papyri. 1911-12. Vols. 8-9 only, corners darkened. Allen
234-714 1978 $20

OZANAM, JACQUES   Dictionnaire Mathematique, Ou Idee Generale
Des Mathematiques. Amsterdam, 1691. Engr. plts., engr. frontis., thick 4to.,
contemp. vellum. Salloch 345-138 1978 $125

OZANAM, JACQUES   Recreations Mathematiques et Physiques, qui
Contiennent Plusieurs Problemes D'Arithmetique.... Paris, 1694. 2 vols., 8vo.,
engrav. plts., fine, contemp. red mor., gilt lozenge centre pieces, first ed., fully
gilt spines, gilt edges. Quaritch 977-127 1978 $1,000

OZANAM, JACQUES   A Treatise of Fortification. 1727. 8vo., contemp. panelled calf, second ed., plts. F. Edwards 1013-593 1978 £75

OZANNE, T. D.   The South As It Is. London, 1863. Ex libris,
hinges cracked, sev. pgs. taped, Bell Wiley's copy. Broadfoot's 44-727 1978
$14

OZINDE, J. B.   The Theory and Practice of the French Tongue.
1756. Fine, contemp. calf, crimson label, first ed., 8vo. Howes 194-409 1978
£32

P

PACIAUDI, PAULO   Monvmenta Peloponnesia Commentariis Explicata. Romae, 1761. 2 vols. in 1, 4to., half calf, lower joint broken, illus., very good. King 7-200 1978 £40

PACIFIC Cumberland Presbyter. Almo, Calif., 1860-1861. Orig. wrps., 1st ed. Ginsberg 16-832 1978 $50.00

THE PACIFIC Northwest. New York, 1883. Folding map, orig. pr. wr., 1st ed. Ginsberg 14-858 1978 $75

PACIFIC Northwest Quarterly. N.P., 1906-1973. Few issued in Xerox, unbound. Ginsberg 14-1035 1978 $725

PACIFIC Rail-Road:A Review of the Reports of the Committees of the Senate and the House...With Remarks by the Author of the Review. New Orleans, 1850. Half mor. Ginsberg 14-864 1978 $75

PACIFICO, ANTONIO   Cronica Veneta Sacra e Profana. Venezia, 1736. 12mo., bds., calf spine rubbed, plts. King 7-201 1978 £50

PACKARD, FRANCIS R.   Life and Times of Ambroise Pare, 1510-1590. New York, 1921. Bit worn. Rittenhouse 49-599 1976 $15

PACKARD, FRANCIS R.   Some Account of the Pennsylvania Hospital. Philadelphia, 1938. First ed. Rittenhouse 49-600 1976 $50

PACKARD, FRANCIS R.   Text-book of Diseases of the Nose, Throat and Ear for the Use of Students and General Practitioners. Philadelphia, 1909. Library marks. Rittenhouse 49-598 1976 $20

PACKARD, J. F.   Grant's Tour Around the World. Cincinnati, 1880. Rebound, clean. Hayman 71-611 1978 $10

PADEN, IRENE D.   Prairie Schooner Detours. New York, 1949. First ed., illus., fine, d.w. Biblo 247-248 1978 $14.50

PADEN, IRENE D.   The Wake of the Prairie Schooner. New York, 1943. Illus. by author. Biblo 248-282 1978 $15

PADMORE, GEORGE   Africa and World Peace. London, 1937. Cr. 8vo, orig. cloth. K Books 239-359 1978 £5

PADOVANI, FABRIZIO   Tractatus duo Alter de Ventis Alter Perbrevis de Terraemotu. Bologna, 1601. Folio, engravings, calf, antique style, scarce, woodcut initial letters. Quaritch 977-245 1978 $1,200

PAGAN, MATHIS   La Gloria et l'honore di ponte Togliati.... 1884. Sm. cr. 4to. George's 635-1220 1978 £20

PAGANO, GRACE   The Encyclopaedia Britannica Collection of Contemporary American Painting. Chicago, 1946. 2nd ed., d.w., sq. 4to., illus. in color & b/w. Biblo 251-234 1978 $20

PAGANO, JO   Golden Wedding. 1943. Austin 79-536 1978 $10

PAGE, C. E.   The Natural Cure of Consumption, Constipation, Bright's Disease, Neuralgia, Rheumatism...A Health Manual for the People. New York, 1884. Sm. 8vo., 1st ed. Morrill 239-193 1978 $12.50

PAGE, F. B.   Prairiedom: Rambles and Scrambles in Texas or New Estremadiera. New York, 1846. Calf, 2nd issue. Jenkins 116-1037 1978 $135

PAGE, HAMILTON   The Lady Resident. London, 1880. 3 vols. in 1, 8vo, original blue cloth, decorated in black, spine gilt (publisher's remainder binding), 1st ed., very good copy. Ximenes 47-221 1978 $60

PAGE, I. MARSHALL   Old Buckingham By the Sea on the Eastern Shore of Maryland. Philadelphia, 1936. Illus., 1st ed., scarce. MacManus 239-1839 1978 $20

PAGE, IRVINE H.   Chemistry of the Brain. Baltimore, 1937. Library marks. Rittenhouse 49-601 1976 $10

PAGE, JESSE   Samuel Crowther, the Slave Boy Who Became Bishop of the Niger. London, n.d., (1889). Orig. pict. cloth, stamped in colors, illus. Americanist 102-16 1978 $20

PAGE, P. K.   As Ten as Twenty. Toronto, (1946). Orig. binding. Wolfe 39-404 1978 $30

PAGE, R. P.   Further Chronicles of the Houghton Fishing Club 1908-1931. London, 1932. Folio, buckram, uncut, illus., t.e.g., ltd. to 350 copies. Wolfe 39-14 1978 $50

PAGE, THOMAS NELSON   The Negro: The South Erner's Problem. NY, 1904. Bell Wiley's copy. Broadfoot's 44-728 1978 $20.00

PAGE, THOMAS NELSON   The Old Gentleman of the Black Stock. New York, 1900. Illus., 1st illus. ed., 1st issue, edges rubbed, bookplt. Biblo BL781-1099 1978 $12.50

PAGE, THOMAS NELSON   The Old Gentleman of the Black Stock. New York, 1900. Cloth, enlarged ed. Hayman 73-200 1978 $7.50

PAGE, THOMAS NELSON   The Old South. New York, 1894. Cloth. Hayman 73-592 1978 $8.50

PAGE, THOMAS NELSON   Social Life in Old Virginia Before the War. 1897. Illus., first ed., very good. Austin 82-695 1978 $20

PAGE, VICTOR W.   The Modern Gasoline Automobile. New York, 1913. Cloth, little worn, dampstaining. Hayman 73-593 1978 $8.50

THE PAGEANT of Newark-on-Trent in Nottinghamshire. 1927. Illus., limited to only 200 copies, good. Nestler Rare 78-75 1978 $25

PAGES, ALPHONSE   Les Grands Poetes Francais. Paris, 1874. Folio, half roan, marbled bds., spine gilt, good uncut copy, portraits, woodcuts. King 7-372 1978 £20

PAGES, PIERRE MARIE FRANCOIS   Travel Round the World in the Years 1767-71. London, 1791. 2 vols., 3/4 mor., first ed. in Eng. Jenkins 116-1038 1978 $250

PAGES, PIERRE MARIE FRANCOIS   Voyages Autour Du Monde.... Paris, 1782. 3 vols. in 2, fldg. maps, colored fldg. plts., 8vo., orig. bds., uncut. Salloch 345-139 1978 $200

PAGES, PIERRE MARIE FRANCOIS   Voyages Autour De Monde.... Berne, 1783. 2nd ed., 3 vols. in 1, contemp. calf, rubbed, sm. split in 1 joint, no half-titles to vol. 1 & 2, orig. cloth, 8vo. Edwards 1012-406 1978 £75

PAGES et Croquis, 1914-18. 1918. Ltd. ed., wood engravings, 5 pts., folio, orig. wrappers in portfolio as issued, rubbed. George's 635-848 1978 £7.50

PAGET, J. OTHO   The Art of Beagling. London, (1932). Illus. Baldwins' 51-550 1978 $10

PAGET, JOHN   Paradoxes & Puzzles: Historical, Judicial and Literary. 1874. 1st. ed., half title, orig. brown cloth, fine. Jarndyce 16-923 1978 £14.50

PAGET, STEPHEN   John Hunter, Man of Science and Surgeon. New York, 1897. Rittenhouse 49-602 1976 $15

PAGET, VIOLET   Ariadne in Mantua; a romance. Oxford and London, 1903. Wrappers, somewhat faded and worn, very good, first ed. Rota 211-299 1978 £15

PAIGE, A.   Mental and Physical Electropathy, or Electricity. Philadelphia, 1852. 8vo., orig. wrs., margins dampstained, 1st ed. Morrill 239-199 1978 $15

PAINE, ALBERT BIGELOW   The Hollow Tree. New York, 1898. 1st ed., profusely illus. by J. M. Conde, boards, one of scarcest Blanck titles, very good copy. Victoria 34-594 1978 $150

PAINE, ALBERT BIGELOW   Mark Twain. 1912. 3 vols., illus., ex-lib. Austin 82-1016 1978 $20

PAINE, ALBERT BIGELOW   Mark Twain, A Biography. New York, 1912. 4 vols. in 2, Bell Wiley's copy. Broadfoot's 44-729 1978 $16

PAINE, ALBERT BIGELOW   Mr. Rabbit's Wedding. New York, (1917). 1st ed., plates by J. M. Conde, colored pictorial cover plate on cloth, very good, scarce. Victoria 34-595 1978 $30

PAINE, MARTYN   Physiology of the Soul and Instinct, as Distinguished from Materialism... New York, 1872. Cloth. Hayman 72-595 1978 $10

PAINE, NATHANIEL   A List of Early American Broadsides, 1860-1800, Belonging to the Library of the American Antiquarian Society. Worcester, 1897. 3/4 mor., slightly rubbed, ltd. to 100 copies. MacManus 238-1023 1978 $40

PAINE, RALPH D.   Joshua Barney. A Forgotten Hero of Blue Water. New York, (1924). Illus., d.j. MacManus 239-1778 1978 $10

PAINE, THOMAS   Common Sense; Addressed to the Inhabitants of America...A New Edition..to Which is Added an Appendix...London. London, 1776. Bound copy, binding worn, good. Nestler Rare 78-174 1978 $225

PAINE, THOMAS   The Complete Writings of... New York, (1945). Fine, boxed, d.w., 2 vols., Biblo 247-32 1978 $17.50

PAINE, THOMAS   Rights of Man. London, 1791. Orig. binding, wanting p. 91-92, 129-130, 151-162. Wolfe 39-407 1978 $25

PAINE, THOMAS   Rights of Man; Part the Second. London, 1792. Title-page cover, sewn. Wolfe 39-408 1978 $25

PAIXHANS, H. J.   Experiences Faites par La Marine Francaise. Paris, 1825. 8vo., contemp. half calf. F. Edwards 1013-167 1978 £20

PAJOT-DES-CHARMES, C.   l'Art du Blanchiment des Toiles, fils et Cotons de Tout Genre. Paris, (1800). 8vo., engr. fldg. plts., modern cloth, inscrip. & lib. blindstamp on title, light foxing, plts. foxed, dampstaining, but good copy, 2nd ed. Norman 5-215 1978 $150

PAKSTAS, KAZYS   Lithuania and World War II. Chicago, 1947. Paper, map. Austin 79-537 1978 $20

PALACE, Museum, Gardens. c. 1852. Plts., text illus., lg. 8vo., orig. coarse-grained mor.-backed cloth, gilt edges. Howes 194-1415 1978 £20

THE PALACE Oᶜ Glass & The Gathering of the People. (1851). 1st. ed., orig. blue cloth, gilt imprint of Crystal Palace, little faded. Jarndyce 16-449 1978 £6.50

PALACE Plays. London, 1930. Fine in worn & chipped d.w. Desmarais B-326 1978 $12.50

PALARDY, JEAN   The Early Furniture of French Canada. Toronto, 1963. Folio, first ed., orig. binding, d.j. Wolfe 39-409 1978 $125

PALATINO, GIOVANBATTISTA   Libro..nel Qual s'Insegna a Scrivere Ogni Sorte Lettera... Rome, 1547. 8vo., old calf, old ink scribbling on title, woodcut portrait and initials. Schumann 511-43 1978 sFr 4,900

PALATINO, GIOVANBATTISTA   Libro... nel Qual s'Insegna a Scrivere Ogni Sorte Lettera... Rome, 1548. Cont. calf, fine. 8vo., woodcut initials, all pages framed by rules in red ink. Schumann 511-44 1978 sFr 3,850

PALENCIA, ISABEL DE   I Must Have Liberty. New York, 1940. First ed. Biblo 247-677 1978 $13.50

PALEOTTI, ALFONSO   Esplicatione del Lenzvolo,.... Bologna, 1598. 4to, engraved plate, double-page folding woodcut, orig. limp vellum, gilt borders, 1st ed. Quaritch 978-119 1978 $1,500

PALEY, WILLIAM   The Principles of Moral and Political Philosophy. London, 1785. 4to., contemp. brown calf, gilt back with mor. label, marbled edges, 1st ed. Gilhofer 74-19 1978 sFr 900

PALEY, WILLIAM   The Principles of Moral and Political Philosophy. 1791. 8th. ed., 2 vols., 8vo., cont. calf, very good. Fenning 32-252 1978 £10.50

PALEY, WILLIAM   A View of the Evidences of Christianity in three parts and the Horae Paulinae. Cambridge, 1850. New ed., prize calf gilt, 8vo. K Books 244-251 1978 £7

PALFREY, FRANCIS W.   The Antietam & Fredericksburg. New York, 1882. Bell Wiley's copy. Broadfoot 46-194 1978 $10

PALFREY, JOHN GORHAM   History of New England. Boston, 1876-1890. 5 vols. Baldwins' 51-403 1978 $75

PALFREY, JOHN GORHAM   History of New England. Boston, 1892. 5 vols., illus., very fine set, orig. cloth. MacManus 239-384 1978 $125

PALGRAVE, F.   The Rise and Progress of the English Commonwealth. 1832. 2 vols., 4to., covers a little stained. George's 635-733 1978 £25

PALGRAVE, F. T.   Gems of English Art of this Century. London, 1868. 24 plts. printed in colours by Leighton Brothers, 4to., cloth, loose in case. Traylen 88-379 1978 £15

PALGRAVE, R. H. I.   Dictionary of Political Economy. 1901-08. 3 vols., 8vo. George's 635-313 1978 £21

PALISSY, BERNARD   Oeuvres... Paris, 1777. Thick tall 4to., 1/2 mor. Salloch 345-140 1978 $500

PALISSY, BERNARD   Les Oeuvres de Maistre Bernard Palissy... Niort, 1888. 2 vols., marbled bds., 8vo., buckram backs, orig. wrs., minor foxing. Quaritch 983-114 1978 $240

PALLADINO, L. B.   Indian and White in the Northwest: A History of Catholicity in Montana, 1831-1891. Lancaster, 1922. 2nd. ed., portraits, illus., 8vo, orig. cloth. Edwards 1012-516 1978 £20

PALLADIO, ANDREA   Architecture.... Venise, 1740. Engraved frontis., maps, 3 vols., folio, full calf. George's 635-87 1978 £100

PALLADIO, ANDREA   Fouᵣ Books of Architecture by Andrea Palladio. London, 1755. Folio, calf, new back, plts., very good. King 7-373 1978 £300

PALLADIO, ANDREA   I Quattro Libri Dell' Architettura di Andrea Palladio. Venice, 1581. 2nd ed., sm. folio, woodcuts, old vellum. Quaritch 978-120 1978 $850

PALLAS, P.   Novae Species Quadrupedam E Glirium Ordine, cum illus. variis...animalium. Erlangae, 1778. Ex-lib, newer binding, leather spined, 8vo., text only. Book Chest 17-277 1978 $40

PALLAS, PETER SIMON   Travels Through the Southern Provinces of the Russian Empire, 1793-94. 1802. 1st. ed., folding maps, plts., mostly coloured, 2 vols., 4to, half calf, slight offsetting. Edwards 1012-212 1978 $450

PALLAS, PETER SIMON   Travels Through the Southern Provinces of the Russian Empire...1793 and 1794. 1812. 2 vols., 4to., maps, plts., contemp. calf. Quaritch 983-350 1978 $750

PALLAVICINO, FERRANTE   Baccinata overo Battarella per le Api Barberini. 1644. 12mo., vellum, paper discoloured throughout. King 7-73 1978 £40

PALLAVICINO, SFORZA   Lettere. Venezia, 1825. Sm. 8vo., marbled bds., calf spine, portrait frontis., very good. King 7-202 1978 £15

PALLAVICINO, SFORZA   Trattato dello Stile e del Dialogo del Padre Sforza Pallavino della Compagnia di Gesu. Modena, 1819. 8vo., marbled bds., calf spine, very good. King 7-203 1978 £15

PALLISER, MRS. BURY
Please turn to
PALLISER, FANNY MARRYAT

PALLISER, FANNY MARRYAT   Historic de la Dentelle. Paris, c. 1867. Plts., some coloured, text illus., roy. 8vo., half red mor., dec. spine. K Books 244-252 1978 £40

PALLISER, FANNY MARRYAT   History of Lace. 1865. 1st. ed., coloured plts., illus., 8vo., orig. cloth, gilt, edges gilt, nice copy. Fenning 32-253 1978 £30

PALLISER, HUGH   The Speech...In a Committee of the House of Commons on Monday the 4th of December, 1780. (c. 1780). 8vo., wrs. F. Edwards 1013-168 1978 £10

PALLISER, JOHN   Solitary Rambles and Adventures of a Hunter in the Prairies. London, 1853. Illus., frontis and plates, half mor., 1st ed. Ginsberg 14-871 1978 $125

PALLU DE LA BARRIERE, L.   Histoire de l'Expedition de Cochinchine en 1861. Paris, 1888. Nouv. ed., large 8vo, maps, orig. covers.   Van der Peet 127-179 1978 Dfl 80

PALMER, ALBERT W.   Orientals in American Life.   1934.   Paper. Austin 79-539 1978 $8.50

PALMER, ALONZO B.   A Treatise on the Science and Practice of Medicine or the Pathology and Therepeutics of Internal Diseases.   New York, 1882. 2 vols., leather, little scuffed.   Hayman 71-612 1978 $10

PALMER, BENJAMIN F.   The Diary of Benjamin F. Palmer, Privateersman. Connecticut, 1914. Wr., illus., limited to only 102 copies.   Nestler Rare 78-25 1978 $45

PALMER, BENJAMIN MORGAN   The Life and Letters of James Henley Thornwell.   Richmond, 1875. Cover speckled, Bell Wiley's copy.   Broadfoot's 44-924 1978 $16

PALMER, ELIHU 1764-1806   Principles of Nature.   London, 1819.   First English ed., contemp. calf, upper joint cracked, 8vo.   Howes 194-410 1978 £15

PALMER, FANNY PURDY   Sonnets.   San Francisco, Tomoye Press, 1909. One of 250 copies, 8vo., bds., prtd. on Fabriano paper made in Italy.   Battery Park 1-210 1978 $50

PALMER, FREDERICK   Bliss, Peacemaker.   The Life and Letters of General Tasker Howard Bliss.   New York, 1934. 1st ed., illus., orig. cloth, d.j., very good.   MacManus 239-722 1978 $12.50

PALMER, FREDERICK   John J. Pershing, General of the Armies.   Harrisburg, (1948). Portrait.   Biblo 247-767 1978 $15

PALMER, GEORGE   Kidnapping in the South Seas.   Edinburgh, 1871. Cloth, shaken, little worn.   Dawson's 127-283 1978 $125

PALMER, H. R.   The Song Queen.   Chicago, 1868. Wrs., moderate wear.   Hayman 73-283 1978 $17.50

PALMER, JAMES E., JR.   Carter Glass, Unreconstructed Rebel.   A Biography.   Roanoke, 1938. Illus.   Biblo BL781-202 1978 $10

PALMER, ROBERT R.   The Procurement and Training of Ground Combat Troops.   1948.   Austin 80-248 1978 $47.50

PALMER, ROBERT ROSWELL   The Army Ground Forces, the Procurement and Training of Ground Combat Troops, US Army in WW II.   Washington, 1948. Presen. copy from other authors to Wiley.   Bell Wiley's copy.   Broadfoot 46-554 1978 $15

PALMER, ROSE A.   The North American Indians...   New York, 1929. Illus. with 85 plts. & text figures.   Hood's 115-762 1978 $60

PALMER, ROSE A.   The North American Indians.   New York, 1929. Illus. with plts. & text figures.   Hood 117-696 1978 $60

PALMER, SAMUEL   An English Version of the Eclogues of Virgil. 1883. Folio, lg. paper, plts. designed by Palmer, Japanese vellum, uncut, bind. restored, ltd. to 135 no. copies.   Quaritch 983-229 1978 $1,900

PALMER, SAMUEL   An English Version of the Eclogues of Virgil. London, 1884. 2nd. ed., plts., folio.   Traylen 88-398 1978 £150

PALMER, SAMUEL   St. Pancras; Being Antiquarian, Topographical, and Biographical Memoranda.   1870. 1st. ed., orig. dark green cloth, good. Jarndyce 16-827 1978 £12.50

PALMER, T. S.   Index Generum Mamalium: A List of the genera and families of Mammals.   1904. Ex-lib, 8vo, orig. cloth.   Book Chest 17-293 1978 $75

PALMER, T. S.   The Jack Rabbits of the United States.   Washington, 1896. Wr.   Jenkins 116-1040 1978 $8.50

PALMER, THOMAS   An Essay of the Meanes How to Make Our Travailes,...   London, 1606. 1st Ed., small quarto, disbound, four-wing cloth wr. with a quarter brown mor slipcase, gilt lettering.   Totteridge 29-77 1978 $375

PALMER, THOMAS   Flores Omnium Pene Doctorum...   Lyons, Roville, 1567. Thick 12mo., pigskin.   Salloch 348-184 1978 $175

PALMER, W. SCOTT   Michael Fairless.   London, 1913. 1st ed., portraits, very good or better.   Limestone 9-103 1978 $13.50

PALMER, WILLIAM   Verbatim Report of the Trial of William Palmer. London, 1856. Binders cloth, 8vo.   K Books 244-430 1978 £16

PALMYRA, Wayne County, New York.   (Rochester), 1907. Illus., 12mo., orig. wrs., 1st ed.   Morrill 241-416 1978 $10

PALOU, FRANCISCO   The Expedition into California of the Venerable Padre Fray Junipero Serra and His Companions in the Year 1769.   San Francisco, 1934. Illus., orig. boards, ltd. to 400 numbered and signed by Watson.   Ginsberg 14-165 1978 $45

PALTO ALTO The Town of the Leland Stanford Junior University.   N.P., n.d. (c. 1900). Wrps.   Hayman 71-79 1978 $8.50

PALOMARES, FRANCISCO ZAVIER DE SANTIAGO   Arte Nueva de Escribir, inventada por el Insigne Maestro Pedro Diaz Morante,....   Madrid, 1776. 1st ed., folio, engraved plates, contemp. calf, rebacked expertly, new endpapers.   Bennett 20-157 1978 $750

PALOU, FRANCISCO   Relacion Historica de la Vida.....   Mexico, 1787. Plate, folding map, full vellum, half mor. slipcase, 1st ed.   Ginsberg 14-915 1978 $1,500

PALTSITS, VICTOR HUGO   Minutes of the Commissioners for Detecting and Defeating Conspiracies in the State of New York.   Albany, 1909. 4to., ex-lib., but good.   Butterfield 21-382 1978 $27.50

PALTSITS, VICTOR HUGO   Minutes of the Executive Council...Administration of Francis Lovelace 1668-1673.   Albany, 1910. 4to., plts., lg. fldg. reprints of 17th Century maps in pockets.   Butterfield 21-137 1978 $25

PALTSITS, VICTOR HUGO   Minutes of the Executive Council of the Province of New York...   Albany, 1910. Documents 1 to 48, 2 vols., thick sm. 4to., ports., plts.   Biblo BL781-170 1978 $18.50

PALTSITS, VICTOR HUGO   Narrative of American Voyages and Travels of Captain William Owen, R.N., and Settlement of the Island of Campobello in the Bay of Fundy, 1766-1771.   New York, 1942. Maps, illus., card cover. Hood 117-266 1978 $50

PALUDAU-MULLER, FREDERIK   The Fountain of Youth.   1867. Frontis, illus., 1/2 morocco, rubbed.   Eaton 45-380 1978 £5

PALUK, WILLIAM   Canadian Cossacks; Essays, Articles and Stories on Ukrainian-Canadian Life.   Winnipeg, 1943. Card cover, ex-lib.   Hood 116-431 1978 $10

PAMBOUR, FRANCOIS MARIE, COMTE GUYONNEAU DE Please turn to GUYONNEAU DE PAMBOUR, FRANCOIS MARIE CCMTE

PAN The Pilgrim: A Vision of Judgment (In Verse).   1877. 1st. ed., plts., illus., coloured printed wrapper, preserved, 4to, roan-backed bds., spine worn, sound & fine internally.   Fenning 32-254 1978 £8.50

PANCIROLI, GUIDO 1523-99   Rerum Memorabilium.   Amberg, 1660. 2 parts in 1 vol., sm. 4to., contemp.sprinkled calf, some age-staining, very good. Howes 194-1441 1978 £65

PANCOAST, HENRY K.   The Head and Neck in Roentgen Diagnosis. Springfield, 1940.   Rittenhouse 49-610 1976 $30

PANCOAST, JOSEPH   A Treatise on Operative Surgery.   Philadelphia, 1846. Second ed., old leather bds. present, but separated.   Rittenhouse 49-609 1976 $12

PANETTA, GEORGE   We Ride a White Donkey.   1944.   Austin 79-540 1978 $10

PANGBORN, J. G.   The New Rocky Mountain Tourist.   Chicago, 1878. Folio, plts., orig. pict pr. wr., 3rd ed.   Ginsberg 14-872 1978 $125

PANHANDLE-PLAINS Historical Review.   Canyon, 1929-1975. 43 vols., complt. set except for 5 vols., fine, mostly mint.   Jenkins 116-1042 1978 $375

PANNETIEE, A.   Lexique francais-Cambodgien. Phom Penh, n.d. (c. 1900). Nouv. ed., large 8vo, rare, orig. covers. Van der Peet 127-180 1978 Dfl 150

PANNETON, J.-E.   Un Sanctuaire Canadien. Montreal, 1897. Wrs. Hood 117-361 1978 $7.50

PANOFSKY, ERWIN   Albrecht Duer. Princeton Univ. Press, 1945. 2nd. ed., 2 vols., 4to. Baldwins' 51-138 1978 $75

PANUNZIO, CONSTANTINE M.   The Soul of an Immigrant. 1921. 1st ed., inscr'd by author. Austin 79-541 1978 $15

PANZANO Y ABOS, MARTINO   De Hispanorum Literatura. Torino, 1758. 1st ed., quarto, full contemporary flecked calf, gilt spine panels, large-margined, fine, rare. Bennett 20-158 1978 $260

PAOLI, PAOLO ANTONIO   Avanzi della Antichita che esistono a Pozzuoli, Cuma e Baia. (Napoli, 1768). Lg. folio, bds. rubbed, half vellum, some damp staining, very good uncut copy, first ed. King 7-204 1978 £500

PAPACINO D'ANTONI, ALESSANDRO VITTORIO   Examen de la Poudre. 1773. Plts., 8vo., old calf, rebacked. F. Edwards 1013-401 1978 £75

PAPACINO D'ANTONI, ALESSANDRO VITTORIO   A Treatise on Gun-Powder. 1789. 8vo., plts., contemp. calf. F. Edwards 1013-594 1978 £300

PAPANICOLAOU, GEORGE N.   Diagnosis of Uterine Cancer by the Vaginal Smear. New York, 1943. Rittenhouse 49-612 1976 $20

PAPANIN, IVAN   Life on an Icefloe. New York, 1939. Trans. from Russian, illus. Hood 117-107 1978 $20

PAPER Industries Inquiry Committee, April 1919. Sm. folio, full lea., copy belonged to Captain Nuttal, with signature. Battery Park 1-452 1978 $250

PAPERS Relating to the Court of Chancery in Ireland. 1819. Unopened, orig. wr., very good. Hyland 128-408 1978 £10

PAPERS Relative to Recruiting in the United States. 1856. Sm. folio, modern blue cloth. Edwards 1012-518 1978 £40

PAPINOT, E.   Dictionnaire d'Historie et de Geographie du Japon... Tokyo, n.d. (c. 1906). Cloth, leather spine and tips, worn. Dawson's 449-172 1978 $55

PAPINOT, E.   Dictionary of the History and Geography of Japan. Illus., cloth, covers bleached, binding loosening. Dawson's 449-171 1978 $40

PAPPUS OF ALEXANDRIA   Frederici Commandini.... Pesaro, 1602. Folio, contemp. calf, woodcuts, third issue of first Latin translation. Gurney 75-80 1978 £150

PAPWORTH, J. B.   Select Views of London: with Historical and Descriptive Sketches of Some of the Most Interesting of Its Public Buildings. Ackermann, 1816. Imp. 8vo., coloured plts., fine copy, contemp. half calf, old backstrip laid down. Quaritch 983-351 1978 $4,000

PAPYRO-Plastics, or the Art of Modelling in Paper: Instructive Amusement for Young Persons of Both Sexes. London, 1825. Color frontis., fldg. plts., sq. 16mo., orig. pink bds., 2nd ed., Harry Houdini's copy. Argosy Special-67 1978 $150

PARACELSUS   Opera Omnia Medico-Chemico-Chirurgica. Geneva, 1658. 3 vols. in 2, folio, portr., contemp. vellum, spine of Vol. 2 repaired, usual foxing & browning because of poor quality paper, very good set, best & most complete Latin ed. Norman 5-*43 1978 $1,250

PARACELSUS   Samtliche Werke. Jena, 1926-32. 4 vols., lg. 8vo., frontis portr., orig. cloth, gilt, cover of Vol. 4 spotted, but very good set, 1st ed. in Modern German. Norman 5-*44 1978 $200

PARACELSUS   Versuch einer Kritik der Echtheit der Paracelsischen Schriften. Berlin, 1894-99. 2 vols. in 3, 8vo., buckram, orig. prtd. wrs. bound in, uncut, fine set, from the library of Henry Sigerist with bklabel & signature, 1st ed. Norman 5-216 1978 $150

PARADIN, CLAUDIUS   The Heroicall Devises of M. Clavdivs Paradin Canon of Beaulieu. London, 1591. 16mo., in 8's, woodcut emblematic figures, minor marginal defects, outer margins cut a little close, calf antique, rare. Quaritch 978-121 1978 $2,400

PARDEE, HAROLD E. B.   Clinical Aspects of the Electrocardiogram. New York, 1933. Third ed. Rittenhouse 49-613 1976 $10

PARDOE, JULIA   The Beauties of the Bosphorus. 1838. First ed., plts., portrait, map, 4 parts, 4to., orig. glazed pict. bds. and qtr. roan. Howes 194-1366 1978 £65

PARDOE, JULIA   The Romance of the Harem. Philadelphia, 1839. 1st Amer. ed., 2 vols., orig. cloth, paper labels, scuffed, good. Greene 78-92 1978 $50

PARE, AMBROISE   Trattato della Peste.... Bologna, 1720. 12mo., old pasteboards, uncut, woodcut, first Italian ed. Gurney 75-81 1978 £50

PAREDES, MARIANO   Manifesto Del Exmo. Mexico, 1846. Original printed wrappers, fine. Jenkins 116-1045 1978 $125

PARENT, ANNE   De La Nature Et Propriete Des Animaux. Paris, 1600. 8vo., contemp. calf, gilt borders on covers, gilt-tooled spine, rare, translated into French. Salloch 345-148 1978 $400

PARENT, ETIENNE   Discours. Quebec, 1878. Worn. Hood 116-710 1978 $7.50

THE PARENT'S Cabinet of Amusement and Instruction. 1859. 2 full pg. coloured illus., text illus., orig. cloth, gilt spine, worn. Eaton 45-382 1978 £5

THE PARENT'S Best Gift:.... York, 1805. 36mo., illus. wrappers, dog-eared and loss of some words. Victoria 34-599 1978 $27.50

PARET, J. PARMLY   Methods and Players of Modern Lawn Tennis. New York, 1915. Cloth, 1st ed., light dampstain on back cover, very good. Hayman 73-594 1978 $7.50

PARIS, JOHN AYRTON   Pharmacologia. New York, 1822. 8vo., contemp. calf, 1st Amer. ed. Morrill 239-200 1978 $50

PARIS, JOHN AYRTON   Pharmacologia: The Art of Prescribing. Vol. 1 only. New York, 1824. Title strip detached, usual scuffing, some staining. Rittenhouse 49-614 1976 $10

PARIS, JOHN AYRTON   Pharmacologia. New York, 1825. 3rd American from 6th London ed., plt., fldg. tables, 2 vols. in 1, 8vo., contemp. calf. Morrill 239-201 1978 $22.50

PARIS, JOHN AYRTON   Philosophy in Sport Made Science in Earnest. London, 1827. 3 vols., 12mo., text woodcuts by George Cruikshank, contemp. half calf, a little worn, first ed. Quaritch 977-128 1978 $95

PARIS, JOHN AYRTON   Philosophy in Sport Made Science in Earnest;.... London, 1827. 3 vols., tall 12mo, engraved vignettes on title-page, illus. and diagrams by George Cruikshank, contemp. marbled boards, rebacked in half dark calf, gilt rules, light foxing, presentation inscription, 1st ed. Bennett 7-82 1978 $200

PARIS, MATTHEW   English History, 1235-73. 1852-54. Frontis., 3 vols., hinges sprung in 1 vol., cr. 8vo., orig. cloth. George's 635-556 1978 £15

PARIS, PIERRE   Manual of Ancient Sculpture. London, 1890. Illus. Biblo 247-293 1978 $12.50

PARIS Exposition 1867. Minerals of the U. S. A. Group V, Class 40. Paris, 1867. Orig. prtd. wrs., 8vo., very good. Americanist 103-61 1978 $32.50

PARISET, R. M.   Nouveau Livre de Principes de Dessein Recuelli... des Etudes des Meilleurs Maitres tout Anciens que Modernes. Paris, (late 18th cent.). Lg. folio, plts., contemp. bds., calf spine and corners worn. Quaritch 983-230 1978 $300

PARISMAS, THOMAS   The History of Capt. Thomas Parismas, Containing a Particular Account of the Cruel and Barbarous Treatment of a Young Lady, Who Was the Wife of Mr. James Negotio, a Merchant in the East Indies. Greenwich, 1812. 12mo., sewn. Morrill 241-443 1978 $10

PARK, LAWRENCE   Gilbert Sturat. New York, 1926. 4 vols., sm. folio in box as issued, blind stamp of former owner on top of title page. Baldwins' 51-137 1978 $400

PARK, MUNGO   The Life and Travels of.... London, c. 1900. Frontis, cr. 8vo, prize calf gilt, slightly marked. K Books 239-362 1978 £6

PARK, MUNGO   Travels in the Interior Districts of Africa. London, 1799. 1st. ed., 3 folding mpas, 5 plts., portraits, 4to, generally dusty & thumbed, repairs to map, few other repairs, old style half calf. K Books 239-361 1978 £140

PARK, THOMAS   Sonnets, and Other Small Poems. London, 1797.
8vo, original pale blue boards, drab paper backstrip (a bit worn), 1st ed., fine
copy. Ximenes 47-222 1978 $125

PARK, WILLIAM LEE   Pioneer Pathways to the Pacific. Clare, (1935).
Cloth, nice, slightly soiled d.j. Hayman 72-596 1978 $12.50

PARKE, JOHN E.   Recollections of Seventy Years and Historical
Gleanings of Allegheny, Pa. Boston, 1886. Port. MacManus 239-1596 1978
$20

PARKE-BERNET GALLERIES   The Celebrated Collection of Americana Formed by
the Late Thomas Winthrop Streeter. New York, 1966-1970. 8 vols., sm. quarto,
illus., vols. 1-7 in blue bds., vol. 8 in blue cloth, fine cond. Petrilla 13-66
1978 $350

PARKER, AMASA J.   Landmarks of Albany County. Syracuse, 1897.
Very thick, tall 8vo, portrs., half lea., rubbed but sound, all edges gilt, good
copy. Butterfield 21-29 1978 $40

PARKER, AMOS A.   Trip to the West and Texas, Comprising a Journey
of Eight Thousand Miles. Concord, 1835. 1st ed., original cloth. Jenkins
116-1046 1978 $275

PARKER, ARTHUR C.   An Analytical History of the Seneca Indians.
1926. Tall 8vo., plts., portrs. Butterfield 21-215d 1978 $25

PARKER, ARTHUR C.   The Archaeological History of New York.
Albany, 1922. 1st ed., 2 vols., illus., plts., orig. wrs., very good. MacManus
239-1205 1978 $35

PARKER, ARTHUR C.   A Contact Period Site...at Factory Hollow...
New York. Plts. Butterfield 21-215e 1978 $7.50

PARKER, ARTHUR C.   Excavations in an Erie Indian Village...at Ripley,
Chautauqua County, N.Y. Albany, 1907. Bound into plain blue bds., tape
backstrip & orig. wr. Butterfield 21-216 1978 $15

PARKER, BISHOP   A Discourse of Ecclesiastical Politie... 1671.
3rd. ed., orig. calf, good. Jarndyce 16-21 1978 £20

PARKER, CHARLES S.   Town of Arlington Past and Present. Arlington,
1907. Illus., map. MacManus 239-1007 1978 $20

PARKER, DOROTHY   After Such Pleasures. New York, 1933. Near
fine in lightly chipped d.w. Desmarais B-501 1978 $12.50

PARKER, DOROTHY   Collected Stories. New York, (1942). 1st
Modern Library Ed., d.w. Biblo 251-600 1978 $8.50

PARKER, DOROTHY   Here Lies the Collected Stories of Dorothy Parker.
New York, 1939. Very fine in lightly worn & chipped d.w. Desmarais B-502
1978 $15

PARKER, GILBERT   The Seats of the Mighty. New York, 1896. 1st
ed. Biblo 251-601 1978 $12.50

PARKER, GILBERT   The Trail of the Sword. London, 1895. First
ed., orig. binding, illus., nice. Rota 211-468 1978 £5

PARKER, GILBERT   The Translation of a Savage. London, 1894.
First ed., orig. binding, nice. Rota 211-467 1978 £5

PARKER, KARL THEODORE   The Drawings of Hans Holbein in the Collection of
His Majesty at Windsor Castle. 1945. Coloured frontis., plts., illus., 4to.
George's 635-186 1978 £15

PARKER, LEONARD F.   Higher Education in Iowa. Washington, 1893.
Original wr., 1st ed. Ginsberg 14-420 1978 $35

PARKER, S.   Journal of an Exploring Tour Beyond the Rocky
Mountains... Ithaca, 1840. Sm. 8vo, 2nd. ed., folding map, orig. cloth, spine
faded, text browned, 2 sm. repairs in map. Edwards 1012-519 1978 £45

PARKER, THEODORE   Lessons from the World of Matter and the World
of Man. Boston, 1865. Portr., 8vo, 1st ed., orig. cloth. Morrill 241-444
1978 $12.50

PARKER, THEODORE   A Sermon for Midsummer Day. Boston, 1859.
Wrs., little soiled. Hayman 73-595 1978 $7.50

PARKER, THEODORE   A Sermon of the Mexican War...June 25, 1848.
Boston, 1848. Unbound, stained, foxed, scarce. Biblo 247-83 1978 $27.50

PARKER, THOMAS JEFFERY   A Textbook of Zoology. London, 1910. 8vo,
illus., 2 vols. Traylen 88-613 1978 £10

PARKER, THOMAS JEFFERY   William Kitchen Parker, a Biographical Sketch.
New York, 1893. Rittenhouse 49-616 1976 $10

PARKER, THOMAS V.   The Cherokee Indians. New York, 1907.
Illus., cover rubbed. Broadfoot 50-165 1978 $30

PARKER, THOMAS V.   The Cherokee Indians. New York, (1907).
Illus., orig. cloth, some staining. MacManus 239-1206 1978 $20

PARKER, WILLIAM B.   Notes Taken During the Exploration Commanded
by Capt. R. B. Marcy, U.S.A., Through Unexplored Texas, in the Summer and
Fall of 1854. Philadelphia, 1856. Original cloth, 1st ed. Jenkins 116-1048
1978 $400

PARKES, E. A.   Researches into the Pathology and Treatment of
the Asiatic or Algide Cholera. London, 1847. First ed. Rittenhouse 49-617
1976 $40

PARKES, MRS. WILLIAM   Domestic Duties; Or, Instructions to Young
Married Ladies... 1828. 3rd. ed., half title, orig. brown bds., paper labels,
very slight rubbing on spine, fine copy in orig. binding. Jarndyce 16-924 1978
£45

PARKHURST, DANIEL BURLEIGH   A Complete Treatise on the Principles and
Technique Necessary to the Painting of Pictures in Oil Colors. Boston, (1898).
Plts., illus., 12mo., 1st ed. Morrill 241-445 1978 $10

PARKINS, ALMON E.   The South. NY, 1933. Illus., Bell Wiley's copy.
Broadfoot's 44-731 1978 $10.00

PARKINSON, JAMES   Medical Admonitions to Families Respecting the
Preservation of Health. Portsmouth, 1803. Orig. bds., hinges weak. Rittenhouse 49-618 1976 $35

PARKINSON, JOHN   The Dinosaur in East Africa. London, (1930).
Plts., text-figures, sketch maps, 8vo, orig. cloth. K Books 239-363 1978 £15

PARKINSON, SIDNEY   A Journal of a Voyage to the South Seas in
H.M.S. The Endeavour. 1773. 1st. ed., portrait, map, engraved copper-plts.,
4to, contemp. tree calf, rebacked, light offsetting. Edwards 1012-362 1978
£1000

PARKMAN, EBENEZER   The Diary of Rev. Ebenezer Parkman, of Westborough, Mass... Westborough, 1899. Illus. MacManus 239-385 1978 $30

PARKMAN, FRANCIS   The Battle for North America. New York, 1948.
First of this ed., fine, d.w. Biblo 247-117 1978 $17.50

PARKMAN, FRANCIS   The Discovery of the Great West. Boston, 1869.
Orig. binding. Wolfe 39-420 1978 $25

PARKMAN, FRANCIS   The Discovery of the Great West. Boston, 1869.
1st ed., orig. cloth. MacManus 239-387 1978 $30

PARKMAN, FRANCIS   A Half-Century of Conflict. Boston, 1929.
2 vols., centenary ed. Hood's 115-128 1978 $20

PARKMAN, FRANCIS   The Jesuits in North America in the Seventeenth
Century. Boston, 1867. Engrav. frontis. map, orig. binding. Wolfe 39-419
1978 $25

PARKMAN, FRANCIS   The Jesuits in North America in the Seventeenth
Century. Toronto, 1899. Hood 116-309 1978 $15

PARKMAN, FRANCIS   La Salle and the Discovery of the Great West.
Boston, 1879. 11th ed., rev'd., 1st of this ed., 1st printing, nice signed inscription by Parkman, maps. Americanist 102-81 1978 $125

PARKMAN, FRANCIS   The Old Regime in Canada. Boston, 1874. 8vo.,
spine faded, 1st ed. Morrill 239-571 1978 $7.50

PARKMAN, FRANCIS   The Old Regime in Canada. Boston, 1875.
Orig. binding. Wolfe 39-421 1978 $17.50

PARKMAN, FRANCIS　　　Oregon Trail. Garden City, 1945. 1 of 1,000 numbered signed by Thomas Hart Benton, illus. in color by Benton, cloth, t.e.g., uncut, publisher's box, fine. Houle 10-254 1978 $85

PARKMAN, FRANCIS　　　Prairie and Rocky Mountain Life; or, the California and Oregon Trail and the States and Territories of our Western Empire... Columbus, 1857. Leather worn, rebacked. Hayman 72-597 1978 $25

PARKMAN, FRANCIS　　　Francis Parkman's Works. Boston, New York, 1902. Frontenac ed., 17 vols., blue buckram, t.e.g., uncut. Wolfe 39-422 1978 $75

PARKS, FANNY　　　Wanderings of a Pilgrim, in Search of the Picturesque, During Four and Twenty Years in the East... 1850. Plts., 21 coloured lithos, 2 vols., imp. 8vo, orig. blue cloth gilt. Edwards 1012-109 1978 £175

PARKS, JOSEPH HOWARD　　　Felix Grundy. Louisiana, 1940. Bell Wiley's copy Broadfoot's 44-733 1978 $20.00

PARKYNS, GEORGE ISHAM　　Monastic and Baronial Remains, with Other Interesting Fragments of Antiquity in England, Wales and Scotland. 1816. 2 vols. in 1, 8vo, plts., contemp. diced calf, rebacked. Quaritch 983-26 1978 $190

PARLANTE, PRISCILLA　　　Ferdinand & Ordella, A Russian Story... 1810. 1st. ed., 2 vols., half titles, rebound in half calf, hand-marbled bds., good. Jarndyce 16-925 1978 £43

PARLEY, PETER
Please turn to
GOODRICH, SAMUEL GRISWOLD

PARMELE, TRUMAN　　　Questions on the Historical Parts of the New Testament. Utica, 1824. 18mo., paper-covered bds., chipped but holding. Butterfield 21-313 1978 $10

PARMENTIER, H.　　　Le Cirque de Mi-Son (Quang-Nam). Hanoi, 1904. Large 8vo, cloth, plts, illus, maps, plans, tables. Van der Peet 127-181 1978 Dfl 125

PARNASO Italiano ovvero Raccolta de' Poeti Classici Italiani D'Ogni genere.... 1784-1791. 56 vols., sm. 8vo., patterned paper wrappers, paper labels, very good, uncut. King 7-205 1978 £600

PARNASSE Des Dames. Paris, 1772. 2 vols., vignette titles, plt., spotted, vol. 1 lacks front end-papers, contemp. panelled calf, gilt spines, corners bumped. Eaton 45-383 1978 £15

PARNELL, J. H.　　　Charles Stewart Parnell, A Memoir. 1916. 1st ed., port., very good, octavo bound in cloth. Hyland 128-321 1978 £6.50

PARNELL, THOMAS　　　Poems Upon Several Occasions Written by ... 1773. Orig. calf, red label, new ed., good. Jarndyce 16-152 1978 £10

PARNELL, THOMAS　　　Poems upon Several Occasions. London, 1773. New ed., contemp. calf, plts., sm. 8vo. K Books 244-431 1978 £15

PARNELL, THOMAS　　　The Poetical Works. Glasgow, Foulis Press, 1786. Folio, contemp. tree calf gilt. Howes 194-272 1978 £55

PARNELL, WILLIAM　　　An Enquiry into the Causes of Popular Discontents in Ireland by an Irish Country Gentleman. 1805. 1st Dublin ed., plain wr., very good. Hyland 128-334 1978 £15

PARNES, R. DE　　　Gazette Anecdotique du Regne de Louis XVI. Paris, 1881. 8vo., illus. wrs., frontis., engr. plts., ltd., uncut. Van der Peet H-64-517 1978 Dfl 45

PARNES, R. DE　　　La Regence, Portefeuille d'un Roue. Paris, 1881. 8vo., orig. covers, engr. frontis., engr. plts., ltd. ed. Van der Peet H-64-518 1978 Dfl 45

THE PAROCHIAL Library of the 18th Century in Christ Church. Boston, Merrymount Press, 1917. Some foxing. Battery Park 1-317 1978 $35

PARPART, ARTHUR K.　　　The Chemistry and Physiology of Growth. Princeton, 1949. Library marks. Rittenhouse 49-619 1976 $12.50

PARR, HARRIET　　　Against Wind and Tide. New York, 1860. 1st Amer. ed. (?), 3 vols. in 1, good. Greene 78-267 1978 $25

PARR, SAMUEL　　　Characters of the Late Charles James Fox. 1809. First ed., contemp. half calf, spines chipped, 2 vols., 8vo. Howes 194-276 1978 £21

PARRISH, ISAAC　　　An Examination of the Principles of the Independent Treasury Bill... Washington, 1840. Disbound, reinforced along binding edge, foxing. Hayman 73-597 1978 $7.50

PARRISH, RANDALL　　　Don Mac Grath. A Tale of the River. Chicago, 1910. Illus., 1st ed., pict. cloth, worn, inner hinges split, bookplt. Biblo BL781-1101 1978 $10

PARRISH, RANDALL　　　Molly McDonald. A Tale of the Old Frontier. Chicago, 1912. Illus., 1st ed. Biblo BL781-1102 1978 $10

PARRISH, RANDALL　　　My Lady of the North. Chicago, 1904. Illus., 1st ed. Biblo 251-602 1978 $22.50

PARRISH, RANDALL　　　My Lady of the South. A Story of the Civil War. Chicago, 1909. Illus. in color, 1st ed., fair. Biblo BL781-1103 1978 $9

PARRISH, THOMAS C.　　　Colorado Springs: Its Climate, Scenery and Society. Colorado Springs, 1889. Illus., original printed wr. bound in half cloth, 1st ed. Ginsberg 14-271 1978 $75

PARROTT, W.　　　London from the Thames. (1840-41). Oblong folio, hand-coloured plts., cloth box, ltd. to 100 copies, this 1 of 13 copies of De Luxe ed. Quaritch 983-352 1978 $900

PARRY, CHARLES HENRY　　　A Memoir of Peregrine Bertie, Eleventh Lord Willoughby de Eresby... 1838. 1st. ed., portrait, 8vo, orig. cloth, printed paper label, very good copy. Fenning 32-255 1978 £10.50

PARRY, EDWARD　　　The Bloody Assize. New York, 1929. Illus. Biblo 251-301 1978 $15

PARRY, WILLIAM EDWARD　　　Journal of a Second Voyage for the Discovery of a North-West Passage from the Atlantic to the Pacific; Performed in the Years 1821-22-23. London, 1824. Illus., thick sq. 4to., full calf, worn, 1st ed. Argosy Special-69 1978 $300

PARRY, WILLIAM EDWARD　　　Journals of the First, Second, and Third Voyages for the Discovery of a North-West Passage From the Atlantic to the Pacific, 1819-25.. 1828. 12mo, 5 vols., orig. cloth, rebacked, new printed labels, sides of 1 vol. affected by ink stain. Edwards 1012-595 1978 £45

PARRY, WILLIAM EDWARD　　　Journals Of the First, Second and Third Voyages For the Discovery of a North-West Passage From the Atlantic to the Pacific.... London, 1828. 5 vols., sm. 8vo, engraved portrait, engraved folding map, plts., some foxing throughout, contemporary cloth, printed paper labels, edges uncut. Deighton 5-166 1978 £115

PARRY, WILLIAM EDWARD　　　Journals of the First, Second and Third Voyages for the Discovery of a North-west Passage from the Atlantic to the Pacific, in 1819, '20, '21, '22, '23, '24 and '25... London, 1828. 5 vols., map, plts., rubbed, scarce. Biblo BL781-47 1978 $87.50

PARSON, THEOPHILUS　　　Slavery. Boston, 1863. 2nd. ed., orig. wraps. as issued. Baldwins' 51-384 1978 $12.50

PARSONS, EDWARD Y.　　　Texas Pacific Railroad. Washington, 1876. Printed wr. Jenkins 116-1052 1978 $20

PARSONS, ELSIE CLEWS　　　American Indian Life. New York, 1925. Sm. 4to., illus. Biblo 247-54 1978 $37.50

PARSONS, FRANCIS　　　The Hartford Wits. Hartford, 1936. 8vo., bds., No. 20 of an ed. of 25 numbered copies. Battery Park 1-48 1978 $50

PARSONS, GEORGE F.　　　The Life and Adventures of James W. Marshall: The Discoverer of Gold in California.... San Francisco, 1935. Original boards, paper label, limited to 500 copies. Ginsberg 14-528 1978 $30

PARSONS, JAMES　　　Remains of Japhet... 1767. 1st. ed., 4to, orig. calf, green label, outer edges of 4 or 5 leaves very slightly affected by damp, o/w superb & most attractive copy. Jarndyce 16-153 1978 £45

PARSONS, ROBERT　　　A Christian Directory, Guiding Men to Eternall Salvation, Commonly Called the Resolution. (London?), 1650. 8vo, short tear in 2 leaves, no loss, little dusty in places, very good copy, full calf antique. Fenning 32-256 1978 £56

PARSONS, USHER　　　Battle of Lake Erie. Providence, 1854. Wr. Butterfield 21-459 1978 $10

PARSONS, USHER   Boylston Prize Dissertation on Inflammation of the Periosteum Eneuresis Irritata.... Boston, 1839. First ed. Rittenhouse 49-620 1976 $17.50

PARSONS, WILLIAM BARCLAY   Robert Fulton and the Submarine. New York, 1922. Lg. 8vo., illus., orig. cloth, gilt, very good copy. Norman 5-118 1978 $40

PARSONS, WILLIAM BARCLAY   Robert Fulton and the Submarine. New York, 1922. Illus., v.g. Nestler Rare78-135 1978 $25

PARTHENIUS, JOSEPHUS MARIANUS   Electricorum libri VI (Commentarii). Rome, 1767. Very rare 1st ed., contemp. vellum, engraved folding plates, 8vo. Gilhofer 75-85 1978 SFr 1,200

A PARTICULAR Account of the Commencement and Progress of the Insurrection of the Negroes in St. Domingo... 1792. 2nd. ed., 8vo, cloth, leather spine. Edwards 1012-737 1978 £35

THE PARTIES and the Men or the Political Issues of 1896... N.P., (1896). Cloth, nice. Hayman 72-646 1978 $10

PARTIN, ROBERT   A Confederate Sergeant's Report to His Wife During the Campaign from Tullahoma to Dalton. Wrs., pres. copy from Partin to Wiley. Broadfoot's 44-414 1978 $8

PARTINGTON, WILFRED   Sir Walter's Post-Bag: More Stories and Side-lights from his Unpublished letter-books. London, (1932). Sole ed., plts., very good or better. Limestone 9-259 1978 $20

PARTON, JAMES   The Life and Times of Aaron Burr. New York, 1858. 1st ed., 3/4 calf, binding rubbed. Biblo 251-100 1978 $37.50

PARTON, JAMES   Life and Times of Benjamin Franklin. Boston, (1864). 2 vols., illus., orig. cloth. MacManus 239-161 1978 $25

PARTON, JAMES   Life of Andrew Jackson. New York, 1861. 3 vols., ports., orig. cloth. MacManus 239-774 1978 $37.50

PARTON, JAMES   Life of Andrew Jackson. New York, 1861. Portrs., 3 vols., 8vo., 2nd prtg. Morrill 241-446 1978 $20

PARTON, JAMES   Life of Andrew Jackson. Boston, 1876. 3 vols., bindings scuffed. Biblo 248-48 1978 $22.50

PARTON, JAMES   The Life of Horace Greeley, Editor of the New York Tribune. New York, 1855. Clean, orig. binding, little worn at bottom of spine. Hayman 71-619 1978 $10

PARTON, JAMES   The Life of Horace Greeley, Editor of the New York, Tribune. New York, 1868. Cloth. Hayman 72-599 1978 $8.50

PARTON, JAMES   Smoking and Drinking. Boston, 1882. 12mo., orig. cloth. Morrill 241-447 1978 $10

PARTON, SARA PAYSON   Fern Leaves from Fanny's Port-folio. Auburn, 1853. Plts., orig. bind., minor stain a lower margins of last few leaves, 1st ed. Petrilla 13-68 1978 $7.50

PARTON, SARA PAYSON   Fern Leaves From Fanny's Port-Folio. Chicago, 1889. Orig. binding, clean. Hayman 71-620 1978 $7.50

PARTRIDGE, ERIC   Robert Eyres Landor: Selections From His Poetry and Prose... 1927. 155 copies, this copy out of series, half vellum, little stained at head of spine otherwise near fine. Jarndyce 16-1211 1978 £20

PARTRIDGE, ERIC   Shakespeare's Bawdy. 1947. 1st. ed., no. 337 of 1040 copies, v.g. Jarndyce 16-1212 1978 £12

PARTY-GIVING On Every Scale. 1885. 8vo, orig. brown cloth, gilt, nice copy. Fenning 32-257 1978 £7.50

PARUTA, PAOLO   Discorsi Politici... Venice, 1629. 4to., vellum. Salloch 348-186 1978 $95

PASCAL, BLAISE   Ludovici Montaltii Litterae Provinciales, de Morali et Politica Jesuitarum Disciplina. 1658. 8vo., first ed. of Latin trans-lation of this famous book. King 7-295 1978 £40

PASCAL, BLAISE   Pensees Sur La Religion et Sur Quelques Autres Sujets... Paris, 1670. Sm. 8vo., vellum. Salloch 348-187 1978 $245

PASCAL, BLAISE   Thoughts on Religion. Edinburgh, Nonesuch Press, (c. 1910). Ed. ltd. to 40 copies on Japanese vellum, sq. 8vo., full parch-ment. George's 635-920 1978 £15

PASCAL, BLAISE   Traitez de l'Equilibre des Liqueurs, et de la Pesanteur de la Masse de l'Air. Paris, 1663. 12mo., contemp. calf, plts., first ed., good. Gurney 75-103 1978 £850

PASCAL, BLAISE   Traitez de l'Equilibre des Liqueurs,.... Paris, 1663. Rare 1st ed., 12mo, engraved folding plates, woodcut, red mor., gilt inside dentelles, gilt edges. Gilhofer 75-86 1978 SFr 4,900

PASCH, MORITZ   Vorlesungen uber neuere Geometrie. Leipzig, (1882). 8vo., contemp. half-cloth, 1st ed. Gilhofer 74-124 1978 sFr 200

PASCHAL, GEORGE WASHINGTON   A History of Printing in North Carolina... Raleigh, 1946. Illus. MacManus 239-1846 1978 $35

PASCHAL, GEORGE WASHINGTON   A History of Printing in North Carolina. Raleigh, 1946. Broadfoot 50-170 1978 $30

PASCHAL, GEORGE WASHINGTON   History of Wake Forest College...1834-1865. Wake Forest, 1935. Vol. I, illus., signed by Francis Paschal. Biblo BL781-35 1978 $13.50

PASCHAL, GEORGE WASHINGTON   History of Wake Forest College 1834-1865. Wake Forest, 1935. Vol. I, some underlining. Broadfoot 50-169 1978 $15

PASCHALL, JOHN   Mr. Paschall's Letter to a Friend in the Country, Stating the Case of Mr. Parkhurst and Himself... 1701. 1st. ed., folio, wrapper, edges uncut, fine. Fenning 32-258 1978 £21.50

PASCOLI, LIONE   Vite de' Pittori, Scultori, ed Architetti Perugini Scritte e Dedicate alla Maesta di Carlo Emmanuel Re di Sardegna. Roma, 1732. 4to., bds., calf spine gilt, good, first ed. King 7-206 1978 £120

PASCOLI, LIONE   Vite de' Pittori, Scultori ed Architetti Perugini. Roma, 1732. 4to., contemp. vellum, 1st ed., fine, marginal waterstain. Gilhofer 74-44 1978 sFr 1,000

PASMA, HENRY K.   Close-Hauled. 1930. Austin 79-544 1978 $17.50

PASQUIN, ANTHONY PSEUD.
Please turn to
WILLIAMS, JOHN, 1761-1818

PASSAVANTI, JACOPO   Lo Specchio di Vera Penitenzia.... Firenze, 1585. 12mo., full contemp. calf, gilt rules, Fletcher of Saltoun copy with sign-ature, crisp and fine. Bennett 20-159 1978 $200

PASSAVANTI, JACOPO   Lo Speechio della vera penitenza.... Firenze, 1723. 8vo., vellum, lettering gilt, woodcut initials. King 7-207 1978 £15

PASSEBOIS, LOUIS F.   Adventures of a Modern Huguenot. Nash-ville, 1940. Illus. Austin 79-545 1978 $32.50

PASTEUR, J.   Studies on Fermentation. London, 1879. Orig. illus., first ed. in English, plts., text diagrams, 8vo. K Books 244-254 1978 £25

PASTEUR, LOUIS   Etudes sur la Biere, ses maladies, causes qui les provoquent, procede pour la rendre inalterable, avec une Theorie Nouvelle de la Fermentation. Paris, 1876. 8vo., contemp. qtr. shagreen, slightly rubbed, plts., pres. copy inscribed by author, fine. Gurney 75-83 1978 £275

PASTEUR, LOUIS   Etudes Sur Le Vin Ses Maladies Causes Qui Les Provoquent Procedes Nouveau Pour Le Conserver Et Pour Le Vieillir. Paris, 1866. 8vo., plts., illus., half black lea., gilt-rule, gilt lettered, foxed, damp.stained, signature of former owner, good copy, 1st ed. Zeitlin 245-309 1978 $350

PASTONCHI: a Specimen of a New Letter for Use on the "Monotype". London, (1928). Marbled bds., vellum back, very fine in slipcase, 1 of 200 copies prtd. by hand on special Fabriano paper. Dawson's 447-107 1978 $225

PASTONCHI: a Specimen of a New Letter for Use on the "Monotype". Trade ed., brown cloth, prtd. on regular paper, no slipcase. Dawson's 447-108 1978 $45

PATANJALI, BHAGWAN SHREE   Aphorisms of Yoga. Very good, first English ed. Bell Book 16-961 1978 £5

PATCHEN, KENNETH   See You in the Morning. London, 1949. First English ed., orig. binding, nice, torn d.w. Rota 211-471 1978 £15

PATCHEN, KENNETH   Sleepers Awake. New York, 1946. First ed., orig. binding, fine, d.w. Rota 211-470 1978 £15

PATER, WALTER   Appreciations with an Essay on Style. London, 1889. 8vo., orig. blue cloth, 1st ed., very good, bookplt. MacManus 238-369 1978 $35

PATER, WALTER   Plato and Platonism. A Series of Lectures. London, 1893. Orig. cloth, 1st ed., good. MacManus 238-370 1978 $35

PATERCULUS, C. VELLEIUS
Please turn to
VELLEIUS PATERCULUS, C.

PATERSON, J.   A Practical Treatise on the Making and Upholding of Public Roads. Montrose, 1819. Sm. 8vo., orig. bds., uncut. Quaritch 977-247 1978 $85

PATERSON, JAMES   The Contemporaries of Burns, and the more recent Poets of Ayrshire. Edinburgh, 1840. 8vo., contemp. half calf, marbled sides, frontispiece, plts. P. M. Hill 142-57 1978 £42

PATERSON, NATHANIEL   The Manse Garden. Glasgow, 1836. 12mo., orig. cloth. K Books 244-255 1978 £8

PATIN, GUI   Lettres Choisies. Rotterdam, 1689. 12mo., contemp. sprinkled calf; gilt on spine, gilt dentelles, worn, light browning, wormtrail, good copy, signatures of early owners, including Mareschal on the endpaper. Zeitlin 245-184 1978 $100

PATIN, GUI   Lettres Choisies De Feu. Paris, 1692. 2 vols., 12mo., frontis. engr. portr., contemp. calf, gilt, ex-lib. of John Earl of Loudoun & Dr. Alfred M. Hellman, very good copy, rare 1st Paris ed. Zeitlin 245-185 1978 $125

PATMORE, COVENTRY   The Unknown Eros. London, 1878. Second ed., orig. binding, nice. Rota 211-472 1978 £15

PATMORE, PETER G.   Mirror of the Months. 1826. 1st. ed., orig. calf, spine rubbed, gilt borders, good. Jarndyce 16-926 1978 £7.50

PATON, WILLIAM AGNEW   Down the Islands... New York, 1887. Illus., 8vo, orig. cloth, cover edge damp-stained. Edwards 1012-735 1978 £15

PATRICK, D.   Chamber's Cyclopaedia of English Literature. 1906. New ed., portraits, 3 vols., imp. 8vo. George's 635-1376 1978 £7.50

PATRICK, REMBERT W.   Florida Under Five Flags. Gainesville, 1945. Signed by author, lg. vol. of many illus., Bell Wiley's copy. Broadfoot's 44-846 1978 $12.00

PATRICK, REMBERT W.   Jefferson Davis and His Cabinet. Baton Rouge, 1944. Bell Wiley's copy. Broadfoot 46-196 1978 $16

PATRICK, SIMON 1626-1707   A Commentary upon the First Book of Moses, Called Genesis. 1695. First ed., sm. 4to., contemp. calf, mor. label. Howes 194-80 1978 £45

PATRIOTIC Appeal to the People of the Country. (New York, 1861). 8vo., unbound. Morrill 241-450 1978 $8.50

PATTEE, FRED LEWIS   Tradition and Jazz. 1925. First ed. Austin 82-697 1978 $12.50

PATTEN, J. H.   The "Immigration Crew". 1935. Austin 79-546 1978 $27.50

PATTERSON, C. L.   Wilson County, Diversified Farming Center of Southwest Texas. Floresville, 1939. 1st ed., printed wr., illus. Jenkins 116-1481 1978 $20

PATTERSON, GILES J.   Journal of a Southern Student 1846-1848. Nashville, 1944. Bell Wiley's copy. Broadfoot's 44-925 1978 $20.00

PATTERSON, HAYWOOD   Scottsboro Boy. New York, (1950). 1st ed. Biblo 251-65 1978 $15

PATTERSON, JAMES W.   Responsibilities of the Founders of Republics. Boston, 1865. 2 vols. in 1, 8vo., half mor., marbled sides, raised bands, ltd. to 250 & 300 copies respectively. Morrill 241-307 1978 $65

PATTERSON, JOHN HENRY   In The Grip of the Nyika. London, 1909. 9 maps, illus., g.t., little thumbed but good, orig. cloth, 8vo. K Books 239-365 1978 £8

PATTERSON, JOHN HENRY   In the Grip of the Nyika. New York, 1909. Respined, TD Carter bookplt., 8vo, orig. cloth, map. Book Chest 17-279 1978 $30

PATTERSON, JOHN HENRY   In The Grip of the Nyika: Further Adventures in British East Africa. 1909. Maps, 8vo, orig. cloth. Edwards 1012-286 1978 £12

PATTERSON, JOHN HENRY   In The Grip of the Nyika. New York, 1909. Maps, illus., 8vo, neatly recased in orig. cloth. K Books 239-366 1978 £7

PATTERSON, JOHN HENRY   The Man-Eaters of Tsavo and Other East African Adventures. London, 1907. Map, illus., slightly thumbed, good reading copy, recased in orig. gilt cloth, 8vo. K Books 239-367 1978 £8

PATTERSON, JOSEPH MEDILL   Rebellion. Chicago, (1911). 1st ed., illus. by Walter Dean Goldbeck. Biblo 251-604 1978 $15

PATTERSON, L.   A Letter to the Church. [Hillsboro,] 1884. Orig. self wr., 1st ed. Ginsberg 14-839 1978 $50

PATTERSON, R.H.   The State, The Poor & The Country, Including Suggestions on the Irish Question. 1870. 1st ed., signed pres. copy, very good. Hyland 128-335 1978 £25

PATTERSON, ROBERT   A Narrative of the Campaign in the Valley of the Shenandoah in 1861. Philadelphia, 1865. Wrs., waterstain. Biblo 247-24 1978 $20

PATTERSON, SAMUEL   Narrative of the Adventures and Sufferings of... Experienced in the Pacific Ocean,.... Palmer, 1817. Full calf 1st ed. Ginsberg 14-873 1978 $250

PATTERSON, SAMUEL   A Narrative of the Adventures, Sufferings and Privations of.... Providence, 1825. 2nd ed., enlarged, half calf. Ginsberg 14-874 1978 $175

PATTIE, JAMES O.   The Personal Narrative of James O. Pattie, of Kentucky during an Expedition from Saint Louis,.... Cincinnati, 1833. Plates, original sheep, leather label, spine repaired, 1st ed., 1st state of text. Jenkins 116-1575 1978 $1,250

PATTISON, GRANVILLE SHARP   A Refutation of Certain Calumnies Published in a Pamphlet, Entitled, "Correspondence Between Mr. Granville Sharp Pattison and Dr. Nathaniel Chapman. Baltimore, 1820. No covers, stain. Rittenhouse 49-603 1976 $30

PATTISON, MARK   Isaac Causaubon 1559-1614. 1892. Second ed., portrait, 8vo., orig. cloth. Howes 194-712 1978 £12

PATTISON, WILLIAM   Poetical Works. (1727)-28. 2 vols., 8vo., 1st ed., portr., plt., contemp. calf, fine set. Quaritch 979-252 1978 $550

PATTON, GEORGE S., JR.   War as I Knew it. 1947. Ex-lib. Austin 80-250 1978 $7.50

PATTON, H.E.   50 Years of Disestablishment. 1922. 1st ed., f.p., illus., very good, octavo bound in cloth. Hyland 128-336 1978 £5

PATTON, JAMES WELCH   Minutes of the Proceedings of the Greenville Ladies Association in Aid of the Volunteers of the Confederate Army. Durham, 1937. Wraps, pres copy from author, inner hinges reinforced, Bell Wiley's copy. Broadfoot's 44-296 1978 $10.00

PATTON, PHILIP   The Natural Defence of an Insular Empire. Southampton, 1810. 4to., half calf, table. F. Edwards 1013-171 1978 £25

PATTON, WILLIAM   Slavery and Fidelity. Cincinnati, (1856). Orig. binding. Wolfe 39-423 1978 $15

PAUKER, JOHN   Excellency. Iowa City, The Stonewall Press, 1967. Illus. by Thomas Kovacks, sm. folio, cloth, portr. on cover, thin, one of 230 copies prtd. by hand, Rivas paper. Battery Park 1-228 1978 $100

PAUL, C. KEGAN   William Godwin: His Friends and Contemporaries. 1876. 1st. ed., portraits, illus., half titles, orig. brown cloth, fine. Jarndyce 16-689 1978 £32

PAUL, ELLIOT   Hugger-Mugger in the Louvre. New York, 1941. Near mint in chipped d.w. Desmara's B-505 1978 $10

PAUL, ELLIOT   Linden on the Saugus Branch. New York, 1947. Near mint in lightly chipped d.w., which is also lightly rubbed at back. Desmarais B-507 1978 $10

PAUL, ELLIOT   Linden on the Saugus Branch. New York, (1947). 1st ed., d.w. slightly frayed. Biblo 251-605 1978 $15

PAUL, ELLIOT   Springtime in Paris. New York, (1950). 1st ed., d.w. Biblo 251-606 1978 $15

PAUL, HERBERT   Queen Anne. London, 1906. Quarto, hand-colored frontis. portrait, red mor. and cloth, original pr. wr. and endstrips bound in, 1st ed., 1 of 800 numbered copies. Bennett 7-83 1978 $135

PAUL, JAMES BALFOUR   The History of the Royal Company of Archers, the Queen's Body-Guard for Scotland. Edinburgh, 1875. Large 8vo, original green cloth, stamped in gilt, 1st ed., laid in report (dusty), fine copy, unopened. Ximenes 47-223 1978 $90

PAUL, JAMES BALFOUR   The Scots Peerage.... Edinburgh, 1904-1914. Coloured frontis, 8 vols., should be 9 lacks vol. 5, roy. 8vo. Traylen 88-456 1978 £90

PAUL, JOHN   Every Landlord or Tenant His Own Lawyer. Dublin, 1782. Lg. 12mo, contemp. mottled calf, wanting the spine label, nice. Fenning 32-259 1978 £18

PAUL, LESLIE   The Living Hedge. 1946. Wood engravings by Reynolds Stone, cr. 8vo. George's 635-214 1978 £5

PAUL, R. B.   The Antiquities of Greece. Oxford, 1835. Engraved plts., fcap. 8vo. George's 635-489 1978 £6.50

PAULDING, HIRAM   Journal of a Cruise of the United States Schooner Dolphin, among the Islands of the Pacific Ocean;.... New York, 1831. 12mo, folding map, orig. pale green cloth, orig. printed paper label on spine, edges uncut, 1st ed., rare. Quaritch 978-62 1978 $950

PAULDING, JAMES KIRKE   The Puritan & His Daughter. New York, 1849. 1st ed., 2 vols. rebound as 1, orig. covers laid-down, new spine, very good. Greene 78-93 1978 $55

PAULDING, K. K.   Letters from the South by a Northern Man. NY, 1835. Foxed, covers worn, Bell Wiley's copy. Broadfoot's 44-735 1978 $35.00

PAULDING, JAMES KIRKE   Slavery in the: United States. New York, 1836. Spine rebacked, Bell Wiley's copy. Broadfoot's 44-736 1978 $26

PAULDING, JAMES KIRKE   Westward Ho. New York, 1832. 1st ed., 2 vols., orig. green cloth covered bds. in fine cond., boxed in marbilized slipcase with brown calf corded spine & gold tooled lettering, better than average copy. Current 24-37 1978 $125

PAULET, AMIAS   The Letter-Books of .... 1874. Octavo, good. Upcroft 10-133 1978 £15

PAULIAN, R.   Coleopteres scarabeides de l'Indochine. Paris, 1945. Large 8vo, illus., map, orig. covers. Van der Peet 127-183 1978 Dfl 60

PAULINE Agassiz Shaw. Boston, 1917. Portr., illus., 8vo., orig. bds., ltd. ed. Morrill 239-605 1978 $9

PAULLIN, CHARLES O.   Commodore John Rodgers, Captain, Commodore, and Senior Officer of the American Navy 1773-1838. Cleveland, 1910. Cloth, 1st ed. Hayman 73-599 1978 $25

PAULLINI, C. F.   Lagographia Curiosa Seu Leporis Descriptio.... Vindel, 1691. 1st ed, sm. 12mo, sm. 8vo, contemp vellum. Book Chest 17-280 1978 $200

PAULO Posprandials. Cambridge, 1883. 4to, illus., title page & edges foxed, buckram. Eaton 45-384 1978 £9

PAULUS JOVIUS
Please turn to
GIOVIO, PAOLO

PAULSEN, FRIEDRICH   The German Universities. New York, 1895. 8vo., ex-lib. Morrill 239-572 1978 $10

PAULSON, J.   Index Lucretianus, Nach Den Ausgaben Von Lachmann, et al. 1926. Sewn. Allen 234-591 1978 $17.50

PAULY, A.   Realenzyklopaedie Der Klassischen Altertumswissenschaft. 1899-1912. Vols. 2-7, ex-lib., buckram, 1 vol. half calf. Allen 234-M 1978 $175

PAUSANIAS   Arx Athenarum a Pausania Descripta in Usum Scholarum ed. O. Jahn et A. Michaelis. 1901. 2 vols., bds., stiff wrs., plt. Allen 234-718 1978 $10

PAUSANIAS   Descriptio Graeciae. 1889-93. 2 vols., half calf. Allen 234-949 1978 $15

PAUSANIAS   Graeciae Descriptio Accurata. Leipzig, 1696. Thick folio, gilt-tooled, orig. vellum, pres. copy, inscr'd by Bernard Pagenstecher, fine copy. Salloch 345-150 1978 $125

PAUW, CORNELIUS DE   Recherches Philosophiques Sur Les Americains. Berlin, 1771. 3 vols., 8vo., calf, binds. rubbed. Salloch 348-188 1978 $70

PAVLOV, IVAN PETROVITCH Die Arbeit Der Verdauungsdrusen. Wiesbaden, 1898. Tall 8vo., illus., contemp. half black shagreen, backstrip chipped off, foxed, very good copy, 1st German ed. Zeitlin 245-186 1978 $450

PAVLOV, IVAN PETROVITCH Conditioned Reflexes. Oxford University Press, 1927. Library marks, otherwise good. Rittenhouse 49-622 1976 $125

PAVLOV, IVAN PETROVITCH Conditioned Reflexes: An Investigation of the Physiological Activity of the Cerebral Cortex. Oxford University Press, 1927. Illus., tall 8vo., buckram, 1st ed. in English. Argosy Special-70 1978 $100

PAWLING, JESSE RANDOLPH Dr. Samuel Guthrie Discoverer of Chloroform, Manufacturer of Percussion Pellets, Industrial Chemist (1782-1848). Watertown, Brewster Press, 1947. Plts. Butterfield 21-269 1978 $7.50

PAXSON, FREDERIC L.   History of the American Frontier, 1763-1893. Boston, (1924). 1st ed. MacManus 239-388 1978 $17.50

PAXTON, JOHN A.   An Alphabetical List of All the Wards, Streets, Roads, Lanes, Alleys, Avenues, Courts, Wharves, Ship Yards, Public Bldgs., &c, in the City & Suburbs of Philadelphia... Philadelphia, (1810). 1st ed., orig. marbled wrs., worn, old libr. bookplate & blindstamps, scarce, 8vo. Americanist 101-110 1978 $60

PAYER, JULIUS   New Lands Within The Arctic Circle... New York, 1877. Coloured frontis, maps, illus., orig. cloth, 8vo, head & tailbands repaired. Edwards 1012-596 1978 £20

PAYER, JULIUS   New Lands Within the Arctic Circle. New York, 1877. 1st Amer. ed., worn binding, 8vo. Book Chest 17-281 1978 $32

PAYN, JAMES   Gleams of Memory. 1894. 1st. ed., half title, orig. blue cloth, v.g. Jarndyce 16-927 1978 £10.50

PAYNE, MRS. ALFRED   Pits and Furnaces... 1869. 1st. ed., half title, orig. blue cloth, v.g., pres. copy from author to her daughter. Jarndyce 16-928 1978 £22

PAYNE, EDWARD F.   The Charity of Charles Dickens. Boston, 1929. Illus., full leather binding, gold lettering on spine and gold ruled edges limited to 425 copies, boxed, good. Nestler Rare 78-255 1978 $15

PAYNE, F.   The Charity of Charles Dickens... Boston, 1929. Only 100 copies printed, half title, orig. cream bds., back hinge slightly worn, otherwise v.g. Jarndyce 16-593 1978 £24

PAYNE, J. F.   Thomas Sydenham. Masters of Medicine. London, 1900. Rittenhouse 49-623 1976 $10

PAYNE, J. T.   Bibliotheca Grevilliana. Parts Second and Third. London, 1842-72. 4 vols., first 3 vols. are med. 8vo., vol. 4 is imp. 8vo. orig. cloth, spines defective, 1 cover detached, 1 joint cracked, text fine and unopened. Forster 130-220 1978 £45

PAYNE, LEONIDAS WARREN, JR.   A Word-List from East Alabama.   Austin, 1909. 8vo., orig. wrs., ex-lib. Morrill 239-235 1978 $8.50

PAYNE, ROGER   Two Bindings by Roger Payne in the Library of Lord Rothschild. Cambridge, 1947. Ltd. to 100 copies, colored plts., folio, orig. bds., cloth back. Forster 130-70 1978 £30

PAYNE, WILLIAM   An Introduction to the Game of Draughts. London, 1756. Small quarto, full contemp. calf, exceedingly rare, 1st ed. Bennett 7-60 1978 $750

PAYNE, WILLIAM W.   Speech of Mr..., of Alabama, on the Bill Making Appropriations for Certain Rivers and Harbors. Delivered in the House...April 5, 1844. N.P., n.d. Disbound. Hayman 72-674 1978 $8.50

PAYNE-GALLWAY, RALPH   The Crossbow. Illus., cr. 4to. Traylen 88-515 1978 £10

PEACOCK, EDWARD   Index to the English Speaking Students Who Have Graduated at Leyden University. London, 1883. 8vo., ex-lib. Morrill 239-573 1978 $15

PEACOCK, THOMAS LOVE   Crotchet Castle. 1831. 1st. ed., sm. 8vo, bound around 1920? in citron morocco, gilt. Hannas 54-234 1978 £85

PEACOCK, THOMAS LOVE   Headlong Hall. London, 1822. 12mo, original quarter cloth and boards, printed paper label (trifle worn), 3rd ed., revised. Ximenes 47-224 1978 $45

PEACOCK, THOMAS LOVE   Headlong Hall. London, 1837. 12mo, original purple cloth, frontispiece (foxed), very good copy, "C" binding, very scarce. Ximenes 47-225 1978 $45

PEACOCK, THOMAS LOVE   The Misfortunes of Elphin. 1829. 1st. ed., 12mo, orig. bds., uncut & unopened, housed in quarter morocco slipcase, A. Edw. Newton's bookplt. Hannas 54-235 1978 £75

PEACOCK, THOMAS LOVE   The Misfortunes of Elphin. London, 1829. 12mo, orig. green and parchment boards, largely unopened, spine chipped at top, rubbing of boards, 1st ed. Bennett 7-84 1978 $175

PEACOCK, THOMAS LOVE   Palmyra, and Other Poems. 1806. 1st. ed., sm. 8vo, frontispiece, orig. paper bds., spine slightly defective, entirely uncut, light foxing. Hannas 54-236 1978 £160

PEAKE, A. S.   An Outline of Christianity, the Story of Our Civilisation. (c. 1925). Coloured illus., 5 vols., roy. 8vo. George's 635-1111 1978 £5.25

PEAKE, MERVYN   The Craft of the Lead Pencil. London, 1946. 8vo, orig. bds., 1st. ed., good copy. Sexton 7-39 1978 £10

PEAKE, MERVYN   How a Romantic Novel was Evolved. Grey Walls Press, 1949. Plts., very good, worn d.w., first English ed. Bell Book 17-715 1978 £7.50

PEAKE, MERVYN   Letters from a Lost Uncle. 1948. Illus. by author, pict. cloth, covers soiled, good, first English ed. Bell Book 17-716 1978 £35

PEAKE, ORA BROOKS   The Colorado Range Cattle Industry. Glendale, 1937. Cloth, gilt top, frontis., fold. maps, facs., 1st ed., fine. Dykes 35-74 1978 $35

PEAKE, R. B.   The Characteristic Costume of France... 1819. 4to., text in French and English, coloured plts., some signed by R. Havell, sl. foxing, contemp. 1/2 dark blue mor., rubbed. Quaritch 983-69 1978 $650

PEALE, ARTHUR L.   Uncas and the Mohegan-Pequot. Boston, 1939. 1st ed., illus. MacManus 239-1207 1978 $10

PEALE, REMBRANDT   Graphics, The Art Of Accurate Delineation,.... Philadelphia, 1850. Old calf leather with marbled boards, rebacked with cloth, plates, map, illus., 8vo. Americanist 101-111 1978 $25

PEARCE, CHARLES E.   Madame Vestris and Her Times. (1920). Orig. cloth, 8vo., plts., spine faded. Howes 194-1273 1978 £6

PEARCE, HAYWOOD J. JR.   Benjamin H. Hill, Secession and Reconstruction. Chicago, 1928. Bell Wiley's copy. Broadfoot's 44-297 1978 $20.00

PEARCE, J. E.   Annual Report of WPA and the University of Texas Archaeological Research. Austin, 1933. Illus. Jenkins 116-1059 1978 $8.50

PEARCE, STEWART   Annals of Luzerne County; A Record of Interesting Events, Traditions, and Anecdotes... Philadelphia, 1860. 1st ed., lg. fold. map, illus., orig. cloth, spine faded, but very fine copy, very scarce. MacManus 239-1541 1978 $100

PEARCE, T. M.   Lane of the Llano, Being the Story of Jim (Lane) Cook. Boston, 1936. 1st ed. Jenkins 116-247 1978 $30

PEARL, RAYMOND   Alcohol and Longevity. New York, 1926. Rittenhouse 49-625 1976 $10

PEARL, RAYMOND   Studies in Human Biology. Baltimore, 1924. Library marks. Rittenhouse 49-624 1976 $25

PEARSE, H. W.   History of the East Surrey Regiment, Vol. II 1914 -17. 1923. Photographs, 8vo. George's 635-850 1978 £7.50

PEARSE, P. H.   The Mother and other Tales. Dundalk, 1916. Second ed., orig. binding, good. Rota 211-481 1978 £7.50

PEARSON, A. F. S.   Thomas Cartwright and Elizabethan Puritanism, 1535-1603. Cambridge, 1925. Octavo, good. Upcroft 10-479 1978 £12.50

PEARSON, EDMUND   Murder at Smutty Nose and Other Murders. New York, (1938). Illus. Biblo BL781-791 1978 $9

PEARSON, EDMUND LESTER   Books in Black and Red. 1923. First ed., signed by Pearson. Austin 82-701 1978 $25

PEARSON, EDMUND LESTER   Books in Black or Red. New York, 1923. 8vo., orig. cloth-backed bds. MacManus 238-1025 1978 $15

PEARSON, F. R.   Roman Yorkshire. 1936. Plt. Allen 234-722 1978 $7.50

PEARSON, FRANK A.   Food. New York, 1944. Biblo 251-367 1978 $10

PEARSON, GEORGE   The Escape of a Princess Pat. Toronto, 1918. Hood 117-143 1978 $20

PEARSON, H. J.   "Beyond Petsora Eastward." London, 1899. Coloured plts., illus., roy. 8vo, joints repaired, pres. copy from author. Traylen 88-592 1978 £18

PEARSON, KARL   The Grammar of Science. London, 1892. 1st ed., 8vo. Gilhofer 75-87 1978 SFr 250

PEARSON, KARL   The Grammar of Science. London, 1892. Rittenhouse 49-525A 1976 $15

PEARSON, KARL   Grammar of Science. Part I, Physical. (London?), 1911. Rittenhouse 49-626 1976 $20

PEARSON, SAMUEL   An Incurable Pioneer. Ft. Worth, 1928. 1st ed., illus. Jenkins 116-1061 1978 $25

PEARSON, T. G.   Birds of America. New York, (1936). Plates by L. A. Fuertes, 4to, orig. cloth. Book Chest 17-282 1978 $20

PEARY, ROBERT EDWIN   The North Pole. 1910. 1st. London ed., folding map, illus., roy. 8vo, orig. cloth. Edwards 1012-598 1978 £20

PEARY, ROBERT EDWIN   The North Pole, Its Discovery in 1909 Under the Auspices of the Arctic Club. New York, 1910. Full-page plts., colored & b/w. Hood 117-108 1978 $50

PEARY, ROBERT EDWIN   Northward over the "Great Ice". London, 1898. 1st. ed., 2 vols., 8vo, frontispieces, illus., orig. blue cloth, gilt, top edge gilt, lib. labels removed, corners trifle bumped, indelible lib. stamp in margins. Deighton 5-167 1978 £75

PEARY, ROBERT EDWIN   Northward Over the "Great Ice"... 1898. 2 vols., portraits, maps, illus., 8vo, orig. cloth. Edwards 1012-597 1978 £35

PEASE, E. M.   Communication... Relative to the Troubles in That State. Washington, 1868. Jenkins 116-1062 1978 $35

PEATTIE, DONALD CULROSS   Audubon's America. Boston, 1940. 1st ed., tall 4to, uncut, illus. in color, ltd. signed ed., fine. MacManus 239-35 1978 $40

PEATTIE, DONALD CULROSS   A Gathering of Birds. New York, 1939. 8vo., orig. cloth. Book Chest 17-283 1978 $22

PEATTIE, RODERICK   The Great Smokies. New York, 1943. Illus. Broadfoot 50-173 1978 $12

PEBRER, PABLO   Historia Administrativa y Estadistica General de las Colonias Inglesas en Todas las Partes del Mundo.... Manila, 1852. 1st ed., quarto, folding tables, quarter calf over grained cloth boards. Bennett 20-162 1978 $125

PECHAM, JOHN   Hamellium, Pascasiu,.... (Paris), 1556. 1st ed., 4to, woodcut printer's device on title, woodcut initials, woodcut diagrams and illus., later marbled wr. Bennett 20-163 1978 $550

PECHLIN, JOHANNES NICOLAAS   Jani Leoniceni Veronenis Metamorphosis Aesculapii & Apollonis Pancreatici. Lugd. Batavorum, 1673. 8vo., half vellum, rare, very scarce. Offenbacher 30-65 1978 $350

PECHLIN, JOHANNES NICOLAAS   Observationum Physico-Medicarum Libri Tres. Hamburgi, 1691. Sm. thick 4to., engr. frontis., plts., contemp. calf, worn, lightly browned, library stamp & ownership inscr. dated 1744, very good copy from the library of Dr. Alfred M. Hellman, 1st ed. Zeitlin 245-187 1978 $275

PECK, CHARLES H.   Annual Report of the State Botanist of New York State. Albany, 1897. 4to., ex-lib., embossed stamp on plts., colored plts. Morrill 239-574 1978 $17.50

PECK, CHARLES H.   The Jacksonian Epoch. New York, 1899. Cloth. Hayman 73-600 1978 $15

PECK, GEORGE   Wyoming: Its History, Stirring Incidents and Romantic Adventures. New York, 1858. Illus., first ed., top of spine torn. Biblo 247-250 1978 $27.50

PECK, GEORGE W.   Adventures of One Terence McGrant. New York, 1871. Orig. binding, clean, slight wear, 1st ed. Hayman 71-234 1978 $12.50

PECKE, RICHARD   Christs Watch-Word. London, 1635. 1st ed., 4to, disbound, top edge slightly trimmed, others uncut. Hannas 54-237 1978 £12.50

PECKER, WILLIAM   A Wedding Ring, fit for the finger:.... Worcester, 1802. Tiny 4" chapbook, flowered wrappers, scarce, spine partly gone. Victoria 34-607 1978 $65

PECKHAM, ANN   The English Cook; or, Prudent Housewife. Leeds, 1767. 12mo, contemporary calf (bit worn), 1st ed., rare, foxed throughout. Ximenes 47-225 1978 $225

PECKHAM, HOWARD H.   Pontiac and the Indian Uprising. Princeton, 1947. Map, illus., scarce. MacManus 239-1208 1978 $20

PECKWELL, ROBERT H.   Cases of Controverted Elections in the Second Parliament of the United Kingdom... London, 1805. 2 vols., 8vo, contemp. calf. Traylen 88-471 1978 £18

PEEL, LAWRENCE   A Sketch of the Life and Character of Sir Robert Peel. 1860. 1st. ed., half title, orig. brown cloth, fine. Jarndyce 16-929 1978 £12

PEEL, SIDNEY   Trooper 8008 I Y. London, 1901. Folding map, illus., covers very shabby, internally good, 8vo, orig. cloth. K Books 239-370 1978 £5

PEELE, GEORGE   The Battell Of Alcazar, Fought in Barbarie, between Sebastian king of Portugall and Abdelmelec king of Marocco. London, 1594. Sm. 4to, floated copy (formerly inlaid) with clever marginal restoration, headlines, catchwords and signatures skillful pen-facsimile, brown mor., gilt edges by Riviere, 1st and only ed. Quaritch 978-122 1978 $3,500

PEET, T. E.   The Cemeteries of Abydos. 1913-14. 3 vols., plts., 4to, orig. printed bds., cloth backs. Edwards 1012-227 1978 £45

PEET, T. E.   The City of Akhenaten, Part I... 1923. 4to, plts., bds., cloth back. Edwards 1012-228 1978 £18

PEETERS, JACQUES   Hongariae Civitates... (Antwerp, c.1670). Engraved title, dedication, plts., oblong 4to, contemp. calf, worn. Traylen 88-441 1978 £800

PEGGE, SAMUEL   Anecdotes of the English Language. 1803. 1st. ed., orig. calf, red labels, v.g. Jarndyce 16-930 1978 £55

PEGGE, SAMUEL   Curialia Miscellanea, or Ancedotes of Old Times.... London, 1814-1818. 2 vols., 8vo, contemp. half calf, from famous Beckford lib. with pencil notes by Beckford. Traylen 88-312 1978 £150

PEGGE, SAMUEL   Curialia Miscellanea, Or Anecdotes of Old Times... 1818. 1st. ed., frontis portrait, half calf, spine gilt, red label, fine. Jarndyce 16-931 1978 £28

PEGUY, CHARLES   Le Mystere De La Charite de Jeanne D'arc. New York, Wells College Press, (1943). One of an ed. of 475 copies, cloth, d.w. Battery Park 1-159 1978 $100

PEIGNOT, GABRIEL   Le Livre des Singularites par G. P. Philomneste, Auteur des Amusents Philogiques. Dijon, 1841. 8vo., marbled bds., calf spine, first ed. King 7-374 1978 £25

PEIRAUD   Nuovo Libro di Scrittura, Ovvero l'Arte d'Imparare a ben Scrivere Senza Maestro. Torino, n.d. (c. 1766). Oblong 4to., wrs., eng. plts. Schumann 511-45 1978 sFr 1,050

PEIRCE, BENJAMIN   A History of Harvard University, from...1636, to the Period of the American Revolution. Cambridge, 1833. Plts., 8vo., orig. bds., cloth back, hinges cracked, 1st ed. Morrill 239-417 1978 $10

PEIRCE, PARKER I.   The Adventures of "Antelope Bill" in the Indian War of 1862. Marshall, 1898. Illus., half mor., 1st ed., rare. Ginsberg 14-877 1978 $350

PEIRSON, A. L.   Memoir of Edward A. Holyoke, M. D., LL.D. Boston, 1829. Facsimile, 8vo., orig. cloth, ex-lib., sm. library labels on spine, 1st ed. Morrill 239-203 1978 $27.50

PELICAN PRESS   Typography: Type Specimens Grouped, Displayed and Numbered for the Ease of Customers Who Desire a Particular Character and Size. London, Pelican Press, n.d. Cloth, light foxing. Dawson's 447-121 1978 $100

PELLATT, EMMA MARY   Western Gleanings. Toronto, 1893. Card cover, illus., signed by author. Hood 117-913 1978 $25

PELLET, ELIAS P.   History of the 114th Regiment, New York State Volunteers. Norwich, 1866. Photos tipped in. Butterfield 21-124 1978 $45

PELLETREAU, WILLIAM S.   History of Putnam County, New York... Philadelphia, 1886. Illus., maps, 4to. MacManus 239-1096 1978 $100

PELLEY, WILLIAM DUDLEY   Drag. 1925. First ed. Austin 82-698 1978 $12.50

PELLEY, WILLIAM DUDLEY   The Greater Glory. 1919. Austin 82-699 1978 $10

PELLOE, E.   West Australian Orchids. Perth, 1930. Sm. 8vo, scarce, color plates, signed, front. in poor facsimile, orig. cloth. Book Chest 17-284 1978 $35

PELLOW, ROBERT E.   When Texas Came Romping into the Union: Tracing Its Footsteps Before and After. Waco, 1935. 1st ed., stiff pict. wr. Jenkins 116-1065 1978 $20

PELTIER, JEAN GABRIEL   Dernier Tableau de Paris... Londres, 1792-93. 1st. ed., 2 vols., 8vo, folding map, half roan, gilt, slightly rubbed, marginal water-stains in vol. 1. Hannas 54-134 1978 £25

PELZER, LOUIS   The Cattlemen's Frontier. Glendale, 1936. Cloth, gilt top, illus., plts., 1st ed., fine. Dykes 35-75 1978 $35

PELZER, LOUIS   The Cattleman's Frontier,.... Glendale, 1936. Uncut, t.e.g., 1st ed. Jenkins 116-1066 1978 $45

PEMBER, EDWARD HENRY   Adrastus of Phrygia and Other Poems.
London, 1897. 1st ed., ltd. 250 copies, laid paper, uncut, 1/4 leather
over bds., pres. copy to Mrs. Coventry Patmore, very good or better.
Limestone 9-229 1978 $30

PEMBER, EDWARD HENRY   Debita flacco, Echoes of Ode and Epode. Chiswick Press, 1891. Ltd. to 250 copies, orig. qtr. calf, a little rubbed. George's
635-479 1978 £5

PEMBERTON, CHARLES REECE   The History of Pel Verjuice. 1853. Sm. 8vo,
slightly foxed, orig. cloth, damp marked. Eaton 45-385 1978 £5

PEMBERTON, HENRY   The Dispensatory of the Royal College of Physicians, London. 1746. 8vo., contemp. sprinkled calf, rebacked, first ed.
Quaritch 977-62 1978 $85

PEMBERTON, J. DESPARD   Facts and Figures Relating to Vancouver Island
and British Columbia... 1860. Maps, modern half calf, few lib. stamps, one
map repaired, 2 mounted on linen, 8vo. Edwards 1012-450 1978 £30

PEMBERTON, MORTON H.   Reuben: His Book. Centralia, 1904. Cloth.
Hayman 73-601 1978 $7.50

PENA, P.   Nova Stirpium Adversaria.... Antwerp, Plantin,
1576. Title within a woodcut border, woodcuts, folio, contemp. vellum, back
cover defective. Traylen 88-614 1978 £550

PENDE, NICOLA   Le Debolezze Di Constituzione. Roma, 1922.
2 vols. in 1, sm. 8vo., orig. brown prtd. upper wr. of Vol. II bound in, brown
library buckram, gilt, marginal pencil notes, stamps, author's pres. inscr., fine
copy, 1st ed. Zeitlin 245-188 1978 $75

PENDLETON, J.   Newspaper Reporting. Battery Park 1-264 1978
$22.50

PENDLETON, WILLIAM C.   Political History of Appalachian Virginia 1776-
1927. Dayton, 1927. Cloth. Hayman 73-717 1978 $15

PENDRILL, C.   Wanderings in Medieval London. 1928. Illus.,
8vo. Upcroft 12-334 1978 £5

PENFIELD, WILDER   Cytology & Cellular Pathology of the Nervous
System. New York, 1932. 3 vols. Rittenhouse 49-630 1976 $35

PENFIELD, WILDER   Epilepsy and Cerebral Localization. Baltimore,
1941. Rittenhouse 49-629 1976 $25

PENHALLOW, SAMUEL   The History of the Indian Wars of New-England,
With the Eastern Indians... Boston, 1924. Fasc. of rare Boston ed., nice, later
cloth, ltd. to 250 copies. MacManus 239-1209 1978 $25

PENHALLOW, SAMUEL   The History of the Wars of New-England With the
Eastern Indians. Cincinnati, 1859. Nice. MacManus 239-1210 1978 $35

PENHALLOW, SAMUEL   The History of the Wars of New-England With
The Eastern Indians... Cincinnati, 1859. Rebound, modern clean. Hayman
71-624 1978 $40

PENICHER, LOUIS   Traite Des Embaumemens Selon Les Anciens Et Les
Modernes. Paris, 1699. 12mo., orig. bds., lightly browned, good copy, 1st ed.
Zeitlin 245-189 1978 $145

PENLEY, AARON   Sketching from Nature in Water-Colours. London, n.d. Illus., orig. water-colour drwgs., plts., 4to. Morrill 241-452 1978
$27.50

PENLEY, AARON   Sketching from Nature in Water-Colours. London, Paris and New York, n.d., (1869?). Illus., folio, orig. cloth, a little
soiled, plts., most in color. Americanist 102-11 1978 $50

PENN, W. A.   The Soverane Herbe. London, 1901. Illus.,
8vo., ex-lib., spine slightly torn, 1st ed. Morrill 241-453 1978 $7.50

PENN, WILLIAM   Correspondence...1700-1750. From the Orig.
Letters in Possession of the Logan Family... Philadelphia, 1870-72. 2 vols.,
tall 8vos., slight wear. Americanist 102-83 1978 $35

PENN, WILLIAM   The Select Works of .... 1825. 4th. ed., 3
vols., half calf, octavo, good. Upcroft 10-135 1978 £30

PENNANT, THOMAS   Indian Ecology. London, 1790. 2nd. ed.,
plts., little foxed, 4to, russia leather, joints weak, many blank leaves bound in.
Traylen 88-615 1978 £48

PENNANT, THOMAS   The Literary Life of the Late Thomas Pennant,
Esq. By Himself. London, 1793. 4to, original marbled boards, drab paper backstrip (bit worn), 1st ed., fine copy. Ximenes 47-227 1978 $125

PENNANT, THOMAS   Some Account of London. 1793. 3rd. ed., 4to,
Frontis map & plts., slight browning of title, otherwise fine handsome copy in orig.
tree calf, red & green labels. Jarndyce 16-818 1978 £54

PENNANT, THOMAS   A Tour in Scotland. Chester, 1771. Plts., 8vo.,
rather thumbed and age-marked throughout, scarce. K Books 244-433 1978 £33

PENNELL, ELIZABETH ROBINS   Charles Godfrey Leland. Boston, 1906. 1st.
ed., illus., 2 vols. Baldwins' 51-178 1978 $15

PENNELL, ELIZABETH ROBINS   The Life of James McNeill Whistler. 1908.
2 vols., 4to., 1st ed., plts., cloth-backed bds. Quaritch 979-328 1978 $40

PENNELL, ELIZABETH ROBINS   Our Philadelphia. Philadelphia, 1914. Illus.,
4to. MacManus 239-1637 1978 $25

PENNELL, ELIZABETH ROBINS   Whistler Journal. Philadelphia, 1921. 1 of
500 copies signed by authors, illus., thick 4to., vellum over cloth, t.e.g., uncut,
fine. Houle 10-257 1978 $95

PENNELL, JOSEPH   The Adventures of an Illustrator Mostly in Following His Authors in America and Europe. Boston, 1925. Tall quarto, buckram,
gilt, illus., colored port. frontis. by William Strang, 1st Trade ed., fine.
Duschnes 220-239 1978 $35

PENNELL, JOSEPH   Etchers and Etching. London, (1920). First of
this ed., 4to., plts. Biblo 247-410 1978 $40

PENNELL, JOSEPH   The Graphic Arts. Modern Men and Modern Methods. Chicago, 1920. Illus., 4to. Biblo BL781-709 1978 $16.50

PENNELL, JOSEPH   The Jew at Home. 1892. Illus. by author.
Austin 79-547 1978 $47.50

PENNELL, JOSEPH   Lithography & Lithographers. London, 1898.
Illus., plts., lg. 4to., orig. parchment very soiled, internally good. K Books
244-434 1978 £70

PENNELL, JOSEPH   Memorial Exhibition of the Works of the Late
Joseph Pennell. Philadelphia, 1926. First ed., tall 8vo., illus., orig. binding.
Americanist 101-9 1978 $25

PENNELL, JOSEPH   Pen Drawing and Pen Draughtsmen. New
York, 1920. 4to., orig. bds., lea. back, open-backed cloth case, 1 of 125
signed copies on Japan paper with orig. drwg. by Pennell. Morrill 241-454
1978 $225

PENNEY, MISS L.   The National Temperance Orator. New York,
1884. Orig. binding, clean. Hayman 71-625 1978 $10

PENNINGTON, EDGAR L.   Apostle of New Jersey, John Talbot, 1645-1727.
Philadelphia, (1938). MacManus 239-1311 1978 $10

PENNSYLVANIA   Inventory of the County Archives of Pa.: No.
6, Berks County. Reading, 1941. Illus., 8vo., orig. binding. Americanist 101-
15 1978 $17.50

PENNSYLVANIA COMMITTEE ON HISTORICAL RESEARCH   Church Music and
Musical Life in Pennsylvania in the Eighteenth Century. Philadelphia, 1926,
1927, 1938 and 1947. 3 vols. in 4, illus., plts., orig. cloth, fine. MacManus
239-1418 1978 $125

PENNSYLVANIA GENEALOGICAL SOCIETY   Publications of. Philadelphia,
1895-1944. 14 vols., orig. 3/4 mor., good. MacManus 239-1467 1978 $225

PENNSYLVANIA Historical Society Bulletin. 1845-1847. Vol. 1, map, view,
scarce. Baldwins' 51-472 1978 $75

PENNSYLVANIA STATE DENTAL SOCIETY Transactions of the Pennsylvania State Dental Society. Lancaster, 1875. 8vo., old cloth, lea. back. Morrill 239-205 1978 $25

PENNYBACKER, A. J.H. A New History of Texas for Schools. Austin, 1900. Illus., maps. Jenkins 116-1067 1978 $15

PENNYPACKER, MORTON The Two Spies Nathan Hale and Robert Townsend. Boston, 1930. 1st ed., ltd. to 780 copies, illus., uncut, slipcase. MacManus 239-616 1978 $25

PENNYPACKER, SAMUEL W. Annals of Phoenixville & Its Vicinity:.... Philadelphia, 1872. 1st ed., tall 8vo, folding fronts, facsimiles, autograph letter signed from Pennypacker, orig. binding. Americanist 101-112 1978 $55

PENNYPACKER, SAMUEL W. Annals of Phoenixville and Its Vicinity: From the Settlement to...1871. Philadelphia, 1872. Fine, rebound, fold. map, inscribed by author, scarce. MacManus 239-1598 1978 $60

PENNYPACKER, SAMUEL W. Pennsylvania In American History. Philadelphia, 1910. 1st ed., only 750 copies, large 8vo, wear, orig. binding. Americanist 101-113 1978 $25

PENNYPACKER, SAMUEL W. Pennsylvania in American History. Philadelphia, 1910. Uncut. MacManus 239-1599 1978 $27.50

PENNYPACKER, SAMUEL W. The Settlement of Germantown, Pa. and the Beginning of German Emigration to North America. Philadelphia, 1899. 1st ed., illus., ltd. to 300 copies, uncut, scarce. MacManus 239-1600 1978 $45

PENQUIN Science News. 1946-50. Complete set, no. 1-54, photographs, drawings, 54 vols., cr. 8vo., orig. wrappers. George's 635-938 1978 £15

PENTLAND, H. C. The Lachine Strike of 1843. 1948. Hood's 115-315 1978 $7.50

PENTRILL, MRS. FRANK Odile, A Tale of the Commune. Dublin, 1886. 1st. & possibly only ed., 8vo, orig. red pictorial cloth, gilt, nice copy. Fenning 32-260 1978 £6

PENTY, A. J. A Guildsman's Interpretation of History. 1923. 8vo. George's 635-736 1978 £5

PENTY, A. J. The Restoration of the Gild System. 1906. 8vo. George's 635-377 1978 £6

PEOPLE of the Old World. Concord, c.1840. Chapbook, lower corner torn, pictorial wrappers, very good. Victoria 34-610 1978 $12.50

THE PEOPLE Poisoned. 1835. 8vo., unbound, scarce. P. M. Hill 142-227 1978 £38

PEPLER, HILARY DOUGLAS C. Concerning Dragons. Ditchling, 1922. 12mo., wood engrs., sewn, 7th ed. Quaritch 979-283 1978 $55

PEPLER, HILARY DOUGLAS C. The Devil's Devices. 1915. 1st ed., illus. by Eric Gill, cr. 8vo., orig. canvas-backed bds., edges uncut. George's 635-172 1978 £20

PEPPER, CHARLES M. Life-Work of Louis Klopsch. Romance of a Modern Knight of Mercy. New York, (1910). Cloth. Hayman 72-609 1978 $10

PEPPER, WILLIAM System of Practical Medicine. Volume V. Diseases of the Nervous System. Philadelphia, 1886. Rittenhouse 49-634 1976 $10

PEPYS, SAMUEL The Diary. London, 1893-99. Lg. paper ed., ltd. to 250 sets, 10 vols.,roy. 8vo., qtr. vellum gilt. K Books 244-256 1978 £60

PEPYS, SAMUEL The Diary of Samuel Pepys. London, 1926. 15mo, 3 vols., gilt lettering on spine, t.e.g., bookplates, light shelf wear, near Mint, 1st ed., collector's cond. Desmarais 1-339 1978 $25

PEPYS, SAMUEL The Diary. 1926-28. 12 vols., plts., frontis., map, pedigrees, cloth, good unopened set in d.ws. Quaritch 979-371 1978 $100

PEPYS, SAMUEL The Diary. 1928. Library ed., plts., 10 vols., demy 8vo., half mor., backs panelled and gilt, gilt tops, other edges untrimmed, attractive. Howes 194-1089 1978 $75

PEPYS, SAMUEL A Last Diary of the Great Warr. 1919. Colored frontis. & plts. by John Kettelwell, cloth-backed bds., very good, first English ed. Bell Book 17-17-492 1978 £6.50

PEPYS, SAMUEL Memories Relating to the State of the Royal Navy of England, for Ten Years, Determin'd December, 1688. (London), 1690. 1st ed., 8vo., 1st issue, frontis, clean & crisp copy, 18th Cent. paneled calf, scarce. Current Misc. 8-36 1978 $850

PEPYS, SAMUEL Memoirs of...His Diary, from 1659 to 1669, and a Selection from His Private Correspondence. London, (c.1870s). Frontis. ports., light foxing, orig. bind. Petrilla 13-71 1978 $8.50

PERATE, A. l'Archeologie Chretienne. Paris, n.d. 8vo., cloth, illus. Van der Peet H-64-184 1978 Dfl 35

PERCIVAL, GERTRUDE Lilian Stanhope, The Clergyman's Orphan... 1882. 8vo, orig. printed wrapper, nice copy. Fenning 32-261 1978 £10.50

PERCIVAL, MAC IVER The Chintz Book. 1923. Lg. 8vo., coloured and plain plts., cloth. Quaritch 983-70 1978 $50

PERCIVAL, MACIVER The Fan Book. New York, (1921). Illus., 8vo., 1st Amer. ed. Morrill 239-581 1978 $25

PERCIVAL, MAC IVER The Walnut Collector. New York, 1927. 31 plts., 47 line drawings. Baldwins' 51-139 1978 $7.50

PERCIVAL, ROBERT An Account of the Island of Ceylon... London, 1803. 1st. ed., 4to, folding engraved map, contemporary sprinkled calf, rebacked with modern calf, red morocco label, corners worn, foxed throughout, some worming. Deighton 5-87 1978 £90

PERCIVAL, ROBERT An Account of the Island of Ceylon... 1803. Folding maps, 4to, half calf, charts browned. Edwards 1012-128 1978 £60

PERCIVAL, WINIFRED Not Only Music, Signora! 1947. Illus., photos. Austin 80-252 1978 $10

PERCY, L. Histoire d'une grande dame au XVIIIe siecle, la Comtesse Helene Potocka. 1888. Half mor., 8vo. George's 635-1256 1978 £5.25

PERCY, THOMAS The Hermit of Warkworth. Alnwick, 1806. 1st ed., engr. by Bewick, plates, illus., rebound in later cloth, scarce. Victoria 34-68 1978 $60

PERCY, THOMAS Reliques of Ancient English Poetry... 1767. 3 vols., 2nd. ed., frontis, old lib. stamp on verso vol. I, half-titles on all vols., orig. calf, rubbed at heads of spines, red labels, good, sound set. Jarndyce 16-154 1978 £48

PERCY, THOMAS Reliques of Ancient English Poetry. 1886. Library ed., 3 vols., orig. cloth, gilt tops, 8vo. Howes 194-1091 1978 £18

PERCY, WILLIAM ALEXANDER The Collected Poems of.... New York, 1943. Bell Wiley's copy. Broadfoot's 44-927 1978 $10

THE PERCY Folio of Old English Ballads and Romances... 1905-10. 4 vols., title in vol. I eng. by Blanche McManus, cloth backed bds., vol. 3 decorated by hand, ltd. ed. of 325 copies. Eaton 45-150 1978 £40

PEREGRINUS, PETER Epistle of Peter Peregrinus of Maricourt to Sygerus of Foncaucout, Soldier, Concerning the Magnet. (London, Chiswick Press, 1902). Sm. 4to., orig. cloth-backed prtd. bds., very fine copy, 1st ed. in English, ed. ltd. to 250 copies rubricated by hand. Norman 5-218 1978 $275

PEREIRA, J. Treatise on Food and Diet. 1843. New buckram, 8vo. George's 635-1347 1978 £10.50

PERELMAN, SIDNEY JOSEPH Acres and Pains. 1947. Illus. Austin 82-700 1978 $10

PERETTI, VINCENZO   Cours de Themes Libres, Ou Par Gradation....
Londres, 1801. 12mo, wrapper, nice copy. Fenning 32-262 1978 £6.50

PEREZ, ISAAC LOEB   Stories and Pictures. 1906. Austin 79-550
1978 $12.50

PEREZ DE MOYA, JUAN   Aritmetica Practica Y Especulativa. Madrid,
1643. Thick 4to., modern vellum. Salloch 345-151 1978 $150

PERFECTION of Military Discipline. 1690. 12mo., contemp. sprinkled sheep,
head of joint split, plts. F. Edwards 1013-404 1978 £250

PERGAMINI, GIACOMO   Il Memoriale della Lingua Italiana. Venezia,
1688. Folio, speckled calf, spine gilt, raised bands. King 7-77 1978 £40

PERIMUTTER, MISCHA   The Rag Bizness. Los Angeles, 1944. Illus.
Austin 79-551 1978 $12.50

PERIZONII, JAC   Rerum Per Europam maxime Gestarum Ab ineunte
Saeculo Sextodecimo usque ad Caroli V. Mortem &c. (Leyden), 1710. Octavo,
full contemp. vellum, sound, all edges red, bookplate. Bennett 20-165 1978
$150

PERKINS, AUGUSTUS   A Private Proof Printed in Order to Preserve Certain Matters Connected with the Boston Branch of the Perkins Family. Boston, 1890.
Signed. Biblo BL781-61 1978 $13.50

PERKINS, C. C.   Italian Sculptors: a History of Sculpture in Northern, Southern and Eastern Italy. 1868. Etchings by author, wood engravings,
4to. George's 635-265 1978 £8.50

PERKINS, D. A.   History of O'Brien County, Iowa. Sioux Falls,
1897. 1st ed., illus., ports., orig. cloth, fine. MacManus 239-980 1978 $50

PERKINS, ELI   Saratoga, 1901. New York, 1872. Illus., 200
photo etchings by author. Baldwins' 51-416 1978 $17.50

PERKINS, G. W.   Historical Sketches of Meriden. West Meriden,
1849. Fold. map, 3/4 calf, lib. marks, fine. MacManus 239-950 1978 $40

PERKINS, MRS. GEORGE A.
Please turn to
PERKINS, JULIA ANNA (SHEPARD)

PERKINS, JAMES H.   Annals of the West... Pittsburg, 1857. Baldwins' 51-566 1978 $20

PERKINS, JAMES H.   Associated Action. An Address Delivered Before
the Oxford Chapter of the Alpha Delta Phi, August 11th, 1840. Cincinnati, 1840.
Disbound. Hayman 72-563 1978 $10

PERKINS, JOHN   A Profitable Booke of Mr. John Perkins, Fellow
of the Inner Temple. London, 1614. 24mo, full early calf, somewhat rubbed,
restored. Bennett 7-86 1978 $200

PERKINS, JOSEPH J.   A Business Man's Estimate of Santa Barbara County,
California: its Climate, Soils and Products. Santa Barbara, 1884. Original printed
wr., 2nd ed. Ginsberg 14-167 1978 $135

PERKINS, JULIA ANNA (SHEPARD) Early Times on the Susquehanna. Binghamton, 1870. Scarce 1st ed., spine faded, rear joint weak, orig. binding, 8vo.
Americanist 101-114 1978 $35

PERKINS, JULIA ANNA (SHEPARD) Early Times on the Susquehanna. Binghamton, 1870. 1st ed. Biblo 247-125 1978 $22.50

PERKINS, JULIA ANNA (SHEPARD) Early Times on the Susquehanna. Binghamton, 1870. 1st ed., orig. cloth, scarce. MacManus 239-1601 1978 $50

PERKINS, MAXWELL E.   Editor to Author: The Letters of Maxwell E. Perkins. New York, 1950. Lg. 8vo., cloth, 1st ed., inscr. J. S. Lawrence 38-
F144 1978 $20

PERKINS, MAXWELL E.   Editor to Author: The Letters of Maxwell E. Perkins. New York, 1950. Red-brown cloth, frontis., 1st ed., 1st issue, fine in
dust jacket. Bradley 49-361 1978 $25

PERLES, ALFRED   The Renegade. 1943. Very good, worn d.w.,
very scarce, first English ed. Bell Book 16-706 1978 £25

PERLES, ALFRED   Round Trip. 1946. Pres. copy inscribed by
author, very good, first English ed. Bell Book 16-707 1978 £16.50

PERLEY, M. H.   A Hand-Book of Information for Emigrants to
New Brunswick. London, 1857. Pamphlet bound in library binding. Hood 117-
268 1978 $90

PERLEY, SIDNEY   The History of Boxford, Essex Co., Mass., From
the Earliest Settlement Known to the Present Time... Boxford, 1880. Illus.,
orig. cloth, lib. marks, fine. MacManus 239-1013 1978 $45

PERLEY, SIDNEY   History of Salem, Mass. Salem, 1924-28. 3
vols., illus., fine. MacManus 239-1050 1978 $60

PERONA, JOHN   El Morocco Family Album. New York, 1937.
Folio, photos. Biblo BL781-171 1978 $15

PERRAUDIERE, R. DE LA   Excursion aux Monuments Khmers. Angers, 1899.
8vo, orig. covers. Van der Peet 127-187 1978 Dfl 30

PERRAULT, CHARLES   Les Hommes Illustres qui ont Paru en France Pendant ce Siecle: avec Leurs Portraits au Naturel. Paris, 1696-1700. Folio, frontis., brown mor., 1st ed. Gilhofer 74-136 1978 sFr 2,000

PERRAULT, JOSEPH FRANCOIS   Extraits ou Precedents des Arrests Tires de Registres du Conseil Superieur de Quebec.... Quebec, 1824. Wolfe 39-425 1978
$150

PERRIN, JEAN   Traite de Chimie Physique. Les Principes. Paris,
1903. 8vo., orig. wrappers, uncut, first ed. Gurney 75-85 1978 £25

PERRIN, JOHN   Entertaining and Instructive Exercises. 1787.
Fifth ed., 12mo., contemp. sheep. Howes 194-299 1978 £10

PERRIN, PORTER G.   The Life and Works of Thomas Green Fessenden.
1925. 1st ed., frontis., orig. cloth, fine. MacManus 239-751 1978 $22.50

PERRIN DU LAC, FRANCOIS MARIE   Travels Through the Two Louisianas...
Phillips, 1807. Modern half calf, 8vo. Edwards 1012-520 1978 £40

PERRIN-DUPORTAL, HENRIETTE   Georgie au Jardin Zoologique. Paris, (1927).
Printed in blue ink, color plates in blue, cover color plate, very good. Victoria
34-611 1978 $10

PERROT, G.   A History of Art in Ancient Egypt. London,
1883. Illus., steel & coloured plts., 2 vols., sm. 4to, orig. pictorial cloth.
Sexton 7-93 1978 £25

PERRUCHOT, H.   Sous la Lumiere Noire. Paris, 1948. 4to., orig.
covers, lithos by Y. Alde, ltd. ed. of 320 numbered copies. Van der Peet H-64-
446 1978 Dfl 75

PERRY, GEORGE   Conchology or the Natural History of Shells....
London, n.d. (1811). Hand-coloured plts., folio, contemp. dark blue morocco,
gilt extra, gilt edges, unusuall clean copy. Traylen 88-616 1978 £600

PERRY, GEORGE   Conchology, or the Natural History of Shells.
1811. Lg. folio, plts., contemp. half mor., gilt spine, t.e.g. Quaritch 983-
354 1978 $2,125

PERRY, M. E.   Hearing a Far Call. Toronto, 1942. Card
cover. Hood 117-821 1978 $7.50

PERRY, M. E.   Song in the Silence and Other Poems. Toronto,
1947. Card cover. Hood 117-822 1978 $7.50

PERRY, MARTHA DERBY   Letters from a Surgeon of the Civil War. Boston,
1906. Illus. from photos, Bell Wiley's copy. Broadfoot's 44-528 1978 $27

PERRY, WILLIAM   The Royal Standard English Dictionary...
Edinburgh, 1804. Oblond 12mo, orig. unlettered sheep, rubbed & worn, but sound,
name cut from extreme upper blank margin of title, trifle dusty, good, sound copy.
Fenning 32-263 1978 £16.50

PERRY, WILLIAM   The Synonymous, Etymological and Pronouncing
Dictionary. 1805. 1st. ed., rebound in half calf, v.g. Jarndyce 16-595 1978
£34

PERRY, WILLIAM S.　　　An Historical Address Delivered in St. John's Church Dubuque, Iowa, on Occasion of the Semi-Centennial Celebration of the Organization of the Parish.　Davenport, 1896.　Original printed wr., lst ed. Ginsberg 14-421 1978 $35

PERSHALL, MISHA　　　About the Hour-Glass and the Scythe.　Woodstock, 1939.　Ltd. ed., author's signed pres., orig. wrs.　Biblo BL781-1105 1978 $10

PERSHING, JOHN J.　　　My Experiences in the World War.　New York, 1931.　2 vols., lst ed., orig. binding, clean.　Hayman 71-634 1978 $10

PERTHES, FREDERICK　　　Life and Times...　Edinburgh, 1858.　Frontis, portrait, attractive half calf, gilt spine, red label, v.g.　Jarndyce 16-932 1978 £5.50

PERZYNSKI, FRIEDRICH　　　Hokusai.　Bielefeld and Leipzig, 1904.　Illus., cloth-covered wrs., (creased and slightly soiled).　Dawson's 449-173 1978 $20

PESAROVIUS, PAUL POMIAN　　　Illuminatus in Veritate Religionis Christianae Hugo Grotius ut et Joannis Clerici De Eligenda Inter Dissentientes Christianos Sententia Liber Unicus.　1721.　Half vellum, spine torn.　Allen 234-1399 1978 $15

PETER, A.　　　Dublin Fragments.　1925.　lst ed., very good, octavo bound in cloth.　Hyland 128-346 1978 £5

PETER, JOHN　　　Artificial Versifying.　London, 1678.　8vo, old half calf (spine quite worn), 2nd ed., revised, very rare.　Ximenes 47-234 1978 $325

PETER PIPER'S Practical Principles Of Plain & Perfect Pronunciation.　Philadelphia, 1836.　12mo, later full straight-grained morocco decor. in gold with marbled end papers, orig. pict. wrs. bound in, hand colored woodcuts.　Americanist 101-115 1978 $300

PETERKIN, JULIA　　　Scarlet Sister Mary.　Indianapolis, (1928). lst ed., very good or better.　Limestone 9-230 1978 $10

PETERS, DEWITT C.　　　Kit Carson's Life and Adventures, from Facts Narrated by Himself.　Hartford, 1873.　Lea., crudely rebacked, enlarged, amateurishly rebacked.　Hayman 73-611 1978 $7.50

PETERS, HARRY T.　　　Currier & Ives, Printmakers to the American People.　Garden City, (1942).　Orig. binding, plts., d.j. slightly worn, fine. Hayman 71-635 1978 $12.50

PETERS, HARRY T.　　　Currier and Ives, Printmakers to the American People.　New York, 1942.　Special ed., 4to., illus.　Biblo 247- 406 1978 $27.50

PETERS, HUGH　　　A Way Propounded to Make the Poor in these and Other Nations Happy.　London, n.d. (1659).　Sm. 4to, modern calf, lst ed. Traylen 88-79 1978 £225

PETERS, JOHN P.　　　Quantitative Clinical Chemistry Interpretations. Volume I.　Baltimore, 1946.　Second ed., library marks, slight tear top of spine. Rittenhouse 49-636 1976 $15

PETERS, JOHN PUNNETT　　　Nippur, or Explorations and Adventures on the Euphrates.　New York, 1897.　Maps, illus., 2 vols., 8vo., ex-lib., lst ed. Morrill 241-460A 1978 $35

PETERS, WILLIAM THEODEORE　　　The Children of the Week.　New York, 1886. lst ed., illus. by Clinton Peters, gilt & enamelled cloth rubbed, good.　Victoria 34-612 1978 $12.50

PETERSON, CHAS. J.　　　Cruising In The Last War.　Philadelphia, 1850. lst ed., disbound, 2 vols., 8vo.　Americanist 101-116 1978 $22.50

PETERSON, EDWARD　　　History of Rhode Island.　New York, 1853.　lst ed., illus., lithographic plts., orig. cloth, very good.　MacManus 239-417 1978 $25

PETIT, J. L.　　　Remarks on Church Architecture.　1841.　Plts., some foxing, 2 vols., half mor.　George's 635-88 1978 £12.50

PETIT, PIERRE　　　Traite Historique Sur Les Amazones...　Leide, 1718.　lst. ed. in French, engraved title-pg., folding maps, plts., engravings, 2 vols., bound in 1, lg. 12mo, contemp. calf, gilt spine, nice.　Fenning 32-264 1978 £32

THE PETITION and Vindication of the Officers of the Armie, under His Excellencie Sir Thomas Fairfax.　1647.　Sm. 4to., unbound as issued.　F. Edwards 1013-405 1978 £20

PETO, SAMUEL MORTON　　　The Resources and Prospects of America.... London & New York, 1866.　lst. ed., 8vo, tinted lithograph plts., orig. green cloth, gilt, cover trifle soiled, lib. label removed, lacks last free endpaper. Deighton 5-52 1978 £25

PETRARCA, FRANCESCO　　　Leben und Werke von Dr. Gustav Koerting. Leipzig, 1878.　8vo., qtr. cloth, good.　King 7-375 1978 £75

PETRARCA, FRANCESCO　　　Opera Quae Extant Omnia.　Basel, 1554.　4 pts. in 2 vols., folio, very rare first collective ed., v.f., late 17th cent. vellum over thick bds.　Schafer 19-33 1978 sFr 3,500

PETRARCA, FRANCESCO　　　Il Petrarca dinvovo ristampeto....　Venetia, 1651.　Engraved title, lacks endpaper, 24mo., calf, rubbed.　George's 635-1449 1978 £7.50

PETRARCA, FRANCESCO　　　De Remediis Utriusque Fortunae.　Venice, 1536.　24mo., new vellum.　Salloch 348-189 1978 $190

PETRARCA, FRANCESCO　　　De Remediis Utriusque Fortunae.　De Contemptu Mundi Colloquiorum Liber.　Rotterdam, 1649.　Very thick 12mo., wallet-edged vellum.　Salloch 348-190 1978 $90

PETRARCA, FRANCESCO　　　Le Rime.　Londra, 1778.　12mo., calf, worn, joints cracking, plts.　King 7-209 1978 £20

PETRARCA, FRANCESCO　　　Le Rime di Francesco Petrarca corrette sopra i testi migliori si aggiungono le considerazioni riveduti e ampliate di Allessandro Tassoni....　Roma, 1821-1822.　2 vols., 8vo., vellum, good, plt.　King 7-211 1978 £40

PETRARCA, FRANCESCO　　　Varie Opere Filosofiche di Francesco Petrarca per la Prima Volta Ridotte in volgare favella.　1824.　Sm. 8vo., bds., calf spine, very good, portrait, plt.　King 7-210 1978 £20

PETRARCA, FRANCESCO　　　Le Vite degl'Imperadori et Pontefici Romani. (Geneva), 1625.　4to., qtr. calf, bds., text in roman letter, slight discoloration of paper.　King 7-80 1978 £40

PETRIE, G.　　　The Ecclesiatical Architecture of Ireland Anterior to the Anglo-Norman Invasion..the Origin & Uses of the Round Towers.　1845. 2nd ed., spine damaged, text very good, octavo bound in cloth.　Hyland 128-347 1978 £17

PETRIE, WILLIAM MATTHEW FLINDERS　　　The Arts & Crafts of Ancient Egypt. Edinburgh, Foulis, 1910.　2nd ed., additional chapter, illus., gilt buckram rather discolored, g.t., 8vo.　K Books 239-373 1978 £7

PETRIE, WILLIAM MATTHEW FLINDERS　　　Egyptian Decorative Art.　London, 1895.　Cr. 8vo., orig. cloth.　K Books 239-374 1978 £6

PETRIE, WILLIAM MATTHEW FLINDERS　　　Naukratis.　1886-88.　2 vols., 4to., orig. printed bds., cloth backs, covers worn.　Edwards 1012-230 1978 £35

PETRIE, WILLIAM MATTHEW FLINDERS　　　Religion and Conscience in Ancient Egypt.　London, 1898.　lst ed., cr. 8vo., orig. cloth, covers slightly marked. K Books 239-376 1978 £6

PETRIE, WILLIAM MATTHEW FLINDERS　　　Roman Portraits and Memphis.　London, 1911.　4to., plts., 4 in color and full page, bds., scarce.　Biblo 247-294 1978 $67.50

PETRIE, WILLIAM MATTHEW FLINDERS　　　Scarabs and Cylinders With Names. 1917.　Plts., 4to., half cloth.　Edwards 1012-231 1978 £30

PETRIE, WILLIAM MATTHEW FLINDERS　　　Tanis.　1885-88.　Plts., 2 vols., 4to., orig. printed bds., rebacked.　Edwards 1012-229 1978 £35

PETRIE, WILLIAM MATTHEW FLINDERS　　　Ten Years' Digging in Egypt 1881-1891. London, 1892.　Map, illus., cr. 8vo., orig. cloth, foxed.　K Books 239-375 1978 £6

PETROFF, P.　　　Ante- Mortem Depositons of P. Petroff.　San Francisco, 1895.　Illus., original cloth, lst ed.　Ginsberg 14-168 1978 $150

PETRONIUS ARBITER   Satyricon cum fragmentis albae Graecae recuper-
atis 1688 nunc demura integrum. 1793. 12mo., calf covered in cloth, front joint
broken. George's 635-490 1978 £5

PETRONIUS ARBITER   The Satyricon. London, 1902. 8vo, binder's
cloth, ltd. ed. of 515 copies. Traylen 88-313 1978 £10

PETTENGILL, S. B.   The College Cavaliers. Chicago, 1883. Ex
libris, cover stained, Bell Wiley's copy. Broadfoot's 44-597 1978 $18

PETTENGILL, S. M.   Pettengill's Newspaper Directory and Advertisers
Handbook for 1878. 1878. Illus. Austin 82-702 1978 $27.50

PETTIGREW, JAMES BELL   Design in Nature. London, 1908. 3 vols., first
and only ed., 4to., portraits, plts., text illus., cloth a little worn. Quaritch
977-129 1978 $70

PETTIGREW, JAMES BELL   Design in Nature. 1908. 3 vols., 4to., illus.
George's 635-42 1978 £30

PETTIGREW, THOMAS JOSEPH   On Superstitions Connected with the History
and Practice of Medicine and Surgery. London, 1844. 8vo., frontis., contemp.
stamped cloth, gilt on spine, very good, uncut copy, bkplts. of Sir William Molesworth & Dr. Alfred M. Hellman, 1st ed. Zeitlin 245-191 1978 $37.50

PETTIGREW, THOMAS LETTSON   Lucien Greville. London, 1833. 3 vols.,
12mo, original grey boards, printed paper labels, three cloth slipcases, green
morocco spines, 1st ed., fine copy in original condition, plates etched by George
Cruikshank, tipped-in india proofs of plates, A.l.s. from Cruikshank. Ximenes
47-235 1978 $250

PETTINGILL, O.   The American Woodcock. Boston, 1936. Plts.,
Inscribed presentation copy to R. C. Murphy, 4to, stiff wr. Book Chest 17-286
1978 $75

PETTIT, EDWARD   The Visions of Government, Wherein the Anti-
Monarchical Principles and Practices of all Fanatical Commonwealths-men,....
London, 1684. 8vo, contemporary mottled calf, spine gilt, 1st ed., emblematic
frontispiece, very good copy. Ximenes 47-236 1978 $150

PETTUS, JOHN   Fodinae Regales. London, 1670. Sm. folio,
portrait, plts., contemp. sheep, rebacked, first 2 leaves of dedication rather
stained. Quaritch 977-248 1978 $400

PETTY, WILLIAM   Five Essays in Political Arithmetick. London,
1687. Sm. 8vo., old calf, rubbed, some soiling on 1st & last leaves, but very
good copy, occas. contemp. notations, bkplt., 1st ed. Norman 5-219 1978
$500

PETTY, WILLIAM   Miscellanea Parliamentaria... London, 1680.
1st. ed., 8vo, contemp. calf, joints cracking. Traylen 88-472 1978 £48

PETTY, WILLIAM   The Petty-Southwell Correspondence. 1928.
3 plts., octavo, good. Upcroft 10-137 1978 £10.50

PETTY, WILLIAM   The Political Anatomy of Ireland. (1691). Reprint, octavo bound in cloth. Hyland 128-968 1978 £7.50

PETULENGRO, GIPSY   A Romany Life. 1936. Illus. Austin 79-
557 1978 $11

PETULENGRO, GIPSY   Romany Remedies and Recipes. London, 1935.
Austin 79-558 1978 $10

PEUCER, GASPARD   Commentarius de Praecipuis Generibus Divina-
tionum.... Wittenberg, 1560. Rittenhouse 49-637 1976 $150

PEVERELLY, CHARLES A.   The Book of American Pastimes... New York,
1866. 1st ed., 8vo., engr. plts., very nice, gilt lettering & decor. on spine,
scarce. Current 24-70 1978 $145

PEVERONE, G.   Arithmetica e Geometria. Lyons, 1581. 2 pts.
in 1 vol., large 8vo., medallion portrait, woodcuts, nineteenth century bds.,
second ed. Quaritch 977-167 1978 $175

PEYTON, COLONEL JESSE E.   Reminiscences Of The Past. Philadelphia, 1895.
1st ed., tall 8vo, illus., orig. binding. Americanist 101-117 1978 $25

PFEIFF, K. A.   Apollon, die Wandlung Seines Bildes in der Griechischen Kunst. 1943. 4to., browned, plts., spine torn. Allen 234-728 1978
$7.50

PFEIFFER, EMILY   Quarterman's Grace and Other Poems. 1879.
Orig. green cloth blocked in black & gold. Eaton 45-387 1978 £5

PFEIFFER, EMILY   Under the Aspens. 1882. Frontis, portraits,
1/2 morocco, rubbed. Eaton 45-388 1978 £6

PFEIFFER, IDA   A Lady's Travels Round the World: Travels From
Vienna to Brazil, Chili, Otaheite, China, The East Indies, Persia and Asia Minor.
1852. 1st. ed. of this translation, sm. 8vo, orig. cloth, very good copy. Fenning
32-265 1978 £10

PFEIFFER, IDA   Visit To The Holy Land, Egypt, and Italy. Lon-
don, 1852. 8vo, tinted lithograph title-pg., tinted lithograph frontispiece, plts.,
paper discoloured, orig. decorative embossed cloth, gilt back. Deighton 5-219
1978 £25

PFINITZING, MELCHIOR   Die Geuerlicheiten und Eins Teils der Geschichten des Loblichen Streitbaren und Hochberumbten... Augsburg, 1519. Folio, v.f.,
early 19th cent. full diced Russia, dec. in gilt, 2nd ed., 2nd issue, woodcut illus.,
bound for the Duke of Bedford. Howell 5-49 1978 $9,500

PFISTER, OSKAR   Was Bietet Dei Psychanalyse Dem Erzieher?
Leipzig, 1923. 8vo., orig. grey prtd. wrs., light browning, marginal pencil
marks, good copy, 2nd ed. Zeitlin 245-192 1978 $50

PFIZENMAYER, E. W.   Siberian Man and Mammoth. 1939. Illus., 8vo.
George's 635-1179 1978 £5.25

PFIZER, GUSTAV   The Life of Luther. 1840. 1st. ed. of this
translation, frontis, roy. 8vo, orig. printed wrapper, nice. Fenning 32-266
1978 £12

PFOHL, E.   Rohstoff und Kolonial Atlas. Berlin, 1938.
Tall 4to, cloth, maps, orig. covers. Van der Peet 127-319 1978 Dfl 75

PHAEDRUS   The Fables. 1753. 2nd. ed., licence leaf,
orig. calf, rebacked, corners worn, o/w v.g. Jarndyce 16-155 1978 £7.50

PHAEDRUS   Phaedri Fabulae, et Publii Syri Sententiae.
Paris, 1729. 24mo, engraved frontis., contemp French red mor. Quaritch
978-126 1978 $340

PHAEDRUS   Fabularum Aesopiorum libri quinque quales omni
parte illustratos publicavit.... Paris, 1824. Engraved plates, 2 vols., cloth.
George's 635-491 1978 £10.50

PHALARIS PSEUDO-   Phalaridis, Agrigentinorum tyranni, epistolae,
ex. Mss. recensuit versione.... Oxonii, (1717). Engraved frontis., contemp.
calf, joint broken. George's 635-492 1978 £8.50

PHALEN, W. C.   The Central Kentucky Phosphate Field. Frankfort, 1915. Tall 8vo., illus., plts. Morrill 239-460 1978 $7.50

PHARIS, GWEN   Dark Harvest, a Tragedy of the Canadian Prairie.
Toronto, 1945. Hood 117-495 1978 $10

PHARMACOPOEA Exquisita Ad Observationes Recentiores Accommodata et Principiis Simplicissimis Superstructa. Stuttgardie, 1798. Rittenhouse 49-642 1976
$35

THE PHARMACOPOEIA of the United States of America. Boston, 1828. 8vo.,
contemp. calf, 2nd ed. Morrill 239-206 1978 $40

THE PHARMACOPOEIA of the United States of America. Philadelphia, 1863.
Sm. 8vo., faded. Morrill 239-207 1978 $15

THE PHARMACOPOEIA of the U.S.A. Fifth Decennial Revision. Philadelphia,
1874. Ex-library. Rittenhouse 49-638 1976 $10

PHARMACOPOEIA of United States. 6th Decennial Revision. New York, 1883.
Cover scuffed, otherwise good. Rittenhouse 49-639 1976 $10

PHARMACOPOEIA of the U.S.A. Seventh Decennial Revision. New York, 1890. Rittenhouse 49-641 1976 $10

THE PHAT Boy's Bird's Eye Map of the St. Lawrence. Rochester, 1885. Folded map, pict. ads, prtd. 16mo. wr., portr., near-mint cond. Butterfield 21-397 1978 $35

PHELAN, MACUM A History of Early Methodism in Texas, 1817-1866. Dallas, 1924. Jenkins 116-911 1978 $45

PHELAN, T. P. Thomas Dongan, Colonial Governor of New York, 1683-1688. New York, 1933. Portrait, octavo, good. Upcroft 10-483 1978 £6

PHELPS, ELIZABETH STUART
Please turn to
WARD, ELIZABETH STUART PHELPS, 1844-1911

PHELPS, HENRY P. The Albany Hand-Book. Albany, 1884. Map, ads, plts. Butterfield 21-30 1978 $15

PHELPS, HENRY P. The Albany Rural Cemetery. Albany & Chicago, 1893. 4to., fldg. map, portrs., near fine copy, orig. cloth, prtd. prospectus laid in, ltd. to 500. Butterfield 21-31 1978 $20

PHELPS, JOHN S. A Letter From...To Citizens Of Arkansas in ..... St. Louis, 1858. Orig. front pr. wr., full leather, lst ed. Ginsberg 14-865 1978 $125

PHELPS, MRS. LINCOLN Our Country, In Its Relations To The Past, Present, and Future. Baltimore, 1864. Sole ed., orig. cloth, every article presented by its author, very good or better. Limestone 9-231 1978 $40

PHELPS, RICHARD H. A History of Newgate in Connecticut, at Simsbury, Now East Granby. Albany, 1860. Tall 8vo., one of few lg. paper copies in a ltd. prtg. of 300, bds. & lea., rubbed but sound, A.L.s. by author tipped in. Butterfield 21-290 1978 $150

PHELPS, RICHARD H. Newgate of Connecticut; Its Origin and Early History. Hartford, 1891. Frontis., orig. cloth. MacManus 239-103 1978 $17.50

PHELPS' Strangers and Citizens' Guide to New York City. New York, (1857). Maps, engrs., lg. fldg. colored map tipped in back, crisp copy in orig. cloth. Butterfield 21-536 1978 $35

PHELPS'S Travellers' Guide Through the United States. New York, 1848. 16mo., orig. lea., pic. covers in gilt & blind, very nice. Morrill 241-461 1978 $30

THE PHENIX. 1707-08. First ed., 2 vols., newly bound in half calf antique, 8vo. Howes 194-415 1978 $55

PHIDIAS et la Sculpture Grecque au Veme Siecle. par Henri Lechat. Paris, 1924. Ed. Nouvelle, illus., wrs. BL781-454 1978 $17.50

PHILADELPHIA a Guide to the Nation's Birthplace. Philadelphia, 1937. 1st ed., illus., nice copy, soiled d.j. MacManus 239-1641 1978 $45

PHILADELPHIA Southern Steamship Manufacturers and Mercantile Register. Philadelphia, 1866. Map. Baldwins' 51-474 1978 $35

PHILES, MANUEL De Animalium Proprietate. Trajecti ad Rhenum, 1730. 4to., woodcut, contemp. vellum over bds., lightly browned, very good, lg. paper copy, ex-lib., lst ed. Zeitlin 245-193 1978 $185

PHILIP IV, KING OF SPAIN Ordonnantie des Coninghs op het Generael Reglement van Sijne Munte. Antwerp, 1652. 4to., bds. Gilhofer 74-73 1978 sFr 500

PHILIP, ALEXANDER PHILIP WILSON A Treatise on Indigestion, and Its Consequences. London, 1821. Nice untrimmed copy, cloth. MacManus 239-391 1978 $30

PHILIP, GEORGE The Story of the last Hundred Years, a Geographical Record, 1834-1934. 1934. Illus., sq. 8vo., orig. wrappers. George's 635-378 1978 £5

PHILIP Vickers Fithian-Journal. Princeton, 1934 & 1945. 2 vols., vol. 2 is ex libris, Bell Wiley's copy. Broadfoot's 44-981 1978 $14

PHILIPPOTEAUX, PAUL Battle of Gettysburg. Boston, 1889. Wrs., fldg. map, Bell Wiley's copy. Broadfoot 46-197 1978 $10

PHILIPS, F. C. Constance, A Novel. 1893. lst. ed., 3 vols., half titles, orig. blue cloth, blocked in gilt & blind, v.g. Jarndyce 16-933 1978 £44

PHILIPSON, DAVID Old European Jewries. 1894. Austin 79-559 1978 $15

PHILLIMORE, L. By an Unknown Disciple. 1918. lst ed., signed pres. copy, Lady Gregory's bookplt., very good, octavo bound in cloth. Hyland 128-352 1978 £9.50

PHILLIMORE, ROBERT The Ecclesiastical Law of the Church of England. 1895. 2nd. ed., 2 vols., recent buckram, octavo, good. Upcroft 10-643 1978 £15

PHILLIP, ARTHUR Copies and Extracts of Letters From ... 1792. 4to, half calf, slight foxing on few leaves. Edwards 1012-341 1978 £1200

PHILLIP, ARTHUR Reise Nach Der Botany-Bay... Hamburg, 1791. Contemp. calf, lst. ed. in German, vignette on title, portrait, engraved plts., folding coloured chart, 8vo. Edwards 1012-340 1978 £100

PHILLIPPO, JAMES M. Jamaica: Its Past and Present State. London, 1843. lst ed., 8vo., illus., orig. brown cloth with spots, new endpapers, partially uncut, text generally clear. Current 24-97 1978 $100

PHILLIPPO, JAMES M. The United States and Cuba. 1857. 8vo, orig. cloth. Edwards 1012-708 1978 £30

PHILLIPS, CABELL Dateline Washington. 1949. Illus. Austin 82-704 1978 $10

PHILLIPS, CATHARINE C. Through the Golden Gate. San Francisco, [1938]. Illus., original cloth, lst ed. Ginsberg 14-169 1978 $20

PHILLIPS, CHARLES The Emerald Isle, A Poem. 1813. 1/2 leather, 4to, f.p. light staining on lower margin, very good, octavo bound in cloth. Hyland 128-353 1978 £17

PHILLIPS, CHARLES The Emerald Isle, A Poem. 1813. 1/2 leather, spine torn, text good. Hyland 128-354 1978 £12

PHILLIPS, CHARLES The Lament of the Emerald Isle. London, 1817. 8vo, disbound, 3rd ed. Ximenes 47-233 1978 $15

PHILLIPS, CHARLES The Ocean Cavern: A Tale of the Tonga Isles. London, 1819. 8vo, disbound, lst ed., vine copy, half-title present. Ximenes 47-239 1978 $80

PHILLIPS, CHARLES Specimens of Irish Eloquence. 1819. lst ed., illus., good, octavo bound in cloth. Hyland 128-355 1978 £10

PHILLIPS, G. F. Principles of Effect and Colour, as Applicable to Landscape Painting... n.d. 3rd ed., oblong 4to., plain and hand-coloured plts., some plts. slightly foxed and soiled, orig. half roan. Quaritch 983-232 1978 $125

PHILLIPS, H. CRANMER Explanation of Improved Capstans; Proposed by... London, 1830. Sm. 8vo., disbound. Paine 78-107 1978 $18.50

PHILLIPS, HARRY Phillips Family History. 1935. Baldwins' 51-263 1978 $12.50

PHILLIPS, J. A General History of Inland Navigation, Foreign and Domestic. London, 1792. 4to., fold. hand coloured map, plts., map and plts. lightly foxed, contemp. half calf, sometime rebacked with orig. gilt spine laid down, first ed. Quaritch 977-249 1978 $600

PHILLIPS, J. V. Report on the Geology of the Mineral Districts Contigious to the Iron Mountain Railroad. St. Louis, 1859. Large folding map, original printed wr., lst ed. Ginsberg 14-594 1978 $100

PHILLIPS, JOHN A Treatise on Geology. London, c. 1840. 2 vols., engraved titles, illus., fcap. 8vo., orig. cloth. K Books 244-138 1978 £15

PHILLIPS, JOHN MARSHALL　　American Silver. New York, (1949). 56 illus. in color & monochrome, text illus., fine copy in d.j. Baldwins' 51-141 1978 $15

PHILLIPS, N.　　Holland and the Canadians. Amsterdam, n.d. Photos., bound. Hood 117-145 1978 $45

PHILLIPS, P. A. S.　　Paul De Lamerie. Profusely illus., folio, ltd. to 500 copies. Traylen 88-516 1978 £18.90

PHILLIPS, R.　　The House Improved. London, 1931. 8vo, orig. cloth, illus., 1st ed., good. Sexton 7-42 1978 £5

PHILLIPS, R. J.　　Spectacles and Eyeglasses. Philadelphia, 1895. 2nd ed., revised, illus., 8vo. Morrill 239-209 1978 $7.50

PHILLIPS, RALPH W.　　The Livestock of China. Washington, D. C., 1945. Decor. wrs., maps, illus., 1st ed., fine copy from the Allred Collection, autographed by Phillips, rare. Dykes 34-122 1978 $35

PHILLIPS, RAY E.　　The Bantu are Coming. London, 1930. 2nd. ed., 4 plts., cr. 8vo, orig. cloth, covers slightly soiled. K Books 239-377 1978 £6

PHILLIPS, SIR RICHARD　　Geography, Illustrated on a Popular Plan for the Use of Schools and Young Persons. c. 1820. Plts., maps, sm. thk. 8vo., full orig. roan. Howes 194-347 1978 £10

PHILLIPS, RICHARD　　Modern London: being the History and Present State of the British Metropolis. 1804. Plts., map, frontispiece, 4to., full contemp. red mor., first ed., first issue. Howes 194-1399 1978 £190

PHILLIPS, S. A.　　Proud Mahaska. Oskaloosa, 1900. Frontis. MacManus 239-979 1978 $37.50

PHILLIPS, SAMUEL　　Political Rules Authoiz'd and Influenc'd by God Our Saviou, to decree and execute Justice:... Boston, 1750. Disbound. Nestler Rare-26 1978 $35

PHILLIPS, STEPHEN　　Ulysses. London, 1902. First ed., orig. binding, nice. Rota 211-483 1978 £5

PHILLIPS, ULRICH BONNELL　The Economic Cost of Slave-Holding in the Cotton Belt. Boston, 1905. Wrs., pres. copy from author, Bell Wiley's copy. Broadfoot 46-199 1978 $12

PHILLIPS, ULRICH BONNELL　A History of Transportation in the Eastern Cotton Belt. NY, 1903. Bell Wiley's copy. Broadfoot's 44-739 1978 $26.00

PHILLIPS, ULRICH BONNELL　Life and Labor in the Old South. Boston, 1929. Illus. & maps, Bell Wiley's copy. Broadfoot's 44-738 1978 $15.00

PHILLIPS, ULRICH BONNELL　The Life of Robert Toombs. NY, 1913. Endpapers faded, Bell Wiley's copy. Broadfoot's 44-301 1978 $40.00

PHILLIPS, ULRICH BONNELL　Plantation and Frontier Documents: 1649-1863... Cleveland, 1909. 2 vols., Bell Wiley's copy. Broadfoot 46-556 1978 $30

PHILLIPS, W. J.　　Colour in the Canadian Rockies. Toronto, 1947. 32 colour plts. Hood's 115-189 1978 $50

PHILLIPS, WATTS　　Amos Clark, or the Poor Dependent. London, 1862. 1st ed., signed & inscribed in French to Eugene Marre Philipon, half-leather, and cloth, good. Greene 78-269 1978 $80

PHILLIPS, WILLARD　　Propositions Concerning Protection and Free Trade. Boston, 1850. 12mo, original black cloth, printed paper label, 1st ed., signature torn from front flyleaf, fine copy. Ximenes 47-240 1978 $40

PHILLIPS MANUFACTURING CO., LTD.　Catalogue L. Toronto, 1922. Card cover, illus., price list. Hood 117-438 1978 $25

PHILLIPS, SAMPSON, AND COMPANY　Catalogue of the Publications of Phillips, Sampson, and Company, with a Circular and List of Some Other Books for Sale by Albert Colby and Co. Boston, 1859. 12mo., orig. cream printed wr., very good copy. Ximenes 47-267 1978 $50

PHILLPOTS, EDEN　　Children of the Mist. London, 1898. 1st ed., frontis. with tissue guard, orig. blue cloth, good, bears owner's name, library blind stamp. Greene 78-270 1978 $60

PHILLPOTTS, EDEN　　Dartmoor Novels. 1927-28. 20 vols., 8vo., Widecombe ed., frontis., bds., parchment backs, little darkened, good set. Quaritch 979-372 1978 $360

PHILLPOTS, EDEN　　Folly and Fresh Air. New York, 1892. 1st Amer. ed., cloth, good. Greene 78-271 1978 $15

PHILLPOTTS, EDEN　　The Grey Room. New York, 1921. Reddish terra-cotta cloth, 1st ed., fine copy, spots on front end papers. Bradley 49-265 1978 $40

PHILLPOTTS, EDEN　　The Transit of the Red Dragon, and other tales. Bristol, 1903. Covers somewhat soiled, else good, first English ed. Bell Book 16-708 1978 £5.50

LE PHILOSOPHE Indien, ou L'Art de Vivre Heureux dans la Societe. Amsterdam, 1760. 12mo., orig. marbled bds., uncut, unopened. Salloch 348-194 1978 $75

LA PHILOSOPHIE De L'Histoire... Amsterdam, 1765. 8vo., contemp. marbled calf, woodcut title. Salloch 348-278 1978 $95

PHILOSTRATUS, FLAVIUS　　Les Images Ou Tableaux De Platte Peinture De Philostrate Lemnien Sophiste Grec. Paris, 1578. Thick 4to., vellum. Salloch 348-195 1978 $115

PHILPOTT, H. S.　　The Province of Nova Scotia, Canada; Resources and Development. Ottawa, 1930. 4th. ed., card cover, illus., fldg. map, ex-lib. Hood's 115-204 1978 $12.50

PHIPPEN, A. R.　　The Schoolmate, Monthly Reader for School and Home Instruction of Youth. New York, 1852. Vol. I, profusely illus., gilt decorated binding faded & moderately worn, contents very good. Victoria 34-615 1978 $22.50

PHIPPS, CONSTANTIN HENRY, MARQUIS OF NORMANBY
Please turn to
NORMANBY, CONSTANTIN HENRY PHIPPS, MARQUIS OF

PHIPPS, HELEN　　Some Aspects of the Agrarian Question in Mexico. Austin, 1925. Jenkins 116-1074 1978 $12.50

PHISTERER, FREDERICK　　Statistical Record. New York, 1886. Bell Wiley's copy. Broadfoot 46-200 1978 $16

PHOENIX, JOHN　　Phoenixiana; or, Sketches and Burlesques. New York, 1856. Cloth, worn, lacking free endpaper in front. Hayman 72-177 1978 $7.50

A PHOTOGRAPHIC Collection of New York's Most Beautiful Views. New York, n.d. (c.1905). Wrps., little soiled. Hayman 71-494 1978 $7.50

PHRENOLOGICAL and Physiological Almanac for 1848. New York, (1847). Pict. wrs. Hayman 73-18 1978 $10

PHYSICIANS', Dentists' and Druggists' Directory of New York and Connecticut. Chicago, 1893. 8vo., ads, illus. Morrill 239-210 1978 $22.50

PIAZZA, ANTONIO　　Il Teatro ovvero Fatti di una Veneziana che lo fanno conoscere. Venezia, 1777. 2 vols. in 1, 8vo., stiff paper bds., spines slightly damaged. King 7-212 1978 £20

PIAZZA, PIETRO　　Specimen Physico-Mathematicum Publice Datum Super Opticae Theorias ad Oculum Hominis Applicatas. Florentiae, 1779. Engr. armorial vignette, fldg. copperplt., lg. 4to., wrs., 1st ed. Offenbacher 30-126 1978 $115

PICARD, CHARLES　　La Vie Privee dans la Grece Classique. Paris, (1930). Illus., orig. wrs. Biblo BL781-455 1978 $10

PICART, B.　　Naaukeurige Beschryving Det Uitwendige Bodts-Dienst-Plichten.... Amsterdam, Rotterdam and The Hague, 1727-38. 6 vols. in 3, vol. 6 in 2 parts, titles printed in red & black, engraved frontis, engraved plts., folio, contemp. vellum. Traylen 88-442 1978 £600

PICCOLOMINI, ENEA SILVIO
Please turn to
PIUS II., POPE

PICHON, JEROME   The Life of Charles Henry County Hoym...Eminent French Bibliophile 1694-1736. Grolier Club, 1899. Portrs., plts., special French paper with watermark of the club, bound in brocaded silk with maroon mor. spine, 1 of 303 copies. Battery Park 1-142 1978 $125

PICHON, JEROME   The Life of County Hoym...Eminent French Bibliophile 1694-1736. New York, Devinne Press, 1899. Trans. into English, 4to., 1 of 300 copies, prtd. on handmade paper, 3/4 lea., silk with floral & geometric designs, fine. Battery Park 1-64 1978 $125

PICHOT, AMEDEE   Les Mormons. Paris, 1854. Half mor., 1st ed. Ginsberg 14-667 1978 $75

PICKARD, MADGE E.   The Midwest Pioneer, His Ills, Cures and Doctors. New York, 1946. Cloth. Hayman 72-614 1978 $7.50

PICKARD, SAMUEL T.   Life and Letters of John Greenleaf Whittier. 1895. Orig. ed., plts., 2 vols., cr. 8vo., orig. cloth. Howes 194-1332 1978 $8.50

PICKARD-CAMBRIDGE, ARTHUR W.   Dithyramb, Tragedy and Comedy. Oxford, 1927. Illus., 8vo. George's 635-493 1978 £5.50

PICKARD-CAMBRIDGE, ARTHUR W.   The Theatre of Dionysus in Athens. Oxford, 1946. Plans, illus., 8vo. George's 635-494 1978 £7

PICKEN, ANDREW   Waltham. Philadelphia, 1833. 1st Amer. ed., cloth with leather label stamped in gold, stained, some interior foxing. Greene 78-94 1978 $85

PICKERING, JOHN   Vocabulary, or Collection of Words and Phrases Which Have Been Supposed to be Peculiar to the United States of America... Boston, 1816. 8vo., modern half calf. Edwards 1012-521 1978 £80

PICKERING, PERCIVAL   A Life Away A Novel. 1893. 1st. ed., 3 vols., half titles, orig. red cloth, blocked in blind, black & gilt, fine. Jarndyce 16-935 1978 £43

PICKERING, THOMAS   Political Essays. Canandaigua, 1812. 1st bound book prtd. in western New York, 16mo., old lea., worn 1st U.S. ed. Butterfield 21-326 1978 $75

PICKERING, WILLIAM   Message of the Governor of the Territory of Washington. Olympia, 1862. Sewn as issued. Ginsberg 14-1037 1978 $100

PICKETT, ALBERT JAMES   History of Alabama, and Incidentally of Georgia and Mississippi, From the Earliest Period. Charlestown, 1851. 2 vols., 3rd ed., illus., cloth, some staining, very scarce. MacManus 239-1853 1978 $75

PICKETT, GEORGE E.   The Heart of a Soldier. New York, 1913. 8vo., slightly dust-soiled. Morrill 241-462 1978 $10

PICKETT, LA SALLE CORBELL   Pickett and His Men. Philadelphia, 1913. Illus., 8vo. Morrill 241-463 1978 $10

PICKFORD, MARY   Demi-widow. Indianapolis, (1935). Signed by author, 1st ed., very good. Houle 10-261 1978 $20

PICKRELL, A. D.   Pioneer Women in Texas. Austin, 1929. 1st ed., original cloth, signed by author. Jenkins 116-1075 1978 $60

PICKTHALL, MARJORIE L. C.   The Complete Poems of Marjorie Pickthall. Toronto, (1927). Frontis., uncut, orig. binding. Wolfe 39-412a 1978 $17.50

PICKTHALL, MARJORIE L. C.   The Drift of Pinions. Montreal, London & New York, 1913. Orig. binding. Wolfe 39-411 1978 $20

PICKTHALL, MARJORIE L. C.   The Wood Carver's Wife. Toronto, (1922). Orig. decor. bds., uncut. Wolfe 39-412 1978 $20

PICKTHORN, K.   Early Tudor Government- Henry VII. Cambridge, 1949. Octavo, good. Upcroft 10-485 1978 £5.50

PICKWELL, G.   Animals in Action. New York, (1940). Soiled orig. binding, 8vo. Book Chest 17-288 1978 $18

PICO, RAFAEL   The Geographic Regions of Puerto Rico. University of Puerto Rico Press, 1950. Illus. Austin 79-560 1978 $27.50

A PICTORIAL History of U. S. S. Massachusetts. N.P., (1945). 4to., illus., few in color, ex-lib., orig. cloth. Morrill 241-695 1978 $15

THE PICTURE Alphabet, or ABC in Rhyme. New Haven, c.1830. Chapbook, woodcuts, illus. wrappers, sewn, very good. Victoria 34-616 1978 $20

PICTURES and Biographies of Brigham Young and His Wives. Salt Lake City, (c.1895). Plts., leather wr., tied. Ginsberg 14-697 1978 $75

PICTURES and Stories. Providence, 1847. 12mo, large woodcuts hand-colored, decorative hand-colored t.p. and upper wrappers, lower one lacking, sewn, very attractive chapbook. Victoria 34-617 1978 $20

PICTURES of Gold Rush California. Chicago, 1949. 12mo., orig. cloth. Morrill 241-250 1978 $7.50

A PICTURESQUE Description of North Wales. 1823. Oblong 4to., hand-coloured plts., contemp. half mor. Quaritch 983-375 1978 $675

PICTURESQUE Hampshire County. Northampton, 1890. Illus., sm. folio, orig. wrs. Morrill 241-343 1978 $15

PICTURESQUE Scandinavia. Denmark -- Sweden -- Norway -- Finland. New York, (1924). 4to., illus., bind. worn, contents fine. Biblo BL781-694 1978 $14.50

PICTURESQUE Watertown. Portland, 1905. Side-opening 8vo., some pages chewed. Butterfield 21-230 1978 $7.50

PIDANSAT DE MAIROBERT, MATHIEU FRANCOIS   Discussion Sommaire sur les Anciennes Limites de L'Acadie.... Basle, 1755. 16mo., wrappers. Wolfe 39-439 1978 $90

PIDGEON, GEORGE C.   The Vicarious Life. Toronto, 1945. Hood's 115-944 1978 $7.50

PIDGIN, CHARLES F.   The Climax or What Might Have Been. A Romance of the Great Republic. Boston, 1902. Cloth, 1st ed. Hayman 72-237 1978 $7.50

THE PIED Piper's Primrose Path. Stamford, 1940. Cloth, fine. Dawson's 447-116 1978 $40

PIEDMONT, ALEXIS OF PSEUD.
Please turn to
RUSCELLI, GIROLAMO

PIEKHANOV, G.   Fundamental Problems of Marxism. (c. 1930). Spine faded, 8vo. George's 635-381 1978 £5

PIEMONTESE, ALESSIO PSEUD.
Please turn to
RUSCELLI, GIROLAMO

PIERCE, A. C.   A Man from Corpus Christi:.... New York, 1894. Illus., 1st and only ed., original cloth, gilt. Jenkins 116-1077 1978 $150

PIERCE, FRANKLIN   Rivers and Harbors. Message from the President of the United States, Communicating...His Reasons for Returning to the House...the River and Harbor Bill of the Last Session... (Washington, 1855). Disbound. Hayman 72-615 1978 $7.50

PIERCE, GILBERT A.   The Dickens Dictionary , A Key to the Characters and...Incidents.... Boston & New York, 1926. Portrait, d.j., very good or better. Limestone 9-85 1978 $13.50

PIERCE, LORNE   The Chronicle of a Century, 1829-1929; the Record of 100 Years of Progress in the Publishing Concerns of the Methodist, Presbyterian, and Congregational Churches in Canada. Toronto, 1929. Card cover. Hood 116-711 1978 $20

PIERCE, LORNE   New History for Old. Toronto, (1931). Printed wrappers. Wolfe 39-440 1978 $17.50

PIERCE, LORNE   William Kirby, Portrait of a Tory Loyalist. Toronto, 1929. Hood's 115-265 1978 $17.50

PIERCE, WESLEY GEORGE   Goin' Fishin', the Story of the Deep-Sea Fishermen of New England. Salem, Southworth-Anthoensen Press, 1934. Illus., lst ed., lg. 8vo., orig. cloth, very good. Americanist 103-74 1978 $35

PIERPONT, JOHN   The Anti-Slavery Poems of. Boston, 1843. 12mo., lacks wrs., lst ed. Morrill 241-464 1978 $7.50

PIERRE-GOSSET, RENEE   Conspiracy in Algiers: 1942-1943. New York, (ca. 1945). Paper. Austin 80-254 1978 $11

PIERRE-VICTOR, BARON DE BESENVAL   Spleen and Other Stories. New York, 1928. Ltd. ed., bookplate. Biblo 247-612 1978 $15

PIERSON, B. T.   Directory of the City of Newark, for 1854-55. Newark, 1854. Fold. map, orig. bds., cloth, bookplt., good. MacManus 239-1308 1978 $40

PIERSON, EMILY CATHARINE   Jamie Parker the Fugitive. Hartford, 1851. Spine worn, Bell Wiley's copy. Broadfoot's 44-740 1978 $30

PIERSON, HAMILTON W.   In the Brush; or Old-Time Social, Political, and Religious Life in the Southwest. New York, 1881. Bell Wiley's copy. Broadfoot 46-557 1978 $10

PIERSON, J. L.   De Achttiende Dynastie Van Ouid-Egypte, 1580-1350 v.e., Vier Pharao's Hun Land Tot een Vereldrijk en Thebe tot een Wereldstad Maakten. Amsterdam, 1936. Illus. Biblo BL781-456 1978 $20

PIESSE, CHARLES HENRY   Olfactics and the Physical Senses. London, 1887. Rittenhouse 49-644 1976 $20

PIETERS, ALEIDA J.   A Dutch Settlement in Michigan. Michigan, Reformed Press, 1923. Illus., lst ed. Austin 79-562 1978 $32.50

PIETRI, J. B.   Voiliers d'Indochine. Saigon, 1943. Folio, plts., coloured frontis., half mor., orig. wrappers bound in, pres. copy inscribed by author. F. Edwards 1013-175 1978 $50

PIETZSCH, L. R.   The Austin Electric Railway System, A Thesis. Austin, 1906. Jenkins 116-1384 1978 $7.50

PIGNA, GIOVANNI BATTISTA   Il Duella.... Venice, 1554. Small quarto, original limp vellum, rubbed, original leather ties, occasional marginal notations, marginal worming, lst ed., Bennett 20-167 1978 $275

PIGNORIUS, LAURENTIUS   De Servis et eorvm apvd veteres ministeriis,.... Padua, 1656. 4to., engraved portrait and woodcut illus., orig. paper boards. Quaritch 978-143 1978 $180

PIGOTT, S.   Hollins; a Study of Industry, 1784-1949. Nottingham, 1949. Coloured frontis., plts., text illus., 4to. George's 635-336 1978 £6

PIGRAY, PIERRE   Epitome des Preceptes de Medecine et Chirurgie. Lyon, 1673. 8vo., contemp. calf, third ed.? Gurney 75-82 1978 £30

PIGRAY, PIERRE   Epitome des Preceptes de Medecine et Chirurgie. Rouen, 1681. 12mo., contemp. vellum. Argosy Special-68 1978 $175

PIJOAN, J.   History of Art. 1933. Coloured plts., text illus., 3 vols., roy. 8vo. George's 635-43 1978 £21

PIKE, NICOLAS   A New and Complete System of Arithmetic. Newbury-Port, 1788. lst ed., full claf, bookplate, very good, firm copy. Victoria 34-618 1978 $75

PIKE, SAMUEL   The Touchstone of Saving Faith. 1757. 8vo., unbound. P. M. Hill 142-202 1978 £6

PIKE, STEPHEN   The Teachers' Assistant; or, A System of Practical Arthimetic... Philadelphia, 1838. New ed., corrections & additions, leather. Hayman 71-637 1978 $10

PIKE, ZEBULON MONTGOMERY   Exploratory Travels Through the Western Territories of North America. London, 1811. Bound with lea. spine & corners, tooled & stamped in gold, marbled edges pages, fldg. map. Hood 117-914 1978 $350

PILCHER, LEWIS STEPHEN   A Surgical Pilgrim's Progress. Philadelphia and London, 1925. Rittenhouse 49-645 1976 $22.50

PILCHER, VERONA   The Searcher: a war play. 1929. 1 of 1000 copies, wood engrav. by Blair Hughes-Stanton, 4to., very good, d.w., first English ed. Bell Book 16-486 1978 £5.50

THE PILGRIM Fathers. Golden Cockerell Press, 1939. Ltd. to 300 copies, wood-engravings by Geoffrey Wales, orig. qtr. mor., linen sides, t.e.g., other uncut. George's 635-904 1978 £85

PILKINGTON, JAMES   The Artist's Guide and Mechanic's Own Book Embracing the Portion of Chemistry Applicable to the Mechanical Arts... Portland, 1847. 8vo., rubbed & faded. Morrill 241-465 1978 $12.50

PILKINGTON, MATTHEW   A General Dictionary of Painters;... London, n.d. New ed., 2 vols., quarto, full brown calf, gilt and blind decor., gilt spines, edges rubbed, gilt edges, bookseller's labels on inside front covers. Totteridge 29-79 1978 $150

PILLEAU, H.   Sketches in Egypt. 1845. Folio, modern half morocco, coloured litho. plts. Edwards 1012-232 1978 £180

PILLING, JAMES CONSTANTINE   Bibliography of the Algonquian Languages. Washington, 1891. Uncut, illus., old 1/2 mor. MacManus 239-1142 1978 $40

PILLING, JAMES CONSTANTINE   Bibliography of the Siouan Languages. Washington, 1887. Prtd. wrs., frayed, loose. Wolfe 39-248 1978 $35

PILLING, JAMES CONSTANTINE   Proof-Sheets of a Bibliography of the Languages of the North American Indians. Washington, D. C., 1885. Reprint of orig., only 100 copies prtd., new. Battery Park 1-460 1978 $45

PILLSBURY, PARKER   Acts of the Anti-Slavery Apostles. Boston, 1884. MacManus 239-849 1978 $30

PIM, BEDFORD   The Gate of the Pacific. 1863. lst. ed., 8vo., coloured lithograph plts., maps, one coloured, orig. blue cloth, gilt back. Deighton 5-53 1978 £45

PIM, BEDFORD   The Gate of the Pacific. 1863. Folding maps, plts., 8 coloured, lithos., orig. cloth, 8vo., cover soiled. Edwards 1012-695 1978 £35

PIM, H.M.   Ascendancy While You Wait. (1915). Wrs., loose, text very good. Hyland 128-359 1978 £5

PIMBLETT, W.   In Africa With the Union Jack. London, c.1894. 8 plts., lacks lst. free endpaper, dec. cloth covers little marked & dull, 8vo. K Books 239-378 1978 £6

PIMENTEL, TOMAS LOPEZ   Esposicion Que Hacen Las Comisiones de Hacienda Y Tejas. Mexico, 1841. Orig. blue pr. wrs., rare. Jenkins 116-1081 1978 $175

PIMENTEL, TOMAS LOPEZ   Espocisicion Que Hacen Las Comisiones De Hacienda Y Tejas.... Mexico, 1841. Original pink printed wr., near mint. Jenkins 116-1030 1978 $125

PINAC, BERTRAND   Tentamen de Visione, Quod, Deo Duce, & Auspice Dei-Para, in Augustissimo Ludoviceo Medico Monspeliensi, Tueri Conabinatur, Auctor. Monspelii, 1785. 8vo., wrs. Offenbacher 30-120 1978 $50

PINCHOT, GIFFORD   Grazing on the Public Lands. Washington, 1905. Wr., superb color folding map. Jenkins 116-1082 1978 $45

PINCHOT, GIFFORD   Just Fishing Talk, Illus. with Photos. New York, 1936. lst ed., nice signed inscript. by Gov. Pinchot, laid in typed letter signed with Pinchot's initials, orig. binding, 8vo. Americanist 101-137 1978 $35

PINCHOT, GIFFORD   A Short Account of the Big Trees of California. Washington, 1900. Illus., large folding tables, original printed wr., lst ed. Ginsberg 14-170 1978 $25

PINCKARD, GEORGE   Notes on the West Indies:.... 1806. 1st ed.,
3 vols., 8vo., quarter calf antique. Quaritch 978-158 1978 $225

PINCKNEY, PAULINE   American Figureheads and their Carvers.   New
York, (1940). 4to., orig. cloth, good. Paine 78-108 1978 $20.00

PINDAR, PETER PSEUD.
Please turn to
WOLCOT, JOHN 1738-1819

THE PINDAR of Wakefield;.... London, c.1800. 12mo, extracted from larger
volume?. Victoria 34-620 1978 $50

PINDARUS   Ode di Pindaro Antichissimo Poeta, e Principe
de' Greci Lirici cioe.... Pisa, 1631. 4to., vellum, illus. King 7-84 1978
£40

PINELLI, BARTOLOMEO   Five Last Days of the Carnival of Rome in a Series
of Five Plates drawn on the spot. 1830. Engrav. plts., foxed, oblong folio, upper
cover detached. George's 635-199 1978 £7.50

PINDER, ULRICH   Speculum Passionis Domini Nostri IJesu Christi.
Nurnberg, 1507. Folio, lacks last blank, woodcuts, 19th century blind-stamped
green mor., bookplt., 1st ed. Gilhofer 74-137 1978 sFr 14,000

PINDER, W.   Der Bamberger Dom und Seine Bildwerke, Aufgeno-
mmen Durch W. Hege. 1927. Folio, plt. Allen 234-14ʳᵛ 1978 $12.50

PINE, JOHN B.   The Story of Gramercy Park. 1921. Illus.,
orig. bds., very good. MacManus 239-372 1978 $10

PINELLI, BARTOLOMEO   Istoria Romana incisa all'acqua forte. 1818-19.
Engrav. plts., oblong roy. 4to., 25 x 18 1/2 inches, contemp. qtr. mor., very
good, entirely untrimmed. Howes 194-1400 1978 £95

PINEVILLE, Where Wyoming Trails Cross. Charleston, 1940. Wrps., very scarce.
Hayman 71-774 1978 $15

PINHEIRO, JOSE FE FELICIANO   Historia Nova, e Completa da America,...
Lisbon, 1800. Sm. 4to., recent 1/2 cloth, vol. I, good. Paine 78-109 1978
$145.00

PINI, VALENTINO   Fabrica de gl'Horologi Solari.... Venice,
1598. Folio, rare 1st ed., old repairs of marginal wormhole, woodcut figures,
old half vellum. Schafer 19-62 1978 sFr. 1,500

PINKERTON, ALLAN   Claude Melnotte as a Detective, and Other
Stories. Chicago, 1875. Cloth, 1st ed. Hayman 73-615 1978 $15

PINKERTON, ALLAN   The Expressman and the Detective. Chicago,
1874. Cloth, worn at extremities. Hayman 73-614 1978 $10

PINKERTON, ALLAN   The Model Town and the Detectives. New York,
1886. Frontis., plts., maroon cloth. Bradley 49-266 1978 $20

PINKERTON, K.   Wilderness Wife. New York, 1939. Illus.
Hood's 115-76 1978 $10

PINKERTON, ROBERT   Extracts of Letters From.... 1817. 1st. ed.,
half-title, 8vo, sewn as issued & uncut. Fenning 32-267 1978 £18

PINNOCK, WILLIAM   A Catechism of Conchology... 1824. 1st. ed.,
12mo, title defective affecting 1st. 3 words, orig. paper wrapper, very good.
Fenning 32-268 1978 £8.50

PINTARD, JOHN   Letters from...to His Daughter Eliza Pintard
Davidson 1816-1833. New York, 1940-41. 4 vols., frontis. MacManus 239-
393 1978 $60

PINTO, EDWARD H.   Treen or Small Woodware Throughout the Ages.
(1949). 4to., illus., cloth. Quaritch 983-Addenda 1 1978 $50

PINTO, EDWARD H.   Treen or Small Woodware Throughout the Ages.
London, (1949). 137 plts. Baldwins' 51-142 1978 $17.50

PIOTROWSKI, R.   Cartels and Trusts, their Origin and Historical
Development from the Economic and Legal Aspect. 1933. 8vo. George's 635-
379 1978 £6

PIOZZI, HESTER LYNCH   Anecdotes of the Late Samuel Johnson during the
Last Twenty Years of his Life. 1786. Sm. 8vo., contemp. calf, spine neatly
repaired, first ed. Howes 194-338 1978 £75

PIOZZI, HESTER LYNCH   British Synonymy; or, An Attempt At Regulating
the Choice of Words in Familiar Conversation. Dublin, 1794. 1st. Irish & 1-vol.
ed., 8vo, contemp. calf, very good copy. Fenning 32-269 1978 £65

PIOZZI, HESTER LYNCH THRALE   Letters to...Johnson
Please turn to
JOHNSON, SAMUEL

PIPER, E.   The Church Towers of Somerset. Bristol, (1898-
c.1900). 2 vols. in 1, folio, etchings signed by Piper, half blue mor. gilt, ltd. to
175 copies. Quaritch 983-47 1978 $240

PIPER, JOHN   The Rape of Lucretia; a symposium. London,
1948. Colour plts. by John Piper, 4to., nice, first ed., orig. binding. Rota 211-
489 1978 £8

PIPER, WATTY   The Little Engine That Could. New York, (1930).
1st ed., rare, very desirable, inner hinge taped and fixed endpapers with tears,
text is very good, cover plate moderately rubbed. Victoria 34-497 1978 $20

PIRANDELLO, LUIGI   The Naked Truth and Eleven Other Stories.
New York, (1934). 1st Amer. ed. Biblo 251-611 1978 $15

PIRENNE, H.   La Fin du moyen age, la desagregation du monde
medieval, 1286-1453. 1931. Binder's cloth, 8vo. George's 635-740 1978
£5

PIROLI, T.   Raccolta di No 22 Mezzi Fogli che Contengono la
Scuola del Disegno ricavati Parts da Antichi Marmi, e Parte Dalle Opere del Gran
Raffaele... Rome, c.1700. Folio, plts., some foxing, half mor., slightly worn.
Quaritch 983-234 1978 $75

PIRONE, P.   Maintenance of Shade and Ornamental Trees.
New York, 1948. 2nd ed., large 8vo, orig. cloth. Book Chest 17-289 1978
$15

PIRSSON, JOHN W.   The Dutch Grants, Harlem Patents and Tidal
Creeks. New York, 1889. Tall 8vo., maps, legal buckram. Butterfield 21-537
1978 $27.50

PISANI, ASCAGNE   Sur L'usage Inoppotun Des Medicamens Essai du
Docteur Ascagne Pisani. Naples, 1846. Rittenhouse 49-647 1976 $17.50

PISANI, FRANCISCUS   De universae philosphiae ornamentis oratio.
(Venice, c. 1520). Sm. 4 to., very rare pamphlet, modern boards. Schafer
19-34 1978 sFr. 550

PITCAIRN, ARCHIBALD   Elementa Medicinae Physico-Mathematica....
London, 1717. 8vo., inscribed, contemp. calf, rebacked, first ed. Quaritch
977-63 1978 $200

PITCHEP, CHARLES A.   The Golden Era of Trenton Falls. Utica, 1915.
Illus. Biblo BL781-172 1978 $9.50

PITISCUS, BARTHOLOMAEUS   Trigonometria. 1630. Sm. 4to., orig. vellum,
soiled. F. Edwards 1013-176 1978 £80

PITKIN, TIMOTHY   A Statistical View of the Commerce of the
United States. Hartford, 1816. 8vo., orig. bds., uncut, hinges repaired, fine
copy, contemp. signature, 1st ed. Norman 5-221 1978 $175

PITMAN, ROBERT C.   Alcohol and the State. New York, 1877.
Cloth, pres. inscrip. on fr. endpaper, Keifer's signature. Hayman 73-617 1978
$12.50

PITTENGER, WILLIAM   Daring and Suffering: a History of the Great
Railroad Adventure. Philadelphia, 1863. New cloth, 1st ed., rebound copy.
Hayman 73-117 1978 $17.50

PITTENGER, WILLIAM   Daring and Suffering. New York, 1887.
Illus., 8vo., binding faded. Morrill 241-466 1978 $15

PITTENGER, WILLIAM   Daring and Suffering: a History of the Andrews Railroad Raid into Georgia in 1862. New York, 1887. Cloth, cover shows wear, inner hinges cracked, newspaper clippings laid in. Hayman 73-118 1973 $10

PITTMAN, PHILIP   The Present State of the European Settlements on the Mississippi... Cleveland, 1906. Reprint of London, 1770 ed., ltd. to 500 copies, ex-lib. MacManus 239-1854 1978 $22.50

PITTON DE TOURNEFORT, JOSEPH
Please turn to
TOURNEFORT, JOSEPH PITTON DE

PITTSBURGH, Pennsylvania, U.S.A. (Pittsburgh, 1898). Wrs., minor wear. Hayman 73-606 1978 $7.50

PIUS II, POPE   Historia Rerum Friderici Tertii Imperatoris ex Mscto optimae notae. 1685. Folio, sheepskin, portrait, plts. King 7-297 1978 £50

PLACER County, California: Its Resources and Advantages. San Francisco, 1886. Illus., map, original printed wr., 1st ed. Ginsberg 14-171 1978 $85

PLAN of the Literary Rooms, Instituted by James Eastburn & Co., at the Corner of Broadway and Pine-Street. New York, 1817. 2nd ed. Butterfield 21-538 1978 $15

PLANCK, MAX   Physikalische Rundblicke. Leipzig, 1922. 8vo., orig. prtd. bds., browning, but very good copy, 1st ed., pres. copy. Norman 5-223 1978 $50

PLANCK, MAX   Treatise on Thermodynamics. London, 1903. 8vo., cloth, 1st English ed. Argosy Special-71 1978 $50

PLANCK, MAX   Uber Gleichgewichtszustande Isotroper Korper in Verschiedenen Temperaturen. Munich, 1880. 8vo., orig. prtd. wrs., uncut, unopened, fine copy, 1st ed. Norman 5-222 1978 $375

PLANS And Views in Perspective, With Descriptions of Buildings Erected in England and Scotland.... London, 1801. 18 full-pg. plts., lg. folio, modern half calf, lib. stamp on title-pg. & at foot of each plt. Traylen 88-404 1978 £150

PLANTENGA, J.H.   Vijftig eeuwen Bouw-Beeldhouw- en Schilder-kunst. Zutphen, 1949. 2 vols., lg. 8vo., cloth, plts., illus. on plts. Van der Peet H-64-187 1978 Dfl 85

PLATERI, FELICIS   Tractatus de Functionum Laesionibus. Basle, 1602. Occasional underlining, some browning. Rittenhouse 49-648 1976 $60

PLATH, SYLVIA   Crystal Gazer; poems. London, Rainbow Press, 1971. Of 400 numbered copies, this is one of only 20 bound by Zachnsdorf in full limp vellum, silk ties, fine, publisher's box, first ed. Rota 211-492 1978 £120

PLATNER, S.   Topography & Monuments of Ancient Rome. 1911. 2nd rev. & enl. ed. Allen 234-736 1978 $10

PLATO   The Dialogues of Plato. Oxford, The Clarendon Press, 1892. 3rd & best ed., 5 vols., 8vo., t.e.g., trans. into English, bound in half golden brown levant mor. with linen bds. & marbled endpapers, pages untrimmed, ribbon bookmarks, shelf wear along bottom edges, else very fine. Current 24-39 1978 $90

PLATO   Dialogues. 1924. 3rd ed., rev. & corrected, 5 vols. Allen 234-737 1978 $60

PLATO   The Dialogues. New York, 1937. 2 vols., 8vo., cloth. Salloch 348-200 1978 $15

PLATO   Euthyphro, Apologia Socratis, Crito, Phaedo, graece ad fidem codd. Mss. Tubing. Lipsae, 1783. Half contemp. calf, 8vo. George's 635-495 1978 £6

PLATO   Opera Omnia. Leipzig and London, 1873. Greek text, folio, vellum with label, gilt-stamped covers. Salloch 348-198 1978 $45

PLATO   The Synposium of Socrates. N.P., 1937. Eight orig. engravings by Ferdinand Springer, large quarto, unopened sheets, orig. wr. and slipcase, one of 150 copies. Totteridge 29-80 1978 $200

PLATO   The Symposium or Supper of .... Nonesuch Press. Sm. 8vo, 1st. ed., no. 307 of 1050 copies, top of canvas spine darkened by dust, o/w fine copy in d.w. Jarndyce 16-1193 1978 £10

PLATO   Timaeus & Critias of Atlanticus. 1944. Allen 234-746 1978 $10

PLATT, GEORGE W.   A History of the Republican Party. Cincinnati, 1904. 1st ed., illus. MacManus 239-394 1978 $30

PLATT, THOMAS COLLIER   Autobiography. New York, 1910. Portrs. in sepia photogravure, 8vo., minor cover stains, 1st ed. Morrill 241-467 1978 $9

PLATTARD, JEAN   The Life of Francois Rabelais. 1930. Orig. ed., plts., roy. 8vo., orig. cloth, spine little faded. Howes 194-1112 1978 £6.50

PLATTER, THOMAS   Thomas Platter's Travels in England 1599. 1937. Octavo, good. Upcroft 10-140 1978 £8.50

PLATTS, JOHN   A Dictionary of English Synonyms. 1825. Orig. bds., leading hinge broken. Jarndyce 16-937 1978 £14

PLAUTUS, TITUS MACCIUS   Comoediae superst. ad. doctissim virorum editiones representate. Amsterodami, 1640. Engraved title, mounted, 32mo., old calf. George's 635-496 1978 £7.50

PLAUTUS, TITUS MACCIUS   Comoediae Superstites XX ad Ultimam. 1721. 24mo., old calf, very shabby, contents fine. Allen 234-754 1978 $12.50

PLAUTUS, TITUS MACCIUS   Comoediae superst. ad. doctissim virorum editiones representate. 1769. 2nd ed., 5 vols., half calf, top of two spines and bottom of one defective, rubbed. George's 635-497 1978 £12.50

PLAUTUS, TITUS MACCIUS   Comoediae. 1893-96. 7 vols. in 4. Allen 234-950 1978 $25

PLAUTUS, TITUS MACCIUS   Comedies. 1899-1913. 2 vols., top of one spine torn. Allen 234-755 1978 $7.50

PLAUTUS, TITUS MACCIUS   Ex Fide, Atque Actoritate Complurium Librorum Manuscriptorum Opera Dionys. (Paris), 1577. Large folio, early style half calf, marbled boards, t.p. soiled and pasted down, fine, wide margined. Bennett 20-168 1978 $275

PLAUTUS, TITUS MACCIUS   Miles Gloriosus. 1890. Half calf, slightly worn, Vol. 4. Allen 234-757 1978 $7.50

PLAYFAIR, G.M.H.   The Cities and Towns of China: A Geographical Dictionary. Hong Kong, 1879. Cloth, rebound or repaired, tips worn and spine lettering rubbed. Dawson's 449-67 1978 $75

PLAZZONI, FRANCESCO   De Partibvs Generationi Inservientibus. 1664. 12mo., bound together in modern vellum over bds. & laid in green cloth slipcase, lightly foxed, very good copy from the library of Dr. Alfred M. Hellman, very rare. Zeitlin 245-194 1978 $250

PLEAS, ELWOOD   Henry Co., Past and Present. New Castle, 1871. Frontis., orig. cloth, lib. marks, fine. MacManus 239-974 1978 $37.50

THE PLEASURES of Matrimony. 1689. Second ed., 12mo., well rebound in full calf antique by Sangorski & Sutcliffe, extremely rare. Howes 194-81 1978 £375

THE PLEDGE: or, the First Step to Fortune. A Sequel to the Bottle. New York, 1850. Disbound. Hayman 72-616 1978 $7.50

PLENDERLEITH, W.A.   Conflict. Toronto, 1950. Hood's 115-450 1978 $10

PLENN, J.H.   Saddie in the Sky: The Lone Star State. New York, 1940. 1st ed., illus., uncut, autographed by author. Jenkins 116-1083 1978 $25

PLETHO, GEMISTHUS   Traite Des Lois... Paris, 1858. Greek and French text, tall 8vo., 1/2 mor. Salloch 348-203 1978 $125

PLETSCH, OSCAR   Little Folks.   London, c.1865. Quarto, colored f.p., large and fine colored illus., tips rubbed, very good. Victoria 34-621 1978 $27.50

PLIMPTON Press Year Book. Norood, 1911. Includes style manual. Baldwins' 51-197 1978 $20

PLINIUS CAECILIUS SECUNDUS, GAIUS   Epistolae et Panegyricus. London, 1722. Buckram, corner soiled. Allen 234-759 1978 $12.50

PLINIUS CAECILIUS SECUNDUS, GAIUS   Epist. Lib. IX.   (Paris), 1599. 2 vols., 16mo., vellum. Allen 234-758 1978 $35

PLINIUS CAECILIUS SECUNDUS, GAIUS   Epistolarum Libri Decem. Venice, Aldus, 1508. 1st Aldine & 1st complete ed., 18th Cent. mottled calf, gilt spine, the Pembroke copy. Thomas 37-48 1978 £100

PLINIUS CAECILIUS SECUNDUS, GAIUS   Epistolarum Libri X. 1790. Thick sm. 8vo., full contemp. crimson mor., all edges gilt. Howes 194-418 1978 £32

PLINIUS CAECILIUS SECUNDUS, GAIUS   Epistularum Libri Novem. 1933. Allen 234-951 1978 $7.50

PLINIUS SECUNDUS, GAIUS   Historia Naturalis. Paris, 1779. Engr. frontis., 6 vols., 8vo., contemp. marbled calf, gilt, rare ed. Salloch 345-153 1978 $100

PLINY THE YOUNGER
Please turn to
PLINIUS CAECILIUS SECUNDUS, GAIUS

PLOMER, HENRY R.   English Printer's Ornaments. London, 1924. 4to., orig. cloth-backed bds., 1st ed., 1 of 500 copies, back cover bruised, otherwise fine. MacManus 238-1026 1978 $75

PLOMER, WILLIAM   The Case is Altered. Hogarth Press, 1932. First ed., nice, d.w., orig. cloth, 8vo. Howes 194-1098 1978 £12.50

PLOSS, HERMANN HEINRICH Woman, an historical, Gynaecological and Anthropological Compendium. London, 1935. 3 vols., coloured plts., lg. 8vo., illus., covers faded, good. K Books 244-258 1978 £30

PLOT, ROBERT   The Natural History of Oxford-shire. Oxford, (1676). Map, plts., folio, contemp. calf, neatly rebacked, orig. label, first ed. Howes 194-82 1978 £215

PLOT, ROBERT   The Natural History of Stafford-Shire. Oxford, 1686. Plts., map, folio, contemp. calf, first ed., upper joint cracked. Howes 194-83 1978 £220

PLOTINUS   On the Beautiful, the 6th Treatise of the 1st Ennead. Stratford on Avon, Shakespeare Head Press, 1914. Ltd. to 510 copies, fcap. 8vo., orig. qtr. linen. George's 635-925 1978 £6.50

PLUES, M.   Rambles in Search of Wild Flowers, and how to distinguish them. 1863. Coloured plates, post 8vo. George's 635-959 1978 £10.50

PLUMMER, C.   Vitae Sanctorum Hiberniae. Oxford, 1910. Good, octavo, 2 vols, cloth. Hyland 128-364 1978 £22.50

PLUMPTRE, C. E.   Giordano Bruno: A Tale of the Sixteenth Century. 1884. 1st. ed., 2 vols., half titles, orig. brown cloth blocked in black & gilt, fine. Jarndyce 16-940 1978 £23

PLUNKET, EMELINE M.   Merrie Games in Rhyme from Ye Olden Time. London, (1886). 1st ed., illus. by Plunket, ornate lettering, vivid red, including ornately decorated covers, fly-leaf gone, fine. Victoria 34-623 1978 $30

PLUNKETT, H.   Ireland in the New Century. 1905. Revised, 3rd ed., wrs., very good, signed pres. copy. Hyland 128-365 1978 £5

PLUTARCHUS   Apophthegmata. (Venice), 1471. Sm. folio, roman letter, crisp, large copy, with orig. manuscript quiring and several uncut edges, old red mor., 1st ed. Quaritch Summer, 1978-36 1978 $6,000

PLUTARCHUS   De Levens van Doorluchtige Grieken en Romeinen Onderling Vergeleeken. Amsterdam, 1789-1809. 13 vols., 8vo., half calf bindings, shaved, engr. portrs. Van der Peet H-64-522 1978 Dfl 450

PLUTARCHUS   The Lives of the Nobel Grecians and Romaines. 1612. Thk. folio, rebound in half calf, antique style, woodcut hand- and tail-pieces and initials. Howes 194-84 1978 £175

PLUTARCHUS   Plutarch's Lives. 1758. Frontis., portrait vignettes, 6 vols., contemp. speckled calf gilt, some joints cracked, 8vo. Howes 194-419 1978 £35

PLUTARCHUS   Lives. 1774. 6 vols., old calf, one joint cracked, lower margins of 3 vols. watermarked. Allen 234-765 1978 $20

PLUTARCHUS   Lives. 1810. New ed., 8 vols., 12mo., tree calf, worn, joints cracked. George's 635-500 1978 £10.50

PLUTARCHUS   Lives. Liverpool, 1883. 3 vols., 8vo. George's 635-501 1978 £10.50

PLUTARCHUS   The Lives of the Noble Grecians and Romanes. Oxford, Shakespeare Head Press, 1928. Ltd. to 500 copies, decor. by Thomas Lowinsky, 8 vols., orig. buckram, covers dull. George's 635-926 1978 £75

PLUTARCHUS   The Lives of the Most Noble Grecians and Romanes. Oxford, Shakespeare Head Press, 1928. 8 vols., 8vo., black cloth, gilt tops, bkplt. each vol., only 500 sets prtd. Quaritch 979-290 1978 $150

PLUTARCHUS   The Lives of the Noble Grecians and Romances ... New York, Shakespeare Head Press, 1928. 8 vols., frontis., 8vo., plts. paper bds., cloth backs, ltd. to 500 copies, v.f., unopened, uncut. Howell 5-53 1978 $200

PLUTARCHUS   Morales De Plutarco. Alcala de Henares, 1548. Folio, mod. mor., translated by Gracian. Salloch 348-205 1978 $350

PLUTARCHUS   Morals. 1871. 5 vols., spot on one cover. Allen 234-764 1978 $30

PLUTARCHUS   Paralellum, Vitae Romanorum et Graecorum Quadraginta Noveum. Florence, 1517. Folio, good, late 18th or early 19th cent. red half mor. Schafer 19-35 1978 sFr 4900

PLUTARCHUS   Sit'ne Rationis Aliqua in Bestiis vis, Tum Utra Animantium Plus Huius Habeant, Terrestria ne, an Aquatica. Basel, 1534. Old vellum. Allen 234-763 1978 $30

POCKET Business Directory of Oakland, California... Oakland, 1881. Original printed 12mo cloth, 1st ed. Ginsberg 14-172 1978 $75

POCOCK, ROGER   Following the Frontier. New York, 1908. Pic. cloth, 1st ed., scarce, very good copy. Dykes 34-156 1978 $45

POE, EDGAR ALLAN   Bells and Other Poems. London, (1912). 1st ed., illus. by Edmund Dulac, 1 of 750 numbered copies signed by Dulac, 4 to., full gilt stamped white vellum, t.e.g., uncut, ties lacking, bookplate, orig. binding, plts. Houle 10-94 1978 $495

POE, EDGAR ALLAN   The Bells and Other Poems. London, n.d. 1st. ed., 4to, cloth gilt extra, coloured plts. & other illus. by Edmund Dulac, pres. copy stamped in blind on title page. Traylen 88-374 1978 £40

POE, EDGAR ALLAN   The Bells and Other Poems. New York and London, n.d. 4to., plts. in color by Edmund Dulac. Biblo 247-349 1978 $125

POE, EDGAR ALLAN   The Centenary Poe. London, (1949). Full mor., t.e.g., ltd. de luxe ed., copy no. 378 of 400 copies printed. Wolfe 39-441 1978 $30

POE, EDGAR ALLAN   La Chute de la Maison Usher. Monte-Carlo, 1948. 8vo., half calf, portfolio, slipcase, colored frontis., colored plts. by Dubout, ltd. ed. of 3000 numbered copies, uncut. Van der Peet H-64-403 1978 Dfl 95

POE, EDGAR ALLAN   The Complete Poems and Stories. New York, 1946. 1st Borzoi ed., 2 vol., fine, d.j., slipcase. Ballinger 11-162 1978 $37.50

POE, EDGAR ALLAN   Eureka: A Prose Poem. New York, 1848. 12mo, later leatherette (worn), 1st ed., slight marginal waterstains. Ximenes 47-242 1978 $75

POE, EDGAR ALLAN   The Fall of the House of Usher. New York, 1931. No. 539 of 1200, wood engrav., fine, burlap. Ballinger 11-163 1978 $22.50

POE, EDGAR ALLAN   The Gift: A Christmas and New Years' Present
for 1840. Philadelphia, (1839). Orig. full blind-stamped mor., 1st ed., bright.
MacManus 238-566 1978 $45

POE, EDGAR ALLAN   The Journal of Julius Rodman. San Francisco,
1947. Orig. boards, 500 copies pr. at Grabhorn Press. Ginsberg 14-880 1978
$25

POE, EDGAR ALLAN   The Literati. New York, 1850. Orig. binding.
Wolfe 39-442 1978 $47.50

POE, EDGAR ALLAN   Nouvelles Choisies d'Edgar Poe. Paris, 1853.
Sm.8vo, tan half morocco, original yellow glazed printed wr. bound in, 1st ed.
in French, very good copy, scarce. Ximenes 47-243 1978 $125

POE, EDGAR ALLAN   Tales of Mystery and Imagination. New York,
1933. Colour plts. by Harry Clarke, first U.S. ed., 4to., pict. cloth, front hinge
weak, good. Bell Book 17-484 1978 £55

POE, EDGAR ALLAN   Tales of Mystery and Imagination. New York,
1933. Color plates, spine lettering dulled, fine. Victoria 34-166 1978 $85

POE, EDGAR ALLAN   Works... New York, 1856. 4 vols., top
extremity of spine chipped, otherwise very good. Americanist 102-92 1978 $25

POE, EDGAR ALLEN   Complete Works. New York, (1902).
1 of 500 numbered sets, illus., Arnheim ed., gilt stamped white vellum over
bds., t.e.g., bookplates of Monte Blue, 10 vols., fine. Houle 10-263
1978 $395

POE, EDGAR ALLAN   The Works of... Plymouth, n.d. Midnight ed.,
on Nelson's India paper, full leather, worn around edges, else good. Austin 82-705
1978 $27.50

POE, JOHN W.   The True Story of the Killing of "Billy the Kid"
(Notorious New Mexico Outlaw) as Detailed by...to E. A. Brininstool in 1919.
Los Angeles, [1923]. Illus., original printed wr., one of 250 numbered copies,
2nd ed. Ginsberg 14-55 1978 $50

POE, WILLIAM HENRY LEONARD   Poe's Brother: The Poems of William
Henry Leonard Poe, Elder Brother of Edgar Allan Poe... New York, (1926).
Illus., blue-gray bds., t.e.g., 1st ed., 1 of 1000, fine in dust jacket, name of
former owner embossed on end paper, slipcase. Bradley 49-267 1978 $40

POELLNITZ, KARL LUDWIG, FREIHERR VON   Memoires. Londres, 1735. 2nd
ed., 4 vols., lg. 12mo., calf. King 7-376 1978 £15

POELLNITZ, KARL LUDWIG, FREIHERR VON   The Memoirs. 1739. 2nd ed.,
2 vols., cont. calf, joints cracked, 8vo. Howes 194-421 1978 £30

POEMS & Ballads of Young Ireland, 1888. 1888. 1st ed., owner initialling on t.p.,
very good. Hyland 128-878 1978 £95

POETAE Minores Graeci. 1684. Sm. 8vo., contemp. panelled calf, unlettered,
slight damage to lower cover. George's 635-502 1978 £10.50

POETIC Gift: containing Barbauld's Hymns in Verse. New Haven, 1841. 16mo,
pictorial wrappers, illus., minor wrapper tears, very good. Victoria 34-624
1978 $10

POETICAL Miscellany. 1701. 8vo., old calf rebacked, title age-soiled, some
old waterstaining in first few leaves, very fair. P. M. Hill 142-292 1978 £100

POETRY Quartos. New York, 1929. 12 vols., orig. wrs., pub. wr., torn, slipcase, 1st ed., ltd. to 475 sets, fine. MacManus 238-740 1978 $85

POETS of Tomorrow. London, Hogarth Press, 1939. First ed., orig. binding,
nice. Rota 211-18 1978 £5

POGANY, G. O.   19th Century Hungarian Painting. Budapest,
(c. 1945). Coloured plts., folio. George's 635-44 1978 £7.50

POGANY, WILLY   The Song of Bilitis. New York, (1926). Lmtd.
ed., signed by Pogany, B&W illus. and plates, lovely endpapers, cover lettering
dulled, fine. Victoria 34-625 1978 $85

POGGI, MAURO   Alfabeto di Lettere Iniziali Inventate...da
Mauro Poggi... N.P., n.d. (c. 1750). Eng. plts., half calf, bookplate of A.
Berard. Schumann 511-46 1978 sFr 2,600

POHLE, ERNST A.   Clinical Radiation Therapy. Philadelphia, 1950.
Library marks. Rittenhouse 49-649 1976 $15

POHLMANN, R. VON   Grundriss der Griechischen Geschichte und Quel-
lenkunde. 1896. New buckram. Allen 234-767 1978 $10

POINSETT, JOEL R.   Report from the Secretary of War in Compliance
with a Resolution...1837,.... Washington, 1838. Folding map, cloth with
leather label. Ginsberg 14-235 1978 $75

POINTER, JOHN   Oxoniensis Academia: or, The Antiquities and
Curiosities of the University of Oxford. 1749. 1st. ed., 12mo, calf, rubbed, old
reback & corners renewed. Jarndyce 16-151 1978 £26

POINTIS, JEAN BERNARD LOUIS DESJEAN DE   A Genuine and Particular
Account of the Taking of Carthagena by the French and Buccaniers in the Year
1697... London, 1740. New cloth, with plan fold in. Baldwins' 51-512 1978
$87.50

POISSON DE GOMEZ, MADELEINE A.   La Belle Assemblee: or, The Adventures
of Twelve Days. Dublin, 1733-31-31. 3rd. ed., engraved plts., 3 vols., 12mo,
contemp. calf, new labels, sm. portion missing from blank margin of 2 plts., nice.
Fenning 32-270 1978 £32.50

POLEHAMPTON, EDWARD T. W.   The Gallery of Nature and Art. 1818. 6
vols., second ed., engrav. plts., contemp. half calf, 8vo. Howes 194-420 1978
£55

POLIAKOV, ALEXANDER   White Mammoths. 1943. Illus. with photos.
Austin 80-256 1978 $11

POLIAKOV, B. G.   Pubimie Igri. Moscow, 1928. Printed wrappers,
fine. Victoria 34-631 1978 $30

POLIDORI, JOHN WILLIAM   The Vampyre; A Tale. 1819. 1st. ed., 8vo,
wanting half-title, little light spotting, very good copy. Fenning 32-271 1978
£65

POLIGNAC, MELCHIOR DE   Anti-Lucretius, sive de Deo et Natura. Paris,
1747. 2 vols., port., 4to, marbled calf, fine contemp. bind., gilt-tooled spine,
very fine set. Salloch 348-207 1978 $175

POLIGNAC, MELCHIOR DE   Anti-Lucretius, Sive, De Deo et Natura, Libri
Novem. 1748. 2 vols. in 1, calf, joints cracked. Allen 234-593 1978 $15

POLISH Acts of Atrocity Against the German Minority in Poland. Berlin-New
York, 1940. 2nd ed. with addenda, illus. with photos, paper. Austin 79-274
1978 $27.50

POLITI, LEO   Pedro the Angel of Olivera Street. New York,
1946. 1st ed., fine, torn d.j. Victoria 34-632 1978 $20

POLITICAL Dialogues Between the Celebrated Statues of Pasquin and Marforio at
Rome. 1736. 1st. ed., 8vo, disbound, title dust-soiled. Hannas 54-238 1978
£10

THE POLITICAL Pilgrim's Progress. 1839. 6 crude woodcuts, stabbed pamphlet,
thumbed. Jarndyce 16-941 1978 £8.50

THE POLITICAL Primer; or, Road to Publich Honours. 1826. 1st. ed., uncut,
orig.blue bds., paper spine, slightly defective at head, paper label rubbed. Jarndyce 16-259 1978 £14.50

POLK, JAMES K.   Approval of the Oregon Bill. Washington, 1848.
Unopened, fine copy. Jenkins 116-1091 1978 $35

POLK, JAMES K.   Correspondence Between the Secretary of War
and Generals Scott and Taylor, and Between General Scott and Mr. Trist...
Washington, 1848. Cloth with leather label, 1st ed. Ginsberg 14-535 1978
$40

POLK, JAMES K.   Polk. The Diary of a President, 1845-1849.
New York, 1929. Frontis. port., illus., orig. cloth, fine. MacManus 239-
395 1978 $15

POLL, HEINRICH   Ueber Schadel Und Skelete Der Bewohner Der
Chatham-Inseln. (Stuttgart, 1902). 8vo., plts., cloth-backed blue bds.,
former owner's stamp on cover, from library of Charles A. Kofoid with bkplt.,
very good. Zeitlin 245-195 1978 $75

POLLARD, A. F.   Henry VIII. London, 1902. Royal quarto, hand-
colored frontis. portrait, early pr. wr. bound in, half red mor., boards covered in
complimentary cloth, 1st ed. Bennett 7-87 1978 $175

POLLARD, ALFRED WILLIAM   Books in the House. Indianapolis, n.d. Ltd. to 500 copies, 8vo. George's 635-1218 1978 £6

POLLARD, ALFRED WILLIAM   Shakespeare's Hand in the Play of 'Sir Thomas More'. Cambridge, 1923. Plts., octavo, good. Upcroft 10-490 1978 £6.50

POLLARD, ALFRED WILLIAM   A Short Title Catalogue of Books Printed in England, Scotland and Ireland.... 2 vols. Traylen 88-58 1978 £40

POLLARD, EDWARD ALFRED   Black Diamonds Gathered in the Darkey Homes of the South. New York, 1860. MacManus 239-850 1978 $27.50

POLLARD, EDWARD ALFRED   The First Year of the War. Richmond, 1862. Orig. green wrs., detached, Bell Wiley's copy. Broadfoot 46-459 1978 $40

POLLARD, EDWARD ALFRED   Observations in the North; Eight Months in Prison and on Parole. Richmond, 1865. Wrs., library stamp on title page, Bell Wiley's copy. Broadfoot 46-461 1978 $125

POLLARD, EDWARD ALFRED   Observations in the North. Richmond, 1865. 8vo., old cloth wrs., orig. prtd. front wr. bound in, cloth wr. loose, 1st ed. Morrill 241-468 1978 $75

POLLARD, EDWARD ALFRED   Southern History of the Great Civil War in the United States. Toronto, 1863. 8vo, orig. cloth, rebacked, engraved portraits. Edwards 1012-547 1978 £12

POLLARD, EDWARD ALFRED   Southern History of the Great Civil War in the United States. Toronto, 1863. Bell Wiley's copy. Broadfoot 46-202 1978 $40

POLLARD, EDWARD ALFRED   Southern History of the War. New York, 1863. Orig. binding, minor wear, clean. Hayman 71-136 1978 $10

POLLARD, EDWARD ALFRED   Southern History of the War. New York, 1864. 8vo, orig. cloth, map, portraits, spotted, spine repaired. Edwards 1012-548 1978 £10

POLLARD, HUGH B. C.   Automatic Pistols. London, (ca. 1920). 8vo., illus. Morrill 241-469 1978 $15

POLLARD, HUGH B. C.   British and American Game-Birds. 1945. 4to., coloured plts. by P. Rickman. George's 635-1013 1978 £32.50

POLLARD, JOSEPHINE   The Decorative Sisters. New York, (1881). 1st ed., chromolithographed plates, including both covers, by Walter Satterlee, very good. Victoria 34-633 1978 $25

POLLARD, JOSEPHINE   The Decorative Sisters. New York, 1881. 8vo., orig. colored pic. bds., cloth back, 1st ed., ex-lib. Morrill 241-470 1978 $30

POLLARD, JOSEPHINE   The Life of George Washington. New York, n.d. Quarto, pictorial cloth, color plates, very good. Victoria 34-634 1978 $7.50

POLLEN, J. H.   Papal Negotiations with Mary Queen of Scots 1561-67. Edinburgh, 1901. Vol. 37, 8vo. George's 635-715 1978 £6.50

POLLNITZ, CHARLES LEWIS, BARON DE
Please turn to
POELLNITZ, KARL LUDWIG, FREIHERR VON

POLLOCK, EDWIN T.   The Hatchet of the United States Ship "George Washington". (New York), 1919. Illus., 8vo. Morrill 241-471 1978 $10

POLLOCK, FREDERICK   The Genius of the Common Law. New York, 1912. 1st Amer. ed. Biblo 251-369 1978 $15

POLLOCK, J.   The Popish Plot; a Study in the History of the Reign of Charles II. 1903. Roy. 8vo, good. Upcroft 10-491 1978 £10

POLLOCK, J.   The Popish Plot; A Study in the History of the Reign of Charles II. Cambridge, 1944. New ed., octavo, good. Upcroft 10-492 1978 £6

POLLOCK, J. E.   Lorenzo and Other Poems. Toronto, 1883. Orig. binding, front cover stained, engrav. frontis. Wolfe 39-410 1978 $12.50

POLLOCK, JOHN HACKETT   Smoking Flax. (c. 1922). Ltd. to 500 copies, wr., 4to, very good. Hyland 128-370 1978 £4.50

POLLOCK, JOHN HACKETT   The Sun-Child, A Poem. 1925. 1st ed., wrs., very good. Hyland 128-368 1978 £4

POLLOCK, JOHN HACKETT   The Tale of Thule. (c. 1923). 1st ed., ltd. 500 copies, wr., 4to, very good. Hyland 128-359 1978 £4

POLLOCK, JOHN HACKETT   William Butler Yeats. 1935. 1st ed., very good, octavo bound in cloth. Hyland 128-885 1978 £7.50

POLLOCK, THOMAS C.   The Philadelphia Theatre in the 18th Century Together with the Day Book of the Same Period. Philadelphia, 1933. 1st ed., frontis., fine. MacManus 239-1645 1978 $37.50

POLLOCK, WALTER HERRIES   Amateur Theatricals. London, 1879. 12mo, 1st ed., rare, covers faded and slightly faded, spine edge chipped. Victoria 34-345 1978 $85

POLLOK, COL.   Wild Sports of Burma, and Assam. London, 1900. Cloth, illus., plts., maps, rare, 8vo. Van der Peet 127-189 1978 Dfl 145

POLLY, G. H.   Domestic Architecture, Furniture & Ornament of England from the 14th to the 18th Century. n.d. Folio, plts. loose on portfolio, lacks spine & ties, blind stamp. Allen 234-1408 1978 $25

POLYBIUS   Historiarum Libri V... N.P., 1608. Sm. 8vo., vellum. Van der Peet H-64-523 1978 Dfl 55

POLYBIUS   History. 1634. Folio, old calf, rebacked, joints tender. Allen 234-770 1978 $75

POLYBIUS   Histoire. 1727-30. 6 vols., 4to., old calf, worn, some joints cracked, fldg. engr. plts. Allen 234-771 1978 $75

POMEROY, E. M.   Archibald Lampman. N.P., n.d. Card cover. Hood 116-265 1978 $7.50

POMEROY, MARCUS MILLS   Home Harmonies. New York, 1876. Orig. binding, clean, faded. Hayman 71-639 1978 $7.50

POMEROY, MARCUS MILLS   Nonsense; or, the Hits and Criticisms on the Follies of the Day. New York, 1868. Signed and inscribed by Pomeroy, orig. cloth, good. Greene 78-328 1978 $25

POMEROY, RALPH LEGGE   The Story of a Regiment of Horse. 1924. 2 vols., imp. 8vo., coloured plts., orig. cloth. F. Edwards 1013-465 1978 £70

POMET, PIERRE   A Compleat History of Druggs. London, 1712. Plts., first English ed., two vols. in one, 4to., contemp. panelled calf, very good. Rota 212-45 1978 £500

POMMEREUL, F. R. J. DE   Campagne du General Buonaparte en Italie pendant les Annees IVe et Ve de la Republique Francaise. Paris, 1797. 2 vols., 12mo., half calf, rubbed, lacks map. King 7-377 1978 £20

POMPONAZZI, PIETRO   Tractatus De Immortalitate Animae. (N.P., 1534). 17th century reissue. 12mo. Salloch 348-208 1978 $450

PONCELET, POLYCARPE   Le Chimica del Gusto e dell'Odorato o sia l' Arte di comporre facilmente.... Fienze, 1782. 8vo., soft bds., plts., very good uncut copy. King 7-213 1978 £120

POND, JOHN   The Sporting Kalendar. (1751). 12mo., old calf, worn. George's 635-1507 1978 £6.50

POND, JOHN   The Sporting Kalendar. 1752. 12mo., old calf. George's 635-1508 1978 £6.50

PONSONBY, FREDERICK   The Grenadier Guards in the Great War of 1914-1918. 1920. Frontis. portraits, plts., 3 vols., 8vo., orig. cloth backed bds. F. Edwards 1013-476 1978 £20

PONTA, GIOACHINO   Il Trionfo Della Vaccinia. Parma, Bodoni Press, 1810. 4to., orig. beige bds., fine lg. paper uncut copy, ownership ms. note inside cover dated August 31st, 1810, 1st ed., 250 prtd. copies. Zeitlin 245-196 1978 $250

PONTANO GIOVANNI GIOVAINO   Gli Orti Delle Esperidi Di Giangiovaino Pontano Con cinque ecoghe.   Venezia, 1761. 8vo., marbled bds., calf spine, portr., nice.   King 7-214 1978 £20

PONTANO GIOVANNI GIOVAINO   Opera Omnia Soluta Oratione Composita. Venice, 1518.   Vol. I, 8vo., vellum.   Salloch 348-209 1978 $145

PONTANO GIOVANNI GIOVAINO   Opera Omnia.   Venice, Aldus, 1518-19. 3 vols., remarkably clean & sound, tall copy, good margins, 19th Cent. dark brown hardgrain mor.   Thomas 37-49 1978 £150

PONTEN, J.   Griechische Landschaften.   1914. Plts., some colored, 2 vols.   Allen 234-772 1978 $7.50

PONTEY, WILLIAM   The Profitable Planter.   1814. Fourth ed., contemp. half calf, mor. labels, 8vo.   Howes 194-132 1978 £25

PONTICELLI, FILIPPO MARIA   Alcune Eresie Dell'Intelletto Umano.   Lucca, 1766. 8vo., bds.   Salloch 348-210 1978 $50

PONTOPPIDAN, D.   Reise til Syd America.   Copenhagen, 1841. 1/4 calf, 8vo., good.   Paine 78-110 1978 $58.50

PONY Express Courier; Telling the Story of California and the Old Trails. Placerville, 1934-1947.   Bound in three folio volumes.   Ginsberg 14-173 1978 $375

POOL, BETTIE FRESHWATER   Literature in the Albemarle.   Baltimore, 1915. Broadfoot 50-175 1978 $25

POOL, EUGENE H.   Surgery at the New York Hospital One Hundred Years Ago.   New York, 1929. Plts., one of 230 numbered copies, printed on hand made paper, signed by author, orig. slipcase.   Wolfe 39-364 1978 $35

POOL, MARIA LOUISE   Chums.   Boston, 1900. Illus., 1st ed.   Biblo BL781-1032 1978 $9

POOL, R.   Views of the Most Remarkable Public Buildings.. of the City of Dublin.   (1780). Reprint, octavo bound in cloth.   Hyland 128-969 1978 £9.50

POOLE, ERNEST   The Bridge. My Own Story.   New York, 1940. 1st ed.   Biblo BL781-1108 1978 $9.50

POOLE, ERNEST   The Great White Hills of New Hampshire.   New York, 1946. Illus., 1st ed., fine, d.j.   MacManus 239-328 1978 $10

POOLE, FRANCIS   Queen Charlotte Islands, a Narrative of Discovery and Adventure in the North Pacific.   London, 1872. 3/4 leather, marbled bds. worn, t.p. and frontis. foxed, otherwise clean.   Hood 116-872 1978 $90

POOLE, JOHN   Hamlet Travestie...   1811. 3rd. ed., half title, uncut, rebound in blue bds., cream paper spine, v.g.   Jarndyce 16-943 1978 £15

POOLE, MATTHEW   A Dialogue between a Popish Priest and an English Protestant....   1670. Stained, corners of some pages wormed, 12mo., old calf worn.   George's 635-1113 1978 £5

POOLE, R. L.   The Exchequer in the Twelfth Century.   Oxford, 1912. 8vo.   Upcroft 12-347 1978 £8.50

POOLE, R. L.   Illustrations of the History of Medieval Thought and Learning.   1932. New ed., 8vo.   Upcroft 12-348 1978 £4.50

POOLE, R. S.   Horae Aegyptiacae: or, The Chronology of Ancient Egypt Discovered From Astronomical and Hieroglyphic Records Upon Its Monuments.   London, 1851. Illus., plts., 8vo, orig. cloth, head of spine damaged.   Sexton 7-95 1978 £7.50

POOLE, WILLIAM F.   An Index to Periodical Literature.   Boston, 1882. 3rd ed., imp. 8vo., full mor.   George's 635-1219 1978 £18

POOLE, WILLIAM F.   The Ordinance of 1787.   Ann Arbor, 1892. Printed wrappers.   Wolfe 39-443 1978 $15

POOR, HENRY VARNUM   An Artist Sees Alaska.   New York, 1945. Illus.   Hood's 115-190 1978 $20

POOR, HENRY VARNUM   An Artist sees Alaska.   New York, 1945. 1st ed., illus.   Biblo BL781-633 1978 $9

POOR Will's Almanack....   Philadelphia, n.d. (1776). Orig. self wrs., worn, 8vo.   Americanist 101-3 1978 $45

POORE, BENJAMIN PERLEY   Life of U. S. Grant.   New York, (1885). Cloth. Hayman 72-618 1978 $10

POPE, ALEXANDER   An Epistle to the Right Honourable Richard Lord Visct.   London, 1733. Folio, disbound, 1st ed., very good copy.   Ximenes 47-256 1978 $150

POPE, ALEXANDER   An Essay on Man.. with the Notes of William, Lord Bishop of Gloucester.   1774. Medallion portrait, frontis eng., contemp. calf, rebacked, orig. label preserved, bookplts. of Roger Senhouse and Hutton Wood.   Eaton 45-390 1978 £10

POPE, ALEXANDER   Essay on Man.   1788. Sm. 8vo., recent marbled bds., plts.   P. M. Hill 142-293 1978 £14

POPE, ALEXANDER   An Essay on Man, To Which is Added The Universal Prayer...   Philadelphia, 1821. Printed bds.   Hayman 71-640 1978 $10

POPE, ALEXANDER   Letters of Mr. Pope, and Several Eminent Persons, From the Year 1705, to 1711 and from the Year 1711.   1735 (Vol. II n.d.). 2 vols. in 1, 8vo., contemp. mottled calf, spine rather worn, lacking label, good.   P. M. Hill 142-203 1978 £140

POPE, ALEXANDER   Of False Taste.   London, 1731. Folio, disbound, 3rd ed., very good copy.   Ximenes 47-257 1978 $70

POPE, ALEXANDER   Of the Characters of Women: An Epistle to a Lady.   London, 1735. Folio, disbound, 1st ed., fine copy.   Ximenes 47-258 1978 $150

POPE, ALEXANDER   Of the Use of Riches, An Epistle to the Right Honourable Allen Lord Bathurst.   London, 1733. Folio, disbound, 2nd ed., nice uncut copy, quite scarce.   Ximenes 47-259 1978 $80

POPE, ALEXANDER   Of the Use of Riches.   1733. 2nd. ed., folio, orig. stabbed issue, rebound in half calf, hand-marbled bds.   Jarndyce 16-162 1978 £36

POPE, ALEXANDER   The Poetical Works of Alexander Pope, Esq. Glasgow, 1785. 3 vols., folio, 1/4 red mor., marbled fore edge & endpapers, spine worn, good set.   Current 24-40 1978 $70

POPE, ALEXANDER   Sober Advice from Horace to the Young Gentleman about Town.   (1734). Folio, 1st ed., modern half mor.   Quaritch 979-254 1978 $175

POPE, ALEXANDER   The Works.   1751. 9 vols., lg. 8vo., contemp. calf, spines fully gilt, plts., fine.   P. M. Hill 142-204 1978 £185

POPE, ALEXANDER   Works in Nine Volumes.   1757. Frontis vol. I, orig. calf, maroon labels, v.g., except for rubbing to heads of spines.   Jarndyce 16-164 1978 £35

POPE, ALEXANDER   Pope's Works.   1778. 4 vols., frontis, plts., orig. speckled calf, gilt borders, spines, dark green labels, fine, handsome set. Jarndyce 16-161 1978 £110

POPE, ALEXANDER   Works.   1882. 9 vols., frontis portrait, orig. blue bds., paper labels, grey spines, uncut & unopened, immaculate set, superb in orig. condition.   Jarndyce 16-944 1978 £60

POPE, HUGH   Saint Augustine of Hippo.   1949. Maps, ex-lib. Allen 234-69 1978 $7.50

POPE, JOHN   The Campaign in Virginia, of July and August, 1862.   Milwaukee, 1863. Wrs., Bell Wiley's copy.   Broadfoot 46-203 1978 $40

POPE, JOSEPH   The Tour of Their Royal Highnesses the Duke and Duchess of Cornwall and York Through the Dominion of Canada in the Year 1901. Ottawa, 1903. Plts.   Hood 117-589 1978 $12.50

POPE, SAXTON   The Adventurous Bowmen.   New York, 1926. Illus., 8vo., lettering on spine flaked, front cover stained, 1st ed.   Morrill 241-472 1978 $25

POPE, WM. F.　　　Early Days in Arkansas, Being for the Most Part the Personal Recollections of an Old Settler... Little Rock, 1895. Illus., half morocco, lst ed. Ginsberg 14-31 1978 $85

THE POPE'S Letter to Maddam Cellier in Relation to Her Great Suffering For the Catholick Cause... (Colophon, 1680). lst. ed., folio, disbound, uncut, paper browned. Hannas 54-47D 1978 $20

POPE-HENNESSY, UNA　　　The Aristocratic Journey. New York, 1931. Bell Wiley's copy. Broadfoot's 44-742 1978 $16

POPHAM, HOME　　　Rules and Regulations to be observed in His Majesty's ship. 1805. 4to., wrappers. F. Edwards 1013-177 1978 £20

POPHAM, JOHN　　　Reports and Cases,... London, 1656. lst ed., small folio, contemp. calf worn, places missing from the spine, pieces cut from free endpaper. Totteridge 29-82 1978 $110

POPPLE, A. E.　　　Snow's Criminal Code of Canada. Toronto, 1939. 5th ed., some wear. Hood 117-409 1978 $17.50

POPULAR Directions For the Prevention and Cure of Headaches, Colds and Indigestion With Medical Prescriptions and Cases by a Medical Practitioner. Philadelphia, 1823. 12mo, orig. bds., untrimmed. Baldwins' 51-355 1978 $27.50

THE POPULAR Rhymes, Sayings and Proverbs of the County of Berwick. Newcastle, 1856. lst. ed., orig. blue cloth, v.g. Jarndyce 16-291 1978 £15.50

THE POPULAR Science Review. 1861-1868. 7 vols., plts., 27 of which are coloured, coloured map, contemp. embossed cloth. Quaritch 977-130 1978 $125

THE POPULAR Story of Blue Beard. Cooperstown, 1839. 24mo., woodcuts, orig. pic. orange wrs. Argosy Special-16 1978 $50

PORCACCHI, THOMMASO　　　Funerali Antichi di diversi popoli, et nation.... Venice, 1591. 4to., 23 engravings, orig. limp vellum, 2nd ed. Quaritch 978-131 1978 $575

PORDEN, ELEANOR A.　　　The Veils. 1815. First ed., contemp. half calf, mor. label, 8vo. Howes 194-424 1978 £18

PORPHYRIVS, MALCHUS　　　De Antro Nympharvm. 1765. 4to., vellum, spine damaged. King 7-378 1978 £25

PORTA, GIOVANNI BATTISTA DELLA　　　De Hvmana Physionomia. Rothomagi, 1650. 8vo., woodcuts, contemp. vellum with overlapping edges, lightly browned, foxed, good copy from the library of Dr. Alfred M. Hellman, rare. Zeitlin 245-197 1978 $150

PORTA, HENRICUS A.　　　De Linguarum Orient ad Omne Doctrinae Genus Praestantia. Milan, 1758. lst ed., quarto, contemp. boards, unopened copy, fine. Bennett 20-169 1978 $225

PORTALIS, ROGER　　　Les Dessinateurs d'Illustration au Dix-Huitieme Siecle. Paris, 1877. Frontis., very thick 8vo., full crimson crushed levant binding, 1 of 50 copies. Argosy Special-72 1978 $200

PORTEOUS, BEILBY　　　Lectures on the Gospel of St. Matthew, 1798-1801. 1802. 2 vols., full contemp. calf, 8vo. George's 635-1114 1978 £6.50

PORTEOUS, BEILBY　　　Sermons on Several Subjects. 1784. Full contemp. calf, 8vo. George's 635-1115 1978 £5

PORTER, ANNA MARIA　　　The Knight of St. John, a Romance. 1817. lst. ed., 3 vols., orig. half calf, marbled bds., v.g. Jarndyce 16-945 1978 £75

PORTER, ANNA MARIA　　　The Knight of St. John: A Romance. 1851. Lg. 12mo, contemp. half calf, very good copy. Fenning 32-272 1978 £8.50

PORTER, ANNA MARIA　　　The Village of Mariendorpt. London, 1821. Four vols., 12mo, contemporary half calf, gilt, lst ed., half-titles present, very good copy. Ximenes 47-261 1978 $200

PORTER, CHARLES T.　　　Review of the Mexican War... Auburn, 1849. 1st ed., rebound, scarce. MacManus 239-309 1978 $40

PORTER, CLYDE　　　Ruxton of the Rockies. Norman, (1950). Illus., lst ed., fine, d.w. Biblo 248-291 1978 $32.50

PORTER, COLE　　　Red Hot and Blue. New York, 1936. Quarto, red, white and blue moire silk cloth, gilt, 1 of 300 copies signed by author and inscription on front fly-leaf, silk is worn, lst ed., fine. Duschnes 220-243 1978 $125

PORTER, DAVID DIXON　　　Allan Dare and Robert le Diable: A Romance. New York, 1885. lst ed. in 2 vols., lg. 8vo, quarter calf & boards, edges rubbed, small spine damage, good. Greene 78-95 1978 $50

PORTER, ELEANOR H.　　　Mary Marie. Boston, 1920. First ed., illus. Biblo 247-573 1978 $12.50

PORTER, ELEANOR H.　　　Pollyanna Grows Up. Boston, 1915. lst ed., illus., fragile binding dulled and rubbed at edges, spine sunned, text about fine, very decent, firm copy, scarce. Victoria 34-635 1978 $50

PORTER, F. T.　　　Gleanings & Reminiscences. 1875. lst ed., cover dull & shaky, text good. Hyland 128-374 1978 £4

PORTER, J. L.　　　The Giant Cities of Bashan and Syria's Holy Places. 1886. Illus., orig. cloth, 8vo. Edwards 1012-81 1978 £12

PORTER, JAMES A.　　　A Prince of Anahuac. Galion, (1894). Cloth, tiny worn spot on spine. Hayman 73-202 1978 $15

PORTER, JANE　　　Sir Edwards Seaward's Narrative of His Shipwreck, and Consequent Discovery of Certain Islands in the Caribbean Sea... London, 1831. 3 vols., rebound circa 1870, half leather, very good copy, waxed. Baldwins' 51-513 1978 $75

PORTER, JANE　　　Sir Edward Seaward's Narrative of his Shipwreck, and consequent Discovery of certain Islands in the Caribbean from 1733 to 1749. 1832. Second ed., 3 vols., 8vo., later "watered" cloth, printed labels, uncut, neat. P. M. Hill 142-208 1978 £30

PORTER, KATHERINE ANNE　　　Flowering Judas and Other Stories. New York, (1935). Orig. cloth, d.j., lst ed., very good. MacManus 238-738 1978 $50

PORTER, KATHERINE ANNE　　　Katherine Anne Porter's French Song-Book. Harrison of Paris: (1933). 4to., orig. cloth-backed bds., d.j., slightly worn, lst ed., 1 of 595 copies, pres. copy, inscribed by author, fine. MacManus 238-806 1978 $250

PORTER, KATHERINE ANNE　　　My Chinese Marriage. New York, 1922. Gold imprint on front cover, t.e.g., name, good, sound copy. Bernard 5-209 1978 $90

PORTER, KATHERINE ANNE　　　Pale Horse, Pale Rider. New York, (1939). Very good. Bernard 5-210 1978 $20

PORTER, KATHERINE ANNE　　　Selected Short Stories. New York, (c.1944). 1st Armed Services ed., No. R-21, oblong 16 mo., pictorial wrappers, ink inscription, good. Houle 10-264 1978 $15

PORTER, MARY H.　　　Eliza Chappell Porter. A Memoir. Chicago, and New York, (1892). Cloth. Hayman 73-619 1978 $22.50

PORTER, NOAH　　　Half-Century Discourse; On Occasion of the Fiftieth Anniversary of His Ordination as Pastor of the First Church, in Farmington, Conn. Farmington, 1857. Wrps., light stains on front wrapper, back wrapper repaired but complete. Hayman 71-642 1978 $7.50

PORTER, NOAH　　　The Human Intellect. London, 1872. 4to., cloth. Salloch 348-211 1978 $20

PORTER, ROBERT KER　　　A Narrative of the Campaign in Russia, during the year 1812. 1814. 3rd ed., 8vo. George's 635-851 1978 £7.50

PORTER, ROBERT KER　　　A Narrative of the Campaign in Russia During the Year 1812. Philadelphia, 1815. Orig. full calf, fold in map torn. Baldwins' 51-362 1978 $20

PORTER, THOMAS   The Carnival: A Comedy. 1664. 1st. ed., 4to, half-morocco, paper browned, few headlines cut into. Hannas 54-239 1978 £90

PORTER, WILLIAM SIDNEY   Let Me Feel Your Pulse. 1910. Illus., first ed. Austin 82-689 1978 $20

PORTER, WILLIAM SIDNEY   Options. New York, 1909. 1st ed., 1st issue. Jenkins 116-1093 1978 $13.50

PORTER, WILLIAM SYDNEY   Postscripts. New York & London, 1923. 1st ed., good. Limestone 9-147 1978 $17.50

PORTER, WILLIAM SYDNEY   Roads of Destiny. New York, 1909. First ed., first state, interior very good. Limestone 9-148 1978 $17.50

PORTER, WILLIAM SYDNEY   Whirligigs. London and New York, (1910). First English ed., good, red cloth, frontis. Limestone 9-149 1978 $15

PORTEUS, T. C.   Calendar of the Standish deeds 1230-1575 pre-served in the Wigan Public Library. 1933. Ltd. to 250 copies, 8vo. Upcroft 12-350 1978 £8.50

A PORTFOLIO of Pictures from the Canadian Section of Fine Arts, British Empire Exhibition, London, 1924. (Toronto, n.d.). Card cover, reproductions. Hood 117-191 1978 $35

PORTFOLIO, Vol. 2. Philadelphia, 1816. Frontis, 3 portraits, browned, 1/2 calf, rebacked & corners repaired. Eaton 45-391 1978 £10

PORTIUS, SIMON
Please turn to
PORZIO, SIMONE

PORTLAND, DUKE OF   Men, Women and Things, Memories. 1927. Illus., imp. 8vo., full crushed mor, gilt. George's 635-1255 1978 £18

PORTLAND. [Portland, 1890]. Illus., orig. pr. wr. Ginsberg 14-841 1978 $35

PORTLOCK, CAPTAIN NATHANIEL   A Voyage Round the World;.... London, 1789. 1st ed., quarto, plates, folding charts, full contemp. calf, tooled in gilt, rebacked, original gilt tooled spine preserved, marbled endpapers, minor off-setting from some of plates. Bennett 20-170 1978 $950

PORTLOCK, ROSA   Twenty-Five Years of Canadian Life. Toronto, 1901. Hood 117-362 1978 $17.50

PORTOLA, GASPAR DE   Diary of...During the California Expedition of 1769-1770. Berkeley, 1909. Illus., original printed wr. Ginsberg 14-174 1978 $10

A PORTRAIT and Biographical Record of Delaware County, Indiana... Chicago, 1894. Mor., spine repaired. Hayman 72-347 1978 $55

PORTRAITS of Illustrious Persons. (c.1800-1820). Ports., marbled bds., minor foxing, else very good. Petrilla 13-74 1978 $100

PORZIO, SIMONE   De Dolore. Florence, 1551. Tall thin 8vo., 1/2 calf. Salloch 345-154 1978 $225

PORZIO, SIMONE   De Humana Mente Disputatio. Florence, 1551. 8vo., 1/2 mor., fine copy. Salloch 345-155 1978 $225

POSENER, S.   Adolphe Cremieux...A Biography. Philadel-phia, 1940. Biblo 251-692 1978 $15

POSSE, BARON NILS   Medical Gymnastics. N.P., 1894. Illus., sm. 8vo., orig. wrs., ex-lib., wrs. chipped. Morrill 239-582 1978 $7.50

POSSELT, E. A.   The Structure of Fibres, Yarns, & Fabrics. 1891. Good. Nestler Rare 78-213 1978 $75

POSSEVINO, ANTONIO   Cultura Ingeniorum e Bibliotheca Selecta... Venice, 1604. 4th rev.d ed., 8vo., 1/2 calf. Salloch 348-212 1978 $145

POST, C. C.   Driven from Sea to Sea. Chicago, 1884. Cloth, with some wear, cover shows wear. Hayman 73-203 1978 $17.50

POST, C. C.   Phil Johnson's Life on the Plains. Chicago, 1888. Cloth, inner hinges strengthened, rare, 1st ed. Hayman 73-618 1978 $100

POST, EMILY   The Title Market. New York, 1909. 1st ed., frontispiece, illus., very good or better. Limestone 9-233 1978 $15

POST, EUGENE J.   The Wig and the Jimmy. New York, 1869. Wrs. Hayman 73-478 1978 $8.50

POST, MARIE CAROLINE   The Life and Memoirs of Comte Regis De Trobriand Major-General in the Army of the United States. New York, 1910. Portrs., new cloth, Bell Wiley's copy. Broadfoot 46-204 1978 $23

POSTEL, GUILELMUS   Syriae Descriptio. N.P. (Paris), 1540. Wood-cut vignette, sm. 8vo., bds. Salloch 345-156 1978 $650

POSTON, CHARLES D.   The Parsees: A Lecture. [Privately printed, 1870]. Illus., original cloth, 1st ed., inscribed presentation copy from "author" to Wm. P. Blake. Ginsberg 14-23 1978 $75

POTE, WILLIAM JR.   Morris Map. Published with Pote's Journal. (New York, 1896). Orig. 8vo., bds., mor. back, map 23 1/2 x 33 1/2 inches. Wolfe 39-444 1978 $25

POTERIUS, PETRUS   Opera Omnia Practica et Chymica, Cum Annot-ationibus & Additamentis. Venice, 1741. 4to., qtr. calf, lacks portrait. Gurney 75-86 1978 £40

POTINIUS, CONRAD   Prognosticum Divinum. Bremen, (1629). Sm. 4to., engr. title illus., contemp. vellum in brown cloth slipcase, browned, signature, good copy from library of Dr. Alfred M. Hellman, very rare. Zeitlin 245-198 1978 $875

POTOCKE, COUNT JOSEPH   Sport in Somaliland. London, 1900. 59 colored illus., 18 pages photos, map, ltd. 200 copies, signed by Rowland Ward, folio, name & inscription in ink on end papers for former owner. Baldwins' 51-551 1978 $100

POTT, A. J.   People of the Book. London, 1932. Map, illus., sm. 8vo., orig. cloth. K Books 239-379 1978 £6

POTT, MRS. HENRY
Please turn to
POTT, CONSTANCE MARY (FEARON)

POTT, CONSTANCE MARY (FEARON)   Francis Bacon and His Secret Society. 1911. 2nd rev. ed., contents dust soiled, cloth, author's pres. copy, blind-stamp on title page. Eaton 45-392 1978 £7

POTT, JOHANN HEINRICH   Animadversiones Physico-Chymicae. Berlin, 1756. Sm. 4to., text illus., buckram, stamp of Wernigerode Library, very good copy, 1st ed. Norman 5-226 1978 $100

POTT, JOHANN HEINRICH   Chymische Untersuchungen. Potsdam & Berlin, 1746-54. 3 parts in 1 Vol., sm. 4to., plt., tables, contemp. vellum, bkplt. of Ernst Graf zu Stolberg, fine copy, 1st ed. Norman 5-225 1978 $300

POTT, JOHANN HEINRICH   Exercitationes Chymicae. Berlin, 1738. Sm. 4to., contemp. vellum, bkplt. of Ernst Graf zu Stolberg, fine copy, 1st collected ed. Norman 5-224 1978 $200

POTTER, BEATRIX   The Fairy Caravan. Philadelphia, (1929). 1st ed., colored illus., green cloth, pictorial cover plate, light inner hinge cracks, very good. Victoria 34-636 1978 $65

POTTER, BEATRIX   The Peter Rabbit Books. London, V.Y. 23 vols., full-page colour plts., sq. cr. 8vo., cloth in d.w. Traylen 88-200 1978 £180

POTTER, BEATRIX   The Roly-Poly Pudding. New York, (1908). 1st Amer. ed., lacks colored t.p., colored endpapers of 1st ed., very good. Victoria 34-637 1978 $15

POTTER, BEATRIX   The Story of A Fierce Bad Rabbit. London, c.1906. Wallet Form, colored plates, wallet tab torn, cover edge partly split, very scarce. Victoria 34-638 1978 $200

POTTER, BEATRIX   The Tailor of Gloucester. London, 1903. 1st trade ed., t.p., plates and endpapers in color, dark green boards with set-in color plate, spine chip, fine. Victoria 34-639 1978 $75

POTTER, BEATRIX   The Tale of Jemima Puddle-Dock. London, 1908. 1st ed., very good, cover spots, light wear at spine bottom. Victoria 34-642 1978 $37.50

POTTER, BEATRIX   The Tale of Mrs. Tiggy-Winkle. London, 1905. 1st ed., several pages soiled, text is very good, spine paper gone, covers very good. Victoria 34-647 1978 $35

POTTER, BEATRIX   The Tale of Mrs. Tittlemouse. London, 1910. 1st ed., color plates, blue boards with colored pictorial set-in, almost fine. Victoria 34-646 1978 $100

POTTER, BEATRIX   The Tale of Mrs. Tittlemouse. London, 1910. 1st ed., negligible soil marks in text, very good. Victoria 34-645 1978 $75

POTTER, BEATRIX   The Tale of Mrs. Tittlemouse. New York, c.1913-18. Very fine. Victoria 34-644 1978 $15

POTTER, BEATRIX   The Tale of The Flopsy Bunnies. London, 1909. 1st ed., very good copy, chip at spinefoot. Victoria 34-641 1978 $45

POTTER, BEATRIX   The Tale of Timmy Tiptoes. New York, (1919). Color plates, virtually mint copy. Victoria 34-643 1978 $15

POTTER, BEATRIX   The Tale of Tom Kitten. London, 1907. 1st ed., faint white powder marks on inner cover edge, very good. Victoria 34-648 1978 $60

POTTER, BEATRIX   The Tale of Two Bad Mice. London, 1904. 1st ed., inscription, small chips at spine ends, minor cracks of papered spine edges, inner hinge cracked but solid, fine, bright copy. Victoria 34-649 1978 $55

POTTER, BEATRIX   Wag-By-Wall. Boston, 1944. 1st ed., limited ed., very good copy, torn d.j. Victoria 34-651 1978 $27.50

POTTER, ERMINE L.   Western Live-Stock Management. New York, 1925. Illus., maps and tables, orig. cloth. Ginsberg 15-882 1978 $15

POTTER, FRANCIS   An Interpretation of the Number 666... Oxford, 1642. Quarto, later half-vellum and cloth, engraved title, bookplate, 1st ed., fine. Bennett 7-88 1978 $225

POTTER, JACK   A Bibliography of John Dos Passos. Chicago, 1950. Orig. cloth, review copy, 1 of 365 copies on laid paper, cloth a bit bubbled, but very good. MacManus 238-906 1978 $37.50

POTTER, JOHN K.   Samuel L. Clemens. First Editions and Values. Chicago, 1932. Sm. 8vo., illus., 1st ed., 1 of 500 copies, nice. MacManus 238-890 1978 $15

POTTER, O. M.   A Little Pilgrimage in Italy. Boston, 1911. Color plts. and illus. Biblo BL781-630 1978 $12

POTTER, STEPHEN   The Theory & Practice of Gamesmanship. 1947. Illus. by F. Wilson, very good, slightly worn d.w., autograph card by author laid in, first English ed. Bell Book 17-741 1978 £10

THE POTTERY & Porcelain of N. J. 1688-1900. Newark, 1947. Good. Nestler Rare 78-83 1978 $25

POTTIER, A.   Revue Retrospective Normande. 1842. New buckram, rubber stamp. Allen 234-1410 1978 $25

POTTIER, EDMOND   Diphilos et les Modeleurs de Terres Cuites Grecques. Paris, (1909). Illus., wrs. Biblo BL781-461 1978 $9

POTTIER, EDMOND   Diphilos et les Modeleurs de Terres Cuites Grecques. Paris,(c.1909). Illus., good. Biblo BL781-370 1978 $10

POTTIER, EDMOND   Douris...and the Painters of Greek Vases. London, 1909. Illus., some in color. Biblo BL781-371 1978 $16.50

POTTIER, EDMOND   Recueil....Etudes d'Art et d'Archeologie. Paris, 1937. Illus., wrs. Biblo BL781-462 1978 $18.50

POTTLE, A.   Index to the Private Papers of James Boswell from Malahide Castle in the Collection of Lt. -Col. R.H. Isham. London, 1937. Ltd. to 1250 copies, med. 8vo., orig. buckram, in slipcase, fine. Forster 130-131 1978 £15

POTTLE, F. A.   The Private Papers of James Boswell from Malahide Castle in the Collection of Lt. Col. R. H. Isham. London, 1931. Ltd. to 415 copies, med. 8vo., orig. buckram, t.e.g., orig. slipcase. Forster 130-130 1978 £30

POTTS, B. F.   Message of the Governor of Montana Territory to the Eighth Session of the Legislative Assembly, January 5, 1874. Virginia City, 1874. Original printed wr., 1st ed. Ginsberg 14-628 1978 $450

POTTS, CHARLES S.   Crime and the Treatment of the Criminal. Austin, 1910. Jenkins 116-1105 1978 $9.50

POTTS, CHARLES S.   Some Practical Problems in Prison Reform. Austin, 1911. 1st ed., printed wr. Jenkins 116-1106 1978 $15

POTTS, EUGENIA D.   The Song of Lancaster, Kentucky. Cambridge, 1876. Cloth. Hayman 72-402 1978 $30

POTVIN, DAMASE   The Saguenay Trip... Montreal, n. d. Card cover, illus., some colour, folding map. Hood's 115-981 1978 $7.50

POUCHET, FELIX ARCHIMEDE   Histoire des Sciences Naturelles au Moyen Age, ou Albert le Grand et son Epoque Consideres Comme Point de Depart de l'Ecole Experimentale. Paris, 1853. 8vo., contemp. green calf, 1st ed., pres. copy, inscr'd by author, slight foxing. Offenbacher 30-127 1978 $75

POUCHOT, M. FRANCOIS   Memoir Upon the Late War in America...1755-60. Roxbury, 1866. 4to., 2 vols., unbound, uncut signatures in plain wrs., plts., maps, 1 of 50 lg. paper sets, total ed. of 200, wrs. frayed, some stains, excellent set for binding, 1st English-language ed. Butterfield 21-182 1978 $75

POUCHOT, M. FRANCOIS   Memoir Upon the Late War in North America, Between the French and English... Roxbury, 1866. 2 vols., fold. maps, illus., blue cloth. MacManus 239-396 1978 $100

POUGHKEEPSIE City Director--1856-'57. Poughkeepsie, (1856). Fldg. map, prtd. bds., loose, backstrip split, pict. ads, woodcuts, some signed by Benson Lossing. Butterfield 21-171 1978 $25

POUJADE, J.   Les Jonques des chinois de Siam. Paris, 1946. 4to, plts., illus., orig. covers. Van der Peet 127-191 1978 Dfl 65

POULSEN, FREDERIK   Roemische Kulturbilder. 1949. Illus., limp bds. Allen 234-779 1978 $15

POULSON'S Town and Country Almanac, for...1805. Philadelphia, (1804). Sewed, some stains. Hayman 72-8 1978 $12.50

POUND, ARTHUR   Johnson of the Mohawks. New York, 1930. Illus., 8vo., lightly dampstained, 1st ed., orig. cloth. Morrill 241-417 1978 $15

POUND, ARTHUR   Johnson of the Mohawks. New York, 1930. Fine. MacManus 239-1211 1978 $15

POUND, EZRA   ABC of Economics. 1933. Covers faded, good, worn d.w., scarce, first English ed. Bell Book 17-742 1978 £45

POUND, EZRA   ABC of Reading. New Haven, 1934. 1st ed., very good. Ballinger 11-164 1978 $25.00

POUND, EZRA   A B C of Reading. Norfolk, (n.d.). Orig. d.j., orig. binding. Wolfe 39-446 1978 $15

POUND, EZRA   The Cantos. New Directions, (1948). Orig.
d.j., orig. binding. Wolfe 39-445 1978 $35

POUND, EZRA   Catholic Anthology 1914-1915. London, 1915.
One of 500 copies, nice, first ed., orig. binding. Rota 211-9 1978 £150

POUND, EZRA   A Draft of Cantos XXXI-XLI. London, (1935).
Fine copy, ownership inscription, d.w. faded. Desmarais B-518 1978 $35

POUND, EZRA   Exultations. London, 1909. 1st ed., 12mo., ads,
spine ends rubbed, previous owner's name on flyleaf, else very fine. Current 24-
41 1978 $125

POUND, EZRA   The Faun. New Haven, 1933. 12mo., handwritten & illuminated in gold & colours, orig. watercolour frontis., decor. paper
wrs., Prokosch bkplt., #3 of 5 copies. Quaritch 979-265 1978 $175

POUND, EZRA   The Fifth Decad of Cantos. 1937. Fine, d.w.,
first English ed. Bell Book 16-711 1978 £25

POUND, EZRA   The Garret. New Haven, 1932. 12mo., handwritten & illuminated in gold & colour, orig. watercolour frontis., decor. paper
wrs., Prokosch bkplt., #2 of 5 copies, duplicate watercolour laid in, inscr. by
Prokosch. Quaritch 979-266 1978 $165

POUND, EZRA   Guides Pol-de Lyon a la Mer-Vallee du Rhone,
etc. (c. 1919). Sm. 8vo., maps, plans, illus., orig. wrs., Ezra Pound's copy
with signature. Quaritch 979-360 1978 $225

POUND, EZRA   Homage to Sextus Propertius. 1934. First separate ed., orig. bds., fine, d.w., 8vo. Howes 194-1100 1978 £25

POUND, EZRA   Indiscretions. Paris, Three Mountains Press,
1923. 1st ed., sm. 4to., handprinted on Isle Saint Louis, 1 of 300 copies, grey bds.
with yellow spine, former owner name, covers lightly soiled, interior near mint,
scarce, printer's notices laid in. Current 24-42 1978 $485

POUND, EZRA   Jefferson and/or Mussolini. New York, 1936.
First U.S. ed., scarce. Bell Book 17-744 1978 £38.50

POUND, EZRA   'Noh' or Accomplishment, a Study of the Classical Stage of Japan. London, 1916. 1st ed., 8vo., only 1250 copies, cover soiling, fine. Current 24-43 1978 $125

POUND, EZRA   Pavannes and Divisions. New York, 1918. First
U.S. ed., portrait, very good, second issue, grey cloth. Bell Book 17-745 1978
£35

POUND, EZRA   Personnae, poems. London, 1909. Bds., nice,
first ed. Rota 212-46 1978 £55

POUND, EZRA   "Prolegomena" and "The Exile". Chicago, 1927.
Orange wrs., 1st issue. Bradley 49-270 1978 $25

POUND, EZRA   Provenca. Boston, (1910). Tan paper bds.
stamped in black, uncut, 1st ed., unusually fine & clean copy. Bradley 49-271
1978 $200

POUND, EZRA   Quia Pauper Amavi. (1919). First ed., roy.
8vo., orig. olive green bds., green buckram spine, uncut, very good, rare, only
500 copies were printed. Howes 194-1101 1978 £75

POUND, EZRA   The Spirit of Romance. London, (1910). 1st ed.,
8vo., clippings laid in, very fine. Current 24-44 1978 $100

POUND, EZRA   The Tea Shop. New Haven, 1933. 12mo., handwritten & illuminated in gold & colours, orig. watercolour frontis., decor. paper
wrs., Prokosch bkplt., #2 of 5 copies, "color model" for frontis. laid in. Quaritch 979-267 1978 $150

POUND, EZRA   Two Poems. New Haven, 1932. 12mo., handwritten & illuminated in gold & colours, orig. watercolour frontis., decor. paper
wrs., Prokosch bkplt., #1 of 5 copies, "color model" for frontis. laid in, inscr.
by Prokosch. Quaritch 979-268 1978 $175

POUND, EZRA   Umbra; early poems. London, 1920. One of
100 numbered copies on handmade paper, signed by author, half parchment, grey
paper bds., first ed. Rota 212-47 1978 £200

POUND, ROSCOE   An Introduction to the Philosophy of Law. New
Haven, 1922. 1st ed. Biblo 251-371 1978 $8.50

POUNDER, ROY M.   Artist, Thinker and Saint. Toronto, 1936.
Hood's 115-945 1978 $7.50

POUQEVILLE, M.   Grece. Paris, 1835. 8vo., bds., roan spine,
woodcut vignette, plts., maps, good. King 7-379 1978 £50

POUSSIN, GUILLAUME T.   The United States; Its Power and Progress. Philadelphia, 1851. 1st U.S. ed. and 1st English ed., fine copy, orig. cloth. Mac-
Manus 239-399 1978 $35

POUTNEY, W. J.   Old Bristol Potteries. Bristol, 1920. Coloured
frontis., illus., roy. 8vo., rebound in half mor. George's 635-234 1978 £12.50

POUVOURVILLE, A. DE   L'Art Indo-Chinois. Paris, 1894. Cloth, illus.,
8vo. Van der Peet 127-192 1978 Dfl 55

POUX, JOSEPH   La Cite de Carcassone - Histoire et Description.
Toulouse, 1922. Plts., illus., stiff wrs., 8vo. Upcroft 12-351 1978 £10

POUYANNE, ALBERT   Catalogue de la Collection Albert Pouyanne;
Ceramique, Ivoires, Pierres sculptees, bronzes, etc.... Paris, 1933. Illus.,
plts., 8vo., orig. covers. Van der Peet 127-283 1978 Dfl 35

POWDERLY, T. V.   Thirty Years of Labor. 1859 to 1889. Columbus,
1890. Cloth. Hayman 73-620 1978 $15

POWELL, AARON M.   Personal Reminiscences of the Anti-Slavery...
New York, 1899. 1st ed., illus. MacManus 239-851 1978 $25

POWELL, ANTHONY   Afternoon Men. 1931. Very good, worn d.w.,
first English ed. Bell Book 16-717 1978 $75

POWELL, BADEN   A General and Elementary View of the Undula-
tory Theory as Applied to the Dispersion of Light. London, 1841. 8vo., fldg.
handcolored frontis., orig. bds., uncut, spine repaired, fine copy, 1st ed., pres.
inscrip. Norman 5-227 1978 $175

POWELL, CAROLINE   Henry & Anna, or the Generous Prince of Algiers.
London, n.d. Inscriptions, 12mo., f.p. and large t.p. cuts in color, plain wrappers,
very good. Victoria 34-652 1978 $27.50

POWELL, DAWN   The Bride's House. 1929. Ltd. to 300 copies,
signed by author. Austin 82-706 1978 $22.50

POWELL, E. T.   The Evolution of the Money Market, (1385-1915)
an Historical and Analytical Study of the Rise and Development of Finance as a
centralised, co-ordinated Force. 1916. 8vo. George's 635-382 1978 £6.50

POWELL, EDWARD ALEXANDER   The End of the Trail, the Far West from New
Mexico to British Columbia. New York, 1919. Illus., map. Hood 116-873
1978 $15

POWELL, EDWARD ALEXANDER   The Last Frontier. New York, 1912. Map,
plts., dec. cloth, g.t., 8vo. K Books 239-380 1978 £8

POWELL, EDWARD ALEXANDER   The Last Frontier. New York, 1919. Map.
plts., dec. cloth, 8vo., g.t. K Books 239-380A 1978 £7

POWELL, EDWARD ALEXANDER   Marches of the North From Cape Breton to
the Klondike. New York, London, 1931. Illus. with photos, folding map.
Hood's 115-608 1978 $20

POWELL, HICKMAN   Ninety Times Guilty. New York, (1939).
1st ed., author's signed pres. Biblo 251-302 1978 $15

POWELL, HICKMAN   What the Citizen Should Know About the Coast
Guard. 1941. Illus. Austin 80-257 1978 $8.50

POWELL, J. H.   Bring Out Your Dead. Philadelphia, 1949. First
ed., fine, d.w., illus. Biblo 247-123 1978 $17.50

POWELL, J. H.   Bring Out Your Dead; the Great Plague of Yellow Fever in Philadelphia in 1793. Philadelphia, 1949. MacManus 239-1731 1978 $15

POWELL, J. H.   Richard Rush. Republican Diplomat. Philadelphia, 1942. Frontis. port., orig. cloth, ex-lib., good. MacManus 239-811 1978 $15

POWELL, LAWRENCE CLARK   Robinson Jeffers: The Man and his Work. Pasadena, San Pasqual Press, 1940. Cloth, d.w., 2nd ed., 1 of 1000 copies, signed by Powell. Dawson's 447-251 1978 $45

POWELL, ROBERT   Depopulation Arraigned, Convicted and Condemned by the Lawes of God and Man... London, 1636. 1st. ed., sm. 8vo, orig. sheep, fine copy. Traylen 88-80 1978 £200

POWELL, WALTER A.   A History of Delaware. Boston, (1928). Illus., maps. Baldwins' 51-232 1978 $25

POWELL, WILLIAM H.   Powell's Records of Living Officers of the United States Army. Philadelphia, 1890. 8vo., inner hinges cracked, 1st ed. Morrill 241-473 1978 $30

POWELL, WILLIS J.   Tachyhippodamia. Philadelphia, 1872. Illus., 12mo., orig. cloth. Morrill 241-474 1978 $10

POWER, E.   Studies in English Trade in the 15th Century. 1933. Roy. 8vo. George's 635-407 1978 £8.50

POWER, MARGUERITE COUNTESS OF BLESSINGTON
Please turn to
BLESSINGTON, MARQUERITE (POWER) FARMER GARDINER, COUNTESS OF

POWER, TYRONE   Impressions of America, During the Years 1833, 1834, and 1835. London, 1836. 2 vols., 1st ed., 8vo., t.e.g., engr. frontis., bound by Stikeman in 3/4 red mor. with marbled bds. & endpapers, raised bands on spine, Power's signature tipped in dated 1840, better than fine. Current 24-98 1978 $365

POWER, TYRONE   Impressions of America, during the Years 1833, 1834, and 1835. London, 1836. 2 vols., 8vo, original blue cloth, printed paper labels, 1st ed. Ximenes 47-262 1978 $200

POWER, TYRONE   The Lost Heir, and The Predicition. 1830. 1st. ed., 3 vols., orig. half calf, v.g. Jarndyce 16-946 1978 £60

POWER, VICTOR O'D.   The Heir of Liscarragh. 1891. 1st. ed., 8vo, orig. cloth, nice copy. Fenning 32- 273 1978 £8.50

THE POWER of Christian Benevolence Illustrated in the Life and Labors of Mary Lyon. New York, (1858). Cloth, new ed. Hayman 73-399 1978 $10

POWERS, STEPHEN   Afoot and Alone; A Walk from Sea to Sea by the Southern Route. Hartford, 1872. Illus., orig. cloth, 1st ed. Ginsberg 14-883 1978 $85

POWERS, W. P.   Some Annals of the Powers Family. Los Angeles, 1924. Illus., orig. cloth, 1st ed. Ginsberg 14-884 1978 $125

POWICKE, F. J.   Robert Browne; Pioneer of Modern Congregationalism. 1910. Plts., octavo, good. Upcroft 10-494 1978 £5

POWICKE, F. M.   The Loss of Normandy, 1189-1204; studies in the history of the Angevin Empire. 1913. 8vo., maps. Upcroft 12-352 1978 £12.50

POWNALL, THOMAS   Topographical Description of the Dominions of the United States of America. Pittsburgh, 1949. Lg. 4to, fold. map, rev. and enlarged ed., first pub. in 1776. MacManus 239-400 1978 $30

POWYS, A. R.   From the Ground Up. 1937. Plts., very good, worn d.w., first English ed. Bell Book 17-746 1978 £6.50

POWYS, JOHN COWPER   The Art of Happiness. 1935. Very good, d.w., first English ed. Bell Book 16-718 1978 £8

POWYS, JOHN COWPER   Confessions of Two Brothers. New York, 1916. First U.S. ed., very good. Bell Book 17-750 1978 £45

POWYS, JOHN COWPER   Confessions of Two Brothers. Rochester, 1916. Cloth, paper label on spine & upper cover. Eaton 45-396 1978 £20

POWYS, JOHN COWPER   Ducdame. 1925. Rare, d.w., very good, first English ed. Bell Book 16-1004 1978 £38.50

POWYS, JOHN COWPER   In Defence of Sensuality. New York, 1930. First U.S. ed., slightly worn d.w. Bell Book 17-747 1978 £12.50

POWYS, JOHN COWPER   In Defence of Sensuality. New York, 1930. 1st Amer. ed., signed. Biblo 251-612 1978 $30

POWYS, JOHN COWPER   Jobber Skald. 1935. Orig. line, very good, later issue d.w., first English ed. Bell Book 16-720 1978 £18.50

POWYS, JOHN COWPER   The Meaning of Culture. New York, 1929. Black cloth, pink paper labels, little shaken. Eaton 45-393 1978 £10

POWYS, JOHN COWPER   A Philosophy of Solitude. New York, 1933. First U.S. ed., lettering on spine rubbed, very good. Bell Book 16-721 1978 £12.50

POWYS, JOHN COWPER   The Pleasures of Literature. 1938. Very good, first English ed. Bell Book 16-722 1978 £18.50

POWYS, JOHN COWPER   Rodmoor. New York, 1916. First U.S. ed., good. Bell Book 16-1006 1978 £37.50

POWYS, JOHN COWPER   The War and Culture. New York, 1914. Blue paper covered bds., paper label on spine, 1st. ed., rebound. Eaton 45-395 1978 £20

POWYS, JOHN COWPER   Wolf Solent. 1929. Fine, d.w., first English ed. Bell Book 16-724 1978 £25

POWYS, JOHN COWPER   Wood and Stone. New York, 1915. 2nd. ed., dark blue cloth, ownership inscpt. on front paste-down. Eaton 45-394 1978 £30

POWYS, LLEWELLYN   Black Laughter. New York, 1924. First U.S. ed., very good. Bell Book 17-751 1978 £12.50

POWYS, LLEWELYN   Black Laughter. New York, 1924. Black cloth with yellow lettering. Eaton 45-397 1978 £6

POWYS, LLEWELLYN   The Cradle of God. New York, 1929. First US ed., fine, dust-soiled d.w. Bell Book 17-752 1978 £12.50

POWYS, LLEWELYN   Dorset Essays. 1935. Photographs by Wyndham Goodden, very good, first English ed. Bell Book 17-753 1978 £10

POWYS, LLEWELYN   Glory of Life. Golden Cockerel Press, 1934. Folio, wood engrs., cloth, vellum back, gilt top, ltd. to 277 copies. Quaritch 979-166 1978 $350

POWYS, LLEWELYN   Now That the Gods are Dead. New York, 1932. 1st ed., limited to 400 copies, signed by both Powys and Ward, plates, spine sunned, fine. Victoria 34-842 1978 $55

POWYS, LLEWELYN   Rats in the Sacristy. London, 1937. Wood-engravings by Gertrude M. Powys, nice, frayed d.w., first ed., orig. binding. Rota 211-505 1978 £10

POWYS, LLEWELYN   Skin for Skin. New York, 1925. Black cloth, yellow lettering, spine & part of upper cover faded. Eaton 45-399 1978 £7

POWYS, LLEWELYN   Skin for Skin. Jonathan Cape, 1926. Ltd. ed., 900 copies, cloth-backed bds., bookplt. of Naomi Mitchison. Eaton 45-398 1978 £12

POWYS, THEODORE FRANCIS   Black Bryony. 1923. 1st ed., woodcuts, orig. green mottled cloth, cr. 8vo., prtd. label, some foxing. Howes 194-1103 1978 £7.50

POWYS, THEODORE FRANCIS   Black Bryony. 1923. Woodcuts, very good, torn d.w., 1st Eng. ed. Bell Book 16-1008 1978 £17.50

POWYS, THEODORE FRANCIS   Bottle's Path and Other Stories. London, 1946. Near mint in lightly soiled & chipped d.w. Desmarais B-524 1978 $25

POWYS, THEODORE FRANCIS   Christ in the Cupboard. London, 1930. 16mo., green prtd. paper wr. somewhat darkened around edges, wholly intact & without chipping, near fine, no. 489 of ed. ltd. to 500 copies, signed by Powys, 1st ed., collector's cond. Desmarais 1-343 1978 $25

POWYS, THEODORE FRANCIS   Innocent Birds. London, 1926. Fine copy, light foxing to edges, d.w. chipped & lightly soiled. Desmarais B-525 1978 $10

POWYS, THEODORE FRANCIS   The Key of the Field. London, 1930. Thin quarto, buckram, t.e.g., woodcut by R. A. Garnett, 1 of 550 copies signed by author, 1st ed., fine. Duschnes 220-245 1978 $35

POWYS, THEODORE FRANCIS   The Key of the Field. London, 1930. Tall 8vo., green cloth, gold lettering, spine faded, t.e.g., fore & bottom edges uncut, fine, 1 of 550 copies numbered & signed by author, 1st ed., collector's cond. Desmarais 1-344 1978 $25

POWYS, THEODORE FRANCIS   Kindness in a Corner. 1930. 1st ed., cloth, drwg. on title page by Gilbert Spencer, lightly soiled, d.w. Eaton 45-400 1978 $7

POWYS, THEODORE FRANCIS   Mr. Weston's Good Wine. London, 1927. Fine, 1st ed., 1 of 450 signed. Ballinger 11-165 1978 $65

POWYS, THEODORE FRANCIS   The Rival Pastors. 1927. 1st ed., no. 65 of 100 copies, signed by author, fine. Jarndyce 16-1213 1978 £36

POWYS, THEODORE FRANCIS   Soliloquies of a Hermit. London, 1918. 8vo., bds., cloth back, fine, Powys autograph laid in, 1st ed., collector's cond. Desmarais 1-345 1978 $30

POWYS, THEODORE FRANCIS   Unclay. 1931. No. 3 of 160 copies signed by author, buckram-backed bds., t.e.g., very good, 1st Eng. ed. Bell Book 16-728 1978 $48.50

POYER, J.   The History of Barbados... 1808. 4to, contemp. quarter mor., some browning in text. Edwards 1012-704 1978 £150

POYNTZ, JOHN   The Present Prospect of the Famous and Fertile Island of Tobago, to the Southward of the Island of Barbadoes. London, 1695. 4to, half mottled calf, gilt, spine gilt, t.e.g., by Riviere, 2nd ed. Ximenes 47-263 1978 $425

POZZO, ANDREA   Perspectiva Pictorum et Architectorum. Rome, 1693-1700. 2 vols., vol. I Latin and Italian, vol. II Latin and French, folio, illus., contemp. Italian, some stains and wear, 1st ed. Gilhofer 74-47 1978 sFr 5,500

POZZO, ANDREA   Rules and Examples of Perspective Proper for Painters and Architects, Etc.,... London, n.d. Folio, green half mor. cracked, green cloth covers, bookplate of C. R. Ashbee, plts. Totteridge 29-83 1978 $400

PRACTICAL Carpentry, Joinery and Cabinet Making. 1839. Engraved title, plts., some soiled, 4to., spanish calf, rubbed. George's 635-249 1978 £40

PRADON, NOCOLAS   Ses Oeuvres. Paris, 1674-1688. 6 vols., tall narrow 24mo., later full calf, gilt backs, inner dentelles, fine. Argosy Special-73 1978 $250

PRADT, DOMINIQUE GEORGES FREDERIC DE RIOM DE PROLHAC DE FOURT DE   The Colonies, and the Present American Revolutions. London, 1817. Leather, gold dec. on spine and covers, mottled end papers, fine. Hood's 116-622 1978 $300

PRAED, WINTHROP MACKWORTH   Poems. 1909. 1 of 440 copies, 16mo., prtd. on fine rag paper of vellum-like quality, bound in half parchment with paper sides & gilt top, India proof portr. of Praed, prospectus laid in, boxed. Battery Park 1-21 1978 $50

PRAEGER, R.L.   Natural History of Ireland. 1950. 1st ed., d.w., very good, octavo bound in cloth. Hyland 128-377 1978 £12

PRAEHISTORICA Asiae Orientalis, Vol 1:.... Hanoi, 1932. Large 8vo, plts, rare, orig. covers. Van der Peet 127-320 1978 Dfl 145

PRATESI, GAETANO   Vita di S. Caterina da Siena Nuovamente compilata Sulle traccie del rinomato scrittore Beato Raimondo da Capua. Siena, 1852. 8vo., half calf, new spine gilt, hand coloured plts., good. King 7-215 1978 £25

PRATT, ANNE   Haunts of the Wild Flowers. 1863. 1st. ed., coloured plts., cr. 8vo, orig. red cloth, gilt, little wear to headbands, nice. Fenning 32-274 1978 £12.50

PRATT, ANNE   Poisonous, Noxious, and Suspected Plants, of our Fields and Woods. London, n.d. Roy. 8vo., orig. limp cloth. K Books 244-260 1978 £22

PRATT, ANNE   Poisonous, Noxious, and Suspected Plants, of our Fields and Woods. London, n.d. Roy. 8vo., orig. printed wrappers. K Books 244-261 1978 £23

PRATT, E. J.   Brebeuf and his Brethren. Toronto, 1940. Orig. d.j., orig. binding. Wolfe 39-447 1978 $15

PRATT, E. J.   Dunkirk. Toronto, 1941. Signed, ltd. ed. Hood 117-823 1978 $40

PRATT, E. J.   Still Life and Other Verse. Toronto, 1943. Hood's 115-894 1978 $25

PRATT, FLETCHER   The Heroic Years. New York, 1934. 1st ed., illus. Biblo 248-196 1978 $16.50

PRATT, FLETCHER   What the Citizen Should Know About Modern War. 1942. Illus. by Andre Jandot. Austin 80-258 1978 $10

PRATT, FOSTER   Legal Relations of Insane Patients. Lansing, 1878. 8vo., orig. wrs., 1st ed. Morrill 239-212 1978 $10

PRATT, H. H.   Early Planters of Scituate. 1929. Illus., ltd. ed. MacManus 239-1051 1978 $35

PRATT, JOSEPH HERSEY   A Year With Osler: 1896-1897. Baltimore, 1949. D.j. Rittenhouse 49-653 1976 $15

PRATT, JOSEPH HYDE   The Mining Industry 1911-1912. Raleigh, 1914. New cloth. Broadfoot 50-178 1978 $15

PRATT, ORSON   Absurdities of Immaterialism; or, A Reply to T. W. P. Taylder's Pamphlet Entitled, "The Materialism of the Mormons or Latter-Day Saints, Examined and Exposed". [Liverpool, 1849]. Disbound. Ginsberg 14-668 1978 $22.50

PRATT, ORSON   Circular Sobre Mormonismo. Salt Lake City, 1879. Orig. pr. wr. Ginsberg 14-1106 1978 $75

PRATT, ORSON   Divine Authenticity of the Book of Mormon. [Liverpool, 1851]. Cloth. Ginsberg 14-669 1978 $60

PRATT, ORSON   Divine Authority; or, The Question, Was Joseph Smith Sent of God? [Liverpool, 1848]. Disbound. Ginsberg 14-670 1978 $25

PRATT, ORSON   Great First Cause; or, The Self Moving Forces of the Universe. [Liverpool, 1851]. Disbound. Ginsberg 14-671 1978 $25

PRATT, ORSON   The Kingdom of God. [Liverpool, 1848]. Disbound. Ginsberg 14-672 1978 $35

PRATT, ORSON   Mormons Bogs Guddommelige Trovaerdighed... Udgived Paa Dansk Af W. Snow. Copenhagen, 1853. Half mor. Ginsberg 14-673 1978 $75

PRATT, ORSON   New Jerusalem; or, The Fulfillment of Modern Prophecy. [Liverpool, 1849]. Disbound. Ginsberg 14-674 1978 $25

PRATT, ORSON   Remarkable Visions. [Liverpool, 1848]. Disbound. Ginsberg 14-675 1978 $25

PRATT, ORSON   Reply to a Pamphlet Printed at Glasgow, with the "Approbation of Clergymen of Different Denominations", Entitled "Remarks on Mormonism". [Liverpool, 1849]. Disbound. Ginsberg 14-676 1978 $20

PRATT, ORSON   Yr Achos Mawr Cyntaf; Neu Alluoedd Hunan-Symudawl Y Bydyssawd. [Merthyr-Tydfil, 1851]. Disbound. Ginsberg 14-678 1978 $35

PRATT, PARLEY   Key to the Science of Theology:... Liverpool, 1855. Full gilt presentation leather, 1st ed., inscribed on front endpaper. Ginsberg 14-1083 1978 $500

PRATT, PARLEY   Proclamation! Sydney, 1852. Close trimmed, half mor. Ginsberg 14-679 1978 $375

PRATT, SAMUEL JACKSON   Emma Corbett or the Miseries of Civil War. London, (1781). Fourth ed., frontispiece in sepia, 3 vols., 12mo., contemp. calf. Howes 194-425 1978 £30

PRATT, SAMUEL JACKSON   Pity's Gift: A Collection of Interesting Tales... 1798. 2nd. ed., illus. with woodcuts, orig. calf, old reback, v.g. Jarndyce 16-167 1978 £45

PRATT, WALTER MERRIAM   Adventure in Vermont. Cambridge, University Press, (1943). Illus., 8vo., d.w., 1st ed. Morrill 239-636 1978 $12.50

PRATTEN, M. A.   My Hundred Swiss Flowers. London, 1887. 8vo., dec. cloth, fine colored plts., rare. Van der Peet H-64-526 1978 Dfl 270

THE PRAYER Book of King Edward VII. (London, 1903). Folio, oak boards, mor. back, metal clasps with leather thongs, gilt stamping on spine, 1 of 400 copies printed in red and black with cuts and borders designed by C. R. Ashbee, engraved by W. Hooper and Miss Clemence Housman, very fine. Duschnes 220-93 1978 $400

PRAZ, M.   Secentismo e Marinismo in Inghilterra... Firenze, 1925. Lg. 8vo, plts., cloth, wrps. bound in, good. Upcroft 10-496 1978 £9

PRE-ASSEMBLY Congress: Addressed Delivered at the Presbyterian Pre-Assembly Congress; also a Report of the Men's Missionary Convention... Toronto, 1913. Hood 116-312 1978 $12.50

PREBLE, GEORGE HENRY   Our Flag. Albany, 1872. 1st ed., orig. 1/2 leather, marbled bds., rubbed but nice, illus., color plts., two A.L.s. from author. MacManus 239-401 1978 $55

PREETORIUS, EMIL   Zehn Blatt Lithographische Original-Zeichnungen. Leipzig, (1911). Folio in sheets, orig. 1/2 vellum portfolio, ltd. ed. of 90 numbered copies prtd. on simili Japan paper, well preserved. Goldschmidt 110-54 1978 $400

PREISSLER, JOHANN DANIEL L'Anatomia Dei Pittori Del Signore Carlo Cesio, das ist: deutliche Answeisung und grundliche Vorstellung von der Anatomie der Mahler. Nurnberg, 1759. Folio, engr. anatomical plts., lea.-backed portfolio with remnants of ties, very good copy, 5th ed., German version. Zeitlin 245-41 1978 $450

PRELIMINARY Announcement of the University of Texas at Austin, Texas, First Session, 1883-84. Austin, 1883. Original printed wr. Jenkins 116-1386 1978 $35

PRELIMINARY List of Churches and Religious Organizations in Oklahoma. Oklahoma City, 1942. Orig. pr. wr., 1st ed. Ginsberg 14-799 1978 $20

PRENDERGAST, JOHN P.   The Cromwellian Settlement of Ireland. 1922. 3rd ed., Irish Academic Press binding of Original Mellifont Press sheets, reprinted charts, light stain on map of Ireland. Hyland 128-918 1978 £14

PRENTISS, A.   History of the Utah Volunteers in the Spanish American War and in the Phillipine Islands... [Salt Lake City, 1900]. Illus., orig. cloth, rebacked, 1st ed. Ginsberg 14-1011 1978 $15

PRENTISS, AUGUSTIN M.   Civil Air Defense. 1941. Illus. Austin 80-259 1978 $10

PRENTISS, ELIZABETH   The Life and Letters of... New York, (1882). Cloth, covers little discolored but good copy. Hayman 72-623 1978 $10

PRESCOTT, GEORGE B.   Electricity and the Electric Telegraph. New York, 1885. 6th ed., rev. & enlarged, 2 vols., cloth, little rubbed. Hayman 73-624 1978 $7.50

PRESCOTT, WILLIAM C.   Report Upon the Mines and Property of the Sterling Silver Mining Company,... New York, 1865. Orig. pr. fr. wr., 1st ed. Ginsberg 14-737 1978 $85

PRESCOTT, WILLIAM HICKLING   Biographical and Critical Miscellanies. 1878. New ed., frontis., portr., prelims & endpaper dust-soiled, contemp. calf, rubbed, spine worn. Eaton 45-401 1978 £5

PRESCOTT, WILLIAM HICKLING History of the Conquest of Mexico, the Reign of Ferdinand and Isabella, the Reign of Philip II, the Conquest of Peru. 1887-93. Plts., 4 vols., cr. 8vo., half calf rubbed. George's 635-744 1978 £5.25

PRESCOTT, WILLIAM HICKLING   History of the Conquest of Peru... New York, 1847. Portr. frontis., map, 2 vols., 1st ed., octavo, orig. blindstamped brown cloth, unusually fine, 1st issue. Totteridge 29-84 1978 $225

PRESCOTT, WILLIAM HICKLING   History of the Reign of Philip II King of Spain 1855-59. Portrs., 3 vols., 8vo. George's 635-738 1978 £10.50

PRESCOTT, WILLIAM HICKLING   History of the Reign of Philip II King of Spain. 1897. Full calf gilt, 8vo. George's 635-739 1978 £18

PRESENT Conditions in Canada. N.P., (1911). Pamphlet. Hood 117-590 1978 $40

THE PRESENT State of Ireland: Together with some Remarques Upon the Antient State Therof. London, 1673. Folding map, modern 1/2 leather, very good, reprint. Hyland 128-379 1978 £60

PRESGRAVE, RALPH   The Dynamics of Study. Toronto, 1944. Orig. binding. Wolfe 39-449 1978 $12.50

PRESGRAVE, RALPH   The Dynamics of Time Study. Toronto, 1944. Hood 117-439 1978 $12.50

PRESTON, E. M.   Nevada County, The Famous Bartlett Pear Belt of California. Nevada City, 1886. Illus., orig. pr. wr., 1st ed. Ginsberg 14-175 1978 $100

PRESTON, LYMAN   Preston's Tables of Interest. Utica, 1828. Orig. bds., red lea. corners & spine, very good. Butterfield 21-314 1978 $25

PRESTON, W. W.   History of Harford County, Maryland. From 1608 to 1812. Baltimore, 1901. Illus., orig. cloth, scarce. MacManus 239-1002 1978 $50

PRESTWICH, G. A.   Life and Letters of Sir Joseph Prestwich. 1899. Plates, text illus., 8vo. George's 635-983 1978 £5

PRESTWICH, JOSEPH   Geology: Chemical, Physical and Stratigraphical. Oxford, 1886. 2 vols., 8vo., cloth, plts., maps, figs. Van der Peet H-64-527 1978 Dfl 45

PRESTWICH, JOSEPH   Geology, Chemical, Physical, and Stratigraphical. Oxford, 1886-1888. Maps, plts., woodcuts, 2 vols., 8vo., waterstained, 1st ed. Morrill 241-475 1978 $17.50

PRESTWICH, JOSEPH   Tables of Temperatures of the Sea. London, 1876. Offprint, 4to., lg. fldg. map, lg. fldg. charts, orig. wrs., very fine copy, 1st ed. Norman 5-228 1978 $75

PRETORIUS, P. J.   Jungle Man. London, (1947). Maps, plts., cr. 8vo., orig. cloth, covers faded. K Books 239-381 1978 £6

PRETORIUS, P. J.   Jungle Man - An Autobiography. New York, 1948. 8vo, orig. cloth. Book Chest 17-290 1978 $10

PRETTY Rhymes About Birds and Animals for Little Boys and Girls. New York, c.1840. Tiny 8pp. chapbook, wrapper, signed "B.F. Pease", fine. Victoria 34-654 1978 $15

THE PRETTY Village. London, c.1851. Sq. 8vo, color plates by Kronheim, ornate gilt and blue decorated flexible boards, spine worn, very good. Victoria 34-655 1978 $20

PREUDHOMME, ROBERT   Essay Instructif de l'Art d'Escriture. Paris, 1639. Sm. 8vo., cont. vellum, first ed. Schumann 511-47 1978 sFr 525

PREVOST, ANTOINE FRANCOIS Histoire de Manon Lescaut et du Chevalier de Grieux. Paris, 1889. 8vo., half calf, frontis., colored plts., illus. by M. Leloir, rare. Van der Peet H-64-448 1978 Dfl 45

PREVOST, JEAN LOUIS   Des Organes Generateurs Chez Quelques Gasteropodes. Geneve, Paris, 1830. 4to., litho. plts., orig. blue wrs., sewn, foxing, very good, lg. paper, uncut, partially unopened copy, author's pres. inscr., rare 1st ed. Zeitlin 245-199 1978 $75

PREYSSINGER, L.   Erganzungs-Texte zum Astronomischen Bilderatlas. Hall, (c. 1840). 8vo., folio, hand-coloured lithographs, orig. printed wrs., plts., loose in orig. cloth folder, a little worn. Quaritch 977-196 1978 $125

PRICE, CARL F.   Wesleyan's First Century. Middletown, 1932. Illus. Biblo BL781-30 1978 $12

PRICE, CARL F.   Wesleyan's First Century. Middletown, 1932.
Ports. Biblo BL781-36 1978 $9.50

PRICE, IRA M.   The Monuments and the Old Testament. Light
from the Near East on the Scriptures. Philadelphia, (1925). New ed., illus.,
maps. Biblo BL781-463 1978 $10

PRICE, ISAIAH   History of the 97th Regt. Penna. Vol. Infantry.
Philadephia, 1875. Illus., scarce, 4to. MacManus 239-902 1978 $35

PRICE, RICHARD   Observations on the Nature of Civil Liberty, the
Principles of Government, and the Justice and Policy of the War With America.
London, 1776. 3/4 leather binding, lacks bottom 3/8 of title page, good. Nestler
Rare 78-176 1978 $75

PRICE, ROSE L.   The Two Americas... 1877. Orig. cloth, 8vo,
plts. Edwards 1012-407 1978 £15

PRICE, SIR F.   Octagamund, A History. Madras, 1908. 4to,
half morocco, cover slightly worn, blank corner cut from title & inscription erased,
folding map, plts. Edwards 1012-110 1978 £45

PRICE, W. H.   The English Patents of Monopoly. Boston, 1906.
8vo. George's 635-384 1978 £8.50

PRICHARD, ETTIE STEPHENS   Old Farm. 1934. First ed., d.j. Austin 82-708
1978 $12.50

PRICHARD, JAMES COWLES   A Treatise on Insanity and Other Disorders
Affecting the Mind. Philadelphia, 1837. 8vo., contemp. calf, covers detached,
foxed, library stamps, former owner's signature, ex-lib., internally good copy,
1st Amer. ed., rare. Zeitlin 245-200 1978 $150

PRIDE, W. F.   The History of Fort Riley. N. P., 1926. Cloth,
fine copy. Hayman 73-633 1978 $10

PRIDEAUX, HUMPHREY   The True Nature of Imposture Fully Display'd in
the Life of Mahomet. London, 1698. 8vo, contemporary calf, gilt, monogram
and crown in gilt on covers, spine gilt, 3rd ed., "corrected", fine copy. Ximenes
47-264 1978 $100

PRIDEAUX, HUMPHREY   The True Nature of Imposture Fully Display'd in
the Life of Mahomet. 1718. 7th. ed., orig. panelled calf, maroon label, fine.
Jarndyce 16-168 1978 $12.50

PRIDEAUX, HUMPHREY   The True Nature of Imposture Fully Displayed in
the Life of Mohomet. 1808. 10th. ed., frontis portrait, orig. half calf, red labels,
marbled bds., good. Jarndyce 16-947 1978 $18

PRIDEAUX, MATHIAS   An Easy and Compendious Introduction for the
Reading All Sorts of Histories. Oxford, 1655. 3rd. ed., 4to, 4 spearate t.p.s.,
orig. calf, very good. Jarndyce 16-22 1978 $36

PRIDEAUX, SARAH TREVERBIAN   An Historical Sketch of Bookbinding. London,
1893. Frontis., 8vo. Traylen 88-59 1978 £10

PRIESSNITZ, VINCENZ   Manuel D'Hydrosudotherapie, ou traitement des
maladies par l'eau froide, la sueur, l'exercise et le regimen. Bruxelles, 1840.
12mo., half brown mor., gilt lettering on spine, light browning & foxing, very
good copy, signature of former owner, 1st ed. Zeitlin 245-201 1978 $65

PRIEST, MICHAEL L.   Medical Companion. Exeter, 1833. Sm. 8vo.,
contemp. calf, 1st ed. Morrill 239-213 1978 $25

PRIEST, WILLIAM   Travels in the United States of America, 1793-97.
1802. 8vo, modern half calf, tinted frontis, soiled & tear repaired, sm. lib. stamp.
Edwards 1012-522 1978 £30

PRIESTLEY, HERBERT INGRAM   Franciscan Explorations in California. Glendale,
1946. Illus., maps, original cloth, 1st ed. Ginsberg 14-176 1978 $35

PRIESTLEY, JOHN BOYNTON   English Journey. London, 1934. Nice, edge
foxing, d.w. chipped with light wear. Desmarais B-527 1978 $15

PRIESTLEY, JOHN BOYNTON   Let the People Sing. London, 1939. First ed.,
orig. binding, very nice, author's autograph signature. Rota 211-514 1978 £6

PRIESTLEY, JOHN BOYNTON   Theatre Outlook. London, (1947). 1st ed.,
8vo., illus., plts., color charts, dust jacket, very good. Houle 10-265 1978
$20

PRIESTLEY, JOHN BOYNTON   They Walk in the City. London, 1936. First ed.,
orig. binding, nice, inscribed by author. Rota 211-513 1978 £8

PRIESTLEY, JOHN BOYNTON   The Town Major of Miraucourt. London,
1930. Full vellum, slightly soiled, 1 of 525 numbered copies signed by author.
Dawson's 447-269 1978 $45

PRIESTLEY, JOSEPH   A Discourse Delivered at the Gravel-Pit Meeting
in Hackney, December 4, 1791... 1791. 1st. ed., fully rebound in half calf,
marbled bds., fine. Jarndyce 16-173 1978 £62

PRIESTLEY, JOSEPH   A Discourse Intended to be Delivered So on After
the Riots in Birmingham. Birmingham, 1791. 1st. ed., rebound in half calf, marbled bds., fine. Jarndyce 16-174 1978 £85

PRIESTLEY, JOSEPH   An Essay on a Course of Liberal Education for
Civil and Active Life.... London, 1765. 8vo, original pale blue boards, white
paper backstrip, 1st ed. Ximenes 47-265 1978 $325

PRIESTLEY, JOSEPH   Free Address to Protestant Dissenters... 1774.
Fully rebound in half-calf, marbled bds., 3rd. ed., good. Jarndyce 16-169 1978
£50

PRIESTLEY, JOSEPH   A Harmony of the Evangelists in Greek. 1777.
2 parts in 1 vol., 4to., orig. bds., entirely uncut, upper joint cracked, entirely
uncut. Howes 194-426 1978 £55

PRIESTLEY, JOSEPH   Histoire de L'Electricite, Traduite de L'Anglois.
Paris, 1771. 3 vols., 12mo., plts., French calf, gilt spines, a little worn. Quaritch 977-131 1978 $100

PRIESTLEY, JOSEPH   Lectures on History and General policy. Dublin,
1788. Contemp. calf, charts, very good, first Dublin ed., 8vo. Howes 194-427
1978 £48

PRIESTLEY, JOSEPH   A Letter to a Layman on the Subject of the Rev.
Mr. Lindsey's Proposal for a Reformed Church... 1774. 1st. ed., fully rebound in
half calf, marbled bds., fine. Jarndyce 16-170 1978 £58

PRIESTLEY, JOSEPH   Letters to Edmund Burke. Birmingham, 1791.
Second ed., uncut in orig. bds., rebacked, 8vo. Howes 194-428 1978 £24

PRIESTLEY, JOSEPH   Memoirs. London, 1806-(07). 2 vols. in 1,
8vo., contemp. calf, rubbed, very good copy, without separate title for Vol. 2.
Norman 5-230 1978 $125

PRIESTLEY, JOSEPH   A Sermon on the Subject of the Slave Trade...
Birmingham, 1788. 1st. ed., fully rebound in half calf, marbled bds., fine.
Jarndyce 16-172 1978 £95

PRIESTLEY, R. E.   Antarctic Adventure: Scott's Northern Party.
1914. Maps, illus., 8vo, orig. cloth. Edwards 1012-599 1978 £75

PRIESTLY, JOHN BOYNTON   Angel Pavement. 1930. Pres. copy inscribed by
author, very good, slightly worn d.w., first English ed. Bell Book 17-754 1978
£10

PRIME, MRS. ALFRED COXE   Three Centuries of Historic Silver. Philadelphia,
1938. 140 plts. & marks. Baldwins' 51-143 1978 $20

PRIME, ALFRED COXE   The Arts & Crafts in Philadelphia, Maryland and
South Carolina, 1721-1785. (Topsfield), 1929-1932. Illus., 2 vols., 8vo., orig.
bds., boxed, partly unopened, mint, special ed. ltd. to 100 copies on Bruce Rogers
all rag paper. Morrill 239-583 1978 $175

PRIME, NATHANIEL S.   A History of Long Island, from Its First Settlement.
New York and Pittsburg, 1845. Ads, fldg. map frontis., neatly rebound, very
good. Butterfield 21-258 1978 $50

PRIME, SAMUEL IRENAEUS   The Power of Prayer. 1859. Austin 82-709
1978 $12.50

PRIME, SAMUEL IRENAEUS   Thoughts on the Death of Little Children. 1865.
Austin 82-710 1978 $11

PRIME, SAMUEL IRENAEUS   Under the Trees. 1874. First ed. Austin 82-
711 1978 $12.50

PRIME, WILLIAM C.   I Go a Fishing. New York, 1873. 1st ed.,
orig. bind., a little worn. Americanist 102-113 1978 $25

THE PRIMER. (London, c.1710). Sm. 8vo, original black-letter type, highlighted
in red throughout, pictorial and decorative woodcut capitals in text, contemporary
full leather, ornate impressed designs and panels of differing leathers, very fine
copy and very scarce. Victoria 34-656 1978 $325

THE PRIMER set Furth by the Kinges Majestie and his Clergie.... (c. 1770). Sm.
8vo., old calf, crudely repaired. George's 635-1116 1978 £5

THE PRIMITIVES of the Greek Tongue. 1758. Contemp. calf, worn, 8vo. George's 635-504 1978 £8.50

PRIMROSE, JAMES   Enchiridion Medicum Practicum. Amsterdam, 1654. 12mo., contemp. vellum, second ed. Gurney 75-87 1978 £40

PRINCE, HARRY   Half-Hours in Old London. New York, n.d. Illus. Biblo 247-725 1978 $12.50

PRINCE, NORMAN C.   Roentgen Technic. St. Louis, 1917. Illus. Rittenhouse 49-654 1976 $15

PRINCE Library...Deposited in the Public Library of the City of Boston. Boston, 1870. Newly rebound in cloth. Battery Park 1-339 1978 $75

THE PRINCETON Bric-a-Brac. Princeton, 1918. Vol. XLII, oblong 8vo., gilt-stamped cloth over bevelled bds., 1st ed., photos, bkplt. J. S. Lawrence 38-F96 1978 $150

THE PRINCETON Bric-a-Brac. Princeton, 1919. Vol. XLIII, oblong 8vo., gilt-stamped cloth over bevelled bds., photos, bkplt. J. S. Lawrence 38-F97 1978 $250

PRINCIPLES Of Design in Architecture. 1809. 1st. ed., orig. half calf, some light damp marking, otherwise v.g. Jarndyce 16-266 1978 £45

PRINGLE, ELIZABETH W. ALLSTON   Chronicles of Chicora Wood. New York, 1923. Bell Wiley's copy. Broadfoot 46-205 1978 $27

PRINGLE, ELIZABETH W. ALLSTON   Chronicles of Chicora Wood. New York, 1923. Illus. MacManus 239-1860 1978 $15

PRINGLE, G. C. F.   In Great Waters, the Story of the United Church Marine Missions. Toronto, 1928. Card cover. Hood 116-314 1978 $15

PRINGLE, JOHN JAMES   Pictorial Atlas of Skin Diseases and Syphilitic Affections...from Models in the Museum of the Saint-Louis Hospital, Paris. London, 1897. Folio, illus., contemp. black half-mor., somewhat rubbed, 1st ed. Gilhofer 74-99 1978 sFr 500

PRINSEP, VAL   Virginie, A Tale of 100 Years Ago. 1890. 1st. ed., 3 vols., half title, bright blue binder's cloth, good. Jarndyce 16-948 1978 £18.50

A PRINTER'S Common-Place Book. Windham, (1937). Decor. bds., 1 of 350 numbered copies, sm. prospectus laid in. Dawson's 447-77 1978 $30

PRINTERS' Flowers: Whimsicalities from the Windsor Press. (San Francisco, 1934). Decor. bds., cloth back, very good, bkplt. of Jackson Burke, 1 of 150 numbered copies, prospectus laid in. Dawson's 447-193 1978 $60

PRINTING in the Twentieth Century. A Survey... London, 1930. 8vo., orig. cloth, plts. MacManus 238-1028 1978 $30

PRIOR, EDWARD S.   A History of Gothic art in England. 1900. Imperial 8vo., illus., modern qtr. mor., buckram sides. Upcroft 12-355 1978 £12.50

PRIOR, MATTHEW   Miscellaneous Works. 1740. 2nd. ed., 8vo, engraved frontis, head & tail pieces, rebound in 1/4 calf gilt, marbled bds. Eaton 45-402 1978 £20

PRIOR, MATTHEW   Occasional Verses 1702-1719. Oxford, 1927. Folio, orig. marbled wrappers, ltd. ed. of 550 copies, good. Sexton 7-177 1978 £12

PRIOR, MATTHEW   An Ode, Humbly Inscrib'd to the Queen. 1706. 1st. ed., folio, disbound, slightly foxed, half-title, little torn & creased. Hannas 54-240 1978 £40

PRIOR, MATTHEW   Poems on Several Occasions. 1709. 2nd. ed., 8vo, frontispiece, slightly cut into at foot, 19th. century half calf, joints beginning to wear. Hannas 54-241 1978 £15

PRIOR, MATTHEW   Poems on Several Occasions. London, 1720. 8vo, contem. vellum, dust-soiled. Hannas 54-242 1978 £24

PRIOR, MATTHEW   Poems on Several Occasions. 1754. 2 vols., 4th. ed., frontis, illus., uniform orig. calf, brown labels, head of spine vol. 1 rubbed, otherwise v.g. Jarndyce 16-175 1978 £17.50

PRIOR, W. D.   Hardy Shrubs. London, 1881. Colored plts., woodcuts, 8vo., orig. colored pic. bds. Morrill 241-476 1978 $17.50

PRITCHARD, H. BADEN   Old Charlton. 1879. 1st. ed., 3 vols., orig. blue remainder cloth, little rubbed. Jarndyce 16-949 1978 $18.50

PRITCHARD, H. H.   Hunting Camps in Wood and Wilderness. London, 1910. 4to, orig. cloth, over 60 plts., illus., good. Sexton 7-127 1978 £10

PRITCHARD, J. C.   An Analysis of the Egyptian Mythology... London, 1838. Lg. 8vo, hand-coloured engraved frontispiece, engraved plts., bound in salmon-pink cloth, printed paper label, cover faded, joints trifle split, inner joints cracked. Deighton 5-220 1978 £33

PRITCHARD, W. A.   Address to the Jury in The Crown vs Armstrong, Heaps, Bray, Ivens, Johns, Pritchard and Queen. Winnipeg, (1920). Card cover. Hood's 115-665 1978 $100

PRITCHETT, H. C.   The School Laws of Texas, Digest of 1891. Austin, 1891. Printed wr., worn. Jenkins 116-1110 1978 $17.50

PRITT, T. E.   North-Country Flies. London, 1886. Coloured plts., second ed., orig. binding. Wolfe 39-15 1978 $25

THE PRIVILEDGES Of the Citizens of London... London, 1682. Sm. 4to, marbled wrappers, title page cropped affecting few letters. Traylen 88-77 1978 £55

THE PROCEEDINGS of a Meeting of Mechanics and Other Working Men, Held at Military Hall, Wooster Street, New York, on Tuesday Evening, Dec. 29, 1829... New York, 1830. Disbound, light foxing. Hayman 72-497 1978 $15

PROCEEDINGS of a Public Meeting of Citizens of Minnesota, In Favor of a Semi-Weekly Overland Mail from Saint Paul to Puget Sound. St. Paul, 1859. Orig. pr. wr. in half mor. slipcase. Ginsberg 14-1041 1978 $1,500

PROCEEDINGS of the Friends of a Rail-road to San Francisco, at Their Public Meeting... Boston, 1849. Orig. pr. wr., 1st ed Ginsberg 14-866 1978 $100

PROCLAMATION of the Twelve Apostles of the Church of Jesus Christ of Latter Day Saints... Liverpool, 1845. Half mor., 1st ed. Ginsberg 14-680 1978 $150

PROCLUS   Fragments that remain of the Lost Writings of Proclus surnamed the Platonic Successor. 1825. Post 8vo., half mor. George's 635-505 1978 £5.25

PROCTOR, B. W.   Marcian Colonna An Italian Tale... 1820. 1st. ed., half title, uncut, rebound in half calf, marbled bds. Jarndyce 16-950 1978 £12.50

PROCTOR, EDNA DEAN   A Russian Journey. Boston, 1872. Sm. 8vo., 1st ed., orig. cloth. Morrill 241-478 1978 $10

PROCTOR, F.   Fox Hunting in Canada and Some Men Who Made It. Toronto, 1929. Inscr'd & signed by author, illus. Hood 117-648 1978 $22.50

PROCTOR, RICHARD A.   Six Lectures on Astronomy. New York, n.d. (circa 1880?). Wrs. Hayman 73-635 1978 $8.50

PROCTOR, ROBERT   An Index of German Books, 1501-1520 In The British Museum. 66 facsimiles. Traylen 88-517 1978 £15

PROCTOR, ROBERT   An Index to the Early Printed Books in the British Museum... Cr. 4to. Traylen 88-518 1978 £25

PROGRAMME Of Studies for the Elementary Schools of Manitoba, July, 1914. (Winnipeg, 1914). Card cover. Hood's 115-407 1978 $10

PROGRAMME of the Jubilee Celebration of the Parish of Nelsonville. (N.P., 1904). Illus., orig. binding. Wolfe 39-156 1978 $35

THE PROGRESS of the Pilgrim Good-Intent. Charlestown, 1801. 2nd Amer. from the 5th London ed., 8vo., old plain wrs. Morrill 239-584 1978 $10

PROGRESSIVE EDUCATION ASSOCIATION   Creative Expression. New York, (1932). Illus., some in color. Biblo BL781-864 1978 $9.50

PROJECTO De Constituicao Para O Imperio do Brazil, Organizado no Conselho de Estado Sobre as Bases Appresentadas Por Sua Majestade Imperial o Senhor D. Pedro I. Imperador Constitucional... Rio de Janeiro, 1823. Vignette, sm. 4to, modern cloth, leather spine, title & last leaf soiled. Edwards 1012-669 1978 £60

PROKOSCH, FREDERIC   The Conspirators. New York & London, 1943. 8vo, cloth, 1st ed., fine. Duschnes 220-247 1978 $12.50

PROKOSCH, FREDERIC   Death at Sea; poems. New York, 1940. First ed., orig. binding, very good. Rota 211-524 1978 £7.50

PROMINENT Americans of Swiss Origin. New York, 1932. Cloth. Hayman 72-650 1978 $10

PROMINENT People of the Maritime Provinces. St. John, 1922. Hood's 115-234 1978 $40

PROMINENT People of the Maritime Provinces. St. John, 1922. Hood 117-269 1978 $45

PROPERT, J. L.   A History of Miniature Art with Notes on Collectors and Collections. London and New York, 1887. Frontis., sm. folio, full gilt-stamped vellum, 1st ed., fine. Howell 5-50 1978 $100

PROPYLAEN-Kunstgeschichte. Berlin, 1923-1932. 22 vols., 8vo., half calf bindings, gilt tooled spines, plts., many in fine colours, rare complete set, fine cond. Van der Peet H-64-76 1978 Dfl 5500

PROROK, COUNT BYRON DE   In Quest of Lost Worlds. London, (1935). Illus., some foxing, orig. cloth, 8vo. K Books 239-382 1978 £6

PROSCH, THOMAS W.   David S. Maynard and Catharine T. Maynard. Seattle, 1906. Illus., original cloth. Ginsberg 14-529 1978 $50

PROSCH, THOMAS W.   McCarver and Tacoma. Seattle, 1906. Illus., orig. cloth, 1st ed. Ginsberg 14-1038 1978 $45

PROTECTION et l'Amelioration du Betail en Indochine. Hanoi, 1931. Large 8vo, plts., illus., tables, orig. covers. Van der Peet 127-193 1978 Dfl 50

PROSPECTUS of the Fort Dodge and Fort Ridgely Railroad and Telegraph Company, Including Organization Survey and Statistics. Fort Dodge, 1878. Folding map, original printed wr., 1st ed. Ginsberg 14-423 1978 $75

PROSPECTUS Of The Forward Mining Development Comapny. Denver, [1904]. Orig. pr. illus. wr., 1st ed. Ginsberg 14-738 1978 $15

PROSPECTUS of the Harmony Gold and Silver Mining Company of Nevada.... New York, [1865]. Plates, colored map laid in, orig. pr. wr., 1st ed. Ginsberg 14-739 1978 $100

PROSPECTUS of the Missouri Iron Company and Missouri and Iron Mountain Cities, Together with a Map of the State...and Plans of the Cities. Boston, 1837. Half morocco, 1st ed. Ginsberg 14-595 1978 $125

A PROTEST Against the Admission of Dakota as a State. [N.P., 1882]. Disbound, 1st ed. Ginsberg 14-322 1978 $75

PROTESTANT Ascendancy & Catholic Emancipation Reconciled by a Legislative Union... Dublin, 1800. 1st ed., plain wrs. Hyland 128-382 1978 £15

PROTESTANT EPISCOPAL CHURCH   Proceedings of the 4th Annual Convocation of the Clergy and Laity of the Protestant Episcopal Church in Oregon and Washington Territories. New York, 1856. Orig. pr. wrs., first ed. Ginsberg 14-842 1978 $50

PROUD, ROBERT   The History of Pennsylvania,...from the Original Institution and Settlement of that Province... Philadelphia, 1797-98. 1st ed., 2 vols., cloth, illus., lacking map, internally fine and clean. MacManus 239-1653 1978 $75

PROUDFOOT, JOHN   The Scotchman in America. Cleveland, 1873. Austin 79-569 1978 $27.50

PROUST, MARCEL   Cities of the Plain. 2 vols., ltd. to 2000 numbered sets, spines dull, very good, first English ed. Bell Book 16-1010 1978 £10

PROUST, MARCEL   Swann's Way. New York, 1923. 2 vols., 1st Amer. ed., edges rubbed, spines dull. Biblo BL781-1110 1978 $9.50

PROUST, MARCEL   Within a Budding Grove. New York, 1924. 2 vols., 1st Amer. ed., edges rubbed, spine dull. Biblo BL781-1111 1978 $12

PROUT, SAMUEL   Prout's Microcosm. The Artist's Sketch-Book of Groups of Figures, Shipping and Other Picturesque Objects. 1841. Folio, plts., orig. cloth, rebacked. Quaritch 983-237 1978 $115

PROUT, WILLIAM   Chemistry Meteorology and the Function of Digestion Considered with Reference to Natural Theology. London, 1834. 8vo., fldg. map in color, half mor., marbled bds., gilt lettered spine, foxing, ex-lib., very good copy. Zeitlin 245-203 1978 $155

PROUT, WILLIAM   The Nature and Treatment of Stomach and Renal Diseases. Philadelphia, 1843. Scuffed shaken. Rittenhouse 49-656 1976 $20

PROUTY, S. S.   Kansas. Topeka, 1887. Sewn as issued, 1st ed. Ginsberg 14-459 1978 $75

PROVERBS for the Nursery. New York, c.1875. Color plates, leaves taped on blank versos, rear wrapper lacking. Victoria 34-657 1978 $8.50

PROVISIONE & Capitoli Attenuti All' Arte Delli Spetiali di Tutto il Felicissimo Dominio Fiorentino per Benefitio Della Vita Humana. Fiorenza, 1576. 4to., wrs., uncut, very scarce, fine copy. Offenbacher 30-40 1978 $125

PROVOL, WILLIAM LEE   The Pack Peddler. Greenville, (1933). Portr., 8vo., 1st ed., pres. copy. Morrill 239-585 1978 $10

PROWETT, C. G.   Religious Equality in Ireland Not Inconsistent with the Maintenance of Our Constitution in Church and State. 1868. First ed., letter to Disraeli signed from author, plain wrs., good. Hyland 128-383 1978 £12

PRUDDEN, T. MITCHELL   Biological Sketches and Letters of T. Mitchell Prudden, M.D. New Haven, 1927. Unmarked. Rittenhouse 49-657 1976 $12.50

PRUDENTIUS CLEMENS, AURELIUS   Opera Omnia. Parma, Bodini Press, 1788. 2 vols. in 1, 4to., contemp. diced russia, spine gilt, excellent copy, handsome binding. Howes 194-528 1978 £85

PRUHOE, LORD   Lord Prudhoe's Journal. London, 1828, 1829. Typescript copy, orig. cloth, 8vo. K Books 239-383 1978 £20

PRUS, CLOVIS RENE   Neue Untersuchungen Uber Die Behandlung Des Magenkrebses, Von Dr. Rene Prus. Wurzburg, 1829. Sm. 8vo., orig. blind-stamped cloth, worn, browned, foxed, dampstains, signatures of former owners & bkplte. of Dr. Alfred M. Hellman. Zeitlin 245-204 1978 $45

PRUSSING, EUGENE E.   The Estate of George Washington, Deceased. Boston, 1927. Illus., scarce. MacManus 239-492 1978 $27.50

PRUSSING, EUGENE E.   The Estate of George Washington, Deceased. Boston, 1927. Cloth, illus., maps. Hayman 73-636 1978 $15

PRYNNE, WILLIAM   Brevia Parliamentaria Rediviva. 1662. 1st. ed., 4to, contemp. calf, rebacked, some worming in lower margin through most of book. Hannas 54-244 1978 £45

PRYNNE, WILLIAM   A Devine Tragedie Lately Acted, or a Collection of Sundry Memorable Examples of Gods Judgements Upon Sabbath-breakers, and Other Like Libertines... N.P., 1636. 4to., later calf-backed marbled bds., 1st ed., rare, signature on front flyleaf, bookplts., good. MacManus 238-137 1978 $250

PRYNNE, WILLIAM   Histrio-Mastix, or, Actors Tragaedi... London, 1633. 1st. ed., 2nd. issue, sm. 4to, blank before the title, few holes, slight waterstaining, little worming in margins, contemp. limp vellum, inside hinges broken, loose in case, but fine large copy. Traylen 88-473 1978 £300

PRYNNE, WILLIAM   The Soveraigne Power of Parliaments and Kingdomes... London, 1643. 1st. & 2nd. parts - 1st. eds., in one vol., sm. 4to, loose in contemp. calf covers. Traylen 88-474 1978 £25

PRYOR, MRS. ROGER A   Reminiscences of Peace and War. NY, 1904. Illus., cover speckled, Bell Wiley's copy. Broadfoot's 44-302 1978 $16.00

PRYS-JONES, A. G.   Poems of Wales. Oxford, 1923. Pres. copy inscribed by author, stiff wraps, very good, first English ed. Bell Book 16-891 1978 £6.50

PRYS-JONES, A. G.   Welsh Poets. 1917. Bds., very good, first English ed. Bell Book 16-892 1978 £4

PSALMANAZAR, GEORGE   Description de l'Isle Formosa en Asie. Amsterdam, 1705. 12mo., cloth, good. King 7-381 1978 £65

PSALMANAZAAR, GEORGE   An Historical and Geographical Description of Formosa.... London, 1926. Cloth, imitation vellum spine, bit soiled, page edges foxed, vol. 2 of The Library of Impostors, 1 of 750 numbered copies. Dawson's 449-68 1978 $50

PSALMANAZAR, GEORGE   Memoirs of. 1765. Second ed., portrait, contemp. mottled calf, rubbed, label missing, contents fine, 8vo. Howes 194-429 1978 £30

PSALMS Carefully Suited to the Christian Worship In The United States of America... Philadelphia, 1793. 32mo, orig. full calf, very good copy. Baldwins' 51-475 1978 $27.50

PSELLUS, MICHAEL   Opus Dilucidum in Quatuor Mathematicas Disciplinas, Arithmeticam, Musicam, Geometriam Et Astronomiam. Paris, 1545. 12mo., contemp. vellum. Salloch 345-157 1978 $400

PSYCHOMETRIC Dictionary. N. P. (Columbus), 1897. Prtd. bds. Hayman 73-637 1978 $7.50

PTOLEMAEUS, CLAUDIUS   De Geographia libri octo .... Basel, 1533. Edito princeps, 17th century marbled calf, gilt panels and spine, red mor. labels and red edges, copy ruled throughout. Gilhofer 75-90 1978 SFr 4,200

PTOLEMAEUS, CLAUDIUS   Geografia, cioe Descrittione Universale della Terra. Venice, 1598-1597. Folio, map, engraved vignette, old half-vellum, mor. labels, very light browning, fine. Gilhofer 74-74 1978 sFr 3,900

PTOLEMAEUS, CLAUDIUS   Operis Quadrupartiti In Latinum Sermonem Traductio Adjectis Libris Posteribus... Louvain, 1548. Sm. 4to., tree calf, gilt, Latin version. Salloch 345-159 1978 $375

PUBLIC Nusance (sic) Considered Under Such Heads of Complaint as are Most Notorious Within the City and Suburbs of London. London, n.d. (1754). 8vo, modern boards, 2nd ed., very good copy. Ximenes 47-182 1978 $125

PUBLICATIONS of Congregational Sabbath-School and Publishing Society. Boston, 1869. Illus. catalogue, sm. 8vo., orig. wrs. Morrill 239-347 1978 $10

THE PUBLICK Spirit of the Whigs. 1714. 4to., 1st ed., modern bds., calf back, fine unopened copy. Quaritch 979-310 1978 $230

PUCKLE, JAMES   The Club. 1817. Engraved portrait and title, foxed, diced calf, rubbed, spine defective, 8vo. George's 635-1456 1978 £7.50

PUDNEY, JOHN   Open the Sky; poems. New York, 1935. First American ed., orig. binding, spine severely faded, very good, inscribed by author. Rota 211-529 1978 £7.50

PUFENDORF, SAMUEL   An Introduction to the History of the Kingdoms and States of Asia, Africa and America... 1705. Thick sm. 8vo, calf, rebacked. Edwards 1012-36 1978 £90

PUFENDORF, SAMUEL   De Jure Nature et Gentium. Amsterdam, 1698. Enlarged ed., thick quarto, full contemp. vellum, early owner's name partially obliterated on front fly, Fletcher's name on rear pastedown. Bennett 20-171 1978 $250

PUFENDORF, SAMUEL   Of the Law of Nature and Nations. London, 1729. 4th ed., thick folio, 1/2 calf, new bind. Salloch 348-213 1978 $225

PUFENDORF, SAMUEL   The Whole Duty of Man According to the Law of Nature. London, 1705. 3rd ed., 8vo., orig. calf, rare. Salloch 348-214 1978 $300

PUGH, E.   Cambria Depicta: a Tour Through North Wales, Illustrated with Picturesque Views... 1816. Folio, coloured frontis., hand-coloured plts., some slight-offsetting mod. half mor. Quaritch 983-355 1978 $1,000

PUGIN, AUGUSTUS CHARLES   Specimens of Gothic Architecture. London, 1821-1823. 4to., 2 vols., engravings, cloth, some lib. stamps, 1st ed. Gilhofer 74-48 1978 sFr 800

PUGIN, AUGUSTUS WELBY NORTHMORE   Contrasts; or a Parallel Between the Noble Edifices of the Fourteenth and Fifteenth Centuries and Similar Buildings of the Present Day... London, 1836. 4to., engravings, cloth, lib. stamps, 1st ed. Gilhofer 74-49 1978 sFr 550

PUGIN, AUGUSTUS WELBY NORTHMORE   Photographs from Sketches by. 1865. 2 vols., roy. 8vo., frontis., pub. half mor. gilt, rather soiled. Quaritch 983-48 1978 $750

PUGNET, J. F. X.   Memoires sur les Fievres Pestilentielles et Insidieuses du Levant, avec un Apercu Physique et Medical du Sayd. Lyon, 1802. 8vo., old cloth, coloured plt., first ed., rare. Gurney 75-88 1978 £40

PUIGBLANCHI, D. ANTONIO   The Inquisition Unmasked. 1816. Engr. plts., 2 vols., contemp. calf badly worn, covers Vol. I detached. George's 635-745 1978 £10.50

PUIGBLANCH, D. ANTONIO   The Inquisition Unmasked. London, 1816. Full calf, bindings rubbed, worn, 2 vols., scarce, engravings. Biblo 247-726 1978 $77.50

PULCI, LUIGI   Il Morgante Maggiore. Paris, 1768. 3 vols., 12mo., full polished Spanish calf. Howes 194-569 1978 £26

PULLAN, MRS.   The Book of Riddles. London, 1855. 2nd ed., fine engraved f.p. and t.p., gilt-decorated impressed cloth, very good. Victoria 34-659 1978 $22.50

PULLEYN, WILLIAM   Church-Yard Gleanings and Epigrammatic Scraps. n.d. Frontis, eng., cloth, spine chipped. Eaton 45-403 1978 £5

PULSZKY, FRANCIS   The Tricolor on the Atlas; or, Algeria and the French Conquest. London, 1854. Gilt cloth, 8vo, 4 double-pg tinted lithos. K Books 239-384 1978 £22

PUNCH and Judy. London, 1873. Illus. by George Cruikshank, 6th ed., frontis., illus., plts., gilt-decor. cover. K Books 244-263 1978 £5

PUNCH'S Guide to the Chinese Collection. London, 1844. Illus., calf, gilt tooled, orig. wrs. bound in, rebacked, old spine laid down, a bit worn at spine end, quite fine. Dawson's 127-312 1978 $85

PUNCH, Or The London Charivari. Vol. I. 1841. 1st. few leaves water-stained, orig. cloth, both covers stained & spine chipped. Eaton 45-404 1978 £15

PUNSHON, W. M.   Lectures and Sermons. Toronto, 1880. 7th ed., spine worn. Hood 117-427 1978 $7.50

PURCELL, E. S.   Life of Cardinal Manning, Archbishop of Westminster. 1896. Frontispieces, 2 vols., 8vo. George's 635-1095 1978 £5.25

PURCELL, HENRY   Orpheus Britannicus. N.P., 1698, 1702. 2 vols., 1st ed., small folio, bound in brown half calf, marbled boards rubbed, gilt lettering and blind decor. on spines, ink notation on verso of frontispiece, some pages foxed, torn and page numbers cropped in vol. one, ink stains on table of contents. Totteridge 29-85 1978 $1,000

PURCELL, J. B.   The Crescent and the Cross. Oxford, 1840. Disbound. Hayman 73-557 1978 $12.50

PURCHAS, SAMUEL   Hakluytus Posthumus, or, Purchas His Pilgrimes. London, 1625. 5 vols., orig. leather bds., some wear on spines, no foxing, illus. with notes, adorned with pictures, fine set of very rare work. Hood's 115-609 1978 $4000

PUREFOY, GEORGE W.   History of the Sandy Creek Baptist Assoc. New York, 1859. Cover worn. Broadfoot 50-181 1978 $30

PURKINJE, JAN EVANGELISTA   De Phaenomeno Generali et Fundamentali Motus Vibratorii Continui in Membranis Cum Externis Tum Internis Animalium Plurimorum et Superiorum et Inferiorum Ordinum Obvii. Wratislaviae, 1835. Lg. 4to., bds., 1st ed. in book form. Offenbacher 30-128 1978 $350

PURRINGTON, W. A.   A Review of Recent Legal Decisions Affecting Physicians, Dentists, Druggists and the Public Health... New York, 1899. 8vo., 1st ed. Morrill 239-214 1978 $17.50

PURRINGTON, WILLIAM A.   Christian Science. New York, 1900. Frontis., facsimile, 8vo., 1st ed. Morrill 241-480 1978 $12.50

PURVIANCE, ROBERT   A Narrative of Events Which Occurred in Baltimore Town During the Revolutionary War. Baltimore, 1849. 1st ed., leatherette, fine. MacManus 239-617 1978 $40

PUSELEY, D.   The Rise and Progress of Australia, Tasmania and New Zealand... 1857. Thick sm. 8vo, orig. cloth, slight repairs to cover. Edwards 1012-342 1978 £60

PUSEY, E. B.   The Minor Prophets. 1906. 8 vols., cr. 8vo., spines faded. George's 635-1117 1978 £5

PUSEY, WILLIAM ALLEN   A Doctor of the 1870's and 80's. Springfield, 1932. Rittenhouse 49-659 1976 $10

PUSH and Pull Pictures. London-New York, c.1885. Sq.8vo., slat book, 5 of 6 slats in working condition, very good. Victoria 34-660 1978 $65

PUSHKIN, ALEXANDER   Gabriel: a Poem in One Song. New York, 1930.
Illus. by Rockwell Kent, full white decor. parchment, 1 of 750 on handmade
paper, acetate dust jacket, slipcase, worn, fine copy. Bradley 49-182 1978
$45

PUSHKIN, ALEXANDER   The Tale of the Golden Cockerel. (1936). 12mo.,
engrs., trellis pattern binding in cloth of gold, ltd. to 100 copies, dust staining
at edges, very good copy. Quaritch 979-353 1978 $280

PUTERSCHEIN, HERMANN   Paraphs. New York, 1928. One of 500 numbered copies, signed by Puterschein. Battery Park 1-81 1978 $50

PUTERSCHEIN, HERMANN   Paraphs. New York, 1928. Decor. bds., cloth,
very fine, slightly browned, 1 of 540 numbered copies signed by author. Dawson's 447-35 1978 $27.50

PUTNAM, GEORGE HAVEN   A Prisoner of War in Virginia 1864-5. New York,
1914. Cover rubbed, Bell Wiley's copy. Broadfoot's 44-562a 1978 $14

PUTNAM, GEORGE HAVEN   Salem Vessels and Their Voyages. Salem, 1924-
30. 4 vols., illus., mint unopened set, series 1-4. MacManus 239-1780 1978
$55

PUTNAM, GEORGE HAVEN   Sentinel of the Coasts. The Log of a Lighthouse
Engineer. New York, (1937). 1st ed., illus. MacManus 239-1781 1978 $10

PUTNAM, J. H.   Egerton Ryerson and Education in Upper Canada.
Toronto, 1912. Hood's 115-408 1978 $40

PUTNAM, JAMES JACKSON   A Memoir of Dr. James Jackson. Boston, 1905.
Illus., 8vo., 1st ed. Morrill 239-215 1978 $12.50

PUTNAM, JAMES JACKSON   A Memoir of Dr. James Jackson. New York,
1905. Rittenhouse 49-661 1976 $15

PUTNAM, RUTH   Life and Letters of Mary Putnam Jacobi. New
York, 1925. Rittenhouse 49-660 1976 $25

PUTZEL, L.   A Treatise on Common Forms of Functional Nervous
Diseases. New York, 1880. Rittenhouse 49-662 1976 $15

PUYDT, R. DE.   Rapport de M. le Colonel de Puydt... Brussels,
1842. Wrps. broken, 8vo., uncut. Paine 78-III 1978 $28.50

PYE, HENRY JAMES   Poems on Various Subjects. 1787. 1st ed., 2
vols., orig. tree calf, spines gilt, maroon & green labels, fine & attractive set.
Jarndyce 16-176 1978 £85

PYE, HENRY JAMES   A Prior Claim; a Comedy. 1805. 1st ed.,
8vo, wrapper, little contemp. doodling on title, fine otherwise. Fenning 32-275
1978 £10.50

PYLE, HOWARD   The Merry Adventures of Robin Hood. New
York, 1883. 1st ed., written and illus. by Pyle, original full-leather covers
modestly rubbed, invisibly rebacked with original label and endpapers, inner
front hinge cracked, fine copy internally. Victoria 34-662 1978 $225

PYLE, HOWARD   Rejected of Men. A Story of To-day. New
York, 1903. Orig. cloth, 1st ed., bookplt. removed, very fine. MacManus
238-567 1978 $30

PYLE, HOWARD   The Story of the Champions of the Round Table.
New York, 1905. 1st ed., illus. by Pyle, fine copy. Victoria 34-663 1978 $45

PYLE, KATHARINE   As the Goose Flies. Boston, (1901). 1st ed.,
written and illus. by Howard Pyle's sister, very good. Victoria 34-665 1978 $20

PYLE, KATHARINE   Six Little Ducklings. New York, 1915. 1st ed.,
plates, very good. Victoria 34-666 1978 $20

PYLE, T.   The Scripture preservative against Popery. 1735.
Contemp. calf, newly rebacked, 8vo. George's 635-1118 1978 £7.50

PYNE, WILLIAM HENRY   The History of the Royal Residences of Windsor
Castle, St. James's Palace, Etc. London, 1819. 3 vols., quarto, contemp. diced
tan calf, 2nd vol. rebacked with old spine over the new, bookplt., fine unwashed
copy, coloured engravings. Totteridge 29-86 1978 $1,750

PYNE, WILLIAM HENRY   On Rustic Figures, in Imitation of Chalk. 1817.
4to., etchings, some slight foxing of text, orig. half mor. Quaritch 983-238
1978 $240

PYNE, WILLIAM HENRY   The Twenty-Ninth of May: Rare Doings at the
Restoration. Dublin, 1825. 1st ed., 2 vols., half title, red morocco, marbled
bds., v.g. Jarndyce 16-953 1978 £58

PYNE, WILLIAM HENRY   Wine & Walnuts... 1824. 2nd. ed., 2 vols.,
half titles, uncut, orig. blue bds., brown paper spines & labels, chipped vol. 1,
v.g. Jarndyce 16-954 1978 £25

Q

QUALEY, CARLTON C.   Norwegian Settlement in the United States. Northfield, 1938. Fine. MacManus 239-404 1978 $20

QUALTROUGH, E. F.   The Sailor's Handy Book... New York, 1881. 1st ed., 12mo., orig. leath., hinges brok. Paine 78-112 1978 $20.00

QUARLES, E. A.   American Pheasant Breeding and Shooting. Wilmington, 1916. Illus., 8vo., orig. wrs., 1st ed. Morrill 241-481 1978 $12.50

QUARLES, FRANCIS   Emblems, Divine and Moral. New York, 1816. 16mo., contemp. calf, wood engrs. Morrill 241-698 1978 $50

QUARLES, FRANCIS   Emblems Moral and Divine. 1859. Woodcuts, octavo, introduction signed W.W., good. Upcroft 10-145 1978 £5

QUARLES, J. A.   The Life of Prof. F. T. Kemper... New York, (1864). Orig. cl., 1st ed. Ginsberg 16-887 1978 $15.00

THE QUARTERLY Theological Review. January, 1819-October, 1819. Philadelphia, 1819. Lea., binding worn, internal dampstains, Vol. II, complete year's run. Hayman 73-639 1978 $10

QUARTO Club Papers, 1926-27. New York, 1927. 1st ed., ltd. to 195 copies, orig. cloth-backed dec. bds., uncut. Americanist 102-97 1978 $25

QUEBEC Almanac; and British American Royal Kalendar, for the Year, 1804. Quebec, (1804). 16mo., orig. plain wrappers. Wolfe 39-450 1978 $125

THE QUEBEC Bridge, Carrying the Transcontinental Line of the Canadian Government Railways Over the St. Lawrence River Near the City of Quebec, Canada. Quebec, 1918. Photos. Hood's 115-983 1978 $17.50

QUEBEC. BUR. OF MINES   Bureau of Mines, Annual Report, 1929, Parts A-D; 1930, Parts A-D. Quebec, 1930, 1931. 8 vols., portfolios of maps, card covers. Hood's 115-565 1978 $30

QUEEN, ELLERY   The American Gun Mystery. New York, 1933. 1st ed., red cloth stamped with pictorial design in black, very good-fine. Houle 10-268 1978 $20

QUEEN Mary's Psalter Miniatures and Drawings by an English Artist of the 14th Century. London, 1912. Med. 4to., orig. half mor., t.e.g. Forster 130-221 1978 £55

QUENNEL, PETER   Baudelaire and the Symbolists. 1929. Plts., buckram, covers faded, very good, first English ed. Bell Book 17-758 1978 £6.50

QUENNELL, PETER   A Letter to Mrs. Virginia Woolf. Hogarth Press, 1932. Very good, wraps, first English ed. Bell Book 16-444 1978 £8.50

QUENSTEDT, F. A.   Handbuch der Petrefaktenkunde. Tubingen, 1885. Marbled boards, cloth spine, very thick and large 8vo. Book Chest 17-292 1978 $80

QUESNAY, FRANCOIS   Traite de la Gangrene. Paris, 1749. 12mo, full contemp. mottled calf, gilt panelled spine, hinges starting, front and back free endpapers missing, 1st ed. Bennett 20-172 1978 $175

QUICK, HERBERT   American Inland Waterways, Their Relation to Railway Transportation... New York, 1909. Illus., map, 1st ed., fine copy. MacManus 239-405 1978 $35

QUIETT, GLENN CHESNEY   They Buildt the West: An Epic of Rails and Cities. New York, 1934. Illus., orig. cloth, 1st ed. Ginsberg 14-886 1978 $12.50

QUILLER-COUCH, ARTHUR THOMAS   Brother Copas. Bristol & London, 1911. 1st ed., good sound copy. Limestone 9-235 1978 $22.50

QUILLER-COUCH, ARTHUR THOMAS   Old Fires and Profitable Ghosts. (1900). Title foxed, else near fine, 1st Eng. ed. Bell Book 17-334 1978 £7.50

QUILLER-COUCH, ARTHUR THOMAS   Poems and Ballads by "Q". London, 1896. 1st ed., uncut, t.e.g., orig. cloth, very good or better. Limestone 9-236 1978 $20

QUILLER-COUCH, ARTHUR THOMAS   Poems and Ballads by 'Q'. 1896. Buckram, t.e.g., very good, 1st Eng. ed. Bell Book 16-733 1978 £5

QUILLER-COUCH, ARTHUR THOMAS   The Ship of Stars. London, 1899. 1st ed., laid paper, uncut, t.e.g., orig. red cloth, very good or better. Limestone 9-237 1978 $14

QUILLER-COUCH, ARTHUR THOMAS   Wandering Heath. London, 1895. 1st ed., orig. cloth, very good. Greene 78-272 1978 $45

QUILTER, HARRY   Giotto. 1880. Coloured frontis., plts., roy. 8vo. George's 635-175 1978 £5

QUILTER, HARRY   Sententiae Artis. 1886. 8vo., orig. cloth, joints weak, Oscar Wilde's copy, bkplt. of Gleeson White. Quaritch 979-365 1978 $1,000

QUINBY, HENRY COLE   Quinby (Quimby) Family in England and America. New York, 1915. Baldwins' 51-264 1978 $22.50

QUINCY, JOSIAH   Essays on the Soiling of Cattle, Illustrated from Experience... Boston, 1860. 2nd ed., orig. cloth, front inner hinge weak, nice copy, inscribed by author. MacManus 239-406 1978 $40

QUINCY, JOSIAH   Essays on the Soiling of Cattle, Illustrated from Experience. New York, 1885. Cloth. Hayman 73-640 1978 $7.50

QUINCY, JOSIAH   Mr. Quincy's Speech in the House...January 19, 1809, on the Bill for Holding an Extra Session of Congress, in May Next. N. P., n.d. (Boston, 1809?). Sewn. Hayman 73-641 1978 $10

QUINCY, JOSIAH   A Municipal History of the Town and City of Boston...1630-1830... Boston, 1852. 1st ed., illus., fine copy. MacManus 239-294 1978 $25

QUINLAN, JAMES ELDRIDGE   History of Sullivan County. Liberty, 1873. Backstrip poor, calf bds. loose, internally clean, needs rebinding, 1st ed., scarce. Butterfield 21-426 1978 $50

QUINLAN, JAMES ELDRIDGE   History of Sullivan County. Liberty, 1873. 8vo., new cloth, 1st ed. Morrill 241-418 1978 $75

QUINN, D. A.   Heroes and Heroines of Memphis. Providence, 1887. Bookplate removed, Bell Wiley's copy. Broadfoot's 44-962 1978 $20

QUINN, D. B.   The Voyages and Colonizing Enterprises of Sir Humphrey Gilbert. London, 1940. 2 vols., illus., fold. maps. Hood 116-649 1978 $200

QUINN, JOHN P.   Fools of Fortune or Gambling and Gamblers, Comprehending a History of the Vice in Ancient and Modern Times. Chicago, 1892. Cloth, moderate wear at extremities, vertical crease on spine, 1st ed. Hayman 73-642 1978 $12.50

QUINN, P. T.   Pear Culture for Profit. New York, 1869. Ex-lib, 12mo, orig. cloth. Book Chest 17-294 1978 $15

QUINT, ALONZO H.   The Potomac and the Rapidan. Army Notes from the Failure at Winchester to the Re-enforcement of Rosecrans 1861-1863. Boston, 1864. Folding map in color, lacks front f/l, Bell Wiley's copy. Broadfoot's 44-525 1978 $16

QUINTANA, DON MANUEL JOSEF Vidas de Españoles Celebres por Don Manuel Josef Quintana. Madrid, 1807. Rare 1st ed., octavo, full contemp. marbled calf, worn. Bennett 20-173 1978 $195

R

RAADT, J. T. DE   Sceaux Armories des Pays-Bas et des Pays Avoisinants. Bruxelles, 1898-1903. 4 vols., 8vo., bds. Van der Peet H-64-528 1978 Dfl 400

RAAEN, AAGOT   Grass of the Earth. 1950. Austin 79-572 1978 $12.50

RABELAIS, FRANCOIS   All the Extant Works of... New York, 1929. 3 vols., folio, illus. in color by Jean De Bosschere, ltd. ed., bds., linen backs, covers faded. Biblo 251-615 1978 $62.50

RABELAIS, FRANCOIS   All the Extant Works of Francois Rabelais. New York, 1929. 3 vols., ed. ltd. to 1300 numbered copies, lg. 4to., map, b & w prts., color illus., plts. mint, binding soiled with faded spines, very fine set. Current 24-46 1978 $110

RABELAIS, FRANCOIS   Ex Reliquiis Venerandae Antiquitatis Lucii Cuspidii Testamentum. Lyons, 1532. 8vo., cont. Lyonnese blindstamped calf, cloth case, first ed. Quaritch 978-132 1978 $4800

RABELAIS, FRANCOIS   Les Songes drolatiques de Pantagruel, 1565. 1869. Woodcut plts., half mor., a little rubbed, 8vo. George's 635-1458 1978 £12.50

RABELAIS, FRANCOIS   La vie tres horrifique du grand Gargantua pere de Pantagruel iadis composee par M. Alcofribas abstracteur de quinte essence. 1919. Contemp. woodcuts, 4 vols., cr. 8vo., half green crushed mor., spines discoloured. George's 635-1459 1978 £10.50

RABELAIS, FRANCOIS   Works. 1849. New ed., 2 vols., frontis, nice tight vols. in orig. stamped cloth, portraits. Eaton 45-405 1978 £6

RACCOLTA de Monumenti piu interressanti del R. Museo Borgonico e di varie Collezioni private. Napoli, 1825. 4to., green mor., good, plts. King 7-216 1978 £20

RACCOLTA de piu belli ed interessant Dipinti Musaiei ed altri monumenti rinveti negli Scavi di Ercolano.... Napoli, 1871. Plts., 4to., orig. bds., rubbed. George's 635-45 1978 £18

RACCONTI Del Vecchio Daniele destinati a dilettare ed istruire la gioventu. Pisa, 1819. Frontis., quite good, sm. 8vo., leather spine, marbled bds., lower bd. renewed, few stains. Thomas 37-46 1978 £110

RACECOURSE and Hunting Field. New York, (1931). Drwgs. in color, 8vo., ltd. to 750 copies. Morrill 241-482 1978 $17.50

RACINE, JEAN BAPTISTE   Theatre, de 1664 a 1667. Paris, 1929-1930. 4 vols. in 1, nice white calf, goldstamped on front side, ltd. ed. of 500 numbered copies on India Paper, 8vo. Van der Peet H-64-451 1978 Dfl 55

RACKHAM, ARTHUR   Arthur Rackham's Book of Pictures. London, 1913. 44 coloured plts., also b/w illus., 4to., ink inscription on fly-leaf. Traylen 88-405 1978 £60

RACKHAM, ARTHUR   A Fairy Book. Garden City, 1923. 1st ed., plts., illus., very good or better. Limestone 9-239 1978 $30

RACKHAM, ARTHUR   Irish Fairy Tales. London, 1920. 1st trade ed., tipped-in color plts. free endpaper gone, very good copy, fine plts. Victoria 34-676 1978 $65

RACKHAM, ARTHUR   King Albert's Book. (London, 1914). 1st ed., tipped-in color plts. by Rackham, Nielsen, etc., spine crack and soiling. Victoria 34-682 1978 $17.50

RACKHAM, ARTHUR   A Midsummer-Night's Dream. New York-London, 1911. 1st ed., 2nd impression, tipped-in color plts, mounted on thick paper, cloth, gilt vignette, almost fine. Victoria 34-678 1978 $110

RACKHAM, ARTHUR   The Peter Pan Portfolio. New York, 1914. Ltd. to 300 copies, lg. folio, tipped-in color plates, tissue guard, all within handsome gilt-lettered and decor. yellow silk covers, spine with silk lacing, silk edge ties lacking, right and upper edge of binding waterstained as are lower corners of sev. tissue guards, plts. very fine, excellent cond. Victoria 34-680 1978 $850

RACKHAM, ARTHUR   Poor Cecco. New York, 1934. Fine color plts., edges rubbwd, library number on t.p., label on endpaper. Victoria 34-684 1978 $35

RACKHAM, ARTHUR   Princess Mary's Gift Book. Liverpool, n.d. Fine tipped-in color plts. by Rackham, etc., covers soiled, text fine. Victoria 34-683 1978 $17.50

RACKHAM, ARTHUR   The Queen's Gift Book. London, (1915). 1st ed., color plate and drawings by Rackham, color plts. by others, faded. Victoria 34-685 1978 $17.50

RACKHAM, ARTHUR   Some British Ballads. London, n.d. (1919). Coloured plts., illus. in b/w by Arthur Rackham, first ed., 4to. Traylen 88-408 1978 £40

RACKHAM, ARTHUR   The Windmill. London, 1923. Color plts. by Rackham, C. Lovat Fraser, and others,1st London ed., cloth spine and orange bds., very good. Victoria 34-692 1978 $65

RACKHAM, BERNARD   A Book of Porcelain. 1910. Coloured plts. by W. Gibb, roy. 8vo., marked on front cover. George's 635-235 1978 £15

RACKHAM, BERNARD   Catalogue of English Porcelain, Earthenware, Enamels, etc., collected by Charles and Lady C. Schreiber, Vol. I Porcelain. 1915. Plts., roy. 8vo., orig. bds. George's 635-237 1978 £7.50

RACKHAM, BERNARD   Early Netherlands Maiolica with Special Reference to the Tiles at the Vyne in Hampshire. (1927). 4to., plain and coloured plts., half mor., gilt top, ltd. to 50 copies signed by author. Quaritch 983-115 1978 $360

RACSTER, OLGA   Dr. James Barry: Her Secret Story. London, (1932). 5 illus., orig. cloth, 8vo. K Books 239-389 1978 £5

RADCLIFF, T.   A Report on the Agriculture of Eastern & Western Flanders: Drawn up at the Desire of the Farming Society of Ireland. 1819. Coloured map, plates, orig. boards, spine torn, very good. Hyland 128-388 1978 £34

RADCLIFFE, ANN   The Mysteries of Udolpho, a Romance. 1795. 3rd. ed., 4 vols., half-titles, rebound in half calf, hand-marbled bds., v.g. Jarndyce 16-177 1978 £68

RADCLIFFE, ANN   The Mysteries of Udolpho, a Romance. 1799. Fourth ed., 4 vols., 12mo., contemp. half calf, good. Howes 194-430 1978 £22

RADCLIFFE, ANN   The Mysteries of Udolpho, a Romance. Dublin, 1800. 3 vols., orig. half calf, marbled bds., good. Jarndyce 16-178 1978 £65

RADCLIFFE, ANN   The Romance of the Forest... London, 1791. 1st. ed., sm. 8vo, 3 vols., old tree calf, red leather labels, little worn, sm. tear in margin of vol. 3 catching one word. Traylen 88-317 1978 £85

RADCLIFFE, FREDERICK P. DELME   The Noble Science. 1839. Plts., roy. 8vo., orig. cloth, faded, spine worn. George's 635-1509 1978 £17.50

RADCLIFFE, FREDERICK P. DELME   The Noble Science, a Few General Ideas on Fox-Hunting. London, 1911. Steel-plt. engrs, hand-colored, wood engrs., 2 vols., 4to., orig. decor. cloth, very good. Americanist 103-92 1978 $55

RADCLIFFE, W.   Fishing from the Earliest Times. 1926. 2nd ed., plates, text illus., 8vo. George's 635-1492 1978 £15

RADDALL, THOMAS HEAD   Halifax. Toronto, 1948. Illus. Hood 117-270 1978 $12.50

RADDALL, THOMAS HEAD   Halifax, Warden of the North. Toronto, (1949). Illus. by Donald C. Mackay, second ed., orig. binding. Wolfe 39-466 1978 $10

RADDALL, THOMAS HEAD   The Pied Piper of Dipper Creek, and Other Tales. Toronto, 1946. Hood's 115-451 1978 $12.50

RADDALL, THOMAS HEAD   Pride's Fancy. Garden City, 1946. Hood 117-536 1978 $10

RADDALL, THOMAS HEAD   Tambour and Other Stories. Toronto, 1945. Decorations by Stanley Turner. Hood's 115-452 1978 $15

THE RADICAL Cure for Ireland; A Letter to the People of England & Scotland Concerning a New Plantation, Communicated Through a Living Friend by Chichester's Ghost. 1890. 1st ed., maps, unopened, very good. Hyland 128-389 1978 £25

RADIN, MAX   The Jews Among the Greeks and Romans. Philadelphia, 1915. Illus. Biblo 247-482 1978 $13.50

RADIN, MAX   Jews Among the Greeks & Romans. 1915. Plt. Allen 234-789 1978 $7.50

RADIN, PAUL   Crashing Thunder. New York, London, 1926. Orig. binding. Wolfe 39-249 1978 $20

RAE, COLIN   Malaboch or Notes From My Diary on the Boer Campaign of 1894... London, 1896. Folding map, 53 plts., gilt dec. cloth, 8vo, few pages roughly opened, repaired. K Books 239-387 1978 £20

RAE, COLIN   Malaboch or Notes From My Diary on the Boer Campaign of 1894.... London, 1896. Folding map, 53 plts., gilt dec. cloth, 8vo. K Books 239-386 1978 £25

RAE, EDWARD   The Country of the Moors. London, 1877. Map, 8 etched plts., cr. 8vo, little thumbed, quarter roan. K Books 239-388 1978 £10

RAE, JOHN   New Adventures of "Alice." Chicago, (1917). Quarto, colored plts., some wear, marginal staining. Petrilla 13-76 1978 $8.50

RAE, PETER 1671-1748   The History of the Rebellion Rais'd Against his Majesty King George I by the Friends of the Popish Pretender. 1746. Second ed., thk. cr. 8vo, contemp. half calf, rebacked. Howe's 194-431 1978 £32

RAE, WILLIAM FRASER   A Modern Brigand. 1888. 3 vols., 1st. ed., beautiful, bright copy in orig. red cloth, blocked in black & blind on leading bd., spines black, blind & gilt, fine. Jarndyce 16-954 1978 £43

RAE, WILLIAM FRASER   Newfoundland to Manitoba; a Guide Through Canada's Maritime, Mining and Prairie Provinces. London, 1881. Maps, illus. Hood 116-650 1978 $95

RAE, WILLIAM FRASER   Newfoundland to Manitoba, Through Canada's Maritime, Mining, and Prairie Provinces. New York, 1881. 1st ed., illus., orig. cloth, very fine copy. MacManus 239-79 1978 $40

RAE, WILLIAM FRASER   Sheridan, A Biography. 1896. 2 vols., portraits, sm. blind-stamp on title pg., cloth, spines chipped. Eaton 45-458 1978 £12

RAE, WILLIAM FRASER   Westward by Rail... 1871. 2nd. ed., map, modern half leather, 8vo. Edwards 1012-523 1978 £20

RAEBURN, HENRY   A Selection from his portraits Reproduced in Photogravure by T. and R. Annan. Edinburgh, 1890. Plts., lg. 4to., orig. cloth. K Books 244-264 1978 £7

RAEMAKERS, LOUIS   Cartoons. 1916. Illus., 2 vols., 4to., half roan, rubbed. George's 635-128 1978 £10.50

RAEMAEKERS, LOUIS   The Great War. 1916-19. 3 vols., roy. folio, port., plain and coloured reproductions, half buckram, slightly rubbed and soiled, ed. de-luxe, ltd. to 1,050 copies, vols. 2 and 3 signed by artist. Quaritch 983-240 1978 $135

RAEMAEKERS, LOUIS   The Great War in 1916. London, 1917. Cartoons, 1 of 1050 copies signed, 60 mounted plts., covers soiled, internally fine, oversize folio (18 x 13). Baldwins' 51-318 1978 $60

RAFFALD, ELIZABETH   The Experienced English Housekeeper For The Use of Ladies, Cooks, etc. Philadelphia, 1818. a new edition, old calf much worn, hinges broken. Baldwins' 51-338 1978 $25

RAFFLES, THOMAS STAMFORD   The History of Java. London, 1830. 2nd. ed., 2 vols., 8vo, half calf, gilt backs. Deighton 5-89 1978 £125

RAFINESQUE, CONSTANTINE SAMUEL   Medical Flora. Philadelphia, 1828-1830. 2 vols., 12mo., plts. prtd. in green, old half calf, mottled bds., gilt on spines, browned, foxed, good copy, 1st ed. Zeitlin 245-205 1978 $1,375

RAFN, CARL CHRISTIAN   Antiquitates Americanae Sive Scriptores Septentrionales Rerum Ante-Columbianarum in America. Copenhagen, 1837. Plts., maps, thick folio, 1/2 calf. Salloch 345-160 1978 $400

RAGATZ, LOWELL JOSEPH   The Fall of the Planter Class in the British Caribbean 1763-1833... New York, (1928). Orig. cloth. MacManus 239-407 1978 $17.50

RAGGUAGLIO ISTORICO   Della Peste Sviluppata In Noja Nell'Anno 1815. Napoli, 1816. 8vo., half contemp. calf, bkplts. of former owners, very good copy. Zeitlin 245-206 1978 $25

RAGOZIN, ZENAIDE ALEXEIEVNA   Chaldea, from the Earliest Times to the Rise of Assyria. London, 1889. 2nd ed., frontis., text illus., map, full prize calf, 8vo. K Books 244-265 1978 £7

RAGOZIN, ZENAIDE ALEXEIEVNA   Media, Babylon and Persia.... 1897. Sm. 8vo., 3rd ed., map, illus., orig. cloth. Edwards 1012-82 1978 £15

RAHT, CARLYLE G.   The Romance of the Davis Mountains and Big Bend Country. El Paso, 1919. 1st ed. Jenkins 116-1123 1978 $57.50

RAIKES, GEORGE ALFRED   Historical Records of the First Regiment of Militia. 1876. Coloured frontis., plates, recent leatherette. George's 635-852 1978 £15

RAIKES, GEORGE ALFRED   Historical Records of the First Regiment of Militia. 1876. 8vo., coloured frontis., plts., orig. cloth, spine worn. F. Edwards 1013-575 1978 £22

RAIKES, GEORGE ALFRED   Roll of the Officers of the 84th York and Lancaster Regiment. 1910. 8vo., orig. cloth, interleaved copy, portrait plts. F. Edwards 1013-536 1978 £18

RAILWAY STAFF NATIONAL TRIBUNAL   Minutes of Proceedings and Documents submitted to the Tribunal, July 1936, July 1937, Jan. 1939, Sept. 1939. 1936-39. 4 vols., folio. George's 635-387 1978 £7.50

RAINE, JAMES WATT   Land of the Saddle Bags. Texarkana, 1924. Illus., new cloth. Broadfoot 50-182 1978 $10

RAINE, WILLIAM MACLEOD   Cattle. Garden City, 1930. 1st ed., pic. cloth, pic. tan end sheets, very good copy, illus., scarce. Dykes 34-63 1978 $25

RAINES, CADWELL WALTON   A Bibliography of Texas. Austin, 1896. Half morocco, 1st ed., limited to 500 numbered copies. Jenkins 116-1128 1978 $125

RAINEY, GEORGE   The Cherokee Strip. Guthrie, 1933. Pic. cloth, illus., 1st ed., edges a little worn else very good, inscribed by author, slipcase. Dykes 35-211 1978 $50

RAINER, P. W.   African Hazard. London, (1940). 4 maps, 8vo, orig. cloth. K Books 239-390 1978 £5

RAINIER, PETER W.   Pipeline to Battle. 1944. Austin 80-261 1978 $7.50

RAINSFORD, W. KERR   From Upton to the Meuse. New York, 1920. Binding spotted, stained, illus. Biblo 247-768 1978 $12.50

RAINSSANT, PIERRE   Discorso Sopra Dodeci Medaglie de' Giochi Secolari dell' Imperator Domiziano. Brescia, 1687. 8vo., limp vellum, plt. King 7-89 1978 £30

RAIT, R. S.   King James's Secret... 1927. Octavo, good. Upcroft 10-146 1978 £8.50

RAITHBY, JOHN   The Study and Practice of the Law, Considered in Their Various Relations to Society... Portland, 1806. 1st. American ed., minor wear, orig. binding. Hayman 71-673 1978 $20

RAJAN, B.   T. S. Eliot: a study of his writings by several
hands. 1947. Portrait, very good, worn d.w., first English ed. Bell Book 16-
316 1978 £6

RAJU, P. V. RAMASWAMI   The Tales of the Sixty Mandarins. London, n.d.
Illus. by Gordon Browne, 2nd ed., binding stained, rubbed. Biblo 251-13 1978
$17.50

RALEIGH, WALTER   An Abridgement of Sir Walter Raleigh's History
of the World, in Five Books. 1698. 1st. ed., engraved portrait, 8vo, some
pencilling, recent half calf, very good copy. Fenning 32-276 1978 £32.50

RALEGH, WALTER   Discoverie of the Large and Bewtiful Empire of
Guiana. London, 1928. Illus., frontis., very fine copy, vellum back, backrum
bds., ltd. to 975 copies. MacManus 239-1782 1978 $60

RALEIGH, WALTER   The Historie of the World. 1677. Maps, folio,
early marbled bds., rebacked with calf, antique style, portrait. Howes 194-85
1978 £80

RALEIGH, WALTER   The Prerogative of Parliaments in England:....
Midelburge, 1628. Quarto, full early blind-stamped calf, gilt-stamped rules and
title on spine. Bennett 7-89 1978 $225

RALEIGH, WALTER   Some Authors: a Collection of Literary Essays,
1896-1916. 1923. Orig. buckram, printed label, 8vo. Howes 194-1113 1978
£6

RALEIGH, WALTER   The War in the Air. Oxford, 1922-37. Plt.,
coloured maps, 7 vols. in 9, 8vo., orig. cloth. F. Edwards 1013-595 1978 £250

RALPH, JULIAN   Dixie or Southern Scenes and Sketches. New
York, 1896. Illus. MacManus 239-1855 1978 $15

RAMAZZINI, BERNARDO   Essai Sur Les Maladies Des Artisans... Paris, 1777.
12mo., contemp. mottled calf, gilt decor. spine, browned, sm. marginal dampstain, very good copy, 1st ed. Zeitlin 245-82 1978 $225

RAMAZZINI, BERNARDO   De Fontivm Mvtinensivm Admiranda Scatvrigine
Tractatvs Physico-Hydrostaticvs. 1601. 4to., new calf by Sangorski and Sutcliffe,
very good, plt., first ed. King 7-90 1978 £240

RAMBACH, C.   Thesaurus Eroticus Linguae Latinae, Sive Theo-
goniae, Legum et Morum Nuptialium Apud Romanos. 1833. New buckram, foxed. Allen 234-791 1978 $20

RAMBAUD, ALFRED   The History of Russia...to 1877. New York,
(1904). Illus., 2 vols. Biblo 247-733 1978 $17.50

RAMBAUD, H.   La Declaration des Abus. Lyons, 1578.
Sm. 8 vo., parallel texts in roman type, phonetic script, orig. limp vellum,
1st ed.,very rare. Quaritch Summer, 1978-37 1978 $7,500

RAMBLE, ROBERT   Stories from the History of Greece. Cincinnati,
1840. Pict. bds. Hayman 73-354 1978 $10

RAMBLES Round Kilmarnock. Kilmarnock, n.d. (c.1870). 2nd. ed., orig. purple
cloth, little faded, good. Jarndyce 16-996 1978 £7.50

RAMEE, LOUISE DE LA
Please turn to
DE LA RAMEE, LOUISE

RAMSAY, ALLAN   The Poems. 1800. New ed., 2 vols., lg. 8vo.,
contemp. sprinkled calf, portrait. P. M. Hill 142-294 1978 £48

RAMSAY, ALAN   The Tea-Table Miscellany. Berwick, 1793. Calf,
spine broken, 4 vols. in 1. Biblo 247-849 1978 $32.50

RAMSAY, ANDREW   The Travels of Cyrus. 1727. Frontispiece, 3
parts in 1 vol., thk. cr. 8vo., contemp. calf, second ed. Howes 194-432 1978
£21

RAMSAY, DAVID   The History of the American Revolution. 1791.
1st. London ed., no half-titles, 2 vols., contemp. calf, 1 joint weak, 8vo.
Edwards 1012-524 1978 £40

RAMSAY, DAVID   The Life of George Washington. New York,
1807. 1st ed., port., rebound, nice copy. MacManus 239-412 1978 $25

RAMSAY, WILLIAM   The Gases of the Atmosphere and the History of
Their Discovery. London & New York, 1896. 8vo., plts., chart, orig. cloth,
gilt, very good copy, 1st ed. Norman 5-233 1978 $125

RAMSAY, WILLIAM   The Life and Letters of Joseph Black. London,
1918. 8vo., ads, plts., orig. cloth, fine copy, 1st ed. Norman 5-36 1978 $40

RAMSDELL, CHARLES WILLIAM   Behind the Lines in the Southern Confederacy.
Baton Rouge, 1944. Review copy, Bell Wiley's copy. Broadfoot's 44-305 1978
$20

RAMSDELL, CHARLES WILLIAM   Reconstruction of Texas. New York, 1910.
Wrs., Bell Wiley's copy. Broadfoot 46-384 1978 $125

RAMSDEN, CHARLES   French Bookbinders 1789-1848. London, 1950.
Plts., cr. 4to., orig. cloth, t.e.g. Forster 130-71 1978 £45

RAMSEY, R. W.   Richard Cromwell, Protector of England. 1935.
Plts., octavo, good. Upcroft 10-500 1978 £8.50

RAMSEY, R. W.   Studies in Cromwell's Family Circle and Other
Papers. 1930. Plts., octavo, good. Upcroft 10-499 1978 £7.50

RAMUS, PETRUS
Please turn to
LA RAMEE, PIERRE DE

RANCH Life in the Buffalo Bill Country. (Chicago, 1928?). Colored pic. wrs.,
maps, illus., 1st ed., very good, scarce. Dykes 34-258 1978 $15

RAND, A. L.   The Southern Half of the Alaska Highway and Its
Mammals. Ottawa, 1944. Card cover, illus. Hood 116-99 1978 $7.50

RAND, CLAYTON   Ink on My Hands. NY, 1940. Pres copy from
author, Bell Wiley's copy. Broadfoot's 44-899 1978 $8.00

RAND, CLAYTON   Men of Spine in Mississippi. Gulfport, 1940.
Pres. copy from author to Bell Wiley. Broadfoot's 44-898 1978 $10

RAND, E.   Orchids. Boston, 1888. 8vo, orig. cloth.
Book Chest 17-296 1978 $65

RAND, EDWARD KENNARD   The Earliest Book of Tours. By...With the Assistance of Leslie Webber Jones. Cambridge, 1934. Folio, illus., orig. cloth, 1st
ed., fine. MacManus 238-982 1978 $35

RAND, EDWARD KENNARD   In Quest of Virgil's Birthplace. Cambridge, 1930.
Illus., maps. Biblo 247-490 1978 $16.50

RAND MCNALLY & CO.   Mileage Map of Texas, Showing Rail Mileage
Between Cities, Towns, and Junctions, Steam and Electric Railroads, All Counties.
Chicago, 1921. Illus., large folding map. Jenkins 116-1131 1978 $35

RAND MCNALLY & CO.   Official Auto Trails Map of Texas,.... Chicago,
1925. Illus., large color folding map. Jenkins 116-1132 1978 $45

RANDALL, E. O.   Ohio Centennial Anniversary Celebration at
Chillicothe, May 20-21, 1903. Columbus, 1903. Cloth. Hayman 73-559 1978
$12.50

RANDALL, HENRY S.   The Life of Thomas Jefferson. New York, 1858.
Cloth, worn, spines worn, with some chipping, internally very good. Hayman
73-644 1978 $10

RANDALL, JAMES G.   Lincoln the President. New York, 1945. Pres.
copy from Randall to Bell Wiley, 4 vols. Broadfoot's 44-308 1978 $36

RANDALL, THOMAS E.   History of the Chippeqa Valley... Eau Claire,
1875. 1st ed., orig. cloth. MacManus 239-1138 1978 $50

RANDOLPH, EDMUND   Address on the History of California from the
Discovery of the Country to the Year 1849... [N.P., 1860]. Original printed
wr. Ginsberg 14-178 1978 $35

RANDOLPH, EDMUND   The New Almaden Mine: The Discussion Reviewed.
San Francisco, 1859. Original pr. wr., 1st ed. Ginsberg 14-179 1978 $150

RANDOLPH, JOHN   Substance of a Speech of Mr... on Retrenchment and Reform, Delivered in the House...First of February, 1828. Washington, 1828. Disbound. Hayman 72-651 1978 $12.50

RANDS, WILLIAM BRIGHTY   Lilliput Levee. New York, 1868. 1st Amer. ed., illus. with plts., front fly-leaf gone and shaken. Victoria 34-693 1978 $17.50

RANGER'S Progress: Consisting of a Variety of Poetical Essays, Moral, Serious, Comic, and Satyrical. London, 1760. 8vo, contemporary calf, gilt, spine gilt, (lower hinge a bit worn), 1st ed., very good. Ximenes 47-250 1978 $275

RANGS, WILLIAM B.   Tangled Talk. London, 1864. Rebound in 1/4 leather. Eaton 45-407 1978 £10

THE RANK & Talent of the Time Being a Dictionary of Contemporary Biography... 1861. 1st. ed., orig. red cloth, spine faded, otherwise v.g. Jarndyce 16-293 1978 £15

RANKE, L.   The History of the Popes, Their Church and State, and Especially of their Conflict With Protestantism in the 16th & 17th Centuries. London, Bohn, 1847. Cr. 8vo, orig. cloth, 3 vols., good. Sexton 7-178 1978 £10

RANKIN, DANIEL J.   The Zambesi Basin and Nyasaland. London, 1893. 3 folding maps, 10 plts., 8vo, orig. cloth. K Books 239-392 1978 £24

RANKIN, FRANCIS H.   Notes on the Care of Infants. (Newport, R. I., 1885). 8vo., orig. wrs., 1st ed. Morrill 239-216 1978 $17.50

RANKIN, JOHN   Letters on Slavery, Addressed to Mr. Thomas Rankin, Merchant at Middlebrook, Augusta County, Virginia. Ripley, 1826. Lea., little worn, solid copy, belonged to the Rankin family. Hayman 73-646 1978 $250

RANKIN, M. WILSON   Reminiscences of Frontier Days, Including an Authentic Account of the Thornburg and Meeker Massacre. Denver, 1938. Orig. cloth, 1st ed. Ginsberg 14-846 1978 $125

RANKIN, MELINDA   Texas in 1850. Boston, 1850. Orig. cloth, gilt, 1st ed., very good. Jenkins 116-1137 1978 $175

RANKIN, REGINALD   A Subaltern's Letters to His Wife. London, 1930. Backstrip faded, g.t., 8vo, orig. cloth. K Books 239-393 1978 £6

RANKIN, S. M.   History of Buffalo Presbyterian Church and Her People, Greensboro, N.C. Greensboro, 1934. Illus., cover speckled. Broadfoot 50-185 1978 $20

RANSAY, HENRIK   Liebig. Helsinki, (1918). 8vo., illus., orig. prtd. wrs., very good copy, 1st ed. Norman 5-182 1978 $25

RANSOM, CAROLINE L.   Studies in Ancient Furniture. 1905. 4to., plt. Allen 234-794 1978 $20

RANSOME, ARTHUR   Edgar Allan Poe; a critical study. London, 1910. Orig. buff buckram, frontispiece water-stained, covers a little used, good, author's signed autograph pres. inscription, first ed. Rota 212-48 1978 £20

RANSOME, ARTHUR   The Picts and the Martyrs. 1943. Drawings by the author, very good, worn d.w., first English ed. Bell Book 16-737 1978 £12.50

RANSOME, ARTHUR   We Didn't Mean to Go to Sea. London, 1937. Illus., coloured maps by the author, first ed., orig. binding, good. Rota 211-539 1978 £7.50

RANSON DE SAINT-MAIGRIN   Du Mouvement Applique Au Traitement De L'Entorse. Paris, 1853. 8vo., disbound, light browning, foxing, dampstains, good copy. Zeitlin 245-207 1978 $35

RAPAPORT, DAVID   Diagnostic Psychological Testing. Chicago, 1945. 2 vols., ex-library. Rittenhouse 49-663 1976 $12.50

RAPER, ARTHUR F.   Preface to Peasantry: A Tale of Two Black Belt Counties. 1936. Illus., Bell Wiley's copy. Broadfoot's 44-863 1978 $16.00

RAPER, CHARLES LEE   North Carolina. A Study in English Colonial Government. New York, 1904. 1st ed., hinge cracked, otherwise fine. MacManus 239-1849 1978 $17.50

RAPER, HOWARD RILEY   Electro-radiographic Diagnosis. St. Louis, 1921. Rittenhouse 49-664 1976 $15

RAPHAEL 1483-1520   I Freschi delle Loggie Vaticane inventati da Raffacle Sanzio. 1851. Vignette portrait, fine engrav. plts., folio, modern binders cloth. George's 635-204 1978 $25

RAPHEL, GEORG   Annotationes in Sacram Scripturam.... Leiden, 1747. 2 vols., thk. 8vo., contemp. vellum, portrait. Howes 194-570 1978 £25

RAPPORTS Des Commissaires Sur Les Pertes de la Rebellion des Annees 1837 et 1838. (Quebec, 1852?). Modern cloth, front blue printed wrapper preserved. Wolfe 39-480 1978 $75

RAQUEZ, A.   Entree gratuite Exposition Hanoi (1903). Saigon, 1903. 4to., boards. Van der Peet 127-322 1978 Dfl 65

RASCOE, BURTON   Before I Forget. 1937. First ed. Austin 82-776 1978 $11

RASCOE, BURTON   Titans of Literature. 1932. Illus. Austin 82-778 1978 $8.50

RASCOE, BURTON   We Were Interrupted. 1947. Austin 82-779 1978 $8.50

RASHDALL, HASTINGS   The Universities of Europe in the Middle Ages. Oxford, 1936, 1942. 3 vols., new ed., 8vo. Upcroft 12-360 1978 £25

RASHLEIGH, WILLIAM   Stubborn Facts from the Factories, by a Manchester Operative. London, 1844. 8vo., ads, stitched, little soiled, but very good copy, 1st ed., inscr'd. Norman 5-236 1978 $125

RASKIN, PHILIP M.   Songs of a Wanderer. Philadelphia, 1917. 12mo., 1st ed. Biblo 251-700 1978 $12.50

RASMUSSEN, ANDREW THEODORE   The Principal Nervous Pathways. New York, 1932. Rittenhouse 49-665 1976 $25

RASMUSSEN, K.   The People of the Polar North... 1908. Roy. 8vo, map, coloured plts., illus., orig. cloth. Edwards 1012-600 1978 £45

RATHBUN, MR.   Speech of ..., of New York, Delivered in the House...January 11, 1844. N.P., n.d. Disbound. Hayman 72-675 1978 $7.50

RATHBUN, J. C.   History of Thurston County, Washington. Olympia, 1895. Brittle, orig. pr. pict. wr., 1st ed. Ginsberg 14-1039 1978 $75

RATHBUN, M.   Fossil Decapod Crustaceans from Mexico. 1930. Wr., 8vo, orig. cloth. Book Chest 17-309 1978 $12.50

RATHER, ETHEL ZIVELY   Recognition of the Republic of Texas by the United States. Austin, 1911. Orig. wr. Ginsberg 14-967 1978 $25

RATHER, ETHEL ZIVLEY   Recognition of the Republic of Texas by the United States. Austin, 1911. Wr., very scarce. Jenkins 116-1140 1978 $45

RATHER Restful Rhymes. Boston, 1898. Orig. hand-colored illus., signed inscr. by Mr. & Mrs. D. L. Griggs, 1st ed., 8vo., orig. cloth, very good. Americanist 103-77 1978 $20

RATHKE, HEINRICH   Entwicklungsgeschichte der Wirbelthiere. Leipzig, 1861. 8vo., half cloth, 1st ed., library stamps, few stains. Offenbacher 30-129 1978 $95

RATHKE, HEINRICH   Untersuchungen Uber Die Aortenwurzelin Und Die Von Ihnen Ausgehenden Arterien Der Saurier. Wien, 1857. 4to., color litho. plts., old bds. backed in buckram, front orig. prtd. wr. bound in, pres. inscr. from author, marginal browning, plts. foxed & loose, signature of H. Grenacher, good copy, 1st separate ed. Zeitlin 245-208 1978 $150

RATHKE, MARTIN HEINRICH
Please turn to
RATHKE, HEINRICH

RATNER, JOSEPH   Intelligence in the Modern World. 1939. 1st Modern Lib. ed. Austin 80-991 1978 $12.50

RATTRAY, ROBERT HALDANE   The Exile: A Poem. London, 1826. 1st. London ed., 8vo, contemp red. straigh-grained morocco, gilt, edges gilt, little rubbed at corners but nice. Fenning 32-277 1978 £12.50

RAU, F.   Biblioteca Di Gius Nautico. Florence, 1785. 2 vols., roy. 8vo., bds., russia spines. F. Edwards 1013-178 1978 £75

RAU, PH.   Jungle Bees and Wasps of Barro Colorado Island with notes on other Insects. Missouri, 1933. 8vo, orig. cloth. Book Chest 17-310 1978 $18.50

RAULSTON, MARION C.   Memories of Owen Humphrey Churchill and His Family. N.P., 1950. Illus., original cloth, 1st ed., inscribed presentation copy from author. Ginsberg 14-239 1978 $40

RAUM, JOHN O.   The History of New Jersey, From Its Earliest Settlement to the Present Time. Philadelphia, (1877). 2 vols., frontis., nice, orig. cloth. MacManus 239-1314 1978 $55

RAUM, JOHN O.   History of the City of Trenton, N.J... Trenton, 1871. Illus., orig. cloth. MacManus 239-1313 1978 $35

RAUSCHNING, HERMAN   The Voice of Destruction. New York, 1940. 1st. ed.,8vo, orig. black cloth, 2 short tears at top of spine, inscription to Winston Churchill. Sawyer 298-102 1978 £90

RAVAGE, M. E.   The Jew Pays. 1919. Austin 79-575 1978 $12.50

RAVELIN, HUMPHREY   The Lucubrations. 1824. 2nd. ed., uncut in orig. brown bds., paper label, v.g. Jarndyce 16-959 1978 £18.50

RAVEN, HENRY CUSHIER   The Anatomy of the Gorilla. New York, 1950. First ed., fine, illus., d.j. Rittenhouse 49-666 1976 $85

RAVENEL, MRS. ST. JULIEN   Charleston The Place and The People. NY, 1906. Illus., Bell Wiley's copy. Broadfoot's 44-928 1978 $14.00

RAVIER, M.H.   Dictionarium Latino-Annamiticum completum et nove ordine Bispositum. Ninh Phu, 1880. 4to, rare, orig. covers. Van der Peet 127-197 1978 Dfl 125

RAVOUX, A.   Memoires, Reminiscences et Conferences de... St. Paul, 1892. Frontis, orig. cloth, French ed. with additions. Ginsberg 14-887 1978 $50

RAVOUX, A.   Reminiscences, Memoirs and Lectures of.... St. Paul, 1890. Frontis, orig. cloth, 1st ed. Ginsberg 14-888 1978 $50

RAWES, WILLIAM   Examples for Youth in Remarkable Instances of Early Piety. New York, 1809. Calf, lacks 4 leaves following t.p., cover wear. Victoria 34-694 1978 $20

RAWLINGS, MARJORIE KINNAN   Cross Creek. New York, 1942. 1st ed. Biblo BL781-1112 1978 $9.50

RAWLINGS, MARJORIE KINNAN   The Yearling. New York, 1939. Illus. in color, decor. blue buckram, 1st ltd. ed., 1 of 770 copies, signed by author & artist, fine in publisher's slipcase. Bradley 49-273 1978 $200

RAWLINGS, THOMAS   The Confederation of the British North American Provinces; Their Past History and Future Prospects... London, 1865. Green lib. bing., fold. map, plts. Hood 116-651 1978 $125

RAWLINSON, H. G.   The History of the 3rd Battalion 7th Rajput Regiment. 1941. Maps, illus., imp. 8vo, cloth. F. Edwards 1013-579 1978 £8

RAWLINSON, GEORGE   The Seventh Great Oriental Monarchy... 1876. Map, illus., thick 8vo, calf. Edwards 1012-83 1978 £30

RAWLINSON, GEORGE   The Sixth Great Oriental Monarchy... London, 1873. 1st. ed., 8vo, half-title, chromolithograph frontispiece, coloured engraved maps, illus., orig. cloth, neatly rebacked, retaining the orig. gilt backstrip. Deighton 5-90 1978 £35

RAWNSLEY, H. D.   The Resurrection of Oldest Egypt. Laleham, 1904. Plts., orig. cloth, 8vo. K Books 239-396 1978 £7

RAWSON, RAWSON W.   Report of the Bahams' Hurricane of October 1866. Nassau, n.d. (1868). 8vo, disbound, 1st ed., folding map, folding table, early library stamp on t.p., scarce Bahamas imprint. Ximenes 47-268 1978 $75

RAWSTORNE, J. G.   An Account of the Regiments of Royal Lancashire Militia, 1759 to 1870. Lancaster, 1874. Imp. 8vo., orig. cloth. F. Edwards 1013-564 1978 £15

RAY, CLARENCE E.   Rube Burrow: King of Outlaws and Train Robbers. Chicago, n.d. Illus., pictorial wr. Jenkins 116-176 1978 $20

RAY, JOHN   A Compleat Collection of English Proverbs. 1737. 2 parts, 8vo, contemp.calf, rebacked. Hannas 54-195 1978 £16

RAY, JOHN   Select Remains. London, 1760. Fine portr., 8vo., contemp. calf, 1st ed., fine copy. Offenbacher 30-130 1978 $140

RAY, JOHN   The Wisdom of God Manifested in the Works of the Creation, In Two Parts. 1692. Second ed., 2 parts in 1 vol., contemp. calf, head of spine chipped, 8vo. Howes 194-86 1978 £65

RAY, JOSEPH   Ray's Arithmetic, First Book. Primary Lessons and Tables in Arithmetic: for Young Learners. Cincinnati, (1857). Pict. bds., rubbed. Hayman 72-652 1978 $7.50

RAY, JOSEPH   Ray's Arithmetic, Third Book. Cincinnati and New York, (1857). Printed bds. Hayman 71-674 1978 $7.50

RAY, JOSEPH   Ray's Arithmetical Key. New York & Cincinnati, (1845). New & improved ed., prtd. bds., worn as usual. Hayman 73-507 1978 $10

RAY, JOSEPH   Ray's New Practical Arithmetic. New York, (copyright 1877). Bds. Hayman 73-645 1978 $7.50

RAY, P. ORMAN   The Repeal of the Missouri Compromise. Cleveland, 1909. Cloth, nice copy, scarce. Hayman 73-647 1978 $25

RAY, WORTH S.   Down in the Cross Timbers. Austin, 1947. 1st ed., limited to 500 copies, illus. Jenkins 116-1143 1978 $30

RAYAEIUS, N.   Responsio ad memoriale quo F. Sebastianus a S. Paulo. Antwerpiae, 1799. Sm. 4to., half calf, rubbed. George's 635-1119 1978 £8.50

RAYE, CHARLES   A Picturesque Tour Through the Isle of Wight, llustrated by Numerous Views. 1825. Oblong 8vo., coloured plts., margins of 1 or 2 plts. a little soiled, orig. half roan, roan label on upper cover. Quaritch 983-356 1978 $540

RAYLEIGH, LORD   Argon, a New Constituent of the Atmosphere. Washington, 1896. Folio, orig. cloth, first ed. Quaritch 977-132 1978 $140

RAYMOND, DORA CEILL   Captain Lee Hall of Texas. Norman, 1940. 1st ed., illus. bu Louis Lundean and Frederic Remington, d.j. Jerkins 116-552 1978 $35

RAYMOND, E. T.   Tecumseh. Toronto, 1915. Illus., fldg. map, lea. Hood 117-698 1978 $12.50

RAYMOND, HARRY   B. I. Barnato. London, 1897. 10 illus., orig. cloth, 8vo, little thumbed, shaken, covers dull. K Books 239-397 1978 £15

RAYMOND, HENRY J.   Disunion and Slavery. (New York, 1860). 8vo., unbound, 1st ed. Morrill 241-484 1978 $10

RAYMOND, THOMAS L.   Stephen Crane. Newark, Carteret Book Club, 1923. 1st ed., 1 of 250 copies, portr., 8vo., orig. cloth, very good. Americanist 103-29 1978 $60

RAYMOND, THOMAS L.   Stephen Crane. Newark, Merrymount Press, 1923. No. 199 of 250 copies prtd., signed pres. copy by author. Battery Park 1-32 1978 $75

RAYMOND, W. O.   Glimpses of the Past. St. John, 1905. Illus. Hood 117-273 1978 $50

RAYMUNDUS DE SABUNDE   Theologia Naturalis Sive Liber Creaturarum... Strassburg, 1501. Folio, stamped pigskin, a few holes. Salloch 348-219 1978 $350

RAYNAL, F. E.   Les Naufrages, ou Vingt Mois Sur un Refic Des Iles Auckland. Paris, 1898. Map, plts., roy. 8vo, orig. red cloth, gilt, nice. Fenning 32-278 1978 £10.50

RAYNAL, GUILLAUME THOMAS FRANCOIS   Histoire Philosophique et Politique des Etablisemens et du Commerce des Europeens Dans Les Deux Indes and Atlas. Geneva, 1781. 10 vols., 8vo. in sprinkled bds., plus atlas 4to. in calf, maps, fine. Salloch 348-220 1978 $300

RAYNAL, GUILLAUME THOMAS FRANCOIS   Histoire Philosophique et Politique des Establissements et du Commerce... Geneva, 1782. Frontis., 10 vols., contemp. calf, 8vo. Howes 194-571 1978 £55

RAYNAL, MAURICE   Histoire du Stadhouderrat, Depuis son Origine Jusqu'a Present. La Haye, 1750. 8vo., orig. covers. Van der Peet H-64-529 1978 Dfl 65

RAYNER, KENNETH   Life and Times of Andrew Johnson, 17th President of the U.S. New York, 1866. 1st ed., orig. cloth, port. MacManus 239-778 1978 $25

REA, LILIAN   The Enthusiasts of Port Royal. New York, 1912. Illus. Biblo 247-735 1978 $17.50

READ, DANIEL   An Address...Delivered Upon the Commencement Occasion, June 30, 1869. N.P., n.d. Unbound as issued. Hayman 73-455 1978 $7.50

READ, HERBERT   Collected Essays in Literary Criticism. 1938. Very good, worn d.w., first English ed. Bell Book 17-766 1978 £8.50

READ, HERBERT   Collected Poems 1913-1925. London, 1926. First ed., orig. binding, spine and edges of covers a little faded, nice. Rota 211-544 1978 £5

READ, HERBERT   The End of a War. 1933. Bds., good, first English ed. Bell Book 16-739 1978 £6.50

READ, HERBERT   Poems 1914-1934. London, 1935. 1st ed., very good or better. Limestone 9-240 1978 $17.50

READ, HERBERT   Reason and Romanticism: Essays in Literary Criticism. 1926. First ed., cr. 8vo., orig. cloth. Howes 194-1115 1978 £6

READ, HERBERT   Songs of Chaos; poems. London, 1915. First ed., wrappers, worn and reapired at spine, good, scarce. Rota 211-543 1978 £15

READ, HERBERT   Staffordshire Pottery Figures. 1929. Colour plts., 4to., covers slightly marked. George's 635-236 1978 £25

READ, HOLLIS   The Christian Brahmun; or, Memoirs of the Life, Writings, and Character of the Converted Brahman, Babajee. New York, 1836. 2 vols. in 1, 12mo, original quarter cloth and boards, printed paper label (bit rubbed), 1st ed., occasional foxing, very good copy. Ximenes 47-269 1978 $27.50

READ, JOHN   The Alchemist in Life Literature and Art. 1947. Illus., 8vo. George's 635-969 1978 £5

READ, JOHN   Prelude to Chemistry. New York, 1937. 8vo., plts., orig. cloth, 1st Amer. ed. Norman 5-237 1978 $25

READ, OPIE   An Arkansas Planter. 1896. Illus., first ed. Austin 82-780 1978 $27.50

READ, OPIE   The Carpetbagger. 1899. Illus., first ed., covers rubbed. Austin 82-781 1978 $12.50

READ, OPIE   My Young Master, a Novel. Chicago, (1896). 1st ed., orig. dec. cloth, covers slightly spotted. Americanist 102-98 1978 $20

READ, WILLIAM A.   Louisiana-French. Baton Rouge, 1931. Illus., original printed wr., 1st ed. Ginsberg 14-509 1978 $25

READ and Circulate, or Extravagance and Galphinism Exposed. N. P., n.d. (1852). Unbound. Hayman 73-625 1978 $7.50

READE, CHARLES   The Cloister & The Hearth. London, n.d. Thick, large 8vo, color plates, drawings, cover color plate, ornate gilt spine, almost fine. Victoria 34-108 1978 $25

READE, CHARLES   The Course of True Love Never Did Run Smooth. 1857. Orig. pictorial bds., rebacked in buckram, paper label. Eaton 45-408 1978 £20

READE, CHARLES   Griffith Gaunt; or Jealousy. London, 1866. 3 vols., orig. cloth, 1st ed., 1st bind., ex-lib. labels removed, cracked inner hinges. MacManus 238-372 1978 $225

READE, CHARLES   Griffith Gaunt; Or Jealousy. 1866. 2nd. ed., 3 vols., half titles, orig. blue cloth, spines worn & dulled, one bd. marked. Jarndyce 16-961 1978 £18.50

READE, CHARLES   Hard Cash. A Matter-of-Fact Romance. London, 1863. 3 vols., orig. cloth, 1st ed., inner hinges cracked, covers worn, otherwise good, bookplt., cloth slipcase. MacManus 238-371 1978 $175

READE, CHARLES   Peg Woffington: A Novel. 1857. New ed., engraved frontis, orig. cloth, faded. Jarndyce 16-960 1978 £6

READE, CHARLES   Peg Woffington. London, 1899. 1st ed., ornate gilt cover and spine, fly-leaf gone, very good. Victoria 34-793 1978 $17.50

READE, CHARLES   Peg Woffington. New York, 1899. 8vo, pict. green cloth, gilt, t.e.g., illus. by Hugh Thomson, fine. Duschnes 220-304 1978 $27.50

READE, CHARLES   A Terrible Temptation. A Story of the Day. London, 1871. 3 vols., orig. cloth, 1st Eng. ed., maroon sand-grained cloth, covers faded and worn, edges a bit torn. MacManus 238-373 1978 $85

READE, CHARLES   A Woman Hater. Edinburgh, 1877. 3 vols., orig. cloth, 1st Eng. ed., edges and extremities a bit worn, but good. MacManus 238-374 1978 $135

READE, MRS. R. H.   The Goldsmith's Ward: A Tale of London City in the 15th. Century. 1891. 1st. & only ed., plts., 8vo, orig. cloth, very good. Fenning 32-279 1978 £10.50

READE, WILLIAM WINWOOD   The African Sketch Book. 1873. Maps, plts., 2 vols., orig. cloth, covers slightly worn, 8vo. Edwards 1012-265 1978 £75

READE, WILLIAM WINWOOD   Savage Africa: Being the Narrative of a Tour in Equatorial, Southwestern and Northwestern Africa... New York, 1864. 1st. American ed., folding map, 28 wood-engravings, old style half calf, 8vo. K Books 239-398 1978 £35

READE, WILLIAM WINWOOD   Savage Africa: Being the Narrative of a Tour in Equatorial, Southwestern and Northwestern Africa... New York, 1864. Folding map, wood-engravings, rebound in half calf, 8vo. K Books 239-399 1978 £30

READE, WINWOOD   The Martyrdom of Man... New York, n.d. (1880's?). 8th ed., cloth, back cover dampstained. Hayman 72-654 1978 $7.50

READER, THOMAS   Squibs and Crackers Let Off on Various Occasions. 1894. 4to, 1/2 morocco. Eaton 45-409 1978 £15

READING, J. H.   The Ogowe Band: A Narrative of African Travel... Philadelphia, 1890. 8vo, orig. cloth, illus. Edwards 1012-266 1978 £20

REAGAN, JOHN H.   Argument of the Hon. John H. Reagan of Texas before the Committee on Commerce on the Railroad Problem. Washington, 1882. Jenkins 116-1147 1978 $45

REAGAN, JOHN H.   Claims for Spoilations Committed by Indians and Mexicans. Washington, 1860. $12.50

REAGAN, JOHN H.   First Annual Report of the Railroad Commission of the State of Texas,.... Austin, 1892. Original cloth, autographed presentation copy to J. J. Arthur from Mrs. John H. Reagan. Jenkins 116-1150 1978 $75

REAGAN, JOHN H.   Report of the Postmaster-General to the President. Montgomery, 1861. Sewn. Jenkins 116-1150 1978 $45

REAGAN, JOHN H.   Speech in the House of Representatives, February 29, 1860. Washington, 1860. Jenkins 116-1152 1978 $35

REAGAN, JOHN H.   Speech...On The State Of The Union. Washington, 1860. Untrimmed. Jenkins 116-1151 1978 $25

REAL Decreto en que S. M. ha Resuelto Ampliar la Concession del Comercio Libre, Contenida en Decreto de 16. de Octubre de 1765. Madrid, 1778. Folio, later marbled bds., vellum back. Wolfe 39-516 1978 $100

THE REAL Devil's Walk. Not by Professor Porson. London, 1830. 12mo, full mottled calf, gilt, a.e.g., by Riviere (trifle rubbed), 1st ed., wood-engravings by Robert Cruikshank. Ximenes 47-251 1978 $40

REASONS Why the Present System of Auctions Ought to be Abolished. New York, 1828. Disbound. Hayman 73-648 1978 $15

REAUMUR, RENE A. F. DE   l'Art de Convertir le fer Forge en Acier, et l'Art d'Adoucir le fer Fondu. Paris, 1722. 4to., fldg. copperplts., contemp. mottled calf, richly gilt spine, dampstaining, but good copy, 1st ed. Norman 5-238 1978 $400

REAVIS, L. U.   Saint Louis: The Future Great City of the World. St. Louis, 1876. Centennial ed., illus., full dec. mor., sm. thick 4to. MacManus 239-1062 1978 $50

REAVIS, L. U.   Texas and Pacific Railway;.... New York, 1878. Orig. pr. wr., 1st ed. Ginsberg 14-969 1978 $85

RECLUS, ELIE   Curious Byways of Anthropology: Sexual Savage and Esoteric Customs of Primitive Peoples. New York, 1932. 1st ed., deluxe, ltd. to 1,000 copies, orig. bind. Petrilla 13-78 1978 $15

RECLUS, ELISEE   North-East Africa. London, c. 1885. 136 text-illus., 5 coloured maps, 38 plts., imperial 8vo, orig. gilt-dec. cloth, g.e. K Books 239-402 1978 £7

RECLUS, ELISEE   North-West Africa. London, c. 1885. 5 colored maps, 38 plts., 205 text-illus., imperial 8vo, orig. gilt-dec. cloth. K Books 239-402A 1978 £7

RECLUS, ONESIME   A Bird's-Eye View of the World. Boston, 1887. 4to., illus. Morrill 239-537 1978 $15

RECLUS, PAUL   L'Anesthesie Localisee par la Cocaine. Paris, 1903. Illus., 12mo., black buckram, orig. wrappers bound in, first ed. Rittenhouse 49-668 1976 $31

RECORD of an Examination Before Kenneth G. White, U.S. Commissioner, in Relation to Forged Checks...in the Name of J. W. Hunter. New York, 1864. Engr. plt., wr., pres. inscr. by defendant. Butterfield 21-541 1978 $10

RECORD of Investigation by Committee from the House of Representatives, 35th Legislature, the State of Texas, of Charges Filed Against James E. Ferguson. Austin, 1917. Original printed wr. Jenkins 116-1546 1978 $25

RECORD of Pennsylvania Volunteers in the Spanish-American War, 1898... N.P., 1901. 2nd ed., 4to., orig. cloth, fine copy. MacManus 239-1685 1978 $17.50

A RECORD of the Ceremony and Oration on the Occasion of the Unveiling of the Monument Commemorating the Great Swamp Fight December 19, 1675 in the Narragansett Country, Rhode Island. 1906. 1st ed., illus., orig. cloth, good copy. MacManus 239-182 1978 $12.50

RECORD of the Courts of Chester County, Pa., 1681-1697. Philadelphia, 1910. Rebound, fine. MacManus 239-1415 1978 $50

A RECORD of the Inscriptions in the Old Town Burying Ground of Newburgh. Newburgh, 1898. Photo frontis., wr. Butterfield 21-334 1978 $22.50

A RECORD of the Proceedings of the Limited Editions Club to Celebrate the 21st Birthday of the Club and the 50th of Its Founder. New York, 1950. Folio, illus. Battery Park 1-31 1978 $35

RECORDING Britain. 1946. Drawings, some tinted or coloured, 4 vols., roy. 8vo. George's 635-1461 1978 £12.50

RECORDS of Holy Trinity Church, Wilmington, Del. N.P., 1890. Frontis. MacManus 239-964 1978 $45

THE RECORDS of the Swedish Lutheran Churches at Raccoon and Penns Neck, 1713-1786. Elizabeth, 1938. Frontis., scarce. MacManus 239-1294 1978 $35

RECUEIL Des Edits, Declarations, Arrests, et Autres Pieces Concernant les Duels & Rencontres. Paris, 1679. 12mo., full calf, ribbed spine, richly gilt tooled, rare, joints cracked, top of spine partly gone, contents good. Van der Peet H-64-609 1978 Dfl 225

RECUPITO, GIULIO CESARE   Vesuviano Incendio Nuntius.... 1639. Sm. 8vo., vellum, very faintly discoloured throughout. King 7-303 1978 £50

RED, WILLIAM S.   A History of the Presbyterian Church in Texas. Austin, 1936. Near mint. Jenkins 116-1157 1978 $25

RED, WILLIAM S.   The Texas Colonists and Religion, 1821-1836. Austin, 1924. 1st ed., some damp stains to outer margins. Jenkins 116-1158 1978 $25

REDDAWAY, T. F.   The Rebuilding of London After the Great Fire. 1940. Plts., octavo, good. Upcroft 10-501 1978 £7.50

REDDING, JOHN M.   Skyways to Berlin. 1943. Austin 80-263 1978 $10

REDE, LUCY LEMAN   Flowers That Never Fade. London, c.1820's. 12mo, hand-colored woodcut, wrappers, very good. Victoria 34-695 1978 $27.50

THE REDEEMED Captive Returning to Zion... Northampton, 1853. Very fine. MacManus 239-1168 1978 $35

DIE REDEN Gotamo Buddhos. Mittlere Sammlung. Munich, 1921. 3 vols., 16mo., bds. Salloch 348-20 1978 $36

REDFIELD, WILLIAM C.   Cape Verde and Hatteras Hurricane, of Aug.--Sept., 1853, with a Hurricane Chart,.... New Haven, 1854. 8vo, original blue printed wr. (spine chipped), 1st ed., presentation copy, inscribed by author on front wr. Ximenes 47-271 1978 $35

REDGRAVE, S.   A Dictionary of Artists of the English-School; Painters, Sculptors, Architects, Engravers and Ornamentists. London, 1874. 8vo, joints little torn, pres. copy. Traylen 88-411 1978 £15

REDGROVE, H. STANLEY   Alchemy: Ancient and Modern. London, 1922. 8vo., plts., orig. cloth, gilt, 2nd ed., revised. Norman 5-239 1978 $25

REDHEAD, H. W.   The Horseman; With Practical Rules to Buyers, Breeders, Breakers, Smiths, &c,...With Numerous Illus. Cleveland, 1855. Only 1 known copy, paper wr., good. Nestler Rare 78-189 1978 $55

REDI, FRANCESCO   Alcune Operette. Venezia, 1830. 2 vols., lg. 16mo., paper bound with title printed on spine, fine uncut unopened copy. King 7-219 1978 £15

REDI, FRANCESCO   Il Bacco in Toscana. Bologna, 1748. 8vo., new cloth, frontis. King 7-218 1978 £20

REDI, FRANCESCO   Bacchus in Tuscany, a Dithyrambic Poem, from the Italian of Francesco Redi, with Notes Original and Select. London, 1825. 12mo, 19th-century green half mor., spine gilt, 1st ed., two blindstamps of early Iowa owner, light dampstains at the beginnings, sound copy. Ximenes 47-147 1978 $60

REDI, FRANCESCO   Sonetti. Firenze, 1702. Lg. folio, cloth, worn at head and foot of spine. King 7-217 1978 £80

REDLICH, H. J.   The Procedure of the House of Commons...
London, 1908. 3 vols., roy. 8vo, scarce. Traylen 88-319 1978 £30

REDMAYNE, PAUL   The Gold Coast Yesterday and Today. London,
1938. 4to, orig. cloth, illus. K Books 239-403 1978 £5

REDMOND-HOWARD, L. G.   Home Rule. 1912. 1st ed., very good, octavo
bound in cloth. Hyland 128-399 1978 £4

REDMOND-HOWARD, L. G.   Six Days of the Irish Republic. Boston, 1916.
Sm. 8vo., torn d.w., orig. cloth. Morrill 241-485 1978 $7.50

REDPATH, JAMES   Hand-book to Kansas Territory and the Rocky
Mountains' Gold Region.... New York, 1859. Maps, orig. cloth, 1st ed. Ginsberg 14-889 1978 $300

REDSLOB, EDWIN   Alt-Danemark Mit 334 Abbildungen 2 Weite
Auflage. Munchen, 1921. 4to. Baldwins' 51-144 1978 $35

REECE, CHARLES S.   A History of Cherry County, Nebraska. N. P.,
(1945). Cloth, fldg. map, illus., 1st ed., very good copy, very scarce. Dykes
34-259 1978 $75

REED, C.   An Historical Narrative of the Origin & Constitution of..the Honourable, the Irish Society. 1855. With supplement to 1878,
very good, octavo bound in cloth. Hyland 128-400 1978 £7

REED, CHESTER A.   Wild Flowers East of the Rockies. Worchester,
Massachusetts, 1910. Color plts. by author, very good or better. Limestone
9-241 1978 $35

REED, EMILY HAZEN   Life of A. P. Dostie; or, The Conflict in New
Orleans. New York, 1868. Frontis, original cloth, 1st ed. Ginsberg 14-510
1978 $75

REED, EMILY HAZEN   Life of A. P. Dostie or the Conflict in New
Orleans. New York, 1868. Bell Wiley's copy. Broadfoot 46-206 1978 $30

REED, HENRY   Lectures on the British Poets. Philadelphia, 1857.
2 vols., covers worn. Biblo 247-850 1978 $12.50

REED, JOHN   Daughter of the Revolution and Other Stories.
New York, (1927). 1st Vanguard ed. Biblo 251-616 1978 $12.50

REED, JOHN   Tamburlaine and Other Verses. (New York),
1917. Blue paper wrs. over bds., uncut, 1st ed., 1 of only 50 copies on Norde-
lung handmade paper, fine copy, scarce. Bradley 49-275 1978 $325

REED, JOSEPH   Tom Jones, A Comic Opera. 1769. 2nd. ed.,
8vo, half-title, dust soiled, disbound. Hannas 54-115 1978 £12.50

REED, JULIUS A.   Reminiscences of Early Congregationalism in
Iowa. Grinnell, 1885. Original printed wr., 1st ed. Ginsberg 14-424 1978
$15

REED, MYRTLE   The Book of Clever Beasts. New York,
(1904). Color frontispiece, illus. by Peter Newell, 1st ed., 8 vo., orig.
decorative red cloth, very good, scarce. House 10-237 1978 $45

REED, PRENTISS B.   Personal Leadership for Combat Officers. 1943.
Austin 80-264 1978 $10

REEDY, WILLIAM MARION   The Law of Love. (East Aurora, 1905). Limp
red lea., binding defect at upper corner of fr. cover, otherwise very good copy.
Hayman 73-271 1978 $7.50

REEKS, MARGARET   The Mother of Goethe 'Frau Aja'. 1911. Gilt,
frontis, portraits, full morocco, gilt panelled, raised bands, a.e.g., inscribed.
Eaton 45-410 1978 £10

REES, J. R.   The Case of Rudolph Hess. 1947. 1st. ed.,
plts., 8vo, orig. cloth, birthday present for Winston Churchill. Sawyer 298-103
1978 £130

REEVE, J. STANLEY   Foxhunting Recollections, A Journal of the Radnor Hounds and Other Packs. Philadelphia, 1928. Illus. Baldwins' 51-552
1978 $15

REEVE, J. STANLEY   Foxhunting Recollections, A Journal of the Radnor
Hounds & Other Packs. Philadelphia, 1928. 1st ed., 1 of 250 special signed
copies, bound in 2-tone cloth, 8vo. Americanist 101-138 1978 $50

REEVE, J. STANLEY   Further Fox-hunting Recollections Including The
Great Lenape Run.... New York, 1935. 1st ed., 1 of 950 copies designed by
Melville E. Stone, printed at Harbor Press, 4to, orig. suede with leather labels.
Americanist 101-139 1978 $40

REEVE, J. STANLEY   Radnor Reminiscences. New York, 1921. Illus.
with photos and silhouettes by author. Baldwins' 51-553 1978 $15

REEVE, J. STANLEY   Radnor Reminiscences. A Foxhunting Journal.
Boston, 1921. Illus. MacManus 239-1654 1978 $17.50

REEVE, W. B.   Daughters of Nijo, a Romance of Japan... New
York, 1904. Illus., coloured plts. Hood 116-494 1978 $22.50

REEVES, J. H.   The Orange County Stud Book, Giving a History
of All Noted Stallions, Bred and Raised in Orange County. New York, 1880.
Illus., 8vo., orig. cloth, 1st ed. Morrill 241-419 1978 $12.50

REEVES, JAMES   Arcadian Ballads. Andoversford, 1977. 4to.,
one of 50 copies bound in leather with marbled end-papers, signed by author &
illus., drawings by Edward Ardizzone, new in slipcase, first English ed. Bell Book
16-477 1978 £60

A REEXAMINATION of the Evidence Concerning the Bay Psalm Book, and the
Eliot Indian Bible, as well as Other Contemporary Books and People. Philadel-
phia, The Cambridge Press, 1945. Illus., 8vo., half dark-green mor. Argosy
Special- 20 1978 $350

THE REFORM Movement. Washington, 1872. Double columns, later wrs. Hayman 73-628 1978 $7.50

REGAMEY, ANGES   Avec des Notices Analytiques par R. Zeller.
Paris, 1946. 4to., bds., plts., many in color. Van der Peet H-64-192 1978
Dfl 35

REGGIO, OCTAVIO   Meditationes Exercitiorum Sancti Patris Ignatii.
Panormi, 1742. 8vo., vellum, first ed., woodcut initials. King 7-220 1978 £15

REGIMEN SANITATIS SALERNITANUM   Regimen Sanitatis Salernitati. London,
1634. 4to., 19th cent. mor., some minor stains. Gurney 75-89 1978 £185

REGIMENTAL History of the 6th Royal Battalion.... Aldershot, 1935. Imp. 8vo.,
cloth. F. Edwards 1013-580 1978 £5

THE REGISTER of Pennsylvania. Devoted to the Preservation of Facts and Documents... Philadelphia, 1828-1834. 16 vols., all but 1 bound in orig. parchment-backed bds., contemp. calf, red. mor. label, good complete set. Mac-
Manus 239-1486 1978 $400

THE REGISTERS OF St. Bene't and St. Peter, Paul's Wharf, London. London,
1909-1912. 4 vols., thick roy. 8vo, full red morocco, extra gilt spines, gilt
edges, superb set. Traylen 88-453 1978 £30

THE REGISTERS Of St. Vedast, Foster Lane and of St. Michael le Quern.
London, 1902. Thick roy. 8vo, full red morocco, gilt extra, g.e. Traylen 88-
452 1978 £10

REGISTRES Des Baptesmes et Sepultures Qui Se Sont Faits Au Fort Duquesne Pendant
Les Annees 1753-56. Nouvelle York, 1859. Orig. cloth, 8vo, front end-paper
missing, only 100 copies printed. Edwards 1012-451 1978 £35

REGLAMENTO, E Instruccion Para Los Presidios Que Se Han De Formar En La
Linea De Frontera De La Nueva Espana. Mexico, 1773. Fine copy handsomely
boxed. Jenkins 116-1163 1978 $3,250

REGLAMENTO y Aranceles Reales Para el Comercio Libre de Espana a Indias de 12.
de Octubre de 1778. Madrid, (1779). 4to., contemp. calf, gilt, engrav. frontispiece. Wolfe 39-515 1978 $400

REGLAS y Constitvciones, qve han de gvardar los senores Inqvisidores,....
Mexico, 1659. Folio, woodcuts, modern quarter mor. Quaritch 978-105 1978
$1,750

REGNAULT, NOEL   Les Entretiens Physiques D'Ariste et D'Eudoxe....
Paris, 1750-55. 5 vols., 12mo., engrav. plts., contemp. calf, gilt spine, bindings wormed. Quaritch 977-133 1978 $160

REGNIER, H. DE   Le Miracle du Fil. Seize Sonnets de Henri de
Regnier et Seize Planches en Couleurs de Yan B. Dyl. Paris, n.d. Folio, coloured plts., vellum, orig. wrs. preserved, #3 of 16 copies on Japon of an ed. of
350, this copy with a signed autograph sonnet by Regnier. Quaritch 983-241 1978
$1,000

REHMANN, ELSA   The Small Place. New York, 1918. Front cover
stained, illus. Biblo 247-313 1978 $15

REIBISCH, FRIEDRICH MARTIN VON   Der Rittersaal. Stuttgart, 1842. Hand-
coloured plts., oblong 4to., orig. wrs., preserved in parchment-backed bds. F.
Edwards 1013-409 1978 £550

REICHEL, LEVIN T.   The Early History of the Church of the United
Brethren Commonly Called Moravians, in North America, 1734-48. Nazareth,
1888. Fine. MacManus 239-1655 1978 $30

REICHEL, WILLIAM C.   The Crown Inn Near Bethlehem, Pa. 1745...
N.P., 1872. Ltd. to 499 copies, nice copy, later cloth. MacManus 239-1656
1978 $25

REICHEL, WILLIAM C.   A History of the Rise, Progress, and Present Condition of the Bethlehem Female Seminary... Philadelphia, 1858. 1st ed., illus.,
orig. 3/4 calf and marbled bds., very good. MacManus 239-1657 1978 $30

REICHEL, WILLIAM C.   Linden Hall Moravian Seminary for Young Ladies,
at Litiz, Lancaster Co., Pa. Founded 1794. Philadelphia, 1863. Orig. printed
wrs., fine. MacManus 239-1658 1978 $8.50

REICHEL, WILLIAM C.   Memorials of the Moravian Church. Philadelphia, 1870. Vol. I, errata slip, fine. MacManus 239-1659 1978 $22.50

REICHENBACH, WILLIAM   Automatic Pistol Marksmanship. Onslow Co.,
(1937). Illus., 12mo., orig. limp cloth. Morrill 241-486 1978 $8.50

REID, ARTHUR   Reminiscences of the Revolution. Utica, 1859.
Prtd. wr., fine, 1st ed. Butterfield 21-383 1978 $35

REID, CHRISTIAN   The Picture of Las Cruces. 1896. First ed. Austin
82-784 1978 $20

REID, EDITH GITTLINGS   The Great Physican, A Short Life of Sir William
Osler. London, New York, Toronto, 1931. Hood's 115-667 1978 $15

REID, EDITH GITTLINGS   The Great Physician. London, 1931. D.j. Rittenhouse 49-669 1976 $10

REID, ERIC   Tanganyika Without Prejudice. London, 1834.
Cr. 8vo., map, frontis, orig. cloth. K Books 239-405 1978 £7

REID, ESCOTT   The Effect of the Depression on Canadian Politics,
1929-32. 1933. Hood's 115-317 1978 $10

REID, FORREST   A Garden by the Sea. Dublin, 1918. Very
nice. Desmarais B-541 1978 $15

REID, FORREST   The Garden God: a tale of two boys. 1905.
Parchment vellum bds. a little damp-stained, good, very scarce, first English ed.
Bell Book 17-768 1978 $65

REID, FORREST   Illustrators of the Sixties. 1928. Plts., roy.
8vo., covers marked. George's 635-47 1978 £50

REID, FORREST   The Milk of Paradise: Some thoughts on Poetry.
1946. First ed., spine faded, orig. cloth, 8vo. Howes 194-1118 1978 £5

REID, FORREST   Peter Waring. 1937. Fine, slightly worn d.w.,
first English ed. Bell Book 17-770 1978 $18.50

REID, G. ARCHDALL   The Principles of Heredity. London, 1905. 8vo.,
ex-lib., 1st ed. Morrill 239-218 1978 $10

REID, J. W.   History of the Fourth Regiment, S.C. Volunteers.
Greenville, 1892. Wrs. detached and chipped, Bell Wiley's copy. Broadfoot's
44-600 1978 $60

REID, JOHN   Essays on Insanity. London, 1816. 8vo., modern
library binder, lightly browned, good copy, rare 1st ed., 1st issue. Zeitlin 245-
209 1978 $150

REID, JOHN   The Life of Major General Andrew Jackson.
Phila., 1828. Binding poor, foxed, Bell Wiley's copy. Broadfoot's 44-750 1978
$10.00

REID, JOHN C.   The Scouting Expeditions of McCulloch's Texas
Rangers. Philadelphia, c.1870. Pictorial cloth. Jenkins 116-1164 1978 $35

REID, MAYNE   The Boy Slaves. Boston, 1865. Illus., orig.
cloth binding, faded & shaken. Eaton 45-411 1978 £5

REID, MAYNE   The Quadroon. London, (1856). 1st
1-vol. ed., orig. green stippled cloth, owner's name on title, very good or
better. Limestone 9-242 1978 $47.50

REID, R. R.   The King's Council in the North. 1921. Folding
map, rebound, clean, octavo. Upcroft 10-506 1978 £10

REID, THOMAS   Essays on the Intellectual Powers of Man. Edinburgh, 1785. Full contemp. calf, neatly rebacked, spine gilt, 1st ed., very good.
Bennett 7-90 1978 $300

REID, THOMAS MAYNE
Please turn to
REID, MAYNE

REID, THOMAS WEMYSS
Please turn to
REID, WEMYSS

REID, WEYMSS   The Life, Letters and Friendships of Richard Monckton Milnes. 1890. Portraits, 2 vols., orig. cloth, 8vo. Howes 194-1047
1978 £12.50

REID, WEYMSS   Life of the Rt. Honourable William Edward
Forster. 1889. Portrait, 8vo. George's 635-1241 1978 £5

REID, WHITELAW   Ohio in the War: Her Statesmen, Her Generals,
and Soldiers. Cincinnati, 1868. 2 vols., new clean, rebound. Hayman 71-134
1978 $45

REID, WHITELAW   Problems of Expansion as Considered in Papers and
Addresses. New York, 1900. Cloth. Hayman 72-658 1978 $7.50

REID, WILLIAM MAXWELL   Lake George and Lake Champlain... New
York, 1910. Thick royal 8vo., illus., fold. colored maps, bookplt., nice copy.
MacManus 239-413 1978 $37.50

REID, WILLIAM MAXWELL   The Story of Old Fort Johnson. New York,
1906. 8vo., illus., light stain bottom of spine, 1st ed., orig. cloth. Morrill
241-420 1978 $25

REID, WILLIAM MAXWELL   The Story of Old Fort Johnson. New York,
1906. Illus. MacManus 239-168 1978 $30

REIFFENSTUEL, JOHANN GEORF   Jus Canonicum Universum clara methodo
juxta titulus Quinque Librorum Decretalium. Venice, 1742. 6 vols. in 3, folio,
good, contemp. vellum, some foxing. Howes 194-572 1978 £60

REIMMANN, JACOB FREDERIC   Idea Sistematis Antiqvitatis Literariae Spect-
atoris Sive Aegypticae Adumbrati. Hillesheim, 1718. 8vo., vellum, first ed.
King 7-382 1978 £35

REINACH, SALOMON   Antiquites Nationales. Description Raisonnee du
Musee de Saint-Germain-en-Laye... Paris, (1889). Illus., 3/4 leather, edges
rubbed. Biblo BL781-464 1978 $24.50

REINACH, SALOMON   Orpheus. A History of Religions. New York,
(1930). Rev'd. ed., illus. Biblo BL781-465 1978 $12

REINACH, SALOMON   Repertoire des Vases Peints. Grecs et Etrusques.
Paris, 1923-24. 2 vols., 2nd ed., illus., orig. wrs. Biblo BL781-466 1978
$27.50

LA REINE Hortense en Italie, en France et en Angleterre Pendant l'Annee 1831. Paris, 1861. 8vo., orig. covers. Van der Peet H-64-353 1978 Dfl 45

REINHARD, J. R.   Mediaeval Pageant. 1939. Lettering on spine rubbed. Allen 234-1419 1978 $10

REINHARDT, MAX   25 Jahre Deutsches Theater. Muenchen, (1930). Illus., 4to., cloth, 1st ed. Argosy Special-75 1978 $45

REINHOLD, ERNST   Beitrag Zur Erlaeuterung Der Pythagorischen Metaphysik. Jena, 1827. 8vo., orig. wrs., uncut. Salloch 348-215 1978 $25

REITZ, DENEY   Commando. 1929. 1st. ed., 8vo, orig. cloth, spine faded, sm. mark on upper cover, otherwise good copy, pres. inscription to Winston Churchill. Sawyer 298-104 1978 £135

REITZ, DENEYS   Commando. London, 1932. 8vo, orig. cloth, folding map. K Books 239-407 1978 £6

RELACAO abbreviada da Republica, que os Religiosos Jesuiticas das Provincias de Portugal & Hespanha... N.p, n.d. (Lisbon, 1757). Sm. 8vo., new leath., fine. Paine 78-20 1978 $115.00

RELATION de ce qu' s'est Passe au Siege de Quebec, et de la Prise du Canada. (Quebec), 1855. Pamphlet, plt. Hood 117-146 1978 $40

RELATION Des Affaires Du Canada, en 1696. Nouvelle-York, 1865. Orig. cloth, 8vo, front-end paper missing. Edwards 1012-452 1978 £35

RELATION of Henri De Tonty Concerning the Explorations of Lasalle from 1678 to 1683. Chicago, 1898. Limited to 197 copies. Jenkins 116-797 1978 $125

RELATIONS de la Louisiane, et du Fleuve Mississippi. Amsterdam, 1720. Plts, full calf, large folding map, plt. (extra). Ginsberg 14-511 1978 $2,000

RELIGIOUS and Christian Advice to a Daughter. 1714. First ed., contemp. panelled calf, gilt, joints weak, 8vo. Howes 194-224 1978 £20

RELIGIOUS Progress on the Pacific Slope... Boston, 1917. Orig. cl., 1st ed. Ginsberg 16-834 1978 $15.00

REMAINS OF St. Mary's Abbey, Dublin, Their Explorations & Researches, A.D., 1886. Dublin, 1887. Wr., plts., good, reprint. Hyland 128-482 1978 £20

REMAK, ROBERT   Uber Methodische Electrisirung Gelahmter Muskeln. Berlin, 1855. 8vo., orig. yellow prtd. wrs., dust-soiled, frayed, browned, good copy, uncut, mostly unopened, 1st ed. Zeitlin 245-210 1978 $125

THE REMARKABLE Life of Dr. Faustus;.... London, n.d. (ca. 1820). 12mo, full polished calf, gilt, spine and inner dentelles gilt, hand-colored frontispiece by George Cruikshank, fine copy from Salomons collection, original blue printed wrappers bound in. Ximenes 47-96 1978 $125

REMARKS on Some Contents of a Letter Relating to the Divisions of the First Church in Salem. (Boston, 1735). 16mo., unbound, orig. cloth, 1st ed. Morrill 241-321 1978 $25

REMARKS Upon the Present Crisis Humbly Address'd to the Knights, Citizens and Burgesses to serve in the Present Parliament. 1736. Sm. 8vo., wrappers. F. Edwards 1013-410 1978 £10

REMARQUE, ERICH MARIA   The Road Back. Boston, 1931. 1st Amer. ed. Biblo BL781-1113 1978 $9

REMARQUES on the Humours and Conversations of the Town. London, 1673. 12mo., contemp sheep, head and tail of spine just torn and neatly repaired. Quaritch 978-133 1978 $575

REMBRANDT VAN RHIJN   Catalogue of Etchings and Dry Points. 1900. Frontis., 8vo., 1 of 210 copies, prtd. on Van Gelder handmade paper, bound in maroon cloth. Battery Park 1-143 1978 $75

REMBRANDT VAN RHIJN   The Complete Works of... History, Description and Heliographic Reproduction of all the Master's Pictures with a Study of His Life and His Art. Paris, 1897-1906. 8 vols., folio, fine set, half brown levant mor., 1 of 75 copies of De Luxe ed., ed. ltd. to 575 copies. Quaritch 983-242 1978 $1,900

THE REMEMBRANCER or, Impartial Repository of Public Events. London, 1776. Rebound. Nestler Rare 78-177 1978 $25

REMINGTON, FREDERIC   Crooked Trails. New York & London, 1898. Pic. cloth, illus. by author, 1st ed., scarce, very good copy, slipcase. Dykes 34-32 1978 $100

REMINGTON, FREDERIC   Crooked Trails. New York and London, 1898. 4to, 1st ed., orange-tan cloth with green pict. decor. on front cover, minimal water damage on bottom cover and top edge, very Good tight copy, illus. by author, collector's cond. Desmarais 1-351 1978 $50

REMINGTON, FREDERIC   Done in the Open. New York, 1902. Cloth & colored pic. bds., unpaged, 1st ed., 1st issue, very good copy, rare, slipcase. Dykes 34-33 1978 $250

REMINGTON, FREDERICK   Stories of Peace and War. New York and London, 1899. Hood's 115-453 1978 $17.50

REMINISCENCES of Scenes and Characters in College. New Haven, 1847. 1st ed., frontis., orig. cloth, fixed, but good copy. MacManus 239-539 1978 $15

REMONDINI, GIUSEPPE   Catalogus Librorum Amplissimus in Typographia Remondinjana Impressorum. Venetis, 1761. Sm. 8vo., soft bds., rare. King 7-221 1978 £100

A REMONSTRANCE Of the State of the Kingdom. London, 1641. Sm. 4to, contemp. white wrappers. Traylen 88-320 1978 £48

REMSBURG, GEORGE J.   Life of Charley Reynolds, Custer's Chief of Scouts. [Potter, 1914-1915]. Proof sheets, 1st ed., very scarce. Ginsberg 14-893 1978 $300

REMY, JULES   A Journey to Great-Salt-Lake City...With a Sketch of the History, Religion, and Customs of the Mormons... London, 1861. 2 vols., illus., map, half mor., 1st English ed. Ginsberg 14-891 1978 $175

REMY, JULES   Voyage au Pays des Mormons:.... Paris, 1860. 2 vols, bound in one, illus., map, half mor., 1st ed. Ginsberg 14-892 1978 $175

RENAN, ERNEST   The Song of Songs. Woodcuts, pict. bds., cloth spine, one of 100 copies on woodcut paper, #70, prtd. in black & orange. Battery Park 1-219 1978 $175

RENAUDOT, EUSEBE   A General Collection of Discourses...Upon... Philosophy, and Other Natural Knowledge. London, 1664-65. 2 vols. in I, sm. folio, full antique calf, gilt, marginal dampstaining, but very good copy, sm. stamp, contemp. signature on flyleaf, 1st ed. in English. Norman 5-240 1978 $950

RENFROW, W. C.   Oklahoma and the Cherokee Strip. Chicago, 1893. Folding map, pr. wr., 1st ed. Ginsberg 14-801 1978 $125

RENKER, ARMIN   Die Kulturgeschicte des Papiers. Insel-Verlag, 1950. Inscr'd & signed pres. copy to Max H. Schmidt, T.L.s, from Renker to Schmidt laid in, illus., samples of papers. Battery Park 1-456 1978 $225

RENKER, ARMIN   Die Reise Nach Filigranistan Eine Geschicte um die Wasserzeichen fur Kinder von zehn bis achtzig Jahren. Illus., 1 of 1000 copies, former library copy, very fine, library rubber stamp, illus. paper over bds. Battery Park 1-457 1978 $100

RENKER, ARMIN   Die Reise nach Filigranistan: Eine Geschichte um die Wasserzeichnen fur Kinder von zehn bis achtzig Jahren. (Mainz, n.d.). Decor. bds. in d.w., near mint, 1 of 1000 copies. Dawson's 447-136 1978 $20

RENNELL, J.   The Geographical System of Herodotus examined and explained by a comparison with those of other ancient Authors and with modern Geography. 1830. Portrait, maps, 2 vols., a little loose in case, covers rubbed. George's 635-472 1978 £7.50

RENNER, FREDERIC G.   A Selected Bibliography on Management of Western Ranges, Livestock, and Wildlife. Washington, D. C., 1938. Wrs., 1st ed., very good copy. Dykes 34-9 1978 $10

RENNIE, D. F.   Peking and the Pekingese During the First Year of the British Embassy at Peking. London, 1865. 1st. ed., 2 vols., cr.8vo, plts. & illus., folding map, orig. maroon cloth, gilt, spines repaired, lib. labels removed. Deighton 5-91 1978 £45

RENO, GEORGE   Buds & Flowers, Of Leisure Hours.   Philadelphia, 1844. 1st ed., tall thin 8vo, worn, orig. binding. Americanist 101-122 1978 $25

RENOUARD, P. V.   History of Medicine, from its Origin to the Nineteenth Century. Cincinnati, 1856. First ed. in English. Rittenhouse 49-671 1976 $35

RENOUARD DE SAINTE-CROIX, CARLOMAN LOUIS FRANCOIS FELIX, MARQUIS
Please turn to
SAINTE-CROIX, CARLOMAN L. F. F. RENOUARD, MARQUIS DE

RENOUF, P. LE PAGE   Lectures on the Origin and Growth of Religion as Illustrated by the Religion of Ancient Egypt. London, 1879. 8vo, orig. cloth, little dusty. K Books 239-408 1978 £7

RENWICK, ROBERT   History of Glasgow. Glasgow, 1921-34. 3 vols., maps, plts., roy. 8vo., covers of vol. 2 a little marked, very good, orig. cloth. K Books 244-435 1978 £22

RENZIUS, RUDY   Hammered Silver Flatware. Toronto, 1945. Illus. Hood 116-195 1978 $7.50

REORGANIZATION of the Legislative Power of Utah Territory.... Washington, 1884. Disbound, 1st ed. Ginsberg 14-1012 1978 $15

REPERTOIRE des Societes anonymes indochinoises. Hanoi, 1944. Large 8vo, tables, orig. covers. Van der Peet 127-199 1978 Dfl 55

REPLY of the Delegates of the Cherokee Nation to the Panphlet of the Commissioner of Indian Affairs. Washington, 1866. Disbound, 1st ed. Ginsberg 14-237 1978 $75

REPPLIER, AGNES   Agnes Irwin. New York, 1935. 1st ed., orig. cloth, frontis. port., signed by Irwin and Repplier. MacManus 239-772 1978 $10

REPPLIER, AGNES   Counter-Currents. Boston, 1916. First ed., pencil writing on fly leaf, good. Biblo 247-615 1978 $10

REPPLIER, AGNES   In Pursuit of Laughter. Boston, 1936. 1st ed., very good, slightly frayed d.w. Biblo BL781-1115 1978 $10

REPTON, HUMPHRY   The Art of Landscape Gardening.... Boston, 1907. 8vo, orig. cloth. Book Chest 17-298 1978 $60

REPTON, HUMPHRY   Sketches and Hints on Landscape Gardening. London, (1794). 1st. ed., aquatint plts., 10 coloured, oblong folio, edges uncut, orig. bds., new calf spine. Traylen 88-618 1978 £1600

REQUA, RICHARD S.   Old World Inspiration For American Architecture. Los Angeles, 1929. 144 plts., sm. folio. Baldwins' 51-145 1978 $17.50

RERESBY, JOHN   The Memoirs of .... 1875. Octavo, good. Upcroft 10-148 1978 £5

RERSBY, TAMWORTH   A Miscellany of Ingenious Thoughts and Reflections, In Verse and Prose... 1721. 4to, contemp. panelled calf, later rebacked. Eaton 45-412 1978 £40

THE RESOURCES and Attractions of San Luis County, California:.... San Luis, 1887. Original pictorial wr., 1st ed. Ginsberg 14-181 1978 $60

RESOURCES of New Mexico. Santa Fe, 1881. Orig. cloth, 1st ed. Ginsberg 14-775 1978 $175

RESOURCES of San Benito County, California:.... Hollister, 1887. Original printed wr., 1st ed. Ginsberg 14-182 1978 $50

THE RESOURCES of the State of Oregon, Revised;.... Salem, 1892. Folding colored map, orig. pr. wr., cloth case. Ginsberg 14-848 1978 $45

RESPONSE a une Adresse de L'Assemblee Legislative, en Date du 16 Mars, 1857- Demandant Copie des Chartres, Permis et Autres Documents en Vertu Desquels, L'Honorable Compagnie de la Baie D'Hudson Pretend a la Propriete du Territoire de la Baie D'Hudson, et de Toutes Cartes y Relatives en la Possession du Gouvernement. Victoria, 1857. Half mor. Ginsberg 14-847 1978 $300

RESTIF DE LA BRETONNE, NICHOLAS EDME   Monsieur Nicolas. 1883. 14 vols., portr., qtr. mor., 8vo. George's 635-1474 1978 £35

RESTIF DE LA BRETONNE, NICHOLAS EDME   Monsieur Nicolas. 1930-31. Portr., plts., 6 vols., roy. 8vo., orig. buckram, a little soiled. George's 635-922 1978 £25

RESTON, JAMES B.   Prelude to Victory. 1942. Austin 80-266 1978 $7.50

RESULT of a Mutual Ecclesiastical Council, Convened at Worcester, Nov. 14, 1820, to Consider the Expediency of Granting the Request of the Rev. Charles A. Goodrich to be Dismissed from the Pastoral Care of the First Church and Parish in Worcester. Worcester, 1820. Sewn. Hayman 73-649 1978 $8.50

RETINGER, J. H.   Conrad and His Contemporaries. New York, 1943. Very fine in d.w. Desmarais B-156 1978 $15

RETURN of Casualties in the Union Forces From the Wilderness to the James River, May-June 1864. N.P., 1864. Wrs., Bell Wiley's copy. Broadfoot 46-212 1978 $9

RETURN Of The Number of Agricultural Labourers Who With Their Families Have Emigrated to New South Wales and Van Diemen's Land... 1835. Sm. Folio, sewn as issued. Edwards 1012-330 1978 £60

RETURN to an Address of the Legislative Assembly for Copies of Certain Seigniorial Documents. Quebec, 1853. Printed wrappers. Wolfe 39-499 1978 $100

RETZIUS, GUSTAF MAGNUS   Anthropologia Suecica. Stockholm, 1902. Folio, maps, plts. in color, orig. half simulated lea., gilt lettered, fine copy, 1st ed. Zeitlin 245-211 1978 $110

RETZIUS, GUSTAF MAGNUS   Crebra Simiarum Illustrata. Stockholm, Jena, 1906. Folio, plts., orig. 3/4 white simulated lea., gilt on spine, as new with d.w., slipcase, 1st ed. Zeitlin 245-213 1978 $250

RETZIUS, GUSTAF MAGNUS   Finska Kranier Jamte Nagra Natur-Och Literatur-Studier Inom Nadra Omraden Af Finsk Antropologi. Stockholm, 1878. Folio, plts., illus., orig. bds. with vignette illus. on covers, gilt on spine, very good copy, 1st ed. Zeitlin 245-214 1978 $75

RETZIUS, GUSTAF MAGNUS   Das Menschenhirn, Studien in Der Makroskopischen Morphologie. Stockholm, 1896. 2 vols., folio, illus., plts., tissue guardsheet, orig. half white composition lea., gilt on spines, fine set, as new, pristine cond., d.w., 1st ed. Zeitlin 245-216 1978 $750

REUSNER, NICOLAS 1545-1602   Symbola Heroica in Tribus Classibus. London, 1664. 12mo., contemp. sheep, inner hinges cracked. Howes 194-87 1978 £15

REVERDY, PIERRE   Au Soleil du Plafond. Paris, 1955. Folio, in sheets, uncut, in orig. pict. wr., slipcover & case, ltd. ed. issued in 220 copies, numbered copy on velin d'Arches paper. Goldschmidt 110-25 1978 $850

REVIEW of Lysander Spooner's Essay on the Unconstitutionality of Slavery. Boston, 1847. Some ink underscorings, disbound. Biblo 247-96 1978 $15

A REVIEW of Some of the Arguments Which are Commonly Advanced Against Parliamentary Interference in Behalf of the Negro Slaves. London, 1823. 8vo, disbound, 1st ed., presentation copy, inscribed "from the author". Ximenes 47-292 1978 $60

REVIEW of the Problem of the Northmen and the Site of Norumbega by Professor Olson of Madison University, Wisconsin, and a Reply by Eben Norton Horsford. N.P., (ca. 1891). 4to., orig. wrs. Morrill 241-209 1978 $10

REVISED Regulations for the Army of the United States 1861. Philadelphia, 1861. Cover crudely taped, Bell Wiley's copy. Broadfoot 46-213 1978 $25

THE REVIVAL of Printing. (London, 1912). 8vo, holland boards and cloth, paper labels, g.t., corners slightly rubbed, front inner hinge tender, 1 of 350 copies, fine. Duschnes 220-253 1978 $75

REVOIL, B. H.   Les Harems du Nouveau Monde-vie des Femmes Chez les Mormons. Paris, 1856. Half mor., 1st ed. Ginsberg 14-1107 1978 $75

REVOLUTIONARY Attempts to Maintain in the House of Representatives its Fraudeulently Elected Members... Washington, 1882. Stitched as issued, sm. piece missing from corner of 1st. leaf, affecting a few letters, tiny hole in one leaf, affecting a few letters. Hayman 71-676 1978 $7.50

THE REVOLUTIONARY Diplomatic Correspondence of the U.S.... 1889. Good, solid set. Nestler Rare 78-184 1978 $55

REWALD, JOHN   The History of Impressionism. New York, (1946). Sm. 4to., plts., many in color. Biblo BL781-720 1978 $12

REY, P.   Dans le Golfe de Siam; les bioussards. Paris, 1907. 3rd ed., 8vo, orig. covers. Van der Peet 127-200 1978 Dfl 45

REYBURN, H. A.   Nietzsche. The Story of a Human Philosopher. London, 1948. 8vo., cloth. Salloch 348-175 1978 $17.50

REYBURN, W.   Some of It was Fun. Toronto, 1949. Illus. by Peter Whalley. Hood 117-147 1978 $15

REYNARD, OVIDE   Album Alphabetique de 500 Lettres Ornees Tirees des Manuscrits des Bibliotheques d'Europe. Paris, n.d. (c. 1880). 8vo., orig. pr. wrs., half cloth. Schumann 511-49 1978 sFr 420

REYNER, EDWARD   A Treatise of the Necessity of Humane Learning for a Gospel Preacher... London, 1663. 8vo., contemp. calf, rebacked, inscription on flyleaf. Salloch 348-221 1978 $75

REYNOLDS, ALEXANDER JACOB   From the Ivory Coast to the Cameroons. London, 1929. 8vo, orig. cloth, folding map, illus., good, ex-lib. K Books 239-409 1978 £5

REYNOLDS, CUYLER   Hudson-Mohawk Genealogical and Family Memoirs. New York, 1911. 4 vols., 4to., engr. portrs., bds. & lea., near fine. Butterfield 21-195 1978 $85

REYNOLDS, EDWARD 1599-1676   Three Treatises of The Vanity of the Creature. 1631. First ed., sm. 4to., 19th cent. calf, very good. Howes 194-88 1978 £42

REYNOLDS, ELDER GEORGE   The Myth of the "Manuscript Found," or the Absurdities of the "Spaulding Story". Salt Lake City, 1883. Clean, orig. binding, front cover little flecked, former owner's name boldly written on title-page. Hayman 71-481 1978 $20

REYNOLDS, FREDERICK   The Free Knights; or, The Edict of Charlemagne. 1810. 1st. ed., 8vo, disbound, title & last page dust-soiled. Hannas 54-248 1978 £5

REYNOLDS, FREDERICK   How to Grow Rich: A Comedy. 1793. 1st. ed., 8vo, disbound. Hannas 54-249 1978 £6

REYNOLDS, FREDERICK   Laugh When You Can: A Comedy. Dublin, 1799. 1st. Irish ed., 12mo, wrapper, nice copy. Fenning 32-282 1978 £7.50

REYNOLDS, HELEN WILKINSON   Dutch Houses in the Hudson Valley before 1776. New York, 1929. Thick 4to., gravure plts., fldg. map, blue & orange cloth, orig. jacket & box, mint copy. Butterfield 21-61 1978 $85

REYNOLDS, HELEN WILKINSON   Dutch Houses in the Hudson Valley Before 1776. New York, 1929. 4to, photos, introduction by F.D. Roosevelt. Baldwins' 51-417 1978 $75

REYNOLDS, HELEN WILKINSON   Dutch Houses in the Hudson Valley Before 1776. New York, 1929. 1st ed., thick 4to., illus., very fine, orig. cloth. MacManus 239-698 1978 $85

REYNOLDS, HELEN WILKINSON   Dutchess County Doorways and Other Examples of Period-Work in Wood 1730-1830. New York, 1931. 4to., numbered plts., prtd. on two sides, very fine, glassine dust jacket, box. Butterfield 21-62 1978 $75

REYNOLDS, HELEN WILKINSON   Dutchess County Doorways, & Other Examples of Period Work in Wood 1730-1830. 1931. Illus., map, very good. Nestler Rare 78-137 1978 $65

REYNOLDS, HELEN WILKINSON   The Records of Christ Church, Poughkeepsie, New York. Poughkeepsie, 1911. Cloth. Hayman 73-482 1978 $12.50

REYNOLDS, J. N.   Voyage of the U. S. Frigate Potomac... New York, 1845. Plts., orig. cloth, badly foxed, 8vo. Edwards 1012-37 1978 $50

REYNOLDS, JOHN   My Own Times, Embracing also the History of My Life. Belleville, 1855. Orig. cloth, 1st ed., very scarce. Ginsberg 14-681 1978 $300

REYNOLDS, JOHN E.   In French Creek Valley. Meadville, 1938. Illus., maps. MacManus 239-1661 1978 $25

REYNOLDS, JOHN N.   The Twin Hells. Chicago, (1890). Clean, orig. binding. Hayman 71-677 1978 $12.50

REYNOLDS, JOHN S.   Reconstruction in South Carolina 1865-1877. Columbia, 1905. Cover speckled, Bell Wiley's copy. Broadfoot's 44-929 1978 $50

REYNOLDS, JOSHUA   A Discourse Delivered to the Students of the Royal Academy on the Distribution of the Prizes, December 10, 1970. 1791. 4to., 1st ed., contemp. marbled wrs., back worn, some staining, pres copy from Reynolds with inscr. in his hand. Quaritch 979-273 1978 $180

REYNOLDS, JOSHUA   The Literary Works of... 1819. 3 vols., 8vo., port., and plt., both spotted, contemp. bds., cloth spines, worn, uncut. Quaritch 983-244 1978 $50

REYNOLDS, JOSHUA   Seven Discourses Delivered in the Royal Academy by the President. London, 1778. Old full calf, spine worn, 1st ed., slightly foxed, otherwise very good. MacManus 238-138 1978 $160

REYNOLDS, JOSHUA   Seven Discourses Delivered in the Royal Academy by the President. 1778. 1st. ed., half title, orig. calf, red label, fine. Jarndyce 16-179 1978 £70

REYNOLDS, JOSHUA   The Works of .... 1801. 3 vols., 8vo, portrait, contemp. half calf, 2 leaves loose, 3rd. ed. Hannas 54-250 1978 £25

REYNOLDS, JOSHUA   The Works of ... 1809. 3 vols., 8vo, portrait, contemp. half calf, 4th. ed. Hannas 54-251 1978 £25

REYNOLDS, HUGHES   The Coosa River Valley from De Soto to Hydro-electric Power. Cynthiana, 1944. Illus., d.j. MacManus 239-1856 1978 $22.50

REYNOLDS, HUGHES   The Coosa River Valley from DeSoto to Hydro-electric Power. Kentucky, 1944. Bell Wiley's copy. Broadfoot's 44-864 1978 $25.00

REYNOLDS, REGINALD   Og and other Ogres. 1946. Drawings by Quentin Crisp, very good, d.w., first English ed. Bell Book 16-202 1978 £6

RHEA, LINDA   Hugh Swinton Legare. Chapel Hill, 1934. Bell Wiley's copy. Broadfoot's 44-930 1978 $12.00

RHEEDE TOT DRAAKESTEIN, HENDRIK ADRIAN VAN   Hortus Indicus Malabaricus. Amsterdam, 1678, 1679, 1682, 1673, (i.e. 1683?). Plates, bound in 2 vols., calf worn, three covers detached and fourth hinge weak. Dawson's 127-313 1978 $17.50

RHEES, J. R.   Diversions of a Bookworm. Battery Park 1-256 1978 $25

RHEES, J. R.   Pleasures of a Bookworm. Battery Park 1-265 1978 $22.50

RHEINWALD, G. F. H.   The Protestant Exiles of Zillertal. 1840. Sm. 8vo., orig. cloth, frontispiece. P. M. Hill 142-27 1978 £8

RHETT, ROBERT G.   Charleston. An Epic of Carolina. Richmond, (1940). Illus., d.j., 4to. MacManus 239-1859 1978 $27.50

RHIND, W. G.   The Tabernacle in the Wilderness. 1842. 2nd ed., hand-coloured engraved plts., rear endpapers defective, folio, orig. cloth. George's 635-1120 1978 £18

RHOADS, SAMUEL N.   Botanica Neglecta. Philadelphia, 1916. Pub. in Paris, 1783. MacManus 239-414 1978 $20

RHOADS, THOMAS L.   My Ancestry...Boyertown, Pa. Reading, 1938. 1st ed., scarce, orig. bind. Petrilla 13-82 1978 $15

RHODES, EBENEZER   Yorkshire Scenery. 1826. First ed., plts., tall 8vo., orig. cloth. Howes 194-1402 1978 £20

RHODES, EUGENE MANLOVE   The Little World Waddies. El Paso, 1946. 1000 copies prtd., pic. cloth, map end sheets, illus., 1st ed., very good copy, slipcase. Dykes 34-65 1978 $65

RHODES, F.   Pageant of the Pacific... (1934). Portrait, 2 vols., imp. 8vo, orig. cloth, signed by author. Edwards 1012-343 1978 £45

RHODES, JAMES FORD   History of the United States From the Compromise of 1850 to the Final Restoration of Homes Rule at the South in 1877. New York, 1906. 7 vols. Baldwins' 51-14 1978 $42.50

RHODES, MAY DAVIDSON   The Hired Man on Horseback: My Story of Eugene Manlove Rhodes. Boston, 1938. Illus., orig. cloth, d.j., 1st ed. Ginsberg 14-894 1978 $35

RHODES, WILLIAM BARNES   Bombastes Furioso. London, 1830. 1st ed., woodcuts, contemporary 3/4 leather with both wrappers bound in, light tip rubbing. Victoria 34-202 1978 $30

RHYS, ERNEST   The Life of Saint David. Newtown, (1927). Quarto, limp vellum, gilt, orig. publisher's slipcase, wood engravings hand colored, fine. Duschnes 220-132 1978 $500

RHYS, ERNEST   Thirty and One Stories. London, 1923. First ed., orig. binding, spine faded, very good. Rota 211-22 1978 £6

RIBADENFYRA, PEDRO DE 1527-1611
Please turn to
RIVADENEIRA, PEDRO DE 1527-1611

RIBBELL, W. R.   A German Traveller in Upper Canada in 1837... n.d. Hood 116-772 1978 $7.50

RIBEYRO, J.   Histoire De L'Isle De Ceylan... Amsterdam, 1701. 1st. published ed., folding map, folding plts., 12mo, contemp. bds., red morocco, spine gilt, uncut. Edwards 1012-129 1978 £60

RIBOT, THEODORE   Experimentelle Psychologie der Gegenwart in Deutschland. Branschweig, 1881. Covers detached, spine chipped. Rittenhouse 49-672 1976 $15

RICARDO, DAVID   Proposals for an Economical and Secure Currency. London, 1816. Modern bds., very good, large copy, first ed. Rota 212-49 1978 £65

RICAULT, PAUL   Istoria delle Stato Presente dell' Impero Ottomano. Venetia, 1672. 4to., soft bds., illus., good uncut copy. King 7-92 1978 £100

RICCI, CORRADO   Beatrice Cenci. New York, 1925. Illus., 2 vols., black cloth, 1st ed. in English, dust jackets, scarce. Bradley 49-276 1978 $15

RICCI, CORRADO   Santi Ed Artisti. Bologna, (1910). 2nd ed., illus. Biblo BL781-721 1978 $9

RICCI, JAMES V.   The Genealogy of Gynaecology. Philadelphia, 1943. Rittenhouse 49-673 1976 $35

RICCI, SEYMOUR DE   The Book Collector's Guide. Philadelphia & New York, 1921. 1st ed., orig. green cloth, upper hinge starting, else very good or better, errata leaf present, No. 535 of 1,100 numbered copies. Limestone 9-80 1978 $85

RICCI, SEYMOUR DE   A Census of Caxtons. 1909. Frontis., 4to., newly rebound, wr. bound in. Battery Park 1-362 1978 $100

RICCI, SEYMOUR DE   English Collectors of Books & Manuscripts. Cambridge, 1930. 1st ed., illus., orig. blue cloth, lower portion of upper cover affected by moisture, else very good or better. Limestone 0-81 1978 $30

RICCIOLI, GIAMB ATTISTA   Astronomiae reformatae tomi duo,.... Bologna, 1665. Rare 1st ed., folio, 2 parts in one vol., engraved maps, old vellum, fine. Gilhofer 75-91 1978 SFr 1,400

RICE, A. H.   The Shennandoah Pottery. 1929. Limited ed., illus., light wear on binding. Nestler Rare 78-208 1978 $55

RICE, A. H.   Shenandoah Pottery. Strasburg, 1929. Illus. with photos. Baldwins' 51-146 1978 $47.50

RICE, DAVID TALBOT   Russian Icons. London, 1947. Colored plts., 12mo., orig. bds., fine. Morrill 241-487 1978 $7.50

RICE, EDMUND   Statement of the St. Paul and Chicago Railway Co.,.... St. Paul, 1867. Map, original printed wrappers, 1st ed. Ginsberg 14-569 1978 $100

RICE, ELMER   A Voyage to Purilla. New York, 1930. 1st ed. Biblo 251-491 1978 $15

RICE, HARVEY   Sketches of Western Reserve Life. Cleveland, 1885. 1st ed., inscribed by author, illus. MacManus 239-381 1978 $25

RICE, J. H.   Collectanea Oratoria. 1808. Thk. cr. 8vo., orig. bds., entirely uncut, woodcut frontis. Howes 194-433 1978 £15

RICE, JESSIE PEARL   J.L.M. Curry. NY, 1949. Bell Wiley's copy. Broadfoot's 44-700 1978 $12.00

RICE, N. L.   Correspondence Between the Believers in the Harmonial Philosophy in St. Louis and.... Cincinnati, 1854. Wrps., minor underlining on front wrapper. Hayman 71-521 1978 $12.50

RICE, NATHAN P.   Trials of a Public Benefactor, as Illustrated in the Discovery of Etherization. New York, 1859. 8vo., nice, 1st ed., sm. broadside tipped in. Morrill 239-220 1978 $75

RICE, WILLIAM W.   Pacific Railroad Commission. Washington, 1878. Orig. pr. wr., 1st ed. Ginsberg 14-867 1978 $15

RICH, E. G.   Hans the Eskimo... Boston and New York, 1934. Illus. by Rockwell Kent. Hood's 115-78 1978 $25

RICH, EDWIN ERNEST, ED.
Please turn to
HUDSON'S BAY COMPANY

RICH, M. B.   History of the First 100 Years in Woolrich, Pa., 1830-1930. N.P., 1930. Illus. MacManus 239-1662 1978 $37.50

RICH, OBADIAH   Bibliotheca Americana Nova. A Catalogue of Books in Various Languages, Relating to Americana, Printed Since the Year 1700. London and New York, 1835. Rebound, 1st ed., 1 of 250 copies. MacManus 238-1031 1978 $50

RICHARD DE BURY
Please turn to
AUNGERVILLE, RICHARD

RICHARD, J. FRAISE   The Florence Nightingale of the Southern Army Experiences of Mrs. Ella K. Newsom, Confederate Nurse in the Great War. NY, 1914. Bell Wiley's copy. Broadfoot's 44-313 1978 $35.00

RICHARDS, IVOR ARMSTRONG   Science and Poetry. 1926. 12mo., cloth-backed bds., covers dull, good, 1st Eng. ed. Bell Book 16-743 1978 £4.50

RICHARDS, J. M.   The Castles on the Ground. The Architectural Press, 1946. Plts. by John Piper, very good, first English ed. Bell Book 17-982 1978 £15

RICHARDS, JOSEPH HAVEN   A Loyal Life. St. Louis, 1913. Orig. binding, clean. Hayman 71-579 1978 $15

RICHARDS, JOHN W.   Penn's Lutheran Forerunners and Friends or Two Hundred and Fifty Years Ago. Columbus, n.d. (1926). Cloth. Hayman 73-652 1978 $7.50

RICHARDS, LAURA E.   The Golden Windows. Boston, 1903. Ownership inscription, very fine. Desmarais B-547 1978 $7.50

RICHARDS, R. D.   The Early History of Banking in England. (1929), reprint 1958. Octavo, good. Upcroft 10-511 1978 £6.50

RICHARDS, THOMAS   Antiquae Linguae Britannicae Thesaurus... Bristol, 1759. Orig. calf, red label, hinges weakening, v.g. Jarndyce 16-71 1978 £54

RICHARDS, THOMAS, LIBRARIAN   A History of the Puritan Movement in Wales 1639-1653. 1920. Octavo, good. Upcroft 10-512 1978 £7.50

RICHARDS, THOMAS, LIBRARIAN   Wales Under the Penal Code (1662-1687).
1925. Octavo, good.   Upcroft 10-513 1978 £6.50

RICHARDS, WALTER   Her Majesty's Army. (c. 1895). Coloured plts.,
vignettes, 3 vols., 4to., half calf. F. Edwards 1013-411 1978 £100

RICHARDS, WALTER   His Majesty's Territorial Army. (c. 1910). 4
vols., 4to., orig. cloth, coloured plts. & frontis. F. Edwards 1013-412 1978
£80

RICHARDS, WILLIAM C.   The Last Billionaire. New York, 1948. Biblo
251-37 1978 $15

RICHARDSON, ALBERT D.   A Personal History of Ulysses S. Grant... Hartford, 1885. Illus., maps. Hayman 72-662 1978 $10

RICHARDSON, BENJAMIN WARD   Diseases of Modern Life. New York, 1883.
Rittenhouse 49-674 1976 $10

RICHARDSON, BENJAMIN WARD   On Alcohol: A Course of Six Cantor Lectures Delivered Before the Society of Arts. New York, 1876. Orig. binding,
clean. Hayman 71-678 1978 $10

RICHARDSON, DOROTHY   Interim. 1919. Spine little faded, very good,
first English ed. Bell Book 16-744 1978 £15

RICHARDSON, DOROTHY M.   Dawn's Left Hand. 1931. 1st. ed., orig. cloth,
covers lightly marked. Eaton 45-413 1978 £7.50

RICHARDSON, DOROTHY M.   Revolving Lights. New York, 1923. 1st. U.S.
ed., orig. cloth. Eaton 45-415 1978 £5

RICHARDSON, DOROTHY M.   Revolving Lights. 1923. 1st. ed., orig. cloth,
spine marked, bookplt. Eaton 45-414 1978 £6

RICHARDSON, E. RAMSAY   Little Aleck, a Life of Alexander H. Stephens.
New York, 1932. Bell Wiley's copy. Broadfoot 46-214 1978 $18

RICHARDSON, E. RAMSAY   Little Aleck, a Life of Alexander H. Stephens.
Pres. copy from author, Bell Wiley's copy. Broadfoot 46-214a 1978 $25

RICHARDSON, EDGAR PRESTON   Washington Allston. (1948). 4to., illus.,
orig. cloth, d.j., fine. MacManus 239-635 1978 $30

RICHARDSON, EDGAR PRESTON   Washington Allston, a Study of the Romantic
Artist in America. Chicago, (1948). 1st ed., fine, d.w., sm. 4to., illus.
Biblo 247-302 1978 $32.50

RICHARDSON, HENRY HANDEL   Christkindleins Wiengenlied. London, 1931.
Decor. paper covers, fine, no. 148 of 250 copies, signed, 1st ed., collector's
cond. Desmarais 1-353 1978 $10

RICHARDSON, HENRY HANDEL   The Fortunes of Richard Mahoney. London,
(1930). Blue cloth, 1st collected ed., fine in dust jacket. Bradley 49-277 1978
$20

RICHARDSON, HENRY HANDEL   The Fortunes of Richard Mahony. London,
1930. Very fine, d.w. chipped. Desmarais B-543 1978 $20

RICHARDSON, HENRY HANDEL   Two Studies. London, 1931. 8vo., bds.,
cloth back, uncut, near mint, ed. ltd. to 500 signed copies, this copy signed but
out of series, 1st ed., collector's cond. Desmarais 1-354 1978 $20

RICHARDSON, HESTER DORSEY   Side-lights on Maryland History, with Sketches
of Early Maryland Families. Baltimore, 1913. 1st ed., uncut, 2 vols., fine set,
scarce. MacManus 239-1841 1978 $50

RICHARDSON, I.   Wealth with the Wind Up. 1935. 1st ed.,
signed pres. copy, very good. Hyland 128-429 1978 £4

RICHARDSON, J.   "The Church Catechism". London, 1712. Orig.
full tooled calf, fine copy, 12mo. Baldwins' 51-335 1978 $75

RICHARDSON, JAMES   Travels in the Great Desert of Sahara, in the
Years 1845 and 1846. London, 1848. 2 vols., frontispieces, both waterstained,
folding map, text-illus., old style half calf, 8vo. K Books 239-410 1978 £60

RICHARDSON, JAMES   Travels in the Great Desert of Sahara, In the
Years of 1845- 46. London, 1848. 1st. ed., 2 vols., 8vo, engraved portrait,
engraved plts., map, woodcut illus., half calf, gilt backs. Deighton 5-21 1978
£65

RICHARDSON, JAMES   Wonders of the Yellowstone. New York, 1873.
Cloth, slightly rubbed. Hayman 73-653 1978 $15

RICHARDSON, JAMES D.   Messages and Papers of the Confederacy.
Nashville, 1905. New cloth, 2 vols., Bell Wiley's copy. Broadfoot's 44-314
1978 $25

RICHARDSON, JOHN   Eight Years in Canada. Montreal, 1847. Autograph pres. inscription from author, orig. binding. Wolfe 39-483 1978 $200

RICHARDSON, JOHN   Movements of the British Legion. London, 1837.
Second ed., illus., autograph signature of Strachan Bethune, orig. binding. Wolfe
39-482 1978 $75

RICHARDSON, JOHN   The Polar Regions. Edinburgh, 1861. Folding
map, orig. cloth, 8vo., cover soiled. Edwards 1012-602 1978 £20

RICHARDSON, LEON BURR   History of Dartmouth College. Hanover, 1932.
1st ed., 2 vols., orig. cloth, fine set. MacManus 239-110 1978 $22.50

RICHARDSON, M. T.   Practical Blacksmithing... New York, 1901-
1903. 2 vols., clean, orig. binding. Hayman 71-680 1978 $12.50

RICHARDSON, RUPERT NORVAL   The Comanche Barrier to South Plains Settlement. Glendale, 1933. 1st ed., illus., orig. cloth, fine. MacManus 239-
1212 1978 $35

RICHARDSON, RUPERT NORVAL   Texas, The Lone Star State. New York,
1943. Author's card laid in, Bell Wiley's copy. Broadfoot's 44-972 1978 $10

RICHARDSON, SAMUEL   Clarisse Harlowe. Geneva, 1785-86. Plts. by
Chodowiecki, 10 vols., demy 8vo., orig. olive bds., printed labels, entirely unpressed and uncut, fine. Howes 194-1403 1978 £175

RICHARDSON, SAMUEL   Clarissa Harlowe. London, (1868). New ed.,
pic. glazed boards, "yellow-back" format, binding damaged. Greene 78-96
1978 $25

RICHARDSON, SAMUEL   The Correspondence. 1804. 1st. ed., 6 vols.,
folding coloured frontis, portrait, folding plts., orig. tree calf, spines little rubbed,
lacking labels, otherwise fine. Jarndyce 16-964 1978 £110

RICHARDSON, SAMUEL   Grandison. 1781. 7th. ed., 7 vols., half title,
engraved frontis in all vols., calf, gilt borders, red labels, a.e.g., v.g. Jarndyce 16-180 1978 £35

RICHARDSON, W.   The Chemical Principles of the Metallic Arts.
Birmingham, 1790. 8vo., half calf, tables, orig. ed. Gurney 75-90 1978 £90

RICHARDSON, W. D.   The Texas Almanac for 1859. Galveston, 1858.
Lacks back wr. Jenkins 116-1321 1978 $225

RICHARDSON, W. D.   The Texas Almanac for 1861. Galveston, 1860.
Cloth binding, lacking wr. Jenkins 116-1322 1978 $225

RICHARDSON, W. D.   The Texas Almanac for 1867. Galveston, 1866.
Bound in cloth with leather label, lacking wr. Jenkins 116-1323 1978 $150

RICHARDSON, WILLIAM   Essays on Shakespeare's Dramatic Characters.
1812. Contemp. calf gilt, lettering piece, 8vo., sixth ed. Howes 194-458 1978
£16.50

RICHARDSON, WILLIAM   Essays on Some of Shakespeare's Dramatic Characters. 1797. 5th. ed., half green calf, slightly rubbed, labels, v.g. Jarndyce 16-181 1978 £16.50

RICHARDSON, WILLIAM L.   The Duties and Conduct of Nurses in Private
Nursing. Leadenhall Press, 1887. Sm. sq. 8vo., bds., first English ed. Bell
Book 16-551 1978 £10

RICHEBOURG, E.   Nagedachtenis. Amsterdam, n.d. (ab. 1930).
Sm. 8vo., fine green calf, richly gilt tooled front cover, a.e.g., text illus., nice
attractive binding, contents browned. Van der Peet H-64-382 1978 Dfl 75

RICHEY, A. G.   Lectures on the History of Ireland to 1534. 1869.
1st ed., 2 vols., cover dull, octavo bound in cloth. Hyland 128-433 1978 £9

RICHEY, A. G.   A Short History of the Irish People Down to the
Date of the Plantation of Ulster. 1887. 1st ed., very good, octavo bound in cloth.
Hyland 128-431 1978 £9

RICHEY, A. G.   A Short History of the Irish People Down to the
Date of the Plantation of Ulster. 1887. 1st ed., bottom of cover stained, good,
octavo bound in cloth. Hyland 128-432 1978 £4

RICHEY, HOMER   Memorial History of the John Bowie Strange Camp,
United Confederate Veterans. Bell Wiley's copy. Broadfoot 46-391a 1978 $20

RICHEY, HOMER   Memorial History of the John Bowie Strange Camp,
United Confederate Veterans. Charlottesville, 1920. Bell Wiley's copy. Broadfoot 46-391 1978 $35

RICHMOND, MRS. I. L.   In My Lady's Garden. Philadelphia, n.d.
Illus., 8vo., ex-lib. Morrill 241-494 1978 $7.50

RICHMOND, JOHN FRANCIS New York and Its Institutions, 1609-1873. New
York, 1873. "Revised ed.", ads, illus., four-leaf clover laid in. Butterfield
21-542 1978 $27.50

RICHMOND, LEONARD   The Technique of the Poster. London, 1933.
4to, tipped-in color plts. Baldwins' 51-198 1978 $60

RICHMOND, MABEL E.   Centennial History of Decatur and Macon County.
Decatur, 1930. 1st ed., illus., orig. cloth, very good. MacManus 239-966
1978 $35

RICHMOND, REBECCA   A Woman of Texas: Mrs. Percy V. Pennybacker.
San Antonio, 1941. Illus., inscribed by author to A. R. Mc Tee., chipped d.j.
Jenkins 116-1058 1978 $17.50

RICHMOND on the James. Philadelphia, (1905). Wrs., slightly soiled. Hayman
73-718 1978 $7.50

RICHTER, AUGUST GOTTLIEB   Traite des Hernies. Bonn, 1788. 4to., old
qtr. sheep, foxed. Gurney 75-91 1978 £30

RICHTER, CONRAD   Brothers of No Kin. New York, Philadelphia,
Chicago, 1924. 1st ed., scarce, very bright, signed. Ballinger 11-171 1978
$100.00

RICHTER, CONRAD   The Sea of Grass. New York, 1937. 1st ed.,
decor. cloth, minor fading of spine, fine copy. Dykes 34-66 1978 $25

RICHTER, CONRAD   The Sea of Grass. New York, 1937. 8vo, decor.
cloth, 1 of 250 copies signed by author and publisher, 1st ed., fine. Duschnes
220-254 1978 $22.50

RICHTER, CONRAD   The Trees. New York, 1940. 8vo, decor. cloth,
d.j., 1st ed., fine. Duschnes 220-255 1978 $10

RICHTER, GEORG GOTTLOB   Opuscula Medica Antehac in Academia Gottin-
gensi Seorsim Edita, Nunc Vero Collecta Studio Io. Christiani Gottlieb Ackerman-
ni, Medicinae Doctoris. Francofurti et Lipsiae, 1780-1781. 3 vols., 4to., contemp. bds., 1st collected ed., very good, with bkplt. Offenbacher 30-131 1978
$250

RICHTER, JEAN PAUL   Titan: A Romance. Boston, 1864. Third ed.,
2 vols., cloth binding, some wear. Greene 78-12 1978 $20

RICHTHOFEN, W. BARON VON   Cattle-Raising on the Plains of North America.
New York, 1885. Original cloth, gilt, 1st ed., very fine. Jenkins 116-1176 1978
$150

RICKETTS, CHARLES   A Defence of the Revival of Printing. London,
Ballantyne Press, 1899. Sm. 8vo., orig. bds., uncut, ltd. ed. on handmade
paper. Goldschmidt 110-58 1978 $80

RICKETTS, CHARLES   Shakespeare's Heroines. n.d. Colour plts. by
Charles Ricketts, oblong 4to., cloth-backed bds., very good, first English ed.
Bell Book 16-492 1978 £6.50

RICKETTS, MAJOR   Narrative of the Ashantee War... 1831. Map,
litho. plts., bds., rebacked, uncut, 8vo, orig. cloth. Edwards 1012-267 1978
£90

RICKMAN, JOHN   Troisieme Voyage de Cook...1776...1780.
Paris, 1783. Contemp. calf, 3rd ed., 8vo., good. Paine 78-35 1978 $125.00

RICKMAN, T.   An Attempt to Discriminate the Styles of Architecture in England from the Conquest to the Reformation. Oxford, 1862. Sixth ed.,
plts., cuts in text. George's 635-89 1978 £7.50

RICORD, F. W.   History of Union County, New Jersey. Newark,
1897. Illus., nice, cloth. MacManus 239-1317 1978 $75

RIDDELL, J. L.   A Monograph on the Silver Dollar, Good and Bad.
New Orleans, 1845. 1st ed., 8vo., unpaginated, illus., bound in brown cloth
backed in black mor., interior fine, unusual book. Current 24-95 1978 $275

RIDDELL, NEWTON N.   Heredity and Prenatal Culture Considered in the
Light of the New Psychology. Chicago, 1900. Fly detached, hinge loose. Rittenhouse 49-675 1976 $10

RIDDELL, ROBERT   The Carpenter and Joiner, Stair Builder and Hand-
Railer. (c. 1860). Plts., folio, binders cloth, stained. George's 635-90 1978
£25

RIDDELL, W. R.   La Rochefoucault-Liancourt's Travels in Canada,
1795... Toronto, 1917. Bound. Hood 116-773 1978 $40

RIDDELL, W. R.   John Richardson... Toronto, n.d. (c.1923).
Hood 116-714 1978 $7.50

RIDDELL, WALTER A.   World Security by Conference. Toronto, 1947.
Illus. Hood 17-591 1978 $15

RIDDING, G.   The Church and Commonwealth, the Visitation
Charges. 1906. 8vo. George's 635-1121 1978 £5.25

RIDDLE, WILLIAM   One Hundred and Fifty Years of School History
in Lancaster. Lancaster, 1905. Plts., 8vo., 1st ed. Morrill 241-459 1978
$7.50

RIDDLE, WILLIAM   The Story of Lancaster: Old and New... Lancaster, 1917. 1st ed., illus., orig. limp leather, ltd. to 100 copies signed by
author, very good. MacManus 239-1529 1978 $42.50

RIDEING, WILLIAM H.   In the Land of Lorna Doone and Other Pleasurable
Excursions in England. New York, (1895). 12mo. Biblo 247-737 1978 $13.50

RIDFLEISCH, EDUARD   A Manual of Pathological Histology to Serve as
an Introduction to the Study of Morbid Anatomy. Volumes I and II. London, 1873.
Rittenhouse 49-676 1976 $30

RIDGAWAY, HENRY B.   The Life of the Rev. Alfred Cookman. New
York, 1874. Cloth, faded & worn. Hayman 73-654 1978 $10

RIDGELEY, HELEN WEST   The Old Brick Churches of Maryland. New
York, 1894. Illus. MacManus 239-1838 1978 $17.50

RIDGELEY, JAMES L.   The Odd-Fellows' Pocket Companion: a Correct
Guide in All Matters Relating to Odd-Fellowship. Cincinnati, 1868. Leather,
mod. wear. Hayman 72-663 1978 $7.50

RIDGELY, MABEL LLOYD   The Ridgelys of Delaware and Their Circle. Portland, 1949. Ltd. ed., fine, lg. 8vo., illus. Biblo 247-34 1978 $57.50

RIDGWAY, ROBERT   Color Standards & Color Nomeclature..With 53
Colored Plates & 1115 Named Colors. 1912. Good. Nestler Rare 78-185 1978
$165

RIDGEWAY, WILLIAM   A Report of the Trial of Edward Kearney upon an
Indictment of High Treason. (1803). 1/2 leather, very good, reprint. Hyland
128-434 1978 £12

RIDGEWAY, WILLIAM   A Report of the Trial of Felix O'Rourke. (1803).
(No. 7), 1/2 leather, very good, reprint. Hyland 128-440 1978 £12

RIDGEWAY, WILLIAM   A Report of the Trial of James Byrne. (1803).
No. 4, 1/2 leather, very good, reprint. Hyland 128-437 1978 £12

RIDGEWAY, WILLIAM   A Report of the Trial of John Begg. (1803).
No. 5, 1/2 leather, very good, reprint. Hyland 128-438 1978 £12

RIDGEWAY, WILLIAM   A Report of the Trial of Owen Kirwan. (1803).
No. 3, 1/2 leather, very good, reprint. Hyland 128-436 1978 £12

RIDGEWAY, WILLIAM   A Report of the Trial of T. M. Roche. (1803).
No. 2., 1/2 leather, very good, reprint. Hyland 128-435 1978 £12

RIDGEWAY, WILLIAM   A Report of the Trial of Walter Clare. 1903.
(No. 6), 1/2 leather, very good, reprint. Hyland 128-439 1978 £12

RIDING, LAURA   14A. London, 1934. Nice, d.w., very scarce,
orig. binding, first ed. Rota 212-50 1978 £80

RIDING, LAURA   Laura and Francisca. Deya, The Seizin Press,
1931. 4to., pict. cover, paper over bds., cloth spine, one of 200 numbered
copies, handmade paper, cover faded. Battery Park 1-226 1978 $200

RIDING, LAURA   The Left Heresy in Literature and Life. 1939.
Good, covers dull, first English ed. Bell Book 16-745 1978 £15

RIDING, LAURA   A Trojan Ending. New York, 1937. 1st print.,
fine, d.j., scarce. Ballinger 11-173 1978 $40.00

RIDLER, ANNE   The Little Book of Modern Verse. 1941. Very
good, d.w., first English ed. Bell Book 16-313 1978 £4.50

RIDLER, ANNE   The Shadow Factory: a nativity play. 1946.
Very good, d.w., first English ed. Bell Book 16-747 1978 £4

RIDLEY, THOMAS 1550-1629   A View of the Civile and Ecclesiasticall Law.
Oxford, 1675. Sm. 8vo., contemp. sheep, sometime rebacked, fourth ed. Howes
194-89 1978 £21

RIDLON, G. T.   Saco Valley Settlements and Families. Portland,
1895. Thick 4to., rebound, illus. MacManus 239-993 1978 $65

RIDPATH, JOHN C.   Das Leben und Wirken von James A. Garfield...
Cincinnati, 1882. Cloth. Hayman 72-664 1978 $10

RIDPATH, PHILIP   Boethius's Consolations of Philosophy. 1785.
8vo., contemp. half calf, marbled sides, corners rubbed. P. M. Hill 142-45
1978 £20

RIEGEL, ROBERT E.   America Moves West. New York, 1930. Orig.
cloth, 1st ed. Ginsberg 14-895 1978 $15

RIEGEL, ROBERT E.   Young America, 1830-40. Norman, (1949).
Illus., first ed., fine, d.w. Biblo 247-149 1978 $17.50

RIEGER, CONRAD   Zur Kenntniss Der Formen Des Hirnschadels.
Kongress, 1887. 4to., fldg. plts. in color, bds. backed in leatherette, ex-lib.,
very good copy, illus. Zeitlin 245-217 1978 $27.50

RIEMANN, B.   Theorie der Abel'schen Functionen. Berlin,
1857. 4to., orig. wrs., upper wrapper detached. Quaritch 977-169 1978 $350

RIESENBERG, FELIX   Portrait of New York. New York, 1939. Sm.
4to., photos by Alland, 1st ed. Biblo 251-241 1978 $27.50

RIESENMAN, JOSEPH   History of Northwestern Pennsylvania... New
York, (1943). 1st ed., 3 vols., 4to., illus., orig. cloth, very fine set. Mac-
Manus 239-1660 1978 $90

RIESS, CURT   Total Espionage. 1941. Austin 80-271 1978
$8.50

RIETHMULLER, C. J.   The Adventures of Nevil Brooke; or How India
Was Won for England. 1877. 1st. ed., 3 vols., orig. red half calf, little rubbed
at head, blue labels, good. Jarndyce 16-963 1978 £24

RIEU, C.   Catalogue of the Persian Manuscripts. Vols. 2
and 3 and Supplement. London, 1881-95. 3 vols., roy. 4to., orig. cloth, covers
of vol. 3 damp-marked. Forster 130-225 1978 £15

RIEU, C.   Supplement to the Catalogue of the Arabic Manuscripts. London, 1894. Roy. 4to., orig. cloth, unopened. Forster 130-226
1978 £18

RIGGS, A. L.   Jesus Htakiniwacinskanpi Okodakiciye. Santee
Agency, 1890. 12mo, orig. pr. wr., 1st ed. Ginsberg 14-724 1978 $45

RIGGS, A. L.   Sunkawakan Wicayuhapi. Santee Agency, 1894.
Orig. pr. pict. wr., 1st ed. Ginsberg 14-725 1978 $45

RIGGS, STEPHEN RETURN   Mary and I. Chicago, (1880). First ed., plts.
Biblo 247-64 1978 $72.50

THE RIGHT Joyous and Pleasant History of the Feasts, Gests, and Prowesses of
the Chevalier Bayard, the Good Knight without Fear and without Reproach. London, 1825. 1st ed., 8vo., t.e.g., 2 vols. in 1, fine cond., 1/2 green mor. with
marbled bds. and endpapers. Current Misc. 8-10 1978 $85

RIGHTHOFEN, WALTER   Cattle-Rraising on the Plains of North America.
New York, 1885. Cloth, decor. end sheets, 1st ed., minor wear, fine copy,
scarce, slipcase. Dykes 34-34 1978 $150

RIGHTMYER, NELSON W.   The Angelican Church in Delaware. Philadelphia,
(1947). MacManus 239-115 1978 $12.50

RIGHTS, DOUGLAS L.   The American Indian in North Carolina. Durham, 1947. 1st ed., d.j., inscribed by author, illus. MacManus 239-1213
1978 $17.50

RIHANI, AMEEN F.   The Quatrains of Abu'l-Ala. New York, 1903.
1st ed. Biblo 251-14 1978 $15

RIIS, JACOB A.   The Battle with the Slum. New York and London, 1902. Plts., 1st ed. Butterfield 21-543 1978 $15

RIIS, JACOB A.   Nibsy's Christman. New York, 1893. Pict.
bds., rubbed, little soiled, some discoloration of endpapers. Hayman 71-235
1978 $10

RIIS, JACOB A.   The Old Town. 1909. Illus. Austin 79-579
1978 $27.50

RIIS, JACOB A.   Out of Mulberry Street. New York, 1898.
Pict. cloth, 1st ed. Butterfield 21-544 1978 $20

RIIS, JACOB A.   Theodore Roosevelt, the Citizen. New York,
1904. Illus., first ed. Biblo 247-152 1978 $12.50

RIKER, JAMES   Revised History of Harlem, Its Origin and Early
Annals... New York, 1904. Illus., orig. cloth, fine. MacManus 239-1086
1978 $45

RILEY, BENNETT   Message from the President of the U. S. in Reply
to a Resolution of the Senate, and Relating to the Protection of the Trade between
Missouri and Mexico. Washington, 1830. Disbound, 1st ed. Ginsberg 14-896
1978 $125

RILEY, J. H.   A Second Collection of Birds from the Provinces
of Yunnan & Szechwan, China. 1931. Wr., 8vo, orig. cloth. Book Chest 17-314
1978 $10.50

RILEY, JAMES   Loss of the American Brig Commerce, Wrecked
on the Western Coast of Africa, 1815... 1817. Folding map, 4to, half calf, spine
gilt. Edwards 1012-241 1978 £120

RILEY, JAMES   Sequel to Riley's Narrative... Columbus,
1851. Map, illus., rebacked, old spine laid down, slight foxing, map torn, 8vo,
orig. cloth. Edwards 1012-242 1978 £40

RILEY, JAMES WHITCOMB   A Child-World. Indianapolis, 1897. 8vo, orig.
red cloth, gilt stamped, t.e.g., near Mint, leather backed slipcase, advance copy
of 1st ed., presentation inscription in Riley's hand. Desmarais 1-355 1978 $125

RILEY, JAMES WHITCOMB   Love Letters of the Bachelor Poet James Whitcomb
Riley to Miss Elizabeth Kahle. Boston, 1921. 4to, boards, cloth back, uncut,
t.e.g., limited to 475 copies, 1st ed. collector's cond. Desmarais 1-43 1978
$20

RILEY, JAMES WHITCOMB   An Old Sweetheart of Mine. Indianapolis, (1902).
First ed., drawings. Biblo 247-616 1978 $27.50

RILEY, JAMES WHITCOMB   Rhymes of Childhood. Indianapolis, 1891. 1st
ed., signed slip from author tipped in, spine ends slightly rubbed, otherwise very
good. MacManus 238-568 1978 $50

RILEY, JOSEPH HARVEY   Birds from Siam & the Malay Peninsula in the US
National Museum Collected by Smith & Abbott. 1938. Wr., 8vo, orig. cloth.
Book Chest 17-299 1978 $15

RILEY, WOODBRIDGE   From Myth to Reason. 1926. Illus., first ed.
Austin 82-787 1978 $17.50

RILKE, RAINER MARIA   Rodin. London, 1948. First English ed., illus.
Biblo 247-423 1978 $8.50

RILKE, RANIER MARIA   Selected Poems. Hogarth Press, 1941. Very
good, d.w., first English ed. Bell Book 16-748 1978 £4.50

RILKE, RAINER MARIA   Wartime Letters, 1914-1921. New York, (1940).
1st Amer. ed., d.w. slightly frayed. Biblo 251-619 1978 $15

RIME Di Diversi Antichi Autori Toscani in dodici libri raccolte. Venezia, 1740.
8vo., vellum. King 7-222 1978 £25

RIMINGTON, CRITCHELL   Fighting Fleets. 1942. Illus. Austin 80-272
1978 $12.50

RIMINGTON, CRITCHELL   Fighting Fleets. New York, (1943). Dust jacket, 8vo., illus., near mint copy, blue cloth slipcase, T.L.s. laid in on White
House stationery, signed in ink in full by President Franklin D. Roosevelt. Current 24-101 1978 $150

RIMMER, ALFRED   Ancient Stone Crosses of England. London, 1875.
Wood engravings. Biblo 247-368 1978 $42.50

RINALDINI, B.   Trattato di Tossicoscopia Chemica per uso dei
Medici et Degli Speziali Incaricati come Periti Delle Analisi Chimico-Guidizarie.
Padua, 1831. 8vo., fine, contemp. green mor. gilt, uncut, partly unopened.
Quaritch 977-65 1978 $100

RIPLEY, ELIZA MC HATTON   Social Life in Old New Orleans... New York,
1912. 1st ed., illus., orig. cloth, fine copy, scarce. MacManus 239-1820
1978 $37.50

RIPLEY, MARY CHURCHILL   The Oriental Rug Book. New York, 1904. 164
illus. Baldwins' 51-147 1978 $25

RIPLEY, PERCY   A Short History of Investment. 1934. 8vo.
George's 635-389 1978 £5

RIPLEY, R. S.   Report of _____, of Operations from August 21
to September 10, 1863. Richmond, 1864. Handbound in 3/4 lea. with marbled
bds., Bell Wiley's copy. Broadfoot 46-441 1978 $150

RIPLEY, THOMAS   They Died with Their Boots On. New York,
1935. Illus., 1st ed., pictorial endsheets. Jenkins 116-1178 1978 $35

RIPLEY, WILLIAM Z.   Railway Problems. New York, (1913). Rev.
ed. Biblo 251-96 1978 $12.50

RISHANGER, WILLIAM DE   The Chronicle of William de Rishanger, of the
Barons' Wars; the Miracles of Simon de Montfort. 1840. 8vo. Upcroft 12-369
1978 £6.50

RISTER, CARL COKE   Border Captives, The Traffic in Prisoners by
Southern Plains Indians 1835-1875. Norman, 1940. Bell Wiley's copy. Broadfoot's 44-973 1978 $14

RITCHIE, LEIGH   Scott & Scotland. 1835. 1st. ed., highly
finished engravings by George Cattermole, some slight foxing, orig. red morocco,
a.e.g., v.g. Jarndyce 16-1023 1978 £15

RITCHIE, LEIGH   Scott and Scotland. 1835. 8vo., plts., some
foxing, pub. red mor. gilt, gilt edges. Quaritch 983-357 1978 $85

RITCHIE, LEITCH   Windsor Castle and its Environs. 1840. First
ed., vignette, plts., contemp. half calf, 8vo. Howes 194-1404 1978 £15

RITSON, JOSEPH   The English Anthology. 1793-94. First ed.,
vignettes, 3 vols., cr. 8vo., contemp. calf, woodcut decor. Howes 194-434
1978 £24

RITSON, JOSEPH   Memoirs of the Celts or Gauls. 1827. 8vo.,
tree calf, gilt, back neatly repaired, fine, first ed. P. M. Hill 142-209 1978
£35

RITSON, JOSEPH   Robin Hood. London, 1885. Woodcuts by
Thomas Bewick, etchings by others, no. 62 of 300 copies, very thick 8vo, vellum
spine mottled. Victoria 34-697 1978 $85

RITSON, JOSEPH   A Select Collection of English Songs with their
Original Airs. 1813. Second ed., woodcuts, 3 vols., cr. 8vo., contemp. grained
calf, rebacked. Howes 194-435 1978 £40

RITSON, JOSEPH   The Works. London, 1783-1832. 16 vols., 12mo,
contemp. tree calf, rubbed, recently rebacked, orig. leather title labels, engravings by William Blake, signed engravings. Totteridge 29-88 1978 $350

RITTENHOUSE, JACK D.   A Guide to Highway 66. Los Angeles, (1946).
Pic. wrs., maps, 1st ed., fine. Dykes 35-207 1978 $12.50

RITTENHOUSE, JESSIE B.   The Little Book of Modern British Verse. Boston,
1924. 12mo., first ed. Biblo 247-853 1978 $9.50

RITTER, ABRAHAM   History of the Moravian Church in Phila., from...
1742 to the Present. Philadelphia, 1857. Illus. MacManus 239-1619 1978
$25

RITTER, ABRAHAM   Philadelphia and Her Merchants as Constituted
50 and 70 Years Ago. Philadelphia, 1860. Illus., orig. cloth. MacManus 239-
1642 1978 $40

RITTER, FREDERIC LOUIS   Music in America. New York, 1883. Orig.
cloth, covers worn, but good copy. MacManus 239-323 1978 $20

RITTER, H. L.   Washington as a Business Man. New York,
(1931). Illus., spine faded. Biblo 248-220 1978 $15

RITTER VON FERNSEE, HEINRICH   Botanische Ergebnisse der Reise Seiner
Majestat des Kaisers von Mexico Maximilian I. nach Brasilien (1859-60). Vienna,
1866. Lg. folio, orig. fr. wrs. mounted on bds., plts. in color, clean. Goldschmidt 110-67 1978 $450

A RITUAL and Illustrations of Freemasonry. London, c. 1880. Plts., fcap. 8vo.,
orig. cloth. K Books 244-125 1978 £9

RITUEL Du Diocese de Quebec. Paris, 1703. Illus., later marbled bds., calf
back. Wolfe 39-491 1978 $400

RITZ, WALTHER   Gesammelte Werke. Oeuvres publiees par la
Societe Suisse de Physique. Paris, 1911. 8vo., orig. wrappers. Gurney 75-92
1978 £25

RITZEMA, H.   Het Nageslacht van Jacob Sybolts, Landbouwer te
Warffum en Geertruid Cornelis'. Groningen, (1925). Thick lg. 8vo., cloth,
plts., portrs. Van der Peet H-64-531 1978 Dfl 75

RIVADENEIRA, PEDRO DE 1572-1611   The Lives of Saints, with Other Feasts of
the Year According to the Roman Calendar. 1669. Plts., thick folio, 19th Cent.
panelled calf, contrasting label, 1st Eng. ed. Howes 194-573 1978 £75

RIVADENEIRA, PEDRO DE 1527-1611   Von dem Leben und Wandel Ignatii Loiole,
Anfengers und Stiffters der Religion, die Societet Iesu Genannt... Ingolstadt,
1590. 4to., old calf over wood bds., lightly rubbed, fine, 1st ed. Gilhofer 74-
75 1978 sFr 900

RIVARD, L. E.   Rivard's Catalog of Popular Music. (Montreal),
1880. 8vo., orig. cloth. Morrill 241-495 1978 $9.50

RIVERIUS, LAZARUS
Please turn to
RIVIERE, LAZARE

RIVERS, HENRY WHEATON   Accidents. Popular Directions for Their Immediate
Treatment. New York, 1845. Rittenhouse 49-678 1976 $15

RIVERS, W. H. R.   The Influence of Alcohol and other Drugs on Fatigue. London, 1908. Ex-lib. Rittenhouse 49-677 1976 $15

RIVES, GEORGE L.   The United States and Mexico 1821-1848.
New York, 1913. 2 vols., t.e.g., maps, fine. Jenkins 116-926 1978 $125

RIVES, GEORGE L.   The United States and Mexico 1821-1848. New
York, 1913. 2 vols., cloth. Hayman 73-656 1978 $50

RIVES, WILLIAM C.   History of the Life and Times of James Madison.
3 vols., old. lib. stamp, nice, orig. cloth., scarce. MacManus 239-789 1978
$55

RIVES, WILLIAM C.   On the Resolution for the Annexation of Texas.
Washington, 1845. Jenkins 116-1180 1978 $25

RIVIERE, LAZARE   Observationum Medicarum, & Curationum insign-
ium Centuriae tres, quibus accesserunt Observationes ab aliis communicatae....
Lyon, 1659. 4to., contemp. calf, repaired, first ed. Gurney 75-93 1978 £65

RIVIERE, ROBERT   Examples of Modern Bookbinding designed and
executed by Robt. Riviere & Son. London, 1919. Ltd. to 200 copies, colored
plts., demy 4to., orig. cloth, t.e.g. Forster 130-74 1978 £50

ROACH, PHILIP A.   Address of...on the 385th Anniversary of the
Discovery of America by Columbus... San Francisco, 1877. Original pr. wr., lst
ed. Ginsberg 14-183 1978 $25

ROADS, SAMUEL JR.   The History and Traditions of Marblehead. Marblehead, 1897. 1st ed., frontis. port., illus., orig. cloth, very fine. Mac-
Manus 239-1036 1978 $50

ROBB, D. M.   Art in the Western World. New York, (1942).
Illus. Biblo 247-414 1978 $17.50

ROBB, W. H.   Thunderbird. Kingston, 1949. Signed by
author. Hood 117-701 1978 $25

ROBBINS, A.   Parnell, The Last Five Years. 1926. lst ed.,
port., good, octavo bound in cloth. Hyland 128-331 1978 £6

ROBBINS, ARCHIBALD   A Journal, Comprising an Account of the Loss of
the Brig Commerce, of Hartford, Con., James Riley, Master, Upon the Western
Coast of Africa, August, 28th, 1815... Hartford, 1817. Sprinkled tree calf,
worn, foxed in spots, lacking most of frontis. map, otherwise good, 1st ed. Petrilla 13-84 1978 $25

ROBBINS, CHANDLER   Address Delivered Before the Patrons and Friends
of the Springfield High School, at Its Opening, January, 1841. Springfield, 1841.
Disbount. Hayman 72-574 1978 $12.50

ROBBINS, GILBERT   The Christian Patriot. Worcester, 1865.
Portr., 12mo., lst ed., orig. cloth. Morrill 241-496 1978 $12.50

ROBE, T.   Ways and Means to Man the Navy with not less
than Fifteen Thousand able Sailors. 1740. 8vo., unbound. F. Edwards 1013-
184 1978 £15

ROBEQUAIN, CH.   l'Indochine Francaise. Paris, 1930. 4to., plts.,
illus. Van der Peet 127-203 1978 Dfl 55

ROBERT, JOSEPH C.   A Ring Tournament in 1864: A Letter from a
Mississipian in the Army of Northern Virginia. Miss, 1941. Wraps, reprint, pres
copy from author. Broadfoot's 44-317 1978 $10.00

ROBERT, PAUL A.   Alpine Flowers. New York, (1945). 4to.,
color plts. from watercolors. Biblo 251-202 1978 $15

ROBERT Louis Stevenson: His Workshop. Boston, 1921. 4to, drab boards, 1/2
vellum, limited to 450 copies, lst ed., collector's cond. Desmarais 1-45 1978
$22.50

ROBERT-HOUDIN, JEAN E.   Memoirs of .... 1860. 8vo, orig. printed
cloth, very good. Fenning 32-283 1978 £28

ROBERTS, C.   Calendarium Genealogicum. 1865. 2 vols.,
4to., new buckram. Allen 234-1428 1978 $25

ROBERTS, C. V.   Early Friends of Upper Bucks County, Pa. with
Some Account of Their Descendants. Philadelphia, 1925. Illus., orig. cloth,
fine. MacManus 239-1402 1978 $65

ROBERTS, CECIL   A Man Arose. 1941. lst. ed., portrait, 8vo,
orig. bds. Sawyer 298-48 1978 £7.50

ROBERTS, CHARLES GEORGE DOUGLAS   Barbara Ladd. Boston, 1902.
Colored plts., illus. by Frank Verbeck. Hood 117-538 1978 $15

ROBERTS, CHARLES GEORGE DOUGLAS   The Feet of the Furtive. New York,
1925. Hood 116-495 1978 $12.50

ROBERTS, CHARLES GEORGE DOUGLAS   The Forge in the Forest. New York,
1896. Plts. Hood 117-539 1978 $15

ROBERTS, CHARLES GEORGE DOUGLAS   The Heart of the Ancient Wood.
New York, 1906. Illus. Hood 117-540 1978 $15

ROBERTS, CHARLES GEORGE DOUGLAS   The House in the Water. Boston,
1908. Plts., lst ed., orig. binding. Petrilla 13-85 1978 $10

ROBERTS, CHARLES GEORGE DOUGLAS   Kings in Exile. London, Melbourne,
Toronto, n.d. Lg. 8vo., illus. Hood 117-541 1978 $17.50

ROBERTS, CHARLES GEORGE DOUGLAS   Poems of Wild Life. London, 1888.
Inscr'd by editor. Hood 117-826 1978 $45

ROBERTS, CHARLES GEORGE DOUGLAS   Red Fox. Boston, 1905. 8vo.,
orig. cloth, plts. by C. L. Bull. Book Chest 17-300 1978 $25

ROBERTS, CHARLES GEORGE DOUGLAS   The Watchers of the Trails. Boston,
1904. lst ed., plts., illus. by C. L. Bull, 8vo., orig. cloth. Book Chest 17-
301 1978 $25

ROBERTS, MRS. D. W.
Please turn to
ROBERTS, LOU CONWAY

ROBERTS, DANIEL W.   Rangers and Sovereignty. San Antonio, 1914.
Cloth, frontis., lst ed., name on front fly else fine. Dykes 35-242 1978 $35

ROBERTS, DAVID   Cattle Breeds and Origin. Waukesha, (1916).
lst ed., pic. cloth, map, illus., very good copy, scarce. Dykes 34-111 1978
$25

ROBERTS, DAVID   The Holy Land, Syria, Idumea, Arabia, Egypt
and Nubia. 1842-49. 3 engraved titles, portrait, map, litho tinted plts., 3 vols.,
folio, half green morocco, some foxing, covers worn & joints repaired. Edwards
1012-84 1978 £2000

ROBERTS, DAVID   The Holy Land, Syria, Idumea, Arabia, Egypt &
Nubia. London, 1855-56. 6 vols. in 3, 4to, tinted lithograph vignette title-
page, tinted lithograph portrait, engraved maps, tinted lithograph plts., very sl.
spotting, orig. blue cloth, gilt bds., all edges gilt, fine copy. Deighton 5-183
1978 £395

ROBERTS, ELLWOOD   Biographical Annals of Montgomery County, Pa...
New York, 1904. 2 vols., illus., 4to., orig. 1/2 leather. MacManus 239-1570
1978 $65

ROBERTS, ELLWOOD   Old Richland Families Inc. Descendants of Roberts,
Lancaster, Lester, Johnson, Foulke, etc. Norristown, 1898. Hinges cracked.
Baldwins' 51-265 1978 $15

ROBERTS, EMMA   Hindostan, Its Landscapes, Palaces, Temples,
Tombs; the Shores of the Red Sea; and...the Himalaya Mountains... (1845). 2
vols. in 1, 4to., frontis., plts., some slight foxing, half red mor. gilt, spine laid
down. Quaritch 983-358 1978 $225

ROBERTS, EMMA   Views In India. London, 1835. lst. ed., 2
vols. in 1, 4to, engraved frontispiece printed in oil colours by G. Baxter, engraved
vignette title-pgs., contemporary polished calf, gilt decorative borders, neatly
rebacked in matching style gilt, clean copy. Deighton 5-221 1978 £75

ROBERTS, EMMA   Views in India, China, and on the Shores of the
Red Sea. London, 1835. 2 vols. bound as 1, frontis. in color by George Baxter,
plts., quarter calf, backstrip faded and moderate wear. Dawson's 127-285 1978
$200

ROBERTS, ELIZABETH MADOX   Black is My Truelove's Hair. 1938. First ed.,
chipped d.j. Austin 82-790 1978 $12.50

ROBERTS, ELIZABETH MADOX   A Buried Treasure. New York, 1931. 8vo, green
buckram, t.e.g. slipcase, 1 of 200 copies signed by author, lst ed., fine. Duschnes 220-263 1978 $25

ROBERTS, ELIZABETH MADOX   The Great Meadow. New York, 1930. 8vo,
green buckram, t.e.g., slipcase, map inserted, lst ed., fine. Duschnes 220-262
1978 $35

ROBERTS, ELIZABETH MADOX   The Time of Man. 1926. Very good, d.j. Austin 82-792 1978 $10

ROBERTS, ELIZABETH MADOX   The Time of Man. 1926. Austin 82-791 1978 $8.50

ROBERTS, ELIZABETH MADOX   The Time of Man.   New York, Viking Press, 1945. 8vo, 1st illus. ed., light gray cloth, wood engravings by Clare Leighton, glassine wr. torn, good clean box, Fine, collector's cond. Desmarais 1-356 1978 $25

ROBERTS, GEORGE S.   Historic Towns of the Connecticut Valley. Schenectady, (1906). Illus., 8vo., inner hinges cracked, 1st ed., orig. cloth. Morrill 241-497 1978 $27.50

ROBERTS, GEORGE S.   Old Schenectady. Schenectady, n.d. (c. 1900). Illus. MacManus 239-1098 1978 $15

ROBERTS, H. N.   Gauntlet, A Series of Open Letters Challenging. 1934. 1st ed., signed pres. copy, wr., very good. Hyland 128-443 1978 £4

ROBERTS, JAMES A.   New York in the Revolution as Colony and State. Albany, 1897. Sm. folio, facsimiles of orig. ms., blue gilt cloth, very good, 1st ed., 1st prtg. Butterfield 21-381 1978 $65

ROBERTS, JAMES A.   New York in the Revolution as Colony and State. Albany, 1898. 2nd ed., illus., facsimiles, 4to., inner front hinge cracked. Morrill 241-421 1978 $25

ROBERTS, KENNETH   Lydia Bailey. Garden City, 1947. Frontis., 1st ed., tall octavo, orig. off-white buckram, spine slightly soiled, gilt top, orig. page of manuscript tipped-in, ltd. to 1000 numbered copies, signed by author. Totteridge 29-90 1978 $75

ROBERTS, KENNETH   Lydia Bailey. Garden City, 1947. 1st ed., octavo, orig. black cloth with gilt lettering, d. j. Totteridge 29-89 1978 $10

ROBERTS, KENNETH   Lydia Bailey. 1947. Maps, limited ed. to 1050 copies, autographed, light discolor on backstrip. Nestler Rare 78-27 1978 $35

ROBERTS, KENNETH   Lydia Bailey. New York, 1947. Orig. cloth, 1st ed., 1 of 1,050 copies, no. and signed by author, boxed, bookplt., fine. MacManus 238-744 1978 $65

ROBERTS, KENNETH   Northwest Passage. New York, 1937. 2 vols., orig. cloth, 1st ed., 1 of 1,050 copies signed by author, fine, d.j. MacManus 238-742 1978 $75

ROBERTS, KENNETH   Northwest Passage. 1938. First Australian ed., paper browning, else good. Austin 82-793 1978 $17.50

ROBERTS, KENNETH   Oliver Wiswell. New York, 1940. 2 vols., orig. cloth, 1st ed., 1 of 1,050 copies numbered and signed by author, bookplt., fine, boxed. MacManus 238-743 1978 $60

ROBERTS, KENNETH   Oliver Wiswell. 1940. First trade ed., very good, d.j. Austin 82-794 1978 $15

ROBERTS, KENNETH   Oliver Wiswell. New York, 1940. Hood 117-542 1978 $15

ROBERTS, KENNETH   Rabble in Arms. 1947. Portraits. First illus. ed. Austin 82-795 1978 $12.50

ROBERTS, KENNETH   Trending into Maine. New York, 1944. Color illus. by N.C. Wyeth. Biblo 247-358 1978 $17.50

ROBERTS, KENNETH L.   Sun Hunting. Indianapolis, (1922). Illus., green cloth, 1st ed., chipped dust jacket, very good copy. Bradley 49-278 1978 $20

ROBERTS, LESLIE   Canada's War in the Air. Montreal, 1943. 3rd ed., photos. Hood 116-139 1978 $27.50

ROBERTS, LESLIE   Canada's War in the Air. Book two. Montreal, 1943. Folio, orig. binding. Wolfe 39-486 1978 $30

ROBERTS, LESLIE   Home from the Cold Wars. Boston, 1948. Hood 117-143 1978 $15

ROBERTS, LLOYD   The Book of Roberts.... Toronto, 1923. Signed by the author. Hood's 115-362 1978 $12.50

ROBERTS, LOU CONWAY   A Woman's Reminiscences of Six Years in Camp with the Texas Rangers. Austin (1928). Wrs., illus., 1st ed., fine, slipcase. Dykes 35-243 1978 $35

ROBERTS, MICHAEL   Critique of Poetry. 1934. Spine faded, good, first English ed. Bell Book 16-582 1978 £4

ROBERTS, MICHAEL   The Faber Book of Modern Verse. London, 1943. 8th Impression of hard-to-find book, light spots on cover, else very good or better. Limestone 9-101 1978 $12.50

ROBERTS, MICHAEL   New Country. Hogarth Press, 1933. Very good, first English ed. Bell Book 17-967 1978 £15

ROBERTS, MICHAEL   New Signatures: Poems by several hands. Hogarth Press, 1932. Orig. bds., spine faded, good, first English ed. Bell Book 16-669 1978 £28.50

ROBERTS, MICHAEL   Poems. London, 1936. First ed., orig. binding, nice. Rota 211-549 1978 £5

ROBERTS, MIRANDA S.   Genealogy of the Descendants of John Kirk... Doylestown, 1912-13. Illus., 4to., scarce. MacManus 239-929 1978 $75

ROBERTS, MIRANDA S.   Genealogy od the Descendants of John Kirk, born 1660, at Alfreton, in Derbyshire, England. Doylestown, 1913. Hinges loose. Baldwins' 51-260 1978 $75

ROBERTS, O. M.   A Description of Texas, Its Advantages and Resources.... St. Louis, 1881. Pres. copy. Baldwins' 51-567 1978 $75

ROBERTS, OCTAVIA   With Lafayette in America. Boston, 1919. 1st. ed., illus from old prints. Baldwins' 51-320 1978 $12.50

ROBERTS, PETER   Immigrant Races in North America. 1910. Illus., 1st ed. Austin 79-583 1978 $12.50

ROBERTS, PETER   The New Immigration. 1912. Austin 79-584 1978 $11

ROBERTS, SOLOMON W.   "Ohio and Pennsylvania Rail-Road." Philadelphia, 1849. Wrps., back wrapper badly soiled. Hayman 71-671 1978 $10

ROBERTS, W. MILNOR   Special Report of a Reconnoissance of the Route for the Northern Pacific Railroad between Lake Supeior and Puget Sound,.... Philadelphi, 1869. Orig. pr. wr., 1st ed. Ginsberg 14-897 1978 $75

ROBERTS, WILLIAM   Centennial: The Oregon Bible Society. [Portland, 1876]. Disbound, 1st ed. Ginsberg 14-850 1978 $25

ROBERTS, WILLIAM   Centennial Sketch: Methodist Episcopal Church in Oregon. [N.P., 1876]. Disbound, 1st ed. Ginsberg 14-849 1978 $25

ROBERTS, WILLIAM   Memoirs of the Life and Correspondence of Mrs. Hannah More. 1834. First ed., portrait, 3 vols., cr. 8vo., orig. cloth, rebacked with old spines laid down. Howes 194-1062 1978 £24

ROBERTS, WILLIAM 1862-1940   Printer's Marks. Chiswick Press. Ltd. to 75 copies on Jap. vellum, #59, full leather, bookplts. of M. C. D. Borden and George Edward Dimock, t.e.g. Battery Park 1-42 1978 $175

ROBERTS, WILLIAM 1862-1940   Rare Books and Their Prices. London, 1895. 1st ed., uncut, t.e.g., orig. green buckram, very good or better. Limestone 9-243 1978 $25

ROBERTSON, A.   The Life of Sir Robert Moray, Soldier, Statesman, and Man of Science (1608-1673). 1922. Octavo, good. Upcroft 10-517 1978 £5.50

ROBERTSON, A.   A Topographical Survey of the Great Road from London to Bath and Bristol... 1792. 2 vols., 8vo., map, fine uncoloured plts., contemp. half red mor., a little rubbed. Quaritch 983-359 1978 $575

ROBERTSON, ALEXANDER F.   Alexander Hugh Holmes Stuart 1807-1891. Richmond, 1925. Uncut, Bell Wiley's copy. Broadfoot 46-215 1978 $15

ROBERTSON, BEN   Red Hills and Cotton. NY, 1942. Typescript from author to Wiley laid in, Bell Wiley's copy. Broadfoot's 44-933 1978 $20.00

ROBERTSON, C. E.   The Attempts Made to Separate the West from the American Union. St. Louis, 1885. Illus., map, orig. wr., 1st ed. Ginsberg 14-898 1978 $37.50

ROBERTSON, C. F.   The Churchman's Answer as to the History and Claims of the Protestant Episcopal Church. St. Louis, 1878. Original printed wr., 1st ed. Ginsberg 14-597 1978 $15

ROBERTSON, C. F.   The Early Days of the Church in Kansas City. [Kansas City, 1883]. Original printed wr., 1st ed. Ginsberg 14-598 1978 $35

ROBERTSON, CHARLES ALEXANDER LOCKHART   On the Want of a Middle Class Asylum in Sussex. London, 1863. 8vo., new wrs. Quaritch 977-66 1978 $40

ROBERTSON, CHARLES ALEXANDER LOCKHART   Pavilion Asylums. London, 1867. 8vo., new wrs., fldg. detailed architectural plan. Quaritch 977-67 1978 $60

ROBERTSON, D. S.   An Englishman in America, 1785. Toronto, 1933. Inscr. & signed by editor. Hood 117-327 1978 $40

ROBERTSON, G.   Memoir of a Chart of the China Sea... 1795. 2nd. ed., 4to, binders' cloth, morocco spine, slight foxing. Edwards 1012-379 1978 £160

ROBERTSON, H.   Examples of Modern French Architecture. London, 1928. Illus., 4to., spine torn. Biblo BL781-547 1978 $22.50

ROBERTSON, HENRY   Natural History of the Atmosphere. Volumes I and II. Edinburgh, 1808. Rittenhouse 49-679 1976 $150

ROBERTSON, J. B.   Texas, The Home For The Emigrant. Houston, 1875. Half morocco. Jenkins 116-1183 1978 $125

ROBERTSON, J. K.   Tayville. Toronto, 1932. Hood 116-774 1978 $12.50

ROBERTSON, J. M.   A History of Freethought. London, 1936. Sq. 8vo, orig. cloth, 4th. ed., 2 vols., d.w., good copy. Sexton 7-179 1978 £10

ROBERTSON, J. R.   Landmarks of Canada, What Art Has Done For Canadian History. Vols. 1 & 2. Toronto, 1917, (1921). Bound. Hood's 115-193 1978 $25

ROBERTSON, JOHN   Michigan in the War. Lansing, 1882. Illus., thick sm. 4to., later cloth. MacManus 239-898 1978 $20

ROBERTSON, MARGARET M.   The Orphans of Glen Elder: a Tale of Scottish Life. London, (c.1870). Color plts., 1st ed., orig. bind. Petrilla 13-87 1978 $7.50

ROBERTSON, WILFRID   Rhodesian Rancher. London & Glasgow, (1935). Cloth, illus., covers little dull, very good copy from the Allred Collection, very scarce. Dykes 34-123 1978 $50

ROBERTSON, WILLIAM, DENTIST   A Practical Treatise on the Human Teeth: Showing the Causes of Their Destruction, and the Means of Their Preservation. Philadelphia, 1841. Plts., binding rubbed, paper spine label chipped, very good, minimal foxing, 1st U.S. ed. Petrilla 13-88 1978 $65

ROBERTSON, WILLIAM, SCOTCH WRITER ON AMERICA   Our American Tour. Edinburgh, 1871. 1st ed., orig. cloth, gilt, beveled edges, very good or better. Limestone 9-6 1978 $50

ROBERTSON, WILLIAM 1721-1793   An Historical Disquisition Concerning the Knowledge Which the Ancients Had of India... Dublin, 1791. 1st Irish ed., lg. fldg. maps, 8vo., contemp. calf, gilt, nice. Fenning 32-284 1978 £12.50

ROBERTSON, WILLIAM 1721-1793   The History of America. 1777. 1st ed., maps, contemp. tree calf, plt., 2 vols., 4to. Howes 194-436 1978

ROBERTSON, WILLIAM 1721-1793   The History of America. 1808. New ed., portr., maps, 2 vols., plts., newly bound in half calf antique, spines gilt. Howes 194-437 1978 £20

ROBERTSON, WILLIAM 1721-1793   The History of Scotland. 1759. 2nd ed., 4to., 2 vols., orig. calf, brown & green labels, slight wear, generally very good. Jarndyce 16-182 1978 £45

ROBERTSON, WILLIAM 1721-1793   The History of the Reign of the Emperor Charles V. London, 1769. 3 vols., quarto, full old calf, very good, hinges weakening, 1st ed. Bennett 7-91 1978 $250

ROBERTSON, WILLIAM 1721-1793   The History of the Reign of the Emperor Charles V. 1769. 3 vols., 4to., fine set, contemp. polished calf. Howes 194-438 1978 £38

ROBERTSON, WILLIAM 1721-1793   History of the Reign of the Emperor Charles V. 1787. Engr. frontis., 4 vols., contemp. calf, rubbed, lacks lettering pieces. George's 635-595 1978 £7.50

ROBERTSON, WILLIAM 1721-1793   Recherches Historiques sur la Connoisance que les Anciens Avoient de l'Inde et sur le Progress du Commerce Avec Cette Partie du Monde Avant le Decouverte... Paris, 1792. 8vo., figured vellum, stained, 1st ed. of French trans. King 7-383 1978 £30

ROBERTSON, WILLIAM 1721-1793   The Works. 1840. 8 vols., engraved frontis., portrait, half titles, polished calf, spines gilt, black labels, handsome set. Jarndyce 16-966 1978 £58

ROBERTSON, WYNDHAM, JR.   Oregon, Our Right and Tilte,.... Washington, 1846. Folding map, contemp. half mor., 1st ed. Ginsberg 14-851 1978 $1,250

ROBESON, ESLANDA GOODE   Paul Robeson, Negro. New York, 1930. 1st prtg., covers rubbed, illus., 8vo., orig. cloth, very good. Americanist 103-18 1978 $30

ROBIN, ABBE CLAUDE   Nouveau Voyage Dans l'Amerique Septentrionale, en l'Annee 1781... Philadelphie et Paris, 1783. 2nd. ed., contemp. calf, 8vo. Edwards 1012-525 1978 £85

ROBINS, BENJAMIN   New Principles of Gunnery. 1742. First ed., plt., 8vo., contemp. bds., calf back. F. Edwards 1013-414 1978 £150

ROBINS, BENJAMIN   New Principles of Gunnery.... 1805. 8vo., plts., contemp. half calf. F. Edwards 1013-186 1978 £60

ROBINS, BENJAMIN   Observations of the Present Convention with Spain. London, 1739. 12mo., disbound. Paine 78-115 1978 $57.50

ROBINS, F. W.   The Story of the Lamp (and the Candle). 1939. Illus., roy. 8vo. George's 635-1475 1978 £8.50

ROBINS, JOHN D.   The Incomplete Anglers. Toronto, 1943. Illus. by Franklin Carmichael. Hood 117-959 1978 $12.50

ROBINSON, BUD   Sunshine and Smiles. Life Story. Flash Lights, Sayings and Sermons. Chicato, (1903). Cloth. Hayman 72-683 1978 $8.50

ROBINSON, C. A.   Alexander the Great: Meeting of East & West in World Government & Brotherhood. 1947. Allen 234-19 1978 $7.50

ROBINSON, C. W.   Life of Sir John Beverley Robinson. Toronto, 1904. Good cond., portr. frontis. Hood 17-328 1978 $50

ROBINSON, CHARLES HENRY   Hausaland or Fifteen Hundred Miles Through the Central Soudan. London, 1900. 3rd. ed., folding coloured map, plts., illus., cr. 8vo, orig. cloth, little foxed. K Books 239-412 1978 £15

ROBINSON, CHARLES NAPIER   Celebrities of the Army. 1900. Lg. 4to., half mor., coloured plts. F. Edwards 1013-415 1978 £10

ROBINSON, CHARLES NAPIER   Celebrities of the Army. London, 1900. 72 coloured plts., folio, gilt dec. cloth, covers slightly marked, 8vo. K Books 239-413 1978 £8

ROBINSON, CHARLES NAPIER   Old Naval Prints. Their Artists and Engravers. London, 1924. 1st ed., folio, illus., plts., many in color, orig. cloth, dust jacket, fine copy, ltd. ed. MacManus 239-1783 1978 $65

ROBINSON, CHARLES NAPIER   Old Naval Prints, their Artists and Engravers. 1924. Illus., 24 in colour, 4to., stain on front cover. George's 635-853 1978 £40

ROBINSON, CHARLES NAPIER   Old Naval Prints, Their Artists and Engravers. London, 1925. Fully illus. some in color, sm. folio, ltd. to 1500 copies, no. 465. Baldwins' 51-514 1978 $37.50

ROBINSON, CHARLES NAPIER   A Pictorial History of the Transvaal and South Africa. London, (1900). Nearly 200 illus., 6 specially prepared maps, roy. 8vo, orig. printed wrappers. K Books 239-414 1978 £14

ROBINSON, CONWAY　　An Account of Discoveries in the West Until 1519... Richmond, 1848. 1st ed., contemp 3/4 calf, bds., rubbed, else very good, scarce. MacManus 239-425 1978 $37.50

ROBINSON, DAVID M.　　A Catalogue of the Greek Vases in the R.O.M. of Archaeology, Toronto. Toronto, 1930. 2 vols., plts. Hood 116-196 1978 $75

ROBINSON, DAVID M.　　Excavations at Olynthus. 1930. 4to., plt., new buckram. Allen 234-808 1978 $35

ROBINSON, E. B. F.　　The True Sphere of the Blind. Toronto, 1896. Hood's 115-668 1978 $10

ROBINSON, EDWARD　　The "Have-more" Plan for a Little Land – a Lot of Living. New York, 1947. Illus. Biblo BL781-866 1978 $8

ROBINSON, EDWIN ARLINGTON　　Cavender's House. New York, 1929. Purple cloth, 1st trade ed., very good in jacket. Bradley 49-279 1978 $10

ROBINSON, EDWIN ARLINGTON　　Cavender's House. New York, 1929. 8vo, boards, cloth back, ex-lib, uncut, near Fine, no. 240 of 500 copies, signed by Robinson, 1st ed., collector's cond. Desmarais 1-360 1978 $30

ROBINSON, EDWIN ARLINGTON　　Cavender's House. New York, 1929. 8vo, blue cloth, gilt stamped, uncut, partially unopened, near Mint in chipped d.w., 1st ed., collector's cond. Desmarais 1-359 1978 $10

ROBINSON, EDWIN ARLINGTON　　Cavender's House. New York, 1929. 8vo, cloth, d.j., 1st ed., fine. Duschnes 220-265 1978 $7.50

ROBINSON, EDWIN ARLINGTON　　Dionysus in Doubt. New York, 1925. First U.S. ed., 1 of 350 numbered copies and signed by author, roy. 8vo., cloth-backed bds., good, A.L.s. from author to Conrad Aiken laid in. Bell Book 16-749 1978 £37.50

ROBINSON, EDWIN ARLINGTON　　The Glory of the Nightingales. New York, 1930. 8vo, green cloth, gilt lettering on spine and cover, near Mint in d.w., 1st ed., collector's cond. Desmarais 1-361 1978 $10

ROBINSON, EDWIN ARLINGTON　　The Man Who Died Twice. New York, 1924. Orig. cloth-backed bds., 1st ed., 1 of 500 no. copies, signed by author, fine, boxed, a little worn. MacManus 238-745 1978 $27.50

ROBINSON, EDWIN ARLINGTON　　Matthias at the Door. New York, 1931. Nice in d.w. Desmarais B-552 1978 $10

ROBINSON, EDWIN ARLINGTON　　Matthias at the Door. New York, 1931. 8vo, cloth, d.j., 1st ed., fine. Duschnes 220-267 1978 $7.50

ROBINSON, EDWIN ARLINGTON　　Nicodemus. New York, 1932. 8vo, cloth, d.j., 1st ed., fine. Duschnes 220-268 1978 $7.50

ROBINSON, EDWARD ARLINGTON　　Nicodemus A Book of Poems. New York, 1932. 8vo, red cloth, uncut, t.e.g., spine sun-faded, else Fine, ed. lmtd. to 253 large paper copies, this no is. 235, signed by Robinson, 1st ed., collector's cond. Desmarais 1-362 1978 $30

ROBINSON, EDWIN ARLINGTON　　Sonnets 1889-1927. New York, 1928. Orig. binding. Wolfe 39-487 1978 $25

ROBINSON, EDWIN ARLINGTON　　Sonnets 1889-1927. New York, 1928. 8vo, boards and cloth, 1 of 561 copies signed by author, typography by W. A. Dwiggins, 1st ed., fine. Duschnes 220-264 1978 $37.50

ROBINSON, EDWIN ARLINGTON　　Talifer. New York, 1933. Bear mint in soiled d.w. Desmarais B-553 1978 $10

ROBINSON, EDWIN ARLINGTON　　Talifer; a narrative poem. New York, 1933. First trade ed., orig. binding, very nice, d.w. Rota 211-550 1978 £5

ROBINSON, EDWIN ARLINGTON　　Tristram. New York, 1927. Rough plum cloth, black buckram spine, 1st ed., 1st state, 1 of 350 signed, good copy. Bradley 49-282 1978 $15

ROBINSON, ELRIE　　Early Feliciana Politics. St. Francisville, 1936. Illus., Bell Wiley's copy. Broadfoot's 44-886 1978 $15.00

ROBINSON, F. A.　　Trail-Tales of Western Canada. Toronto, n.d. (about 1914). Illus. Hood 117-918 1978 $15

ROBINSON, FAYETTE　　An Account of the Organization of the Army of the United States... Philadelphia, 1848. 1st ed., 2 vols., 12mo, illus., cloth. MacManus 239-426 1978 $37.50

ROBINSON, H.A.　　Further Memories of Irish Life. 1924. 1st ed., very good, octavo bound in cloth. Hyland 128-446 1978 £5

ROBINSON, H. C.　　Journal April 5-May 20, 1882. N.P., [ca. 1882]. Original printed wr., 1st ed. Ginsberg 14-184 1978 $60

ROBINSON, HENRY MARTIN　　The Great Fur Land. New York, 1879. Illus., orig. binding. Wolfe 39-488 1978 $30

ROBINSON, JOAN　　Essays in the Theory of Employment. Oxford, 1947. Biblo BL781-867 1978 $9.50

ROBINSON, JOHN　　Old John Robinson's Sketches of Animated Nature. Cincinnati, (1872). Illus., 8vo., orig. pic. wrs., text loose in wrs., stained. Morrill 241-498 1978 $10

ROBINSON, JOHN R.　　Miniature Illustrated Railway Guide of the Lake Shore and Michigan Southern Railway, the Great South Shore Route. December, 1872. Illus., fold. map, wrs., sm. piece lacking from corner of back wrapper. Hayman 72-682 1978 $15

ROBINSON, P. J.　　Toronto During the French Regime; a History of the Toronto Region from Brule to Simcoe, 1615-1793. Toronto, 1933. Illus. by C.W. Jefferys, ed. limited to 500 copies. Hood 116-775 1978 $75

ROBINSON, PHILIP STEWART　　Sinners and Saints. Boston, 1883. 1st ed., mustard cloth, top edge stained yellow, very good. Greene 78-329 1978 $65

ROBINSON, SELMA　　City Child. New York, 1931. 1st ed., illus. by Rockwell Kent, fine. Victoria 34-457 1978 $20

ROBINSON, SOLON　　Hot Corn.... New York, 1854. Orig. binding, clean, little worn, illus. Hayman 71-236 1978 $10

ROBINSON, STANFORD FREDERICK HUDSON　　Celtic Illuminative Art... Dublin, 1908. Roy. 4to., plts., some coloured, buckram. Quaritch 983-246 1978 $160

ROBINSON, STANFORD FREDERICK HUDSON　　Celtic Illuminative Art. 1908. Cover shaky, very good, octavo bound in cloth, reprint. Hyland 128-448 1978 £42.50

ROBINSON, THERESE L. VON J.　　Talvi's History of the Colonization of America. 1851. 2 vols. in 1, thick 8vo, orig. cloth, cover faded. Edwards 1012-526 1978 £18

ROBINSON, VICTOR　　The Story of Medicine. New York, 1931. Top cover stained. Rittenhouse 49-680 1976 $10

ROBINSON, W.　　My Wood Fires and Their Story, Showing the Beauty and Use of the Wood Fire. London, 1917. 4to, orig. cloth, little soiled. Sexton 7-180 1978 £12

ROBINSON, WILL H.　　The Story of Arizona. Phoenix, (1919). 1st ed., illus., orig. cloth, hinges cracked, lacking front flyleaf, otherwise a very good copy, scarce. MacManus 239-1897 1978 $40

ROBINSON, WILLIAM　　The Intriguing Milliners and Attornies Clerks. 1738. 1st. ed., sm. 8vo, frontispiece, contemp. calf, rebacked, title soiled & traces of use throughout. Hannas 54-252 1978 £85

ROBINSON, WILLIAM MORRISON　　The Confederate Privateers. New Haven, 1928. Bell Wiley's copy. Broadfoot 46-217 1978 $40

ROBINSON AND HARCUM　　A Catalogue of Greek Vases. Toronto, 1930. Vol. II only, plts., inner hinge sprung, covers stained. Biblo BL781-469 1978 $27.50

ROBISON, DANIEL M.　　Bob Taylor and the Agrarian Revolt in Tennessee. Chapel Hill, 1935. Cloth, book is fine, dust jacket very slightly worn. Hayman 73-660 1978 $10

ROBISON, DANIEL M.   Bob Taylor and the Agrarian Revolt in Tennessee.
Chapel Hill, 1935. Presen. copy from author to Wiley. Bell Wiley's copy.
Broadfoot 46-559 1978 $9

ROBISON, JOHN   A System of Mechanical Philosophy. Edinburgh,
1822. 4 vols., 8vo., plts., some plts. foxed & one cut into at fold, orig. cloth
backed bds., printed paper labels, two joints torn, uncut. Quaritch 977-250
1978 $175

ROBLES, VITO ALESSIO
Please turn to
ALESSIO ROBLES, VITO

ROBSON, ALBERT H.   J. E. H. MacDonald. Toronto, 1946. Card
cover, colored plts. Hood 117-221 1978 $20

ROBSON, ALBERT H.   Paul Kane. Toronto, 1933. Card cover,
color plts. Hood 117-222 1978 $25

ROBSON, GEORGE FENNELL   Scenery of the Grampian Mountains:....
London, 1819. Folio, contemp. diced half calf, marbled boards, joints split, gilt,
maroon cloth folding box, coloured aquatints, 2nd ed. Totteridge 29-91 1978
$850

ROBSON, JOHN S.   How a One-Legged Rebel Lives, Reminiscences of
the Civil War. Charlottesville, 1891. Wraps, front wrap detached and chipped,
Bell Wiley's copy. Broadfoot's 44-659 1978 $50

ROBSON, WILLIAM   The Old Play-Goer. 1844. Fcap. 8vo., covers
faded. George's 635-1413 1978 £5.25

ROBY, J.   Traditions of Lancashire. First and Second Series.
1829. 4 vols., roy. 8vo., lg. paper, plts., green levant mor., gilt backs, fine
copy, bookplt. of Hugh Perkins. Quaritch 983-360 1978 $525

ROCCO, ANTONIO   Esercitationi Filosofiche le Quali Versano in
Considerare le Positioni, & Obiettioni, che si Contengono nel Dialogo del Signor
Galileo Galilei Linceo Contra la Dottrina d'Aristotile. Venetia, 1633. Woodcut diagrams, 4to., contemp. limp vellum, 1st ed., very rare, fine copy. Offenbacher 30-50 1978 $750

ROCHE, ARTHUR SOMERS   Loot. 1916. Illustrated. Austin 82-797 1978
$12.50

ROCHE, EUGENIUS   London In A Thousand Years With Other Poems.
1830. 1st ed., frontis portrait, light dampstaining affecting bottom half of book
throughout, orig. cloth, paper label. Jarndyce 16-969 1978 £14.50

ROCHE, JAMES JEFFREY   Life of John Boyle O'Reilly. 1891. Ex-lib.
Austin 79-586 1978 $17.50

ROCHEMONTEIX, CAMILLE DE   Les Jesuites et la Nouvelle-France au XVIIe
Siecle d'Apres Beaucoup de Documents Inedits. Paris, 1895, 1896. 3 vols.,
portraits. Hood's 117-347 1978 $175

ROCHON, ALEXIS   A Voyage to Madagascar, and The East Indies.
1792. Folding map, calf rebacked, 8vo. Edwards 1012-321 1978 £120

ROCHON-DUVIGNEAUD, A.   Les Yeux et la Vision des Vertebres. Paris, 1943.
Illus., thick lg. 8vo., black buckram, orig. wrappers bound in, first ed. Rittenhouse 49-681 1976 $95

ROCK, D.   Did the Early Church in Ireland Acknowledge
the Pope's Supremacy? Answered in a Letter to Lord John Manners. 1844. 1st ed.,
1/2 leather, very good. Hyland 128-450 1978 £7

ROCKEFELLER, JOHN D.   Random Reminiscences of Men and Events. New
York, 1909. Inscribed to Mr. John K. Earnest. Baldwins' 51-185 1978 $15

ROCKLEY, ALICIA MARGARET (TYSSEN AMHERST) CECIL, BARONESS   A
History of Gardening in England. London, 1896. 2nd ed., illus., roy. 8vo.,
little worn. Traylen 88-529 1978 £15

ROCKLEY, ALICIA MARGARET (TYSSEN-AMHERST) CECIL, BARONESS   A
History of Gardening in England. 1910. 3rd ed., plts., octavo, good. Upcroft
10-255 1978 £18

ROCKWELL, A. D.   Lectures on Electricity in its Relations to Medicine
and Surgery. New York, 1879. Rittenhouse 49-682 1976 $10

ROCKWELL, CHARLES   The Catskill Mountains and the Region Around.
New York, 1867. Frontis., 8vo., 1st ed., autographed. Morrill 239-553 1978
$25

THE ROCKY Mountains of Canada. Montreal, n.d. Views in colour, card cover.
Hood 116-875 1978 $15

A ROD for the Back of the Binder. Chicago, Lakeside Press, 1928. Sm. 4to.,
decor. cloth, illus. Battery Park 1-280 1978 $22.50

A ROD For the Back of the Binder. Some Considerations of Binding with Reference
to the Ideals of the Lakeside Press. Chicago, 1928. 4to., orig. cloth, 1st ed.,
cover label a bit scratched, otherwise fine. MacManus 238-865 1978 $30

RODD, FRANCIS R.   General William Eaton the Failure of an Idea.
New York, 1932. Illus., map, fine. MacManus 239-748 1978 $10

RODD, RENNEL   Ballads of the Fleet and Other Poems. 1897.
1st. ed., photogravure frontis, 8vo, orig. cloth gilt, t.e.g., others uncut, pres.
copy to Winston Churchill. Sawyer 298-106 1978 £80

RODDICK, AMY REDPATH   The Flag and Other Poems, 1918. Montreal,
1918. Hood's 115-903 1978 $10

RODDICK, AMY REDPATH   The Iroquois Enjoy a Perfect Day. Montreal,
1939. Frontis. portrait, autograph inscription by author, orig. binding. Wolfe 39-
489 1978 $25

RODEN, ROBERT F.   The Cambridge Press. 1638-1692. A History of
the First Printing Press Established in English America... New York, 1905. 12mo.,
orig. bds., 1 of 50 copies on Japan vellum, slightly soiled. MacManus 238-860
1978 $50

RODENWALDT, GERHART   Die Kunst Der Antike. Berlin, (1927). 4to.
Baldwins' 51-148 1978 $50

RODGERS, ANDREW D.   "Noble Fellow." New York, 1940. Orig.
binding, clean, nice copy in d.j. Hayman 71-581 1978 $7.50

RODGERS, CLEVELAND   New York: The World's Capital City. New
York, (1948). Illus., spine faded. Biblo 251-73 1978 $12.50

RODGERS, CLEVELAND   New York: The World's Capital City. New
York, (1948). Illus. Biblo BL781-174 1978 $10

RODGERS, H. J.   Twenty-Three Years Under a Sky-Light...
Hartford, 1872. 1st ed., illus., errata leaf, orig. cloth, fine. MacManus 239-
392 1978 $40

RODGERS, WOODES   A Cruising Voyage Round The World... London,
1718. 2nd. ed., corrected, 8vo, 4 of 5 engraved folding maps, one torn without
loss, contemporary mottled calf, neatly rebacked, morocco label, gilt. Deighton
5-189 1978 £140

RODIN, AUGUSTE   A la Venus de Milo. Paris, 1945. 4to., orig.
wr., uncut, 1st ed., numbered copy on velin paper. Goldschmidt 110-60 1978
$45

RODKER, JOHN   Hymns. (London), Ovid Press, 1920. 1 of
190 copies, tall 8vo., orig. cloth-backed bds., uncut, largely unopened, very
good. Americanist 103-66 1978 $55

RODMAN, SELDEN   The Airmen; a poem. New York, 1941. First
ed., orig. binding, very nice, author's signed autograph pres. inscription, A.L.s.
from author loosely inserted. Rota 211-555 1978 £12

RODMAN, SELDEN   The Amazing Year; a diary in verse. New York,
1947. First ed., orig. binding, nice, d.w., author's initialled autograph pres.
inscription. Rota 211-556 1978 £10

RODMAN, SELDEN   Mortal Triumph and Other Poems. New York,
(1932). 1st ed., d.w. slightly soiled. Biblo 251-621 1978 $12.50

RODNEY, C. A.   The Reports on the Present State of the United
Provinces of South America. 1819. Folding map, offset on title, modern half
calf, 8vo. Edwards 1012-671 1978 £85

RODNEY, GEORGE BRYDGES   As a Cavalryman Remembers. Caldwell, 1944.
Dec. cloth, illus., frontis., 1st ed., very good, d.w., very scarce. Dykes 35-
153 1978 $32.50

RODRIGUEZ, D. THOMAS   Borrascas del Corazon. 1850. 8vo, lib. stamp on lst. title pg., 1/2 calf, rubbed, Madrid. Eaton 45-430 1978 £10

RODRIGUEZ, ALPHONSUS 1526-1616   The Practice of Christian Perfection. London, 1697-99. 3 vols., sm. 4to., 19th cent. half mor., first ed. Howes 194-90 1978 £70

RODT, C. VON   Reise Einer Schweizerin um die Welt. Neuenburg, 1903. 4to., pict. cloth, illus. Van der Peet H-64-532 1978 Dfl 95

RODWAY, J.   In The Guiana Forest. 1911. Illus., 8vo, orig. d.w., orig. cloth. Edwards 1012-672 1978 £15

RODWAY, PHYLLIS P.   Philip Rodway and a Tale of Two Theatres. Birmingham, 1934. Coloured plts., illus., roy. 8vo., orig. cloth. Howes 194-1276 1978 £5

RODWELL, G. F.   South by East. London, 1877. Illus., 8vo., ex-lib., lst ed., orig. cloth. Morrill 241-500 1978 $10

ROE, ALFRED SEELYE   The Ninth New York Heavy Artillery, a History of Its...Marches, Camps, Battles...Personal Sketches, and a Complete Roster. Worcester, 1899. Tall thick 8vo., plts., red pict. cloth, very good. Butterfield 21-125 1978 $50

ROE, ALFRED SEELYE   The Thirty-Ninth Regiment Massachusetts Volunteers, 1862-1865. Worcester, 1914. Illus., 8vo., orig. cloth, lst ed. Morrill 241-348 1978 $20

ROE, ALFRED SEELYE   Worcester in the Spanish War. Worcester, 1905. Illus., tall 8vo., lst ed., orig. cloth. Morrill 241-347 1978 $10

ROE, CHARLES F.   Custer's Last Battle. New York, 1927. Illus., original pictorial folio wr. Ginsberg 14-298 1978 $50

ROE, CLIFFORD G.   Panders and Their White Slaves. New York, (1910). Orig. binding, clean. Hayman 71-682 1978 $7.50

ROE, E. P.   Nature's Serial Story. New York, 1885. 8vo, orig. cloth, illus. by W. H. Gibson & Dielman. Book Chest 17-318 1978 $15.50

ROE, ELIZABETH   Friendship in Death. 1750. Orig. calf, old reback, leading bd. detached. Jarndyce 16-183 1978 £5

ROEDER, RALPH   Juarez...and His Mexico. New York, 1947. First ed., one signature sprung, 2 vols. Biblo 247-79 1978 $20

ROEHRICHT, WOLF   Hochofen. Munich, 1925. Lg. folio in sheets, matted, orig. half leather portfolio, ltd., issued in 180 copies, one of 30 preferred copies, orig. watercolor over charcoal signed by artist, printed on Japan paper. Goldschmidt 110-62 1978 $350

ROEMER, FERDINAND   Texas, With Particular Reference to German Immigration and the Physical Appearance of the Country. San Antonio, 1935. Folding map, d.j., lst ed. in English. Jenkins 116-1191 1978 $85

ROESEL VON ROSENHOF, AUGUST JOHANN   Monatlich Herausgegebene Insektenbelustigung. Nuernberg, (1749-1764). 4 vols., portr., engr. frontis's in colors, thick 4to., contemp. calf, ed. in book form, fine set. Salloch 345-163 1978 $2,000

ROESSLER, BALTHAZAR   Speculum Metallurgiae Politissimum Oder Hellpolierter Berg-Bau-Spiegel. Dresden, 1700. Folio, plts., modern bds. covered with old vellum antiphonal sheets, foxed & some dampstaining, but very good copy, lst ed. Norman 5-*45 1978 $850

ROGER, P.   Percement de l'Isthme Americain par un Canal Interoceanique... Paris, 1864. 4to., wrs. Gilhofer 74-76 1978 sFr 400

ROGER OF WENDOVER   Flowers of History, the History of England to 1235 formerly ascribed to Matthew Paris. 1892. 2 vols., cr. 8vo., orig. cloth. George's 635-558 1978 £10.50

ROGERS, A. N.   Communication Relative to the Location of the U.P.R.R. Across the Rocky Mountains Through Colorado Territory. Central City, 1867. Original printed yellow wr. Ginsberg 14-272 1978 $350

ROGERS, BENJAMIN A.   Report on the International Congress for the Prevention and Repression of Crime, Made to the Governor of Texas. Austin, 1873. Printed wr., scarce. Jenkins 116-1193 1978 $115

ROGERS, BETTY   Will Rogers, His Wife's Story. Indianapolis & New York, (1941). lst ed., fabricoid, orange top, illus., fine copy in d.w., reinforced. Dykes 34-161 1978 $10

ROGERS, BRUCE   Paragraphs on Printing Elicited from Bruce Rogers in Talks with James Hendrickson on the Functions of the Book Designer. New York, 1943. Decor. bds., cloth spine, mostly unopened, very fine, worn slipcase, 1 of 199 lg. paper copies signed by Rogers. Dawson's 447-139 1978 $200

ROGERS, BRUCE   Paragraphs on Printing Elicited from Bruce Rogers in Talks with James Hendrickson on the Functions of the Book Designer. 1943. Occas. notes, illus., frontis., sm. 4to. Battery Park 1-28 1978 $75

ROGERS, BRUCE   Report on the Typography of the Cambridge University Press, Prepared in 1917 at the Request of the Syndics. Cambridge, 1950. Bds., cloth back, very fine, 1 of 500 copies. Dawson's 447-140 1978 $65

ROGERS, HENRY   Essays selected from Contributions to the Edinburgh Review. 1850. 2 vols., 8vo. George's 635-1476 1978 £12.50

ROGERS, HENRY C.   History of the Town of Paris, and the Valley of the Sauquoit. Utica, 1881. Frontis., clippings laid in, scarce, very good. Butterfield 21-317 1978 $75

ROGERS, HOWARD S.   History of Cass County, From 1825 to 1875. Cassopolis, 1875. 1st ed., orig. cloth, fine. MacManus 239-1056 1978 $42.50

ROGERS, J.   Seventeen Sermons on Several Occasions. 1736. Full calf gilt, 8vo. George's 635-1122 1978 £5.25

ROGERS, J.   Sport in Vancouver and Newfoundland. New York, 1912. Illus. & maps by author. Hood's 115-611 1978 $17.50

ROGERS, J. E.   Among Green Trees. Chicago, 1902. 4to, orig. cloth. Book Chest 17-302 1978 $12.50

ROGERS, J. GUINNESS   J. Guinness Rogers; An Autobiography. 1903. lst ed., illus., very good, octavo bound in cloth. Hyland 128-451 1978 £6.50

ROGERS, JAMES EDWIN THOROLD   A History of Agriculture and Prices in England, 1259-1793. Oxford, 1866. 2 vols., 8vo. George's 635-390 1978 £18.50

ROGERS, JAMES EDWIN THOROLD   Six Centuries of Work and Wages. New York, 1891. Wrs., charts. Hayman 71-683 1978 $8.50

ROGERS, JAMES H.   America Weighs Her Gold. New Haven, 1931. Biblo BL781-868 1978 $8

ROGERS, J. S.   History of Arkansas Baptists. Little Rock, 1948. Illus., original cloth, d.j., lst ed. Ginsberg 14-33 1978 $22.50

ROGERS, J. W.   Madame Surratt, a Drama in Five Acts. Washington, D.C., 1926. Spine worn. Broadfoot 50-187 1978 $15

ROGERS, JOHN WILLIAM   Finding Literature on the Texas Plains. Dallas, (1931). Cloth & bds., lst ed., fine copy, frontis., 1 of 300 copies, very scarce. Dykes 34-10 1978 $90

ROGERS, JULIA ELLEN   Among Green Trees. Chicago, 1902. Photogravure plts., illus., 4to., lst ed. Morrill 241-502 1978 $15

ROGERS, PATRICK   Father Theobald Mathew. 1945. Austin 79-587 1978 $10

ROGERS, ROBERT   A Concise Account of North America. n.d. Lea.-bound copy, missing regular title-page, duodecimo, 18th century ed., fr. hinges loose. Hood 117-592 1978 $500

ROGERS, ROBERT   Reminiscences of the French War. Concord, 1831. Illus., orig. bds., worn, frontis. portrait. Wolfe 39-489a 1978 $110

ROGERS, SAMUEL   Human Life, a Poem. 1819. lst. ed., 4to, half title, orig. grey bds., paper label, some chipping of spine, otherwise v.g. Jarndyce 16-970 1978 £36

ROGERS, SAMUEL   Human Life--a Poem. 1819. Cr. 8vo, contemp. calf, panelled in gilt and blind, rebacked. Eaton 45-418 1978 £10

ROGERS, SAMUEL   Human Life, A Poem. 1819. 1st. ed., 8vo, half title, thick paper copy, very marked grey wraps bound in, neat modern cloth, paper label. Jarndyce 16-971 1978 £9.50

ROGERS, SAMUEL   Italy, a Poem. 1823. Part the 1st., 2nd. ed., half title, orig. cloth, v.g., pres. copy, inscribed by author. Jarndyce 16-972 1978 £15

ROGERS, SAMUEL   Italy, a Poem. 1830. 1st. ed., vignette illus. many by Turner, calf, gilt borders, spine rubbed, new label, internally bright & crisp. Jarndyce 17-973 1978 £12.50

ROGERS, SAMUEL   Poems. 1834. 1st. ed., vignettes, many by Turner, binding bright & crisp, calf, gilt borders. Jarndyce 16-974 1978 £12.50

ROGERS, SAMUEL   Recollections of the Table-Talk. 1856. 2nd. ed., half title, orig. brown cloth, slightly loose, otherwise v.g. Jarndyce 16-975 1978 £6.50

ROGERS, SAMUEL   Recollections. 1859. 1st. ed., half title, orig. red cloth, paper label, v.g. Jarndyce 16-976 1978 £13.50

ROGERS, THOMAS   The Faith, Doctrine, and Religion, Professed and Protected in the Realme of England, and Dominions of the Same. 1625. 4to, contemp. limp vellum, slight marginal worming, edges of title frayed. Hannas 54-253 1978 £35

ROGERS, WALTER T.   A Manual of Bibliography. New York, 1891. Coloured frontis., spine chipped, 1st U.S. ed., orig. bind. Petrilla 13-89 1978 $17.50

ROGERS, WILL   The Illiterate Digest. New York, 1924. Cloth, illus., 1st ed., covers dull, very good copy. Dykes 34-162 1978 $7.50

ROGERSON, SIDNEY   Both Sides of the Road, a Book about Farming. 1949. Illus. by Charles Tunnicliffe, roy. 8vo. George's 635-218 1978 £6.25

ROGERSON, SYDNEY   Our Bird Book. London, 1947. Coloured plts., text illus., 4to., d.w., orig. cloth. K Books 244-268 1978 £10

ROGNETTA, FRANCESCO   Traite Philosophique et Clinique d'Ophthalmologie Base sur les Principes de la Therapeutique Dynamique. Paris, 1844. 8vo., contemp. half calf, 1st ed., paper discolored in some places. Offenbacher 30-121 1978 $115

ROGOFF, HARRY   An East-Side Epic. London, 1930. Austin 79-588 1978 $10

ROGUES DE FURSAC, JOSEPH   Manual of Psychiatry. 1911. Back & front cover water damaged. Austin 80-942 1978 $12.50

ROHDE, ELEANOUR SINCLAIR   Oxford's College Gardens, Described. London, 1932. Plts., 8vo., orig. cloth. Book Chest 17-303 1978 $30

ROHDE, ELEANOUR SINCLAIR   The Story of the Garden... London, 1932. Plts. 5 in colour, roy. 8vo, little worn. Traylen 88-619 1978 £6

ROHDE, ERWIN   Der Griechische Roman und Seine Vorlaeufer. 1900. Half calf, top of spine missing. Allen 234-820 1978 $10

ROHDE, ERWIN   Psyche. 1925. 2 vols. in 1, sewn. Allen 234-821 1978 $10

ROHDE, W. S.   Garden-Craft in the Bible and other Essays. Plates, 8vo, orig. cloth. Book Chest 17-304 1978 $22.50

ROHMER, SAX   The Day The World Ended. Garden City, 1930. 1st ed., 8 vo., pictorial d.j., very good-fine. Houle 10-231 1978 $70

ROHMER, SAX   The Day the World Ended. Garden City, 1930. Cloth, 1st ed. Hayman 72-191 1978 $7.50

ROHOLD, S. B.   The War and the Jew.... Toronto, 1915. Hood's 115-131 1978 $15

ROKITANSKY, CARL FREIHERR VON   Handbuch der pathologischen Anatomie. Vienna, 1842-1846. 3 vols., perfect, 8 vo., rare 1st ed., contemp. half calf. Schafer 19-63 1978 sFr. 2,500

ROKITANSKY, CARL FREIHERR VON   A Manual of Pathological Anatomy. London, 1849-1854. 4 vols., 8vo., green stamped cloth, gilt lettering on spines, very good copy, bkplts. of Drs. James Gilpin Houseman & Alfred M. Hellman. Zeitlin 245-219 1978 $150

ROLAND, ANDRE F.   Le Grand Art d'Ecrire Necessaire a Ceux qui Veulent se Perfectionner dans cette Science. Paris, n.d. (c. 1758). Imp. folio, folded, cont. paper wrs., uncut, spine defective, first ed. Schumann 511-50 1978 sfr 5000

ROLFE, MRS. A.   The Oath of Allegiance. 1847. 2 vols., frontis, etchings, orig. cloth, blocked in blind on corners, gilt lettering on spines. Eaton 45-419 1978 £30

ROLFE, FREDERICK WILLIAM   Chronicles of the House of Borgia. 1901. Roy. 8vo., buckram, t.e.g., plts., very good, scarce, first English ed. Bell Book 16-190 1978 £85

ROLFE, FREDERICK WILLIAM   Chronicles of the House of Borgia. 1901. First ed., plts., thick roy. 8vo., red binders cloth, gilt top. Howes 194-1125 1978 £40

ROLFE, FREDERICK WILLIAM   The Desire and Pursuit of the Whole. London, 1934. 8vo., green cloth, gilt panel on spine, 1st binding, near mint, slightly chipped d.w., 1st ed. Desmarais 1-104 1978 $45

ROLFE, FREDERICK WILLIAM   Hubert's Arthur. 1935. Very good, first English ed. Bell Book 16-979 1978 £12.50

ROLL, CHARLES   Indiana. 1931. Illus., very good. Nestler Rare 78-70 1978 $40

ROLL of Honor: Names of Soldiers, Victims of the Rebellion, Buried in National Cemetries in Maine,.... Washington, 1866. Wr. Jenkins 116-1194 1978 $27.50

ROLLESTON, HUMPHRY DAVY   The Right Honourable Sir Thomas Clifford Allbutt, K.B.C. London, 1929. D.j. Rittenhouse 49-685 1976 $15

ROLLESTON, T. W.   The High Deeds of Finn. 1910. 1st ed., 16 col. illus. by S. Reid, very good, octavo bound in cloth. Hyland 128-453 1978 £12

ROLLIN, CHARLES   The Ancient History of the Egyptians, Carthaginians.... Glasgow, 1826. 2 vols., maps, illus., full red calf, 8vo. K Books 244-269 1978 £18

ROLLIN, M.   The Ancient History of the Egyptians, Carthagians, Assyrians, Babylonians, Medes and Persians, Grecians and Macedonians, etc. London, 1839. 3 vols., 8vo., half calf, maps, bindings shaved, & damaged. Van der Peet H-64-533 1978 Dfl 150

ROLLINS, CARL PURINGTON   Off the Dead Bank. 1949. Bds., cloth back, fine, 1 of 675 copies. Dawson's 447-177 1978 $13.50

ROLLINSON, JOHN K.   Pony Trails in Wyoming. Caldwell, 1941. Cloth, illus., 1st ed., fine, inscribed by author, slipcase, scarce. Dykes 35-148 1978 $35

ROLT, RICHARD c. 1725-70   An Impartial Representation of the conduct of the Several Powers of Europe, engaged in the late General War. 1749-50. 4 vols., fine, contemp. full polished calf, first ed. Howes 194-440 1978 £45

ROLVAAG O. E.   Giants in the Earth. 1927. 1st ed., very good. Austin 79-589 1978 $47.50

ROMAINS, J.   Les Hommes de Bonne Volonte. Paris, 1954. 4 vols., thick lg. 8vo., full modern calf bound, slipcases, out of print. Van der Peet H-64-453 1978 Dfl 350

ROMAN DE LA ROSE   C'y est le Rommant de la Rose. Ou tout l'art d'amour est Enclose Hystoires et Auctoritez et Maintz Beaulx Propos Vsitez qui a este Nouvellement Corrige Suffisantement et Cotte Bien a Lavantaige... Paris, 1531. Folio, woodcut, contemp. limp vellum, red mor. box. Gilhofer 74-133 1978 sFr 7,700

ROMANCERO General, en que se contienen todos los Romances que andan impressos. Madrid, 1604. 4to., dark green mor. by Bedford, gilt edges, 1st com. ed. Quaritch 978-134 1978 $6,000

ROMANCES of Old Japan. London, (1920). Illus., decor. cloth, bit worn and bumped, 2nd printing. Dawson's 449-176 1978 $25

ROMANNE-JAMES, C.   Herb-lore for Housewives. London, 1938. 8vo., orig. cloth, illus. K Books 244-270 1978 £6

ROMANO, FIORAVANTE MARTINELLI   Roma ricercata nel suo Sito con tutte le curiosita, che in esso si ritrovano tanto antiche, come moderne. Rome, 1769. Woodcuts, 12mo., contemp. bleached vellum. Argosy Special-77 1978 $250

THE ROMANS in Greece. Boston, 1799. Sm. 8vo., orig. bds., uncut, slight age staining. Quaritch 979-16 1978 $60

ROMER, A.   Anecdotal and Descriptive Natural History. 1873. Chromolitho. plts., illus., 8vo, orig. red cloth, edges gilt, gilt, bright, fresh copy. Fenning 32-286 1978 £10.50

ROMER, FRANCOIS FLORIAN   Resultats Generaux de Mouvement Archeologique en Hongrie. Budapest, 1878. Illus., map, 3/4 leather, rubbed. Biblo BL781-470 1978 $34.50

ROMER, FRANK   100 Years of Books. 100th Anniversary of the Davey Company. Jersey City, (1942). Illus. Biblo BL781-774 1978 $10

ROMILLY, SAMUEL   Memoirs of the Life... 1840. 1st. ed., 3 vols., frontis portrait, half calf, marbled bds., good. Jarndyce 16-977 1978 £18

ROMINE, W. B.   The Story of Sam Davis. Pulaski, 1928. Wrs., Bell Wiley's copy. Broadfoot 46-218 1978 $20

ROMINE, W. B.   A Story of the Original Klu Klux Klan. Pulaski, 1924. Wrs., pres. copy from Mr. Romine to Bell Wiley. Broadfoot's 44-321 1978 $30

RONDOT, NATALIS   Notice du Vert de Chine... Paris, 1858. Lg. 8vo., fldg. litho. plts., cloth samples, contemp. half calf, gilt, rubbed, upper hinge repaired, some light foxing & dampstaining, but very good copy, inscr'd by Natalis Randot, 1st ed. Norman 5-242 1978 $275

RONDTHALER, EDWARD   Life of John Heckewelder. Philadelphia, 1847. Frontis., fine. MacManus 239-1488 1978 $32.50

RONSARD, PIERRE DE   Abrege de l'Art Poetique Francois. Eragny Press, 1903. Contemp. full red crushed mor., fine, woodcut title borders and vignette, 8vo. Howes 194-846 1978 £165

RONSARD, PIERRE DE   Abrege de L'Art Poetique Francois. Eragny Press, 1903. Ltd. to 226 copies, woodcut initials, orig. patterned bds.. spine darkened, edges uncut. George's 635-890 1978 £100

RONSARD, PIERRE DE   Choix de Sonnets. Eragny Press, 1902. Contemp. full red crushed mor., raised bands, gilt edges, fine, 8vo., only 226 copies printed by Lucien and Esther Pissarro in Ricketts' Vale type. Howes 194-847 1978 £165

RONY, GEORGE   This, Too, Shall Pass Away. Creative Age Press, 1945. Frontis., 1st ed., inscr'd by author. Austin 79-590 1978 $20

ROO VAN ALDERWERELD, J. K. H. DE   De Ondergang van het Tweede Keizerrijk. Schiedam, 1870. 2 vols., 8vo., half cloth, illus., fldg. maps, ex-lib., shaved. Van der Peet H-64-534 1978 Dfl 55

ROOME, WILLIAM J. W.   Through the Lands of Nyanza. London, (1930). Folding map, plts., cr. 8vo, spine faded, orig. cloth. K Books 239-416 1978 £7

ROOME, WILLIAM J. W.   Tramping Through Africa. London, 1930. Map, 32 plts., covers dull, orig. cloth, 8vo. K Books 239-415 1978 £6

ROOPER, WILLIAM   The Life and Death of Sir Thomas More... London, 1729. Fold. plt., 8vo., 1/2 calf. Salloch 348-166 1978 $125

ROOS, CHARLES F.   Stabilization of Employment. Bloomington, 1933. Biblo BL781-869 1978 $9.50

ROOS, JOHN FREDERICK FITZGERALD DE
Please turn to
DE ROS, JOHN FREDERICK FITZGERALD

ROOSEVELT, ELEANOR   This I Remember. New York, (1949). Illus., 1st ed. Biblo BL781-240 1978 $8.50

ROOSEVELT, ELEANOR   This Troubled World. New York, 1938. Sm. 8vo., d.w., 1st ed. Morrill 241-503 1978 $7.50

ROOSEVELT, FRANKLIN D.   The Happy Warrior, Alfred E. Smith. Boston, 1928. 8vo., d.w., 1st ed. Morrill 241-699 1978 $12.50

ROOSEVELT, FRANKLIN D.   The Wit and Wisdom of... New York, 1950. 1st ed. Biblo 251-107 1978 $12.50

ROOSEVELT, T.   A Book-Lovers Holidays in the Open. New York, 1916. 8vo., orig. cloth. Book Chest 17-321 1978 $14

ROOSEVELT, THEODORE   African Game Trails. 1910. Illus., first ed. Austin 82-798 1978 $15

ROOSEVELT, THEODORE   East of the Sun and West of the Moon. 1926. Illus., first ed., very good. Austin 82-802 1978 $20

ROOSEVELT, THEODORE   Hunting In Many Lands. New York, 1895. 1st ed., plts., large 8 vo., t.e.g., very good or better. Limestone 9-244 1978 $55

ROOSEVELT, THEODORE   Hunting Trips of a Ranchman... New York, 1885. Medora ed., plts., etchings, imp. 8vo, orig. cloth, ltd. ed. of 500 copies. Edwards 1012-527 1978 £65

ROOSEVELT, THEODORE   Huntings Trips of a Ranchman... 1902. Imp. 8vo, portrait & illus. by A. B. Frost, contemp. half calf, slightly rubbed, 1 joint repaired. Edwards 1012-528 1978 £15

ROOSEVELT, THEODORE   Letters to Kermit...1902-1908. New York, 1946. Illus., 1st ed., d.w. Biblo BL781-245 1978 $9

ROOSEVELT, THEODORE   The New Nationalism. 1910. Dark red cloth, first ed., inscribed by former owner. Austin 82-800 1978 $27.50

ROOSEVELT, THEODORE   Outdoor Pastimes of an American Hunter. 1908. Illus. Austin 82-801 1978 $12.50

ROOSEVELT, THEODORE   The Summer Birds of the Adirondacks in Franklin County, NY. by.... New York, 1925. Limited to 200 copies, very good. Nestler Rare 78-139 1978 $25

ROOSEVELT, THEODORE   The Wilderness Hunter: An Account of the Big Game of the United States and Its Chase With Horse, Hound and Rifle. 1902. 8vo, illus., contemp. half calf, slightly rubbed, 1 joint repaired, Standard Lib. ed., Edwards 1012-529 1978 £15

ROOT, FRANK A.   The Overland Stage to California. Columbus, 1950. Illus., reprint of Topeka 1901 Ed., fine, d.w. Biblo 248-289 1978 $27.50

ROOT, GEORGE F.   The Prize. Chicago, (1870). Oblong 12mo., orig. bds., lightly dampstained, 1st ed. Morrill 241-505 1978 $12.50

ROOT, ROBERT K.   The Poetical Career of Alexander Pope. 1938. Portrait, orig. cloth, 8vo. Howes 194-1099 1978 £6.50

ROOT, SIDNEY   Primary Bible Questions for Young Children. Atlanta, 1864. Wrs., Bell Wiley's copy. Broadfoot 46-463 1978 $37

ROOT, WAVERLEY   The Secret History of the War. 1945. Vol. II. Austin 80-277 1978 $10

ROPER, WILLIAM   Life of Sir Thomas More. 1822. New ed., half calf, rubbed, plts. Allen 234-1371 1978 $7.50

ROPES, MRS. H. A.   Six Months in Kansas. Boston, 1856. Orig. cloth, fine. MacManus 239-1935 1978 $25

ROPES, JOHN CODMAN   The Army Under Pope. New York, 1881. Bell Wiley's copy. Broadfoot 46-219 1978 $12

ROPES, JOHN CODMAN   The Story of the Civil War. New York, 1894-98. Coloured maps, 3 vols., 8vo., orig. cloth, pres. copy. F. Edwards 1013-416 1978 £40

ROQUE, J. DE LA   Voyage Fait Par Ordre Du Roy Louis XIV Dans la Palestine... Paris, 1717. Engraved plts., sm. 8vo, calf, rebacked, lib. stamp on title.   Edwards 1012-85 1978 £90

ROQUELAURE, DUC. DE   Secret Memoirs. 1896. Ltd. to 1,000 copies, 4 vols., cr. 8vo., orig. parchment. George's 635-923 1978 £5.25

ROS, AMANDA M.   Poems of Puncture. London, n.d. (1912). Wrappers, discoloured and chipped at spine, scarce, first ed. Rota 212-51 1978 £35

ROSCOE, HENRY E.   A Treatise on Chemistry. New York, 1878-1889. 3 vols. in 8, 8vo., illus., orig. cloth, worn, but very good set, bkplts., 1st Amer. ed. Norman 5-243 1978 $125

ROSCOE, J.   The Baganda: An Account of Their Native Customs and Beliefs. 1911. Illus., 8vo, orig. cloth. Edwards 1012-287 1978 £25

ROSCOE, THOMAS   Belgium: in a Picturesque Tour. 1841. Sm. 4to., engravings, some slight foxing, orig. dec. cloth gilt. Quaritch 983-361 1978 $105

ROSCOE, THOMAS   The Italian Novelists... 1825. 4 vols., half-titles, frontis, vignettes, foxed, 1/4 calf, spines rubbed. Eaton 45-420 1978 £15

ROSCOE, THOMAS   Lanscape Annual, 1831. Cheapside, 1831. Light wear on binding, illus., fore edge painting. Nestler Rare 78-247 1978 $65

ROSCOE, THOMAS   The Life of William the Conqueror. n.d. (1846). Frontis portrait & engraved t.p., orig. cloth, v.g. Jarndyce 16-978 1978 £8.50

ROSCOE, THOMAS   The London and Birmingham Railway. London, (1839). 8vo., coloured folding map, plts., orig. cloth, gilt, spine faded. Quaritch 977-251 1978 $135

ROSCOE, THOMAS   The Tourist in France... 1834. 8vo., lg. paper, frontis., plts., pub. mor. Quaritch 983-362 1978 $120

ROSCOE, THOMAS   Wanderings and Excursions in North and South Wales. 1836, n.d. 2 vols., roy. 8vo., plts., vignettes, contemp. half calf. Howes 194-1405 1978 £55

ROSCOE, THOMAS   Wanderings and Excursions in North Wales. 1853. 8vo., plts., orig. green cloth gilt. Quaritch 983-363 1978 $145

ROSCOE, WILLIAM 1753-1831   The Life of Lorenzo de Medici. 1796. Second ed., 2 vols., 4to., contemp. half russia, rebacked. Howes 194-385 1978 £42

ROSCOE, WILLIAM 1753-1831   Monandrian Plants of the Order Scitamineae... Liverpool, (1823)-28 (29). Plts. engraved & coloured by G. Graves, 1 plt. foxed, impl. folio, contemp. half green morocco, little rubbed, fine copy, ltd. to 150 copies. Traylen 88-659 1978 £1650

ROSCOE, WILLIAM 1753-1831   The Wrongs of Africa, A Poem. Part the First. London, 1777. Bound with Part the Second, 2 vols. in 1, 4to, modern cloth, 1st ed., uncommon, very rare. Ximenes 47-275 1978 $250

ROSCOE, WILLIAM E.   History of Schoharie County. Syracuse, 1882. Illus. & biographical sketches, 4to., plts., hinges cracked, needs rebacking, text & plts. tight & clean. Butterfield 21-406 1978 $65

ROSE, HERBERT JENNINGS   Handbook of Greek Literature from Home to the Age of Lucian. 1948. 3rd ed., revised. Allen 234-831 1978 $8.50

ROSE, HUGH JAMES   A New General Biographical Dictionary. 1857. 12 vols., half calf gilt, rubbed, 4 covers detached, 2 spines a little defective, 8vo. George's 635-1258 1978 £30

ROSE, STUART   The Maryland Hunt Cup. New York, 1931. 4to, illus. Baldwins' 51-291 1978 $37.50

ROSE, THOMAS   Westmoreland, Cumberland, Durham & Northumberland Illustrated from Original Drawings by Thomas Allom. London, 1832. Plts., 4to., good, half calf. K Books 244-271 1978 £60

ROSE, WILLIAM STEWART   Apology Addressed to the Travellers Club or Anecdotes of Monkeys. 1825. 1st. ed., modern olive cloth, paper label, v.g. Jarndyce 16-979 1978 £7.50

THE ROSE: Being a Detection of the Pernicious Tendency of Two Libels...In the Old England Journal, and The Thistle. (1747). 8vo., new qtr. roan. P. M. Hill 142-214 1978 £28

ROSE Window. London, 1939. Pres. binding, full blue roan, first ed., very good. Rota 211-19 1978 £5

ROSEBOOM, EUGENE H.   The Civil War Era 1850-1873. Columbus, 1944. Bell Wiley's copy. Broadfoot's 44-589 1978 $16

ROSELLI, BRUNO   Vigo. Boston, 1933. 1st ed., very good, inscr'd by author. Austin 79-591 1978 $27.50

ROSEN, ERWIN   Der Deutsche Lausbub in Amerika. Stuttgart, (1913). 3 vols. Biblo 247-153 1978 $20

ROSEN, GEORGE   400 Years of a Doctor's Life. New York, 1947. Rittenhouse 49-686 1976 $7.50

ROSENAU, M. J.   Disinfection and Disinfectants. Philadelphia, 1902. Library marks. Rittenhouse 49-687 1976 $15

ROSENBACH, ABRAHAM SIMON WOLF 1876-   The All-Embracing Doctor Franklin. Philadelphia, 1932. Frontis., 1 of 198 numbered copies, half lea. Battery Park 1-481 1978 $150

ROSENBACH, ABRAHAM SIMON WOLF 1876-   An American Jewish Bibliography. Baltimore, 1926. Facs. MacManus 239-233 1978 $40

ROSENBACH, ABRAHAM SIMON WOLF 1876-   A Book Hunter's Holiday. Boston, 1936. One of 760 numbered copies, signed by Rosenbach, from Jean Hersholt's library with bkplt. & signature. Battery Park 1-480 1978 $100

ROSENBACH, ABRAHAM SIMON WOLF 1876-   A Book Hunter's Holiday Adventures with Books and Manuscripts. Boston, 1936. Illus., orig. buckram, 1st ed., ltd. to 760 copies signed by author, pub. slipcase. MacManus 238-1034 1978 $65

ROSENBACH, ABRAHAM SIMON WOLF 1876-   A Book Hunter's Holiday. Adventures with Books and Manuscripts. Boston, 1936. Illus., orig. cloth, dust jacket, worn, 1st ed., bkplt., good. MacManus 238-1035 1978 $20

ROSENBACH, ABRAHAM SIMON WOLF 1876-   A Book Hunter's Holiday. Adventures with Books and Manuscripts. Boston, (1936). Illus., orig. cloth, dust jacket, worn, inscr'd by author. MacManus 238-1036 1978 $25

ROSENBACH, ABRAHAM SIMON WOLF 1876-   Books and Bidders. Boston, 1927. Illus., orig. cloth-backed bds., paper label, 1st ed., pres. copy, ltd. to 785 copies signed by author, covers somewhat worn, bkplt. MacManus 238-1037 1978 $75

ROSENBACH, ABRAHAM SIMON WOLF 1876-   Books and Bidders. The Adventures of a Bibliophile. Boston, 1927. 8vo., orig. cloth, 1st ed. MacManus 238-1038 1978 $20

ROSENBACH, ABRAHAM SIMON WOLF 1876-   Henry C. Folger as a Collector. N.P., n.d. Orig. wrs., 1st ed., pres. copy, inscr'd by author, very good. MacManus 238-1039 1978 $25

ROSENBACH, ABRAHAM SIMON WOLF 1876-   The Unpublishable Memoirs. New York, 1917. 12mo., orig. cloth, 1st ed. MacManus 238-1040 1978 $35

ROSENBACH, ABRAHAM SIMON WOLF 1876-   The Unpublishable Memoirs. London, (1924). Frontis., orig. cloth, 1st Eng. ed., bkplt., nice. MacManus 238-1041 1978 $30

ROSENBAUM, S.   Against Home Rule. 1912. 1st ed., 1/2 leather, very good. Hyland 128-457 1978 £10.50

ROSENBERGER, JESSE L.   The Pennsylvania Germans, A Sketch Of Their History & Life, Of the Mennonites, & Of Side Lights From the Rosenberger Family. Chicago, (1923). 1st ed., photos, 8vo., orig. binding. Americanist 101-124 1978 $20

ROSENGARTEN, J. G.   American History From German Archives with
Reference to the German Soldiers in the Revolution and Franklin's Visit to Germany.
Lancaster, 1904. Illus., scarce. MacManus 239-1664 1978 $25

ROSENGARTEN, J. G.   French Colonists and Exiles in the U.S. Philadelphia, 1907. Fine copy. MacManus 239-427 1978 $17.50

ROSENHAIN, WALTER   Glass Manufacture. New York, 1912. Orig.
binding. Wolfe 39-210 1978 $17.50

ROSENSTEIN, I. G.   Theory and Practice of Homoeopathy. Louisville,
1840. Sm. 8vo., 1st ed. Morrill 239-221 1978 $40

ROSENTHAL, LEONARD   The Kingdom of the Pearl. New York, (1920).
Large quarto, 1st Amer. ed., no. 4 of 675 copies, tipped-in illuminated color
plates, white cloth spine, silver-decor. boards, fine. Victoria 34-255 1978
$235

ROSENTHAL, LUDWIG   Incunabula, Xylographica et Chalcographica.
Munich, 1892. Illus., tall 4to., orig. stiff wrs., text in French & German, torn
along backstrip. Morrill 239-592 1978 $15

THE ROSETTA Stone. (Philadelphia, 1859). 2nd ed., spine restored, covers a
bit worn, illus. MacManus 238-552 1978 $100

ROSINI, GIOVANNI   La Monaca Di Monza Storia Del Secolo XVII.
Pisa, 1829. 3 vols., frontis engraving in vol. I, contemp. calf, later rebacked,
gilt spines. Eaton 45-421 1978 £35

ROSOSPINA, F.   Pinacoteca della Pontificia Accademia delle belli
arti in Bologna. Bologna, 1830. Plts., lg. folio, full recent mor. George's 635-
50 1978 £35

ROSOSPINA, F.   Pinacoteca della pontificia Accademia delle belli
arti in Bologna. Bologna, 1830. Plts., folio, half roan, worn. George's 635-
51 1978 £12.50

ROSS, ALEXANDER 1590-1654   Pansebeia; or A View of All Religions in the
World.... London, 1675. 5th ed., portrait frontis., 8vo., contemp. calf, neatly
rebacked, leather label, N2 torn otherwise good condition. Traylen 88-321 1978
£50

ROSS, ALEX. M.   The Butterflies and Moths of Canada. Toronto,
1873. Ex-lib., cover slightly scuffed, illus. Hood 117-960 1978 $25

ROSS, ALEXANDER   Adventures of the First Settlers on the Oregon and
Columbia Rivers:.... London, 1849. Map, half mor., 1st ed. Ginsberg 14-899
1978 $300

ROSS, ALEXANDER 1591-1654   The History of the World: The Second Part, in
Six Books. 1652. Contemp. calf, neatly rebacked, first ed., folio. Howes 194-
91 1978 £50

ROSS, CHARLES   Correspondence of Charles, First Marquis Cornwallis. 1859. Second ed., maps, 3 vols., 8vo., orig. brown cloth. F. Edwards
1013-271 1978 £30

ROSS, CHRISTIAN K.   The Father's Story of Charley Ross, the Kidnapped
Child: Containing a Full and Complete Account of the Abduction of Charles Brewster Ross... Philadelphia, (1876). Cloth, worn at extremities. Hayman 72-688
1978 $8.50

ROSS, D. BARTON   A Southern Speaker. 1901. New ed. Austin
82-803 1978 $15

ROSS, ELLEN   The Wreck of the White Bear, East Indiaman.
New York, 1873. 4th. ed., 2 vols. in 1, 10 colored plts. Hood's 115-454 1978
$25

ROSS, FREDERICK   The Ruined Abbeys of Britain. Mackenzie,
c.1880. 2 vols., folio, coloured wood cut plts., orig. cloth, a little soiled.
Quaritch 983-27 1978 $150

ROSS, GEORGE   Case of the Hepatic Artery. Montreal, 1877.
Rittenhouse 49-587A 1976 $55

ROSS, GEORGE   Case of the Hepatic Artery. Montreal, 1877.
Rittenhouse 49-588 1976 $65

ROSS, GEORGE   The Senate of Canada; Its Constitution, Powers,
and Duties Historically Considered. Toronto, 1914. Hood's 115-612 1978 $25

ROSS, ISHBEL   Highland Twilight. 1934. First ed. Austin 82-
804 1978 $12.50

ROSS, ISHBELL   Through the Lich-Gate. New York, 1931. Illus.,
4to., full vellum, silk doublures, gilt top, uncut, boxed, fine, ed. ltd. to 175
copies, signed by Otis Skinner. Morrill 239-554 1978 $40

ROSS, JOHN   Narrative of a Second Voyage in Search of a
North-West Passage... (183?). 8vo., orig. cloth, engraved plts. Edwards 1012-
603 1978 £25

ROSS, JOHN   Narrative of a Second Voyage in Search of a
North-West Passage, and of a Residence in the Arctic Regions During the Years
1829-1833. London, 1835. Plts., frontis. missing, fldg. map, thick 4to., calf.
Salloch 345-164 1978 $175

ROSS, JOHN   Relation du Second Voyage Fait a la Recherche
d'un Passge au Nord-Quest.... Paris, 1835. 2 vols., plts., map, orig. half mor.,
Queen Marie Louise's set with her stamp. Ginsberg 14-900 1978 $225

ROSS, JOHN D.   Burnsiana: A Collection of Literary Odds and
Ends relating to Robert Burns. London, c. 1890. 3 vols. in 1, cr. 4to., orig.
cloth. K Books 244-272 1978 £12

ROSS, PETER   The Scot in America. New York, 1896. 1st
ed. MacManus 239-428 1978 $30

ROSS, ROBERT   Aubrey Beardsley. 1909. Plts., cloth gilt,
t.e.g., very good, scarce, first English ed. Bell Book 16-056 1978 £22.50

ROSS, VICTOR   Petroleum in Canada. Toronto, 1917. Illus.
Hood's 115-731 1978 $10

ROSS, WILLIAM WILSON   10,000 Miles by Land and Sea. Toronto, 1876.
Orig. cloth, 1st ed. Ginsberg 14-901 1978 $50

ROSS-OF-BLADENSBURG, JOHN FOSTER GEORGE   The Coldstream Guards
1914-1918. 1928. 3 vols., portrait frontis., roy. 8vo., orig. cloth. F. Edwards 1013-477 1978 £25

ROSS-OF-BLADENSBURG, JOHN FOSTER GEORGE   A History of the Coldstream Guards, 1815-95. 1896. Maps, illus. by Lt. N. R. Wilkinson, some
coloured, roy. 8vo. George's 635-854 1978 £15

ROSSETTI, CHRISTINA   New Poems, Hitherto Unpublished or Uncollected. London & New York, 1896. 1st ed., portrait, uncut, orig. cloth,
very good or better. Limestone 9-245 1978 $40

ROSSETTI, CHRISTINA   A Pageant and Other Poems. London, 1881.
1st ed., uncut, orig. cloth, bookplate, very good or better. Limestone 9-246
1978 $110

ROSSETTI, CHRISTINA   The Prince's Progress and Other Poems. London,
1866. 1st ed., 12mo., frontis., title page & design for cloth cover all by Dante
Rossetti, spine soiled, sm. spots to bottom of fr. bd., otherwise, very fine copy,
scarce. Current 24-47 1978 $245

ROSSETTI, CHRISTINA   The Prince's Progress and Other Poems. 1866.
Sm. 8vo., 1st ed., orig. cloth, pencilled notes, scarce, name & date on endpaper. Quaritch 979-276 1978 $170

ROSSETTI, CHRISTINA   The Prince's Progress and other poems. 1866.
Vignette, fscp. 8vo., contemp. half mor., covers rubbed, good, first English ed.
Bell Book 17-774 1978 £8.50

ROSSETTI, CHRISTINA   Speaking Likenesses. London, 1874. Illus. by
Arthur Hughes, 1st ed., sm. 8vo., a.e.g., 1st issue, fr. bd. decor. in gilt, orig.
blue cloth with gilt decor's & lettering, bds. soiled & worn at extremities, still a
good copy. Current 24-48 1978 $135

ROSSETTI, CHRISTINA   Verses. Eragny Press, 1906. One of 175 copies,
pr. in red and black, woodcut borders and initials, orig. patterned bds., edges uncut. George's 635-891 1978 £80

ROSSETTI, DANTE GABRIEL   Ballads and Narrative Poems. (Hammersmith,
Kelmscott Press, 1893). One of 310 copies on handmade paper, 8vo., orig.
vellum, silk ties, fine, slipcase. Houle 10-178 1978 $550

ROSSETTI, DANTE GABRIEL   The Blessed Damozel. Aiken, Palmetto Press, 1900. 12mo., orig. white wrs. prtd. in gold, 1 of 500 numbered copies, bkplt. of Thos. Bird Mosher, fronts., very good. Americanist 103-67 1978 $30

ROSSETTI, DANTE GABRIEL   Collected Works. 1890. 2 vols., sm. 8vo., quarter blue mor., gilt backs, gilt tops, neat inscr. each vol. Quaritch 979-277 1978 $70

ROSSETTI, DANTE GABRIEL   The Early Italian Poets from Ciullo d'Alcamo to Dante Alighieri (1100-1200-1300). 1861. Sm. 8vo., 1st ed., orig. cloth, little worn. Quaritch 979-278 1978 $150

ROSSETTI, DANTE GABRIEL   The Early Italian Poets From Ciullo D'Alcamo to Dante Alighieri... 1861. 1st. ed., orig. cloth, gilt, joints cracking & corners bumped. Eaton 45-422 1978 £20

ROSSETTI, DANTE GABRIEL   The House of Life. Cambridge, 1894. 1 of 500 copies prtd. on French handmade paper, paper over bds. Battery Park 1-45 1978 $115

ROSSETTI, DANTE GABRIEL   Italian Poets Chiefly Before Dante. Oxford, 1925. Reissue, very good, uncut, mussed signature on front end sheet. Limestone 9-247 1978 $22.50

ROSSETTI, DANTE GABRIEL   The Letters of. London, 1928. 1 of 560 numbered copies, 1st ed., gilt stamped cloth, t.e.g., uncut, fine. Houle 10-283 1978 $75

ROSSETTI, DANTE GABRIEL   Poems. London, 1870. 1st ed., 8vo., orig. gilt decor. cloth & endpapers, fine copy, bkplt. Current Misc. 8-57 1978 $135

ROSSETTI, DANTE GABRIEL   Poems. 1904. Plts., 2 vols., cr. 4to., half vellum. Howes 194-1130 1978 £21

ROSSI, GIAN VITTORIO   Pinocotheca Imaginum Illustrium, Doctrinae vel ingenii laude,.... Leipzig, 1692. 2nd ed., octavo, engraved frontispiece, full contemporary blind-stamped calf, Andrew Fletcher copy with signature in back paste-down. Bennett 20-68 1978 $175

ROSTER and Brief History of Co. K, Third Regiment, Minute Men. N. P. (Carver?), n.d. Portrs., 16mo., orig. cloth. Morrill 241-349 1978 $10

ROSTER Of Union War Veterans Residing in Washington County, Ohio, October 1st, 1914. N.P., (1914). Wrps., frontispiece portrait. Hayman 71-135 1978 $8.50

ROSTOVTZEFF, M.   History of the Ancient World. Oxford, 1928-30. Maps, plts., figs., 2 vols., roy. 8vo., ex-library copy. George's 635-1180 1978 £10.50

ROSTOVTZEFF, M.   History of the Ancient World. Rome, n.d. Vol. 2, plt. Allen 234-833 1978 $15

ROSWITHA OF GANDERSHEIM
Please turn to
HROTSVIT, OF GANDERSHEIM

ROTH, C. H.   The Eye. Boston, 1878. Frontis., 8vo., orig. wrs., 1st ed. Morrill 239-222 1978 $15

ROTH, CECIL   Haggadah. London, (1939). Lg. 4to., full pub. levant mor., hand sewn and hand bound, gilt panels and symbols by Sangorski & Sutcliffe, matching box, one of 250 on vellum, signed by illus. and author, miniature paintings in colors by Arthur Szyk. Duschnes 220-302 1978 $2,500

ROTH, ERNEST D.   American Etchers. New York, (1929). 4to., plts., vol. I, bds., edges rubbed. Biblo BL781-710 1978 $12

ROTH, HENRY LING   Oriental Silverwork. Malay and Chinese. A Handbook for Connoisseurs, Collectors, Students and Silversmiths. 1910. 4to., illus. Quaritch 983-130 1978 $140

ROTH, KELLY   Experiences and Travels. Illus., inscr'd by author. Austin 79-601 1978 $27.50

ROTH, SAMUEL   Jews Must Live. Golden Hind Press, 1934. Illus. Austin 79-602 1978 $17.50

ROTHENSTEIN, JOHN   Sixteen Letters from Oscar Wilde. London, Curwen Press, 1950. No. 352 of 550 numbered copies prtd. on Van Gelder paper, boxed. Battery Park 1-53 1978 $50

ROTHENSTEIN, WILLIAM   Men and Memories. New York, 1935. 1st U.S. ed., orig. bind. Petrilla 13-91 1978 $10

ROTHFELS, HANS   Die Deutsche Opposition Gegen Hitler. Krefeld, 1949. Hinges cracking, orig. bind., 1st ed. Petrilla 13-92 1978 $8.50

ROTHSCHILD, ALONZO   "Honest Abe". Boston, 1917. 1st ed., illus., ports., orig. cloth-backed bds., ltd. to 330 copies, fine. MacManus 239-891 1978 $27.50

ROTHROCK, MARY U.   The French Broad-Holston Country. Knoxville, 1946. Illus., 8vo., 1st ed., orig. cloth. Morrill 241-569 1978 $17.50

ROTTENSTEIN, J. B.   Traite Theorique Et Pratique D' Anesthesie Chirur-gicale Avec Applications A L'Obstetrique, a l'Ophthalmologie, a l'Art Dentaire. Paris, 1879. 8vo., frontis. portr., wood engrs., orig. blue prtd. wrs., library stamps & bkplt., good uncut copy, pres. inscr. from author, 1st ed. Zeitlin 245-310 1978 $87.50

ROUAULT, GEORGES   Soliloques. Neuchatel, 1944. Lg. 8vo., orig. wr., uncut, ltd. ed., numbered copy on Verge creme paper, illus. Goldschmidt 110-54 1978 $75

ROUGE, JACQUES, VICOMTE DE   Geographie Ancienne de la Basse-Egypt. Paris, 1891. Map, half green mor. gilt, ex-lib., 8vo. K Books 239-115 1978 £12

ROUGHLEY, T. C.   Wonders of the Great Barrier Reef. Australia, 1936. Plates, 8vo., orig. cloth. Book Chest 17-307 1978 $23.50

ROURKE, C.   Audubon. New York, (1936). Illus., plates, 8vo., orig. cloth. Book Chest 17-308 1978 $12.50

ROURKE, THOMAS   Simon Bolivar...Man of Glory. New York, 1939. Illus., 1st ed. Biblo BL781-104 1978 $9

ROUSSAT, RICHARD   Des Elements Et Principes D'Astronomie. Paris, 1552. 8vo., vellum, rare. Salloch 345-165 1978 $350

ROUSSEAU, JEAN-BAPTISTE   Oeuvres de J.B. Rousseau. Paris, 1820. 5 vols., 8vo, portrait, contemp. vellum gilt, occasional faint foxing, fine copy, nouvelle ed. Hannas 54-254 1978 £75

ROUSSEAU, JEAN JACQUES   The Confessions. New York, 1928. 2 vols. in 1, thick 8vo., cloth. Salloch 348-225 1978 $10

ROUSSEAU, JEAN JACQUES   The Confessions of... London, Nonesuch Press, 1938. 2 vols., 8vo, orig. niger morocco, spines darkened, ltd. ed. of 800 copies. Traylen 88-322 1978 £25

ROUSSEAU, JEAN JACQUES   The Confessions. Nonesuch Press, 1938. 2 vols., orig. pigskin, gilt tops, fine, ed. ltd. to 800 copies, printed on mould-made paper, 8vo. Howes 194-1440 1978 £42

ROUSSEAU, JEAN JACQUES   Correspondance Originale et Inedite de .... Paris, 1803. 2 vols., 12mo, rebound, cloth, 3 1/2 x 5", inscribed on endpaper by Lady Elinor Butler of Llangollen. Eaton 45-423 1978 £20

ROUSSEAU, JEAN-JACQUES   A Discourse upon the Original and Foundation of the Inequality among Mankind. 1761. First English ed., rare, contemp. calf, binding wormed at sides but sound, 8vo. Howes 194-441 1978 £75

ROUSSEAU, JEAN JACQUES   Discours Sur L'Origine Et Fondemens De L'Inegalite Parmi Les Hommes. London, 1782. Frontis. by Moreau, 12mo., calf. Salloch 348-222 1978 $50

ROUSSEAU, JEAN JACQUES   Eloisa. London, 1810. 3 vols., covers missing. Biblo 247-854 1978 $22.50

ROUSSEAU, JEAN JACQUES   Emile, Ou De L'Education. Amsterdan, 1762. 1st. ed., frontis, 4 vols., sm. 8vo, contemp. mottled calf, gilt spines, leather labels, joints weakening, good copy. Traylen 88-443 1978 £20

ROUSSEAU, JEAN JACQUES   Emile, Ou L'Education. Geneva, 1780. 4 vols., 8vo., orig. old paper bind. Salloch 348-223 1978 $55

ROUSSEAU, JEAN JACQUES   Emilies and Sophia. 1733. Vols. 1 and 2 (ex 4), sm. 8vo., contemp. calf. George's 635-1477 1978 £8.50

ROUSSEAU, JEAN JACQUES   Oeuvres Completes. Paris, 1839. 8 vols., contemp. half navy calf, 8vo. Howes 194-1443 1978 £40

ROUSSEAU, JEAN JACQUES   Oeuvres Politiques. Basle, 1795. 2 vols., sm. 8vo., contemp. calf with labels. Salloch 348-224 1978 $60

ROUSSEAU, JEAN JACQUES   The Social Contract. New York, n.d. 8vo., cloth. Salloch 348-226 1978 $8

ROUSSEAU, JEAN JACQUES   Traites sur la Musique. Geneva, 1781. Orig. ed., contemp. calf, rubbed, green and red mor. labels on spine. Gilhofer 75-93 1978 SFr 500

ROUSSEL, NAPOLEAN   A Mes Enfants. Paris, 1855. Engravings, cr. 8vo, embossed paper bds., gilt, edges rubbed. Eaton 45-424 1978 £5

ROUSSET, J.   Memoires du Regne de Catherine Imperatrice & Souveraine de toute la Russie.... Amsterdam, 1729. 12mo., marbled bds., calf spine, plts., second ed. King 7-384 1978 £25

"ROUTE Step!" Toledo, 1896. Orig. binding, clean, some soiling of cover. Hayman 71-560 1978 $10

ROUTES and Rates for Summer Tours 1883 (via) Utica and Black River Railroad. Utica, 1883. Railroad maps, illus., pict. ads, covers chipped, front detached, maps & text near-fine. Butterfield 21-395 1978 $25

ROUTH, M. J.   Reliquae sacrae. Oxonii, 1846-58. 7 vols., full calf, spines faded, 8vo. George's 635-1123 1978 £42.50

ROUVIER, F.   Trois Apotres de la Nouvelle Fance: Les P.P. Jean de Brebeuf, Is. Jogues, et G. Lalment. Bruges, n.d. Unopened. Hood's 115-613 1978 $15

ROUX, PHILIBERT JOSEPH   A Narrative of a Journey to London, in 1814. London, 1816. 2nd ed., 8vo., orig. bds., lightly browned, bkplts. & library stamps, good uncut copy. Zeitlin 245-312 1978 $85

ROUX, PHILIBERT JOSEPH   Relation D'un Voyage Fait A Londres En 1814. Paris, 1815. 8vo., contemp. half calf, bds., lightly browned, bkplt., library stamps, signatures of former owners, good copy, 1st ed. Zeitlin 245-311 1978 $175

ROWAN, A. H.   The Autobiography of.... (1840). Octavo bound in cloth, reprint. Hyland 128-970 1978 £5.50

ROWAN, JOHN J.   The Emigrant and Sportsman in Canada. London & Stanford, 1876. Fldg. map, 1st ed. Austin 79-603 1978 $37.50

ROWAN-ROBINSON, H.   England, Italy, Abyssinia. London, 1935. 8 vo, maps, illus., orig. cloth. K Books 239-417 1978 £5

ROWBOTHAM, G. F.   Acute Injuries of the Head. Baltimore, 1942. Ex-library. Rittenhouse 49-689 1976 $15

ROWE, DOROTHY   The Rabbit Lantern and Other Stories of Chinese Children. New York, 1925. Color plates and signed inscription by Rowe, 1st ed., very good. Victoria 34-706 1978 $10

ROWE, ELIZABETH   Friendship in Death... 1745. Title laid-down, browned, several contemp. signatures in ink, contemp. tree calf, joints weak. Eaton 45-426 1978 £20

ROWE, ELIZABETH   Friendship in Death... 1753. 2 vols., old calf. Eaton 45-427 1978 £20

ROWE, ELIZABETH   The Works. 1796. 4 vols., sm. 8vo., contemp. calf, one joint cracked, best ed. Howes 194-442 1978 £35

ROWE, GEORGE STRINGER   Fiji and The Fijians. London, 1858. 1st. ed., 2 vols., sm. 8vo, chromolithograph frontispiece, plts., 2 coloured, illus., folding map, neatly repaired, quarter calf, gilt backs. Deighton 5-100 1978 £65

ROWE, GEORGE STRINGER   Fiji and the Fijians. 1858. 2 vols., sm. 8vo, map, 3 coloured, plts., illus., slightly soiled, orig. cloth. Edwards 1012-371 1978 £34

ROWELL, GEORGE AUGUSTUS   An Essay on the Beneficient Distribution of the Sense of Pain. London, Edinburgh & Oxford, 1862. 2nd ed., 8vo., orig. prtd. wrs., slightly dust-soiled, good copy. Zeitlin 245-221 1978 $22.50

ROWELL, N. W.   The British Empire and World Peace; Being the Burwash Memorial Lectures. Toronto, 1922. Hood 116-652 1978 $25

ROWLAND, MRS. DUNBAR   Andrew Jackson's Campaign Against the British or the Mississippi Territory in the War of 1812. NY, 1926. Illus., pres. copy from author, Bell Wiley's copy. Broadfoot's 1978 $16.00

ROWLAND, DUNBAR   History of Mississippi: The Heart of the South. Chicago, 1925. Chicago, 1925. 2 vols., Bell Wiley's copy. Broadfoot's 44-901 1978 $60

ROWLAND, DUNBAR   Jefferson Davis, Constitutionalist. Jackson, 1923. 10 vols. & index, defects on rear board, fine, Bell Wiley's copy. Broadfoot's 44-326 1978 $150

ROWLAND, DUNBAR   Jefferson Davis' Place in History as Revealed in His Letters, Papers, and Speeches. Jackson, 1923. Wraps, Bell Wiley's copy. Broadfoot's 44-327 1978 $9.00

ROWLAND, DUNBAR   Publications of the Mississippi Historical Society Centenary Series. Jackson, Miss., 1916. 2 vols., presen. copy from Rowland to Wiley. Bell Wiley's copy. Broadfoot 46-560 1978 $25

ROWLAND, DUNBAR   A Symposium on the Place of Discovery of the Mississippi River by Hernando DeSoto. Jackson, 1927. Worn spot on front cover, Bell Wiley's copy. Broadfoot's 44-902 1978 $14

ROWLAND, ERON   Varina Howell, Wife of Jefferson Davis. New York, 1927. Faded, 2 vols., pres. copy from author to Bell Wiley. Broadfoot's 44-328 1978 $30

ROWLAND, EVA EICKEMEYER   In and Out of the Nursery. (1900). Oblong folio. Victoria 34-707 1978 $17.50

ROWLAND, LENORE   The Romance of La Puente Rancho. (Puente, 1948). Wrs., 1st ed., fine copy autographed by author, numerous corrections & additions in her hand. Dykes 34-241 1978 $15

ROWLANDS, H.   Mona Antiqua Restaurata... Dublin, 1723. 4to., 1st ed., engraved plts., a little spotted, contemp. mottled calf gilt. Quaritch 983-28 1978 $95

ROWLANDS, RICHARD PSEUD.
Please turn to
VERSTEGEN, RICHARD FL. 1565-1620

ROWLANDSON, THOMAS   Journal of Sentimental Travels in the Southern Provinces of France, Shortly Before the Revolution. 1821. Roy. 8vo., coloured plts., tall copy, crimson mor., gilt top, other edges uncut, bookplts. Quaritch 983-364 1978 $525

ROWLANDSON, THOMAS   Loyal Volunteers of London and Environs, Infantry and Cavalry in Their Respective Uniforms... (1798-99). Imp. 4to., handcoloured aquatints, red. mor. gilt, gilt edges by Bayntun, good copy. Quaritch 983-71 1978 $6,000

ROWLANDSON, THOMAS   Loyal Volunteers of London and Environs.... Ackermann, (1798-99). Finely coloured aquatint plts., 4to., full mor., matching slipcase. F. Edwards 1013-417 1978 £2,600

ROWLEY, HUGH   Puniana; or, Thoughts Wise and Other-Wise.... Lond., 1866. Over 100 illus. by Rowley, orig. cloth binding bevelled edges, edges gilt, very good cond. Greene 78-330 1978 $75.00

ROWLEY, O. R.   The Anglican Episcopate of Canada and Newfoundland. Milwaukee, 1923. Spine worn. Hood 117-366 1978 $35

ROWNING, JOHN   A Compendious System of Natural Philosophy. 1753. Plts., 4 parts in 2 vols., nice, contemp. calf, spines gilt, 8vo. Howes 194-443 1978 £50

ROWNTREE, B. SEEBOHM   Poverty: A Study of Town Life. 1902. 4th. ed., maps, 8vo., orig. cloth, nice. Fenning 32-287 1978 £5

ROWSON, SUSANNA   Charlotte Temple, A Tale Of Truth. Philadelphia, 1809. 2 vols. in 1, 8th Amer. ed., 12mo., orig. calf, rubbed, scarce early ed. Americanist 101-125 1978 $40

ROY, J. EDMOND   Histoire de la Seigneurie de Lauzon. Volume 1.
Levis, 1897. Orig. wrappers, bound in half mor.   Wolfe 39-493 1978 $40

ROY, J. EDMOND   Histoire de la Seigneurie de Lauzon. Volume III.
Levis, 1900. Half calf, autograph inscription signed by author.   Wolfe 39-494
1978 $40

ROY, J. EDMOND   In and Around Tadousac. Levis, 1891. Orig.
printed wrappers.   Wolfe 39-492 1978 $20

ROY, JULES   Turenne, Sa Vie, les Institutions Militaires de
son Temps. Paris, 1884. Thick imp. 8vo., orig. cloth, calf spine, portraits,
coloured plts., maps.   F. Edwards 1013-440 1978 $30

ROY, PIERRF GEORGES   La Famille le Compte Dupre. Levis, 1941.
Card cover, pgs. unopened.   Hood 116-50 1978 $17.50

ROY, PIERRE GEORGES   Old Manors Old Houses. Quebec, 1927. First
series, numerous half-tones, full calf, joint cracked.   Wolfe 39-495 1978 $80

ROY, WILLIAM   The Military Antiquities of the Romans in Britain.
1793. Lg. folio, contemp. calf, rebacked, plts.   F. Edwards 1013-419 1978
£65

ROY, WILLIAM   The Military Antiquities of the Romans in North
Britain and Particularly their Ancient System of Castrametation.... London, 1793.
1st. ed., lg. folio, engraved plts., half calf, neatly rebacked retaining orig. backstrip, morocco label, frontispiece, fine copy.   Deighton 5-139 1978 £135

ROYAL CANADIAN YACHT CLUB, TORONTO   Annals of the Royal Canadian
Yacht Club, 1852-1937.... Toronto, 1937. Photos & sketches.   Hood 117-763
1978 $40

ROYAL DISPENSARY FOR DISEASES OF THE EAR   Prospectus of the Royal Dispensary for Diseases of the Ear, for the Relief of the Poor, Dean Street, Soho
Square. London, 1824. Folio, unbound.   Quaritch 977-68 1978 $75

THE ROYAL Fusiliers in an Outline of Military History, 1685-1932. Aldershot,
1933. Illus., 8vo.   George's 635-855 1978 £5.25

A ROYAL Guest. Oxford: Daniel Press, 1900. 8vo., orig. light grey wrs., 1 of
110 copies, front cover very slightly torn, but fine.   MacManus 238-788 1978
$125

THE ROYAL Highland Regiment. Edinburgh, 1913. Coloured frontis., plts., imp.
8vo., orig. cloth.   F. Edwards 1013-513 1978 £18

ROYAL ONTARIO MUSEUM OF ARCHAEOLOGY   European Tapestries XV to
XVIII Centuries; Catalogue of a Loan Exhibition. Toronto, 1945. Card cover,
illus.   Hood 116-165 1978 $7.50

ROYCE, WILLIAM HOBART   A Balzac Bibliography. Chicago, 1929-30.
2 vols., blue bds. & cloth, 1st ed., vol. I with dust jacket, vol. II without jacket, very good.   Bradley 49-32 1978 $20

ROYLE, J. F.   An Essay on the Antiquity of Hindoo Medicine.
London, 1837.   Rittenhouse 49-691 1976 $175

ROZE, LOUISE-ANDREE   Josette et Jehan de Reims. Paris, n.d. Large
quarto, plate in pochoire and illus., very good.   Victoria 34-211 1978 $32.50

RUARK, ROBERT   Grenadine Etching. Garden City, 1947. Very
good, dw.   Bernard 5-231 1978 $15

RUCELLAI, GIOVANNI   Le Opere D. M. Giovanni Rucellai Ora Per La
Prima Volta in un Volume Raccolte... Padua, 1772. Cr. 8vo, engraved frontis,
wood-eng. initials & head & tail pieces, vellum.   Eaton 45-432 1978 £10

RUCKER, ELIZABETH HOYLE   The Genealogy of Peiter Heyl and His Descendants. Shelby, 1938.   Broadfoot 50-191 1978 $75

RUDBECK, OLOF   Insidiae Structae, Olai Rudbeckii Sueci Ductus
Hepaticis Aquosis, & vasis Glandularum Serosis. Lugduni Batavorum, 1654.
Sm. woodcuts, sm. 8vo., half vellum, 1st ed., very rare, fine copy.   Offen-
bacher 30-133 1978 $450

RUDD, P.   An Answer to the Pamphlet..in Letters to Edward
Cooke..Letter the Second. Dublin, 1799. 1st ed., plain wrs.   Hyland 128-466
1978 £8

RUDE, HANS   William S. Knudsen. 1945. Illus. with photos, paper, written in Danish.   Austin 79-606 1978 $17.50

RUDIMENTS of Ancient Architecture, Containing an Historical Account of the
Five Orders, with Their Proportions, and Examples of Each from Antiques... 1804.
3rd ed., enlarged, 8vo., plts., contemp. half calf.   Quaritch 983-49 1978 $45

RUDOLPH, JOSEPH   Pickups from the "American Way", Early Life
and Civil War Reminiscences of Capt. Joseph Rudolph. N.P., 1941. Wrs.,
Bell Wiley's copy.   Broadfoot's 44-585 1978 $10

RUETLINGER, JOHANN CASPAR   Neuw Zugerichte Schreibkunst. Zurich, 1648.
Sm. folio, half vellum, plts., fine with wide margins.   Schumann 511-51 1978
sFr 8,500

RUFF, SIEGFRIED   Grundriss Der Luftfahrtmedizin. Leipzig, 1939.
8vo., illus., orig. blue cloth, silver letter, d.w., author's pres. inscr. dated
July 1939, ex-lib., 1st ed.   Zeitlin 245-222 1978 $85

RUFFHEAD, OWEN   The Life of A. Pope. 1769. Plt., contemp.
mottled calf, first ed., 8vo.   Howes 194-423 1978 £45

RUFFHEAD, OWEN   The Life of Alexander Pope. 1769. 8vo., tree
calf gilt, rebacked, marbled edges and endpapers, frontispiece, first ed.   P. M.
Hill 142-206 1978 £55

RUFFIN, EDMUND   An Essay on Calcareous Manures. Shellbanks,
1835. Foxed, new cloth, Bell Wiley's copy.   Broadfoot's 44-985 1978 $30.00

RUFFINI, GIOVANNI   Doctor Antonio, A Tale. Edinburgh, 1855.
1st. ed., attractive half calf, gilt spine, red label, v.g.   Jarndyce 16-982
1978 £14.50

RUFFINI, GIOVANNI   Doctor Antonio. New York, 1874. Orig. cloth,
good.   Greene 78-97 1978 $15

RUFFNER, E. H.   Report of a Reconnaissance in the Ute Country
Made in the Year 1873. Washington, 1874. Folding map, half mor., 1st ed.
Ginsberg 14-902 1978 $60

RUGGLES, ALICE MC GUFFEY   The Story of the McGuffeys. 1950. Illus.
Austin 82-809 1978 $11

RUGGLES, SAMUEL B.   Law of Burial. Albany, 1858. Disbound.
Butterfield 21-396 1978 $17.50

RUGGLES, SAMUEL B.   Resources of the United States. New York,
1864. Disbound, minor defect at binding edge.   Hayman 73-663 1978 $7.50

RUHRAH, JOHN   Pediatric Biographies. Baltimore, n.d. Pres.
copy signed by author.   Rittenhouse 49-693 1976 $35

THE RUINOUS Tendency of Auctioneering, and the Necessity of Restraining It
for the Benefit of Trade, Demonstrated in a Letter to the Right Hon. Lord Bathhurst,
President of the Board of Trade. London, 1828. Disbound.   Hayman 73-664
1978 $20

THE RULES and Constitutions For Governing and Managing the Maiden-Hospital....
Edinburgh, 1731. Sm. 8vo., unbound.   P. M. Hill 142-215 1978 £18

RULES and Forms of Procedure in the Church Courts of the Presbyterian Church in
Canada, Adopted by the General Assembly of 1889. Toronto, 1889. Hood 116-
316 1978 $12.50

RUMBAUGH, JACOB   Reminiscences of... N.P., 1910. Illus., orig.
cloth, 1st ed.   Ginsberg 14-903 1978 $60

RUMFORD, SIR BENJAMIN THOMPSON, COUNT   Experimental Essays,
Political, Economical and Philosophical. Dublin, 1796. 3rd ed., illus., plts.,
8vo., recent bds., nice.   Fenning 32-328 1978 £24

RUMP: or an Exact Collection of the Choycest Poems and Songs Relating to the Late
Times. London, 1662. 8vo, full black 19th-century morocco, gilt, spine gilt,
a.e.g., by J. Clarke, morocco solander case, 2nd ed., fine copy, engraved title,
facing frontispiece, and longitudinal half-title, contemporary signature of
Fabian Phillipps.   Ximenes 47-245 1978 $375

RUMPEL, J.   Lexicon Pindaricum. 1833. Half calf.   Allen
234-735 1978 $20

RUNKLE, BERTA   The Helmet of Havarre. 1901. Illus., first ed.
Austin 82-810 1978 $11

RUNYON, DAMON   Damon Runyon Favorites. New York and Cleveland, (1946). Pages browned, good, in chipped d.w. Bernard 5-234 1978 $15

RUNYON, DAMON   My Old Man. 1940. Drawings by Josef, very
good, worn d.w., first English ed. Bell Book 16-753 1978 £5.50

RUNYON, DAMON   Short Takes. New York, (1946). Very good in
chipped dw. Bernard 5-235 1978 $20

RUNYON, DAMON   Short Takes. London, (1948). Very good.
Bernard 5-236 1978 $15

RUPP, FREDERICK A.   John Montcalm, Heretic: A Tale of the Maryland
Hills. Reading, 1908. Rittenhouse 49-696 1976 $10

RUPP, I. DANIEL   A Collection of Upwards of 30,000 Names of
German, Swiss, Dutch, French and Other Immigrants in Pennsylvania from 1727 to
1776. Philadelphia, 1876. 2nd rev'd. and enlarged ed., very fine. MacManus
239-1665 1978 $25

RUPP, I. DANIEL   He Pasa Ekklesia. Philadelphia, 1844. Full
calf, lst ed. Ginsberg 14-682 1978 $75

RUPP, I. DANIEL   He Pasa Ekklesia. Philadelphia, 1844. Austin 79-609 1978 $47.50

RUPPANER, ANTOINE   Hypodermic Injections in the Treatment of Neuralgia, Rheumatism, Gout, and Other Diseases. Boston, 1865. lst ed., sm. 8vo.,
rare, rebacked, orig. cloth bds., interior fine, library stamp. Current 24-125
1978 $675

RUPPELL, E.   Systematische Uebersight der Vogel Nord-Ost-
Afrika's. Frankfurt, 1845. Hand coloured litho. plts., roy. 8vo, binder's cloth,
scarce. Traylen 88-660 1978 £400

RUPPIN, ARTHUR   Der Aufbau Des Landes Israel. Berlin, 1919.
In German. Austin 79-610 1978 $27.50

RUPPIN, ARTHUR   The Jews of Today. New York, 1913. Biblo
251-701 1978 $12.50

RUSCELLI, GIROLAMO   Espositioni et Introduttioni Universali, sopra
tutta la Geografia di Tolomeo. Venetia, 1573. 4to., wrs. Argosy Special-74
1978 $50

RUSCELLI, GIROLAMO   Tre Discorsi.... Venice, 1553. lst ed., small
quarto, contemp. limp vellum, marginal notations, marginal staining throughout,
woodcut title device, woodcut initials, Fletcher & Saltoun copy. Bennett 20-176
1978 $225

RUSCHENBERGER, W. S. W.   Three Years in the Pacific. London, 1835.
2 vols., 8vo, contemp. calf, rebacked. Edwards 1012-673 1978 £175

RUSCONI, MAURO   Descrizione Anatomica Degli Organi Della Circolazione Delle Larve Delle Salamandre Acquatiche.... Pavia, 1817. lst ed.,
folio, fold-out engraved colored plate, full green straight-grained mor., floral
gilt borders, spine lightly faded else fine. Bennett 20-177 1978 $1,250

RUSCONI, MAURO   Histoire Naturelle Developpement et Metamor-
phose de la Salamandre Terrestre.... Pavie, 1854. lst ed., folio, fold-out hand
colored engravings, red pebbled cloth, fine, gilt on spine, large copy, extremely
rare. Bennett 20-178 1978 $1,250

RUSH, BENJAMIN   Sixteen Introductory Lectures to Courses of Lectures Upon the Institutes and Practice of Medicine. Philadelphia, 1811. Cover
has spots, usual wear, title strip present, contents remarkably free of foxing and
browning. Rittenhouse 49-695 1976 $275

RUSH, JACOB   Charges, and Extracts of Charges, on Moral
and Religious Subjects..by..Pres. of 3rd District of Court of Common Pleas...
(New York), 1815. Very good. Nestler Rare 78-48 1978 $15

RUSH, JAMES   Philosophy of the Human Voice. Philadelphia,
1855. Fourth ed., worn, some foxing. Rittenhouse 49-694 1976 $10

RUSH, RICHARD   A Letter to Albert Gallatin, on the French
Claims to the Newfoundland Fisheries... New York, 1890. Orig. bds., ltd. to
250 copies, covers soiled, hinges cracked. MacManus 239-429 1978 $10

RUSH, RICHARD   Memoranda of a Residence at the Court of London From 1819 to 1825. Philadelphia, 1845. MacManus 239-430 1978 $27.50

RUSH, SAMUEL   A Discourse on the Moral Influence of Sounds...
Philadelphia, 1839. 8vo., orig. wrs., trimmed close, slightly uneven, lst ed.
Morrill 239-223 1978 $25

RUSHFORTH, G. M.   Latin Historical Inscriptions, Illustrating the History of the Early Empire. 1930. 2nd ed. Allen 234-836 1978 $9.50

RUSHWORTH, JOHN   Historical Collections of Private Passages of
State.... 1721. 8 vols., folio, full contemp. calf, some light age-browning.
Howes 194-444 1978 £175

RUSK, THOMAS J.   Speech of Hon. Thomas J. Rusk, of Texas, on
the Mexican War. Washington, 1848. Sewn. Jenkins 116-1203 1978 $65

RUSKAY, SOPHIE   Horsecars and Cobblestones. Beechhurst
Press, 1948. Illus. Austin 79-611 1978 $10

RUSKIN, JOHN   Arrows of the Chase. Being a Collection of
Scattered Letters, Etc. Sunnyside, Orpington, Kent, 1880. 2 vols., orig. paper
covered bds., lst ed., spines somewhat worn, otherwise very good. MacManus
238-375 1978 $45

RUSKIN, JOHN   Arrows of the Chace. 1880. lst. ed., 2 vols.,
4to, lg. paper copy, half titles, frontis, uncut, orig. grey bds., paper labels,
hinges little worn, good, inserted are 3 photos. Jarndyce 16-983 1978 £38

RUSKIN, JOHN   Catalogue of I: a collection of Drawings in
City, Town & Hamlet by Albert Goodwin, II: A Series of Drawings made for St.
George's Guild. 1886. Good, in chipped wraps, first English ed. Bell Book
16-756 1978 £4

RUSKIN, JOHN   Catalogue of the Ruskin Centenary Exhibition;
held at the Royal Academy, Oct.-Nov. 1919. 1919. Good, wraps, first English
ed. Bell Book 16-757 1978 £4

RUSKIN, JOHN   The Crown of Wild Olive. Philadelphia,
1891. 1 of 550 numbered copies, thick 8vo., plts., figures, orig. blue
cloth, t.e.g., uncut, fine. Houle 10-285 1978 $20

RUSKIN, JOHN   The Elements of Drawing; in Three Letters to
Beginners. 1857. Post 8vo., lst ed., illus. by author, orig. cloth. Quaritch
983-249 1978 $110

RUSKIN, JOHN   The Elements of Drawing. London, 1857.
Illus. by author, 8vo., lst ed., orig. cloth. Morrill 241-510 1978 $25

RUSKIN, JOHN   The Elements of Drawing; In Three Letters to
Beginners. London, 1857. Octavo, full original blind-stamped green publisher's
cloth, lst ed. Bennett 7-93 1978 $85

RUSKIN, JOHN   The Elements of Drawing, in Three Letters to Beginners. 1857. Second ed., illus. drawn by author, cr.8vo. George's 635-208
1978 £5

RUSKIN, JOHN   The Elements of Perspective. 1859. 8vo., orig.
cloth, good copy, scarce. Quaritch 983-250 1978 $60

RUSKIN, JOHN   Lectures on Art. Oxford, 1870. Good, first
English ed. Bell Book 16-754 1978 £12

RUSKIN, JOHN   Letters upon Subjects of General Interest to
Various Correspondents. London, (For T. J. Wise) 1892. First ed., orig. binding,
very nice. Rota 211-804 1978 £25

RUSKIN, JOHN   Modern Painters... 1903. 4th ed., 6 vols., 8
8vo., coloured and plain plts., half calf, gilt spines. Quaritch 983-251 1978
$75

RUSKIN, JOHN   The Nature of Gothic. Hammrsmith, Kelmscott
Press, 1892. 8vo., vellum, illus., one of 500 copies, fine. Duschnes 220-167
1978 $225

RUSKIN, JOHN   Notes on Samuel Prout and William Hunt, in Illustration of a Loan Collections of Drawings. 1880. Folio, plts., half leather,
gilt top. Quaritch 983-252 1978 $75

RUSKIN, JOHN   On the Old Road. A Collection of Miscellaneous
Essays, Pamphlets, Etc. Sunnyside, Orpington, Kent, 1885. 3 vols., orig. paper
covered bds., 1st ed., spines a bit worn, outer hinges cracked, otherwise very
good, 1,000 copies printed. MacManus 238-376 1978 $85

RUSKIN, JOHN   The Poems. Orpington, 1891. First ed., plts.
by the author, 2 vols., 4to., orig. half vellum, entirely uncut, only 800 copies
were printed. Howes 194-1137 1978 £36

RUSKIN, JOHN   Poems. Orpington, 1891. 2 vols., 4to, plts.,
cloth. Eaton 45-433 1978 £20

RUSKIN, JOHN   Praeterita: Outlines of Scenes and Thoughts
Perhaps Worthy of Memory in My Past Life. Orpington, 1885-89. First ed., in
the orig. 28 parts as issued, plts., 4to., 12 x 9 1/2 inches, orig. printed wrappers,
uncut, partly unopened, fine. Howes 194-1138 1978 £120

RUSKIN, JOHN   Sesame and Lilies. 1864. Stitching weak,
cloth, gilt. Eaton 45-434 1978 £6

RUSKIN, JOHN   Studies in Both Arts: Being 10 Subjects, Drawn
and Described. Orpington, 1895. Folio, plain and coloured plts., dec. cloth,
slightly dust-soiled, uncut. Quaritch 983-253 1978 $100

RUSKIN, JOHN   Unto This Last. Edinburgh, Ballantyne Press,
1902. Orig. vellum, with ties, uncut, 8vo., ed. ltd. to 400 copies, on hand-made
paper. Howes 194-607 1978 £25

RUSKIN, JOHN   Works. London, 1903-1912. Illus., 39 vols.,
plts. some coloured, facsimiles, thick roy. 8vo, orig. buckram. Traylen 88-
326 1978 £500

RUSLING, J. F.   Men and Things I Saw in the Civil War Days.
New York, 1899. 8vo, half morocco, joints cracked, portraits. Edwards 1012-
549 1978 £10

RUSS, D.   Der Wellensittich, Seine Naturgeschichte,
Pflage, und Bucht. 12mo, orig. cloth. Book Chest 17-325 1978 $28.50

RUSS, K.   Die Prachfinken. Magdeburg, 1898. 12mo,
orig. cloth. Book Chest 17-324 1978 $32

RUSSELL, LADY   The Rose Goddess and other Sketches of Mystery
and Romance. 1910. Collotypes, illus., roy. 8vo. George's 635-753 1978
£8.50

RUSSELL, A. J.   On Champlain's Astrolabe, lost on the 7th June,
1613 and Found in August, 1867. Montreal, 1879. Card cover mended, folding
map. Hood's 115-614 1978 $45

RUSSELL, A. J.   The Red River Country, Hudson's Bay and North-
west Territories, Considered in Relation to Canada... Ottawa, 1869. Illus.,
map, wrs. Hood 116-876 1978 $115

RUSSELL, BERTRAND   Human Knowledge: its scope and limits. 1948.
Very good, d.w., first English ed. Bell Book 16-759 1978 £4.50

RUSSELL, BERTRAND   The Principles of Mathematics. Cambridge,
University Press, 1903. Vol. 1, lg. 8vo., orig. cloth, gilt, uncut, little worn,
but fine copy, newsclippings pasted on endpaper, 1st ed. Norman 5-246 1978
$250

RUSSELL, C.   The Parnell Commission; The Opening Speech
for the Defence. 1889. 1st ed., a.e.g., full leather, front loose, good.
Hyland 128-325 1978 £10

RUSSELL, C.   The Parnell Commission; The Opening Speech
for the Defence. 1889. Revised, shaky, octavo bound in cloth, reprint. Hyland
128-326 1978 £4

RUSSELL, CHARLES EDWARD   Songs of Democracy and Other Themes. New
York, 1909. 1st ed., fr. cover spotted. Biblo 251-623 1978 $15

RUSSELL, CHARLES H.   Charles Howland Russell, 1851-1921. By His Son.
New York, 1935. Illus. Biblo BL781-224 1978 $8.50

RUSSELL, CHARLES M.   Good Medicine. Garden City, 1930. 1st ed.,
decor. cloth, colored pic. end sheets, illus., scarce, very good copy, slipcase.
Dykes 34-35 1978 $75

RUSSELL, GEORGE, OF DURBAN   The History of Old Durban, and Reminiscences of an Emigrant of 1850. Natal, 1899. Plts., decor. cloth, 8vo. K
Books 244-437 1978 £25

RUSSELL, GEORGE WILLIAM   Dark Weeping. London, 1929. Lg. paper ed.,
signed, near mint. Desmarais B-5 1978 $25

RUSSELL, GEORGE WILLIAM   Imaginations and Reveries. Dublin, 1915. 1st
ed., orig. cloth, d.j., a little worn, fine, rare in d.j. MacManus 238-602
1978 $50

RUSSELL, GEORGE WILLIAM   Some Passages from the Letters of AE to W.B.
Yeats. Dublin, Cuala Press, 1936. One of 300 copies, linen-backed bds., very
good, English first ed. Bell Book 16-001 1978 £40

RUSSELL, JOHN   Essays and Sketches of Life and Character.
1821. 2nd. ed., calf, leading hinge weakening, otherwise v.g. Jarndyce 16-
985 1978 £14.50

RUSSELL, JOHN SCOTT   On the Nature, Properties, and Applications of
Steam, and on Steam Navigation. 1841. 8vo., table, plts. printed on india paper,
woodcuts, 3 plts. soiled and slightly frayed in margins & another torn, contemp.
half calf, rebacked. Quaritch 977-252 1978 $100

RUSSELL, LINDSAY   America to Japan. 1915. Austin 79-612
1978 $17.50

RUSSELL, MICHAEL   History and Present Condition of the Barbary
States. Edinburgh, 1835. Map, 11 illus., sm. 8vo, orig. cloth, paper label.
K Books 239-420 1978 £8

RUSSELL, MICHAEL   View of Ancient and Modern Egypt... Edinburgh, 1832. 2nd. ed. revised, map, illus., sm.8vo, orig. cloth, paper label,
joints repaired. K Books 239-421 1978 £7

RUSSELL, MICHAEL   View of Ancient and Modern Egypt... Edinburgh, 1838. 3rd. ed. revised & enlarged, sm. 8vo, orig. cloth, illus., map,
paper label, little thumbed & backstrip clipped. K Books 239-422 1978 £8

RUSSELL, PHILLIPS   Benjamin Franklin...The First Civilized American. New York, 1926. Illus. Biblo 251-38 1978 $8.50

RUSSELL, PHILLIPS   Red Tiger. New York, 1929. Illus. Biblo 251-
53 1978 $15

RUSSELL, R. C.   The Old and Young Lands. Oxford, 1916. Cr.
8vo, orig. cloth. K Books 239-424 1978 £6

RUSSELL, R.L.   The Child & His Pencil, Adventures in a Country
School, Foreword by St. J. Ervine. 1936. Illus., very good, reprint, octavo
bound in cloth. Hyland 128-469 1978 £4.50

RUSSELL, RACHEL   Letters of ... 1773. 1st. ed., 4to, half title,
orig. calf, brown label, hinges weak, otherwise good. Jarndyce 16-184 1978
£12.50

RUSSELL, RACHEL   Letters. 1820. Portrait, fcap. 8vo., contemp.
calf, one spine label missing, pres. copy from William Wilberforce. Howes 194-
519 1978 £40

RUSSELL, RICHARD   A Dissertation Concerning the Use of Sea Water
in Diseases of the Glands... Oxford, 1753. 8vo., plts., contemp. calf, gilt
on spines, gilt dentelles, light browning, signature of former owner, very good
copy, 1st authorized ed. in English. Zeitlin 245-223 1978 $225

RUSSELL, RICHARD   De Tabe Glandulari, sive de usu Aquae Marinae
in Morbis Glandularum Dissertatio. Oxford, 1750. 8vo., plts., fine lg. copy,
contemp. red mor. gilt, gilt edges, first ed. Quaritch 977-69 1978 $125

RUSSELL, ROBERT   Natal. Pietermaritzburg, 1899. 6th. ed.,
map in pocket, cr. 8vo., orig. cloth, lacks 1st. free endpaper. K Books 239-
423 1978 £8

RUSSELL, ROBERT   Natal. The Land and its Story. Maritzburg, 1904. 10th ed., frontis., maps in pocket, cr. 8vo., edges somewhat marked, dec. cloth. K Books 244-438 1978 £6

RUSSELL, ROBERT HOWARD   The Edge of the Orient. New York, 1896. Illus., 8vo., ex-lib., covers soiled, 1st ed., orig. cloth. Morrill 241-511 1978 $7.50

RUSSEL, W. CLARK   The Emigrant Ship. New York, (1893). 1st Amer. ed., 3 vols. in 1, light green cloth, good. Greene 78-97 1978 $20

RUSSELL, W. CLARK   The Emigrant Ship. 1893. Austin 79-613 1978 $10

RUSSELL, W. CLARK   The Good Ship Mohock. New York, 1895. 1st Amer. ed., quarter calf, marbled boards, good. Greene 78-273 1978 $20

RUSSELL, W. CLARK   A Strange Elopement. New York, 1892. 1st. Amer. ed., illus., orig. cloth, good. Greene 78-99 1978 $25

RUSSELL, WILLIAM HOWARD   Canada: Its Defences, Condition, and Resources. London, 1865. Rebound in green fab. Hood's 115-615 1978 $17.50

RUSSELL, WILLIAM HOWARD   My Diary in India, In the Year 1858-9. London, 1860. 1st. ed., 2 vols., 8vo, tinted lithograph plts., some repairs, rebound in cloth, gilt, ex-lib. copy. Deighton 5-92 1978 £33

RUSSELL, WILLIAM HOWARD   My Diary North and South. Boston, 1863. Bound in simulated red lea., Bell Wiley's copy. Broadfoot 46-220a 1978 $20

RUSSELL, WILLIAM HOWARD   My Diary North and South. New York, 1863. Illus., new cloth, Bell Wiley's copy. Broadfoot 46-220 1978 $16

RUSSELL, WILLIAM T.   Maryland, the Land of Sanctuary... Baltimore, 1907. Frontis. MacManus 239-1835 1978 $22.50

RUSSELL PASHA, THOMAS   Egyptian Service 1902-1946. London, (1949). Maps, illus., lacks 1st. free endpaper, 8vo, orig. cloth. K Books 239-425 1978 £5

RUSSO, ANTHONY   A Bibliography of James Whitcomb Riley. Indianapolis, 1944. 8vo., orig. cloth. MacManus 238-1032 1978 $20

RUSSO, DOROTHY RITTER   A Bibliography of George Ade 1866-1944. Indianapolis, 1947. 1st ed., orig. bind. Americanist 102-1 1978 $30

RUSSO, DOROTHY RITTER   A Bibliography of Booth Tarkington, 1869-1946. Indianapolis, 1949. 1st ed., very fine cond. Victoria 34-773 1978 $35

RUSSO, DOROTHY RITTER   A Bibliography of Booth Tarkington 1896-1946. Indiana, 1949. Fine. Ballinger 11-91 1978 $25.00

RUST, GEORGE   A Letter of Resolution Concerning Origen and The Chief of His Opinions. (London, 1661), Facsimile Reprint, New York, 1933. Octavo, good. Upcroft 10-150 1978 £5.50

RUSTED'S Humourous and Entertaining Jester or Pabulum of Life. London, n.d. (ca.1800). 12mo, 19th-century half calf, 1st ed., engraved frontispiece by Haynes, very good uncut copy, very rare. Ximenes 47-162 1978 $90

RUTER, H.   Zeit und Heimat der Homerischen Epen vom Zorn des Achilleus und von der Heimkehr des Odysseys. 1937. Plts. Allen 234-454 1978 $7.50

RUTGERS College. The Celebration of the 150th Anniversary of Its Founding as Queens College, 1766-1916. (Princeton), 1917. Illus., 8vo., ex-lib. Morrill 239-544 1978 $7.50

RUTHERFORD, ANWORTH   Squawberry Canyon. 1932. Mor., pic. end sheets, gilt top, illus., 1st ed., 1 of 25 no. copies signed by author, fine, plastic d.w., slipcase. Dykes 35-154 1978 $25

RUTHERFORD, ERNEST   Radiations from Radioactive Substances. Cambridge, University Press, 1930. 8vo., illus., orig. cloth, gilt, hinges cracked, but very good copy, 1st ed. Norman 5-*47 1978 $75

RUTHERFORD, ERNEST   Radio-activity. Cambridge, 1904. 8vo., text-illus., orig. cloth, a little worn, first ed. Quaritch 977-134 1978 $325

RUTHERFORD, ERNEST   Radioactivity. Cambridge, University Press, 1904. 8vo., plt., text illus., orig. cloth, gilt, bkplt., fine copy, 1st ed. Norman 5-247 1978 $300

RUTHERFORD, ERNEST   Radio-Activity. Cambridge, University Press, 1905. 8vo., illus., orig. cloth, fine copy, 2nd ed. Norman 5-248 1978 $150

RUTHERFORD, ERNEST   Die Radioaktivitat. Berlin, 1907. 8vo., diagrs., tables, modern cloth, fine copy, 1st ed. in German with author's final revisions. Norman 5-*46 1978 $100

RUTHERFORD, J.   The Secret History of the Fenian Conspiracy, Its Origins, Objects & Ramifications. 1877. 1st ed., 2 vols., good, octavo bound in cloth. Hyland 128-470 1978 £20

RUTHERFORD, MILDRED LEWIS   Jefferson Davis & Abraham Lincoln 1861-1865. NP, 1916. Cover soiled, Bell Wiley's copy. Broadfoot's 44-330 1978 $10.00

RUTLEDGE, A.   Life's Extras. New York, (1945). New enlarged, illus., very fine in dw. Bernard 5-237 1978 $7.50

RUTLEDGE, ANNA WELLS   Artists in the Life of Charleston, Through Colony & State, From Restoration to Reconstruction. Philadelphia, 1949. 4to., orig. pic. wrs., illus., very good. Americanist 103-89 1978 $40

RUTLEDGE, ARCHIBALD   Home by the River. 1941. Illus., pres. copy, signed by author, illus. Austin 82-81 1978 $27.50

RUTLEDGE, ARCHIBALD   Peace in the Heart. 1937. Austin 82-812 1978 $11

RUTTENBER, EDWARD M.   History of the Town of Newburgh. Newburgh, 1859. Illus. by Charles W. Tice, tall 8vo., cloth covers worn but sound, frontis. view, woodcut scenes in text, 1st ed., inscr'd by William W. Belknap. Butterfield 21-335 1978 $65

RUTTER, J.   Delineations of the North Western Division of the County of Somerset, and of Its Antediluvian Bone Caverns... 1829. Roy. 8vo., lg. paper, coloured map, plts., woodcuts, half calf. Quaritch 983-29 1978 $160

RUTTER, OWEN   The First Fleet. Golden Cockerel Press, 1937. Folio, engrs., cloth, ltd. to 375 copies. Quaritch 979-169 1978 $450

RUTTY, JENNIE C.   Letters of Love and Counsel for "Our Girls". Anderson, 1899. Cloth, inner hinges cracking. Hayman 73-667 1978 $7.50

RUYSBROECK, JAN VAN
Please turn to
JAN VAN RUYSBROECK

RUXTON, GEORGE FREDERICK   Life in the Far West. New York, 1855. 2nd Amer. ed., sm. 8vo., orig. cloth, cover slightly worn. Edwards 1012-530 1978 $25

RUYSCH, FREDERICK   Observationum Anatomico-Chirurgicarum Centuria. Amstelodami, 1691. 2 parts in 1 vol., copperplts., 4to., contemp. vellum, soiled, 1st ed. Offenbacher 30-134 1978 $500

RYAN, ARTHUR RIDGEWAY   Brief History of St. Bernadette's Roman Catholic Shrine Church in Dyker Heights. 1937. Illus. Austin 79-614 1978 $12.50

RYAN, E.   The History of the Effects of Religion on Mankind. 1802. 2nd ed., (1st Dublin ed.), bookplt. of Knight of Kerry, full leather (rubbed), text very good. Hyland 128-476 1978 £25

RYAN, J.   Irish Monasticism, Origins & Early Development. (1931). Reprint, octavo bound in cloth. Hyland 128-971 1978 £8

RYAN, J.   The Life of William the Third. 1836. 1st ed., map, port., original cloth (worn), good. Hyland 128-478 1978 £15

RYAN, JOHN J.   Historical Sketch of Loyola College. Baltimore, 1852-1902. Illus., 4to. Baldwins' 51-292 1978 $10

RYAN, KATE   Old Boston Museum Days. Boston, 1915. Illus.,
first ed. Biblo 247-908 1978 $17.50

RYAN, MARAH ELLIS   For the Soul of Rafael. 1906. Illus., first ed.
Austin 82-813 1978 $27.50

RYCAUT, P.   The History of the Turkish Empire, 1623-1677...
1680. Portraits, illus., folio, calf, slightly worn, corner of title slightly frayed,
8vo. Edwards 1012-55 1978 £180

RYD, VALERIUS ANSELMUS   Catalogus annorum et principum geminus ab
homine conditio,.... Berne, 1540. 1st ed., small folio, 19th century blind-
stamped vellum, contemp. marginal entries, woodcuts, fine. Gilhofer 75-95
1978 SFr 3,900

RYDER, DUDLEY   Diary, 1715-16. 1939. Plts., 8vo. George's
635-1259 1978 £5.25

RYE, W. B.   A List of the Books of Reference in the Reading
Room of the British Museum. London, 1871. Second ed. revised, demy 8vo.,
orig. cloth. Forster 130-227 1978 £10

RYERSON, EGERTON   "The Story of My Life," by the Late.... Toronto,
1883. T.p. missing, frontis., plts. Hood 116-299 1978 $25

RYERSON, JOHN   Hudson's Bay; or, a Missionary Tour in the Territory of the Hon. Hudson's Bay Company... Toronto, 1855. Orig. bind., pp. 115
and 116 missing, illus. Hood 116-593 1978 $50

RYLAND, FREDERICK   A Treatise on the Diseases and Injuries of the
Larynx and Trachea. London, 1936. Rittenhouse 49-698 1976 $20

RYLAND, R.H.   The History, Topography & Antiquities of Waterford. 1824. 1st ed., 1/2 leather, spine leather missing, all maps and plts. present, very good. Hyland 128-479 1978 £30

RYLE, JOHN A.   Natural History of Disease. London, 1936. Rittenhouse 49-699 1976 $20

RYMER, THOMAS   The English Monarch: An Heroic Tragedy. London, 1691. New cloth, 4to., 2nd ed., slightly soiled. MacManus 238-139
1978 $75

RYMILL, J.   Southern Lights: The Official Account of the
British Graham Land Expedition, 1934-1937. 1938. 1st. ed., maps, illus., roy.
8vo, orig. cloth. Edwards 1012-504 1978 £35

RYNNING, OLE   Ole Rynning's True Account of America. 1926.
Paper, both Norwegian & English text. Austin 79-615 1978 $12.50

S

S., J.   The History of the Life and Acts of the Most Reverend Father in God, Edmund Grindal. 1710. First ed., folio, frontis., orig. panelled calf, hinges weak, v.g. Jarndyce 16-101 1978 £36

S., P. D.   Mrs. Tomkins In Town. 1882. 8vo, orig. pink printed paper wrapper, fine. Fenning 32-289 1978 £9

SAABYE, HANS-EGEDE   Greenland... 1818. lst. English ed., map, bds., corners worn, cloth spine, uncut, 8vo. Edwards 1012-605 1978 £100

SABBATH Desecration: a National Tract. Buffalo, 1850. Disbound. Hayman 73-474 1978 $7.50

SABELLICUS, MARCUS ANTONIUS   Rerum Venetarum Decades. Venice, 1487. First ed., historiated with contemp. water-colour drawing, folio, 18th cent. half vellum, few wormholes in upper margins, arms of the Gabrielli Family of Venice enclosed within a watercolour design. Thomas 37-59 1978 £3500

SABINE, EDWARD   The North Georgia Gazette, And Winter Chronicle. London, 1821. lst. ed., 4to, half-title, quarter vellum, green bds., gilt back, morocco label, pres. copy. Deighton 5-169 1978 £70

SABINE, EDWARD   Report on the Variations of the Magnetic Intensity Observed at Different Points of the Earth's Surface. London, 1838. Offprint, 8vo., plts., orig. cloth, very good copy, inscr'd, lst ed. Norman 5-250 1978 $275

SABINE, JAMES   Glorying in The Cross... Charlestown, 1819. 2nd. ed., disbound, some age stains. Hayman 71-685 1978 $7.50

SABINE, LORENZO   Biographical Sketches of Loyalists of the American Revolution, with an Historical Essay. Boston, 1864. 2 vols., 8vo., bindings waterstained, partly discolored, otherwise sound, enl. ed. Morrill 239-593 1978 $30

SABSOVICH, KATHARINE   Adventures in Idealism. Stratford Press, 1922. Illus. with photos. Austin 79-616 1978 $27.50

SACCO, LUIGI   Trattato di Vaccinazione con Osservazioni sul Giavardo e Vajuolo Pecorino. Milan, 1809. 4to., contemp. half calf, portrait, coloured plts., first ed., fine. Gurney 75-95 1978 £65

SACHS, CURT   World History of the Dance. 1938. Plts., imp. 8vo. George's 635-1537 1978 £25

SACHS, HANS   Der Fursten Schatz. Strassburg, 1538. Fine copy, sm. 4 to., modern half vellum. Schafer 19-37 1978 sFr. 1,500

SACHS, HEINRICH   Vortrage Uber Bau Und Thatigkeit Des Grosshirns Und Die Lehre Von Der Aphasie Und Seelenblindheit Fur Aerzte Und Studirende. Breslau, 1893. 8vo., plts., contemp. half calf, lightly browned, pencilled notes, very good copy, lst ed. Zeitlin 245-225 1978 $75

SACHSE, JULIUS FRIEDRICH   Benjamin Franklin as a Free Mason. Philadelphia, 1906. lst ed., illus., nice copy, orig. cloth, ltd. to 200 copies. MacManus 239-154 1978 $40

SACHSE, JULIUS FRIEDRICH   The German Pietists of Provincial Pennsylvania. 1694-1708. Philadelphia, 1895. 1st ed., thick 4to., illus., orig. cloth, ltd. to 500 copies, very good. MacManus 239-1666 1978 $85

SACHSE, JULIUS FRIEDRICH   The German Sectarians of Pennsylvania. 1708-1742... Philadelphia, 1899. 1st ed., illus., orig. cloth, ltd. to 350 copies, front flyleaf lacking, otherwise very good copy. MacManus 239-1667 1978 $75

SACHSE, JULIUS FRIEDRICH   The Wayside Inns of the Lancaster Roadside Between Philadelphia and Lancaster. Lancaster, 1912. Illus., scarce. MacManus 239-1668 1978 $35

SACKVILLE WEST, EDWARD   A Flame in Sunlight: the life and works of Thomas de Quincey. 1936. First ed., plts., 8vo., orig. cloth. Howes 194-779 1978 £5

SACKVILLE-WEST, EDWARD   The Rescue. 1945. Colour plts. by Henry Moore, very good, slightly worn d.w., first English ed. Bell Book 17-496 1978 £12.50

SACKVILLE-WEST, VICTORIA   The Dark Island. 1934. Covers dull and somewhat rubbed, else good, first Eng. ed. Bell Book 16-760 1978 #6

SACKVILLE-WEST, VICTORIA   The Edwardians. Hogarth Press, 1930. First ed., cr. 8vo., fine, d.w., orig. cloth. Howes 194-1142 1978 £7.50

SACKVILLE-WEST, VICTORIA   Family History. Hogarth Press, 1932. Covers somewhat soiled, else very good, first English ed. Bell Book 17-780 1978 £12.50

SACKVILLE-WEST, VICTORIA   The Garden. 1946. Very good, worn d.w., first English ed. Bell Book 17-781 1978 £5.50

SACKVILLE-WEST, VICTORIA   Orchard and Vineyard. 1921. Linen-backed bds., worm-hole 1 3/4" across through lower bd., fine, near unopened, worn d.w., signed by author, first English ed. Bell Book 17-782 1978 £45

SACKVILLE-WEST, VICTORIA   Pepita. New York, 1937. First U.S. ed., portrait, very good, worn d.w. Bell Book 17-783 1978 £8.50

SACRAE Scripturae Locorum Quorundam Versio Metrica. Oxoniae, 1736. 8vo., XIXth Century half calf, a trifle rubbed. George's 635-1124 1978 £7.50

SACY, LOUIS DE   A Discourse of Friendship. 1707. 8vo., contemp. panelled calf, lacks label, good. P. M. Hill 142-212 1978 £48

SADE, DONATIEN ALPHONSE FRANCOIS, COMTE   Dialogue Between a Priest and a Dying Man. Chicago, 1927. Ltd. ed., edges rubbed. Biblo BL781-924 1978 $14.50

SADGER, J.   Sleep Walking and Moon Walking: a Medico-Literary Study. New York, 1920. Tall 8vo., pr. wrs., uncut. Argosy Special-79 1978 $25

SADLER, A. L.   The Maker of Modern Japan: The Life of Tokugawa Ieyasu. London, (1937). Cloth, 1 spot of wear, spine faded, illus. Dawson's 449-176 1978 $25

SADLER, RALPH 1507-87   Letters and Negotiations of Sir Ralph Sadler. Edinburgh, 1720. First ed., contemp. panelled calf, upper joint cracked, last leaves browned, 8vo. Howes 194-446 1978 £20

SADLIER, MRS. J.   The Confederate Chieftains: A Tale of the Irish Rebellion of 1641. New York, 1864. Orig. cloth, spine defective. Eaton 45-436 1978 £8

SADLIER, MRS. J.   The Confederate Chieftains, A Tale of the Irish Rebellion of 1641. n.d. Very good, octavo bound in cloth, reprint. Hyland 128-480 1978 £8

SADLIER, MICHAEL   Trollope. A Commentary. New York, 1947. Good, dw. Greene 78-274 1978 $20

SAENGER, GERHART   Today's Refugees, Tomorrows Citizens. 1941. Austin 79-617 1978 $11

SAFFELL, W. T. R.   Records of the Revolutionary War. Philadelphia, 1858. 1st ed., scarce. MacManus 239-618 1978 $37.50

SAFFORD, A. K.   Resources of Arizona Territory with a Description of the Indian Tribes;.... San Francisco, 1871. Orig. pr. wr., 1st ed., Philip Ashton Rollins' copy with his bookplt., slipcase, pages stained. Ginsberg 14-25 1978 $150

SAFFORD, MARION F.   The Story of Colonial Lancaster. Rutland, 1937. Illus., d.j. MacManus 239-1031 1978 $15

SAFFORD, MILDRED R.   Sugar Babe. A Sketch of Plantation Life in the Seventies. New York, 1940. 12mo., author's pres., d.w. Biblo BL781-128 1978 $10

SAFFORD, WILLIAM H.   The Life of Harman Blennerhassett... Chillicothe, 1850. Cloth, minor wear, scarce, 1st ed. Hayman 72-691 1978 $35

THE SAGA of King Olaf Tryggwason who Reigned over Norway A.D. 995-1000. 1895. Cr. 4to., orig. cloth backed bds., spine worn. Howes 194-1143 1978 £7.50

SAGE, BALTHASAR GEORGES   Experiences Propres A Faire Connoitre Que L'Alkali Volatil-Fluor Est Le Remede Le Plus Efficace Dans Les Asphyxies. Paris, 1777. 8vo., contemp. mottled calf, gilt ornamented spine, very good copy, Paris ed. Zeitlin 245-226 1978 $150

SAGE, DEAN   A Supplement to the Catalogue of Books on Angling Collected by Mr. Dean Sage of Albany, N.Y. New York, 1904. Sq. 4to., uncut, orig. cloth, ltd. to 50 copies. Wolfe 39-17 1978 $30

SAGE, RUFUS B.   Scenes in the Rocky Mountains, and in Oregon, California,.... Philadelphia, 1846. Calf gilt, map, early issue of 1st ed., rare. Jenkins 116-1212 1978 $800

SAGLIO, ANDRE   French Furniture. London, n.d. 50 illus. Baldwins' 51-150 1978 $12.50

THE SAILOR'S Almanack, for...1845. New York, (1844). Hayman 73-15 1978 $8.50

SAIN, EZRA   Seven Months in the Wilderness of Conviction... N.P., n.d. (Toledo?, 1870's?). Unbound as issued. Hayman 72-570 1978 $8.50

SAINT JAMES CATHEDRAL, TORONTO   Reports and Financial Statements for the Year Ending Feb. 28, 1914. Wrs. Hood 117-368 1978 $10

SAINT Catherine: 25 Novembre 1946. (Paris), 1946. Color & black & white lithos, thin 4to, stiff pic. wrs., orig. glassine, 1 of 1150 numbered copies on velin du Marais. Argosy Special-80 1978 $75

SAINT-AMAND, IMBERT DE   The Last Years of Louis XV. Boston, 1893. Trans. from French, photogravures by Goupil, 4to., orig. bds., cloth back, ed. ltd. to 150 copies. Morrill 239-594 1978 $15

SAINT-AMAT, PIERRE CHARLES DE   Voyage en Californie 1850-1851... Paris, 1851. Orig. wr. in vellum. Ginsberg 14-185 1978 $125

SAINT-AUBIN, AUGUSTIN DE   Mes Gens ou les Commissionnaires Ultramontains au Service de qui Veut Les Payer. Paris, (1766-1770). Sm. folio, half-mor., marbled bds., very nice, 1st ed. Gilhofer 74-138 1978 sFr 2,000

SAINT-CROIX, F. R. DE   Reise nach Ostindien, den Philippinischen Inseln und China; nebst einigen Nachrichten uber Cochinichina und Tunkin. Berlin, 1811. Half calf, boards, rare, 8vo. Van der Peet 127-207 1978 Dfl 175

SAINT-EVREMOND, CHARLES DE 1613-1703   Works. 1700. Portrait, 2 vols., contemp. panelled calf, neatly rebacked with double mor. labels, new endpapers, first English ed. Howes 194-94 1978 £35

SAINT-EXUPERY, ANTOINE DE   The Little Prince. New York, (1943). 1st ed., illus. in color, fine in slightly torn dj. Victoria 34-237 1978 $45

SAINT-EXUPERY, ANTOINE DE   Night Flight. New York, 1932. First U.S. ed., very good. Bell Book 17-786 1978 £8.50

SAINT EXUPERY, ANTOINE DE The Wild Garden. New York, 1938. Thin 8vo, boards, cloth backstrip, decor. by John O'Hara Cosgrave II, 1 of 1000 copies, 1st Amer. ed., fine. Duschnes 220-272 1978 $12.50

SAINT-GAUDENS, AUGUSTUS   The Reminiscences of Augustus Saint Gaudens. New York, 1913. 2 vols., illus. MacManus 239-701 1978 $30

SAINT-GELAIS, MELLIN DE   Sophonisba. Sm. 8vo., civilite type, dark green mor. gilt, gilt edges, by Bauzonnet-Trautz. Quaritch 978-136 1978 $4,000

SAINT GEORGES, GEORGES GUILLET DE
Please turn to
GUILLET DE SAINT GEORGES, GEORGES

SAINT JOHN, CHRISTOPHER Ellen Terry. London, 1907. Illus., first edition. Biblo 247-913 1978 $15

SAINT JOHN, HENRY, VISCOUNT BOLINGBROKE
Please turn to
BOLINGBROKE, HENRY ST. JOHN 1678-1751

SAINT JOHN, JOHN   Observations on the Land Revenue of the Crown. 1788. 1st. ed., 4to, orig. bds., uncut, backstrip defective, o/w v.g., orig. condition. Jarndyce 16-186 1978 £18.50

SAINT JOHN, S.   Life in the Forests of the Far East. 1862. 2 vols., maps, 4 coloured plts., 12 tinted litho. plts., 8vo, orig. cloth, fine set. Edwards 1012-173 1978 £100

SAINT-JOHN, SPENSER   Hayti, or the Black Republic. 1889. second ed., map, sm. 8vo., half calf. Edwards 1012-719 1978 £15

SAINT LEGER, ALEXIS   Anabsis. London, 1930. Text in French and English, trans. and signed by T.S. Eliot, 8vo, orig. cloth, first ed., ltd. 350 copies, v.f., glassine wr., slipcase worn and soiled. Howell 5-22 1978 $175

SAINT-LEGER, ALEXIS   Anabasis. London, 1930. 1st ed., thin tall octavo, orig. green cloth, gilt top, 1 of 350 numbered copies, signed by T. S. Eliot. Totteridge 29-36 1978 $250

SAINT-LO, GEORGE   England's Safety. 1693. Sm. 4to., half calf. F. Edwards 1013-194 1978 £200

SAINT-LO, GEORGE   England's Safety. 1693. Second ed., woodcut frontis., sm. 4to., contemp. wrappers. F. Edwards 1013-195 1978 £120

SAINT MAURICE, FAUCHER DE   Le Contre-Amiral Byng Devant Ses Juges et Devant l'Histoire. 1893. Hood's 115-671 1978 $10

SAINT OMER L'AINE   Abrege de la Graphometrie. Paris, n.d. (c. 1800). Eng. plts., folio, bds., leather back, some stains, plts. Schumann 511-52 1978 sFr 600

SAINT OMER L'AINE   Declaration des Droits de l'Homme et du Citoyen ... Paris, 1790. Folio, orig. paper wrs., eng. leaves. Schumann 511-53 1978 sFr 4,300

SAINT OMER L'AINE   Traite des Vrais Principes de l'Ecriture. Paris, n.d. (c. 1800). Eng. plts., 8vo., orig. wrs. Schumann 511-54 1978 sFr 435

SAINT-ONGE, LOUIS N.   Alphabet Yakama. Montreal, 1872. Orig. photo. port., woodcuts, orig. pr. wr. bound in half mor. Ginsberg 14-1040 1978 $125

SAINT-PALAYE, JEAN BAPTISTE DE LA CURNE DE   The Literary History of the Troubadours. 1779. First English ed., pres. copy inscribed from author, contemp. calf, joints cracked, label rubbed, 8vo. Howes 194-447 1978 £35

SAINT PALAYE, JEAN BAPTISTE DE LA CURNE DE   Memoires sur l'Ancienne Chevalerie. Paris, 1759. 2 vols., sm. 8vo., contemp. calf, spines gilt, first ed. Howes 194-574 1978 £25

SAINT-PALAYE, JEAN BAPTISTE DE LA CURNA DE   Memoirs of Ancient Chivalry. 1784. Contemp. calf, gilt back, first English ed., 8vo. Howes 194-448 1978 £28

SAINT-PIERRE, JACQUES HENRI BERNARDIN DE   Pablo y Virginia. Philadelphia, 1810. Contemp. 3/4 lea., blue marbled paper, cover tips rubbed, sm. spine edge split, very scarce copy, very good. Victoria 34-710 1978 $75

SAINT-PIERRE, JACQUES HENRI BERNARDIN DE   Paolo e Virginia. Napoli, 1821. 2 vols. in 1, 12mo., cloth, spine faded, engr. frontis. King 7-385 1978 £15

SAINT-PIERRE, JACQUES HENRI BERNARDIN DE   Paul and Virginia. Edinburgh, 1881. Illus., ltd. ed., full lea., rubbed. Biblo BI781-628 1978 $15

SAINT-PIERRE, JACQUES HENRI BERNARDIN DE   Paul et Virginie. Paris, 1837. 8vo., illus., polished brown calf. Traylen 88-444 1978 £10

SAINT-PIERRE, JACQUES HENRI BERNARDIN DE   Paul and Virginia. 1888. Roy. 8vo., engrs., half blue mor., gilt panelled back, gilt top, other edges uncut. Quaritch 979-284 1978 $85

SAINT-PIERRE, JACQUES HENRI BERNARDIN DE   Studies of Nature. 1798. 1st ed., contemp. sheep, joints cracked, spine slightly worn, 8vo. Howes 194-449 1978 £12.50

SAINT-PIERRE, JACQUES HENRI BERNARDIN DE   A Voyage to the Island of Mauritius. 1775. Contemp. mottled calf, 8vo., 1st Eng. ed. Edwards 1012-322 1978 £225

SAINT-SIMON, LOUIS DE ROUVROY DE   Memoires. Boston, 1899. 8vo., 4 vols., green cloth, paper labels, uncut, t.e.g., illus., spine darkened, shelf wear, covers insign. spotted, near fine, tight copies, scarce set, Versailles Ed., ltd. to 800 sets of which this is no. 187, 1st ed. Desmarais 1-363 1978 $55

SAINT-SIMON, LOUIS DE ROUVROY DE   Memoirs of...on the Times of Louis XIV and the Regency. London, 1899. Half vellum, bds., spines faded, rubbed, fine, 4 vols., illus. Biblo 247-741 1978 $57.50

SAINT-SIMON, LOUIS DE ROUVROY DE   The Memoirs of... New York, 1901. 4 vols. Biblo 247-742 1978 $28.50

SAINT-SIMON, LOUIS DE ROUVROY DE   Memoirs, on the Times of Louis XIV and the Regency. 1915. Illus., 4 vols. George's 635-755 1978 £5

SAINT-SIMON, LOUIS DE ROUVROY DE   Memoirs, on the Times of Louis XIV and the Regency. Boston, 1919. Ed. ltd. to 600 copies, illus., 4 vols., lg. 8vo., spines faded. George's 635-754 1978 £5

SAINT VRAIN, CERAN   Las Animas, or Vigil and St. Vrain Grant. [N.P., c. 1872]. New wr., 1st ed. Ginsberg 14-776 1978 $75

SAINT WHITTY, J. S.   The Flaming Wheel; Nature Studies in Dublin Cont'd & Wicklow. 1924. 1st ed., d.w., very good, octavo bound in cloth. Hyland 128-779 1978 £5

SAINTE-BEUVE, C. A.   Portraits of the Eighteenth Century, Historic and Literary. New York and London, 1906. Plts., 2 vols., orig. cloth, leather labels, spines discoloured, covers faded, 8vo. Howes 194-1144 1978 £6.50

SAINTE-CROIX, CARLOMAN L. F. F. RENOUARD, MARQUIS DE   Voyage Commercial et Politique aux Indes Orientales... Paris, 1810. First ed., maps, coloured in outline, 3 vols., orig. wrs., rebacked, uncut, 8vo. Edwards 1012-214 1978 £90

SAINTINE, M. X. B.   Picciola. Bruxelles, 1837. 1/2 leather, rubbed, lib. stamp on verso of title-pg. Eaton 45-437 1978 £5

SAINTSBURY, GEORGE   A History of English Prose Rhythm. 1922. Orig. cloth, demy 8vo. Howes 194-1145 1978 £6

SAINTSBURY, GEORGE   A History of the French Novel. 1917-19. First ed., 2 vols., newly rebound in qtr. rose calf, 8vo. Howes 194-1146 1978 £15

SAINTSBURY, GEORGE   A Last Scrap Book. London, 1924. Orig. half-buckram and parchment, 1st ed., 1 of 250 lg. paper copies signed by author, parchment very slightly discolored, otherwise fine. MacManus 238-377 1978 £35

SAINTSBURY, GEORGE   A Scrap Book. London, 1922. Signed, 1 of 300 ltd. ed., large paper copies, uncut, partly unopened, handmade paper, white cloth backed bds., very good or better. Limestone 9-252 1978 $45

SAINTYVES, P.   Les Cinquante Jugements de Salomon ou les Arrets des Bons Juges d'Apres la Tradition Populaire. Paris, n.d. Slipcase, colored illus. by J. Touchet, loose plts., ltd. ed. of 500 numbered copies only, 8vo., orig. covers. Van der Peet H-64-454 1978 Dfl 125

SAKER, E. M.   Alfred Saker. London, 1929. 2nd. ed., map, frontispiece, cr. 8vo, orig. cloth. K Books 239-426 1978 £5

SALA, ANGELUS   Angelus Sala, Liebarzt des Herzogs Johann Albrecht II von Mecklenburg-Gustrow. Berlin, 1933. 8vo., frontis. portr., orig. prtd. wrs. Norman 5-251 1978 $25

SALA, GEORGE AUGUSTUS   America Revisited: From the Bay of New York to the Gulf of Mexico... 1882. 2 vols., cloth gilt, name on titles, 1 joint repaired, woodcut engravings, 8vo. Edwards 1012-531 1978 £15

SALA, GEORGE AUGUSTUS   A Journey Due North.... London, 1858. 1st. ed., 8vo, half-title, half calf, gilt back. Deighton 5-140 1978 £28

SALA, GEORGE AUGUSTUS   Living London Being "Echoes" Re-Echoed. 1883. 1st. ed., frontis & other illus., unusual engraved title, orig. red cloth, pictorial imprint on leading bd. & spine in black silver & gilt, v.g. Jarndyce 16-831 1978 £22

SALA, GEORGE AUGUSTUS   My Diary in America. London, 1865. 2 vols., Bell Wiley's copy. Broadfoot 46-221 1978 $35

SALA, GEORGE AUGUSTUS   Paris Herself Again in 1878-79. London, 1880. 5th ed., 2 vols., illus. Biblo 247-743 1978 $32.50

SALA, GEORGE AUGUSTUS   Rome & Venice... 1869. 1st. ed., half title, orig. green cloth, good. Jarndyce 16-988 1978 £9.50

SALA, GEORGE AUGUSTUS   William Hogarth: Painter, Engraver and Philosopher. 1866. 1st. ed., frontis & illus., half title, orig. brown cloth, little rubbed, good. Jarndyce 16-987 1978 £14.50

SALAMAN, MALCOLM CHARLES   The Etchings of Sir Francis Seymour Haden. London, 1923. Ltd. ed. of 200 copies, plts., one woodcut, lg. 4to., gilt cloth, new calf spine. K Books 244-439 1978 £30

SALAMAN, MALCOLM CHARLES   The Great Painter-Etchers From Rembrandt to Whistler. London, The Studio, 1914. 4to., orig. wrappers, little frayed & worn, plts. Sexton 7-46 1978 £7

SALAMAN, MALCOLM CHARLES   Londoners Then and Now as Pictured by Their Contemporaries. London, 1920. Plts., some color, bevelled cloth, very good or better. Limestone 9-253 1978 $25

SALAMAN, MALCOLM CHARLES   Old English Mezzotints. London, 1910. 4to., orig. wrappers, plts., good. Sexton 7-36 1978 £12

SALAUN, L.   l'Indochine. Paris, 1903. 4to, plts., orig. covers. Van der Peet 127-208 1978 Dfl 150

SALE, EDITH TUNIS   Interiors of Virginia Houses of Colonial Times from the Beginnings of Virginia to the Revolution... Richmond, 1927. Ltd. ed., illus., plts. MacManus 239-1874 1978 $35

SALE, EDITH TUNIS   Interiors of Virginia Houses of Colonial Times From the Beginnings of Virginia to the Revolution. 1927. Ltd. ed. Baldwins' 51-530 1978 $22.50

SALE, JOHN B.   The Tree Named John. 1929. Silhouettes, first ed., d.j. Austin 82-814 1978 $27.50

SALE, JOHN B.   The Tree Named John. Chapel Hill, 1929. 22 silhouettes, front cover slightly speckled, Bell Wiley's copy. Broadfoot's 44-903 1978 $10.00

SALE, RICHARD   Not too Narrow...Not too Deep. New York, 1936. 1st ed., covers faded. Biblo BL781-965 1978 $9.50

SALE at Public Auction...1854...the Interest of the State of California in Water Lot Property in the City of San Francisco by Order of the California Land Commission. [San Francisco, 1854]. Original printed wr. in half morocco, 1st ed. Ginsberg 14-194 1978 $275

SALIGNAC, BERNARD   Algebrae Libri Duo. Frankfurt, 1580. 4to., wrs. Salloch 345-166 1978 $110

SALIMBENE, FRANCISCAN   From St. Francis to Dante; a translation of all that is of passing interest in the Chronicle of the Franciscan Salimbene, 1221-1288. 1907. Second ed., revised, calf, gilt, a.e.g., sm. nick in spine, 8vo. Upcroft 12-386 1978 £8.50

SALIS MARCHLINS, KARL ULYSSES VON   Travels through Various Provinces of the Kingdom of Naples, in 1789. London, 1795. First Eng. ed., 8vo., maps, plts., some hand colored, cont. speckled calf, worn, joints weak. Deighton 5-226 1978 £48

SALISBURY, ALBERT   Two Captains West. Seattle, (1950). 4to, drawings by Carter Lucas, Ltd. to 350 copies, signed by both authors, fine, d.w., boxed. Biblo 248-270 1978 $82.50

SALLEY, A. S.   The History of Orangeburg County, South Carolina. Orangeburg, 1898. Fold. map. MacManus 239-1121 1978 $85

SALLEY, A. S.   Sack and Destruction of the City of Columbia, S. C. N.P., 1937. Bell Wiley's copy. Broadfoot 46-375 1978 $16

SALLEY, A. S.   South Carolina Troops in Confederate Service Vol. III. Columbia, 1930. Bell Wiley's copy. Broadfoot 46-374 1978 $20

SALLUSTIUS CRISPUS, GAIUS   Belli Catilinarii et Jugurthini Historiae. 1738. 16mo., old calf, joints cracked, lacks flyleaves, corner stained. Allen 234-840 1978 $10

SALLUSTIUS CRISPUS, GAIUS   Belli Catilinarii et Jugurthini Historiae. Glasguae, 1749. Sm. 8vo., contemp. calf, rubbed. George's 635-507 1978 £7.50

SALLUSTIUS CRISPUS, GAIUS   Crispi Sallustii Belli Catilinarii et Jugurthini Historiae. Glasguae, 1749. Foolscap octavo in fours, quarter-calf over original boards, expertly repaired. Bennett 20-181 1978 $175

SALLUSTIUS CRISPUS, GAIUS   Opera. (Venice, 1494-1500.) 1st illus. ed., folio, marbled boards with vellum spine and corners, two leaves rather browned, early marginal notes. Bennett 20-180 1978 $1,100

SALLUSTIUS CRISPUS, GAIUS   Opera auae Supersunt, Omnia. Foulis Press, 1751. Contemp. russia gilt, sm. 8vo. Howes 194-273 1978 £25

SALLUSTIUS CRISPUS, GAIUS   Opera Omnia, Quae Exstant. Francofurti, 1707. 8vo., full vellum. Van der Peet H-64-538 1978 Dfl 65

SALLUSTIUS CRISPUS, GAIUS   Opera quae extant. Birmingham, Baskerville Press, 1773. 4to., full contemp. English straight grained mor., all edges gilt, first Baskerville ed. Howes 194-154 1978 £110

SALLUSTIUS CRISPUS, GAIUS   Opera omnia, excusa ad edilionem Cortiicum....
1789. Contemp. mottled calf, gilt, 8vo.   George's 635-506 1978 £7.50

SALLUSTIUS CRISPUS, GAIUS   Opera. 1828-35. Old calf, worn, Vols. 1-2,
index bound before text of vol. I.   Allen 234-838 1978 $12.50

SALLUSTIUS CRISPUS, GAIUS   Quae Exstant. Norimbergae, 1783. Sm. 8vo.,
bds. Van der Peet H-64-539 1978 Dfl 45

SALMON, D. E.   Contagious Diseases of Domesticated Animals.
Washington, 1833. Jenkins 116-1213 1978 $17.50

SALMON, EDWARD   General Wolfe. Toronto, 1909. Frontis. port.,
fold. map, orig. binding.   Wolfe 39-558 1978 $15

SALMON, WILLIAM   Botanologia. London, 1710-11. Title-pg. in
red & black, engraved frontis, illus., bound in 2 vols., folio, old panelled calf,
rebacked gilt, leather labels. Traylen 88-623 1978 £525

SALMON Fishing on the Great Wacheeshoo. Montreal, n.d. Illus., orig. binding, covers separated at spine. Wolfe 39-18 1978 $45

SALPOINTE, J. B.   A Brief Sketch of the Mission of San Xavier Del
Bac with a Description of its Church... San Francisco, 1880. Original front
printed wr. Ginsberg 14-26 1978 $125

SALT, HENRY   A Voyage to Abyssinia... 1814. Folding maps,
engraved plts., 4to, cover slightly worn, orig. cloth, I map repaired, few leaves
of text little soiled. Edwards 1012-288 1978 £175

SALT Lake City. (Brooklyn, 1904). Wrs., photo. views. Hayman 72-759 1978
$7.50

SALTER, EDWIN   A History of Monmouth and Ocean Counties,
N.J... Bayonne, 1890. Illus., scarce, nice. MacManus 239-1318 1978
$85

SALTER, J. T.   Boss Rule. Portraits in City Politics. New York,
(1935). Biblo BL781-870 1978 $9

SALTER, WILLIAM   Iowa. The First Free State in the Louisiana Purchase. Chicago, 1905. 1st ed., illus., ports., orig. pic. cloth, foxing, soiling,
but good copy. MacManus 239-214 1978 $10

SALTMARSH, JOHN d. 1647   Holy Discoveries and Flames. 1640. 12mo.,
rebound in full calf antique, first ed. Howes 194-95 1978 £45

SALTONSTALL, WILLIAM G.   Ports of Piscataqua Soundings in the Maritime
History of the Portsmouth, N.H., Customs District... Cambridge, 1941. 1st ed.,
4to., illus., orig. cloth bds., fine. MacManus 239-1784 1978 $25

SALTUS, EDGAR   Parnassians Personally Encountered. Cedar
Rapids, 1923. One of only 200 copies, spine soiled, very good. Bernard 5-274
1978 $35

SALVAGE, JEAN GALBERT   Anatomie Du Gladiateur Combattant... Paris,
1812. Royal folio, copperplates, frontis., plts. prtd. in black & red, full contemp.
calf, fine gilt decor. frame border, gilt ornamented spine panel, gilt inner dentelles, minor crease in last plt., fine copy from the Herbert M. Evans Library of
Medical Classics, 1st ed., scarce. Zeitlin 245-228 1978 $2,750

SALVESTE, E.   The Occult Sciences. 1846. 2 vols., ex-libris
copy, covers soiled and worn, 8vo. George's 635-1434 1978 £18

SALZMAN, L. F.   English Industries of the Middle Ages. Oxford,
1923. Illus., cr. 8vo. George's 635-393 1978 £5

SAMBIN, HUGUES   Oeuvre de la diversite des termes. Lyons,
1572. Folio, woodcuts, excellent copy, contemp. limp vellum, 1st ed., 1st
issue. Quaritch Summer, 1978-38 1978 $4,500

SAMPSON, EZRA   The Brief Remarker on the Ways of Man. Canandaigua, 1821. Full calf, extremities worn, tight, internally clean. Butterfield
21-327 1978 $17.50

SAMPSON, JOHN   In Lighter Moments. Liverpool, 1934. 8vo,
orig. bds., illus. by Lawrence Wright, good. Sexton 7-182 1978 £5

SAMS, CONWAY WHITTLE   The Conquest of Virginia, The Forest Primeval...
New York, 1916. Illus., maps. Baldwins' 51-531 1978 $20

SAMUEL, MAURICE   Beyond Woman. 1934. Austin 79-621 1978
$17.50

SAMUEL, MAURICE   The Gentleman and the Jew. 1950. Orig.
ed. Austin 79-623 1978 $8.50

SAMUEL, MAURICE   The Great Hatred. 1940. Austin 79-624
1978 $8.50

SAMUEL, MAURICE   Harvest in the Desert. 1947. Austin 79-625
1978 $7.50

SAMUEL, MAURICE   Prince of the Ghetto. 1948. Austin 79-627
1978 $7.50

SAMUELS, M. M.   Power Unleashed. New York, (1943). 8vo.,
dust wrapper, 1st ed. Morrill 241-512 1978 $10

SAMUELS, MAURICE V.   A Pageant of the Strong. 1923. Paper. Austin 79-630 1978 $20

SAMUELS, P. I.   The Early Life, Correspondence and Writings of
the Right Honorable Edmund Burke... Cambridge, 1923. First ed., illus. Biblo
247-663 1978 $25

SAMUEL, SIGMUND   The Seven Years War in Canada, 1756-1763.
Toronto, 1934. Illus., fldg. maps. Hood 117-152 1978 $50

SAN ANTONIO: A History and Guide Compiled by Workers of the Writers' Program
of the Work Project Administration in the State of Texas. San Antonio, 1941. Wr.,
illus., maps. Jenkins 116-112 1978 $15

SAN DIEGO California, City and County. San Diego, [1919]. Illus., original
printed wr., 1st ed. Ginsberg 14-186 1978 $15

SAN FRANCISCO. ORDINANCES   An Act in Relation to a Sea-Wall or Bulkhead
in the City and County of San Francisco. San Francisco, 1858. Folio, stitched as
issued. Ginsberg 14-68 1978 $150

SAN Francisco. San Francisco, 1913. Illus., original printed wr., 1st ed.   Ginsberg 14-187 1978 $20

SAN JUAN County, New Mexico. [Chicago, 1893]. Map, plates, orig. pr. wr.,
1st ed. Ginsberg 14-777 1978 $75

SANBORN, F. B.   The Life and Letters of John Brown... Boston,
1885. Orig. cloth, fine. MacManus 239-729 1978 $17.50

SANBORN, KATE   Old Time Wall Papers. Greenwich, 1905. 4to.,
illus., some in color, new cloth, ltd. ed. MacManus 239-702 1978 $60

SANCTA Croce: a Nicotian Treatise with Illustrative Antitheses. Worcester,
Publisher's Private Press, 1887. 1 of 125 numbered copies, orig. prtd. parchment
wrs., fronts, 8vo., very good. Americanist 103-99 1978 $30

SAND, GEORGE   Francis the Waif. London, 1889. Illus., half-
calf, cloth side, t.e.g., good. Greene 78-275 1978 $35

SAND, GEORGE   The Mosaic Workers: A Tale, and the Orco;
A Tradition. London, 1844. 1st Eng. ed., chromolithograph frontis., quarter
leather binding, pres. copy from L. Maria Child to Anne Whitney, 12 mo. Greene
78-276 1978 $95

SANDARS, MARY F.   George Sand. 1927. Plts., orig. cloth, 8vo.,
spine slightly faded. Howes 194-1148 1978 £4

SANDBURG, CARL   Abraham Lincoln. New York, 1926. 6 vols.,
cuts of cartoons, pres. set inscribed by Sandburg to Wiley, half-tones of photos.
Broadfoot's 44-334a 1978 $75

SANDBURG, CARL   Abraham Lincoln, The Prairie Years. New York,
(1926). First ed., 2 vols., illus., maps. Biblo 247-82 1978 $22.50

SANDBURG, CARL   Abraham Lincoln...the War Years. New York,
(1939). 4 vols., illus., 1st ed. Biblo BL781-121 1978 $27.50

SANDBURG, CARL   Abraham Lincoln: The War Years. New York,
(1943). Half-tones of photos, cuts of cartoons, letters, documents, 4 vols., 8vo.
Morrill 239-595 1978 $30

SANDBURG, CARL   The American Songbag. New York, (1927).
Lg. 8vo., d.w., tears in d.w., 1st ed. Morrill 241-513 1978 $17.50

SANDBURG, CARL   Chicago Poems. New York, 1916. Cloth, fine.
Dawson's 447-270 1978 $50

SANDBURG, CARL   Cornhuskers. New York, 1918. Bds., name &
date, 1st state. Dawson's 447-271 1978 $50

SANDBURG, CARL   Cornhuskers. New York, 1918. 8vo, 1st ed.,
light green boards with dark green lettering, corners bumped and slightly worn,
bookplate, Fine, collector's cond. Desmarais 1-364 1978 $27.50

SANDBURG, CARL   Cornhuskers. 2nd state, somewhat worn at extre-
meties. Dawson's 447-272 1978 $30

SANDBURG, CARL   Good Morning, America. New York, 1928.
Cloth, clipping laid in. Dawson's 447-273 1978 $20

SANDBURG, CARL   Remembrance Rock. New York, (1948). 2 vols.,
orig. cloth, 1st ed., 1 of 1,000 copies signed by Carl Sandburg, fine. MacManus
238-569 1978 $80

SANDBURG, CARL   Remembrance Rock. New York, 1948. 16vo,
dark blue cloth, d.w. slightly chipped and repaired at top of spine, near Mint,
signed, 1st ed. Desmarais 1-365 1978 $32.50

SANDBURG, CARL   Selected Poems of. New York, (c.1944).
1st Armed Services ed., No. N-6, oblong 16 mo., pictorial wrappers, very
good. Houle 10-286 1978 $25

SANDBURG, CARL   Slabs of the Sunburnt West. New York, 1922.
8vo, orange cloth with green lettering, spine slightly darkened, very Nice, 1st
issue, 1st ed., collector's cond. Desmarais 1-366 1978 $35

SANDBURG, CARL   Storm Over the Land. New York, (1942).
Illus., 8vo., d.w., 1st ed. Morrill 241-514 1978 $10

SANDEMAN, FRASER   By Hook and by Crook. 1862. Illus. by author,
sq. cr. 8vo., binders cloth. George's 635-1493 1978 £12.50

SANDER, H. F. C.   Reichenbachia. London, 1886-1895. 1st. &
2nd. series, chromolithographed plts., edition de luxe with plts. printed on thick
cards, 4 vols., bound in 8, lg. folio, contemp. half green morocco, gilt panelled
spines, gilt edges, only 25 copies produced. Traylen 88-624 1978 £6000

SANDERS, ALVIN HOWARD   At the Sign of the Stock Yard Inn. Chicago,
1915. Mor. & cloth, illus., frontis. in color, 1st ed., minor moisture stains,
plts., inscr. by author, scarce. Dykes 34-78 1978 $25

SANDERS, ALVIN HOWARD   The Cattle of the World. Washington, D. C.,
1926. Fabricoid, illus., 1st ed., very good copy. Dykes 34-127 1978 $10

SANDERS, ALVIN HOWARD   Shorthorn Cattle. Chicago, (1900). 2nd ed.,
cloth, illus., very good copy. Dykes 34-113 1978 $15

SANDERS, ALVIN HOWARD   Shorthorn Cattle. Chicago, (1918). Cloth,
illus., updated, fine copy. Dykes 34-114 1978 $25

SANDERS, ALVIN HOWARD   The Story of the Herefords. Chicago, 1914.
Cloth, illus., 1st ed., very good copy. Dykes 34-112 1978 $35

SANDERS, CHARLOTTE   Holidays at Home. 1806. 2nd. ed., engraved
frontis, orig. calf, good. Jarndyce 16-989 1978 £18

SANDERS, GEORGE A.   Reality: or Law and Order vs. Anarchy and Socialism. A Reply to Edward Bellamy's Looking Backward and Equality. Cleveland,
1898. Cloth. Hayman 72-692 1978 $15

SANDERS, J. T.   Farm Ownership and Tenancy in the Black
Prairie of Texas. Washington, 1922. Wr., illus. Jenkins 116-1217 1978 $10

SANDERS, JOHN   Memoirs on the Military Resources of the Valley
of the Ohio,.... Pittsburgh, 1845. Printed wr. Jenkins 116-1218 1978 $175

SANDERS, JOHN   Memoirs on the Military Resources of the Valley
of the Ohio,.... Washington, 1845. Half morocco. Jenkins 116-1219 1978
$125

SANDERS, L.   The Holland House Circle. 1908. Illus., 8vo.
George's 635-1261 1978 £5

SANDERS, TOM   Her Golden Hour. Houston, 1929. 1st ed.,
wr. Jenkins 116-1220 1978 $20

SANDERS, W. H.   A Compend for the Members of the Organized
Medical Profession of Alabama. Montgomery, 1913. 8vo., ex-lib. Morrill
239-1 1978 $10

SANDERS, WILEY BRITTON   Juvenile Courts in North Carolina. Chapel
Hill, 1948. Broadfoot 50-193 1978 $10

SANDERS, WILEY BRITTON   Nergo Child Welfare in North Carolina. Chapel
Hill, 1933. New cloth. Broadfoot 50-194 1978 $12

SANDERSON, HOWARD K.   Lynn in the Revolution. Boston, 1909. 2 vols.,
ltd. no. ed., 4tos., illus., maps. MacManus 239-1034 1978 $42.50

SANDERSON, J. E.   Messengers of the Churches... Toronto, 1901.
2nd series, bookplt., ports., illus. Hood 116-317 1978 $12.50

SANDERSON, JOHN P.   Republican Landmarks. 1856. 1st ed. Austin 79-631 1978 $32.50

SANDERSON, THOMAS   Original Poems. Carlisle, 1800. 12mo,
19th-century half calf, spine gilt, 1st ed., fine copy. Ximenes 47-278 1978
$75

SANDERSON, THOMAS W.   20th Century History of Youngstown and Mahon-
ing County, Ohio and Representative Citizens. Chicago, 1907. Double columns,
new cloth. Hayman 73-552 1978 $60

SANDES, EDWARD WARREN CAULFEILD   The Indian Sappers and Miners.
Chatham, 1948. Plts., orig. cloth, 8vo., coloured maps. F. Edwards 1013-581
1978 £12

SANDFORD, FRANCIS   A Genealogical History of the Kings of England,
and Monarchs of Great Britain. London, 1677. Title page in red & black, illus.,
engravings, folio, red straight-grained morocco gilt, panelled sides, gilt, edges
marbled & gilt, most attractive vol. with pencil notes by Beckford. Traylen 88-
460 1978 £550

SANDHAM, ALFRED   Ville-Marie. Montreal, 1870. Engrs., orig.
binding. Hood 117-594 1978 $85

SANDHAM, E.   The Grandfather: or, The Christmas Holidays.
1810. 2nd. ed., 12mo, frontis, eng., contemp. panelled calf, corners & edges
rubbed. Eaton 45-439 1978 £5

SANDOZ, MARI   Old Jules. Boston, 1935. Fine copy in worn
d.w. Desmarais B-567 1978 $7.50

SANDOZ, MARI   The Tom-Walker. New York, 1947. Orig. cloth,
d.j., 1st ed. Ginsberg 14-909 1978 $40

SANDOZ, MAURICE   The House Without Windows. 1950. First ed.,
coloured plts. by Salvador Dali, roy. 8vo., d.j. George's 635-134 1978 £18

SANDOZ, MAURICE   On the Verge. New York, 1950. Illus., 1st
ed., sq. 8vo., d.w., pres. copy from Salvador Dali. Argosy Special-32 1978
$275

SANDS, FRANK   A Pastoral Prince... Santa Barbara, 1893.
Pic. cloth, illus., 1st ed., scarce, frontis. taped, else very good, slip case.
Dykes 35-60 1978 $175

SANDS, FRANK   Santa Barbara at a Glance;.... Santa Barbara,
1895. Illus., original printed wr., 1st ed. Ginsberg 14-189 1978 $75

SANDS, WILLIAM FRANKLIN   Our Jungle Diplomacy. Chapel Hill, 1944.
Biblo 251-54 1978 $12.50

SANDSTROM, IVAR   On A New Gland in Man and Several Mammals.
Baltimore, 1938. Rittenhouse 49-700 1976 $30

SANDWELL, A. H.   Planes Over Canada. London, 1938. Illus.
Hood's 115-134 1978 $22.50

SANDWICH, JOHN, EARL OF   The Private Papers of...First Lord of the Admiralty, 1771-1782. 1932-1938. 4 vols., illus., orig. cloth, fine. MacManus
239-1785 1978 $75

SANDYS, EDWIN   Europae Speculum. 1629. Sm. 4to., contemp.
calf, joints little worn, first authorized ed. Howes 194-96 1978 £55

SANDYS, EDWIN   Europae Speculum, or a View or Survey of the
State of Religion in the Westerne parts of the World. N.P., 1629. Quarto, full
early calf, 1st ed. Bennett 7-94 1978 $275

SANDYS, GEORGE   Sandys Travailes... London, 1652. Fifth ed.,
sm. folio, engraved & printed title-pgs., folding engraved map, some leaves torn,
without loss of printed surface, some staining, manuscript notes in contemporary
hand, quarter calf, marbled bds., back defective at head & tail, joints weak.
Deighton 5-222 1978 £145

SANDYS, J. E.   Harvard Lectures on the Revival of Learning. Cambridge, 1905. 8vo. Upcroft 12-391 1978 £7.50

SANDYS, WILLIAM   Christmastide, Its History, Festivities, and Carols. London, c.1860. Lithographs, text vignettes, imitation-wood cloth, gold-ruled, tips rubbed, very good. Victoria 34-711 1978 $50

SANDZEN, BIRGER   The Smoky Valley. Kansas City, 1922. Bds., 20 lithographs, spine little chipped & repaired. Hayman 71-687 1978 $10

SANFORD, MRS. D. P.   A Houseful of Children. New York, 1877. B&W plates signed by T. Cobb, Stevens & others, superb gilt binding, very good. Victoria 34-712 1978 $20

SANFORD, L. G.   The History of Erie County, Penna., From Its First Settlement. N.P., 1894. New enlarged ed., illus., maps, fine. Mac-Manus 239-1669 1978 $35

SANFORD, MRS. N.   History of Marshall County, Iowa. Clinton, 1867. Cloth, illus., 1st ed., top of spine worn else very good, plastic d.w., very scarce. Dykes 35-160 1978 $75

SANGER, WILLIAM W.   The History of Prostitution. New York, 1858. Orig. binding, backstrip chipped. Wolfe 39-497 1978 $30

SANGSTER, MARGARET E.   Life on High Levels. Cincinnati, 1897. Orig. binding, clean. Hayman 71-688 1978 $10

SANKEY, JOHN   Diary of a Trip... Manchester, 1888. Orig. cloth, inscribed pres. copy from author, mint. Jarndyce 16-990 1978 £12.50

SANSOM, JOSEPH   Letters from Europe, During a Tour Through Switzerland and Italy, in the Years 1801 and 1802. Philadelphia, 1805. 2 vols., contemp. full calf, a bit worn, 1st ed., former owner's name stamped on each t.p., rare. MacManus 238-570 1978 $40

SANSON, WILLIAM   Westminster in War. 1947. 8vo, orig. cloth, photos, pres. copy to Winston Churchill. Sawyer 298-107 1978 £55

SANSOVINO, FRANCESCO   Del Governo Et Amministratione Di Diversi Regni Et Republiche... Venice, 1583. 4to., vellum. Salloch 348-229 1978 $200

SANSOVINO, FRANCESCO   Dell'Historia Universale dell'Origine et Imperio de Turchi. Venice, 1560. Rare 1st ed., 4to, 2 vols. in one, old brown mor., gilt arms on panels, gilt edges. Gilhofer 75-96 1978 SFr 1,100

SANTA Barbara, California, Morning Press, Special Edition. Santa Barbara, 1887. Illus., map, original large printed wr. Ginsberg 14-190 1978 $65

SANTA CLARA County, California: .... San Jose, 1890. Illus., original printed wr. Ginsberg 14-191 1978 $65

SANTA Cruz and Monterey. San Francisco, 1880. Original printed wr., map on wr., 1st ed. Ginsberg 14-157 1978 $85

SANTANGELO, ORAZIO DE ATTELLIS   Protest Against the Convention of April 11, 1839, Between the U.S.A. and the Republic of Mexico,.... Washington, 1842. Half mor., 1st ed. Ginsberg 14-970 1978 $300

SANTAYANA, GEORGE   Lucifer. A Theological Tragedy. Chicago, 1899. 12mo., orig. cloth, 1st ed., very good. MacManus 238-572 1978 $50

SANTAYANA, GEORGE   Sonnets and Other Poems. New York, 1896. 12mo., orig. cloth, new ed., very good. MacManus 238-571 1978 $50

SANTE, L. R.   The Chest. Annals of Roentgenology. A Series of Monographic Atlases. Volume XI. New York, 1931. Shaken, cover not fresh. Rittenhouse 49-701 1976 $12.50

SANTEE, ROSS   Apache Lande. New York, 1947. 1st. ed., illus. by author, bookplate, fine. Baldwins' 51-568 1978 $15

SANTEE, ROSS   Apache Land. New York, London, 1947. Pic. cloth, 1st ed., fine copy in d.w. from the Allred Collection & inscr'd to him, orig. watercolors by Santee, illus., slipcase. Dykes 34-206 1978 $150

SANTEE, ROSS   Cowboy. New York, 1928. Pic. cloth, illus., 1st ed., fine copy in slipcase. Dykes 34-67 1978 $37.50

SANTORELLI, ANTONIO   Antonii Santorelli Nolani, Philosophi, et Medici, Et in Gymnasi Neapolitano, primi olim Philosophiae Interpretis.... 1622. 4to., limp vellum, lower hinge split, first ed., rare. King 7-99 1978 £120

SANUTUM, PETRUM AURELIUM   Soli Deo Honor et Gloria. Venetiis, 1543. 1st ed., quarto, 19th-century half-vellum over flecked boards, title backed. Bennett 20-183 1978 $150

SAPPER, PSEUD.
Please turn to
MC NEILE, HERMAN CYRIL

SAPPHO   Sappho Revocata. 1928. Plts., roy. 8vo., orig. buckram gilt, ltd. to 350 copies. Howes 194-1149 1978 £25

SAPPINGTON, JOHN   The Theory and Treatment of Fevers. Arrow Rock, 1844. 12mo., contemp. calf, worn, rebacked with gilt lettering, foxed, signatures of former owners, good copy, 1st ed. in English. Zeitlin 245-229 1978 $150

THE SARATOGA Association for the Improvement of the Breed or Horses. August 1908. Race Course, Saratoga Springs, New York. (New York, 1908). Wrs. Hayman 72-498 1978 $7.50

SARBAH, JOHN MENSAH   Fanti Customary Laws. London, 1904. 2nd. ed., revised, amateur half calf, 8vo. K Books 239-428 1978 £22

SARDINI, GIACOMO   Congetture sopra un'antica stampa.... Firenze, 1793. 4to., Italian calf, good margins, first ed. King 7-232 1978 £30

SARG, TONY   Tony Sarg's New York. New York, 1926. 4to., illus. in color, 1st ed. Biblo 251-180 1978 $32.50

SARGENT, GEORGE B.   Lecture on the "West";..... Davenport, 1858. Original printed wr. bound in cloth, 1st ed. Ginsberg 14-425 1978 $75

SARGENT, GEORGE H.   A Busted Bibliophile and His Books. Being a Most Delectable History of the Diverting Adventures of That Renowned Book-collector A. Edward Newton of Daylesford in Penna... Boston, 1928. Illus., orig. cloth-backed marbled bds., 1st ed., 1 of 600 copies, bookplts., very good. MacManus 238-999 1978 $35

SARGENT, GEORGE H.   A Busted Bibliophile and His Books. Boston, 1928. 8vo., orig. cloth-backed bds., 1st ed., ltd. to 600 copies, illus. MacManus 238-998 1978 $27.50

SARGENT, JOHN S.   The Work. 1903. Plts., lg. folio. George's 635-52 1978 £12.50

SARGENT, MRS. JOHN T.   Sketches and Reminiscences of the Radical Club of Chestnut Street, Boston. Boston, 1880. Heliotypes, 8vo., all edges gilt, 1st ed. Morrill 241-515 1978 $17.50

SARGENT, JOHN WILLIAM   Toasts for the Times in Pictures and Rhymes. New York, 1904. Prtd. on one side only, pictured by Nella Fontain Binckley. Hayman 73-669 1978 $7.50

SARGENT, LUCIUS M.   Dealings with the Dead.... Boston, 1856. 2 vols., orig. full pub. mor., a.e.g., 1st ed., slightly worn, but very good pub. gift bind., rare in this bind. MacManus 238-573 $75

SARGENT, M. P.   Pioneer Sketches: Scenes and Incidents of Former Days... Erie, 1891. Cloth, faded and worn. Hayman 72-694 1978 $35

SARGEANT, P. W.
Please turn to
SERGEANT, PHILIP WALSINGHAM

SARGENT, WINTHROP   The History of an Expedition Against Fort Du Quesne, in 1755... Philadelphia, 1855. 1st ed., orig. cloth. MacManus 239-166 1978 $45

SAROYAN, WILLIAM   The Assyrian. New York, (1950). Fine in very good dw. Bernard 5-241 1978 $10

SAROYAN, WILLIAM   The Daring Young Man on the Flying Trapeze. New York, 1934. Near mint in chipped d.w. with faded spine. Desmarais B-570 1973 $70

SAROYAN, WILLIAM   Don't Go Away Mad and Two Other Plays. New York, (1949). 1st ed., d.w. Biblo 251-625 1978 $12.50

SAROYAN, WILLIAM   Hilltop Russians in San Francisco. (San Francisco, Grabhorn Press), 1941. Color plts., sm. 4to., first ed., ltd. to 500 copies, fine, d.w. Howell 5-30 1978 $100

SAROYAN, WILLIAM   Inhale and Exhale. 1936. First ed. Austin 82-817 1978 $20

SAROYAN, WILLIAM   Peace. 1939. 177 pages. Austin 82-819 1978 $10

SAROYAN, WILLIAM   The Saroyan Special: Selected Short Stories. New York, (1948). Illus., rear bd., little smudged, 1st ed. Petrilla 13-99 1978 $8

SAROYAN, WILLIAM   So Help Me. 1943. 240 pages. Austin 82-822 1978 $8.50

SARPI, PAOLO   Discorso dell'origini, forma, leggi, ed vso dell' Vfficio del' Inqvisitione nella Citta, e Dominio di Venetia. 1639. 4to., marbled bds., lettering piece gilt, roman letter, some discoloration of paper. King 7-100 1978 $30

SARPI, PAOLO   Historia del Concilio Tridentino. London, 1619. Very rare 1st ed., folio, contemp. half-vellum. Gilhofer 75-97 1978 SFr 3,600

SARPI, PAOLO   A Treatise of Beneficiary Matters. Westminster, 1727. Contemp. calf, label missing, 8vo. Howes 194-450 1978 £22

SARR, LOUIS VICTOR   Pledge the Canadian Maiden. New York, 1928. Hood 117-818 1978 $10

SARRANS, B.   Memoirs of General Lafayette and of the French Revolution of 1830. New York, 1833. 2 vols., 1st U.S. ed., very fine, orig. cloth. MacManus 239-781 1978 $40

SARRAZIN DE MONTFERRIER, A. A. W.   De Principes et des Procedes du Magnetisme Animal.... Paris, 1819. 2 vols. in 1, 8vo, contemp. calf gilt, new label, somewhat worn. Quaritch 977-71 1978 $175

SARTAIN, JOHN   The Reminiscences of a Very Old Man, 1808-1897. New York, 1899. Illus., 1st ed. MacManus 239-812 1978 $25

SARTON, MAY   The Bridge of Years. New York, 1946. 16mo, green cloth, gilt stamped, stated 1st ed., Fine, 6 line inscription by author. Desmarais 1-367 1978 $20

SARTORIS, RAMON   Three Plays. N.P., 1944. 1st ed., illus., 4to., orig. bds., slight wear. Americanist 102-19 1978 $65

SARTORIO, ENRICO C.   Social and Religious Life of Italians in America. Boston, (1918). Author's signed pres. to William Roscoe Thayer, Thayer's bkplt., stains on binding & upper margins. Biblo 251-375 1978 $15

SARTORIUS, C.   Mexico: Landscapes and Popular Sketches. New York, n.d. (ca. 1860). Steel engrs., 4to., 3/4 mor. Argosy Special-78 1978 $850

SARTRE, JEAN-PAUL   The Age of Reason. 1947. Good, first English ed. Bell Book 17-797 1978 £5

SARTRE, JEAN PAUL   L'Etre et le Neant. Paris, 1943. 1st ed., 8vo, orig. pr. wr. Gilhofer 75-98 1978 SFr 450

SARTRE, JEAN-PAUL   Existentialism and Humanism. 1948. Very good, slightly worn d.w., first English ed. Bell Book 17-798 1978 £6.50

SASSOON, SIEGFRIED   The Heart's Journey. New York and London, 1927. One of 590 copies, signed by author, fine, d.w., first ed., orig. binding. Rota 211-583 1978 £100

SASSOON, SIEGFRIED   The Heart's Journey. London, 1928. Orig. cloth, 1st ed., fine, slightly soiled d.j. MacManus 238-746 1978 $20

SASSOON, SIEGFRIED   In Sicily. London, (1927?). 1st ed., color plt., pictorial wr., very good or better. Limestone 9-254 1978 $12.50

SASSOON, SIEGFRIED   Memoirs of a Fox-Hunting Man. 1928. First ed., cr. 8vo., very good, repaired d.w., orig. cloth. Howes 194-1150 1978 £12.50

SASSOON, SIEGFRIED   Memoirs of an Infantry Officer. 1930. 1st. ed., blue cloth, spine faded. Eaton 45-441 1978 £10

SASSOON, SIEGFRIED   Memoirs of an Infantry Officer. London, 1930. Orig. blue buckram, 1st ed., 1 of 750 copies on Eng. hand-made paper, signed by author, fine. MacManus 238-747 1978 $65

SASSOON, SIEGFRIED   Memoirs of an Infantry Officer. 1931. First illus. ed., drawings in colour, pict. cloth, fine. Bell Book 16-764 1978 £15

SASSOON, SIEGFRIED   The Old Huntsman and Other Poems. London, 1917. 8vo, grey boards, paper label, 1st issue with errata slip pasted in, cover bumped, Fine in damaged d.w., 1st ed. Desmarais 1-368 1978 $60

SASSOON, SIEGFRIED   Picture Show; poems. Cambridge, 1919. First ed., one of 200 copies, nice, orig. binding, author's autograph signature. Rota 211-582 1978 £85

SASSOON, SIEGFRIED   Poems by Pinchbeck Lyre. 1931. Sm. 8vo., 1st ed., bds., fine copy. Quaritch 979-285 1978 $25

SASSOON, SIEGFRIED   Rhymed Ruminations; poems. London, 1940. First Trade ed., orig. binding, very nice. Rota 211-584 1978 £8

SASSOON, SIEGFREID   The Road to Ruin. 1933. Mint, d.w., first English ed. Bell Book 16-765 1978 £28.50

SASSOON, SIEGFRIED   A Suppressed Poem. (Milwaukee), The Unknown Press, 1919. Portr., self-wrs., 1st separate ed., #5 of numbered ed. of 50, light dampstain, rare. Bradley 49-288 1978 $50

SASSOON, SIEGFRIED   To My Mother. London, (1928). 1st ed., color plt., pictorial wr., very good or better. Limestone 9-255 1978 $12.50

SATCHELL, JOHN   Thornton Abbey: Or, The Persecuted Daughter. n.d. (c.1825). 1st. ed., half calf, head of spine worn, lacks leading free endpaper, good. Jarndyce 16-991 1978 £8.50

THE SATIRIST. London, 1803-1813. Available October 1, 1807-April 1, 1813, 9 vols., half calf, handcolored plts., lg. fldg. plts., tinted, rare set. Van der Peet H-64-281 1978 Dfl 750

SATIS, G.   Classical Exercises Upon the Rules of the French Syntax... 1792. 8vo, contemp. calf, worn, paper label. Eaton 45-442 1978 £10

SAUCERMAN, SOPHIA   International Transfers of Territory in Europe. 1937. Austin 79-634 1978 $12.50

SAUGNIER   Voyages to the Coast of Africa. London, 1792. First ed. in English, map, good, contemp. calf, 8vo. K Books 244-273 1978 £80

SAULEY, F. DE   Narrative of a Journey Round the Dead Sea and In the Bible Lands, 1850-51... 1854. Folding map, 2 vols., 8vo, half morocco. Edwards 1012-86 1978 £45

SAUMAISE, CLAUDE DE   Claudii Salmasii Plinianae Exercitationes in Caii Julii Solini Polyhistora. (Utrecht), 1689. 2nd ed., fine, thick folio, 2 vols. in 1, contemp. vellum over boards, blind-stamped devices and borders on covers, paneled spine, occasional foxing. Bennett 20-184 1978 $325

SAUNDERS, E. M.   The Life and Letters of the Rt. Hon. Sir Charles Tupper, Bart. New York, 1916. Photogravure plts., 2 vols. Hood 117-330 1978 $65

SAUNDERS, FREDERICK   Salad for the Social. New York, 1856. Illus., sm. 8vo., binding slightly faded, 1st ed. Morrill 239-596 1978 $12.50

SAUNDERS, FREDERICK   Some Famous Books. Battery Park 1-263 1978 $22.50

SAUNDERS, JOHN CUNNINGHAM   The Anatomy of The Human Ear...Diseases of That Organ. Philadelphia, 1821. First Amer. ed., browning, otherwise tight and clean. Rittenhouse 49-702 1976 $55

SAUNDERS, LOUISE   The Knave of Hearts. Racine, 1925. 1st ed., sq. 4to., spiral binding, illus., pic. paper covers, very fine. Current Misc. 8-35 1978 $285

SAUNDERS, LOUISE   The Knave of Hearts. New York, 1925. Sm. folio, very good, pictures by Maxfield Parrish. Baldwins' 51-151 1978 $300

SAUNDERS, LOUISE   The Knave of Hearts. New York, 1925. 1st ed., cover color plate, margins thumbed, covers a bit rubbed, light foxing, cloth ed., all plates very good. Victoria 34-603 1978 $225

SAUNDERS, O. ELFRIDA   English Illumination. Florence, (1928). Collotype plts. of reproductions, 2 vols., folio, orig. buckram, d.w. Traylen 88-64 1978 £120

SAUNDERS, MARSHALL   'Tilda Jane. An Orphan in Search of a Home. Boston, 1901. Illus., 1st ed. Biblo BL781-1033 1978 $10

SAUNDERS, WILLIAM   Agricultural Colleges and Experimental Farm Stations. Ottawa, 1886. Wrs. Hood 117-962 1978 $12.50

SAUNDERS, WILLIAM   A Treatise on the Structure, Economy, and Diseases of the Liver. Walpole, 1810. 12mo., contemp. calf, 2nd Amer. ed. Morrill 239-225 1978 $20

SAUNDERSON, HENRY H.   History of Charleston, N.H. Claremont, (1876). 1st ed., illus., orig. cloth, minor wear, scarce. MacManus 239-1065 1978 $60

SAUSSURE, HORACE BENEDICT DE   Essais sur l'Hygrometrie. Neuchatel, 1783. 4to., copperplts., orig. wrs., uncut, mostly unopened, spine repaired, very good copy, 1st ed. Norman 5-252 1978 $300

SAUSSURE, NICHOLAS-THEODORE DE   Recherches Chimiques sur la Vegetation. Paris, 1804. 8vo., fldg. tables, fldg. copperplt., contemp. half calf, little rubbed, but fine copy, 1st ed. Norman 5-253 1978 $275

SAUVEUR, L.   Chats with The Little Ones. Boston, 1876. 1st ed., illus. by J.M.D. and F.T. Merrill, moderate cover wear, text very good. Victoria 34-714 1978 $8.50

SAVAGE, D. S.   Mysticism & Aldous Huxley. Yonkers, New York, 1947. 1 of 750 copies, 8 vo., stiff pictorial wrappers, fine. Houle 10-288 1978 $25

SAVAGE, GEORGE H.   Insanity and Allied Neuroses. Practical and Clinical. London, 1891. Third ed. Rittenhouse 49-703 1976 $10

SAVAGE, JOHN   The Life and Public Services of Andrew Johnson, Seventeenth President... New York, 1866. 8vo., illus., fine, 1st ed., orig. cloth. Morrill 241-516 1978 $18.50

SAVAGE, M.W.   R. L. Sheil's Legal & Political Sketches. 1855. 1st ed., 2 vols., slight wear on spine, very good, octavo bound in cloth. Hyland 128-518 1978 £15

SAVAGE, RICHARD   The Works of. 1777. New ed., 2 vols., 8vo., calf rebacked. P. M. Hill 142-213 1978 £48

SAVAGE, RICHARD HENRY   My Official Wife. London, 1891. Pict. glazed boards, "yellow-back" format in poor condition, interior good. Greene 78-100 1978 $15

SAVAGE, ROSEMARY L.   American Concern over Canadian Railway Competition in the North-West, 1885-1890. (Ottawa, 1942). Hood's 115-984 1978 $7.50

SAVARD, F. A.   L'Abatis, Dessins d'Andre Morency. Montreal, 1943. Card cover. Hood 116-318 1978 $10

SAVARY, CLAUDE   Morale de Mohamet. 1784. 12mo., green polished calf. King 7-386 1978 £25

SAVELLE, MAX   The Diplomatic History of the Canadian Boundary, 1749-1763. New Haven, 1940. Fldg. map. Hood 117-595 1978 $40

SAVERIEN, ALEXANDRE   Histoire des Progres de l'Esprit Humain dans les Arts.... Paris, 1766. 1st ed., octavo, full contemp. blond blind-stamped pig, frontis. by Massard, exquisite copy. Bennett 20-186 1978 $150

SAVETH, EDWARD N.   American Historians and European Immigrants 1875-1925. 1948. 1st ed. Austin 79-636 1978 $15

SAVI, GAETANO   Flora Italiana Ossia Raccolta Delle Piante Piu Belle Che Si Coltivano Nei Giardini d'Italia. Pisa, 1818-1824. Lg. plts., printed in colours, 3 vols., lg. folio, contemp. quarter russia leather, bd. sides, spines gilt, some slight foxing. Traylen 88-661 1978 £4800

SAVIGNY, MRS. A. G.   A Heart-Song of To-Day. Toronto, 1886. Inscr'd by author on flyleaf. Hood 117-543 1978 $35

SAVIGNY, J. B. H.   Narrative of a Voyage to Senegal in 1816... 1818. Coloured portrait, orig. cloth-backed bds., repaired at head of spine, 8vo, marginal staining at end. Edwards 1012-268 1978 £90

SAVILE, GEORGE, MARQUIS OF HALIFAX
Please turn to
HALIFAX, GEORGE SAVILE, MARQUIS OF

SAVONAROLA, GIROLAMO   De Simplicitate Christianae Vitae. Florence, (1496). 1st ed., fine, quarto, dark brown crushed levant mor., Hamsworth Library copy, bookplate of Clifford Rattey. Bennett 20-185 1978 $1,750

SAVOYARD, PSEUD.   Essays on Men, Things and Events.
Please turn to
NEWMAN, EUGENE WILLIAM

SAWTELLE, ITHAMAR B.   History of the Town of Townsend, Middlesex Co., Mass... Fitchburg, 1878. Illus., 3/4 calf, lib. marks, very good. MacManus 239-1053 1978 $35

SAWYER, CHARLES JAMES   English Books 1475-1900. A Signpost for Collectors. Westminster, 1927. 2 vols., 8vo., orig. cloth, d.j., worn, 1st ed., illus., ltd. MacManus 238-1049 1978 $85

SAWYER, CHARLES JAMES   English Books 1475-1900. London, 1927. 2 vols., plts., illus., nice, 8vo., orig. cloth, d.w. K Books 244-274 1978 £40

SAWYER, J. C.   Odorographia, a Natural History of Raw Materials and Drugs Used in the Perfume Industry. London, 1892-94. 2 vols., 8vo., illus., cloth, one vol. rebacked, odd spine laid down. Quaritch 977-253 1978 $200

SAWYER, J. C.   Rhodologia. A Discourse on Roses and the Odour of the Rose. Brighton, 1894. 8vo., map, orig. wrappers, worn. Quaritch 977-254 1978 $40

SAWYER, JAMES A.   Wagon Road from Niobrara to Virginia City.... Washington, 1866. Disbound, 1st ed. Ginsberg 14-910 1978 $35

SAWYER, JOHN   History of Cherry Valley from 1740 to 1898. Cherry Valley, 1898. One inner hinge weak, good copy. Butterfield 21-347 1978 $35

SAWYER, JOSEPH DILLAWAY   Washington. New York, 1927. 2 vols., illus., 1st ed., edges rubbed, top of spine of vol. I nicked. Biblo 248-221 1978 $27.50

SAWYER, JOSEPH DILLAWAY   Washington. New York, 1927. 1st ed., 2 vols., illus., orig. cloth, d.j., fine set. MacManus 239-503 1978 $35

SAWYER, ROBERT V.   Water Gardens and Goldfish. New York, 1928. 8vo, orig. cloth. Book Chest 17-329 1978 $15

SAWYER, RUTH   Folkhouse. 1932. 266 pages. Austin 82-823 1978 $11

SAXE, MAURICE, COMTE DE 1696-1750   Reveries, or Memoirs Upon the Art of War. 1757. Copperplts., 4to., contemp. calf, repaired, rebacked. F. Edwards 1013-420 1978 £70

SAXE-COBURG AND GOTHIA, ERNEST I, DUKE OF   Reise Des Herzogs Ernst... Leipzig, 1864. Coloured engraved title, maps, coloured plts. by Robert Kretschmer, oblong folio, rebacked, orig. cloth, some foxing. Edwards 1012-281 1978 £75

SAXI, F.   British Art and the Mediterranean. 1948. Illus., lg. folio. George's 635-53 1978 £5

SAXON, ISABELLE PSEUD.
Please turn to
SUTHERLAND, MRS. REDDING

SAXON, LYLE   Children of Strangers. 1937. Austin 82-824 1978 $10

SAXON, LYLE   Fabulous New Orleans. 1930. Illus. Austin 82-930 1978 $11

SAXON, LYLE   Father Mississippi. 1927. Illus., first ed., very good. Austin 82-825 1978 $27.50

SAXON, LYLE   Father Mississippi. NY, 1927. Many illus., cover speckled, Bell Wiley's copy. Broadfoot's 44-904 1978 $12.00

SAXON, LYLE   Old Louisiana. 1929. Illus., first ed., v.g. Austin 82-931 1978 $27.50

SAXTORPH, MATTHIAS   Gesammelte Schriften Geburtshulflichen, Praktischen und Physiologischen Inhalts. Kopenhagen, 1803. 2 parts in 1 vol., fldg. copperplts., 8vo., contemp. bds., fine copy. Offenbacher 30-135 1978 $150

SAY, JEAN-BAPTISTE   A Treatise on Political Economy... Philadelphia, 1830. Contemp calf, stained. MacManus 239-431 1978 $25

SAYER, JOSEPH   The Law of Damages. Dublin, 1792. 12mo., contemp. calf, rebacked. Morrill 239-593 1978 $7.50

SAYERS, DOROTHY L.   Even the Parrot. Exemplary Conversations for Enlightened Children. London, (1944). Illus. by Sillince, orig. cloth, d.j., chipped, 1st ed., very good, scarce. MacManus 238-748a 1978 $75

SAYERS, DOROTHY L.			Even the Parrot: Exemplary Conversation
For Enlightened Children. London, 1944. 1st ed., illus., d.j., very good
or better. Limestone 9-256 1978 $30

SAYERS, DOROTHY L.			Gaudy Night. 1935. Covers somewhat rubbed,
good, first English ed. Bell Book 16-259 1978 £12.50

SAYERS, DOROTHY L.			In the Teeth of the Evidence, and other stories.
1939. Good, first English ed. Bell Book 16-260 1978 £12.50

SAYERS, DOROTHY L.			The Man Born to be King. A Play Cycle on the
Life of Our Lord and Saviour Jesus Christ. London, 1943. Orig. cloth, d.j.,
slightly worn and dust-soiled, 1st ed., very good. MacManus 238-748 1978 $35

SAYERS, DOROTHY L.			Murder must Advertise & Hangman's Holiday.
New York, n.d. Very good, covers slightly marked. Bell Book 16-261 1978
£4

SCADDING, HENRY			Toronto of Old; Collections and Recollections Il-
lustrative of the Early Settlement and Social Life of the Capital of Ontario. Toronto, 1873. 1st ed., orig. bds., signed by Henry Morgan, bind. a little scuffed.
Hood 116-776 1978 $100

SCADDING, HENRY			Toronto: Past and Present: Historical and Des-
criptive... Toronto, 1884. Ltd. ed., illus. Hood 116-777 1978 $100

SCAIFE, ARTHUR H.			The War to Date (March 1, 1900). London,
1900. 46 plts., cr. 8vo, slightly thumbed ex-Smiths copy neatly recased in orig.
dec. cloth. K Books 239-429 1978 £9

SCALIGER, JULIUS CAESAR		Exotericarum Exercitationum Liber Quintus
Decimus De Subtilitate, ad Hieronymum Cardanum. Lutetiae Parisiorum (Paris),
1557. Sm. 4to., full antique calf, old signature crossed out, fine copy, 1st ed.
Norman 5-254 1978 $450

SCAMMON, J. YOUNG			Chicago Historical Society, November 19, 1868,
Introductory Address by.... Chicago, 1877. Wrps. Hayman 71-313 1978 $7.50

THE SCARLET Beast, Stripped Naked... n.d. (1680). 1st. ed., folio, disbound.
Hannas 54-47F 1978 £24

SCARLET Book of Free Masonry. New York, (1880). Colored frontis., illus.,
8vo., orig. cloth. Morrill 241-518 1978 $12.50

SCARPA, ANTONIO			Saggio Di Osservazioni E D'Esperienze Sulle
Principali Malattie Degli Occhi. Venezia, 1802. 8vo., engr. medallion portr.,
engr. plts., contemp. beige bds., marginal wormtrail, very good uncut copy with
bkplt. of former owner. Zeitlin 245-230 1978 $250

SCEARCE, S.				Northern Lights to Fields of Gold. Caldwell,
1939. Illus. & full-page plts. by R.H. Hall. Hood's 115-79 1978 $35

SCENERY of the Catskill Mountains as Described by Irving, Cooper, Bryant...
Thomas C9le and Other Eminent Writers. New York, (1860). Prtd. wr. Butterfield 21-100 1978 $15

SCENES in Our Parish. Philadelphia, 1834. Bds., some wear. Hayman 73-670
1978 $7.50

SCENIC Gems of Maine. Portland, 1893. Illus., lg. oblong 8vo. Morrill 239-
500 1978 $12.50

SCHAACK, HENRY C. VAN		The Life of Peter Van Schaack. New York,
1842. Portr., soundly rebound, 3/4 lea. & bds. Butterfield 21-389 1978 $65

SCHAARSCHMIDT, FR.			Zur Geschichte der Dusseldorfer Kunst, Insbeson-
dere im XIX Jahrhundert. Dusseldorf, 1902. 4to., cloth, plts., illus. Van der
Peet H-64-196 1978 Dfl 65

SCHABOL, JEAN ROGER		La Practique du Jardinage. Paris, 1774. Con-
siderably enlarged ed., frontis and engraved plates by Jean Robert, all hand-
colored, contemp. red mor., gilt inside dentelles, triple gilt fillets on panels,
gilt back, splendid set. Gilhofer 75-100 1978 SFr 1,200

SCHACHNER, NATHAN			Alexander Hamilton. New York, (1946). First
ed., d.w. Biblo 247-130 1978 $15

SCHACHNER, NATHAN			The Mediaeval Universities. 1938. Allen 234-
1446 1978 $7.50

SCHACHNER, NATHAN			The Price of Liberty. New York, 1948. Biblo
251-702 1978 $12.50

SCHAEFER, FRIEDRICH			Georg Christoph Lichtenberg Als Psychologe
Und Menschenkenner. Leipzig, 1899. Port., illus., 8vo., pamphlet bind., orig.
wrs. bound in. Salloch 348-118 1978 $10

SCHAEFER, HENRICH			Amarna in Religion und Kunst. Leipzig, 1931.
Illus., 12mo., wrs. Biblo BL781-472 1978 $9

SCHAEFFER, CASPER			Memoirs and Reminiscences Together with
Sketches of the Early History of Sussex County, N.J... Hackensack, 1907.
Illus., ltd. to 250 copies, scarce. MacManus 239-1319 1978 $65

SCHAEFFER, CHARLES WILLIAM	Early History of the Lutheran Church in
America, from the Settlement of the Swedes on the Delaware to the Middle of the
Eighteenth Century. Philadelphia, 1857. Orig. cloth, good copy, lib. marks.
MacManus 239-261 1978 $12.50

SCHAEFFER, J. PARSONS		The Nose. Philadelphia, 1920. Some wear on
cover, trifle loose. Rittenhouse 49-704 1976 $35

SCHAFF, MORRIS			The Sunset of the Confederacy. Boston, (1910).
Cloth. Hayman 73-119 1978 $10

SCHALCK, ADOLF W.			History of Schylkill County, Pa. N.P., 1907.
2 vols., 4tos., later cloth w/leather labels, illus. Americanist 101-132 1978 $95

SCHANTZ, F. J. F.			The Domestic Life and Characteristics of the
Pennsylvania-German Pioneer... Lancaster, 1900. 1st ed., illus., orig. cloth,
bookplt., signed by author. MacManus 239-1670 1978 $32.50

SCHANZ, M.				Geschichte der Roemischen Literatur. 1898-1904.
4 vols., half calf, rubber stamps on title. Allen 234-856 1978 $35

SCHARF, JOHN THOMAS		The Chronicles of Baltimore. Baltimore, 1874.
Rebound. MacManus 239-997 1978 $42.50

SCHARF, JOHN THOMAS		History of Delaware, 1609-1888. Philadelphia,
1888. Orig. ed., rebacked in red buckram, 2 vols. Baldwins' 51-233 1978 $400

SCHARF, JOHN THOMAS		History of Philadelphia 1609-1884. Philadelphia,
1884. 3 vols., illus., maps. MacManus 239-1620 1978 $125

SCHARF, JOHN THOMAS		History of Philadelphia, 1609-1884. Philadel-
phia, 1884. 3 vols., illus., maps, 4to, rebound in red lib. buckram. Baldwins'
51-478 1978 $90

SCHARF, JOHN THOMAS		History of the Confederate States Navy. NY, 1887.
Ex libris, hinges cracked, spine wrinkled, torn, pictorial cover, Bell Wiley's copy.
Broadfoot's 44-335 1978 $40.00

SCHARLING, HENRIK			Nicolai's Marriage: A Picture of Danish Family
Life. 1876. First English ed., 2 vols., cr. 8vo., orig. decor. cloth. Howes
194-1154 1978 £8.50

SCHAUINGER, J. HERMAN		William Gaston, Carolinian. Milwaukee, 1949.
Broadfoot 50-195 1978 $20

SCHAUSS, HAYYIM			The Lifetime of a Jew. New York, 1950. Illus.,
1st ed. Austin 79-637 1978 $12.50

SCHEER, CHARLES H. E.		Conad History: Continental Advance Section,
Communcations Zone, European Theater of Operations, U.S. Army. (Heidelberg,
1945). Sm. folio, colored plts., 1st ed., signed by historian. Petrilla 13-101
1978 $16

SCHEFFER, FREDERICK		The Toast, An Epic Poem, in Four Books. Dub-
lin, 1732. 8vo, disbound, 1st genuine Dublin ed., very good copy. Ximenes
47-168 1978 $250

SCHEFFLER, K.			Adolph Menzel. Berlin, 1938. 8vo., bds.,
illus. Van der Peet H-64-197 1978 Dfl 35

SCHEFFLER, K.			Deutsche Maler und Zeichner im Neunzehnten
Jahrhundert. Leipzig, 1919. 8vo., cloth, illus. Van der Peet H-64-84 1978
Dfl 35

SCHEIBEN, SIMON			De Victu Disputatio Ordinaria Instituta...
Leipzig, 1559. 4to., wrs. Salloch 345-167 1978 $60

SCHEIBERT, JUSTUS			The Franco-German War, 1870-71. Chatham,
1894. 1st. ed. of this translation, plt., folding maps, 8vo, orig. cloth, sm.
portion cut from blank f/l & inside joints weak, very good copy. Fenning 32-
291 1978 £9.50

SCHELHAMMER, GUNTHER CHRISTOPH	De Auditu Liber Unus. Lugduni-Ba-
tavorum, 1684. Engr. frontis., illus. on fldg. copperplts., 8vo., contemp. limp
bds., uncut, 1st ed., very rare, fine copy. Offenbacher 30-136 1978 $300

SCHELL, JAMES P.			History of the Early Presbyterian Church of North
Dakota. (Fargo, 1885?). Orig. pr. wr. Ginsberg 14-323 1978 $25

SCHELLING, FRIEDRICH WILHELM JOSEPH   Philosophische Schriften.   Landshut, 1809.   8vo., contemp. cloth, 1st ed.   Salloch 348-233 1978 $450

SCHELLING, FRIEDRICH WILHELM JOSEPH   System Des Transcendentalen Idealismus.   Tuebingen, 1800.   8vo., 1/2 calf, 1st ed.   Salloch 348-231 1978 $250

SCHELLING, FRIEDRICH WILHELM JOSEPH   Vorlesungen Ueber Die Methode Des Akademischen Studiums.   Tuebingen, 1803.   8vo., marbled bds., uncut, 1st ed.   Salloch 348-232 1978 $250

SCHELSTRATE, EMMANUEL 1649-92   De Disciplina Arcani contra Disputationem Ernesti Tentzelli Disseratio Apologetica.   Patavil, 1743.   Contemp. blind stamped pigskin over wooden bds., metal clasps, sm. 4to.   Howes 194-575 1978 £25

SCHENCK, DAVID   North Carolina, 1780-81. Being a History of the Invasion of the Carolinas.   Raleigh, 1889.   Fold. map.   Broadfoot 50-196a 1978 $30

SCHENCK, DAVID   North Carolina, 1780-81. Being a History of the Invasion of the Carolinas.   Raleigh, 1889.   New cloth.   Broadfoot 50-196b 1978 $25

SCHENCK, ELIZABETH H.   The History of Fairfield.   New York, 1889-1905. 2 vols., sm. 4tos., fine set.   MacManus 239-946 1978 $75

SCHENCK, J. H.   The Wild Ranger of Santa Fe.   [Philadelphia, c. 1895].   Illus., orig. pict. wr., 1st ed.   Ginsberg 14-779 1978 $150

SCHENCK, JOHN S.   History of Ionia and Montcalm Counties, Michigan.   Philadelphia, 1881.   Lib. marks, lg. 4to., illus., very nice, orig. calf-backed cloth bds.   MacManus 239-1058 1978 $100

SCHENCK, R. C.   No Compromise with Treason.   (Washington, 1864).   Disbound, age-browned.   Hayman 73-671 1978 $7.50

SCHENDEL, A. VAN   De Berg Van Droomen.   Amsterdam, 1913. Sm. 8vo., crushed black calf, sm. gilt borders tooled on both sides, very nice binding, contents fine.   Van der Peet H-64-387 1978 Dfl 150

SCHENDEL, A. VAN   Drogon.   Amsterdam, 1906.   Sm. 8vo., black mor., broad gilt tooled lace-work border on both sides, gilt tooled spine, t.e.g., plts. by M. Bauer, scarce, excellent binding.   Van der Peet H-64-384 1978 Dfl 200

SCHENDEL, A. VAN   De Mensch Van Nazareth.   Amsterdam, 1916. Sm. 8vo., crushed black calf, sm. gilt borders tooled on both sides, bound in very attractive binding.   Van der Peet H-64-386 1978 Dfl 150

SCHENDEL, A. VAN   Verhalen.   Amsterdam, n.d. (ab. 1925).   Sm. 8vo., crushed black calf, sm. gilt borders tooled on both sides, uncut, attractive binding.   Van der Peet H-64-385 1978 Dfl 125

SCHEPPEGRELL, WILLIAM   Hayfever and Asthma. Care, Prevention and Treatment.   Philadelphia, 1922.   Ex-library.   Rittenhouse 49-705 1976 $15

SCHERER, JAMES A. B.   Three Meiji Leaders: Ito, Togo, Nogi.   Tokyo, 1936. Cloth.   Dawson's 449-182 1978 $10

SCHERER, W.   A History of German Literature.   1886.   Orig. ed., 2 vols., buckram, 8vo.   Howes 194-1155 1978 £7.50

SCHERFFER, P. C.   De Emendatione Telescopiorum Dioptricorum per Vitrum Objectivum compositum recens a Dollondo in Anglia inventa, Dissertatio.   Vienna, 1762.   4to., bds., plt., vignette, first ed.   Gurney 75-32 1978 £60

SCHERJON, W.   Vincent van Gogh's Great Period.   Amsterdam, 1937. 4to., cloth, portr., plts., out of print, rare.   Van der Peet H-64-85 1978 Dfl 150

SCHERMERHORN, FRANK E.   American & French Flags of the Revolution. 1948. Colored plates, good.   Nestler Rare 78-178 1978 $25

SCHERMERHORN, FRANK E.   American and French Flags of the Revolution. Philadelphia, 1948.   Illus., in color, scarce.   MacManus 239-619 1978 $25

SCHERMERHORN, WILLIAM E.   The History of Burlington, N.J.   Burlington, 1927. Illus., fine, scarce.   MacManus 239-1320 1978 $45

SCHERZER, JOSEPH   Lehrbuch der Militar-Chemie als Leitfadur für die Vorlesungen im k.k. Bombardier-Corps.   Wien, 1845.   Fldg. litho. plts., 8vo., contemp. green cloth, back gilt, 1st ed.   Offenbacher 30-137 1978 $85

SCHERZER, KARL   Narrative of the Circumnavigation of the Globe by the Austrian Frigate Novara, 1857-59.   1861-63.   Maps, illus., 3 vols., binders cloth, lib. stamps on titles.   Edwards 1012-38 1978 £60

SCHETKY, JOHN CHRISTIAN   Illustrations of Walter Scott's Lay of the Last Minstrel...   1808.   1st ed., 4to, 12 plts., offset, probably lacking half-title, contemp. calf, spine worn.   Hannas 54-297 1978 £30

SCHEUBEL, JOANNES   Algebrae Compendiosa Facilisque Descriptio, qua Depromuntur Magna Arithmetices Miracula.   Paris, 1551.   Sm. 4to., disbound, slipcase, first separate ed., first issue.   Quaritch 977-170 1978 $3,000

SCHEUBEL, JOANNES   Algebrae in Compendiosa Facilisque Descriptio, Qua Depromuntur Magna Arithmetices Miracula.   Paris, 1551.   Woodcut vignette, tall 8vo., marbled bds., 1st & only ed.   Salloch 345-168 1978 $350

SCHEUCHZER, JOHANN JACOB   Kupfer-Bibel, in Welcher Die Physica Sacra Oder Geheiligte Natur-Wissenschafft Derer in Hl.   Augsburg & Ulm, 1731-1733. Engr. frontis., portr., plts., 4 vols., folio, 1/2 calf, few stains in margins, fine set, plts. in excellent cond.   Salloch 345-169 1978 $2,000

SCHEURLEER, D. F.   Van Varen en Vechten.   's-Gravenhage, 1914. 3 vols., 8vo., half cloth, frontis's, contents & edges brown spotted.   Van der Peet H-64-541 1978 Dfl 75

SCHEYER, HANS EGON   Five Anthropometric Studies of Southern Chinese Women...   Canton, (1932)-1936.   8vo., mostly in wrs. or unbound, stapled, from the library of Dr. Alfred M. Hellman.   Zeitlin 245-231 1978 $37.50

SCHIERN, F.   Life of James Hepburn, Earl of Bothwell.   Edinburgh, 1880.   8vo.   George's 635-562 1978 £5.25

SCHIFF, MORITZ   Lecons sur la Physiologie de la Digestion, Faites au Museum d'Histoire Naturelle de Florence.   Florence & Turin, 1867.   8vo., orig. prtd. wrs., uncut, 2 vols., 1st ed., stamps on wrs.   Offenbacher 30-138 1978 $150

SCHILD, M.   Old English Costumes.   (c. 1865).   Engraved plts. in colour, 4to., orig. cloth worn.   George's 635-243 1978 £25

SCHILDER, PAUL   The Image and Appearance of the Human Body. New York, 1950.   Rittenhouse 49-706 1976 $12.50

SCHILLER, JOHANN CHRISTOPH FRIEDRICH VON   The Death of Wallenstein.   1800.   1st ed., orig. bds., uncut, spine little worn, generally very good, orig. cond.   Jarndyce 16-390 1978 £85

SCHILLER, JOHANN CHRISTOPH FRIEDRICH VON   The Fight with the Dragon. A Romance.   1825.   1st Eng. ed., plts., contemp. half calf, head of spine chipped, 4to.   Howes 194-1156 1978 £25

SCHILLER, JOHANN CHRISTOPH FRIEDRICH VON   Fridolin.   1824.   1st Eng. ed., plts., German & English texts prtd. en face, contemp. half calf, 4to. Howes 194-1157 1978 £21

SCHILLER, JOHANN CHRISTOPH FRIEDRICH VON   Fridolin Or, The Road to The Iron Foundry.   1824.   1st. ed., illus., 4to, uncut, orig. grey bds., lg. paper label on leading bd., little loose & some foxing, otherwise good.   Jarndyce 16-993 1978 £27

SCHILLER, JOHANN CHRISTOPH FRIEDRICH VON   Mary Stuart, A Tragedy. 1824.   1st. ed., orig. half calf, good.   Jarndyce 16-992 1978 £16

SCHILLER, JOHANN CHRISTOPH FRIEDRICH VON   The Poems and Ballads of ... 1844.   1st. ed., 2 vols., half title, brown morocco, raised bands, spines & borders gilt, a.e.g., fine.   Jarndyce 16-994 1978 £34

SCHILLER, JOHANN CHRISTOPH FRIEDRICH VON   Umrisse zu Liede von der Glocke nebft Undeutungen, von M. Retsch.   Stuttgart, 1837.   Plts., some foxing, sm. oblong folio, half calf, worn.   George's 635-206 1978 £7.50

SCHILLER, JOHANN CHRISTOPH FRIEDRICH VON   William Tell.   London, 1823.   Sm. margin rips., pict. bds., heavily rubbed, roan spine, v.g.   Victoria 34-299 1978 $40

SCHILLINGLAW, JOHN J.   A Narrative of Arctic Discovery, From the Earliest Period to the Present Time.   London, 1850.   1st. ed., 8vo, folding engraved maps, orig. blue blind stamped cloth, gilt, neatly rebacked retaining orig. backstrip, gilt, some staining.   Deighton 5-170 1978 £35

SCHILPP, PAUL A.   The Philosophy of Ernst Cassirer.   Evanston, 1949. 4to., cloth.   Salloch 348-28 1978 $25

SCHLABRENDORFF, FABIAN VON   Revolt Against Hitler.   1948.   1st. ed., 12 mo, orig. cloth, illus., slightly faded, pres. copy to Winston Churchill.   Sawyer 298-108 1978 £125

SCHLAGINTWEIT, ROBERT VON   Californie en Zijne Bevolking...Deventer, 1873. Deventer, 1873. Illus., orig. prtd. wr., 1st ed. Ginsberg 14-192 1978 $125

SCHLAGINTWEIT, ROBERT VON   Die Eisenbahn Zwischen den Stadten New York und Mexiko Nebst Einer Allgemeinen Schilderung Mexikos. Weimar, [ca. 1873]. Orig. pr. wr. Ginsberg 14-911 1978 $75

SCHLATTER, R. B.   The Social Ideas of Religious Leaders 1660-1688. Oxford, 1940. Octavo, good. Upcroft 10-527 1978 £7.50

SCHLEGEL, FRIEDRICH   Ueber die Sprache und Weisheit de Indier. Heidelberg, 1808. 8vo., light spotting, old marbled boards, cloth spine, rare 1st ed. Quaritch 978-137 1978 $400

SCHLEICH, KARL LUDWIG   Schmerzlose Operationen. Berlin, 1899. 8vo., illus., some in color, orig. red cloth, gilt lettered, fine copy, 4th ed. Zeitlin 245-232 1978 $65

SCHLEIMANN, HEINRICH   Troja. Ergebnisse Meiner Neuesten Ausgrabungen auf der Baustelle von Troja... Leipzig, 1884. 8vo., illus., color maps, orig. pub. cloth, lib. stamp on title, 1st ed. Gilhofer 74-50 1978 sFr 400

SCHLESINGER, ABRAHAM   Einfuhrung in Den Zionismus. 1921. Paper, in German, 1st ed., paper browning. Austin 79-638 1978 $37.50

SCHLESINGER, RUDOLF   Federalism in Central and Eastern Europe. New York, 1945. Biblo BL781-871 1978 $9

SCHLEUSNER, T. E.   Novum lexicon Graeco-Latinum in Novum Testamentum.... Glasguae, 1824. 2 vols., calf rubbed, lacks letteringpieces from Vol. 1, 8vo. George's 635-1125 1978 £5.50

SCHLEY, WINFIELD S.   Report of...Commanding Greely Relief Expedition of 1884. Washington, 1887. Plts., maps. Hood 117-110 1978 $55

SCHLIEMANN, HENRY   Mycenae. New York, 1878. Maps, plans, illus., plts. in color, lg. 8vo. Morrill 239-599 1978 $37.50

SCHLOSSER, J. VON   Die Kunst des Mittelalters. Berlin, ab. 1923. Sm. 4to., cloth, illus., colored plts. Van der Peet H-64-86 1978 Dfl 30

SCHLOSSER, L. B.   A Selection from Collection of...An Exhibition of Books on Papermaking. Wr., thin, 1 of 300 copies, prtd. on handmade "Bird & Bull" paper made by J. Barcham Green. Battery Park 1-341 1978 $100

SCHLYTTER, LESLIE EVAN   The Tall Brothers. 1921. First ed., d.j., very good. Austin 82-826 1978 $20

SCHMALZ, G. A. HEINRICH   Ein Fall Von Aphasie In Folge Luetischer Hirnaffection. Leipzig, (1870). Sm. 8vo., unbound, browned, good copy. Zeitlin 245-233 1978 $45

SCHMID, M.   Kunstgeschichte des XiX. Leipzig, 1904. 4to., cloth, illus., colored plts. Van der Peet H-64-40 1978 Dfl 40

SCHMID, NOCOLAUS   Von den Weltkorpern. N. P., 1766. 8vo., contemp. calf, rubbed, but very good copy, 1st ed. Norman 5-255 1978 $150

SCHMIDT, ADOLF   The Examination of the Function of the Intestines by Means of The Test Diet.... Philadelphia, 1909. Library marks. Rittenhouse 49-707 1976 $10

SCHMIDT, C. F.   Greek Revival Architecture in the Rochester (NY) Area. 1946. Illus., limited ed., good. Nestler Rare 78-210 1978 $20

SCHMIDT, CHARLES   Etudes Sur Le Mysticisme Allemand Au XIVe Siecle. Paris, 1847. Folio, 1/2 vellum with label. Salloch 348-234 1978 $85

SCHMIDT, HEINRICH   Philosophisches Woerterbuch. Leipzig, 1934. 9th ed., 8vo., cloth. Salloch 348-235 1978 $7.50

SCHMIDT, HUBERT G.   Rural Hunterdon... New Brunswick, 1946. Illus., orig. cloth, very good. MacManus 239-1321 1978 $20

SCHMIDT, JOHANN ADAM   Uber die Krankheiten des Thranenorgans. Wien, 1803. Copperplts., prtd. in sepia, 8vo., contemp. half calf, 1st ed., very good copy. Offenbacher 30-122 1978 $375

SCHMIDT, M. C. P.   Kulturhistorische Beitraege zur Kenntnis des Griech. 1914. Sewn. Allen 234-860 1978 $10

SCHMIDT, RUDOLPH   Pain. Philadelphia, (1911). 2nd ed., 8vo. Morrill 239-226 1978 $7.50

SCHMIED, FRANCOIS LOUIS   Peau-Brune. Lyons, 1931. 4to., contemp. full dark blue levant mor., inner gilt mor. border, brown suede doublures & fly leaves, uncut, orig. wr., backstrip bound in, slipcase, bound by G. Crette, ltd. ed. issued in 135 copies, 1 of 90 numbered copies on Arches paper, signed by artist, illus. by F. L. Schmied, superb copy, pristine cond. Goldschmidt 110-65 1978 $2,400

SCHMITZ, JOSEPH W.   Thus They Lived: Social Life in the Republic of Texas. San Antonio, 1936. Cloth. Jenkins 116-1167 1978 $20

SCHMITZ, LUDOWICO MICHAELI   De Sonnambulismo Spontaneo. Coloniae ad Rhenum, 1833. Rittenhouse 49-708 1976 $17.50

SCHMITZ, Y.   Guillaume Ier et la Belgique. Paris, 1945. 8vo., orig. covers. Van der Peet H-64-542 1978 Dfl 45

SCHMUCKER, S. S.   The American Lutheran Church, Historically, Doctrinally, and Practically Delineated. Springfield, 1851. A.e.g. MacManus 239-260 1978 $12.50

SCHNABEL, CARL   Handbook of Matallurgy. London, 1898. Illus., 2 vols., 8vo., 1st English ed., orig. cloth. Morrill 241-520 1978 $20

SCHNEERSOHN, JOSEPH I.   Lubavitcher Rabbi's Memoirs. Brooklyn, 1949. Ex-lib. Austin 79-639 1978 $27.50

SCHNEIDER, CARL CAMILLO   Vorlesungen Ueber Tierpsychologie. Leipzig, 1909. Illus., tall 8vo., 3/4 lea. Salloch 345-171 1978 $30

SCHNEIDER, HERBERT WALLACE   A History of American Philosophy. 1946. Austin 82-827 1978 $27.50

SCHNEIDER, ISIDOR   The Judas Time. New York, 1946. 1st ed., d.w. frayed. Biblo 251-626 1978 $13.50

SCHNEIDER, O.   Typen-Atlas. Dresden, 1892. 4to., cloth, 4th rev. ed., plts., illus., map. Van der Peet H-64-543 1978 Dfl 45

SCHNIDLER, ANTON F.   The Life of Beethoven... 1841. 1st. ed. in English, portrait, folding plts. of facsimiles, 2 vols., 8vo, orig. blue cloth, very slight wear to 1 headband, bright fresh copy. Fenning 32-292 1978 £32

SCHNITZLER, ARTHUR   Flint and Fliederbusch. Berlin, 1917. Wrappers. Eaton 45-443 1978 £5

SCHNITZLER, ARTHUR   The Lonely Way: Intermezzo. New York, 1915. 1st Amer. ed. Biblo 251-627 1978 $16.50

SCHOENBERNER, FRANZ   The Inside Story of an Outsider. 1949. Austin 79-640 1978 $10

SCHOEPF, JOHANN DAVID   Materia Medica Americana Potissimum Regni Vegetabilis. Erlangen, 1787. 8vo., half mor. in the style of the period, back gilt, 1st ed., rare, fine copy. Offenbacher 30-139 1978 $2,500

SCHOETTLE, EDWIN J.   Sailing Craft... (New York), 1928. 4to., illus., orig. cloth, bookplt., spine darkened, otherwise a very good copy. MacManus 239-1786 1978 $30

SCHOFIELD, F. H.   The Story of Manitoba. Winnipeg, 1913. 3 vols., illus., lea. spines & corners worn. Hood 117-919 1978 $150

SCHOFIELD, JOHN M.   Forty-Six Years in the Army. New York, 1897. 8vo., portr., ex-lib., 1st ed., orig. cloth. Morrill 241-521 1978 $20

THE SCHOLARTIS PRESS   List for May-June, 1929, with a Full Description of All Previous Publications. London, (1929). 12mo., orig. wrs. Morrill 241-522 1978 $7.50

SCHOLES, P. A.   The Mirror of Music, 1844-1944. 1947. Illus., 2 vols., covers a little rubbed, 8vo. George's 635-1414 1978 £8.50

SCHOLL, WILLIAM M.   The Human Foot. Chicago, (1915). 8vo., 1st ed. Morrill 239-227 1978 $25

SCHOLL, WILLIAM M.   Practipedics. Scinece of Giving Foot Comfort and Correcting the Cause of Foot and Shoe Troubles. Chicago, 1917. Rittenhouse 49-709 1976 $12.50

SCHOMBURGK, ROBERT H.   A Description of British Guiana, Geographical and Statistical... 1840. Folding map, outline coloured, binders' cloth, 8vo, slightly soiled. Edwards 1012-674 1978 £65

SCHONGAUER, M.   Katalog der Kupferstiche Martin Schongauers. Vienna, 1925. 4to., plts. of watermarks, sewed. Quaritch 983-255 1978 $150

SCHOOCK, M.   De Sternutatione Tractatus Copiosus.   Amsterdam, 1664. 12mo., contemp. red mor., gilt panelled sides and back, gilt edges. Quaritch 977-72 1978 $200

SCHOOLCRAFT, HENRY ROWE   Historical and Statistical Information, Respecting the History, Condition and Prospects of the Indian Tribes of the United States. Philadelphia, 1851-55. 5 vols., 4to., illus., first ed., bind. worn, some foxing, some plts. stained, pres. copies signed by L. Lea and G. W. Manypenny, lacks vol. 6. Biblo BL781-77 1978 $600

SCHOOLCRAFT, HENRY ROWE   Notes on the Iroquois. Albany, 1847. Colored portrs., ads, enlarged ed., orig. backstrip reinforced with tape, otherwise good. Butterfield 21-219 1978 $35

SCHOOLING, WILLIAM   Alliance Assurance, 1824-1924. 1924. Illus., sq. 8vo. George's 635-394 1978 £6

SCHOOLING, WILLIAM   The Governor and Company of Adventures of England Trading Into Hudson's Bay During 250 Years, 1670-1920. 1920. 4to, wrapper, 2 coloured portraits, maps, illus. Edwards 1012-453 1978 £25

SCHOOLING, WILLIAM   The Governor and Company of Adventurers of England Trading into Hudson's Bay During Two Hundred and Fifty Years, 1670-1920. London, 1920. Card cover, illus., fold. map. Hood 116-594 1978 $30

SCHOPENHAUER, ARTHUR   Briefe. Leipzig, (1894). 12mo., cloth. Salloch 348-240 1978 $9

SCHOPENHAUER, ARTHUR   Complete Essays. New York, 1942. Thick 4to., cloth. Salloch 348-237 1978 $15

SCHOPENHAUER, ARTHUR   On the Fourfold Root of the Principle of Sufficient Reason; On the Will in Nature. London, 1910. Rev'd ed., 8vo., cloth. Salloch 348-239 1978 $10

SCHOPENHAUER, ARTHUR   Parerga and Paralipomena. Munich, 1913. Vol. I, 4to., cloth. Salloch 348-238 1978 $20

SCHOPENHAUER, ARTHUR   Werke. Leipzig, n.d. 5 vols., 8vo., cloth, India paper. Salloch 348-236 1978 $75

SCHOTT, CASPAR   Organum Mathematicum. Wuerzburg, 1668. Engr. Plts., very thick 4to., lea.-backed bds., front hinge repaired. Salloch 345-172 1978 $450

SCHOTTER, HOWARD W.   The Growth & Development Of The Pennsylvania Railroad...1846-1926.... (Philadelphia), 1927. 2nd pr., map, illus., large 8vo, orig. binding. Americanist 101-121 1978 $20

SCHOUTEN, G. DE   Voiage Aux Indes Orientales, 1658-65. Amsterdam, 1707. Frontis, plts., 2 vols., 12mo, contemp. calf, vol. I rebacked, slight worming in 1st. part of vol. I. Edwards 1012-215 1978 £100

SCHRADER, FREDERICK FRANKLIN   Handbook Political, Statistical and Sociological for German Americans. 1916. Illus., paper. Austin 79-643 1978 $20

SCHRADER, HANS   Phidias. Frankfurt, 1924. 325 plts., 4to. Baldwins' 51-152 1978 $40

SCHREBER, JOHANN CHRISTIAN DANIEL   Die Saeugthiere in Abbildungen Nach Der Natur. Mit Beschreibungen. Erlangen, 1775-1778. Plts., some hand-colored, thick 4to., fine contemp. binding of gilt-tooled marbled calf with lea. labels, polychromed edges, lavishly illus. Salloch 345-173 1978 $600

SCHREIBER, J.   Meteorology in the Service of Medicine. Louisville, 1878. 8vo., orig. wrs., autographed by Giddings. Morrill 239-228 1978 $12.50

SCHREINER, OLIVE   Dreams. 1891. Portrait, decor. cloth, good, first English ed. Bell Book 17-801 1978 £8.50

SCHREINER, OLIVE   Losse Gedachten Over Zuid-Afrika. Haarlem, 1900. Portrait frontis, cr. 8vo, orig. cloth-backed printed bds. K Books 239-433 1978 £18

SCHREINER, OLIVE   The Story of an African Farm. 1883. Good, orig. patterned cloth, 2 vols., first English ed. Bell Book 16-767 1978 £95

SCHREVELIUS, C.   Lexicon manuale Graeco-Latinum et Latino-Graecum. 1661. Engraved title, first few pages damp-stained, panelled calf, bottom of spine defective. George's 635-508 1978 £7.50

SCHREVELIUS, C.   Lexicon manuale Graeco-Latinum et Latino-Graecum. 1699. Old calf, unlettered, 8vo. George's 635-509 1978 £8.50

SCHRICK, MICHAEL   Von den usz gebrenten wassern.... Strassburg, 1519. Small 4to., Gothic letter, extensive notes in early hand touched by binder in some margins, modern boards. Quaritch 978-138 1978 $1,650

SCHRIJNEN, J.   Nederlandsche Volkskunde. Zutphen, n.d. 2 vols., 8vo., cloth. Van der Peet H-64-200 1978 Dfl 45

SCHROETER, JOHANN HIERONYMUS   Selenotogographishe Fragmente zur Genauern Kenntniss de Mondflache.... Gottingen, 1791-1802. 1st ed., 2 vols., quarto, occasional contemp. MS notes, rare. Bennett 20-189 1978 $3,150

SCHROYER, M. S.   Company "G" History, Lamented Comrade's Writings Tell of Service of Locally Recruited, Civil War Unit in 147th Regiment. N.P., 1939. Bell Wiley's copy. Broadfoot's 44-594 1978 $16

SCHRUMPF-PIERRON, P. M. D.   Tobacco and Physical Efficiency. New York, 1927. Rittenhouse 49-710 1976 $15

SCHUBART, W.   Papyri Graecae Berolinenses. 1911. Folio, plts. Allen 234-863 1978 $15

SCHUBRING, P.   Die Italienische Plastik des Quattrocento. Potsdam, 1924. 4to., plts., illus., half cloth. Quaritch 983-256 1978 $35

SCHUCHHARDT, C.   Alteuropa. 1935. 4to., plts., illus., pencilled, few notes in ink. Allen 234-864 1978 $10

SCHULBERG, BUDD   The Disenchanted. New York, (1950). 8vo., cloth, d.j., 1st ed., 1st prtg. J. S. Lawrence 38-F148 1978 $10

SCHULBERG, BUDD   The Disenchanted. 1950. Austin 82-828 1978 $8.50

SCHULBERG, BUDD   The Harder They Fall. 1947. First ed. Austin 82-829 1978 $10

SCHULL, JOSEPH   I, Jones, Soldier. Toronto, 1944. Hood 116-840 1978 $10

SCHULTZ, ALFRED P.   Race or Mongrel. 1908. Austin 79-645 1978 $27.50

SCHULTZ, CHRISTIAN   Travels on an Inland Voyage through the States of New York, Pennsylvania, Virginia, Ohio, Kentucky and Tennessee and through the Territories of Indiana, Louisiana, Mississippi and New-Orleans; Performed in the Years 1807 and 1808. New York, 1810. 1st ed., 8vo., 2 vols. in 1, portr., plts., maps, old 1/2 calf over marbled bds. rebacked, very scarce. Current Misc. 8-38 1978 $895

SCHULTZ, HAROLD S.   Nationalism and Sectionalism in South Carolina 1852-1860. Durham, 1950. Bell Wiley's copy. Broadfoot's 44-937 1978 $16.00

SCHULTZE, A.   The Sultanate of Bornu. London, 1913. Cr. 8vo, 2 folding maps, orig. cloth. K Books 239-434 1978 £10

SCHULZ, ELLEN D.   Texas Wild Flowers. Chicago & New York, 1928. 1st ed., illus., color, very good or better. Limestone 9-257 1978 $35

SCHULZE, ERNST   Die Bezauberte Rose. Leipzig, 1837. Cr. 8vo, frontis portrait, 6 plts. by Schumacher, orig. bds., stained. Eaton 45-444 1978 £5

SCHULZE, F.   Die Deutsche Napoleon-Karikatur. Weimar, 1916. 4to., full vellum, colored plts. out of text, other plts., rare. Van der Peet H-64-282 1978 Dfl 400

SCHULZE, W.   Reise-und Lebens-Bilder aus Neuholland, Neuseeland, un Californien. Magdeburg, 1853. Half morocco. Ginsberg 14-193 1978 $150

SCHUMAN, F. L.   Europe on the Eve. New York, 1939. First ed. Biblo 247-745 1978 $10

SCHUMPETER, JOSEPH A.   Business Cycles. New York, 1939. 2 vols. Biblo BL781-872 1978 $16.50

SCHUNKE, I.   Leben und Werk Jakob Krauses. Leipzig, (1943). Colored plts., illus., demy 4to., marbled bds., cloth back. Forster 130-79 1978 £25

SCHURIG, MARTIN   Spermatologia Historico-Medica, h.e. Seminis Humani Consideratio Physico-Medico-Legalis, qua ejus Natura et Usus, Insimulque Opus Generationis et Varia de Coitu Aliaque Huc Pertinentia... Francofurti ad Moenum, 1720. 4to., contemp. half vellum, 1st ed. Offenbacher 30-140 1978 $225

SCHUYLER, GEORGE L.   Correspondence and Remarks Upon Bancroft's History of the Northern Campaign of 1777 and the Character of Major-Gen. Philip Schuyler. New York, 1867. 1st ed., royal 8vo., 1 of only 2 copies on tinted paper, only 202 copies prtd. in all, wrs. with some soiling & wear, spine patched. Current 24-103 1978 $100

SCHUYLER, R. L.   The Fall of the Old Colonial System, a Study in British Free Trade, 1770-1870. 1945. 8vo. George's 635-396 1978 £5

SCHWAB, GUSTAV   Gods & Heroes, Myths & Epics of Ancient Greece. 1947. Allen 234-865 1978 $7.50

SCHWARTZ, E.   Die Konigslisten des Eratosthenes und Kastor mit Excursen uber die Interpolationen bei Africanus und Eusebios. Gottingen, 1894. Lg. 8vo., cloth. Van der Peet H-64-544 1978 Dfl 50

SCHWARTZ, JACOB   The Writings of Alfred Edgar Coppard. 1931. No. 646 of 650 copies signed by Coppard, this being one of 50 for pres., qtr. linen, very good, first English ed. Bell Book 16-187 1978 £22.50

SCHWARTZ, LOUIS   Cosmetics and Dermatitis. New York, 1946. Rittenhouse 49-711 1976 $10

SCHWARZ, IGNATIUS   Imperii Princeps Ecclesiasticus... Augsburg, 1733. Frontis., pits., folio, marbled bds., leather label. Salloch 348-243 1978 $175

SCHWARZ, LEO W.   A Golden Treasury of Jewish Literature. 1937. Illus. Austin 79-646 1978 $12.50

SCHWARZ, LEO W.   The Jewish Caravan. 1935. Austin 79-648 1978 $12.50

SCHWARZ, LEO W.   Memoirs of My People. 1943. Austin 79-649 1978 $12.50

SCHWARZE, EDMUND   History of the Moravian Missions Among Southern Indian Tribes of the United States. Bethlehem, 1923. Illus. MacManus 239-1215 1978 $35

SCHWATKA, FREDERICK   Along Alaska's Great River... Chicago, 1900. Illus., front inner hinge repaired. MacManus 239-16 1978 $17.50

SCHWATKA, FREDERICK   A Summer in Alaska... St. Louis, 1894. Illus., maps, orig. pic. cloth. MacManus 239-19 1978 $20

SCHWEDIAUR, FRANCOIS XAVIER
Please turn to
SWEDIAUR, FRANCOIS XAVIER

SCHWEDLER, JOSEFA H.   Come Back With Me. Hollywood, 1950. Austin 79-650 1978 $17.50

SCHWEINFURTH, GEORG   The Heart of Africa. 1873. 1st. ed. in Eng., 2 vols., 8vo., plts., one of which is coloured, maps, illus., some neat repairs, half calf, gilt backs, ex-lib. copy, lib. stamps throughout. Deighton 5-22 1978 £75

SCHWEINFURTH, GEORG   The Heart of Africa. London, 1878. 2 vols., folding map, many plts., text-illus., cr. 8vo, slight foxing, nice bright copy, orig. dec. cloth. K Books 239-435 1978 £30

SCHWENKE, PAUL   Festchrift zur Gutenbergfeir. 1900. Pres. copy, A.L.s. from Schwenke, newly rebound in 3/4 lea. & marbled paper over bds., 4to. Battery Park 1-155 1978 $125

SCHWETTMANN, MARTIN W.   Santa Rita: The University of Texas Oil Discovery. Austin, 1933. Illus. by Tom Lea. Jenkins 116-1233 1978 $12.50

SCHWOB, MARCEL   Annabella et Giovanni: conference. Paris, 1894. First French ed., very good, wraps. Bell Book 16-768 1978 £4

SCHWOB, MARCEL   The Children's Crusade. Boston, Heintzemann Press, 1898. 12mo., finely prtd. on handmade paper, pict. bds., 1 of 500 copies, old Italian handmade paper, upper spine loose. Battery Park 1-167 1978 $50

SCHWOB, MARCEL   La Porte des Reves. Paris, 1899. 4to., orig. pict. wr., uncut, 1st ed., 220 numbered copies prtd. on Japan paper, illus. by Georges de Feure, autograph inscription from author, fine copy. Goldschmidt 110-23 1978 $975

SCHWOB, RENE   Chagall et L'ame Juive. Paris, 1931. Sq. 8vo., orig. pict. wr., ltd. ed., 565 numbered copies prtd., numbered on Alfa paper, illus. by Chagall, autograph inscription, signed & dated from Chagall. Goldschmidt 110-12 1978 $60

THE SCIENTIFIC American Reference Book. New York, 1876. Orig. binding, clean, little rubbed. Hayman 71-692 1978 $7.50

SCIOPPIUS, GASPAR   Infamia Famiani.... 1658. 12mo., cloth. King 7-311 1978 £20

SCLATER, P. L.   The Book of Antelopes. 1894-1900. 4 vols., 4to., illus., hand-coloured plts., orig. cloth, a little worn, joints of vol. 4 repaired, but clean. Quaritch 983-365 1978 $5,250

SCLATER, WILLIAM LUTLEY   The Geography of Mammals. London, 1899. Ex-lib with blindstamp, 1st ed., binding worn, bookplt., 8vo, orig. cloth. Book Chest 17-334 1978 $65

SCOALA Romana din Roma. 1937-38. Vols. 7-8 only, folio, sewn, plt. Allen 234-822 1978 $12.50

SCOBEE, BARRY   Old Fort Davis. San Antonio, 1947. 1st ed., illus. Jenkins 116-1234 1978 $15

SCOBLE, JOHN   The Rise and Fall of Krugerism. London, 1900. Good, 8vo., orig. cloth. K Books 244-440 1978 £15

SCOFIELD, C. L.   The Life and Reign of Edward the Fourth. 1923. 2 vols., orig. cloth, recased, 8vo. Upcroft 12-396 1978 £17.50

SCORESBY, WILLIAM   Journal of a Voyage to the Northern Whale-Fishery... Edinburgh, 1823. 1st. ed., 8vo, half-title, folding & other engraved maps & plts., some spotting of text, blue polished half calf, matching bds., gilt, morocco label gilt. Deighton 5-168 1978 £285

SCORTIA, JOANNES BAPTISTA   De Natura Et Incremento Nili. Lyons, 1617. Sm. 8vo., modern calf. Salloch 345-174 1978 $225

SCOT, MICHAEL   Phisionomia. Paris, n.d. (early 16th c.). Sm. 8vo., vellum, with ties, fine woodcut, lib. stamp, attractive. Gurney 75-96 1978 £175

SCOT, REGINALD   The Discoverie of Witchcraft. 1930. Ltd. ed., sm. folio. George's 635-1435 1978 £25

SCOTLAND Illustrated. London, 1850. Plts., woodcut tailpieces, 4to., half calf. K Books 244-275 1978 £65

SCOTT, ANNA M.   Day Dawn In Africa... New York, 1858. 11 plts., cr. 8vo, frontispiece, folding map, rather foxed, head & tail of spine slightly frayed, orig. cloth. K Books 239-436 1978 £30

SCOTT, CAROLINE LUCY   Trevelyan. London, 1833. 3 vols., 12mo, contemporary brown figured cloth (a trifle worn), 1st ed., very good copy. Ximenes 47-279 1978 £60

SCOTT, CAROLINE LUCY   Trevelyan. 1837. Engraved frontis, 8vo, orig. cloth, nice. Fenning 32-293 1978 £7.50

SCOTT, CLEMENT   The Drama of Yesterday and Today. 1899. First ed., portrait, plts., 2 vols., orig. cloth, 8vo. Howes 194-1277 1978 £15

SCOTT, EDMUND   An Exact Discourse Of the Subtilties, Fashihions (sic),.... 1606. 1st ed., rare, small 4to, small round wormhole in upper margins affecting several headlines, dark blue levant mor., gilt edges, by Riviere. Quaritch 978-49 1978 $2,000

SCOTT, EVELYN   Bread and A Sword. 1937. Austin 82-831 1978 $10

SCOTT, EVELYN   A Calendar of Sin. 1931. 2 vols., first ed. Austin 82-832 1978 $27.50

SCOTT, EVELYN   Eva Gay. 1933. 799 pages. Austin 82-833 1978 $11

SCOTT, EVELYN   Migrations. 1927. First ed. Austin 82-834 1978 $20

SCOTT, EVELYN   The Shadow of the Hawk. 1941. First ed., d.j. Austin 82-835 1978 $22.50

SCOTT, EVELYN   The Viking Bodleys. 1896. Illus. colored covers, very good. Austin 82-839 1978 $20

SCOTT, EVELYN   The Wave. 1929. First ed. Austin 82-836 1978 $20

SCOTT, EVELYN   The Wave. 1929. 625 pages. Austin 82-837
1978 $7.50

SCOTT, F. R.   Canada and the Commonwealth. Toronto, (1938).
Card cover. Hood 116-653 1978 $30

SCOTT, F. R.   Labour Conditions in the Men's Clothing Industry.
Toronto, 1935. Card cover, ex-lib. Hood 116-356 1978 $15

SCOTT, G. D.   The Stones of Bray & The Stories They Can
Tell of the Ancient Times in the Barony of Rathdown. 1913. 1st ed., wr., illus.,
very good. Hyland 128-488 1978 £15

SCOTT, GENIO C.   Fishing in American Waters. New York, 1869.
Illus., orig. binding. Wolfe 39-19 1978 $25

SCOTT, GEORGE   Scott's New Coast Pilot for the Lakes, Containing
a Complete List of All the Lights and Light-Houses, Fog Signals and Buoys, on Both
the American and Canadian Shores... Detroit, 1916. Printed bds., some wear,
9th ed. Hayman 72-696 1978 $12.50

SCOTT, HUGH STOWELL   The Phantom Future. London, 1888. 2 vols.,
orig. cloth, 1st ed., front inner hinge cracked in vol. 1, slightly worn, but very
good, Hugh Walpole's Brackenburn bookplt. MacManus 238-331 1978 $125

SCOTT, HUGH STOWELL   Young Mistley. London, 1888. 2 vols., orig.
cloth, 1st ed., covers worn and soiled, inner hinges cracking, rare. MacManus
238-330 1978 $125

SCOTT, J. D.   Combination Atlas Map of Bucks County, Pennsylvania. Philadelphia, 1876. 1st ed., folio, illus., maps, many colored,
orig. cloth, rebacked, very good copy. MacManus 239-1400 1978 $200

SCOTT, J. W. ROBERTSON   The Story of the Pall Mall Gazette, of its first
editor Frederick Greenwood and of its founder George Murray Smith. 1950. 8vo.,
illus. George's 635-1445 1978 £5.25

SCOTT, JOHN   Critical Essays on Some of the Poems, of Several
English Poets by ... 1785. Uncut in orig. bds., spine chipped o/w v.g.
Jarndyce 16-187 1978 £28

SCOTT, JOHN   Narratives of two Families exposed to the Great
Plague of London 1665. 1832. Fcap. 8vo., half calf, rubbed. George's 635-
1126 1978 £6

SCOTT, JOHN   The Poetical Works. 1786. 2nd. ed., frontis
vignette, orig. calf, gilt spine, slight rubbing of leading bd., otherwise v.g.,
bookplt. of Wm. Mylen & signed by him. Jarndyce 16-188 1978 £58

SCOTT, JOHN   Poetical Works. 1782. 8vo., 1st ed., plts.,
contemp. calf, gilt panelled back, frontis. Quaritch 979-50 1978 $200

SCOTT, LYDIA   A Marriage in High Life. 1828. 1st. ed., 2
vols., uncut, rebound in half calf, marbled bds., v.g. Jarndyce 16-998 1978
£28

SCOTT, MICHAEL   The Cruise of the Midge. Edinburgh, 1836. 2
vols., 12mo., orig. cloth, 1st ed., bookplts., very good set, bind. B, spine ends
worn. MacManus 238-378 1978 $125

SCOTT, MICHAEL   Tom Cringles Log. Philadelphia, 1833. 1st Amer.
ed., half-cloth and boards with paper labels, very good, 2 vols. Greene 78-101
1973 $65

SCOTT, R. W.   Recollections of Bytown, Some Incidents in the
History of Ottawa. Ottawa, (1911). Card cover, signed by author. Hood 116-
778 1978 $35

SCOTT, ROBERT FALCON   Scott's Last Expedition. 1913. 2nd. ed.,
maps, portraits, coloured plts., illus., 2 vols., roy. 8vo., orig. cloth. Edwards
1012-607 1978 $30

SCOTT, SARAH   A Description of Millenium Hall and the Country
Adjacent. 1764. Second ed., 12mo., old half calf, frontispiece. P. M. Hill
142-188 1978 £48

SCOTT, SARAH   Millenium Hall. 1762. 1st. ed., engraved
frontis, full calf, not contemp., v.g. Jarndyce 16-189 1978 £100

SCOTT, TEMPLE   Oliver Goldsmith. Bibliographically and Biographically Considered... New York, 1928. 4to., colored frontis. port., orig.
embossed cloth, pub. box, 1st ed., 1 of 1,000 copies, inscribed by publisher,
mint. MacManus 238-931 1978 $50

SCOTT, THOMAS A.   Statements...Before the House Committee on the
Pacific Railroad. Washington, 1875. Sewn. Jenkins 116-1238 1978 $17.50

SCOTT, THOMAS A.   The Texas and Pacific Railway. Washington,
1878. Printed wr. Jenkins 116-1237 1978 $35

SCOTT, THOMAS A.   Texas Pacific Railroad. Washington, 1875.
Sewn. Jenkins 116-1239 1978 $25

SCOTT, W. B.   The British School of Sculpture: Illustrated from
the Finest Works of Deceased Masters of the Art. 1871. Folio, plts., illus., cloth.
Quaritch 983-257 1978 $65

SCOTT, W. W.   Two Confederate Items--Diary of Capt. H. W.
Wingfield & Reminiscences of the Civil War. Richmond, 1927. Wrs., Bell Wiley's
copy. Broadfoot 46-392 1978 $14

SCOTT, WALTER   The Abbott. Edinburgh, 1820. 1st. ed., 3 vols.,
12mo, lacks half-titles, ealy 20th century mottled calf, gilt, some slight foxing,
nice set. Hannas 54-259 1978 £15

SCOTT, WALTER   The Abbot. Edinburgh, 1820. 3 vols., 1st ed.,
mor. Quaritch 979-286 1978 $20

SCOTT, WALTER   Anne of Geierstein. Edinburgh, 1829. 3 vols.,
12mo., 1st ed., orig. drab bds., green paper backs, uncut, spines defective,
signature of Andrew Fletch of Salton, good copy. Quaritch 979-287 1978 $55

SCOTT, WALTER   Anne of Geierstein: or, The Maiden of the Mist.
Edinburgh, 1829. 1st. ed., 3 vols., half titles, rebound buckram, paper labels on
spine. Eaton 45-445 1978 £10

SCOTT, WALTER   Anne of Geierstein; or The Maiden of the Mist.
1829. 1st. ed., 3 vols., half titles, uncut, blue bds., grey cloth spines, paper
labels, good. Jarndyce 16-1038 1978 £16

SCOTT, WALTER   Anne of Geierstein; or, The Maiden of the Mist.
Edinburgh, 1829. 1st. ed., 3 vols., lg. 12mo, half-titles, orig. bds., new cloth
spines, uncut. Hannas 54-260 1978 £20

SCOTT, WALTER   Anne of Geierstein; or the Maiden of the Mist.
1829. Contemp. half calf, ex-lib. copy, some traces of use, 1st. ed., 3 vols., lg.
12mo. Hannas 54-261 1978 £6

SCOTT, WALTER   The Antiquary. 1816. 1st. ed., blue bds.,
grey cloth spines, paper labels, good. Jarndyce 16-1026 1978 £14.50

SCOTT, WALTER   En Bedstefaders Fortaelling... Copenhagen,
1834. 1st. Danish ed., 3 vols. in 1, 8vo, half calf. Hannas 54-262 1978 £10

SCOTT, WALTER   Bergslottet i Dumfries eller Stjerntydaren och
Sigenerskan. Stockholm, 1822. 1st. Swedish ed., 3 vols. in 1, 8vo, contemp.
half calf, worn. Hannas 54-264 1978 £15

SCOTT, WALTER   The Border Antiquities of England and Scotland.
1814. 2 vols., 4to., contemp. half calf, plts. Howes 194-1407 1978 £65

SCOTT, WALTER   The Border Antiquities of England and Scotland.
London, 1814-17. Orig. ed., 2 vols., plts., 4to., uncut, orig. qtr. roan, bds.
sides. K Books 244-276 1978 £45

SCOTT, WALTER   Chronicles of the Canongate. Edinburgh, 1827.
2 vols., 1st. ed., 1st. series, endpapers foxed, 1/2 calf, worn. Eaton 45-447
1978 £10

SCOTT, WALTER   Chronicles of the Canongate. Edinburgh, 1828.
1st. ed., 3 vols., 8vo, contemp. half calf, lacks one label, occasional foxing.
Hannas 54-265 1978 £15

SCOTT, WALTER   Chronicles of the Canongate. 1828. 2nd.
series, 1st. ed., 3 vols., half titles, blue bds., grey cloth spines, paper labels,
good. Jarndyce 16-1037 1978 £12.50

SCOTT, WALTER   The Complete Waverley Novels. 1836-39. 48
vols. in 25, thick 12mo., illus., plts. foxed, contemp. half black mor. Howes
194-1159 1978 £50

SCOTT, WALTER   The Complete Waverley Novels. 1842-47.
Plts., wood engravings, 12 vols., thick roy. 8vo., full polished tree calf. Howes
194-1158 1978 £110

SCOTT, WALTER   The Doom of Devorgoil, a Melo-Drama. Edin-
burgh, 1830. 1st. ed., half title, uncut, later half maroon calf, v.g. Jarndyce
16-1017 1978 £36

SCOTT, WALTER   The Field of Waterloo; a Poem. Edinburgh,
1815. 8vo, disbound, 1st ed., half-title present. Ximenes 47-280 1978 $17.50

SCOTT, WALTER   Fielding og Smollett. Christiania, n.d. (1834).
2nd. Norweigan ed., sm. 8vo, contemp. wrappers, torn, unopened. Hannas 54-
266 1978 £15

SCOTT, WALTER   The Fine Art Scott.   Complete set of 28 vols.,
cr. 8vo, orig. red cloth, 1 vol. little spotted, illus. by J. A. Hammerton, good.
Sexton 7-183 1978 £45

SCOTT, WALTER   En Fortaelling om Montrose. Copenhagen, 1825.
1st. Danish ed., 2 vols. in 1, 8vo, contemp. half calf, rubbed. Hannas 54-267
1978 £10

SCOTT, WALTER   The Fortunes of Nigel. Edinburgh, 1822. 1st.
ed., 3 vols., half titles, orig. half calf, v.g. Jarndyce 16-1008 1978 £22

SCOTT, WALTER   The Fortunes of Nigel. Edinburgh, 1822. 3
vols., orig. bds., spines repaired, front cover detached on vol. 1, 1st ed., very
good. MacManus 238-379 1978 $50

SCOTT, WALTER   Fortunes of Nigel. 1822. 1st. ed., 3 vols.,
blue bds., grey cloth spines, paper labels, good. Jarndyce 16-1032 1978 £12.50

SCOTT, WALTER   The Fortunes of Nigel. Edinburgh, 1822. 1st.
ed., 3 vols., 8vo, lacks half-titles, contemp. half calf, little worn. Hannas
54-268 1978 £12.50

SCOTT, WALTER   Guy Mannering; or The Astrologer. 1815. 2nd.
ed., 3 vols., half titles, frontis, blue bds., grey cloth spines, paper labels, good.
Jarndyce 16-1025 1978 £15.50

SCOTT, WALTER   Guy Mannering. Edinburgh, 1815. 3rd ed., 3
vols., contemp. half calf, one joint weak, 8vo. K Books 244-277 1978 £14

SCOTT, WALTER   Guy Mannering; or, The Astrologer. Edinburgh,
1820. 6th. ed., 3 vols., half titles, uncut, orig. grey bds., paper labels, some
rubbing to hinges otherwise v.g. Jarndyce 16-1003 1978 £12.50

SCOTT, WALTER   Halidon Hill; A Dramatic Sketch, From Scottish
History. Edinburgh, 1822. Modern 1/4 green morocco, marbled bds. Eaton 45-
446 1978 £20

SCOTT, WALTER   Harold the Dauntless: A Poem. Edinburgh, 1817.
1st. ed., orig. grey bds., paper label, uncut, good. Jarndyce 16-1001 1978 £36

SCOTT, WALTER   Ivanhoe; A Romance. Edinburgh, 1820. 1st.
ed., 3 vols., 8vo, half-titles lacking, mottled, gilt, 1 joint worm damaged, 1 leaf
torn & repaired, some foxing. Hannas 54-270 1978 £12.50

SCOTT, WALTER   Ivanhoe; A Romance. Edinburgh, 1820. 1st.
ed., half-titles, contemp. half calf, vol. 1 broken with lower cover missing.
Hannas 54-271 1978 £5

SCOTT, WALTER   The Journal. Edinburgh, 1890. First ed., 2
vols., portrait frontis., orig. cloth, 8vo., ex-library, inner hinges cracked.
Howes 194-1161 1978 £6

SCOTT, WALTER   Kenilworth: A Romance. 1821. 1st. ed., 3
vols., orig. half calf, marbled bds., good. Jarndyce 16-1004 1978 £18

SCOTT, WALTER   Kenilworth; A Romance. 1821. 1st. ed., 3 vols.,
blue bds., grey cloth spines, paper labels, good. Jarndyce 16-1030 1978 £14.50

SCOTT, WALTER   The Lady of the Lake; a Poem. Edinburgh,
1810. 1st. ed., 4to, portrait, contemp. blue straight-grained morocco, gilt, little
rubbed. Hannas 54-272 1978 £25

SCOTT, WALTER   The Lady of the Lake; a Poem. Edinburgh,
1811. 1st. ed., engraved title, 6 plts. by Rich. Westall, contemp. diced russia,
gilt, joints cracked, 4to. Hannas 54-273 1978 £22

SCOTT, WALTER   The Lady of the Lake. New York, 1813. 1st
miniature Amer. ed., calf, very good. Victoria 34-717 1978 $15

SCOTT, WALTER   Letters From a Gentleman in the North of Scotland... 1818. 5th. ed., half calf, heads of spines rubbed. Jarndyce 16-1002
1978 £36

SCOTT, WALTER   Letters on Demonology & Witchcraft. 1831. 2nd.
ed., frontis, half title, orig. brown cloth, worn at head & tail of spine, good.
Jarndyce 16-1018 1978 £9.50

SCOTT, WALTER   The Life of Napoleon Bonaparte, Emperor of the
French. Philadelphia, 1827. 1st. American ed., 3 vols., frontis portrait, orig.
red binders cloth, good. Jarndyce 16-1011 1978 £15

SCOTT, WALTER   Life of Napoleon Buonaparte. Edinburgh, 1834-
35. 9 vols., fcap. 8vo., contemp. half red mor., frontis. Howes 194-1162 1978
£28

SCOTT, WALTER   Marmion: A Tale of Flodden Field. Edinburgh,
1808. 1st. ed., 4to, half title, rebound in half calf, handmarbled bds., v.g.
Jarndyce 16-1000 1978 £42

SCOTT, WALTER   Military Memoirs of the Great Civil War...
Edinburgh, 1822. 1st. ed., 4to, half title, lacks following free endpaper, half
calf, spine gilt, light foxing, v.g., only 500 copies printed. Jarndyce 16-1005
1978 £38

SCOTT, WALTER   Mindetale Over Hertugen af York. 1827. 1st.
Danish ed., sm. 8vo, contemp. limp bds. Hannas 54-275 1978 £12.50

SCOTT, WALTER   Minstrelsy of the Scottish Border. Edinburgh, 18
1821. 5th. ed., 3 vols., orig. bds., uncut, paper labels, good, 8vo. K Books
244-279 1978 £15

SCOTT, WALTER   The Monastery. 1820. 1st. ed., 3 vols., blue
bds., grey cloth spines, paper labels, good. Jarndyce 16-1029 1978 £14.50

SCOTT, WALTER   The Monastery. Edinburgh, 1820. 1st. ed.,
3 vols., 12mo, half-titles, contemp. half calf, 2 spines defective. Hannas 54-
276 1978 £6

SCOTT, WALTER   Original Memoirs Written During the Great Civil
War; Being the Life of Sir Henry Slingsby... Edinburgh, 1806. Roy. 8vo, portrait,
modern cloth-backed bds., good. Upcroft 10-154 1978 £15

SCOTT, WALTER   Peveril of the Peak. Edinburgh, 1822. 1st. ed.,
4 vols., 8vo, half-titles, contemp. calf, lacks one label, very good set. Hannas
54-277 1978 £20

SCOTT, WALTER   Peveril of the Peak. 1822. 1st. ed., 4 vols.,
blue bds., grey cloth spines, paper labels, good. Jarndyce 16-1033 1978 £12.50

SCOTT, WALTER   Peveril of the Peak. Edinburgh, 1822. 1st.
ed., half titles, 4 vols., 8vo, orig. cloth-backed paper bds., uncut, spines with
printed numbers otherwise unlettered, fine. Fenning 32-294 1978 £55

SCOTT, WALTER   The Pirate. Edinburgh, 1822. First ed., 3 vols.,
contemp. half calf, 8vo. K Books 244-278 1978 £18

SCOTT, WALTER   The Pirate. Edinburgh, 1822. 1st. ed., 3 vols.,
8vo, lacks half-titles, contemp. half calf. Hannas 54-278 1978 £12.50

SCOTT, WALTER   The Pirate.... Edinburgh, 1822. 3 vols.,
small octavo, orig. boards, uncut edges, some wear and chipping on spines, 1st
ed. Bennett 7-95 1978 $125

SCOTT, WALTER   The Pirate. Edinburgh, 1822. 3 vols., post
8vo., contemp. cloth, good, first English ed. Bell Book 16-771 1978 £10

SCOTT, WALTER   The Pirate. 1822. 2nd. ed., 3 vols., blue bds.,
grey cloth spines, paper labels, good. Jarndyce 16-1031 1978 £9.50

SCOTT, WALTER   The Poetical Works. Edinburgh, 1821. 10 vols.,
engrav. title-vignettes, contemp. russia gilt, head of backstrip of Vol. 1 chipped
away, good, 8vo. K Books 244-281 1978 £20

SCOTT, WALTER   The Poetical Works. Edinburgh, 1822. Portrait,
8 vols., 12mo., full contemp. crimson mor. Howes 194-1160 1978 £35

SCOTT, WALTER   The Poetical Works of Sir Walter Scott. London,
1833. 12 vols., 12mo., 1/2 green calf with marbled bds., paneled spine with gilt
decor's, engr. frontis, binding heavily rubbed & scuffed, but firm, interiors fine.
Current 24-49 1978 $50

SCOTT, WALTER   The Poetical Works. London, c. 1875. Illus.,
blue prize calf gilt, 8vo. K Books 244-280 1978 £6

SCOTT, WALTER   Provincial Antiquities and Picturesque Scenery of
Scotland. 1826. First ed., 2 vols. in 1, 4to., contemp. half mor., gilt edges,
very good, plts. Howes 194-1408 1978 £75

SCOTT, WALTER   Quentin Durward. Edinburgh, 1823. 3 vols.,
1st. ed., half-titles, contemp. gilt spines, rubbed. Eaton 45-448 1978 £25

SCOTT, WALTER Quentin Durward. 1823. 1st. ed., 3 vols., blue bds., grey cloth spines, paper labels, good. Jarndyce 16-1034 1978 £14.50

SCOTT, WALTER Quentin Durward... Edinburgh, 1823. 3 vols., small octavo, full early grey calf, gilt spines, tooled covers. 1st ed., fine. Bennett 7-96 1978 $100

SCOTT, WALTER Quentin Durward. 1823. 3 vols., orig. half calf, marbled bds., good. Jarndyce 16-1007 1978 £18

SCOTT, WALTER Redgauntlet. 1824. 1st. ed., 3 vols., orig. half calf, marbled bds., v.g. Jarndyce 16-1010 1978 £18

SCOTT, WALTER Redgauntlet. A Tale of the Eighteenth Century. Edinburgh, 1824. 3 vols., contemp. 3/4 calf, 1st ed., slightly worn, but very nice. MacManus 238-380 1978 $85

SCOTT, WALTER Redgauntlet, A Tale of the 18th Century. 1824. 1st. ed., 3 vols., half titles, blue bds., grey cloth spines, paper labels, good. Jarndyce 16-1036 1978 £14.50

SCOTT, WALTER Redgauntlet, a Tale of the Eighteenth Century. Edinburgh, 1824. 1st. ed., 3 vols., 8vo, lacks half-titles, contemp. half calf. Hannas 54-280 1978 £18

SCOTT, WALTER Redgauntlet, a Tale of the Eighteenth Century. Edinburgh, 1824. 1st. ed., 2nd. state, half-titles, early 20th. century mottled calf, gilt, fine set, 3 vols., 8vo. Hannas 54-281 1978 £20

SCOTT, WALTER Religious Discourses By a Layman. 1828. 1st. ed., half titles, bound in half calf, marbled bds., fine. Jarndyce 16-1013 1978 £45

SCOTT, WALTER Rob Roy. 1818. 1st. ed., 3 vols., blue bds., grey cloth spines, paper labels, good. Jarndyce 16-1028 1978 £17.50

SCOTT, WALTER Rob Roy. Boston, 1839. 2 vols., orig. paper wrs., remarkable condition considering age, fragility of paper bindings. Greene 78-102 1978 $25

SCOTT, WALTER Rokeby: A Poem. Edinburgh, 1813. First ed., 4to., contemp. tree calf. Howes 194-1164 1978 £14

SCOTT, WALTER Rokeby; a Poem. Edinburgh, 1813. 1st. ed., 4to, half-title, contemp. tree calf, upper cover detached. Hannas 54-282 1978 £15

SCOTT, WALTER St. Ronan's Wall. 1824. 1st. ed., 3 vols., orig. half calf, marbled bds., good. Jarndyce 16-1009 1978 £18

SCOTT, WALTER St. Ronan's Well. 1824. 1st. ed., 3 vols., blue bds., grey cloth spines, good, paper labels. Jarndyce 16-1035 1978 £12.50

SCOTT, WALTER St. Ronan's Well. Edinburgh, 1824. 1st. ed., 3 vols., 8vo, lacks half-titles & blank leaves, contemp. half calf, gilt spine. Hannas 54-283 1978 £18

SCOTT, WALTER Tales of A Grandfather. 1829. 2nd. series, 3 vols., 1st. ed., frontis, engraved titles, orig. bds., red morocco spines, rubbed. Jarndyce 16-1015 1978 £6.50

SCOTT, WALTER Tales of A Grandfather. 1830. 3rd. series, 3 vols., 1st. ed., frontis, engraved title, orig. bds., red morocco spines, rubbed, bds. little worn. Jarndyce 16-1016 1978 £6.50

SCOTT, WALTER Tales of My Landlord, First Series. Edinburgh, 1816. 1st. ed., 4 vols., 12mo, half-titles, contemp. calf, rebacked. Hannas 54-284 1978 £25

SCOTT, WALTER Tales of My Landlord. 1816. 1st. ed., 4 vols., half titles, blue bds., grey cloth spines, paper labels, good. Jarndyce 16-1027 1978 £14.50

SCOTT, WALTER Tales of My Landlord, Third Series. Edinburgh, 1819. 1st. ed., 4 vols., 12mo, half-titles, contemp. half calf, one spine damaged, some foxing. Hannas 54-285 1978 £15

SCOTT, WALTER Tales of My Landlord. Fourth and Last Series. London, 1832. 4 vols., orig. bds., paper labels, 1st ed., spines repaired, otherwise very good. MacManus 238-382 1978 $85

SCOTT, WALTER Tales of My Landlord, Fourth Series. Edinburgh, 1832. 1st. ed., 4 vols., 12mo, half-titles, contemp. German half calf, worn, new end-papers, some waterstains. Hannas 54-286 1978 £18

SCOTT, WALTER The Vision of Don Roderick; a Poem. Edinburgh, 1811. 1st. published ed., 1st. issue with signature Q, 4to, thick paper, half-title, orig. bds., spine & label defective, uncut. Hannas 54-287 1978 £24

SCOTT, WALTER The Vision of Don Roderick; a Poem. Edinburgh, 1811. 1st. published ed., issue ending with signature R, 4to, half morocco, heavily foxed, 4to, orig. bds. Hannas 54-288 1978 £10

SCOTT, WALTER The Vision of Don Roderick: A Poem. Edinburgh, 1811. First ed., 4to., orig. bds., entirely uncut, very good, orig. state. Howes 194-1165 1978 £21

SCOTT, WALTER The Vision of Don Roderick: A Poem. Edinburgh, 1811. Second ed., contemp. diced calf, first octavo ed. Howes 194-1166 1978 £12.50

SCOTT, WALTER Waverly; or, 'tis Sixty Years Since. Edinburgh, 1814. 2nd. ed., 3 vols., 12mo, half-titles, contemp. half calf, spine little defective, some foxing. Hannas 54-289 1978 £15

SCOTT, WALTER Waverley; or, 'Tis Sixty Years Since. 1814. 2nd. ed., 3 vols., blue bds., grey cloth spines, paper labels, good. Jarndyce 16-1024 1978 £24

SCOTT, WALTER Waverley Novels. London, 1892. Portrait, finely etched plts., 48 vols., 8vo. Traylen 88-329 1978 £25

SCOTT, WALTER Woodstock; or, the Cavalier. A Tale of the Year Sixteen Hundred and Fifty-One. London, 1826. 3 vols., orig. bds., paper labels, slightly worn, 1st ed., fine, half mor. slipcase. MacManus 238-381 1978 $85

SCOTT, WALTER Woodstock; or The Cavalier. Edinburgh, 1826. 1st. ed., half titles, uncut, orig. bds., paper labels, v.g. Jarndyce 16-1012 1978 £32

SCOTT, WALTER Woodstock; or, The Cavalier. Edinburgh, 1826. 1st. ed., 3 vols., 8vo, half-titles, early 20th. century mottled calf, gilt, little foxing, very good set. Hannas 54-290 1978 £18

SCOTT, WILLIAM ROBERT The Constitution and Finance of English, Scottish and Irish Joint-Stock Companies to 1720. Cambridge, 1910-12. 3 vols., spine of Vol. 2 dull, 8vo. George's 635-397 1978 £21

SCOTT-GILES, C. WILFRED The Romance of Heraldry. London, (1929). Illus. Baldwins' 51-266 1978 $10

SCOTT-O'CONNOR, V. C. The Silken East. London, 1928. Thick 8vo., cloth, illus., colored plts., scarce. Van der Peet 127-212 1978 Dfl 115

SCOTT'S Specialized Catalogue of United States Postage Stamps. New York, 1923. Illus., narrow 12mo, orig. limp lea., 1st ed. Morrill 241-523 1978 $8.50

SCOTTISH History and Life. Glasgow, 1902. Plates, text, illus., folio. George's 635-757 1978 £10.50

SCOTUS, MICHAEL
Please turn to
SCOTT, MICHAEL

SCOUGAL, HENRY A Sermon Preach'd on the 25th of December, Being the Nativity of Our Saviour. Boston, 1737. 16mo., homemade wrs., very scarce. Morrill 241-524 1978 $22.50

SCOUTETTEN, H. Memoir on the Radical Cure of Club-Foot. (Philadelphia, 1840). 8vo., bds., plts., illus. Gurney 75-97 1978 £30

SCRAPS of Biography. Salt Lake City, 1883. Orig. cloth, 1st ed. Ginsberg 14-684 1978 $15

SCRIBANUS, CAROLUS Adolescens Prodigus. Antwerp, 1621. 8vo., 1/2 calf, fine. Salloch 348-244 1978 $125

SCRIPPS, JOHN LOCKE Life of Abraham Lincoln. New York, 1860. 8vo., sewn, partly torn along spine, 2nd ed. Morrill 239-601 1978 $57.50

SCRIVENOR, H. History of the Iron Trade. 1854. Cover faded, 8vo. George's 635-398 1978 £7.50

SCRIVERIUS, PETRUS   Respublica Roma, Honori Urbis Aeternae P. Scriverius Restituit. Leiden, 1629. 16mo., vellum, 2nd ed., lacks flyleaves, 2 leaves misbound. Allen 234-870 1978 $25

SCROGGS, WILLIAM O.   Filibusters and Financiers, the Story of William Walker and His Associates. New York, 1916. Presen. copy from author to Wiley. Bell Wiley's copy. Broadfoot 46-561 1978 $8

SCROPE, G. POULETT   The Geology and Extinct Volcanoes of Central France. London, 1858. 8vo, original terra cotta cloth, 2nd ed., enlarged and "improved", frontispiece, plates, folding map, fine copy. Ximenes 47-231 1978 $45

SCRUGG, MRS. GRASS R.   Gardening in the Southwest. Dallas, 1932. 1st ed., autographed. Jenkins 116-1241 1978 $7.50

SCRYMGEOUR, DANIEL   The Poetry and Poets of Britain. Edinburgh, 1866. New ed., frontis, photo portrait, facsimile signature of Tennyson, orig. cloth, dec. in gold & black, a.e.g. Eaton 45-449 1978 £12

SCUDAMORE, CHARLES   Observations on M. Laennec's Method of Forming a Diagnosis of the Diseases of the Chest by Means of the Stethoscope, and of Percussion. London, 1826. 8vo., contemp. bds., spine damaged, uncut, 1st ed., very clean copy. Offenbacher 30-79 1978 $200

SCUDAMORE, CHARLES   A Treatise on the Nature and Cure of Gout and Rheumatism. Philadelphia, 1819. 8vo., contemp. tree calf, worn, browned, owner's signature, internally a good copy, 1st Amer. ed. Zeitlin 245-234 1978 $75

SCUDDER, HORACE E.   The Bodley Grandchildren and Their Journey in Holland. 1882. Illus. colored covers, very good. Austin 82-838 1978 $20

SCUDDER, HORACE E.   Recollections of Samuel Breck with Passages from His Note Books. Philadelphia, 1877. MacManus 239-727 1978 $15

SCUDDER, V. D.   The Franciscan Adventure; a study of the first hundred years of the Order of St. Francis of Assisi. 1931. Ex-library copy, qtr. mor., 8vo. Upcroft 12-397 1978 £5

SCUDERY, MADELEINE DE   Conversations Upon Several Subjects. London, 1683. 2 vols. in 1, fcap. 8vo, contemp. red morocco, sides elaborately gilt, gilt. Traylen 88-330 1978 £220

SCULLY, C. ALISON   The Course of the Silver Greyhound. New York, 1936. Map. Biblo 247-770 1978 $15

SEABORN, EDWIN   The Asiatic Cholera in 1832 in the London District. 1937. Hood 116-779 1978 $10

SEABORN, EDWIN   The March of Medicine in Western Ontario. Toronto, 1944. 112 illus. Hood's 115-672 1978 $40

SEABROOK, WILLIAM   The White Monk of Timbuctoo. New York, (1934). 29 illus., 8vo, orig. cloth. K Books 239-437 1978 £7

SEAGRAVE, GORDON S.   Burma Surgeon Returns. 1945. Illus. Austin 80-286 1978 $10

SEALSFIELD, CHARLES   The Cabin Book or, National Characteristics. London, 1852. Orig. cloth, 1st English ed., fine. Jenkins 116-1222a 1978 $125

SEALSFIELD, CHARLES   Life in the New World; or, Sketches of American Society. New York, (1844). Half mor. Ginsberg 14-914 1978 $225

SEARCHING For Truth. New York, (1902). 2nd. ed., orig. binding, clean. Hayman 71-693 1978 $7.50

SEARIGHT, THOMAS B.   The Old Pike. Uniontown, 1894. 1st ed., illus., ports., orig. cloth, very good. MacManus 239-433 1978 $35

SEARLES, HERBERT LEON   The Study of Religion in State Universities. 1927. Paper. Austin 79-658 1978 $17.50

SEARS, J. E.   The Architects' Compendium and Catalogue. London, 1930. Thick 4to, orig. cloth, binding worn, illus., good. Sexton 7-4 1978 £10

SEARS, J. MONTGOMERY   Catalogue of the Library of J. Montgomery Sears, Including the Poetical Library of Ferdinand Freiligrath. Cambridge, 1882. 4to., full contemp. calf, back cover dampstained. Morrill 241-525 1978 $17.50

SEARS, LORENZO   Wendell Phillips. Orator and Agitator. New York, 1909. 1st ed., orig. cloth, very good. MacManus 239-803 1978 $10

SEARS, LOUIS M.   George Washington. New York, (1932). Maps. Biblo 247-222 1978 $16.50

SEARS, ROBERT   Pictorial History of China and India. New York, 1852. Engravings, fold. maps, plts., good copy, orig. bind. Petrilla 13-104 1978 $10

SEARS, ROEBUCK AND CO.   Our Grocery List, January-February, 1907...., Chicago. (Chicago, 1906?). Wrs., illus. Hayman 72-325 1978 $7.50

SEASONABLE and Affecting Observations on the Mutiny Bill, Articles of War, and Use and Abuse of a Standing Army. 1701. 8vo., unbound. F. Edwards 1013-244 1978 $15

SEAVER, JAMES E.   Deh-he-wa-mis: or a Narrative of the Life of Mary Jemison. 1842. 1st Batavia ed., orig. cloth, worn, spine repaired, text foxed, rare. Butterfield 21-220a 1978 $75

SEAVER, JAMES E.   Deh-he-wa-mis: or a Narrative of the Life of Mary Jemison. 1842. 2nd Batavia ed., orig. cloth, some wear, tight copy. Butterfield 21-220b 1978 $50

SEAVER, JAMES E.   Deh-he-wa-mis: or a Narrative of the Life of Mary Jemison. Devon & London, 1842. 4th English ed., ads, orig. bds. & label. Butterfield 21-220c 1978 $35

SEAVER, JAMES E.   Deh-He-Wa-Mis. Devon & London, 1847. 16mo., contemp. calf, ex-lib., crudely rebacked with white tape. Morrill 241-526 1978 $15

SEAVER, JAMES E.   Deh-he-wa-mis: or a Narrative of the Life of Mary Jemison. 1856. 1st New York, Auburn & Rochester ed., shabby copy, frayed orig. cloth. Butterfield 21-220d 1978 $15

SEAVER, JAMES E.   Deh-he-wa-mis: or a Narrative of the Life of Mary Jemison. 1877. 2nd Buffalo ed., good copy. Butterfield 21-220e 1978 $35

SEAVER, JAMES E.   Deh-he-wa-mis: or a Narrative of the Life of Mary Jemison. New York, 1929. Reprint of the rare 1824 1st ed., #638 of 950 copies, very good. Butterfield 21-220f 1978 $12.50

SEAVER, JAMES E.   Deh-he-wa-mis: or a Narrative of the Life of Mary Jemison. New York, 1932. Complete ed., new copy in dust jacket. Butterfield 21-220g 1978 $35

SEAVER, JAMES E.   Deh-he-wa-mis: or a Narrative of the Life of Mary Jemison. New York, 1949. Modern paperback "Edition of 1949", illus., good. Butterfield 21-220h 1978 $7.50

SEAWARD, J.   Observations on the Re-building of London Bridge. London, 1824. 8vo., frontispiece, plts., orig. bds., joints weak, pres. copy from author. Quaritch 977-255 1978 $200

SEBA, ALBERTUS   Locupletissimi Rerum Naturalium. Amsterdam, 1734-65. Engraved frontis, portrait, printed titles in red & black with vignettes, engraved plts., 4 vols., lg. folio, contemp. red morocco, gilt, g.e., unusually fine copy. Traylen 88-626 1978 £3300

SEBERUS SULANUS, WOLFGANG   Argus Homericus Sive Index Vocabulorum in Omnia Homeri Poemata. Amsterdami, 1649. 4to., vellum, index in Greek letter in three columns. King 7-312 1978 £20

SEBITZ, MELCHIOR   Historia Memorabilis De Foemina Quadam Argentoratensi... Argentinae, 1627. Sm. 4to., engr. plts., rebound in old liturgical vellum leaf over bds., browned, good copy, bkplt. of Dr. Alfred M. Hellman, laid in brown linen slipcase, 1st ed. Zeitlin 245-235 1978 $325

SECCOMBE, THOMAS   The Bookman Illustrated History of English Literature. 1906. Plts., 2 vols., sm. folio, orig. qtr. roan. George's 635-1385 1978 £5

SECCOMBE, THOMAS   An English Garner. 1903. 12 vols., orig. blue cloth, gilt tops, other edges untrimmed, complete set, 8vo., orig. issue. Howes 194-843 1978 £75

SECKER, THOMAS   A Sermon Preached Before the Society Corresponding With the Incorporated Society in Dublin... 1757. Engraved vignette title-pg., 4to, wrapper, final leaf contains Oliver's Booklist of 75 titles. Fenning 32-295 1978 £10.50

SECOMB, DANIEL F.   History of the Town of Amherst, Hillsborough Co., N.H. Concord, 1883. 1st ed., illus., ports., orig. cloth, lib. marks, fine. MacManus 239-1063 1978 $50

SECOMBE, CAPT. Army and Navy Drolleries, Alphabetical Descriptions. (c. 1865). Designs by author printed in colour by Kronheim, 4to., orig. pictorial cloth, rebacked qtr. mor. George's 635-858 1978 £32.50

SECOND, JEAN EVERAERTS Les Baisers, precedes du Mois de Mai, Poeme. 1770. Copperplt., 8vo., contemp. calf. Argosy Special-81 1978 $100

THE SECOND Book of the Rhymer's Club. London, 1894. 8vo, brown cloth, gilt lettering on spine, bookplate, Fine, scarce, Bodley Head imprint with ed. ltd. to 450 copies for England and 150 for U.S., 1st ed., collector's cond. Desmarais 1-352 1978 $100

THE SECOND Chapter of Accidents & Remarkable Events, Containing Caution & Instruction for Children. Philadelphia, 1807. Copperplts., 24mo., contemp. marbled wrs., very fine copy, rare. Argosy Special-31 1978 $125

SECOND Part of the Tragedy of Amboyna... London, 1653. 8vo., orig. bds., ex-lib., lacks spine, ed. ltd. to 95 copies. Morrill 239-603 1978 $10

THE SECRET History of Persia. 1745. 12mo., contemp. calf, joints weak, label missing. Howes 194-1442 1978 £21

THE SECRET History of the Most Renown'd Q. Elizabeth, and Earl of Essex. Cologne (i.e. London), 1767. 12mo, 2 parts, woodcut frontispiece, contemp. coarse linen, worn. Hannas 54-52 1978 £18

SECRET Journals of the Senate of the Republic of Texas, 1836-1845. Austin, 1911. Fine copy. Jenkins 116-1490 1978 $17.50

THE SECRET Springs of Dublin Song. 1918. Very good, reprint, octavo bound in cloth. Hyland 128-489 1978 £17.50

SEDDALL, H. Edward Nangle, The Apostle of Achil, A Memoir & A History. 1884. 1st ed., illus., very good. Hyland 128-170 1978 £12.50

SEDGEFIELD, S. W. Notes on the Practice of the Office of Titles of Victoria. Melbourne, 1879. 1st. ed., 8vo, orig. cloth, little wear to headbands, very good copy. Fenning 32-296 1978 £14

SEDGWICK, THEODORE A Memoir of the Life of William Livingston, Member of Congress in 1774, 1775, and 1776... New York, 1833. 1st ed., frontis., contemp. calf-backed marbled bds., foxed. MacManus 239-1291 1978 $40

SEDGWICK, WILLIAM T. Principles of Sanitary Science and the Public Health. New York, 1902. 8vo., fine, 1st ed. Morrill 239-229 1978 $25

SEDLEY, HENRY Dangerfield's Rest; or, Before the Storm. A Novel of American Life and Manners. New York, 1864. Cloth, little worn at ends of spine and upper edges. Hayman 72-238 1978 $12.50

SEDWICK, THEODORE Thoughts on the Proposed Annexation of Texas to the United States. New York, 1844. Original pink printed wr., 1st ed., 1st issue. Jenkins 116-1223a 1978 $55

SEEBOHM, HENRY A Monograph of the Turdidae, or Family of Thrushes. London, 1902. Portrait, hand coloured plts. by Keulemans, 2 vols., half dark blue morocco, folio, cloth sides to match, gilt tops, fine copy. Traylen 88-662 1978 £1800

SEEBOHM, FREDERIC The English Village Community, examined in its relation to the Manorial and Tribal Systems and to the Common or Open Field System of Husbandry. 1913. Maps, plts., 8vo. George's 635-758 1978 £7.50

SEEBOHM, FREDERIC The Oxford Reformers; John Colet, Erasmus and Thomas More. 1887. 3rd. ed., prize morocco, gilt, a.e.g., octavo, good. Upcroft 10-529 1978 £9

SEEBOHM, HENRY A History of British Birds. London, 1883-5. 1st ed., large 8vo, 4 vols., color plates, spine end creasing. Book Chest 17-335 1978 $85

SEED, JEREMIAH Discourses on Several Important Subjects. 1745. 2nd. ed., 2 vols., orig. calf, red labels, v.g. Jarndyce 16-190 1978 £5.50

SEEING San Francisco. (San Francisco, 1915). Booklet of 23 unused tinted postcards. Hayman 73-155 1973 $7.50

SEELEN, IO. H. Miscellanea... Lubecas, 1734. 8vo., fine old vellum, engr. frontis. Van der Peet H-64-545 1978 Dfl 60

SEELEY, E. L. Artists of the Italian Renaissance. (London), 1907. Late in 8vo., forrel, coloured plts., uncut, very good, coloured woodcut frontis. King 7-387 1978 £15

SEELEY, JOHN ROBERT The Growth of British Policy, an Historical Essay. Cambridge, 1895. Portrait, 2 vols., cr. 8vo., ex-library copy. George's 635-759 1978 £5.25

SEELEY, JOHN ROBERT The Growth of British Policy. Cambridge, 1897. Second ed., 2 vols., octavo, good. Upcroft 10-530 1978 #7.50

SEELINGSON, LELIA A History of Indianola. Cuero, n.d. Wraps. Jenkins 116-184 1978 $15

SEELY, CHARLES S. Russia and the Battle of Liberation. 1945. Austin 80-288 1978 $8.50

SEEMAN, CLARA F. Memories of Mother Pauline P. Freestone. Ca. 1937. Illus., paper. Austin 79-660 1978 $27.50

SEGALE, BLANDINA At the End of the Santa Fe Trail. Milwaukee, (1949). Cloth, 3rd printing. Hayman 72-697 1978 $7.50

SEGALL, JEAN B. Wings of the Morning. Toronto, 1945. Ex-lib. Hood's 115-135 1978 $15

SEGELHANDBUCH Fur Den Golf Von Bengalen. Berlin, 1907. 8vo., cloth, colored illus. Van der Peet H-64-546 1978 Dfl 65

SEGRE, ALFREDO Mahogany. 1944. Pres. copy to authors uncle, first ed., d.j. Austin 82-840 1978 $20

SEGUIN, MARC Des Ponts en fil de fer. Paris, 1824. Fldg. copperplts., 8vo., bds., 1st ed. Offenbacher 30-141 1978 $125

SEGUIN, PIERRE Selecta Numismata Antiqua Ex Museo Petri Seguini. 1684. 4to., calf, rubbed, very good. King 7-313 1978 £70

SEGUR, LOUIS PHILIPPE DE Memoires ou Souvenirs et Anecdotes. Paris, 1825-26. Folding engrav. map, portraits, 3 vols., 8vo., contemp. red glazed bds., flat spines, gilt with green mor. labels, little worn, from Beckford lib. with pencil notes by Beckford. Traylen 88-445 1978 £210

SEIDLITZ, WOLDEMAR VON Geschichte des japanischen Farbenholzschnitts. Dresden, 1923. Illus., tipped-in color plts., boards, cloth back, edges worn, 4th ed. Dawson's 449-183 1978 $45

SEITZ, DON C. Artemas Ward. 1919. Illus., first ed. Austin 82-841 1978 $20

SEITZ, DON C. The Buccaneers. New York, 1912. 1st ed., fine inked inscription by Seitz, lightly rubbed, very good. Victoria 34-661 1978 $35

SEITZ, DON C. Horace Greeley Founder of the New York Tribune. Indianapolis, (1926). Illus. MacManus 239-759 1978 $8.50

SEITZ, DON C. Training for the Newspaper Trade. 1916. First ed. Austin 82-842 1978 $17.50

SEITZ, DON C. Under the Black Flag. 1925. First ed., ex-lib. Austin 82-843 1978 $12.50

SEITZ, DON C. Writings By and About James Abbott McNeill Whistler. A Bibliography. Edinburgh, 1910. 12mo., orig. cloth, 1st ed., 1 of 350 copies, very good. MacManus 238-1075 1978 $40

SELDEN, JOHN The Duello or Single Combat. 1610. First ed., sm. 4to., 19th cent. half calf. F. Edwards 1013-421 1978 £175

SELDEN, JOHN Table-Talk. 1696. Second ed., 8vo., contemp. sprinkled sheep, very good. P. M. Hill 142-307 1978 £65

SELDEN, JOHN Table Talk: Being the Discourses of ..., Esq; or His Sense of Various Matters of Weight and High Consequence... London, 1716. 12mo., later full calf, mor. label, 3rd ed., inscription, covers rubbed. MacManus 238-140 1978 $35

SELDEN, JOHN The Table Talk. 1892. Orig. roxburghe binding, gilt top, 8vo. Howes 194-1171 1978 £6

SELDEN Ancestry. Oil City, (1931). 1st ed., thick 8vo., illus., orig. cloth, pres. copy, hinges weak, otherwise very good. MacManus 239-938 1978 $32.50

SELDES, GEORGE The Catholic Crisis. 1939. 1st ed., signed letter by Seldes Tipped on to front flyleaf. Austin 79-663 1978 $17.50

SELECTAE e Profanis Scriptoribus Historiae.... Londini, 1741. 12mo., contemp. calf, unlettered. George's 635-1479 1978 £8.50

A SELECTION from the Best Anti-Slavery Authors. Salem, 1849. 12mo., orig. wr., foxed, Ist ed. Morrill 241-13 1978 $25

SELKIRK, THOMAS DOUGLAS, EARL OF   Observations on the Present State of the Highlands of Scotland. London, 1805. Contemp. bds., backstrip worn. Wolfe 39-504 1978 $100

SELKIRK, THOMAS DOUGLAS, EARL OF   Observations on the Present State of the Highlands of Scotland... London, 1805. Half-title pg. missing, lea. binding with gold tooling, new endpapers. Hood's 115-236 1978 $185

SELL, J. C.   20th Century History of Altoona and Blair County Pennsylvania. Chicago, 1911. Illus., 4to., full leather, fine. MacManus 239-1673 1978 $60

SELLAR, ROBERT   Hemlock; a Tale of the War of 1812; Gleaner Tales. Huntington, 1918. Hood 116-498 1978 $35

SELLAR, ROBERT   The History of the County of Huntingdon and of the Seigniories of Chateauguay and Beauharnois.... Huntingdon, 1888. Orig. binding. Wolfe 39-500 1978 $100

SELLAR, ROBERT   Morven. Huntingdon, 1911. Orig. binding. Wolfe 39-503 1978 $15

SELLAR, ROBERT   The U.S. Campaign of 1813 to Capture Montreal. Huntingdon, 1913. Printed wrappers. Wolfe 39-502 1978 $20

SELLAR, ROBERT   The Tragedy of Quebec: The Expulsion of its Protestant Farmers. Huntingdon, 1907. Orig. binding. Wolfe 39-501 1978 $25

SELLARDS, E.H.   The Geology and Mineral Resources of Bexar County. Austin, 1919. Illus., color folding map. Jenkins 116-113 1978 $7.50

SELLE, RALPH   Here Comes Texas: A Centennial. Houston, 1935. Ist ed. Jenkins 116-1224a 1978 $15

SELLERS, CHARLES   Oporto, Old and New, an Historical Record of the Port Wine Trade and a Tribute to British Commercial Enterprize in the North of Spain. 1899. Illus., roy. 8vo. George's 635-399 1978 £7.50

SELLERS, CHARLES COLEMAN   Charles Willson Peale. Hebron, 1939, Philadelphia, 1947. Ist eds., 2 vols., illus., orig. cloth, fine, very scarce. MacManus 239-696 1978 $60

SELLERS, EDWIN JAQUETT   De Carpentier Allied Ancestry...of New Netherland. Philadelphia, 1928. Ltd. to 100 copies. MacManus 239-918 1978 $40

SELLERS, EDWIN JAQUETT   Early History of the Draper Family of Sussex County, Delaware. Philadelphia, 1929. Ltd. to 100 copies. MacManus 239-929 1978 $30

SELLERS, EDWIN JAQUETT   Fenwick Allied Ancestry. Philadelphia, 1916. Ltd. to 100 copies. MacManus 239-923 1978 $40

SELLERS, EDWIN JAQUETT   Genealogy of Dr. Francis Joseph Pfeiffer of Philadelphia, Pa., and His Descendants. Philadelphia, 1899. Frontis., ltd. to 200 copies. MacManus 239-934 1978 $30

SELLERS, EDWIN JAQUETT   Genealogy of the Hollock Family of Sussex County, Delaware. Philadelphia, 1897. Ltd. to 200 copies. MacManus 239-930 1978 $30

SELLERS, EDWIN JAQUETT   Jaudon Family of Pennsylvania. Philadelphia, 1924. Ltd. to 150 copies. MacManus 239-928 1978 $20

SELLERS, EDWIN JAQUETT   Sellers Family of Pennsylvania and Allied Families. Philadelphia, 1925. Orig. cloth, fine, ltd. to 150 copies. MacManus 239-939 1978 $25

SELLERS, EDWIN JAQUETT   Van Hecke Allied Ancestry. Philadelphia, 1933. Ltd. to 100 copies. MacManus 239-942 1978 $30

SELLERS, JAMES BENSON   Slavery in Alabama. University, 1950. Bell Wiley's copy. Broadfoot's 44-839 1978 $12

SELLERS, WILLIAM   A Treatise on Machine Tools as Made by William Sellers & Co. Philadelphia, 1884. 6th. ed., revised. Baldwins' 51-479 1978 $17.50

SELLERY, G. C.   Medieval Foundations of Western Civilization. 1929. Maps. Allen 234-1451 1978 $10

SELLEY, E.   Village Trade Unions in Two Centuries. 1920. Cr. 8vo. George's 635-400 1978 £5

SELMI, FRANCESCO   Sulla Esistenza Di Principii Alcaloidi Naturali Nei Visceri Freschi Et Putrefatti Onde IL Periot Chimico Puo Essere Condotto A Conclusioni Erronee... Bologna, 1872. 4to., plts., wrs., foxed, very good copy, Ist ed. Zeitlin 245-236 1978 $150

SELOUS, F. C.   Sunshine and Storm in Rhodesia. London, 1896. Ist. ed., map, illus., 8vo, orig. cloth, shabby but sound copy. K Books 239-438 1978 £15

SELOUS, F. C.   Sunshine and Storm in Rhodesia. London, 1896. 2nd. ed., map, plts., cr. 8vo, zebra-skin pattern endpapers, orig. cloth, spine faded. K Books 239-439 1978 £20

SELOUS, FREDERICK F.   A Hunter's Wanderings in Africa... 1895. 4th. ed., folding map, plts., orig. cloth, 8vo, gilt, nice. Fenning 32-297 1978 £24.50

SELVAGIUS, J. L.   Antiquitatum christianarum institutiones nova methodo in quatuor libris tributae.... Patavii, 1780. Text ptd. in dble-columns, 3 vols. in 2, sm. 4to., contemp. mottled calf, gilt. George's 635-1127 1978 £10

SELWYN, CECIL E.   Rhyming Snapshots of an Idle Fellow. Toronto, 1924. Hood's 115-905 1978 $17.50

SELYE, HANS   Stress. General Adaptation-Syndrome and the Diseases of Adaptation. Montreal, 1950. Ex-library. Rittenhouse 49-714 1976 $12.50

SEMALLE, COMTE DE   Quatre Ans a Pekin; Aout 1880-Aout 1884. Paris, about 1933. Large 8vo, illus., plts., orig. covers. Van der Peet 127-215 1978 Dfl 45

SEMI-Annual List of Choice New Dwellings Constructed and For Sale by Charles Buek & Co., Architects...500 Madison Ave. Orig. wr. Butterfield 21-504 1978 $15

THE SEMI-CENTENNIAL of Anaesthesia. Boston, 1897. Rittenhouse 49-18 1976 $65

SEMMES, JOHN E.   John H. B. Latrode and His Times 1803-1891. Baltimore, (1917). Ltd. ed., illus., uncut, fine. MacManus 239-782 1978 $45

SEMMES, RAPHAEL   Captains and Mariners of Early Maryland. Baltimore, 1937. Sm. thick 4to., scarce, fine. MacManus 239-1825 1978 $50

SEMMES, RAPHAEL   Crime and Punishment in Early Maryland. Baltimore, 1938. Fine copy, scarce. MacManus 239-1828 1978 $25

SEMMES, T. J.   Address of Congress to the People of the Confederate States. Richmond, c.1864. Jenkins 116-1226a 1978 $100

SENAULT, LOUIS   Nouveau Livre d'Ecriture Representant Naivement toutes les Plus Rares Curiosites des Lettres Financieres et Italiennes Bastardes. Paris, n.d. (c.1670). Oblong folio, 19th cent. half mor., engravings, very rare. Schumann 511-55 1978 sFr 1,200

SENEBIER, JEAN   Catalogue Raisonne des Manuscrits Conserves dans la Bibliotheque de la Ville & Republique de Geneva. Geneva, 1779. First ed., contemp. calf, upper joint cracked, labels missing, 8vo. Howes 194-281 1978 £25

SENEBIER, JEAN   Histoire Litteraire de Geneve. Geneve, 1786. First ed., 3 vols., 8vo., contemp. calf, labels missing. Howes 194-282 1978 £35

SENECA, LUCIUS ANNAEUS   ....Answer to Lucilius His Quaere: Why Good Men Suffer Misfortunes Seeing There is a Divine Providence? London, 1648. 12mo., contemp. calf, rehinged, lacks last blank. Salloch 348-247 1978 $125

SENECA, LUCIUS ANNAEUS   The Epistles. London, 1786. Ist ed., 2 vols. in 1, 3/4 period style calf over marbled boards, gilt-panelled spine with stamped devices, title on morocco label, gilt, rare. Bennett 20-187 1978 $250

SENECA, LUCIUS ANNAEUS   Los Libros De Beneficiis. Madrid, 1629. 4to., vellum. Salloch 348-246 1978 $95

SENECA, LUCIUS ANNAEUS   Los. V. libros de Seneca... Toledo, 1510. Sm. folio, Gothic letter, woodcut, 19th-century red mor., 2nd ed in vernacular. Quaritch 978-139 1978 $2,400

SENECA, LUCIUS ANNAEUS   Oeuvres Completes. 1879. 2 vols. Allen 234-875 1978 $10

SENECA, LUCIUS ANNAEUS   Opera Omnia. Tauchnitz, 1832. 6 vols. in 3, half calf, labels on spine faint. Allen 234-874 1978 $12.50

SENECA, LUCIUS ANNAEUS   Opera, Quae Extant Omnia. Batav, 1619. 8vo., half calf, binding shaved. Van der Peet H-64-547 1978 Dfl 45

SENECA, LUCIUS ANNAEUS   Oratorum et Rhetorum Sententiae Divisiones Colores. 1922. Lower portion of spine torn. Allen 234-954 1978 $10

SENECA, LUCIUS ANNAEUS   De Quatuor Virtutibus Cardinalibus. Nuremberg, 1507. Thin 4to., 1/2 calf. Salloch 348-245 1978 $175

SENECA, LUCIUS ANNAEUS   Tragoedia. Venice, 1517. Sm. 8vo., contemp. full vellum, 1st Aldine press ed., fine, inscription. Howell 5-3 1978 $350

SENECA, LUCIUS ANNAEUS   The Tenne Tragedies of Seneca. 1887. From the orig. ed. of 1581, 2 vols., sm. 4to., orig. wrappers. Howes 194-12121 1978 £18

SENECA, LUCIUS ANNAEUS   Tragoediae. Venetiis, 1517. 1st Aldine ed., octavo, full red crushed morocco, Aldine device stamped in gold on both covers, gilt rules on spine, title and all edges gilt, Syston Park bookplate, former owner's light MS notes on free marbled endpaper. Bennett 20-189 1978 $350

SENECA FALLS. CHARTERS   Charter and By-Laws and Rules and Orders of the Village of Seneca Falls. Seneca Falls, 1860. Wrs., light stains, good sound copy. Butterfield 21-410 1978 $25

SENN, EMANUEL J.   Principles of Surgery. Philadelphia, 1909. Fourth ed. Rittenhouse 49-716 1976 $10

SENN, NICHOLAS   A Nurse's Guide for the Operating Room. Chicago, 1902. Rittenhouse 49-717 1976 $10

SENNEP, JEHAN   Le Milieu. Paris, 1934. 8vo., illus. wr., loose illus. Van der Peet H-64-283 1978 Dfl 45

SENNERT, DANIEL   De Chymicorum Cum Aristotelicis et Galenicis Consensu ac Dissensu. Wittenberg, 1619. 8vo., old vellum, some browning due to poor quality paper, but fine copy, stamp of Wernigerode Library, bkplt. of Ernst Graf zu Stolberg, old signature on title, 1st ed. Norman 5-256 1978 $350

SEPET, M.   Jeanne d'Arc. Tours, n.d. 4to., half calf, illus. Van der Peet H-64-548 1978 Dfl 65

SEPP, D.   Tresoor der Zee-en Landreizen. 's-Gravenhage, 1939-1957. 2 vols., lg. 8vo., cloth, uncut, fine cond. Van der Peet H-64-549 1978 Dfl 195

SEPP, J. N.   Orient und Occident. Berlin, 1903. 8vo., orig. covers, scarce. Van der Peet H-64-550 1978 Dfl 40

SERGEANT, ADELINE   The Mistress of Quest. New York, 1895. 1st Amer. ed., quarter calf & marbled boards, good. Greene 78-103 1978 $15

SERGEANT, ADELINE   Out of Due Season. New York, 1895. 1st Amer. ed., quarter calf & marbled boards, good. Greene 78-104 1978 $20

SERGEANT, PHILIP WALSINGHAM   Little Jennings & Fighting Dick Talbot. 1913. 1st ed., 2 vols., illus., very good, octavo bound in cloth. Hyland 128-491 1978 $8.50

SERLE, AMBROSE   Horae Solitariae. Philadelphia, (1799) and 1801. 2 vols., 8vo., contemp. calf, nice, 1st Amer. ed. Morrill 239-604 1978 $20

SERMONS Preached at the Church of St. Paul the Apostle, New York...1865 and 1866. New York, 1867. Orig. cl., 1st ed. Ginsberg 16-835 1978 $15.00

SERRE, MICHEL   Traite de la Reunion Immediate et de son in- influence sur les Progres recens de la Chirurgie dans toutes les Operations. Paris, 1830. 8vo., old qtr. calf, plts., first ed. Gurney 75-98 1978 £36

SERVICE, ROBERT W.   Ballads of a Bohemian. Toronto, New York, 1921. Hood 117-827 1978 $15

SERVICE, ROBERT W.   Ballads of a Bohemian. New York, (1921). 8vo., green cloth, gilt stamped, very Nice, inscribed by author, 1st ed. Desmarais 1-370 1978 $20

SERVICE, ROBERT W.   The House of Fear. London, 1930. Hood's 115-457 1978 $15

SERVICE, ROBERT W.   Songs of a Sour-dough. Toronto, 1908. 8vo., green cloth, gilt lettering, Fine, 1st ed. Desmarais 1-371 1978 $15

SERVIEZ, J. R. DE   Roman Empresses. 1913. 2 vols., spines faded. Allen 234-879 1978 $10

SETH, JAMES   English Philosophers and Schools of Philosophy. London, 1925. 8vo., cloth. Salloch 348-249 1978 $12.50

SETON, ERNEST THOMPSON   Bird Portraits. Boston, 1901. Plts., cover scuffed. Hood 116-199 1978 $60

SETON, ERNEST THOMPSON   Boy Scouts of America. New York, 1910. 1st ed. of First Boy Scout Handbook, illus., pictorial cloth, moderately dust-soiled, scarce, very good. Victoria 34-92 1978 $85

SETON, ERNEST THOMPSON   Lives of the Hunted, Containing a True Account of the Doings of Five Quadrupeds & Three Birds. New York, 1901. 1st ed., 8vo., orig. ink drwg. by Seton-Thompson, signed, hinges reinforced, very good, orig. green decor. cloth. Current Misc. 8-39 1978 $100

SETON, ERNEST THOMPSON   Monarch - The Big Bear of Tallac. New York, 1904. 8vo., orig. cloth. Book Chest 17-336 1978 $20

SETON, ERNEST THOMPSON   Wild Animals I Have Known. New York, 1898. 1st ed., 1st issue, fine internally, covers faded, very good. Victoria 34-788 1978 $75

SETON, GRACE (GALLATIN)   A Woman Tenderfoot. New York, 1900. Plts., 8vo., orig. cloth. Book Chest 17-338 1978 $27.50

SETON-THOMPSON, GRACE GALLATIN
Please turn to
SETON, GRACE (GALLATIN)

SETTLE, ELKANAH   Absalom Senior: or, Achitophel Transpos'd. 1682. 1st. ed., folio, lacking final blank leaf, disbound, title dust-soiled, little torn. Hannas 54-298 1978 £55

SETTLE, ELKANAH   The Character of a Popish Successour, and What England May Expect From Such a One. 1681. 1st. ed.?, folio, disbound. Hannas 54-300 1978 £22.50

SETTLE, M. L.   Empire on Wheels. Stanford, (1949). 1st ed., small 4to, fine, d.w. Biblo 248-293 1978 $17.50

SEVENTEENTH Century Studies Presented to Sir Herbert Grierson. Oxford, 1938. Plts., rear bd. little marked, octavo, good. Upcroft 10-341 1978 £14

77e Anniversaire du 22 Septembre 1792, Celebre par les Republicains, de Langue Francaise, de St. Louis, Mo., Etats-Unis D'Amerique... St. Louis, [1869]. Disbound, 1st ed. Ginsberg 14-599 1978 $35

SEVERANCE, FRANK H.   Old Trails on the Niagra Frontier. Cleveland, 1903. 2nd ed., fold. map, fine. MacManus 239-434 1978 $17.50

SEVERANCE, FRANK H.   Old Trails on the Niagara Frontier. Cleveland, 1903. 2nd ed., fldg. map, damp-staining lower margin. Butterfield 21-308 1978 $7.50

SEVERANCE, HENRY O.   Michigan Trailmakers. Ann Arbor, 1930. Cloth. Hayman 73-445 1978 $7.50

SEVERIN, ERNEST   Svenskarne I Texas I Ord Och Bild: 1838-1918. Austin, 1919. Photos. Jenkins 116-1227a 1978 $25

SEVERUS, SULPICIUS   Opera Omnia quae extant. Leyden, 1643. 1st issue, 12mo, engraved copperplate t.p., full long-grained red morocco, gold lines on back and sides, all edges gilt, ex-Beckford, ex-Sir John Thorold with bookplate of Syston Park on verso of top cover. Bennett 20-190 1978 $95

SEVERUS, SULPICIUS   Quae exstant opera omnia, cum notis J. Vorstii. 1703. Woodcut device on title, text browned, sm. 8vo., contemp. vellum. George's 635-510 1978 £5.25

SEVESTRE, N.   Loup-Blanc. Paris, 1915. Large 8vo, boards,
illus. Van der Peet 127-216 1978 Dfl 65

SEVIGNE, MARIE (DE RABUTIN CHANTAL) MARQUISE DE   Letters from the
Marchioness De Sevigne to Her Daughter the Countess de Grignon. 1801. 7 vols.,
lg. 12mo., contemp. mottled calf, gilt ruled spines, double lettering pieces, nice.
Fenning 32-298 1978 £21.50

SEWALL, SAMUEL   Letter-Book. Boston, 1886-1888. 2 vols.,
orig. cloth, good set. MacManus 239-436 1978 $50

SEWALL, THOMAS   Memoir of Dr. Godman; Being an Introductory
Lecture Delivered November 1, 1830. New York, 1832. Paper covers sewn.
Rittenhouse 49-718 1976 $25

SEWARD, ANNA   Letters written between the years 1784 and 1807.
Edinburgh, 1811. 6 vols., cr. 8vo., full contemp. navy straight grained mor.,
frontis. Howes 194-1445 1978 £65

SEWARD, ANNA   Monody on Major Andre. 1781. Orig. marbled
paper covers, uncut. Baldwins' 51-364 1978 $75

SEWARD, ANNA   Poem to the Memory of Lady Miller. 1782.
1st. ed., 4to, disbound, loose, title & following leaf foxed. Hannas 54-302
1978 £22.50

SEWARD, OLIVE R.   William H. Seward's Travels Around the World.
New York, 1873. Rebound copy of 1st. ed., clean, many illus. Hayman 71-695
1978 $10

SEWARD, W. W.   Topographia Hibernica. 1795. 4to, map,
leather (worn), text good, no plates. Hyland 128-492 1978 £50

SEWARD, WILLIAM H.   Life and Public Services of John Adams. Auburn,
1850. Portr. MacManus 239-717 1978 $8.50

SEWARD, WILLIAM H.   Speech of William H. Seward for the Immediate
Admission of Kansas into the Union. (Washington, 1856). Unbound as issued.
Hayman 71-392 1978 $7.50

SEWELL, ELIZABETH MISSING   Ivors. 1856. 1st. ed., 2 vols., orig. green
cloth, half titles, v.g. Jarndyce 16-1039 1978 £45

SEWELL, ELIZABETH MISSING   Margaret Percival. New York, 1854. Amer.
ed., 2 vols., orig. cloth, good. Greene 78-105 1978 $25

SEWELL, WILLIAM GRANT   The Ordeal of Free Labor in the British West
Indies. New York, 1862. 12mo, original blue-violet cloth, 1st ed., 2nd issue,
old town library bookplate, very good copy. Ximenes 47-282 1978 $27.50

SEYBERT, ADAM   Statistical Annals... Philadelphia, 1818. 1st
ed., lg. 4to, later cloth. MacManus 239-437 1978 $65

SEYDEWITZ, MAX   Civil Life in Wartime Germany. 1945. Austin
80-291 1978 $12.50

SEYFFERT, OSKAR   A Dictionary of Classical Antiquities. London-
New York, 1895. Lg. thick 8vo., cloth, text illus., spine damaged. Van der
Peet H-64-551 1978 Dfl 55

SEYFFERT, OSKAR   A Dictionary of Classical Antiquities, Mythology,
Religion, Literature and Art. London, 1908. 3rd ed., text illus., 4to., gilt-
decor. cover. K Books 244-282 1978 £9

SEYMORE, D. J.   Handbook For Famers in South Africa. London,
(1935). 13 maps, 3rd. enlarged ed.,roy. 8vo., orig. cloth, covers shabby, working
copy. K Books 239-442 1978 £7

SEYMOUR, MR.   Remarks of ..., of New-York, Delivered in the
House...January 9, 1844. N.P., n.d. Disbound. Hayman 72-676 1978 $7.50

SEYMOUR, CHARLES   The Intimate Papers of Colonel House. Boston,
1926. 2 vols. Bell Wiley's copy. Broadfoot 46-563 1978 $10

SEYMOUR, CHARLES   The Intimate Papers of Colonel House. Boston,
1926. 2 vols., cloth. Hayman 72-699 1978 $10

SEYMOUR, E. S.   Sketches of Minnesota, the New England of the
West. New York, 1850. Illus., original cloth, 1st ed. Ginsberg 14-571 1978
$37.50

SEYMOUR, GEORGE DUDLEY   William F. Hopson and His Bookplates. Washington, 1929. 4to., frontis. port., orig. parchment-backed bds., 1st ed., 1 of
100 copies signed by Hopson and Seymour, a bit rubbed, otherwise very good. Mac-
Manus 238-872 1978 $50

SEYMOUR, HAROLD J.   Design for Giving. 1947. Austin 80-292 1978
$10

SEYMOUR, HORATIO   Address of..., Before the Saratoga County Fair.
Delivered at Saratoga, N.Y., September 10th, 1868. Columbus, (1868). Unbound as issued. Hayman 72-639 1978 $10

SEYMOUR, JOHN F.   Centennial Address Delivered at Trenton, N. Y.,
July 4, 1876. Utica, 1877. Wr., inscr'd by author. Butterfield 21-319 1978
$15

SEYMOUR, ROBERT   Seymour's Humorous Sketches. London, 1878.
Tall 8vo., mild foxing, plts. clear & fine, gilt, black & red pict. cover & spine,
faded, minor spotting back cover, ex-lib. copy, few blindstamps. Current 24-
50 1978 $140

SEYMOUR, ST. JOHN D.   Anglo-Irish Literature 1200-1582. 1929. Orig.
ed., orig. cloth, 8vo. Howes 194-1172 1978 £7.50

SEYS, JOHN   Extraordinary Trial of the Rev. John Seys, Pastor
of the Bedford Street Methodist Episcopal Church, New-York City, for an Alled-
ged Assault and Battery on Mrs. Elizabeth Cram. (New York, 1847). 2nd ed.,
uncut, wr., loose. Butterfield 21-489 1978 $17.50

SEZAN, CLAUDE   Les Poupees Anciennes. Paris, 1930.
8 vo., stiff pictorial wrappers, color frontispiece, illus., mostly uncut &
unopened, good-very good. Houle 10-239 1978 $22.50

SHACKLETON, ELIZABETH   Touring through France. Philadelphia, 1925. Illus.
Biblo 247-746 1978 $15

SHACKLETON, ERNEST HENRY   The Heart of the Antarctic, Being the Story
of the British Antarctic Expedition 1907-1909. London, 1909. 1st ed., 2 vols.,
maps in pocket, colored plts., roy. 8vo., orig. decor. cloth. K Books 244-
283 1978 £25

SHACKLETON, ROBERT   The Book of New York. Philadelphia, (1917).
Illus. Biblo BL781-176 1978 $8.50

SHADWELL, THOMAS   The Virtuoso. A Comedy. London, 1676. Sm.
4to, half calf (bit rubbed), 1st ed., very good large copy. Ximenes 47-283
1978 $275

SHAFFER, ELLEN   The Garden of Health. (San Francisco), 1957.
Woodcut illus., 4to., orig. bds., buckram back, plain d.w., fine, ed. ltd. to
300 copies. Morrill 239-230 1978 $100

SHAFTER, RICHARD A.   Destroyers in Action. Cornell Martime Press,
1945. Illus. Austin 80-293 1978 $12.50

SHAFTON, PIERS   The Compliments of the Season or How to Give
an Evening Party. 1849. Illus., orig. cloth, good. Jarndyce 16-1041 1978 £12

SHAKESPEARE, WILLIAM   As You Like It. New York, 1900. 1 of
200 numbered copies printed on Japan vellum, plts., 4 to., half green mor.
over gilt stamped green cloth, t.e.g., uncut, protective box, fine. Houle
10-290 1978 $100

SHAKESPEARE, WILLIAM   Mr. William Shakespeares Comedies, Histories,
and Tragedies. London, 1632. Tall folio, full calf with blind-stamped covers and
paneled spine, title washed and pressed, scarce 2nd folio., handsome copy. Bennett 7-98 1978 $4,500

SHAKESPEARE, WILLIAM   Mr. William Shakespeares Comedies, Histories,
& Tragedies. (1807). Portrait, folio, contemp. calf, rebacked. Howes 194-453
1978 £70

SHAKESPEARE, WILLIAM   Shakespeares Comedies, Histories, & Tragedies.
Oxford, 1902. Folio, orig. brown suede, rebacked with orig. spine over the new,
lacks orig. ties, endpapers foxed, ink inscription, 1,000 copies pr. and signed by
Sidney Lee. Totteridge 29-95 1978 $125

SHAKESPEARE, WILLIAM   Shakespeare's Comedies, Histories and Tragedies.
Oxford, 1902. Folio, rough calf, from the Chatsworth copy. Quaritch 979-291
1978 $450

SHAKESPEARE, WILLIAM   The Comedies, Histories & Tragedies. New York,
Limited Editions Club, 1939. 37 vols., decor. bds., cloth spine, 1 of 1950 numbered sets, illus. Dawson's 447-148 1978 $475

SHAKESPEARE, WILLIAM The Dramatic Works. 1820. 12 vols., frontis portrait, half title in all vols., orig. blue bds., paper labels, uncut, some brown spotting on spines otherwise v.g. in orig. condition. Jarndyce 16-1045 1978 £25

SHAKESPEARE, WILLIAM The Dramatic Works. (Chiswick Press), 1856. Portrait, vignettes, 10 vols., orig. cloth, paper labels, entirely uncut, 8vo. Howes 194-1176 1978 £18.50

SHAKESPEARE, WILLIAM The Merchant of Venice. n.d. Colour plts. by James D. Linton, no. 17 of 500 copies, signed by artist, 4to., full vellum gilt, t.e.g., covers slightly soiled, silk ties missing, very good, first English ed. Bell Book 17-494 1978 £20

SHAKESPEARE, WILLIAM The Merry Wives of Windsor. London, 1910. Illus. by Hugh Thomson, first ed., tipped-in coloured plts., illus., 4to., gilt-dec. cloth. K Books 244-285 1978 £18

SHAKESPEARE, WILLIAM Pericles. Oxford, 1905. Ltd. ed., 4 to., full gilt stamped vellum, uncut, very good. Houle 10-291 1978 $65

SHAKESPEARE, WILLIAM Pericles. Oxford, 1905. No. 421 of ltd. ed., published by subscription, orig. buckram backed bds., with ties, nearly fine. Limestone 9-260 1978 $35

SHAKESPEARE, WILLIAM The Phoenix & Turtle. (Flansham), Pear Tree Press, (1938). 1st ed., ltd. to 200 copies, unbound sheets, woodcut illus., 8vo., orig. cloth, very good. Americanist 103-136 1978 $25

SHAKESPEARE, WILLIAM The Plays of... London, 1765. 8 vols., port., full contemp. polished calf, red mor. labels, 1st ed. MacManus 238-141 1978 $450

SHAKESPEARE, WILLIAM Poems... London, 1640. First ed., 8vo., orig. sheep, bootom of spine chipped, minimal restoration, fine. Quaritch 978-141 1978 $18,500

SHAKESPEARE, WILLIAM Bell's Edition of Shakespeare's Plays as they are now performed. 1773-74. Portrait, 9 vols., sm. 8vo., fairly recently rebound in calf, first ed. Howes 194-454 1978 £45

SHAKESPEARE, WILLIAM Plays. 1797. Woodcuts, 8 vols., thk. sm. 8vo. contemp. calf, a few joints cracked and labels missing. Howes 194-455 1978 £30

SHAKESPEARE, WILLIAM Romeo and Juliet. Batsford, 1936. Colour plts. by Oliver Messel, 4to., very good, first English ed. Bell Book 17-495 1978 £12.50

SHAKESPEARE, WILLIAM Shakespeare's Sonnets 1897. University Press. One of 750 copies prtd. on English handmade paper, paper over bds., spine worn. Battery Park 1-44 1978 $100

SHAKESPEARE, WILLIAM The Sonnets of Shakespeare from the First Edition of 1609. Elston Press, 1901. One of 210 copies. Battery Park 1-86 1978 $150

SHAKESPEARE, WILLIAM The Sonnets of ... Cambridge, 1924. Sq. 8vo, cloth-backed bds. rubbed, good. Upcroft 10-155 1978 £5.50

SHAKESPEARE, WILLIAM The Tempest. London, 1908. 1st ed., quarto, tipped-in color plates by Woodroffe, gilt vignettes on cover and spine, very good copy. Victoria 34-883 1978 $50

SHAKESPEARE, WILLIAM The Tragedy of Hamlet, Prince of Denmark. (New York, Limited Editions Club, 1933). Engrs., full pigskin, bit soiled, bkplt., fine, slightly faded slipcase, 1 of 1500 numbered copies, signed by Eric Gill. Dawson's 447-43 1978 $85

SHAKESPEARE, WILLIAM Twelfth Night. London, n.d. Illus. by W. Heath Robinson, color plts., 4 to., gilt stamped green cloth, very good. Houle 10-280 1978 $95

SHAKESPEARE, WILLIAM The Works of ... 1725. 1st. ed., 6 vols., 4to, portrait, orig. panelled calf, hinges weak or cracked, otherwise v.g. Jarndyce 16-191 1978 £200

SHAKESPEARE, WILLIAM Works. 1890. 3 vols., thick 8vo., half crimson mor., gilt tops. Howes 194-1175 1978 £24

SHAKESPEARE, WILLIAM Works. Cambridge, 1929. 22 vols., sm. 8vo. Traylen 88-331 1978 £12

SHAKESPEARE, WILLIAM Works. London, Nonesuch Press, 1929. 7 vols., roy. 8vo, full niger morocco, gilt top, other edges uncut, contents lettered, ltd. ed. of 1600 copies. Traylen 88-332 1978 £300

SHAKESPEARE, WILLIAM The Works of... New York: The Nonesuch Press, 1929-32. 7 vols., lg. 8vo., full russet mor., 1 of 1,600 copies, leather darkened and somewhat rubbed, bookplts., very good. MacManus 238-840 1978 $500

SHAKESPEARE, WILLIAM The Works. New York, Nonesuch Press, 1929-33. 7 vols., lg. 8vo., full niger gilt ruled mor., reprint of first folio of 1623, v.f., uncut. Howell 5-47 1978 $650

SHAKESPEARE, WILLIAM Complete Works. Garden City, 1936. Cambridge ed., 1 of 750 signed and illus. by Rockwell Kent, folio, blue cloth, vellum labels, t.e.g., uncut, 2 vols., plts., very good. Houle 10-181 1978 $225

SHAKESPEARE, WILLIAM The Complete Works of William Shakespeare. Garden City, 1936. Illus. by Rockwell Kent, large 8vo., very good in dw which is ragged at edges. Bernard 5-144 1978 $30

SHAKESPEARE, WILLIAM The Complete Works of William Whakespeare. Garden City, 1936. Cambridge ed. text, small folio, buckram, vellum labels, gilt, t.e.g., illus. by Rockwell Kent, 1 of 750 copies, all rag paper signed by artist, 2 vols., fine. Duschnes 220-173 1978 $250

SHAKESPEARE: A Review and a Preview. New York, Limited Editions Club, n.d. 4to., nice. Bell Book 16-570 1978 £10

SHALER, N. S. Aspects of the Earth. London, 1890. Plts., illus., roy. 8vo. Traylen 88-628 1978 £20

SHAMBAUGH, BENJAMIN F. The Messages and Proclamations of the Governors of Iowa. Iowa City, 1903-1905. Vols. I, II, III, IV, V & VII. Bell Wiley's copy. Broadfoot 46-565 1978 $40

SHANKS, HENRY THOMAS The Papers of Willie Person Mangum. Raleigh, 1950. 5 vols., Bell Wiley's copy. Broadfoot's 44-917 1978 $15

SHANKS, HENRY THOMAS The Secession Movement in Virginia 1847-1861. Richmond, 1934. Bell Wiley's copy. Broadfoot's 44-669 1978 $14.00

SHANNON, C. HAZLEWOOD The Pageant. London, 1896. Plts., 4to., orig. cloth. K Books 244-429 1978 £24

SHANNON, FRED ALBERT The Civil War Letters of Sergeant Onley Andrus. Urbana, 1947. Some margins stained and repaired, Bell Wiley's copy. Broadfoot's 44-469 1978 $17

SHANNON, FRED ALBERT The Organization and Administration of the Union Army 1861-65. Cleveland, 1928. Bright set, 2 vols., Bell Wiley's copy. Broadfoot's 44-336 1978 $50

SHANNON, MARTHA A. S. Boston Days of William Morris Hunt. Boston, 1923. Portr., reproductions of Hunt's paintings, 8vo., new cloth, fine, 1st ed., ltd. Morrill 239-515 1978 $9.50

THE SHANNON Hydro-Electric Scheme. C. 1926. Wrs., very good, reprint. Hyland 128-495 1978 £5

SHAPIRO, KARL Essay on Rime; a poem. New York, 1945. First ed., orig. binding, spine faded, nice, torn d.w. Rota 211-592 1978 £6

SHAPLEY, RUFUS EDMONDS Solid for Mulhooly. New York, 1881. Cloth, moderate wear at ends of spine, minor spotting on cover. Hayman 73-204 1978 $12.50

SHARAKU, KURTH J. Sharaku. Zweite, Starke Bearbeitete Auflage. Munich, 1922. 4to., plts., some coloured, orig. bds., cloth back. Quaritch 983-145 1978 $130

SHARE, H. Under Great Bear and Southern Cross, Forty Years afloat and ashore. 1932. Illus., 8vo. George's 635-859 1978 £8.50

SHARP, A. Cantor Lectures on Cycle Construction and Design. London, 1899. Large 8vo., illus., orig. wrappers, repaired. Quaritch 977-256 1978 $55

SHARP, D. E. Franciscan Philosophy at Oxford in the Thirteenth Century. Oxford, 1930. 8vo. Upcroft 12-403 1978 £15

SHARP, DANIEL   Christian Mourning. A Discource Delivered at the Funeral of Rev. Lucius Bolles, D. D... Boston, 1844. Disbound. Hayman 72-700 1978 $7.50

SHARP, E. A.   Lyra Celtica. Edinburgh, 1932. 2nd ed., 8vo., orig. cloth. K Books 244-403 1978 £5

SHARP, LUKE PSEUD.
Please turn to
BARR, ROBERT

SHARP, R. F.   Catalogue of the Pamphlets, Newspapers, and Manuscripts relating to the Civil War, Commonwealth, and Restoration, collected by G. Thomason 1640-61. London, 1908. 2 vols., roy. 8vo., orig. cloth, t.e.g. Forster 130-233 1978 £40

SHARP, SAMUEL   Letters from Italy, Describing the Customs and Manners of that Country, in the Years 1765 and 1766. 1766. Contemp. calf, First ed., label missing, 8vo. Howes 194-460 1978 £28

SHARP, WILLIAM   Pharais. A Romance of the Islea. Derby, 1894. 12mo., orig. patternd bds., 1st ed., fine. MacManus 238-383 1978 $85

SHARP, WILLIAM   Vistas. Derby, 1894. 12mo., orig. patterned bds., 1st ed., very slightly worn, but fine. MacManus 238-384 1978 $75

SHARPE, BILL   Tar on my Heels. Winston-Salem, 1946. Broadfoot 50-200 1978 $10

SHARPE, RICHARD BOWDLER   A Monograph of the Alcedinidae: or, Family of Kingfishers. 1868-71. 2 vols., roy. 4to., map, hand-coloured plts. by Keulemans, contemp. quarter calf. Quaritch 983-366 1978 $8,750

SHARPE, RICHARD BOWDLER   A Monograph of the Paradiseidae... 1891-98. 2 vols., imp. folio, hand colored plts., cloth backed bds., bookplate of Alexander Lawson Duncan. Quaritch 983-367 1978 $20,000

SHARPE, RICHARD SCRAFTON   Smiles for All Seasons:.... London, 1825. 12mo, full green crushed levant, gilt, spine gilt, t.e.g., by Bumpus, 2nd ed., revised, plate in five compartments by George Cruikshank, original printed wr. (a bit rubbed) bound in at end, bookplate of Sir David Salomons, very scarce. Ximenes 47-234 1978 $80

SHARPHAM, EDWARD   Cupid's Whirligig. Golden Cockerel Press, 1926. Sm. 8vo., full mor., gilt, gilt top. Quaritch 979-170 1978 $40

SHARPLESS, ISAAC   A History of Quaker Government in Pennsylvania. Philadelphia, (1900). 2 vols., ltd. to 600 copies, sm. 4tos., untrimmed set, t.e.g., 1/2 mor., spines scuffed. MacManus 239-1675 1978 $35

THE SHASTA Route in All of Its Grandeur. Chicago, n.d. (Early 20th Century). Wrps., photographic views in color. Hayman 71-672 1978 $8.50

SHAVER, LILLIE TERRELL   Flashlights on Texas. Austin, (1928). Decor. fabricoid, illus., 1st ed., pres. copy from author, full lea. d.w. with Mr.-Mrs. Jack Munger in gilt on front cover. Dykes 34-261 1978 $22.50

SHAW, ANNA HOWARD   The Story of a Pioneer. New York, (1928). Cloth. Hayman 73-673 1978 $7.50

SHAW, ANNIE S.   Hazell and Sons, Brewers. Cincinnati, n.d., (c.1900). Orig. binding, clean. Hayman 71-243 1978 $8.50

SHAW, CHARLES   Topographical and Historical Description of the Town of Boston. Boston, 1817. 1st ed., illus., plts., paper-backed bds., nice untrimmed copy, scarce. MacManus 239-298 1978 $30

SHAW, CHARLES RUSSELL   Knots Useful and Ornamental. Boston, 1924. Illus., 8vo., 1st ed., orig. cloth. Morrill 241-529 1978 $10

SHAW, FRANK L.   The Building Trades. 1916. Austin 80-841 1978 $8.50

SHAW, FRANK L.   The Printing Trades. 1916. Austin 80-842 1978 $8.50

SHAW, FRED G.   The Complete Science of Fly Fishing and Spinning. London, 1920. Illus., second ed., orig. binding. Wolfe 39-20 1978 $25

SHAW, G. A.   Madagascar and France... 1885. Illus., plts., portrait, folding map, orig. cloth, 8vo. Edwards 1012-324 1978 £15

SHAW, GEORGE BERNARD   The Admirable Bashville. London, 1909. First Separate ed., wrappers, good. Rota 211-593 1978 £6

SHAW, GEORGE BERNARD   The Adventures of the Black Girl in Her Search For God. 1932. 1st. ed., 1st. printing, wood-engravings, end-papers, covers & other dec. by John Farleigh, 8vo, orig. paper covered bds., inscribed by author. Sawyer 299-134 1978 £145

SHAW, GEORGE BERNARD   Androcles and the Lion, Overruled, Pygmalion. 1916. First ed., cr. 8vo., orig. cloth. Howes 194-1185 1978 £5

SHAW, GEORGE BERNARD   The Apple Cart. London, 1930. Olive green cloth, 1st ed., fine, brittle dust jacket. Bradley 49-289 1978 $12.50

SHAW, GEORGE BERNARD   Back to Methuselah. London, 1945. New ed., orig. binding, nice. Rota 211-595 1978 £8

SHAW, GEORGE BERNARD   Bernard Shaw through the Camera. London, 1948. Photographs, fine, d.w., first ed., orig. binding. Rota 211-599 1978 £7.50

SHAW, GEORGE BERNARD   Bernard Shaw through the Camera. 1950. 8vo., illus., cloth with d.w., pres. copy from Shaw with inscr., T.L.s. tipped in. Quaritch 979-294 1978 $400

SHAW, GEORGE BERNARD   Cashel Byron's Profession. Chicago, 1901. 1st authorized Amer. ed., extremities of spine a bit worn, but very good. MacManus 238-751 1978 $50

SHAW, GEORGE BERNARD   Cashel Byron's Profession. Chicago, 1901. 1st of this ed., covers scuffed, otherwise a good copy. Biblo 251-628 1978 $20

SHAW, GEORGE BERNARD   Cashel Byron's Profession. Chicago, 1901. First American ed., orig. binding. Rota 212-52 1978 £40

SHAW, GEORGE BERNARD   Collection of Works. London, V.Y. 16 vols., 8vo. Traylen 88-335 1978 £10

SHAW, GEORGE BERNARD   Common Sense about the War. 1914. First ed., 4to., stitched as issued, fine, orig. state. Howes 194-1186 1978 £30

SHAW, GEORGE BERNARD   The Common Sense of Municipal Trading. 1904. Orig. blue cloth, very good, scarce, first English ed. Bell Book 16-774 1978 £10

SHAW, GEORGE BERNARD   The Doctor's Dilemma, Getting Married, and The Shewing-Up of Blanco Posnet. 1911. First ed., cr. 8vo., orig. cloth, gilt top. Howes 194-1187 1978 £5

SHAW, GEORGE BERNARD   An Essay – On Going to Church. Boston, 1905. 12mo., first Luce ed. Biblo 247-622 1978 $12.50

SHAW, GEORGE BERNARD   Fabianism & The Empire, A Mantifesto by the Fabian Society. 1900. 1st ed., wr. (worn), text very good. Hyland 128-501 1978 £15

SHAW, GEORGE BERNARD   The Intelligent Woman's Guide to Socialism and Capitalism. New York, 1928. 1st Amer. ed., orig. bind. Petrilla 13-107 1978 $10

SHAW, GEORGE BERNARD   Love Among the Artists. Chicago, 1900. Orig. dec. cloth, 1st ed., spine darkened, otherwise good. MacManus 238-750 1978 $60

SHAW, GEORGE BERNARD   Man and Superman. Westminster, 1903. 1st ed., green cloth, gilt tops, john Quinn's bkplt., Alfred A. Knopf's Hovel bkplt., protective fldr., fine cond., half mor. slipcase. Bradley 49-290 1978 $60

SHAW, GEORGE BERNARD   Plays: Pleasant and Unpleasant. London, 1898. Engr. portr., 2 vols., light green cloth, gilt tops, 1st ed., fine, green half mor. slipcase. Bradley 49-291 1978 $45

SHAW, GEORGE BERNARD   Plays: Pleasant and Unpleasant. London, 1898. 2 vols., frontis. port., 1st ed., spines a bit darkened, but very good. MacManus 238-749 1978 $75

SHAW, GEORGE BERNARD   Prefaces. 1934. Lg. 8vo, woodcut title, cloth. Eaton 45-452 1978 £6

SHAW, GEORGE BERNARD   Saint Joan. 1924. Ltd. ed. of 750 copies, 12 coloured & 4 monochrome plts., folio, orig. linen-backed dec. bds., d.w., good copy, autograph inscription by author. Sawver 299-133 1978 £140

SHAW, GEORGE BERNARD   The Sanity of Art... 1908. Wrappers, foot of spine torn. Eaton 45-453 1978 £5

SHAW, GEORGE BERNARD   Too True To Be Good, Village Wooing & On The Rocks. London, (1934). 8vo, cloth, d.j., t.e.g., Standard ed. of Works, fine. Duschnes 220-283 1978 $20

SHAW, HENRY   Dresses and Decorations of the Middle Ages, from the Seventh to the Seventeenth Centuries. 1858. 2 vols., imp. 8vo, hand-coloured plts., woodcuts, orig. half roan, bind. worn but contents clean. Quaritch 983-90 1978 $250

SHAW, HENRY   The Encyclopedia of Ornament. Edinburgh, 1898. Coloured frontis., plts., 4to. George's 635-54 1978 £18

SHAW, HENRY   Specimens of Ancient Furniture, Drawn from Existing Authorities... 1836. Folio, lg. paper, hand-coloured plts., orig. cloth, mor. back, recased, fine copy. Quaritch 983-91 1978 $420

SHAW, HENRY WHEELER   Josh Billings' Spice Box. New York, n.d. Engrs., 4to., orig. wrs. Morrill 241-530 1978 $8.50

SHAW, IRWIN   The Gentle People. New York, (1939). Illus., 1st ed., signed, very good, d.w. Biblo 251-629 1978 $17.50

SHAW, IRWIN   Report on Israel. 1950. Illus., photos. Austin 79-666 1978 $27.50

SHAW, IRWIN   The Young Lions. New York, 1948. First U.S. ed., very good, worn d.w. Bell Book 17-806 1978 $8.50

SHAW, JAMES   Early Reminiscences of Pioneer Life in Kansas. N.P., (1886). 1st ed., frontis., fine copy, orig. cloth, slightly spotted. MacManus 239-1933 1978 $35

SHAW, JAMES   Twelve Years in America.... London, Dublin, Chicago, 1867. Clean, lacks free endpaper, 1st. ed., orig. binding. Hayman 71-327 1978 $40

SHAW, PETER   Chemical Lectures. London, (1734). 8vo., contemp. calf, rebacked, very good copy, 1st ed. Norman 5-257 1978 $200

SHAW, PRINGLE   Ramblings in California... Toronto, (1857). Sm. 8vo, orig. cloth, cover worn, name in ink on preface, preserved in cloth case. Edwards 1012-532 1978 £100

SHAW, REUBEN COLE   Across the Plains in Forty-Nine. Chicago, 1948. 12mo., orig. cloth. Morrill 241-249 1978 $7.50

SHAW, ROBERT K.   All Saints Church. Worcester, 1835-1935. Baldwins' 51-404 1978 $7.50

SHAW, S. M.   A Centennial Offering... Cooperstown, 1886. 12mo. MacManus 239-334 1978 $35

SHAW, W. A.   The History of Currency, 1252-1894, an Account of the Gold and Silver Monies and Monetary Standards of Europe and America. (1895). 8vo. George's 635-401 1978 £7.50

SHAW, WILLIAM H.   History of Essex and Hudson Counties, N.J. Philadelphia, 1884. 2 vols., illus., 4to., rebound. MacManus 239-1322 1978 $100

SHAWVER, LONA   Chuck Wagon Windies and Range Poems. San Antonio, 1934. 1st ed., limited ed., numbered, inscribed and autographed by Ms. Shawver. Jenkins 116-1230a 1978 $20

SHAY, FELIX   Elbert Hubbard of East Aurora. New York, 1926. Frontis., illus., fine copy, 1st ed., torn but complete dust jacket. Butterfield 21-210 1978 $15

SHAY, FELIX   Elbert Hubbard of East Aurora. 1926. Austin 82-846 1978 $10

SHAY, FRANK   A Little Book of Vagabond Songs. New York, 1931. 12mo., etchings by Philip Kappel, 1st ed. Biblo 251-631 1978 $15

SHEA, JOHN GILMARY   The Cross and the Flag. 1900. Illus., huge vol. Austin 79-667 1978 $47.50

SHEA, JOHN GILMARY   Early Voyages. Albany, 1902. 500 copies reprinted, this is #241, initialed by John McDonough, grey bds., beige cloth backstrip, inscr'd by McDonough. Austin 79-668 1978 $125

SHEA, JOHN GILMARY   History of the Catholic Church in the United States. New York, 1886-92. 4 vols., illus., orig. cloth. MacManus 239-438 1978 $110

SHEA, JOHN GILMARY   Life and Times of the Most Rev. John Carroll. 1888. Illus., rebound. Austin 79-669 1978 $37.50

SHEA, JOHN GILMARY   Perils of the Ocean and Wilderness... Boston, 1857. 1st ed., 12mo., cloth. Paine 78-116 1978 $16.50

SHEAHAN, JAMES W.   The Life of Stephen A. Douglas. New York, 1860. 1st ed., frontis. port., orig. cloth, staining, but good copy. MacManus 239-744 1978 $15

SHEARING, JOSEPH   Airing in a Closed Carriage. London, n.d. (1943). 1st ed. Biblo BL781-943 1978 $10

SHEARMAN, H.   Anglo-Irish Relations. 1948. 1st ed., d.w., near fine, octavo bound in cloth. Hyland 128-516 1978 £5

SHEARWOOD, MRS. F. P.   By Water and The Word: A Transcription of the Diary of the Right Reverend J. A. Newnham... Toronto, 1943. Hood's 115-80 1978 $30

SHEDD, W. G. T.   The Nature and Importance of a Natural Rhetoric. Auburn, 1852. 8vo., orig. wrs., 1st ed., pres. copy. Morrill 239-606 1978 $10

SHEDD, WILLIAM B.   Italian Population in New York. 1934. Maps, paper. Austin 79-670 1978 $7.50

SHEE, GEORGE   An Essay on the Situation, Customs and Manners of the Ancient Germans. Cambridge, 1804. 8vo., unbound. P. M. Hill 142-216 1978 £18

SHEE, MARTIN ARCHER   The Life of .... London, 1860. 2 vols., 8vo, half red morocco. Traylen 88-413 1978 £15

SHEEAN, VINCENT   Between the Thunder and the Sun. 1943. Austin 80-294 1978 $10

SHEEHAN, D.D.   Ireland Since Parnell. 1921. 1st ed., spine faded, very good, octavo bound in cloth. Hyland 128-324 1978 £6.50

SHEFFIELD, JOHN, DUKE OF BUCKINGHAM AND NORMANBY
Please turn to
BUCKINGHAM, JOHN SHEFFIELD, DUKE OF

CAUTION: He was also Earl of Mulgrave
SHEFFIELD, JOHN, FL. 1643-1647

SHEFFY, L. F.   The Life and Times of Timothy Dwight Hobart. Canyon, 1950. Cloth, map end sheets, illus., 1st ed., fine copy, scarce. Dykes 34-68 1978 $25

SHEFFY, L. F.   The Life and Times of Timothy Dwight Hobart 1855-1935. Canyon, 1950. Cloth, map, illus., 1st ed., covers a little rubbed else fine, autographed by author. Dykes 35-262 1978 $40

SHELDON, CHARLES M.   In His Steps. Chicago, 1898. Orig. binding, clean. Hayman 71-238 1978 $8.50

SHELDON, GEORGE   Half Century at the Bay, 1636-1686. Boston, 1905. 8vo., 1st ed. Morrill 239-607 1978 $15

SHELDON, LIONEL A.   Letters of Gov...Written to the Santa Fe New Mexican Review While on a Visit to the City of Mexico. N.P., 1884. Orig. pr. wr., 1st ed. Ginsberg 14-916 1978 $85

SHELDON, W. H.   The Varieties of Human Physique. New York, 1940. Rittenhouse 49-722 1976 $12.50

SHELLABARGER, S.   Disfranchisement of Rebels, Speech of Hon. S.
Shellabarger, of Ohio.   Washington, 1866. Wrs., Bell Wiley's copy. Broadfoot
46-225 1978 $8

SHELLEY, GEORGE ERNEST   Monograph of the Nectariniidae, or Family of
Sunburds. London, 1876-80. Hand coloured plts., thick 4to, full brown morocco,
spine dec., gilt edges, little foxing in text, plt. entirely clean, colouring is
unusually brillant. Traylen 88-629 1978 £3750

SHELLEY, MARY WOLLSTONECRAFT GODWIN   The Last Man. Paris, 1826.
1st continental ed., 3 vols., 12mo., orig. wrs., paper labels, uncut. Hannas
54-303 1978 £36

SHELLEY, MARY WOLLSTONECRAFT GODWIN   Lodore. Brussels, 1835. 8vo.,
orig. quarter cloth, marbled bds., somewhat shaken, first continental ed., scarce.
Ximenes 47-285 1978 $100

SHELLEY, PERCY BYSSHE   Adonais. Oxford, 1891. Orig. blue
beveled cloth, gilt, t.e.g., very good or better. Limestone 9-264 1978
$30

SHELLEY, PERCY BYSSHE   Alastor; or, The Spirit of Solitude: and Other
Poems. London, 1885. Reprint of 1st ed., brown buckram, near fine, unopened,
1 of 4 copies prtd. on vellum. Dawson's 447-274 1978 $175

SHELLEY, PERCY BYSSHE   Alastor. London, 1885. Ltd. 404, (350,
like this 1, on toned paper), orig. bds., label chipped, corners bumbed, very
good or better. Limestone 9-265 1978 $25

SHELLEY, PERCY BYSSHE   The Cenci. London, 1819. 1st. ed., 8vo, blue
morocco, gilt, pres. copy to Thomas Jefferson from author, preserved in brown
morocco, backed slip-in case gilt & buckram sleeve, association copy. Sawyer
299-135 1978 £2850

SHELLEY, PERCY BYSSHE   The Cenci. London, 1821. Three-quarters brown
mor. & marbled bds., spine gilt, t.e.g., marbled end papers, 2nd ed., nice copy.
Bradley 49-292 1978 $150

SHELLEY, PERCY BYSSHE   I Cenci Tragedia in cinque atti...Tradotta da
Adolfo de Bosis. Roma, 1898. Lg. 4to., decor. wrappers, illus., lg. paper,
uncut. King 7-234 1978 £25

SHELLEY, PERCY BYSSHE   Epipsychidion. Montagnola, 1923. Quarto,
vellum over boards, ltd to 222 copies, covers slightly warped, bookplt., fine.
Duschnes 220-222 1978 $250

SHELLEY, PERCY BYSSHE   Essays, Letters From Abroad, Translations and
Fragments. 1840. 1st. ed., 2 vols., 12mo, lacks half-title in vol. 2, binder's
cloth, slightly worn. Hannas 54-304 1978 £30

SHELLEY, PERCY BYSSHE   The Lyrical Poems and Translations. Florence
Press, 1918. One of 250 numbered copies on large paper, full vellum, gilt, first
English ed. Bell Book 17-361 1978 £18.50

SHELLEY, PERCY BYSSHE   The Masque of Anarchy. London, 1832. 1st ed.,
full olive levant, gilt, t.e.g., inner dentelles gilt, marbled end papers, engr.
bkplt. of former owner, very fine copy. Bradley 49-293 1978 $185

SHELLEY, PERCY BYSSHE   The Masque of Anarchy. 1832. 1st. ed., half
title, orig. bds., hinges weak, otherwise v.g., orig. condition. Jarndyce 16-
1046 1978 £90

SHELLEY, PERCY BYSSHE   The Narrative Poems. Florence Press, 1927.
2 vols., orig. cloth-backed bds., gilt tops, other edges untrimmed, 8vo. Howes
194-1194 1978 £6.50

SHELLEY, PERCY BYSSHE   The Poetical Works of ... 1839. 4 vols.,
1st. authorized collected ed., sm. 8vo, portrait, foxed, orig. cloth, head-bands
worn. Hannas 54-307 1978 £40

SHELLEY, PERCY BYSSHE   Poetical Works. 1908. Portrait, half crimson
mor., gilt top, 8vo. Howes 194-1192 1978 £7.50

SHELLEY, PERCY BYSSHE   Posthumous Poems. London, 1824. 1st ed., contemp. calf & marbled bds., fine, firm copy, new lea. spine, bkplt. of Geoffrey
Ecroyd, very good copy, scarce. Bradley 49-294 1978 $250

SHELLEY, PERCY BYSSHE   Posthumous Poems. London, 1824. 1st. ed.,
8vo, orig. bds., uncut, new boards spine with fragmentary remains preserved,
bookplt. removed from flyleaf. Traylen 88-336 1978 £80

SHELLEY, PERCY BYSSHE   Prometheus Unbound. (London, Essex House
Press, 1904). 1 of 200 copies printed on handmade paper, frontispiece draw-
ings, sm. folio, full white vellum stamped in gold, green silk ties, fine.
Houle 10-292 1978 $295

SHELLEY, PERCY BYSSHE   Queen Mab. London, 1821. Portr., 3/4 red mor.
& cloth, 1st published ed., 1st issue, very good copy, internally sound. Bradley
49-367 1978 $200

SHELLEY, PERCY BYSSHE   Queen Mab. 1821. 8vo., 1st published ed.,
contemp. olive binders cloth, uncut, bkplt. of John Clawson. Quaritch 979-295
1978 $120

SHELLEY, PERCY BYSSHE   Queen Mab. London, 1821. Octavo, bound in
contemp. grey-green boards, morocco label, all edges uncut, N. Brinsley Acworth's
copy, armorial bookplate and signature. Bennett 20-191 1978 $425

SHELLEY, PERCY BYSSHE   Queen Mab. London, 1821. 2nd ed., sm. 4to.,
t.e.g., frontis, fine interior, 3/4 blue mor. Current Misc. 8-40 1978 $300

SHELLEY, PERCY BYSSHE   Queen Mab. 1829. Uncut, tall 8vo, grey-
green morocco, elaborate gilt borders & dentelles, silk endpapers, hinges rubbed,
otherwise v.g. Jarndyce 16-1047 1978 £28

SHELLEY, PERCY BYSSHE   Queen Mab: A Philosophical Poem, with Notes.
New York, 1831. Rebound in very handsome 3/4 calf and marbled boards, gilt
rules and spine decorations, raised bands, desirable ed. Victoria 34-729 1978
$35

SHELLEY, PERCY BYSSHE   The Revolt of Islam; a Poem, In Twelve Cantos.
1829. 8vo, title & several leaves spotted, contemp. calf, joints weak. Eaton 45-
454 1978 £30

SHELLEY, PERCY BYSSHE   Rosalind and Helen, a Modern Eclogue...
1819. 1st. ed., 8vo, half-title, 3/4 red crushed morocco, t.e.g., others uncut,
binding signed by Chiroux, preliminary leaves misbound, few tears in margin
repaired. Hannas 54-306 1978 £85

SHELLEY Memorials: From Authentic Sources. 1862. 2nd. ed., frontis, half calf,
ex-lib. binding. Eaton 45-456 1978 £15

SHELTON, F. W.   Up the River. New York, 1853. Cloth, some
staining on cover. Hayman 72-704 1978 $7.50

SHELTON, LOUISE   Beautiful Gardens in America. New York,
1915. Plates, 4to, orig. cloth. Book Chest 17-340 1978 $18

SHELTON, LOUISE   Beautiful Gardens in America. New York, 1924.
Rev. ed., illus., 4to., boxed, fine, box partly broken. Morrill 239-608 1978
$10

SHELTON, WILLIAM HENRY   The Salmagundi Club. 1918. Illus., ltd. to 500
copies, signed by author, ex-lib. Austin 82-847 1978 $20

SHENSTONE, WILLIAM   Men and Manners. Golden Cockerel Press,
1927. Cr. 8vo., orig. qtr. mor., gilt top, ltd. to 500 numbered copies. Howes
194-896 1978 £18

SHENSTONE, WILLIAM   Poetical works.... Edinburg, 1778. 2 vols.,
12mo, contemp. vellum gilt in style of Edwards of Halifax bindery, roll-tool borders,
blue wash on sides, monochrome watercolour drawings on each cover, underside of
vellum, gilt spines, excellent cond. Quaritch 978-14 1978 $2,000

SHENSTONE, WILLIAM   Poetical Works. Stanhope Press, 1806. 2 vols.,
sm. 8vo., contemp. full vellum. Howes 194-463 1978 £7.50

SHENSTONE, WILLIAM   The Works in Poetry and Prose. London, 1773.
3 vols., octavo, full contemp. calf, most complete ed., very good. Bennett
7-99 1978 $45

SHENSTONE, WILLIAM   The Works in Verse and Prose. 1764. First
collected ed., 2 vols., contemp. polished calf, joints cracked, frontispieces,
vignettes. Howes 194-462 1978 £25

SHENSTONE, WILLIAM   The Works in Verse and Prose. Edinburgh, 1765.
2 vols., 12mo., contemp. calf, lacking labels, first Scottish ed. P. M. Hill 142-
295 1978 £20

SHENSTONE, WILLIAM   The Works in Verse and Prose. 1764-69. 3
vols., 8vo., full polished calf gilt, frontispieces, vignettes, first ed. P. M. Hill
142-305 1978 £75

SHENSTONE, WILLIAM   The Works in Verse & Prose With Decorations. 1791. 6th. ed., 3 vols., frontis, vignettes, folding plt., calf, black labels. Jarndyce 16-194 1978 £20

SHEPARD, A. K.   The Land of the Aztecs: or, Two Years in Mexico. Albany, 1859. Original cloth, gilt, 1st and only ed. Jenkins 116-1235a 1978 $125

SHEPARD, CHARLES UPHAM   Notice of Lion River, South Africa, Meteoric Iron. New Haven, 1853. 8vo, orig. pale pink pr. wr., 1st ed., illus., light dampstains, very good copy. Ximenes 47-286 1978 $25

SHEPARD, ODELL   Connecticut. Past and Present. New York, 1939. 1st ed., illus. Biblo 251-67 1978 $15

SHEPERD, WILLIAM   Prairie Experiences in Handling Cattle and Sheep. New York, 1885. Illus., orig. cloth. Ginsberg 14-917 1978 $35

SHEPHARD, CHARLES   An Historical Account of the Island of Saint Vincent. 1831. Engraved plts., early cloth binding, rebacked, sides slightly worn, plts. & some pgs. browned, 8vo. Edwards 1012-742 1978 £95

SHEPHERD, C. W.   The North-West Peninsula of Iceland.... London, 1867. 1st. ed., 8vo, coloured lithograph view, folding lithograph map, gilt back, quarter calf. Deighton 5-141 1978 £48

SHEPHERD, JOB   Poor Job, 1752. Newport, (1751). 12mo., sewn, orig. cloth. Morrill 241-492 1978 $75

SHEPHERD, JOB   Poor Job, 1754. Newport, (1753). 12mo., sewn, orig. cloth. Morrill 241-493 1978 $30

SHEPHERD, THOMAS H.   Metropolitan Improvements. 1827. Plts., 4to., orig. half mor., frontis. Howes 194-1409 1978 £120

SHEPHERD, THOMAS H.   Metropolitan Improvements... 1847. Illus. by James Elmes, new ed., almost all very clean, orig. red cloth, gilt, dec. spine, a.e.g., v.g. Jarndyce 16-823 1978 £68

SHEPHERD, W.   Prairie Experiences in Handling Cattle and Sheep. London, 1884. Pic. cloth, black end sheets, illus., 1st British ed., near fine copy, slipcase. Dykes 34-36 1978 $75

SHEPHERD, W.   Prairie Experiences in Handling Cattle and Sheep. 1885. 1st Amer. ed., very good copy, slipcase. Dykes 34-37 1978 $40

SHEPHERD, WILLIAM R.   The Story of New Amsterdam. New York, 1926. Illus., 1st ed. Biblo BL781-177 1978 $8.50

SHEPPARD, ELIZABETH SARA   Almost a Heroine. Boston, 1860. 1st Amer. ed., 3 vols. in 1, orig. cloth, damp stained throughout, poor copy. Greene 78-106 1978 $30

SHEPPARD, ROBERT D.   Great Americans of History. Abraham Lincoln. A Character Sketch... Milwaukee, 1903. Cloth, minor wear. Hayman 72-431 1978 $7.50

SHERARD, ROBERT H.   The Life, Work and Evil Fate of Guy de Maupassant. 1926. Plts., orig. cloth, 8vo. Howes 194-1041 1978 £5

SHERBROOKE Fair. Aug. 27th to Sept. 1st, 1933. Official Programme. (Sherbrooke), 1933. Printed wrappers, some evidence of wear. Wolfe 39-163 1978 $7.50

SHERER, JOSEPH MOYLE
Please turn to
SHERER, MOYLE

SHERER, MOYLE   The Story of A Life. 1825. 3rd. ed., 2 vols., orig. half calf, labels, little rubbed. Jarndyce 16-1049 1978 £22.50

SHERIDAN, FRANCES   The Discovery. A Comedy in Five Acts. London, 1924. Ltd. to 210 copies, fine, slightly frayed, faded d.w., uncut, scarce. Biblo BL781-1012 1978 $37.50

SHERIDAN, PHILIP H.   Personal Memoirs. New York, 1888. Maps, illus., 2 vols., 8vo., 1st ed., orig. cloth. Morrill 241-531 1978 $13.50

SHERIDAN, RICHARD BRINSLEY   The Duenna: A Comic Opera. Dublin, 1794. 1st Irish ed., 12mo., wrapper, fine. Fenning 32-299 1978 £16.50

SHERIDAN, RICHARD BRINSLEY   Jone's British Theatre. Vol. V & VI. Dublin, 1795. 1st collected ed., portraits, 2 vols., 12mo., contemp. calf, little light spotting, very good. Fenning 32-301 1978 £45

SHERIDAN, RICHARD BRINSLEY   Plays. 1901. 8vo., blue calf, gilt panelled back, gilt edges. Quaritch 979-297 1978 $30

SHERIDAN, RICHARD BRINSLEY   The Rivals, A Comedy. Dublin, 1775. 1st Irish ed., 12mo., wrapper, nice. Fenning 32-300 1978 £35

SHERIDAN, RICHARD BRINSLEY   The School for Scandal. Oxford: The Shakespears Head Press, 1930. 4to., orig. vellum-backed bds., 1 of 475 copies, fine. MacManus 238-844 1978 $45

SHERIDAN, RICHARD BRINSLEY   The School for Scandal. 1949. Color plts. by Cecil Beaton, sm. 4to., cloth gilt, very good, d.w., 1st Eng. ed. Bell Book 17-077 1978 £5

SHERIDAN, RICHARD BRINSLEY   The School for Scandal. Toronto, n.d. 1st Canadian ed., tipped-in color plates, handsome over-all gilt pictorial cloth, fine. Victoria 34-795 1978 $75

SHERIDAN, RICHARD BRINSLEY   The School for Scandal. London, n.d. Tipped-in color plates, limited to 350 copies, signed by Thomson, bound in full vellum, endpapers foxed, fine, bright copy. Victoria 34-803 1978 $200

SHERIDAN, SOL N.   Ventura County California. San Francisco, n.d. Illus., maps, original pictorial colored wr., 1st ed. Ginsberg 14-196 1978 $45

SHERIDAN, THOMAS   A Complete Dictionary of the English Language. 1790. 3rd. ed., rebound in half calf, marbled bds., v.g. Jarndyce 16-73 1978 £44

SHERIDAN, THOMAS   A Course of Lectures on Elocution:... London, 1762. 1st ed., quarto, contemp. red half mor., marbled boards, recently rebacked, orig. leather title label, browned throughout. Totteridge 29-96 1978 $175

SHERIDAN'S Veterans. Boston, 1883. Wrs., illus., a souvenir of their two campaigns in the Shenandoah Valley, Bell Wiley's copy. Broadfoot 46-226 1978 $17

SHERLOCK, THOMAS   A Letter From the Bishop of London to the Clergy and People of London and Westminster on the Occasion of the Late Earthquakes. 1750. 1st. ed., rebound, half cloth, marbled bds. Jarndyce 16-196 1978 £12.50

SHERMAN, CHRISTOPHER E.   A Journey to the Land of Kingdom Come, and Other Journeys in Prose and Verse. Columbus, 1936. Cloth. Hayman 72-403 1978 $7.50

SHERMAN, FREDERIC FAIRCHILD   Early American Portraiture. New York, 1930. 4to., 1 of 250 copies, prtd. on heavy paper, illus., orig. cloth, very good. Americanist 103-15 1978 $45

SHERMAN, FREDERIC FAIRCHILD   Sonnets Suggested by Books in the Library of J. Pierpont Morgan. New York, 1909. Sm. 4to., prtd. on pure vellum, orig. bds., vellum back, binding little soiled, internally clean, ltd. to 15 copies. Quaritch 979-298 1978 $150

SHERMAN, JOHN   Recollections of Forty Years in the House, Senate, and Cabinet. Chicago, 1895. 1st. ed., illus. with portraits, orig. cloth, gilt, fine, bright, 2 vols. Baldwins' 51 16 1978 $17.50

SHERMAN, JOHN   John Sherman's Recollections of Forty Years in the House, Senate and Cabinet. New York, 1895. 2 vols., illus. MacManus 239-814 1978 $20

SHERMAN, JOHN   John Sherman's Recollections of Forty Years in the House, Senate and Cabinet. An Autobiography. Chicago, (1896). Illus., 1 vol. ed. Hayman 72-705 1978 $7.50

SHERMAN, ORRAY TAFT   Meteorological and Physical Observations on the East Coast of British America. Washington, 1883. 4to., orig. wrs. Morrill 241-532 1978 $17.50

SHERRILL, CHARLES H.   French Memories of 18th Century America. New York, 1915. Illus. MacManus 239-439 1978 $12.50

SHERRILL, HUNTING   A Review of the Diseases of Dutchess County from 1809 to 1825. New York, 1826. Rittenhouse 49-723 1976 $35

SHERRILL, LEWIS JOSEPH   The Rise of Christian Education. 1944. Austin 79-672 1978 $12.50

SHERRIN, R. A.   Early History of New Zealand...   New Zealand, 1890. Coloured frontis, illus., sm. 4to, orig. half morocco gilt, spine faded, some slight foxing. Edwards 1012-352 1978 £35

SHERRINGTON, CHARLES S.   Integrative Action of the Nervous System. New York, 1906. Ex-library, some wear. Rittenhouse 49-724 1976 $15

SHERROD, ROBERT   Tarawa. 1944. Illus. Austin 80-295 1978 $7.50

SHERWIN, REIDER T.   The Viking and the Red Man. 1940. Ex-lib. Austin 79-673 1978 $12.50

SHERWOOD, A.   Conversation in a Tent. Macon, n.d. Wrs., Bell Wiley's copy. Broadfoot 46-465 1978 $40

SHERWOOD, BOB   Hold Yer Hosses! 1932. Long inscription by author, illus., first ed. Austin 82-848 1978 $20

SHERWOOD, CHRISTOPHER   Sally Bowles. Hogarth Press, 1937. First ed., fcap. 8vo., very good, frayed d.w., orig. cloth. Howes 194-953 1978 £28

SHERWOOD, ISAAC R.   Memories of the War. Toledo, 1923. Orig. binding, clean, pres. copy. Hayman 71-137 1978 $17.50

SHERWOOD, ISAAC R.   Memories of the War. Toledo, 1923. Full page illus., pres. copy from Gen. Sherwood's daughter. Broadfoot's 44-587 1978 $20

SHERWOOD, J. ELY   California:.... New York, 1848. Illus., plain wr. in half morocco slipcase. Ginsberg 14-197 1978 $1,250

SHERWOOD, J. M.   Memoirs of Rev. David Brainerd, Missionary to the Indians of North America... New York, 1884. Cloth. Hayman 72-706 1978 $10

SHERWOOD, ROBERT E.   There Shall Be No Night. New York, 1940. Very fine in chipped d.w. Desmarais B-580 1973 $12.50

SHETRONE, HENRY C.   The Mound-Builders a Reconstruction of the Life of a Prehistoric American Race... New York, 1930. Illus., 1st ed., scarce, very fine, d.j., worn. MacManus 239-1216 1978 $40

SHEW, JOEL   The Water-Cure Manual. New York, 1847. Engr. portr., sm. 8vo., half lea., fr. cover loose, some dampstains in text. Morrill 239-231 1978 $8.50

SHIEL, M. P.   The Best Short Stories. 1948. Spine faded, good, first English ed. Bell Book 17-810 1978 £7.50

SHIEL, M.P.   The Yellow Danger. London, 1900. Pict. cloth binding. Greene 78-278 1978 $20.00

SHIELDS, BENJAMIN G.   Speech of the Hon. Benjamin G. Shields, of Alabama, on the Loan Bill. Washington, 1842. Disbound, neatly reinforced along binding edge. Hayman 73-675 1978 $7.50

SHIELLS, ROBERT   Marriage: A Poetical Essay. London, 1748. 4to, title page damaged, laid down, lacking the 'P' of Poetical, rest of text not affected, 1/2 morocco, rubbed. Eaton 45-457 1978 £20

SHIELS, G.   Professor Tim & Paul Twyning. 1927. 1st ed., boards with cloth spine, very good. Hyland 128-521 1978 £6

SHIELS, W. EUGENE   Gonzalo De Tapia (1561-1594). 1934. Map, ex-lib. Austin 79-674 1978 $17.50

SHILLABER, BENJAMIN PENHALLOW   The Double-Runner Club or the Boys of Rivertown. 1881. Illus. Austin 82-849 1978 $17.50

SHILLINGTON, V. M.   The Commercial Relations of England and Portugal. (1926). Map, cr. 8vo. George's 635-402 1978 £5.25

SHIMEALL, R. C.   End of Prelacy. 1852. Austin 79-675 1978 $27.50

SHIMMELL, LEWIS S.   Border Warfare in Pennsylvania During the Revolution. Harrisburg, 1901. Orig. wrs. MacManus 239-1676 1978 $27.50

SHINKOKAI, KOKUSAI BUNKA   Introduction to Classic Japanese Literature. Tokyo, 1948. Cloth, second printing. Dawsons 449-136 1978 $30

SHINN, CHARLES HOWARD   Mining Camps. New York, 1948. First Borzoi ed., d.w. Biblo 247-264 1978 $17.50

SHINN, CHARLES HOWARD   The Story of the Mine as Illustrated by the Great Comstock Lode of Nevada. New York, 1896. Illus., orig. cloth, 1st ed. Ginsberg 14-741 1978 $35

SHIPLEY, J. W.   Pulp and Paper-Making in Canada. Toronto, 1929. Hood 117-452 1978 $15

SHIPMAN, MRS. O. L.   Taming the Big Bend: A History of the Extreme Western Portion of Texas, From Fort Clark to El Paso. N.P., 1926. Near mint, 1st ed., rare. Jenkins 116-1239a 1978 $135

SHIPP, J. E. D.   Giant Days, or- The Life and Times of William H. Crawford. Georgia, 1909. Cover speckled, Bell Wiley's copy. Broadfoot's 44-868 1978 $10.00

SHIPPEE, LESTER B.   Bishop Whipple's Southern Diary 1843-1844. Minneapolis, 1937. Bell Wiley's copy. Broadfoot's 44-762 1978 $16.00

SHIPPEN, NANCY   Nancy Shippen, Her Journal Book... Philadelphia, 1935. Map end papers. MacManus 239-1677 1978 $10

SHIRAS, GEORGE   Hunting Wild Life with Camera and Flashlight. Washington, (1935). 2 vols., sm. 4to., orig. bind. Petrilla 13-108 1978 $12.50

SHIRLEY, JOHN fl. 1680-1702 The Accomplished Ladies Rich Closet of Rarities. London, 1651. Third ed., 12mo., modern calf, scarce. Quaritch 977-73 1978 $550

SHIROKOGROFF, S. M.   Ethnological and Linguistical Aspect of the Ural-Altaic Hypothesis. Leipzig, 1931. 8vo., orig. covers. Van der Peet H-64-552 1978 Dfl 30

SHIRREFS, J.   Inquiry into the Life, Writings, and Character of the Rev. Dr. William Guild. Aberdeen, 1799. 2nd ed., lacks a prelim. leaf, later half mor., spine gilt. George's 635-1244 1978 £5.25

SHOEMAKER, HENRY W.   Elizabethan Days. Reading, 1912. Scarce. Baldwins' 51-480 1978 $20

SHOEMAKER, HENRY W.   Mountain Minstrelsy of Pennsylvania. Philadelphia, 1931. Fine, orig. cloth. MacManus 239-1678 1978 $35

SHOEMAKER, JOHN V.   Ointments and Oleates Especially in Diseases of the Skin. Philadelphia, 1890. 2nd ed., revised & enlarged, 8vo. Morrill 239-232 1978 $7.50

SHOEMAKER, JOHN V.   A Practical Treatise on Diseases of the Skin. New York, 1895. 2nd ed., revised & enlarged, chromogravure plts., illus., 8vo., half lea. Morrill 239-233 1978 $10

SHOEMAKER, VAUGHN   '41 and '42 A. D. Cartoons. Chicago, 1942. Illus., 8vo., orig. bds., cloth back, 1st ed., signed orig. pen & ink drwg. by Shoemaker. Morrill 241-533 1978 $20

SHONNARD, FREDERIC   History of Westchester Co., New York... New York, 1900. Thick 4to., rebound, illus. MacManus 239-1103 1978 $70

SHOOK, CHARLES A.   The True Origin of the Book of Mormon. Cincinnati, 1914. Illus. Austin 79-676 1978 $27.50

SHORE, HENRY N. BARON TEIGNMOUTH
Please turn to
TEIGNMOUTH, HENRY N. SHORE BARON

SHORRT, W. T. P.   Collectanea Curiosa Antiqua Dunmonia... Exeter, c.1842. 8vo., plts., fine copy, orig. cloth. Quaritch 983-30 1978 $85

SHORT, BOB   A Treatise on The Game of Draughts; or Short Rules for Short Memories. 1823. 12mo, orig. brown wrappers, paper label, v.g. Jarndyce 16-1050 1978 £6.50

SHORT, ERNEST H.   The Painter in History. Philadelphia, n.d. Illus. Biblo BL781-737 1978 $14.50

A SHORT Account of the First Settlements of the Provinces of Virginia,.... 1630. Limited to 790 copies, fine. Nestler Rare 78-84 1978 $20

A SHORT Account of the First Settlement of the Provinces of Virginia, Maryland, New York, New Jersey, and Pennsylvania, by the English. London, 1735. Reprinted N.P., 1922, ltd. to 790 numbered copies, fold. map, fine copy, cloth bds., sm. 4to. MacManus 239-441 1978 $27.50

A SHORT Account of the Worshipful Company of Stationers, presented to the Arch-bishop of Canterbury and the Guests on the Celebration of the 500th Anniversary of the Foundation of the Company. 1903. Coloured frontis. plates, half calf. George's 635-403 1978 £30

A SHORT Authentic Account of the Expedition Against Quebec in the year 1759. Quebec, 1872. Orig. printed wrappers. Wolfe 39-459 1978 $35

SHORT Authentic Account of the Expedition Against Quebec in the Year 1759 Under Major-General James Wolfe, by a Volunteer Upon that Expedition. Que-bec, 1872. Paper covers. Hood 117-153 1978 $35

A SHORT Bibliography of English Books on Japan. Tokyo, 1936. Decor. wrs., 3rd ed., revised. Dawson's 449-185 1978 $10

A SHORT Biography of Daniel B. Wood and Family. San Marcos, (1904). Wrps., some paper worn from spine. Hayman 71-265 1978 $12.50

A SHORT History and Photographic Record of the 101st U.S. Field Artillery. Cam-bridge, 1918. 4to., wrs. Biblo 247-762 1978 $17.50

A SHORT History of Insects. Norwich, (? 1797). Sm. 8vo., hand-coloured plts., contemp. sheep, rebacked, inscr. dated 1819. Quaritch 979-88 1978 $120

A SHORT Plea for Human Nature and Common Sense. Dublin, 1787. 8vo., unbound, dust soiled, 1st ed. Morrill 241-165 1978 $10

SHORTER, CLEMENT KING   George Borrow and His Circle. Boston, 1813. Illus. Baldwins' 51-329 1978 $8.50

SHORTER, DORA (SIGERSON) Verses. 1893. 1st ed., very good, octavo bound in cloth. Hyland 128-522 1978 £12.50

SHORTHOUSE, JOSEPH HENRY   Blanche, Lady Falaise. London, 1891. First ed., cloth binding, very good cond. Greene 78-279 1978 $35

SHORTHOUSE, JOSEPH HENRY   Sir Percival, A Story of the Past and of the Present. London, 1836. 1st ed., orig. salmon colored cloth, very good. Greene 78-107 1978 $35

SHORTT, ADAM   Documents Relating to Canadian Currency, Ex-change and Finance During the French Period. Ottawa, 1925. 2 vols., card covers. Hood 116-357 1978 $45

SHOSKES, HENRY   No Traveler Returns. 1945. Austin 79-677 1978 $12.50

THE SHOSOIN: An Eighth Century Repository. Tokyo, n.d. Wrs., folded, foxed, somewhat worn. Dawson's 449-186 1978 $10

SHOTOVER Papers. Oxford, (1875). Sq. 8vo., orig. white buckram, soiled in cloth slipcase. George's 635-1480 1978 £15

SHOTWELL, J. T.   The See of Peter. 1927. Allen 234-1452 1978 $17.50

SHOVE, FREDEGOND   Daybreak. Hogarth Press, 1922. Patterned bds., good, only 250 copies printed, first English ed. Bell Book 17-457 1978 £25

SHOWERMAN, GRANT   Eternal Rome, the City & Its People from the Earliest Times. 1924. 2 vols., plt. Allen 234-830 1978 $10

SHPALL, LEO   The Jews in Louisiana. 1936. Paper. Austin 79-680 1978 $12.50

SHRIDHARANI, K.   My India My America. 1941. Austin 79-678 1978 $10

SHRINER, CHARLES A.   Paterson, N.J. Its Advantages for Manufacturing, Its Industries... Paterson, 1890. Lg. 4to., illus., very fine. MacManus 239-1324 1978 $35

SHRIVER, WILLIAM P.   Immigrant Forces. 1913. Photos. Austin 79-679 1978 $10

SHRYOCK, RICHARD HARRISON   The Development of Modern Medicine. New York, 1947. First Borzoi ed., d.j. Rittenhouse 49-725 1976 $17.50

SHUB, D.   The Jewish World Almanac 1927. New York, 1927. In Yiddish. Austin 79-371 1978 $17.50

SHUCKBURGH, E. S.   Augustus, Life & Times of the Founder of the Roman Empire. 1905. Top of spine slightly torn. Allen 234-75 1978 $8

SHUEY, AUDREY M.   Personality Traits of Jewish and Non-Jewish Stu-dents. 1944. #290, paper. Austin 79-681 1978 $27.50

SHUGG, ROGER W.   Origins of Class Struggle in Louisiana. Baton Rouge, 1939. Bell Wiley's copy. Broadfoot's 44-888 1978 $12.00

SHUMARD, BENJAMIN F.   Report on the Chouteau League Tract;.... St. Louis, 1873. Plts., maps, orig. front pr. wr., 1st ed. Ginsberg 14-600 1978 $100

SHURLEY-DIETRICH-ATKINS CO. LTD.   Saws, Saw Tools, Machine Knives and Files. Galt, 1950. Card cover, illus. Hood 116-358 1978 $15

SHURREFF, JAFFUR   Qanoon-E-Islam, Or, The Customs of the Moosul-mans of India... London, 1832. 1st. English ed., 8vo, engraved frontispiece, lithograph plts., contemporary polished calf, gilt & blind-stamped borders, neatly rebacked retaining orig. backstrip, gilt, morocco label. Deighton 5-93 1978 £85

SHURROCKS, A. A.   Indian Artifacts Collected on Nantucket. Cape Cod 22-170 1978 $9

SHURTER, EDWIN D.   Woman Suffrage: Bibliography and Selected Argu-ments. Austin, 1915. Very fine. Jenkins 116-1497 1978 $18.50

SHURTLEFF, NATHANIEL B.   A Topographical and Historical Description of Boston. Boston, 1871. Tall 8vo., 1st ed. Morrill 239-516 1978 $25

SHUTE, HENRY A.   The Real Diary of a Real Boy. Boston, 1902. Tall 16mo., 3rd ed, 1903, orig. bind. Petrilla 13-109 1978 $7.50

SIAM; Nature and Industry. Bangkok, 1930. Large 8vo, cloth, maps, plans, plts. Van der Peet 127-219 1978 Dfl 65

SICKELS, IVIN   Exercises in Wood-Working. New York, 1890. 8vo., ex-lib. Morrill 239-609 1978 $10

SIDDONS, SARAH   The Story of Our First Parents Selected from Milton's Paradise Lost. London, 1822. Abridged, 8vo, papered boards, original spine label, spine with cracks, and a chip, very good, scarce. Victoria 34-733 1978 $40

SIDELL, W. H.   Report of the Secretary of War Communicating... W. H. Sidell's Survey of a Route for a Railroad from the Great Bend River, to Providence, on the Mississippi River. Washington, 1851. Disbound. Ginsberg 14-512 1978 $20

SIDNEY, ALGERNON 1622-83 Discourses Concerning Government. 1698. First ed., folio, contemp. panelled calf, minor damp stain throughout. Howes 194-97 1978 £65

SIDNEY, PHILIP   Astrophel & Stella. (London), 1931. 8vo, decor. boards, inner matching wr., slipcase, 1 of 1200 copies printed on handmade paper, fine. Duschnes 220-219 1978 $50

SIDNEY, PHILIP   The Countesse of Pembrokes Arcadia. 1638. Folio, title within woodcut border, lacks initial blank leaf, contemp. calf, rebacked, faint water-stains throughout. Hannas 54-308 1978 £85

SIEBERT, WILBUR HENRY   The Flight of American Loyalists to the British Isles. Columbus, 1911. Card cover, some underlining. Hood 116-654 1978 $22.50

SIEBERT, WILBUR HENRY   Kentucky's Struggle with Its Loyalist Proprietors. Columbus, 1920. Card cover. Hood 116-655 1978 $20

SIEBERT, WILBUR HENRY   The Tory Proprietors of Kentucky Lands. Colum-bus, 1919. Card cover. Hood 116-656 1978 $20

SIEBOLD, ALEXANDER FREIHERRN VON   Phillip Franz von Siebold's letzte Reise nach Japan, 1859-1962. Berlin, 1903. Illus., cloth, soiled and worn, hinges weak, lacking free endpapers, bookseller's sticker on t.p. Dawson's 449-187 1978 $25

SIEGENBEEK VAN HEUKELOM, DANIEL ELIZA   Recueil De Travaux, Anato-mo-Pathologiques du Laboratoire Boerhaave. 1888-1898. Leide, 1899. 2 vols., 8vo., plts., some in color, half grained lea., gilt, library initials stamped on spine, pencil underlinings, library stamps, very good copy, 1st collected ed. Zeitlin 245-237 1978 $75

SIENKIEWICZ, HENRYK   Dust and Ashes or Demolished. New York, (1899). Cloth. Hayman 73-676 1978 $7.50

SIENKIEWICZ, HENRYK   "Quo Vadis". Boston, 1897. 1st Amer. ed., rubbed, very good. Victoria 34-734 1978 $15

SIGAUD DE LA FOND, JOSEPH-AIGNAN   Precis Historique et Experimental des Phenomenes Electriques. Paris, 1785. 8vo., fldg. plts., contemp. calf, rubbed, very good copy, contemp. signature on title, 2nd & best ed., revised & with additional plt. Norman 5-258 1978 $275

SIGERSON, DORA
Please turn to
SHORTER, DORA SIGERSON

SIGNAL Fires on the Trail of the Pathfinder. New York, 1856. 12mo., 1st ed., orig. cloth. Morrill 241-658 1978 $17.50

SIGOURNEY, LYDIA HOWARD   Gleanings. Hartford, 1860. First ed., 8vo., inscription by author, upper cover almost loose. Victoria 34-735 1978 $22.50

SIGOURNEY, LYDIA HUNTLEY   Moral Pieces in Prose and Verse. Hartford, 1815. First ed., printed bds., text almost fine. Victoria 34-736 1978 $40

SIGSBY, WILLIAM   Life and Adventures of Timothy Murphy. 1893. 18mo., wr., covers torn & patched with tape. Butterfield 21-407 1978 $15

SIGSBY, WILLIAM   Life and Adventures of Timothy Murphy, the Benefactor of Schoharie. 1912. Plts., ads, stiff wr. Butterfield 21-408 1978 $17.50

SIKES, J. G.   Peter Abailard. Cambridge, 1932. 8vo. Upcroft 12-405 1978 £8.50

SILCOX, C. E.   Church Union in Canada; Its Causes and Consequences. New York, 1933. 1st ed. Hood 116-319 1978 $40

THE SILENT Dormitory. New York, 1887. Author's presentation. Biblo 247-494 1978 $15

SILIUS ITALICUS, CAIUS   The Second Punick War Between Hannibal and the Romanes. London, 1661. First ed., plts., folio, newly rebound in qtr. calf antique style, some stains. Howes 194-92 1978 £50

SILL, EDWARD ROWLAND   Hermione and Other Poems. Boston, (1899). 1st ed., bkplt. Biblo 251-633 1978 $9.50

SILLARD, R.M.   Barry Sullivan & His Contemporaries; A Histrionic Record. 1901. 1st ed., 2 vols., illus., good, octavo bound in cloth. Hyland 128-588 1978 £10

SILLIMAN, BENJAMIN   A Description of the Recently Discovered Petroleum Region in California. New York, 1855. 8vo, original tan printed wr., fine copy, rare and important piece, folding plan. Ximenes 47-283 1978 $450

SILLIMAN, BENJAMIN   Professor Silliman's Report Upon the Oil Property of the Pacific Coast Petroleum Company, of New-York,.... New York, 1865. 8vo, original pink glazed we., 1st ed., colored map, slight oxidation of wr., very fine, very rare. Ximenes 47-289 1978 $600

SILLIMAN, BENJAMIN   Remarks Made on a Short Tour Between Hartford and Quebec, in the Autumn of 1819. New Haven, 1820. Modern cloth, damp stains internally, engrav. views crudely hand-coloured. Wolfe 39-507 1978 $65

SILLIMAN, BENJAMIN   Tour to Quebec, in the Autumn of 1819. London, 1822. 2nd ed., rebound in black cloth, gold stamping, engrs. Hood 117-597 1978 $90

SILLIMAN, BENJAMIN   United Reese River Silver Mining Company, Mines Located in Austin, Lander County..... Boston, 1865. Orig. front pr. wr., printed for private distribution, 1st ed. Ginsberg 14-742 1978 $100

SILONE, IGNAZIO   Bread and Wine. New York, 1937. 1st Amer. ed. Biblo 251-634 1978 $8.50

SILONE, IGNAZIO   Mr. Aristotle. New York, (1935). 1st Amer. ed. Biblo 251-635 1978 $8.50

SILTZER, FRANK   The Story of British Sporting Prints. (c. 1925). Coloured illus., orig. cloth, rubbed. George's 635-55 1978 £45

SILVER, ROLLO G.   The Boston Book Trade 1800-1825. New York, 1949. Printed wrappers, very fine. Victoria 34-737 1978 $20

SILVER Mines of Nevada. New York, 1865. Folding map, orig. pr. wr. Ginsberg 14-743 1978 $150

SILVER Mines of Virginia and Austin, Nevada. Boston, 1865. Orig. pr. wr., 1st ed. Ginsberg 14-744 1978 $150

SILVERSTRE, PAUL JOSEPH   Cavalry in Action in the Wars of the Future. 1905. 1st. ed. in English, lg. folding map, 8vo, orig. cloth, gilt, few neat pencil notes, very good copy. Fenning 32-302 1978 £16

SILVESTRE, A.   Les Tocasson. Paris, 1883. Sm. 4to., pict. cloth, colored caricatural plts. by R. Tinant, loose in binding. Van der Peet H-64-284 1978 Dfl 55

SIMAK, CLIFFORD   Cosmic Engineers. New York, (1950). Fine. Bernard 5-419 1978 $17.50

SIMCOE COUNTY PIONEER AND HISTORICAL SOCIETY   Pioneer Papers:... Barrie, 1908-1917. Nos. 1-6, bound in 1 vol., 1st ed. Hood 116-780 1978 $60

SIMES, THOMAS   The Military Guide for Young Officers. 1776. Thick 8vo., sprinkled calf, mor. label. F. Edwards 1013-596 1978 £110

SIMKIN, RICHARD   The Boy's Book of British Battles from 1704 to 1882. (1889). Coloured plts., illus., oblong 8vo., orig. stiff paper covers. F. Edwards 1013-424 1978 £45

SIMKINS, FRANCIS BUTLER   Pitchfork Ben Tillman. Baton Rouge, 1944. Pres copy from author to Wiley, Bell Wiley's copy. Broadfoot's 44-938 1978 $12.00

SIMKINS, FRANCIS BUTLER   South Carolina During Reconstruction. Chapel Hill, 1932. Illus., pres. copy from author to Bell Wiley. Broadfoot's 44-612 1978 $36

SIMKINS, FRANCIS BUTLER   The South Old and New. New York, 1947. Illus., pres. copy from author to Bell Wiley. Broadfoot's 44-764 1978 $8

SIMKINS, FRANCIS BUTLER   The Tillman Movement in South Carolina. Durham, 1926. Pres copy from author, ex libris, cover stained, Bell Wiley's copy. Broadfoot's 44-939 1978 $12.00

SIMMENDINGER, ULRICH   True and Authentic Register of Persons...Who in the Year 1709, Under the Wonderful Providences of the Lord Journeyed from Germany to America. 1930-35. Index, prtd. in German, wrs., very good. Butterfield 21-277g 1978 $7.50

SIMMONS, ERNEST   Pushkin. 1937. Orig. ed., plts., lg. 8vo., orig. cloth, cover trifle dust-soiled. Howes 194-1110 1978 £6

SIMMONS, JOHN   An Account of a Simple, Easy and Effectual Method for Preserving His Majesty's Navy. 1774. 4to., contemp. wrappers, signed by author. F. Edwards 1013-203 1978 £60

SIMMS, FREDERICK WALTER   Practical Tunnelling. London, 1877. 3rd ed., illus., fldg. plts., 4to. Morrill 241-535 1978 $32.50

SIMMS, HENRY H.   Life of Robert M. T. Hunter. Richmond, 1935. Bell Wiley's copy. Broadfoot's 44-339 1978 $30.00

SIMMS, JEPTHA ROOT   History of Schoharie County, and Border Wars of New York. Albany, 1845. Illus. with engrs., facsimiles, 1st ed., publisher's calf, fine bright copy. Butterfield 21-416 1978 $90

SIMMS, JEPTHA ROOT   History of Schoharie County, and Border Wars of New York. Albany, 1845. Calf bind., rubbed, foxed, fair. Biblo BL781-178 1978 $27.50

SIMMS, JEPTHA ROOT   Trappers of New York, or a Biography of Nicholas Stoner & Nationel Foster. Albany, 1871. Plts., orig. gilt-stamped cloth, little faded & rubbed, completely sound, sm. private bkplt., inscr'd in pencil on blank fly. Butterfield 21-417 1978 $45

SIMMS, P. MARION   The Bible in America, Versions That Have Played Their Part in the Making of the Republic. 1936. Illus., good. Nestler Rare 78-28 1978 $12

SIMMS, WILLIAM GILMORE   Egeria or Voices of Thought and Counsel.... Philadelphia, 1853. First ed., very good. Austin 82-852 1978 $27.50

SIMMS, WILLIAM GILMORE   The Life of Nathanael Green. Major-General in the Army of the Revolution. New York, n.d.(c.1849). Eng. frontis., illus., orig. cloth, spine decor. in gilt, covers blocked in blind, very good. Greene 78-332 1978 $75

SIMMS, WILLIAM GILMORE   The Life of the Chevalier Bayard. New York, 1847. Illus., orig. cloth, interior foxing, contemp. inscrip., good. Greene 78-331 1978 $65

SIMMS, WILLIAM GILMORE   Marie de Berniere: A Tale of the Crescent City. Philadelphia, 1853. Orig. cloth, 1st ed., covers worn, foxed, bookplt. removed. MacManus 238-574 1978 $60

SIMMS, WILLIAM GILMORE   The Partisan.   New York, n.d. (1880's?). New & rev. ed., cloth, later ed. Hayman 73-205 1978 $7.50

SIMMS, WILLIAM GILMORE   Richard Hurdis: or, the Avenger of Blood. Philadelphia, 1833. 2 vols., 12mo, early purple half calf, gilt, spines gilt, 1st ed., bookplates of a seminary library, fine and attractive copy. Ximenes 47-290 1978 $275

SIMMS, WILLIAM GILMORE   Southward Ho! A Spell of Sunshine. New York, n.d. (1880's?). Later ed., cloth. Hayman 73-206 1978 $7.50

SIMMS, WILLIAM GILMORE   The Yemassee: A Romance of Carolina. Atlanta, ND. Hinges cracked, cover stained, Bell Wiley's copy. Broadfoot's 1978 44-940 $7.00

SIMON, CHARLES E.   The De Lamar Lectures 1926-27 of the School of Hygiene and Public Health, John Hopkins Univ. 1928. Austin 80-946 1978 $17.50

SIMON, GUSTAV   Mittheilungen aus der Chirurgischen Klinik des Rostocker Krankenhauses Wahrend der Jahre 1861-1865. Prag, 1869. 2 parts in 1 vol., woodcut plts., illus., 8vo., contemp. gilt & decor. cloth. Offenbacher 30-142 1978 $175

SIMON, J.   Essay on Irish Coins..with Mr. Snellings Supplement, also, an Additional Plate Containing 19 Coins Never Before Published. Dublin, 1810. Original boards, plts., worm traces on inside margins, spine worn, good, reprint. Hyland 128-528 1978 £45

SIMON, JOHN   English Sanitary Institutions...   London, Paris, New York & Melbourne, 1890. 8vo., orig. cloth, gilt on spine, bkplt. & library stamps, good copy, 1st ed. Zeitlin 245-313 1978 $250

SIMON, JOHN   English Sanitary Institutions, Reviewed in Their Course of Development and in Some of Their Political and Social Relations. London, 1897. 2nd ed., 8vo., orig. cloth. Gurney 75-99 1978 £25

SIMON, JOHN   Public Health Reports. London, 1887. 2 vols., 8vo., portrs., orig. cloth, gilt on spines, foxing, bkplts. & library stamps, very good copy, pres. inscr., 1st ed. Zeitlin 245-314 1978 $375

SIMON, OLIVER   Printing of Today. 1928. Reproductions, folio, covers rubbed and a little stained. George's 635-1222 1978 £30

SIMOND, LOUIS   Journal of a Tour and Residence in Great Britain, During the Years 1810 and 1811 by a French Traveller. Edinburgh, 1815. 2 vols., 1st ed., 8vo., aquatint plts., fldg. tables, contemp. old diced calf with blind & gilt decor. spines, interior fine. Current 24-191 1978 $210

SIMONDE DE SISMONDI, JEAN CHARLES LEONARD   Historical View of the Literature of the South of Europe. 1823. 4 vols., cont. calf, 8vo. Howes 194-1200 1978 £20

SIMONIN, LOUIS LAURENT   Le Monde Americain; Souvenirs de Mes Voyages aux Etats-Unis. Paris, 1876. Orig. pr. wr., 1st ed. Ginsberg 14-919 1978 $65

SIMONIN, LOUIS LAURENT   Les Pierres Esquisses Mineralogiques. Paris, 1869. Wood engravings, plts. in chromolithograph, maps printed in colour, roy. 8vo, leather spine, upper joint weak. Traylen 88-630 1978 £15

SIMONIN, LOUIS LAURENT   A Travers Les Etats-Unis de L'Atlantique au Pacifique. Paris, 1875. Orig. pr. wr., 1st ed. Ginsberg 14-920 1978 $85

SIMPKINSON, C.H.   Life & Times of William Laud, Arch-Bishop of Canterbury. 1894. 1st ed., good, octavo bound in cloth. Hyland 128-529 1978 £5

SIMPSON, BERTRAM L.   The Re-Shaping of the Far East. Macmillan, 1905. 1st ed., lg. folding map, plts., 2 vols., 8vo, orig. cloth, very good. Fenning 32-303 1978 £18.50

SIMPSON, C. R.   The History of Lincolnshire Regiment, 1914-18. 1931. Illus. by C. Simpson, roy. 8vo. George's 635-838 1978 £12.50

SIMPSON, FRANK EDWARD   Radium Therapy. St. Louis, 1922. Rittenhouse 49-731 1976 $15

SIMPSON, GEORGE   Narrative of a Journey round the World, during the Years 1841 and 1842. London, 1847. 1st ed., octavo, 2 vols., frontispiece portrait, original blind-stamped cloth, spines sun-faded. Bennett 20-240 1978 $450

SIMPSON, GEORGE   Narrative of a Voyage to California Ports in 1841-1842,.... San Francisco, 1930. Map, plate, orig. pr. stiff wr., limited to 250 copies pr. Ginsberg 14-922 1978 $75

SIMPSON, H. T.   Archaeologia Adelensis, or a History of the Parish of Adel, in the West Riding of Yorkshire... 1879. 8vo., frontis., plts., etchings by W. Lloyd Gerguson, orig. cloth, slightly worn. Quaritch 983-31 1978 $65

SIMPSON, HENRY   The Lives of Eminent Philadelphians, Now Deceased, Collected from Original and Authentic Sources. Philadelphia, 1859. Illus. with fine engrs., 1st ed., lg. 8vo., orig. cloth, very good. Americanist 103-70 1978 $30

SIMPSON, HENRY   The Lives of Eminent Philadelphians, Now Deceased. Philadelphia, 1859. Illus., lg. paper ed. MacManus 239-1629 1978 $50

SIMPSON, HENRY   The Lives of Eminent Philadelphians, Now Deceased. Philadelphia, 1859. Rebound. MacManus 239-1630 1978 $30

SIMPSON, J. Y.   Clinical Lectures on Diseases of Women. Philadelphia, 1863. Rittenhouse 49-732 1976 $25

SIMPSON, JAMES H.   ...Report of the Secretary of War, Communicating ...Captain Simpson's Report and Map of Wagon Road Routes in Utah Territory.... Washington, 1859. Large folding map, cloth, 1st ed. Ginsberg 14-923 1978 $125

SIMPSON, JAMES H.   Route from Fort Smith to Santa Fe.... Washington, 1850. Plates, folding map, disbound. Ginsberg 14-924 1978 $75

SIMPSON, JAMES YOUNG   Anaesthesia. Philadelphia, 1849. 8vo., orig. cloth, fine, rare, lib. stamp on title. Gurney 75-100 1978 £350

SIMPSON, T.   Narrative of the Discoveries on the North Coast of America... London, 1843. 1st. ed., 8vo, folding engraved maps, half calf, gilt back. Deighton 5-54 1978 £165

SIMPSON, T.   The Nature and Laws of Chance. London, 1740. 4to., contemp. half calf, rebacked. Quaritch 977-171 1978 $300

SIMPSON, WILLIAM   The Seat of War in the East. London, (1855). 1st series, acquatint plates, 1st ed., folio, 19th century cloth covers, coloured lithos., later maroon mor. spine, gilt lettering, rubbed, some spotting and staining mainly to the front and rear. Totteridge 29-97 1978 $1,000

SIMPSON, WILLIAM   The Seat of War in the East. 1855-56. Tinted litho plts., 2 vols. in 1, folio, contemp. red morocco, wide borders on sides gilt, some slight foxing. Edwards 1012-56 1978 £400

SIMPSON, WILLIAM   The Seat of War in the East. London, (1855-6). 2 vols. bound in 1, 1st ed., folio, contemp. maroon mor., gilt, some spotting and staining mainly to the first part, rebacked, tinted litho. plts. Totteridge 29-98 1978 $1,000

SIMPSON, WILLIAM JOHN   Report on Plague in the Gold Coast in 1908. London, 1909. Folio, plts., orig. blue prtd. bds. backed in buckram, very good copy, 1st ed. Zeitlin 245-238 1978 $35

SIMS, GEORGE R.   Ballads & Poems. London, (1883). 1st ed., good, a.e.g., decorative cloth. Limestone 9-267 1978 $15

SIMS, JOSEPH PATTERSON   Old Philadelphia Colonial Details. New York, 1914. Plts., folio, orig. prtd. bds., cloth back & corners, 1st ed. Morrill 241-460 1978 $27.50

SIMS, WILLIAM   Report of the Kansas State Board of Agriculture... Containing a Topographical Description of the State,... Topeka, 1884. Cloth, 1st ed. Ginsberg 14-462 1978 $65

SIMSAR, MUHAMMED AHMED   Oriental Manuscripts of the John Frederick Lewis Collection in the Free Library of Phila... Philadelphia, 1937. 8vo., orig. cloth, illus. MacManus 238-926 1978 $10

SINCLAIR, CATHERINE   Modern Accomplishments, or the March of Intellect.... NY, 1836. Fir. Am. Ed., cloth binding, damaged, designs blocked in blind, lacks end papers, generally foxed. Greene 78-280 1978 $30.00

SINCLAIR, CATHERINE   Modern Flirtations; or, A Month at Harrowgate. Edinburgh, n.d. (183-). 3 vols., second thousand, half titles, orig. purple/brown cloth, blocked in blind, fine copy. Jarndyce 16-1052 1978 £48

SINCLAIR, CATHERINE   Modern Society: or, the March of Intellect.
The Conclusion of Modern Accomplishments. NY, 1837. Fir. Am. Ed., cloth
binding w/very damaged spine, damp stain. Greene 78-281 1978 $30.00

SINCLAIR, CATHERINE   Scotland and the Scotch. Edinburgh, 1840.
8vo., rebound in bds. K Books 244-287 1978 £14

SINCLAIR, G.Q   Hortus Gramineus Woburnensis: Grasses & Plants.
England, 1824. Rebound, 8vo. Book Chest 17-345 1978 $55

SINCLAIR, GORDON   Bright Paths to Adventure. Toronto, 1947. Illus.
Hood 116-715 1978 $10

SINCLAIR, GORDON   Loose Among Devils. London, c. 1935. Illus.,
8vo, orig. cloth. K Books 239-446 1978 £5

SINCLAIR, JOHN   The Code of Health and Longevity. Edinburgh,
1807. 2nd ed. of vol. 1, 1st ed. of vols. 2-4, 4 vols., engrav. frontispieces,
good, rubbed half calf, 8vo. K Books 244-288 1978 £35

SINCLAIR, MAY   Mrs. & Mrs. Nevill Tyson. Edinburgh, 1898.
Orig. cloth, 1st ed., owner's bookplate, good. Greene 78-282 1978 $55

SINCLAIR, UPTON   The Brass Check. Pasadena, (1919?).
1st ed., orig. pr. wr., worn, very good or better. Limestone 9-268
1978 $30

SINCLAIR, UPTON   The Cry for Justice. New York, (1915). Illus.,
signed by Sinclair, d.w. Biblo 251-636 1978 $27.50

SINCLAIR, UPTON   The Goslings. Pasadena, (1924). 1st ed.
Biblo 251-637 1978 $17.50

SINCLAIR, UPTON   The Jungle. New York, 1906. 1st. ed., orig.
binding, clean. Hayman 71-697 1978 $12.50

SINCLAIR, UPTON   The Jungle. New York, 1906. 1st ed., 2nd
issue, spine faded, fr. inner hinge weak, otherwise good copy, scarce. Biblo
251-638 1978 $27.50

SINCLAIR, UPTON   The Jungle. New York, 1906. Decor. cloth,
signature inside front cover, fine & bright. Dawson's 447-275 1978 $25

SINCLAIR, UPTON   Oil! New York, 1927. 1st ed., edges rubbed.
Biblo 251-639 1978 $15

SINDING, PAUL C.   History of Scandinavia. 1866. 9th ed., fldg.
map. Austin 79-690 1978 $20

SINESIO, SECONDO   De Vita et Rebus Gestis Guilelmi II, Sicillae
Regis, Monregalensis Ecclesiae Fundatoris. 1769. Folio, vellum, vignette on title,
very good, text in double column, Latin and Italian. King 7-235 1978 £35

SINFULNESS of Maintaining Christian Fellowship with Slave-Holders. Edinburgh, 1847. 8vo., unbound, 1st ed. Morrill 241-536 1978 $25

SINGER, CHARLES   A Short History of Biology. Oxford, 1931. 8vo,
orig. cloth, illus., good. Sexton 7-207 1978 £6

SINGER, DOROTHEA WALEY   Catalogue of Latin and Vernacular Alchemical
Manuscripts in Great Britain and Ireland Dating From Before the XVI Century.
Brussels, 1928-31. 8vo, orig. wrappers, frontis, 3 vols. Traylen 88-65 1978
£18

SINGER, H. W.   Stories of the German Artists. London, 1911.
8vo., cloth, plts., some colored. Van der Peet H-64-201 1978 Dfl 35

SINGER, S. W.   Some Account of the Book Printed at Oxford in
MCCCCLXVII, Under the Title of Exposicio Sancti Jeronimi in Simbolo Aposto-
lorum in which is Examined Its Claim to be Considered the First Book Printed in
England. London, 1812. 1st ed., thin 8vo., bound in orig. brown bds., pages
uncut, illus., light & occas. foxing, interior fine, very scarce. Current 24-240
1978 $145

SINGLETON, ESTHER   Social New York Under the Georges 1714-1776.
New York, 1902. Illus., 1st ed. Butterfield 21-138 1978 $20

SINGLETON, ESTHER   The Story of the White House. New York, 1907.
2 vols., illus. MacManus 239-442 1978 $20

SINGLETON, OTHO R.   Texas Pacific Railroad. Washington, 1878.
Large folding map, orig. pr. wr., 1st ed. Ginsberg 14-972 1978 $45

THE SINGULAR Adventures of Two Hermits, Who Dwelt on the Pyrenean Mountains
Which Divide Spain from France. London, 1802. 1st ed., no covers, extracted
from a bound volume. Victoria 34-739 1978 $20

THE SINN Fein Rebellion Handbook, Easter, 1916. 1916. 2nd ed., wr., very
good. Hyland 128-531 1978 £12

SINTELAER, JOHN   The Scourge of Venus and Mercury... London,
1709. 8vo., frontis. engr. portr., fldg. engr. plt., contemp. calf, gilt rule,
rebacked, browning, stains, good copy from the library of Dr. Alfred M. Hellman, 2nd ed., very rare. Zeitlin 245-239 1978 $150

SIOUSSAT, ANNIE LEAKIN   Old Baltimore. New York, 1932. 18 illus.
Baldwins' 51-294 1978 $12.50

SIPE, C. HALE   Fort Ligonier and Its Times... Harrisburg, 1932.
Illus., fine. MacManus 239-1679 1978 $40

SIPE, C. HALE   Mount Vernon and the Washington Family.
Butler, 1929. Enlarged ed., illus., orig. cloth, fine. MacManus 239-502 1978
$7.50

SIPPL, LEOPOLD   Idea Sapientis, id est Philosophiae Morum
Pars Prima, Secunda and Tertia: Ethica, Theo-Politica and Oeconomica...
Vienna, 1746. 1 vol., frontis., plts., 8vo., contemp. calf, gilt-tooled. Sal-
loch 348-252 1978 $175

SIR Edward Burne-Jones. London, (1905). Plts., cloth backed bds., very good or
better. Limestone 9-45 1978 $18

SIR GAWAIN
Please turn to
GAWAIN AND THE GREEN KNIGHT

SIREN, O.   Chinese Sculpture from the Fifth to the Fourteenth
Century... 1925. 4 vols., 4to., plts., buckram, good copy. Quaritch 983-
32 1978 $840

SIRINGO, CHARLES A.   Riata and Spurs. Boston, 1927. 1st ed., 1st
issue. Jenkins 116-1245 1978 $75

SIRINGO, CHARLES A.   Riata and Spurs. Boston & New York, 1927.
Decor. fabricoid, 1st ed., illus., scarce, fine copy in orig. d.w., slipcase,
from the Allred Collection. Dykes 34-69 1978 $75

SIRINGO, CHARLES A.   Riata and Spurs. 1st ed., fine copy, minus the
d.w., slipcase. Dykes 34-70 1978 $65

SIRINGO, CHARLES A.   A Texas Cowboy. New York, (1950). Cloth,
illus., very good copy. Dykes 34-49 1978 $25

SIRR, H. C.   Ceylon and The Cingalese... 1850. Map,
plts., 2 vols., 8vo, rebacked. Edwards 1012-130 1978 £20

SISMONDI, JEAN CHARLES LEONARD DE
Please turn to
SIMONDE DE SISMONDI, JEAN CHARLES LEONARD

SISSON, C. J.   The Judicious Marriage of Mr. Hooker and the
Birth of 'The Laws of Ecclesiastical Polity'. Cambridge, 1940. Octavo, good.
Upcroft 10-539 1978 £8.50

SISSON, C. J.   Lost Plays of Shakespeare's Age. Cambridge,
1936. Illus., octavo, good. Upcroft 10-538 1978 £7

SISSON, C. J.   Thomas Lodge and Other Elizabethans. Cambridge, 1933. Plts., octavo, good. Upcroft 10-537 1978 £12

SISSON, JONATHAN   Second Letter to the Right Hon. Earl Grey....
1832. 1st. ed., corner of 2 leaves lacking affecting few letters, 8vo, unbound,
sewn as issued, uncut, inscribed by author. Fenning 32-304 1978 £9.50

SISSONS, C. B.   Bi-Lingual Schools in Canada. London, Toronto, 1917. Hood 117-964 1978 $30

SISSONS, C. B.   Egerton Ryerson; His Life and Letters. Toronto,
1937, 1947. 2 vols. Hood's 115-268 1978 $100

SITTERSON, JOSEPH CARLYLE   The Secession Movement in North Carolina.
Chapel Hill, 1939. Autographed by author, signed twice by Wiley, new cloth.
Broadfoot 50-359 1978 $15

SITTL, KARL   Archaeologie der Kunst, Nebst Einem Anhang Ueber die Antike Numismatik. 1895. New buckram, lacks atlas of illus. Allen 234-886 1978 $12.50

SITWELL, EDITH   Aspects of Modern Poetry. London, 1934. First ed., orig. binding, nice. Rota 211-620 1978 £9

SITWELL, EDITH   Bucolic Comedies. 1923. Sm. 8vo., lst ed., bds., back little darkened, trifle worn, bkplt. of Richard Hughes, pres. copy inscr. by author. Quaritch 979-362 1978 $110

SITWELL, EDITH   Bucolic Comedies. London, 1923. First ed., orig. binding, nice. Rota 211-617 1978 £25

SITWELL, EDITH   The Canticle of the Rose: Selected Poems, 1920-1947. London, 1949. 8vo, blue cloth, spine gilt, d.w. spine somewhat darkened, unusually Fine, six line inscription from author and two page a.l.s. from author to J.G. Wilson on stationery of Sesame Imperial and Pioneer Club laid in, lst ed. Desmarais 1-373 1978 $150

SITWELL, EDITH   Clown's Houses. Oxford, (1918). First ed., sq. 8vo., orig. decor. limp bds., printed label, nice, partly unopened. Howes 194-1201 1978 £28

SITWELL, EDITH   Facade. Kensington, 1922. 8vo, original red patterned boards (spine worn), printed paper side-label, lst ed., author's rarest and most significant books, privately printed, only 150 copies, numbered and signed, presentation copy, inscribed, laid-in A.l.s. from author. Ximenes 47-291 1978 $700

SITWELL, EDITH   Facade, poems. Kensington, Favil Press, 1922. Coloured frontispiece by G. Severini, one of 150 numbered copies, signed by the author, orange paper bds., first ed., spine worn, nice, very scarce. Rota 211-616 1978 £200

SITWELL, EDITH   Five Variations on a Theme. (London), 1933. First ed., 8vo., bds., fine, d.j., pres. copy, inscribed by author. Houle 10-293 1978 $95

SITWELL, EDITH   Gold Coast Customs. 1929. Near fine, d.w., first English ed. Bell Book 16-779 1978 £32.50

SITWELL, EDITH   I Live Under A Black Sun. New York, 1938. 8vo, green cloth, uncut, spine darkened, lst Amer. ed., very Nice, collector's cond. Desmarais 1-374 1978 $15

SITWELL, EDITH   The Pleasure of Poetry, Second Series. London, 1931. 8vo, orange cloth, gilt lettering on spine, d.w. spine sun-faded, Fine, 11 line inscription from Sitwell to John Hayward, lst ed., collector's cond. Desmarais 1-375 1978 $75

SITWELL, EDITH   The Pleasures of Poetry. 1932. 3rd series, very good, first English ed. Bell Book 16-780 1978 £6

SITWELL, EDITH   Poems New and Old. London, 1940. First ed. of this selection, very nice, orig. binding. Rota 211-621 1978 £6

SITWELL, EDITH   Popular Song; a poem. London, (1928). One of 500 numbered copies, signed by author, first ed., orig. binding, nice. Rota 211-619 1978 £15

SITWELL, EDITH   The Song of the Cold. 1945. Pres. copy inscribed by author, very good, first English ed. Bell Book 16-781 1978 £21

SITWELL, EDITH   The Song of the Cold. London, 1945. 8vo, black cloth, gilt lettering on spine, Fine in d.w., lst ed., collector's cond. Desmarais 1-376 1978 $12.50

SITWELL, EDITH   Wheels, 1920 (Fifth Cycle). 1928. Dec. bds., buckram spine. Eaton 45-459 1978 £9

SITWELL, OSBERT   All at Sea; a social tragedy. London, 1927. First ed., orig. binding, good. Rota 211-633 1978 £7.50

SITWELL, OSBERT   Argonaut and Juggernaut. 1919. Very good, first English ed. Bell Book 16-782 1978 £6.50

SITWELL, OSBERT   Argonaut and Juggernaut. London, 1919. 8vo, brown cloth, paper label, spine darkened and label worn, Nice copy, lst ed., 1 of 1,000 copies pr. with 4 line inscription by author, collector's cond. Desmarais 1-378 1978 $70

SITWELL, OSBERT   At the House of Mrs. Kinfoot. London, Favil Press, 1921. Drawings by William Roberts, one of 101 numbered copies, signed by author, wrappers, nice, first ed. Rota 211-624 1978 £75

SITWELL, OSBERT   Before the Bombardment. 1926. Pres. copy inscribed from author, covers faded, good, first English ed. Bell Book 16-783 1978 £8.50

SITWELL, OSBERT   Demos the Emperor: a secular oratorio. 1949. Pict. wraps, good, first English ed. Bell Book 16-785 1978 £4

SITWELL, OSBERT   Discursions on Travel, Art and Life. London, 1925. First ed., orig. binding, illus., good, scarce. Rota 211-626 1978 £9

SITWELL, OSBERT   Discursions on Travel, Art and Life. London, 1925. First ed., orig. binding, illus., nice, inscribed by author. Rota 211-627 1978 £25

SITWELL, OSBERT   Dumb Animal. London, 1930. 8vo, purple cloth, gilt lettering, partially unopened, unusually Fine bright copy, lst ed., inscribed. Desmarais 1-379 1978 $55

SITWELL, OSBERT   Dumb-Animal and other stories. London, 1930. First ed., orig. binding, spine faded, nice, inscribed by author. Rota 211-629 1978 £21

SITWELL, OSBERT   Left Hand, Right Hand! London, 1945-50. 8vo, 5 vols., red cloth, all in fine cond. except for Laughter with some soiling and fading of cover, lst 3 vols. in d.w.'s with tears and soiling, Good set, lst ed., collector's cond. Desmarais 1-380 1978 $65

SITWELL, OSBERT   The Man Who Lost Himself. London, 1929. Fine, d.w. rumpled & chipped. Desmarais B-586 1978 $15

SITWELL, OSBERT   Miracle on Sinai. London, 1933. First ed., orig. binding, spine a little soiled, nice. Rota 211-630 1978 £6

SITWELL, OSBERT   Noble Essences. Boston, 1950. lst Amer. ed., d.w. Biblo 251-640 1978 $13.50

SITWELL, OSBERT   Out of the Flame; poems. London, 1923. First ed., orig. binding, upper cover creased, nice. Rota 211-625 1978 £5

SITWELL, OSBERT   Penny Foolish, A Book of Tirades and Panegyrics. 1935. First ed., covers faded, 8vo. George's 635-1329 1978 £7.50

SITWELL, OSBERT   The People's Album of London Statues. 1928. First ed., illus., roy. 8vo., orig. white buckram, gilt top, other edges untrimmed, special ed. on hand made paper, signed by author and artist, ltd. to 116 copies only. Howes 194-1202 1978 £18

SITWELL, OSBERT   Victoriana; a symposium of Victorian wisdom. London, 1931. First ed., frontispiece in colour by Max Beerbohm, orig. binding, spine darkened, nice. Rota 211-632 1978 £12

SITWELL, OSBERT   The Winstonburg Line. 1919. lst. ed., 4to, orig. wrappers, covers little discoloured, corners slightly worn, otherwise very good, very scarce. Sawyer 298-49 1978 £45

SITWELL, SACHEVERELL   Conversation Pieces, a Survey of English Domestic Portraits and their Painters. 1936. Plts., some coloured, sm. 4to. George's 635-57 1978 £10

SITWELL, SACHEVERELL   Doctor Donne and Gargantua. 1930. First ed., slim roy. 8vo. George's 635-1330 1978 £5

SITWELL, SACHEVERELL   Exalt the Eglantine and other poems. London, 1926. Illus. by Thomas Lowinsky, one of 370 numbered copies, first ed., orig. binding, spine and covers faded, very nice. Rota 211-636 1978 £35

SITWELL, SACHEVERELL   Far from My Home. London, 1931. First ed., orig. binding, very nice. Rota 211-637 1978 £6

SITWELL, SACHEVERELL   The Hundred and One Harlequins; poems. London, 1922. First ed., orig. binding, spine darkened, nice. Rota 211-634 1978 £9

SITWELL, SACHEVERELL   The Hunters and the Hunted. New York, 1943. Very nice, d.w. somewhat chipped & worn. Desmarais B-587 1978 $12.50

SITWELL, SACHEVERELL   Primitive Scenes and Festivals. 1942. First ed., plts., orig. cloth, 8vo. Howes 194-1203 1978 £6

SITWELL, SACHEVERELL   The Thirteenth Caesar and other poems. London, 1924. First ed., orig. binding, spine darkened and covers rather marked, very good. Rota 211-635 1978 £5

SIX Mois chez les Sauvages par un Missionaire. Limoges (186-). Dec. cloth, 8vo., good. Paine 78-117 1978 $45.00

SIX Thousand Years of Bread. 1944. Illus. Austin 80-729 1978 $11

SIXTEENTH Annual Fair of the Tippecanoe County Agricultural Association... Lafayette, 1882. Wrs., some paper worn from spine. Hayman 72-366 1978 $12.50

SIXTY Five Years of History: A Church With A World Wide Influence-First Presbyterian Church, Berkeley, Ca., 1878-1943. (Berkeley, 1943). Orig. pr. wrps., lst ed. Ginsberg 16-836 1978 $7.50

SJODAHL, J. M.   Joseph Smith. Salt Lake City, 1891. Disbound. Ginsberg 14-685 1978 $17.50

SKEAT, W. W.   A Moeso-Gothic Glossary. London & Berlin, 1868. Sq. 8vo., scarce, orig. cloth. Howes 194-803 1978 $7.50

SKEEN, W.   Adam's Peak: Legendary, Traditional and Historic Notices of the Samanala and Sri-Pada... Colombo, 1870. Map, sq. 8vo, cloth sides, leather spine. Edwards 1012-131 1978 £20

SKELTON, JOHN   Charles I. London, 1898. Royal quarto, red mor. over cloth, gilt rules, orig. wr. and backstrips bound in, lst ed., engravings, hand colored frontis. Bennett 7-100 1978 $175

SKELTON, JOHN   Mary Stuart. London, 1898. Quarto, bound in quarter straight-grained red mor. and cloth boards, hand colored frontis., illus. Bennett 7-101 1978 $150

SKENE, ALEXANDER J. C.   Treatise on the Diseases of Women. New York, 1889. Cover worn in places, separating at hinge. Rittenhouse 49-733 1976 $12.50

SKENE, ALEXANDER J. C.   Treatise on the Diseases of Women. New York, 1895. 2nd ed., revised & enlarged, engrs., chromolithographs, 8vo., half lea. Morrill 239-234 1978 $10

SKENE, JOHN   The Lawes and Acts of Parliament Maid Be King James the First and His Successours. Esinburgh, 1597. Title surrounded by portraits, thick folio, old calf, covers loose, title page mounted & some staining on lst. few leaves. Traylen 88-475 1978 £30

SKETCHES Of Grange and Neighbourhood. Kendal, 1850. Frontis, plts., orig. green cloth, good. Jarndyce 16-262 1978 £12

SKETCHES of the Character and Writings of Eminent Living Surgeons and Physicians of Paris. Boston, 1831. Library stamp on title. Rittenhouse 49-57 1976 $75

SKIFF, FREDERICK WOODWARD   Adventures in Americana. Recollections of Forty Years Collecting Books, Furniture, China, Guns and Glass. Portland, 1935. 8vo., orig. cloth, ltd. to 800 no. copies, signed by author. MacManus 238-1052 1978 $10

SKILLMAN, W. D.   The Western Metropolis; or, St. Louis in 1846. St. Louis, 1846. Map, original cloth, lst ed. Ginsberg 14-601 1978 $300

SKINNER, CHARLES   Henrici's Molds, Yeasts and Actinomycetes. New York, 1947. Second ed., ex-library. Rittenhouse 49-734 1976 $10

SKINNER, L.   Politicians by Accident. 1946. lst ed., illus., good, octavo bound in cloth. Hyland 128-532 1978 $5

SKINNER, L.   Politicians by Accident. 1946. lst ed, signed pres. copy from author, 1/4 cloth, very good, illus. Hyland 128-533 1978 £9

SKINNER, STEPHEN   Dictionary, Etymologicon Linguae Anlicanae. 1671. lst ed., folio, orig. calf, spine gilt, red label, surface of bds. rubbed, good sound copy. Jarndyce 16-14 1978 £95

SKINNER, STEPHEN   Etymologicon Linguae Anglicanae... Londini, 1671. lst. ed., folio, lg. paper, contemp. calf, rebacked, lg. gilt arms of Tighe Family on covers. Hannas 54-198 1978 £100

SKINNER, THOMAS E.   Sermons, Addresses and Reminiscences. Raleigh, 1894. Cover stained. Broadfoot 50-202 1978 $30

SKIOLDEBRAND, A. F.   A Picturesque Journey to the North Cape. London, 1813. lst English ed., 8vo., fldg. map, orig. half calf binding, marbled bds., maps & plts. fine. Current 24-192 1978 $210

SKIPSEY, JOSEPH   Carols from the Coal-Fields. London, 1886. Cr. 8vo., a little dusty, orig. cloth. K Books 244-441 1978 £6

SKODA, JOSEPH   Abhandlung uber Perkussion und Auskultation. Vienna, 1839. 8 vo., very fine copy, rare lst ed., orig. printed, light green boards. Schafer 19-64 1978 sFr. 3,400

SKOMOROVSKY, BORIS   The Siege of Liningrad. 1944. Illus. Austin 80-298 1978 $8.50

SKOTTOWE, AUGUSTINE   The Life of Shakespeare... 1824. lst. ed., polished calf, black & green labels, spines gilt, slight scratch to one bd., otherwise v.g. Jarndyce 16-1044 1978 £22

SKUES, GEORGE EDWARD MAC KENZIE   Minor Tactics of the Chalk Stream and kindred subjects. 1914. 2nd ed., coloured frontis, 8vo. George's 635-1494 1978 £10.50

SKUES, GEORGE EDWARD MAC KENZIE   Nymph Fishing for Chalk Stream Trout. 1939. Coloured frontis, plts., 8vo. George's 635-1495 1978 £7.50

SKUES, GEORGE EDWARD MAC KENZIE   Side-Lines, Side-Lights and Reflections, Fugitive Papers of a Chalkstream Angler. 1932. Plts., 8vo. George's 635-1496 1978 £12.50

SKUES, GEORGE EDWARD MAC KENZIE   The Way of a Trout with a Fly and some Further Studies in Minor Tactics. 1935. 3rd ed., plts., 2 in colour, 8vo. George's 635-1497 1978 £10.50

SLACK, HENRY A.   Bird Notes from Farview. (Albany, 1901). Orig. illus., wr., thumbed, marginal drawings by author, #34 of 300 copies. Butterfield 21-43 1978 $15

SLADEN, DOUGLAS   More Queer Things about Japan. London, 1905. Rebound in cloth, (pages browned and foxed), illus. Dawson's 449-188 1978 $20

SLADE, F.   Catalogue of the Collection of Glass Making Formed by... 1871. Sm. folio, plain and coloured plts., woodcuts, half mor., rubbed, good copy. Quaritch 983-116 1978 $600

SLAFTER, CARLOS   A Record of Education. Dedham, 1905. 8vo., orig. cloth, binding rubbed & stained, lst ed. Morrill 241-351 1978 $10

SLARE, FREDERICK   Experiments and Observations upon Oriental and other Bezoar-Stones. London, 1715. 8vo., contemp. panelled sheep, first ed. Gurney 75-101 1978 £70

SLATE Pictures for the Instruction and Amusement of the Young. Troy, c.1840. Wrappers, wrappers taped, small corner chip, plates are fine. Victoria 34-740 1978 $27.50

SLATER, JOHN HERBERT   Book Collecting. London, 1892. Illus., orig. cloth, first ed., one of 500 lg. paper copies, rubbed. MacManus 238-1053 1978 $25

SLATER, JOHN HERBERT   Book Collecting. London, 1892. First ed., illus., orig. pict. cloth, v.g. Limestone 9-269 1978 $20

SLATER, JOHN HERBERT   Engravings and their Value. London, 1900. 2nd ed., cr. 8vo., gilt dec. spine. K Books 244-289 1978 £16

SLATER, JOHN HERBERT   Engravings and Their Value. 1921. 5th. ed., plts., illus., 8vo, orig. cloth, nice. Fenning 32-305 1978 £12.50

SLATER, JOHN HERBERT   The Library Manual. London, (1883). 1st ed., spine sunned, sm. hole in front free end sheet, very good or better. Limestone 9-270 1978 $21.50

SLATER, JOHN HERBERT   Round and About the Book-Stalls. London, 1891. 1st ed., orig. cloth, very good or better. Limestone 9-271 1978 $20

SLATTERY, CHARLES LEWIS   Felix Reville Brunot 1820-1898: A Civilian in the War for the Union: President of the First Board of Indian Commissioners. New York, 1901. Illus., original cloth, lst ed. Ginsberg 14-63 1978 $22.50

SLAVERY, as it Relates to the Negro, or African Race, Examined in the light of ...Holy Scriptures. Albany, 1843. Orig. cloth, rubbed but sound. Butterfield 21-72 1978 $25

SLEEMAN, W. H.   Rambles and Recollections of an Indian Official. 1844. lst. ed., 32 coloured plts., 2 vols., half green morocco, slight dampstaining of few plts., 8vo. Edwards 1012-111 1978 £60

SLEIDANUS, JOHANNES   De Quatuor Monarchils Libri Tres. London, Cambridge, 1686. 12mo., contemp. calf, joints slightly cracked. Howes 194-98 1978 £32

SLESSOR, JOHN   Strategy for the West. New York, 1954. lst. ed., 8vo, orig. cloth, pres. copy to Winston Churchill. Sawyer 298-109 1978 £135

SLEVOGT, MAX   Abenteuer. Berlin, 1923. Folio, publisher's 1/2 vellum portfolio, ltd. ed. issued in 150 numbered copies only, reproductions of watercolors by Slevogt, excellent. Goldschmidt 110-68 1978 $300

SLICK, SEWELL E.   William Trent and the West. Harrisburg, 1947. D.j. MacManus 239-1702 1978 $15

SLIDELL, JOHN   A Year in Spain. NY, 1830. Orig. half-cloth, boards w/paper labels, hinges broken, boards loose, contents good. Greene 78-283 1978 $25.00

SLOAN, JOHN   Gist of Art. New York, (1939). Illus., signed in pencil. Baldwins' 51-154 1978 $50

SLOANE, HANS   An Account of a most Efficacious Medicine for Soreness, Weakness, and Several Other Distempers of the Eyes. (?1750). 8vo., unbound, good. P. M. Hill 142-171 1978 £38

SLOANE, HANS   Catalogus Plantarum Quae in Insula Jamaica Spinte Proveniunt.... London, 1696. Sm. 8vo, old calf, newly rebacked, fine copy of rare work. Traylen 88-632 1978 £220

SLOSSON, ANNIE T.   Seven Dreamers. New York, 1891. Orig. binding, clean, covers slightly soiled. Hayman 71-239 1978 $7.50

SLOVER, JOHN   Indian Atrocities. Cincinnati, 1867. Unbound, one of 500 copies. Wolfe 39-246 1978 $90

SLYVESTER, JAMES JOSEPH   Spring's Debut. A Town Idyll. In Two Centuries of Continuous Thyme. (Baltimore), (1880). 8vo., orig. wrs., 1st ed., pres. copy, inscribed, fine. Howell 5-57 1978 $75

SMALL, HAROLD ADAMS   The Road to Richmond. Berkeley, 1939. Bell Wiley's copy. Broadfoot's 44-516 1978 $16

SMALL, HENRY BEAUMONT   The Canadian Handbook and Tourists' Guide... Montreal, 1866. Illus. with photos. Hood 117-599 1978 $60

SMALL, HENRY BEAUMONT   The Canadian Handbook and Tourist's Guide. Montreal, 1867. Orig. binding. Wolfe 39-438 1978 $50

SMALLEY, GEORGE W.   London Letters and Some Others. 1890. 1st. ed., 2 vols., half title, orig. cloth, good. Jarndyce 16-1054 1978 £10

SMALLMAN, H. F.   Diary of a Retired Official. Ajmer, 1915. Hood 117-331 1978 $7.50

SMALLRIDGE, GEORGE   Twelve Sermons on Several Occasions. Oxford, 1717. 1st. ed., orig. panelled calf, v.g. Jarndyce 16-197 1978 £12.50

SMART, BENJAMIN H.   Practical Logic: or Hints to Young Theme-Writers, for the Purpose of Leading Them to Think and Reason With Accuracy. 1823. 1st. ed., lg. 12mo, orig. bds., uncut, printed paper label, fine. Fenning 32-306 1978 £10.50

SMART, HARLEY   At Fault. London, (1897). New ed., 3 vols. in 1, pict. glazed board, "yellow-back" format, shows wear. Greene 78-108 1978 $40

SMART, THOMAS B.   The Bibliography of Matthew Arnold. London, 1892. Orig. cloth, 1st ed., bookplt. partially removed. MacManus 238-855 1978 $45

SMATHERS, GEORGE H.   The History of Land Titles in Western Carolina. Asheville, 1938. Fold. map, front flyleaf torn. Broadfoot 50-203 1978 $30

SMEATON, JOHN   Experimental Enquiry Concerning the Natural Powers of Wind and Water to Turn Mills and Other Machines. 1794. Royal 8vo., plts., rebound in half mor., uncut, first book ed. Quaritch 977-260 1978 $175

SMEATON, JOHN   A Narrative of the Building and a Description of the Construction of the Edystone Lighthouse With Stone. 1793. Second ed., royal folio, plts., contemp. half calf. Quaritch 977-259 1978 $750

SMEATON, JOHN   A Narrative of the Building and a Description of the Construction of the Edystone Lighthouse with Stone... 1793. 2nd ed., roy. folio, plts., contemp. half calf, 1st ed. appeared in 1731. Quaritch 983-369 1978 $915

SMEATON, OLIPHANT   The Medici and the Italian Renaissance. Edinburgh, 1901. Biblo 251-277 1978 $15

SMEDLEY, E.   Erin, A Geographical & Descriptive Poem. 1810. 1st ed., 2 parts, colored map, 4to, 1/4 leather, mostly unopened, very good. Hyland 128-534 1978 £40

SMEDLEY, FRANK E.   Frank Fairlegh. 1904. Plts. by George Cruikshank, new ed., 12mo., good, first English ed. Bell Book 16-482 1978 £4

SMEDES, SUSAN DABNEY   A Southern Planter. NY, 1914. Bell Wiley's copy. Broadfoot's 44-768 1978 $10.00

SMELLIE, WILLIAM   The Philosophy of Natural History. Edinburgh, 1790. 4to., contemp. sprinkled calf, very good, first ed. Howes 194-464 1978 £58

SMELLIE, WILLIAM   The Philosophy of Natural History. Edinburgh, 1790. Quarto, full early blond calf, Sir Michael Shaw Stewart's bookplate, 1st ed., very good. Bennett 7-102 1978 $175

SMELLIE, WILLIAM   A Set of Anatomical Tables, with Explanations, and an Abridgment, of the Practice of Midwifery... London, 1754. Royal folio, copperplts., modern half calf, marbled bds., gilt, lightly browned, marginal repairs, very good copy, rare 1st ed., only 100 copies. Zeitlin 245-240 1978 $1,750

SMELLIE, WILLIAM   A Set of Anatomical Tables. London, 1761. Royal folio, 2nd ed., plts., uncut, brown cloth fldr. with ties, very good copy from the library of Dr. Alfred M. Hellman, reprint, rare. Zeitlin 245-241 1978 $250

SMELT, LEONARD   The Speech of Leonard Smelt, Esq. York, 1780. 4to., disbound, 1st ed., very uncommon. Ximenes 47-2 1978 $100

SMET, PIERRE JEAN DE   Missien Van Den Oregon en Reizen Naar De Rotsbergen.... Gent, 1849. Illus., maps, plts., orig. front pr. wr. Ginsberg 14-812 1978 $100

SMET, PIERRE JEAN DE   Voyages dans L'Amerique Septentrionale. Brussels/Paris, 1874. Marbled bds., cloth back, engrav. frontis. port. Wolfe 39-510 1978 $36

SMETIUS, HENRICUS   Prosodia, quae Syllabarum Positione et Diphthongis carentium quantitates. Rouen, 1648. 18th cent. calf, some marginal damp-staining, 8vo. Howes 194-576 1978 £12.50

SMILES, SAMUEL   The Huguenots, their Settlements, Churches and Industries in England and Ireland. 1867. Stained, 8vo. George's 635-760 1978 £5.25

SMILES, SAMUEL   The Huguenots in England & Ireland. 1889. Very good, reprint, octavo bound in cloth. Hyland 128-535 1978 £9

SMILES, SAMUEL   Life & Labour... 1887. 1st. ed., half title, orig. maroon cloth, blocked in blind & gilt, v.g. Jarndyce 16-1056 1978 £12.50

SMILES, SAMUEL   Life of a Scotch Naturalist: Thomas Edward Associate of the Linnean Society. London, 1876. 1st. ed., portrait, illus. by George Reid, 8vo, orig. cloth, good. Sexton 7-208 1978 £7.50

SMILES, SAMUEL   Life of a Scotch Naturalist. New York, 1877. 1st Amer. ed., ex-lib., 8vo, orig. cloth. Book Chest 17-348 1978 $13.50

SMILES, SAMUEL   The Life of George Stephenson and of His Son Robert Stephenson... New York, 1868. Illus., fine. MacManus 239-443 1978 $20

SMILES, SAMUEL   A Publisher and his Friends, Memoir and Correspondence of John Murray. 1911. Portraits, cr. 8vo. George's 635-1216 1978 £5.25

SMILIN' Jack and the Escape from Death Rock. Racine, (1943). Edges rubbed, very good. Bernard 5-350 1978 $7.50

SMIRKE, ROBERT   Review of a Battalion of Infantry Including the Eighteen Manoeuvers. New York, 1811. 2nd. American from the 4th London ed., 8vo, orig. full calf, fine copy. Baldwins' 51-322 1978 $100

SMIT, D. H.   Johan Van Heemskerck, 1597-1656. Amsterdam, 1933. 8vo., orig. covers, lg. fldg. genealogical table, torn. Van der Peet H-64-388 1978 Dfl 45

SMITH, A.   On the Irish Coins of Edward 4th. 1840. 4 plts., R.I.A. Offprint, plain wr., good, reprint. Hyland 128-536 1978 £5

SMITH, A. DONALDSON   Through Unknown African Countries. London, 1897. 6 folding maps, plts., text-illus., roy. 8vo, orig. cloth, covers shabby, otherwise good. K Books 239-449 1978 £20

SMITH, ADAM   Essays on Philosophical Subjects. London, 1795. 4to., contemp. calf, rubbed, rebacked but fine copy, bkplt., 1st ed. Norman 5-*48 1978 $750

SMITH, ADAM   An Inquiry Into the Nature and Causes of the
Wealth of Nations. London, 1776. 1st. ed., 2 vols., 4to, half red morocco,
gilt tops, other edges uncut. Traylen 88-82 1978 £3650

SMITH, ADAM   An Inquiry Into the Nature and Causes of the
Wealth of Nations. Dublin, 1785. 4th. ed., 2 vols., 8vo, later half calf, gilt
spines, double labels, very good. Fenning 32-307 1978 £65

SMITH, ADAM   An Inquiry into the Nature and Causes of the
Wealth of Nations. London, 1793. 7th ed., 3 vols., 8vo., contemp. marbled
calf, labels, binds. rubbed, 1 hinge cracking. Salloch 348-253 1978 $60

SMITH, ADAM   An Inquiry into the Nature and Causes of the
Wealth of Nations. London, 1802. Tenth ed., 3 vols., contemp. calf, 8vo.
K Books 244-290 1978 £35

SMITH, ADAM   An Inquiry into the Nature and Causes of
the Wealth of Nations. Hartford, 1804. 2 vols., 2nd American ed., good
sound copies, orig. or contemp. calf over heavy bds., gilt-leather, vol. 1
lacks blank end sheet. Limestone 9-273 1978 $50

SMITH, ADAM   An Inquiry into the Nature and Causes of the
Wealth of Nations. 1811. 3 vols., orig. bds., entirely uncut, mainly unopened,
nice unpressed copy in orig. state, 8vo. Howes 194-465 1978 £45

SMITH, ADAM   An Inquiry into the Nature and Causes of the
Wealth of Nations... Edinburgh, 1863. New ed., thick 8vo., inner hinges split,
covers stained, good. Biblo BL781-877 1978 $16.50

SMITH, ALBERT RICHARD   The Adventures of Mr. Ledbury & His Friend Jack
Johnson. 1844. 1st. ed., 3 vols., frontis & illus. by John Leech, calf, gilt
borders & spines, brown labels, t.e.g., fine. Jarndyce 16-1057 1978 £70

SMITH, ALEXANDER   City Poems. Boston, 1858. 1st Amer. ed.,
spine torn, covers worn & stained, one signature sprung. Biblo 251-641 1978
$18.50

SMITH, ALFRED E.   Autobiography: Up to Now. 1929. Austin
79-695 1978 $7.50

SMITH, ALFRED E.   Progressive Democracy. 1928. Austin 79-696
1978 $8.50

SMITH, ALICE RAVENEL HUGER   The Dwelling Houses of Charleston. Philadelphia, 1917. 128 illus., ltd. ed., scarce. Baldwins' 51-532 1978 $90

SMITH, ALSON J.   The Christian Front. Ca. 1939. Illus., paper.
Austin 79-172 1978 $12.50

SMITH, ANN ELIZA (BRAINERD)   Atla: A Story of the Lost Island. NY, 1866.
Fir. Ed., orig. pict. cloth binding, good cond. Greene 78-284 1978 $60.00

SMITH, ARTHUR D. HOWDEN   Fighting the Turk in the Balkans. 1908. First
ed. Austin 82-857 1978 $27.50

SMITH, ARTHUR D. HOWDEN   Mr. House of Texas. New York, 1940. 1st ed.
Jenkins 116-665 1978 $8.50

SMITH, ARTHUR D. HOWDEN   Old Fuss and Feathers, the Life and Exploits of
Lt. Genl. Winfield Scott. New York, 1937. 1st ed., illus., d.j. MacManus
239-813 1978 $15

SMITH, ARTHUR H.   China in Convulsion. New York, 1901. 2 vols.,
illus., cloth, spines faded. Dawson's 449-77 1978 $60

SMITH, ASHBEL   Addresses at the Commencement Exercises of the
University of Texas, Delivered June 14, 1884. Austin, 1884. Original printed wr.,
rare. Jenkins 116-1246 1978 $35

SMITH, ASHBEL   Reminiscences of the Texas Republic. Galveston,
1876. 1/2 morocco, gilt, slipcased, exceedingly rare 1st ed., only 100 copies,
only about 50 copies released. Jenkins 116-1247 1978 $275

SMITH, BENJAMIN H.   Atlas of Delaware County. Philadelphia, 1880.
Folio, maps. Baldwins' 51-482 1978 $300

SMITH, BETTY   A Tree Grows in Brooklyn. New York, (1943).
1st ed., dust jacket, 8vo., A.L.s. loosely laid in, 1st issue, orig. green cloth,
paper spine label, fine. Current 24-51 1978 $95

SMITH, MRS. BURNETT   A Vexed Inheritance. Toronto, (1890). Orig.
cloth, 1st ed., good. Greene 78-289 1978 $15

SMITH, C. ALPHONSO   O. Henry Biography. New York, 1916. Broadfoot 50-304 1978 $10

SMITH, C. B.   First Annual Report of the State Historical Society
of Iowa. Des Moines, 1857. Half morocco, 1st ed., rare. Ginsberg 14-426 1978
$100

SMITH, C. C.   The Life and Work of Jacob Kenoly. Cincinnati, (1912). Cloth, title page little foxed, sm. & light dampstain at top of some
pages. Hayman 73-677 1978 $8.50

SMITH, C. ERNEST   Religion Under the Barons of Baltimore. Baltimore, 1899. Frontis. Austin 79-697 1978 $27.50

SMITH, C. HENRY   The Mennonites of America. Goshen, 1909.
Illus. MacManus 239-304 1978 $25

SMITH, CALEB B.   Fort Ridgely and South Pass Wagon Road. Washington, 1862. Disbound, 1st ed. Ginsberg 14-572 1978 $20

SMITH, CARROLL E.   Pioneer Times in the Onondaga Country.
Syracuse, 1904. Illus. Butterfield 21-324 1978 $45

SMITH, CHARLES   Antient & Present State of the County of Kerry.
1756. 1st ed., lacks map, plts., back cover loose, good, octavo bound in cloth.
Hyland 128-537 1978 £40

SMITH, CHARLES HAMILTON   The Ancient Costume of Great Britain and Ireland,
from the 7th to the 16th Century. 1848. Improved ed., folio, frontis., hand-
coloured plts., half mor., gilt spine. Quaritch 983-72 1978 $450

SMITH, CHARLES HAMILTON   Costume of the Army of the British Empire,
According to the Last Regulations, 1814... 1815. Color aquatint plts., half
calf, 4to. F. Edwards 1013-428 1978 £2750

SMITH, CHARLES W.   Pacific Northwest Americana. A Checklist of
Books and Pamphlets Relating to the History of the Pacific Northwest. New York,
1921. 8vo., orig. cloth, 2nd ed., rev'd. and enlarged. MacManus 238-1054
1978 $30

SMITH, CHARLES W.   Roger B. Taney: Jacksonian Jurist. Chapel Hill,
1936. Bell Wiley's copy. Broadfoot's 44-892 1978 $8.00

SMITH, D. E. HUGER   A Carolina Rice Plantation of the Fifties. New
York, 1936. 30 paintings in water color by Alice R. Huger, 4to. Baldwins' 51-
533 1978 $15

SMITH, DAVID EUGENE   A History of Japanese Mathematics. Chicago,
1914. Illus., 8vo., orig. cloth, 1st ed. Argosy Special-82 1978 $25

SMITH, DAVID EUGENE   A History of Japanese Mathematics. Chicago,
1914. Illus., cloth, spine faded. Dawson's 449-189 1978 $30

SMITH, E. BALDWIN   Early Christian Iconography and a School of Ivory
Carvers in Provence. Princeton, 1918. Sm. 4to., illus., shaken, rebinding copy.
Biblo 247-298 1978 $42.50

SMITH, E. BOYD   The Story of Noah's Ark. Boston, 1905. 1st ed.,
colored pictorial boards, almost fine copy, color plts. Victoria 34-742 1978 $60

SMITH, E. W.   The Ila-Speaking Peoples of Northern Rhodesia.
1920. 1st. ed., map, illus., 2 vols., modern half morocco, 8vo. Edwards 1012-
309 1978 £75

SMITH, E. WILLARD   With Fur Traders in Colorado, 1839-40: The
Journal of E. Willard Smith. N.P., n.d. Original wr., illus., one of 100
numbered copies signed by LeRoy Hafen. Ginsberg 14-273 1978 $12.50

SMITH, EDGAR C.   A Short History of Naval and Marine Engineering.
Cambridge, University Press, 1937. 8vo., illus., orig. cloth, gilt, very good
copy. Norman 5-205 1978 $40

SMITH, EDGAR FAHS   Old Chemistries. New York & London, 1927.
4to., orig. cloth, plts., gilt, fine copy, 1st ed. Norman 5-260 1978 $50

SMITH, EDGAR FAHS   Priestley in America, 1794-1804. Philadelphia,
(1920). Scarce, fine. MacManus 239-445 1978 $15

SMITH, EDGAR FAHS   Priestly In America 1794-1804. Philadelphia,
1920. 1st ed., small 8vo., orig. binding. Americanist 101-120 1978 $15

SMITH, EDWARD   William Cobbett, a Biography. 1878. 1st. ed.,
2 vols., frontis, half titles, orig. dark green cloth, black & gilt imprint, v.g.
Jarndyce 16-388 1978 £25

SMITH, EDWARD C.   History of Lewis County, West Virginia. Weston, 1920. Map. MacManus 239-1135 1978 $35

SMITH, EDWIN W.   The Golden Stool. London, 1926. Folding map, cr. 8vo, orig. cloth. K Books 239-450 1978 £6

SMITH, EGERTON   The Elysium of Animals; A Dream. 1836. 1st. ed., engraved frontis, plts. by George Cruikshank, half morocco, marbled bds., spine little worn. Jarndyce 16-1058 1978 £16

SMITH, ELDER A. J.   The Light of Other Days; Or, Passing Under the Rod. Dayton, 1878. Orig. binding, clean. Hayman 71-702 1978 $12.50

SMITH, ELIAS   The American Physician, and Family Assistant. Boston, 1826. 4 parts, lea., rebacked, free endpaper lacking in fr. Hayman 73-424 1978 $50

SMITH, ELIZABETH   Fragments in Prose and Verse by ... 1818. New ed., frontis, 1/2 calf, rubbed, bookplt. of Thomas Delves Broughton. Eaton 45-461 1978 £6

SMITH, ELLEN HART   Charles Carroll of Carrollton. Cambridge, 1942. Illus. MacManus 239-735 1978 $17.50

SMITH, ELLEN HART   Charles Carroll of Carrollton. Cambridge, 1942. Bell Wiley's copy. Broadfoot's 44-893 1978 $8.00

SMITH, ERNEST BRAMAH   English Farming and Why I Turned It Up. London, 1894. Stiff wrappers, first ed., nice, scarce. Rota 211-46 1978 £10

SMITH, ERNEST BRAMAH   Kai Lung's Golden Hour. London, 1924. 8vo, boards, cloth spine, leather labels, near Mint in d.w., 1 of 250 copies signed by author, 1st ed. Desmarais 1-51 1978 $30

SMITH, ERNEST BRAMAH   Max Carrados. London, (1914). 1st ed., red cloth, bookplate of Scott Cunningham, inscribed by Ellery Queen. Houle 10-43 1978 $175

SMITH, ERNEST BRAMAH   The Specimen Case. London, (1924). 1st ed., creased d.j., fine. Houle 10-44 1978 $55

SMITH, ERNEST BRAMAH   The Wallet of Kai Lung. London, 1900. 1st ed., 1st issue, green pictorial cloth stamped in yellow, white and black with design, ink signed by author, very good-fine. Houle 10-45 1978 $125

SMITH, ERNEST BRAMAH   The Wallet of Kai Lung. London, 1900. 1st ed., 1st issue, green pictorial cloth, good. Houle 10-46 1978 $45

SMITH, ETHAN   Two Sermons on One Subject. Windsor, 1805. 8vo, unbound, 1st ed. Morrill 241-537 1978 $10

SMITH, EUSTACE   Clinical Studies of Disease in Children. London, 1876. Prize calf binding, fine, 8vo. K Books 244-291 1978 £18

SMITH, F. BERKELEY   How Paris Amuses Itself. New York, 1903. 3rd ed., illus by author & others, pictorial cloth, fine. Limestone 9-274 1978 $15

SMITH, F. BERKELEY   Madame Mesange. Garden City, 1912. 1st ed., color frontis., pres. copy from author to Mrs. Samuel Page, very good or better, keepsake format, cloth. Limestone 9-275 1978 $20

SMITH, F. BERKELEY   Parisians Out of Doors. New York & London, 1905. Illus. by author & others, water-color frontis., 1st ed., pictorial cover, fine, pen & ink drawings. Limestone 9-276 1978 $15

SMITH, F. BERKELEY   The Real Latin Quarter. New York, 1901. Illus. by author, colored pictorial spine & upper cover, cloth, virtually new condition. Limestone 9-277 1978 $25

SMITH, FRANCIS HOPKINSON   Colonel Carter of Cartersville. Boston, 1891. Orig. binding, 1st issue of 1st ed., clean, private lib. bkplt., very good copy, slight rubbing. Hayman 71-241 1978 $25

SMITH, FRANCIS HOPKINSON   Colonel Carter of Cartersville. Boston, 1891. Illus., green cloth, 1st ed., 1st state, bkplt., good copy, lightly worn, few spots, protective green linen jacket. Bradley 49-299 1978 $50

SMITH, FRANCIS HOPKINSON   Colonel Carter's Christmas. New York, 1903. Cloth, 1st ed. Hayman 72-239 1978 $7.50

SMITH, FRANCIS HOPKINSON   The Fortunes of Oliver Horn. New York, 1902. Orig. binding, 1st ed., clean. Hayman 71-240 1978 $7.50

SMITH, FRANCIS HOPKINSON   Kennedy Square. New York, 1911. Cloth, 1st ed. Hayman 71-241 1978 $7.50

SMITH, FRANCIS HOPKINSON   Novels, Stories and Sketches. New York, 1904. Beacon ed., Vols. 1-20, 22 and 23, together 22 vols., cr. 8vo., spines faded. George's 635-1482 1978 £15

SMITH, FRANCIS HOPKINSON   Peter. A Novel of Which He is Not the Hero. New York, 1908. Cloth, 1st ed. Hayman 72-240 1978 $7.50

SMITH, FRANK   A History of Dedham. Dedham, 1936. Illus., 8vo., nice, 1st ed. Morrill 239-517 1978 $15

SMITH, GEORGE 1804-1882   History of Delaware County, Pa. Philadelphia, 1862. Maps, illus. MacManus 239-1439 1978 $50

SMITH, GEORGE BARNETT   Shelley A Critical Biography. Edinburgh, 1877. 1st. ed., half title, orig. dark green cloth, blocked in black & gilt, slight rubbing otherwise v.g. Jarndyce 16-1048 1978 £24

SMITH, GEORGE G.   The Life and Letters of James Osgood Andrew. Nashville, Tenn., 1882. Bell Wiley's copy. Broadfoot 46-568 1978 $12

SMITH, GEORGE G.   The Life and Times of George Foster Pierce, D. D., LL.D., Bishop of the Methodist Episcopal Church, South. Nashville, 1888. Portrs., 8vo., orig. cloth, 1st ed. Morrill 241-538 1978 $10

SMITH, GEORGE K.   The Insertion of the Capsular Ligament of the Hip Joint and Its Relation to Intra-Capsular Fracture. New York, 1862. Rittenhouse 49-737 1976 $10

SMITH, GERRIT   Abstract of the Argument..."Are the Christians of a Given Community the Church of Such Community?" Albany, 1847. Butterfield 21-418a 1978 $7.50

SMITH, GERRIT   Defends His Aid to John Brown and to Runaway Slaves in Upstate New York. New York, 1860. Butterfield 21-418c 1978 $15

SMITH, GERRIT   Speeches of Gerrit Smith in Congress 1853-'4. Washington, 1854. Butterfield 21-418f 1978 $12.50

SMITH, GERTRUDE   The Beautiful Story of Doris and Julie. New York, 1906. 1st ed., color plates, fine. Victoria 34-743 1978 $20

SMITH, GERTRUDE   The Boys of Marmiton Prairie. Boston, 1899. 1st ed., illus., almost fine. Victoria 34-744 1978 $10

SMITH, GOLDWIN   Essays on Questions of the Day. New York, 1897. 2nd ed., rev. Biblo 251-378 1978 $12.50

SMITH, GOLDWIN   Irish History and Character. 1861. 1st ed., good, octavo bound in cloth. Hyland 128-538 1978 £5

SMITH, GOLDWIN   Irish History and Irish Character. 1862. 2nd ed., good, octavo bound in cloth. Hyland 128-539 1978 £6

SMITH, GOLDWIN   Reminiscences. New York, 1910. Orig. binding, clean, minor spotting, sm. snag at top of spine. Hayman 71-703 1978 $7.50

SMITH, HANNAH WHITALL   John M. Whitall, The Story Of His Life. Philadelphia, 1879. 1st ed., portr., orig. binding, 8vo. Americanist 101-134 1978 $25

SMITH, HAROLD CLIFFORD   Jewellery. 1908. Plts., 4 coloured, illus., roy. 8vo, orig. cloth, gilt, t.e.g., nice. Fenning 32-309 1978 £14.50

SMITH, HARRY BACHE   First Nights & First Editions. Boston, 1931. Signed by author, illus., 1 of 260 numbered copies, t.e.g. Battery Park 1-485 1978 $75

SMITH, HARRY BACHE   A Sentimental Library. New York, 1914. T.e.g. Battery Park 1-484 1978 $150

SMITH, HENRY JUSTIN   Chicago, a Portrait. 1931. Illus., first ed., v.g.
Austin 82-932 1978 $27.50

SMITH, HENRY NASH   Virgin Land. Cambridge, 1950. First ed., fine,
d.w., illus. Biblo 247-265 1978 $17.50

SMITH, HENRY PERRY   History of Broome County. Syracuse, 1885.
4to., orig. gilt-stamped 1/2 lea. & cloth, all edges gilt. Butterfield 21-77 1978
$75

SMITH, HENRY PERRY   History of the City of Buffalo and Erie County...
Syracuse, 1884. 2 vols., fine, rebound. MacManus 239-1080 1978 $90

SMITH, HERBERT MAYNARD   Frank, Bishop of Zanzibar. London, 1926.
7 plts., name cut from end-paper, 8vo, orig. cloth. K Books 239-451 1978 £5

SMITH, HOMER W.   Kamongo. 1932. First ed. Austin 82-858 1978
$11

SMITH, HORACE   Brambletye House; or, Cavaliers and Roundheads.
1826. 1st. ed., 3 vols., lg. 12mo, contemp. half calf, rubbed, some stains.
Hannas 54-315 1978 £18

SMITH, HORACE   Brambletye House; or, Cavaliers and Roundheads.
Paris, 1826. 1st. continental ed., 3 vols., 12mo, orig. wrappers, paper labels,
uncut. Hannas 54-316 1978 £15

SMITH, HORACE   The Midsummer Medley for 1830. 1830. First
ed., 2 vols., 12mo, contemp. half calf. Howes 194-1209 1978 £30

SMITH, HORACE   Rejected Addresses: or The New Theatrum Poetarum. 1812. 1st. ed., half title, uncut, orig. marbled bds., paper spine, little
chipped, rare, orig. condition. Jarndyce 16-1060 1978 £58

SMITH, HORACE   Rejected Addresses: or The New Theatrum
Poetarum. London, 1812. 12mo, contemporary half calf, rebacked, spine gilt,
1st ed. Ximenes 47-295 1978 $70

SMITH, HORACE   Rejected Addresses. 1813. 12mo., half calf,
label missing. Howes 194-466 1978 £7.50

SMITH, HORACE   The Tor Hill. 1826. First ed., 3 vols., contemp. half green coarse-grained mor., 8vo. Howes 194-1208 1978 £32

SMITH, HORACE WEMYSS   Life and Correspondence of the Rev. William
Smith, D.D., First Provost of the College and Academy of Philadelphia. Phila-
delphia, 1879-80. 1st ed., 2 vols., illus., frontis., t.e.g., untrimmed, rebound.
MacManus 239-1680 1978 $40

SMITH, HUGH   Letters to Married Ladies. New York, 1827.
Sm. 8vo., orig. bds., cloth back, 1st Amer. ed. Morrill 239-235 1978 $47.50

SMITH, HUGH MC CORMICK   The fresh-water fishes of Siam; or Thailand.
Washington, 1945. Illus., plts, 8vo, orig. covers. Van der Peet 127-224
1978 Dfl 55

SMITH, MRS. J. GREGORY
Please turn to
SMITH, ANN ELIZA (BRAINERD)

SMITH, J. H.   An Authentic Narrative of the Causes Which
Led to the Death of Major Andre ... 1808. 1st. ed., map, portrait, plts., some
slight browning, sm. tear in title repaired, calf, 8vo. Edwards 1012-463 1978
£95

SMITH, JAMES EDWARD   Lachesis Lapponica, or a Tour in Lapland...
London, 1811. 2 vols., 1st ed., royal 8vo., ads, pen & ink sketches, endpapers,
orig. paper covered bds., uncut leaf edges, very nice copy, delicate & scarce
book. Current 24-193 1978 $235

SMITH, JAMES EDWARD   A Specimen of the Botany of New Holland.
London, 1793. Coloured engraved plts., half-title, 4to, orig. four paper parts as
issued, parts 1 & 2 in brown wrappers, paper label on part 1, parts 3 &4 blue
printed wrappers. Traylen 88-663 1978 £3300

SMITH, JAMES FRAZER   White Pillars. New York, 1941. 4to, illus. by
author. Baldwins' 51-534 1978 $15

SMITH, JAMES FRAZER   White Pillars. NY, 1941. Illus., Bell Wiley's
copy. Broadfoot's 44-769 1978 $14.00

SMITH, JAMES REUEL   Springs and Wells of Manhattan and the Bronx...
at the End of the Nineteenth Century. 1938. 4to., 1st ed., illus., photos.
Butterfield 21-546 1978 $8

SMITH, JOHN, DEALER IN PICTURES   A Catalogue Raisonne of the Works of
the Most Eminent Dutch, Flemish and French Painters. 1829-42. Plts., 9 vols.,
roy. 8vo., spines faded. George's 635-59 1978 £65

SMITH, JOHN 1580-1631   Advertisements for the Unexperienced Planters
of New England or Anywhere. Boston, 1865. Fine uncut copy, ltd. to 250
copies. MacManus 239-444 1978 $40

SMITH, JOHN 1580-1631   A Description of New England. Boston, 1865.
1st facsimile ed., 1 of 6 copies on India paper, 1 of 25 lg. quarto copies, fine,
full brown mor., gilt lettering on spine, scarce. Current Misc. 8-41 1978 $100

SMITH, JOHN 1580-1631   A True Relation of Virginia. Boston, 1866.
Lg. fold. map, orig. cloth, very good, ltd. to 250 copies. MacManus 239-1882
1978 $40

SMITH, JOHN 1618-1652   Select Discourses.... London, 1660. 1st ed.,
quarto, contemp. calf, armorial bookplate of John Hay, Marquis of Tweeddale
and Earl of Gifford. Bennett 20-194 1978 $175

SMITH, JOHN fl. 1633-1673   England's Improvement Reviv'd; Digested into
Six Books. (London), 1670. Lg. paper copy of 1st. ed., 4to, old calf, joints
repaired. Traylen 88-83 1978 £400

SMITH, JOHN 1747-1807   General View of the Agriculture of the County of
Argyll. Edinburgh, 1798. First ed., table, contemp. half calf, 8vo. Howes
194-133 1978 £30

SMITH, JOHN E.   Our County and Its People. Boston, 1890. Thick
tall 8vo., portrs., maps, half lea., very good. Butterfield 21-267 1978 $65

SMITH, JOHN GUTHRIE   Digest of the Law of Scotland relating to the
Poor. Edinburgh, 1859. Backstrip frayed, 8vo., orig. cloth. K Books 244-442
1978 £7

SMITH, JOHN JAY   Recollections of. Philadelphia, 1892. Fine,
illus., rebound. MacManus 239-1325 1978 $30

SMITH, JOHN THOMAS   A Book For A Rainy Day... 1845. 1st. ed.,
nice copy, orig. light blue cloth, trifle loose. Jarndyce 16-1061 1978 £28

SMITH, JOHN THOMAS   A Book For a Rainy Day. 1845. 2nd. ed.,
orig. green cloth, dulled. Jarndyce 16-1062 1978 £14

SMITH, JOHN THOMAS   Nollekens and His Times. Comprehending a Life
of that Celebrated Sculptor, and Memoirs of Several Contemporary Artists. 1829.
2nd. ed., 2 vols. extended to 4, 4to., ports., hand-coloured aquatints, half blue
mor. gilt. Quaritch 983-Addenda m 1978 $750

SMITH, JOHN THOMAS   Nollekens and His Times.... London, 1920.
Plts., 2 vols., 8vo. Traylen 88-396 1978 £15

SMITH, JOSEPH   Bibliotheca Anti-Quakeriana. London, 1873.
1st ed., very good, unopened. Austin 79-699 1978 $95

SMITH, JOSEPH   Bibliotheca Smithiana seu catalogus librorum D.
Josephi Smithii Angli per Cognomina Authorum dispositus. Venetiis, 1755. 2
parts in 1 vol., 1st ed., f'scap. 4to., contemp. vellum. Forster 130-228 1978
£220

SMITH, JOSEPH   The Doctrine and Covenants, of the Church of
Jesus Christ of Latter-Day Saints.... Salt Lake City, 1883. Clean, orig. binding,
former owner's name on title-page. Hayman 71-483 1978 $10

SMITH, JOSHUA HETT   An Authentic Narrative of the Causes Which Led
to the Death of Major John Andre...to Which is Added a Monodny on the death
of Maj. Andre, by Miss Seward. New York, 1809. 1st Amer. ed., port., rebound,
good. Nestler Rare 78-179 1978 $40

SMITH, JOSHUA TOULMIN   The Northmen in New England, or America in the Tenth Century. Boston, 1839. Maps, worn, stained and foxed, a mess but a readable copy, scarce. Biblo 247-45 1978 $20

SMITH, JULIA A.   Sunshine and Shade in Central Africa.   London, 1908. 12 plts., cr. 8vo, dec. cloth.   K Books 239-452 1978 £5

SMITH, JUSTIN H.   The Annexation of Texas. NY, 1941. Bell Wiley's copy. Broadfoot's 44-975 1978 $25.00

SMITH, JUSTIN H.   Our Struggle for the Fourteenth Colony; Canada and The American Revolution. New York, London, 1907. 2 vols., 315 illus., 23 maps. Hood's 115-616 1978 $75

SMITH, JUSTIN H.   The War with Mexico. New York, 1919. 2 vols. Jenkins 116-931 1978 $150

SMITH, L. H.   Bermuda's Oldest Inhabitants - Tales of Plant Life. England, 1950. 3rd ed., colored illus. by M. Middleton, 8vo, orig. cloth. Book Chest 17-352 1978 $15

SMITH, L. M.   Cluny in the Eleventh and Twelfth Centuries. 1930. Plts., 8vo. Upcroft 12-411 1978 £8.50

SMITH, L. M.   The Early History of the Monastery of Cluny. Oxford, 1920. 8vo. Upcroft 12-410 1978 £7.50

SMITH, LAWRENCE B.   Dude Ranches and Ponies. New York, 1936. Cloth, illus., 1st ed., fine copy inscr. by Irving Larom & autographed by author, d.w. Dykes 34-233 1978 $25

SMITH, LAWRENCE B.   Modern Shotgun Shooting. New York, 1935. 1st ed., illus., good, tattered d.j. Limestone 9-278 1978 $17.50

SMITH, LILLIAN   Killers of the Dream. New York, (1949). 1st ed. Biblo 251-642 1978 $7.50

SMITH, LILLIAN   Killers of the Dream. 1949. First ed., very good, d.j. Austin 82-859 1978 $20

SMITH, LOGAN PEARSALL   Unforgotten Years. London, 1949. 2nd printing, frontis., nice. Limestone 9-322 1978 $8

SMITH, LUCIUS E.   Heroes and Martyrs of the Modern Missionary Enterprise. Providence, 1856. Portrs., 8vo., 1st ed., orig. cloth. Morrill 241-539 1978 $15

SMITH, M.   Al-Ghazali the Mystic. 1944. 8vo. Upcroft 12-412 1978 £6.50

SMITH, NATHAN   Medical and Surgical Memoirs. Baltimore, 1831. Portr., plts., 8vo., contemp. calf, 1st ed. Morrill 239-236 1978 $87.50

SMITH, PAUL JORDON   Man With the Gold-Headed Cane. New York, (1943). 1 of 300 copies, 8 vo., patterned wrappers, stiff bds., fine, T.L.s. from author. Houle 10-294 1978 $30

SMITH, PHILIP H.   Legends of the Shawangunk and Its Environs... Pawling, 1887. 1st ed., 4to, illus., scarce. MacManus 239-349 1978 $45

SMITH, R.A.L.   Canterbury Cathedral Priory; a study in monastic administration. Cambridge, 1943. 8vo. Upcroft 12-413 1978 £8.50

SMITH, R. C.   Life, Incidents and Voyages of...Giving Interesting Notes of His Voyages Around the World,.... [Oakland], 1889. Orig. pr. wr., 1st ed. Ginsberg 14-929 1978 $50

SMITH, R. F.   Doniphan County, Kansas, History and Directory for 1868-1869 :.... [Wathena], 1868. Original cloth, 1st ed. Ginsberg 14-463 1978 $150

SMITH, RALPH D.   The History of Guilford, Connecticut, From Its First Settlement in 1639. Albany, 1877. Plts., unbound signatures, uncut & unopened, little dusty, good binding copy. Butterfield 21-291 1978 $15

SMITH, REED   South Carolina Ballads. Cambridge, 1928. Bell Wiley's copy. Broadfoot's 44-941 1978 $20

SMITH, RICHARD   A Tour of Four Great Rivers, the Hudson, Mohawk, Susquehanna and Delaware in 1769. New York, 1906. Plts., internally clean, uncut copy, ltd. to 780. Butterfield 21-419 1978 $25

SMITH, ROBERT   Speech of Mr..., of Illinois, on the Improvement of the Western Waters. Delivered in the House...January 17, 1844. N.P., n.d. Disbound. Hayman 72-678 1978 $7.50

SMITH, ROBERT 1689-1768   A Compleat System of Opticks in Four Books, Viz. Cambridge, 1738. First ed., quarto, 2 vols., plts., full cont. calf, v.f. Bennett 20-195 1978 $635

SMITH, ROBERT 1689-1768   A Compleat System of Opticks in Four Books, viz. a Popular, a Mathematical, a Mechanical, and a Philosophical Treatise. Cambridge, 1738. Fldg. copperplts., 4to., contemp. calf, 1st ed., fine set. Offenbacher 30-143 1978 $475

SMITH, ROBERT METCALF   The Shelley Legend. New York, 1945. 1st ed., frontis., illus., d.j., very good. Limestone 9-325 1978 $25

SMITH, ROSWELL C.   Smith's First Book in Geography. New York, 1846. 1st ed., sq. 12mo, engravings and maps in color, text foxed, pict. boards rubbed at edge, spine tips moderately worn. Victoria 34-745 1978 $25

SMITH, S. R.   The Story of the Wyoming Valley. Kingston, 1906. Illus., inscribed by author. MacManus 239-1682 1978 $10

SMITH, S. COMPTON   Chile Con Carne. New York, 1857. Ads, new cloth, rebound copy, plts. Hayman 73-680 1978 $20

SMITH, SAMUEL 1584-1662   The Admirable Convert. London, 1632. First ed., sm. 8vo., contemp. sheep, neatly rebacked, some damp-staining. Howes 194-99 1978 £20

SMITH, SAMUEL 1720-1776   History of the Province of Pennsylvania. Philadelphia, 1913. MacManus 239-1681 1978 $25

SMITH, SAMUEL B.   The Mark of the Beast, and the Renunciation of Popery. New York, 1835. 8th ed., wr., woodcut cartoon signed on cover. Butterfield 21-54 1978 $17.50

SMITH, SAMUEL STANHOPE   An Essay on the Causes of the Variety of Complexion and Figure in the Human Species to Which are Added Strictures on Lord Kaim's Discourse, on the Original Diversity of Mankind. Philadelphia, 1787. 8vo., contemp. wrs., unopened, red half mor. fldr., 1st ed. Offenbacher 30-144 1978 $250

SMITH, SAMUEL STANHOPE   An Essay on the Causes of the Variety of Complexion and Figure in the Human Species. New-Brunswick, 1810. 8vo., contemp. half shagreen, gilt on spine, lightly browned, foxed, good copy, author's pres. inscr. Zeitlin 245-242 1978 $150

SMITH, SAMUEL STANHOPE   Sermons. Newark, 1799. 8vo., contemp. calf. Morrill 241-540 1978 $27.50

SMITH, SIDNEY   The Matchless Couple; Shakespeare & Scott... n.d. (c.1865). 1st. ed., orig. red cloth, blocked in black & gilt, v.g. Jarndyce 16-1063 1978 £18.50

SMITH, SOLOMON FRANKLIN   Theatrical Management in the West and South for Thirty Years... New York, 1868. Illus., portr., cloth. Hayman 72-713 1978 $40

SMITH, STEVIE   Mother, What is Man? 1942. Very good, sl. worn d.w., first English ed. Bell Book 17-814 1978 £18.50

SMITH, STEVIE   Novel on Yellow Paper. 1936. Covers slightly soiled, else very good, first English ed. Bell Book 17-815 1978 £22.50

SMITH, SYLVANUS   Fisheries of Cape Ann. Gloucester, 1915. 1st ed., illus., orig. dec. cloth, fine. MacManus 239-285 1978 $15

SMITH, SYLVANUS   Fisheries of Cape Ann. Gloucester, 1915. Fine, orig. cloth, 8vo. Paine 78-118 1978 $35.00

SMITH, T. R.   Poetica Erotica...Rare and Curious Amatory Verse. New York, 1921. 3 vols., spines creased, 1st ed., #132 of 1,500 copies, orig. bind. Petrilla 13-112 1978 $27.50

SMITH, T. R.   Poetica Erotica.   New York, 1927. 1 of
1,250 copies, 1st ed., 8 vo., half cloth, uncut, 2 vols., very good. Houle
10-386 1978 $55

SMITH, T. R.   Poetica Erotica: A Collection of Rare and
Curious Amatory Verse. New York, (1949). Thick 8 vo., d.j., fine.
Houle 10-295 1978 $15

SMITH, THOMAS   Speech of Mr..., of Indiana, on the Improvement
of the Western Waters: Delivered in the House... January 17, 1844. Washington,
1844. Disbound. Hayman 72-677 1978 $8.50

SMITH, THOMAS 1513-1577   The Common-Wealth of England and the Manner
of Gouvernement Thereof. London, 1621. Black letter, printer's device on title
page, sm. 4to, half calf. Traylen 88-476 1978 £60

SMITH, WILLIAM 1728-1793   The History of the Province of New York, from
the First Discovery to the Year 1732. Philadelphia, 1792. Second ed., modern
buckram, title badly dampstained. Wolfe 39-511 1978 $85

SMITH, WILLIAM 1728-1793   Histoire de la Nouvelle-York, Depuis la Decouverte de Cette Province. Londres, 1767. 16mo., 1st ed. in French, contemp.
calf, raised bands, gilt panels on spine, worn but holding. Butterfield 21-420
1978 $65

SMITH, WILLIAM 1728-1793   History of New-York. Albany, 1814. Bds. &
backstrip worn, internally clean, uncut copy, complete ed. Butterfield 21-421
1978 $35

SMITH, WILLIAM 1813-1893   A Dictionary of Christian Antiquities, a Continuation of the Dictionary of the Bible. 1876. Cuts in text, 2 vols., ex-libris, 8vo.
George's 635-1130 1978 £10.50

SMITH, WILLIAM 1813-1893   A Dictionary of Christian Biography, Literature,
Sects and Doctrines, a Continuation of The Dictionary of the Bible. 1877. Vols.
1-3 (ex 4), 8vo. George's 635-1131 1978 £10.50

SMITH, WILLIAM 1813-1893   A Dictionary of the Bible, its Antiquities, Biography, Geography, and Natural History. 1863. Cuts in text, 3 vols., ex-libris,
8vo. George's 635-1129 1978 £15

SMITH, THOMAS E. V.   The City of New York in the Year of Washington's
Inauguration, 1789. New York, 1889. Fldg. map, 8vo., 1st ed. Morrill 239-
555 1978 $10

SMITH, THORNE   The Night Life of the Gods. 1934. Very good,
worn d.w., first English ed. Bell Book 17-816 1978 £10

SMITH, THORNE   Rain in the Doorway. New York, 1933. Illus.,
first ed. Biblo 247-624 1978 $17.50

SMITH, TRUMAN   An Examination of the Question of Anaesthesia
Arising on the Memorial of Charles Thomas Wells Presented to the United States
Senate. New York, 1858. 8vo., engr. portrs. laid in, orig. black stamped
cloth, library bkplt. & stamp, very good copy, pres. inscr. from author, rare.
Zeitlin 245-318 1978 $145

SMITH, TRUMAN   An Examination of the Question of Anaesthesia,
Arising on the Memorial of Charles Thomas Wells. New York, 1859. 8vo.,
orig. cloth, lea. back. Morrill 239-237 1978 $25

SMITH, TRUMAN   An Examination of the Question of Anesthesia,
Arising on the Memorial of Charles Thomas Wells. New York, 1859. Some wear
on spine. Rittenhouse 49-736 1976 $105

SMITH, TRUMAN   An Inquiry into the Origin of Modern Anaesthesia.
Hartford, 1867. Portr. of Horace Wells, 8vo., portion of covers & endleaves
dampstained, 1st ed. Morrill 239-238 1978 $35

SMITH, TRUMAN   An Inquiry into the Origin of Modern Anaesthesia.
Hartford, 1867. 8vo., portr., orig. cloth, gilt lettered, fine pres. copy, inscr'd
by author. Zeitlin 245-243 1978 $150

SMITH, TRUMAN   On the Bill to Admit California into the Union,
to Establish Territorial Government for Utah and New Mexico, Making Proposals
to Texas for the Establishment of its Western and Northern Boundaries. Washington,
1850. Jenkins 116-1261 1978 $45

SMITH, TRUMAN   Speech of Hon. T. Smith, of Connecticut, on
the Proposition of Hon. Mr. Douglas, of Illinois, to Authorize a Levy of Tonnage
Duties by the States for the Improvement of Rivers and Harbors. Washington,
n.d. (1852). Double columns, disbound. Hayman 73-626 1978 $8.50

SMITH, TUNSTALL   Richard Snowden Andrews. N.P., 1910.
Ex libris, cover soiled and worn, Bell Wiley's copy. Broadfoot's 44-518 1978
$14

SMITH, W. B.   On Wheels and How I Came There. New York,
1892. Cover worn & frayed, signature loose, Bell Wiley's copy. Broadfoot's
44-466 1978 $10

SMITH, W. E. L.   Episcopal Appointments and Patronage in the
Reign of Edward II; a study in the relations of church and state. Chicago, 1938.
Royal 8vo. Upcroft 12-414 1978 £9.50

SMITH, W. H.   Canada: Past, Present and Future, Being a Historical, Geographical, Geological and Statistical Account of Canada West.
Toronto, 1851. 2 vols., orig. black cloth binding with gold stamping on cover &
spine, spine edges slightly worn. Hood's 115-617 1978 $110

SMITH, W. H.   Canada: Past, Present and Future... Toronto,
(1852). 2 vols., roy. 8vo, orig. cloth, engraved title, vignette, maps. Edwards
1012-455 1978 £50

SMITH, W. J.   A Synopsis of the Origin and Progress of Architecture: to Which is Added, a Dictionary of General Terms. 1831. 8vo., plts.,
occasional foxing, orig. bds., cloth back. Quaritch 983-50 1978 $35

SMITH, W. L. G.   The Life and Times of Lewis Cass. New York,
1856. 1st ed., fine, orig. cloth. MacManus 239-736 1978 $45

SMITH, W. W.   The Story of a Dark Plot. Montreal, 1898.
Orig. binding. Wolfe 39-167 1978 $12.50

SMITH, WALLACE   Bessie Cotter. 1935. 1st. ed., banned book
when published. Eaton 45-462 1978 £5

SMITH, WALLACE   Garden of the Sun. Los Angeles, (1939).
Cloth, illus., 1st ed., fine, very scarce. Dykes 35-61 1978 $40

SMITH, WALTER C.   Selections from the poems of. Glasgow, 1893.
Full prize calf, 8vo. K Books 244-292 1978 £6

SMITH, WALTER G.   Brief History of the Louisiana Territory. St.
Louis, 1904. Orig. cloth. MacManus 239-446 1978 $10

SMITH, WILLIAM   Animaversions on the Speeches of Mr. Saurin &
Mr. Bushe... Dublin, 1800. 1st ed., plain wrs. Hyland 128-546 1978 $9

SMITH, WILLIAM   Letter to H. Grattan... Dublin, 1800. 1st ed.,
plain wrs. Hyland 128-544 1978 £10

SMITH, WILLIAM   Review of a Publication Entitled the Speech of the
Rt. Hon. John Foster..in a Letter. Dublin, 1799. 3rd ed., plain wrs. Hyland
128-545 1978 £5

SMITH, WILLIAM 1813-1893   Dictionary of Greek and Roman Antiquities.
London, 1842. Thick 8vo., half calf, wood eng. Van der Peet H-64-555 1978
Dfl70

SMITH, WILLIAM 1813-1893   Dictionary of Greek and Roman Biography and
Mythology. 1844. Wood engravings, 3 vols., binder's buckram. George's 635-
511 1978 £18

SMITH, WILLIAM 1813-1893   Dictionary of Greek and Roman Geography.
1870. Wood engravings, 2 vols., binder's buckram. George's 635-512 1978
£12.50

SMITH, WILLIAM CARLSON   Americans in the Making. 1939. Austin 79-
701 1978 $17.50

SMITH, WILLIAM HENRY   Bacon & Shakespeare... 1857. 1st. ed., orig.
green cloth, blocked in gilt & blind, v.g. Jarndyce 16-1065 1978 £14.50

SMITH MANUFACTURING COMPANY   "Dollars". (Chicago?, n.d. c.1900?). Wrps. Hayman 71-96 1978 $8.50

SMITH & Sheldon's Stove Directory, for 1857. Troy, 1857. 12th ed., plts., illus., 8vo., orig. wrs. Morrill 241-561 1978 $22.50

SMOLKA, H. P.   40,000 Against the Arctic; Russia's Polar Empire. New York, 1937. Illus. Hood 116-101 1978 $20

SMOLLETT, TOBIAS GEORGE   The Adventures of Peregrine Pickle. London, 1751. 1st. ed., 4 vols., sm. 8vo, old bds., cancel leaf L12 in vol. 3, new calf spines. Traylen 88-337 1978 £180

SMOLLETT, TOBIAS GEORGE   The Adventures of Peregrine Pickle. 1751. 1st. ed., 4 vols., 12mo, lacks final blank leaves in vols. 2 & 3, vol. 3 pg. 12 is a cancel & 2 pages are apparently inserted from another copy, contemp. calf, very worn, faint water-stains in vol. 4. Hannas 54-317 1978 £100

SMOLLETT, TOBIAS GEORGE   The Adventures of Peregrine Pickle. London, 1751. 4 vols., 12mo., 1st ed., contemp. calf, fine set, cloth slipcase. Quaritch 979-300 1978 $800

SMOLLETT, TOBIAS GEORGE   The Adventures of Peregrine Pickle...and Memoirs of a Lady of Quality. Harrisburg, 1807. 3 vols., orig. calf, a little rubbed. Americanist 102-108 1978 $20

SMOLLETT, TOBIAS GEORGE   The Expedition of Humphrey Clinker. London, 1671. 3 vols., contemp. calf, 19th century rebacking, some rubbing, 1st ed., contemp. bookplt. and signature of Thomas Tindal, very good set, quarter mor. slipcase. MacManus 238-143 1978 $475

SMOLLETT, TOBIAS GEORGE   The Expedition of Humphry Clinker. London, 1771. 2nd ed., 12mo., 3 vols., 3/4 tan calf with marbled bds. & endpapers, fine or better. Current 24-52 1978 $100

SMOLLETT, TOBIAS GEORGE   The History of England... London, 1848. 4 vols, new ed., full calf, mottled edges. Biblo 247-747 1978 $72.50

SMOLLETT, TOBIAS GEORGE   Novels. Boston, 1926. 1 of 500 numbered sets, large paper, illus. by George Cruikshank, large 8 vo., 3/4 green mor., t.e.g., gilt stamped backs, bookplates, 11 vols., fine. Houle 10-296 1978 $600

SMOLLETT, TOBIAS GEORGE   Peregrine Pickle. 1769. 4th. ed., 4 vols., orig. calf, spines gilt dec., red labels, handsome set, Earl of Hereford's bookplt. Jarndyce 16-199 1978 £38

SMOLLETT, TOBIAS GEORGE   The Regicide; or, James the First of Scotland. 1749. 1st. ed., 8vo, disbound. Hannas 54-318 1978 £140

SMOLLETT, TOBIAS GEORGE   Travels Through France and Italy. 1766. 1st. ed., 2 vols., 8vo, half-titles, modern mottled calf, gilt, old style. Hannas 54-319 1978 £120

SMOLLETT, TOBIAS GEORGE   Works. 1884. 6 vols., roy. 8vo., well prtd. on fine paper, portr., half brown levant mor., gilt panelled backs, gilt top, other edges uncut, fine set, ltd. to 500 copies. Quaritch 979-373 1978 $325

SMYTH, ALBERT H.   The Philadelphia Magazines and Their Contributors, 1741-1850. Philadelphia, 1892. Scarce. MacManus 239-1684 1978 $25

SMYTH, ALBERT H.   Writings of Benjamin Franklin. New York, 1907. 10 vols., fine, orig. cloth. MacManus 239-153 1978 $150

SMYTH, G. S.   First Letter to a Noble Lord on the Subject on the Union. Dublin, 1799. 2nd ed., plain wrs. Hyland 128-549 1978 £6

SMYTH, HENRY DE WOLF   A General Account of the Development of Methods of Using Atomic Energy for Military Purposes. (Washington, D. C.), 1945. 8vo., orig. prtd. wrs., very good copy, 1st published ed. Norman 5-261 1978 $575

SMYTH, HENRY DE WOLF   A General Account of the Development of the Methods of Using Atomic Energy for Military Purposes Under the Auspices of the United States Government 1940-1945. 1945. Paper. Austin 80-302 1978 $27.50

SMYTH, JAMES W.   History of the Catholic Church in Woonsocket and Vicinity, From the Celebration of the First Mass in 1828, to the Present Time. Woonsocket, 1903. Illus. with photos. Austin 79-702 1978 $47.50

SMYTH, JOHN FERDINAND DALZIEL   A Tour in the United States of America. London, 1784. 1st ed., 3/4 leather, marbled bds., stamp on t.p. of either vol., otherwise fine. Broadfoot 50-305a 1978 $425

SMYTH, JOHN FERDINAND DALZIEL   A Tour in the United States of America. London, 1784. 1st ed., 8vo., 2 vols., rebound in blue marbled bds. & 3/4 calf, gilt decorated spine, interior with some scattered light spotting, scarce. Current 24-194 1978 $675

SMYTH, JOHN FERDINAND DALZIEL   A Tour of the United States of America. Vol. I (only). London, 1784. Contemp. calf. Wolfe 39-512 1978 $100

SMYTH, JOHN FERDINAND DALZIEL   A Tour in the United States of America. Paris, 1791. 2 vols. in 1, new leather spine. Broadfoot 50-305b 1978 $200

SMYTH, NEWMAN   Passing Protestantism and Coming Catholicism. 1912. Austin 79-703 1978 $10

SMYTH, WILLIAM   Lectures on Modern History from the Irruption of the Northern Nations to the Close of the American Revolution. Cambridge and London, 1848. 5 vols., full green calf, spines gilt, lacks some lettering pieces. George's 635-761 1978 £15

SMYTH, WILLIAM H.   The Life and Services of Captain Phillip Beaver, Late of His Majesty's Ship Nisus. 1829. 1st. ed., 8vo, recent cloth, fine. Fenning 32-310 1978 £21.50

SMYTHE, MRS.   Ten Months in the Fiji Islands. 1864. 1st. ed., illus. by 9 chromolithographs, 4 colour 5 tinted, woodcuts, maps, orig. red cloth, very fine copy except for slight marking of spine. Jarndyce 16-664 1978 £48

SMYTHE, AUGUSTINE T.   The Carolina Low Country. New York, 1932. Color illus., some foxing, Bell Wiley's copy. Broadfoot's 44-943 1978 $15

SMYTHE, HENRY   Historical Sketch of Parker County and Weatherford, Texas. St. Louis, 1877. 1st ed., later cloth, original backstip laid down. Jenkins 116-1050 1978 $485

SNELL, ADA L. F.   Palatines Along the Mohawk and Their Church in the Wilderness. 1948. Illus. Austin 79-704 1978 $12.50

SNELL, JAMES P.   History of Hunterdon and Somerset Counties, N.J... Philadelphia, 1881. 4to., very scarce, fine. MacManus 239-1327 1978 $150

SNELL, PH. L.   Kurzer Abriss Der Geschichte Der Philosophie. Giessen, 1819. 2 vols. in 1, sm. 8vo., contemp. bds. Salloch 348-254 1978 $30

SNIDER, CHARLES HENRY JEREMIAH   The Glorious "Shannon's" Old Blue Duster and Other Faded Flags of Fadeless Fame. Toronto, 1923. Some colour illus. Hood's 115-985 1978 $20

SNIDER, CHARLES HENRY JEREMIAH   Under the Red Jack; Privateers of the Maritime Provinces of Canada in the War of 1812. Toronto, n.d. Insc. & signed by author. Hood's 115-237 1978 $30

SNODGRASS, J. J.   Narrative of the Burmese War... 1827. 1st. ed., folding map, laid down, plts., half calf, 8vo. Edwards 1012-157 1978 £50

SNOW, ALPHEUS H.   The Administration of Dependencies... New York, 1902. 1st ed., very scarce. MacManus 239-447 1978 $30

SNOW, CHARLES PERCY   Death Under Sail. 1932. Covers somewhat worn, good, scarce, first English ed. Bell Book 16-263 1978 £15

SNOW, CHARLES PERCY   The Light and the Dark. London, 1947. Second impression, spine faded, nice, author's signed autograph pres. inscription, first ed., orig. binding. Rota 212-54 1978 £20

SNOW, EDGAR   The Battle for Asia. 1941. Ex-lib., new lib. binding. Austin 80-303 1978 $12.50

SNOW, EDWARD ROWE   Famous New England Lighthouses. Boston, (1945). Illus., 1st ed., fine. MacManus 239-1787 1978 $12.50

SNOW, EDWARD ROWE   A Pilgrim Returns to Cape Cod. Boston, (1946). Illus., 1st ed. Biblo BL781-147 1978 $10

SNOW, EDWARD ROWE   Pirates and Buccaneers of the Atlantic Coast. Boston, (1944). Illus., 8vo., 1st ed., orig. cloth. Morrill 241-541 1978 $10

SNOW, EDWARD ROWE   Strange Tales From Nova Scotia to Cape Hatteras. New York, 1949. Illus. Hood's 115-238 1978 $20

SNOW, ELLIOT   The Sea, The Ship and The Sailor. Salem, 1925.
Plts., 8vo., orig. cloth. F. Edwards 1013-204 1978 £20

SNOW, ELLIOT   The Sea, the Ship and the Sailor... Salem,
1925. Illus. MacManus 239-1788 1978 $25

SNOW, ERASTUS   One Year in Scandinavia:.... Liverpool, 1851.
Disbound. Ginsberg 14-687 1978 $22.50

SNOW, LORENZO   The Italian Mission. London, 1851. Cloth, 1st
ed. Ginsberg 14-688 1978 $60

SNOW, M. L. H. ARNOLD   Mechanical Vibration and Its Therapeutic Application. New York, 1904. Illus., 8vo., few spots on fr. cover, 1st ed. Morrill
239-239 1978 $10

SNOW, WILLIAM PARKER   Southern Generals... New York, 1865. Ports.,
1st ed., rebound. Biblo BL781-18 1978 $28.50

SNOW, WILLIAM PARKER   A Two Year Cruise Off Tierra Del Fuego...
London, 1857. 2 vol., contemp. embos. cloth, color. plts., hinges crack., 8vo.
Paine 78-119 1978 $167.50

SNOWDEN, JAMES R.   A Description of the Medals of Washington...
Philadelphia, 1861. Illus., very nice copy, old 1/2 leather, inscribed by author.
MacManus 239-491 1978 $75

SNOWDEN, YATES   Marching with Sherman. Columbia, 1929.
Wraps, pres copy from author, Bell Wiley's copy. Broadfoot's 44-344 1978
$15.00

SNYDER, JOHN FRANCIS   John Francis Snyder: Selected Writings. Springfield, 1962. Orig. binding, clean. Hayman 71-326 1978 $10

SNYDER, ROSE E.   A Narrative. N.P., 1925. Original cloth, 1st
ed., inscribed presentation copy from author. Ginsberg 14-427 1978 $55

SOAMES, JANE   The Coast of Barbary. London, (1938). 2 maps,
4 plts., 8vo., orig. cloth. K Books 239-454 1978 £5

SOBIESKI, JOHN   The Life-Story and Personal Reminiscences of
Col. John Sobieski. 1900. Illus., 1st ed., long inscr. by author on flyleaf.
Austin 79-705 1978 $47.50

SOBY, J. T.   Twentieth-Century Italian Art. New York,
(1949). Sm. 4to., illus., plts. in color, pres., signed by Barr. Biblo BL781-738
1978 $13.50

SOCIAL Visits; or, a Few Chesnuts for the Children, & a Dinner for the Old Folks.
Charleston, 1854. 1st ed., 12mo., orig. cloth, very good. Americanist 103-90
1978 $32.50

SOCIETY FOR THE PREVENTION OF PAUPERISM   The Second Annual Report
of the... New York, 1820. Prtd. wr., good. Butterfield 21-533 1978 $20

SOCIETY OF THE PREVENTION OF PAUPERISM   The Fourth Annual Report of
the... New York, 1821. Uncut, unopened, prtd. wr. Butterfield 21-534 1978
$17.50

THE SOCIETY of the New York Hospital, 1771-1921. (New York, 1921). Illus.,
orig. binding. Wolfe 39-366 1978 $25

SOGLOW, O.   Pretty Pictures. New York, (1931). 1st ed.,
4to. Biblo 251-182 1978 $12.50

SOIKA, KARL   Judentum-Deutschtum. New York, 1934. In
German, paper, underlined. Austin 79-706 1978 $22.50

SOLINUS, CAIUS JULIUS   De Mirabilibus Mondi. Brescia, 1498. Folio
18th-century full blind-tooled calf, rebacked, edges rubbed. Bennett 20-197
1978 $950

SOLIS Y RIBADENEYRA, ANTONIO DE   Histoire de la Conquete du Mexique...
Paris, 1691. First French ed., 2nd issue, maps, plts., 4to., calf. F. Edwards
1012-696 1978 £120

SOLIS Y RIBADENEYRA, ANTONIO DE   Historia de la Conquista de Mexico...
Barcelona, 1770. 3 vols., 12mo., vellum. King 7-388 1978 £20

SOLLEYSELL, JACQUES DE   The Compleat Horseman: Discovering the Surest
Marks of the Beauty, Goodness, Faults and Imperfections of Horses. London, 1696.
Fold. plts. in fine crisp cond., orig. calf rebacking, worn front hinge loose, sm.
folio, portrait. Baldwins' 51-544 1978 $350

SOLMI, EMONDO   Le Fonti dei Manoscritti di Leonardo. Turin,
1908. 8vo., illus., contemp. half mor. Norman 5-L13 1978 $35

SOLON, M. L.   A Brief History of Old English Porcelain and its
Manufactories. 1903. Coloured plts., roy. 8vo. George's 635-238 1978 £21

SOLORZANO, PEREIRA, JOANNES DE   Emblemata Centum Regiopolitica. (Madrid, 1652). Thick folio, vellum. Salloch 348-255 1978 $30

SOLVYNS, B.   The Costume of Hindostan...1798 and 1799.
(1823). Folio, text in English and French, coloured plts., contemp. red. mor.
Quaritch 983-73 1978 $450

SOMARE, ENRICO   Exhibition of Italian 19th Century Paintings...
New York, 1949. 4to., plts., some in color, wrs. Biblo BL781-739 1978
$12.50

SOMBART, WERNER   Die Juden und das Wirtschaftsleben. 1918.
Paper, in German. Austin 79-708 1978 $20

SOME Account of the Pennsylvania Hospital; from its First Rise to the Beginning of
the Fifth Month, called May 1754. Philadelphia, 1817. Rittenhouse 49-631
1976 $25

SOME Early Vermont Invitations, from the Collection of Bella C. Landauer.
New York, 1930. Limited to only 60 copies, good. Nestler Rare 78-29 1978
$30

SOME Pertinent Information: San Diego and Its Future. San Diego, [1895]. Original 16mo printed wr., 1st ed. Ginsberg 14-198 $50

SOME Remarks on the Late Lord Bolingbroke's Famous Letter to Sir William Windham.
1753. 8vo., stitched as issued, uncut, fine. P. M. Hill 142-46 1978 £15

SOME Remarks Upon the Revd. Mr. Anderson's Positions Concerning the Unlawfulness of Stage-Plays. Edinburgh, 1733. 1st ed., 8vo., disbound. Hannas 54-333
1978 £55

SOMERS, ROBERT   The Martyr of Glencree. 1878. 1st. ed., 3
vols., orig. brown cloth, leading bd. of vol. 1 string marked, otherwise v.g.
Jarndyce 16-1066 1978 £48

SOMERS, ROBERT   The Southern States Since the War 1870-71.
NY, 1871. Lg. folding map w/slight tears, Bell Wiley's copy. Broadfoot's
44-771 1978 $26.00

SOMERS, ROBERT   The Southern States Since the War 1870-1.
London and New York, 1871. 1st ed., illus., fold. map in color, cloth, some
staining. MacManus 239-1857 1978 $30

SOMERSET---One Of The First Flowers of Civilization in Ohio. N.P., n.d.
(Early 20th Century). Wrps. Hayman 71-576 1978 $8.50

SOMERVILLE, EDITH ANNE OENONE   An Enthusiast. 1921. Covers damp
stained, else good, first English ed. Bell Book 16-787 1978 £4

SOMERVILLE, EDITH ANNE OENONE   An Enthusiast. 1921. Spine somewhat
faded, else very good, first English ed. Bell Book 17-819 1978 £12.50

SOMERVILLE, EDITH ANNE OENONE   A Foxhunt in the Irish Hills. London,
(1926). Author's signed autograph note, first ed., orig. binding. Rota 212-55
1978 £300

SOMERVILLE, EDITH ANNE OENONE   Further Experiences of an Irish R.M.
1908. First ed., illus. by E. E. Somerville, lacks blank endpaper, cr. 8vo.,
covers dull. George's 635-1331 1978 £5

SOMERVILLE, EDITH ANNE OENONE   Further Experiences of an Irish R. M.
1908. Illus. by author, very good, first English ed. Bell Book 16-788 1978
£12.50

SOMERVILLE, EDITH ANNE OENONE   In Mr. Knox's Country. 1915. Very
good, plts., first English ed. Bell Book 16-789 1978 £8.50

SOMERVILLE, EDITH ANNE OENONE   An Incorruptible Irishman (Being an
Account of Chief Justice C. Kendal Bushe...1767-1843). 1932. 1st ed., illus.,
cover dull, text good. Hyland 128-557 1978 £12

SOMERVILLE, EDITH ANNE OENONE   Mount Music. 1919. Spine faded,
good, first English ed. Bell Book 16-790 1978 £6.50

SOMERVILLE, EDITH ANNE OENONE   A Patrick's Day Hunt. (1901). 1st ed., plts., pict. cover, oblong folio, good. Hyland 128-556 1978 £40

SOMERVILLE, EDITH ANNE OENONE   The States through Irish Eyes. 1931. 8vo., 1st ed., plts. & decor. by author, cloth, fine with d.w., pres. inscr. initialled by author. Quaritch 979-301 1978 $30

SOMERVILLE, WILLIAM   The Chace. 1735. 4to., 1st ed., engr. frontis., contemp. sprinkled calf, rebacked, clean copy. Quaritch 979-302 1978 $210

SOMERVILLE, WILLIAM   The Chace. 1735. 3rd. ed., rebound, 1/4 leather. Eaton 45-463 1978 £10

SOMERVILE, WILLIAM   The Chase: a Poem. 1802. Roy. 8vo., wood-cuts, half mor., gilt panelled back, somewhat rubbed, bookplt. Quaritch 983-370 1978 $185

SOMERVILLE, WILLIAM   The Chace. 1802. Roy. 8vo., woodcuts, half mor., gilt panelled back, bkplt. Quaritch 979-303 1978 $150

SOMMER, H. OSKAR   The Kalender of Shepherds. London, 1892. No. 4 of 300 copies, orig. bds., joints cracked, v.g., 3 vols. in 1, inscribed pres. copy from author to Sir Henry H. Howorth, A.L.s. laid in. Houle 10-300 1978 $150

SOMMER, H. OSKAR   Le Roman De Merlin. London, 1894. 1 of only 12 copies on handmade paper, sm. folio, later cloth, fine, uncut, mostly unopened, rare. Houle 10-299 1978 $425

SOMMERS, JOHN   The Judgement of Whole Kingdoms and Nations, Concerning the Rights, Power, and Prerogative of Kings,.... London, 1771. Octavo, half modern calf over old marbled boards, some light staining. Bennett 7-103 1978 $100

SOMMERVILLE, MAXWELL   Siam on the Meinam from the Gulf to Ayuthia. Philadelphia, 1897. Illus., 8vo., ex-lib., 1st ed., orig. cloth. Morrill 241-543 1978 $10

SONDERN, FREDERIC E.   Outline of Preventive Medicine. New York, 1932. Second ed. Rittenhouse 49-741 1976 $10

SONDES, GEORGE   Authentic Memorials of Remarkable Occurences and Affecting Calamities in the Family of .... n.d. (c.1793). Orig. bds., spine missing, octavo, good. Upcroft 10-160 1978 £15

A SONGE Made in Edward IV Hys Tyme of Ye Battele of Hexhamme, in Northumberland MCCCCLXIV. Newcastle, (c.1850). Orig. yellow wrappers, good. Jarndyce 16-263 1978 £8.50

SONGS of the Grove: records of the Ancient World. Vine Press, 1921. 1 of 550 numbered copies, woodcut title, cloth-backed bds., covers littled soiled, good, first English ed. Bell Book 16-864 1978 £12

SONGS of the Woodland, the Garden, and the Sea. New York, 1859. Colored lithos., 8vo. Morrill 241-544 1978 $12.50

SONNE, NIELS HENRY   Liberal Kentucky 1780-1828. NY, 1939. Bell Wiley's copy. Broadfoot's 44-878 1978 $12.00

SONNENKALB, VICTOR   Du Rontgen-Diagnostik Des Nasen-Und Ohren-arztes Von Dr. Sonnenkalb. Jena, 1914. Tall 8vo., photo. plts., illus., orig. grey prtd.cloth, good copy, former owner's signature & stamp, 1st ed. Zeitlin 245-244 1978 $25

SOON We'll Be Three Years Old. Racine, 1936. Illus., lg. sq. 8vo., orig. colored pict. wrs. Morrill 241-114 1978 $7.50

SOPER, GEORGE A.   A Report to the Chicago Real Estate Board on the Disposal of the Sewage and Protection of the Water Supply of Chicago. (Chicago), 1915. 8vo., orig. limp cloth, ex-lib., 1st ed. Morrill 239-433 1978 $7.50

SORBIERE, SAMUEL DE   Discours de Monsieur de Sorbiere, Touchant Divers Experiences de la Transfusion du Sang. Paris, 1668. 4to., full red crushed mor. Jansenist style, 1st ed., rare, very fine copy. Offenbacher 30-145 1978 $2,500

SOREL, GEORGES   Reflexions sur la violence. Paris, 1908. 1st ed., orig. pr. wr., 8vo. Gilhofer 75-101 1978 SFr 400

SORELL, HELEN   You, Who Love Life. (New York, 1956). 1st ed., plates, very fine, dust jacket. Victoria 34-459 1978 $40

SORGE, ERNST   With 'Plane, Boat and Camera in Greenland. New York, 1936. Illus. Biblo BL781-8 1978 $12.50

SORROWS of Seduction, in Eight Delineations, with Other Poems. London, 1806. 2nd ed., mezzotint plates are hand-colored, full leather binding by Morrell of London, ornate gilt borders and gilt decorated spine, gilt dentelles, very fine copy. Victoria 34-747 1978 $35

THE SORROWS of Yamba; or the Negro Woman's Lamentation. Boston, 1819. Chapbook, original plain wrappers, almost fine. Victoria 34-748 1978 $65

SORTAIS, G.   Ilios et Iliade. Paris, 1894. 8vo., half calf, map. Van der Peet H-64-556 1978 Dfl 70

SOTHEBY, SAMUEL LEIGH   Ramblings in the Elucidation of the Autograph of Milton. London, 1861. Sm. folio, frontis., ports., contemp. green mor., 1st ed., pres. copy, rubbed, inscribed. MacManus 238-135 1978 $150

SOTHEBY, WILLIAM   Ellen; or, The Confession: A Tragedy in Five Acts. 1816. Green buckram, paper label. Eaton 45-464 1978 £5

SOUANCE, C. DE   Iconographie Des Perroquets Non Figures Dans Les Publications de Levaillant et de M. Bourjot Saint-Hilaire. Paris, Bertrand, 1857. Hand-coloured plts., lg. folio, preserved in cloth case, fine, lg. paper copy in orig. wrapper. Traylen 88-633 1978 £3000

SOUERS, P. W.   The Matchless Orinda (Harvard Studies in English V). Cambridge, 1931. 4 plts., octavo, good. Upcroft 10-544 1978 £8.50

SOUPAULT, PHILIPPE   Ode to Bombed London. 1944. Orig. wraps, very good, scarce. Bell Book 17-821 1978 £15

SOUREK, K.   Umeni na Solvensku, Odkar Zeme a Lidu. Melangrich, 1938. Thick 4to., half calf, illus., plts. in color. Van der Peet H-64-203 1978 Dfl 125

SOUSA, JOHN PHILIP   The Fifth String. 1902. Illus., first ed. Austin 82-862 1978 $12.50

SOUSA PINTO, ANTONIO JOSE   Elementos de Pharmacia, Chymica, e Botanica Para Uso Dos Principiantes. Lisboa, 1805. 4to., full modern calf, 1st ed., very good copy. Offenbacher 30-146 1978 $125

SOUSA PINTO, ANTONIO JOSE   Elementos de Pharmacia, Chymica, e botanica, Para uso dos Principiantes. Lisbon, 1805. 8vo., contemp. calf, gilt spine, new endpapers, title page a little soiled. Quaritch 977-74 1978 $75

THE SOUTH: A Letter from a Friend in the North. Philadelphia, 1856. 8vo., unbound, 1st ed. Morrill 241-85 1978 $12.50

THE SOUTH And East African Year Book & Guide. London, 1932. 38th ed., cr. 8vo., maps, orig. cloth. K Books 239-459 1978 £5

SOUTH KENSINGTON MUSEUM   Ancient and Modern Furniture and Woodwork in the.... 1874. Roy. 8vo., coloured frontis., cloth, leather spine. Quaritch 983-Addenda n 1978 $65

SOUTH KENSINGTON MUSEUM   A Descriptive Catalogue of the Historical Collection of Water-Colour Paintings in the... 1876. Roy. 8vo., plts., roxburghe, old backstrip laid down, rebacked. Quaritch 983-258 1978 $40

THE SOUTH in the Building of the Nation... Richmond, (1909). 12 vols., mor., binds. broken, colored frontis in each vol., plts., some covers detached. Hayman 72-719 1978 $35

SOUTH CAROLINA- A Guide to the Palmetto State. New York, 1942. Bell Wiley's copy. Broadfoot's 44-944 1978 $15

SOUTH Carolina Raw Materials. Columbia, 1949. Illus., 8vo., d.w., 1st ed. Morrill 241-547 1978 $12.50

SOUTHERN California: An Authentic Description of Its Natural Features,.... Los Angeles, 1892. Illus., original pictorial wr., 1st ed. Ginsberg 14-199 1978 $35

SOUTHERN Historical Society Papers. Complete set 52 vols., hand bound in gray buckram, most wrs. bound in, good condition, Bell Wiley's copy. Broadfoot's 44-701 1978 $1200

SOUTHERN Table Book: A New Selection of Arithmetical Tables.... Charleston, 1857. Wrps. Hayman 71-386 1978 $10

SOUTHESK, JAMES CARNEGIE, EARL OF   Saskatchewan and the Rocky Mountains. Edinburgh, 1875. 1st ed., 8vo., fldg. maps prtd. on linen & coloured in outline, litho. plts., wood engr. plts., illus., half calf, spine & corners rubbed, joint cracked in center, some fraying & soiling of margins of maps. Deighton 5-55 1978 £75

SOUTHESK, JAMES CARNEGIE, EARL OF   Saskatchewan and the Rocky Mountains. A Diary and Narrative of Travel, Sport, and Adventure, During a Journey Through the Hudson's Bay Company's Territories in 1859 and 1860. Edinburgh, 1875. Maps, illus., lib. binding. Hood 116-883 1978 $120

SOUTHEY, ROBERT   The Annal Anthology. Bristol, 1799-1800. Octavo, handsomely rebacked early marbled boards, raised spine bands, sole ed. Bennett 7-104 1978 $125

SOUTHEY, ROBERT   The Doctor, &c's. New York, 1836. 1st Amer. ed., orig. cloth, good. Greene 78-109 1978 $30

SOUTHEY, ROBERT   Letters from England. New York, 1836. 1 vol. ed., disbound. Greene 78-285 1978 $25

SOUTHEY, ROBERT   The Life of Nelson. London, 1813. 2 vols., pott octavo, orig. boards, spines calf, gilt titles, front hinge weak, 1st ed. Bennett 7-105 1978 $125

SOUTHEY, ROBERT   Madoc, A Poem. 1805. 1st. ed., 4to, engraved title, half title, orig. half calf, green label, fine. Jarndyce 16-1069 1978 £50

SOUTHEY, ROBERT   Poems: Containing the Retrospect, Odes, Elegies, Sonnets &C. 1795. 1st. ed., 8vo, contemp. tree calf, rebacked, orig. spine laid down, good, very rare, A.L.S. with autograph poem signed by author loosely inserted. Sawyer 299-136 1978 £750

SOUTHEY, ROBERT   Roderick, the Last of the Goths. 1815. 2 vols., contemp. straight-grained crimson mor., gilt edges, 8vo. Howes 194-469 1978 £12.50

SOUTHEY, ROBERT   Roderick, The Last of the Goths. London, 1816. 2 vols., 4th. ed., 12mo, contemp. mottled calf, hinges cracked, half titles. Sexton 7-185 1978 £15

SOUTHEY, ROBERT   Specimens of the Later English Poets, With Preliminary Notices. 1807. 1st. ed., 3 vols., 8vo, recent bds., nice. Fenning 32-312 1978 £18.50

SOUTHEY, ROBERT   Wat Tyler, A Dramatic Poem. 1817. 1st. ed., half titles, orig. buff wrappers, uncut. Jarndyce 16-1067 1978 £38

SOUTHEY, ROBERT   Wat Tyler, A Dramatic Poem. 1817. New ed., half title, uncut, orig. buff wrappers, fine, orig. condition. Jarndyce 16-1068 1978 £32

SOUTHEY, ROSAMOND   Storm & Sunshine in South Africa. London, 1910. Plts. gilt cloth, g.t., 8vo, bright copy. K Books 239-460 1978 £8

SOUTHWEST Missouri. St. Louis, 1888. Illus., plates, folding maps, original pictorial printed wr., 1st ed. Ginsberg 14-602 1978 $125

SOUVENIR Album Perron Boulevard Gaspe Co., Que. Montreal, (n.d. c. 1928). Oblong 8vo, printed wrappers, lg. sepia halftone views. Wolfe 39-196 1978 $15

SOUVENIR Book of the Cleveland Industrial Exposition June 7-19, 1909. Cleveland, 1909. Bds., label on fr. cover. Hayman 73-153 1978 $7.50

SOUVENIR Book Silver Anniversary 1887-1912 Borough of Wilkinsburg October the 3rd, 4th and 5th. N. P., (1912). Wrs., ads. Hayman 73-608 1978 $8.50

SOUVENIR Booklet of the Visit to Toronto of His Eminence Cardinal Villeneuve, Archbishop of Quebec, June 5-9, 1934. Toronto, 1934. Illus., bound. Hood 117-372 1978 $15

A SOUVENIR: Descriptive of the Adirondack Mountains, Lake George...Saratoga...Reached by the Delaware & Hudson. Albany, n.d. (1880s). Lg. fldg. map, wr., illus. from photos. Butterfield 21-152D 1978 $12.50

SOUVENIR Ex-Winesberger's Reunion 1910. Cleveland, (1910). Wrs., photos. Hayman 73-543 1978 $8.50

SOUVENIR of Austin, Texas, 1911. Austin, 1911. Fine illus. Jenkins 116-1389 1978 $18.50

SOUVENIR Of Columbus, Ohio. (Columbus, n.d. c.1884). Wrps. Hayman 71-526 1978 $8.50

SOUVENIR of Sarnia. N.P., n.d. (about 1925). Fldr. of 10 fold-out picture cards. Hood 117-764 1978 $10

SOUVENIR of Scotland. Edinburgh, 1889. Cr. 4to., decor. cloth. K Books 244-443 1978 £33

SOUVENIR Of Springfield. (Portland, n.d. 190-?). Wrps., light offset on 1st. leaf from front wrapper. Hayman 71-328 1978 $8.50

SOUVENIR of the Thousand Islands and River St. Lawrence. Grand Rapids (ca. 1912). Color plts., card cover. Hood 117-765 1978 $20

SOUVENIR of Toledo, Ohio. (Portland, n.d., c. 1904). Wrs. Hayman 72-555 1978 $8.50

SOUVENIR Programme given by the Theatrical and Musical Professions as a Tribute to Miss Ellen Terry on the Occasion of her Jubilee, June 12th, 1906. 1906. Plts., sm. folio, stiff pict. bds. George's 635-1417 1978 £12.50

SOUVENIR Volume Of the American Testimonial Banquet to H. M. Stanley, on May 30, 1890, in London. 1890. Photos, 8vo, brown leather, embossed with arms of U.S.A. Edwards 1012-290 1978 £75

SOWERBY, A.   A Naturalist's Holiday by the Sea. 1923. 8vo, orig. cloth. Book Chest 17-356 1978 $15

SOWERBY, J.G.   Afternoon Tea, Rhymes for Children. New York, 1881. 1st Amer. ed., colored pictorial boards, worn at edges. Victoria 34-749 1978 $20

SOWERBY, JAMES   English Botany. (1832-) 46. 2nd ed., coloured plts., 12 vols., binders cloth, badly worn, some spines missing and defective. George's 635-961 1978 £175

SOWERBY, JAMES   Sowerby's English Botany. 1863-70. 7 vols., 8vo, colour plts., green cloth, vol. 3 bound in slightly different cloth, John Ruskin's copy. Quaritch 979-280 1978 $735

SOWERBY, JAMES   English Botany.... London, 1877-1892. Coloured plts., 13 vols., thick roy. 8vo, half morocco, spines little dull, lib. stamps at foot of some text pages, sound set. Traylen 88-634 1978 £200

SPAFFORD, HORATIO GATES   A Gazetteer of State of N.Y. Albany, 1824. Map, some wear on binding. Nestler Rare 78-141 1978 $55

SPALDING, C. C.   Annals of the City of Kansas:.... Columbia, 1950. Illus., original cloth, boxed. Ginsberg 14-464 1978 $15

SPALDING, CHARLES   Love at First Flight. Boston, 1943. Illus. by Carl Rose. Austin 80-304 1978 $8.50

SPALDING, H. S.   Catholic Colonial Maryland. A Sketch. Milwaukee, (1931). Illus. MacManus 239-1826 1978 $15

SPALDING, JAMES ALFRED   Dr. Lyman Spalding, the Originator of the United States Pharmacopoeia. Boston, 1916. Portr., 8vo, ex-lib., nice, no external marks, 1st ed. Morrill 239-240 1978 $17.50

SPALDING, JAMES ALFRED   Maine Physicians of 1820. Lewiston, 1928. 8vo., ex-lib., 1st ed. Morrill 239-241 1978 $15

SPALDING, RUFUS P.   Confiscation of Rebel Property. Speech of Hon..., of Ohio, Delivered in the House...January 22, 1864. (Washington, n.d., 1864). Unbound as issued. Hayman 72-133 1978 $7.50

SPALLANZANI, LAZZARO   Dell' Azione Del Cuore Ne' Vasi Sanguigni Nuove Osservazioni. (Modena, 1768). 8vo., modern half vellum, browned, light foxing, sm. library stamp, very good copy, 1st ed. Zeitlin 245-246 1978 $375

SPALLANZANI, LAZARO   Experiences Sur La Circulation Observee Dans L' Universalite Du Systeme Vasculaire. Paris, (1800). 8vo., engr. plts., orig. blue bds., minor brown spots, very good copy with old bkplt. of Dr. Honnorat, rare. Zeitlin 245-247 1978 $175

SPALLANZANI, LAZZARO   De'Fenomeni Della Circolazione Osservata Nel Giro Universale De'Vasi. Modena, 1773. 8vo., fine frontis. engr., copperplt., vellum over bds., gilt ornamented spine, foxing, very good copy, 1st ed. Zeitlin 245-245 1978 $425

SPALLANZANI, LAZZARO   Travels in the Two Sicilies and some parts of the Apennines. London, 1798. 4 vols., 8vo., diced calf sides, rebacked in calf gilt, good, plts. King 7-237 1978 £140

SPALLANZANI, LAZZARO   Viaggi alle due Sicilie e in alcune parte dell'Appennino.... Pavia, 1792-1797. 1st ed., 8vo, 6 vols., contemp. half-calf, lightly rubbed, gilt back, red mor. Gilhofer 75-102 1978 SFr 1,100

SPALTEHOLZ, WERNER   Handatlas Der Anatomie Des Menschen. Leipzig, 1909. Tall 8vo., illus., mostly in color, orig. blue cloth, gilt lettered, signature of former owner, good copy, 6th ed. Zeitlin 245-248 1978 $45

SPANGENBERG, JOHANNES 1484-1550   Postilla: von Ostern bis auff das Advent. Erfurt, 1561. Woodcut illus., sm. 8vo., newly bound in full mor. antique style, leaf 153 defective with loss of 1/3 of text, rare. Howes 194-577 1978 £120

SPANGLER, EDWARD W.   Caspur Baltzer and Henry and George Spengler Who Settled in York County Respectively, 1729, 1732 and 1751. York, 1896. Baldwins' 51-243 1978 $85

SPANISH-English Dictionary. Paris, 1803. Sm. cr. 8vo, 1/4 vellum, marbled bds., bookplt. of Lord Rendlesham. Eaton 45-465 1978 £5

SPANISH Grants in New Mexico. Washington, 1884. Folding map, orig. pr. wr., rebacked, 1st ed. Ginsberg 14-781 1978 $100

SPARGO, JOHN   Two Bennington-born Explorers and Makers of Modern Canada. (N.P.), 1950. Illus., orig. binding. Wolfe 39-517 1978 $10

SPARKE, E.   Scintillula altaris. Between 1652-1700. Sm. 8vo., some staining, lacks title, engraved plts., calf gilt, worn, joints cracking. George's 635-1132 1978 £7.50

SPARKS, E. E.   The English Settlement in Illinois... Cedar Rapids, 1907. Ltd. to 250 copies, mint copy. MacManus 239-1929 1978 $25

SPARKS, E. E.   The Wonders of the Colorado Desert, Southern California. Its Rivers and Its Mountains, Its Canyons and Its Springs... Boston, 1906. 2 vols., illus., fold. map, 1st ed., fine. MacManus 239-1930 1978 $32.50

SPARKS, JARED   The Life of George Washington. Boston, 1839. 1st ed., illus., orig. full calf, nice copy. MacManus 239-501 1978 $25

SPARKS, JARED   The Life of Gouverneur Morris... Boston, 1832. 3 vols., port., orig. bds., rebacked. MacManus 239-796 1978 $55

SPARLING, R. A.   History of the 12th Service Battalion York and Lancaster Regiment. (1920). Illus., covers faded and stained, 8vo. George's 635-860 1978 £5

SPARO, JOHN   The Potters and Potteries of Bennington. Boston, 1926. Special ltd. ed. 800 numbered copies, 4to, plts. Baldwins' 51-155 1978 $75

SPARRMAN, ANDERS   A Voyage Round the World With Captain James Cook... Golden Cockerel Press, 1944. Folio, folding map, wood-engravings by P. Barker-Mill, orig. cloth, 8vo. Edwards 1012-364 1978 £320

SPAULDING, E. WILDER   His Excellency George Clinton, Critic of the Constitution. New York, 1938. Ports., map, d.j., fine. MacManus 239-740 1978 $12.50

SPAULDING, JOHN H.   Historical Relics of the White Mountains. Mt. Washington, (1858). Frontis., vignette, 12mo., 3rd ed., orig. cloth. Morrill 241-393 1978 $30

SPAULDING, JONAH   The Female's Guide to Health. Skowhegan, 1837. 12mo., orig. bds., cloth back, 1st ed. Morrill 239-242 1978 $45

SPAULDING, JONAH   A Summary History of Persecution, From the Crucifixion of Our Saviour to the Present Time. Hallowell, 1819. Leather-backed bds., worn, spine chipped. Hayman 71-706 1978 $12.50

SPEAKMAN, HAROLD   Mostly Mississippi. NY, 1927. colored frontis, illus., Bell Wiley's copy. Broadfoot's 44-907 1978 $15.00

SPEARING, H. G.   The Childhood of Art or the Ascent of Man. London, 1930. 2nd ed. revised, fully illus., 2 vols. Baldwins' 51-156 1978 $32.50

SPEARS, E. L.   Prelude to Victory. 1939. 1st. ed., illus., maps, 8vo, orig. cloth, good copy. Sawyer 298-41 1978 £12.50

SPEARS, EDWARD   Assignment to Catastrophe, Vol. II, The Fall of France, June, 1940. 1954. 1st. ed., pres. copy to Winston Churchill, plts., maps, 8vo, orig. red cloth, spine slightly soiled, good copy. Sawyer 298-111 1978 £120

SPEARS, JOHN RANDOLPH   The American Slave-Trade. NY, 1900. Lower spine & pages stained, Bell Wiley's copy. Broadfoot's 44-773 1978 $12.00

SPEARS, JOHN RANDOLPH   Captain Nathaniel Brown Palmer. New York, 1922. 12mo., orig. cloth, good. Paine 78-120 1978 $15.00

SPEARS, JOHN RANDOLPH   The History of Our Navy...1775-1898. New York, 1899. Illus., maps, 5 vols. MacManus 239-1789 1978 $37.50

SPECTOR, BENJAMIN   A History of Tufts College Medical School. (Boston, 1943). Illus., 8vo., 1st ed., pres. copy. Morrill 239-243 1978 $16.50

SPECULUM. 1932-45. Bindings not uniform, Vols. 7-3,20, 24-26. Allen 234-N 1978 $15

SPEECHES Delivered at the Great Meeting..St. James's Hall,..May 6th, 1868 in Support of the United Church of England & Wales. 1868. Disbound, very good, octavo bound in cloth, reprint. Hyland 128-560 1978 £12

SPEED, JOHN   The History of Great Britaine Under the Conquests of Ye. London, 1614. Folio, quarter pigskin, blue-grey boards, corners repaired, gilt lettering on spine, bookplate, several pages tipped in, neat repairs, worm hole in margin. Totteridge 29-99 1978 $200

SPEEDY, TOM   The Natural History of Sport in Scotland with Rod and Gun. Edinburgh, 1920. Illus. by J. G. Millais, frontis., plts., illus., 4to., gilt-dec. cloth. K Books 244-293 1978 £20

SPEELMAN, C.   Journaal der Reis van den Gezant der O. I. Compagnie Joan Cunaeus naar Perzie in 1651-1652. Amsterdam, 1908. 8vo., bds., map. Van der Peet H-64-557 1978 Dfl 45

SPEER, EMORY   Lincoln, Lee, Grant and Other Biographical Addresses. New York, 1909. Front hinge starting, cover speckled, Bell Wiley's copy. Broadfoot's 44-345 1978 $30

SPEER, OCIE   Texas Jurists. N.P., 1936. Illus. Jenkins 116-1269 1978 $75

SPEIDEL, HANS   Invansion, 1944. Chicago, 1950. Biblo 247-790 1978 $9.50

SPEKE, JOHN HANNING   Journal of the Discovery of the Source of the Nile. New York, 1864. Map, portr., woodcut illus., tall thick 8vo., cloth, 1st Amer. ed. Argosy Special-83 1978 $100

SPEKE, JOHN HANNING   Journal of the Discovery of the Source of the Nile. New York, 1864. 1st. American ed., folding map, 1 other map, plts., text-illus., roy. 8vo., minor foxing, nice fresh copy, orig. gilt-lettered cloth. K Books 239-461 1978 £60

SPEKE, JOHN HANNING   What Led to the Discovery of the Source of the Nile. 1864. 1st. ed., 8vo., half title, engraved frontispiece, folding engraved map, modern half calf, gilt back. Deighton 5-23 1978 £105

SPELL, LOTA M.   Music in Texas. Austin, 1936. Jenkins 116-1270 1978 $17.50

SPELMAN, HENRY   The English Works. 1723. Portrait, second ed., contemp. calf, rebacked, folio, 2 parts in 1 vol. Howes 194-471 1978 £38

SPELMAN, HENRY   De Non Tremerandis Ecclesiis, Churches Not to be Violated. Oxford, 1668. 4th. ed., orig. calf, little worn, good. Jarndyce 16-23 1978 £25

SPENCE, H.D.M.   Cloister Life in the Days of Coeur de Lion. London, 1892. 1st ed., quarto, B&W plates, text illus., handsome gilt decor. cloth binding, very good. Victoria 34-750 1978 $17.50

SPENCE, JAMES L. T. C.   Myths & Legends of Ancient Egypt. 1917. Plts., 16 coloured, 8vo, orig. cloth, gilt, t.e.g., nice. Fenning 32-314 1978 £8.50

SPENCE, JAMES L. T. C.   Myths & Legends of Babylonia & Assyria. 1916. Plts., 8 coloured, 8vo, orig. cloth, gilt, nice. Fenning 32-315 1978 £7.50

SPENCE, JOSEPH   Anecdotes, Observations and Characters of Books and Men. 1820. 8vo., 1st ed., portr., orig. bds., back and upper joint cracked. Quaritch 979-304 1978 $85

SPENCE, JOSEPH   Polymetis:.... London, 1747. Folio, full contemporary red morocco, covers decorated with wide gilt border, spine richly gilt, a.e.g., 1st ed., frontispiece portrait by Vertue, plates by Boitard, some foxing, fine and elegant copy. Ximenes 47-299 1978 $450

SPENCE, L.   The Myths of Mexico and Peru. 1913. Coloured frontis., maps, illus., orig. cloth, 8vo. Edwards 1012-697 1978 £10

SPENCE, LEWIS   The Myths of the North American Indians. New York, 1914. Colour plts., very good cond. Hood 116-438 1978 $60

SPENCE, LEWIS   The Myths of the North American Indians. New York, n.d. Plts., in colour, other illus. MacManus 239-1217 1978 $12.50

SPENCE, MISS N.   Their Name Liveth: A Memoir of the Boys of Parkdale Collegiate Institute Who Gave Their Lives in the Great War. Toronto, (1919). Hood 116-141 1978 $17.50

SPENCELEY, J. W.   A Descriptive Checklist of the Etched & Engraved Book-Plates by J. W. Spenceley. Boston, The Troutsdale Press, 1905. Illus., t.e.g. Battery Park 1-294 1978 $75

SPENCER, BENJAMIN   A Dumb Speech or, A Sermon Made But No Sermon Preached... 1646. 1st. ed., 16mo, orig. calf, gilt borders, good. Jarndyce 16-24 1978 £30

SPENCER, CLAIRE   Gallow's Orchard. 1930. First ed. Austin 82-863 1978 $12.50

SPENCER, DAVID   Historic Germantown. Germantown, (1908). Illus., fine. MacManus 239-1614 1978 $12.50

SPENCER, EDMUND   Travels in European Turkey in 1850 Through Bosnia, Servia, Bulgaria, Macedonia, Thrace, Albania and Epirus. London, 1851. 2 vols., 1st ed., ads, lg. fldg. map, tinted litho. frontis., orig. blind stamped binding, spines a bit faded, interiors fine. Current 24-195 1978 $125

SPENCER, ELEANOR P.   The Printer's Relict. Baltimore, The Amphora Press, 1937. 12mo., cloth, thin. Battery Park 1-3 1978 $25

SPENCER, ICHABOD S.   Fugitive Slave Law. New York, 1850. 8vo., unbound. Morrill 241-549 1978 $7.50

SPENCER, J. W.   The Duration of Niagara Falls and the History of the Great Lakes. New York, (1895). "2nd ed." Butterfield 21-305 1978 $12.50

SPENCER, JOHN   A Discourse Concerning Prodigies... London, 1665. 2 parts in 1 vol., sm. 8vo, orig. calf gilt spine. Traylen 88-339 1978 £35

SPENCER, ORSON   Letters Exhibiting the Most Prominent Doctrines of the Church of Jesus Christ of the Latter Days Saints.... Liverpool, 1879. Leather, 6th ed. Ginsberg 14-689 1978 $25

SPENCER, ORSON   The Prussian Mission of the Church of Jesus Christ of Latter Day Saints. Liverpool, 1853. Disbound, 1st ed. Ginsberg 14-690 1978 $50

SPENCER, ROBERT CAVENDISH   Letter-Book of Captain R. C. Spencer of H.M.S. Madagascar. 1828-30. Folio, rough calf. F. Edwards 1013-206 1978 £120

SPENCER, THEODORE C.   The Struggle for Religious and Political Liberty. New York, (1887). Cloth. Hayman 72-721 1978 $12.50

SPENCER'S Roster of Native Sons (and Daughters). Bath, 1941. Alphabetical index, T.L.s. by author laid in, scarce. Butterfield 21-422 1978 $35

SPENDER, H.   Home Rule. (1912). 2nd ed., wr., good. Hyland 128-562 1978 £5

SPENDER, JOHN KENT   Therapeutic Means for the Relief of Pain. London, 1874. 8vo., 1st ed. Morrill 239-244 1978 $22.50

SPENDER, STEPHEN   The Edge of Being. 1949. Very good, d.w., first English ed. Bell Book 16-794 1978 £5.50

SPENDER, STEPHEN   Poems. 1933. Very good, d.w., first English ed. Bell Book 16-795 1978 £45

SPENDER, STEPHEN   Selected Poems. London, 1940. First ed. of this selection, orig. binding, covers dust-marked, nice. Rota 211-654 1978 £5

SPENDER, STEPHEN   Spiritual Exercises; poems. London, 1943. One of 125 numbered copies, wrappers, nice, inscribed by author, first ed. Rota 212-56 1978 £80

SPENDER, STEPHEN   Trial of a Judge, a Tragedy in Five Acts. 1938. First ed., 8vo. George's 635-1332 1978 £5

SPENDLOVE, F. ST. GEORGE   The Face of Early Canada. Toronto, (1958). 4to., illus., d.j., no. 39 of ltd. ed., signed by author, orig. binding. Wolfe 39-518 1978 $150

SPENGLER, OSWALD   The Decline of the West. New York, 1939. 2 vols. in 1, thick 4to., cloth. Salloch 348-258 1978 $30

SPENGLER, OSWALD   Der Untergang Des Abendlandes... Leipzig, 1918. 4to., 3/4 cloth, 1st ed. Salloch 348-256 1978 $50

SPENGLER, OSWALD   Der Untergang Des Abendlandes. Munich, 1919. 4th ed., 4to., wrs., paper yellowing. Salloch 348-257 1978 $10

SPENSER, EDMUND   Complete Works in Verse and Prose. 1882-84. 9 vols., sm. 4to., facsimiles, illus., half grey-green levant mor., gilt backs, gilt tops, other edges uncut, fine set. Quaritch 979-305 1978 $200

SPENSER, EDMUND   The Faerie Queen: The Shepheards Calendar... (London), 1611. 1 vols., illus., sm. folio, contemp. gilt-stamped calf, 1st collected ed., 2nd issue, light marginal waterstain, else fine. Howell 5-55 1978 $450

SPENSER, EDMUND   Faerie Queene. 1758. 1st. ed., 2 vols., 4to, orig. calf, red labels, fine. Jarndyce 16-201 1978 £75

SPENSER, EDMUND   Spenser's Fairie Queen. London, 1894. Illus. by Walter Crane, 19 vols., orig. pict. wrs., 1st of this ed., wr. wear, very good set. MacManus 238-144 1978 $250

SPENSER, EDMUND   The Poetical Works. 1825. 5 vols., half titles, frontis, portrait in vol. I, lib. stamp on titles & several leaves, lib. bookplts., cloth, paper labels, few sm. tears at head of spines. Eaton 45-466 1978 £15

SPENSER, EDMUND   The Poetical Works. 1909-10. Orig. issue, 3 vols., lg. 8vo., orig. buckram, paper labels. Howes 194-1211 1978 £17.50

SPENSER, EDMUND   The Shepherd's Calendar. London, 1732. F.p. portrait by Vertue, engraved plates by Fourdrinier, fine, crisp copy, rebound in modern half-leather, marbled boards. Victoria 34-752 1978 $50

SPENSER, EDMUND   The Shepheardes Calender. London, The Cresset Press, 1930. Tall 4to., t.e.g., ed. ltd. to 350 copies, prtd. on Barcham Green handmade paper, illus., orig. linen covered bds., spotted, vellum back with gilt lettering better than fine, text clean, binding firm. Current 24-53 1978 $135

SPENSER, EDMUND   Works of That Famous English Poet..Viz. London, 1679. Frontis, title-pg. in red & black, folio, contemp. calf, rebacked with gilt spine & leather label. Traylen 88-340 1978 £80

SPERLING, W.   Tierkarikaturen-Zeichenschule. Leipzig, 1937. 8vo., orig. covers, text illus. Van der Peet H-64-285 1978 Dfl 35

SPERONI, SPERON   Dialogi del Sig. Venice, 1596. Quarto, full contemp. vellum, Meietti's device on t.p., Fletcher of Saltoun copy. Bennett 20-199 1978 $250

SPERONI, SPERON   Orationi del Sig. Venice, 1596. 1st ed., quarto, full contemp. vellum, sound. Bennett 20-200 1978 $250

SPEYER, LEONORA   Naked Heel. New York, 1931. Author's signed pres. copy, cloth. Eaton 45-467 1978 £5

THE SPHYNX: A New and Original Collection of Double Acrostics. 1867. Orig. cloth, gilt. Eaton 45-161 1978 £5

SPICER, DOROTHY GLADYS   Folk Festivals and the Foreign Community. Woman's Press, 1923. Illus. Austin 79-712 1978 $12.50

SPICER-SIMSON, THEODORE   Men of Letters of the British Isles. New York, 1924. 4to., 1 of 520 numbered copies prtd. on Rives paper, bds., cloth spine. Battery Park 1-23 1978 $150

SPIEGELBERG, OTTO   A Text Book of Midwifery. London, 1887-1888. Illus., 2nd German ed., 2 vols., 8vo., ex-lib., lacks spine & back cover. Morrill 239-245 1978 $7.50

SPIELMANN, MARION HARRY   The History of "Punch". London, 1895. Illus., large paper ed. ltd. to 250 copies, no. 30. Baldwins' 51-365 1978 $17.50

SPIELMANN, MARION HENRY   Hugh Thomson: his art, letters, humour & charm. 1931. Coloured plts., text illus., covers dull, good, first English ed. Bell Book 17-502 1978 £30

SPIELMAN, MARION HENRY   Kate Greenaway. London, 1905. Illus., orig. cloth, spine worn and faded, but good. MacManus 238-936 1978 $35

SPIELMANN, MARION HARRY   The Title-Page of the First Folio of Shakespeare's Plays. A Comparative Study of the Droeshout Portrait and the Stratford Monument. London, 1924. 8vo., orig. bds., 1st ed., plts. MacManus 238-1050 1978 $40

SPIERS, R. P.   The Orders of Architecture. 1897. Plts., folio. George's 635-91 1978 £7.50

SPIERS, R. P.   The Orders of Architecture, Greek, Roman and Italian. London, Batsford, 1902. 4th. ed., plts., folio, orig. cloth. Sexton 7-50 1978 £8

SPILLER, ROBERT   Fenimore Cooper, Critic of His Times. 1931. Illus., very good. Nestler Rare 78-142 1978 $20

SPILSBURY, F. B.   Account of a Voyage to the Western Coast of Africa... London, 1807. Folding map, 5 plts., generally dusty, new bds., 8vo. K Books 239-462 1978 £18

SPILSBURY, FRANCIS   A Treatise on the Method of Curing the Gout, Scurvy, Leprosy, Elephantiasis, Evil and Other Cutaneous Eruptions. c.1775. Half-title, 8vo, orig. wrapper, uncut, slight worming in 2 places, o/w nice. Fenning 32-316 1978 £65

SPINA, ARNOLD   A History of Tuberculosis, from the Time of Sylvius to the Present Day. Cincinnati, 1883. 12mo., cloth. Rittenhouse 49-744 1976 $37

SPINGARN, J. E.   Critical Essays of the Seventeenth Century. Oxford, 1908, 1957. 3 vols., octavo, good. Upcroft 10-645 1978 £15

SPINGARN, J. E.   The New Criticism. New York, 1911. 8vo, red cloth, gilt stamped, Fine, tight copy, badly worn and split d.w., Thomas' Hardy's copy, Max Gate bookplate, 6-line inscription from author, 1st ed. Desmarais 1-381 1978 $40

SPINOZA, BENEDICTUS DE   Opera Posthuma, Quarum series post Praefationem exhibetur. Amsterdam, 1677. 1st ed., quarto, 19th-century half-vellum over boards, very good. Bennett 20-201 1978 $1,400

SPINOZA, BENEDICTUS DE   Traite Des Ceremonies Superstitieuses Des Juifs Tant Anciens Que Modernes. Amsterdam, 1678. Thick 12mo., contemp. mor. gilt, gilt edges. Salloch 348-259 1978 $300

THE SPIRIT OF Irish Wit... n.d. (1811). 2nd. ed., coloured frontis, half calf, little rubbed, good. Jarndyce 16-761 1978 £12.50

SPIROKOGOROFF, S.M.   Social Organization of the Northern Tungus; with introductory chapters concerning grographical distribution and history of these groups. Shanghai, 1933. Cloth, illus. Dawson's 449-74 1978 $45

THE SPITALFIELDS Weaver; or, Tom Shuttle and Blousalinda, a Dolorous Ditty:... London, 1821. 12mo, full green crushed levant, gilt, spine gilt, t.e.g., by Bumpus, chapbook, hand-colored frontispiece, inscribed at the bottom by George Cruikshank, extremely rare, original printed front wr. bound in, fine copy. Ximenes 47-252 1978 $275

SPIVAK, JOHN L.   Plotting America's Pogroms. 1934. Paper, paper browning, good. Austin 79-714 1978 $15

SPIVAK, JOHN L.   Shrine of the Silver Dollar. 1940. Illus. Austin 79-173 1978 $7.50

SPIX, JOHANN BAPTIST VON   Travels in Brazil, in the Years of 1817-1820. 1st. ed. in Eng., 2 vols., 8vo, half title in vol. 2, aquatint plts., modern half calf, gilt backs. Deighton 5-56 1978 £165

SPOIL of the North Wind. Chicago, Blue Sky Press, (1900). Decor. gray bds., 1 of 500 on Shandon paper, spine ends worn. Bradley 49-23 1978 $35

SPOFFORD, HARRIET PRESCOTT   Sir Rohan's Ghost. A Romance. Boston, 1860. Orig. cloth, 1st ed., spine faded. MacManus 238-575 1978 $30

SPOKESFIELD, WALTER E.   The History of Wells County, North Dakota and Its Pioneers. Jamestown, (1928). Orig. binding, clean. Hayman 71-502 1978 $50

SPOONER, LYSANDER   The Unconstitutionality of Slavery. Boston, 1845. Disbound. Biblo 247-97 1978 $27.50

SPOONER, SHEARJASHUB   Anecdotes of Painters, Engravers, Sculptors and Architects, and Curiosities of Art. New York, 1865. 3 vols., 8vo., orig. bds., cloth backs, pencil notes, illus. Morrill 241-550 1978 $15

SPOONER, THOMAS   Records of William Spooner, of Plymouth, Mass., and His Descendants. Cincinnati, 1883. Vol. I, cloth. Hayman 73-232 1978 $20

SPOTTISWOOD, JOHN   The History of the Church and State of Scotland. 1677. Folio, 2 portraits, contemp. calf, rebacked, slight marginal water-stains, 2 gatherings reversed. Hannas 54-320 1978 £15

SPOTTISWOOD, JOHN   An Introduction to the Knowledge of the Stile of Writs, Simple and Compound.... Edinburgh, 1708. Sm. 4to, old calf, rough cloth spine. Traylen 88-477 1978 £10

SPRAGUE, JOHN TITCOMB   The Treachery in Texas, the Secession of Texas, and the Arrest of the United States Officers, and Soldiers Serving in Texas. New York, 1862. Orig. prtd. wr. Jenkins 116-1271 1978 $25

SPRAGUE, JOHN TITCOMB   The Treachery in Texas, ... New York, 1862. Orig. pr. wr. Ginsberg 14-975 1978 $35

SPRAGUE, JOHN TITCOMB   The Treachery in Texas, the Secession of Texas. New York, 1862. Wrs., Bell Wiley's copy. Broadfoot 46-386 1978 $25

SPRAGUE, MARY A.   An Earnest Trifler. Boston, 1880. Orig. binding, clean. Hayman 71-242 1978 $8.50

SPRAGUE, WILLIAM B.   Annals of the American Unitarian Pulpit... New York, 1865. Frontis., orig. cloth, spine chipped, otherwise nice copy. MacManus 239-448 1978 $40

SPRAT, THOMAS   The History of the Royal Society of London, For the Improving of Natural Knowledge. London, 1667. 1st ed., quarto, contemp. calf, rebacked, gilt spine rules with green morocco label, gilt, R.E. Myddelton copy, with bookplate of Chirk Castle, portrait missing. Bennett 20-202 1978 $400

SPRETER, JOHANN   VOnn Weltlicher und Geistlicher Oberkeyt, Adel und Ritterschafft, Kriegen unnd Kriegfleuten.... Basel, 1543. Sm. 4 to., rare 1st ed., modern half vellum. Schafer 19-38 1978 sFr. 450

SPRING, AGNES W.   Casper Collins. The Life and Exploits of an Indian Fighter of the Sixties. New York, 1927. Illus., 1st ed., fine, d.j. MacManus 239-1218 1978 $25

SPRING, GARDINER   First Things. New York, 1851. 2 vols., 8vo., 1st ed., orig. cloth. Morrill 241-551 1978 $12.50

SPRING, HOWARD   There is No Armour. 1948. Pres. copy inscribed by author, very good, slightly worn d.w., three A.L.s. by author laid in, first English ed. Bell Book 17-825 1978 £15

SPRING, LEVERETT W.   Kansas, the Prelude to the War for the Union. Boston, 1896. Cloth, nice copy. Hayman 73-684 1978 $7.50

SPRINGER, ANTON   Handbuch der Kunstgeschichte. Band VI – Die Aussereuropaische Kunst. Ostasiatische - Indische - Islamische - Afrikanische... Leipzig, 1929. Sm. 4to., illus., color plts. Biblo BL781-669 1978 $16.50

SPROAT, AMASA D.   An Endeavor Towards a Universal Alphabet. Chillicothe, 1857. Wrs., some wear. Hayman 73-573 1978 $10

SPROEGEL, JOHANN ADRIAN THEODOR   Dissertatio Inauguralis Medica Sistens Experimenta Circa Varia Venena in Vivis Animalibus Instituta. Gottingae, (1753). 4to., contemp. gilt bds., library stamp, some browning, very good copy, 1st ed., rare. Zeitlin 245-249 1978 $97.50

SPROGLE, HOWARD   The Philadelphia Police, Past and Present. Philadelphia, 1887. Illus., fine copy, orig. cloth. MacManus 239-1644 1978 $40

SPRUNT, ALEXANDER, JR.   South Carolina Bird Life. Columbia, 1949. Lg. thick 4to., illus. MacManus 239-1863 1978 $25

SPRUNT, JAMES   Chronicles of the Cape Fear River. Raleigh, 1916. 2nd ed., simulated leather. Broadfoot 50-306 1978 $125

SPRUNT, JAMES   Derelicts. Wilmington, 1920. Frontis., 8vo., 1st ed., orig. cloth. Morrill 241-552 1978 $40

SPURZHEIM, JOHANN GASPAR   Phrenology.   London, n.d. (1825).   8vo.,
orig. qtr. cloth, back slightly torn, 3rd ed., plts.   Gurney 75-102 1978 £20

SPURZHEIM, JOHANN GASPAR   Phrenology, or the Doctrine of the Mental
Phenomena...   Boston, 1834. 2 vols., 3rd Amer. ed., tall 8vos., orig. cloth,
some spine wear, plts.   Americanist 102-90 1978 $37.50

SPYRI, JOHANNA   Cornelli.   Philadelphia, (1920). Color plates by
Maria L. Kirk, pictorial cloth lightly dulled, fine.   Victoria 34-753 1978 $10

SQUADRON A: A History of Its First Fifty Years, 1889-1939.   New York, 1939.
Illus. Biblo 247-85 1978 $15

SQUAIR, J.   La Grammaire Par Eugene Labiche.   Toronto,
1906. School textbook in drama form.   Hood's 115-365 1978 $10

SQUANQUERILLO, COSTANTINO   Trattato di Anatomia Pittorica.   Rome,
(1839)-1841. Very rare 1st ed., lithographs, contemp. half-vellum, folio. Gilhofer 75-103 1978 SFr 3,900

SQUARIO, EUSEBIO   Dell' Elettricismo: o sia delle forze elettriche de'
corpi Svelate dalla Fisica Sperimentale.   Napoli, 1747. Sm. 8vo., lg. engr.
vignettes, woodcut, contemp. vellum over bds., chipped, lightly browned &
foxed, marginal dampstains, ownership inscr., good copy, rare Naples ed.
Zeitlin 245-250 1978 $75

SQUIER, EPHRIAM GEORGE   Nicaragua: Its People, Scenery, Monuments and
the Proposed Interoceanic Canal.   London, 1852. 1st. English ed., 2 vols., 8vo,
lithograph maps, tinted lithograph plts., wood engraved illus., rebound in modern
half calf, sl. dust soiling in margins, o/w very good copy.   Deighton 5-223 1978
£125

SQUIER, EPHRAIM GEORGE   Waikna; or, Adventures on the Mosquito Shore.
New York, 1855. 1st ed., illus., sm. 8vo., orig. cloth, slightly rubbed. Edwards
1012-685 1978 $30

SQUIRE, JANE   A Proposal to Determine our Longitude.   1743.
Second ed., 8vo., plts., contemp. full mor., special pres. copy on fine paper,
A.L. s. by author inserted.   F. Edwards 1013-207 1978 £120

SQUIRE, JANE   A Proposal to Determine Our Longitude.   London,
1743. 8vo., contemp. calf, 2nd ed., fine copy.   Offenbacher 30-147 1978
$125

SQUIRE, JOHN COLLINGS   The Cambridge Book of Lesser Poems.   Cambridge, 1927. 1st ed., valuable, very good or better.   Limestone 9-279
1978 $15

SQUIRE, JOHN COLLINGS   The Moon.   (London, 1920). No. 142 of
ltd. 200 copies, signed, large 8 to., on Abbey Mill laid paper, orig. cloth,
very good or better.   Limestone 9-280 1978 $25

SQUIRE, LORENE   Wildfowling with a Camera.   Philadelphia,
(1938). 4to., plts. Biblo BL781-696 1978 $17.50

SQUIRE, S.   A Sermon preached in the Abbey Church of Westminster, Jan. 30th 1762.... 1762. Cr. 4to., wrappers, worn. George's 635-
1133 1978 £6

SQUIRE, WILLIAM   The Unreasonableness of the Romanists Requiring
our Communion with the Present Roman Church.   1670. Sm. 8vo., 19th century
full calf, licence leaf, plt., only ed.   P. M. Hill 142-11 1978 £20

SQUPAULT, PHILIPPE   William Blake.   London, 1928. Illus.,
plts., very good or better.   Limestone 9-28 1978 $22.50

SRESCI, GIOVANNI FRANCESCO   L'Idea con le Circonstanze Naturali, che
a Quella si Ricercano...   Milan, 1622. 4to., half leather, first ed., fine, wide
margins. Schumann 511-14 1978 sFr 700

STACY, EDMUND   The Country Gentleman's Vade Mecum.   1699.
8vo., contemp. sheep rebacked, very good.   P. M. Hill 142-12 1978 £220

STAEL-HOLSTEIN, ANNE LOUISE GERMAIN NECKER, BARONNE DE
Corinne, or Italy.   1807. 3 vols., sm. 8vo., contemp. half red roan. Howes
194-472 1978 £21

STAEL-HOLSTEIN, ANNE LOUISE GERMAINE NECKER, BARONNE DE
Corinne, or, Italy.   Philadelphia, 1836. 2 vols., 3rd Amer. ed., orig. cloth,
paper labels, scuffing, good.   Greene 78-286 1978 $25

STAEL-HOLSTEIN, ANNE LOUISE GERMAINE· NECKER, BARONNE DE
Letters on the Writings and Character of J. J. Rousseau.   Dublin & Edinburgh,
1814. 8vo., half calf.   Hannas 54-256 1978 £15

STAEL-HOLSTEIN, ANNE LOUISE GERMAINE NECKER, BARONNE DE   Ten
Years' Exile.   1821. Contemp. diced calf, crack in lower joint, 1st Eng. ed.,
8vo.   Howes 194-473 1978 £21

STAEL HOLSTEIN, ANNE LOUISE GERMAINE NECKER, BARONNE DE   Trea-
surers of Thought.   1819. 1st ed., half title, orig. bds., uncut, spine little worn,
otherwise v.g., orig. state.   Jarndyce 16-462 1978 £5

STAFFORD, E. A.   The Need of Minstrelsy and Other Sermons.   Toronto, 1892. Some wear. Hood 116-320 1978 $10

STAFFORD, JEAN   Boston Adventure.   1944. First ed., covers
rubbed around edges. Austin 82-864 1978 $12.50

STAFFORD, T.   Pacata Hibernia, Ireland Appeased & Reduced
or a History of the Wars of Ireland in the Reign of Queen Elizabeth.   London,
1821. 2 vols., maps, plans, trimmed, modern cloth, reprint, very good. Hyland
128-564 1978 £80

THE STAG at Eve.   New York, (1931). 4to., cartoons, 1st ed. Biblo 251-183
1978 $15

THE STAGE-PLAYERS Complaint.   1641. Printed wrappers, quarter roan, lib.
stamps, no. 41 of 100 copies printed, inscribed by author. Hannas 54-334 1978
£15

STAGG, JOHN 1770-1824   The Minstrel of the North.   1810. First ed.,
contemp. half calf, 8vo.   Howes 194-474 1978 £25

STAHL, P. J.   Contes Celebres de la Litterature Anglaise.   Paris,
c.1865. 8vo., illus. by G. Fath, handsome leather and cloth, rubbed, very good.
Victoria 34-755 1978 $22.50

STAIR, JOHN DALRYMPLE, 5TH EARL OF   Observations on a Late Publication
Entitled "Memoirs of Great Britain, by Sir John Dalrymple,".... London, 1773.
4to., disbound, 1st ed. Ximenes 47-67 1978 $20

STAIR, JOHN DALRYMPLE, 5TH EARL OF   The State of the National Debt,....
Edinburgh, 1776. 12mo., disbound, 1st Edinburgh ed., half-title present, very
scarce. Ximenes 47-66 1978 $60

STALEY, E.   The Guilds of Florence.   1906. Lg. 8vo.,
plts., illus., library qtr. mor., cloth sides. Upcroft 12-420 1978 £10

STALEY, V.   Hierurgia Anlicana.... 1902-3. 2 vols.,
plts., octavo, good. Upcroft 10-163 1978 £12.50

STALLINGS, LAURENCE   The First World War.   New York, 1933. 1st ed.,
4to. Biblo 251-242 1978 $27.50

STAMER, WILLIAM   The Gentleman Emigrant: His Daily Life, Sports,
and Pastimes in Canada, Australia, and the United States.   1874. 1st. & only ed.,
half-titles, 2 vols., 8vo, orig. cloth, bindings worn & stained, but sound, good,
clean internally. Fenning 32-319 1978 £24

STAMFORD 50th Anniversary, 1900-1950.   Stamford, 1950. Wr., illus. Jenkins
116-1563 1978 $12.50

STAMPA, GASPARA   Rime di Madonna Gaspara Stampa.... Venezia,
1738. 8vo., marbled bds., portraits. King 7-238 1978 £50

STAN, ANISOARA   They Crossed Mountains and Oceans.   William-
Frederick Press, 1947. Illus. with woodcuts. Austin 79-715 1978 $12.50

STANARD, MARY NEWTON   Colonial Virginia, Its People and Customs.
Philadelphia, 1917. Thick 4to., ltd. ed., illus., uncut. MacManus 239-1867
1978 $27.50

STANDARD, MARY NEWTON   Richmond, Its People and Its Story.   Philadelphia,
1923. 83 illus. Baldwins' 51-535 1978 $12.50

STANDARD, PAUL   Calligraphy's Flowering, Decay, & Restauration,
with Hints for its Wider Use Today.   Chicago, 1947. Cloth, fine, author's
signed pres. inscr. & dated. Dawson's 447-163 1978 $30

STANDARD VOTING MACHINE CO.   The Standard Voting Machine Adopted
by the Cities of Buffalo, Rochester, Utica, Ithaca, Poughkeepsie and Auburn.
Rochester, (1900). 16mo., plts., wr. covers. Butterfield 21-446 1978 $7.50

STANFORD, JOHN   Divine Benevolence to the Poor.   New York,
1816. Sewn, uncut, prtd. wr. Butterfield 21-478 1978 $10

STANHOPE, GEORGE   Pious Breathings... 1714. 4th. ed., engraved frontis, orig. panelled calf, v.g. Jarndyce 16-203 1978 £7.50

STANHOPE, LOUISA SIDNEY   The Bandit's Bride. Exeter, 1837. Amer. ed., 3 vols. in 2, full contemp. calf, gilt decor. spines, good. Greene 78-110a 1978 $65

STANHOPE, LOUISA SIDNEY   The Bandit's Bride. Philadelphia, 1851. 3 vols. in 1 very thick vol., full leather, stamped in blind front & back covers, spine lettered in gilt, gilt design, edges rubbed, very good copy. Greene 78-110b 1978 $35

STANHOPE, PHILIP DORMER
Please turn to
CHESTERFIELD, PHILIP DORMER STANHOPE

STANISLAVSKY, CONSTANTIN   My Life in Art. New York, 1924. Lg. 8vo., illus., 1st Amer. ed., orig. cloth. Morrill 241-553 1978 $10

STANLEY, CLARK   Something Interesting to Read. Providence, n.d. (ca. 1900). Illus., 8vo. Morrill 239-246 1978 $10

STANLEY, HENRY M.   Coomassie and Magdala. London, n.d. New ed., 2 parts in 1 vol., 2 maps, 26 illus., cr. 8vo, gilt-dec. cloth. K Books 239-465 1978 £15

STANLEY, HENRY M.   How I Found Livingstone; Travels, Adventures and Discoveries in Central Africa... London, 1872. 1st. ed., thick 8vo, orig. pictorial cloth, little worn & sm. snag at foot of spine. Sexton 7-117 1978 £65

STANLEY, HENRY M.   How I found Livingstone, Travels, adventures, and Discoveries in Central Africa. New York, 1906. Maps, plts., illus., orig. pict. decor. cloth, 8vo. K Books 244-297 1978 £9

STANLEY, HENRY M.   In Darkest Africa... 1890. Folding maps, portraits, plts., illus., 2 vols., 8vo, orig. cloth. Edwards 1012-289 1978 £45

STANLEY, HENRY M.   In Darkest Africa. New York, 1890. 2 vols., 2 maps supplied in facsimile, illus., roy. 8vo, orig. dec. cloth, somewhat shaken. K Books 239-467 1978 £20

STANLEY, HENRY M.   In Darkest Africa. New York, 1890. 2 vols., 2 maps, 2 portraits, 150 other illus., roy. 8vo, neatly recased in orig. dec. cloth, covers little chafed. K Books 239-466 1978 £25

STANLEY, HENRY M.   In Darkest Africa, or the Quest, Rescue & Retreat of Emin, Governor of Equatoria. New York, 1891. 2 vols., 8vo, orig. cloth. Book Chest 17-359 1978 $85

STANLEY, HENRY M.   Through the Dark Continent. New York, 1878. Maps, woodcuts, 2 vols., 8vo., half mor., marbled bd. sides, 1st Amer. ed. Morrill 241-554 1978 $35

STANLEY, HENRY M.   Through the Dark Continent. London, 1878. 1st ed., 2 vols., maps, plts., illus., roy. 8vo., orig. brown cloth, top edges dust-soiled, otherwise good. K Books 244-444 1978 £45

STANLEY, THOMAS B.   The Technique of Advertising Production. New York, (1948). Illus., 4to., some underscoring. Biblo BL781-527 1978 $9

STANLEY, WILLIAM   Commentaries on Ireland. 1833. Cover worn, text very good, reprint. Hyland 128-565 1978 £12

STANLEY, WILLIAM   A Discourse Concerning the Devotions of the Church of Rome.... 1685. 1st. ed., 4to, wrapper, fine. Fenning 32-320 1978 £10.50

STANSFIELD, ALFRED   The Electric Furnace, Its Evolution, Theory and Practice. Toronto, New York, 1907. Illus. Hood 117-454 1978 $20

STANSTEAD, L. C.   The Canadian Reader. Stanstead, 1834. Full calf. Wolfe 39-168 1978 $100

STANTON, DANIEL   A Journal of the Life, Travels, and Gospel Labours, of a Faithful Minister of Jesus Christ... Philadelphia, 1772. Contemp. calf, bookplts., very nice copy. MacManus 239-1686 1978 $25

STANTON, FRANK L.   Songs from Dixie Land. Indianapolis, 1900. Bell Wiley's copy. Broadfoot's 44-775 1978 $14.00

STANTON, MARY ALMSTED   A System of Practical and Scientific Physiognomy.. Philadelphia, 1890. 2 vols., profusely illus. Baldwins' 51-367 1978 $20

STANTON, THEODORE   Elizabeth Cady Stanton. As Revealed in Her Letters, Diary and Reminiscences. New York, (1922). 1st ed., 2 vols., illus., orig. cloth, very good. MacManus 239-819 1978 $22.50

STANWELL-FLETCHER, T. C.   Driftwood Valley. Boston, 1946. Illus. Hood 116-888 1978 $12.50

STANYAN, ABRAHAM   An Account of Switzerland Written in the Year 1714. 1714. 1st. ed., orig. panelled calf, hinges weak. Jarndyce 16-213 1978 £28

STANYAN, TEMPLE d. 1752   The Grecian History. 1756. Frontispiece, map, plts., 2 vols., contemp. calf, 8vo. Howes 194-475 1978 £21

STAPLER, H.B.B.   A Detailed Description of the Scenes and Incidents Connected with a Trip Through the Mountains and Parks of Colorado,.... Wilmington, 1871. Orig. cloth, small cover stains, leaves partly stained, cloth slipcase, Littell copy with his bookplt., signed pres. from Gause. Ginsberg 14-274 1978 $150

STAPLES, ARTHUR G.   Jack in the Pulpit. Lewiston, 1921. First ed., ltd. to 1500 copies, signed by author, with inscription. Austin 82-621 1978 $37.50

STAPLES, ARTHUR G.   Just Talks on Common Themes. 1919. Ltd. to 1050 copies, signed by author. Austin 82-622 1978 $20

STAPLES, THOMAS S.   Reconstruction in Arkansas 1862-1874. NY, 1923. New cloth, pres copy to Wiley from author, Bell Wiley's copy. Broadfoot's 44-433 1978 $36.00

STAPLES, WILLIAM R.   Rhode Island in the Continental Congress... Providence, 1870. Fine uncut copy, orig. cloth. MacManus 239-620 1978 $35

STAPLETON, THOMAS   Promptuarium Morale Super Evangelia Dominicalia Totius Anni. Lyons, 1594. Vol. I only. Allen 234-1460 1978 $45

STAPART   L'Art de Graver au Pinceau: Nouvelle Methode... Paris, 1773. 12mo., half leather. Schumann 511-56 1978 sFr 1,100

STARK, CHARLES R.   Groton, Conn. Stonington, 1922. Illus., ltd. to 300 copies, fine, orig. cloth. MacManus 239-949 1978 $45

STARK, CORDELIA   The Female Wanderer. Boston, 1829. Crude paper wr. Nestler Rare 78-143 1978 $35

STARK, FREYA   Baghdad Sketches. Baghdad, 1932. Illus. by E. N. Prescott, very nice, first ed., orig. binding, author's signed autograph pres. inscription, very scarce. Rota 211-658 1978 £35

STARK, JAMES H.   The Loyalists of Massachusetts and the Other Side of the American Revolution. Boston, (1907). Illus., uncut, fold. map, scarce. MacManus 239-621 1978 $35

STARKE, R. G.   The Lord of Lanoraie, A Canadian Legend. Montreal, 1898. Illus. Hood's 115-908 1978 $17.50

STARKEY, G. R.   Drs. Starkey and Palen's Treatment by Inhalation with their Original Compound Oxygen. Philadelphia, (1888). Illus., 16mo., orig. wrs. Morrill 239-247 1978 $10

STARKEY, JAMES   Twenty Five Lyrics. 1933. 1 of 150 copies, very good, octavo bound in cloth, reprint. Hyland 128-312 1978 £20

STARLING, ELIZABETH   Noble Deeds of Woman; Or, Examples of Female Courage and Virtue. Boston, 1860. Orig. binding, clean, some wear. Hayman 71-709 1978 $7.50

STARLING, ERNEST H.   Elements of Human Physiology. Philadelphia, 1892. First ed. Rittenhouse 49-747 1976 $12.50

STARR, CHESTER G.   From Salerno to the Alps. Washington, (1948). Maps. Biblo 247-791 1978 $17.50

STARR, FREDERICK   The Ainu Group at the Saint Louis Exposition. Chicago, 1904. Boards, joints splitting, general wear, illus., still tight. Dawson's 449-191 1978 $8.50

STARRETT, VINCENT   Ambrose Bierce. Philadelphia, 1929. No. 14 of
lg. paper ed., ltd. to 45 copies, signed by author, frontis. Austin 82-869 1978
$12.50

STARRETT, VINCENT   Bookman's Holiday. The Private Satisfactions of
an Incurable Collector. New York, (1942). Cloth, 1st print., nice., slightly
worn d.j. Hayman 72-724 1978 $12.50

STARRETT, VINCENT   Bookman's Holiday. New York, 1942. 1st print.,
fine, d.j. Ballinger 11-85 1978 $25.00

STARRETT, VINCENT   Dead Man Inside. 1931. First ed. Austin 82-
870 1978 $12.50

STARRETT, VINCENT   Dead Man Inside. New York, 1931. First U.S.
ed., very good. Bell Book 17-267 1978 £5

STARRETT, VINCENT   Penny Wise and Book Foolish. New York, 1929.
Orig. cloth, d.j., 1st ed. MacManus 238-1055 1978 $15

STATE And National Platforms of the Democratic Party. N.P., n.d. (1876).
Stitched. Hayman 71-647 1978 $7.50

THE STATE of Iowa, U.S.A.: Its Statistics and Resources. Des Moines, 1876.
12mo, disbound, 1st ed. Ginsberg 14-428 1978 $35

A STATEMENT of Facts, with Remarks, &c. in Answer to a Pamphlet, Published
at Brooklyn, in Relation to the Steam Boat Ferry. Brooklyn, 1822. Wr., pages
uncut & loose, two signatures of Capt. Francis H. Ellison. Butterfield 21-485
1978 $25

A STATEMENT of the Claim of the West India Colonies to a Protecting Duty Against
East India Sugar. London, 1823. 8vo, disbound, 1st ed. Ximenes 47-331 1978
$70

STATEMENT of the Disposition of Some of the Bodies of Deceased Union Soldiers
and Prisoners of War Who Remains Have Been Removed to National Cemeteries in
the Southern and Western States. Washington, 1869. Wr. Jenkins 116-1276
1978 $15

STATHAM, E. P.   A Jacobean Letter-Writer; The Life and Times
of John Chamberlain. 1920. Octavo, good. Upcroft 10-546 1978 £5

STATHAM, E. P.   Privateers and Privateering. New York, 1910.
Illus., orig. pic. cloth, very good, bookplt. MacManus 239-1790 1978 $15

STATHAM, F. REGINALD   Paul Kruger and His Times. London, 1898.
Portrait, folding map, generally little dusty & thumbed, head of backstrip snicked,
orig. cloth, 8vo. K Books 239-468 1978 £8

STATHEM, H. HEATHCOTE   Modern Architecture. New York, 1898. 1st
Amer. ed., 8vo, spine sunned, very good. Victoria 34-756 1978 $25

STATIUS, PUBLIUS PAPINIUS   Opera. denuo ac ferio emendatus. Amsterodami,
1624. Engraved title, 32mo., contemp. calf, rubbed. George's 635-513 1978
£6

STATIUS, PUBLIUS PAPINIUS   Silvarum Libri Quinque. 1728. Fine, 4to.,
contemp. polished calf. Howes 194-476 1978 £24

STATUES of Sam Houston and Stephen F. Austin Erected in Statuary Hall of the
Capitol Building at Washington. Washington, 1905. Jenkins 116-47 1978 $12.50

STATUTES of the Most Honourable Order of the Bath. 1812. 4to., contemp.
crimson mor., all edges gilt. Howes 194-407 1978 £21

STATZ, D.   Gotisches Musterbuch. Zweite Auflage. Leipzig, 1905. Folio, plts., some in color, bind. badly torn and worn. Biblo BL781-
548 1978 $47.50

STAUNTON, G. L.   An Historical Account of the Embassy to the
Emperor of China... 1797. Maps, vignette title, frontis by Stothard, illus.,
engraved plts., half calf, slight dampstaining on 3 plts., 8vo. Edwards 1012-
198 1978 £40

STAUNTON, GEORGE   Authentic Account of an Embassy From the King
of Great Britain to the Emperor of China... 1798. Portraits, 2 vols., 4to, folio
atlas, plts., half calf. Edwards 1012-197 1978 £350

STAUNTON, GEORGE THOMAS   Miscellaneous Notices Relating to China,
and Our Commercial Intercourse with That Country, Including a Few Translations
from the Chinese Language. London, 1850. 2nd ed., 8vo, contemp. roan
back & corners, marbled sides, ex-lib. Morrill 241-555 1978 $47.50

STAVELEY, T.   The History of Churches in England. 1712.
Panelled calf, worn, joints cracked, 8vo. George's 635-1134 1978 £5.25

STEAD, CHRISTINA   Seven Poor Men of Sydney. 1934. 1st. ed., orig.
cloth, very good. Eaton 45-468 1978 £12

STEAD, WILLIAM T.   Real Ghost Stories. New York, 1921. New ed.,
1st Amer. ed. Biblo BL781-966 1978 $7.50

STEALEY, O. O.   Twenty Years in the Press Gallery... New York,
1906. Cloth. Hayman 72-725 1978 $12.50

STEARN, C. H.   University and Community in the Canadian Democracy. Hamilton, 1948. Card cover, illus. Hood 116-387 1978 $7.50

STEARNS, CHARLES   The Black Man of the South, and the Rebels.
NY, 1872. Cover slightly worn, Bell Wiley's copy. Broadfoot's 44-348 1978
$35.00

STEARNS, EZRA S.   History of Ashburnham Mass., from the Grant of
Dorchester Canada to the Present... Ashburnham, 1887. Illus., nice, orig.
cloth. MacManus 239-1008 1978 $55

STEARNS, EZRA S.   History of the Town of Rindge, N.H... Boston, 1875. 1st ed., illus., ports., orig. cloth, very good. MacManus 239-
1076 1978 $50

STEARNS, HAROLD E.   America Now. An Inquiry into Civilization in the
United States. New York, 1938. 1st ed. Biblo BL781-878 1978 $9.50

STEARNS, HAROLD E.   The Street I Know. 1935. First ed. Austin 82-
871 1978 $15

STEARNS, JOHN G.   An Inquiry into the Nature and Tendency of Speculative Free-Masonry:.... Utica, 1829. 5th ed., rev'd. and corrected, leather.
Hayman 72-726 1978 $15

STEARNS, MARTHA GENUNG   The Transplanting. 1928. Illus. with photos.
Austin 79-40 1978 $11

STEARNS, W.   New England Bird Life. Boston, 1881-3.
2 vols., 8vo, orig. cloth. Book Chest 17-360 1978 $80

STEBBING, HENRY   The Christian in Palestine. (1847). First ed.,
vignette title, map, plts., 4to., orig. mor.-backed cloth, gilt edges. Howes
194-1367 1978 £75

STEBBING, HENRY   Lives of the Italian Poets. 1832. Second ed.,
3 vols., cr. 8vo., contemp. half blue mor. gilt. Howes 194-1214 1978 £18.50

STEBBINS, RUTH   Extracts from a Number of the Most Eminent and
Celebrated Medical Authors. N.P., n.d. (Hartford? ca. 1822). 8vo., sewn,
scarce. Morrill 239-248 1978 $47.50

STEBER, BENJAMIN   Complete Street Directory of the Village of Ilion
...1921. Utica, 1921. Ads, wr. Butterfield 21-205 1978 $12.50

STEDMAN, EDMUND C.   Alice of Monmouth. New York, 1864. 1st ed.,
12mo., orig. terra cotta cloth faded at spine, otherwise better than fine, newspaper clipping tipped in. Current 24-75 1978 $100

STEDMAN, JOHN G.   Narrative of a Five Years' Expedition Against
the Revolted Negroes of Surinam on the Wild Coast of South America
from the Year 1772 to 1777. London, 1796. 1st ed., 2 vols., 4to., engrs. from
d·wgs made by author, fldg. maps, fldg. plt., orig. full calf neatly rebacked bindings with rubbing, all else fine. Current 24-196 1978 $695

STEED, WICKHAM   That Bad Man. 1942. 1st. ed., 8vo, orig. cloth,
spine faded, pres. copy to Winston Churchill. Sawyer 298-112 1978 £110

STEEL, FLORA ANNIE   The Hosts of the Lord. New York, 1900. 1st
Amer. ed., orig. cloth, t.e.g., spine darkened, owner's name on end paper, good.
Greene 78-111 1978 $20

STEEL, JOHANNES   Men Behind the War. 1942. Ex-lib. Austin
80-309 1978 $8.50

STEEL, JOHN H.   An Analysis of the Congress Spring, with Practical
Remarks on Its Medical Properties. New York, 1856. Frontis., 12mo., inserted
are 2 ads. Morrill 239-250 1978 $15

STEELE, ASHBEL   Chief of the Pilgrims: Or, the Life and Times of William Brewster. Philadelphia, 1857. 1st ed., illus., orig. cloth, fine. Mac-Manus 239-728 1978 $17.50

STEELE, HARWOOD   Ghosts Returning. Toronto, 1950. Hood's 115-458 1978 $15

STEELE, MATTHEW FORNEY   American Campaigns. Washington, 1909. Maps color coded, 2 vols., Bell Wiley's copy. Broadfoot's 44-349 1978 $50

STEELE, MATTHEW FORNEY   Civil War Atlas to Accompany Steele's American Campaigns. West Point, 1941. 136 double-page maps, inscribed to Wiley w/2 letters from author to Wiley, laid in overlays on revisions & changes, Bell Wiley's copy. Broadfoot's 44-350 1978 $100.00

STEELE, OLIVER G.   Steele's Western Guide Book and Emigrant's Directory;.... Buffalo, [1849]. Maps, 17th ed, orig. cloth. Ginsberg 14-930 1978 $250

STEELE, RICHARD   The Englishman:... London, 1714. 1st ed., small quarto, disbound, sewn with white paper cover, two wing-cloth cover, maroon cloth slipcase. Totteridge 29-100 1978 $100

STEELE, RICHARD   The Guardian. 1756. 2 vols., eng. frontis, title vignette, blind-stamps on titles, old calf, worn. Eaton 45-469 1978 £10

STEELE, RICHARD   The Romish Ecclesiastical History of Late Years. 1714. Frontispiece, contemp. calf, rebacked, first ed., 8vo. Howes 194-477 1978 £21

STEELE, ROBERT   Huon of Bordeaux. 1895. First ed., sq. 8vo., orig. buckram, illus. Howes 194-1216 1978 £6.50

STEELE, ROBERT   Renaud of Montauban. 1897. First ed., plts., orig. buckram, binding soiled, 8vo. Howes 194-1217 1978 £6.50

STEEN, MARQUERTIE   William Nicholson. 1943. Coloured plts., very good, worn d.w., first English ed. Bell Book 16-671 1978 £5

STEEN, RALPH W.   Twentieth Century Texas: An Economic and Social History. Austin, 1942. 1st ed., illus. Jenkins 116-1279 1978 $15

STEENSTRUP, JOHANNES JEPETUS SMITH   Ueber den Generationswechsel, oder die Fortpflanzung und Entwickelung durch abwechselnde Generationen... Copenhagen, 1842. 8vo., old qtr. shagreen, plts., 1st German ed. Gurney 75-104 1978 £80

STEEVENS, G. W.   From Capetown to Ladysmith; An Unfinished Record of the South African War. London, 1900. First ed., orig. binding, nice. Rota 211-660 1978 £8

STEFANSSON, VILHJALMUR   My Life with the Eskimo. New York, 1913. Maps, photo illus., some binding wear, orig. cloth, 8vo. Book Chest 17-363 1978 $45

STEGER, H. P.   The Letter of Harry Peyton Steger, 1899-1912. Austin, 1915. Very rare, only a few copies printed. Jenkins 116-1230 1978 $150

STEGNER, WALLACE   One Nation. 1945. Illus. with photos. Austin 79-716 1978 $12.50

STEGNER, WALLACE   The Preacher and the Slave. 1950. Austin 79-717 1978 $10

STEIG, WILLIAM   All Embarrassed. New York, (1944). 1st ed., signature of Oriana Atkinson on flyleaf, good, d.w. Biblo 251-184 1978 $12.50

STEIG, WILLIAM   The Lonely Ones. New York, (1942). 1st ed. Biblo 251-185 1978 $12.50

STEIG, WILLIAM   Persistent Faces. New York, (1945). 1st ed., d.w. Biblo 251-186 1978 $12.50

STEIGMAN, B. M.   The Unconquerable Tristan. New York, 1933. First ed., illus. Biblo 247-889 1978 $15

STEIN, AUREL   On Alexander's Track to the Indus... 1929. 8vo, folding maps, numerous illus., modern half red morocco. Edwards 1012-112 1978 £30

STEIN, GERTRUDE   L'Arbalete; revue de litterature. 1944. First ed., one of 2150 numbered copies, handset and handprinted, imp. 8vo., wrappers, fine. Rota 211-661 1978 £15

STEIN, GERTRUDE   The Autobiography of Alice B. Toklas. New York, 1933. First ed., frontis., v.g. or better. Limestone 9-282 1978 $35

STEIN, GERTRUDE   Brewsie and Willie. New York, (1946). 8vo, cloth, 1st ed., fine. Duschnes 220-285 1978 $45

STEIN, GERTRUDE   Dix Portraits. Paris, (1930). White wrs., 1st ed., in English and French, 1 of 400 on Alfa paper, fine, unopened copy, glassine dust jacket. Bradley 49-300 1978 $125

STEIN, GERTRUDE   An Elucidation. Paris, 1927. 8vo, tan paper wr., near Mint, 1st ed., collector's cond. Desmarais 1-382 1978 $75

STEIN, GERTRUDE   Four Saints in Three Acts. New York, (1934). 4 to., illus., pictorial wrappers, good-fine. Houle 10-307 1978 $25

STEIN, GERTRUDE   Four Saints in Three Acts. Hartford, 1934. 1st ed., folio, stiff pink wrappers, very good, inscribed by Virgil Thomson. Houle 10-305 1978 $50

STEIN, GERTRUDE   Four Saints in Three Acts. (New York), 1934. 1st ed., folio, illus. deluxe souvenir New York program, stiff white wrappers, good-fine. Houle 10-306 1978 $35

STEIN, GERTRUDE   How To Write. Paris, (1931). 1 of 1,000 copies, extremely fine copy in grey boards, enclosed in cloth slipcase. Houle 10-308 1978 $135

STEIN, GERTRUDE   Ida. New York, (1941). 1 of 2,000 copies, 1st ed., ink inscription, d.j., fine. Houle 10-309 1978 $75

STEIN, GERTRUDE   Lucy Church Amiably. Paris, 1930. 1 of 1,000 copies, 1st ed., blue bds., very good, bright copy of fragile book. Houle 10-310 1978 $175

STEIN, GERTRUDE   The Making of Americans Being a History of a Family's Progress. Paris, Three Mountains Press, (1925). 1st Amer. ed., thick 4to, rare, orig. red & black decor. cloth, black cloth spine, light warping of bds., name of former owner, interior near mint. Current 24-54 1978 $475

STEIN, GERTRUDE   Morrow's Almanack For...1928. New York, (1927). 1st ed., fine, d.j., cloth slipcase. Houle 10-313 1978 $50

STEIN, GERTRUDE   Paris France. New York, 1940. 1st ed., fine, in scarce d.j. Ballinger 11-176 1978 $25.00

STEIN, GERTRUDE   Two Poems (Hitherto Unpublished. New York, 1948. 12mo., pr. wrs., 1 of 200 printed at Banyan Press on French, Italian and Chinese papers, 1st ed., fine. Duschnes 220-286 1978 $55

STEIN, GERTRUDE   Wars I Have Seen. Batsford, 1945. Plts., very good, d.w., first English ed. Bell Book 16-796 1978 £10

STEIN, GERTRUDE   Wars I Have Seen. New York, (1945). 1st ed., fine. Houle 10-319 1978 $45

STEIN, GERTRUDE   A Wedding Bouquet: Ballet. London, (1936). 1st ed., folio, stiff rose wr., fine, cloth slipcase. Houle 10-320 1978 $95

STEIN, LEO   ABC of Aesthetics. New York, 1927. 1st ed., half cloth over bds., cloth slipcase, very good. Houle 10-323 1978 $45

STEIN, MARK AUREL   On Alexander's Track to the Indus. London, 1929. 1st ed., sm. 4 to., gilt stamped tan cloth, t.e.g., illus., maps, fine. Houle 10-324 1978 $95

STEIN, MARK AUREL   Ruins of Desert Cathy. London, 1912. 1st ed., thick sm. 4 to., illus., color plts., maps, orig. tan cloth, t.e.g., uncut, bookplates, 2 vols., very good. Houle 10-325 1978 $225

STEINACH, ADELRICH   Geschichte Und Leben Der Schweizer Kolonien in den Vereinigten Staaten von Nord-Amerika, unter Mitwirkung des Nord-Ameri-kanischen Gruttl-Bundes. New York, 1889. Scarce, good, sound cond. Austin 79-719 1978 $97.50

STEINBECK, JOHN   Bombs Away. The Story of a Bomber Team... New York, 1942. Photos., cloth, 1st ed., fine, d.j. Hayman 72-728 1978 $15

STEINBECK, JOHN   Cannery Row. New York, 1945. Prtd. blue wrs., 1st ed., very fine copy, blue protective wr. & slipcase. Bradley 49-302 1978 $500

STEINBECK, JOHN   Cannery Row. 1945. Fine, d.w., first English ed. Bell Book 16-797 1978 £12.50

STEINBECK, JOHN   Cannery Row. 1945. Austin 82-907a 1978 $11

STEINBECK, JOHN   Cannery Row. 1945. Yellow cloth, second printing, d.j. Austin 82-873 1978 $12.50

STEINBECK, JOHN   Cannery Row. 1945. Book Club ed., d.j. Austin 82-874 1978 $10

STEINBECK, JOHN   Cup of Gold. 1929. First ed., good sound copy. Austin 82-875 1978 $225

STEINBECK, JOHN   Cup of Gold. New York, (1936). 2nd ed., binding a bit dusty, good. Bernard 5-258 1978 $8

STEINBECK, JOHN   Cup of Gold. (1929). 1936. Austin 82-907b 1978 $17.50

STEINBECK, JOHN   The Forgotten Village. New York, 1941. Sm. quarto, 1st ed. Petrilla 13-115 1978 $10

STEINBECK, JOHN   The Forgotten Village. 1941. Austin 82-878 1978 $25

STEINBECK, JOHN   The Grapes of Wrath. 1939. Very good, repaired but good d.j. Austin 82-882 1978 $12.50

STEINBECK, JOHN   The Grapes of Wrath. 1939. First ed., good. Austin 82-879 1978 $20

STEINBECK, JOHN   The Grapes of Wrath. New York, 1939. First U.S. ed., orig. pict. linen, very good, torn d.w. Bell Book 17-829 1978 £55

STEINBECK, JOHN   The Grapes of Wrath. 1939. Later printing, fine, d.j. Austin 82-880 1978 $12.50

STEINBECK, JOHN   The Grapes of Wrath. New York, 1939. 16mo, tan cloth with maroon pict. design, d.w. with minimal chipping, 1st issue, near Pristine cond., 1st ed. Desmarais 1-384 1978 $80

STEINBECK, JOHN   The Grapes of Wrath. 1939. Bookplt., very good, somewhat soiled d.w., first English ed. Bell Book 17-830 1978 £38.50

STEINBECK, JOHN   The Grapes of Wrath. New York, (1939). 8vo, cloth, d.j., top colored yellow indicating 1st state, 1st ed., fine. Duschnes 220-287 1978 $100

STEINBECK, JOHN   The Grapes of Wrath. 1939. Austin 82-907c 1978 $20

STEINBECK, JOHN   The Grapes of Wrath. 1940. Later printing, frayed d.j. Austin 82-881 1978 $10

STEINBECK, JOHN   In Doubious Battle. 1936. Austin 82-907d 1978 $12.50

STEINBECK, JOHN   The Long Valley. 1938. First ed., very good, d.j. Austin 82-883 1978 $47.50

STEINBECK, JOHN   The Long Valley. New York, 1938. First U.S. ed., very good, slightly worn d.w. Bell Book 17-831 1978 £47.50

STEINBECK, JOHN   The Long Valley. 1938. First ed., top edge faded. Austin 82-884 1978 $20

STEINBECK, JOHN   The Long Valley. New York, 1938. Terra-cotta cloth, beige buckram spine, 1st ed., fine in dust jacket. Bradley 49-307 1978 $65

STEINBECK, JOHN   The Long Valley. 1939. Austin 82-885 1978 $11

STEINBECK, JOHN   The Moon is Down. 1942. First ed., illus., first issue, paper. Austin 82-887 1978 $37.50

STEINBECK, JOHN   The Moon is Down. New York, 1942. Near fine in slightly rubbed & darkened d.w. Desmarais B-593 1978 $7.50

STEINBECK, JOHN   The Moon is Down. New York, 1942. First ed., d.w. Biblo 247-626 1978 $17.50

STEINBECK, JOHN   The Moon is Down. New York, 1942. First U.S. ed., very good, d.w. Bell Book 16-798 1978 £10

STEINBECK, JOHN   Of Mice and Men. New York, 1937. First U.S. ed., near fine. Bell Book 17-832 1978 £18.50

STEINBECK, JOHN   Of Mice and Men. 1937. First ed., second issue, very good, frayed d.j. Austin 82-888 1978 $12.50

STEINBECK, JOHN   Of Mice and Men. 1937. Backstrip darkened. Austin 82-889 1978 $10

STEINBECK, JOHN   The Pastures of Heaven. Cleveland and New York, (1946). Borders of pages browned, good or better in chipped dw. Bernard 5-250 1973 $7.50

STEINBECK, JOHN   The Pearl. 1947. First ed., d.j., drawings. Austin 82-892 1978 $17.50

STEINBECK, JOHN   The Red Pony. New York, 1937. Orig. bds., 1st ed., 1 of 699 copies on hand-made paper, signed by author, very good. MacManus 238-753 1978 $150

STEINBECK, JOHN   A Russian Journal. New York, 1948. Tall 8vo, boards and cloth, d.j., photos by Robert Capa, 1st ed., fine. Duschnes 220-288 1978 $25

STEINBECK, JOHN   A Russian Journal. 1948. Pictures, first ed., very good, d.j. Austin 82-893 1978 $27.50

STEINBECK, JOHN   Sea of Cortez. 1941. First ed., illus., frayed and repaired but complete d.j. Austin 82-894 1978 $97.50

STEINBECK, JOHN   Tortilla Flat. 1935. First Modern Lib. ed., illus. Austin 82-898 1978 $10

STEINBECK, JOHN   Tortilla Flat. 1935. Illus. Austin 82-897 1978 $11

STEINBECK, JOHN   Tortilla Flat. New York, (1946). Illus., 12mo, 1st Penguin paperback ed., pulp paper, orig. wrs. Biblo 251-644 1978 $10

STEINBECK, JOHN   The Wayward Bus. New York, 1947. 16vo., orange-red cloth, fine copy, 1st ed., collector's cond. Desmarais 1-385 1978 $20

STEINBECK, JOHN   The Wayward Bus. 1947. First ed. Austin 82-900 1978 $7.50

STEINBECK, JOHN   The Wayward Bus. New York, 1947. First U.S. ed., very good, somewhat worn d.w. Bell Book 17-834 1978 £12.50

STEINBERG, FRANZ ANTON VON   Gruendliche Nachricht Von Dem in Dem Inner-Crain Gelegenen Czirknitzer See... Leibach, 1758. Engr. portr., plts., 4to., panelled calf. Salloch 345-177 1978 $200

STEINBERG, MILTON   The Making of the Modern Jew. 1934. Austin 79-720 1978 $10

STEINBERG, MILTON   A Partisan Guide to the Jewish Problem. 1945. Austin 79-721 1978 $7.50

STEINDLER, ARTHUR   Mechanics of Normal and Pathological Locomotion in Man. Baltimore, 1935. Ex-library. Rittenhouse 49-749 1976 $25

STEINDLER, ARTHUR   The Traumatic Deformities and Disabilities of the Upper Extremity. Springfield, 1946. Ex-library. Rittenhouse 49-750 1976 $20

STEINDORFF, G.   Die Bluetezeit des Pharaonenreichs. Bielefeld, 1900. Illus., stiff wrs. Biblo BL781-487 1978 $10

STEINER, BERNARD CHRISTIAN   The Life and Correspondence of James Mc Henry, Secretary of War Under Washington and Adams. Cleveland, 1907. Illus., fine, untrimmed, later cloth. MacManus 239-785 1978 $35

STEINER, BERNARD CHRISTIAN   Maryland During the English Civil Wars. Baltimore, 1906-7. Cloth. MacManus 239-1833 1978 $30

STEINER, EDWARD A. From Alien to Citizen. 1914. Illus., 1st ed., inscr'd by author. Austin 79-722 1978 $20

STEINER, EDWARD A. From Alien to Citizen. 1914. Illus. Austin 79-723 1978 $7.50

STEINER, EDWARD A. The Immigrant Tide: Its Ebb & Flow. 1909. Austin 79-724 1978 $8.50

STEINER, EDWARD A. Introducing the American Spirit. 1915. Austin 79-725 1978 $12.50

STEINER, EDWARD A. Old Trails and New Borders. 1921. Austin 79-726 1978 $12.50

STEINER, EDWARD A. On The Trail of the Immigrant. New York, (1906). Orig. binding, clean. Hayman 71-711 1978 $10

STEINER, EDWARD A. On the Trail of the Immigrant. 1906. Illus., 1st ed., very good. Austin 79-727 1978 $12.50

STEINER, JACOB Die Geometrische Konstruktion Ausgefuhrt mittels der geraden Linie und eines festen Kreises. Berlin, 1833. 8vo., contemp. half-cloth, 1st ed. Gilhofer 74-125 1978 sFr 700

STEINER, JACOB Systematische Entwicklung der Abhangigkeit Geometrischer Gestalten von Einander, mit Berucksichtigung der Arbeiten Alter und Neuer Geometer Uber Porismen, Projections-Methoden, Geometrie der Lage, Transversalen, Dualitat und Reciprocitat, etc. Berlin, 1832. Fldg. plts., 8vo., contemp. half calf, 1st ed. Offenbacher 30-148 1978 $250

STEINER, NANCY HUNTER A Closer Look at Ariel: A Memory of Sylvia Plath. Mint in d.w. Desmarais B-513 1978 $10

STEINMAN, D. B. The Builders of the Bridge. 1945. Illus. Austin 79-731 1978 $10

STEINMETZ, CHARLES P. America and the New Epoch. 1916. Austin 79-732 1978 $7.50

STEINWAY Collection of Paintings by American Artists. New York, 1919. Folio, mounted color plts., ltd. ed., spine chipped, sm. tears at top & bottom, edges rubbed. Biblo 251-251 1978 $10

STELLMAN, LOUIS J. Port O' Gold. A History--Romance of the San Francisco Argonauts. Boston, (1922). Illus., 1st ed. Biblo BL781-299 1978 $10

STELZLE, CHARLES A Son of the Bowery. 1926. Austin 79-733 1978 $8.50

STELZLE, CHARLES Why Prohibition! New York, (1918). Cloth. Hayman 72-730 1978 $7.50

STENBOCK, ERIC Shorter Stories from Balzac. n.d. (c.1896). Cloth gilt, t.e.g., very good, first English ed. Bell Book 17-835 1978 £12.50

STENDHAL
Please turn to
BEYLE, MARIE HENRI

STENELAUS And Amylda; A Christmas Legend... 1858. 1st. ed., illus. by Geo. Cruikshank, half title, orig. light blue printed wrappers, spine defective, otherwise v.g. Jarndyce 16-439 1978 £35

STENELAUS And Amylda; A Christmas Legend... 1858. 1st. ed., illus. by George Cruikshank, bound in polished green morocco, spine gilt, pictorial blue paper wrappers, superb copy. Jarndyce 16-438 1978 £55

STENHOUSE, THOMAS B.H. The Rocky Mountain Saints: A Full and Complete History of the Mormons. New York, 1873. Illus. Biblo 247-253 1978 $37.50

STENHOUSE, WILLIAM Illustrations of the Lyric Poetry and Music of Scotland. 1853. Orig. cloth, gilt. Eaton 45-470 1978 £6

STENTON, F. M. The First Century of English Feudalism, 1066-1166. Oxford, 1932. 8vo. Upcroft 12-423 1978 £6.50

STEPHANUS, CAROLUS
Please turn to
ESTIENNE, CHARLES

STEPHANUS, HENRICUS
Please turn to
ESTIENNE, HENRI

STEPHEN, G. A. Die Moderne Grossbuchbinderei. 1916. Illus., newly bound in cloth. Battery Park 1-283 1978 $75

STEPHEN, J. The Crisis of the Sugar Colonies... 1802. Half calf, some age discoloration in text, 8vo. Edwards 1012-743 1978 £85

STEPHEN, JAMES FITZJAMES Horae Sabbaticae. 1892. 1st. 2nd. & 3rd. series, 3 vols., half titles, orig. cloth, v.g. Jarndyce 16-1077 1978 £15

STEPHEN, LESLIE Dictionary of National Biography. London, 1908, 1909 and 1912. 25 vols. in all, 8vo., full red mor., some scuffing shelf wear, fine. Current 24-212 1978 $485

STEPHEN, LESLIE Studies of a Biographer. 1898. 1st. ed., 2 vols., half titles, orig. olive cloth, v.g. Jarndyce 16-1074 1978 £14.50

STEPHENS, ALEXANDER H. The Reviewers Reviewed. New York, 1872. 1st ed., orig. cloth, spine slightly torn, but fine copy. MacManus 239-908 1978 $35

STEPHENS, FREDERIC G. English Children as Painted by Sir Joshua Reynolds. London, 1867. 4to., neatly recased in orig. gilt cloth, photographs. K Books 244-298 1978 £30

STEPHENS, GEORGE Handbook of The Old-Northern Runic Monuments of Scandinavia and England. Edinburgh & Copenhagen, 1884. 1st. quarto ed., 4to, plts., illus., maroon half morocco, gilt line borders, t.e.g., other edges uncut, gilt, marbled endpapers. Deighton 5-142 1978 £60

STEPHENS, H. L. Father Tom and The Pope or A Night at the Vatican. t.p. lacking, inscription dated 1861, covers loose, spine gone, rare, text is very good. Victoria 34-757 1978 $10

STEPHENS, JAMES The Crock of Gold. London, 1912. Orig. cloth, rubbed, 1st ed., worn, covers stained. MacManus 238-755 1978 $75

STEPHENS, JAMES The Crock of Gold. 1926. 1st ed., illus. by T. MacKenzie, very good, octavo bound in cloth. Hyland 128-569 1978 £22.50

STEPHENS, JAMES The Crock of Gold. New York, 1942. Color plts., orig. bind. Petrilla 13-117 1978 $12

STEPHENS, JAMES Deirdre. 1st U.S. ed., good, octavo bound in cloth. Hyland 128-570 1978 £5

STEPHENS, JAMES Etched in Moonlight. New York, 1928. 8vo, boards, cloth back, t.e.g., slipcase, 1 of 750 copies signed by author, 1st Amer ed., fine. Duschnes 220-291 1978 $50

STEPHENS, JAMES Five New Poems. 1913. Sm. 8vo., 1st ed., decor's, orig. wrs. Quaritch 979-306 1978 $15

STEPHENS, JAMES Five New Poems. 1913. Hand-coloured decor. by Lovat Fraser, wraps, very good, first English ed. Bell Book 16-595 1978 £15

STEPHENS, JAMES The Hill of Vision. Maunsel, 1912. 1st ed., 1/4 cloth, good. Hyland 128-567 1978 £5

STEPHENS, JAMES The Insurrection in Dublin. Dublin and London, 1916. Cloth, little marked, 1st. ed. Eaton 45-471 1978 £15

STEPHENS, JAMES Irish Fairy Tales. London, 1920. Quarto, limited to 520 copies, signed by Arthur Rackham, tipped-in color plates, mounted on cream "linen", vellum spine darkened, text and plates very fine, superior copy. Victoria 34-675 1978 $385

STEPHENS, JAMES Julia Elizabeth. New York, 1929. Sq. quarto, decor. boards, cloth back, 1 of 861 copies signed by author, 1st ed., fine. Duschnes 220-293 1978 $37.50

STEPHENS, JAMES On Prose and Verse. New York, 1928. 12mo, decor. boards, 1 of 5r copies of 1000 signed by author, 1st ed., fine. Duschnes 220-292 1978 $37.50

STEPHENS, JAMES   Reincarnation. London, 1918. Thin 8vo, cloth, gilt, 1st ed., name and date on endpaper, fine. Duschnes 220-290 1978 $37.50

STEPHENS, JAMES   Theme and Variations. New York, 1930. 12mo, green cloth, gilt, slipcase, 1 of 892 copies signed by author, 1st ed., as new. Duschnes 220-294 1978 $22.50

STEPHENS, JOHN   An Historical Discourse. London, 1661. Sm. 4to, contemp. vellum. Traylen 88-341 1978 £15

STEPHENSON, JOHN   Medical Botany. 1831. 4 vols., 8vo., hand-coloured plts., orig. cloth, repaired, leather labels, entirely uncut. Quaritch 977-76 1978 $1,000

STEPHENSON, JOHN   Medical Botany. 1835. Vols. 2 and 3 and collection of 48 plts. from Vol. 1, coloured engraved plts., 2 vols., roy. 8vo., half rough calf worn, plt. from Vol. 1 loose. George's 635-962 1978 £75

STEPHENSON, JOHN   Medical Zoology, and Mineralogy. 1838. 8vo., hand coloured lithographed plts., orig. cloth, uncut. Quaritch 977-75 1978 $285

STEPHENS, JOHN   A Practical Treatise on Consumption. London, 1761. First ed., 19th (?) Century half leather marbled bds. Rittenhouse 49-751 1976 $30

STEPHENS, JOHN LLOYD   Incidents of Travel in Central America, Chiapas and Yucatan. New Brunswick, 1949. Illus., 2 vol. in 1. Biblo 251-55 1978 $20

STEPHENS, JOHN LLOYD   Incidents of Travel in Greece, Turkey, Russia and Poland. New York, 1842. Folding map, illus., 2 vols., sm. 8vo, orig. cloth. Edwards 1012-58 1978 £50

STEPHENS, JOHN LLOYD   Incidents of Travel in Yucatan. London, 1843. 1st. English ed., 2 vols., 8vo, folding map, folding engraved plts., rebacked in modern calf, lettered in gilt on spines, some plts. slightly cut due to trimming by binder, o/w very good copy. Deighton 5-224 1978 £80

STEPHENS, LORENZO DOW   Life Sketches of a Jayhawker of '49. N.P., 1916. Illus., original wr., 1st ed. Ginsberg 14-200 1978 $100

STEPHENS, ROBERT NEILSON   Captain Ravenshaw or, the Maid of Cheapside. Boston, 1901. Cloth, spine faded. Hayman 73-208 1978 $8.50

STEPHENS, W. A.   Hamilton; And Other Poems and Lectures. Toronto, 1871. 2nd. ed. Hood's 115-909 1978 $30

STEPHENSON, NATHANIEL WRIGHT   George Washington. New York, 1940. 2 vols., boxed, Bell Wiley's copy. Broadfoot's 44-777 1978 $16

STEPHENSEN, P. R.   The Legend of Aleister Crowley. 1930. 8vo., orig. wrappers. George's 635-1423 1978 £5

STEPHENSON, SYDNEY   Ophthalmia Neonatorum, with Expecial Reference to Its Causation and Prevention. London, 1907. Rittenhouse 49-753 1976 $20

STEPHENSON, WENDELL H.   The Civil War Diary of Willie Micajah Barrow, Sept. 23, 1861-July 13, 1862. N.P., n.d. Wrs., Bell Wiley's copy. Broadfoot 46-337 1978 $12

STEPNEY, GEORGE   An Epistle, in Verse, To Charles Montague Esq.; on His Majesty's Voyage to Holland. 1691. 1st. ed., folio, disbound, uncut, paper faintly stained. Hannas 54-339 1978 £50

STERLAND, W.   The Birds of Sherwood Forest. London, 1869. Worn binding, 8vo, orig. cloth. Book Chest 17-365 1978 $65

STERLING, ADA   A Belle of the Fifties. New York, 1904. 1st ed., rear hinge pulling, very good or better. Limestone 9-56 1978 $45

STERLING, ADA   The Jew and Civilization. 1924. Austin 79-735 1978 $8.50

STERLING, EDWARD 1773-1847   The Letters of Vetus, from March 10 to May 10, 1812. 1812. 2 parts in 1 vol., contemp. calf, spine gilt, 8vo. Howes 194-478 1978 £14

STERLING, GEORGE   Lilith. 1920. 1 of 350 copies prtd. Battery Park 1-13 1978 $45

STERLING, GEORGE   Robinson Jeffers: The Man and the Artist. New York, 1926. Cloth, very good. Dawson's 447-252 1978 $30

STERLING, GEORGE   Thirty-Five Sonnets. 1917. 1 of 300 numbered copies prtd. Battery Park 1-12 1978 $50

STERLING, ROBERT T.   Lighthouses of the Maine Coast & the Men Who Keep Them. Brattleboro, Stephen Daye Press, 1935. Illus., 1st ed., fronts., 8vo., orig. cloth, very good. Americanist 103-84 1978 $25

STERN, SELMA   The Court Jew. 1950. Austin 79-737 1978 $12.50

STERNBERG, COUNT   My Experiences of the Boer War. London, 1901. 8vo, orig. cloth, little foxed, corners bumped. K Books 239-471 1978 £10

STERNE, LAURENCE   Letters to His Most Intimate Friends. 1776. New ed., 3 vols., frontis vol. 1, orig. calf, red labels, fine. Jarndyce 16-211 1978 £43

STERNE, LAURENCE   The Life and Opinions of Tristram Shandy, Gentleman. Vol. 1 & 2, N.P., 1760, 3 & 4, 1761, 5 & 6, 1762-67. 1st. ed., 9 vols., author's signature in vols. 5, 7 & 9, frontis, contemp. calf, except vol. 7 in contemp. 1/2 red calf, marbled bds., bindings worn, 3 covers detached. Eaton 45-472 1978 £450

STERNE, LAURENCE   The Life and Opinions of Tristram Shandy, Gentleman. Waltham St. Lawrence: The Golden Cockerel Press, 1929. Illus., 3 vols., orig. maroon buckram, 1 of 500 copies, very good. MacManus 238-798 1978 $100

STERNE, LAURENCE   A Sentimental Journey Through France and Italy. By Mr. Yorick. London, 1768. 2 vols., 12mo., contemp. polished calf, rebacked with matching calf and mor. labels, 1st ed. MacManus 238-145 1978 $350

STERNE, LAURENCE   A Sentimental Journey Through France and Italy by Mr. Yorick. Dublin, 1768. 2nd. ed., 2 vols. in 1, 12mo, orig. calf, excellently rebacked, maroon label. Jarndyce 16-208 1978 £23

STERNE, LAURENCE   A Sentimental Journey Through France and Italy by Mr. Yorick. 1768. 2nd. ed., 2 vols., half-titles, orig. calf, red labels, fine. Jarndyce 16-207 1978 £46

STERNE, LAURENCE   A Sentimental Journey through France and Italy by Mr. Yorick. 1768. 2 vols. in 1, sm. 8vo., 1st ed., portr. frontis., fldg. plt., contemp. calf. Quaritch 979-307 1978 $300

STERNE, LAURENCE   A Sentimental Journey Through France and Italy. London, 1768. 8mo., 2 vols., 2nd ed., bound in 3/4 calf with marbled bds. & endpapers, paneled spine with gilt fillets, fr. hinges tender, near fine throughout. Current 24-55 1978 $115

STERNE, LAURENCE   A Sentimental Journey Through France and Italy by Mr. Yorick. 1770. 2 vols., new ed., orig. calf, little rubbed, hinges weakening, sound set. Jarndyce 16-209 1978 £18.50

STERNE, LAURENCE   A Sentimental Journey Through France and Italy by Mr. Yorick. Paris, 1783. 2nd. ed., revised, 12mo, orig. calf, corners worn, rebacked, new endpapers. Jarndyce 16-210 1978 £24

STERNE, LAURENCE   A Sentimental Journey through France and Italy. 1809. New ed., 12mo., plain cloth, early 19th century, over original bds., uncut, frontispiece, plt. P. M. Hill 142-218 1978 £45

STERNE, LAURENCE   A Sentimental Journey Through France and Italy. New York, 1884. Illus. in photogravure, 4to., orig. pic. wrs., orig. illus. cloth box with fldg. flaps & ribbon ties. Morrill 241-556 1978 $25

STERNE, LAURENCE   A Sentimental Journey Through France and Italy. Paris: The Black Sun Press, 1929. Illus. by Polia Chentoff, orig. wrs., pub. box a bit worn, 1 of 335 copies on Arches paper, very fine. MacManus 238-777 1978 $65

STERNE, LAURENCE   The Sermons of Mr. Yorick. (1760)-69. 7 vols., sm. 8vo., contemp. full calf, spines gilt. Howes 194-479 1978 £120

STERNE, LAURENCE   The Sermons of Mr. Yorick. 1777. 6 vols., new ed., frontis portrait, orig. calf, red labels, vol. labels missing, otherwise v.g., handsome set. Jarndyce 16-205 1978 £25

STERNE, LAURENCE   The Sermons of Mr. Yorick. 1777-1779. New ed., 6 vols., orig. calf, red labels, fine set. Jarndyce 16-206 1978 £35

STERNE, LAURENCE   The Works of ...; in Four Volumes... 1819. 4 vols., frontis, portraits, lib. stamp on title pg., rebound in cloth, a.e.g. Eaton 45-473 1978 £45

STERNE, LAURENCE   The Works of... Stratford-Upon-Avon, 1926. 7 vols., port., illus. by Cruikshank and Rowlandson, orig. cloth-backed bds., 1 of 500 lg. paper sets, few spines slightly damp-stained, otherwise very good. MacManus 238-146 1978 $250

STERNS, JUSTIN   Osru. New York, 1911. Orig. binding, clean, 1 inch strip cut from top of free endpaper in front, o/w very good copy. Hayman 71-713 1978 $10

STETTINIUS, EDWARD R.   Lend-Lease. 1944. Illus. Austin 80-310 1978 $7.50

STEUART, J. A.   Self-Exiled: A Story of the High Seas and East Africa. London, 1899. Cr. 8vo, gilt-dec. cloth, little dull, plts. by J. Schonberg. K Books 239-472 1978 £6

STEUBEN, FRIEDRICH WILHELM, BARON VON   Regulations for the Order & Discipline of the Troops of the US. Philadelphia, 1798. Small 8vo, contemp. leather-backed marbled boards, rubbed, marginal repairs, good complete copy, plates. Americanist 101-140 1978 $325

STEUBEN GLASS, INC.   Collection of Designs in Glass by Twenty-Seven Contemporary Artists. New York, (1940). Illus., sm. 8vo., orig. wrs., plts., 2nd ed. Morrill 241-83 1978 $7.50

STEVANS, CHARLES MC CLELLAN
Please turn to
STEVENS, CHARLES MC CLELLAN

STEVENS, ABEL   A Compendious History of American Methodism. New York, (1867). Cloth. Hayman 72-731 1978 $10

STEVENS, ABEL   Madame De Stael, A Study of Her Life and Times. 1881. 1st. ed., 2 vols., frontis portraits, half titles, orig. grey cloth, good. Jarndyce 16-463 1978 £6.50

STEVENS, BERTHA   Boys and Girls in Commercial Work. Austin 80-843 1978 $8.50

STEVENS, CHARLES MC CLELLAN   Lucky Ten Bar of Paradise Valley. Chicago, (1900). Illus., orig. decor. cloth, 1st ed. Ginsberg 14-931 1978 $75

STEVENS, FLORA ELLICE   Shores of Nothing. Waco, 1942. Stiff printed wr., limited to 115 copies, printed by Carl Hertzog., mint copy, original glassine. Jenkins 116-627 1978 $350

STEVENS, G. R.   Fourth Indian Division, 1939-1945. (c. 1948). Thick roy. 8vo., coloured frontis., plts., maps, orig. cloth. F. Edwards 1013-582 1978 £10

STEVENS, G. W.   From Capetown to Ladysmith and Egypt in 1898. London, 1900. 2 maps, cr. 8vo, orig. cloth. K Books 239-469 1978 £6

STEVENS, G. W.   From Capetown to Ladysmith and Egypt in 1898. London, 1900. 2nd. impression, 2 maps, cr. 8vo, orig. cloth, slight foxing. K Books 239-470 1978 £5

STEVENS, GEORGE ALEXANDER   A Lecture on Heads. 1802. Orig. calf, hinge weakening, designs by Thurston. Jarndyce 16-1075 1978 £16

STEVENS, GEORGE ALEXANDER   Songs, Comic and Satyrical. 1788. New ed., 12mo, 19th-century calf, g.e. P. M. Hill 142-297 1978 £25

STEVENS, GEORGE T.   Three Years in the Sixth Corps. N.P., 1866. Steel engravings, front hinge starting, tips of spine worn, Bell Wiley's copy. Broadfoot's 44-559 1978 $16

STEVENS, HAZARD   The Life of Isaac Ingalls Stevens. Boston and New York, 1901. 2 vols., orig. binding, maps & illus., clean. Hayman 71-714 1978 $18.50

STEVENS, HENRY   Recollections of Mr. James Lenox of New York and the Formation of His Library. Chiswick Press. 16mo., prtd. on fine paper, 3/4 cloth, marbled paper over bds., binding worn. Battery Park 1-43 1978 $50

STEVENS, ISAAC I.   Campaigns of the Rio Grande and of Mexico. New York, 1851. Original printed wr., rebacked. Ginsberg 14-539 1978 $450

STEVENS, JAMES   The Auroras of Autumn. New York, 1950. 8vo, cloth, d.j., 1st ed., fine. Duschnes 220-296 1978 $60

STEVENS, LEWIS T.   The History of Cape May County, New Jersey From the Aboriginal Times to the Present Day... Cape May City, 1897. Illus. MacManus 239-1328 1978 $90

STEVENS, SYLVESTER K.   Pennsylvania, Titan of Industry. New York, 1948. 3 vols., 4to., illus. Americanist 102-86 1978 $45

STEVENS, THADDEUS   Speech of Hon. T. Stevens, of Pennsylvania, Delivered in the House...March 19, 1867, on the Bill...Relative to Damages to Loyal Men, and for Other Purposes. N. P., n.d. (Washington, 1867). Double columns, disbound, bit dust soiled. Hayman 73-686 1978 $8.50

STEVENS, WALLACE   Harmonium. New York, 1923. 1st ed., 8vo., orig. blue cloth, light wear at extremities, spine faded, very nice copy. Current 24-56 1978 $300

STEVENS, WALLACE   The Man With the Blue Guitar and Other Poems. New York, 1937. 1st ed., more than respectable. Ballinger 11-177 1978 $32.50

STEVENS, WALLACE   New Poems: 1940, An Anthology of British and American Verse. New York, 1941. Illus., light gray buckram, 1st ed., fine in chipped dust jacket. Bradley 49-310 1978 $35

STEVENS, WALLACE   A Primitive Like an Orb. (New York, Banyan Press, 1948. Green wrs., uncut, stitched, 1 of 500 copies, name of former owner, covers a little browned, fine copy, scarce. Bradley 49-311 1978 $150

STEVENS, WALLACE   Transport to Summer. New York, 1947. 12mo, cloth and boards, d.j., 1st ed., fine. Duschnes 220-295 1978 $65

STEVENS, WILLIAM OLIVER   Annapolis, Anne Arundel's Town. New York, 1937. Illus., d.j. MacManus 239-1823 1978 $10

STEVENS, WILLIAM OLIVER   Charleston, Historic City of Gardens. New York, 1939. Illus. by author. Baldwins' 51-536 1978 $12.50

STEVENS, WILLIAM OLIVER   Old Williamsburg and Her Neighbors. New York, 1941. Illus. Biblo BL781-255 1978 $10

STEVENSON, ADLAI E.   Something of Men I Have Known... Chicago, 1909. 1st ed., illus., ports., orig. cloth, very good. MacManus 239-449 1978 $20

STEVENSON, J.   The Truth about John Wyclif, his life, writings, and opinions. 1885. 8vo. Upcroft 12-425 1978 £6.50

STEVENSON, JOHN   The New Cattegat, Baltic, and Gulf of Finland Pilot. London, 1797. Sm. 4to. disbound. Paine, 78-122 1978 $18.50

STEVENSON, O. J.   Ontario High School English Grammar. Toronto, 1926. Hood 116-388 1978 $7.50

STEVENSON, R. RANDOLPH   The Southern Side; or, Andersonville Prison. Baltimore, 1876. Illus., 1st ed. Biblo BL781-21 1978 $37.50

STEVENSON, R. SCOTT   Morrell Mackenzie. London, 1946. Illus., 8vo. Morrill 239-251 1978 $10

STEVENSON, ROBERT LOUIS   Ballads. 1890. First ed., cr. 8vo., orig. navy buckram, gilt tops. Howes 194-1221 1978 £12.50

STEVENSON, ROBERT LOUIS   The Best Things in Edinburgh. San Francisco, 1923. Thin quarto, holland boards, cloth backstip, 1 of 250 copies, typography design by Edwin E. Grabhorn, fine. Duschnes 220-298 1978 $30

STEVENSON, ROBERT LOUIS   A Cadger's Creel. 1925. Cloth-backed bds., rather soiled d.w. Eaton 45-475 1978 £10

STEVENSON, ROBERT LOUIS   A Child's Garden of Verses. New York, 1885. 1st Amer. ed., blue cloth spine lightly faded, tips rubbed, blue boards rubbed at tips, lightly dust-soiled, text almost fine, scarce. Victoria 34-759 1978 $85

STEVENSON, ROBERT LOUIS   A Child's Garden of Verses. London, 1885. 1st. ed., 12mo, orig. blue cloth, gilt lettering, gilt top, other edges uncut. Traylen 88-201 1978 £180

STEVENSON, ROBERT LOUIS   A Child's Garden of Verses. London, 1885. 8vo, 1st ed., bright blue cloth, edges bevelled, 2 small water marks on back cover, endpapers browned, t.e.g., uncut, copy crisp, near Mint, blue mor. backed solander case. Desmarais 1-387 1978 $350

STEVENSON, ROBERT LOUIS   A Child's Garden of Verses. London, 1885. "Second Edition", blue cloth, gilt vignette, bevelled edges, text fine. Victoria 34-760 1978 $40

STEVENSON, ROBERT LOUIS   A Child's Garden of Verses. London, 1896. 2nd printing, cover cloth a little dulled, very good. Victoria 34-699 1978 $35

STEVENSON, ROBERT LOUIS   A Child's Garden of Verses. (New York), (1944). Illus., pict. slip-case, fine. Victoria 34-265 1978 $10

STEVENSON, ROBERT LOUIS   A Christmas Sermon. New York, 1900. 8vo, pr. boards, cloth back, edges somewhat rubbed, Nice, 1st ed., collector's cond. Desmarais 1-388 1978 $8

STEVENSON, ROBERT LOUIS   Collected Works. 1906-07. Pentland ed., frontispieces, 20 vols., orig. black buckram, gilt tops, other edges uncut, 8vo. Howes 194-1220 1978 £45

STEVENSON, ROBERT LOUIS   The Dynamiter. London, 1885. 12mo., orig. printed wrs., 1st ed., front wr. torn, otherwise good, cloth fold. case. MacManus 238-389 1978 $25

STEVENSON, ROBERT LOUIS   Essays of Travel. 1905. First ed., cr. 8vo., orig. buckram, gilt top. Howes 194-1222 1978 £5

STEVENSON, ROBERT LOUIS   Father Damien, An Open Letter to the Reverend Doctor Hyde of Honolulu. London, 1490. 1st. ed., 8vo, orig. printed wrappers. Traylen 88-342 1978 £20

STEVENSON, ROBERT LOUIS   Father Damien. Sydney, 1890. 1st ed., rare, 8vo., stapled pamphlet, 1 of 25 copies, very fine copy, text clean & tight, near mint, encased in green cloth fldg. box with gilt lettering. Current 24-57 1978 $1,300

STEVENSON, ROBERT LOUIS   Father Damien. 1890. Sm. 8vo., 1st published ed., binder's cloth, orig. brown prtd. wrs. bound in. Quaritch 979-308 1978 $75

STEVENSON, ROBERT LOUIS   A Footnote to History: Eight Years of Trouble in Samoa. 1892. First ed., frontis. map, cr. 8vo., orig. green cloth, scarce, nice. Howes 194-1223 1978 £18

STEVENSON, ROBERT LOUIS   A Footnote to History. 1892. 1st. ed., half title, orig. dark green cloth, good. Jarndyce 16-1078 1978 £20

STEVENSON, ROBERT LOUIS   In the South Seas: Experiences and Observations in the Marquesas. 1900. First English ed., orig. buckram, gilt top, 8vo. Howes 194-1224 1978 £5

STEVENSON, ROBERT LOUIS   In the South Seas. London, 1900. Good, fore-edge foxed. Desmarais B-600 1978 $20

STEVENSON, ROBERT LOUIS   An Inland Voyage. London, 1878. Woodcut title by Walter Crane, orig. pict. cloth, 1st ed., spine and covers darkened, but good unopened copy, cloth fold. box. MacManus 238-387 1978 $150

STEVENSON, ROBERT LOUIS   Island Nights' Entertainment. 1893. First ed., map, plts., orig. blue-green pict. cloth, 8vo. Howes 194-1225 1978 £12.50

STEVENSON, ROBERT LOUIS   Island Nights' Entertainments. 1893. 1st. ed., 1st. issue, illus. by Gordon Browne & W. Hatherell, half title, orig. dull blue cloth, gilt imprint, slightly rubbed, but good copy. Jarndyce 16-1079 1978 £14.50

STEVENSON, ROBERT LOUIS   Island Nights' Entertainments Consisting of the Beach of Galesa, the Bottle Imp, the Isle of Voices. London, 1893. 1st ed., 1st issue, with inked price change, illus., uncut, gilt, pictorial cloth, very good or better. Limestone 9-283 1978 $40

STEVENSON, ROBERT LOUIS   Island Nights Entertainment. London, 1893. 8vo., orig. cloth, 1st ed., 1st issue, good, half-mor. fold. box. MacManus 238-391 1978 $50

STEVENSON, ROBERT LOUIS   Kidnapped Being Memoirs of the Adventures of David Balfour. (London), 1886. Fold. map, orig. cloth, 1st ed., 1st issue, signature, very good. MacManus 238-390 1978 $125

STEVENSON, ROBERT LOUIS   Kidnapped, being Memoirs of the Adventures of David Balfour in the Year 1751. (London), 1886. 1st ed., scarce 2nd issue, 8vo., hinges repaired, spine soiled, fine. Current Misc. 8-58 1978 $85

STEVENSON, ROBERT LOUIS   The Master of Ballantrae. 1889. Good, pict. cloth, first English ed. Bell Book 16-799 1978 £6.50

STEVENSON, ROBERT LOUIS   The Meaning of Friendship. Chicago, 1909. Prtd. in red & black, d.w. Battery Park 1-82 1978 $50

STEVENSON, ROBERT LOUIS   The New Amphion. Edinburgh, 1886. Bound in vellum, orig. ties, one torn, side silk ties, uncut, t.e.g., excel. cond., orig. board box, sides broken. Greene 78-288 1978 $125

STEVENSON, ROBERT LOUIS   Poems by Robert Louis Stevenson. Boston, 1921. 4to., drab bds., half vellum, uncut, t.e.g., ltd. to 450 copies, 1st ed., collector's cond. Desmarais 1-44 1978 $25

STEVENSON, ROBERT LOUIS   Prayers Written at Vailima. London, (1910). Sm. 4to., vellum, base of spine chipped, back cover spotted. Biblo 251-645 1978 $37.50

STEVENSON, ROBERT LOUIS   St. Ives. London, 1898. 1st English ed., uncut, orig. cloth, very good or better. Limestone 9-284 1978 $27.50

STEVENSON, ROBERT LOUIS   The Sea Fogs. San Francisco, 1907. Near mint. Desmarais B-601 1978 $25

STEVENSON, ROBERT LOUIS   The Silverado Squatters. London, 1883. Pic. cloth, bkplt., 1st state of 1st published ed. Dawson's 447-276 1978 $100

STEVENSON, ROBERT LEWIS   Strange Case of Dr. Jekyll and Mr. Hyde. New York, 1886. 1st ed., orig. paper wrs., lacks rear wrap, spine almost flaked off, cover some stains, contemp. inscrip. Greene 78-333 1978 $150

STEVENSON, ROBERT LOUIS   The Suicide Club. New York, Marchbanks Press, 1941. Orig. aquatint etchings by Karl Schrag, ltd. ed. issued in 100 numbered copies on Vidalon paper, 8vo., orig. wr., uncut, pristine cond. Goldschmidt 110-56 1978 $200

STEVENSON, ROBERT LOUIS   Tales and Fantasies. 1905. First ed., orig. buckram, gilt top, 8vo. Howes 194-1226 1978 £5

STEVENSON, ROBERT LOUIS   Treasure Island. New York, (1927). First Amer. ed., tipped in color plts., gilt lettered cloth, v.g., illus. by E. Dulac. Victoria 34-260 1978 $65

STEVENSON, ROBERT LOUIS   Treasure Island. 1949. Drawings by Mervyn Peake, very good, d.w., first English ed. Bell Book 17-724 1978 £35

STEVENSON, ROBERT LOUIS   Treasure Island. Avon, n.d. Illus. by Edward A. Wilson, mint in slipcase. Bernard 5-263 1978 $15

STEVENSON, ROBERT LOUIS   Treasure Island. New York, n.d. Color plts., very good. Victoria 34-261 1978 $20

STEVENSON, ROBERT LOUIS   Underwoods. London, 1887. Dark blue cloth, 1st ed., 1st issue. Bradley 49-312 1978 $40

STEVENSON, ROBERT LOUIS   Vallima Letters: Being Correspondence addressed by Robert Louis Stevenson to Sidney Colvin.... 1895. First ed., plts., cr. 8vo., orig. buckram gilt, gilt top. Howes 194-1227 1978 £6.50

STEVENSON, ROBERT LOUIS   Virginibus Puerisque and Other Papers. London, 1881. Orig. cloth, 1st ed., 2nd issue, spine faded, hinges weak, otherwise good. MacManus 238-388 1978 $45

STEVENSON, ROBERT LOUIS   War in Samoa. 1893. 8vo., orig. wrs. contained in cloth case. Quaritch 979-309 1978 $135

STEVENSON, ROBERT LOUIS   Weir of Hermiston. An Unfinished Romance. London, 1896. Fine copy, some foxing. Desmarais B-602 1978 $25

STEVENSON, ROBERT LOUIS   Weir of Hermiston. 1896. First ed., orig. buckram, gilt top, upper side trifle spotted, 8vo. Howes 194-1229 1978 £7.50

STEVENSON, ROBERT LOUIS   Works. 1922-23. 26 vols., lg. 8vo., Vailima ed., illus., buckram, backs faded slightly, good copy. Quaritch 979-374 1978 $400

STEVENSON, ROBERT LEWIS   The Wrecker. London, 1892. 1st Eng. ed., blue cloth, very good. Greene 78-334 1978 $40

STEVENSON, ROBERT LOUIS   The Wrong Box. 1889. Covers somewhat marked, good, first English ed. Bell Book 17-840 1978 £15

STEVENSON, ROBERT LOUIS   The Wrong Box. 1889. 1st. ed., orig. red cloth, spine faded. Eaton 45-476 1978 £10

STEVENSON, S. W.   A Dictionary of Roman Coins, Republican and Imperial. London, 1889. 700 textual illus., thick roy. 8vo, cloth. Traylen 88-415 1978 £15

STEVENSON, W. H.   The Early History of St. John's College. Oxford, 1939. Plts., octavo, good. Upcroft 10-548 1978 £5

STEVERS, MARTIN D.   Steel Trails. The Epic of the Railroads. New York, (1933). Illus. Biblo BL781-232 1978 $7.50

STEVOGT, MAX   Alte Marchen. 1920. Drawings, oblong folio, orig. bds., stained. George's 635-61 1978 £5

STEWART, A.   Speech of Mr. A. Stewart, of Pennsylvania, on the Portion of the President's Message and Treasury Report Relating to the Tariff. Delivered in the House...9th of December, 1845. Washington, (1845?). Unbound, little dust soiled. Hayman 73-688 1978 $7.50

STEWART, D.   The Covenanters of Teviotdale and Neighbouring Districts. 1908. Octavo, good. Upcroft 10-549 1978 £8.50

STEWART, DONALD OGDEN   A Parady Outline of History. New York, 1921. Illus., 1st ed., good, little shaken in slightly warped cover. Limestone 9-285 1978 $12.50

STEWART, DUGALD   Elements of the Philosophy of the Human Mind. London, 1792. Demy quarto, contemp. quarter-calf, marbled boards, hinges seperating, boards rubbed, 1st ed. Bennett 7-108 1978 $150

STEWART, DUGALD   Philosophical Essays. Edinburgh, 1810. Quarto, full contemp. diced calf, red mor. label, front hinge strenghtened expertly, 1st ed. Bennett 7-109 1978 $250

STEWART, DUGALD   Postscript to Mr. Stewart's Short Statement of Facts Relative to the election of Professor Leslie. Edinburgh, 1806. Octavo, half modern calf over grey-mottled boards, 1st and last leaves discolored, sole ed. Bennett 7-110 1978 $125

STEWART, FRANK H.   Notes on Old Gloucester County, N.J. (Camden), 1917. 3 vols., vol. 1 pub. in 1917, illus. MacManus 239-1329 1978 $27.50

STEWART, G. C.   The Hierophant. Newark, 1859. 12mo., 1st ed., lacks plt., orig. cloth. Morrill 241-557 1978 $10

STEWART, GEORGE R.   Take Your Bible in One Hand:.... San Francisco, 1939. Illus., folio cloth, 1st ed., limited to 750 copies. Ginsberg 14-982 1978 $15

STEWART, HARRY EATON   Diathermy and its Application to Pneumonia. New York, 1923. Rittenhouse 49-754 1976 $10

STEWART, J.   Plocacosmos: or the Whole Art of Hair Dressing; Wherein is Contained, Ample Rules for the Your Artizan, More Particularly for Ladies, Women, Valets,... 1782. Lg. 8vo., frontis., plts., lacking half title, half calf, gilt top. Quaritch 983-Addenda o 1978 $900

STEWART, JOHN   An Account of Jamaica, and Its Inhabitants. London, 1803. 1st. ed., 8vo, title-pg., rebound in polished half calf, marbled bds., gilt back, raised bands, morocco label gilt. Deighton 5-57 1978 £65

STEWART, JOHN   The Stable Book. New York, 1856. Illus., 8vo., few spots on fr. cover. Morrill 239-615 1978 $17.50

STEWART, N.   History of the Worshipful Company of Gold and Silver Wyre-Drawers and of the Origin and Development of the Industry which the Company represents. Leadenhalt Press, 1891. Roy. 8vo., illus. by E. D'Avigdor. George's 635-405 1978 £10.50

STEWART, OLIVER   The Strategy and Tactics of Air Fighting. 1925. Diagrams, cr. 8vo., covers rubbed and marked. George's 635-861 1978 £10.50

STEWART, W. B.   A Stewart Family and Some Others. Cleveland, 1947. Bell Wiley's copy. Broadfoot's 44-354 1978 $10.00

STEWART, W. C.   The Practical Angler. Edinburgh, 1861. 4th ed., illus., fcap. 8vo., orig. cloth. K Books 244-299 1978 £8

STEWART, WILLIAM M.   Bondholder's Conspiracy to Demonetize Silver. San Francisco, 1885. Orig. pr. wr., 1st ed. Ginsberg 14-746 1978 $75

STIBBS, JOHN HOWARD   Andersonville and the Trial of Henry Wirz. Iowa City, c.1912. Pres. copy from Stibb's grandson to Bell Wiley. Broadfoot's 44-355 1978 $12

STICK, DAVID   Fabulous Dare. Kitty Hawk, 1949. New cloth. Broadfoot 50-309 1978 $8

STICKELBERGER, EMANUEL   Das Ex Libris in der Schweiz und in Deutschland. Basel, 1904. 8vo., pict. cover, illus., ex-lib. Battery Park 1-293 1978 $100

STICKNEY, ALBERT   The Transvaal Outlook. New York, 1900. 4 folding maps, 8vo, orig. cloth. K Books 239-473 1978 £16

STIEGLITZ, ALFRED   America and Alfred Stieglitz: a collective portrait. New York, 1934. First U.S. ed., plts., very good, worn d.w. Bell Book 17-841 1978 £10

STIFF, EDWARD   The Texan Emigrant: Being a Narration of the Adventures of the Author in Texas. Cincinnati, 1840. Original cloth, spine gilt, folding map, 1st ed, rare and valuable. Jenkins 116-1287 1978 $375

STIGAND, C. H.   The Game of British East Africa. 1909. 8vo, orig. cloth, illus. Edwards 1012-291 1978 £45

STIKEMAN, H. HEWARD   Special Lectures of the Law Society of Upper Canada on Taxation, 1944. Toronto, 1944. Blank fly leaf torn. Hood's 115-675 1978 $12.50

STILES, HENRY REED   Bundling, Its Origin, Progress & Decline in America. Harrisburg, 1928. 1 of "less than 1000", signed by Aurand, orig. binding, 8vo. Americanist 101-141 1978 $20

STILES, HENRY REED   The Civil, Political, ...History and Commercial and Industrial Record of the County of Kings and the City of Brooklyn, N.Y. New York, (1884). 2 vols. in 1, rebound, illus., lg. thick 4to. MacManus 239-1091 1978 $125

STILL, ANDREW T.   Osteopathy, Research and Practice. Kirksville, 1910. Rittenhouse 49-755 1976 $50

STILLE, ALFRED   Therapeutics and Materia Medica. Philadelphia, 1868. 3rd ed., revised & enlarged, 2 vols., 8vo., contemp. calf. Morrill 239-252 1978 $15

STILLE, CHARLES J.   Major-General Anthony Wayne and the Pennsylvania Line in the Continental Army. Philadelphia, 1893. 1st ed., illus., frontis., t.e.g., orig. cloth, hinges cracking, bookplts. removed. MacManus 239-622 1978 $40

STILLINGFLEET, EDWARD 1635-99   An Answer to Mr. Cressy's Epistle Apologetical to a Person of Honour Touching his Vindication of Dr. Stillingfleet. 1675. First ed., modern buckram binding, little age-staining, 8vo. Howes 194-101 1978 £22

STILLINGFLEET, EDWARD 1635-99   A Discourse Concerning the Idolatry Practised in the Church of Rome. 1676. Fourth ed., modern buckram binding, some age-staining, 8vo. Howes 194-102 1978 £22

STILLMAN, CLARA G.   Samuel Butler: A Mid-Victorian Modern. 1932. Orig. ed., roy. 8vo., plts., orig. cloth. Howes 194-689 1978 £5

STILLMAN, ETHAN   A Discourse, Delivered at the Unadilla-Forks, July 9th, 1837...on the Subject of the Sabbath. DeRuyter, 1840. Sewn, never bound. Butterfield 21-265 1978 $7.50

STILLMAN, JACOB DAVIS BABCOCK   The Horse in Motion as Shown by Instantaneous Photography... Boston, 1882. Sm. folio, very good copy. Baldwin;s 51-554 1978 $400

STILLWELL, MARGARET BINGHAM   Gutenberg and the Catholicon of 1460. New York, 1936. Folio, full brown leather stamped in blind, gilt lettering, protective wrs and slipcase to match, De Luxe ed., fine. Duschnes 220-137 1978 $2,500

STILLWELL, MARGARET BINGHAM   Incunabula and Americana 1450-1800. A Key to Bibliographical Study. New York, 1931. 8vo., orig. cloth, 1st ed., scarce. MacManus 238-1058 1978 $65

STILLWELL, MARGARET BINGHAM   Incunbula and Americana, 1450-1800... New York, 1931. Very good, 4to. Ballinger 11-89 1978 $35.00

STIMSON, E. R.   History of the Separation of Church and State in Canada. Toronto, 1887. 2nd ed. Hood 116-321 1978 $25

STIMSON, F. J.   The American Constitution. New York, 1908. Biblo BL781-879 1978 $9

STINE, J. H.   History of the Army of the Potomac. Washington, (1893). 2nd. ed., hinges cracked & loose. Baldwins' 51-208 1978 $20

STIRLING, EDWARD   Old Drury Lane... 1881. 1st. ed., 2 vols., half titles, orig. green cloth little rubbed. Jarndyce 16-1081 1978 £18.50

STIRLING, JAMES HUTCHISON   The Secret of Hegel... 1865. 1st. ed., 2 vols., half titles, orig. brown cloth, v.g. Jarndyce 16-728 1978 £18.50

STIRLING, M. W.   The Natives Peoples of New Guinea. 1943. Illus., paper. Austin 80-313 1978 $8.50

STIRNER, MAX   The Ego and His Own. New York, 1907. 8vo., gilt edges, cloth, 1st ed. of Eng. trans. Salloch 348-261 1978 $15

STIRNER, MAX   Der Einzige und sein Eigenthum. Leipzig, 1845. 8vo., contemp. half calf, gilt back, 1st ed., very fine. Gilhofer 74-20 1978 sFr 1,300

A STITCH in Time. 4to., marbled paper over bds., one of 1525 numbered copies. Battery Park 1-215 1978 $15

STOCK, JOSEPH   A Narrative of what passed at Killalla in the County of Mayo, and the Parts Adjacent, during the French Invasion, 1798. Dublin, 1800. 8vo., half calf. F. Edwards 1013-430 1978 £20

STOCK, RALPH   The Confessions of a Tenderfoot. London, 1913. Cloth, illus., 1st ed., very good copy from the Allred Collection. Dykes 34-105 1978 $40

STOCKARD, MISS S. W.   The History of Alamance. Raleigh, 1900. Pres. copy with Archibald Henderson's bookplt., cover rubbed. Broadfoot 50-310 1978 $50

STOCKDALE, PERCIVAL   The Poet. A Poem. London, 1773. 4to, disbound, 1st ed., fine copy. Ximenes 47-301 1978 $80

STOCKER, RHAMANTHUS M.   Centennial History of Susquehanna County, Pennsylvania. Philadelphia, 1887. 1st ed., thick 4to., illus., ports., orig. 3/4 calf and bds., spine worn, but very good copy, scarce. MacManus 239-1692 1978 $150

STOCKET, LETITIA   Baltimore. A Not Too Serious History. Baltimore, 1936. Illus., signed. MacManus 239-1824 1978 $22.50

STOCKTON, FRANK RICHARD   The Adventures of Captain Horn. 1895. Austin 82-908 1978 $10

STOCKTON, FRANK RICHARD   The Captain's Toll-Gate. With a Memorial Sketch and a Bibliography. New York, 1903. Orig. vellum-backed bds., 1st ed., 1 of 160 lg. paper copies with Stockton's signature tipped in, fine. Mac-Manus 238-578 1978 $50

STOCKTON, FRANK RICHARD   The Captain's Toll Gate... 1903. Illus., first ed. Austin 82-909 1978 $12.50

STOCKTON, FRANK RICHARD   The Casting Away of Mrs. Lecks and Mrs. Aleshine. New York, (1886). Orig. cloth, spine ends slightly rubbed, spine a bit faded, 1st state, fine, box. MacManus 238-577 1978 $65

STOCKTON, FRANK RICHARD   The Girl at Cobhurst. 1898. First ed. Austin 82-910 1978 $12.50

STOCKTON, FRANK RICHARD   The Great Stone Face of Sardis. New York, 1898. Cloth, illus. by Peter Newell, 1st ed. Hayman 73-210 1978 $10

STOCKTON, FRANK RICHARD   Fable and Fiction. 1949. Illus. in color. Austin 82-911 1978 $12.50

STOCKTON, FRANK RICHARD   Kate Bonnet. 1907. Illus., first ed., cover spots. Austin 82-912 1978 $12.50

STOCKTON, FRANK RICHARD   The Lady, or the Tiger? And Other Stories. New York, 1884. Orig. cloth, 1st ed., worn, box. MacManus 238-576 1978 $75

STOCKTON, FRANK RICHARD   The Late Mrs. Null. New York, 1886. 8vo., patterned cloth, nice, first ed. Desmarais 1-390 1978 $15

STOCKTON, FRANK RICHARD   Mrs. Cliff's Yacht. 1896. Illus., first ed. Austin 82-913 1978 $12.50

STOCKTON, FRANK RICHARD   Personally Conducted. New York, 1890. 1st ed., illus. by Joseph Pennell and others, ex-library, spine faded, very good. Victoria 34-761 1978 $10

STOCKTON, FRANK RICHARD   Pomona's Travels. (New York, 1894). Cloth. Hayman 73-209 1978 $7.50

STOCKTON, FRANK RICHARD   The Squirrel Inn. 1891. First ed., illus. Austin 82-914 1978 $15

STOCKTON, FRANK RICHARD   Ting A Ling. New York, 1870. 1st ed., gilt covers ornaments bright, tips lightly rubbed, very minor cover soil marks, internally fine copy, very scarce. Victoria 34-762 1978 $185

STOCKTON, FRANK RICHARD   The Watchmaker's Wife and Other Stories. New York, 1893. Near fine, ownership inscription, bkplt. Desmarais B-605 1978 $10

STOCKTON, ROBERT F.   A Sketch of the Life of..., Navy Dept. Corres. New York, 1856. Baldwins' 51-570 1978 $25

STOCKWELL, I. H.   Preserve Your Eyes. Worcester (ca. 1860s-1870s). Orig. wrs., 4 x 2 1/2 inches, nice. Morrill 239-253 1978 $12.50

STODDARD, AMOS   Sketches, Historical and Descriptive of Louisiana. Philadelphia, 1812. Full calf, 1st ed. Ginsberg 14-514 1978 $250

STODDARD, HENRY L.   As I Knew Him. New York, 1927. Illus. Biblo 247-138 1978 $15

STODDARD, JOHN L.   Portfolio of Photographs of Famous Scenes, Cities and Paintings. Chicago, (c. 1895). Photographs, oblong folio, half mor., rubbed. George's 635-1517 1978 £5.50

STODDARD, JOHN L.   Scenic America. Chicago, n.d. (c.1900). Orig. binding, clean, views. Hayman 71-715 1978 $12.50

STODDARD, LOTHROP   Luck. 1929. 336 pages. Austin 82-915 1978 $11

STODDARD, LOTHROP   Reforging America. 1927. Austin 79-740 1978 $10

STODDARD, LOTHROP   The Rising Tide of Color Against White World Supremacy. 1922. Austin 79-742 1978 $8.50

STODDARD, LOTHROP   Stakes of the War. 1918. Austin 79-743 1978 $12.50

STODDART, DAYTON   Lord Broadway. New York, 1941. First ed.,
illus. Biblo 247-911 1978 $12.50

STODDART, JOHN   Remarks on Local Scenery & Manners in Scotland
during the Years 1799 and 1800. London, 1801. 2 vols., engrav. titles, map,
plts., roy. 8vo., half dark calf gilt. K Books 244-446 1978 £70

STOEFFLER, JOHANN   Ephemeridum reliquiae Ioannis Stoeffleri
Germani,.... Tubingen, 1548. Very rare ed., portrait of Stoeffler by Holbein,
contemp. blind-stamped calf, repaired, light waterstain. Gilhofer 75-104 1978
SFr 900

THE STOIC and Epicurean Philosophers. New York, 1940. 8vo., cloth. Salloch
348-262 1978 $15

STOKER, BRAM   Famous Imposters. 1910. 1st. ed., orig. cloth,
t.e.g., illus., one gathering slightly springing, otherwise v.g. Jarndyce 16-
1214 1978 £10.50

STOKER, BRAM   The Man. 1905. Very good, scarce, first English ed. Bell Book 16-800 1978 £25

STOKER, BRAM   The Mystery of the Sea. 1902. Very good, first
English ed. Bell Book 17-842 1978 £22.50

STOKER, BRAM   Personal Reminiscences of Henry Irving. 1906.
Plts., 2 vols., orig. cloth gilt, very good, first English ed. Bell Book 17-843
1978 £15

STOKER, BRAM   Personal Reminiscences of Henry Irving. New
York, 1906. 2 vols., frontis, portraits, plts., orig. red cloth, gilt, little soiled,
slightly shaken. Eaton 45-264 1978 £10

STOKER, BRAM   The Shoulder of Shasta. London, 1895. 1st ed.,
covers and edges a little dust-soiled, 8vo., orig. cloth. K Books 244-445 1978
£18

STOKES, C. S.   Sanctuary. CapeTown, 1941. 1st. ed., illus.,
sm. 4to, orig. cloth, slightly worn, slight foxing on half title & last leaf, pres.
letter to Winston Churchill pasted to front paste down end-paper. Sawyer 298-
113 1978 £65

STOKES, I. N.   American Historical Prints Early Views of American Cities. New York, 1933. Illus. MacManus 239-704 1978 $85

STOKES, ROBERT   New Imperial Ideals. 1930. 1st. ed., map, 8vo,
orig. cloth, pres. copy to Winston Churchill. Sawyer 298-114 1978 £125

STOKES, WHITLEY   Gwreans An Bys. Berlin, 1863. Cover stained,
8vo. K Books 244-300 1978 £15

STOKES, WHITLEY   Irish Glosses, A Mediaeval Tract..Irish Arch.
& Celtic Soc., 1860. Fine modern 1/4 leather binding, very good, reprint.
Hyland 128-577 1978 £45

STOKES, WILLIAM   Lectures on the Theory and Practice of Physic.
Philadelphia, 1837. Cover spotted, worn at hinges, foxed. Rittenhouse 49-757
1976 $32.50

STOKES, WILLIAM   William Stokes, His Life and Work, 1804-1878.
Masters of Medicine. London, 1898. Rittenhouse 49-758 1976 $12.50

STOLBERG, BENJAMIN   Tailor's Progress. 1944. Illus. Austin 79-744
1978 $8.50

STOLLER, JAMES H.   Geological Excursions. Schenectady, (1931).
Butterfield 21-403 1978 $7.50

STONE, BENJAMIN   Sir Benjamin Stone's Pictures, Records of National
Life and History...Festivals, Ceremonies, and Customs... London, 1906. 4to.,
orig. dec. cloth, rubbed. Americanist 102-89 1978 $75

STONE, EDWIN M.   History of Beverly, Civil and Ecclesiastical,
From Its Settlement in 1630 to 1842. Boston, 1843. 1st ed., frontis., orig. cloth,
fine, inscribed by author. MacManus 239-1010 1978 $45

STONE, EDWIN M.   Our French Allies...of the American Revolution.
Providence, 1884. 4to, illus., maps, rebound. MacManus 239-623 1978 $35

STONE, HARLAN FISKE   Public Control of Business... New York, (1940).
Biblo BL781-881 1978 $12

STONE, HERBERT STUART   First Editions of American Authors. A Manual for
Book Lovers... Cambridge, 1893. 12mo., orig. cloth, 1st ed., good, 450 copies
were printed. MacManus 238-1060 1978 $75

STONE, HUGH E.   A Flora of Chester County, Pennsylvania...
Philadelphia, 1945. 2 vols., illus., scarce. MacManus 239-1412 1978 $75

STONE, I. F.   This is Israel. 1948. Illus. with photos. Austin 79-745 1978 $27.50

STONE, I. F.   Underground to Palestine. 1946. Austin 79-
746 1978 $12.50

STONE, IRVING   Sailor on Horseback. Cambridge, (1938). Illus.,
name, otherwise very good, dw. Bernard 5-169 1978 $10

STONE, JACOB LEON   A Reply to Bishop Colenso's Attack upon the
Pentateuch,.... San Francisco, 1863. Original cloth, 1st ed. Ginsberg 14-201
1978 $75

STONE, JAMES W.   Festival of the Sons of New Hampshire: with the
Speeches of Webster, Woodbury and Others...Nov. 7, 1849. Boston, 1850.
Ports., 1st ed., scarce. Biblo BL781-142 1978 $38.50

STONE, JAMES W.   Trial of Prof. John W. Webster-Indicted for the
Murder of Dr. George Parkman. Boston, 1850. Bound in bds. Rittenhouse 49-
759 1976 $85

STONE, REYNOLDS. A Book of Lettering. London, (1935). Bds. with cloth
back, soiled, very good. Dawson's 447-164 1978 $115

STONE, W. E.   Walton Stone, a Bunyan, Boone, Crockett, a
Robinson Crusoe. New York, 1931. Archibald Henderson's bookplt. Broadfoot
50-311 1978 $15

STONE, WILBUR MACEY   The Gigantick Histories of Thos. Boreman.
Portland, 1933. 1st ed., 1 of 250 signed copies, illus., orig. bind. Americanist
102-114 1978 $30

STONE, WILBUR MACEY   A Snuff-Boxful of Bibles. Newark, 1926. Illus.,
orig. cloth-backed bds., 1st ed., 1 of 200 copies, fine. MacManus 238-1062
1978 $35

STONE, WILLIAM L.   The Life and Times of Sa-Go-Ye-Wat-Ha, or
Red-Jacket. Albany, 1866. One of 500 orig. light red cloth, paper label, minor
cover defects. Baldwins' 51-418 1978 $32.50

STONE, WILLIAM L.   The Life and Times of Sa-Go-Ye-Wat-Ha, or
Red Jacket...with a Memoir of the Author, by His Son. Albany, 1866. Lg. 4to.,
old 1/2 mor., marbled bds., uncut, 1 of 75 lg. paper copies, ltd. to 575 copies.
Americanist 102-6 1978 $135

STONE, WILLIAM L.   The Poetry and History of Wyoming... New
York, 1841. Frontis., contemp. 3/4 calf, marbled bds., fine copy, A.L.s. by
author tipped-in. MacManus 239-1687 1978 $35

STONE, WILLIAM L.   A Refutation of the Fabulous History of the Arch-
impostor Maria Monk. N.P., n.d. Wrs. Hood 117-373 1978 $27.50

STONE, WILLIAM S.   The Ship of Flame. New York, 1945. 4to,
orig. cloth backed paper bds., little worn on corners, illus. by Nicolas Mordvinoff.
Sexton 7-51 1978 £12

STONE Henge, a Poem. 1792. 1st. ed., 4to, inscribed to Edward Jerningham Esq.,
rebound in brown bds., v.g. Jarndyce 16-31 1978 £50

STONEHOUSE, JOHN HARRISON   Green Leaves, New Chapters in the Life
of Charles Dickens. 1931. No. 268 of 535 copies, 10 fine illus., blue d.w.,
fine. Jarndyce 16-594 1978 £9.50

STONEY, SAMUEL GAILLARD   Plantations of the Carolina Low Country. Charleston, 1938. Ltd. ed., sm. folio, dust jacket, illus., fine. MacManus 239-703
1978 $65

STONIER, G. W.   The Memoirs of a Ghost. London, 1947. First
ed., orig. binding, nice, d.w., author's signed autograph pres. inscription. Rota
211-668 1978 £5

STOPES, C. C.   The Life of Henry, Third Earl of Southampton, Shakespeare's Patron.   Cambridge, 1922. Plts., octavo, good.   Upcroft 10-550 1978 £8.50

STOPES, MARIE C.   Enduring Passion.   1928. 8vo., orig. cloth, slightly rubbed, first ed.   Quaritch 977-78 1978 $45

STOPES, MARIE C.   The Human Body.   1926. 8vo., colour plts., illus., cloth, binding marked, first ed.   Quaritch 977-79 1978 $30

STOPES, MARIE C.   Radiant Motherhood.   1920. 8vo., orig. cloth, slightly rubbed, first ed.   Quaritch 977-77 1978 $45

STORACE, BALDASSARE   Istoria della Famiglia Acquaviva Reale D'Aragona. Roma, 1738. Lg. 4to., calf, rubbed, illus., very good.   King 7-239 1978 £20

STORER, J.   Fifteen Engravings, Being Views of the Ancient Town of Hertford, and Its Vicinity, and Christ's Hospital, London.   1830. 8vo., plts., orig. printed wrs., back worn.   Quaritch 983-371 1978 $85

STORIES About Mortimer.   London, n.d. Inscription dated 1834, hand-colored plates, cloth, very good.   Victoria 34-767 1978 $110

STORRS, RONALD   A Record of the War.   n.d. lst. ed., illus., maps, 8vo, orig. cloth, spine little dull, pres. copy to Winston Churchill.   Sawyer 298-115 1978 £75

STORY, GEORGE WALTER   A Continuation of the Impartial History of the Wars With Ireland.   1693. Sm. 4to, folding plts., half sheepskin, rubbed, sound, half-title & title browned & repaired.   Upcroft 10-166 1978 £35

STORY, ISAAC   A Sermon, Preached August the 15th, 1798, at Hamilton, at the Ordination of the Rev. Daniel Story, to the Pastoral Care of the Church in Marietta, and Its Vicinity...   Salem, 1798. Printed wrs.   Hayman 72-577 1978 $125

STORY, JOSEPH   The Opinion of Judge Story, in the Case of Ezekiel Foster, the Suffolk Insurance Company et alii Claiman's of Schooner Boston and Cargo, and Appellants, vs. John Gardiner, et alii Libellants for Salvage, and Appellees.   Boston, 1833. 8vo., orig. wrs., old handwritten label on fr. cover, backstrip torn, lst ed.   Morrill 239-616 1978 $15

STORY, R. H.   William Carstares; A Character and Career of the Revolutionary Epoch (1649-1715).   1874. Octavo, good.   Upcroft 10-551 1978 £10

STORY, WILLIAM WETMORE   Nature & Art: a Poem Delivered Before the Phi Beta Kappa Soc. of Harvard University.   Boston, 1844. lst ed., scarce, 8vo., orig. cloth, very good.   Americanist 103-94 1978 $20

THE STORY of Blue-Beard, or, the Effects of Female Curiousity.   Glasgow, n.d. (c. 1840). Illus. text and wrappers, colored cuts, fine.   Victoria 34-80 1978 $10

THE STORY of Ellen and Mary: or, the Advantage of Humility.   London, 1822. 2nd ed., stipple-engraved plates (colored), covers lacking.   Victoria 34-764 1978 $10

THE STORY of Our Darling Nellie.   Boston, 1858. First ed., binding stained, 12mo., illus.   Biblo 247-558 1978 $17.50

THE STORY of Samson.   New York, c.1860. 12mo, wrappers, color plates, on linen, illus. by A. Lumley, light foxing, rubbing, very good.   Victoria 34-765 1978 $12.50

THE STORY Of 'South Africa' Newspaper and Its Founder.   London, 1903. 4to, many illus., orig. cloth.   K Books 239-457 1978 £12

STORY of the Nations.   1885-1916. Subscription ed., 66 vols., maps, illus., lg. cr. 8vo., orig. blue cloth.   George's 635-764 1978 £50

STOTZ, CHARLES MORSE   The Early Architecture of Western Pennsylvania. Pittsburgh, 1936. Lg. 4to., illus., lib. marks, fine copy.   MacManus 239-705 1978 $100

STOTHARD, CHARLES ALFRED   The Monumental Effigies of Great Britain;.... N.P., 1817-1832. lst ed., folio, contemp. maroon half mor., marbled boards, gilt lettering on spine, edges worn, gilt edges, offsetting of plates.   Totteridge 29-101 1978 $300

STOUDT, JOHN B.   The Liberty Bells of Pennsylvania.   Philadelphia, 1930. Illus., ltd. to 1,000 copies, fine, unopened.   MacManus 239-1688 1978 $25

STOUDT, JOHN B.   Pennsylvania Folk Art, an Interpretation.   Allentown, 1948. Illus., some in color, d.j.   MacManus 239-1689 1978 $30

STOUGHTON, JOHN 1807-1897   History of Religion in England From the Opening of the Long Parliament to the End of the 18th Century.   1881. 6 vols., orig. cloth, little marked, octavo, good.   Upcroft 10-553 1978 £25

STOUGHTON, JOHN 1807-1897   William Penn, The Founder of Pennsylvania. 1882. 1st ed., port., unopened, very good, octavo bound in cloth.   Hyland 128-340 1978 £7.50

STOUGHTON Collection of Church Music.   Boston, 1829. Oblong 8vo., contemp. calf with outer contemp. protective calf covering, lst ed.   Morrill 241-559 1978 $20

STOUT, WESLEY W.   Great Engines and Great Planes.   1947. 8vo., illus. in color & black & white, lst ed.   Morrill 239-295 1978 $10

STOUT, WESLEY W.   "Tanks.   1946. Illus.   Austin 80-314 1978 $8.50

STOWE, HARRIET BEECHER   Earthly Care, a Heavenly Discipline.   Philadelphia, 1858. Orig. wraps, 16mo.   Baldwins' 51-363 1978 $17.50

STOWE, HARRIET BEECHER   Uncle Tom's Cabin.   London, 1852. 1st English & lst illus. ed. in book form, 8vo., a.e.g., frontis., illus. by George Cruikshank, rebound in full tan calf by Bayntun with gilt fillets, inner dentelles, gilt decor. paneled spine, orig. covers & spine bound in at end, very fine copy throughout with no foxing.   Current 24-58 1978 $145

STOWE, HARRIET BEECHER   Uncle Tom's Cabin.   Boston, 1852. 2 vols., illus., rare presentation binding, red cloth with over-all gilt decorations, pictorial vignettes on both covers and spine, edges rubbed, very good.   Victoria 34-766 1978 $70

STOWE, HARRIET BEECHER   Uncle Tom's Cabin.   1852. Full calf, rubbed.   Eaton 45-477 1978 £10

STOWE, HARRIET BEECHER   Uncle Tom's Cabin; Or, Life Among the Lowly. Boston, Cleveland, 1852. 2 vols., little foxed, orig. cloth gilt, faded, early issue.   Eaton 45-478 1978 £35

STOWE, HARRIET BEECHER   Uncle Tom's Cabin.   Cambridge, 1892. 2 vols., no. 158 of 250 copies, bound in full rust-brown suede with handsome impressed vignettes, black satin endpapers, plates and drawings by E. W. Kemble, fine.   Victoria 34-763 1978 $100

STOWE, HARRIET BEECHER   Uncle Tom's Cabin.   Cambridge, 1896. 1 of 250 copies signed in full & dated by author, 8 vo., orig. grey cloth, large paper ed., uncut, mostly unopened, 2 vols., engraved frontispieces, very good, scarce.   Houle 10-333 1978 $150

STOWE, WALTER HERBERT   Immigration and the Growth of the Episcopal Church.   1942.   Austin 79-747 1978 $15

STRABOLGI, LORD   The Campaign in the Low Countries, The First Full-Length Account of the Epic Struggle in Holland and Belgium.   n.d. Maps, 8vo, orig. cloth, illus., pres. copy to Winston Churchill.   Sawyer 298-116 1978 £65

STRACHEY, JOHN   The Coming Struggle for Power.   New York, (1935). Rev'd. ed.   Biblo BL781-883 1978 $9

STRACHEY, LYTTON   Books and Characters, French and English.   London, 1922. 8vo, green cloth, paper label, uncut, unopened, Fine in darkened d.w., lst ed.   Desmarais 1-392 1978 $20

STRACHEY, LYTTON   Characters and Commentaries.   1933. Portrait, buckram, very good, first English ed.   Bell Book 16-801 1978 £6.50

STRACHEY, LYTTON   Characters and Commentaries.   1933. First ed., frontis., orig. buckram, 8vo.   Howes 194-1232 1978 £5.50

STRACHEY, LYTTON   Elizabeth and Essex: a Tragic History.   1928. First ed., plts., orig. buckram, d.w., 8vo.   Howes 194-1233 1978 £5.50

STRACHEY, LYTTON   Elizabeth and Essex.   1928. Plts., good, first English ed.   Bell Book 17-845 1978 £6.50

STRACHEY, LYTTON   Portraits in Miniature, and other Essays.   1931. First ed., orig. buckram, fine, d.w., 8vo.   Howes 194-1234 1978 £7.50

STRACHEY, LYTTON   Portraits in Miniature, and other essays. 1931. Buckram, bookplt., near fine, first English ed. Bell Book 16-802 1978 £5

STRAHAN, EDWARD   A Century After: Picturesque Glimpses of Philadelphia and Pennsylvania... Philadelphia, 1875. Lg. 4to., illus., fine. MacManus 239-1690 1978 $40

STRAHAN's Grand Annual For the Young. n.d. Illus. some by Millais, buckram, gilt spine. Eaton 45-479 1978 £5

STRAHORN, ROBERT E.   The Hand-book of Wyoming and Guide to the Black Hills and Big Horn Regions for Citizen, Emigrant and Tourist. Cheyenne, 1877. Illus., orig. cloth, 1st ed. Ginsberg 14-1081 1978 $250

THE STRAIGHTENING of the Chicago River. Chicago, 1926. Illus., charts, diags., 8vo., orig. bds., ex-lib., nice, 1st ed. Morrill 239-439 1978 $10

STRAIN, ISAAC G.   Cordillera and Pampa. New York, 1853. 8vo., 1st ed., pres. copy, orig. cloth. Morrill 241-562 1978 $17.50

STRAIT, NEWTON A.   Alphabetical List of Battles 1754-1900. Washington, D.C., 1902. MacManus 239-450 1978 $15

STRANG, E. D.   Olmsted County, Minnesota and Its Advantages of Soil, Climate and Location, with Rochester as a Most Favorable Point for Manufacturing. Rochester, 1884. Double page map, woodcut views, original pr. wrs., 1st ed. Ginsberg 14-573 1978 $75

STRANG, HERBERT   Brown of Moukden: A Story of the Russo-Japanese War. 1906. First ed., plt. by William Rainey, maps, orig. pict. cloth, nice, 8vo. Howes 194-975 1978 £6.50

STRANG, HERBERT   Kobo: A Story of the Russo-Japanese War. 1905. First ed., plts., maps, orig. pict. cloth gilt, 8vo., fine. Howes 194-976 1978 £6.50

STRANG, JOHN   Glasgow and its Clubs. Glasgow, 1864. 3rd ed., cr. 4to., orig. hard-grain mor. gilt, joints rubbed. K Books 244-447 1978 £15

STRANG, WILLIAM   The Earth Fiend. London, 1892. One of 150 numbered copies, signed by author/artist, folio, fine, first ed., orig. binding. Rota 211-672 1978 £50

STRANGE, K.   With the West In Her Eyes; The Story of a Modern Pioneer. Toronto, 1945. Card cover. Hood's 115-271 1978 $10

STRANGE, RICHARD   The Life and Gests of S. Thomas Cantilupe, Bishop of Hereford.... Gant (Ghent), 1674. 1st. ed., sm. 8vo., contemp.vellum, leather label, arms of the Signet lib. on covers. Traylen 88-344 1978 £95

STRANGE, THOMAS ARTHUR   A Guide to Collectors. London, 1950. 4to., cloth. Van der Peet H-64-204 1978 Dfl 70

STRANGE, W.   Canada, the Pacific and War. Toronto, 1937. Fldg. map. Hood 117-157 1978 $10

A STRANGERS' and Tourists' Guide to Chicago. Chicago, 1866. 16mo, illus., orig. cloth. Edwards 1012-480 1978 £18

STRASBURGER, EDUARD   Ueber Den Theilungsvorgang Der Zellkerne Und Das Verhaltniss Der Kerntheilung Zur Zelltheilung. Bonn, 1882. 8vo., fldg. plts., orig. prtd. wrs., chipped, very good uncut & unopened copy from the library of Dr. Herbert M. Evans, 1st separate ed. Zeitlin 245-252 1978 $150

STRASSBURGER, RALPH B.   Pennsylvania German Pioneers: A Publication of the Original Lists of Arrivals in the Port of Philadelphia.... Norristown, 1934. 4tos, handsomely custom-bound 3/4 morocco with raised bands, housed in protective case. Americanist 101-142 1978 $125

STRATEMEYER, EDWARD   Under Otis in the Philippines, or a Young Officer in the Tropics. Boston, 1899. Illus., 8vo., 1st ed. Morrill 241-563 1978 $10

STRATFORD, NICHOLAS   The Lay-Christian's Obligation to Read the Holy Scriptures. 1687. 1st. ed., 4to, wrapper, fine. Fenning 32-317 1978 £8.50

STRATHESK, JOHN   Bits from Blinkbonny, or, Bell O' the Manse. Toronto, 1885. Orig. illus. Hood 116-716 1978 $7.50

STRATHY, E. G.   A Guide to the Cathedral Church of St. James, Toronto. Toronto, 1932. Card cover, illus. Hood 117-375 1978 $10

STRATTAN'S Dublin, Cork & South of Ireland. 1892. Pres. copy, very good, octavo bound in cloth, reprint. Hyland 128-578 1978 £15

STRATTON, A.   The Orders of Architecture: Greek, Roman and Renaissance... 1931. 4to., plts., slight worming of front end-papers, cloth, back faded. Quaritch 983-51 1978 $50

STRATTON-PORTER, GENE   The White Flag. New York, 1923. First ed., frontis. in color, first ed. Biblo 247-627 1978 $17.50

STRATZ, C. H.   Die Korperformen in Kunst und Leben der Japaner. Stuttgart, 1904. German text, illus., color plts., rebound in fabrikoid, bold ownership signature across title. Dawson's 449-193 1978 $25

STRAUCH, AEGIDIUS E.   Astrognosia, Synoptice et Methodice in usum Gymnasiorum et Academiarum Adornata. Wittenberg, 1678. 12mo., frontispiece, plts., contemp. vellum slightly stained. Quaritch 977-198 1978 $100

STRAUS, OSCAR S.   Under Four Administrations. 1922. Austin 79-747 1978 $15

STRAUS, OSCAR S.   Under Four Administrations. From Cleveland to Taft. Boston, 1922. Illus., 1st ed. Biblo BL781-225 1978 $9

STRAUS, RALPH   A Whip for the Woman. London, 1931. First ed., orig. binding, fine, frayed d.w., with slip bearing the author's signature mounted on fly-leaf. Rota 211-674 1978 £7.50

STRAUS, ROGER WILLIAMS   Religious Liberty and Democracy. 1939. Austin 79-749 1978 $8.50

STREATFIELD, FRANK N.   Reminiscences of an Old 'Un. London, 1911. 7 plts., 8vo, orig. cloth, slightly thumbed. K Books 239-475 1978 £6

STREET, GEORGE E.   Mount Desert. Boston, 1905. 1st ed., frontis. port., illus., orig. pic. cloth, very good, bookplt. MacManus 239-989 1978 $25

STREET, A. B.   The Poems of Alfred B. Street. New York, 1867. 2 vols., tear in contents page, good set. Nestler Rare 78-144 1978 $20

STRETZER, THOMAS   Merryland. New York, (1932). Ltd. ed. Biblo 251-646 1978 $12.50

STRETZER, THOMAS   Merryland. New York, (1932). Ltd. to 777 copies, orig. bind. Petrilla 13-119 1978 $10

STRIBLING, THOMAS SIGISMUND   Backwater. 1930. Austin 82-916 1978 $8.50

STRIBLING, THOMAS SIGISMUND   The Store. 1932. Austin 82-917 1978 $7.50

STRIBLING, THOMAS SIGISMUND   Strange Moon. 1929. First ed. Austin 82-918 1978 $11

STRIBLING, THOMAS SIGISMUND   These Bars of Flesh. 1938. First ed. Austin 82-919 1978 $12.50

STRICKLAND, AGNES   Lives of the Queens of England, from the Norman Conquest with Anecdotes of their Courts. 1841. 2nd ed., engraved title and portrait, 12 vols., post 8vo., spines faded. George's 635-765 1978 £10.50

STRICKLAND, AGNES   The Moss-House... London, 1822. 1st. ed., plts., 12mo, orig. quarter leather. Traylen 88-202 1978 £40

STRICKLAND, SAMUEL   Twenty-seven Years in Canada West. London, 1853. Two vols., later library cloth, calf back. Wolfe 39-522 1978 $60

STRICKLER, THEODORE D.　　When and Where We Met Each Other On Shore and Afloat Battles, Actions, Skirmishes - 1861-1866. Washington, 1899. Wraps, Bell Wiley's copy. Broadfoot's 44-356 1978 $16.00

STRINDBERG, AUGUST　　The Creditor. Philadelphia, 1910. Brown cloth, 1st. ed. in English. Eaton 45-480 1978 £5

STRINDBERG, AUGUST　　The German Lieutenant and Other Stories. Chicago, 1915. 1st Amer. ed. Biblo 251-647 1978 $17.50

STRINDBERG, AUGUST　　The Inferno. 1912. Good, first English ed. Bell Book 16-803 1978 £5

STRINDBERG, AUGUST　　Tales. 1930. Near fine, first English ed. Bell Book 16-1012 1978 £4.50

STRINGER, ARTHUR　　The Door of Dread. Indianapolis, 1916. Some wear. Hood's 115-460 1978 $10

STRINGER, ARTHUR　　The Silver Poppy. New York, 1924. Pages browned. Hood 117-544 1978 $12.50

STRINGER, HARRY R.　　Heroes All! Washington, (1919). 2 colored plts., should be 3. Biblo 247-772 1978 $17.50

STRINGFIELD, JOHN K.　　Complete Closing Out Sale of the Melbourne Stud, the Property of William S. Barnes. Lexington, (1903). Wrs., moderate wear. Hayman 73-369 1978 $10

STROBEL, P. A.　　The Salzburgers and Their Descendants... Baltimore, 1855. Illus., 1st ed., fine. MacManus 239-1812 1978 $37.50

STRODE, HUDSON　　South by Thunderbird. New York, (1937). Illus. Biblo BL781-118 1978 $10

STRODE, HUDSON　　Sweden, Model for a World. New York, (1949). Illus. Biblo 247-748 1978 $12.50

STROMGREN, H. L.　　Die Zahnheilkunde im Achtzehnten Jahrhundert. Copenhagen, 1935. Rittenhouse 49-760 1976 $25

STRONG, ADAM　　The Electrical Eel... 1777. 4to, half title, dusted, uncut, edges little worn, rebound in bds., new ed., additions. Jarndyce 16-214 1978 £54

STRONG, CHARLES AUGUSTUS　　The Origin of Consciousness. London, 1918. Underlining. Rittenhouse 49-761 1976 $10

STRONG, DONALD S.　　Organized Anti-Semitism in America...1930-40. Washington, (1941). Wrs. Biblo 251-379 1978 $12.50

STRONG, EUGENIE　　Catalogue of the Greek and Roman Antiques in the Possession of the Right Hon. Lord Melchett... Oxford, 1928. 4to, plts. Traylen 88-25 1978 £5

STRONG, HENRY W.　　My Frontier Days and Indian Fights on the Plains of Texas. Dallas, 1926. 1st ed., original pictorial wr. Jenkins 116-1290 1978 $25

STRONG, ISOBEL　　Memories of Vallima and R. L. Stevenson. 1903. First English ed., portrait, orig. buckram, gilt top, 8vo. Howes 194-1230 1978 £5

STRONG, J. BARRY　　The Legitimate Origin of All the Epidemics in Man and Beast. Taylor, 1882. Frontis, 8vo., orig. wrs., scarce. Morrill 239-254 1978 $67.50

STRONG, JOSIAH　　Our Country: Its Possible Future and Its Present Crisis. New York, (1885). Cloth. Hayman 72-734 1978 $12.50

STRONG, LEONARD ALFRED GEORGE　　The Big Man, Furnival Books. 1931. 1st ed., ltd. 550 copies, cover worn, text very good, octavo bound in cloth. Hyland 128-580 1978 £8

STRONG, LEONARD ALFRED GEORGE　　The Big Man. London, 1931. One of 550 numbered copies, signed by author, nice, 1st ed., orig. binding. Rota 211-678 1978 £5

STRONG, LEONARD ALFRED GEORGE　　A Defence of Ignorance. New York, 1932. One of 200 numbered copies, signed by author, very nice, 1st ed., orig. binding. Rota 211-680 1978 £15

STRONG, LEONARD ALFRED GEORGE　　Dewer Rides. London, 1929. 1st ed., orig. binding, fine, d.w., author's autograph signature, preserved in red cloth fldr. & slipcase. Rota 211-677 1978 £15

STRONG, LEONARD ALFRED GEORGE　　Difficult Love; Poems. Oxford, 1927. 1st ed., orig. binding, fine. Rota 211-676 1978 £5

STRONG, LEONARD ALFRED GEORGE　　John McCormack. 1941. Illus., ex-lib. Austin 79-752 1978 $8.50

STRONG, LEONARD ALFRED GEORGE　　Northern Light. London, 1930. Thin quarto, cloth, gilt, t.e.g., 1 of 275 copies signed by author, fine. Duschnes 220-300 1978 $20

STRONG, LEONARD ALFRED GEORGE　　The Minstrel Boy (A Portrait of Tom Moore). 1937. 1st ed., good, octavo bound in cloth. Hyland 128-158 1978 £5

STRONG, MARGARET MIRIAM　　Genealogy of the Ragland Families and Numerous Other Families of Prominence in America With Whom They Have Intermarried. St. Louis, 1928. Orig. binding, clean. Hayman 71-264 1978 $12.50

STRONG, MARTIN　　An Essay on the Usefullness of Mathematical Learning. 1701. 1st ed., orig. panelled calf, leading hinge broken otherwise v.g. Jarndyce 16-215 1978 £20

STRUTT, G.　　The Regal and Ecclesiastical Antiquities of England... Bohn, 1842. Roy. 4to., coloured plts., orig. half mor., orig. ed. pub. in 1777. Quaritch 983-92 1978 $450

STRUTT, JACOB GEORGE　　Sylva Britannica. 1826. Imp. 8vo., full calf, rubbed, spine defective, joint broken. George's 635-979 1978 £65

STRUTT, JACOB GEORGE　　Sylva Britannica. 1826. Etched title, plts., imp. folio, half red mor., rubbed. George's 635-978 1978 £300

STRUTT, JOHN W.　　Argon. Washington, 1896. Folio, orig. prtd. wrs., uncut, fine copy, 1st ed. Norman 5-265 1978 $200

STRUTT, JOHN W.　　The Becquerel Rays and the Properties of Radium. London, 1904. 8vo., ads, photolitho. plts., text illus., orig. cloth, uncut, fine copy, 1st ed. Norman 5-266 1978 $175

STRUTT, JOSEPH　　Glig-Gamena Angel-Doed:... London, 1801. Quarto, bound in brown half mor., marbled boards, gilt spine, gilt top, some slight browning throughout, 1st ed., hand-coloured plts. Totteridge 29-102 1978 $300

STRUVE, FRIEDRICH GEORGE WILHELM　　Beobachtungen des Halleyschen Cometen bei Seinem Erscheinen im Jahre 1835. St. Petersburg, 1839. Folio, plts., orig. bds., new cloth spine. Quaritch 977-199 1978 $125

STRYKER, LLOYD PAUL　　Andrew Jackson. NY, 1914. Bell Wiley's copy. Broadfoot's 44-781 1978 $14.00

STRYKER, WILLIAM S.　　The Battle of Monmouth. Princeton, 1927. Illus., 1st ed., fine, d.j., scarce. MacManus 239-625 1978 $37.50

STUART, MRS. A. H. H.　　Washington Territory: Its Soil, Climate, Productions and General Resources. Olympia, 1875. Orig. pr. wr., 1st ed. Ginsberg 14-1043 1978 $150

STUART, ARABELLA W.　　The Lives of Mrs. Ann H. Judson and Mrs. Sarah B. Judson, with a Biographical Sketch of Mrs. Emily C. Judson, Missionaries to Burmah. Auburn, 1852. Cloth, moderate wear, slight foxing. Hayman 73-689 1978 $8.50

STUART, GILBERT　　An Historical Dissertation concerning the Antiquity of the English Constitution. Edinburgh, 1768. Quarto, early quarter-calf, marbled boards, 1st ed. Bennett 7-111 1978 $150

STUART, GILBERT　　An Historical Dissertation Concerning the Antiquity of the English Constitution. Edinburgh, 1768. Fine, contemp. polished calf, first ed., 8vo. Howes 194-480 1978 £25

STUART, JAMES 1775-1849　　Three Years in North America. Edinburgh, 1833. 3rd. ed., folding map, no half-titles, 2 vols., sm. 8vo, contemp. diced calf, coloured labels. Edwards 1012-410 1978 £45

STUART, JESSE   Foretaste of Glory. New York, 1946. Red cloth, 1st ed., scarce, signed & dated by author, in chipped dust jacket. Bradley 49-315 1978 $100

STUART, JESSE   Trees of Heaven. New York, 1940. 1st ed. Biblo 251-648 1978 $17.50

STUART, M.   Romeinsche Geschiedenissen. 's-Gravenhage-Amsterdam, 1824-1826. 20 vols., sm. 8vo., half calf bindings, nice set, frontis. Van der Peet H-64-558 1978 Dfl 450

STUART, MARGARET   Scottish Family History. Edinburgh, 1930. 8vo., orig. cloth. K Books 244-302 1978 £8

STUART, ROBERT   The Discovery of the Oregon Trail. New York, 1935. Illus., orig. cloth, 1st ed. Ginsberg 14-933 1978 $40

STUART, ROBERT   Views and Notices of Glasgow in Former Times. Glasgow & Edinburgh, 1848. 4to., orig. blind-stamped cloth, joints repaired, plts. Howes 194-1411 1978 £45

STUART, THOMAS   Stuart's Fancy Drinks and How to Mix Them. New York, (1904). 12mo., orig. wrs., back wr. partly torn. Morrill 241-564 1978 $10

STUART-WATT, EVA   Africa's Dome of Mystery. London, c.1930. 36 plts., map, 4to, orig. cloth. K Books 239-476 1978 £12

STUART-WORTLEY, EMMELINE CHARLOTTE ELIZABETH MANNERS   Travels in the United States, etc. During 1849 and 1850. London, 1851. 1st ed., 12mo., 3 vols., exceptionally nice copies in orig. blue cloth, bright gilt lettering on spine. Current 24-203 1978 $210

STUART-WORTLEY, EMMELINE CHARLOTTE ELIZABETH MANNERS   Travels in the United States, During 1849 and 1850. New York, 1851. 1st U.S. ed., nice copy, orig. cloth, fine copy. MacManus 239-536 1978 $27.50

STUBBS, GEORGE   The Anatomy of the Horse. London, 1853. Folio, orig. plum-colored cloth, faded, taped crudely at hinges, 8vo.,plts. Book Chest 17-372 1978 $200

STUBBS, GEORGE   The Anatomy of the Horse. 1766, 1899. Engraved plts., folio, orig. qtr. cloth, rubbed. George's 635-1019 1978 £27.50

STUBBS, R. ST. G.   Lawyers and Laymen of Western Canada. Toronto, 1939. Hood 116-54 1978 $22.50

STUBBS, W.   Germany in the early Middle Ages, 476-1250. 1908. Maps, 8vo. Upcroft 12-433 1978 £6

STUBBS, W.   Historical Introductions to the Rolls Series. 1902. 8vo. Upcroft 12-432 1978 £6.50

STUBBS, W.   Registrum Sacrum Anglicanum. Oxford, 1897. 4to. Upcroft 12-431 1978 £10

STUCKI, JOHN S.   Family History Journal of...A Handcart Pioneer of 1860. Salt Lake City, 1932. Illus., cloth, 1st ed. Ginsberg 14-691 1978 $125

STUDIES in Child Training - Series I, No. 9. 1925. Pamphlet. Austin 80-811 1978 $8.50

STUDIES in Southern History and Politics. New York, 1914. Bell Wiley's copy. Broadfoot's 44-782 1978 $25

STUDIES in Verse. Chicago, 1899. Ltd. to 225 copies. Biblo 247-628 1978 $17.50

STUKELEY, WILLIAM   Palaeographia Sacra or, Discourses on Sacred Subjects. 1763. 1st. ed., 4to, frontis, orig. mottled calf, old reback, fine copy. Jarndyce 16-216 1978 £32

THE STUNDISTS. New York, n.d. (20th Century). 8vo., orig. wrs., chipped, front wr. loose. Morrill 241-565 1978 $10

STUNKARD, HORACE W.   Parasitic Diseases and American Participation in the War. Vol. XLIV. Austin 80-315 1978 $10

STUR, D.   Die Culm-Flora des Mahrisch-Schlesischen Dach-schieffers. Wien, 1875. Folio, illus., litho. plts. out of text, back cover missing, loose, 8vo., orig. covers. Van der Peet H-64-559 1978 Dfl 65

STURGE, C.   Cuthbert Tunstal; Churchman, Scholar, Statesman, Administrator. 1938. Table, plts., octavo, good. Upcroft 10-555 1978 £10

STURGE, JOSEPH   A Visit to the United States in 1841. 1842. 8vo., orig. cloth, cover faded. Edwards 1012-533 1978 £30

STURGE-MOORE, THOMAS
Please turn to
MOORE, THOMAS STURGE

STURGIS, R. C., JR.   Bookplates by Frederick G. Hall. Boston, The Troutsdale Press, 1905. Bkplt. of Sheldon Cheney. Battery Park 1-291 1978 $50

STURGIS, W. H.   Fly-Tying. New York, 1940. Coloured frontis., photographs and drawings, 8vo. George's 635-1498 1978 £6

STURGIS, WILLIAM   The Oregon Question. Boston, 1845. Folding map, orig. pr. wr., 1st ed. Ginsberg 14-853 1978 $75

STURM, JOHANN CHRISTOPHE 1635-1703   Mathesis Enucleata, cujus Praecipua Contenta sub finem Praefationis.... Nuremburg, 1695. First ed., plts., thick sm. 8vo., contemp. English panelled calf, joints cracked. Howes 194-578 1978 £21

STURRIDGE, ERNEST   Dental Electro-Therapeutics. Philadelphia, 1918. Second ed., thoroughly revised. Rittenhouse 49-765 1976 $12.50

STUTFIELD, HUGH EDWARD MILLINGTON   Climbs and Explorations in the Canadian Rockies. 1903. 8vo., orig. cloth, maps, illus. Edwards 1012-456 1978 £20

STUVEN, JOHANN FRIEDERICH   De Vero novi orbis inventore dissertatio historico-critica. Frankfurt a.M., 1714. Very rare 1st ed., 8vo, half vellum, some browning. Gilhofer 75-105 1978 SFr 500

STYLES, W. A. I.   Unusual Facts of Canadian History. Toronto, 1947. Hood 117-601 1978 $17.50

SUARES, ANDRE   Bouclier du Zodiaque. Paris, 1920. Royal 8vo., orig. pict. wr., uncut, ltd. ed. issued in 440 numbered copies on Lafuma paper, illus. with orig. woodcuts by D. Galanis. Goldschmidt 110-23A 1978 $35

SUBSCRIPTIONS to the Chicago Relief Fund, by Citizens and Associations of California...From Oct. 11, 1871 to Jan. 31, 1872. Original printed wr., 1st ed. Ginsberg 14-202 1978 $35

THE SUBSTANCE OF A Conversation With John Bellingham, the Assassin of the Late Rt. Hon. Spencer Perceval... 1812. 1st. ed., browned, tear from top corner of title, disbound. Jarndyce 16-274 1978 $12.50

SUCCESS MANUFACTURING COMPANY   All-Steel Refrigerators. Gloucester, n.d. (ca. 1915). Illus., 8vo., orig. wrs. Morrill 239-588 1978 $15

SUCCO, FRIEDRICH   Katsukawa Shunsho (Haruaki). Plauen im Vogt-land, 1922. German text, illus., plts., boards, cloth spine, covers a little worn. Dawson's 449-194 1978 $37.50

SUCKLEY, MARGARET L.   The True Story of Fala. New York, 1942. Illus., photographs, 1st ed., d.j., very good. Houle 10-334 1978 $15

SUCKLING, JOHN   Works. 1719. 12mo, frontis, portrait, divisional titles, faint blind-stamp on title, 1/2 calf. Eaton 45-481 1978 £15

SUCKLING, JOHN   The Works of Sir John Suckling. Dublin, 1766. Octavo, 19th century half mottled calf, marbled boards, joints tender, occasional light spotting, 1st Dublin ed. Bennett 7-112 1978 $50

SUDWORTH, G.   Forest Trees of the Pacific Slope. 1908. Wr., maps, 8vo, orig. cloth. Book Chest 17-374 1978 $20

SUE, EUGENE   L'Ebreo Errante. Napoli, 1848. 4 vols.,
16mo., contemp. roan-backed bds., 1st Italian ed. Morrill 241-566 1978 $15

SUE, EUGENE   Le Juif Errant. Paris, 1845. 4 vols., Lg. 4to.,
half roan, some joints cracking, plts. King 7-389 1978 £30

SUESS, EDWARD   La Face de la Terre. 1905-13. Coloured
maps, illus., 3 vols. in 5, orig. wrappers soiled and frayed. George's 635-985
1978 £20

SUETONIUS TRANQUILLUS, CAIUS   History of Twelve Caesars. 1899. 2
vols., sq. 8vo., orig. buckram-backed bds. Howes 194-1298 1978 £9.50

SUFFLING, ERNEST R.   English Church Brasses. London, 1910. First ed.,
illus. Biblo 247-320 1978 $37.50

SUGDEN, ALAN VICTOR   A History of English Wallpaper 1509-1914.
(1925). Roy. 4to., plain and coloured illus., cloth, scarce. Quaritch 983-93
1978 $540

SUGDEN, EDWARD BURTENSHAW   A Series of Letters to a Man of Property on
the Sale, Purchase, Leasing, Settlement and Devising of Estates. 1812. Second
ed., orig. bds., entirely uncut, nice, orig. state, 8vo. Howes 194-481 1978
£12

SUGIMOTO, ELSA INAGAKI   A Daughter of the Samurai. 1928. Illus.
Austin 79-753 1978 $11

SUGRANES, EUGENE   The Old San Gabriel Mission. San Gabriel,
(1921). Wrps. Hayman 71-81 1978 $7.50

SULLIVAN, A. M.   New Ireland. 1878. 2 vols., v.g., octavo,
cloth, reprint. Hyland 128-585 1978 £12

SULLIVAN, ALLAN   Aviation in Canada, 1917-1918; Being a Brief Account of the Work of the R.A.F.C., the Aviation Department of the Imperial Muni-
tions Board and Canadian Aeroplanes Limited. Toronto, 1919. Photos. Hood
116-146 1978 $30

SULLIVAN, ARABELLA   Recollections of A Chaperon. 1833. 1st. ed.,
3 vols., orig. half calf, marbled bds., good. Jarndyce 16-1083 1978 £45

SULLIVAN, EDWARD   The Book of Kells. 1914. 1st ed., very good,
octavo bound in cloth. Hyland 128-589 1978 £25

SULLIVAN, EDWARD   The Book of Kells. 1914. 1st ed., piece torn
from spine, very good, octavo bound in cloth. Hyland 128-590 1978 £20

SULLIVAN, EDWARD   Rambles and Scrambles in North and South America
London, 1852. Orig. cloth, 1st ed. Ginsberg 14-934 1978 $125

SULLIVAN, JAMES   Interesting Correspondence Between...Gov.
Sullivan and Col. Pickering in Which the Latter Vindicates Himself Against the
Groundless Charges and Insinuations Made by the Governour and Others. Boston,
1808. Unbound, buckram case. Biblo 247-110 1978 $42.50

SULLIVAN, MARK   Our Times, 1900-1925. New York, 1926-1935.
Fully illus., 6 vols. Baldwins' 51-17 1978 $30

SULLIVAN, MARK   Our Times. The United States. New York.
Illus. MacManus 239-452 1978 $40

SULLIVAN, R. J.   A View of Nature in Letters to a Traveller among
the Alps. 1794. 6 vols., full tree calf, somewhat rubbed, 8vo. George's 635-
939 1978 £50

SULLIVAN, ROBERT   The Spelling-Book Superseded. New York,
(1866). Printed bds., moderate wear. Hayman 71-718 1978 $7.50

SULLIVAN, T. D.   Irish Penny Readings. n.d. 3 vols., very good,
reprint, octavo bound in cloth. Hyland 128-592 1978 £15

SULLIVAN, T.D.   Recollections of Troubled Times in Irish Politics.
1905. 1st ed., port., good, octavo bound in cloth. Hyland 128-591 1978 £7

SULLIVAN, WILLIAM KIRBY   Facts & Theories; or the Real Prospects of the
Beet-Sugar Manufacture in Ireland. 1852. 1st ed., ex lib, pres. copy from
author, 1/2 leather, very good. Hyland 128-596 1978 £50

SULLIVAN, WILLIAM T.   The Political Class Book;... Boston, 1837. Leather, joints cracking. Hayman 72-735 1978 $10

SULLY, MAXIMILIAN DE BETHUNE DUC DE   Memoires des Sages et Royalles
Oeconomies D'Estat,.... N.D., (1638). 4 vols. bound in 3, bound in full
early calf, with spine-panels, gilt, hinges weak on all volumes, leather rubbed.
Bennett 20-204 1978 $850

SULTE, BENJAMIN   La Guerre des Iroquois 1600-1653. 1897.
Hood 116-440 1978 $7.50

SULTE, BENJAMIN   La Mort de Cavalier de La Salle. 1898. Hood
116-660 1978 $7.50

SULTE, BENJAMIN   L'Organisation Militaire du Canada, 1636-1648.
1896. Hood 116-147 1978 $12.50

SULTZER, KARL   Beschreibung Eines Neu-Entdeckten Eingeweide-
Wurmes Im Menschlichen Koerper. Strasbourg & Paris, 1802. Thin 8vo., contemp.
bds., rare. Salloch 345-178 1978 $25

A SUMMARY Account of the Viceroyalty of Buenos Ayres... (1806). Folding map,
modern half calf, 8vo. Edwards 1012-630 1978 £120

SUMMER In The Antarctic Regions... (1848). 12mo, map, illus., orig. cloth.
Edwards 1012-609 1978 £25

SUMMER Shore Resorts. Boston, 1891. Illus., tall 8vo., orig. wrs. Morrill
241-353 1978 $10

SUMMERFIELD, CHARLES   The Rangers and Regulars of the Tanaha; or, Life
Among the Lawless: A Tale of the Republic of Texas. New York, 1856. Original
cloth, gilt, some wear to spine, foxed, 1st ed. Jenkins 116-1291 1978 $45

SUMMERS, GEORGE W.   The Mountain State. A Description of the Natural Resources of West Virginia. Charleston, 1893. 1st ed., orig. printed wrs.,
worn, but good. MacManus 239-1889 1978 $17.50

SUMMERS, GEORGE W.   Pages from the Past. Charleston, 1935. Wrs.,
prtd. on rather poor quality newsprint, fine cond. Hayman 73-745 1978 $12.50

SUMMERS, LEWIS PRESTON   Annals of Southwest Virginia. 1769-1800. Abing-
don, 1929. 1st ed., thick 8vo., frontis. port., illus., orig. cloth, fine copy.
MacManus 239-1864 1978 $55

SUMMERS, LEWIS PRESTON   History of Southwest Virginia, 1746-1786, Washington County, 1777-1870. Richmond, 1903. Illus., maps. MacManus 239-
1870 1978 $50

SUMMERS, M.   Discovery of Witches. 1928. Cr. 4to., orig.
wrappers, front wrapper and frontis. torn. George's 635-1436 1978 £5

SUMNER, CHARLES   Prophetic Voices Concerning America. Boston,
1874. 8vo, green cloth, blind stamped, bevelled edges, near Mint, 1st ed.
Desmarais 1-394 1978 $20

SUMNER, CHARLES   Prophetic Voices Concerning America. Boston,
1874. Orig. binding, clean, former owner's name on title-pg. Hayman 71-719
1978 $10

SUMNER, CHARLES   The Republican Party; Its Origin, Necessity and
Permanence. Speech of Hon..., Before the Young Men's Republican Union of New-
York, July 11th, 1860. (New York, 1860). Disbound. Hayman 72-632 1978
$8.50

SUMNER, CHARLES   Speech...on the Bill for the Admission of Kansas
as a Free State, in the U.S. Senate, June 4, 1860. Washington, 1860. Disbound.
Biblo 247-98 1978 $32.50

SUMNER, GEORGE   A Compendium of Physiological and Systematic Botany. Hartford, 1820. Sm. 8vo., engr. plts., orig. tree calf, browned, good copy, lst & only ed., very rare. Zeitlin 245-253 1978 $75

SUMNER, WILLIAM G.   The Financier and the Finances of the American Revolution. New York, 1891. Orig. cloth, some wear, 2 vols. MacManus 239-627 1978 $65

SUNBEAM, SUSIE   The Picture Alphabet, with Stories. New York, (1856). Cloth. Hayman 72-384 1978 $7.50

SUNDAY Reading for Young and Old for 1886. New York, 1886. Quarto, chromo-lithographed f.p. and cover plate by T. Pym, very good. Victoria 34-768 1978 $15

SUNDAY Reading for the Young. New York, 1892-1904. 4tos., orig. cloth-backed color pic. bds., color fronts, black & white illus., very good. Americanist 103-95 1978 $95

SUPAN, A.   Die territoriale Entwicklung der Europaischen Kolonien. Gotha, 1906. Large 8vo, boards, folding maps in color. Van der Peet 127-325 1978 Dfl 55

SUPERANTIUS, HIERONYMUS   Oratio Ad Venetos Adolescentes Venetiis Publice Habita. Venice, n.d. 8 leaves, 4to., wrs. waterstained. Salloch 348-263 1978 $175

SUPPLEMENT to the Book of Faces. Chicago, n.d. (ca. 1933). Biblo 251-253 1978 $17.50

SURIA, TOMAS DE   Journal of Tomas De Suria of His Voyage with Malaspina to the Northwest Coast of America in 1791. Glendale, 1936. Illus., plts., orig. wr., 100 copies. Ginsberg 14-935 1978 $55

SURMELIAN, LEON Z.   I Ask You, Ladies and Gentlemen. 1945. Austin 79-758 1978 $8.50

SURR, THOMAS SKINNER   A Winter in London or, Sketches of Fashion, A Novel. 1824. 13th. ed., 3 vols., half calf, black labels, very attractive set. Jarndyce 16-1084 1978 £25

SURRATT, JOHN H.   Trial of...in the Criminal Court for the District of Columbia. Washington, 1867. 2 vols., old 3/4 mor., scuffed, but nice, scarce. MacManus 239-909 1978 $65

SURREY Archaeological Collections, Relating to the History and Antiquities of the County. London, 1858-1968. Complete set from vol. 1 to vol. 65 & 4 extra vols., lacks vol. 5 and vol. 6 part 2, 8vo, 15 vols. in orig. wrps. remainder in cloth. Traylen 88-26 1978 £150

SURREY Archaeological Collections, Relating to the History and Antiquities of the County. London, 1869. Cloth, shaken, illus., Vol. IV. Biblo 251-142 1978 $25

SURREY Archaeological Collections, Relating to the History and Antiquities of the County. Guildford, 1931-68. Vols. 39-60, lacking vol. 53, 8vo, most cloth. Traylen 88-27 1978 £30

SURTEES, ROBERT SMITH   Handley Cross. 1854. First illus. ed., hand-coloured plts., wood-engrav., full polished calf. Howes 194-1412 1978 £50

SURTEES, ROBERT SMITH   Town and Country Papers. London & New York, 1929. 4to, ltd. to 125 copies, illus. by George D. Armour. Baldwins' 51-537 1978 $25

SUSIL, FR.   Moravske Narodni Pisne. Praha, 1941. Lg. thick 4to., cloth, plts. Van der Peet H-64-206 1978 Dfl 50

SUTCLIFF, ROBERT   Travels in Some Parts of North America in the Years 1804, 1805 and 1806. Philadelphia, 1812. Orig. grey bds., uncut. Baldwins' 51-18 1978 $100

SUTCLIFF, ROBERT   Travels in Some Parts of North America, 1804-06. York, 1815. 2nd. ed., plts., sm. 8vo, modern half calf, browning on plts. & some pgs. of text, repair to title & 4 pgs. Edwards 1012-534 1978 £30

SUTCLIFFE, THOMAS   The Earthquake of Juan Fernandez... Manchester, 1839. Litho., orig. printed wrappers, 8vo, orig. cloth, edges slightly frayed. Edwards 1012-678 1978 £30

SUTHERLAND, DUCHESS, COUNTESS OF   Views in Orkney and On the North-eastern Coast of Scotland, Taken in 1805. 1807. Ltd. ed. of 120 copies, half-title, etchings, bound in straight-grained red mor., gilt, marbled endpapers, all edges gilt, Caroline, Dutchess of Leinster's Copy, good. Deighton 5-137 1978 £245

SUTHERLAND, DAVID   A Tour Up The Straits, From Gibraltar to Constantinople. London, 1790. 2nd. ed., corrected, 8vo, half calf, gilt back. Deighton 5-144 1978 £50

SUTHERLAND, MRS. REDDING   Five Years Within the Golden-Gate. London, 1868. Orig. cloth, lst ed. Ginsberg 14-936 1978 $65

SUTHERLAND, WILLIAM   The Ship-Builder's Assistant. 1766. Fourth ed., plts., sm. 4to., antique style half calf. F. Edwards 1013-211 1978 £350

SUTRO, EMIL   Duality of Voice. New York, 1899. 8vo., lst ed., inscr. by Louis Prang. Morrill 239-255 1978 $10

SUTTER, JOHN A.   New Helvetia Diary: a Record of Events Kept by... 1845-1848. San Francisco, 1939. Illus., map, original cloth boards, 950 copies printed. Ginsberg 14-203 1978 $75

SUTTON, J. J.   History of the Second Regiment, West Virginia Cavalry Volunteers During the War of the Rebellion. Portsmouth, 1892. Illus., pages soiled, hinges cracked, tips of spine worn, Bell Wiley's copy. Broadfoot's 44-674 1978 $24

SUTTON, JOHN D.   History of Braxton County and Central West Virginia. Sutton, 1919. Cloth, facsimile of scarce orig. Hayman 73-746 1978 $20

SUTTON, RICHARD VINCENT   A Record of His Life Together With Extracts From His Private Papers. 1922. Roy. 8vo, frontis, portrait, illus., some leaves with finger-marks, orig. bds., linen spine, soiled. Eaton 45-158 1978 £10

SUTTON, SAMUEL   An Historical Account of a New Method For extracting the foul Air out of Ships.... 1745. Plt., sm. 8vo., wrappers. F. Edwards 1013-210 1978 £95

SUTTON, SAMUEL   An Historical Account of a New Method for extracting the Foul Air out of Ships.... London, 1749. Second ed., 8vo., old calf, joint cracked, plt. Gurney 75-75 1978 £65

SUTTON-ON-THE-ELK. Charleston, 1941. Wrps. Hayman 71-776 1978 $15

SUZUKI, BEATRICE ERSKINE LANE   Impressions of Mahayana Buddhism. Kyoto, London, 1940. Limp boards, somewhat soiled and yellowed. Dawson's 449-195 1978 $20

SVEHLA, J.   Ceska Karikatura v XIX Stoleti. Praze, 1941. 4to., cloth, text illus., plts. Van der Peet H-64-287 1978 Dfl 65

SVIRSKY, L.   Your Newspaper. 1947. Austin 82-680 1978 $12.50

SVORONOS, J. N.   L'Helenisme Primitif de la Macedoine Prouve par la Numismatique et l'or du Pangee. 1919. 4to., sewn., plt. Allen 234-696 1978 $17.50

SWAIM, WILLIAM   Cases of Cures Performed by the Use of Swaim's Panacea. Philadelphia, 1829. Sm. 8vo., orig. prtd. bds., lea. backed, worn, browned, stained, pencil signature of early owner, lst ed., very rare. Zeitlin 245-254 1978 $45

SWAIN, GEORGE FILLMORE   Conservation of Water by Storage. New Haven, 1915. Illus., tall 8vo., lst ed., only 1000 prtd. Morrill 239-617 1978 $12.50

SWAINSON, WILLIAM   Swainson's Exotic Conchology. London, 1834-1968. 4to, limited ed., reproduction, orig. cloth. Book Chest 17-376 1978 $25

SWALLOW, GEORGE CLINTON   Geological Report of the Country Along the Line of the Southwestern Branch of the Pacific Railroad... St. Louis, 1859. Illus., lg. fldg. map with plts., old buckram, lst ed. Ginsberg 14-868 1978 $30

SWALLOW, GEORGE CLINTON   Report on the Mineral Lands of Messrs. Woods Christy and Co., and Messrs Christy and Woods, in Franklin County Missouri. St. Louis, (1866). Tinted maps and plates, orig. printed wrs., lst ed. Ginsberg 14-603 1978 $150

SWALLOW, SILAS C.   III Score and X or Selections, Collections, Recollections of Seventy Busy Years. Harrisburg, n.d. (c. 1909). Cloth, front cover
somewhat spotted but good. Hayman 72-736 1978 $10

SWAMI, S. P.   Aphorisms of Yoga. 1938. 1st ed., d.w.,
very good, octavo bound in cloth. Hyland 128-884 1978 £11

SWAMMERDAMM, JAN   Bibel de Natur, worinen die Insekten in gewisse
Classen vertheilt,.... Leipzig, 1752. 1st ed. in German, folio, engraved plts.,
very good, quarter cloth over boards. Bennett 20-205 1978 $750

SWAN, CARROLL J.   My Company. Company D. 101st Engineers, 26th
Division. Boston, 1918. Illus. Biblo 247-773 1978 $15

SWAN, JOHN   Speculum Mundi. 1670. Fourth ed., sm. 4to.,
full contemp. calf, neatly rebacked, first and last leaves soiled, good. Howes
194-103 1978 £75

SWAN, TIMOTHY   The Songster's Assistant:.... Suffield, [1801?].
8vo., some light browning, modern half mor., orig. back wr. preserved, rare.
Quaritch 978-144 1978 $1,500

SWANDER, J. I.   The Reformed Church. Dayton, (1889). Cloth.
Hayman 73-577 1978 $10

SWANK, JAMES M.   History of the Manufacture of Iron in All Ages,
& Particularly in the U.S....1585-1885. Philadelphia, 1884. Good, rebound
copy. Nestler Rare 78-214 1978 $55

SWANK, JAMES M.   Introduction to a History of Ironmaking and Coal
Mining in Pennsylvania. Philadelphia, 1878. Bookplt., very fine, scarce.
MacManus 239-1694 1978 $35

SWANK, JAMES M.   History of the Manufacture of Iron in All Ages
and Particularly in the United States,1595-1885. Philadelphia, 1884. Baldwins'
51-19 1978 $17.50

SWANN, H. KIRKE   A Monograph of the Birds of Prey (Order Accip-
tres). London, 1924-45. Ltd. to 412 copies, scarce, colored plts., folio, orig.
parts with wr, chromoliths by Gronvold. Book Chest 17-377 1978 $600

SWANSON, NEIL H.   The Perilous Fight. New York, (1945). Illus.,
maps, 1st ed. Biblo BL781-260 1978 $9

SWARBRICK, JOHN   Robert Adam and his Brothers, their Lives, Work
and Influence on English Architecture Decoration and Furniture. (1915). Illus.,
imp. 8vo. George's 635-74 1978 £35

SWARTWOUT, R. E.   The Monastic Craftsman. Cambridge, 1932.
Illus., 8vo. George's 635-62 1978 £5.25

SWAYNE, R.   Seventeen Trips Through Somaliland. England,
1895. Leather, maps, illus., 8vo, orig. cloth, TD Carter bookplt. Book Chest
17-378 1978 $65

SWEDENBORG, EMANUEL   De Coelo et ejus Mirabilibus, et de Inferno, ex
Auditis & Visis. London, 1758. 1st ed., quarto, 18th-century calf, rebacked,
armorial bookplate, inscription on t.p. Bennett 20-206 1978 $150

SWEDENBORG, EMANUEL   The Doctrine of the New Jerusalem Concerning the
Lord. New York, 1866. Wrs., minor wear. Hayman 72-737 1978 $7.50

THE SWEDES and Finns in New Jersey. (Bayonne), 1938. Illus. MacManus
239-1258 1978 $25

SWEDIAUR, FRANCOIS XAVIER   A Complete Treatise on the Symptoms, Effects,
Nature and Treatment of Syphilis. Philadelphia, 1815. 8vo., contemp. calf,
1st Amer. ed. Morrill 239-256 1978 $40

SWEDIAUR, FRANCOIS XAVIER   Syphilis; A Complete Treatise on the Symptoms,
Effects, Nature and Treatment. Philadelphia, 1815. Translated from the fourth
French ed. Rittenhouse 49-767 1976 $30

SWEDISH INSTITUTE IN ROME   Opuscula Archaeologica. 1946. Vol. 4,
4to., sewn. Allen 234-911 1978 $12.50

SWEENY, CHARLES   Moment of Truth. 1943. Austin 80-317 1978
$8.50

SWEET, ALEXANDER EDWIN   Sketches from "Texas Sittings". New York, 1882.
1st ed., illus., orig. gilt pict. cloth, good. Greene 78-335 1978 $70

SWEET, ALEXANDER EDWIN   Sketches from "Texas Siftings". New York, 1882.
Illus. Jenkins 116-1294 1978 $25

SWEET, H.   The Epinal Glossary, Latin and Old-English, of
the 8th Century. (1883), reprint 1936. Lg. 4to., cloth-backed bds. soiled.
Upcroft 12-435 1978 £12.50

SWEET, H.   The Oldest English Texts. (1885), reprint 1938.
8vo. Upcroft 12-436 1978 £15

SWEET, WILLIAM W.   Religion in Colonial America. New York, 1942.
1st ed. MacManus 239-454 1978 $15

SWEETSER, M. F.   Views in the White Mountains. Portland, 1879.
Heliotypes, 12mo., text plus plts., 1st ed. Morrill 239-540 1978 $15

SWEETSER, M. F.   Views in the White Mountains. Portland, 1879.
12 heliotype pictures. Baldwins' 51-405 1978 $20

SWIFT, DEANE   An Essay Upon the Life, Writings and Character of
Dr. Jonathan Swift. 1755. First ed., contemp. calf, label missing, 8vo. Howes
194-485 1978 £38

SWIFT, JOHN F.   Soscol. San Francisco, 1865. Original self
wr., 1st ed. Ginsberg 14-204 1978 $75

SWIFT, JONATHAN   Baucis and Philemon:... London, 1710. Small
octavo, recently bound in quarter brown mor., gilt lettering along spine, bookplate.
Totteridge 29-103 1978 $200

SWIFT, JONATHAN   A Defence of English Commodities. Dublin,
London, 1720. 8vo., unbound, first London ed. P. M. Hill 142-220 1978 £120

SWIFT, JONATHAN   Directions to Servants. Golden Cockerel
Press, 1926. 4to., full vellum binding, #27 of 380 copies, signed by John Nash.
Battery Park 1-112 1978 $150

SWIFT, JONATHAN   An Essay Upon the Life, Writings and Character
of ... 1755. Orig. calf, rebacked, v.g. Jarndyce 16-218 1978 £55

SWIFT, JONATHAN   Gulliver's Travels. London, n.d. Black &
white illus. by Arthur Rackham, sm. 8vo, spine dull. Traylen 88-409 1978 £8

SWIFT, JONATHAN   The Hibernian Patriot. London, Dublin, 1730.
Contemp. calf, joint cracked, leather worn from foot of upper bd., first London ed.
Howes 194-482 1978 £75

SWIFT, JONATHAN   The Intelligencer. Dublin, London, 1729. First
ed. in book form, orig. panelled calf, joints split, 8vo. Howes 194-486 1978
£80

SWIFT, JONATHAN   Prose Works. 1897-1908. Frontis., 12 vols.,
cr. 8vo., orig. cloth, orig. ed. Howes 194-1239 1978 £48

SWIFT, JONATHAN   Prose Writings of...Chosen and Arranged by
Walter Lewin. 1886. First ed., v.g., octavo, cloth. Hyland 128-600 1978 £5

SWIFT, JONATHAN   Selections from the Prose Writings. London,
1884. 8vo., full brown crushed levant, 1 of 50 numbered copies, lg. paper ed.
Argosy Special-84 1978 $85

SWIFT, JONATHAN   The Swearer's Bank. Dublin, London, 1720.
8vo., unbound, first London ed. P. M. Hill 142-219 1978 £85

SWIFT, JONATHAN   A Tale of a Tub. Written for the Universal Improvement of Mankind. To Which is Added, an Account of a Battel Between the
Antient and Modern Books in St. James's Library. London, 1704. 8vo., full
straight grain red mor., a.e.g., 1st ed. MacManus 238-148 1978 $800

SWIFT, JONATHAN   Tale of a Tub. 1727. 7th. ed., frontis, plts.
by J. Clark, orig. calf, with author's apology & explanatory notes. Jarndyce 16-
217 1978 £20

SWIFT, JONATHAN   Les Voyages de Gulliver. Paris, 1946. 4to., bds., portfolio, bds. slipcase, illus., 1 of 45 copies on "Arches", orig. water-color of artist, total ed. of 1865 numbered copies. Van der Peet H-64-456 1978 Dfl 125

SWIFT, JONATHAN   A Voyage to Lilliput by Dr. Lemuel Gulliver. A Voyage to Brobdingnag Made by Dr. Lemuel Gulliver in the Year mdccii. New York, 1950. 2 vols., frontis. maps, folio, 64mo., pict. bds., ltd. to 1,500 copies, fine, slipcase a little worn. Howell 5-56 1978 $100

SWIFT, JONATHAN   The Works... 1720. 1st ed., 2 vols., folio, frontis portrait, orig. calf, hinges slightly worn, green & black labels, good. Jarndyce 16-221 1978 £80

SWIFT, JONATHAN   Works. 1856. 2 vols., thick roy. 8vo., contemp. half buff calf, portrait. Howes 194-1238 1978 £12.50

SWIFT, JONATHAN   The Works of Jonathan Swift. London, 1766/68/69. 24 vols., 16mo., bound as set, copperplt. engrs., bkplt. of The Library of Hart House, bound in calf contemp. with publication, labels missing, covers loose, cracked spines, signatures loose, interiors very good to excellent. Current 24-59 1978 $185

SWIFT, JOSEPH   The Grand Question Debated:.... London, 1732. 8vo, disbound, very possibly the 1st ed., very good copy, complete. Ximenes 47-302 1978 $400

SWIFT, LOUIS F.   The Yankee of the Yards. Chicago & New York, 1927. 2nd prtg., decor. cloth, illus., fine copy, d.w., reinforced. Dykes 34-165 1978 $7.50

SWIFT, LOUIS F.   The Yankee of the Yards. New York, (1927). Illus., bind. dull. Biblo BL781-93 1978 $9

SWIFT, SAMUEL   History of the Town of Middlebury, in the County of Addison, Vermont... Middlebury, 1859. Illus., rebound, lib. marks, good. MacManus 239-1126 1978 $35

SWIFT, T.   Hear Him! Hear Him! In a Letter to the Rt. Hon. John Foster. 1799. 1st Dublin, plain wrs. Hyland 128-613 1978 £8

SWIFT, T.   The Utility of Union..In a Letter..To the Marquis Cornwallis. Dublin, 1800. 1st ed., plain wrs. Hyland 128-614 1978 £8

SWIGGETT, S. A.   The Bright Side of Prison Life. Baltimore, 1897. Bell Wiley's copy. Broadfoot 46-332 1978 $30

SWINBURNE, ALGERNON CHARLES   Astrophel & Other Poems. 1894. 1st ed., half title, dark blue cloth, good. Jarndyce 16-1099 1978 £10.50

SWINBURNE, ALGERNON CHARLES   Atalanta in Calydon. 1866. 1st ed., half title, dark blue cloth, good. Jarndyce 16-1085 1978 £12.50

SWINBURNE, ALGERNON CHARLES   Atalanta in Calydon. 1908. 8vo., cloth, somewhat faded. Quaritch 979-313 1978 $20

SWINBURNE, ALGERNON CHARLES   A Century of Roundels. London, 1883. 1st ed., (only 1,000 printed), very good, dedication to Christina Rossetti unopened. Limestone 9-286 1978 $25

SWINBURNE, ALGERNON CHARLES   Charles Dickens. London, 1913. 1st ed., orig. blue cloth, gilt, t.e.g., illus., very good or better. Limestone 9-287 1978 $40

SWINBURNE, ALGERNON CHARLES   The Duke of Gandia. 1908. 1st ed., orig. black cloth, untrimmed, good. Jarndyce 16-1102 1978 £6.50

SWINBURNE, ALGERNON CHARLES   Early Letters from Algernon Charles Swinburne to John Nichol. London, 1917. Half blue calf, orig. wrappers, nice, first ed. Rota 212-57 1978 £125

SWINBURNE, ALGERNON CHARLES   Erechtheus: A Tragedy. 1876. 1st ed., half title, dark blue cloth, good. Jarndyce 16-1089 1978 £8.50

SWINBURNE, ALGERNON CHARLES   Grace Darling. 1893. 4to., 1st ed., parchment, bkplt., little worn. Quaritch 979-314 1978 $65

SWINBURNE, ALGERNON CHARLES   Laus Veneris. Paris, 1923. Lg. 8vo., orig. wr., uncut, ltd. ed., issued in 443 numbered copies on Arches paper, illus. with two-tone woodcuts by Raphael Drouart. Goldschmidt 110-22A 1978 $25

SWINBURNE, ALGERNON CHARLES   Locrine, A Tragedy. 1887. 1st ed., half title, dark blue cloth, good. Jarndyce 16-1096 1978 £6.50

SWINBURNE, ALGERNON CHARLES   Locrine, A Tragedy. London, 1887. 8vo., green cloth, gilt stamped, owners blindstamp on rear flyleaf, spine rubbed, nice, 1st ed., collector's cond. Desmarais 1-395 1978 $30

SWINBURNE, ALGERNON CHARLES   Marino Faliero. 1885. 1st ed., blind-stamp on several leaves, 1/2 morocco, ex-lib. binding. Eaton 45-486 1978 £8

SWINBURNE, ALGERNON CHARLES   Mary Stuart, A Tragedy. 1881. 1st ed., very slight chip to bottom corner of spine, dark blue cloth, good. Jarndyce 16-1093 1978 £5.50

SWINBURNE, ALGERNON CHARLES   Mary Stuart. London, 1881. 1st ed., orig. gilt stamped green cloth, uncut, ink signature on title, fine. Houle 10-335 1978 $45

SWINBURNE, ALGERNON CHARLES   Miscellanies. 1886. 1st ed., half title, dark blue cloth, good. Jarndyce 16-1095 1978 £7.50

SWINBURNE, ALGERNON CHARLES   Note of An English Republican on the Muscovite Crusade. London, 1876. Demy octavo, bound, as issued, in mottled-grey paper wr., sole appearance. Bennett 7-113 1978 $45

SWINBURNE, ALGERNON CHARLES   A Note on Charlotte Bronte. 1877. 1st. ed., 3rd. issue, half title, inserted dedication leaf, orig. dark blue cloth, gilt borders & spine, v.g. Jarndyce 16-311 1978 £38

SWINBURNE, ALGERNON CHARLES   Pasiphae. A Poem. (London: The Golden Cockerel Press, 1950). 8vo., illus., full vellum, 1 of 100 copies bound with 1 extra engraving, t.e.g., fine. MacManus 238-799 1978 $100

SWINBURNE, ALGERNON CHARLES   Poems and Ballads. 1866. 2nd. ed., partly unopened, orig. cloth, recased, new endpapers. Eaton 45-488 1978 £5

SWINBURNE, ALGERNON CHARLES   Poems & Ballads. 1866. 2nd ed., half title, orig. green cloth, good. Jarndyce 16-1086 1978 £8.50

SWINBURNE, ALGERNON CHARLES   Poems and Ballads. 1878. Sm. 8vo., 1st ed., orig. cloth, uncut, H. Buxton Forman's copy with bkplt. Quaritch 979-316 1978 $65

SWINBURNE, ALGERNON CHARLES   Poems and Ballads. 1878. 2nd. series, sm. cr. 8vo, 1/2 green calf, ex-lib. binding. Eaton 45-489 1978 £5

SWINBURNE, ALGERNON CHARLES   Poems & Ballads. 1889. 3rd series, half title, dark blue cloth, good. Jarndyce 16-1097 1978 £6.50

SWINBURNE, ALGERNON CHARLES   Posthumous Poems. 1917. Blind-stamp on title-pg., cloth. Eaton 45-484 1978 £5

SWINBURNE, ALGERNON CHARLES   Rosamund, Queen of the Lombards. 1899. 1st. ed., blind-stamp on title pg., 1/2 morocco ex-lib. binding. Eaton 45-485 1978 £6

SWINBURNE, ALGERNON CHARLES   Rosamund, Queen of the Lombards, A Tragedy. 1899. Orig. cream cloth, browned, 1st ed., good. Jarndyce 16-1101 1978 £5.50

SWINBURNE, ALGERNON CHARLES   Selected Poems. London, (1928). Plts., illus. by Harry Clarke, 4to., gilt stamped black pict. cloth, fine, uncut, unopened copy. Houle 10-69 1978 $95

SWINBURNE, ALGERNON CHARLES   The Sisters, A Tragedy. 1892. 1st ed., half title, dark blue cloth, good. Jarndyce 16-1098 1978 £8.50

SWINBURNE, ALGERNON CHARLES   A Song of Italy. 1867. 1st ed., orig. green cloth, good. Jarndyce 16-1087 1978 £9.50

SWINBURNE, ALGERNON CHARLES　　Songs of the Springtides. 1880. 1st ed., half title, dark blue cloth, good. Jarndyce 16-1092 1978 £7.50

SWINBURNE, ALGERNON CHARLES　　Songs of the Springtides. 1880. 1st. ed., orig. green cloth, gilt. Eaton 45-487 1978 £5

SWINBURNE, ALGERNON CHARLES　　The Springtide of Life. London, (1918). 4 to., gilt stamped green cloth, illus. by Arthur Rackham, fine. Houle 10-277 1978 $135

SWINBURNE, ALGERNON CHARLES　　The Springtide of Life. London, (1918). Quarto, white boards with vellum back, gilt, g.t., illus., color plts., binding shabby, internally fine. Duschnes 220-249 1978 $135

SWINBURNE, ALGERNON CHARLES　　Studies in Prose and Poetry. 1894. 1st ed., half title, dark blue cloth, good. Jarndyce 16-1100 1978 £7.50

SWINBURNE, ALGERNON CHARLES　　Studies in Song. 1880. 1st ed., sm. paint mark in leading bd., dark blue cloth, good. Jarndyce 16-1091 1978 £5.50

SWINBURNE, ALGERNON CHARLES　　A Study of Ben Jonson. 1889. Blind-stamp on title pg., edges dust-soiled, cloth. Eaton 45-483 1978 £8

SWINBURNE, ALGERNON CHARLES　　A Study of Victor Hugo. 1886. 1st ed., half title, dark blue cloth, good. Jarndyce 16-1094 1978 £8.50

SWINBURNE, ALGERNON CHARLES　　William Blake: A Critical Essay. 1868. 2nd. ed., 8vo, 3 plain & 6 hand-coloured facsimile plts., 1/2 red morocco, joints and corners rubbed, lib. crest on upper cover. Eaton 45-482 1978 £30

SWINBURNE, ALGERNON CHARLES　　The Complete Works of .... London, 1925. Ed. ltd. to 780 set in 20 vols., this set is 17 vols. only, lacking vol. 7, 9, and 16, orig. cloth, 8vo. Sexton 7-188 1978 £75

SWINBURNE, HENRY　　Travels Through Spain, In the Years 1775 and 1776. London, 1779. 1st. ed., 4to, folding engraved map, engraved plts., contemporary calf, neatly rebacked, retaining the orig. backstrip & morocco label, sl. fraying in margins of map, clean copy internally. Deighton 5-145 1978 £95

SWINBURNE, JOHN　　A Typical American. Albany, 1888. Illus., 8vo. Morrill 239-257 1978 $12.50

SWINDEN, JAN H. VAN　　Recueil de Memoires sur l'Analogie de l'Electricite et du Magnetisme. The Hague, 1748. 3 vols., 8vo., plts., lg. fldg. table, orig. wrs., uncut, mostly unopened, very light foxing on titles, light dampstaining upper margin of one plt., but fine set, 1st ed. Norman 5-267 1978 $350

SWINDEN, JOHN　　Junius Lord Chatham, and the "Miscellaneous Letters" proved to be spurious. 1833. 8vo., orig. cloth uncut, portrait. P. M. Hill 142-156 1978 £8

SWINDLEHURST, W. J.　　First Biennial Report of the Department of Labor and Industry 1913-1914. Helena, 1914. Original wr. Ginsberg 14-632 1978 $22.50

SWINDLER, MARY HAMILTON　　Ancient Painting from the Earliest Times to the Period of Christian Art. 1929. 4to., illus., plts. Allen 234-912 1978 $40

SWINDLER, MARY HAMILTON　　Ancient Painting From the Earliest Times to the Period of Christian Art. New Haven, 1929. 640 illus., 4to. Baldwins' 51-157 1978 $50

SWINEY, G. C.　　Historical Records of the 32nd Light Infantry. 1893. Frontis., coloured plts., illus., 8vo., orig. cloth. F. Edwards 1013-507 1978 £70

SWINNERTON, FRANK　　The Georgian Literary Scene, 1910-1935. New York, (1949). 6th ed., illus., fine, d.j., made from English sheets. Limestone 9-289 1978 $13.50

SWINNERTON, FRANK　　Sketch of a Sinner. London, (1930). First ed., orig. binding, fine, torn d.w. Rota 211-685 1978 £10

SWINTON, E.　　Twenty Years After, the Battlefields of 1914-18, then and now. (1938). Illus., 3 vols., 4to. George's 635-863 1978 £10.50

SWIRE, H. L. R.　　A Bibliography of the Works of Joseph Hergesheimer. Philadelphia, 1922. Frontis. port., orig. cloth-backed bds., 1st ed., ltd. to 300 copies, very good. MacManus 238-943 1978 $25

SWISHER, JACOB A.　　The Iowa Department of the Grand Army of the Republic. Iowa City, 1936. Library stamp on front fly, Bell Wiley's copy. Broadfoot 46-333 1978 $10

SWISHER, JAMES　　How I Know. Cincinnati, 1880. Decor. cloth, illus., recased, top & bottom spine neatly repaired, some foxing, good copy, slipcase, rare. Dykes 34-38 1978 $50

SWISS-AMERICAN HISTORICAL SOCIETY　　Prominent Americans of Swiss Origin. 1932. Illus. with photos. Austin 79-762 1978 $20

SWITZLER, WM. F.　　Report on the Internal Commerce of the U.S., 1189. Washington, 1839. Near mint. Jenkins 116-1297 1978 $20

SWORD and Womankind. 1900. Ltd. to 1000 copies, etched frontis., 8vo. George's 635-1518 1978 £12.50

SYBEL, HEINRICH VON　　The History and Literature of the Crusades. n.d. (c. 1908). New ed., sm. 8vo. Upcroft 12-437 1978 £5

SYDNEY, W. C.　　England and the English in the 18th Century, Chapters in the Social History of the Times. Edinburgh, (1891). Plts., 2 vols. George's 635-766 1978 £6.25

SYDNOR, CHARLES SACKETT　　Slavery in Mississippi. NY, 1933. Bell Wiley's copy. Broadfoot's 44-903 1978 $15.00

SYKES, CHRISTOPHER　　Orde Wingate. 1959. 8vo, orig. cloth, maps, photo illus., pres. copy to Winston Churchill. Sawyer 298-117 1978 £130

SYKES, J.　　The Amalgamation Movement in English Banking, 1825-1924. 1926. 8vo. George's 635-408 1978 £6

SYLVESTER, HARRY　　Dayspring. 1945. First ed., d.j. Austin 82-935 1978 $12.50

SYLVESTER, HERBERT MILTON　　Indian Wars of New England. Boston, 1910. 3 vols., fine. Biblo 247-66 1978 $150

SYLVESTER, HERBERT MILTON　　Maine Pioneer Settlements. Boston, 1909. 5 vols., Ltd. ed., front inner hinge of vol. 1 split, very good, scarce. Biblo 248-78 1978 $87.50

SYLVESTER, NATHANIEL BARTLETT　　History of Rensselaer Co. Philadelphia, 1880. Illus. & biographical sketches, lg. 4to., plts., color map, orig. 1/2 lea. & cloth, lightly worn, all edges gilt, clean, tight copy. Butterfield 21-365 1978 $75

SYLVIUS, JACOBUS, OF AMIENS
Please turn to
DU BOIS, JACQUES

SYMES, MICHAEL　　An Account of An Embassy to the Kingdom of Ava... 1800. 1st. ed., lg. paper copy, maps, engraved plts., 4to, calf, rebacked. Edwards 1012-158 1978 £250

SYMES, MICHAEL　　Relazione Dell'Ambasciata Inglese Spedita Nel 1795 Nel Regnid'Ava o nell'Impero dei Birmani. Naples, 1832. 4 vols. in 1, hand-colored plts., thick 8vo., vellum, Italian translation. Salloch 345-179 1978 $150

SYMINGTON, J. A.　　The Brotherton Library. Leeds, 1931. Illus., demy 4to., orig. buckram. Forster 130-253 1978 £25

SYMMES, FRANK R.　　History of the Old Tennent Church, Monmouth County, New Jersey. Cranbury, 1904. Illus., orig. bind. Petrilla 13-121 1978 $12.50

SYMMES, FRANK R.　　History of the Old Tennent Church... Cranbury, 1904. 2nd ed., illus., orig. cloth, fine. MacManus 239-1330 1978 $27.50

SYMONDS, E.M.　　A Study of Prejudices. New York, 1895. 1st Amer. ed., quarter calf, marbled boards, good. Greene 78-268 1978 $15

SYMONDS, JOHN ADDINGTON   Essays Speculative and Suggestive. 1890. 2 cols., copious pencil notes by Roger Senhouse, orig. cloth rather worn. Eaton 45-490 1978 £6

SYMONDS, JOHN ADDINGTON   In the Key of Blue and Other Prose Essays. 1893. Ist ed., orig. cream cloth, gilt, spine now dull & rubbed, t.e.g., others uncut. George's 635-1333 1978 £5

SYMONDS, JOHN ADDINGTON   The Principles of Beauty. 1857. Plts., foxed, roy. 8vo. George's 635-63 1978 £10.50

SYMONDS, JOHN ADDINGTON   The Principles of Beauty. London, 1857. 8vo, half green morocco, gilt, spine gilt, Ist ed., attractive copy, plates at end foxed. Ximenes 47-303 1978 $35

SYMONDS, JOHN ADDINGTON   Shakespeare's Predecessors in the English Drama. London, 1884. First ed., orig. binding, spine faded, very good, scarce. Rota 211-687 1978 £25

SYMONDS, ROBERT WEMYSS   Old English Walnut and Lacquer Furniture. London-1923. Plts., 4to. Traylen 88-416 1978 £25

SYMONS, ALPHONSE JAMES ALBERT   Frederick Baron Corvo. London, Curwen Press, 1927. One of 199 numbered copies, wrappers, very nice, inscribed by author, first ed. Rota 212-10 1978 £45

SYMONS, ALPHONSE JAMES ALBERT   H. M. Stanley. 1933. Ist ed., pres. copy with inscr. by author, 8vo., orig. cloth, d.w. Sawyer 299-138 1978 £75

SYMONS, ALPHONSE JAMES ALBERT   The Nonesuch Century. London, 1923. Cloth, near mint, d.w., half mor. fldg. case, 1 of 750 numbered copies, copy belonged to Oliver Simon. Dawson's 447-100 1978 $650

SYMONS, ALPHONSE JAMES ALBERT   The Quest for Corvo: An Experiment in Biography. 1934. Plts., buckram, good, Ist Eng. ed. Bell Book 16-194 1978 £15

SYMONS, ALPHONSE JAMES ALBERT   The Quest for Corvo. 1934. Pres. copy, Ist ed., inscr. by author, illus., 8vo., orig. cloth, d.w., fine. Sawyer 299-137 1978 £225

SYMONS, ALPHONSE JAMES ALBERT   The Quest for Corvo. New York, 1934. First U.S. ed., illus., very good. Bell Book 17-182 1978 £17.50

SYMONS, ARTHUR   Colour Studies in Paris. London, 1918. Ist ed., portrait, illus., red cloth, very good or better. Limestone 9-291 1978 $15

SYMONS, ARTHUR   From Catullus, Chiefly Concerning Lesbia. London, 1924. Thin 4to, full blue mor., gilt dentelles, ltd. ed., fine, 1 of 200 signed copies. Argosy Special-85 1978 $100

SYMONS, ARTHUR   Knave of Hearts. 1894-1908. New York, 1913. Ist Amer. ed. Biblo 251-651 1978 $17.50

SYMONS, ARTHUR   Mes Souvenirs. One of 200 numbered copies signed by author, copy #23, Velin de Rives paper, bound in beige bds. Battery Park 1-171 1978 $200

SYMONS, ARTHUR   Notes on Joseph Conrad. London, 1925. Fine in damaged d.w. Desmarais B-154 1978 $42.50

SYMONS, ARTHUR   A Study of Thomas Hardy. 1927. One of 350 numbered copies, portrait, sm. 4to., cloth-backed bds., covers faded, very good, first English ed. Bell Book 17-849 1978 £18.50

SYMONS, HARRY   Three Ships West. Toronto, 1949. Hood's 115-461 1978 $10

SYMONS, THOMAS W.   ...Information Respecting the Navigable Waters of the Upper Columbia River and Its Tributaries, and of the Country Adjacent Thereto. Washington, 1882. Plates, map, cloth with leather label, Ist ed. Ginsberg 14-937 1978 $35

SYMPSON, SAMUEL   A New Book of Cyphers... London, n.d. (1739). 8vo., Janssenist blue mor., inner gilt dentelles, by Cuzin, fresh and flawless copy, eng. plts. Schumann 511-57 1978 sFr 1100

SYNGE, JOHN MILLINGTON   The Aran Islands. 1912. Library Ed., illus. by Jack B. Yeats, very good, octavo bound in cloth. Hyland 128-619 1978 £15

SYNGE, JOHN MILLINGTON   The Aran Islands. 1926. Rebound in cloth, very good, reprint. Hyland 128-617 1978 £21

SYNGE, JOHN MILLINGTON   Deirdre of the Sorrows. 1911. Ist U. S. ed., very good, octavo bound in cloth. Hyland 128-621 1978 £12

SYNGE, JOHN MILLINGTON   The Dramatic Works of...1915. 1915. Ist collected ed., very good, octavo bound in cloth. Hyland 128-626 1978 £15

SYNGE, JOHN MILLINGTON   In Wicklow and West Kerry. 1912. Fscp. 8vo., qtr. vellum, good, Ist Eng. ed. Bell Book 16-823 1978 £5

SYNGE, JOHN MILLINGTON   In Wicklow and West Kerry. 1912. Bds. with parchment spine, very good, reprint. Hyland 128-618 1978 £8

SYNGE, JOHN MILLINGTON   The Shadow of the Glen and Riders to the Sea. 1905. Wrs., good, reprint. Hyland 128-630 1978 £25

SYNGE, JOHN MILLINGTON   The Tinker's Wedding. A Comedy in Two Acts. Dublin, 1907. Orig. cloth-backed bds., Ist ed., near-fine. MacManus 238-757 1978 $40

SYNGE, JOHN MILLINGTON   The Well of the Saints. London, 1905. Orig. cloth-backed bds., Ist ed., fine. MacManus 238-756 1978 $50

SYNGE, JOHN MILLINGTON   The Well of the Saints. 1905. Very good, octavo, cloth, reprint. Hyland 128-629 1978 £17.50

SYNGE, JOHN MILLINGTON   Complete Works. 1910. 4 vols., ex-lib., covers worn, text good, octavo bound in cloth. Hyland 128-622 1978 £26

SYR GAWAIN
Please turn to
GAWAIN AND THE GREEN KNIGHT

SZYK, ARTHUR   Ink and Blood. New York, Heritage Press, 1946. First ed., 4to., numbered plts., ltd. to 1000 copies for pres., colored frontis., plts., signed by artist, simulated batique box, full black mor., v.f. Current 24-241 1978 $235

SZYK, ARTHUR   Le Livre d'Esther. Paris, (1925). 8vo., orig. wrs., slipcase as issued, text in French and Hebrew, illus. in color, one of 175 copies on Jap. vellum, fine, with extra set of illus. in b/w. Duschnes 220-301 1978 $350

T

TABLE Rock Album, and Sketches of the Falls and Scenery Adjacent. Buffalo, 1855. 3/4 leather. Hood's 115-849 1978 $50

TABOR, GRACE   The Landscape Gardening Book. Philadelphia, 1911. Illus., tall 8vo., 1st ed. Morrill 239-618 1978 $7.50

TACHE, ALEXANDRE ANTONIN   Une Page de l'Histoire des Ecoles de Manitoba; Etude des Cinq Phases D'une Periode de 75 Annees. Montreal, 1894. Hood 116-890 1978 $50

TACITUS, GAIUS CORNELIUS   Annals. 1904-09. 2 vols., quite ex-lib., worn, Books I-VI & XI-XVI. Allen 234-918 1978 $15

TACITUS, GAIUS CORNELIUS   Gli Annali di Cornelio Tacito. Venetia, 1582. 4to., blind-stamped vellum, some waterstaining. King 7-103 1978 $30

TACITUS, GAIUS CORNELIUS   Opera. Lugduni, 1684. Sm. 8vo., vellum, wrongly paged, brownspotted & wormholes. Van der Peet H-64-561 1978 Dfl 60

TACITUS, GAIUS CORNELIUS   Opera. 1812. 5 vols., some joints cracked, one inner hinge stained. Allen 234-914 1978 $25

TACITUS, GAIUS CORNELIUS   Works. 1737. Second ed., 4 vols., contemp. calf, very good, 8vo. Howes 194-488 1978 £38

TACITUS, GAIUS CORNELIUS   Works. 1813. 2 vols., roy. 8vo., contemp. qtr. calf with vellum corners, entirely uncut. Howes 194-489 1978 £20

TACOMA and Vicinty. (Tacoma), 1888. Illus., tinted plts., orig. pict. cloth, 1st ed. Ginsberg 14-1044 1978 $50

TACOMA Illustrated, Published Under the Auspices of the Tacoma Chamber of Commerce. Chicago, 1889. Illus., folio stiff wr., 1st ed. Ginsberg 14-1046 1978 $75

TACOMA: The City With a Snow-Capped Mountain in Its Dooryard. Tacoma, 1912. Illus., orig. pr. colored wr. Ginsberg 14-1045 1978 $30

TACOMA, The Pacific Terminus of the Northern Pacific Railroad. Tacoma, 1884. Lithographed maps, plates, orig. pr. wr., 1st ed. Ginsberg 14-1048 1978 $100

TACOMA, Washington Territory, the Western Terminus of the Northern Pacific Railroad. St. Paul, 1888. Orig. pr. wr. Ginsberg 14-1047 1978 $50

TAFT, HENRY W.   A Century and a Half at the New York Bar. New York, 1938. Plts., lacks front free endpaper, otherwise fine, boxed as issued. Butterfield 21-549 1978 $10

TAFT, ROBERT   Photography and the American Scene. New York, 1938. Illus., 1st ed. MacManus 239-710 1978 $35

TAGLIENTE, GIOVANNI ANTONIO   Lo Presente Libro Insegna la Vera Arte de lo Excellete Scrivere de Diverse Varie Sorti le Quali se fano per Geometrica Ragione... Venice, 1531. Sm. 4to., vellum with some damp marks, woodcut. Schumann 511-58 1978 sfr 5,750

TAGLIENTE, GIOVANNI ANTONIO   Lo Presente Libro Insegna la Vera arte de lo excellete Scrivere de Diverse Varie Sorti de Litere le Quali se Fano per Geometrica Ragione... Venice, 1560. Sm. 4to., paper cover, woodcut. Schumann 511-60 1978 sFr 3,000

TAISNIER, JEAN   Opusculum...de Natura Magnetis, et eius Effectibus. Cologne, 1562. 4to., woodcut portr., 19th Cent. Spanish or Peruvian mottled calf, very light dampstain, pen doodle on portr., but fine copy, old signature on flyleaf, bkplt., 1st ed. Norman 5-269 1978 $2,250

TAIT, GEORGE   A Summary of the Powers and Duties of a Justice of the Peace in Scotland. Edinburgh, 1821. 3rd. ed., full calf, somewhat rubbed and stained, 8vo. K Books 244-304 1978 £8

TAIT, JOHN   The Cave of Morar, the Man of Sorrows. 1775. 2nd. ed., half-title, 4to, disbound in folder. Hannas 54-340 1978 £8.50

TAIT, R. H.   "The Trail of the Caribou"; the Royal Newfoundland Regiment, 1914-1819. Boston, (1933). Suede cover, signed by author. Hood's 115-910 1978 $40

TAIT, WILLIAM SURGEON   Magdalenism... Edinburgh, 1842. 2nd. ed., orig. brown cloth, v.g. Jarndyce 16-1103 1978 £20

TAJA, AGOSTINO MARIA   Lettera, e Poetici Componimenti.... Roma, 1705. Folio, vellum, plt. King 7-240 1978 £20

TAKEKOSHI, YOSOBURO   The Economic Aspects of the History of the Civilization of Japan. London, (1930). 3 vols., cloth, endpapers browned. Dawson's 449-196 1978 $60

TALAEUS, AUDOMARUS   Rhetorica. Frankfurt, 1583. 8vo., 1/2 calf, rare. Salloch 348-265 1978 $250

TALBOT, CATHERINE   The Works of the Late .... 1795. Lg. 12mo, contemp. calf, gilt, nice. Fenning 32-323 1978 £12.50

TALBOT, CHARLES R.   Don Quixote, Jr. Boston, (1879). 1st ed., illus. by L. Hopkins, very good. Victoria 34-110 1978 $10

TALBOT, EDITH ARMSTRONG   Samuel Chapman Armstrong, a Biographical Study. New York, 1904. Orig. binding, clean, few sm. dents in back cover. Hayman 71-720 1978 $7.50

TALBOT, ELEANOR W.   Jack O'Lantern and Other Rhymes. London, (1883). Pictorial cover boards rubbed at edges, fine. Victoria 34-771 1978 $25

TALBOT, F.   Saint Among Savages; the Life of Isaac Jogues. New York and London, 1935. Hood 116-270 1978 $25

TALBOT, JOHN   History of North America... Leeds, 1820. 1st ed., 2 vols., contemp. calf, marbled bds., covers worn, illus., maps, plts. MacManus 239-456 1978 $25

TALBOT, THEODORE   The Journals of...1843 and 1849-52 with the Fremont Expedition of 1843 and with the First Military Company in Oregon Territory 1849-1852. Portland, 1931. Orig. cloth, 1st ed. Ginsberg 14-939 1978 $30

TALBOT-BOOTH, E. C.   Merchant Ships, 1943. London, 1944. Oblong 4to., illus. & line drwgs., orig. cloth, very good. Americanist 103-85 1978 $45

TALBOT-BOOTH, E. C.   What Ship is That? N.P., 1944. Illus. Austin 80-318 1978 $17.50

TALBOTT, JOHN L.   The Western Practical Arithmetic. Cincinnati, 1845. Bds., worn, cover worn. Hayman 71-721 1978 $8.50

TALCOTT, J. FREDERICK   Swift and Still Waters. Lifetime Recollections and Reflections....and Genealogy. New York, (1943). Illus., author's signed pres. Biblo BL781-94 1978 $22.50

A TALE of a Tub. 1704. Sm. 8vo., 1st ed., contemp. panelled calf, gilt back, very good unpressed copy. Quaritch 979-311 1978 $700

THE TALE of Gamelyn. Elston Press, 1901. 1 of 200 copies, 16mo., without decor. Battery Park 1-88 1978 $100

THE TALE of King Florus and the Fair Jehane. Kelmscott Press, 1893. 16mo, 1st ed., bds., linen back, trifle soiled, very good copy, scarce, 350 copies prtd. Quaritch 979-356 1978 $250

TALES for Males. New York, (1945). Very good, chipped dustwrapper. Bernard 5-16 1978 $7.50

TALES of the Academy. London, 1820 and 1821. 2 vols., 1st ed., 12mo, finely engraved f.p. in each vol, upper margins t.p.'s clipped where owner's signature appeared, marbled paper boards, leather spine, very good. Victoria 34-772 1978 $85

TALES of the Wonder Club. n.d. (c. 1898-1900). Illus., 3 vols., 8vo, 1st ed., orig. plum cloth, fine, rare. Quaritch 979-249 1978 $125

TALFOURD, THOMAS NOON   Ion; A Tragedy. n.d. 1st. ed., half title, orig. cloth, v.g. Jarndyce 16-1104 1978 £15

TALFOURD, THOMAS NOON   Vacation Rambles and Thoughts;.... London, 1845. 2 vols., large 12mo, original green cloth, 1st ed., very good copy. Ximenes 47-304 1978 $60

TALLACK, WILLIAM   Friendly Sketches in America. London, 1861. 1st ed., cloth. MacManus 239-457 1978 $30

TALLANT, ROBERT   Mrs. Candy and Saturday Night. 1947. First ed., frayed d.j. Austin 82-939 1978 $11

TALLANT, ROBERT   Mr. Preen's Salon. 1949. First ed. Austin 82-938 1978 $11

TALLENT, ANNIE D.   The Black Hills; or, the Last Hunting Ground of the Dakotas... St. Louis, 1899. Illus., original cloth, 1st ed. 14-324 1978 $100

TALLIS, JOHN   Tallis's Illustrated London. London, 1851. 3 vols, plts., orig. cloth, vol. I rather unpleasantly stained affecting the corner of about 20 plts., 8vo. K Books 244-305 1978 $45

TALLMADGE, BENJAMIN   Memoir of Col. Benjamin Tallmadge Prepared by Himself at the Request of His Children. New York, 1858. 1st ed., 8vo., pres. from the editor, A.L.s. tipped in, orig. brown bds., gilt lettering rebacked, otherwise very fine, obituary notices tipped in. Current 24-106 1978 $315

TALMAN, JAMES J.   Travel in Ontario Before the Coming of the Railway. 1933. Hood's 115-986 1978 $7.50

TAMURA, T.   Art of the Landscape Gardens of Japan. Japan, 1935. Wr., 8vo. Book Chest 17-379 1978 $15

TANGENT, PARTICK QUINN   The New Columbia or the Re-United States. Findlay, 1909. Orig. binding, clean. Hayman 71-636 1978 $15

TANGYE, R.   Notes on My Fourth Voyage to the Australian Colonies... Birmingham, 1886. Orig. wrappers, spine slightly defective, 8vo. Edwards 1012-344 1978 £45

TANNANT, T. R.   Eastern Washington Territory and Oregon:.... (Portland, 1881). Orig. pr. wr. bound in cloth, 1st ed. Ginsberg 14-940 1978 $175

TANNENBAUM, FRANK   Darker Phases of the South. New York, 1924. Pres. copy from author to Bell Wiley. Broadfoot's 44-785 1978 $17

TANNER, EDWIN P.   The Province of New Jersey 1664-1738. New York, 1908. Orig. wrs., chipped. MacManus 239-1331 1978 $35

TANNER, GEORGE CLINTON   Fifty Years of Church Work in the Diocese of Minnesota 1857-1907. St. Paul, 1909. Illus., original cloth, 1st ed. Ginsberg 14-574 1978 $25

TANNER, HENRY SCHENCK   Memoir on The Recent Surveys, Observations and Internal Improvement in the United States. Philadelphia, 1829. Baldwins' 51-20 1978 $65

TANNER, HUDSON C.   "The Lobby" and Public Men From Thurlow Weed's Time. Albany, (1888). 1st. ed.?, cr. 8vo, orig. cloth, gilt, pres. copy from publisher. Fenning 32-324 1978 £10.50

TANNER, JOHN   Memoires de. Paris, 1835. Two vols. in one, modern buckram. Wolfe 39-524 1978 $125

TANNER, JOSEPH ROBSON   Constitutional Documents of the Reign of James I, A.D. 1603-1625. Cambridge, 1930. Octavo, good. Upcroft 10-170 1978 £5.50

TANNER, JOSEPH ROBSON   English Constitutional Conflicts of the 17th Century, 1603-1689. Cambridge, 1937. Octavo, good. Upcroft 10-559 1978 £6

TANNER, JOSEPH ROBSON   Tudor Constitutional Documents A.D. 1485-1603. Cambridge, 1930, 1951. 2nd. ed., octavo, good. Upcroft 10-169 1978 £5.50

TANNER, THOMAS HAWKES   Index of Diseases and Their Treatment. Philadelphia, 1867. Rittenhouse 49-768 1976 $15

TANSILL, CHARLES CALLAN   The Foreign Policy of Thomas F. Bayard, 1885-1897. New York, 1940. Baldwins' 51-21 1978 $15

TANSILLO, LUIGI   The Nurse, a Poem. London, 1798. 4to., old half mor., marbled bds., gilt lettered on backstrip, worn, lightly browned & foxed, lg. paper copy from the library of Dr. Alfred M. Hellman, 1st English ed., rare. Zeitlin 245-258 1978 $125

TANSILLO, LUIGI   Opere. Venezia, 1738. 4to., soft bds., text in double column, uncut. King 7-241 1978 £40

TANQUEREL DES PLANCHES, LOUIS JEAN CHARLES   Lead Diseases. Lowell, 1848. 8vo., light dampstains, 1st ed. in English. Morrill 239-258 1978 $47.50

TAPIE, MICHEL   Mirobolus Macadam & Cie. Paris, 1946. 4to., orig. wr., uncut, ltd. ed., 730 copies on heavy velin d'Arches paper, illus. with one orig. color litho. by Jean Dubuffet, copy signed by author, painter & illus'r. Goldschmidt 110-20 1978 $550

TAPLEY, HARRIET S.   Chronicles of Danvers. Danvers, 1923. Illus., cloth-backed bds., 1st ed., scarce. MacManus 239-1024 1978 $30

TAPPAN, EVA MARCH   The Children's Hour. Boston, 1907. 10 vols., frontis., plts., 8vo., 3/4 blue mor., gilt spines, first ed., ltd. to 1000 copies, v.f., partially unopened, uncut. Howell 5158 1978 $200

TARAVAL, SIGISMUNDO.   The Indian Uprising in Lower California 1734-1737. Los Angeles, 1931. Plates, original boards, one of 665 numbered copies. Ginsberg 14-205 1978 $75

TARBELL, F. B.   A History of Greek Art. Chautauqua, 1905. Illus. Biblo BL781-490 1978 $7.50

TARBELL, IDA M.   The Life of Abraham Lincoln. New York, 1908. 2 vols., illus., edges rubbed. Biblo 248-62 1978 $16.50

TARDIEU, ANDRE   The Truth About the Treaty. Indianapolis, (1921). Cloth. Hayman 72-738 1978 $7.50

TARG, WILLIAM   Carrousel for Bibliophiles... New York, 1947. 1st ed., fine, d.j. Hayman 72-739 1978 $20

TARGA, C.   Ponderationi Sopra La Contrattatione Maritima. Genoa, 1692. Sm. 4to., vellum. F. Edwards 1013-213 1978 £28

TARKINGTON, BOOTH   Alice Adams. 1921. Illus., d.j. Austin 82-940 1978 $11

TARKINGTON, BOOTH   Beasley's Christmas Party. 1909. Illus., first ed. Austin 82-941 1978 $11

TARKINGTON, BOOTH   Beasley's Christmas Party. 1909. Illus., later ed. Austin 82-942 1978 $8.50

TARKINGTON, BOOTH   Claire Ambler. 1928. First ed. Austin 82-943 1978 $10

TARKINGTON, BOOTH   The Collectors of Whatnot. Boston & New York, (1923). Pen & ink illus. by Tarkington, signed by all 3 authors, d.j., fair. Baldwins' 51-158 1978 $50

TARKINGTON, BOOTH   The Fascinating Stranger and Other Stories. 1923. Austin 82-944 1978 $11

TARKINGTON, BOOTH   Gentleman from Indiana. 1899. First ed., second state, signed by author. Austin 82-945 1978 $27.50

TARKINGTON, BOOTH   The Gentleman from Indiana. New York, 1899. 8vo, green pict. cloth, uncut, 2nd issue, covers rubbed and spotted, hinges beginning to loosen, Nice, signed by Takington, 1st ed. Desmarais 1-397 1978 $20

TARKINGTON, BOOTH   Gentleman from Indiana. (1902). 1916. Illus. Austin 82-946 1978 $8.50

TARKINGTON, BOOTH   The Guest of Quesnay. 1917. Austin 82-947 1978 $7.50

TARKINGTON, BOOTH   Harlequin and Columbine. 1923. Frontis., first English ed. Austin 82-948 1978 $12.50

TARKINGTON, BOOTH   Image of Josephine. 1945. First ed., frayed d.j. Austin 82-949 1978 $8.50

TARKINGTON, BOOTH   Image of Josephine. 1945. Austin 82-950 1978 $7.50

TARKINGTON, BOOTH   Little Orvie. 1934. Illus., first ed. Austin 82-952 1978 $10

TARKINGTON, BOOTH   Little Orvie. 1934. Illus., first ed., frayed d.j. Austin 82-951 1978 $11

TARKINGTON, BOOTH   The Lorenzo Bunch. 1936. First ed., frayed d.j. Austin 82-953 1978 $12.50

TARKINGTON, BOOTH   The Magnificent Ambersons. 1918. Illus. Austin 82-954 1978 $10

TARKINGTON, BOOTH   The Magnificent Ambersons. 1925. Austin 82-955 1978 $8.50

TARKINGTON, BOOTH   Mr. White, the Red Barn, Hell and Bridewater. 1935. First ed. Austin 82-956 1978 $10

TARKINGTON, BOOTH   Penrod and Sam. 1916. Illus., first ed. Austin 82-957 1978 $12.50

TARKINGTON, BOOTH   Ramsey Milholland. 1919. Illus. Austin 82-958 1978 $8.50

TARKINGTON, BOOTH   Seventeen. 1915. Illus. Austin 82-959 1978 $8.50

TARKINGTON, BOOTH   The Show Piece. 1947. First ed., frayed d.j. Austin 82-960 1978 $12.50

TARKINGTON, BOOTH   Three Selected Short Hovels. 1947. First ed., d.j. Austin 82-961 1978 $12.50

TARKINGTON, BOOTH   The Two Vanrevels. 1902. Illus. Austin 82-962 1978 $10

TARKINGTON, BOOTH   The Two Vanrevels. 1916. Illus. Austin 82-963 1978 $8.50

TARKINGTON, BOOTH   Works. Garden City, 1922. 1 of 1,075 sets signed by author, half cloth, 18 vols., Seawood Ed., very good. Houle 10-336 1978 $150

TARKINGTON, BOOTH   The Works of... 1922-24. Seawood ed., ltd. to 1975 numbered copies, vols. I-XVII, not signed. Austin 82-965 1978 $125

TARKINGTON, BOOTH   The World Does Move. 1928. Austin 82-966 1978 $10

TARKINGTON, BOOTH   The World Does Move. 1928. First ed. Austin 82-964 1978 $12.50

TARKINGTON, BOOTH   Young Mrs. Greeley. 1929. First ed. Austin 82-953a 1978 $10

TARLETON, BANASTRE   A History of the Campaigns of 1780-1781 in the Southern Provinces of North America. London, 1787. 1st ed., fold. maps, partially colored, some foxing and stains, 3/4 leather. Broadfoot 50-313 1978 $600

TARTAGLIA, NICCOLO   Nova Scientia. (Venice, 1537). Sm. 4to., famous woodcut frontis., fine text woodcuts & diagrs., limp vellum, 16th Cent. style, fine copy, 1st ed. Norman 5-*49 1978 $2,750

TARTAGLIA, NICCOLO   Regola Generale di Solevare Ogni Fondata Nave et navilii con regione. Venice, 1562. Sm. 4to., vellum, illus., woodcuts. F. Edwards 1013-214 1978 £70

TARUFFI, CESARE   Intorno Alla Macrosomia. Bologna, 1888. 4to., illus., disbound, uncut, mostly unopened copy. Zeitlin 245-259 1978 $45

TASISTRO, LOUIS FITZGERALD   Random Shots and Southern Breezes. New York, 1842. 2 vols., foxed, Bell Wiley's copy. Broadfoot's 44-786 1978 $30

TASSE, JOSEPH   Les Canadiens de l'Ouest. Montreal, 1873. 2 vols., 3/4 lea. marbled bds., spine worn at head. Hood 17-332 1978 $90

TASSMAN, I. S.   The Eye Manifestations of Internal Diseases. St. Louis, 1946. Second ed. Rittenhouse 49-769 1976 $20

TASSO, TORQUATO   Aminta Favola Boscareccia di Torquato Tasso Ristampata.... 1725. 16mo., new calf binding, good, plt. King 7-242 1978 £30

TASSO, TORQUATO   Delle Rime.... Brescia, 1592-93. 2 vols. in 1, 8vo., Roman and Italic letter, old dark green mor. gilt, gilt arms on sides of Hon. Thomas Grenville, gilt edges. Quaritch 978-148 1978 $425

TASSO, TORQUATO   Discorso Della Virtu Heroica E Della Charita. Venice, 1582. 10 leaves, 4to., bds., 1st ed. Salloch 348-266 1978 $125

TASSO, TORQUATO   Il Forno, Overo Della Nobilita Dialogo. Vicenza, 1581. 4to., 3/4 red mor., fine. Salloch 348-267 1978 $150

TASSO, TORQUATO   Gerusalemme Liberata Del Sig. Torquato Tasso. Caslamaggiore, 1581. Sm. 4to., vellum gilt, first complete ed. Quaritch 978-146 1978 $650

TASSO, TORQUATO   Gierusalemme Liberata,.... Ferrara, 1581. Sm. 4to., red mor. gilt, gilt edges. Quaritch 978-147 1978 $340

TASSO, TORQUATO   Godfrey of Bulloigne. 1687. Cr. 8vo., contemp. calf, lettering piece. Howes 194-105 1978 £40

TASSO, TORQUATO   Jerusalem Delivered, an Heroic Poem. 1811. Engraved portrait, roy. 8vo., half calf, neatly rebacked. George's 635-1519 1978 £7.50

TASSO, TORQUATO   La Jerusalem Delivree.... Paris, 1841. Lg. 8vo., half calf, corners worn, plts., illus., vignettes, very good. King 7-390 1978 £20

TASSO, TORQUATO   La Jerusalem Delivree Vingt-quatre Planches Hors Texte en Couleurs de O.D.-V. Guillonnet. Paris, (1921). Lg. 8vo., half calf, portrait, woodcuts, plts. in soft colours, unblemished copy. King 7-391 1978 £20

TASSO, TORQUATO   Manoscritti inediti di Torquato Tasso ed altri pregevoli documenti per servire alla biografia del medesimo posseduti.... 1837. Folio, marbled bds., calf spine gilt, portrait frontis., plts., handmade paper, very good uncut copy, first and only ed. King 7-243 1978 £75

TASSONI, ALLESANDRO   Paragone degli Ingegni Antichi e Moderni. Venezia, 1827. Sm. 8vo., marbled bds., calf spine, very good. King 7-244 1978 £40

TATE, ALLEN   A Southern Vanguard, The John Peale Bishop Memorial Volume. New York, 1947. Bell Wiley's copy. Broadfoot's 44-787 1978 $8

TATE, ALLEN   Stonewall Jackson. The Good Soldier. 1930.
Port. frontis., plts., sq. 8vo., orig. cloth. F. Edwards 1013-340 1978 £10

TATE, ALLEN   The Vigil of Venus: Pervigilium Veneris. N.P.,
Cummington Press, 1943. 4to, black cloth, uncut, Latin text, near Mint, torn
tissue wr., no. 20 of 105 numbered copies, 1st ed. Desmarais 1-109 1978 $40

TATE, GEORGE   A Treatise on Hysteria. Philadelphia, 1831.
8vo., orig. bds., cloth back, 1st Amer. ed. Morrill 239-259 1978 $15

TATE, NAHUM   An Elegy on the Most Reverend Father in God,
His Grace, John Tillotson, Late Lord Archbishop of Canterbury. 1695. 1st. ed.,
folio, disbound. Hannas 54-341 1978 £55

TATE, NAHUM   On the Sacred Memory of Our Late Sovereign
Charles II: With a Congratulation to His Present Majesty. 1685. 1st. ed., folio,
disbound, slight worming, touching 6 letters, scribbles on last page. Hannas 54-
342 1978 £45

TATE, NAHUM   A Poem on the Late Promotion of Several Eminent
Persons in Church and State. 1694. 1st. ed., folio, thick paper, disbound.
Hannas 54-343 1978 £60

TATE, NAHUM   Poems Written on Several Occasions. 1684.
2nd. ed., enlarged, 8vo, contemp. calf, rebacked. Hannas 54-344 1978 £85

TATLER   The Lucubrations of Isaac Bickerstaff Esq. 1723.
Orig. panelled calf, spines little rubbed, otherwise v.g. Jarndyce 16-222 1978
£22

TATTERSALL, C. E. C.   A History of British Carpets From the Introduction
of the Craft Until the Present Day. 1934. Coloured frontis, plts., 54 of these in
colour, roy. 4to. Traylen 88-417 1978 £40

TATUM, RICHARD P.   Tatum Narrative. Philadelphia, 1925. Mac-
Manus 239-941 1978 $30

TAUBES, F.   Studio Secrets. New York, (1945). Sm. 4to.,
illus., 3rd ed., name on t.p. Biblo BL781-749 1978 $9

TAULER, JOHANNES   Meditationi Pie, et Divote di M. Giovanni
Taulero. Fiorenza, 1572. 12mo, full contemp. limp vellum, partial circuit,
devices on covers, gilt, title on spine in contemp. hand, library of Andrew Fletcher
with signature on t.p. Bennett 20-208 1978 $95

TAUNTON, E. L.   The History of the Jesuits in England 1580-1773.
1901. Plts., octavo, good. Upcroft 10-560 1978 £5.50

TAUSSIG, C. W.   Rum, Romance and Rebellion. (c. 1930). 8vo.,
drawings by P. Kappel, covers faded. George's 635-409 1978 £8.25

TAVERNER, PERCY ALGERNON   Birds of Canada. Ottawa, 1934. Illus.,
colored plts., 1st ed., signed by author. Hood 116-55 1978 $45

TAVERNER, PERCY ALGERNON   Birds of Canada. Ottawa, 1934. 87 plts. in
color. Baldwins' 51-369 1978 $25

TAVIANI, SIRO   Il Moto Umano in Leonardo da Vinci. Florence,
1942. 8vo., illus., orig. prtd. wrs. Norman 5-L31 1978 $15

TAWNEY, R. H.   The Agrarian Problem in the 16th Century. 1912.
Coloured maps, 8vo. George's 635-410 1978 £7.50

TAXES No Charge; In A Letter From a Gentleman, to a Person of Quality. London, 1690. Sm. 4to, half leather. Traylen 88-84 1978 £55

TAYLER, WILLIAM   Thirty-Eight Years in India... 1882. 8vo,
plts., illus., 2 vols., half red calf, slightly worn. Edwards 1012-113 1978 £35

TAYLOR, MRS.   Maternal Solicitude for a Daughter's Best
Interests. London, 1822. 12mo., full cont. maroon mor., gilt and blind
tooling, frontis., fine, joints rubbed, with fore-edge painting. Duschnes
220-102 1978 $150

TAYLOR, A.   Original Poems. 1868. Illus., orig. cloth gilt,
charming engravings, paper cutting concerning author tipped-in. Eaton 45-492
1978 £5

TAYLOR, ALEXANDER   Climates for Invalids. London, 1866. 12mo.,
orig. publisher's binding in blind-stamped orange cloth, gilt lettering on spine,
worn, good copy, reprint of 3rd ed. Zeitlin 245-260 1978 $22.50

TAYLOR, ALFRED SWAINE   Medical Jurisprudence. Philadelphia, 1866.
Rittenhouse 49-770 1976 $10

TAYLOR, ALRUTHEUS AMBUSH   The Negro in South Carolina During the
Reconstruction. Washington, 1924. Bell Wiley's copy. Broadfoot's 44-945
1978 $25.00

TAYLOR, BAYARD   Colorado: A Summer Trip. 1867. Sm. 8vo,
half green morocco, marginal stain affecting title & 2 leaves. Edwards 1012-535
1978 £30

TAYLOR, BAYARD   Eldorado or Adventures in the Path of the Empire.
New York, 1949. Illus., fine, d.w. Biblo 247-267 1978 $17.50

TAYLOR, BAYARD   Hannah Thurston: A Story of American Life.
New York, 1864. 1st ed. Biblo 251-652 1978 $37.50

TAYLOR, BAYARD   The Lake Regions of Central Africa: or, Life and
Landscapes from Egypt to the Negro Kingdoms of the White Nile. New York, 1854.
10th. ed., folding map, frontispiece, 4 litho plates, cr. 8vo, generally little age-
marked, gilt cloth faded, backstrip slightly chafed. K Books 239-482 1978 £20

TAYLOR, BAYARD   Views Afoot, or Europe Seen With Knapsack &
Staff. 1869. 1st ed., very good, octavo bound in cloth. Hyland 128-638 1978
£5

TAYLOR, C. C.   Toronto "Called Back", from 1886 to 1850. Its ...
Growth...as an Importing Centre with the Development of Its Manufacturing Industries... Toronto, 1886. Illus., map. Hood 116-782 1978 £40

TAYLOR, EDMOND   The Strategy of Terror. 1940. Austin 80-322
1978 $8.50

TAYLOR, ELIZABETH   At Mrs. Lippincote's. 1945. Covers soiled,
else good, first English ed. Bell Book 16-825 1978 £5.50

TAYLOR, ELIZABETH   A View of the Harbour. 1947. Very good,
slightly worn d.w., first English ed. Bell Book 17-853 1978 £10

TAYLOR, EMERSON GIFFORD   New England in France, 1917-1919. Boston,
1920. Maps, illus. Biblo 247-774 1978 $15

TAYLOR, ERNEST M.   History of Brome County, Quebec. Montreal,
1908. Vol. I, illus., orig. binding. Wolfe 39-171 1978 $40

TAYLOR, ERNEST M.   History of Brome County, Quebec. Montreal,
1937. Vol. II, orig. binding. Wolfe 39-172 1978 $40

TAYLOR, FITCH W.   A Voyage Round the World... New Haven,
1847. Plts., illus., 2 vols. in 1, sm. 8vo., orig. cloth. Edwards 1012-39 1978
£60

TAYLOR, FRANK H.   Philadelphia in the Civil War, 1861-1865.
Philadelphia, 1913. Illus., fold. map, t.e.g., orig. cloth. MacManus 239-
1695 1978 $7.50

TAYLOR, FREDERICK WINSLOW   The Principles of Scientific Management.
New York, 1911. 8vo., cloth, backstrip stained, 1st trade ed. Argosy Special-
86 1978 $200

TAYLOR, FREDERICK WINSLOW   The Principles of Scientific Management.
New York, 1911. 1st ed., 8vo., very fine copy. Current 24-126 1978 $395

TAYLOR, GEORGE   Maps of the Roads of Ireland. (1778). Octavo
bound in cloth, reprint. Hyland 128-974 1978 £10

TAYLOR, GEORGE COFFIN   Essays of Shakespeare, An Arrangement. New York, 1947. 8vo, orig. cloth, pres. copy to Winston Churchill. Sawyer 298-118 1978 £90

TAYLOR, GRIFFITH   Canada: A Study of Cool Continental Environments and Their Effect on British and French Settlement. New York, n.d. Plts., illus. Hood 116-661 1978 $30

TAYLOR, GRIFFITH   Enviroment and Nation: Geographical Factors in the Cultural and Political History of Europe. Toronton, 1936. 1st ed. Hood 116-662 1978 $50

TAYLOR, GRIFFITH   With Scott: The Silver Lingin. 1916. Maps, illus., orig. cloth, 8vo. Edwards 1012-610 1978 £75

TAYLOR, H. B.   The Apples of England. 1946. Coloured plts., roy. 8vo. George's 635-963 1978 £7.50

TAYLOR, H. J.   Capetown to Kafue. London, c.1916. Frontis, 8 plts., cr. 8vo, orig. cloth, little thumbed. K Books 239-483 1978 £6

TAYLOR, H. J.   Yosemite Indians and Other Sketches. San Francisco, 1936. Illus., limited to 500 copies, wr. Ginsberg 14-206 1978 $25

TAYLOR, HENRY   Autobiography, 1800-1875. 1885. 2 vols., portrait, spines slightly faded, orig. cloth, 8vo. Edwards 1012-199 1978 £16

TAYLOR, HENRY   The Bee-Keeper's Manual. London, 1860. 6th ed., fcap. 8vo., illus., orig. cloth. K Books 244-30 1978 £16

TAYLOR, ISAAC   Elements of Thought. 1833. 12mo, orig. cloth, dark red spine label, uncut, nice. Fenning 32-325 1978 £14.50

TAYLOR, ISAAC   Scenes in Africa,... London, 1820. 1st ed., 12mo, orig. printed boards title "African Scenes" and maroon mor. spine, rubbed, hand colored engravings. Totteridge 29-104 1978 $75

TAYLOR, ISAAC   Scenes in Africa, For the Amusement and Instruction of Little Tarry-at-Home Travellers. London, 1821. 2nd. ed., folding map, plts., fcap. 8vo, orig. printed bds., leather spine. Traylen 88-203 1978 £30

TAYLOR, ISAAC   Scenes in Africa, For the Amusement and Instrucction of Little Tarry-at-Home Travellers. London, 1826. 5th. ed., illus., plts., fcap. 8vo, bds., leather spine. Traylen 88-203A 1978 £28

TAYLOR, ISAAC   Scenes in England for the Amusement and Instruction of Little Tarry-at-Home Travellers. London, 1822. 1st ed., engravings and plates, foxed, boards rubbed, minor margin tears. Victoria 34-778 1978 £50

TAYLOR, ISAAC   Scenes in Europe for the Amusement and Instruction of Little Tarry at Home Travellers. 1818. Sm. 8vo., fldg. maps, engrs., orig. paper bds., lea. back. Quaritch 979-342 1978 $180

TAYLOR, ISAAC   Scenes of British Wealth, In Produce, Manufactures and Commerce... London, 1823. 1st. ed., sm. 8vo, orig. quarter leather, printed board sides, folding engraved map, illus., plts., good. Traylen 88-204 1978 £50

TAYLOR, ISAAC L.   Campaigning with the First Minesota Ed. by Hazel Wolf. St. Paul, 1944. Cover speckled, Bell Wiley's copy. Broadfoot's 44-535 1978 $17

TAYLOR, JANE   Busy Idleness. New York, 1834. Chapbook, bound in modem wrappers. Victoria 34-783 1978 $7.50

TAYLOR, JANE   A Day's Pleasure. New York, 1830. 1st Amer. printing, extracted from a bound volume, foxed. Victoria 34-780 1978 $15

TAYLOR, JANE   Essays in Rhyme, or Morals and Manners. Boston, 1816. 1st Amer. ed., original boards, upper hinge cracked, text foxed, very good. Victoria 34-779 1978 $115

TAYLOR, JANE   Little Ann and Other Poems. London, n.d. (1882, 1883). Illus. by Kate Greenaway, orig. glazed pict. bds., 1st ed., preliminaries foxed, otherwise very nice. MacManus 238-256 1978 $65

TAYLOR, JANE   Little Ann and Other Poems. London, n.d. Illus. in color by Kate Greenaway, pict. bds. Biblo BL781-1026 1978 $12.50

TAYLOR, JANE   The Writings of Jane Taylor. Boston, 1831-2. 5 vols., 1st complete ed., cloth, spine paper labels, some cover soiling, fine. Victoria 34-782 1978 $85

TAYLOR, JEFFERYS   Aesop in Rhyme, with some Originals. 1823. Sm. 8vo., frontis., engrs., orig. mottled bds., 2nd ed., neatly rebacked, neat inscr. Quaritch 979-343 1978 $100

TAYLOR, JEFFERYS   A Month in London. 1832. Sm. 8vo., engr. frontis., engr. plts., orig. grey cloth, gilt & blind decor. Quaritch 979-344 1978 $150

TAYLOR, JEFFREYS.   Ralph Richards, The Miser. London, 1821. 1st ed., original boards, leather spine with small chip, moderate rubbing, sev. leaves pulled. Victoria 34-784 1978 $35

TAYLOR, JEFFREYS   The Young Islanders, And What Came of Their Adventures. (c.1859). Woodcut frontis & vignette, post. 8vo, orig. coloured pic. bds., backstrip worn, cover loose, David Livingstone's copy with his signature, linen box. Sawyer 299-127 1978 £95

TAYLOR, JEREMY   The Great Exemplar... 1667. 4th ed., shaky, octavo bound in cloth. Hyland 128-640 1978 £6

TAYLOR, JEREMY   The Rule and Exercises of Holy Dying. London, 1847. Rebound in lea., rubbed. Biblo 251-607 1978 $57.50

TAYLOR, JEREMY   The Rule and Exercises of Holy Living. 1706. Engraved frontis. and plts., top halves of pages stained, diced calf, spine worn, joints cracked, 8vo. George's 635-1136 1978 £6.50

TAYLOR, JEREMY   XXVIII Sermond Preached at Golden Grove.... London, 1651. Engraved vignette on title ruled in red, 1st. ed., folio, old calf, rebacked. Traylen 88-345 1978 £58

TAYLOR, JEREMY   Symbolon Ethiko-Polemikon. 1657. Portrait, vignette, folio, rebound in full reversed calf, orig. spine neatly mounted, new endpapers, first ed., very good. Howes 194-106 1978 £65

TAYLOR, JEREMY   The Worthy Communicant. 1678. Sm. 8vo., half calf, front joint cracked. Howes 194-107 1978 £24

TAYLOR, JOHN 1580-1653   The Water Poet... London, 1621. 12mo., 19th century half straight grained mor. and cloth sides, 1st ed., good copy, rare. MacManus 238-150 1978 $400

TAYLOR, JOHN 1580-1653   "The Water Poet". London, 1630. 1st. collected ed., folio, red levant morocco, gilt extra, gilt edges, joints little rubbed, preserved in quarter morocco case. Traylen 88-347 1978 £425

TAYLOR, JOHN 1580-1653   All the Workes of ... 1630. 1st. collected ed., folio, additional engraved title, author's portrait, woodcut portraits, 19th century morocco, a.e.g., sm. tears in titles, lacks initial blank leaf, scribbles on printed title & last page. Hannas 54-345 1978 £350

TAYLOR, JOHN 1711-1788   Sermons, on Different Subjects. 1788. 8vo., contemp. calf, nice, first ed. P. M. Hill 142-151 1978 £35

TAYLOR, JOHN 1757-1832   Poems on Various Subjects. London, 1827. 1st. ed., 2 vols., 8vo., orig. cloth, paper labels, spines worn. Traylen 88-346 1978 £18

TAYLOR, MARY   A History of the Memminger Normal School. NP, c. 1941. Pres copy from author, illus., Bell Wiley's copy. Broadfoot's 44-946 1978 $12.00

TAYLOR, MARY SNYDER   Annals of a Bucks County Family of Old Taylorsville, Pennsylvania. (N.P., 1940). Plts., rubbed, 1st and only ed., very scarce, orig. bind. Petrilla 13-123 1978 $35

TAYLOR, NATHANIEL W.   Life on a Whaler, or, Antartic Adventures in the Isle of Desolation. New London, 1929. Illus. by William T. Peters, ltd. to 900 copies. MacManus 239-1791 1978 $45

TAYLOR, NATHANIEL W.   A Sermon, Addressed to the Legislature of the State of Connecticut, at the Annual Election in Hartford, May 7, 1823...   New-Haven, 1823. 2nd ed., scarce, some stains.   Hayman 72-740 1978 $8.50

TAYLOR, PHILLIP MEADOWS.   Confessions of a Thug.   London, 1839. 3 vols., octavo, lacking the publisher's cat. from vol. one, rebound, by Riviere and Son, 3/4 mottled calf and boards, gilt tooled spine and gilt ruling on upper and lower covers, 1st ed., t.e.g.   Bennett 7-115 1978 $195

TAYLOR, PHILIP MEADOWS   Confessions of a Thug.   London, 1879. 3 vols. in 1, new ed., orig. cloth, spine darkened, good.   Greene 78-115 1978 $30

TAYLOR, RACHEL ANNAND   The End of Fiametta; poems.   London, 1923. First ed., orig. binding, good.   Rota 211-696 1978 £5

TAYLOR, RACHEL ANNAND   Poems.   London, 1904. First ed., orig. binding, nice, author's autograph pres. inscription.   Rota 211-695 1978 £5

TAYLOR, RICHARD   Te Ika A Maui, or New Zealand and Its Inhabitants...   1855. Frontis, folding map, coloured plts., illus., 8vo, orig. cloth, map torn, cover repaired.   Edwards 1012-353 1978 £45

TAYLOR, ROBERT LEWIS   Professor Fodorski.   1950. First ed., frayed d.j.   Austin 82-967 1978 $10

TAYLOR, SAMUEL   A Discussion of the Propisition Whether Immersion in Water is the Only Christian Baptism?... Frankfort, 1844. Tall 8vo., modern quarter lea. with marbled bds., some foxing.   Americanist 103-96 1978 $100

TAYLOR, THEODORE   Thackeray. The Humourist and the Man of Letters. The Story of His Life, Including a Selection from His Characteristic Speeches...   London, 1864. Frontis. port., illus., full mor., 1st ed., very good.   MacManus 238-398 1978 $30

TAYLOR, THOMAS 1576-1633   A Commentarie upon the Epistle of S. Paul written to Titus.   Cambridge, 1612. First ed., sm. 4to., contemp. calf, sm. paper flaw in pp. 227/8 affecting a few letters only, good untrimmed copy.   Howes 194-108 1978 £50

TAYLOR, THOMAS E.   Running the Blockade: A Personal Narrative of Adventure, Risks, and Escapes During the American Civil War.   London, 1912. Folding map, spine faded, embossed sign. on title page margin, Bell Wiley's copy.   Broadfoot's 44-359 1978 $20.00

TAYLOR, THOMAS J.   A History of the Tar River Baptist Association 1830-1921.   N.P., 1924.   Broadfoot 50-315 1978 $15

TAYLOR, W. S.   The Mourning Dove.   Austin, 1916. Wr., illus.   Jenkins 116-1310 1978 $7.50

TAYLOR, WALTER C.   Counsels to Woman.   Springfield, 1871. Wear on cover.   Rittenhouse 49-771 1976 $10

TAYLOR, WALTER H.   General Lee: His Campaigns in Virginia 1861-1865.   Norfolk, 1906. Folding maps in color, cover speckled, Bell Wiley's copy.   Broadfoot's 44-360 1978 $80

TAYLOR, WILLIAM   Historic Survey of German Poetry.   1828-30. First ed., 3 vols., contemp. half green mor., 8vo.   Howes 194-1242 1978 £60

TAYLOR and His Generals. A Biography of Major-General Zachary Taylor...   Philadelphia, 1847. Illus., ports., cloth, orig. printed wrs. bound in, good copy.   MacManus 239-310 1978 $27.50

TEALE, EDWIN WAY   Dune Boy.   New York, 1943. 8vo, orig. cloth.   Book Chest 17-381 1978 $12

TEALE, EDWIN WAY   The Lost Woods.   New York, 1945. 4to, orig. cloth.   Book Chest 17-382a 1978 $22.50

TEALE, EDWIN WAY   The Lost Woods.   New York, 1945. 8vo, 5th printing, orig. cloth.   Book Chest 17-382b 1978 $12

TEALE, T. PRIDGIN   Dangers to Health.   London, 1881. 3rd ed., plts., 8vo., ex-lib., nice, pres. copy.   Morrill 239-260 1978 $10

THE TEARS of the Foot Guards, Upon Their Departure for America:....   London, 1776. 4to, disbound, 1st ed., half-title present; short tear in inner margins, very scarce.   Ximenes 47-253 1978 $250

TEASDALE, T. C.   Sermon on Baptism Delivered in West Chester, Pa. on the Evening of Jan. 19, 1834.   Philadelphia, 1834.   Baldwins' 51-484 1978 $75

TEDDER, LORD   With Prejudice.   Illus.   Austin 80-324 1978 $12.50

TEDLOCK, E. W., JR.   The Frieda Lawrence Collection of D.H. Lawrence Manuscripts.   Albuquerque, 1948. 8vo., cloth, 1st ed., label on spine rubbed.   J.S. Lawrence 38-L159 1978 $20

TEEGAN, T. H.   With the Grand Army to Moscow, An Historical Novel.   (c. 1900). 1st ed., signed pres. copy from author to Knight of Kerry, map, illus., damage to back cover, very good, octavo bound in cloth.   Hyland 128-643 1978 £15

TEGETMEIER, WILLIAM BERNHARD   Horses, Asses, Zebras, Mules and Mule Breeding.   London, 1895. Engr. plts., text illus., spine faded.   Morrill 239-620 1978 $30

TEGETMEIER, WILLIAM BERNHARD   Pigeons: Their Structure, Varieties, Habits & Management.   England, (1870). Chromoliths by Harrison Weir, new spine, sev. plate margins chipped, 8vo., orig. cloth.   Book Chest 17-383 1978 $95

TEGNER, ESIAS   The Tale of Frithiof.   1872. Half title, orig. red cloth, v.g.   Jarndyce 16-1071 1978 £6

TEIGNMOUTH, HENRY NOEL SHORE, BARON   Old Foye Days, Being the True Story of a Cornish Haven.   1896-1907. 2 vol., sm. 4to., orig. bds. cloth backed, plts.   F. Edwards 1013-198 1978 £15

TELEGRAPHIC Cypher.   Milwaukee, 1868. Rev. ed., 12mo., orig. lea., spine lacking.   Morrill 239-621 1978 $12.50

TELESIO, BERNARDINO   Varii De Naturalibus Rebus Libelli Ab Antonio Presio Editi.   Venetiis, 1590. 1st ed., 4to, full contemp. vellum, expertly rebacked, small worm holes in gutter of 1st few leaves, rare.   Bennett 20-209 1978 $1,500

TELFAIR, NANCY   A History of Columbus, Georgia 1828-1928.   Columbus, Ga., 1929. Bell Wiley's copy.   Broadfoot 46-574 1978 $20

TELLER, H. M.   Letter From...Transmitting...Copies of Documents and Correspondence Relating to Leases of Lands in Indian Territory to Citizens of the U. S. for Cattle-Grazing and Other Purposes.   Washington, 1884. Folding maps, diagram, half mor., 1st ed.   Ginsberg 14-802 1978 $150

TELLER, H. M.   Letter from...Transmitting...Report of Commissioner of Indian Affairs Submitting Copies of Sioux Agreements to Cession of Land to the U.S.,....   Washington, 1884. Large folding map, disbound, 1st ed.   Ginsberg 14-925 1978 $25

TELLIER, JULES   Abd-er-Thaman in Paradise.   (Waltham St. Lawrence): The Golden Cockerel Press, 1928. Wood-engravings by Paul Nash, orig. cloth-backed marbled bds., ltd. to 400 copies, extremities slightly worn, but good.   MacManus 238-800 1978 $45

TEMPLE, EDMOND   The Life of Pill Garlick; Rather a Whimsical Sort of Fellow.   Dublin, 1813. 1st. ed., orig. half calf, marbled bds., good.   Jarndyce 16-1105 1978 £18

TEMPLE, JACOB PAXON   Collection of Early American Furniture and Objects of Art.   1922. Illus.   Baldwins' 51-159 1978 $20

TEMPLE, JOHN B.   Address Delivered to the Graduates of the Erodelphian Society, of Miami University, August 12, 1840.   Cincinnati, 1840. Disbound, foxed.   Hayman 73-578 1978 $12.50

TEMPLE, JOSIAH HOWARD   History of North Brookfield, Mass... 1887. Illus., very fine, orig. cloth.   MacManus 239-1042 1978 $35

TEMPLE, JOSIAH HOWARD   History of the Town of Palmer, Mass... Illus., maps, front hinge weak, orig. cloth, lib. marks.   MacManus 239-1044 1978 $30

TEMPLE, OLIVER P.   East Tennessee and the Civil War. Cincinnati, 1899. Bell Wiley's copy. Broadfoot 46-380 1978 $65

TEMPLE, SARAH BLACKWELL GOBER   The First Hundred Years. Atlanta, 1935. Bell Wiley's copy. Broadfoot's 44-872 1978 $45.00

TEMPLE, WILLIAM   Memoirs of What Passed in Christendom from the War Begun 1671 to the Peace Concluded 1670. 1692. Contemp. calf, ex lib Evelyn Shirley with Bookplt., good, reprint. Hyland 128-644 1978 £25

TEMPLE, WILLIAM   Observations Upon the United Provinces of the Netherlands. London, 1673. 8vo., full old calf, 2nd ed., corrected & augmented, top of spine damaged, worn. Van der Peet H-64-552 1978 Dfl 200

TEMPLE Bar, The City Golgotha. 1853. 1st. ed., sq. octavo, coloured frontis, and 1 plt., orig. green cloth, gilt dec., good. Jarndyce 16-825 1978 £10

TEMPLER, CLAUD   Poems and Imaginings. Paris, 1920. First ed., portraits, orig. printed bds., 8vo. Howes 194-1243 1978 £10

TEMPORAL Prosperity and Spiritual Delcine: Or, Free Thoughts on Some Aspects of Modern Methodism, by a Wesleyan Minister. London, 1866. Restored. Hood's 115-948 1978 $30

TEN Lithographic Coloured Flowers with Botanical Descriptions Drawn and Coloured by a Lady. Edinburgh, 1826. 1st ed., folio, illus. with forty full-page hand-colored lithographic plates, full contemp. blue straight-grained mor., tooled in gilt, blind on the upper and lower covers, gilt on spine, a.e.g., very rare. Bennett 20-228 1978 $4,750

THE TEN Little Niggers. London, c.1875. Sewn, pictorial wrappers rubbed and darkened, color plates, very good, worn wrappers modestly priced. Victoria 34-785 1978 $25

TENISON, LOUISA   Castile and Andalucia. 1853. Imp. 8vo., frontis., plts., orig. cloth, gilt, fine copy, text in mint cond. Quaritch 983-261 1978 $390

TENNANT, J. L.   A Study of Rural Schools in Runnels County, Texas. Austin, 1924. Folding map, scarce. Jenkins 116-1201 1978 $12.50

TENNENT, JAMES E.   Ceylon: An Account of the Island... 1859. Maps, 2 folding, frontispieces, text illus., 2 vols., 8vo, half green morocco gilt. Edwards 1012-132 1978 £50

TENNENT, JAMES E.   Sketches of the Natural History of Ceylon... 1861. Illus., sm. thick 8vo, orig. cloth. Edwards 1012-133 1978 £30

TENNENT, JOHN   Physical Enquiries. London, 1742. Sm. 8vo., disbound, good copy, 1st ed., rare. Zeitlin 245-261 1978 $275

TENNEY, J. B.   The Mineral Industries of Arizona. Tucson, 1928. Original printed wr., 1st ed. Ginsberg 14-28 1978 $15

TENNEY, S.   A Manual of Zoology, for Schools, College & General Reader. New York, 1873. 8vo, orig. cloth. Book Chest 17-384 1978 $13

TENNYSON, ALFRED   Carmen Saeculare. 1887. 8vo., orig. stiff wrs., gilt edges enclosed in cloth slipcase, bkplts. in slipcase. Quaritch 979-317 1978 $95

TENNYSON, ALFRED   The Death of Oenone, Akbar's Dream and other Poems. 1892. First ed., sm. 8vo., orig. cloth. Howes 194-1246 1978 £5

TENNYSON, ALFRED   Demeter and other Poems. 1889. First ed., fcap. 8vo. George's 635-1334 1978 £5

TENNYSON, ALFRED   Demeter and other Poems. 1889. First ed., sm. 8vo., orig. cloth. Howes 194-1247 1978 £5

TENNYSON, ALFRED   Enoch Arden, etc. Moxon, 1864. Sm. 8vo., 1st ed., orig. cloth, back faded, little stained. Quaritch 979-318 1978 $10

TENNYSON, ALFRED   Enoch Arden. 1864. 1st. ed., orig. green calf, spine gilt, red label, fine. Jarndyce 16-1107 1978 £8

TENNYSON, ALFRED   Enoch Arden, etc. 1864. Orig. cloth, cloth of Frieze. Eaton 45-493 1978 £10

TENNYSON, ALFRED   The Foresters: Robin Hood and Maid Marian. 1892. First ed., fcap. 8vo., orig. cloth. Howes 194-1248 1978 £5

TENNYSON, ALFRED   Gareth and Lynette. 1872. First published ed., sm. 8vo., orig. cloth. Howes 194-1250 1978 £5

TENNYSON, ALFRED   The Holy Grail and Other Poems. London, 1870. 8vo, green blind-stamped cloth, flyleaves foxed, spine rubbed, Nice, 1st ed., collector's cond. Desmarais 1-398 1978 $20

TENNYSON, ALFRED   Idylls of the King. 1859. First ed., sm. 8vo., full contemp. green mor., gilt panelled sides and spine, all edges gilt. Howes 194-1251 1978 £8.50

TENNYSON, ALFRED   Idylls of the King. 1859. 2nd. ed., orig. cloth. Eaton 45-494 1978 £5

TENNYSON, ALFRED   In Memoriam. 1850. 1st. ed., 1st. issue, frontis, orig. cloth, v.g. Jarndyce 16-1106 1978 £60

TENNYSON, ALFRED   In Memoriam. Boston, 1852. First U.S. ed., orig. patterned cloth, good. Bell Book 17-854 1978 £12.50

TENNYSON, ALFRED   The Lover's Tale. 1879. 1st. ed., orig. cloth. Eaton 45-495 1978 £6

TENNYSON, ALFRED   Lyrical Poems. London, 1885. Ed. ltd. to 500 copies on lg. paper, 8vo., t.e.g., signed by artist, pen & ink sketches, full crushed red levant, spine gilt with raised bands, green crushed mor. doublures, marblized box. Current Misc. 8-43 1978 $650

TENNYSON, ALFRED   Maud and other Poems. 1855. First ed., fcap. 8vo., cover faded. George's 635-1335 1978 £5

TENNYSON, ALFRED   Maud and Other Poems. 1855. 1st. ed., 8vo, orig. green cloth, nice. Fenning 32-326 1978 £24

TENNYSON, ALFRED   Poems, 1830. 1862. 3/4 dark green morocco by Riviere, front green printed wrapper bound in. Baldwins' 51-371 1978 $135

TENNYSON, ALFRED   Poems. MDCCCXXX. MDCCCXXXIII. 1862. 12mo., orig. wrs., unopened, fine. MacManus 238-392 1978 $75

TENNYSON, ALFRED   Poems. 1864. Thick 8vo., contemp. binding of full dark green hard grain mor, raised bands, gilt edges. Howes 194-1244 1978 £30

TENNYSON, ALFRED   Poems by Two Brothers. 1893. Lg. 8vo., orig. cream cloth, printed on fine paper, ltd. lg. paper ed. of 300 copies only. Howes 194-1254 1978 £12

TENNYSON, ALFRED   Poetical Works. 1909. Portrait, half crimson mor. gilt, gilt top, 8vo. Howes 194-1245 1978 £7.50

TENNYSON, ALFRED   Queen Mary. 1875. 8vo., 1st ed., orig. cloth. Quaritch 979-319 1978 $25

TENNYSON, ALFRED   Tiresias and other Poems. 1885. First ed., fcap. 8vo. George's 635-1336 1978 £5

TENNYSON, ALFRED   The Works of Alfred, Lord Tennyson. Boston, 1892-95. 12 vols., octavo, bound in 3/4 grained mor. over cloth, gilt borders, raised spine bands and gilt floral motif stamped on spines, 1 of 1,000 copies, Ed. de Luxe. Bennett 7-116 1978 $450

TENNYSON, CHARLES   Alfred Tennyson. 1949. Plts., d.w., orig. cloth, 8vo. Howes 194-1252 1978 £5.50

TENNYSON, CHARLES   Sonnets and Fugitive Pieces. Cambridge, 1830. Orig. bds., 1st. ed. Baldwins' 51-372 1978 $85

TENNYSON, HALLAM   Alfred Lord Tennyson, a Memoir. London, 1897. 1st. ed., 2 vols., very good. Baldwins' 51-370 1978 $20

TENNYSON, HALLAM   Alfred Lord Tennyson: A Memoir by his Son. 1897. First ed., plts., 2 vols., orig. cloth, 8vo. Howes 194-1253 1978 £14

TENNYSON D'EYNCOURT, EUSTACE H. W.   A Shipbuilder's Yarn. n.d. lst. ed., illus., 8vo, orig. cloth, spine slightly dull, pres. copy to Winston Churchill. Sawyer 298-119 1978 £75

TENORIO DE LEON, ALVARO   Atomos Que Neuvamente Se Han Descubierto Con Las Luzes De Apolo, en la Controversia Celebre del vso de las Sangrias, assi en los Afectos Superiores Como en las Calenturas. (N. P., n.d.), (Cadiz, ca. 1680). Sm. 4to., woodcut, modern blue Spanish calf, gilt tooled, sm. marginal worm-trail, very good copy, scarce. Zeitlin 245-262 1978 $125

THE 10TH Royal Hussars in the Second World War, 1939-1945. Aldershot, 1948. Cloth, port., plts., maps, 8vo. F. Edwards 1013-470 1978 £4

TENTZELIUS, W. E.   Exercitationes selectae in duos partes. Lipsae et Francofurti, 1692. Sm. 4to., loose in old vellum covers. George's 635-1137 1978 £5

TERENCE
Please turn to
TERENTIUS AFER, PUBLIUS

TERENTIUS AFER, PUBLIUS   Comoediae seu Ex Dan Heinsii Recentione. Amsterodami, 1640. 16mo., nice full calf, binding shaved. Van der Peet H-64-563 1978 Dfl 110

TERENTIUS AFER, PUBLIUS   Comoediae Sex. 1731. Contemp. panelled sheep, 8vo. Howes 194-490 1978 £10

TERENTIUS AFER, PUBLIUS   Comedies made English. 1741. Recent qtr. calf, 8vo. George's 635-515 1978 £7.50

TERENTIUS AFER, PUBLIUS   Comedies made English. 1741. 12mo., contemp. calf, joint broken. George's 635-514 1978 £5

TERENTIUS AFER, PUBLIUS   Publii Terentii afri Comediae Sex:.... Glasquae, 1742. lst ed., large Crown 8vo, in fours, full contemp. calf, gilt-paneled spine, lacks front and back free-endpapers. Bennett 20-210 1978 $225

TERENTIUS AFER, PUBLIUS   Comedies made English. 1743. Sm. 8vo., contemp. vellum. George's 635-516 1978 £8.50

TERENTIUS AFER, PUBLIUS   The Comedies of Terence. 1768. Plts., 2 vols., contemp. half calf, second ed. Howes 194-491 1978 £21

TERENTIUS AFER, PUBLIUS   The Comedies of Terence.... 1768. Folding, engraved plts., 2 vols., 8vo., contemp. calf, nice. Fenning 32-327 1978 £21.50

TERENTIUS AFER, PUBLIUS   Comedies. 1768. 2 vols., fldg. plt., old calf, worn, shabby, joints cracked. Allen 234-930 1978 $15

TERENTIUS AFER, PUBLIUS   Comoediae. 1854. 4to., full contemp. calf, all edges gilt. Howes 194-1255 1978 £15

TERENTIUS AFER, PUBLIUS   Comedies. 1908. 2nd ed., some pencillings. Allen 234-928 1978 $7.50

TERENTIUS AFER, PUBLIUS   Lustspiele. 1799. 2 vols., half calf. Allen 234-932 1978 $8.50

TERHUNE, ALBERT PAYSON   Syria from the Saddle. Boston, 1896. 8vo., illus., ex-lib., orig. cloth, lst ed. Morrill 241-570 1978 $12.50

TERHUNE, ALFRED MC KINLEY   The Life of Edward Fitzgerald. New Haven, 1947. First ed., frontis., maps, d.j., v.g. Houle 10-247 1978 $30

TERHUNE, MARY VIRGINIA (HAWES)   Colonial Homesteads and Their Stories. New York, 1912. 167 illus., 2 vols. in 1. Baldwins' 51-254 1978 $22.50

TERHUNE, MARY VIRGINIA (HAWES)   Moss-Side. New York, 1857. Cloth, rubbed, lst ed. Hayman 72-242 1978 $7.50

TERMAN, LEWIS MADISON   The Stanford Study of Gifted Children. (Stanford?, 1946). 8vo., author's photo. portr., gray prtd. wrs., good copy. Zeitlin 245-263 1978 $25

TERRELL, A. W.   Address of Judge A. W. Terrell before the Athenaeum and Rusk Socities of the University of Texas. Austin, 1884. Jenkins 116-1314 1978 $25

TERRY, ALLEN   A Correspondence. New York, Fountain Press, 1931. No. 931 of 3000 copies, roy. 8vo., buckram, t.e.g., spine faded, very good, largely unopened. Bell Book 17-855 1978 £15

TERRY, C. S.   The Life and Campaigns of Alexander Leslie, 1st Earl of Leven. 1899. Maps, illus., 8vo. George's 635-837 1978 £7.50

TERRY, C. S.   The Life and Campaigns of Alexander Leslie, First Earl of Leven. 1899. Maps, plts., octavo, good. Upcroft 10-563 1978 £12

TERRY, E.   A Voyage to East-India... 1777. Folding map, engraved portrait, plts., half calf, fore-edge of map frayed & short tear, 8vo. Edwards 1012-114 1978 £120

TERRY, S. B.   The Financing of the Hundred Years War, 1337-60. 1914. 8vo. George's 635-411 1978 £5.25

TESSAN, FRANCOIS DE   Promenades au Far-West. Paris, 1912. Orig. pr. wr., lst ed. Ginsberg 14-947 1978 $45

TESSIN, CARL GUSTAV   Letters from an Old Man to a Young Prince.... 1756. First English ed., 2 vols., 12mo., contemp. calf. Howes 194-226 1978 £32

TESTIMONIAL Dinner Given to Mr. Raymond Orteig by His Friends in Appreciation of the Great Services He has Rendered Aviation in the United States and France...Nov. 2, 1927, Waldorf-Astoria Hotel, New York. (New York, 1928). Illus., 8vo., orig. wrs., scarce. Morrill 241-34 1978 $25

TETAU, J.   Les Apothicaires de Nancy au XVIIIe. 1932. George's 635-412 1978 £5

TETU, CHARLES   Analyse et Observations sur les Droits Relatifs aux Eveques de Quebec et de Montreal.... Montreal, 1842. Covers missing. Wolfe 39-525 1978 $100

TEUFFEL, WILHELM SIGISMUND   History of Roman Literature. 1900. 2 vols. Allen 234-986 1978 $22.50

TEXAS   Inventory of the County Archives of Texas: Bandera County. San Antonio, 1940. Jenkins 116-61 1978 $15

TEXAS   Inventory of the County Archives of Texas: Fayette County. San Antonio, 1940. Map. Jenkins 116-430 1978 $17.50

TEXAS   Inventory of the County Archives of Texas: Marion County. San Antonio, 1940. Map. Jenkins 116-886 1978 $15

TEXAS   Inventory of the County Archives of Texas: Milam County. San Antonio, 1941. Map. Jenkins 116-942 1978 $15

TEXAS   Inventory of the County Archives of Texas: Mills County. San Antonio, 1940. Map. Jenkins 116-948 1978 $13.50

TEXAS   Inventory of the County Archives of Texas: Robertson County. San Antonio, 1941. Jenkins 116-1185 1978 $17.50

TEXAS   Inventory of the County Archives of Texas: Rockwall County. San Antonio, 1940. Map. Jenkins 116-1190 1978 $15

TEXAS   Inventory of the County Archives of Texas: Sabine County. San Antonio, 1939. Map. Jenkins 116-1210 1978 $17.50

TEXAS   Inventory of the County Archives of Texas: Somervell County. San Antonio, 1940. Map. Jenkins 116-1263 1978 $15

TEXAS   Inventory of the County Archives of Texas: Wilson County. San Antonio, 1939. Map. Jenkins 116-1479 1978 $12.50

TEXAS. CONSTITUTION   Constitution of the State of Texas Adopted by the Constitutional Convention... Austin 1922. Orig. cloth, scarce. Jenkins 116-955 1978 $35

TEXAS. CONSTITUTIONAL CONVENTION   Journal of the Constitutional Convention of the State of Texas.   Galveston, 1875. Rare, John Henry Brown's copy. Jenkins 116-756 1978 $185

TEXAS. LAWS   Texas–General Laws of the Ninth Legislature of the State of Texas.   Houston, 1862. Wrs., Bell Wiley's copy.   Broadfoot 46-450 1978 $150

TEXAS & PACIFIC RAILWAY COMPANY. CHARTERS   Charter and Other Legislation Relating to the Texas and Pacific Railway Company.   N.P., c. 1875. Half mor. Jenkins 116-211 1978 $200

TEXAS HISTORICAL RECORDS SURVEY   Inventory of the County Archives of Texas...Prepared by...Work Projects Administration.   San Antonio, 1940. Wrs. Hayman 72-744 1978 $12.50

TEXAS Almanac and State Industiral Guide for 1904.   Galveston, 1904. Original pictorial wr. Jenkins 116-1324 1978 $45

TEXAS Almanac and State Industrial Guide, 1914.   Dallas, 1914. 1st ed., pict. wr., illus., maps. Jenkins 116-1325 1978 $35

TEXAS Memorial Museum Information Pamphlets.   Austin, 1939-1944. No. 1 to 33 complete. Jenkins 116-1329 1978 $125

TEXAS Under Six Flags, Together with a Brief Sketch of Paris and Lamar County. Paris, 1936. 1st ed., wr., illus., map. Jenkins 116-789 1978 $15

TEXTE, JOSEPH   J. J. Rousseau and the Cosmopolitan Spirit in Literature.   1899. Orig. buckram, 8vo., spine little faded. Howes 194-1136 1978 £6

TEY, JOSEPHINE   The Franchise Affair.   London, (1949. Biblo 251-455 1978 $8.50

THACHER, AMOS BATEMAN   Turkoman Rugs.   55 plts., cr. 4to, ltd. to 500 copies. Traylen 88-523 1978 £18

THACHER, JAMES   American Modern Practice or a Simple Method of Prevention and Cure of Diseases.   Boston, 1817. Orig. bds., clean, very little foxing. Rittenhouse 49-773 1976 $35

THACHER, JAMES   History of the Town of Plymouth; From Its First Settlement in 1620, to 1832.   Boston, 1832. Frontis., rebound. MacManus 239-1046 1978 $35

THACHER, JOHN BOYD   The Cabotian Discovery.   1897. Fold. plt. Hood 116-663 1978 $15

THACHER, JOHN BOYD   The Collection of...in the Library of Congress. Incunabula – Books Relating to the French Revolution – Autograph Letters. Washington, 1915, 31, 31. 3 vols., 8vo., orig. mor.-backed cloth, some slight rubbing. MacManus 238-1066 1978 $40

THACKERAY, WILLIAM MAKEPEACE   The Adventures of Philip on His Way Through the World...   1862. 1st. ed., 3 vols., half title, orig. brown cloth, fine. Jarndyce 16-1133 1978 £135

THACKERAY, WILLIAM MAKEPEACE   Ballads.   London, 1865. Contemp. half calf over cloth, very good or better. Limestone 9-292 1978 $15

THACKERAY, WILLIAM MAKEPEACE   Ballads, Critical Reviews, Tales.... 1899. Illus., half green levant mor., gilt top, 8vo. Howes 194-1257 1978 £6.50

THACKERAY, WILLIAM MAKEPEACE   Christmas Books.   1857. New ed., illus., engraved tailpiece, folding frontis, orig. half red morocco, marbled bds., v.g. Jarndyce 16-1123 1978 £12

THACKERAY, WILLIAM MAKEPEACE   A Collection of Letters of W. M. Thackeray 1847-1855.   London, 1887. 1st ed., portrait, illus., tall 4to., orig. brown cloth, gilt, beveled edges, very good or better. Limestone 9-296 1978 $35

THACKERAY, WILLIAM MAKEPEACE   Denis Duval.   1867. 1st ed., orig. pink cloth, v.g., bookplt. Jarndyce 16-1136 1978 £20

THACKERAY, WILLIAM MAKEPEACE   Doctor Birch & His Young Friends.   1849. 1st. ed., hand coloured frontis, vignette & plts., sm. lib. stamp on reverse of plts., half calf, v.g. Jarndyce 16-1115 1978 £16

THACKERAY, WILLIAM MAKEPEACE   English Humourists of the Eighteenth Century.   London, 1853. Orig. cloth, 1st pub. ed., very good. MacManus 238-394 1978 $75

THACKERAY, WILLIAM MAKEPEACE   The English Humourist.   1853. 2nd. ed., half title, orig. cloth, v.g. Jarndyce 16-1118 1978 £6.50

THACKERAY, WILLIAM MAKEPEACE   Etchings.   n.d. Plts., orig. card wrappers, cloth spine, slight damage to front bd., contents v.g. Jarndyce 16-1137 1978 £8.50

THACKERAY, WILLIAM MAKEPEACE   The Four Georges.   1861. 1st. ed., illus., half title, some foxing of prelims., orig. green cloth, bright. Jarndyce 16-1128 1978 £14.50

THACKERAY, WILLIAM MAKEPEACE   The Four Georges.   1861. 1st. ed., illus., half title, orig. green cloth, good. Jarndyce 16-1130 1978 £12.50

THACKERAY, WILLIAM MAKEPEACE   The Four Georges.   1861. 1st. ed., illus., half title, orig. green cloth, dulled. Jarndyce 16-1129 1978 £10.50

THACKERAY, WILLIAM MAKEPEACE   The Four Georges.   1862. 2nd. ed., illus., half title, orig. green cloth, good. Jarndyce 16-1131 1978 £6

THACKERAY, WILLIAM MAKEPEACE   The Four Georges.   1866. Early ed., illus., half title, orig. green cloth, good. Jarndyce 16-1132 1978 £6

THACKERAY, WILLIAM MAKEPEACE   The History of Henry Esmond, Esq.   1852. 1st. ed., 3 vols., half titles, untrimmed in full calf, gilt borders & dentelles, gilt spines, dark green labels, fine handsome set. Jarndyce 16-1117 1978 £120

THACKERAY, WILLIAM MAKEPEACE   The History of Henry Esmond, Esq.   1853. 2nd. ed., 3 vols., half titles, frontis, orig. brown cloth, paper labels replaced with facsimiles, v.g. Jarndyce 16-1119 1978 £22.50

THACKERAY, WILLIAM MAKEPEACE   The History of Henry Esmond, Esq. Colonel in the Service of Her Majesty Queen Anne....   New York, 1831. Orig. paper wr., edges frayed, back cover detached, good. Greene 78-116 1978 $25

THACKERAY, WILLIAM MAKEPEACE   The History of Pendennis.   London, 1848-1850. Orig. 24 parts in 23, yellow pict. wrs., 1st ed., some wr. defects and soiling, very good, cloth boxes. MacManus 238-393 1978 $275

THACKERAY, WILLIAM MAKEPEACE   The History of Pendennis.   London, 1849-50. 2 vols., 1st ed., octavo, bound in half wine mor., gilt spines, spines faded, plts. Totteridge 29-105 1978 $100

THACKERAY, WILLIAM MAKEPEACE   The History of Pendennis.   New York, 1850. 1st Amer. ed., 2 vols., illus. wood eng., orig. cloth, good. Greene 78-336 1978 $50

THACKERAY, WILLIAM MAKEPEACE   The History of Pendennis.   London, 1898. 8vo., half calf, t.e.g., frontis. & illus. by author. Van der Peet H-64-406 1978 Dfl 55

THACKERAY, WILLIAM MAKEPEACE   The History of Samuel Titmarsh and the Great Hoggarty Diamond.   London, n.d. (1849??). 8vo, original white glazed boards, printed in dark blue and light green, "yellowback", very fine condition. Ximenes 47-305 1978 $50

THACKERAY, WILLIAM MAKEPEACE   The Kickleburys on the Rhine.   1850. 1st. ed., illus., half title, half brown morocco, little rubbed otherwise v.g. Jarndyce 16-1116 1978 £12

THACKERAY, WILLIAM MAKEPEACE   The Kickleburys on the Rhine.   1866. 4th ed., frontis, engraved title & plts., orig. purple cloth, gilt imprint on leading bds., v.g. Jarndyce 16-1135 1978 £10

THACKERAY, WILLIAM MAKEPEACE   Lovel the Widower.   1861. 1st. ed., frontis & plts., lib. stamp on title, finely bound in half calf, spine heavily gilt, labels, good. Jarndyce 16-1127 1978 £14

THACKERAY, WILLIAM MAKEPEACE   Miscellaneous Essays Sketches & Reviews. 1885. Illus., half title, orig. green cloth, mint. Jarndyce 16-1139 1978 £8.50

THACKERAY, WILLIAM MAKEPEACE   Mrs. Perkin's Ball. n.d. (1847). 1st. ed., illus., half green morocco, spine rubbed. Jarndyce 16-1113 1978 £9.50

THACKERAY, WILLIAM MAKEPEACE   Mrs. Perkin's Ball. n.d. (1874). 1st. ed., half title, illus., orig. covers bound in at end, 3/4 red morocco, gilt spine, t.e.g., fine. Jarndyce 16-1112 1978 £18.50

THACKERAY, WILLIAM MAKEPEACE   Mr. Brown's Letters to a Young Man About Town. Cambridge, The Riverside Press, 1901. 1 of 500 numbered copies prtd., marbled paper over bds., cloth spine. Battery Park 1-20 1978 $50

THACKERAY, WILLIAM MAKEPEACE   The Newcomes. London, 1853-5. Illus. by Richard Doyle, orig. printed wrs., orig. 24 parts in 23, 1st ed. in orig. parts, nice, boxed. MacManus 238-395 1978 $400

THACKERAY, WILLIAM MAKEPEACE   The Newcomes. 1854-55. 2 vols., illus. by Richard Doyle, foxed, rebound in cloth. Eaton 45-497 1978 £8

THACKERAY, WILLIAM MAKEPEACE   The Newcomes. London, 1854-5 Full-page plates, textual drawings on steel and wood by Richard Doyle, 2 vols., 1st ed., octavo, bound in blue half mor., gilt spines, gilt edges, light foxing. Totteridge 29-106 1978 $100

THACKERAY, WILLIAM MAKEPEACE   The Newcomes. London, 1854-55. 2 vols. octavo, engraved plates, many illus. and vignettes, bound by Bayntun in 3/4 crimson mor., gilt borders, t.e.g., orig. cloth covers and backstrips bound in, 1st ed. Bennett 7-117 1978 $95

THACKERAY, WILLIAM MAKEPEACE   The Newcomes. 1854-5. 1st. ed., 2 vols., illus. by Richard Doyle, some foxing of plts., half green calf, maroon labels, v.g. Jarndyce 16-1120 1978 £20

THACKERAY, WILLIAM MAKEPEACE   The Newcomes. 1854-5. 1st. ed., 2 vols., engraved frontis & vignette, tailpieces by Richard Doyle, some rather foxed, orig. cloth, worn. Jarndyce 16-1121 1978 £10.50

THACKERAY, WILLIAM MAKEPEACE   The Newcomes. 1854-5. 1st. ed., 2 vols., illus. on steel & wood by Richard Doyle, half red calf, labels, rubbed & heads of spines worn. Jarndyce 16-1122 1978 £5.50

THACKERAY, WILLIAM MAKEPEACE   The Newcomes. London, 1900. Thick 8vo., half calf, t.e.g., frontis., plts. Van der Peet H-64-405 1978 Dfl 55

THACKERAY, WILLIAM MAKEPEACE   Notes of a Journey From Cornhill to Grand Cairo. 1846. 1st. ed., coloured frontis, illus., half calf, good. Jarndyce 16-1110 1978 £15

THACKERAY, WILLIAM MAKEPEACE   Notes of a Journey From Cornhill to Grand Cairo. 1846. 2nd. ed., hand-coloured frontis, orig. red cloth, gilt imprint recased, fine & bright. Jarndyce 16-1111 1978 £10

THACKERAY, WILLIAM MAKEPEACE   The Orphan of Pimlico and Other Sketches, Fragments and Drawings. London, 1876. 1st ed., lg. 8vo., cloth over bds., spine chipped, plts., very good or better. Limestone 9-293 1978 $65

THACKERAY, WILLIAM MAKEPEACE   The Orphan of Pimlico & Other Sketches. 1876. 1st. ed., folio, frontis portrait, facsimiles & drawings, half title, orig. blue cloth, gilt & black imprint, fine copy, except for slight damp marking of back bd. Jarndyce 16-1138 1978 £14

THACKERARY, WILLIAM MAKEPEACE   The Orphan of Pimlico., & Other Sketches, Fragments & Drawings. Philadelphia, 1876. 1st Amer. ed., newly rebound quarter morocco, cloth sides, marbled end papers, very good. Greene 78-337 1978 $55

THACKERAY, WILLIAM MAKEPEACE   The Paris Sketch Book. 1840. 1st. ed., 2 vols., numerous designs, orig. brown cloth, new endpapers, slight wear to head, otherwise v.g. Jarndyce 16-1109 1978 £22

THACKERAY, WILLIAM MAKEPEACE   Rebecca and Rowena. London, 1850. First ed., plts., illus., orig. half mor., over maroon stippled cloth, raised bds., v.g. or better. Limestone 9-294 1978 $35

THACKERAY, WILLIAM MAKEPEACE   Roundabout Papers. 1863. 1st. ed., engraved frontis, half red morocco, marbled bds., v.g. Jarndyce 16-1134 1978 £12

THACKERAY, WILLIAM MAKEPEACE   Roundabout Papers. London, 1863. Illus., orig. cloth, 1st ed., very good. MacManus 238-397 1978 $50

THACKERAY, WILLIAM MAKEPEACE   Sultan Stork & Other Stories & Sketches. London, 1887. Olive green cloth, very good, solander case, side broken. Greene 78-291 1978 $65

THACKERAY, WILLIAM MAKEPEACE   Stray Papers. Being Reviews, Verses & Sketches (1821-1847). Philadelphia, n.d. (1901). 1st Amer. ed., orig. cloth, front end paper damaged, good. Greene 78-290 1978 $45

THACKERAY, WILLIAM MAKEPEACE   Thackerayana Notes and Anecdotes Lond., 1898. New Ed., colored frontispiece, orig. cloth, good, some int. foxing. Greene 78-292 1978 $35.00

THACKERAY, WILLIAM MAKEPEACE   Vanity Fair. 1848. 1st. ed., illus., orig. blue cloth, slight splitting locally on hinges, otherwise v.g. in orig. cloth. Jarndyce 16-1114 1978 £110

THACKERAY, WILLIAM MAKEPEACE   Vanity Fair. London, 1896. 8vo., half calf, t.e.g., frontis. portr. Van der Peet H-64-408 1978 Dfl 55

THACKERAY, WILLIAM MAKEPEACE   The Virginians. 1857-9. 1st. ed., 24 parts, illus., orig. yellow wrappers, some little worn, boxed, good set. Jarndyce 16-1125 1978 £140

THACKERAY, WILLIAM MAKEPEACE   The Virginians. A Tale of the Last Century. London, 1857-1859. 24 parts, orig. printed wrs., 1st ed., slight chipping, nice, half mor. solander case. MacManus 238-396 1978 $375

THACKERAY, WILLIAM MAKEPEACE   The Virginians. London, 1858. 2 vols., 1st ed., 1st issue, lacking half title, steel engraved plts., wood engravings, contemp. half calf, marbled bds., gilt spines, very good or better. Limestone 9-295 1978 $65

THACKERAY, WILLIAM MAKEPEACE   The Virginians. 1858-9. 1st. ed., 2 vols., illus. on steel & wood, very slight foxing, half green morocco, handsome set. Jarndyce 16-1126 1978 £38

THACKERAY, WILLIAM MAKEPEACE   The Virginians. 1858-59. 2 vols., illus., foxed, rebound in cloth. Eaton 45-496 1978 £8

THACKERAY, WILLIAM MAKEPEACE   The Virginians. London, 1899. 8vo., half calf, t.e.g., frontis. portr., illus. by author. Van der Peet H-64-407 1978 Dfl 55

THACKERAY, WILLIAM MAKEPEACE   The Virginian. New York, 1911. Illus. by Charles M. Russell & Frederic Remington, signed on half title, fr. flyleaf torn out, new ed. Baldwins' 51-575 1978 $50

THACKERAY, WILLIAM MAKEPEACE   The Works. 1888-91. Frontispieces, illus., 13 vols., orig. green cloth, 8vo. Howes 194-1255a 1978 £22

THACKERAY, WILLIAM MAKEPEACE   The Works. 1908-09. Biographical ed., portraits, illus. by author, 13 vols., half red crushed mor., raised bands, gilt tops, 8vo. Howes 194-1256 1978 £105

THACKERAY, WILLIAM MAKEPEACE   Works. New York & London, 1910-11. 26 vols., lg. 8vo., centenary biographical ed., coloured frontis., illus., half brown mor., panelled backs, gilt tops, bkplt. Quaritch 979-375 1978 $360

THANE, ERIC   The Majestic Land. (1950). First ed., fine, d.w., illus. Biblo 247-268 1978 $17.50

THARIN, R. S.   Arbitrary Arrests in the South. New York, 1863. 12mo., ex-lib., lacks top half of spine, 1st ed. Morrill 239-624 1978 $17.50

THARP, BENJAMIN C.   The Vegetation of Texas. Houston, 1939. 1st ed., wr. Jenkins 116-1339 1978 $10

THARP, LOUISE HALL   The Peabody Sisters of Salem. Boston, 1950. 1st ed., illus., very good. Victoria 34-787 1978 $8.50

THATCHER, FRANKLIN   The Friend to Health. Boston, 1826. Some damp stains, spine repaired, cover worn. Rittenhouse 49-774 1976 $20

THAXTER, CELIA   Stories and Poems for Children. 1895. First ed. Austin 82-969 1978 $17.50

THAYER, JOHN ADAMS   Astir. 1910. First ed., v.g. Austin 82-970 1978 $12.50

THAYER, JOHN ADAMS   Astir. A Publisher's Life-Story. Boston, 1910. 1st ed., edges rubbed. Biblo BL781-775 1978 $10

THAYER, WILLIAM M.   The Ferry-Boy and the Financier. Boston, 1864. Orig. bind. Petrilla 13-125 1978 $8.50

THAYER, WILLIAM ROSCOE   Theodore Roosevelt...An Intimate Biography. Boston, (1919). Illus. Biblo 251-108 1978 $12.50

THAYER, WILLIAM ROSCOE   Theodore Roosevelt. Boston, (1919). Illus. Biblo BL781-246 1978 $8

THAYER, WILLIAM SYDNEY   The Malarial Fevers of Baltimore: an Analysis of 616 Cases. Baltimore, 1895. Color plts., folding tables, tall 8vo., printed wrs. loose and torn. Rittenhouse 49-776 1976 $25

THAYER, WILLIAM SYDNEY   Osler and Other Papers. Baltimore, 1931. Rittenhouse 49-775 1976 $15

THAYER-SMITH, HOLLIS RANDOLPH   Sonnets of a Sorehead. Cambridge, 1925. 1st ed., wr., very good or better. Limestone 9-299 1978 $25

THEAL, GEORGE MC CALL   The Portuguese in South Africa. London, 1896. Maps, 8vo, orig. cloth. K Books 239-484 1978 £22

THEAL, GEORGE MC CALL   South Africa. London, 1897. 8vo, half green morocco, 4th. ed., Rugeley Grammar School Prize label, good. Sexton 7-118 1978 £10

THE THEATRE; or The Letters of Candidus... Edinburgh, 1802. 1st. ed., 12mo, contemp. bds., later cloth spine, uncut, title dust-soiled & ink blobs in 2 final leaves, corner of 2 leaves torn with loss of some text. Hannas 54-335 1978 £15

THEBAUD, A.J.   Ireland, Past & Present. New York, 1901. Good, octavo bound in cloth, reprint. Hyland 128-645 1978 £10.50

THELLER, E. A.   Canada in 1837-38; Showing, by Historical Facts, the Causes of the Late Attempted Revolution, and of its Failure. Philadelphia, 1841. 2 vols., covers slightly worn. Hood's 115-851 1978 $165

THEOBALD, LEWIS   A Complete Key to the Last New Farce the What d've call it. 1715. 8vo, 1st ed., disbound, preserved in cloth, mor. back. Quaritch 979-152 1978 $400

THEOBALD, LEWIS   Harlequin Sorcerer: With the Loves of Pluto and Proserpine. 1752. 8vo, half-title. Hannas 54-346 1978 £17.50

THEOBALD, LEWIS   Orpheus and Eurydice; an Opera. 1740. 1st. octavo ed., disbound. Hannas 54-347 1978 £10

THEOCRITUS   Idyllia. 1760. Old calf, cover detached, spines torn, illus. Allen 234-990 1978 $10

THEOCRITUS   Idylls. 1925. Ltd. to 750 copies, roy. 8vo., orig. qtr. parchment. George's 635-881 1978 £7.50

THEOCRITUS   Theocriti Syracusil quae supersunt. Oxford, 1770. 2 vols., 4to., Greek text, contemp. vellum. Howes 194-492 1978 £35

THEOCRITUS   Theocritus Translated into English Verse. Cambridge and London, 1869. First ed., good, orig. green cloth, scarce. Limestone 9-49 1978 $32.50

THEOCRITUS   Works. 1950. 2 vols. Allen 234-987 1978 $40

THEODORUS GAZA   Liber De Mensibus Atticis. Basle, 1536. Sm. 8vo., modern 1/2 calf. Salloch 345-180 1978 $400

THEOPHRASTUS   The Characters of... London, 1831. Illus., sm. 8vo., 3/4 calf, with labels. Salloch 345-182 1978 $25

THEOPHRASTUS   Opera Omnia. Leyden, 1613. Folio, vellum, fine copy, from the library of Jean Barbeyrac (1674-1744). Salloch 345-181 1978 $275

THERY, R.   l' Indochine Francaise. Paris, 1931. Illus., maps, 8vo, orig. covers. Van der Peet 127-243 1978 Dfl 35

THESAURUS Linguae Latinae. 1900-12. 4to., Vols. 1-4, Vols. 1-3 in half mor., rubbed, Vol. 4 in buckram. Allen 234-O 1978 $250

THESE Are Our Lives. Chapel Hill, 1939. Bell Wiley's copy. 44-789 1978 $14

THEURIET, A.   Le Secret de Gertrude. Paris, 1890. Lg. 8vo., orig. covers, illus. & plts. by E. Adan. Van der Peet H-64-457 1978 Dfl 65

THEVET, ANDRE   Historia Dell'India America detta Altramente Francia Antartica.... Venice, 1561. Contemp. vellum. Wolfe 39-527 1978 $350

THIAN, RAPHAEL P.   Legislative History of the General Staff of the Army of the United States .... Washington, 1901. Orig. cloth, 1st ed. Ginsberg 14-980 1978 $37.50

THIBAULT, GIRARD   Academie de l'Espee, ou se demonstrent par reigles mathematiques sur le fondement d'un cercle mysterieux la theorie et pratique des vrais et jusqu'a present incognus secrets due maniement des armes a pied et a cheval. (Leyden), 1628. Engr. portr., full brown mor., blind-tooled, light soiling & waterstaining, light foxing, internally fine, engr. bkplt., 1st ed. Dawson's 447-294 1978 $2,800

THICKNESS, PHILIP   Useful Hints to those who make the Tour of France. 1768. 8vo., contemp. qtr. calf, marbled sides, first ed. P. M. Hill 142-306 1978 £75

THIERS, M. A.   The History of the French Revolution. London, 1838. Extra-illus., 1st ed., 5 vols. expanded to 10, royal 8vo., t.e.g., unique, 2 A.L.s., full blue crushed levant, elab. inner dentelles, raised bands, crimson endpapers, bkplt. of Samuel Barger, perfect cond., rare. Current Misc. 8-44 1978 $1,000

THIERS, M. A.   The History of the French Revolution. 1838. Illus., engraved plts., some foxing, 5 vols., full calf, rubbed. George's 635-770 1978 £10

THIESS, FRANK   The Voyage of Forgotten Men (Tsushima). Indianapolis, (1937). Cloth, very good. Dawson's 127-316 1978 $15

THINGS I Shouldn't Tell. Philadelphia, 1925. Illustrated. Biblo 247-650 1978 $15

THIRKELL, ANGELA   Three Houses. London, 1931. Fine in faded, soiled & lightly damaged d.w. Desmarais B-613 1978 $10

THIRLWALL, C.   A History of Greece. London, 1835. 8 vols., sm. 8vo., clothbound, nice set. Van der Peet H-64-564 1978 Dfl 100

THISTLETON, FRANK   The Art of Violin Playing for Players and Teachers. London, 1924. Diagrams, cr. 8vo., covers dull. K Books 244-449 1978 £6

THOLDE, JOHANN   Letztes Testament Darinnen die Geheime Bucher vom Grossen Stein der Uralten Weisen. Strassburg, 1651. 2 vols. in 1, 12mo., engrs. in text, old vellum, stamp of Wernigerode Library, some foxing, old underlining, but good copy, bkplt. of Ernst Graf zu Stolberg, 3rd ed. & 1st ed. to include books 3 thru 5. Norman 5-291 1978 $500

THOLDE, JOHANN   The Triumphal Chariot of Antimony. London, 1893. Ads, orig. cloth, good copy. Norman 5-292 1978 $75

THOLUCK, FRIEDRICH AUGUST GOTTREU   Sufism sive Theosophia Persarum Pantheistica... Berlin, 1821. 8vo., bds. Salloch 348-270 1978 $55

THOM, ADAM   The Claims to the Oregon Territory Considered. London, 1884. 8vo, unbound as issued. Baldwins' 51-571 1978 $42.50

THOM, CHARLES   The Aspergilli. Baltimore, 1926. Library copy. Rittenhouse 49-778 1976 $17.50

THOM, WILLIAM   Rhymes and Recollections of a Hand-Loom Weaver. London, 1844. 8vo, original purple cloth, 1st ed., fine copy. Ximenes 47-308 1978 $45

THOMA, KURT H.   Oral Abscesses. Boston, 1916. Plts., many in color. Rittenhouse 49-779 1976 $25

THOMANN, TH. H.   Pagan; Ein Jahrtausend Buddhistischer Tempelkunst (in Burma). Stuttgart, 1923. Half cloth, colored frontis., colored plts., 8vo. Van der Peet 127-244 1978 Dfl 65

THOMAS A KEMPIS   The Christian's Pattern. 1733. Engraved frontis. contemp. calf, joints cracked, worn, 8vo. George's 635-1140 1978 £5

THOMAS A KEMPIS   The Christian's Pattern. 1898. Ed. ltd. to 660 copies, text ptd. in red and black, plts., orig. limp vellum, t.e.g., others uncut. George's 635-1141 1978 £15

THOMAS A KEMPIS   Imitatio Christi
Please turn to
IMITATIO CHRISTI

THOMAS OF ERCELDOUNE   Sir Tristrem: A Metrical Romance of the Thirteenth Century. Edinburgh, 1811. Roy. 8vo., contemp. calf, spine gilt, lg. paper ed. Howes 194-1279 1978 £15

THOMAS, A. H.   Calendar of Select Pleas and Memoranda of the City of London AD 1381-1412. Cambridge, 1922. Royal 8vo. Upcroft 12-445 1978 £7.50

THOMAS, A. R.   Practical Guide for Making Post-Mortem Examinations and for the Study of Morbid Anatomy. Philadelphia, 1873. Rittenhouse 49-780 1976 $12.50

THOMAS, ALLEN C.   A History of the Friends in America. Philadelphia, 1919. 5th ed., orig. cloth, very good. MacManus 239-169 1978 $15

THOMAS, ANNIE   No Alternative. Philadelphia, n.d. (c.1860). 1st Amer. ed. (?), orig. cloth edges rubbed. Greene 78-293 1978 $25

THOMAS, ANNIE   On Guard, A Novel. 1865. 1st. ed., 3 vols., half titles, contemp. half brown cloth, marbled bds., externally generally rubbed, marbled paper from bottom of back bd. missing. Jarndyce 16-1141 1978 £18.50

THOMAS, ARAD   Pioneer History of Orleans County. Albion, 1871. 2 indexes, portrs., orig. cloth, light wear on spine, very good, sound copy. Butterfield 21-336 1978 $45

THOMAS, ARTHUR H.   Company Laboratory Apparatus and Reagents.... Philadelphia, 1921. Baldwins' 51-485 1978 $22.50

THOMAS, BENJAMIN P.   Portrait for Posterity, Lincoln and His Biographers. New Brunswick, 1947. Pres. copy from author to Bell Wiley. Broadfoot's 44-361 1978 $10

THOMAS, BERT   In Red and Black. 1928. Plts. in two colours, 4to., bottom of spine defective. George's 635-129 1978 £5

THOMAS, BERTRAM   Arabia Felix. New York, 1932. 8vo, red cloth, gilt lettering on cover and spine, 1st ed., spine badly sunned and somewhat spotted, Good copy, collector's cond. Desmarais 1-273 1978 $17.50

THOMAS, CHARLES G.   Johannesburg in Arms 1895-96. London, 1896. 6 plts., cr. 8vo, orig. cloth, inscribed from author. K Books 239-485 1978 £20

THOMAS, CYRUS   The Agricultural and Pastoral Resources of Southern Colorado and Northern New Mexico... London, 1872. Disbound. Ginsberg 14-981 1978 $75

THOMAS, CYRUS   Contributions to the History of the Eastern Townships. Montreal, 1866. Orig. binding. Wolfe 39-173 1978 $85

THOMAS, CYRUS   The Rev. John and a Few Philanthropists. Montreal, 1903. Inscribed by author. Hood 116-499 1978 $35

THOMAS, CYRUS   The Rev. John and a Few Philanthropists. Montreal, 1903. Orig. binding. Wolfe 39-174 1978 $25

THOMAS, DAVID Y.   Arkansas in War and Reconstruction 1861-1874. Little Rock, 1926. Illus., Bell Wiley's copy. Broadfoot's 44-434 1978 $35.00

THOMAS, DYLAN   Deaths and Entrances. 1946. Sm. 4to., 1st ed., orig. cloth, slightly torn d.w., fine copy. Quaritch 979-320 1978 $65

THOMAS, DYLAN   Deaths and Entrances. 1946. Fine, d.w., first English ed. Bell Book 16-827 1978 £55

THOMAS, DYLAN   Deaths and Entrances. London, 1946. 8vo, orange cloth, gilt lettering on spine, 1st ed., ownership inscription, Nice, tight copy. Desmarais 1-400 1978 $75

THOMAS, DYLAN   18 Poems. London, 1934. 8vo, black cloth, 1st ed., 2nd issue, rounded spine, tipped in leaf, near Mint in torn d.w. Desmarais 1-401 1978 $250

THOMAS, DYLAN   18 Poems. Fortune Press, 1934. 2nd ed., bds., very good, later issue binding. Bell Book 16-829 1978 £15

THOMAS, DYLAN   18 Poems. Fortune Press, (1942). Second ed., later issue, bds., very good, d.w. Bell Book 17-859 1978 £35

THOMAS, DYLAN   The Map of Love: verse and Prose. 1939. Portrait, good, first issue, in smooth cloth, first English ed. Bell Book 16-830 1978 £38.50

THOMAS, DYLAN   Portrait de l'Artiste en Jeune Chien. Paris, 1947. First French ed., 1 of 100 numbered copies on alfa, wraps, fine unopened copy. Bell Book 16-831 1978 £15

THOMAS, EDITH M.   Mary at The Farm and Book of Recipes Complied During Her Visit Among the "Penna. Germans". Norristown, 1915. Recased, illus., few pages mended. Baldwins' 51-486 1978 $25

THOMAS, EDWARD   Last Poems. 1918. First ed., orig. bds., edges untrimmed, rare, 8vo. Howes 194-1448 1978 £65

THOMAS, EDWARD   Rest and Unrest. 1910. Very good, first English ed. Bell Book 16-838 1978 £16.50

THOMAS, EDWARD   The Selected Poems of Edward Thomas. Gregynog Press, 1927. Prospectus laid in, #266 of a numbered ed. of 275 copies. Battery Park 1-139 1978 $250

THOMAS, GABRIEL   An Account of Pennsylvania and West New Jersey. Cleveland, 1903. Ltd. to 250 copies, very fine untrimmed copy, orig. bds., reprint from 1698 copy. MacManus 239-1696 1978 $37.50

THOMAS, HELEN   As It Was. 1927. 1st. U.S. ed., lettered in pink on upper cover. Eaton 45-499 1978 £6

THOMAS, HENRY   Early Spanish Bookbindings XI-XV Centuries. London, 1939. Plts., demy 4to., orig. bds., holland back, fine. Forster 130-93 1978 £20

THOMAS, HENRY   Short-title Catalogue of Books printed in France and of French Books printed in other countries from 1470 to 1600. London, 1924. Demy 8vo., orig. cloth. Forster 130-232 1978 £6

THOMAS, HENRY W.   History of the Doles-Cook Brigade Army of Northern Virginia C.S.A. Atlanta, 1903. Illus., new cloth, Bell Wiley's copy. Broadfoot's 44-463 1978 $80.00

THOMAS, ISAIAH   The History of Printing in America. Frontis. engr. Battery Park 1-180 1978 $55

THOMAS, JOHN JACOBS   The American Fruit Culturist. Auburn, 1849, 1875. 8vo, orig. cloth. Book Chest 17-385 1978 $30

THOMAS, JOHN JACOBS   The Illustrated Annual Register of Rural Affairs and Cultivator Almanac, for the Year 1859... Albany, 1859. Wrs., engravings. Hayman 72-749 1978 $7.50

THOMAS, JOHN JACOBS   The Illustrated Annual Register of Rural Affairs and Cultivator Almanac, for the Year 1866. Albany, 1866. Wrps., engravings. Hayman 71-730 1978 $7.50

THOMAS, JOSEPH B.   Hounds and Hunting Through the Ages. New York, 1937. 4to, illus. Baldwins' 51-555 1978 $15

THOMAS, KATHERINE ELWES   The Real Personages of Mother Goose. New York, 1930. Very good, d.j. Ballinger 11-94 1978 $17.50

THOMAS, NATHANIEL S.   Convocational Sermon...On the Semi-Centenary of the Church in Wyoming... [Douglas, 1918]. Orig. pr. wr., 1st ed. Ginsberg 14-1082 1978 $30

THOMAS, NORMAN   After the New Deal, What? New York, 1936. 1st ed., Dorothy Thompson's unique bkplt. Biblo 251-381 1978 $18.50

THOMAS, NORMAN   Appeal to the Nations. New York, (1947). 1st ed., d.w. Biblo 251-382 1978 $12.50

THOMAS, NORMAN   We Have a Future. Princeton, 1941. 1st ed. Biblo 251-384 1978 $15

THOMAS, NORTHCOTE W.   Timne-English Dictionary. London, 1916. 2 vols., orig. cloth, 8vo, covers very faded. K Books 239-487 1978 £8

THOMAS, ROBERT   Modern Practice of Physic. Philadelphia, 1817. Orig. bds. & title strip. Rittenhouse 49-781 1976 $25

THOMAS, ROBERT   The Modern Practice of Physic. New York, 1822. 6th Amer. ed., lg. thick 8vo, contemp. calf, very good. Americanist 103-134 1978 $40

THOMAS, ROBERT A.   A Century of Methodism in Germantown. 1895. 1st ed., illus., orig. cloth, fine. MacManus 239-1697 1978 $10

THOMAS, S.   The Banker's Sure Guide. 1771. 16mo., sheep, worn. George's 635-989 1978 £7.50

THOMAS, T. GAILLARD   Abortion and Its Treatment, from the Standpoint of Practical Experience. New York, 1894. 12mo., revised by author. Morrill 239-261 1978 $8.50

THOMAS, T. M.   Eleven Years in Central South Africa. 1872. Folding map, portrait, plts., cover worn, orig. cloth, 8vo, short tear in map. Edwards 1012-310 1978 £45

THOMAS, WILLIAM I.   The Polish Peasant in Europe and America. Chicago, University of Chicago Press, 1918. 2 vols., 1st ed., good. Austin 79-770 1978 $67.50

THOMAS, WILLIAM J.   Human Longevity. London, 1873. 8vo., ex-lib., 1st ed. Morrill 239-262 1978 $12.50

THOMAS Dangerfield's Answer to A Certain Scandalous Lying Pamphlet, Entituled Malice Defeated. 1680. 1st. ed., folio, disbound. Hannas 54-47A 1978 £15

THOMAS Simms Bettens. New York, Gilliss Press, 1909. 1st ed., 1 of 250 copies prtd. on Imperial Japan vellum, full brown pigskin with raised bands on spine, full pigskin doublures & moire silk endpapers, photogravure illus., 8vo., very good. Americanist 103-115 1978 $45

THOMASON, JOHN W.   Jeb Stuart, With Illustrations by the Author. New York, 1934. Inscribed by author, front hinge cracked, cover stained. Broadfoot's 44-362 1978 $16

THOMAZI, A.   La conquete de l'Indochine. Paris, 1923. Maps, illus., 8vo, orig. covers. Van der Peet 127-246 1978 Dfl 35

THOME, JAMES A.   Emancipation in the West Indies... New York, 1838. 1st ed., orig. cloth, some wear, fold. map. MacManus 239-852 1978 $35

THOMES, WILLIAM H.   Life in the East Indies. 1873. First ed., illus., covers worn. Austin 82-971 1978 $20

THOMES, WILLIAM H.   The Whaleman's Adventures in the Sandwich Islands and California. 1873. Illus., hinges loose, covers worn. Austin 82-972 1978 $12.50

THOMIRE, P-P.   Fonderu-Ciseleur, 1751-1843. Sa Vie-Son Oeuvre... Paris, (1947). 4to., plts., good copy, orig. wrs., pres. inscription from author. Quaritch 983-Addenda p 1978 $40

THOMLINSON, MATTHEW H.   The Garrison of Fort Bliss, 1849-1916. El Paso, 1945. Bds., map, illus., 1st ed., minor stain on back cover else very good, d.w., scarce. Dykes 35-263 1978 $35

THOMPSON, A. HAMILTON   The English Clergy, and their Organization in the later Middle Ages. Oxford, 1947. 8vo. George's 635-1144 1978 £6.50

THOMPSON, SIR BENJAMIN, COUNT RUMFORD
Please turn to
RUMFORD, SIR BENJAMIN THOMPSON, COUNT

THOMPSON, BENJAMIN FRANKLIN   History of Long Island. New York, 1839. Lithos., 8vo., binding partly faded, few stains, sound, 1st ed. Morrill 239-556 1978 $60

THOMPSON, C. M.   Reconstruction in Georgia Economic, Social, Policital 1865-1872. New York, 1915. MacManus 239-1811 1978 $35

THOMPSON, C. MILDRED   Reconstruction in Georgia...1865-1872. New York, 1915. Pres. copy from author to Wiley, wrs., Bell Wiley's copy. Broadfoot 46-325 1978 $25

THOMPSON, CHARLES JOHN SAMUEL   The History and Evolution of Surgical Instruments. New York, 1942. Shelf marks on spine and lower cover. Rittenhouse 49-782 1978 $17.50

THOMPSON, CHARLES JOHN SAMUEL   The Mystery and Lore of Monsters. New York, 1931. Plts., orig. binding, foxing in spots, 1st Amer. ed. Petrilla 13-128 1978 $8

THOMPSON, CLAUDE WILLETT   Vagrant Verses. Quebec, 1926. One of 100 numbered copies signed by author, orig. binding. Wolfe 39-526 1978 $17.50

THOMPSON, DOROTHY   Let the Record Speak. 1939. Austin 80-326 1978 $7.50

THOMPSON, EDGAR T.   Race Relations and the Race Problem. Durham, 1939. Bell Wiley's copy. Broadfoot's 44-790 1978 $16.00

THOMPSON, EDWARD J.   The Knight Mystic & Other Verses. 1907. Parchment wrappers, paper label on spine, unopened, alteration in ink on pg. 41. Eaton 45-500 1978 £5

THOMPSON, EDWARD P.   The Passions of Animals. London, 1851. 1st ed., 8vo., orig. brown cloth, gilt lettering on spine, blind stamped bds., very good copy. Current 24-127 1978 $95

THOMPSON, EDWARD P.   Roentgen Rays and Phenomena of the Anode and Cathode. New York, (1896). 8vo., illus., photo. portr., orig. black cloth, gilt lettering on spine, good copy with bkplt. of Frederick Finch Strong, 1st ed. Zeitlin 245-315 1978 $75

THOMPSON, ERNEST SETON
Please turn to
SETON, ERNEST THOMPSON

THOMPSON, FLORA   Still Glides the Stream. London, 1948. First ed., drawings by Lynton Lamb, nice, orig. binding, d.w. Rota 211-288 1978 £5

THOMPSON, FRANCIS   Poems. London, 1893. Frontis., orig. bds., 1st ed., spine rubbed, otherwise very good, 500 copies printed. MacManus 238-399 1978 $65

THOMPSON, FRANCIS   Poems. London, 1893. 8vo, decor. boards, front hinge started, top and bottom of spine worn, Nice, 1 of 500 copies, 1st ed. Desmarais 1-402 1978 $55

THOMPSON, FRANCIS   Saint Ignatius Loyola. London, 1909. Illus., orig. cloth, 1st ed., good copy. MacManus 238-401 1978 $45

THOMPSON, FRANCIS   Selected Poems. Glasgow, 1909. Portrait, full sage green levant mor., 8vo. Howes 194-1280 1978 £6.50

THOMPSON, FRANCIS   Sister Songs. London, 1895. Frontis. by Laurence Housman, orig. dec. cloth, 1st ed. MacManus 238-400 1978 $25

THOMPSON, FRANK V.   Schooling of the Immigrant. 1920. Austin 79-772 1978 $12.50

THOMPSON, GEORGE   Africa in a Nutshell for the Million; or, Light on the "Dark Continent." Oberlin, 1881. Cloth. Hayman 72-750 1978 $10

THOMPSON, GEORGE   Prison Life and Reflections...of Work, Burr, and Thompson, Who Suffered an Unjust and Cruel Imprisonment in Missouri Penitentiary, for Attempting to Aid Some Slaves to Liberty. Hartford, 1850. 3 parts in 1 vol., good, orig. bind. Petrilla 13-127 1978 $12.50

THOMPSON, GEORGE S.   Bat Masterson: The Dodge City Years. Topeka, 1943. 1st ed., printed wr. Jenkins 116-893 1978 $17.50

THOMPSON, HARRIET DIANA   The Witch of Melton Hall: A Tale. c.1896. Sm. 8vo, orig. cloth, gilt, lettered "The Granville Popular Library", nice. Fenning 32-329 1978 £6

THOMPSON, HENRY T.   Ousting the Carpetbagger from South Carolina. Columbia, 1926. Illus., cover worn, Bell Wiley's copy. Broadfoot's 44-613 1978 $20.00

THOMPSON, HENRY YATES   Thirty-Two Miniatures from the Book of Hours of Joan II, Queen of Navarre, a MS. of the 14th Century. London, Chiswick Press, 1899. Collotype plts., folio, full crimson crushed levant gilt decor., gilt dentelles. Argosy Special -87 1978 $250

THOMPSON, HUBERT O.   New York Water Supply. New York, Feb. 1882. Lg. folded map. Butterfield 21-553 1978 $7.50

THOMPSON, JAMES WESTFALL   Byways in Bookland. Berkeley, 1935. 12mo., cloth. Battery Park 1-490 1978 $25

THOMPSON, JOHN   The Life of. Worcester, 1856. 1st ed., rebound. MacManus 239-853 1978 $50

THOMPSON, JOSEPH P.   Abraham Lincoln; His Life and Its Lessons. New York, 1865. Wrps., black-bordered front wrapper. Hayman 71-423 1978 $20

THOMPSON, LEANDER   Memorial of James Thompson, 1630-1682 and of Eight Generations of His Descendants. Boston, 1887. Illus., good. Biblo BL781-62 1978 $12.50

THOMPSON, MARGARET   Phrenological Character of Reuben Dunbar, with a Short Treatise on the Causes and Prevention of Crime. Albany, 1851. Disbound. Butterfield 21-45 1978 $15

THOMPSON, MAURICE   Alice of Old Vincennes. Frontis. in color, plts., green pic. cloth, 1st ed., illus., nice & bright. Bradley 49-322 1978 $20

THOMPSON, PAUL W.   What the Citizen Should Know About the Army Engineers. 1942. Illus. by Andre Jandot. Austin 80-327 1978 $8.50

THOMPSON, R. A.   Conquest of California. Santa Rosa, 1896. Illus., original wr. Ginsberg 14-208 1978 $75

THOMPSON, RAY M.   The Land of Lafitte the Pirate. Jefferson Parish, (1943). Photo. by Eugene Delacroix, drawings by Tilden Landry, illus., spiral binding, boards. Biblo 248-216 1978 $15

THOMPSON, RICHARD W.   Recollections of Sixteen Presidents from Washington to Lincoln. Indianapolis, 1894. 1st ed., 2 vols., illus., orig. cloth, very good set. MacManus 239-459 1978 $32.50

THOMPSON, RICHARD W.   Recollections of Sixteen Presidents from Washington to Lincoln. Indianapolis, 1894. 2 vols., cloth, rubbed, flecking on covers, "edition de luxe". Hayman 73-700 1978 $8.50

THOMPSON, ROBERT   The Gardener's Assistant. London, 1859. Coloured plts., illus., qtr. green calf, roy. 8vo., faint heat stain on front cover, good. K Books 244-309 1978 £20

THOMPSON, ROBERT   The Gardener's Assistant, Practical and Scientific. 1878. New ed., plts., some in colour, text illus., roy. 8vo., half mor., rubbed. George's 635-964 1978 £12.50

THOMPSON, ROBERT   The Gardener's Assistant, Practical and Scientific. 1909. New ed., coloured plts., text illus., 6 divisional vols., roy. 8vo. George's 635-965 1978 £10.50

THOMPSON, ROBERT T.   Colonel James Neilson.... New Brunswick, 1940. Fine. MacManus 239-1332 1978 $25

THOMPSON, RUTH PLUMLY   Pirates in Oz. Chicago, (1931). Illus., some spotting on rear cover, very good, tight copy. Bernard 5-514 1978 $25

THOMPSON, RUTH PLUMLY   Silver Princess in Oz. Chicago, (1938). Illus., very good. Bernard 5-515 1978 $25

THOMPSON, S.   Reminiscences of Canadian Pioneer for the Last Fifty Years. Toronto, 1884. Hood's 115-274 1978 $60

THOMPSON, SLASON   The Humbler Poets. Chicago, 1888. 2nd ed., 8vo. Morrill 239-626 1978 $10

THOMPSON, SLASON   A Short History of American Railways, Covering Ten Decades. Chicago, 1925. Illus., spine dulled, else very good, 1st ed., signed by author, orig. bind. Petrilla 13-129 1978 $12

THOMPSON, THEOPHILUS   Annals of Influenza or Epidemic Catarrhal Fever in Great Britain from 1510 to 1837. London, 1852. 8vo., orig. green blind-stamped cloth, light foxing, ex-lib., very good copy, 1st ed. Zeitlin 245-264 1978 $45

THOMPSON, THOMAS P.   Louisiana Writers Native and Resident... New Orleans, 1904. 8vo., ex-lib. Morrill 239-436 1978 $17.50

THOMPSON, TOMMY   The Script Letter. Its Form, Construction and Application. London & New York, (1949). Sq. 8vo, cloth, gilt, illus., 3rd impression, fine. Duschnes 220-59 1978 $17.50

THOMPSON, W. M.   The Holy Land, Egypt, Constantinople, Athens, Etc., Etc. London, c.1865. 1st. ed., 4to, photos, some spotting, orig. blue cloth, gilt, all edges gilt. Deighton 5-175 1978 £265

THOMPSON, W. M.   The Land and the Book. London, 1870. Map, frontis., coloured plts., illus., full green mor., 8vo. K Books 244-310 1978 £12

THOMPSON, ZADOCK   Guide to Lake George, Lake Champlain, Montreal and Quebec...from Albany, Burlington, Montreal, & c. Burlington, 1845. 18mo., tall, narrow fldg. woodcut map tipped in, plts., prtd. wr. in fine cond. Butterfield 21-19 1978 $75

THOMPSON, ZADOCK   History of Vermont, Natural, Civil, and Statistical, in Three Parts. Burlington, 1842. Map, engrs., 8vo., contemp. calf, 1st ed. Morrill 241-594 1978 $40

THOMPSON, ZADOCK   History of Vermont, Natural, Civil and Statistical. Burlington, 1853. 1st ed., fold. map, cloth, very good. MacManus 239-468 1978 $35

THOMS, HERBERT   Classical Contributions to Obstetrics and Gynecology. Springfield, 1935. First ed., shelf number on spine, clean, fresh. Rittenhouse 49-783 1976 $30

THOMS Irish Almanac & Official Directory. 1876. Map, (small tear in map), good, reprint, octavo bound in cloth. Hyland 128-647 1978 £7.50

THOMSON, A. LANDSBOROUGH   Britain's Birds and their Nests. London, 1910. Coloured plts., 4to., gilt-decor. cover. K Books 244-307 1978 £15

THOMSON, A. LANDSBOROUGH   Problems of Bird-Migration. London, 1926. Maps, diagrams, 8vo., orig. cloth. K Books 244-308 1978 £6

THOMSON, A. M.   A Political History of Wisconsin. Milwaukee, 1900. Thick 4to, rebound, illus. MacManus 239-531 1978 $35

THOMSON, ANDREW   Substance of the Speech Delivered at the Meeting of the Edinburgh Society for the Abolition of Slavery, on October 19, 1830. Edinburgh, 1830. 8vo., unbound, 1st ed. Morrill 241-575 1978 $15

THOMSON, ANTHONY TODD   Conspectus of The Pharmacopeoias of The London, Edinburgh and Dublin Colleges of Physicians and of The United States Pharmacopeoias.   New York, 1844. One cover detached, but present, spine much worn, scuffed, some foxing.   Rittenhouse 49-784 1976 $20

THOMSON, ARTHUR S.   The Story of New Zealand: Past and Present; Savage and Civilized. 1859. Maps, illus., 2 vols., sm. 8vo, frontis repaired, covers slightly worn, orig. cloth.   Edwards 1012-354 1978 £45

THOMSON, CHARLES   Causes of the Alienation of the Delaware and Shawanese Indians From the British Interest.   Philadelphia, 1867. Ed. ltd. to 250 copies, rebound.   MacManus 239-1219 1978 $45

THOMSON, CHARLES WYVILLE   The Voyages of the "Challenger".   London, 1877. Ist ed., 2 vols., 8vo., portr., maps, plts., many coloured in outline, wood-engr. illus., orig. green cloth, gilt, t.e.g., neatly recased, lib. labels removed.   Deighton 5-194 1978 £68

THOMSON, CLARA L.   Samuel Richardson. 1900. First ed., plts., orig. cloth, 8vo.   Howes 194-1121 1978 £7.50

THOMSON, D. CROAL   The Paris Exhibition 1900. London, 1901. Roy. 4to., illus., covers rather shabby, good.   K Books 244-253 1978 £12

THOMSON, EDWARD   Sketches Biographical and Incidnetal... Cincinnati, 1857. Cloth, foxed.   Hayman 72-578 1978 $17.50

THOMSON, IGNATIUS   The Patriot's Monitor for Vermont.   Randolph, 1810. 12mo, papered oak boards chipped, upper hinge partly split.   Victoria 34-798 1978 $32.50

THOMSON, JAMES 1700-1748   The Castle of Indolence: An Allegorical Poem. London, 1748. 4to, disbound, Ist ed., couple of very small library stamps, sound copy.   Ximenes 47-309 1978 $125

THOMSON, JAMES 1700-1748   The Seasons. 1730. Ist. collected ed., 4to, title vignette, 5 eng. plts., very light marginal foxing, contemp. calf, gilt spine, joints & edges rubbed, subscription ed.   Eaton 45-502 1978 £40

THOMSON, JAMES 1700-1748   Les Saisons, Poeme Traduit de L'Anglois de Thomson.   London, 1779. Frontis, eng., 12mo, 2 1/2 x 4 3/4", contemp. mottled calf.   Eaton 45-503 1978 £5

THOMSON, JAMES 1700-1748   The Seasons. 1797. Plts., imp. 4to. 18 x 14 inches, full contemp. straight grained mor., very clean.   Howes 194-1413 1978 £125

THOMSON, JAMES 1700-1748 The Works... 1738. 2 vols., vol. I, Ist. leaf recto blank, half title, vignette titles, 5 eng. plts., contemp. mottled calf, gilt spines, joints cracked.   Eaton 45-501 1978 £50

THOMSON, JAMES 1700-1748 The Works. 1762. Orig. calf, spines gilt, labels, one new, joints cracking, 2 vols., plts., otherwise fine.   Jarndyce 16-223 1978 £30

THOMSON, JAMES 1800-1883 Retreats: a Series of Designs, Consisting of Plans and Elevations for Cottages, Villas, and Ornamental Buildings. 1833. 4to., hand-coloured plts., very slight foxing, contemp. half green mor., Ist ed., 2nd issue, fine.   Quaritch 983-52 1978 $1,200

THOMSON, JAMES 1834-1882 Walt Whitman: the man and the poet. 1910. Fine unopened copy, orig. wraps, first English ed.   Bell Book 16-842 1978 £6

THOMSON, JOHN   Descriptive Catalogue of the Writings of Sir Walter Scott.   Philadelphia, 1898. Tall 8vo., orig. wrs.   Morrill 239-627 1978 $12.50

THOMSON, JOHN ARTHUR   The New Natural History. (c. 1910). Colored plts., illus., 3 vols., 4to.   George's 635-1001 1978 £5

THOMSON, JOSEPH JOHN   Electricity and Matter. London, 1904. 8vo., text diagrams, orig. cloth, first ed.   Quaritch 977-136 1978 $125

THOMSON, JOSEPH JOHN   Notes on Recent Researches in Electricity and Magnetism. Oxford, Clarendon Press, 1893. 8vo., ads, text illus., orig. cloth, gilt, uncut, fine copy, prize pres. slip on pastedown, Ist ed.   Norman 5-*51 1978 $200

THOMSON, MORTIMER   Doesticks: What He Says. 1855. Illus., brown cloth, first ed.   Austin 82-973 1978 $17.50

THOMSON, MORTIMER   Doesticks: What He Says. 1855. Illus., red cloth, first ed., worn around edges.   Austin 82-974 1978 $12.50

THOMSON, MORTIMER   Nothing to Say. 1857. Illus., first ed., worn around edges.   Austin 82-975 1978 $12.50

THOMSON, MORTIMER   Plu-Ri-Bus-Tah. 1856. Illus., first ed.   Austin 82-976 1978 $17.50

THOMSON, MORTIMER   Plu-Ri-Bus-Tah. 1856. Backstrip worn.   Austin 82-977 1978 $12.50

THOMSON, RICHARD   Chronicles of London Bridge by an Antiquary. 1827. Ist. ed., 56 embellishments, engraved title pg., orig. half calf, bds. rubbed.   Jarndyce 16-820 1978 £20

THOMSON, SAMUEL   The Guide to Health. Columbus, 1827. Bds., rubbed, 3rd ed.   Hayman 73-425 1973 $40

THOMSON, W. W.   Chester County and Its People. Chicago, 1898. Illus., thick 4to., very scarce, orig. leather bds., cloth.   MacManus 239-1698 1978 $90

THORBECKE, ELLEN   People in China: Thirty-two photographic studies from life. London, 1935. Boards, cloth back, dust wrs., d.w. browned and waterstained, tipped-in gravure portraits.   Dawson's 449-83 1978 $50

THORBURN, ARCHIBALD   British Mammals. 1920-21. 2 vols., 4to., colored plts., orig. red cloth, gilt tops.   Quaritch 983-372 1978 $656

THORBURN, ARCHIBALD   Game Birds and Wild-Fowl of Great Britain and Ireland. London, 1923. Fine coloured plts., lg. 4to., orig. cloth gilt, covers a little marked and soiled.   K Books 244-450 1978 £295

THORBURN, GRANT   Fifty Years Reminiscences of New York, or, Flowers from the Garden of Laurie Todd. New York, (1845). 12mo, orig. cloth, front hinge weak, else nice, frontis.   MacManus 239-460 1978 $20

THORBURN, S. S.   David Leslie A Story of the Afghan Frontier. 1879. Ist. ed., 2 vols., half titles, orig. red cloth, blocked in black & gilt, fine.   Jarndyce 16-1142 1978 £26

THOREAU, HENRY DAVID   Cape Cod. Boston, 1865. 12mo., orig. cloth, 1st ed., covers somewhat worn, bookplt. removed.   MacManus 238-580 1978 $150

THOREAU, HENRY DAVID   Cape Cod. Boston, 1896. Illus. in color, 2 vols., orig. cloth, 1st of this ed., spines faded, otherwise fine.   MacManus 238-581 1978 $75

THOREAU, HENRY DAVID   The Maine Woods. Boston, 1864. Orig. cloth, 1st ed., bookplt., spine faded, else fine.   MacManus 238-579 1978 $85

THOREAU, HENRY DAVID   The Maine Woods. New York, (1909). Gold stamped binding, hinge inner front cracking, 8vo.   Book Chest 17-386 1978 $15

THOREAU, HENRY DAVID   Summer: From the Journal of Henry D. Thoreau. Boston, 1884. 8vo, green orig. cloth, some foxing, ownership sign. on flyleaf, Fine, Ist ed., collector's cond.   Desmarais 1-403 1978 $70

THOREAU, HENRY DAVID   Walden or Life In The Woods. 1854. Ist. ed. with May adv., very good copy.   Baldwins' 51-406 1978 $350

THOREAU, HENRY DAVID   Walden, or Life in the Woods. Boston, 1854. Ist ed., 12mo., ads, occas. light foxing.   Current 24-61 1978 $785

THOREAU, HENRY DAVID   Walden; or, Life in the Woods. Boston, 1897. 2 vols., illus., orig. cloth, near-fine.   MacManus 238-582 1978 $45

THOREAU, HENRY DAVID   A Week on the Concord and Merrimack Rivers. Boston & Cambridge, 1849. Rare Ist ed., with author's corrections, good copy, boxed in wooden case with snap cover.   Current Misc. 8-45 1978 $1,850

THOREAU, HENRY DAVID   A Week on the Concord and Merrimack Rivers. Boston and Cambridge, 1849. 8vo, original dark brown cloth, green half morocco slipcase, 1st ed., author's first book, very fine bright copy, exceptionally clean. Ximenes 47-310 1978 $1600

THORN, WILLIAM   Memoir of the War in India. 1818. Folding map, 4to, calf, rebacked, lib. stamp on verso of title & last pg. Edwards 1012-115 1978 £60

THORNBOROUGH, LAURA   The Great Smoky Mountains. New York, 1937. Broadfoot 50-317 1978 $15

THORNDIKE, HERBERT   Just Weights and Measures... 1680. 4to, recent bds., very good. Fenning 32-330 1978 £21.50

THORNE, JAMES   Handbook to the Environs of London. London, 1876. 2 vols., covers a little dull, 8vo. K Books 244-211 1978 £8

THORNTON, ELIZABETH   Truth and Falsehood. A Romance. London, 1844. 3 vols., 12mo, contemporary half cloth and marbled boards, morocco labels, 1st ed., very scarce. Ximenes 47-311 1978 $90

THORNTON, JAMES H.   Memories of Seven Campaigns. 1895. 8vo., orig. cloth, illus. F. Edwards 1013-435 1978 £10

THORNTON, JAMES H.   Memories of Seven Campaigns. Constable, 1895. 1st. ed., illus., 8vo, orig. cloth, spine faded & little foxing in place, nice. Fenning 32-331 1978 £12.50

THORNTON, P. M.   The Stuart Dynasty: Short Studies of Its Rise, Course and Early Exile. London, 1890. Demy. 8vo, orig. cloth, little worn, illus., good. Sexton 7-190 1978 £6

THORNTON, RICHARD H.   An American Glossary. Philadelphia, 1912. 2 vols. Baldwins' 51-22 1978 $20

THORNTON, W. T.   A Plea for Peasant Proprietors with the Outlines of a Plan for Their Establishment in Ireland. 1874. Very good, reprint, octavo bound in cloth. Hyland 128-648 1978 £12

THORNWELL, JAMES HENLEY   Hear the South! New York, 1861. 8vo., unbound, 1st separate ed. Morrill 241-576 1978 $10

THORP, JOSEPH   B. H. Newdigate: Scholar-Printer 1869-1944. Oxford, 1950. Roy. 8vo., orig. holland-backed bds., facsimiles, some coloured. George's 635-1217 1978 £18

THORP, JOSEPH   Eric Gill. 1929. 4to., plts., cloth, fine with d.w. Quaritch 979-160 1978 $120

THORP, JOSEPH   Eric Gill. 1929. Portrait, plts., 4to. George's 635-174 1978 £25

THORP, WILLARD   The Lives of Eighteen from Princeton. Princeton, 1946. 8vo., cloth, d.j., 1st ed., fine. J. S. Lawrence 38-F150 1978 $25

THORPE, THOMAS B.   The Hive of "The Bee-Hunter". NY, 1854. Steel engraving, small spot on front cover, Bell Wiley's copy. Broadfoot's 44-792 1978 $75.00

THORPE, THOMAS B.   Our Army on the Rio Grande, Being a Short Account of the Events from the Removal of the Army of Occupation from Corpus Christi to the Surrender of Matamoros,.... Philadelphia, 1846. Original cloth, 1st ed. Jenkins 116-1349 1978 $285

THORPE, THOMAS EDWARD   Essays in Historical Chemistry. New York, 1902. Lg. 8vo., ads, orig. cloth, gilt, uncut, unopened, very good copy, 2nd ed. Norman 5-273 1978 $30

THORPE, WILLIAM ARNOLD   A History of English and Irish Glass. 1929. 2 vols., imp. 8vo., coloured frontis., cloth, spines faded, orig. ed. Quaritch 983-117 1978 $360

THORPE, WILLIAM ARNOLD   A History of English and Irish Glass. Illus., cr. 4to, 2 vols. in 1, ltd. to 500 copies. Traylen 88-524 1978 £18

THORSETH, MATTHEA   Cradled in Thunder. 1946. Austin 79-774 1978 $12.50

THOUSAND Islands and St. Lawrence River. Watertown, (1917). Reproduced in sepia, side-opening 8vo. Butterfield 21-427 1978 $12.50

THOUSAND Islands and St. Lawrence River. "The Venice of America". Watertown, n.d. Card cover, photos, some coloured. Hood 116-784 1978 $17.50

THE THOUSAND Islands and the River St. Lawrence. Grand Rapids, n.d. (ca. 1900). Fldg. map, card cover. Hood 117-767 1978 $20

THE THOUSAND Islands and the River of St. Lawrence. Grand Rapids, n.d., (c.1900). Folding map, card cover. Hood's 115-852 1978 $17.50

THOUMAS, GENERAL   Autour Du Drapeau, 1789-1889. Paris, (c. 1890) Illus., 4to., binder's cloth. F. Edwards 1013-436 1978 £45

THOURET, MICHEL AUGUSTIN   Recherches Et Doutes Sur Le Magnetisme Animal. Paris, 1784. 12mo., contemp. half calf, gilt lettering, very lightly foxed, very good copy, 1st ed. Zeitlin 245-265 1978 $125

THOYTS, E. E.   History of the Royal Berkshire Militia. Reading, 1897. Plts., 8vo., orig. cloth, portraits. F. Edwards 1013-557 1978 £12

THRALL, HOMER S.   Pictorial History of Texas. St. Louis, 1883. Folding map, best (enlarged) ed., pictorial cloth. Jenkins 116-1351 1978 $125

THRASHER, MARION   Long Life in California. Chicago, [1915]. Illus., orig. cloth, 1st ed., inscribed presentation copy to Theodore Hittell from author. Ginsberg 14-1090 1978 $22.50

THREE Courses and a Dessert: Comprising Three Sets of Tales, West Country, Irish, and Legal; and a Melange. London, 1888. Illus. by George Cruikshank, unopened copy. Petrilla 13-132 1978 $8.50

THREE Speeches Against Continuing the Army. 1718. Sm. 8vo., stitched, uncut. F. Edwards 1013-437 1978 £10

THRELFALL, T. R.   The Story of the King's Liverpool Regiment. 1916. Coloured frontis., plts., 8vo., orig. cloth. F. Edwards 1013-487 1978 £12

THE THRIFT Campaign in the Schools of Ontario... Toronto, (1919?). Hood's 115-414 1978 $7.50

THROCKMORTON, JAMES W.   Texas and Pacific Railway. Washington, 1877. Printed wr. Jenkins 116-1352 1978 $35

THRUMM, THOMAS G.   Hawaiian Almanac and Annual for 1876. Honolulu, 1876. 8vo., orig. blue pr. wr., lower half back wr. missing, Quaritch 978-73 1978 $135

THRUPP, S.   The Merchant Class of Medieval London, 1300-1500. Chicago, 1948. 8vo. Upcroft 12-452 1978 $8.50

THRUSTON, G. P.   The Antiquities of Tennessee and the Adjacent States... Cincinnati, 1897. 2nd. ed., roy. 8vo, plts., illus., orig. cloth. Edwards 1012-636 1978 £18

THUCYDIDES   De Bello Peloponnesiaco Libri VIII. Venice, 1502. Edito princeps, folio, old calf, rebacked. Gilhofer 75-106 1978 SFr 6,500

THUCYDIDES   De Bello Peloponnesiaco, Libri VIII; iidem Latine, ex Interpretatione L. Vallae, ab Henrico Stephano recognita. (Geneva), 1588. Folio, contemp. full calf, floral gilt spine, foxing in text, 2nd ed. Argosy Special-88 1978 $150

THUCYDIDES   Maps and Plans illustrative of Thucydides. Oxford, (c. 1830). Engraved maps, plans, plts., half roan worn. George's 635-517 1978 £10.50

THUILLIER, HENRY F.   Gas in the Next War. 1939. 8vo, orig. cloth, pres. copy to Winston Churchill. Sawyer 298-120 1978 £72

THURBER, JAMES   Fables for Our Times and Famous Poems Illustrated. 1940. Illus, first ed., d.j. Austin 82-980 1978 $17.50

THURBER, JAMES   Fables for Our Time and Famous Poems Illustrated. 1940. Illus., first ed. Austin 82-979 1978 $12.50

THURBER, JAMES   Men, Woman and Dogs. 1943. First ed. Austin 82-983 1978 $11

THURBER, JAMES   My World - And Welcome To it. 1942. Drawings by author, covers soiled, good, first English ed. Bell Book 17-863 1978 £5

THURBER, JAMES   My World and Welcome to It. 1942. Illus. Austin 82-984 1978 $8.50

THURBER, JAMES   The Thurber Carnival. New York, 1945. Bkplt. partly removed, fine copy in lightly soiled & chipped d.w. Desmarais B-621 1978 $15

THURBER, JAMES   The White Deer. New York, 1945. Nice in somewhat tattered d.w. Desmarais B-622 1978 $12.50

THURLOW, S.   The Land Surveyor's Ready Reckoner. (c. 1835). Folding frontis., 16mo., diced calf. George's 635-942 1978 £5

THURMAIER, JOHANN   Des Hochgelerten weitberumbten Beyerischen Geschichtschreibers Chronica... Frankfurt, 1580. Folio, 18th cent. calf, gilt back, rubbed, some underlining, otherwise fine, 2nd German ed. Gilhofer 74-139 1978 sFr 1,500

THURMAN, ALLEN G.   The Campaign in Ohio. Speech of Hon..., at Sandusky, Ohio, September 7th, 1868. Columbus, (1868). Unbound as issued. Hayman 72-640 1978 $15

THUCYDIDES   Thucydides Translated into English. Chelsa, Ashendene Press, 1930. One of 260 copies, folio, bound in white pigskin, fine, cloth slipcase. Houle 10-14 1978 $1,600

THWAITES, REUBEN G.   Daniel Boone. New York, 1902. Illus. Broadfoot 50-320 1978 $15

THWAITES, REUBEN G.   The Revolution on the Upper Ohio, 1775-1777. Madison, 1908. 1st ed., orig. cloth, ltd. to 1,200 copies. MacManus 239-628 1978 $30

TIBBATS, JOHN W.   Speech of Mr..., of Kentucky, on the Question of the Reannexation of Texas; Together with His Remarks on the Tariff: Delivered in the House...May 7, 1844. Washington, 1844. Wrs. Hayman 72-747 1978 $12.50

TIBERI, GIUSEPPE   Trattenimenti Letterarj di Cionesio Licio P.A. Dedicati a suoi amici. 1786. 8vo., vellum, portrait, very good. King 7-245 1978 £20

TIBBUTT, H. G.   The Life and Letters of Sir Lewis Dyve (1599-1669). 1948. Portraits, wrps., octavo, good. Upcroft 10-568 197 8 £5

TIBULLUS, ALBIUS   Carmina Libri Tres. Lipsiae, 1817. 8vo., half calf. Van der Peet H-64-565 1978 Dfl 55

TIBULLUS, ALBIUS   Elegies. 1798. Orig. calf, worn, 3 vols. Allen 234-998 1978 $17.50

TICE, JOHN H.   Over the Plains and on the Mountains. St. Louis, 1872. Illus., 1st ed., some foxing, text stained, orig. cloth, scarce. Biblo BL781-301 1978 $22.50

TICKELL, THOMAS   A Poem, To His Excellency. 1713. 1st ed., folio, disbound, loose, title frayed affecting line border, filing holes punched in inner margin, text wholly intact, very good working copy. Hannas 54-348 1978 £10

TICKNOR, GEORGE   History of Spanish Literature... 1855. New ed., 3 vols., 1/2 tan morocco, rubbed. Eaton 45-504 1978 £20

TICKNOR, GEORGE   Life, Letters, and Journals. Boston, 1876. Portraits, first ed., 2 vols., orig. cloth. Howes 194-1282 1978 £18

TIELKE, JOHANN G. 1731-87   An Account of Some of the Most Remarkable Events of the War between the Prussians, Austrians, and Russians, from 1756 to 1763. 1787-88. Plts., 2 vols., roy. 8vo., uncut in orig. bds., printed paper labels, fine, 2 hinges cracked. Howes 194-494 1978 £48

TIEPOLI, G. B.   Le Cahier de Dessiens des Tiepolo au Musee Correr de Venise. Par G. Lorenzetti. Venice and Paris, 1946. Roy. folio, bds., vellum corners, ltd. to 700 no. copies in Italian and 1,300 in French. Quaritch 983-262 1978 $90

TIGHE, R. S.   Letters to Lord Tenterden... 1828. 1st. ed., uncut, unopened, stitched as issued, good. Jarndyce 16-1143 1978 £12.50

TILDEN, SAMUEL J.   The New York City "Ring". New York, 1873. Butterfield 21-550e 1978 $15

TILDEN, WILLIAM AUGUSTUS   Chemical Discovery and Invention in the Twentieth Century. London & New York, (1917). 8vo., illus., orig. cloth, gilt, very good copy, 1st ed. Norman 5-274 1978 $25

TILDEN, WILLIAM AUGUSTUS   William Ramsay, Memorials of His Life and Work. London, 1918. 8vo., illus., orig. cloth, uncut, very good copy, 1st ed. Norman 5-234 1978 $20

TILDEN, WILLIAM T.   Match Play and the Spin of the Ball. New York, 1925. Illus., 8vo., half mor., bottom of spine worn, ltd. to 350 copies signed by Tilden & editor. Morrill 241-577 1978 $15

TILDEN & Hendricks Reform Songs for the Centennial Campaign of 1876. N.P., (1876). Wrps. Hayman 71-648 1978 $15

TILGHMAN, OSWALD   History of Talbot County, Maryland, 1661-1861. Baltimore, 1915. 1st ed., nos. on spine, otherwise nice set, 2 vols., illus., 4to., very scarce. MacManus 239-1006 1978 $50

TILLEY, ARTHUR   The Dawn of the French Renaissance. 1918. Orig. ed., plts., thick 8vo., orig. half buckram, scarce. Howes 194-1283 1978 £8

TILLEY, ARTHUR   The Literature of the French Renaissance. 1904. Orig. ed., 2 vols., orig. cloth, 8vo. Howes 194-1284 1978 £8.50

TILLEY, M. P.   A Dictionary of the Proverbs in England in the Sixteenth and Seventeenth Centuries... Ann Arbor, 1950. 4to, good. Upcroft 10-171 1978 £15

TILLIER, CLAUDE   Mein Onkel Benjamin. Munich, (1909). 8vo., publisher's full lea., ltd. ed., 1 of 63 numbered copies on rag paper, lea. binding, clean. Goldschmidt 110-55 1978 $125

TILLOTSON, JOHN 1630-94   The Works. 1707. Portrait, folio, contemp. panelled calf, rebacked, orig. label preserved. Howes 194-495 1978 £30

TILLVARO, FYRTIOARIGA   Historik ofver Forsta Svenska Baptistforsamlingens Vestkusten-San Francisco, 1925. Illus., in Swedish, paper. Austin 79-775 1978 $17.50

TILLYARD, AELFRIDA   Cambridge Poets, 1900-13. Cambridge, 1913. Cloth gilt, t.e.g., very good, first English ed. Bell Book 17-014 1978 £12.50

TILNEY, FREDERICK   The Brain from Ape to Man. New York, 1928. Tall 4to., 2 vols., illus., orig. black cloth, pic. endpapers, bkplts. & library stamps, good copy, 1st ed. Zeitlin 245-316 1978 $200

TILTON, ELEANOR M.   Amiable Autocrat. 1947. Austin 82-988 1978 $10

TIM Bobbin's Lancashire Dialect and Poems. 1833. Plts. by George Cruikshank, engraved frontis., orig. grey bds., cloth spine, uncut, spine little worn, otherwise good. Jarndyce 16-433 1978 £22

TIMBS, JOHN   Clubs & Club Life in London. n.d. (1872). Frontis & numerous other illus., half title, maroon morocco, gilt borders, a.e.g., v.g. Jarndyce 16-828 1978 £18.50

TIMBS, JOHN   Lady Bountiful's Legacy to Her Family & Friends. 1868. 1st. ed., orig. green cloth, blocked in black & gilt, fine. Jarndyce 16-1144 1978 £8.50

TIMBS, JOHN   A Picturesque Promenade round Dorking in Surrey.
1823. Second ed., 12mo., orig. cloth-backed bds., uncut, fine, woodcuts. P.
M. Hill 142-226 1978 £36

TIMELY TIPS To Texas Truckers. Houston, c.1900's. Printed wr. Jenkins
116-1354 1978 $20

THE TIMES History of the War. 1915-21. Illus., 21 vols., folio, orig. half roan,
a little rubbed. George's 635-862 1978 £21

TIMMONS, BASCOM N.   Garner of Texas: A Personal History. New York,
1948. 1st ed., illus. Jenkins 116-490 1978 $10

TIMMONS, BASCOM N.   Garner of Texas: A Personal History. New York,
1948. 1st ed., illus. Jenkins 116-491 1978 $7.50

TIMMS, W. R.   The Art of Illuminating as Practiced in Europe
from the Earliest Times. London, n.d. Plts. in color, rebound. Battery Park I-
491 1978 $150

TIMPERLEY, C. H.   Encyclopaedia of Literary and Typographical
Anecdote... London, 1842. Thick 8vo, inner joints little weak, 2nd. ed.,illus.,
portraits. Traylen 88-69 1978 £48

TINDAL, N.   A Guide to Classical Learning or Polymetis
Abridged. 1777. 4th. ed., illus., engraved frontis, plts., orig. calf, red label,
v.g. Jarndyce 16-224 1978 £9.50

TINEL, J.   Nerve Wounds. New York, 1918. Ex-library.
Rittenhouse 49-787 1976 $17.50

TINGLING, MARION   The Secret Diary of William Byrd of Westover,
1739-1741. Richmond, 1942. Baldwins' 51-519 1978 $15

TINGREY, PIERRE FRANCOIS   The Painter and Varnisher's Guide. London,
1804. 8vo., fldg. copperplts., fldg. table, contemp. half calf, antique marbled
paper on covers, fine copy, 1st ed. in English. Norman 5-275 1978 $250

TINKCOM, H. M.   John White Geary Soldier-Stateman. Philadelphia, 1940. MacManus 239-1465 1978 $8.50

TIPPING, H. AVRAY   English Homes. Period IV...Late Stuart, 1649-
1714. 1929. Vol. I, folio, illus., buckram, gilt edges. Quaritch 983-53 1978
$180

TIPPING, H. AVRAY   English Homes. London, V.Y. Complete set
except for vol. 2, 8 vols., plts., illus., folio. Traylen 88-419 1978 £400

TIPPING, H. AVRAY   The Story of the Royal Welsh Fusiliers. (1915).
Coloured frontis. & plts., 8vo., orig. white parchment. F. Edwards 1013-497
1978 £20

TIPPLE, BERTRAND M.   Alien Rome. Washington, D. C., 1924. Austin 79-776 1978 $15

TIREBUCK, WILLIAM   The Little Widow and Other Eposides English, Irish, Welsh and Scotch. London, 1894. 1st ed., laid paper, blue
cloth, A.L.s. laid in, very good or better. Limestone 9-302 1978 $18

TISSANDIER, GASTON   Bibliographie Aeronautique. Paris, 1887. Sm.
folio, orig. prtd. wrs., uncut & unopened, little soiled, but fine copy, 1st ed.
Norman 5-277 1978 $75

TISSOT, ROGER   Mont Blac. London, (1924). Illus., 8vo.,
orig. cloth. Morrill 241-578 1978 $10

TISSOT, SIMON ANDRE   Advice to the People in General, with Regard to
Their Health.... London, 1767. 2 vols. Rittenhouse 49-790 1976 $35

TISSOT, SIMON ANDRE   Essai sur les Maladies des Gens du Monde. Paris,
1771. Troisieme ed. originale, clean, tight, orig. binding. Rittenhouse 49-789
1976 $30

TISSOT, SIMON ANDRE   L'Onanisme. Dissertation sur les Maladies Pro-
duites par la Masturbation. Tolouse, 1765. Dixieme ed., orig. binding, very
good. Rittenhouse 49-788 1976 $30

TISSOT, SIMON ANDRE   Three Essays. Dublin, 1772. 8vo., contemp.
calf, some light foxing, library stamps, bkplts. of former owners, rare. Zeitlin
245-266 1978 $155

TIT for Tat or the Reviewer Reviewed..an Examination of Mr. Smith's Review..of
the Speech of the Rt. Hon. John Foster.... Dublin, 1799. 1st ed., plain wrs.
Hyland 128-271 1978 £8

TITLE Papers of the Lower California Company, to Lands, etc. in the Territory of
Lower California, and in the States of Sonora and Sinaloa of the Republic of
Mexico. New York, 1870. Orig. wr., 1st ed. Ginsberg 14-209 1978 $50

TITTLE, WALTER   Roosevelt as an Artist Saw Him... New York,
(1948). Ports., illus., cloth, 1st ed., very good, d.j. Hayman 72-753 1978
$7.50

TITYRICAE Decisiones De Lana Caprina. 1610. 4to., wrs. Salloch 345-81 1978
$35

TIXIER, VICTOR   Tixier's Travels on the Osage Prairies. Norman,
1940. Illus., folding maps, orig. cloth,1st ed. Ginsberg 14-985 1978 $17.50

TIZAC, H. D'ARDEENE DE   Animals in Chinese Art: A Collection of Examples.
London, 1923. Gravure plts., cloth, moderately worn and foxed, some fading to
covers, 1 of 250 numbered copies. Dawson's 449-85 1978 $185

TOALDO, GIUSEPPE   Della vera influenza degli Astri, delle Stagioni,
a Mutazioni di Tempo.... Padova, 1770. 4to., contemp. decor. paper bds.,
plt., illus., fine, uncut, first ed. King 7-246 1978 £100

TOALDO, GIUSEPPE   Tavole di Vitalita. Padua, 1787. 4to., limp
bds. Gurney 75-105 1978 £25

TOBIE, H.E.   No Man Like Joe. Portland, (1949). 1st ed.,
signed, illus., fine copy, d.w. Biblo 248-276 1978 $27.50

TOBIN, JOHN   The Curfew: A Play in Five Acts. 1807. 7th.
ed., cloth. Eaton 45-505 1978 £8

TOBIN, RICHARD L.   Invasion Journal. 1944. Austin 80-329 1978
$8.50

TOD, J.   Travels in Western India... 1839. Engraved
plts., 4 vignettes, 4to, binders' cloth, lib. stamps on plts., title & last pg.
Edwards 1012-116 1978 £45

TOD, M. N.   A Selection of Greek Historical Inscriptions to the
end of the Fifth Century B.C. Oxford, 1946-50. Second ed., 2 vols., 8vo.
George's 635-518 1978 £7.50

TOD, T.   Observations on Dr. M'Farlan's Inquiries Concerning the State of the Poor. Edinburgh, 1783. 1st. ed., roy. 8vo, very fine
copy in orig. mottled wrappers, edges uncut. Traylen 88-85 1978 £40

TOD, W. M.   Farming. London, 1903. No. 41 of 150 copies,
full vellum with gold pictorial stampings on cover and spine, Haddon Hall Library,
endpapers, head and tail pieces by Rackham, extra color plate laid-in, fine.
Victoria 34-672 1978 $200

TODAY'S Children. 1937. 312 pages, illus. with photos. Austin 82-860 1978
$12.50

TODD, CHARLES   Life of Colonel Aaron Burr, Vice President of the
United States. New York, 1879. Reprint, wrs. torn and frayed. Biblo BL78-194
1978 $12

TODD, CHARLES BURR   The History of Redding Conn., From Its First Settlement to the Present Time. New York, 1880. Frontis., orig. cloth, lib. marks,
very nice. MacManus 239-955 1978 $30

TODD, J.H.   The Last Age of the Church by J. Wyclyffe Now
First Printed from a Manuscript in the University Library, Dublin. 1840. Boards,
lacks cloth spine, text good, reprint. Hyland 128-649 1978 £7.50

TODD, JOHN A.   The World's Cotton Crops. London, 1915. Illus.
Biblo BL781-885 1978 $12

TODD, RUTHVEN   Tracks in the Snow. Grey Walls Press, 1946.
Plts., illus., very good, d.w., first English ed. Bell Book 17-110 1978 £8.50

TODD, RUTHVEN   Tracks in the Snow. (1946). Illus., d.w.
Eaton 45-506 1978 £8

TODD, RUTHVEN   Until Now: poems. Fortune Press, (1942).
Very good, browned d.w., first English ed. Bell Book 16-848 1978 £5

TODD, VINCENT HOLLIS   Baron Christoph von Graffenried's New Bern Adventures. Chicago, 1913. Wrs., maps. Broadfoot 50-321 1978 $35

TODD, W. E.   Birds of Western Pennsylvania. 1940. 4to,
22 plts. in color, illus., orig. drawings by George Miksch Sutton. Baldwins' 51-
487 1978 $50

TODHUNTER, JOHN   Isolt of Ireland, A Legend in Aprologue & Acts,
and, The Poison Flower. 1927. 1st ed., 1/4 cloth, very good.. Hyland 128-652
1978 £10

TODHUNTER, JOHN   Selected Poems. 1929. 1st ed., 1/4 cloth, very
good. Hyland 128-651 1978 £12.50

TODHUNTER, JOHN   A Sicilian Idyll. London, 1890. 4to, boards,
paper label, uncut, unopened, near Fine, no. 166 of 250 small paper copies,
stamped with Elkin Mathews' oval stamp on flyleaf, 1st ed., collector's cond.
Desmarais 1-404 1978 $50

TODHUNTER, JOHN   A Sycilian Idyll. London, 1890. 1 of 250
numbered copies, 1st ed., 8 vo., half Japan vellum over grey bds., uncut,
unopened, frontispiece, bookplate of Allan Giles, good-fine. Houle 10-339
1978 $45

TODRIN, BORIS   The Plundered Heart. 1948. First ed., d.j.
Austin 82-990 1978 $12.50

TOFFTEEN, OLOF A.   Myths and Bible. Minneapolis, 1899. Inscr'd
by author. Austin 79-778 1978 $27.50

TOISAGE Des Bois A La Marque et Celui Des Batimens. Rouen, 1772. Sm. 8vo.,
contemp. calf. F. Edwards 1013-217 1978 £28

TOLAND, JOHN   Amyntor:.... London, 1699. 1st ed., small
octavo, contemp. calf, expertly rebacked preserving original spine, armorial
bookplate of the Earl of Hopetoun, obliterated signature on t.p. Bennett
20-211 1978 $250

TOLAND, JOHN   Amyntor: or, A Defence of Milton's Life. London,
1699. Small octavo, contemp. calf, expertly rebacked preserving original spine,
armorial bookplate of Earl of Hopetoun, fine copy, 1st ed. Bennett 7-119 1978
$250

TOLAND, JOHN   A Critical History of the Celtic Religion &
Learning: Containing an Account of the Druids... 1815. Original boards, good,
reprint. Hyland 128-653 1978 £35

TOLAND, JOHN   The Life of John Milton, Containing, Besides the
History of His Works, Several Extraordinary Characters of Men and Books, Sects,
Parties, and Opinions. London, 1699. Disbound, 1st separate ed., signature on
t.p., foxing throughout. MacManus 238-134 1978 $50

TOLEDO, FRANCISCO 1532-96   Summa Casuum Conscientiae Absolutissima....
1633. Contemp. calf, thk. 8vo. Howes 194-579 1978 £25

THE TOLEDO Blue Book, a Family and Social Directory...Fifth Issue, 1895-6.
Toldeo, n.d. (1895?). Cloth, inner hinges cracking. Hayman 72-580 1978
$7.50

TOLKIEN, JOHN RONALD REUEL   Farmer Giles of Ham. London, 1949. Illus,
plts. in color, tan bds., first ed., fine, d.j., scarce. Bradley 49-323 1978 $75

TOLLER, ERNST   Hoppla, Wir Leben! Potsdam, 1927. 1st ed.,
d.w. Biblo 251-656 1978 $17.50

TOLLER, ERNST   Die Maschinenstrumer. Leipzig, 1922. 1st ed.
Biblo 251-655 1978 $15

TOLLER, ERNST   No More Peace! 1937. Very good, buckram,
first English ed. Bell Book 16-031 1978 £35

TOLSTOY, LEV NICOLAEVICH   Anna Karenina. Philadelphia, (c. 1920s).
Colored plts., mor. and cloth, slight chip to upper spine, otherwise good. Petrilla
13-133 1978 $8.50

TOLSTOY, LEV NIKOLAEVICH   Essays from Tula. London, 1948. 1st ed., top
of spine torn. Biblo 251-657 1978 $13.50

TOLSTOY, LEV NICOLAEVICH   Labor: The Divine Command. The Suppressed
Book of the Peasant Bondareff. New York, 1890. 12mo., wrs., frayed, 1st
Amer. ed. Biblo BL781-886 1978 $10

TOLSTOY, LEV NIKOLAEVICH   Life and Works. 1928-37. 21 vols., sm.
8vo., Tolstoy centenary ed., frontis., maps, cloth, d.ws., fine unopened set.
Quaritch 979-376 1978 $450

TOLSTOY, LEV NICOLAEVICH   The Two Pilgrims, or Love and Good Deeds.
(Boston, 1887). 12mo., orig. wrs., lacks ribbon ties, wrs. & text loose, 1st
Amer. ed. Morrill 241-579 1978 $10

TOLSTOY, LEV NICOLAEVICH   What Men Live By. New York, (1888). 1st
Amer. ed., 12mo., orig. cloth. Morrill 241-580 1978 $12.50

TOLSTOY, LEV NIKOLAEVICH   Work While Ye Have the Light. A Tale of the
Early Christians. New York, 1890. First Amer. ed., orig. wrappers, very good.
Greene 78-294 1978 $55

TOLTZ, JOHANNES   Eyn Sermonn von der vilfeltigen frucht des
gestorbnen weytzkomlen.... Leipzig, 1526. Sole ed., sm. 4 to., modern
half vellum. Schafer 19-39 1978 sFr. 600

TOM Thumb's Play Book to Teach Children Their Letters by a New and Pleasant
Method. Alnwick, c.1825. 12mo, woodcuts, one on wrapper by Thomas Bewick,
pictorial yellow wrappers, fine. Victoria 34-801 1978 $50

TOMKINS, E.   Poems on various subjects. 1804. New ed.,
illus., fcap. 8vo., contemp. tree calf, very good. Howes 194-496 1978 £12.50

TOMLINSON, EVERETT T.   In the Camp of Cornwallis Being the Story of
Reuben Denton and His Experience During the New Jersey Campaign of 1777.
1902. Illus., first ed. Austin 82-992 1978 $12.50

TOMLINSON, EVERETT T.   Old Fort Schuyler. Philadelphia, 1901. 1st ed.,
illus., good. Biblo BL781-1034 1978 $9

TOMLINSON, HENRY MAJOR   All Our Yesterdays. London, 1930. 8vo, black
cloth, gilt stamped, 1st issue, error in running head, d.w. lightly worn, Fine, 4
line inscription from author to John Middleton Murry on flyleaf, 1st ed. Desmarais
1-405 1978 $35

TOMLINSON, HENRY MAJOR   Between the Lines. Cambridge, 1930. 8vo,
blue cloth, gilt lettering on spine, Fine in slightly chipped d.w., 1st ed., collector's cond. Desmarais 1-406 1978 $10

TOMLINSON, HENRY MAJOR   Cote D'Or. 1929. First ed., cr. 8vo., orig.
bds., cover faded, special ed., ltd. to 300 copies signed by the author. Howes
194-1287 1978 £5

TOMLINSON, HENRY MAJOR   Cote D'Or. 1929. One of 300 copies on handmade paper, numbered & signed by author, bds., covers somewhat faded, nice,
first English ed. Bell Book 17-867 1978 £6.50

TOMLINSON, HENRY MAJOR   Illusion: 1915. London, 1929. 8vo, patterned
boards, cloth back, uncut, unopened, t.e.g., near Mint in d.w., 1st ed.
Demarais 1-407 1978 $10

TOMLINSON, HENRY MAJOR   Illusion: 1915. 1929. 1st. ed. in book form,
cloth. Eaton 45-509 1978 £5

TOMLINSON, HENRY MAJOR   London River. New York, 1921. 8vo, blue
cloth, paper label, spine darkened, very Nice, 1st pr., no. 1189 of 2100 copies,
1st ed. Desmarais 1-408 1978 $15

TOMLINSON, HENRY MAJOR   Norman Douglas. 1931. 1st. ed., d.w., good.
Jarndyce 16-1219 1978 £6

TOMLINSON, HENRY MAJOR   Out of Soundings.   London, 1931.   Nice in chipped, lightly faded d.w.   Desmarais B-624   1978 $10

TOMLINSON, HENRY MAJOR   The Sea and the Jungle.   London, 1912.   8vo, green cloth, gilt stamped, t.e.g., 1st issue, Nice, 1st ed., collector's cond.   Desmarais 1-409   1978 $60

TOMLINSON, HENRY MAJOR   The Sea and The Jungle.   1912. 1st. ed., cloth, faded & edges worn.   Eaton 45-506   1978 £8

TOMLINSON, HENRY MAJOR   The Sea and The Jungle.   1912. 1st. ed., frontis, 8vo, orig. cloth, some spotting in text.   Edwards 1012-679   1978 £18

TOMLINSON, HENRY MAJOR   The Snows of Helicon.   1933. 1st. ed., d.w.   Eaton 45-508   1978 £5

TOMLINSON, HENRY MAJOR   The Snows of Helicon.   London, 1933.   Nice, repaired d.w.   Desmarais B-625   1978 $10

TOMLINSON, HENRY MAJOR   Thomas Hardy.   New York, 1929.   4to, fore and bottom edges uncut, very Good copy, 1 of 761 copies signed by author and artist, 1st ed., collector's cond.   Desmarais 1-410   1978 $25

TOMLINSON, HENRY MAJOR   Waiting for Daylight.   London, 1922.   8vo, maroon cloth, gilt lettering on spine and cover, Fine in dust-stained d.w., 1st ed.   Desmarais 1-411   1978 $15

TOMLINSON, J. T.   The Prayer Book, Articles and Homilies.   1897.   Octavo, good.   Upcroft 10-571   1978 £6.50

TOMLINSON, WILLIAM P.   Kansas in 1858...a History of the Recent Troubles in the Territory.   New York, 1859.   1st ed., nice copy, cloth.   MacManus 239-1934   1978 $20

TOMPKINS, D. A.   History of Mecklenburg County and the City of Charlotte from 1740-1903.   Charlotte, 1903.   Vol. 1.   Broadfoot 50-322   1978 $40

TOMPKINS, DANIEL D.   A Columbia College Student in the Eighteenth Century.   New York, 1940.   Portr., facsimiles, 12mo., 1st ed., autographed by Jacobsen.   Morrill 239-557   1978 $12.50

TOMPKINS, STUART R.   Promyshlinnik and Sourdough.   Norman, 1945.   1st ed., maps.   Biblo 248-14   1978 $16.50

TOMS, ISAAC   The Shining Convert.   1747.   8vo., unbound.   P. M. Hill 142-229   1978 £7

TONEY, MARCUS B.   The Privations of a Private.   Nashville, 1907.   Cover soiled, snag in upper spine, Bell Wiley's copy.   Broadfoot's 44-617   1978 $40

TONNA, CHARLOTTE E.   Osric, a Missionary Tale, With, The Garden and Other Poems.   1826.   2nd. ed., half title, lg. 12mo, recent bds., very good.   Fenning 32-332   1978 £12.50

TONY Sarg's Saving Book.   Cleveland-New York, (1946).   1st ed., oblong quarto, mint, d.j.   Victoria 34-713   1978 $10

TOOKE, GEORGE   A collection of his very rare writings in verse and prose,....   London, c. 1652-1660.   Sm. 4to., 5 works in 1, engraved plate by William Marshall, orig. black mor., gilt panels, gilt edges.   Quaritch 978-149   1978 $3,500

TOOKE, WILLIAM   The Life of Catherine II, Empress of Russia.   Dublin, 1800.   Fifth ed., map, 3 vols., contemp. tree calf.   Howes 194-199   1978 £25

TOOLEY, E. V.   Maps and Map Makers.   London, (1949).   First ed., d.w., illus., some in color, sm. 4to.   Biblo 247-454   1978 $20

TOPELIUS, A.   Times of Battle and of Rest.   Chicago, 1883.   Fir. Am. Ed., orig. cloth binding, good cond.   Greene 78-295   1978 $35.00

TOPINARD, PAUL   L'Anthropologie.   Paris, 1876.   8vo., illus., orig. cloth, rubbed, some staining, 1st ed.   Gilhofer 74-102   1978 sFr 100

TOPLADY, AUGUSTUS M.   1740-78   Historic Proof of the Doctrinal Calvinism of the Church of England.   1774.   First ed., 2 vols., contemp. sheep, rebacked, good, 8vo.   Howes 194-497   1978 £30

TORINUS, ALBANUS   Paraphrases in Libros Omnes Alexandri Tralliani.   Basle, 1541.   Folio, bound in medieval vellum ms. leaf.   Salloch 345-183   1978 $150

TORIO DE LA RIVA Y HERRERO, D. TORCUATO   Arte de Escribir Reglas y con Muestras...   Madrid, 1802.   4to., cont. vellum, engravings, 2nd ed.   Schumann 511-63   1978 sFr 1,300

TORNQUIST, KARL G.   The Naval Campaigns of Count De Grasse During the American Revolution.   Philadelphia, 1942.   Illus.   MacManus 239-1792   1978 $20

TORONTO PUBLIC LIBRARY   Canadian Book of Printing.   Toronto, 1940.   Hood 117-80   1978 $35

TORONTO PUBLIC LIBRARY   Catalogue of the Books in the Circulating Library.   Toronto, 1889, 1896.   Vols. 1 & 2.   Hood 117-81   1978 $30

TORONTO, the Capital of Ontario...   Toronto, 1921.   Reproductions of etchings, spine slightly worn.   Hood 116-785   1978 $40

TORRANCE, MARY FISHER   The Story of Old Rensselaerville.   New York, 1939.   Frontis., fldg. maps, writing on margins & underlining in ink.   Butterfield 21-35   1978 $15

TORRE, VINCENT   Seeds.   The Ink-Well Press, 1961.   4to., cloth decor. cover, illus., #22 of 100 numbered copies, prtd. on Japanese handmade paper.   Battery Park 1-182   1978 $125

TORRENS, ROBERT   Colonization of South Australia.   London, 1835.   1st ed., octavo, folding map, half red morocco and marbled boards, stamps from Kings Inn Dublin Library and Eastern Command P.O.W. Camp on verso to t.p. and on last page, rare.   Bennett 20-212   1978 $475

TORREY, D.   A Contribution Toward a Genealogy of All Torreys in America.   Detroit, 1890.   8vo.   Morrill 239-628   1978 $12.50

TORREY, JESSE JR.   The Intellectual Torch.   1912.   Ex-lib., good.   Nestler Rare 78-146   1978 $10

TORRICELLI, EVANGELISTA   Lezioni Accademiche.   Firenze, 1715.   4to., engr. portr. of Torricelli by Pietro Anichini, contemp. vellum, fine copy, 1st ed.   Norman 5-278   1978 $950

TORRICELLI, EVANGELISTA   Lezioni Accademiche.   Florence, 1715.   4to., old half calf, portrait, vignette, woodcuts, first ed.   Gurney 75-107   1978 £350

THE TORRINGTON Diaries.   1934-38.   4 vols., 8vo., fldg. genealogical table, plts., illus., buckram, fine set.   Quaritch 979-363   1978 $200

TORTIERE, DRUE   The House Near Paris.   1946.   Illus.   Austin 80-319   1978 $8.50

TORY, GEOFFROY   Champfleury.   Paris, 1529.   Extremely rare 1st ed., 1st issue, red mor., gilt inside dentelles, five raised bands, gilt back, panels and edges, illus., superb copy.   Gilhofer 75-107   1978 SFr 45,000

TORY, H. M.   A History of Science in Canada.   Toronto, 1939.   Hood 116-664   1978 $25

TOSI, JACOBO LORENZO   Raccolta d'Opuscoli Sopra l'Opinioni Filosofiche di Newton.   Firenze, 1774.   8vo., half vellum.   Offenbacher 30-110   1978 $125

TOTHEROH, DAN   Deep Valley.   1942.   Very good, d.j., first ed.   Austin 82-991   1978 $17.50

TOTT, BARON DE   Memoirs of...   1785.   8vo, 2 vols., calf, joints repaired.   Edwards 1012-59   1978 £50

TOUCH Me Gently, Father Time.   Cincinnati, (1877).   Wrs., fr. cover litho. view.   Hayman 73-570   1978 $7.50

TOUCHATOUT, PSEUD.
Please turn to
BIENVENU, CHARLES LEON

TOUDOUZE, GUSTAVE   Le Roy Soleil. Paris, 1908. 1st ed., folio, slight edge rubbing, fine copy. Victoria 34-492 1978 $100

TOURGEE, ALBION W.   An Appeal to Caesar. New York, 1884. Clean, orig. binding, slightly rubbed. Hayman 71-734 1978 $12.50

TOURGEE, ALBION W.   Bricks without Straw. 1880. Frontis. Austin 82-995 1978 $10

TOURGEE, ALBION W.   Bricks Without Straw. 1880. First ed., with erratum slip, v.g. Austin 82-994 1978 $37.50

TOURGEE, ALBION W.   A Fool's Errand. 1879. Illus., first ed., front hinge cracked where 15 page letter has been inserted, letter signed. Austin 82-993 1978 $47.50

TOURGEE, ALBION W.   A Fools Errand. 1879. Austin 82-996 1978 $11

TOURGEE, ALBION W.   A Fool's Errand...and the Invisible Errand... 1879. 1880. 2 parts complete in 1 vol., illus. ed. Austin 82-997 1978 $12.50

TOURGEE, ALBION W.   A Fool's Errand. New York, (1880). Two parts complete in 1 vol., illus. ed., cloth. Hayman 73-703 1978 $12.50

THE TOURIST in Wales. Comprising Views of Picturesque Scenery, Towns, Castles, Antiquities, Seats of the Nobility, Gentry... c.1850. Roy. 8vo., plts., half calf. Quaritch 983-376 1978 $335

THE TOURISTS' Guide, Containing Maps of Mount Hope Bay, Narragansett Bay, Long Island Sound, East and Hudson River... Boston, n.d. (@1899). 16mo., fldg. maps, mint cond., wr., covers chipped. Butterfield 21-261 1978 $15

TOURISTS' Guide to Down the Harbor, Hull and Nantasket, Downer Landing, Hingham, Cohasset... Boston, 1893. Fldg. maps, illus., 12mo., orig. wrs. Morrill 241-354 1978 $17.50

THE TOURISTS' Hand-Book to the British Islands. 1880. Illus., folding maps, half title, orig. limp green cloth, gilt. Jarndyce 16-310 1978 £10.50

TOURISTS' New North-Eastern Reference Book of Summer Travel. New York, (1882). 4to., maps, pict. ads. Butterfield 21-435 1978 $20

TOURNEFORT, JOSEPH PITTON DE   Beschryving Van Eene Reize De Levant... Amsterdam, 1737. 1st. ed. Dutch translation, 2 parts in 1 vol., 4to, engraved plts., contemporary mottled calf, neatly rebacked, retaining orig. back, light browning, and foxing, good copy. Deighton 5-94 1978 £295

TOURNEUR, CYRIL   The Works of Cyril Tourneur. Fanfrolico Press, 1929. Illus. by Frederick Carter, 1 of 750 numbered copies, Pannekoek mould-made paper. Battery Park 1-97 1978 $200

TOURSCHER, F. E.   The Hogan Schism and Trustee Troubles in St. Mary's Church Phila., 1820-29. Philadelphia, (1930). MacManus 239-1624 1978 $15

TOURTELLOT, A. B.   The Charles. New York, (1941). Illus. by E. J. Donnelly. Biblo 251-106 1978 $15

TOUSEY, THOMAS G.   Military History of Carlisle, Pa., and Carlisle Barracks. Richmond, 1939. Illus., signed by author, scarce. MacManus 239-1701 1978 $25

TOUSSAINT, PIENE   Memoirs of .... Boston, 1854. Frontis. Baldwins' 51-385 1978 $17.50

TOUSSENEL, ALPHONSE   L'esprit des Betes. Paris, (1868). Lg. 8vo., 1/2 green hardgrain mor., 1st illus. ed., illus. by Emile Bayard. Goldschmidt 110-3 1978 $40

TOUT, THOMAS FREDERICK   Chapters in the Administrative History of Mediaeval England. 1920-28. Vols. 1-4, ex-lib., 3 vols., scratched, spine of Vol. 2 badly. Allen 234-1480 1978 $45

TOUT, THOMAS FREDERICK   The Place of the Reign of Edward II in English History. 1914. 8vo. Upcroft 12-455 1978 £8.50

TOUT, THOMAS FREDERICK   The Place of the Reign of Edward II in English History. Manchester, 1914. Lacks endpapers, covers dull, 8vo. George's 635-772 1978 £7.50

TOWER, REUBEN   An Appeal to the People of the State of New-York, in Favor of the Construction of the Chenango Canal,.... Utica, 1830. 8vo, sewn, as issued, 1st ed., very good copy, uncut and unopened. Ximenes 47-312 1978 $75

TOWERS, JOSEPH   Memoirs of the Life and Times of Frederick the Third, King of Prussia. 1788. 2 vols., 8vo., contemp. tree calf. P.M. Hill 142-112 1978 £28

TOWLER, J.   The Silver Sunbeam: A Practical and Theoretical Text-Book on Sun Drawing and Photographic Printing... New York, 1864. Clean, orig. binding, slight wear, very good copy. Hayman 71-735 1978 $100

TOWNE, CHARLES HANSON   Ambling through Acadia. New York, 1923. Drwgs. by W. E. Heitland. Hood 117-276 1978 $15

TOWNE, CHARLES HANSON   Autumn Loiterers. New York, 1917. 1st ed., illus., frontis., uncut, pictorial cloth, pen &ink drawings, very good or better. Limestone 9-303 1978 $15

TOWNE, CHARLES HANSON   Jogging Around New England. New York, 1939. Illus., 1st ed. Biblo BL781-148 1978 $8.50

TOWNE, CHARLES HANSON   This New York of Mine. New York, 1931. 1st ed., lacks label on spine, illus. Biblo 248-88 1978 $12.50

TOWNE, CHARLES HANSON   Shaking Hands with England. New York, (1919). Author's signed pres. Biblo 247-775 1978 $13.50

TOWNE, CHARLES HANSON   Two Singers. New York, Village Press, 1928. 1st ed., 1 of 350 signed copies, tall thin 8vo., orig. cloth-backed bds., uncut, very good. Americanist 103-131 1978 $20

TOWNE, CHARLES WAYLAND   Shepherd's Empire. Norman, 1945. 1st ed., cloth, maps, illus., fine copy, autographed by Towne, Edward Wentworth & Harold Bugbee, scarce. Dykes 34-283 1978 $50

TOWNE, CHARLES WAYLAND   Shepherd's Empire. 1st ed., fine in d.w. Dykes 34-283a 1978 $17.50

TOWNSEND, C. W.   Beach Grass. Boston, 1923. Signed copy, 8vo, orig. cloth. Book Chest 17-387 1978 $16.50

TOWNSEND, EDWARD WATERMAN   "Chimmie Fadden". 1895. Illus., 1st ed. Austin 82-998 1978 $12.50

TOWNSEND, EDWARD WATERMAN   "Chimmie Fadden", Major Max and Other Stories. New York, (1895). Cloth. Hayman 73-212 1978 $7.50

TOWNSEND, G.   The Oedipus Romanus. 1819. Contemp. calf, 8vo. George's 635-1437 1978 £10.50

TOWNSEND, GEORGE ALFRED   Campaigns of a Non-Combatant, and His Romaunt Abroad During the War. New York, 1866. Baldwins' 51-209 1978 $17.50

TOWNSEND, J. W.   The Old "Main Line". 1922. Illus., inscribed copy. Baldwins' 51-488 1978 $10

TOWNSEND, JOHN KIRKE   Narrative of a Journey Across the Rocky Mountains, to the Columbia River, and a Visit to the Sandwich Islands, Chili... Boston, 1839. 1st ed., tall 8vo., orig. patterned cloth, a little worn, piece gone from foot of spine, front blanks gone. Americanist 102-116 1978 $325

TOWNSEND, RICHARD E. A.   Visions of the Western Railways. London, 1838. Plain contemp. wrappers. Wolfe 39-537 1978 $100

TOWNSEND, VIRGINIA F.   Our Presidents, or the Lives of the 23 Presidents of the United States. New York, 1889. Tall 8vo., steel portrs., untrimmed, ex-lib., ed. ltd. to 500 copies. Morrill 239-630 1978 $10

TOWNSEND, W. G. P.   Modern Decorative Art in England, Vol. 1. 1922. Illus., in colour, folio. George's 635-260 1978 £25

TOWNSEND, W. J.   New History of Methodism. 1909. Illus., 2 vols., lg. 8vo. George's 635-1101 1978 £7.50

TOWNSEND, WILLIAM H.   Lincoln, the Litigant. Boston, 1925. Illus., ltd. ed. Biblo 248-63 1978 $32.50

TOWNSHEND, CHARLES   The Barrier-Treaty Vindicated. 1712. 1st. ed., 8vo, disbound, half-title, 1 corner water-stained. Hannas 54-349 1978 £12.50

TOWNSHEND, D.   Life and Letters of Mr. Endymion Porter, Sometime Gentleman of the Bedchamber to King Charles I. 1897. Illus., octavo, good. Upcroft 10-572 1978 £6.50

TOWNSHEND, R. B.   Last Memories of a Tenderfoot. New York, 1926. Cloth, 1st Amer. ed. Hayman 73-704 1978 $12.50

TOWNSON, T.   A Discourse on the Evangelical History, from the Internment to the Ascension of our Lord Jesus Christ. Oxford, 1793. Full calf, joint cracking, 8vo. George's 635-1145 1978 £7.50

TOYNBEE, ARNOLD J.   Armenian Atrocities. London, 1915. Map, paper, 1st ed. Austin 79-781 1978 $20

TOYNBEE, ARNOLD J.   A Study of History, Vols. 1-6. 1934-48. 6 vols., 8vo. George's 635-773 1978 £7.50

TOYNBEE, ARNOLD J.   A Study of History. London, 1948. 10 vols., 2 slipcases, presen. copy from author to Wiley. Bell Wiley's copy. Broadfoot 46-577 1978 $75

TOYNBEE, ARNOLD J.   Survey of International Affairs, 1924. 1926. 8vo. George's 635-774 1978 £6

TOYNBEE, PAGET   Dante Studies and Researches. 1902. 8vo. George's 635-1289 1978 £5

TOYNBEE, PAGET   Satirical Poems Published Anonymously by William Mason. Oxford, Clarendon Press, 1926. 4to, orig. bds., d.w., portraits, good. Sexton 7-159 1978 £10

TOYNBEE, PHILIP   Tea with Mrs. Goodman. 1947. Very good, first English ed. Bell Book 16-1015 1978 £4

TRACY, MILTON C.   The Colonizer: A Saga of Stephen F. Austin. El Paso, 1941. 1st ed., fine, d.j., illus. Jenkins 116-48 1978 $12.50

TRAGIC Dramas From Scottish History. Edinburgh, 1859. 2nd. ed., orig. green cloth, v.g. Jarndyce 16-999 1978 £9.50

TRAHERNE, THOMAS   Poetical Works. 1903. Frontis., cr. 4to., orig. white cloth, cover slightly soiled. Howes 194-1288 1978 £12.50

THE TRAIL of the Tiger. New York, 1928. Cartoon illus., 8vo., d.w., partly torn & ink stain on spine, 1st ed. Morrill 241-697 1978 $15

TRAILL, CATHERINE PARR   The Backwoods of Canada... Nattali and Bond, (1840). Map, illus., 12mo, orig. cloth. Edwards 1012-457 1978 £20

TRAILL, CATHERINE PARR   The Backwoods of Canada: Being Letters From the Wife of an Emigrant Officer... Toronto, 1929. Illus. by Owen Staples, spine faded. Hood's 115-854 1978 $25

TRAILL, HENRY DUFF   Social England, a Record of the Progress of the People. 1894. 6 vols., 8vo. George's 635-762 1978 £10.50

TRAILL, HENRY DUFF   Social England, a Record of the Progress of the People. 1902-04. Illus., a few in colour, 6 vols., imp. 8vo. George's 635-763 1978 £21

TRAIN, ARTHUR   No Matter Where. New York, 1933. 1st ed., 8 vo., d.j., fine. Houle 10-341 1978 $15

TRAIN, ARTHUR   No Matter Where. New York, 1933. 1st ed., 8 vo., d.j., very good-fine. Houle 10-340 1978 $25

TRAIN, CHARLES R.   Closing Argument in Behalf of the Petitioners for the Annexation of Dorchester to Boston.... Boston, 1869. Wrps. Hayman 71-446 1978 $7.50

TRAIN and Bank Robbers of the West...Missouri's Daring Outlaws. Chicago, 1882. Cloth, some wear & spotting of cover. Hayman 73-339 1978 $35

TRALL, RUSSELL THACHER   The Hydropathic Encyclopedia. New York, 1852. Engr. illus., 8vo., dampstained, occas. foxing, 1st ed. Morrill 239-263 1978 $20

TRALL, RUSSELL THACHER   Sexual Physiology: A Scientific and Popular Exposition of the Fundamental Problems in Sociology. New York, 1866. Wear signs. Rittenhouse 49-792 1976 $10

TRALL, RUSSELL THACHER   Uterine Diseases and Displacements. New York, 1854. Rittenhouse 49-791 1976 $20

TRANT, THOMAS A.   Narrative of a Journey Through Greece, in 1830. 1830. 1st. & only ed., plts., illus., 8vo, light signs of use, very good, cont. calf. Fenning 32-333 1978 £28.50

TRAPP, JOSEPH   The Royal Sin: or, Adultery Rebuk'd in a Great King... London, 1738. 8vo., stitched as issued, uncut, 1st ed., fine. MacManus 238-151 1978 $65

TRAQUAIR, RAMSAY   The Old Architecture of Quebec. Toronto, 1947. 4to., illus., orig. binding. Wolfe 39-531 1978 $360

TRATADO Da Abolica Do Trafico de Escravos Em Todos os Lugares Da Costa De Africa ao Norte do Quador... Rio de Janeiro, 1815. Sm. folio, unbound, slight split in title, sm. wormhole in text repaired affecting a few words. Edwards 1012-677 1978 £75

TRATADO De Amizade, e Allianca Entre os Muito Altos e Muito Poderosos Senhorses O Principe Regente de Portugal e El Rey do Reino Unido da Grande Bretanha e Irlanda... Rio de Janeiro, 1810. Sm. folio, wrappers, browned. Edwards 1012-680 1978 £75

TRATADO DE Commercio Regente De Portugal... Rio de Janeiro, 1810. Sm. folio, wrappers, few pages spotted, crease in 6 leaves cracked. Edwards 1012-681 1978 £75

TRAUM, SAMUEL W.   Mormonism Against Itself. 1910. Illus. Austin 79-782 1978 $22.50

A TRAVELLER'S Criticism on Our Health Resorts, Their Scenery, Climatic Peculiarities and Curative Influence. Boston, 1885. Illus., 12mo., orig. pict. wrs. Morrill 239-12 1978 $12.50

TRAVELS into Several Remote Nations of the World, in Four Parts, by Lemuel Gulliver, first a Surgeon, and then a Captain of Several Ships. 1726. 2 vols., 8vo., portr., maps, plans, contemp. calf, very nice copy, bkplt. of Samuel Whitbread. Quaritch 979-312 1978 $650

THE TRAVELS Of Several Learned Missioners of the Society of Jesus... 1714. 2 folding plts., calf, rebacked, 8vo. Edwards 1012-24 1978 £75

TRAVELS Over The Land and Over The Sea. London, c.1805. Hand-colored plates, stitches are gone, leaves are loose, bound in later but early cloth, cloth spine present as narrow strip, minor margin edge staining, contents very good, leather label darkening. Victoria 34-806 1978 $135

TRAVELS Through the Interior Parts of America. Boston, 1923. 2 vols., orig. bds., very good set, reprint of the rare 1789 ed., ltd. to 575 sets, one spine worn, else very good. MacManus 239-27 1978 $55

TRAVEN, B.   Die Brucke im Dschungel. Berlin, 1929. 1st ed., tall 8vo., covers little soiled, scarce, orig. cloth, very good. Americanist 103-100 1978 $45

TRAVERS, BENJAMIN   An Inquiry concerning that disturbed state of the Vital Functions usually denominated Constitutional Irritation. London, 1826. 8vo., half calf, first ed. Gurney 75-106 1978 £25

TRAVERS, MORRIS   The Discovery of the Rare Gases. London, 1928. Lg. 8vo., frontis., & text illus., orig. cloth-backed bds., d.w., little soiled, but fine copy, pres. stamp, 1st ed. Norman 5-235 1978 $85

TRAVERS, P.L.   Mary Poppins. New York, (1934). 1st Amer. ed., illus., signed by Miss Travers, front free endpaper lacking, covers slightly faded, pictorial d.j. Victoria 34-807 1978 $50

TRAYLOR, JOHN H.   Memorial of Kate C. Sturgis and Stella J. Chambers, Heirs of General T. J. Chambers. Austin, ca. 1888. Jenkins 116-208 1978 $85

TRAYSER, DONALD G.   Barnstable Three Centuries of a Cape Cod Town. Hyannis, 1939. Illus., d.j., fine. MacManus 239-1009 1978 $17.50

TREADWELL, EDWARD F.   The Cattle King. New York, 1931. First ed., d.w. frayed, illus. Biblo 247-241 1978 $35

TREADWELL, EDWARD F.   The Cattle King. New York, 1931. Port., front inner hinge sprung. Biblo BL781-291 1978 $10

TREATISE on Arithmetic. Toronto, Hamilton, 1853. Cover worn. Hood 117-965 1978 $40

A TREATISE on the Approaching Commercial Intercourse between Gt. Britain and France. 1814. Wrappers, 8vo. George's 635-416 1978 £12.50

TREBA, FRIEDRICH W. H. VON   Erfahrungen Vom Innern der Gebirge. Dessau & Leipzig, 1785. Folio, handcolored vignettes, handcolored fldg. plts., full antique calf, slightly rubbed, light soiling on title, little dampstaining in margin of some plts., but fine copy, 1st ed.   Norman 5-*52 1978 $950

TRECCO, GIOVANNI BATTISTA   Coltivazione e Governo del Lino Marzuolo Con dodici Travole in Rame. Vicenza, 1792. 4to., bds., a few paper flaws in margins, first ed.   King 7-247 1978 £65

TREDGOLD, THOMAS   A Practical Treatise on Rail-Roads and Carriages. London, 1825. 8vo., ads, engr. plts., orig. bds., uncut, spine repaired, fine copy, 1st ed.   Norman 5-279 1978 $350

TREDGOLD, THOMAS   A Practical Treatise on Rail-roads and Carriages... with the Theory, Effect and Expense of Steam Carriages... London, 1835. Plts., bds., disbound. Petrilla 13-137 1978 $45

TREDGOLD, THOMAS   Principles of Warming and Ventilating Public Buildings, Dwelling-Houses, Manufactories, Hospitals, Hot-Houses, Conservatories, etc.... London, 1824. 8vo., ads, plts., illus., orig. bds. neatly rebacked, light scattered interior foxing, tight copy, uncut leaf edges. Current 24-128 1978 $185

TREDGOLD, THOMAS   The Steam Engine. London, 1827. 4to., qtr. calf, uncut, plts., woodcuts, first ed.   Gurney 75-108 1978 £135

TREDWELL, D. M.   Sketch of Life of Apollonius of Tyana... 1886. Inscr'd, map. Allen 234-37 1978 $15

TREE, HERBERT BEERBOHM   Thoughts and After-Thoughts. 1913. Decorations by Lovat Fraser, very good, first English ed. Bell Book 16-596 1978 £5.50

TREFFEL'S History of Roman Literature. 1891. 2 vols., blind-stamp on title-pgs., cloth, little shaken, head of spines worn. Eaton 45-515 1978 £10

TREGASKIS, RICHARD   Stronger than Fear. 1945. Austin 80-332 1978 $8.50

TREGELLES, S. P.   Account of the Printed Text of the Greek New Testament. 1854. Library stamp on title, new endpapers, 8vo. George's 635-1146 1978 £5

TRELAWNEY-ANSELL, E. C.   I Followed Gold. London, 1938. 8vo, orig. cloth, pres. inscription from author. K Books 239-491 1978 £8

TRELAWNY, EDWARD JOHN   Adventures of a Younger Son. London, 1890. New ed., 3 vols. in 1, cloth, foxing, good, orig. boards. Greene 78-296 1978 $25

TRELAWNY, EDWARD JOHN   Records of Shelley, Byron & The Author. 1878. 1st. ed., half titles, frontis, orig. black cloth, gilt borders, fine. Jarndyce 16-1147 1978 £48

TREMBLEY, ABRAHAM   Memoires Pour Servir a l'Histoire d'un Genre de Polypes d'eau Douce, a Bras en Forme de Cornes. Leide, 1744. Fldg. copper-plts., 4to., contemp. vellum, 1st ed., very fine copy. Offenbacher 30-152 1978 $575

TRENCH, HERBERT   New Poems. 1907. First ed., orig. buckram, 8vo., A.L.s. from author loosely inserted. Howes 194-1289 1978 £6

TRENCHARD, JOHN   Free Thoughts Concerning Officers in the House of Commons. (1698). 4to., unbound. P. M. Hill 142-13 1978 £14

TRENCK, FRIEDRICH VON DER   The Life of Baron Frederic Trenck. 1788. 3 vols., portrait, 12mo., contemp. sheep, first English ed. Howes 194-499 1978 £28

TRENTSENSKY, M.   Exercises in Coloring-French Military. Vienna, (c. 1860). Coloured plts., oblong sm. folio, orig. wrappers. F. Edwards 1013-439 1978 £60

TRESSALL, ROBERT   The Ragged Trousered Philanthropists. 1914. Orig. cloth, neatly rebacked, good, first English ed. Bell Book 17-868 1978 £12.50

TREVELYAN, C. E.   The Irish Crisis. (c. 1847). Bound in green silk, pres. copy "With Author's Compliments", a.e.g., spine worn, very good, reprint. Hyland 128-696 1978 £25

TREVELYAN, G. O.   The Ladies in Parliament... Cambridge, 1869. 1st. collected ed., half title, orig. brown cloth, fine. Jarndyce 16-1148 1978 £12.50

TREVELYAN, GEORGE MACAULAY   England in the Age of Wycliffe. 1925, 1946. Maps. 8vo. Upcroft 12-459 1978 #4.50

TREVELYAN, GEORGE MACAULAY   England in the Age of Wycliffe. 1946. Maps. Allen 234-1483 1978 $10

TREVELYAN, M. C.   William the Third and the Defence of Holland 1672-4. 1930. Plts., maps, octavo, good. Upcroft 10-575 1978 £7.50

TREVER, A. A.   History of Civilization. 1936-39. 2 vols., plt., color of bindings not uniform. Allen 234-1006 1978 £12.50

TREVES, FREDERICK   The Cradle of the Deep. New York, 1908. Maps, photo illus., colored front., 8vo, orig. cloth. Book Chest 17-388 1978 $32.50

TREVES, FREDERICK   The Tale of a Field Hospital. London, 1900. 14 plts., cr. 4to, neatly recased in orig. gilt-lettered limp leather, g.t. K Books 239-492 1978 £8

TREVISICK, C.   Fancy Pheasants, Jungle Fowl & Peafowl for Beginners. London. Color plates, 12mo, orig. cloth. Book Chest 17-389 1978 $13.50

TREVOR-BATTYE, A.   Ice-Bound on Kolguev... 1895. Maps, illus., orig. cloth, 8vo, cover slightly worn, few sm. lib. stamps. Edwards 1012-611 1978 £20

TRIAIRE, PAUL   Dominique Larrey Et Les Campagnes De La Revolution Et De L'Empire 1768-1842. Tours, 1902. Tall 8vo., frontis. portr., half mor., gilt lettering, worn, lightly browned, bkplt. & library stamps, early owner-ship inscr., good copy, 1st ed. Zeitlin 245-306 1978 $87.50

TRIAL of William Bushnell, M. D., Samuel Gregg, M. D., and Others, All of Boston, for Practising Homeopathy While They Were Members of the Massachusetts Medical Society, Before Jeremiah Spofford, M. D., George Hayward, M. D., and Others. Boston, 1873. 8vo., orig. wrs., 1st ed. Morrill 239-264 1978 $17.50

THE TRIBUNE Almanac and Political Register for 1864. New York, (1863). Wrps., minor wear. Hayman 71-16 1978 $7.50

THE TRIBUNE Almanac and Political Register for 1865. New York, (1864). Wrs. Hayman 72-17 1978 $7.50

A TRIBUTE To A. Edward Newton. Washington, (1940). 1 of 1000 copies, orig. blue wrs., 8vo. Americanist 101-106e 1978 $20

A TRIBUTE to the Fair. New York, 1864. 12mo., 1st ed. Morrill 239-502 1978 $10

TRIBUTE to the Memory of De Witt Clinton, Comprehensive Sketch of His Life. Albany, 1828. Orig. bds. & 1/2 lea. Butterfield 21-129 1978 $15

TRICASSO, PATRICIO   Epitoma Chyromantico. Venice, 1538. 8vo., woodcuts, vellum. Salloch 345-184 1978 $110

THE TRICKS of Trade in the Adulteration of Food and Physic. 1856. Fcap. 8vo., covers faded. George's 635-1348 1978 £5.25

TRIMEN, ROLAND   South-African Butterflies... London, 1887-1889. Map, 12 coloured & 1 plain plt., 3 vols. in 2, roy. 8vo, half brown morocco. Traylen 88-636 1978 £65

TRIMMER, SARAH   An Essay on Christian Education. 1812. First ed., contemp. half calf, 8vo. Howes 194-500 1978 £21

TRIMMER, SARAH   Fabulous Histories, or, the History of the Robins. London, 1840. Engraved plates, marbled boards, gilt-lettered leather spine, two signatures lightly pulled, fine. Victoria 34-808 1978 $40

TRIMMER, SARAH   Scripture Lessons Designed to Accompany A Series of Prints from the New Testament. London, 1825. Matching leather, spine ends chipped, very good set. Victoria 34-809 1978 $35

TRINITY COLLEGE, TORONTO. CHARTERS   The Act of Incorporation, Royal Charter, Statues and By-Laws of Trinity College, Toronto. Toronto, 1903. Bound. Hood's 117-929 1978 $15

A TRIP Through London: Containing Observations on Men and Things. London, 1728. 8vo, modern boards, 2nd ed., rare. Ximenes 47-183 1978 $150

A TRIP to Alaska... San Francisco, (1884). 1st ed., orig. decorated cloth, very good copy. MacManus 239-21 1978 $30

TRIPLETT, FRANK   History, Romance and Philosophy of Great American Crimes and Criminals. Hartford, 1885. Engrs., 8vo., inner hinges cracked, orig. cloth. Morrill 241-581 1978 $15

TRIPP, ALONZO   Crests from the Ocean-World or, Experiences in a Voyage to Europe..1847-48. Foxed, 8vo, orig. cloth. Book Chest 17-390 1978 $20

TRIPP, ALONZO   Crests from the Ocean World... Boston, 1853. Austin 82-1000 1978 $27.50

TRIPP, GEORGE HENRY   Student-Life at Harvard. Boston, 1876. 8vo., bookplate removed, 1st ed. Morrill 239-418 1978 $7.50

TRISTRAM, H. B.   Pathways to Palestine... (1881). Mounted photos, 4to, rebacked, lib. stamps on title & half title, 1st. series of 2. Edwards 1012-87 1978 £75

TRISTRAM, WILLIAM OUTRAM   Coaching Days and Coaching Ways. 1888. Imp. 8vo., 1st ed., frontis., very slight foxing on prelims, orig. decor. cloth, little worn. Quaritch 983-373 1978 £125

TRITHEIM, JOHANN   Polygraphiae Libri Sex. (1518). Sm. folio, unnumbered leaves, late 18th Cent. half calf, gilt, little rubbed, occas. browning, dampstaining, worming, but very good copy, 1st ed. Norman 5-280 1978 $2,250

TROBRIAND, PHILIPPE   Army Life in Dakota. Chicago, 1941. Trans. from French, cloth. Hayman 73-705 1978 $10

TROGUS POMPEIUS
Please turn to
JUSTINUS, MARCUS JUNIANUS

TROIL, UNO VON   Letters on Iceland... London, 1780. 8vo, engraved plt., folding engraved map, some spotting, half calf, gilt back. Deighton 5-147 1978 £95

TROLLOPE, ANTHONY   The American Senator. New York, (1940). Orig. cloth, pub. box, ltd. to 310 copies, fine. MacManus 238-995 1978 $25

TROLLOPE, ANTHONY   Avala's Angel. London, n.d. (ca.1884). 8vo, original pictorial glazed boards (bit worn), attractive "yellowback", very decent. Ximenes 47-314 1978 $35

TROLLOPE, ANTHONY   The Bertrams. Leipzig, 1859. 2 vols., sq. 8vo, contemp. quarter morocco. Hannas 54-351 1978 £15

TROLLOPE, ANTHONY   Can You Forgive Her?.... London, 1864. 2 vols., octavo, illus., woodcut and engraved, full contemp. calf, gilt inner dentelles, spines gilt, 1st ed. Bennett 7-120 1978 $175

TROLLOPE, ANTHONY   The Complete Chronicles of Barsetshire. 1891. 8 vols., cr. 8vo., half brown mor., frontis., fine. Howes 194-1291 1978 £85

TROLLOPE, ANTHONY   Doctor Thorne. Leipzig, 1858. 2 vols., sq. 8vo, contemp. quarter morocco. Hannas 54-352 1978 £15

TROLLOPE, ANTHONY   The Duke's Children. A Novel. London, 1880. 3 vols., orig. cloth, 1st ed., good, lib. labels removed, worn, cloth slipcase. MacManus 238-404 1978 $185

TROLLOPE, ANTHONY   Four Lectures...Printed Verbatim from the Original Texts. London, (1938). Orig. cloth, 1st ed., ltd. to 150 copies, very fine. MacManus 238-405 1978 $85

TROLLOPE, ANTHONY   Framley Parsonage. New York, 1861. 1st Amer. ed., plates by Millais, orig. cloth, good. Greene 78-118 1978 $50

TROLLOPE, ANTHONY   Framley Parsonage. New York, 1862. 12mo, brown-black cloth rubbed with some bubbles and one small tear on front cover, corners rubbed, some foxing, front free endpaper absent, ownership sign. on flyleaf, Fair copy, 1st ed., collector's cond. Desmarais 1-412 1978 $50

TROLLOPE, ANTHONY   The Golden Lion of Granpere. London, 1872. Orig. cloth, 1st ed., 1st bind., covers worn, inner hinges cracked, otherwise good, bookplt. MacManus 238-403 1978 $100

TROLLOPE, ANTHONY   Harry Heathcote of Gangoil: A Tale of Australian Bush Life. Leipzig, 1874. Sq. 8vo, contemp. quarter morocco. Hannas 54-353 1978 £15

TROLLOPE, ANTHONY   He Knew He Was Right. 1869. First ed., plts., illus., 2 vols., contemp. full calf, spines gilt, 8vo. Howes 194-1292 1978 £45

TROLLOPE, ANTHONY   He Knew He Was Right. 1869. 1st. ed., 2 vols. in 1, illus. by Marcus Stone, half calf, gilt spine, rather worn. Eaton 45-510 1978 £40

TROLLOPE, ANTHONY   The Kellys and the O'Kelleys. New York, 1860. Orig. cloth, dull, spine faded. Eaton 45-511 1978 £10

TROLLOPE, ANTHONY   Last Chronicle of Barset. 1867. 2 vols., 8vo., 1st ed., plts., half blue mor. gilt, neat signature. Quaritch 979-321 1978 $200

TROLLOPE, ANTHONY   The Last Chronicles of Barset. New York, 1867. 1st Amer. ed., illus. by George H. Thomas, 2 vols. in 1, cloth, spine damaged, interior good. Greene 78-119 1978 $50

TROLLOPE, ANTHONY   The Last Chronicle of Barset. 1867. 2 vols., 1st. ed., illus. by George H. Thomas, few leaves & plts. foxed, mostly marginal, orig. blue cloth, gilt decorations on upper covers & spines, head of spines fraying. Eaton 45-512 1978 £40

TROLLOPE, ANTHONY   Miss Mackenzie. London, c. 1880. Cr. 8vo., 5th ed., half red mor. K Books 244-314 1978 £7

TROLLOPE, ANTHONY   North America. Philadelphia, 1862. Two vols. in one, orig. binding. Wolfe 39-533 1978 $25

TROLLOPE, ANTHONY   North America. New York, 1862. Bell Wiley's copy. Broadfoot 46-578 1978 $15

TROLLOPE, ANTHONY   North America. Harper, 1862. Browned, orig. cloth, dull, joints split, pirated 1st. U.S. ed. Eaton 45-513 1978 £10

TROLLOPE, ANTHONY   Orley Farm. 1862. First ed., plts., 2 vols., contemp. half green calf, good, 8vo. Howes 194-1293 1978 £45

TROLLOPE, ANTHONY   Orley Farm. New York, 1862. 1st Amer. ed., 2 vols. in 1, illus. by J.E. Millais, orig. cloth, good. Greene 78-120 1978 $50

TROLLOPE, ANTHONY   Ralph the Heir. London, 1871. 1st ed., orig. brown cloth, weak hinges, good copy, 3 vols. Greene 78-121 1978 $175

TROLLOPE, ANTHONY   Sir Harry Hotspur of Humblethwaite. London, 1871. Orig. cloth, 1st ed., covers worn, some pencil scoring, bookplts. MacManus 238-402 1978 $85

TROLLOPE, ANTHONY   Thackeray. Lond., 1874. Fir. Ed., red cloth binding, spine ends worn, interior very good, contemp. name plate, coated end papers. Greene 78-298 1978 $50.00

TROLLOPE, ANTHONY   Thackeray. 1879. Covers somewhat soiled, good, first English ed. Bell Book 16-853 1978 £15

TROLLOPE, ANTHONY   The Three Clerks. New York, 1860. 12mo, blue stamped boards with corners bumped and slightly worn, top and bottom of spine rubbed, some foxing, ownership sign. on flyleaf, generally Fine copy, 1st ed. Desmarais 1-413 1978 $150

TROLLOPE, ANTHONY   The Three Clerks. New York, 1860. Orig. cloth, 3 vols. in 1, good. Greene 78-122 1978 $15

TROLLOPE, ANTHONY   Travelling Sketches. 1866. 1st. ed., orig. red cloth, v.g. Jarndyce 16-1151 1978 £60

TROLLOPE, ANTHONY   Travelling Sketches. Lond., 1866. Red cloth binding, bevelled edges, coated end papers, very fine bright, tight clean copy. Greene 78-299 1978 $85.00

TROLLOPE, ANTHONY   Victoria & Tasmania. London, 1875. Pict. glazed boards, "yellow-back" format, ex-library copy with stamps, new ed., good. Greene 78-123 1978 $40

TROLLOPE, ANTHONY   The West Indies and The Spanish Main. Leipzig, 1860. Sq. 8vo, contemp. quarter morocco. Hannas 54-354 1978 £12.50

TROLLOPE, FRANCES   The Blue Belles of England. Paris, 1842. First one-volume ed., contemp. half calf, spine neatly rebacked, very good. Bell Book 17-869 1978 £15

TROLLOPE, FRANCES   Charles Chesterfield. Paris, 1842. First one-volume ed., contemp. half calf, very good. Bell Book 17-870 1978 £15

TROLLOPE, FRANCES   Domestic Manners of the Americans. New York, 1949. Illus. from orig. ed., cloth bind. in dw, very good. Greene 78-301 1978 $20

TROLLOPE, FRANCES   Domestic Manners of the Americans. New York, 1949. Bell Wiley's copy. Broadfoot 46-579 1978 $10

TROLLOPE, FRANCES   The Life and Adventures of Michael Armstrong, the Factory Boy. 1840. Plts., contemp. half green calf, spine gilt, 8vo., first single-vol. ed. Howes 194-1294 1978 £25

TROLLOPE, FRANCES   The Life and Adventures of Michael Armstrong, the Factory Boy. 1840. First one-volume ed., engrav. plts., full contemp. calf, covers somewhat rubbed, good. Bell Book 17-871 1978 £18.50

TROLLOPE, FRANCES   Paris and The Parisians in 1835. 1836. 2nd. ed., 2 vols., engraved frontis & numerous illus., orig. diced calf, spines faded, otherwise v.g. Jarndyce 16-1150 1978 £75

TROLLOPE, FRANCES   Paris and The Parisians in 1835. 1836. 2nd. ed., 2 vols., engraved frontis & numerous illus., orig. diced calf, spines faded, o/w v.g. Jarndyce 16-1149 1978 £42

TROLLOPE, FRANCES   Petticoat Government. 1857. Sm. 8vo, contemp. half calf, very good. Fenning 32-336 1978 £8.50

TROLLOPE, FRANCES   The Ward of Thorpe-Combe. Paris, 1842. First one-volume ed., contemp. half calf, good. Bell Book 17-872 1978 £15

TROLLOPE, HENRY M.   The Life of Moliere. 1905. Portrait, thick roy. 8vo., orig. cloth. Howes 194-1057 1978 £6.50

TROLLOPE, THOMAS ADOLPHUS   Dream Numbers. Philadelphia, n.d.(1869?) 1st Amer. ed.(?), 3 vols. in 1, orig. cloth, damaged interior good. Greene 78-125 1978 $20

TROLLOPE, THOMAS ADOLPHUS   Lindisfarne Chase. New York, 1864. 1st Amer. ed., 3 vols. in 1, orig. cloth, good. Greene 78-126 1978 $35

TROLLOPE, THOMAS ADOLPHUS   A Summer in Western France. London, 1841. Orig. cloth, lacks color frontis, plts. by Hervieu, small numbers on spine, edges rubbed, good. Greene 78-124 1978 $75

TROLLOPE, THOMAS ADOLPHUS   What I Remember. 1887. 1st. ed., 2 vols., frontis portrait, half title, good. Jarndyce 16-1152 1978 £34

TROMP, MAARTEN HARPERTSZOON   The Journal of Maarten Harpertszoon Tromp, Anno 1639. Cambridge, 1930. Lg. 8vo., cloth, plts., maps. Van der Peet H-64-566 1978 Dfl 65

TROTSKY, LEON   The History of the Russian Revolution to Brest-Litovsk. 1919. Spine faded, very good, first English translation. Bell Book 16-854 1978 £10

TROTTER, BEECHAM   A Horseman and the West. Toronto, 1925. Ex-lib. Hood 116-595 1978 $20

TROTTER, R. G.   Canadian Federation. Toronto, 1924. Fldg. map. Hood 117-603 1978 $35

TROTTER, R. G.   Canadian History; A Syllabus and Guide to Reading. Toronto, 1934. New and enlarged ed. Hood's 115-42 1978 $35

TROTTER, THOMAS   View of the Nervous Temperament. Troy, 1808. Orig. bds., usual wear, some light foxing. Rittenhouse 49-793 1976 $30

TROUP, ROBERT   A Letter to the Hon. Henry Brockholst Livingston ...on the Canal Policy of the State of New York...with...Additional Documents. Albany, 1822. Prtd. wr., sewn, uncut, unopened, near mint copy, labeled slipcase. Butterfield 21-98 1978 $50

TROUSSEAU, ARMAND   Des Principaux Alimens Envisages Sous le Point de Vue de Leur Digestibilite et de Leur Puissance Nutritive. Paris, 1837. Lg. 4to., contemp. bds., rebacked, 1st ed., Trousseau's own copy, ms. additions, very good cond. Offenbacher 30-153 1978 $1,500

TROW DIRECTORY, PRINTING & BOOKBINDING CO.   Specimen Book of Type, Borders, Ornaments, Initials. (New York, 1905). Covers faded along edges, 8vo., orig. cloth, very good. Americanist 103-102 1978 $35

TROWBRIDGE, JOHN TOWNSEND   Cudjo's Cave. Boston, 1864. 1st ed., 2nd state, rebound in 3/4 mor., bkplt. Biblo 247-631 1978 $30

TROWBRIDGE, JOHN TOWNSEND   The South. Hartford, 1866. Bell Wiley's copy. Broadfoot's 44-797 1978 $22

TROYER, L. E. MRS.   The Sovereignty of the Holy Spirit. California, 1934. Illus. with photos., paper. Austin 79-783 1978 $27

TRUDEAU, EDWARD LIVINGSTON   Autobiography. Philadelphia, 1916. Illus., 8vo., 1st ed. Morrill 239-265 1978 $12.50

TRUDEAU, EDWARD LIVINGSTON   An Autobiography. New York, 1916. Rittenhouse 49-794 1976 $7.50

THE TRUE History of the War, Parts 1 to 4. London, 1900. 4 vols., imperial 8vo, new wrappers. K Books 239-493 1978 £30

TRUE Loyalty and the Independence of the Church. St. Louis, 1865. Original printed wr., 1st ed. Ginsberg 14-605 1978 $35

TRUEMAN, A. W.   The Story of the United Empire Loyalists. Toronto, 1946. Illus. Hood 117-277 1978 $7.50

TRUESDALE, JOHN   The Blue Coats, and How They Lived, Fought and Died For the Union. Philadelphia, (1867). Rebound, clean. Hayman 71-139 1978 $7.50

TRUESDELL, LEON E.   The Canadian Born in the United States. Yale University Press, 1943. Austin 79-784 1978 $27.50

TRUITT, CHARLES J.   Historic Salisbury, Maryland, Including Historical Sketches of the Eastern Shore. New York, 1932. Illus. Baldwins' 51-295 1978 $7.50

TRUITT, CHARLES J.   Historic Salisbury, Md. New York, (1932). Illus. MacManus 239-1005 1978 $22.50

TRUMAN, BEN C.   From the Crescent City to the Golden Gate via the Sunset Route of the Southern Pacific Company. San Francisco, 1890. 1st ed., disbound, illus. Ginsberg 14-211 1978 $50

TRUMAN, GEORGE   Journal of Rachel Wilson Moore.... Philadelphia, 1867. Baldwins' 51-383 1978 $12.50

TRUMBLE, ALFRED   Sword and Scimitar: The Romance of the Crusades. New York, 1890. Folio, illus., bind. rubbed, one signature loose, very good. Biblo BL781-617 1978 $18.50

TRUMBO, DALTON   Johnny Got His Gun. 1939. Austin 82-1001 1978 $10

TRUMBULL, BENJAMIN   A Funeral Sermon, Delivered November 12, 1811, at the Interment of the Rev. Noah Williston, Pastor of the Church at West-Haven. New Haven, 1812. Unbound as issued, reinforced along binding edge. Hayman 73-706 1978 $10

TRUMBULL, HENRY   History of the Discovery of America... Boston, 1833. Fold. plts., rebound. MacManus 239-462 1978 $25

TRUMBULL, JOHN   Autobiography, Reminiscences and Letters of... New York, 1841. 1st ed., maps, illus., fine copy, orig. cloth. MacManus 239-711 1978 $40

TRUMBULL, JOHN   M'Fingal: A Modern Epic Poem.. Hartford, 1782. Port., bound in 3/4 morocco. Nestler Rare 78-180 1978 $35

TRUMPET of Freedom. Boston, 1864. Wrs. soiled, Bell Wiley's copy. Broadfoot's 44-368 1978 $30

TRUSLER, JOHN   The Progress of Man and Society. London, 1791. 12mo, later calf, 1st ed., illus. with woodcuts by Bewick, nice copy, pictorial half-title. Ximenes 47-315 1978 $250

TRUSS, SELDON   Turmoil at Brede. New York, 1931. 1st ed., d.j., very good. Houle 10-342 1978 $20

TSCHICHOLD, JAN   An Illustrated History of Writing and Lettering. New York, Columbia University Press, (1948). Plts., bds. in d.w. Dawson's 447-168 1978 $25

TSCHUDI, J.J. VON   Travels in Peru, During the Years 1838-1842... London, 1847. 8vo, frontispiece, vignette title-pg. ex-lib. copy, with lib. stamps, rebound in polished half calf, morocco labels gilt, new end-papers. Deighton 5-58 1978 £78

T'SERSTEVENS, A.   Monsieur Santeuil, les nymphes et les saintes. 1926. Wood cuts by J.-L. Perrichon, ltd. numbered ed. George's 635-930 1978 £6.50

TSUDA, NORITAKE   Handbook of Japanese Art. Tokyo, 1935. Cloth, illus. Dawson's 449-201 1978 $35

TUBERKULOSESTUDIEN   Virchows Archiv Fur Pathologische Anatomie Und Physiologie Und Fur Klinische Medizin. Berlin, 1907. 8vo., fldg. plts., illus., half mor., gilt on spine, ex-lib., very good copy. Zeitlin 245-270 1978 $25

TUCK, RUTH   Not With the Fist. 1946. Austin 79-785 1978 $12.50

TUCKER, CHARLOTTE MARIE   The Lake of the Woods. Edinburgh, n.d. (c.1850). 1st ed.(?), cloth, edges gilt, rubbed, very good. Greene 78-338 1978 $50

TUCKER, CHARLOTTE MARIA   Old Friends with New Faces. London, 1853. Sm. 8vo, original bright blue cloth, decorated in gilt, 1st ed., engraved frontispiece and t.p., very good copy. Ximenes 47-316 1978 $15

TUCKER, GEORGE   The Theory of Money and Banks Investigated. Boston, 1839. Baldwins' 51-374 1978 $17.50

TUCKER, JOSIAH   Four Letters on Important National Subjects. Glocester, 1783. 8vo., new qtr. calf, marbled sides. P. M. Hill 142-230 1978 £28

TUCKER, P.   Origin, Rise & Progress of Mormonism. 1867. Lacks backstrip, good copy. Nestler Rare 78-147 1978 $25

TUCKER, ST. GEORGE   A Dissertation on Slavery With a Proposal For The Gradual Abolition of It, In the State of Virginia. Philadelphia, 1796. Disbound. Baldwins' 51-387 1978 $100

TUCKER, SARAH   The Rainbow in the North... 1853. Sm. 8vo, 4th. ed., map, engraved title, plts., orig. cloth. Edwards 1012-458 1978 £25

TUCKER, WILLARD D.   Gratiot County, Michigan. Saginaw, 1913. Orig. binding, clean, scarce. Hayman 71-468 1978 $60

TUCKERMAN, BAYARD   William Jay and the Constitutional Movement for the Abolition of Slavery. New York, 1893. Illus., ex-lib. MacManus 239-854 1978 $12.50

TUCKERMAN, HENRY THEODORE.   Poems. Boston, 1851. 8vo, original green cloth, decorated in gilt, 1st ed., fine presentation copy, inscribed by author. Ximenes 47-317 1978 $35

TUCKWELL, W.   A. W. Kinglake. London, 1902. First ed., illus., orig. blue cloth, pres. copy from author, very good or better. Limestone 9-167 1978 $20

TUDOR, WILLIAM   Letters on the Eastern States. Boston, 1821. 2nd ed., old 1/2 mor. MacManus 239-463 1978 $37.50

TUDOR-CRAIG, ALGERNON   Armorial Procelain of the Eighteenth Century.' London, 1925. Many plts., 3 in colour, 4to, buckram, scarce, ltd. ed. of 1000 numbered copies. Traylen 88-420 1978 £42

TUER, ANDREW WHITE   Bartolozzi and His Works. London, Leadenhall Presse, (1882). 2 vols., quarto, orig. vellum with gilt lettering on covers and spines, plts. Totteridge 29-107 1978 $125

TUER, ANDREW WHITE   Old London Street Cries. London, Leadenhall Press, 1885. Newly rebound in marbled paper over bds., cloth spine. Battery Park 1-197 1978 $50

TUER, ANDREW WHITE   Old London Street Cries and The Cries of To-Day. 1885. Illus., 16mo, orig. fancy bds., printed paper label, with ties, backstrip neatly renewed, very good. Fenning 32-337 1978 £8.50

TUER, ANDREW WHITE   Old London Street Cries. London, Leadenhall Press, 1885. 16mo., marbled paper over bds., ties. Battery Park 1-196 1978 $75

TUER, ANDREW WHITE   1,000 Quaint Cuts from Books of Other Days.... London, Leadenhall Press, (1886). 1st ed., sq. octavo, printed blue boards, blue cloth spine, bookplate, ltd. ed. printed on one side only. Totteridge 29-108 1978 $100

TUER, ANDREW WHITE   Pages and Pictures from Forgotten Children's Books. London, 1898-9. 1st ed., illus., gilt-illus. cover and spine, invaluable ref. tool. Victoria 34-811 1978 $55

THE TUFTS College Graduate. Tufts College, 1904-1918. 16 vols. in 9, 8vo., bound in 3 different kinds of buckram, ex-lib. Morrill 239-518 1978 $30

TUGWELL, REXFORD   The Stricken Land, the Story of Puerto Rico. 1947. Orig. ed. Austin 79-786 1978 $12.50

TULLY, MISS   Narrative of a Ten Years' Residence at Tripoli in Africa...Comprising Authentic Memoirs and Anecdotes of the Reigning Bashaw... 1817. 4to., fold. map. coloured plts., some foxing, half calf. Quaritch 983-374 1978 $210

TULLY, JIM   Blood on the Moon. New York, (1931). 1st ed., very good or better. Limestone 9-305 1978 $15

TULLY, JIM   Emmett Lawler. 1922. Ex-lib. Austin 82-1002 1978 $11

TUNNEY, THOMAS J.   Throttled! 1919. Illus. from photos. Austin 79-787 1978 $20

TUNNICLIFFE, CHARLES FREDERICK   Bird Portraiture - How To Do It. London, (1946). Color plates, 8vo., orig. cloth. Book Chest 17-391 1978 $13.50

TUNNICLIFFE, CHARLES FREDERICK   My Country Book. 1942. Coloured plts., illus., roy. 8vo. George's 635-216 1978 £5

TUPPER, F. B.   Family Records; Containing Memoirs of Major-Gen. Sir Isaac Brock, Lieut. E. W. Tupper and Col. Wm. de Vic Tupper... Guernsey, 1835. Orig. bind., inscribed by editor. Hood 116-665 1978 $250

TUPPER, MARTIN FARQUHAR   Proverbial Philosophy: A Book of Thoughts and Arguments. 1838. Originally treated, 1st. ed., orig. cloth, rebacked. Eaton 45-517 1978 £20

TUPPER, MARTIN FARQUHAR   The Rides and Reveries of the Late Mr. Aesop Smith. Philadelphia, (1858?). Sole American ed., rear end sheet cut out, very good or better. Limestone 9-306 1978 $25

TURGENEV, IVAN   A Sportsman's Notebook. London, 1950. 16mo, dark blue cloth boards, gilt stamped, d.w., near Mint cond., lst ed. Desmarais 1-414 1978 $20

TURNBULL, A.   A Treatment of the Diseases of the Eye, By Means of Prussic Acid Vapour, and Other Medicinal Agents. London, 1843. 8vo., plt., orig. blindstamped cloth, paper label, pres. copy inscribed by author. Quaritch 977-80 1978 $85

TURNBULL, W. ROBERTSON   History of Moffat. Edinburgh & Moffat, 1871. Sm. 8vo., covers faded and shabby, a little dusty throughout. K Books 244-451 1978 £8

TURNELL, MARTIN   Poetry and Crisis. Paladin Press, 1938. Bds., very good, worn d.w., first English ed. Bell Book 16-585 1978 £4

TURNER, A. A.   Villas on the Hudson. New York, 1860. Photolithos., plts., diags., oblong folio, some foxing, very scarce. Morrill 239-558 1978 $300

TURNER, CHARLES   Sonnets. London, and Cambridge, 1864. 8vo., original green cloth, lst ed., inner hinges tender, very good copy. Ximenes 47-318 1978 $60

TURNER, DANIEL   Divine Songs, Hymns, and Other Poems. Reading, 1747. 8vo, contemp. sheep (spine worn), lst ed., old library bookplate, sound copy, very scarce book. Ximenes 47-319 1978 $100

TURNER, FREDERICK JACKSON   The Frontier in American History. New York, 1920. Bell Wiley's copy. Broadfoot 46-580 1978 $10

TURNER, FREDERICK JACKSON   The United States, 1830-1850. The Nation and Its Sections. New York, (1935). Maps, lst ed. Biblo BL781-257 1978 $13.50

TURNER, J. B.   Mormonism in All Ages;.... New York, [1842]. Original cloth, lst ed., very scarce. Ginsberg 14-693 1978 $100

TURNER, JOSEPH MALLORD WILLIAM   The Harbours of England, Engraved by Thomas Lupton from Original Drawings Made Expressly for the Work by.... (1856). Folio, mezzotint plts., margin of title repaired, orig. red cloth gilt, orig. backstrip laid down, gilt edges. Quaritch 983-264 1978 $375

TURNER, JOSEPH MALLORD WILLIAM   The Rivers of France, from Drawings By... London, c. 1840. Roy. 8vo., engr. frontis., engr. title page, slight spotting, orig. dark blue cloth, gilt borders, all edges gilt. Deighton 5-148 1978 £65

TURNER, LAURENCE   Decorative Plasterwork in Great Britain. (1927). Folio, frontis., buckram, dust wrs. Quaritch 983-94 1978 $150

TURNER, ORASMUS   History of the Pioneer Settlement of Phelps and Gorham's Purchase. Rochester, 1851. Deluxe copy of the lst ed. in half vellum with gilt title, crimson cloth sides, all edges gilt, text fresh & crisp. Butterfield 21-450 1978 $75

TURNER, ORASMUS   History of the Pioneer Settlement of Phelps and Gorham's Purchase. lst ed., bound in black buckram. Butterfield 21-451 1978 $45

TURNER, ORSAMUS   Pioneer History of the Holland Purchase of the Western Part of New York... Buffalo, 1849. lst ed., illus. MacManus 239-357 1978 $60

TURNER, ORASMUS   Pioneer History of the Holland Purchase of Western New-York. Buffalo, 1850. Maps, plts., half lea. & cloth, good clean copy. Butterfield 21-452 1978 $65

TURNER, ORASMUS   Pioneer History of the Holland Purchase of Western New-York. Lacking the frontis. portr. of Joseph Ellicott, full lea., sound, maps, plts. Butterfield 21-453 1978 $35

TURNER, SAMUEL   An Account of an Embassy to the Court of the Teshoo Lama, in Tibet... 1800. lst. ed., lg. paper copy, folding map, engraved plts., 4to, calf, rebacked. Edwards 1012-143 1978 $300

TURNER, THOMAS   Diary (1754-1765). London, 1925. 12mo., orig. cloth. Morrill 241-582 1978 $7.50

TURNER, WILLIAM d. 1568   A Booke of the natures and properties, as well of the bathes in England and Italy, very necessary for all seik persones that can not be healed with the helpe of natural bathes. (Cologne), 1562. Folio, calf, first ed. Gurney 75-109 1978 £265

TURNER, WILLIAM 1653-1701   A Compleat History of the most Remarkable Providences, both of Judgement and Mercy.... 1697. First ed., 3 parts in 1 vol., folio, 19th cent. tan calf, joints weak. Howes 194-109 1978 £80

TURNER, WILLIAM 1658-1726   Exercises to the Accidence and Grammar.. Consisting Chiefly of Moral Sentences. 1783. 14th. ed., 6mo, contemp. sheep, worn. Eaton 45-516 1978 £8

TURNER-TURNER, J.   Three Years' Hunting and Trapping in America and The Great North-West. 1888. Portrait, maps, illus., imp. 8vo, orig. bds., cloth spine, worn. Edwards 1012-459 1978 £25

TURNING a New Leaf; or the Story of Charles Terry. New York, 1866. Cloth. Hayman 72-386 1978 $7.50

TURNOR, EDMUND   Collections for the History of the Town and Soke of Grantham. Lg. 4to., handcolored map, engr. plts., vignettes, orig. bds., uncut, unopened, new calf spine, worn, offsetting of title, but fine copy, lst ed. Norman 5-*39 1978 $300

TURTON, WILLIAM   Conchylia Insularum Britannicarum. The Shells of the British Islands... London, 1822. Color plts., laid in loosely, 4to., calf. Salloch 345-185 1978 $125

TUSON, EDWARD WILLIAM   The Dissector's Guide. Boston, 1833. Illus. by woodcuts, lst Amer. ed., sm. 8vo. Morrill 239-266 1978 $15

TUSSAUD, JOHN T.   The Romance of Madame Tussaud's. New York, (1920). Illus., covers dull. Biblo BL781-757 1978 $10

TUTTIETT, M. G.   Ribstone Pippins. New York, 1898. lst Amer. ed., cloth, good. Greene 78-211 1978 $15

TUTTLE, CHARLES R.   The Annual New England Official Directory and General Hand-Book for 1878-79. Boston, 1878. 8vo., lst issue, orig. cloth. Morrill 241-583 1978 $15

TUTTLE, CHARLES R.   History of the Border Wars of Two Centuries... Chicago, 1874. Illus., rebound, lst ed. MacManus 239-1220 1978 $25

TUTTLE, CHARLES R.   Our North Land: Being a Full Account of the Canadian North-West and Hudson's Bay Route, Together with a Narrative of the Experiences of the Hudson's Bay Expedition of 1884. Toronto, 1885. Maps, engravings, t.p. worn, rebound. Hood 116-893 1978 $40

TUTTLE, JAMES H.   Wam-Dus-Ky: A Descriptive Record of a Hunting Trip to North Dakota. Mineapolis, 1893. Illus., original cloth, lst ed. 14-325 1978 $400

TUTTLE, JASON H.   Headquarters For All Articles Used by Horsemen. (Jersey City, n.d., c.1880). Wrps. Hayman 71-87 1978 $12.50

TUTTLE, WILLIAM P.   Bottle Hill and Madison, N.J. Glimpses and Reminiscences from Its Earliest Settlement to the Civil War. (Madison, 1917). Illus., scarce, ltd. to 500 copies. MacManus 239-1334 1978 $45

TWAMLEY, LOUISA ANNE
Please turn to
MEREDITH, LOUISA ANNE (TWAMLEY)

TWELVE English Statesmen. 1888. 12 vols., cr. 8vo. George's 635-779 1978 £5

A TWENTIETH Century History of Southwest Texas. Chicago, 1907. 2 thick quarto vols., half morocco, gilt, very rare. Jenkins 116-1401 1978 $550

THE TWIN Pagodas of Zayton: A Study of Later Buddhist Sculpture in China. Cambridge, 1935. Gravure plts., cloth, slight scuffing. Dawson's 449-87 1978 $45

TWO Centuries of the Church of the Brethren or the Beginnings of Brotherhood. Bi-centennial Addresses at the Annual Conference, Held at Des Moines, Iowa, June 3-11, 1908. Elgin, 1908. Cloth, back cover dampstained. Hayman 72-116 1978 $7.50

TWO of the Saxon Chronicles.... Oxford, 1892-99. 2 vols., cr. 8vo. George's 635-781 1978 £10

THE TWO Putnams Israel and Rufus in the Havana Expedition 1762... Hartford, 1931. Cloth bds., boxed, very fine, unopened. MacManus 239-403 1978 $35

TWO Years Behind a Plough, or The Experience of a Pennsylvania Farm-Boy. Philadelphia, 1878. Austin 82-278 1978 $27.50

TWOMEY, A. C.   Needle to the North. London, n.d. (1940?). 1st ed., illus. Hood 117-111 1978 $25

TWYSDEN, JOHN   Medicina Veterum Vindicata. London, 1666. Sm. 8vo., contemp. mottled calf, gilt-ruled, gilt dentelles, fine lg. paper copy, only 1 copy in the U. S., 1st ed., scarce. Zeitlin 245-271 1978 $675

TYLER, GEORGE W.   The History of Bell County. San Antonio, 1936. 1st ed., illus., folding maps, signed by C. W. Macune. Jenkins 116-89 1978 $45

TYLER JOHN   Proceedings...Relative to Texas, from the Injunction of Secrecy has been Removed. Washington, 1844. Jenkins 116-1403 1978 $60

TYLER, ROBERT LEE   Lawyer Bell from Boston. New York, (1893). Sm. 8vo., 1st ed. Morrill 239-631 1978 $20

TYLER, ROBERT OGDEN   Memoir of...Brevet Major-General, U.S. Army. Together with His Journal of Tow Month's Travel in British and Farther India. Philadelphia, 1878. 4to., pres., signed. Biblo BL781-258 1978 $20

TYLER, MASON WHITING   Recollection of the Civil War. New York, 1912. Illus., Bell Wiley's copy. Broadfoot's 44-530 1978 $16

TYLOR, EDWARD B.   Anthropology. London, 1881. Illus., cr. 8vo., orig. cloth. K Books 244-5 1978 £5

TYMMS, W. P.   The Church's Floral Kalandar. London, (1861). 1st ed., tissue-guarded color plates, some minor edge rubbing, very good with legible friese. Victoria 34-816 1978 $135

TYMMS, W. P.   The Child. London, c.1860's. Chromoligho-graphed plates, Victorian binding, signed by Tymms, flowery design, blocked in gold, blank leaves foxed as are t.p. and 1st plate in margin, gilt covers fine and bright. Victoria 34-815 1978 $65

TYNAN, KATHERINE
Please turn to
HINKSON, KATHERINE TYNAN

TYNDALE, WALTER   Below the Cataracts (Egypt). Philadelphia, 1907. Plts., in color by author, 8vo., ex-lib., 1st Amer. ed. Morrill 241-584 1978 $7.50

TYNDALL, JOHN   Comparative View of the Cleavage of Crystals and Slate Rocks. 1856. 8vo., illus., orig. wrs., good copy, inscr'd by author. Norman 5-281 1978 $40

TYNDALL, JOHN   Contributions to Molecular Physics in the Domain of Radiant Heat. London, 1872. 8vo., ads, fldg. plts., orig. cloth, gilt, uncut, fine copy, 1st ed. Norman 5-287 1978 $185

TYNDALL, JOHN   Essay on the Floating-Matter of the Air in relation to Putrefaction and Infection. London, 1881. 8vo., orig. cloth, illus., first ed. Gurney 75-110 1978 £60

TYNDALL, JOHN   Faraday as a Discoverer. London, 1868. 8vo., port., orig. blind stamped cloth, uncut, fine, first ed. Norman 5-101 1978 $95

TYNDALL, JOHN   Fragments of Science. New York, 1905. Sm. 8vo, 2 vols., orig. cloth. Book Chest 17-393 1978 $14.50

TYNDALL, JOHN   Heat Considered as a Mode of Motion. London, 1863. 8vo., plt., text illus., orig. blindstamped pebbled cloth, gilt, uncut, spine faded but very good copy, contemp. pencil signature on title, 1st ed. Norman 5-283 1978 $185

TYNDALL, JOHN   Lectures on Light. New York, 1873. 8vo., ads, text illus., orig. cloth, gilt, bklabel, sm. stamp on endpaper, but very fine, fresh copy, 1st ed. Norman 5-288 1978 $85

TYNDALL, JOHN   On the Passage of Radiant Heat Through Dry and Humid Air. 1863. Offprint, 8vo., orig. wrs., pres. copy. Norman 5-284 1978 $35

TYNDALL, JOHN   Remarks on Recent Researches on Radiant Heat. 1862. Offprint, 8vo., very good copy. Norman 5-282 1978 $35

TYNDALL, JOHN   Rough Notes of a Portion of a Course of 6 Lectures for Boys and Girls on Water and Air. 1879-80. 8vo., orig. prtd. wrs., very good copy. Norman 5-289 1978 $25

TYNDALL, JOHN   Sound. London, 1867. 8vo., ads, frontis. portr., text illus., orig. bright blue blindstamped cloth, gilt, uncut, worn & back cover little spotted, good copy, 1st ed. Norman 5-286 1978 $95

TYNECASTLE COMPANY   Tynecastle Canvas: Vellum: Textures: Compo: Wood Mouldings: Adaptable and Fibrous Plaster... Edinburgh and London, (1923 and 1934). Folio, illus., cloth, loose, wrs. as issued. Quaritch 983-95 1978 $55

TYPES: a Description of Brown's Patent Type Setting & Distributing Machinery. With a Brief History of the Art of Printing & Its Labor-Saving Appliances. Boston, 1870. Later cloth, orig. pic. wrs. bound in, illus., 8vo., very good. Americanist 103-103 1978 $25

TYPES, Borders and Miscellany of Taylor & Taylor, with Historical Brevities on their Derivation and Use. San Francisco, 1939. Cloth with lea. spine, slightly soiled & worn slipcase, 1 of 330 numbered copies. Dawson's 447-170 1978 $90

TYPES of the Times. By Old Tom of Oxford. London, 1820. 8vo, disbound, 1st ed., very good copy. Ximenes 47-254 1978 $40

A TYPICAL American; or, Incidents in the Life of Dr. John Swinburne of Albany, the Eminent Patriot, Surgeon, and Philanthropist. Albany, 1888. Plts. Butterfield 21-270 1978 $35

TYPOGRAPHIA. An Ode on Printing. Inscrib'd to the Honourable William Gooch, Esq; His Majesty's Lieutenant-Governor, and Commander in Chief of the Colony of Virginia. Roanoke, 1926. Orig. calf-backed marbled bds., pub. slipcase, 1 of 515 copies, very good. MacManus 238-1071 1978 $35

A TYPOGRAPHICAL Commonplace-Book. New York, 1932. Cloth, 1 of 595 numbered copies on Montgolfier Annonay vellum. Dawson's 447-76 1978 $75

TYPOTIUS, JACOBUS   Symbola Divina Humana Pontificum Imperatorum Regum... Frankfurt, 1642. 3 parts in 1 vol., folio, plts., sm. light water-stain on corner of a few leaves, old calf, worn, 3rd ed. Quaritch 983-265 1978 $250

TYRRELL, ELEANOR   South African Snapshots for English Girls. London, 1910. 7 plts., cr. 8vo., orig. cloth. K Books 239-494 1978 £6

TYRRELL, J. B.   Algonquian Indian Names of Places in Northern Canada. 1914. Card cover. Hood's 115-44 1978 $12.50

TYRRELL, R. Y.   Echoes from Kottabos. 1906. Sm. 4to., qtr. buckram, very good, first English ed. Bell Book 16-918 1978 £12.50

TYRWHITT, R. ST. JOHN   A Handbook of Pictorial Art. Oxford, 1875. Coloured and tinted lithos and diagrams, full calf gilt, 8vo. George's 635-65 1978 £12.50

TYSON, JAMES   The Cell Doctrine, its History and Present State, for the Use of Students in Medicine and Dentistry. Philadelphia, 1870. Rittenhouse 49-795 1976 $25

TYSSEN-AMHERST, ALICIA MARGARET, HON. MRS. EVELYN CECIL
Please turn to
ROCKLEY, ALICIA MARGARET (TYSSEN-AMHERST) CECIL, BARONESS

TYTLER, ALEX F.   Elements of General History, Ancient & Modern. Edinburgh, 1807. 4th. ed., 2 vols., 7 lg. handcoloured maps, half calf, rubbed, hinges weak. Jarndyce 16-1154 1978 £12.50

TYTLER, ANN FRASER   Leila. 1839. Sm. 8vo., half red calf, gilt back, frontispiece, nice. P. M. Hill 142-77 1978 £28

TYTLER, ANN FRASER   Leila in England. 1842. Sm. 8vo., half red calf, gilt back, frontispiece, nice. P. M. Hill 142-78 1978 £28

TYTLER, PATRICK FRASER   Historical View of the Progress of Discovery on the More Northern Coasts of America From the Earliest Period to the Present Time. Edinburgh, 1833. 2nd. ed., illus. by map & 9 engravings by Jackson, orig. binding carefully restored with new endpapers. Hood's 115-622 1978 $60

TYTLER, PATRICK FRASER   The Northern Coasts of America, and The Hudson's Bay Terrirories. 1853. Sm. 8vo, map, engraved title, plts., browned, cover slightly worn, orig. cloth.   Edwards 1012-460 1978 £20

TYTLER, SARAH   Days of Yore. 1866. Ist. ed., half titles, orig. brown cloth, v.g. Jarndyce 16-1155 1978 £28

TYTLER, WILLIAM 1711-92   An Inquiry, Historical and Critical, Into the Evidence against Mary Queen of Scots.... Edinburgh, 1772. Third ed., contemp. calf, 8vo. Howes 194-383 1978 £25

U

UBALDIS, ANGELUS DE   Super Prima Infortiati.... Venice, 1504.
2 parts in 1, title & printer's device in red, lg. folio, old limp calf, spine
defective, marginal worming, stained at end. Traylen 88-482 1978 £280

UDALL, W.   The Historie of the Life and Death of Mary
Stuart Queene of Scotland. 1636. 1st. ed., frontispiece, portrait, woodcut t.p.,
fully rebound in half calf, marbled bds., fine. Jarndyce 16-25 1978 £65

UDDEN, J.A.   Review of the Geology of Texas. Austin, 1916.
Folding maps, cloth. Jenkins 116-1406 1978 $8.50

UEBERWEG, FRIEDRICH   Grundriss Der Geschichte Der Philosophie Des
Altertums. Berlin, 1920. 11th ed., thick 4to., 1/2 cloth. Salloch 348-273
1978 $25

UEBERWEG, FRIEDRICH   A History of Philosophy, From Thales to the
Present Time. 1875-76. 2nd. ed., 2 vols., 8vo, orig. cloth, spines worn, but
sound, clean copy. Fenning 32-338 1978 £12.50

UFFENBACH, PHILIPP   De Quadratura Circuli Mechanici... Nuernberg,
1653. 2 vols. in 1, plts., sm. 4to., bds. Salloch 345-186 1978 $175

UHDE, WILHELM   Life and Works of Vincent Van Gogh. Vienna,
(1936). 4to., plts. mostly in color. Biblo 247-440 1978 $30

ULLIAC-TREMADEURE, MLLE.   Les Jeunes Natualistes ou Entretiens sur l'Histoire
Naturelle des Animaux des Vegetaux et des Mineraux. Paris, 1852. Cinquieme
ed., 2 vols., sm.8vo, foxed, edges rubbed, cover gilt very handsome, superb
bindings and plates. Victoria 34-817 1978 $40

ULLIAC-TREMADEUR, MLLE.   Phenomenes Et Metamorphoses. Paris, 1854.
Color plts., illus., tall 8vo, orig. plychrome & gold decor. cloth, fine romantic
binding. Salloch 345-187 1978 $110

ULRICH, C. F.   Kup Books & Printing. New York, 1943. Wr.,
fine. Battery Park 1-492 1978 $50

ULRICH, SIMPRECHT   Gloriosorum Christi Confessorum Vdalrici and
Symperti... Augsburg, 1516. First ed., sm. 4to., woodcuts, bds. Quaritch 978-
150 1978 $750

ULRICI, H.   Geschichte der Hellenischen Dichtkunst. 1835.
2 vols., sewn, covers loose. Allen 234-1008 1978 $7.50

ULSTER Journal of Archaeology. 1853-62. Vols. 1-9, Plt., maps, new buckram,
rubber stamp on title. Allen 234-P 1978 $125

ULTIMOS Communicaciones Entre El Govierno Mexicano Y...Los Estados-Unidos,
Sobre La Cuestion De Tejas. Mexico, 1846. Rare. Jenkins 116-1407 1978 $175

ULTZMANN, R.   Neuroses of the Genito-Urinary System in the
Male, with Sterility and Impotence. Philadelphia, 1890. Rittenhouse 49-796
1976 $12.50

ULYSSES, CHARLES
Please turn to
SALIS MARCHLINS, KARL ULYSSES VON

UNDER Sapphire Skies in San Antonio. N.P., 1916. Illus., paper wr. Jenkins
116-1521 1978 $30

UNDERHILL, EVELYN   The Miracles of Our Lady Saint Mary: Brought
Out of Divers Tongues and Newly Set Forth in English. New York, 1906. Good
copy, 1st U.S. ed., orig. bind. Petrilla 13-140 1978 $7.50

UNDERHILL, EVELYN   Ruysbroek. 1914. Ex-library copy, rebound,
buckram, 8vo. Upcroft 12-466 1978 £4

UNDERHILL, GEORGE F.   The Helter Skelter Hounds or, Mr. Flopkins
Sporting Memoirs. 1894. 1st. ed., numerous illus. by Lance Thackeray, half
title, orig. pictorial bds., little rubbed, good. Jarndyce 16-1156 1978 £8.50

UNDERRICHT der newen Jrsaln und Sect halben, so yetzt an vil orten im heyligen
Reich entsteen, un sunderlich wider die jhenigen so mit treumen.... (Nuremberg,
c. 1525/1529). Sm. 4 to., fine copy, pamphlet, modern half vellum.
Schafer 19-41 1978 sFr. 1,200

UNDERWOOD, EDNA W.   Letters from a Prairie Garden. 1919. First ed.
Austin 82-1017 1978 $12.50

UNDERWOOD, FRANCIS H.   Quabbin. Boston, 1893. Illus., 8vo., orig.
cloth, cover stains. Morrill 241-355 1978 $10

UNDERWOOD, JOHN J.   Alaska an Empire in the Making. New York,
1913. Orig. binding, clean, 1st. ed. Hayman 71-740 1978 $10

UNDERWOOD, MICHAEL   Traite des Maladies des Enfans. Paris, 1786.
8vo., contemp. mottled calf, 1st French ed. Argosy Special-90 1978 $300

UNDERWOOD, MICHAEL   Treatise on the Diseases of Children with General
Directions for the Management of Infants from the Birth. Philadelphia, 1793.
New ed., revised & enlarged, 12mo., contemp. calf, hinges cracked, 1st Amer.
ed., lacks 12 pages. Morrill 239-267 1978 $15

UNDERWOOD, MICHAEL   Treatise on the Diseases of Children and Management of Infants from the Birth. Boston, 1806. 3 vols. in one, good, slight cracking at hinge. Rittenhouse 49-797 1976 $45

UNDERWOOD, REGINALD   Hidden Lights. Fortune Press, 1937. Portrait,
very good, d.w., first English ed. Bell Book 16-363 1978 £5

UNITED CHURCH OF CANADA   Forms of Service for the Offices of the Church.
Toronto, 1926. Hood 117-376 1978 $10

UNITED CHURCH PUBLISHING HOUSE   History of... Toronto, n.d. Hood
117-84 1978 $7.50

A UNITED Nation Backs Them Up. n.d. (ca. 1943). Pamphlet. Austin 80-337
1978 $7.50

UNITED STATES. CONGRESS. HOUSE   Debates in the House of Representatives, on the Bills for Carrying into Effect the Louisiana Treaty. Philadelphia,
1804. Half lea., 1st ed. Ginsberg 14-497 1978 $325

UNITED STATES. CONGRESS. SENATE   The Select Committee of the Senate
Appointed to Inquire into the Late Invasion and Seizure of the Public Property at
Harper's Ferry. (Washington, 1860). Clean, rebound copy. Hayman 71-771
1978 $27.50

UNITED STATES. CONSTITUTION   Constitutions des Treize Etats-Unis de
l'Amerique a Philadelphie. Paris, 1783. First ed., one of 500 copies, 8vo., v.f.,
orig. calf, hinges loose, spine ends worn. Current 24-77 1978 $450

UNITED STATES. DEPT. OF COMMERCE   Agriculture. 1922. Vol. 6, Part I.
Austin 80-489 1978 $47.50

UNITED STATES. DEPT. OF COMMERCE   Annual Report of the Chief of the
Bureau of Statistics on the Commerce and Navigation of the U.S. for the Fiscal
Year Ended June 30, 1876. Washington, 1877. Thick 8vo. Biblo 251-309 1978
$15

UNITED STATES. DEPT. OF COMMERCE   Central Electrical Light and Power
Stations and Street and Electrical Railways. 1915. Austin 80-486 1978 $75

UNITED STATES. DEPT. OF COMMERCE   Electrical Railways. 1920. Paper.
Austin 80-488 1978 $27.50

UNITED STATES. DEPT. OF COMMERCE   Manufactures. Part I: United States
by Industries. 1902. Vol. VII. Austin 80-479 1978 $47.50

UNITED STATES. DEPT. OF COMMERCE   Manufactures. Part II: States and
Territories. 1902. Vol. VIII. Austin 80-480 1978 $47.50

UNITED STATES. DEPT. OF COMMERCE   Manufactures. Part III: Special Reports on Selected Industries. 1902. Vol. IX. Austin 80-482 1978 $47.50

UNITED STATES. DEPT. OF COMMERCE   Occupations. 1904. Austin 80-483
1978 $75

UNITED STATES. DEPT. OF COMMERCE   Telephones 1907. 1910. Illus. Austin 80-484 1978 $67.50

UNITED STATES. DEPT. OF COMMERCE   Transportation by Water 1916. 1920. Illus. Austin 80-487 1978 $37.50

UNITED STATES. DEPT. OF COMMERCE   Wealth, Debt, and Taxation. 1907. Austin 80-485 1978 $95

UNITED STATES. DEPT. OF THE NAVY   Introduction to Naval Aviation. 1946. Illus. with many photos. Austin 80-346 1978 $20

UNITED STATES. DEPT. OF THE NAVY   Nomenclature of Naval Vessels. 1942. Austin 80-345 1978 $12.50

UNITED STATES. DEPT. OF WAR   Browning Machine Guns. April, 1945. Paper. Austin 80-350 1978 $17.50

UNITED STATES. DEPT. OF WAR   Dictionary of United States Army Terms. 1944. Paper. Austin 80-348 1978 $12.50

UNITED STATES. DEPT OF WAR   Omaha Beachhead. 1945. Illus., maps, fold. , photos, paper. Austin 80-245 1978 $27.50

UNITED STATES. DEPT. OF WAR   Ordnance Maintenance. April 6, 1945. Illus., paper. Austin 80-351 1978 $12.50

UNITED STATES. DEPT. OF WAR   Ordnance Maintenance Browning Machine Gun. Oct. 23, 1944. Illus., paper. Austin 80-349 1978 $17.50

UNITED STATES. DEPT. OF WAR   Technical Manual Army Instruction. April 19, 1943. Illus., paper. Austin 80-352 1978 $12.50

UNITED STATES. LAWS   An Act to Admit the State of Texas to Representation in the Congress of the United States. Washington, 1870. 8vo. Jenkins 116-1154 1978 $12.50

UNITED STATES. LAWS   An Act to Define the Boundaries of the State of Iowa, and to Repeal so Much of the Act of the Third of March, 1845, as Relates to the Boundaries of Iowa... Washington, 1846. Folio, disbound, laid in half mor. slipcase, rare. Ginsberg 14-406 1978 $250

UNITED STATES. LAWS   A Bill Concerning the Lead Mines in the County of Washington, in the Territory of Missouri. Washington, 1815. Folio, very rare. Jenkins 116-952 1978 $85

UNITED STATES. LAWS   ...Bill Providing for the Admission of the State of Dakota into the Union, and for the Organization of the Territory of North Dakota. Washington, 1886. Disbound, first ed. Ginsberg 14-305 1978 $30

UNITED STATES. LAWS   The Laws of the United States of America. Philadelphia, 1796. 1st ed., 8vo., 3 vols., orig. sheep, interiors mostly clear and bright, bookplts. Current 24-107 1978 $285

UNITED STATES. SUPREME COURT   December Term, 1863: Green C. Bronson and James T. Soutter...vs. The La Crosse and Milwaukie Railroad Company et al. N.P., n.d. (1863). Sewn. Hayman 73-766 1978 $8.50

UNITED States in the Light of Prophecy. Battle Creek, Steam Press, 1872. 12mo., 1st ed., orig. cloth. Morrill 241-585 1978 $12.50

UNIVERSAL Harmony or the Gentleman & Ladies Social Companion:.... London, 1745. Quarto, bound in dark red half mor., bookseller's ticket on inside front cover, pages foxed, few small holes and neat repairs, eng. plts. Totteridge 29-110 1978 $300

AN UNIVERSAL History from the Earliest Accounts to the Present Time. London, 1779-81. 18 vols., plts., contemp. calf, endpapers discoloured, 8vo. K Books 244-453 1978 £45

THE UNIVERSAL Penman. London, 1743. New York, 1941. Folio, orig. cloth-backed bds., facs. ed., 1 of 1,000 copies, slightly worn, but good. MacManus 238-881 1978 $40

UNIVERSITY OF PENNSYLVANIA   Medical Graduates with an Historical Sketch of the Origin, Progress and Present State of the Medical Department. Philadelphia, 1836. Rittenhouse 49-798 1976 $35

UNIVERSITY Almanac and Business Book, 1870. New York, 1870. 12mo., illus., orig. wrs. Morrill 239-268 1978 $12.50

UNIVERSITY of Toronto Roll of Service, 1914-1918. Toronto, 1921. Hood 116-151 1978 $17.50

THE UNIVERSITY Of Toronto Song Book. Toronto, n.d. (c.1887). Hood's 115-911 1978 $25

UNLUCKY John and his Lump of Silver. (London), c.1825. 1st ed., engravings on both wrappers, 12mo, very scarce, very good. Victoria 34-819 1978 $125

UNTERMAN, ISAAC   Jewish Youth in America. Federal Press, 1941. Austin 79-793 1978 $12.50

UNTERMEYER, LOUIS   Omar Khayyam. Rubaiyat. New York, (1947). Illus. in color. Biblo BL781-634 1978 $7.50

UNWIN, G.   Finance and Trade under Edward III. 1918. Spine dull, 8vo. Upcroft 12-467 1978 £7

UNWIN, G.   Finance and Trade Under Edward III, by Members of the History School. Manchester, 1918. 8vo. George's 635-323 1978 £8.50

UNWIN, WILLIAM   Selfemployment in Secret. Left Under the Hand Writing of the Rev. Mr. Corbet... Charlestown, 1807. Bds. Hayman 72-760 1978 $10

UNZER, JOHN AUGUSTUS   The Principles of Physiology. London, 1851. 8vo., two works in 1 vol., orig. green stamped cloth, gilt lettering on spine, binder's ticket, bkplts. of Drs. James Gilpin Houseman and Alfred M. Hellman, very good copy, rare. Zeitlin 245-272 1978 $75

UPDIKE, DANIEL BERKELEY   In the Day's Work. Cambridge, 1924. One of 260 numbered copies, ltd., signed by Updike, marbled cloth. Battery Park -1-493 1978 $100

UPDIKE, DANIEL BERKELEY   Printing Types, Their History, Forms and Use. Cambridge, 1937. 2nd. ed., illus., 2 vols. Baldwins' 51-199 1978 $42.50

UPDIKE: American Printer & His Merrymount Press: Notes on the Press & Its Works by Danl B. Updike. New York, 1947. 1st ed., 8vo., orig. cloth, very good. Americanist 103-104 1978 $25

UPDIKE, JOHN   Three Texts From Early Ipswich. Ipswich, 1968. 1 of 26 lettered & signed hardbound copies, tan cloth, mint, glassine jacket. Houle 10-347 1978 $275

UPDIKE, WILKINS   A History of the Episcopal Church in Narragansett, Rhode Island. Boston, 1907. 3 vols., 2nd ed., illus. Biblo BL781-149 1978 $42.50

UPPER Missouri Mining and Prospecting Company for the Purpose of Purchasing, Working, and Selling Gold, Silver, and Other Mines in Montana Territory. New York, 1865. Cloth, 1st ed. Ginsberg 14-633 1978 $175

UPSHUR, ABEL P.   A Brief Enquiry into the True Nature and Character of our Federal Government: Being a Review of Judge Story's Commentaries on the Constitution of the United States. Phila., 1863 Wraps, reprint of 1840 Bell Wiley's copy. Broadfoot's 44-372 1978 $25.00

UPTON, BERTHA   The Golliwog's Fox-Hunt. London, n.d. c.1905. Coloured illus. by Florence K. Upton, oblong 4to, orig. printed wrappers, slightly defective. Traylen 88-207 1978 £25

UPTON, BERTHA   Golliwog in the African Jungle. London, 1909. Coloured illus. by Florence K. Upton, oblong 4to, picture bds., cloth spine. Traylen 88-206 1978 £30

UPTON, FLORENCE K.   The Adventures of Two Dutch Dolls. London, (1895). 1st ed., oblong 4to., 1st issue, colored pict. bds., soiled, very good copy. Current 24-229 1978 $100

UPTON, FLORENCE K.   The Adventures of two Dutch Dolls. London, (1895). 1st ed., colored plates, boards dust-soiled, very good, frayed leaves, text defects. Victoria 34-820 1978 $20

UPTON, FLORENCE K.   The Adventures of two Dutch Dolls and a "Golliwog". (1895). Oblong 8vo., colour illus., pic. bds., cloth back, good copy. Quaritch 979-93 1978 $105

UPTON, JOHN   Critical Observations on Shakespeare. 1748. Second ed., contemp. calf, 8vo. Howes 194-459 1978 £21

UPTON, NICHOLAS   De Studio Militari Libri Quatuor. 1654. Sm. folio, 18th cent. russia, portrait, plts. F. Edwards 1013-442 1978 £90

UPTON, SARAH B.   Sketch of the Life of Sarah B. Upton. Philadelphia, 1886. 2nd ed., cloth. Hayman 73-707 1978 $7.50

URBAN, JOHN W.   Battle Field and Prison Pen, or Through the War, and Thrice a Prisoner in Rebel Dungeons. N.P., (1887). Cloth, inner hinges cracking, minor wear. Hayman 72-136 1978 $7.50

URBANUS, BOLZANI   Bellunensis. Institutiones Graecae Grammaticae. Venice, Aldus, 1497-98. First ed., first issue, little soiled, otherwise very clean and sound, good margins, an early 19th cent. dark blue straight-grain mor., qto. Thomas 37-50 1978 £1850

URE, ANDREW   A Dictionary of Arts, Manufactures, and Mines. London, 1853. Fourth ed., 2 vols., roy. 8vo., handsome, full prize calf, woodengravings. K Books 244-316 1978 £50

URING, NATHANIEL   A History of the Voyages and Travels of... 1726. lst. ed.. maps, slight repairs to 2 maps, some marginal staining, 8vo, old style panelled calf. Edwards 1012-745 1978 £200

URQUHART, D.   The Spirit of the East. London, 1839. 2nd. ed., 2 vols., 8vo, folding frontispiece map, lithograph plt., orig. cloth, gilt, covers trifle faded, joints little split, some foxing. Deighton 5-227 1978 £115

USEFUL Essays, and Instructive Stories Selected for the Improvement of the Minds, and the Forming of the Manners,.... Bennington, 1807. 12mo, marbled paper partly gone, oak boards chipped. Victoria 34-821 1978 $15

USENER, H.   Goetternamen. 1929. New buckram. Allen 234-1010 1978 $15

USHER, A. P.   The Early History of Deposit Banking in Mediterranean Europe. Cambridge, 1943. Label removed from front cover, spine dull, 8vo. George's 635-417 1978 $7.50

USHER, JAMES WARD   An Art Collector's Treasures, Illustrated and Described. London, 1916. 80 illus. in colour, thick folio, orig. leather, ltd. ed. of 300 copies. Traylen 88-421 1978 £25

USHER, JAMES WARD   An Art Collector's Treasures, Illustrated and Described by Himself... 1916. Folio, coloured plts., full mor., ed. ltd. to 300 copies. Quaritch 983-266 1978 $150

USHER, R. G.   The Pilgrims and Their History. New York, 1918. Illus., good. Biblo BL781-40 1978 $9

USSHER, A.   The Magic People. 1950. lst ed., very good, octavo bound in cloth. Hyland 128-714 1978 £8

USSHER, JAMES   Annales Veteris Testamentia, A Prima Mundi Origine Deducti... London, 1650. Rebound in full leather, very good, reprint. Hyland 128-717 1978 £27.50

USSHER, JAMES   Annales Veteris Et Novi Testament..Quibus Omnibus Praefixa Est..Vita, A Th. Smitho, S.T.D. Geneva, 1722. Folio, rebacked, contemp. calf with blind impress crest on cover, very good. Hyland 128-718 1978 £85

USSHER, JAMES   An Answer to a Challenge Made by a Jesuit in Ireland.... 1625. lst London ed., 4to, text very good, needs rebinding. Hyland 128-914 1978 £105

USSHER, JAMES   Answer to a Jesuit; With Other Tracts on Poetry. 1835. Spine chipped, very good, octavo bound in cloth, reprint. Hyland 128-715 1978 £10

USSHER, JAMES   The Judgement. 1657. Portrait, fcap. 8vo., 19th cent. half calf. Howes 194-110 1978 £21

USSHER, JAMES   Veterum Epistolarum Hibernicarum Sylloge... Dublin, 1632., lst ed., full contemp. calf, very good. Hyland 128-716 1978 £75

UTAH   Inventory of County Archives of Utah, No. 25, Utah County. Odgen, 1940. Illus., orig. pict. pr. wrs., lst ed. Ginsberg 14-1005 1978 $25

UZANNE, OCTAVE   The Mirror of the World. Liverpool, 1890. Roy. 8vo., illus., dec. ornaments by P. Avril, full turquoise mor. Quaritch 983-267 1978 $375

UZANNE, OCTAVE   La Reliure Moderne Artistique et Fantaisiste. Paris, 1887. Ltd. to 1500 copies on "papier velin", plts., roy. 8vo., mor., t.e.g. Forster 130-96 1978 £35

V

THE VACATION; or, the Four Cousins. New Haven, c.1835. Sewn, wrappers, plates, fine. Victoria 34-822 1978 $12.50

VACHELL, H. A.   The Hill, a Romance of Friendship. 1905. First ed., illus. by Percy Wadham, cr. 8vo., covers rubbed. George's 635-1338 1978 £7.50

VACHON, MARIUS   Les Arts et les Industries du Papier en France 1871-94. Paris, (1894). Decor. bds., calf back. Forster 130-97 1978 £50

VACQUERIE, AUGUSTE   Tragaldabas. Paris, 1886. 4to., contemp. 1/2 crimson mor., uncut, bound by Fechoz, ltd. ed. issued in 600 copies only, numbered copy on velin paper, illus. by F. Meaulle after Edouard Zier, clean, well preserved. Goldschmid; 110-33 1978 $50

VAENIUS, OTTO
Please turn to
VEEN, OCTAVIO VAN

VAIL, ALFRED   The American Electro Magnetic Telegraph. Philadelphia, 1845. 8vo., text illus., contemp. half mor., rubbed & endpapers foxed, but very good copy, 1st ed. Norman 5-290 1978 $175

VAIL, ROBERT WILLIAM GLENROIE   Alice in Wonderland. The Manuscript and Its Story. New York, 1928. 12mo., illus., orig. cloth pres. binding, 1st ed., pres. copy, inscr'd by A. S. W. Rosenbach, spine a little rubbed and faded, otherwise very good. MacManus 238-1047 1978 $85

VAIL, ROBERT WILLIAM GLENROIE   The Revolutionary Diary of Leut. Obadiah Gore, Jr. New York, 1929. Tall 8vo., plts., wr., ex-lib. Butterfield 21-388 1978 $10

VAIL, ROBERT WILLIAM GLENROIE   The Voice of the Old Frontier. New York, (1949). Dust jacket. MacManus 239-465 1978 $27.50

VALAMONT, P. DE   La Verite sur la Colonie de Port-Breton et sur le Marquis de Rays. Nimes, 1889. Printed wrappers, frayed, brittle. Wolfe 39-540 1978 $30

VALCK, G.   Fantastic Costumes of Trades and Professions. 36 plts., imp. 4to. Traylen 88-525 1978 £10

VALE, E.   The Track of the Irish Mail. n.d. Pen & ink sketches by F.H. Glazebrook & R.M. Hutchings, wrs., very good, reprint. Hyland 128-722 1978 £5

VALENTIN, GABRIEL GUSTAV   Der Gebrauch des Spektroskopes zu physiologischen und arztlichen Zwecken. Leipzig & Heidelberg, 1863. Lg. 8 vo., 1st ed., wood-engraved figures, cloth bound, orig. wr. pasted on cover. Schafer 19-65 1978 sFr. 600

VALENTINE, DAVID THOMAS   Manual...
Please turn to
NEW YORK (CITY)

VALENTINE, J.   Irish Memories. Bristole, (c.1925). Port., illus., very good, octavo bound in cloth, reprint. Hyland 128-722 1978 £5

VALENTINER, WILHELM REINHOLD   Rembrandt Paintings in America. New York, 1931. Folio, plts., 1st ed. Biblo 247-413 1978 $47.50

VALENTINI, MICHAEL BERNHARD   Amphitheatrum zootomicum tabulis aeneis quamplurimus exhibens historia animalium anatomicam.... Frankfurt a.M., 1720. Very rare 1st ed., contemp. calf, lightly rubbed, light browning, folio, 3 parts in 2 vols., plts. Gilhofer 75-108 1978 SFr 2,900

VALERIANUS, JOANNES PETRUS   Oratio In Funere Hieronymi Turriani. (Venice), (1506). 4to., wrs. Salloch 345-188 1978 $125

VALERIUS MAXIMUS   Dictorum et factorum memorabilium libri novem. Aldi Romani, 1502. Octavo, full contemp. vellum, restored expertly, ownership inscription of Sebastiano Marchetti, variant copy. Bennett 20-213 1978 $350

VALIERO, ANDREA   Historia Della Guerra Della Guerra Di Candia. Venice, 1679. 1st ed., quarto, full contemp. calf, hinges cracked, t.p. a little stained else fine, signature of Andrew Fletcher on title, rare. Bennett 20-214 1978 $225

VALLANCE, A.   English Church Screens, Being Great Roods, Screenwork and Rood-Lofts of Parish Churches in England and Wales. 1936-47. Coloured frontis., illus., 2 vols., 4to., cloth. Quaritch 983-54 1978 $95

VALLE DI VENAFRO, GIOVANNI BATTISTA DELLA   Vallo Libro continente appertinente a Capitanij,.... Venice, April, 1543. 8 vo., rare, illus. pocket-manual, woodcut figures, repairs on upper margins, recent binding with old leather over limp bds. Schaffer 19-66 1978 sFr. 8.30

VALLEE, LEON   Catalogue Des Velins de la Section Des Cartes... Bibliotheque Nationale Les Lilas. 1917. 4to., pres. copy from Vallee, holographic signed inscription, 3/4 lea., marbled bds. Battery Park 1-343 1978 $125

VALLENTIN, ANTONINA   Leonardo Da Vinci, ...the Tragic Pursuit of Perfection. New York, 1938. Illus., color plts., 1st ed. Biblo BL781-581 1978 $9

VALLENTIN, ANTONINA   Mirabeau. New York, 1948. Illus. Biblo 247-715 1978 $7.50

VALLET, L.   Le Chic a Cheval.... Paris, 1891. Coloured plts., illus., lg. 4to., orig. cloth, repaired. F. Edwards 1013-443 1978 £50

VALLEY, L. A.   Travers L'Europe: Croquis de Cavalerie. Paris, 1893. Roy. 4to., coloured plts and illus. by author, half mor., orig. pic. wr. bound in. Quaritch 983-74 1978 $135

VALLEYFIELD, Canada, the Cotton Factory Town of Canada. n.d. (ca. early 1900s). Illus., oblong 8vo., orig. wrs. Morrill 239-633 1978 $10

VALLISNIERI, ANTONIO   Opere Diverse del Sig. Venezia, 1715. 2 vols., 4to., vellum, first ed., good, plts. King 7-249 1978 £125

VALOUR And Victory. London, c.1900. Coloured frontis, many full-page & other illus., 4to, orig. de. cloth, g.e. K Books 239-496 1978 £10

VAMBERY, ARMINIUS   The Coming Struggle for India. London, 1885. Map, 8vo., 1st ed., ex-lib., orig. cloth. Morrill 241-587 1978 $7.50

VAN ALSTYNE, LAWRENCE   Diary of An Enlisted Man. New Haven, 1910. Cover spotted, Bell Wiley's copy. Broadfoot's 44-561 1978 $30

VAN BEMMELEN, A.   Lessen Over De Algebra Of Stelkunst. The Hague, 1840-1841. 2 vols. in I, 8vo., contemp. gilt-tooled calf with red label, very fine copy. Salloch 345-189 1978 $45

VAN BRAAM, FREDERICK A.   World Collectors Annuary. Vol. I - 1946-49. Delft, (1950). 4to., illus. Biblo BL781-716 1978 $25

VAN BRUYSSEL, E.   The Population of an Old Pear Tree; or, Stories of Insect Life. New York, 1870. Illus., good, 1st Amer. ed., orig. bind. Petrilla 13-142 1978 $10

VAN BUREN, MARTIN   The Autobiography of Martin Van Buren. Washington, 1920. Cloth, dampstain on fr. cover. Hayman 73-711 1978 $10

VAN BUREN, MARTIN   Information Concerning the Boundary between the U.S. and the Republic of Mexico. Washington, 1837. Boards, morocco label. Jenkins 116-1414 1978 $65

VAN BUREN, MARTIN   Speech of the Hon..., Delivered at the Capitol, in the City of Albany, Before the Albany County Meeting, Held on the 10th July, 1827. Albany, 1827. Disbound. Hayman 72-763 1978 $15

VANCE, A.   The Green Book; or Reading Made Easy of the Irish Statutes. 1862. 1st ed., unopened, good, octavo bound in cloth. Hyland 128-726 1978 £20

VANCE, JOHN   Travels of John Davis in the United States of America 1798 to 1802. Boston, 1910. 2 vols., pr. privately, ltd. to 487 sets. Nestler Rare 78-36 1978 $65

VANCE, RUPERT   All These People: The Nation's Human Resources in the South. 1945. Bell Wiley's copy. Broadfoot's 44-799 1978 $12.00

VANCE, RUPERT   Human Geography of the South: A Study in Regional Resources and Human Adequacy. 1935. Autographed by author, Bell Wiley's copy. Broadfoot's 44-800 1978 $14.00

VAN COTT, MAGGIE N.   The Harvest and the Reaper. Reminiscences of Revival Work. New York, (1876). New cloth. Hayman 72-764 1978 $12.50

VANCOUVER, GEORGE   A Voyage of Discovery to the North Pacific Ocean, and Round the World,.... London, 1801. 6 vols., calf, illus., some joints weak, endpapers stained. Dawson's 127-293 1978 $650

VAN DALE, A.   Dissertationes IX. Amsterdam, 1702. Engraved vignette on title, plts., thick sm. 4to, 18th. century red morocco, 3 line border gilt. Traylen 88-446 1978 £380

VANDERBILT, GERTRUDE L.   The Social History of Flatbush, and Manners and Customs of the Dutch Settlers in Kings County. New York, 1881. 1st ed., illus., fine copy, orig. cloth. MacManus 239-358 1978 $25

VANDERBILT, WILLIAM KISSAM   Taking One's Own Ship Around the World... New York. Sm. folio, ltd. to 500 copies, levant back, inscr'd. Baldwins' 51-516 1978 $50

VANDERBILT, WILLIAM KISSAM   To Galapagos on the Ara, 1926... 1927. One of 900 copies, cloth. Baldwins' 51-515 1978 $42.50

VANDERBILT, WILLIAM KISSAM   West Made East with the Loss of a Day... New York, 1933. One of 800 copies, cloth, sm. folio. Baldwins' 51-517 1978 $37.50

VANDERCOOK, JOHN W.   Black Majesty. New York, 1928. First ed., drawings, spine faded. Biblo 251-56 1978 $15

VANDERCOOK, JOHN W.   Caribbee Cruise. 1938. Illus., first ed. Austin 82-1023 1978 $11

VANDERCOOK, JOHN W.   Discover Puerto Rico. 1939. Illus., first ed. Austin 82-1024 1978 $8.50

VANDERCOOK, JOHN W.   The Fool's Parade. 1930. Illus., first ed. Austin 82-1025 1978 $11

VANDERCOOK, JOHN W.   Murder in Fiji. 1936. First ed. Austin 82-1026 1978 $11

VANDERVELDE, EMILE   Collectivism and Industrial Evolution. Chicago, 1901. Wrs. Hayman 73-710 1978 $10

VAN DEUSEN, JOHN G.   Economic Bases of Disunion in South Carolina. NY, 1928. Folding map, Bell Wiley's copy. Broadfoot's 44-949 1978 $25.00

VAN DE VELDE, C. W. M.   Narrative of a Journey Through Syria and Palestine, 1851-52... 1854. Map, plts., 2 vols., 8vo, orig. cloth, covers slightly worn. Edwards 1012-88 1978 £75

VAN DE VELDE, MARTHA   French Fiction of Today. London, 1891. 1st ed., 2 vols., blue cloth, illus., photographs, very good. Greene 78-303 1978 $75

VAN DE WATER, FREDERIC F.   Glory-Hunter. A Life of General Custer. Indianapolis, (1934). Cloth, 1st ed. Hayman 73-712 1978 $27.50

VAN DE WATER, FREDERIC F.   Glory-Hunter...General Custer. Indianapolis, (1934). Illus., 1st ed. Biblo BL781-302 1978 $14.50

VAN DE WATER, FREDERIC F.   Glory-Hunter. A Life of General Custer. New York, (1934). Illus., 1st ed., scarce, bright copy. MacManus 239-1910 1978 $25

VAN DE WATER, FREDERIC F.   Hidden Ways. 1935. First ed. Austin 82-1029 1978 $12.50

VAN DE WATER, FREDERIC F.   A Home in the Country. 1937. Austin 82-1028 1978 $10

VAN DE WATER, FREDERICK F.   Lake Champlain and Lake George. Indianapolis and New York, (1946). Plts., dust jacket, American Lakes Series. Butterfield 21-240 1978 $8.50

VAN DE WATER, FREDERIC F.   Rudyard Kipling's Vermont Feud. 1937. First ed. Austin 82-1027 1978 $12.50

VAN DE WATER, FREDERIC F.   We're Still in the Country. 1938. Austin 82-1030 1978 $11

VANDEWATER, ROBERT J.   The Tourist, or, Pocket Manual for Travellers on the Hudson River, the Western Canal and the Stage Road to Niagara Falls. New York, 1835. 12mo., 4th ed., bds., good. Biblo BL781-179 1978 $16.50

VANDERWATER, ROSALIE   Two Tea Parties. New York, London, (1882). Color plates, boards rubbed at edges, fine. Victoria 34-825 1978 $25

VAN DIEMAN'S Land Royal Kalendar... Launceston, 1848. 2 coloured plts., sm. 8vo, bds., leather back. Edwards 1012-345 1978 £75

VAN DINE, S. S.
Please turn to
WRIGHT, WILLARD HUNTINGTON

VANDIVER, FRANK E.   Confederate Blockade Running Through Bermuda 1861-1865. Austin, 1947. Illus, Bell Wiley's copy. Broadfoot's 44-374 1978 $30.00

VAN DOREN, CARL   American and English Literature Since 1890. 1925. Austin 82-1038 1978 $12.50

VAN DOREN, CARL   Benjamin Franklin. New York, 1938. First ed., illus. Biblo 247-48 1978 $13.50

VAN DOREN, CARL   Benjamin Franklin. New York, 1938. Ports., 1st ed. Biblo BL781-51 1978 $9.50

VAN DOREN, CARL   Benjamin Franklin. New York, 1945. Biblo 247-49 1978 $7.50

VAN DOREN, CARL   Carl Van Doren: Selected by Himslef. 1945. First ed., d.j. Austin 82-1031 1978 $11

VAN DOREN, CARL   The Great Rehearsal. New York, 1948. Illus., 1st ed. Biblo 251-88 1978 $9.50

VAN DOREN, CARL   James Branch Cabell. 1928. Austin 82-1032 1978 $7.50

VAN DOREN, CARL   Many Minds. 1926. Austin 82-1034 1978 $11

VAN DOREN, CARL   Mutiny in January. New York, 1943. Illus., 1st ed., signed, very good, d.w. Biblo BL781-238 1978 $10

VAN DOREN, CARL   The Ninth Wave. 1926. Austin 82-1035 1978 $10

VAN DOREN, CARL   The Patriotic Anthology. 1941. Austin 82-1036
1978 $8.50

VAN DOREN, CARL   Secret History of the American Revolution. New
York, 1941. First ed., ltd. to 590 numbered copies, signed, fine, boxed, illus.
Biblo 247-147 1978 $57.50

VAN DOREN, CARL   Secret History of the American Revolution.
New York, 1941. 1 of 590 large paper copies, 1st ed., thick 8 vo., red cloth,
leather labels, t.e.g., very good. Houle 10-349 1978 $45

VAN DOREN, CARL   Secret History of the American Revolution.
New York, 1941. 1st ed., illus. Biblo 248-202 1978 $15

VAN DOREN, CARL   Three Worlds. 1936. Austin 82-1037 1978
$10

VAN DOREN, DOROTHY   Brother and Brother. 1928. Austin 82-1039
1978 $10

VAN DOREN, DOROTHY   Dacey Hamilton. 1942. First ed., frayed d.j.
Austin 82-1040 1978 $12.50

VAN DOREN, DOROTHY   Those First Affections. 1938. First ed. Austin 82-
1041 1978 $12.50

VAN DOREN, MARK   The Country Year. New York, 1946. 16mo,
pastoral cloth decor., d.w. slightly rubbed, signed by author, Fine copy, laid in
postcard signed by Van Doren, 1st ed. Desmarais 1-415 1978 $15

VAN DOREN, MARK   Liberal Education. 1943. Austin 82-1043 1978
$11

VAN DOREN, MARK   Shakespeare. 1939. Austin 82-1044 1978
$11

VAN DOREN, MARK   The Travels of William Bartram. New York,
1928. Bell Wiley's copy. Broadfoot's 44-802 1978 $12

VAN DOREN, MARK   Windless Cabins. 1940. First ed. Austin 82-
1045 1978 $15

VAN DRUTEN, JOHN   Young Woodley: a play. 1928. Very good,
pres. copy inscribed by author, autograph post-card by author attached to inside
front cover, first English ed. Bell Book 16-859 1978 £4.50

VAN DUSEN, CONRAD   The Indian Chief: an Account of the Labours,
Losses, Sufferings and Oppression of Ke-zig-ko-e-ne-ne.... London, 1867.
Orig. bds. restored. Hood 116-444 1978 $185

VAN DYKE, HARRY STOE   Theatrical Portraits; With Other Poems. 1822.
1st ed., sm. 8vo, woodcut portrait inserted, half-title, contemp. half roan, gilt.
Hannas 54-337 1978 £35

VAN DYKE, HENRY   The House of Rimmon. New York, 1908. 1st
ed. Biblo 251-660 1978 $8.50

VAN DYKE, HENRY J.   The Character and Influence of Abolitionism.
New York, 1860. 8vo., unbound, 1st ed. Morrill 241-588 1978 $7.50

VAN DYKE, JOHN C.   The New New York. New York, 1909. Illus.
by Joseph Pennell. Baldwins' 51-419 1978 $15

VAN DYKE, THEODORE S.   Flirtation Camp: Or, The Rifle, Rod, and Gun
in California. New York, 1881. Orig. binding, clean, front free endpaper
detached but present, inner hinges cracking. Hayman 71-244 1978 $10

VANE, CAPEL   The Desire of the Moth. NY, 1895. Fir. Am.
Ed., quarter calf, marbled boards, good cond. Greene 78-304 1978 $15.00

VANE, DENZIL   Like Lucifer. A Novel. London, 1886. 3 vols.,
orig. cloth, 1st ed., covers a bit worn and soiled, lib. labels. MacManus 238-
353 1978 $85

VANE, W. L.   The Durham Light Infantry. 1914. Coloured
plts.,roy. 8vo., publisher's half mor. F. Edwards 1013-527 1978 £35

VAN EECHOUT, EDOUARD P.   Campagnes et Stations sur les Cotes de L'Amerique du Nord Par L. du Hailly. Paris, 1864. Half mor., 1st ed. Ginsberg 14-
1016 1978 $85

VAN EECHOUT, EDOUARD P.   Campagnes et Stations sur les Cotes de l'Amerique du Nord.... Paris, 1864. Half mor. Ginsberg 14-212 1978 $125

VANEL   Intrigues Galantes de la Cour de France, depuis
le commencement de la Monarchie jusqu a present. Cologne, 1695. Frontis., 2
vols. in 1, thick sm. 8vo., contemp. calf. Howes 194-580 1978 £21

VAN EPPS, PERCY M.   Contributions to the History of Glenville. Mimeo-
graphed articles in loose-leaf wr., 4to., newspaper supplement laid in. Butterfield 21-404 1978 $15

VAN EVERY, DALE   Charles Lindbergh, His Life. New York, 1927.
Illus., 1st. ed., d.j. Baldwins' 51-179 1978 $12.50

VAN EVERY, EDWARD   Sins of New York as "Exposed" by the Police
Gazette. New York, 1930. 4to., illus., frayed dust jacket, nice copy, 3rd
prtg. Butterfield 21-552 1978 $15

VAN EYCK, H.   J. Hubert et Jean Van Eyck. Par E. Durand-
Greville. Brussels, 1910. 4to., plts., half leather. Quaritch 983-268 1978
$75

VAN GOGH, VINCENT
Please turn to
GOGH, VINCENT VAN

VAN HEURCK, HENRI   A Treatise on the Diatomaceae.... London,
1896. Text figures, 4to, buckram, t.e.g., fine copy of orig. & best ed.
Traylen 88-637 1978 £65

VAN HOFFMAN, CARL   Jungle Gods. London, 1929. 16 illus., orig.
cloth, 8vo, little thumbed. K Books 239-504 1978 £6

VAN HORNE, THOMAS B.   History of the Army of the Cumberland. Cincinnati, 1875. 3 vols., ex-lib., nice, orig. cloth, scarce. MacManus 239-
910 1978 $85

VAN HORNE, THOMAS B.   History of the Army of the Cumberland. Cincinnati, 1875. Atlas only, maps, cover spotted, Bell Wiley's copy. Broadfoot's
44-376 1978 $25

VANINUS, JULIUS CAESAR   Amphitheatrum Aeternae Providentiae Divino-
Magicum, Christiano-Physicum and Astro-Catholicum. Lyon, 1615. 8vo., 1/2
calf. Salloch 348-275 1978 $300

VAN LAER, A. J. F.   Correspondence of Jeremias van Rensselaer 1651-
1674. Albany, 1932. Butterfield 21-36 1978 $8.50

VAN Loan's Catskill Mountain Guide. New York, 1879. Maps, illus., folded
& partly colored maps, wr., very good, scarce. Butterfield 21-101 1978 $35

VAN LOON, HENDRIK WILLEM   The Arts. New York, 1937. Illus., some
in color, 1st ed. Biblo BL781-753 1978 $10

VAN LOON, HENDRIK WILLEM   The Arts. New York, 1937. Color plates,
fine, d.j. Victoria 34-824 1978 $12.50

VAN LOON, HENDRIK WILLEM   The Life and Times of Simon Bolivar. New
York, 1943. Illus. by author, 1st ed., d.w. Biblo 251-57 1978 $17.50

VAN LOON, HENDRIK WILLEM   Lives. New York, 1942. First ed., illus.
Biblo 247-753 1978 $16.50

VAN LOON, HENDRIK WILLEM   Lives.   New York, 1942.   Illus., some in color, 1st ed.   Biblo BL781-638 1978 $10

VAN LOON, L. G.   Crumbs from an Old Dutch Closet.   The Hague, 1933.   4to., wr., prospectus laid in.   Butterfield 21-164 1978 $17.50

VAN PELT, JOHN V.   Masterpieces of Spanish Architecture.   Romanesque and Allied Styles.   New York, 1925.   Plts., illus., 4to., covers rubbed.   Biblo BL781-550 1978 $20

VAN REES PRESS   Specimens of Types.   New York, (1930).   1 of 500 copies, orig. dec. cloth.   Americanist 102-117 1978 $35

VAN RENSSELAER, SOLOMON   A Narrative of the Affair of Queenstown in the War of 1812...   New York and Boston, 1836.   Orig. cloth bind., fold. map.   Hood 116-787 1978 $200

VAN RENSSELAER, STEPHEN   Check List of Early American Bottles and Flasks.   New York, 1921.   Illus., 8vo., fr. cover bit soiled & wrinkled, 1st ed.   Morrill 239-634 1978 $15

VAN RENSSELAER, STEPHEN   Check List of Early American Bottles and Flasks.   Peterborough, 1926.   Revised ed., 162 plts., signed copy.   Baldwins' 51-161 1978 $55

VAN SINDEREN, ADRIAN   The Story of the Six Years of Global War.   1946.   Austin 80-355 1978 $12.50

VANSITTART, HENRY   A Narrative of the Transactions in Bengal, 1760 to 1764.   1766.   First ed., 3 vols., contemp. calf, joints cracked, tall copy, 8vo.   Howes 194-501 1978 £85

VAN SWEITEN, GERARDI B. DE   Commentaria.   Bassani, 1788.   Old leather, clean.   Rittenhouse 49-804 1976 $75

VAN TASSEL, CHARLES SUMNER   The First Hundred Years of Bowling Green, Ohio...1833-1933.   (Bowling Green, 1933?).   Cloth, very scarce.   Hayman 72-590 1978 $17.50

VAN TASSEL, CHARLES SUMNER   Story of the Explorers of the Great Northwest.   N.P., (Bowling Green?), 1941.   Maps., wrs., scarce.   Hayman 72-765 1978 $7.50

VAN TASSEL, CHARLES SUMNER   Story of the Maumee Valley, Toldeo, and the Sandusky Region.   Chicago, 1929.   4 vols., cloth.   Hayman 72-584 1978 $60

VAN TYNE, CLAUDE H.   The Causes of the War of Independence and the War of Independence, American Phase.   Boston, 1922-1929.   2 vols.   MacManus 239-629 1978 $27.50

VAN TYNE, CLAUDE H.   The War of Independence, American Phase.   Being the Second Volume of a History of the Founding of the American Republic.   Boston, 1929.   1st ed., orig. cloth, d.j., fine.   MacManus 239-630 1978 $12.50

VAN URK, J. BLAN   The Story of American Foxhunting From Challenge to Full Cry, 1650-1906.   New York, 1940-41.   2 vols., sm. folio.   Baldwins' 51-543 1978 $200

VAN VECHTEN, CARL   In The Garret.   New York, 1920.   1st ed., uncut, orig. bds., very good or better.   Limestone 9-309 1978 $25

VAN VOORHIS, JOHN S.   The Old and New Monongahela.   Pittsburgh, 1893.   1st ed., port., very scarce.   MacManus 239-1704 1978 $60

VAN WINKLE, DANIEL   Old Bergen.   Jersey City, (1902).   Maps, illus., 8vo., ex-lib., 1st ed., orig. cloth.   Morrill 241-400 1978 $22.50

VAN WINKLE, DANIEL   Old Bergen History and Reminiscences.   Jersey City, (1902).   1st ed., illus., ports., orig. cloth, fine.   MacManus 239-1335 1978 $35

VAN WYCK, FREDERICK   Select Patents of New York Towns.   Boston, 1938.   Plts., maps, stiff wr., corrected reprint ed., 1 of only 75 copies, 4 added maps not in 1st prtg.   Butterfield 21-456 1978 $35

VAQUEZ, HENRI LOUIS   Les Arythmies Par Le Docteur H. Vaquez.   Paris, 1911.   8vo., illus., orig. maroon cloth, gilt lettering, very good copy, bkplt. of Carleton B. Chapman, M. D., 1st ed.   Zeitlin 245-273 1978 $75

VAQUEZ, HENRI LOUIS   Les Troubles Du Rythme Cardiaque.   Paris, 1926.   8vo., illus., orig. green cloth, gilt lettering, very good copy from library of Carleton B. Chapman, M. D., 1st ed.   Zeitlin 245-274 1978 $75

VARAGINE, JACOBUS DE
Please turn to
JACOBUS DE VARAGINE

VARCHI, BENEDETTO   Storia Fiorentina di Messer Benedetto Varchi Nella quale principalmente si contengono l'ultime Revolutioni....   1721.   Folio, vellum, very good, rare first issue of first ed.   King 7-250 1978 £150

VARDON, ROGER   English Bloods.   Ottawa, 1930.   Printed wrappers.   Wolfe 39-119 1978 $55

VAREN, BERNARD   Geographia Generalis.   Amsterdam, 1650.   12mo., fldg. charts, contemp. vellum, light dampstaining, but fine copy, 1st ed.   Norman 5-293 1978 $950

VARET, ALEXANDRE LOUIS   The Nunns Complaint Against the Fryars.   Being the Charge Given in to the Court of France, by the Nunns of St. Katherine near Provins, Against the Fathers Cordeliers Their Confessors.   London, 1676.   12mo., contemp. calf, rebacked with later calf and mor. label, 1st Eng. ed., worn, spine detached, signature on t.p., bookplt.   MacManus 238-118 1978 $100

VARGAS, ALPHONSUS DE   Alphonsi de Vargas Toletani Relatio Ad Reges et Principes Christianos....   1641.   12mo., bds., calf spine gilt, edges red-stained.   King 7-107 1978 £35

VARIGNON, PIERRE   Traite du Mouvement,....   Paris, 1725.   1st ed., quarto, folding engraved plates, contemp. mottled calf, red morocco label, very good large paper.   Bennett 20-215 1978 $475

VARIGNY, C. DE   Nouvelle Geographie Moderne des cinq Parties du Monde.   Paris, n.d. (ab. 1910).   3 vols., lg. 8vo., half calf, richly illus.   Van der Peet H-64-568 1978 Dfl 175

VARILLAS, ANTOINE   The Secret History of the House of Medicis.   London, 1686.   1st. ed., 8vo, contemp. calf, rebacked.   Traylen 88-349 1978 £68

VARLO, C.   A New System of Husbandry....   Philadelphia, 1785.   Vol. 1 only, orig. full calf.   Baldwins' 51-490 1978 $35

THE VARSITY.   Toronto, 1880-81.   Folio, contemp. bds., scuffed, front cover loose.   Wolfe 39-543 1978 $50

VARTHEMA, LUDOVICO DI   The Itinerary of Ludovico di Varthema of Bologna from 1502 to 1508.   London, Argonaut Press, 1928.   Ltd. ed., maps, illus., 4to., orig. buckram, somewhat soiled, internally good.   K Books 244-454 1978 £12

VASARI, GIORGIO   Lives of the Artists.   New York, (1946).   Illus., some in color.   Biblo BL781-755 1978 $9

VASARI, GIORGIO   Lives of the Most Eminent Painters, Sculptors and Architects.   1912-15.   100 coloured & 401 plain plts., 10 vols., roy. 8vo, orig. buckram, gilt tops, other edges uncut.   Traylen 88-422 1978 £230

VASARI, GIORGIO   Lives of the Most Eminent Painters.   Verona, 1966.   1 of 1,500 numbered copies signed by Mardersteig, sm. folio, illus., bookplate, d.j., 2 vols., as new, slipcase.   Houle 10-350 1978 $125

VASARI, GIORGIO   Ragionamenti.   Arezzo, 1762.   Second ed., 4to., new half calf, portrait of Vasari as frontispiece.   King 7-251 1978 £40

VASSAL, G. M.   On and off duty in Annam.   London, 1910.   Cloth, illus., photos by author, map, 8vo., orig. covers.   Van der Peet 127-255 1978 Dfl 55

VASSOS, RUTH   Contempo. New York, 1929. 4to., publisher's cloth, slipcase, ltd. ed. issued in 166 copies, numbered copy signed by artist & Ruth Vassos, illus. Goldschmid-110-74 1978 $45

VAUCANSON, JACQUES DE   Le Mecanisme du Fluteur Automate. Paris, 1738. 4to., frontis., old red mor., gilt, fine copy, 1st ed. Norman 5-294 1978 $1,100

VAUDOYER, JEAN-LOUIS   Suzanne et L'Italie, Lettres Familieres. Paris, 1909. 4to, wrappers, 3-line pencil inscription by author, ltd. ed. of 500 copies. Eaton 45-518 1978 £5

VAUDRY, M. O.   Savage Family. A Sketch of the Life of Captain John Savage, J.P. Lennoxville, (1921). Printed wrappers. Wolfe 39-160 1978 $20

VAUGHAN, HENRY   The Works. 1914. Orig. issue, 2 vols., fine, d.w., 8vo., orig. cloth. Howes 194-1300 1978 £10

VAUGHAN, OWEN   Old Fireproof. London, 1912. Pictorial cloth, plts. by Edgar Holloway, 8vo. K Books 239-501 1978 £6

VAUGHAN, T.   Recent Madreporaria of the Hawaiian Islands and Laysan. 1907. Plates, folio, orig. wr. lacking, uncut, 8vo. Book Chest 17-396 1978 $55

VAUX, ROBERTS   Memoirs of the Life of Anthony Benezet. York, 1817. Frontispiece, sm. 8vo, half calf. Edwards 1012-245 1978 £30

VAY DE VAYA   The Inner Life of the United States. London, 1908. Austin 79-801 1978 $20

VAZQUEZ, GABRIELE   De Cultu Adorationis libri tres. (Alcala), 1594. 1st ed., quarto, full-page plate, full contemp. vellum, original ties, some wear and soiling of vellum. Bennett 20-216 1978 $125

VEATCH, A. C.   Evolution of the Congo Basin. London, 1935. Folding map, 9 plts., roy. 8vo, orig. cloth. K Books 239-502 1978 £12

VEATCH, J. O.   Soil Survey of San Saba County, Texas. Washington, 1917. Folding map, printed wr. Jenkins 116-1224 1978 $7.50

VECCHIERELLO, HUBERT   Einstein and Relativity. Paterson, 1934. 8vo., orig. bds., cloth back, ex-lib. Morrill 241-590 1978 $8.50

VECHTEN, CARL VAN
Please turn to
VAN VECHTEN, CARL

VEDDER, JESSIE V. V.   History of Green County, Vol. I, 1641-1800. N.P., (1927). Prtd. wr. Butterfield 21-200 1978 $20

VEDRES, NICOLE   Images du Cinema Francais. Paris, 1945. 4to., illus., wraps, very good. Bell Book 17-166 1978 £8.50

VEECH, JAMES   The Monongahela of Old, or, Historical Sketches of South-Western, Pa., to the Year 1800. Pittsburgh, (1910). Port. MacManus 239-1705 1978 $45

VEGA, CHRISTOPHER   A. Comentaria in librum Galeni de differentia febrium. Compluti, 1553. 1st ed., small 8vo, folding table, full contemp. vellum, light staining of 1st part of text. Bennett 20-217 1978 $350

VEGA, GARCILASO DE LA
Please turn to
GARCILASO DE LA VEGA

VEITCH, H. N.   Sheffield Plate, its History, Manufacture and Art. 1908. Plts., imp. 8vo., covers worn. George's 635-255 1978 £12.50

VEITCH, JOHN   The History and Poetry of the Scottish Border, Their main Features and Relations. Edinburgh, 1893. New ed., 2 vols., 8vo., orig. cloth. K Books 244-317 1978 £15

VELASQUEZ, D.   Diego Velasquez und Sein Jahrhundert. Von C. Justi. Dritte Auflage. Bonn, 1922-23. 2 vols., roy. 8vo., plts., half leather. Quaritch 983-269 1978 $70

VELAZQUEZ DE VELASCO, LUIS JOSE   Ensayo Sobre los Alphabetos de las Letras Desconocidas que se Encuentran en las mas Antiguas Medallas, y Monumentos de Espana. Madrid, 1752. 4to., half leather, eng. plts. Schumann 511-64 1978 sFr 350

VELLEIUS PATERCULUS C.   M. Velleii Paterculi quae supersunt. Oxford, 1693. First English printing, vignette on title, 8vo., contemp. calf. Howes 194-111 1978 £30

VELLEIUS PATERCULUS, C.   Opera quae supersunt: cum Variis Lectionibus Optimarum Editionum. Oxford, 1711. Vignette, contemp. panelled calf, joints cracked, label missing, 8vo. Howes 194-411 1978 £14

VELLEIUS PATERCULUS, C.   C. Velleii Paterculi Quae Supersunt. Lugduni, 1744. Octavo, full cont. vellum, sound. Bennett 20-160 1978 $195

VELNET, MARY   An Affecting History of the Captivity and Suffering of an Italian Lady, Who Was Seven Years a Slave in Tripoli. Boston, n.d. 1st. American ed., woodcut frontis, orig. boards, worn. Baldwins' 51-388 1978 $27.50

VELOX   Velocipedes, Bicycles and Tricycles: How to Make and How to Use Them. London, 1869. 8vo., text illus., orig. prtd. bds., rubbed, rebacked, retaining orig. advertisement endpapers, very good copy, 1st ed. Norman 5-31 1978 $500

VELPEAU, ALFRED ARMAND LOUIS MARIE   An Elementary Treatise on Midwifery. Philadelphia, 1831. 8vo., modern cloth, gilt lettering, browned, foxed, signature & stamp, good copy from Library of Dr. Alfred M. Hellman, 1st Amer. ed. Zeitlin 245-274 1978 $75

VELPEAU, ALFRED ARMAND LOUIS MARIE   Nouveaux Elements de Medecine Operatoire. Bruxelles, 1834-1835. 1 vol., 8vo., atlas sm. folio, half-calf, some lib. stamp, 1st ed. Gilhofer 74-104 1978 sFr 650

VEN, D. J. VAN DER   Van Vrijen en Trouwen Op 't Boerenland. Amsterdam-Mechelen, 1929. 8vo., cloth, illus., plts. Van der Peet H-64-215 1978 Dfl 30

VENEGAS, MIGUEL   Naturalische und Bergerlische Geschichte von Californien... Lemgo, 1769-1770. 3 vols. bound in 1, folding map, boards. Ginsberg 14-213 1978 $250

VENERONI, GIOVANNI   The New Italian Grammar... 1711. 1st. English ed., 8vo, contemp. calf, slightly worn. Hannas 54-199 1978 £20

VENETUS, PAULUS NICOLETTUS   Universalia Predicamenta sexque principia. Venice, 1494. Editio Princeps, folio, printer's mark of O. Scutus on final leaf, quarter calf boards. Bennett 20-218 1978 $1,375

VENICE. Parti dell' Illustrissima Signoria di Venetia in Materia delle Stampa. 4to., unbound. Argosy Special-91 1978 $75

VENN, J. A.   Foundations of Agricultural Economics. Cambridge, 1923. Plts., illus., maps, 8vo. Traylen 88-87 1978 £6

VENNER, TOBIAS   Via Recta Ad Vitam Longam. London, 1650. Sm. 4to., woodcut, contemp. blind-stamped calf, gilt, lightly browned, good copy from library of Dr. Alfred M. Hellman. Zeitlin 245-276 1978 $200

VENNING, MARY ANNE   A Geographical Present:.... London, 1817. 1st ed., hand-colored plates, 12mo, 3rd ed. Victoria 34-833 1978 $150

VENTURI, LIONELLO   Impressionists and Symbolists. New York, 1950. First ed., d.w., illus. Biblo 247-441 1978 $17.50

VERDIZOTTI, GIO. MARIO   Cento favole morali. Venice, 1570. Sm. 4 to., woodcut border, full-page woodcuts, very good, recent brown mor. gilt, 1st ed. Quaritch Summer, 1978-43 1978 $2,100

VERGA, ETTORE   Gli Studi Intorno a Leonardo. Rome, 1923. 8vo., orig. prtd. wrs., uncut, unopened, lacks back wr., Chauncey Leake's copy with his signature on fr. wr. & title. Norman 5-L24 1978 $30

VERGA, GIOVANNI   Cavalleria Rusticana and Other Stories. London, (1928). 8vo., cloth, d.j., 1st ed., fine, scarce in d.j. J.S. Lawrence 38-L14 1978 $100

VERGA, GIOVANNI   Little Novels of Sicily. New York, 1925. 1st ed., 1st issue, dark red cloth, 8vo., cloth. J.S. Lawrence 38-L49 1978 $25

VERGA, GIOVANNI   Mastro-Don Gesualdo. New York, 1923. 8vo., cloth, d.j., 1st ed., spine of d.j. tanned with some chipping, but fine. J.S. Lawrence 38-L57 1978 $150

VERGENNES, C. G.   Memoire Historique et Politique sur la Louisiane. Paris, 1802. 1st ed., half calf, worn, interior very fine. Jenkins 116-1570 1978 $175

VERGILIUS MARO, PUBLIUS   Virgil's Aeneis. Edinburgh, 1710. New ed., folio, little age-staining, fine, bound c. 1870 in full dark green mor., gilt edges, translated into Scottish Verse. Howes 194-249 1978 £85

VERGILIUS MARO, PUBLIUS   Aeneis. Wien, 1784. Sm. 8vo., full calf, 7 parts in 1 vol., binding shaved, damaged, joint weak. Van der Peet H-64-574 1978 Dfl 80

VERGILIUS MARO, PUBLIUS   Bucolica, Georgica, et Aeneis. Birmingham, Baskerville Press, 1757. 4to., 19th cent. polished calf, first ed. Howes 194-155 1978 £85

VERGILIUS MARO, PUBLIUS   Bucolica, Georgica, et Aeneis. Glasguae, Foulis Press, 1778. 2 vols. in 1, folio, contemp. calf, crimson label. Howes 194-274 1978 £45

VERGILIUS MARO, PUBLIUS   Les Bucoliques. Paris, 1953. 4to., dark blue levant mor., panels of glazed royal blue, light blue and green calf, uncut, orig. wrs. and backstrip bound in half mor. slipcover and case, bound by Creuzevault, ltd. ed., 245 numbered copies on Arches paper, trans. by Paul Valery, illus. with lithos. by Jacques Villon. Goldschmidt 110-77 1978 $2,400

VERGILIUS MARO, PUBLIUS   Les Eglogues de Virgile. Weimar, Cranach Press, 1927. 4to., in sheets, uncut, in orig. wr., publisher's 1/2 vellum portfolio, ltd. ed., 1 of 250 numbered copies on hemp & fibre paper, illus. by Maillol. Goldschmidt 110-46 1978 $1,500

VERGILIUS MARO, PUBLIUS   Georgiques de Virgile.... Paris, 1770. Lg. 8vo., calf, raised bands, plts. King 7-393 1978 £30

VERGILIUS MARO, PUBLIUS   The Georgics. 1928. Cr. 4to., first ed., woodcuts, orig. green cloth. Howes 194-1302 1978 £6

VERGILIUS MARO, PUBLIUS   The Georgics of... New York, 1931. Folio, engrs., ltd. ed., bds., lea. back, spine torn, scuffed, otherwise very good copy. Biblo 251-430 1978 $37.50

VERGILIUS MARO, PUBLIUS   P. Virgili Maronis Opera;.... Batavor, 1636. 12mo, folding plate, full ong-grained crushed morocco, a.e.g. Bennett 20-219 1978 $60

VERGILIUS MARO, PUBLIUS   Opera, cum Veterum Omnium Commentariis et Selectis Recentiorum Notis. (Leyden), 1646. 4to., cont. calf, spine gilt. Howes 194-581 1978 £30

VERGILIUS MARO, PUBLIUS   Opera. Amstelaedami, 1730. Sm. 8vo., old vellum. Van der Peet H64-572 1978 Dfl 60

VERGILIUS MARO, PUBLIUS   Opera. Paris, 1832. Sm. 8vo., cloth. Van der Peet H64-571 1978 Dfl 40

VERGILIUS MARO, PUBLIUS   Opera. 1950. 2 vols. Allen 234-1016 1978 $15

VERGILIUS MARO, PUBLIUS   The Works of Virgil, In Latin and English. 1778. 3rd. ed., folding map, plts., 4 vols., 8vo, contemp. mottled calf, gilt spines, red & black labels, nice. Fenning 32-339 1978 £45

VERINI, GIOVANNI BATTISTA   Incipit Liber Primus Elementorum Litterarum... N.P., n.d. (Toscolano, c. 1526-27). 4 parts in 1, full brown mor., sm. 4to., bookplate, fine, complete copy, from the Landau-Finaly lib., with bookplate, first ed., woodcuts. Schumann 511-65 1978 sFr 11,000

LE VERITABLE Riel Tel Que Depeint Dans des Lettres de sa Grandeur Mgr. Grandin... Montreal, 1887. Bound in contemporary mottled bds. with linen spine. Hood's 115-275 1978 $110

VERLAINE, PAUL   Oeuvres Poetiques. Lausanne, 1943-1944. 3 vols., 8vo., half calf, gilt headband, ltd. ed. of 100 numbered copies on "Papier du Marais", total ed. of 2000 numbered copies, orig. cover bound up, nice set. Van der Peet H-64-459 1978 Dfl 175

VERLAINE, PAUL   Poems. Chicago, 1895. Illus., 8vo., orig. green cloth, fine, 1 of 100 copies on Japan vellum, A.L.s. inserted. Morrill 241-592 1978 $50

VERMIGLI, PIETRO MARTIRE   Most Learned and Fruitful Commentaries. London, 1568. 1st. ed. in English, black letter, title within woodcut border, thick folio, lacking last leaf, contemp. blind stamped calf over wooden bds., worn, browned in outer margin, few edges frayed. Traylen 88-350 1978 £70

VERMILYEA, THOMAS E.   An Introductory Address to the Course of Lectures. Albany, 1837. Disbound. Butterfield 21-292e 1978 $7.50

VERMONT, E. DE V.   American Heraldica. New York, 1886. Illus. by Henry Rykees in color, folio, binding broken loose. Baldwins' 51-267 1978 $50

THE VERMONT & New York Almanac..1810. Middlebury, 1810. Excellent, bound copy. Nestler Rare 78-1 1978 $20

VERNE, JULES   The American Gun Club. New York, 1874. Some int. foxing, illus., orig. blue cloth, gilt lettering, edges rubbed, good. Greene 78-305 1978 $20

VERNE, JULES   From Earth to Moon. New York, 1874. Illus., spine cloth rippled, fine bright copy. Greene 78-306 1978 $35

VERNE, JULES   The Survivors of the Chancellor Diary of J.R. Kazaalon, Passenger and Martin Paz. London, 1875. 1st Eng. ed., full page illus. by Riou, "very handsome" ed., interior good. Greene 78-128 1978 $125

VERNE, JULES   The Tour of the World in 80 Days. Boston, 1874. Orig. cloth, edges stained red, 12 mo. Greene 78-307 1978 $15

VERNE, JULES   The Wreck of the Chancellor. Boston, 1875. 12mo, 1st Amer. ed., no illus., gilt cover vignette, almost fine. Victoria 34-834 1978 $35

VERNER, WILLOUGHBY   The First British Rifle Corps. 1890. Coloured frontis., sm. 8vo., orig. cloth. F. Edwards 1013-548 1978 £15

VERNER, WILLOUGHBY   History and Campaigns of the Rifle Brigade, 1800-1813. 1912-19. 2 vols., 4to., orig. cloth, coloured plts. F. Edwards 1013-547 1978 £90

VERNET, HORACE   Salon d'Horace Vernet.... Paris, 1822. 8vo., contemp. half calf. F. Edwards 1013-444 1978 £22

VERNEY, FRANCES PARTHENOPE   Memoirs of the Verney Family During the Civil War. 1892. Illus., plts., 2 vols., 8vo. George's 635-785 1978 £10.50

VERNEY, FRANCES PARTHENOPE   Memoirs of the Verney Family During the Civil War, during the Commonwealth and from the Restoration to the Revolution. 1892-99. Portrs., 4 vols., 8vo., lib. ed., illus., bkplt., cloth. Quaritch 979-323 1978 $125

VERNEY, FRANCES PARTHENOPE   The Memoirs of the Verney Family. 1899, reprint 1970. 4 vols., 8vo., illus. Traylen 88-352 1978 £10

VERNEY, RALPH   Verney Papers; Notes of Proceedings in the Long Parliament. 1845. Octavo, good. Upcroft 10-176 1978 £6.50

VERNON, EDWARD   Original Papers Relating to the Expedition to Carthagena. N.P. (London), 1744. Together 2 vols., 8vo, contemporary calf, gilt, spines gilt, 1st ed., uniformly bound and labelled, splendid condition. Ximenes 47-321 1978 $275

VERNON, GEORGE   The Life of the Learned and Reverend Dr. Peter
Heylyn, Chaplain to Charles I and Charles II. 1682. Sm. 8vo., contemp. sheep,
rebacked, new endpapers, preserving orig. blank leaves, first ed. Howes 194-59
1978 £35

VERRI, ALESSANDRO   The Roman Nights. 1798. 12mo., recent full
calf, first ed. in English. P. M. Hill 142-195 1978 £55

VERRIEN, NICOLAS   Recueil d'Emblemes, Devises, Medailles, et
Figures Hieroglyphiques... Paris, 1696. Plts., 8vo., dark green mor. Janssenist
binding, by Cuzin, splendid copy, portrait. Schumann 511-66 1978 sFr 1120

VERRIEN, NICOLAS   Recueil d'Emblemes, Devises, Medailles, et
Figures Hieroglyphiques... Paris, 1724. Frontis., plts., 8vo., cont. calf, gilt
back. Schumann 511-67 1978 sFr 1,000

VERRO, SEBASTIANUS   Physicorum Libri Decem. Basileae, 1581. Sm.
8vo., woodcut, illus., contemp. limp vellum, two ties, marginal dampstain,
very good copy, very rare ed. Zeitlin 245-277 1978 $450

VERSTEGEN, RICHARD FL. 1565-1620   A Restitution of Decayed Intelligence.
London, 1628. Octavo, half calf and marbled bds., calf worn. Bennett 7-92
1978 $75

VERSTEGEN, RICHARD FL. 1565-1620   A Restitution of Decayed Intelligence...
London, 1634. Small quarto, full sprinkled calf, recently rebacked, lea. title
labels, slim bkplt. of Charles Norton, woodcuts. Totteridge 29-93 1978 $125

VERTANES, CHARLES A.   Armenia Reborn. 1947. Maps, illus. Austin
79-803 1978 $27.50

VERTUMNUS; or, The Progress of Spring: A Poetical Essay. Glasgow, 1761.
8vo., modern calf, 1st ed., half-title present, very good copy, very scarce.
Ximenes 47-255 1978 $125

VERVIERS, E.   De Nederlandsche Handelspolitiek tot aan de
Toepassing der Vrijhandelsbeginselen. Leiden, 1914. 8vo., orig. covers. Van
der Peet H-64-569 1978 Dfl 40

VERWORN, MAX   De Sogenannte Hypnose Der Thiere. Jena, 1898.
8vo., illus., cloth backed bds., orig. prtd. upper cover pasted on, library stamps,
ex-lib., very good copy, rare 1st ed. Zeitlin 245-278 1978 $45

VERZAMELING van Dagorders Betrekking Hebbende op Toegekende Belooningen
aan hen die zich Onderscheidden bij Krijgsverrichtingen van het Koninklijk Neder-
landsch-Indisch Leger van 1818 t/m Heden. Batavia, 1939. 8vo., cloth, scarce.
Van der Peet H-64-570 1978 Dfl 135

VESALIUS, ANDREAS   De Humani Corporis Fabrica Libri Septem. Basileae, (1555). Folio, woodcuts, blind-stamped pigskin, edged in lea., fine tall
copy, marginal worming, 3 leaves tipped in with manuscript notes in contemp.
hand, 3-page note by 19th Cent. owner to new owner laid in, bkplt., 3rd ed.
Zeitlin 245-279 1978 $12,500

VESALIUS, ANDREAS   De humani corporis fabrica libri septem.
Venice, 1568. Folio, woodcuts, very good, recent blindstamped mor., 4th (1st
Italian) ed. Quaritch Summer, 1978-44 1978 $3,500

VESEY-FITZGERALD   Game Fish of the World. London, (1949).
Colored front, color plates, royal 8vo., orig. cloth. Book Chest 17-398 1978
$30

VESLINGUS, JOHANNES 1598-1649   The Anatomy of the Body of Man. 1677.
Plts., folio, contemp. calf, extremely rare. Howes 194-112 1978 £385

VESPA, AMLETO   Secret Agent of Japan. London, 1938.
1st ed., Left Book Club (not for sale to public), cloth, very good or better.
Limestone 9-310 1978 $17.50

THE VESPERS of Palermo. Edinburgh, 1840. 12mo., full brown polished calf,
very good. Current Misc. 8-19 1978 $885

VESPUCIUS, AMERICUS   The First Four Voyages of.... New York, 1902.
1 of 50 copies, spine mended. Hood 116-667 1978 $60

VESTAL, STANLEY   King of the Fur Traders; the Deeds and Deviltry of
Pierre Esprit Radisson. Boston, 1940. Maps. Hood 116-597 1978 $30

VETERUM Mathematicorum Athenaei, Apollodori, Philonis, Bitonis, Heronis et
Aliorum Opera, Graece et Latine Pleraque Nunc Primum Edita. Parisiis, 1693.
Folio, contemp. calf, rebacked. Offenbacher 30-154 1978 $750

VEYRAT, G.   La Caricature a Travers les Siecles. Paris,
1895. Lg. 8vo., illus. wrs., caricatural text illus., wrs. damaged. Van der Peet
H-64-290 1978 Dfl 40

VIALART, CHARLES   Geographia Sacra. Amsterdam, 1703. Maps,
vignettes, folio, contemp. half vellum, marbled bds., bookplt. of J. Bellamy,
handsome production on fine paper. Thomas 37-35 1978 £150

VIANNA KELSCH, G. DE   Canon Tibirtius. 's-Gravenhage, 1931. 3 parts,
4to., cloth, fine plts. Van der Peet H-64-217 1978 Dfl 45

THE VICAR of Iver. 1821. 12mo., old half calf, hinges cracked, frontispiece.
P. M. Hill 142-196 1978 £30

VICARS, A.   Index to the Prerogative Wills of Ireland 1536-1810.
Very good, octavo bound in cloth, reprint. Hyland 128-733 1978 £30

VICAT, J.L.   A Practical and Scientific Treatise on Calcareous
Mortars and Cements, Artificial and Natural;.... London, 1837. 1st ed. in
English, octavo, full-page plate, original publisher's blindstamped cloth, lettered in
gold on spine. Bennett 20-220 1978 $175

VICENTINO, LUDOVICO   The Calligraphic Models of Ludovico degli Arrighi
surnamed Vicentino. Paris, 1926. Paste-paper bds., 1 of 300 copies prtd. Dawson's 447-112 1978 $225

VICKERS, ROY   Murdering Mr. Velfrage. 1950. Very good,
torn d.w., first English ed. Bell Book 17-271 1978 £10

VICTOR, BENJAMIN   The Widow of the Wood. 1755. 1st. ed., 12mo,
half title, sm. repair to last leaf, speckled calf, gilt borders, lacking label, a.e.g.,
v.g. Jarndyce 16-225 1978 £80

VICTOR, FRANCES FULLER   The River of the West. Columbus, 1950. Reprint,
fine, d.w., engravings. Biblo 247-272 1978 $27.50

VICTOR RECORDS   Catalog of Victor Records. Camden, (1938).
Wrs., complete, compact. Hayman 73-96 1978 $7.50

VICTORIA, QUEEN   Letters, a Selection, 1837-61. 1907. Plates,
3 vols., 8vo. George's 635-787 1978 £5

THE VICTORY Won: a Memorial of the Rev. Wm. J. Hoge, D.D., Late Pastor of
the Tabb St. Presbyterian Church, Petersburg, Va. Richmond, 1864. 1st and
only ed., orig. printed wrs. Americanist 102-32 1978 $85

VIDA, MARCO GIROLAMO   Les Vers a Soie Suivi du Poeme des Echecs, et de
Pieces Fugitives. 1809. Allen 234-1487 1978 $12.50

VIDAL, DOMINGO   Cirugia Forense O Arte De Hacer Las Relaciones
Chirurgico-Legales. Madrid, 1802. 12mo., contemp. mottled calf, gilt, worn,
sm. wormtrail, library stamp, good copy. Zeitlin 245-281 1978 $75

VIDAL, GORE   The City and the Pillar. 1948. Black cloth, first
ed., good clean copy. Austin 82-1049 1978 $20

VIDAL, GORE   The Season of Comfort. 1949. First ed., v.g.,
frayed d.j. Austin 82-1050 1978 $27.50

VIDAL, LOUIS-ANTOINE   Les Instruments a Archet. Illus. with 122 plts.
by F. Hillemacher, cr. 4to, 3 vols. Traylen 88-526 1978 £30

VIDAL, PIERRE   Les Heures de la Femme a Paris. Paris, Editions
Boudet, 1903. Sm. 4to., full Prussian blue levant mor., uncut edges, orig. wr.
bound in, slipcase, bound by Ch. Meunier, 1907, ltd. ed., 250 copies prtd., 1 of
25 numbered copies on Japan, plts., orig. watercolors by Pierre Vidal, signed &
dated. Goldschmid-110-75 1978 $1,350

VIDE, V. V.   Sketches of Aboriginal Life. New York, 1846.
MacManus 239-1221 1978 $22.50

VIERA, M. LAFFITTE   West Philadelphia Illustrated...   Philadelphia, 1903. 1st ed., sm. 4to., illus., scarce. MacManus 239-1650 1978 $60

VIERO, FRANCESCO   Descrizione d'un Apparecchio di Macchine Per Cavare e Mannigiare le Arie Generalmente Dette Fisse. Bologna, 1788. Engr. vignette, fldg. copperplts., 8vo., contemp. blue wrs., spine damaged, lst ed. Offenbacher 30-155 1978 $115

LES VIES Et Motz Dorez Des Sept Sages De Grece:.... Paris, 1554. 16mo., Roman and Italic letter, small round wormhole in lower blank margins, contemp. Parisian calf, gilt centre and corner-pieces, careful repairs to head and foot of spine. Quaritch 978-140 1978 $1,100

VIEUCHANGE, MICHEL   Smara.   London, (1933). Folding map, 29 illus., cr. 8vo, orig. cloth. K Books 239-503 1978 £6

VIEWS of Buffalo. Buffalo & Portland, (1905). Side opening 8vo, unnumbered pages, plts. from photos. Butterfield 21-82 1978 $15

VIEWS of Portsmouth, Ohio, U. S. A. N.P., (1890). Cloth. Hayman 72-572 1978 $15

VIEWS of the Department of Medicine of the University of Texas, Galveston. Galveston, c.1895. Printed wr. Jenkins 116-486 1978 $15

VIEWS of the University of Texas. Austin, 1911. Photos and illus. Jenkins 116-1390 1978 $12.50

VIGENERE, BLAISE DE   Traicte des Chiffres, ou Secretes Manieres d'Escrire. Paris, 1587. Woodcuts, 4to., cont. calf, first ed., second issue. Schumann 511-68 1978 sFr 1,400

VIGERUS, F.   De praecipuis Graecae dictionis idiotaismis liber, cum animadversionibus H. Hoogeveri, quibus adjunxit et suas J. C. Zeunius. Lipsae, 1788. Contemp. calf, 8vo. George's 635-519 1978 £7.50

VIGNOLA, GIACOMO BAROZZI DA   Livre Nouveau Ou Regles Des Cinq Ordres D'Architecture, Par Jaques Barozzio de Vignole... Paris, 1767. Folio, plts., t.p. sl. soiled, mottled calf gilt, corners rubbed. Quaritch 983-55 1978 $725

VIGNOLES, O.J.   Memoir of Sir Robert P. Stewart, Mus. Doc. 1898. lst ed., ex lib, lacks fly, very good, octavo bound in cloth. Hyland 128-574 1978 £8.50

VILA, VINCENTE   The Portola Expedition of 1769-1770: The Diary of... Berkeley, 1911. Original printed wr. Ginsberg 14-214 1978 $15

VILAS, WILLIAM F.   Letter from...Transmitting the Report of the Commission to Negotiate with the Band of Ute Indians in Southern Colorado for Such Modification of Their Treaty and Other Rights... Washington, 1889. Folding map, disbound, lst ed. Ginsberg 14-1015 1978 $25

VILAS, WILLIAM F.   Letter from...Transmitting the Report of the Surveyor-General of New Mexico on Private Land Claim No. 156, Known as Los Ranchos. Washington, 1880. Folding map, disbound, lst ed. Ginsberg 14-782 1978 $25

VILLANI, FILIPPO   Le Vite D'Uomini Illustri Fiorentini.... Venezia, 1747. 4to., marbled bds., calf spine, very good, first ed. King 7-253 1978 £50

VILLARD, OSWALD GARRISON   John Brown, 1800-1859. Boston, 1910. Illus., 8vo., lst ed., orig. cloth. Morrill 241-595 1978 $20

VILLARD, OSWALD GARRISON   John Brown, 1800-1859. Boston, 1910. Illus., lst ed., inner hinges split. Biblo 248-68 1978 $20

VILLARI, L.   Giovanni Segantini, the Story of his Life. 1907. Reproductions in half-tone and photogravure, imp. 8vo. George's 635-210 1978 £7.50

VILLARI, PASQUALE   The Life and Times of Girolamo Savonarola. London, 1888. Cloth, covers faded, illus., 2 vols. Biblo 247-483 1978 $17.50

VILLARI, PASQUALE   Life and Times of Girolamo Savonarola. New York, 1896. Illus., top of spine chipped. Biblo 251-276 1978 $15

VILLARI, PASQUALE   Life & Times of Girolamo Savonarola. (1909). Plt. Allen 234-1444 1978 $7.50

VILLE, ANTOINE DE   Les Fortifications, Contenans la Maniere de Fortifier Toute Sorte de Places... Paris, 1666. 8vo., plts., contemp. mottled calf gilt. Quaritch 983-56 1978 $130

VILLEGAS, DON ESTEVAN MANUEL DE   Las Eroticas o Amatorias. Naxera, 1618. 1st ed., quarto, notes in 19th-century hand bound in, full contemporary limp vellum, lightly foxed, rare. Bennett 20-221 1978 $725

VILLENEUVE, MARQUIS DE   Charles X et Louis XIX en exil. 1889. Half mor., 8vo. George's 635-789 1978 £5.25

VILLERMONT, COMTESSE MARIE DE   Histoire de la Coiffure Feminine. Bruxelles, 1891. Color frontis., plts. in black & white, illus., 4to., half mor., marbled bd. sides, dampstained, nice, lst ed. Morrill 241-596 1978 $112.50

VILLETTE, JOHN   A Genuine Account of the Behaviour and Dying Words of William Dodd. 1777. 2nd. ed., 8vo., binder's cloth, author's signature on title cut into. Hannas 54-88 1978 £10

VILLIERS, ALAN J.   The Making of a Sailor. London, 1938. Sm. 4to, orig. cloth, illus. with over 200 photos. Sexton 7-169 1978 £12

VILLIERS, GEORGE, DUKE OF BUCKINGHAM
Please turn to
BUCKINGHAM, GEORGE VILLIERS, DUKE OF

VILLIFRANCHI, GIOVANNI   Descrizione Della Barriera, e Della Mascherata, Fatta in Firenze a' XVII. Firenze, 1613. 4to., bds., lst ed. Offenbacher 30-51 1978 $350

VILLON, FRANCOIS   Autres Poesies de Maistre Francois Villon et de son Ecole. Eragny Press, 1901. Ltd. to 226 copies, printed in red and black, woodcut frontis., orig. patterned bds., edges uncut. George's 635-892 1978 £105

VILLON, FRANCOIS   Les Oevres. La Haye, 1942. 8vo., bds., ltd. ed. of 325 copies. Van der Peet H-64-460 1978 Dfl 60

VINCENT, FRANCIS   A History of the State of Delaware From Its First Settlement Until the Present Time... Philadelphia, 1870. Orig. 15 parts bound in vol. I. Baldwins' 51-236 1978 $55

VINCENT, LEON H.   De Witt Miller. Cambridge, 1912. Pres. inscrip., signed by Vincent. Battery Park 1-27 1978 $75

VINCENT, WILLIAM 1739-1815   The Periplus of the Erythrean Sea. 1800-05. Portrait, first ed., table, plts., maps, 2 vols., 4to., contemp. sprinkled calf. Howes 194-502 1978 £55

VINES, RICHARD   The Hearse of the Renowned, Robert Earle of Essex and Ewe.... 1646. Engraved portrait, text browned, sm. 4to., neat in full diced calf. George's 635-1148 1978 £10.50

VINEY, JOHNNY   Sailors are Gobs of Fun, Hattie. 1943. Illus. by Poucher. Austin 80-357 1978 $10

VINOGRADOFF, P.   English Society in the Eleventh Century; essays in English medieval history. Oxford, 1908. 8vo. Upcroft 12-477 1978 £8.50

VIRCHOW, RUDOLPH   Cellular Pathology as Based Upon Physiological and Pathological Histology. New York, n.d. First Amer. ed. Rittenhouse 49-805 1976 $75

VIRGIL
Please turn to
VERGILIUS MARO, PUBLIUS

VIRKUS, FREDERICK ADAMS   The Abridged Compendium of American Genealogy. Chicago, 1925. Vol. I. Baldwins' 51-268 1978 $25

VISCONTI, E. Q.   Oeuvres, Musce Pie-Clementin. Milan, 1820. Plts., many stained, 4to., half mor., rubbed. George's 635-66 1978 £18

VISIT To The Chinese Coast and Other Books for the Young. (New York, n.d. c.1850?). Clean, orig. binding. Hayman 71-387 1978 $8.50

VISITS To 'The Religious World'. 1829. 1st. ed., orig. calf, leading hinge & tail of spine worn. Jarndyce 16-260 1978 £10.50

VISSING, MARY L.   Sawdust. Boston, 1945. Frontis., first ed., d.j., ex-lib. Austin 82-294 1978 $20

VITAL Records of Winchendon...to the End of the Year 1849. Worcester, 1909. 8vo. Morrill 239-519 1978 $7.50

VITALIS DE FURNO   Pro Conservanda Sanitate, Tvendaqve prospera Valetvdine, ad Totivs Hvmani Corporis Morbos et aegritvdines, salvtarivm remediorvm. Mogvntiae, 1531. Sm. folio, woodcut, modern vellum over bds., faint dampstain, slight browning, fine copy, 1st ed., rare. Zeitlin 245-282 1978 $1,750

VITI, LUDOVICO   Chi cerca, truova Dialoghi D'un Romano.... 1713. 8vo., limp vellum, slightly damaged. King 7-254 1978 £35

VITRUVIUS POLLIO, MARCUS   De Architectura Livri Dece traducti de Latino in Vulgare affigurati. Como, 1521. 1st ed., folio, full-page, half-page and smaller woodcuts, vellum over boards. Gilhofer 75-109 1978 SFr 19,500

VITRUVIUS POLLIO, MARCUS   I Dieci Libri dell' Architettura di M. Vitruvio. Venetia, 1629. Folio, limp vellum, woodcut illus., woodcut initials. King 7-110 1978 £135

VITRUVIUS POLLIO, MARCUS   The Architecture of Marcus Vitruvius Pollio, in Ten Books. 1826. 1st. ed., engraved plts., engraved vignettes on india paper, 4to, contemp. calf, gilt, possible a lg. paper copy of which only 25 were issued. Fenning 32-340 1978 £36

VITRUVIUS POLLIO, MARCUS   The Ten Books of Architecture. Cambridge, 1914. Roy. 8vo., plts., cloth. Quaritch 983-57 1978 $65

VIVA, DOMENICO   Damnatae Theses ab Alex. VII.... Padua, 1711. Portrait, 4 parts in 1 vol., contemp. vellum, label missing, 8vo. Howes 194-582 1978 £20

VIZETELLY, HENRY   Paris in Perils. 1882. 1st. ed., 2 vols., illus., half titles, orig. cloth, fine. Jarndyce 16-1158 1978 £18.50

VLEKKE, BERNARD HUBERTUS MARIA   Hollanders Who Helped Build America. 1942. Illus., ex-lib. Austin 79-804 1978 $37.50

VLOBERG, M.   l'Eucharistie Dans l'Art. Grenoble-Paris, 1946. 2 vols., colored plts. & other plts., 8vo., orig. covers. Van der Peet H-64-219 1978 Dfl 70

A VOCABULARY Or Such Words in the English Language as are of Dubious or Unsettled Accentuation in Which the Pronunciation of Sheridan, Walker and Other Orthoepists is Compared. 1797/ 1st. ed., orig. blue bds., paper spine, uncut. Jarndyce 16-74 1978 £38

VOET, P.   Ac Philosophiae in academ ultraj.... 1646. 12mo., vellum. George's 635-1522 1978 £10.50

VOGEL, JULIUS   The Official Handbook of New Zealand. 1875. 1st. ed., mounted photo plts., folding maps, plts., illus., 8vo, orig. cloth-backed printed paper wrapper, nice. Fenning 32-341 1978 £28.50

VOGEL-JORGENSEN T.   Peter Lassen Af California. 1937. Illus., in Danish. Austin 79-807 1978 $27.50

A VOICE from Greece, in Appeal to the Sympathies and Charities of America. (New York), 1828. Disbound. Hayman 73-720 1978 $12.50

VOILIER, JEAN   Ville Ouverte. Paris, 1942. Sm. 4-o., orig. pict. wr., uncut, ltd. ed., 430 numbered copies prtd. on Docelles paper, illus. by Paul Valery. Goldschmidt 110-70 1978 $45

VOJAN, E. S.   Velky New York. 1908. Illus., fldg. map. Austin 79-808 1978 $37.50

VOLATERRANUS, RAPHAEL
Please turn to
MAFFEI, RAFFAELE

VOLAVKA, V.   Praha. Praha, 1948. 4to., cloth, colored frontis., plts., text illus. Van der Peet H-64-220 1978 Dfl 65

THE VOLCANO Under the City. New York, 1887. 16mo., good copy, 1st ed., orig. bind. Petrilla 13-145 1978 $14

VOLLENHOVEN, M. W. R. VAN   Het Geslacht Van Vollenhoven (Oud-Overijselsch Geslacht). Brussel, 1918. Lg. 4to., colored frontis., portrs., facs.-illus. Van der Peet H-64- 576 1978 Dfl 150

VOLNEY, CONSTANTIN F.   Voyage En Syrie et en Egypte, 1783-1785. 1787. Maps, folding views, 2 vols., contemp. calf, 8vo, repaired. Edwards 1012-89 1978 £60

VOLTA, ALESSANDRO   Collezione dell'Opere. Florence, 1816. 8vo., 5 parts in 3 vols., port. of author, fold plts., contemp. half-vellum, fine, 1st ed. Gilhofer 74-127 1978 sFr 1,700

VOLTA, ALESSANDRO   Lettere sulla Meteorologia Elettrica. Pavia, (1788). 8vo., 3 vols., plts., contemp. half calf, marbled bds., red mor. labels, gilt back, very fine set, rare, 1st ed. Gilhofer 74-126 1978 sFr 3,000

VOLTAIRE, FRANCOIS MARIE AROUET DE   Amelie ou Le Duc De Foix, Tragedie. London, 1753. 8vo., wr., fine. Fenning 32-342 1978 £18

VOLTAIRE, FRANCOIS MARIE AROUET DE   Kandide Oder die Beste Welt. Munich, 1920. Sm. 4to., publisher's 1/2 cloth, illus. with pen & ink compositions by Paul Klee. Goldschmidt 110-33 1978 $100

VOLTAIRE, FRANCOIS MARIE AROUET DE   Candide. New York, 1928. Illus., embossed, gilt buckram, fine, 1 of 1470 numbered copies signed by Rockwell Kent, flannel-lined slipcase. Dawson's 447-84 1978 $60

VOLTAIRE, FRANCOIS MARIE AROUET DE   Candide. New York, 1930. Illus. & decor. by Rockwell Kent, imp. 8vo., spine faded. George's 635-188 1978 £8.50

VOLTAIRE, FRANCOIS MARIE AROUET DE   Candide and Other Romances. London, n.d. Drawings, very good or better. Limestone 9-311 1978 $10

VOLTAIRE, FRANCOIS MARIE AROUET DE   Candide. Illus. by Rockwell Kent, 1470 copies, numbered, signed by Rockwell Kent. Battery Park 1-188 1978 $100

VOLTAIRE, FRANCOIS MARIE AROUET DE   La Henriade avec des Variantes et des Notes. Londres, 1734. 2 parts in 1 vol., sm. 8vo., contemp. calf, spine gilt. Howes 194-505 1978 £15

VOLTAIRE, FRANCOIS MARIE AROUET DE   The History of the War of Seventeen Hundred and Forty-One. London, 1756. 1st Eng. ed., octavo, contemp. speckled calf, rubbed. Bennett 20-222 1978 $150

VOLTAIRE, FRANCOIS MARIE AROUET DE   The History of the War of Seventeen Hundred and Forty-One. 1756. Contemp. calf, lettering piece, 8vo. Howes 194-506 1978 £30

VOLTAIRE, FRANCOIS MARIE AROUET DE   Huit Contes. Nantes-Paris, 1947. Lg. 8vo., orig. covers, prtd. in red & black, watercolor illus. by Bruneau, ltd. ed. of 300 numbered copies, extra set of plts. Van der Peet H-64-461 1978 Dfl 125

VOLTAIRE, FRANCOIS MARIE AROUET DE   L'Ingenu. 1934. Ltd. ed., colored plts. by B. Saint-Andre, 4to., decor. bds. George's 635-1523 1978 £12.50

VOLTAIRE, FRANCOIS MARIE AROUET DE   The Princess of Babylon. Nonesuch Press, 1927. Decor. by T. Lowinsky, ltd. ed., on Batchelor's Kelmscott handmade paper, fcap. 8vo., orig. qtr. parchment. George's 635-919 1978 £10

VOLTAIRE, FRANCOIS MARIE AROUET DE   The Princess of Babylon. None-such Press, 1927. 1st ed., no. 5 of 1500 copies, illus. by Thomas Lowinsky, top & tail of spine little darkened, otherwise very good. Jarndyce 16-1216 1978 £8.50

VOLTAIRE, FRANCOIS MARIE AROUET DE   The Princess of Babylon. London, 1927. 12mo., marbled bds. with vellum back, decor. by Thomas Lowinsky, 1 of 1500 copies prtd. on handmade paper, fine. Duschnes 220-218 1978 $15

VOLTAIRE, FRANCOIS MARIE AROUET DE   The Princess of Babylon. London, Nonesuch Press, 1927. Sm. 8vo., bds., frontis. & illus. by Th. Lowinsky, ltd. ed. of 1500 numbered copies, uncut. Van der Peet H-64-409 1978 Dfl 50

VOLTAIRE, FRANCOIS MARIE AROUET DE   La Pucelle D'Orleans... 1762. Nouvelle ed., 20 engrs., full modern calf, raised bands, gilt spine. Eaton 45-520 1978 £30

VON BORCKE, HEROS   Memoirs of the Confederate War for Independence. New York, 1938. 2 vols., map, 1st pub. in 1866. MacManus 239-911 1978 $32.50

VONDEL, J. VAN DEN   Adam in Ballingschap, of Aller Treurspeelen Treur-spel. Maastricht, 1922. Lg. 8vo., ltd. ed. of 580 numbered copies only. Van der Peet H-64-389 1978 Dfl 35

VON HASE, K.   Handbook to the Controversy with Rome. 1906. 2 vols., roy. 8vo., covers faded. George's 635-1147 1978 £7.50

VON HASSELL, ULRICH   Diaries, 1938-1944. New York, 1947. 1st Amer. ed. Biblo 247-752 1978 $15

VON HUTTEN, BETTINA   He and Hecuba. 1905. Austin 82-1046 1978 $8.50

VON HUTTEN, BETTINA ,   Our Lady of the Beeches. New York, 1902. Very slightly spotted, dec. cloth, spine soiled, bookplt. of Bessie & Alan Sullivan. Eaton 45-522 1978 £5

VON HUTTEN, BETTINA   Our Lady of the Beeches. 1902. First ed. Austin 82-1047 1978 $12.50

VON KLARWILL, VICTOR   The Fugger News-Letters 1568-1605. 1924. Illus. Austin 80-622 1978 $20

VON POLLNITZ, K. L.   The Amorous Adventures of Augustus of Saxony. 1929. Plts., 8vo. George's 635-1230 1978 £5.25

VOORHIES, FELIX   Acadian Reminiscenses, with the True Story of Evangline. Opelousas, 1907. Illus. Hood 117-279 1978 $25

VOORHIES, FELIX   Acadian Reminiscences. Louisiana, 1907. Illus., autographed by author, cover stained, Bell Wiley's copy. Broadfoot's 44-891 1978 $12.00

VORAGINE, JACOBUS
Please turn to
JACOBUS DE VARAGINE

VORSE, MARY HEATON   Time and the Town. New York, 1942. 1st ed., nice copy, d.j. MacManus 239-297 1978 $15

VOSE, JAMES W.   Catalogue of Piano-Fortes Manufactured by James W. Vose, Amory Hall Building, No. 323 Washington St., Boston. Boston, 1859. 8vo., original tan printed wrs., very good copy. Ximenes 47-313 1978 $35

VOSSIUS, GERARDUS JOANNES   De Artis Poeticae Natura, ac Constitutione Liber. Amsterdam, 1647. Vellum, binding and pages crinkled by damp. Allen 234-1491 1978 $30

VOSSIUS, GERARDUS JOANNES   Gerardi Ioannis Vossii de Quatuor Artibus Popularibus de Philologia et Scientiis Matematicis cui Operi Subjungitur... Amstelaedami, 1660. Quarto, half vellum over marbled bds., fine. Bennett 20-223 1978 $225

VOSSIUS, GERARDUS JOANNES   Lattina Grammatica..In Usum Scholarum. Amsterdam, 1680. 12mo., full vellum, fine. Victoria 34-837 1978 $85

VOSSLER, KARL   Mediaeval Culture. 1929. 2 vols., 8vo., green cloth, faded. Eaton 45-135 1978 £8

VOUTE, EMILE   The Passport. 1915. First ed., frayed d.j., pres. copy inscribed by author. Austin 82-1048 1978 $27.50

THE VOYAGE of the First Hessian Army from Portsmouth to New York, 1776. New York, (1915). Sm. 4to., bds., uncut, backstrip chipped, one of 110 copies printed. Wolfe 39-236 1978 $25

VOYCE, ARTHUR   Russian Architecture. New York, (1948). Illus. Biblo 247-315 1978 $12.50

VOYNICH, ETHEL LILLIAN   The Gadfly. NY, 1897. Fir. Ed., floral end papers, orig. cloth binding, lacks front end paper, good copy. Greene 78-308 1978 $30.00

VREDEMANN DE VRIES, JOANNES
Please turn to
VRIES, JAN VREDEMAN DE

VRIES, HUGO DE   Di Mutationslehre. Leipzig, 1901-1903. 1st ed., cloth, orig. pr. wr. bound in, 2 vols., 4to. Gilhofer 75-30 1978 SFr 800

VRIES, JAN VREDEMAN DE   Perspective. Leyden, 1604-05. Very rare, first ed., oblong folio, 2 parts in 1 vol., cont. limp vellum, plts., fine. Gilhofer 75-111 1978 sFr 3800

VRIESLAND, V. E. VAN   Het Werk en de Mens Nico van Suchtelen. Amsterdam, 1948. 8vo., cloth, frontis. portr. Van der Peet H-64-390 1978 Dfl 30

VULLIAMY, C. E.   Aspasia: The Life and Letters of Mary Granville, Mrs. Delany. 1935. Plts., orig. cloth, 8vo. Howes 194-777 1978 £6.50

VULLIAMY, C. E.   Outlanders. London, (1938). Frontis, 3 maps, orig. cloth, 8vo, covers dull. K Books 239-506 1978 £6

VUILLIER, GASTON   La Danza.... Milano, 1899. Illus., sm. folio, half parchment. George's 635-1418 1978 £18

VULPES, BENEDETTO   Onori Funebre Renduti a Domenico Cotugno. Napoli, 1824. 4to., frontis. portr., calf backed blind-stamped blue floral bds., gilt on spine, very good copy, 1st ed. Zeitlin 245-48 1978 $122.50

VYNER, ROBERT T.   Notitia Venatica. London, 1841. 1st ed., royal 8vo., handcolored prints by Alken, 3/4 red mor., marbled bds., very fine, near mint. Current 24-242 1978 $225

VYNNE, HAROLD R.   The Woman That's Good. A Story of the Undoing of a Dreamer. Chicago, (1900). Cloth, slight wear, rare. Hayman 72-243 1978 $10

W

W., H.　　　　　　Something New Out of Africa. London, 1934.
4 maps, 108 illus., 4to., orig. cloth. K Books 239-507 1978 £7

WAAGEN, DR.　　　Treasures of Art in Great Britain. 1854. 3 vols.,
drawings, 8vo. George's 635-67 1978 £6.50

WACHTEL, CURT　　　Chemical Warfare. 1941. Austin 80-358 1978
$12.50

WACK, HENRY WELLINGTON　　The Story of the Congo Free State. New York,
1905. Folding coloured map, 1 other map, 120 plts. & illus., roy. 8vo, neatly
recased in orig. cloth. K Books 239-508 1978 £10

WADD, WILLIAM　　　Comments on Corpulency, Lineaments of Lean-
ness, Mems on Diet and Diatetics. London, 1829. 8vo., plts. by author, near
contemp. cloth, leather label, a little worn. Quaritch 977-81 1978 £35

WADDEL, JOHN N.　　　Memorials of Academic Life. Richmond, 1891.
Bell Wiley's copy. Broadfoot's 44-804 1978 $14.00

WADDELL, ALFRED-MOORE　　A Colonial Officer and His Times 1754-1773, a
Biographical Sketch of Gen. Hugh Waddell of N.C. Raleigh, 1890. Broadfoot
50-324 1978 $40

WADDELL, HELEN　　　Beasts and Saints. 1934. Woodcuts by R. Gibbings, 8vo. George's 635-162 1978 £5

WADDELL, J. JEFFREY　　Rambles through Lanarkshire. Hamilton, 1911.
Illus., cr. 8vo., orig. cloth. K Books 244-457 1978 £5

WADDELL, JAMES D.　　　Biographical Sketch of Linton Stephens. Georgia,
1877. Pres. copy from author, cover worn. Broadfoot's 44-874 1978 $35

WADDELL, JOSEPH A.　　　Annals of Augusta County, Virginia...with a
Diary of the War 1861-5 and a Chapter on Reconstruction. Richmond, 1886.
Hinges cracked, Bell Wiley's copy. Broadfoot's 44-673 1978 $40

WADDELL, LAWRENCE A.　　　Lhasa and Its Mysteries, With a Record of the
Expedition of 1903-1904. 3rd. ed., coloured frontis, coloured illus., lg. folding
map & other maps, plts., 8vo, orig. cloth, binding dull but sound, very good.
Fenning 32-343 1978 £24

WADDINGTON, GEORGE　　A Visit to Greece, In 1823 and 1824. London,
1825. 8vo, half-title, folding engraved map, leaf of addendum, polished half
calf, marbled bds., gilt back, pres. inscription. Deighton 5-149 1978 £48

WADDINGTON, MARY KING　Chateau and Country Life in France. New York,
1908. Illus. Biblo 247-755 1978 $15

WADDINGTON, SAMUEL　　Arthur Hugh Clough. London, 1883. 8vo,
original blue cloth (a trifle rubbed), 1st ed., very good copy. Ximenes 47-322
1978 $22.50

WADE, HOUSTON　　　The Dawson Men of Fayette County. Houson,
1932. Jenkins 116-304 1978 $35

WADE, JOHN DONALD　　Augustus Baldwin Longstreet. NY, 1924.
Bell Wiley's copy. Broadfoot's 44-875 1978 $15.00

WADSWORTH, E.　　　Sailing Ships and Barges of the Western Mediterranean and Adriatic Seas. 1926. Ltd. to 450 copies, map, plts. and vignettes
hand-coloured, sm. folio, orig. qtr. linen, cloth sides, slightly faded, edges uncut.
George's 635-864 1978 £110

WAETZOLDT, WILHELM　　Durer und Seine Zeit. Vienna, Phaidon Press,
(1935). Plts., many mounted & in color. Biblo 251-197 1978 $42.50

WAFA, SHAIKH　　　Commentarius in Ruzname Naurus sive Tabulae
aequinoctiales novi Persarum & Turcarum anni. Augsburg, 1676. 4to, engraved
plts. by Melchior Haffner, light water-staining in upper margins, leaves embrowned
due to quality of paper, contemp. vellum, 1st ed. Quaritch 978-124 1978
$1,900

WAFER, LIONEL　　　A New Voyage and Description of the Isthmus of
America... London, 1699. Fldg. map, fldg. plts., 8vo., modern calf. Salloch
345-192 1978 $600

WAFER, LIONEL　　　A New Voyage and Description of the Isthmus of
America, Giving an Account of the Author's Abode there, the Form and the Make
of the Country. London, 1699. 1st ed., sm. 8vo., except. scarce, fine copy,
fldg. map, plts., interior clean & crisp, full calf with raised bands, rare. Current Misc. 8-46 1978 $985

WAFER, LIONEL　　　Les Voyages de Lionnel Waffer Contenant une
Description Tres-exacte de l'Isthme de l'Amerique et de Toute la Nouvelle Espagne.
Paris, 1706. Calf, 1st French ed., nice copy. Hayman 72-771 1978 $125

WAGENKNECHT, EDWARD　　Great Modern American Stories. 1920. Austin
82-488a 1978 $15

WAGER, DANIEL E.　　　Col. Marinus Willett. Utica, 1891. Wrps.,
sm. piece missing from corner of front wrapper, not affecting printing. Hayman
71-499 1978 $7.50

WAGER, DANIEL E.　　　Our County and Its People...Oneida County
New York. Boston, 1896. Lg. thick 4to., rebound. MacManus 239-1095
1978 $75

WAGGONER, CLARK　　History of the City of Toledo and Lucas County,
Ohio. New York & Toledo, 1888. New, clean. Hayman 71-562 1978 $55

WAGNER, A. R.　　　A Catalogue of English Mediaeval Rolls of Arms.
1950. Lg. 8vo., plts. Upcroft 12-481 1978 £5.50

WAGNER, D. P.　　　War Service Records, 1939-1945. Toronto, 1947.
Ltd. ed., illus. Hood 117-158 1978 $25

WAGNER, DANIEL　　　Uber das Kalium, die Verbindungen der Ersten
Stufe der Zusammensetzung Desselben und Uber das Atzkali. Wien, 1825. 8vo.,
orig. prtd. wrs., uncut, 1st ed. Offenbacher 30-156 1978 $50

WAGNER, FELIX　　　A Handbook of Chiropody. London, 1909. 8vo.,
2nd ed., illus., text dampstained. Morrill 239-270 1978 $8.50

WAGNER, HENRY RAUP　　California Voyages, 1539-1541. San Francisco,
1925. Illus., orig. cloth. Ginsberg 14-1019 1978 $85

WAGNER, HENRY RAUP　　The Cartography of the Northwest Coast of
America to the Year 1800. Berkeley, 1937. First ed., fine, d.w., boxed, 2 vols,
4to., maps. Biblo 247-456 1978 $200

WAGNER, HENRY RAUP　　Sir Francis Drake's Voyage Around the World:....
San Francisco, 1926. Illus., orig. cloth, 1st ed. Ginsberg 14-1020 1978 $125

WAGNER, J.　　　The Boxer. New York, 1947. 8vo, orig. cloth.
Book Chest 17-401 1978 $17

WAGNER, RICHARD　　Drei Operndichtungen nebst einer Mittheilung
an seine Freunde als Vorwort. Leipzig, 1852. 1st ed., 8vo, contem. half-cloth,
lightly rubbed. Gilhofer 75-112 1978 SFr 900

WAGNER, RICHARD　　"Lohengrin." London, (c. 1890s). Colored plts.,
full-grained blue mor., hand-marbled endpapers, orig. bind., linen slipcase
Petrilla 13-146 1978 $45

WAGNER, RICHARD　　My Life. 1911. Best English ed., frontispieces,
2 vols., orig. cloth, 8vo. Howes 194-1306 1978 £12

WAGNER, RICHARD　　Oper und Drama. Leipzig, 1852. 1st ed.,
contemp. half-cloth. Gilhofer 75-113 1978 SFr 1,100

WAGNER, RICHARD　　The Rhine-Gold. New York, Merrymount Press,
1907. Prtd. in several colors, t.e.g. Battery Park 1-203 1978 $22.50

WAGNER, RICHARD　　The Rhinegold and the Valkyrie. 1939. Coloured
plts. by Arthur Rackham, roy. 8vo. George's 635-202 1978 £30

WAGNER, RICHARD   The Tale of Lohengrin, Knight of the Swan. London, n.d. 1st ed., Pictorial gilt cover and spine, fine, original labelled pictorial slip-case, reinforced.   Victoria 34-626 1978 $150

WAGNER, RICHARD   Tannhauser. London, (1911). Printed on grey paper, tipp-in color plates, very fine, original pictorial box, reinforced.   Victoria 34-627 1978 $165

WAGNER, RUDOLPH   Icones Zootomicae. Leipzig, 1841. Folio, engr. plts., orig. cloth-backed bds., lightly browned & foxed, marginal dampstains, good copy, ex-lib., 1st ed.   Zeitlin 245-283 1978 $150

WAGSTAFFE, WILLIAM   A Comment Upon the History of Tom Thumb. London, 1711. 8vo, disbound, 1st ed., very good copy.   Ximenes 47-323 1978 $250

WAIN, LOUIS   Peter. A Cat O'One Tail. New York-London, 1892. 1st Amer. ed., text illus., pictorial boards of heavily bandaged and damaged, very good.   Victoria 34-838 1978 $30

WAINEWRIGHT, LATHAM   The Literary and Scientific Pursuits. 1815. 8vo., contemp. calf gilt, fine.   P. M. Hill 142-101 1978 £20

WAIT, BENJAMIN   Letters from Van Dieman's Land, Written During Four Years Imprisonment for Political Offences Committed in Upper Canada... Buffalo, 1843. Orig. bds. worn, some foxing.   Hood 116-272 1978 $185

WAITE, ARTHUR EDWARD   The Holy Grail, its Legends and Symbolism. 1932. Roy. 8vo.   George's 635-1438 1978 £12.50

WAITE, ARTHUR EDWARD   Lives of Alchemystical Philosophers Based on Materials Collected in 1815 and Supplemented by Recent Researches... London, 1888. Orig. bind.   Americanist 102-4 1978 $50

WAITE, ARTHUR EDWARD   A New Encyclopaedia of Freemasonry... London, 1923. 2 vols., sm. 4to, orig. cloth, plts., illus.   Sexton 7-142 1978 £16

WAITE, C. V.   The Mormon Prophet and His Harem;.... Cambridge, 1886. Illus., orig. cloth, 1st ed.   Ginsberg 14-694 1978 $25

WAITE, F. D.   San Diego: The City and the County. San Diego, 1888. Map, original pict. wr., 1st ed.   Ginsberg 14-215 1978 $65

WAITE, FREDERICK CLAYTON   The First Medical College in Vermont. Castleton, 1818-1862. Montpelier, 1949.   Rittenhouse 49-808 1976 $12.50

WAKA Sanju-Rokkasen. c. 1610. Unobtrusive wormholes filled in at beginning and end, orig. fukoro-toji with prussian blue covers decorated with floral motif, enclosed in later brocade case.   Quaritch 978-86 1978 $5,000

WAKE, H.   Swift and Bold. Aldershot, 1949. Plts., port., maps, 8vo., orig. cloth, mint, orig. d.j.   F. Edwards 1013-523 1978 £12

WAKEFIELD, H. R.   The Clock Strikes Twelve. Sauk City, 1946. One of 4,000 copies, good in mint dw.   Bernard 5-435 1978 $30

WAKEFIELD, PRISCILLA 1751-1832   An Introduction to the Natural History and Classification of Insects. 1816. First ed., plts., fcap. 8vo., orig. bds., entirely uncut, one joint cracked, spine worn, good copy in orig. state.   Howes 194-349 1978 £25

WAKELEY, J. B.   The Heroes of Methodism: Containing Sketches of Eminent Methodist Ministers. Toronto, n.d. 11th. ed.   Hood's 115-950 1978 $10

WAKEMAN, STEPHEN H.   The Stephen H. Wakeman Collection of Nineteenth Century American Writers...First Editions, Inscribed Presentation and Personal Copies, Original Manuscripts and Letters of Nine American Authors.... New York, 1924. Orig. cloth, paper label, fine.   MacManus 238-1072 1978 $40

WAKSMAN, S.   Humus. London, 1936. 8vo, orig. cloth.   Book Chest 17-402 1978 $35

WALBURGA, ST.   Sacerdos Eystettensis des, ac Thaumaturgae Virgini et ordinis Sacreti Benedicti abbatissae Heiden heimensi divae Walburgae devotus.... Eystadii, 1722. Sm. 8vo., old sheep worn.   George's 635-1149 1978 £5

WALCOTT, EARLE A.   Blindfolded. Indianapolis, (1906). Cloth, 1st ed. in book form.   Hayman 73-30 1978 $8.50

WALCOTT, MARY VAUX   North American Wild Flowers. Washington, 1925. Color plts., 5 vols., ex-lib, folio, orig. cloth.   Book Chest 17-403 1978 $100

WALD, LILLIAN D.   Windows on Henry Street. Boston, 1934. Illus. with drwgs., 1st ed. in slightly frayed dust jacket.   Austin 79-811 1978 $15

WALD, LILLIAN D.   Windows on Henry Street. 1934. Drwgs., 1st ed., frayed dust jacket, inscr'd by author.   Austin 79-810 1978 $17.50

WALD, LILLIAN D.   Windows on Henry Street. 1934. Illus. with drwgs.   Austin 79-812 1978 $12.50

WALDEGRAVE, JAMES   Memoirs from 1754-58. 1821. First ed., 4to., portrait, contemp. half calf.   Howes 194-508 1978 £21

WALDEN, ARTHUR TREADWELL   A Dog-Puncher on the Yukon. Boston, 1928. Illus.   Hood's 115-83 1978 $20

WALDENMAIER, N. P.   Some of the Earliest Oaths of Allegiance to the U.S. 1944. Good.   Nestler Rare 78-181 1978 $20

WALDIE, GEORGE   A History of the Town and Palace of Linlithgow. Linlithgow, 1868. 2nd ed., frontis., map, illus., cr. 8vo., covers and endpapers very dust-marked, inscribed from the author.   K Books 244-455 1978 £5

WALDMAN, MILTON   Americana. New York, 1925.   Battery Park 1-494 1978 $35

WALDMANN, EMIL   Griechische Originale. Leipzig, 1923. 2nd ed., illus.   Biblo BL781-507 1978 $17.50

WALDO, FULLERTON   The Saga of a Supercargo. Philadelphia, (1926). Illus.   Biblo BL781-10 1978 $9

WALDO, S. PUTNAM   The Life and Character of Stephen Decatur... Middletown, 1822. Lib. stamp, illus., plts., cloth.   MacManus 239-743 1978 $22.50

THE WALDOS. New York, (1849). Plts., some foxing, dampstains, 16mo., orig. cloth.   Morrill 241-601 1978 $7.50

WALDRON, FRANCIS GODOLPHIN 1744-1818   Heigho for a Husband! A Comedy. 1794. Frontispiece, first ed., old calf-backed bds., 8vo.   Howes 194-509 1978 £18

WALDRON, GEORGE   The Compleat Works, In Verse and Prose. N.P., (London), 1731. 1st. collected ed., folio, lg. paper, woodcuts, modern half calf, very good copy, rare.   Hannas 54-167 1978 £275

WALDRON, M.   Snow Man; John Hornby in the Barren Lands. Boston, 1931. Ex-lib., cover scuffed.   Hood's 115-84 1978 $20

WALDSTEIN, CHARLES   Greek Sculpture and Modern Art. Cambridge, 1914. Illus.   Biblo BL781-508 1978 $18.50

WALDSTEIN, CHARLES   The Work of John Ruskin, its Influence upon Modern Thought and Life. 1894. First ed., portrait, cr. 8vo.   Howes 194-1141 1978 £5

WALES, WILLIAM W.   Sketch of St. Anthony and Minneapolis, Minnesota Territory. Minneapolis, 1857. Woodcuts, original printed wr., rare issue.   Ginsberg 14-575 1978 $125

WALEY, ARTHUR   Chinese Poems. 1946. Very good, worn d.w., first English ed.   Bell Book 16-868 1978 £5.50

WALEY, ARTHUR   The No Plays of Japan. 1921. Plts., near fine, unopened, first English ed.   Bell Book 16-869 1978 £15

WALFORD, C.   Gilds, their Origin, Constitution, Objects and Later History. 1879. Roy. 8vo.   George's 635-419 1978 £5

WALFORD, C.   Gilds, their Origin, Constitution, Objects and Later History. 1888. Roy. 8vo., new and enlarged ed.   George's 635-419 1978 £5

WALKER, ALEXANDER   Intermarriage: The Mode in Which, and the Causes Why, Beauty, Health and Intellect, Result from Certain Unions.... New York, 1842. Rittenhouse 49-809 1976 $40

WALKER, ALEXANDER   Woman Physiologically Considered as to Mind, Morals, Marriage, Matrimonial Slavery, Infidelity, and Divorce. 1840. Second ed., 12mo., 19th-century half calf, gilt back. P. M. Hill 142-232 1978 £35

WALKER, C. B.   The Mississippi Valley and Prehistoric Events... Burlington, 1879. 1st. ed., orig. binding, clean. Hayman 71-754 1978 $25

WALKER, C. IRVINE   The Life of Lieutenant General Richard Heron Anderson of the Confederate States Army. Charleston, 1917. Pres. copy from Virginia S. White, great neice of Anderson, annotations by Mrs. White, cover speckled, Bell Wiley's copy. Broadfoot's 44-378 1978 $75

WALKER, E. RONALD   The Australian Economy in War and Reconstruction. New York, 1947. Biblo 251-386 1978 $17.50

WALKER, EDWARD A.   Our Finest Year of Army Life, An Anniversary Address Delivered to First Regiment of Connecticut Volunteers Heavy Artillery. New Haven, 1862. Wrs., wrs. soiled, spine chipped, Bell Wiley's copy. Broadfoot's 44-438 1978 $16

WALKER, ERIC ANDERSON   The Great Trek. London, 1938. 2nd. ed., 3 maps, 4 plts., 8vo, orig. cloth. K Books 239-509 1978 £12

WALKER, ERIC ANDERSON   A History of South Africa. London, 1935. 12 maps, enlarged reissue, 8vo, orig. cloth. K Books 239-510 1978 £6

WALKER, FRANCIS A.   History of the Second Army Corps in the Army of the Potomac. New York, 1886. Maps, portrs., 8vo., 1st ed., orig. cloth. Morrill 241-602 1978 $15

WALKER, FRANKLIN   A Literary History of Southern California. Berkeley, 1950. Original cloth, d.j., 1st ed. Ginsberg 14-216 1978 $12.50

WALKER, G. A.   The Costume of Yorkshire Illustrated by a Series of Forty Engravings Being Facsimiles of Original Drawings. Leeds, 1885. Lg. folio, coloured frontis., plts., contemp. half mor., orig. pub. in 1814, ltd. to 600 numbered copies. Quaritch 983-77 1978 $700

WALKER, GEORGE LEON   History of the First Church in Hartford, 1633-1883. Hartford, 1884. 1st ed., illus., orig. cloth, fine copy. MacManus 239-99 1978 $30

WALKER, JAMES SCOTT   An Accurate Description of the Liverpool and Manchester Rail-Way... Liverpool, 1831. 3rd. ed., engravings, folding plts., dedicated to George Stephenson, rebound in brown cloth, fine copy. Jarndyce 16-955 1978 £75

WALKER, JOHN   A Critical Pronouncing Dictionary and Expositor of the English Language. 1797. 2nd. ed., 4to, orig. tree calf, red label, corners knocked, hinges weakening, generally v.g. Jarndyce 16-69 1978 £45

WALKER, JOHN   Great American Paintings from Smibert to Bellows, 1729 to 1924. New York, 1943. 4to., plts., some in color. Biblo 247-442 1978 $37.50

WALKER, JOHN   A Rhyming Dictionary answering at the same time the purposes of Spelling and Pronouncing the English Language. 1824. 2 vols., post 8vo., binders cloth. George's 635-1472 1978 £6.50

WALKER, JOSEPH COOPER   Historical Memoir on Italian Tragedy, from the Earliest Period to the Present Time. London, 1799. 4to., half calf, vignettes, first ed. King 7-394 1978 £50

WALKER, JUDSON ELLIOTT   Campaigns of General Custer in the North-west and the Final Surrender of Sitting Bull. New York, 1881. Illus., original wr., 1st ed. Ginsberg 14-300 1978 $125

WALKER, R. A.   Some Unknown Drawings of Aubrey Beardsley Collected and Annotated. London, 1923. 1 of 500 numbered copies, 4to., illus. with plates & photographs, uncut, d.j., fine. Houle 10-24 1978 $145

WALKER, ROBERT J.   Abstract of Mr. Walker's Speech on the Texas Treaty. Washington, 1844. Jenkins 116-1428 1978 $65

WALKER, ROBERT J.   Letter Relative to the Annexation of Texas,.... Washington, 1844. 1st ed., 1st issue, scarce. Jenkins 116-1429 1978 $60

WALKER, WILLIAM   Memoirs of the Distinguished Men of Science of Great Britain Living in the Years 1807-08. London, 1862. 8vo., frontis., orig. cloth, uncut, case, v.g. Norman 5**7 1978 $95

WALKER, WILLIAM   A Treatise of English Particles, Shewing Much of the Variety of Their Significations and Uses in English. 1679. 7th. ed., engraved title, neatly rebound in half calf, old marbled bds., very good. Jarndyce 16-26 1978 £38

WALKER, WILLIAM SIDNEY   The Appeal of Poland. Cambridge, 1816. 8vo, disbound, 1st ed., rare. Ximenes 47-324 1978 $60

WALKER, WILLIAM SIDNEY   The Heroes of Waterloo. London, 1815. 8vo. disbound, 1st ed., very uncommon. Ximenes 47-325 1978 $60

WALKINSHAW, ROBERT   On Puget Sound. New York, 1929. Cloth, private bkplt. Hayman 73-721 1978 $10

WALL, E. BERRY   Neither Pest nor Puritan. Memoirs. New York, 1940. Illus. Biblo BL781-259 1978 $9

WALL, JOHN F.   Thoroughbred Bloodlines. Washington, 1946. 3rd. ed., revised in 1 vol. with errata slip & supplement, folio. Baldwins' 51-556 1978 $47.50

WALL, MARTIN   Dissertations on Select Subjects in Chemistry and Medicine. Oxford, 1783. 8vo., woodcut illus., brown wrs., good copy, 1st ed. Zeitlin 245-284 1978 $150

WALL, W.   The History of Infant Baptism in Two Parts. 1707. 2nd. ed., 4to, orig. calf. Jarndyce 16-226 1978 £10.50

WALLACE, A. F.   Land Cruising and Prospecting... Columbus, (1908). Cloth. Hayman 72-774 1978 $7.50

WALLACE, ADAM   The Parson of the Islands: A Biography of the Late Rev. Joshua Thomas. Philadelphia, 1872. Orig. binding, clean. Hayman 71-756 1978 $10

WALLACE, ALFRED RUSSEL   The Geographical Distribution of Animals With A Study of the Relations of Living and Extinct Faunas as Elucidating the Past Changes of the Earth's Surface. London, 1876. 1st. ed., 2 vols., 8vo, maps, illus., immaculate copy. Traylen 88-638 1978 £180

WALLACE, ALFRED RUSSELL   Island Life. 1880. First ed., maps, text illus. George's 635-948 1978 £45

WALLACE, ALFRED RUSSEL   Tropical Nature and other essays. London, 1878. First ed., 8vo., orig. cloth. K Books 244-319 1978 £20

WALLACE, ANTHONY F. C.   King of the Delawares, Teedyuscung. Philadelphia, 1949. Fine. MacManus 239-1222 1978 $25

WALLACE, CRANMORE   A Geography of New Hampshire, With a Sketch of Its Natural History for Schools. Boston, 1829. Colored folding map, illus., printed boards, lacks first fly. Nestler Rare 78-30 1978 $55

WALLACE, DILLON   The Lure of the Labrador Wild. Toronto, 1905. Illus., maps. Hood 17-280 1978 $17.50

WALLACE, EDGAR   Day of Uniting. New York, 1930. 1st ed., d.j., fine. Houle 10-355 1978 $17.50

WALLACE, EDGAR   One-Act Play Parade. 1935. Orig. cloth, d.w. Eaton 45-526 1978 £20

WALLACE, EDGAR   Sanders of the River. n.d. Covers soiled, good, signed by author, first English ed. Bell Book 17-272 1978 £12.50

WALLACE, EDGAR   Writ in Barracks. Methuen, 1900. Edges spotted, orig. cloth, several ink spots on covers, scarce. Eaton 45-524 1978 £10

WALLACE, FRANCIS B.   Memorial of the Patriotism of Schuylkill County, in the American Slaveholder's Rebellion. Pottsville, 1865. 1st ed., frontis., cloth. MacManus 239-1672 1978 $22.50

WALLACE, FREDERICK WILLIAM   In the Wake of the Wind-Ships.   Toronto, (1927). Illus., orig. binding. Wolfe 39-548 1978 $55

WALLACE, FREDERICK WILLIAM   Record of Canadian Shipping. Toronto, (1929). Illus., dust jacket, orig. binding. Wolfe 39-549 1978 $45

WALLACE, FREDERICK WILLIAM   Under Sail in the Last of the Clippers. Glasgow, (1936). 4to., illus., orig. binding. Wolfe 39-550 1978 $75

WALLACE, HENRY A.   The Western Range: Letter from the Secretary of Agriculture. Washington, 1936. Tables, orig. wr. Ginsberg 14-1021 1978 $45

WALLACE, LEW   Autobiography. New York, 1906. Illus., 2 vols., 8vo., lst ed. Morrill 239-642 1978 $9.50

WALLACE, LEW   Ben-Hur. New York, (1899). Illus., 2 vols., 3/4 crimson levant, t.e.g., fine set, de luxe Garfield ed. Bradley 49-330 1978 $50

WALLACE, LEW   The Fair God...Conquest of Mexico. Boston, 1899. 2 vols., plts., illus., spine rubbed, else very good, orig. bind. Petrilla 13-148 1978 $27.50

WALLACE, LEW   The Prince of India or Why Constantinople Fell. New York, 1893. 1st ed., 2 vols., blue cloth, pictorial, very nice. Limestone 9-312 1978 $40

WALLACE, LEW   The Wooing of Malkatoon Commodus. 1898. Illus., first ed., some cover defects, else good. Austin 82-1051 1978 $15

WALLACE, PAUL A. W.   Conrad Weiser 1696-1760, Friend of Colonist & Mohawk. Philadelphia, 1945. lst ed., large 8vo, maps, orig. binding. Americanist 101-145 1978 $25

WALLACE, PAUL A. W.   Conrad Weiser, 1696-1760, Friend of Colonist and Mohawk. Philadelphia, 1945. Map. MacManus 239-1709 1978 $35

WALLACE, PAUL A. W.   The Muhlenbergs of Pennsylvania. University of Pennsylvania Press, 1950. Illus. Austin 79-813 1978 $12.50

WALLACE, ROBERT L.   The Canary Book. London, (1893). 3rd ed., coloured plts., illus., cloth, covers rather marked but good. K Books 244-456 1978 £9

WALLACE, SARAH A.   The Journal of Benjamin Moran 1857-1865. Chicago, 1948. 2 vols., Bell Wiley's copy. Broadfoot's 44-380 1978 $30

WALLACE, W. G.   These Forty Years-and After. Toronto, 1927. Hood 117-377 1978 $7.50

WALLER, EDMUND   Poems. 1711. 8th. ed., 10 plts., portraits, panelled & speckled calf, skilfully rebacked & corners repaired, v.g. Jarndyce 16-227 1978 £26

WALLER, EDMUND   The Poems. 1893. Sm. 8vo, good. Upcroft 10-179 1978 £5

WALLER, EDMUND   Works in Verse and Prose. 1744. Frontis, portrait, 2 plts., one folding, orig. calf, red label, spine rubbed. Jarndyce 16-228 1978 £12

WALLER, JOHN   The Merry Ghosts. 1946. Pres. copy inscribed by author, portrait, hinges weak, good, worn d.w., first English ed. Bell Book 16-871 1978 £4

WALLER, JOHN   Middle East Anthology. 1946. Very good, d.w., first English ed. Bell Book 16-014 1978 £6

WALLER, WILLARD   The Veteran Comes Back. 1944. Austin 80-359 1978 $8.50

WALLICH, NATHANIEL   Plantae Asiaticae Rariores... London, 1830-32. Map, hand-coloured litho. plts., 3 vols., lg. folio, 3/4 green morocco, gilt top, other edges uncut, very fine copy, only 254 copies issued. Traylen 88-664 1978 £6000

WALLING, HENRY F.   New Topographical Atlas of...Pennsylvania. 1872. Plates, dampstains, rebound. Nestler Rare 78-46 1978 $55

WALLING, ROBERT ALFRED JOHN   The Diaries of John Bright. 1931. Illus., frontis. Austin 80-445 1978 $12.50

WALLIS, J. P. R.   The Matabele Mission. 1945. Roy. 8vo, portraits, folding map, orig. red cloth, gilt, t.e.g., other edges uncut. Deighton 5-25 1978 £25

WALLIS, JOHN   Grammatica Linguae Anglicanae. Oxford, 1653. Sm. 8vo, old sheep, worn, first ed. Gurney 75-111 1978 £200

WALLIS, JOHN   Grammatica linguae Anglicanae cui praefigitur de loquela.... 1765. Engrav. portrait, full crimson roan, rubbed, spine faded, 8vo. George's 635-1372 1978 £7.50

WALMSLEY, E.   Physiognomical Portraits. One Hundred Distinguished Characters, from Undoubted Originals... 1822-24. 2 vols. in 1, 4to., lg. paper, plts., half mor. gilt. Quaritch 983-272 1978 $140

WALPOLE, HORACE, EARL OF ORFORD, 1717-1797   The Castle of Otranto, a Gothic Story. 1786. 5th ed., contemp. calf, rebacked with orig. label preserved, 8vo. Howes 194-511 1978 £25

WALPOLE, HORACE, EARL OF ORFORD, 1717-1797   The Castle of Otranto and the Mysterious Mother. (London), Chiswick Press, 1925. Color engrs., decor. blue cloth, uncut, 1 of 220 copies for the U.S., fine in chipped dust jacket. Bradley 49-333 1978 $25

WALPOLE, HORACE, EARL OF ORFORD, 1717-1797   A Catalogue of Engravers Who Have Been Born or Resided in England... 1765. 2nd ed., 4to., numerous fine portrs., orig. calf, very good. Jarndyce 16-229 1978 £58

WALPOLE, HORACE, EARL OF ORFORD, 1717-1797   A Catalogue of the Royal and Noble Authors of England, with Lists of Their Works. London, 1759. Sm. octavo, 2 vols., frontis., full tan speckled calf, red lea. labels, gilt, 2nd ed. Bennett 7-122 1978 $95

WALPOLE, HORACE, EARL OF ORFORD, 1717-1797   A Catalogue of the Royal and Noble Authors of England with Lists of Their Works. 1759. 2nd ed., 2 vols., frontis., half title, orig. tree calf, rebacked. Jarndyce 16-231 1978 £42

WALPOLE, HORACE, EARL OF ORFORD 1717-1797   A Catalogue of the Royal and Noble Authors of England, With Lists of Their Works. 1759. 2nd ed., 2 vols., frontis., cont. calf, rebacked. Eaton 45-527 1978 £20

WALPOLE, HORACE, EARL OF ORFORD, 1717-1797   A Catalogue of the Royal and Noble Authors of England, Scotland and Ireland. 1806. Portrs., 5 vols., full contemp. straight-grained mor., 8vo. Howes 194-512 1978 £85

WALPOLE, HORACE, EARL OF ORFORD 1717-1797   Journal of the Printing Office at Strawberry Hill. London, 1923. 8vo., orig. parchment backed spine, ltd. to 650 copies. d.j. MacManus 238-1073 1978 $60

WALPOLE, HORACE, EARL OF ORFORD, 1717-1797   Letters to Sir Horace Mann, British Envoy at the Court of Tuscany. 1834. Portr., foxed, 3 vols., cr. 8vo., contemp. half calf. Howes 194-1311 1978 £15

WALPOLE, HORACE, EARL OF ORFORD, 1717-1797   Letters to the Earl of Hertford, During His Lordship's Embassy in Paris. 1825. 4to., portr., contemp. half calf, lst ed. Howes 194-513 1978 £25

WALPOLE, HORACE, EARL OF ORFORD, 1717-1797   Letters. 1890. lst ed., 2 vols., portrs., illus., half titles, orig. maroon cloth, very good. Jarndyce 16-1161 1978 £14.50

WALPOLE, HORACE, EARL OF ORFORD, 1717-1797   The Letters. 1903-05. Portrs., 16 vols., orig. crimson buckram, special lg. paper ed., prtd. on handmade paper, signed by editor and ltd. to 260 sets. Howes 194-1310 1978 £75

WALPOLE, HORACE, EARL OF ORFORD 1717-1797   Memoirs of the Reign of King George the Third...N.P., n.d. 4 vols., first ed., octavo, orig. cloth. Bennett 20-224 1978 $150

WALPOLE, HORACE, EARL OF ORFORD 1717-1797   The Mysterious Mother. Dublin, 1791. Sm. octavo, cont. straight grain tan mor. Totteridge 29-112 1978 $150

WALPOLE, HORACE, EARL OF ORFORD, 1717-1797   Private Correspondence of... London, 1820. 4 vols., 8vo., half lea., spines damaged & back strips partly missing. Sexton 7-191 1978 £10

WALPOLE, HORACE, EARL OF ORFORD 1717-1797 Reminiscences Written by
Mr. ... in 1788... Oxford, 1924. 4to., illus., orig. cloth backed bds., ltd.
to 500, v.g. MacManus 238-152 1978 $35

WALPOLE, HORACE, EARL OF ORFORD, 1717-1797   Strawberry Hill Accounts.
Oxford, 1927. 4to., illus. Battery Park 1-488 1978 $125

WALPOLE, HORACE, EARL OF ORFORD, 1717-1797   The Works. 1798. 5 vols.,
4to., contemp. tree calf, plts., 1st ed., 2nd issue. Howes 194-510 1978 £85

WALPOLE, HORACE, EARL OF ORFORD 1717-1797   The Works of Horatio Walpole, Earl of Orford. London, 1798. 1st ed., quarto, brown half mor. with
marbled boards, gilt spines, some hinges tender, top edges gilt, 5 vols., illus.,
plts. Totteridge 29-113 1978 $275

WALPOLE, HORATIO 1678-1757   An Answer to Lord Bolingbroke's Letters on
the Study of History. 1762. 1st ed., 4to., orig. calf, red label, spine little
rubbed, otherwise fine, inscr'd on title 'From Lord Walpole'. Jarndyce 16-232
1978 £14

WALPOLE, HORATIO 1678-1757   An Answer to the Latter Part of Lord Bolingbroke's Letters on the Study of History. 1763. Contemp. calf, 8vo. Howes 194-
181 1978 £21

WALPOLE, HORATIO 1678-1757   An Answer to the Latter Part of Lord Bolingbroke's Letters on the Study of History. London, 1763. 8vo., contemp. full red
mor., gilt, spine gilt, a.e.g., 1st published ed., very handsome copy, attractively bound. Ximenes 47-326 1978 $150

WALPOLE, HUGH   The Blind Man's House. New York, 1942.
Very fine in damaged d.w. Desmarais B-640 1978 $10

WALPOLE, HUGH   Fortitude. London, (1913). Red cloth, 1st ed.,
bkplt. of A. Watson Armour III. Bradley 49-334 1978 $7.50

WALPOLE, HUGH   Reading, an Essay. New York, 1926. Bds.,
1st ed., nice copy in dust jacket, slipcase. Hayman 73-723 1978 $7.50

WALPOLE, R.   Memoirs Relating to European and Asiatic Turkey,
and Other Countries of the East. 1820. Maps, plts., 2 vols., 4to, orig. bds.,
rebacked, rubber stamps partly erased from titles, uncut. Edwards 1012-61 1978
£160

WALPOLE, R.   Specimens of Scarce Translations of the Seventeenth
Century from the Latin Poets to which are added miscellaneous Translations from
the Greek, Spanish, Italian. 1805. Sm. 8vo., 1st ed., red straight-grained mor.,
gilt edges, from the Hamilton Palace (Beckford) Library. Quaritch 979-25 1978
$170

WALROND, THEODORE   Letters and Journals of James Bruce, Eighth Earl
of Elgin... 1873. 2nd. ed., 8vo, orig. cloth, fine. Fenning 32-344 1978
£18.50

WALSH, C. C.   Early Days on the Western Range. Boston, 1917.
Bds., illus., 1st ed., fine copy in slipcase. Dykes 34-39 1978 $50

WALSH, C. C.   Early Days on the Western Range. 1st ed., minor
wear to top & bottom of spine, very good copy, slipcase. Dykes 34-40 1978
$40

WALSH, CORREA MOYLAN   The Political Science of John Adams. New
York, 1915. Orig. cloth. MacManus 239-10 1978 $15

WALSH, CORREA MOYLAN   The Political Science of John Adams. New York,
1915. Biblo 248-2 1978 $17.50

WALSH, J. J.   High Points of Medieval Culture. 1938. Allen
234-1492 1978 $7.50

WALSH, JOHN HENRY   Archery, Fencing, and Broadsword. London,
1865. 12mo, original yellow pictorial glazed boards, nice copy, uncommon
"yellowback". Ximenes 47-327 1978 $45

WALSH, L.J.   John Mitchel. 1934. 1st ed., very good,
octavo bound in cloth. Hyland 128-127 1978 £4

WALSH, PETER   Four Letters on Several Subjects, to Persons of
Quality. (London), 1686. 1st. ed., 8vo, contemp. unlettered calf, sm. lib.
stamp on title, fine copy otherwise. Fenning 32-345 1978 £85

WALSH, R.   A Residence At Constantinople, During A Period
Including The Commencement, Progress, and Termination of the Greek and Turkish
Revolutions. London, 1836. 1st. ed., 2 vols., engraved portrait, engraved plts.,
woodcuts, folding engraved map, neatly repaired, half calf, gilt backs. Deighton
5-150 1978 £50

WALSH, ROBERT   An Appeal from the Judgements of Great Britain
Respecting the United States... Philadelphia, 1819. 1st ed., rebound. Mac-
Manus 239-469 1978 $25

WALSH, W.   The Jesuits in Great Britain; an Historical
Inquiry into Their Political Influence. 1903. Octavo, good. Upcroft 10-585
1978 £5

WALSHE, E. H.   Golden Hills, A Tale of the Irish Famine.
(c.1865). Illus., a.e.g., very good, reprint, octavo bound in cloth. Hyland
128-747 1978 £7

WALSHE, ELIZABETH   Cedar Creek. London, (n.d.). Illus., orig.
binding. Wolfe 39-552 1978 $30

WALSTON, CHARLES   Alcamenes...and the Establishment of the Classical Type in Greek Art. Cambridge, 1926. Sm. 4to., illus. Biblo BL781-314
1978 $22.50

WALT Whitman in Camden. Camden, 1933. Photos by Arnold Genthe, pres.
slip laid in, 1 of 1100 copies prtd. & bound. Battery Park 1-132 1978 $125

WALTERS, ALAN   Palms & Pearls, or Scenes in Ceylon. 1892.
1st. & only ed., frontis, 8vo, orig. cloth, gilt, very good. Fenning 32-346
1978 £12

WALTERS, H. B.   The Art of the Greeks. London, (1906). 1st ed.,
illus. Biblo BL781-509 1978 $16.50

WALTERS, H. B.   History of Ancient Pottery. Greek, Etruscan and
Roman. New York, 1905. 2 vols., illus., some color plts., good. Biblo BL781-
510 1978 $45

WALTERS, H. B.   History of Ancient Pottery, Greek, Etruscan &
Roman. 1905. Vol. 2 only, plt. Allen 234-1037 1978 $15

WALTERS, LORENZO   Tombstone's Yesterday. Tucson, 1928. Illus.,
orig. cloth, 1st ed. Ginsberg 14-1085 1978 $100

WALTERS, LORENZO   Tombstone's Yesterday. Tucson, 1928. Illus.,
original cloth, 1st ed. Ginsberg 14-29 1978 $75

WALTERS, RAYMOND   Alexander James Dallas, Lawyer--Politician--
Financier. Philadelphia, 1943. Orig. cloth, frontis. MacManus 239-1431
1978 $15

WALTERS, RAYMOND   The Bethlehem Bach Choir. 1918. Austin 79-
814 1978 $12.50

WALTERS, RAYMOND   Bethlehem, Long Ago and To-day. Bethlehem,
1923. Plts., 1st ed., orig. bind. Petrilla 13-150 1978 $9.50

WALTHAM, T. ERNEST   Tangerine. London, 1907. 80 illus., dec.-
cloth, 8vo, generally little dusty. K Books 239-515 1978 £5

WALTON, G.   New Treatise and Practical Guide to Staircasing
and Handrailing. Manchester. (c. 1850). Plts., folio, half roan, rubbed, joints
cracked. George's 635-92 1978 £25

WALTON, IZAAK   The Complete Angler. 1784. 4th. ed., plts.,
illus., engraved frontis, 8vo, contemp. calf, gilt, name erased from sm. portion
of title resulting in very sm. hole, handsome copy. Fenning 32-347 1978 £32.50

WALTON, IZAAK   The Complete Angler. 1835. 3rd major ed.,
thick 16mo., t.e.g., reprinted on cheap paper, illus., copperplts., woodcuts,
extra plts., some handcolored, bound in full green mor., gilt fillets, gilt decor.
paneled spine, marbled endpapers, bds reattached, text & plts. near fine, scarce.
Current 24-62 1978 $175

WALTON, IZAAK   The Complete Angler, or the Contemplative Man's
Recreation...with Original Memoirs and Notes by Sir Harris Nicolas. Pickering,
1836. 2 vols., roy. 8vo., lg. paper, 1st Nicolas ed., port., illus., half mor.,
foxing. Quaritch 983-377 1978 $500

WALTON, IZAAK   The Complete Angler. London, 1869.
8 vo., orig. gilt stamped cloth, good-fine. Houle 10-357 1978 $35

WALTON, IZAAK   The Compleat Angler. 1929. 8vo., illus., niger mor., rough gilt top. Quaritch 979-246 1978 $180

WALTON, IZAAK   The Compleat Angler, or the Contemplative Man's Recreation. 1931. 4to., ed. de luxe, plts. in colour, black & white illus., ltd. ed., signed by artist. Quaritch 979-272 1978 $400

WALTON, IZAAK   The Lives of Dr. John Donne, Sir Henry Wotton, Mr. Richard Hooker, Mr. George Herbet, and Dr. Robert Sanderson. London, 1825. Lg. paper copy, 8vo, contemp. green morocco, gilt spine, gilt borders, gilt edges. Traylen 88-355 1978 £55

WALTON, JOSEPH S.   Conrad Weiser and the Indian Policy of Colonial Pennsylvania. Philadelphia, (1909). 1st ed., illus., orig. cloth, rubbed, but nice. MacManus 239-1715 1978 $50

WALTON, WILLIAM   A Narrative of the Captivity and Sufferings of Benjamin Gilbert and His Family... Philadelphia, 1848. 3rd ed., rebound. MacManus 239-1167 1978 $27.50

WALTZ: an Apostrophic Hymn. 1813. 4to., 1st ed., brown mor., extremely rare. Quaritch 979-74 1978 $5,500

WALWORTH, ELLEN HARDIN   Battles of Saratoga 1777. Albany, (1891). 4to., plts., ads, attractively bound. Butterfield 21-390 1978 $10

WALZEL, O.   Deutsche Dichtung von Gottsched bis zur Gegenwart. Potsdam, 1930. 4to., cloth, plts., many in color, text illus. Van der Peet H-64-477 1978 Dfl 70

WALZEL, O.   Gehalt und Gestalt im Kunstwerk des Dichters. Berlin, 1923. 4to., cloth, plts., text illus. Van der Peet H-64-478 1978 Dfl 50

WAMPUM, J. B.   Morning and Evening Prayer, the Administration of the Sacraments and Certain Other Rites and Ceremonies of the Church of England. London, (1866). Hood 117-713 1978 $75

WANDELL, SAMUEL H.   Aaron Burr. New York, 1925. 2 vols., illus., uncut. MacManus 239-731 1978 $17.50

WANLEY, NATHANIEL   The History of Man... Dublin, 1791. 2 vols., bound in 1, 8vo, contemp. mottled calf, nice. Fenning 32-348 1978 £14

WANLEY, NATHANIEL   The Wonders of the Little World. 1678. First ed., folio, contemp. calf, very good. Howes 194-113 1978 £80

WANN, PAULUS   Sermones de Tempore in Evangeliis. Hagenau, 1507. Folio, finely printed in Gothic Letter in double columns, full 19th cent. mor., all edges gilt, fine. Howes 194-583 1978 £250

WANSEY, HENRY   An Excursion to the United States of North America in the Summer of 1794. Salisbury, 1798. 2nd ed., fldg. plt., very good cond., bound in full maroon fine grain mor., decor. corded spine with gold tooled lettering, marble endpapers. Current 24-198 1978 $195

WANSEY, HENRY   The Journal of an Excursion to the United States of North America in the Summer of 1794. Salisbury, 1796. First ed., 12mo., portrait frontis., spine repaired, some foxing, v.g. Current 24-199 1978 $250

THE WANTON Jesuit. 1731. 8vo., unbound, scarce. P. M. Hill 142-62 1978 £65

WAQUET, H.   l'Art Breton. Grenoble-Paris, 1942. 2 vols., 8vo., orig. covers, text illus., colored plts. Van der Peet H-64-222 1978 Dfl 75

WAR BIRDS, Diary of an Unknown Aviator. 1927. 2nd. printing, coloured frontis, other illus. by Clayton Knight, 8vo, orig. blue cloth gilt, slightly worn, fine pres. inscription to Winston Churchill. Sawyer 298-121 1978 £125

WAR Commemoration Book, 1914-1918. 1920. Coloured plts., lg. 4to., illus., orig. cloth, portrait frontis. F. Edwards 1013-553 1978 £30

WAR Papers, Read Before the Commandery of the State of Maine, Military Order of the Loyal Legion of the United States. Portland, 1902. Uncut, Vols. II, III, & IV, Bell Wiley's copy. Broadfoot 46-271 1978 $12

WAR Records, South Carolina College Cadets in the War Bulletin of U. S. C. Columbia, 1908. Wrs., Bell Wiley's copy. Broadfoot 46-377 1978 $9

WAR Songs, for Anniversaries and Gatherings of Soldiers to Which is Added a Selection of Songs and Hymns for Memorial Day. Boston, (1883). Cloth, mod. wear. Hayman 72-776 1978 $7.50

WARBASSE, JAMES PETER   Medical Sociology. New York, 1909. 8vo., 1st ed. Morrill 239-271 1978 $15

WARBURTON, ELIOT   Memoirs of Horace Walpole and his Contemporaries. 1851. First ed., frontispieces, 2 vols., orig cloth, 8vo. Howes 194-1312 1978 £14

WARBURTON, ROWLAND EYLES EGERTON   Hunting Songs, Ballads, etc. Chester, 1834. Illus., full red mor. by Riviere. Baldwins' 51-557 1978 $100

WARBURTON, WILLIAM   Letters from...to the Hon. Charles Yorke, from 1752-1770. 1812. Lg. 4to., orig. bds., uncut, backstrip partly defective. P. M. Hill 142-233 1978 £32

WARD, ADOLPHUS WILLIAM   A History of English Dramatic Literature to the Death of Queen Anne. 1899. New ed., 3 vols., orig. cloth, 8vo. Howes 194-1313 1978 £18

WARD, ADOLPHUS WARD   The Cambridge History of English Literature. Cambridge, 1933. 15 vols., orig. blue cloth, backs faded, 8vo. Howes 194-703 1978 £35

WARD, ARTEMUS   Speech of the Hon. Artemus Ward. Boston, 1814. Sewn. Wolfe 39-553 1978 $50

WARD, ARTEMUS PSEUD.
Please turn to
BROWNE, CHARLES FARRAR 1834-1867

WARD, CHRISTOPHER   Dutch and Swedes on the Delaware 1609-1664. Philadelphia, 1930. MacManus 239-119 1978 $30

WARD, CHRISTOPHER   The Delaware Continentals, 1776-1783. Wilmington, 1941. Maps, d.j., fine. MacManus 239-631 1978 $35

WARD, CHRISTOPHER   The Delaware Continentals, 1776-1783. Wilmington, 1941. Subscribers ed., ltd. to 395 copies, no. 283, signed. Baldwins' 51-237 1978 $32.50

WARD, CHRISTOPHER   The Delaware Continentals 1776-1783. Wilmington, 1941. 1st ed., 1 of 395 numbered copies, signed by Ward, lg. 8vo., nice copy in d.w. & box, color fronts, maps. Americanist 103-113 1978 $50

WARD, E. F.   Christopher Monck, Duke of Albemarle. 1915. Plts., octavo, good. Upcroft 10-586 1978 £6

WARD, EDWARD   Boston in 1682 and 1699. Providence, 1905. Fine untrimmed copy, cloth bds., ltd. to 100 copies. MacManus 239-282 1978 $30

WARD, ELIZABETH STUART PHELPS 1844-1911   Burglars in Paradise. 1886. First ed., orig. paper covered ed., bound with front cover in. Austin 82-703 1978 $20

WARD, EMILY   Three Travellers in North Africa. London, 1921. Folding map, illus., cr. 8vo., orig. cloth. K Books 239-516 1978 £6

WARD, GEORGE W.   History of the Second Penna. Veteran Heavy Artillery, from 1861 to 1866. Philadelphia, 1904. Rebound, revised, illus. MacManus 239-912 1978 $27.50

WARD, H.   A Voice from the Congo, Comprising of stories, anecdotes & descriptive notes. New York, 1910. T.D. Carter bookplt., Lang name stamp, worn binding, 8vo. Book Chest 17-404 1978 $45

WARD, MRS. H. D.
Please turn to
WARD, ELIZABETH STUART PHELPS 1844-1911

WARD, HARRIET   Five Years in Kaffirland.... London, 1848. 2nd. ed., 2 vols., sm. 8vo, lithograph portrait frontispieces, lithograph plt. & map, quarter calf, gilt backs. Deighton 5-26 1978 £75

WARD, HENRY A.   Annals of Richfield. Utica, 1898. Scarce. Butterfield 21-349 1978 $15

WARD, HERBERT   Mr. Poilu, Notes and Sketches with the Fighting French. 1916. Ltd. to 150 signed copies, plates, some tinted, 4to. George's 635-867 1978 £8.50

WARD, HERBERT   A Voice From the Congo. New York, 1910. Numerous plts., 8vo, orig. cloth. K Books 239-517 1978 £10

WARD, MRS. HUMPHREY
Please turn to
WARD, MARY AUGUSTA ARNOLD

WARD, J.S.M.   The Hung Society: or The Society of Heaven and Earth. London, 1925-26. Illus., 3 vols., cloth, little soiled, 1 of 1500 numbered sets. Dawson's 449-89 1978 $55

WARD, JAMES   Psychological Principles. Cambridge, 1918. 1st ed., orig. publisher's cloth, 8vo. Gilhofer 75-114 1978 SFr 100

WARD, JOHN   The Good-Will of Him That Dwelt on the Bush. 1645. Good. Jarndyce 16-6 1978 £9.50

WARD, LESTER   Young Ward's Diary. New York, (1935). 8vo., d.w., 1st ed. Morrill 241-604 1978 $22.50

WARD, LYND   Prince Bantam. New York, 1929. 1st ed., colored f.p., B&W plates, handsome binding with color vignette, edges faded, very fine in d.j. Victoria 34-843 1978 $25

WARD, LYND   Wild Pilgrimage. New York, 1932. 1st ed., large 8vo, scarcest of Ward's novels, woodcut plates, fine. Victoria 34-845 1978 $85

WARD, LYND   Madman's Drum. New York, (1930). 1st ed., signed, woodcuts. Biblo 251-663 1978 $75

WARD, MAISIE   Insurrection Versus Resurrection. 1937. Frontis, 1st ed., slightly frayed dust jacket. Austin 79-817 1978 $20

WARD, MARY AUGUSTA (ARNOLD)   Eleanor. 1900. 1st ed., plts., 8vo., orig. cloth, nice. Fenning 32-349 1978 £24

WARD, MARY AUGUSTA (ARNOLD)   Fields of Victory. (1919). Pres. copy inscr'd by author, plts., map, chart, very good, 1st Eng. ed. Bell Book 17-889 1978 £6

WARD, MARY AUGUSTA (ARNOLD)   Helbeck of Bannisdale. London, 1898. Orig. cloth, 1st ed., fine. MacManus 238-406 1978 $50

WARD, MARY AUGUSTA (ARNOLD)   Fenwick's Career. London, 1906. Orig. cloth, 1st ed. MacManus 238-407 1978 $20

WARD, MARY AUGUSTA (ARNOLD)   Towards the Goal. London, 1917. 1st ed., orig. binding, spine faded, very good, author's autograph pres. inscr. Rota 211-737 1978 £40

WARD, MRS. R.   The Child's Guide to Knowledge. London, 1888. 57th ed., qtr. leather, 16mo., slightly shaken. K Books 244-321 1978 £6

WARD, RICHARD   The Life of Henry More. London, 1710. 8vo., calf. Salloch 348-162 1978 $110

WARD, RICHARD HERON   The Powys Brothers: a study. 1935. Portraits, some foxing, very good, first English ed. Bell Book 16-730 1978 £7.50

WARD, ROBERT PLUMER   Tremaine, or the Man of Refinement. 1825. 2nd. ed., engraved frontis, 3 vols., lg. 12mo, contemp. half calf, nice. Fenning 32-350 1978 £24

WARD, ROBERT PLUMER   Tremaine. 1825. 3 vols., 12mo., calf gilt, frontispiece in Vol. I, fine, first ed. P. M. Hill 142-197 1978 £85

WARD, THOMAS   England's Reformation. 1747. 2 vols. in I, frontis, 15 eng. plts., browned, Victorian panelled calf, rebacked. Eaton 45-528 1978 £25

WARD, THOMAS   England's Reformation. 1747. 2 vols., sm. 8vo., contemp. calf, attractive. Howes 194-514 1978 £42

WARD, THOMAS   England's Reformation: A Poem. Manchester, 1815. Engraved plts., 8vo, some browning & spotting, sound, good copy, contemp. calf. Fenning 32-351 1978 £7.50

WARD, W.   Life of John Henry Cardinal Newman. 1913. 2 portraits, 2 vols., covers dull, 8vo. George's 635-1104 1978 £5.50

WARD, W. C.   Sir John Vanbrugh. London, 1893. Portr., 2 vols., 8vo., ex-lib., ltd. to 750 copies, orig. cloth. Morrill 241-605 1978 $15

WARD, W. E. F.   A History of the Gold Coast. London, 1948. 11 maps, 8 plts., 8vo, orig. cloth. K Books 239-518 1978 £6

WARD, WILLIAM RANKIN   Down the Years. A History of the Mutual Benefit Life Insurance Company. 1845 to 1932. (Newark, 1932). Illus. Biblo BL781-99 1978 $9.50

WARDE, FREDERICK   Printers Ornaments Applied to the Composition of Decorative Borders, Panels and Patterns. London, 1928. Leaves prtd. in color on one side only on heavy colored stock, cloth. Dawson's 447-186 1978 $60

WARDEN, C.F.   The Battle of Waterloo; a Poem; in Two Parts. London, 1817. 8vo, disbound, 1st ed., frontispiece portrait of Wellington, very good copy, unusual illus. poem. Ximenes 47-328 1978 $125

WARDEN, D. B.   A Statistical, Political and Historical Account of the United States of North America; From the Period of Their First Colonization to the Present. Edinburgh, 1819. 1st ed., 3 vols., cloth, illus., fine set. Mac-Manus 239-480 1978 $100

WARDEN, FLORENCE   The Mis-Rule of Three. NY, 1903. Fir. Am. Ed., orig. cloth binding. Greene 78-313 1978 $15.00

WARDEN, WILLIAM   Letters Written on Board His Majesty's Ship the Northumbrugh.... (1816). Port. frontis., plt., 8vo., orig. bds., first ed. F. Edwards 1013-448 1978 £15

WARDEN, WILLIAM A.   Genealogy of the Dexter Family in America. Worcester, 1905. Illus. Biblo BL781-56 1978 $17.50

WARDLAW, JOHN   A Diary/Log Book of his Travels and Cruises in his Yachts Eugenie and Fair Rosamund in the 1850s and '60s. London. 4to., orig. roan, loose and shaken. K Books 244-322 1978 £25

WARDMAN, GEORGE   A Trip to Alaska. Boston, 1885. Cloth. Hayman 73-724 1978 $12.50

WARE, F. B.   History of Cronyn Memorial Church, London, Ontario, 1873-1949. (St. Thomas, 1949). Hood 117-378 1978 $12.50

WARE, MRS. HIBBERT   His Dearest Wish. A Novel. London, 1883. 3 vols., orig. cloth, 1st ed., lib. labels removed, worn. MacManus 238-354 1978 $75

WARE, J.   The Whole Works..Concerning Ireland Revised & Improved. 1739/46. 3 vols. in 2, contemp. calf, plts. in vol. II, some wear on cover, bookplt. of the Knight of Kerry in both vols., reprint. Hyland 128-748 1978 £105

WARE, J.   The Whole Works..Concerning Ireland Revised & Improved. 1739/1762. 2 vols., plts., binding on vol. II split, reprint. Hyland 128-749 1978 £100

WARFIELD, DAVID   Ghetto Silhouettes. 1902. Austin 79-818 1978 $17.50

WARFIELD, J. D.   The Founders of Anne Arundel and Howard Counties, Maryland. Baltimore, 1905. Orig. cloth, stained, 1st ed., ports., very scarce. MacManus 239-995 1978 $60

WARING, GEORGE E.   Sewerage and Land Drainage. New York, 1889. 2nd ed., plts., 4to., ex-lib., library binding, inner hinges cracked. Morrill 241-606 1978 $50

WARING, JANET   Early American Wall Stencils, Their Origin, History and Use. New York, 1937. 100 photos, 4to. Baldwins' 51-163 1978 $50

WARING, JOHN BURLEY   Masterpieces of Industrial Art and Sculpture at the International Exhibition, 1862. 1863. Plts., text in English and French, 3 vols., folio, orig. mor. fully gilt, rubbed. George's 635-68 1978 £150

WARINGTON, SMYTH H.   Chase and Chance in Indo-China. Edinburgh and London, 1934. Cloth, illus., maps, 8vo. Van der Peet 127-262 1978 Dfl 35

WARINGTON, SMYTH H.   Notes of a Journey on the Upper Mekong, Siam. London, 1895. Half calf, plts., maps, illus., rare, 8vo, orig. covers. Van der Peet 127-263 1978 Dfl 65

WARMAN, CY   The Story of the Railroad. New York, 1898. 1st ed., illus., orig. cloth, fine. MacManus 239-411 1978 $10

WARMOTH, HENRY CLAY   War, Politics and Reconstruction. Stormy Days in Louisiana. New York, 1930. 1st ed., d.j., fine, port. MacManus 239-1821 1978 $20

WARMOTH, HENRY CLAY   War, Politics and Reconstruction. New York, 1930. Cover speckled, Bell Wiley's copy. Broadfoot's 44-513 1978 $24

WARNER, CHARLES DUDLEY   My Summer in a Garden. Boston, 1871. 12mo., 1st ed., A.L.s. tipped in. Morrill 239-644 1978 $15

WARNER, CHARLES DUDLEY   My Summer in a Garden. Boston, 1871. 12mo., very nice, 1st ed. Morrill 239-645 1978 $7.50

WARNER, CHARLES DUDLEY   My Summer in a Garden. Boston, (1912). Pic. green cloth, fine, bright, illus. Bradley 49-335 1978 $8.50

WARNER, CHARLES DUDLEY   The People for Whom Shakespeare Wrote. 1897. Illus., first ed., backstrip darkened. Austin 82-1054 1978 $12.50

WARNER, ELISHA   History of Spanish Fork. Spanish Fork, 1930. Orig. cloth, 1st ed. Ginsberg 14-1013 1978 $30

WARNER, ESTHER   New Song in a Strange Land. London, 1949. Woodcut illus., slight foxing, 8vo, orig. cloth. K Books 239-519 1978 £5

WARNER, F.   History of Ireland, Volume the 1st. 1763. 1st ed., full leather, hinges weak, text very good. Hyland 128-750 1978 £10

WARNE, FRANK JULIAN   The Tide of Immigration. 1916. Austin 79-819 $12.50

WARNER, GEORGE F.   Illuminated Manuscripts...Miniatures, Borders and Initials. London, 1903. 4 series in 1 vol., ltd. to 500 copies, plts. in gold and colours, imp. 4to., half mor., 1 joint cracked, rubbed, t.e.g. Forster 130-235 1978 £110

WARNER, H. H.   Warner's Artist's Album. (Rochester, 1888). Pict. wrps. in full color. Hayman 71-91 1978 $10

WARNER, OLIVER   An Introduction to British Marine Painting. 1948. Coloured frontis., plts., imp. 8vo., orig. cloth. F. Edwards 1013-219 1978 £20

WARNER, REX   The Professor. New York, 1939. 1st Amer. ed., d.w. Biblo 251-664 1978 $12.50

WARNER, REX   Views of Attica and its Surroundings. 1950. Plts., very good, d.w., first English ed. Bell Book 17-890 1978 £5

WARNER, SUSAN BOGART   The Old Helmet. New York, 1864. 1st ed., 2 vols., orig. cloth, very good. Greene 78-314 1978 $35

WARNER, SUSAN BOGART   Queechy. 1853. Frontis, engraved title pg., sm. 8vo, contemp. half calf, very good. Fenning 32-352 1978 £6

WARNER, SUSAN BOGART   Say and Seal. Philadelphia, 1860. 1st ed., 2 vols., orig. cloth bind. Greene 78-315 1978 $40

WARNER, SYLVIA TOWNSEND   The Cat's-Cradle Book. New York, 1940. Illus. by Bertram Hartman, 1st ed., d.w. slightly frayed. Biblo 251-665 1978 $15

WARNER, SYLVIA TOWNSEND   Elinor Barley. Cresset Press, 1930. One of 350 numbered copies signed by author, plts., roy 8vo., quarter vellum, t.e.g., bds. somewhat rubbed, spine dust-spotted, good, first English ed. Bell Book 17-891 1978 £12.50

WARNER, SYLVIA TOWNSEND   Lolly Willowes or the Loving Huntsman. 1926. First ed., d.j. Austin 82-1055 1978 $20

WARNOD, ANDRE   3 Petites Filles Dans la Rue. Paris, 1925. Sm. 4to., 3/4 red mor., color onlays, orig. wr. & backstrip bound in, ltd. ed. issued in 710 copies, numbered copy on velin blanc paper, illus. by Jules Pascin. Goldschmidt 110-50 1978 $125

WARNSINCK, J. C. M.   De Vloot van den Koning-Stadhouder 1689-1690. Amsterdam, 1934. 8vo., cloth, plts. Van der Peet H-64-578 1978 Dfl 45

WARR, G. W.   Canada as It is. London, 1847. Orig. pamphlet cover bound in 3/4 lea. Hood 117-771 1978 $140

WARRACK, GUY   Sherlock Holmes and Music. 1947. Very good, slightly worn d.w., first English ed. Bell Book 17-809 1978 £6

WARREN, ALBERT H.   The Promises of Jesus Christ. (1866). Printed in gold & colours, sm. 4to, orig. reddish brown cloth, block in gold & blind, white paper mandorla inlay, edges gilt, binding signed AW, fine. Fenning 32-353 1978 £24

WARREN, BENJAMIN HARRY   Report on the Birds of Pennsylvania, with Special Reference to the Food-habits.... Harrisburg, 1890. Large thick 8vo, orig. 1/2 morocco with marbled boards, edges & tips rubbed, new spine & end papers, plates, 2nd ed. Americanist 101-146 1978 $65

WARREN, BENJAMIN HARRY   Report on the Birds of Pennsylvania, with special reference to their food-habits. 1890. Newer leather spine, plates, 2nd enlarged, revised ed., 8vo, orig. cloth. Book Chest 17-405 1978 $110

WARREN, BENJAMIN HARRY   Report on the Birds of Penna. Harrisburg, 1890. 2nd ed., rev'd., 4to., later cloth, plts. in full color. MacManus 239-1712 1978 $50

WARREN, CHARLES   On The Veldt in the Seventies. London, 1902. 2 folding maps, 18 plts., g.t., 8vo, orig. cloth. K Books 239-520 1978 £20

WARREN, CHARLES   The Supreme Court in United States History, 1789-1918. Boston, (1926). 2 vols. Baldwins' 51-23 1978 $20

WARREN, EDWARD   An Epitome of Practical Surgery, for Field and Hospital. Richmond, 1863. 1st ed., 8vo., orig. stamped cloth, lightly browned, dampstains, library stamps, bkplt., good copy, very rare. Zeitlin 245-317 1978 $650

WARREN, EDWARD   The Life of John Collins Warren, M.D. Boston, 1860. 2 vols., some wear, weak at hinges. Rittenhouse 49-813 1976 $30

WARREN, EDWARD   Life of John Warren. Boston, 1874. Some chipping at top of spine. Rittenhouse 49-814 1976 $50

WARREN, EDWARD PERRY   The Prince Who Did Not Exist. Merrymount Press, (1900). 12mo., 1 of 350 copies, #118, illus. by Arthur J. Gaskin, bds., vellum spine, prtd. on fine paper. Battery Park 1-201 1978 $50

WARREN, G. K.   Preliminary Report of Explorations in Nebraska and Dakota, in the Years 1855-56-57. Washington, 1875. Folding maps, orig. wr. Ginsberg 14-1024 1978 $65

WARREN, GARNET   The Romance of Design. New York, 1926. Illus., color & black & white, 4to., orig. bds., cloth back, 1st ed. Morrill 241-607 1978 $7.50

WARREN, INA RUSSELLE   The Doctor's Window. Buffalo, 1898. Rittenhouse 49-812 1976 $10

WARREN, J. B. L.   A Guide to the Study of Book-Plates. Manchester, 1900. Second revised ed., plts., demy 8vo., orig. cloth. Forster 130-112 1978 £10

WARREN, J. RUSSELL   Magpie Murder. New York, (1942). First ed., d.w. Biblo 247-532 1978 $16.50

WARREN, JOSEPH   Hamilton's Catechism of the Organ. 1842. Orig. cloth, 12mo., plts., nice. P. M. Hill 142-199 1978 £16

WARREN, RAYMOND   The Prairie President. Chicago, (1930). Illus. Biblo 248-63 1978 $32.50

WARREN, ROBERT PENN   At Heaven's Gate. 1943. First ed., some fade to spine, else good. Austin 82-1056 1978 $27.50

WARREN, ROBERT PENN   John Brown: The Making of a Martyr. New York, 1929. First ed., scarce. Biblo 248-69 1978 $95

WARREN, ROBERT PENN   World Enough and Time. New York, 1950. First U.S. ed., very good, worn d.w. Bell Book 17-895 1978 £12.50

WARREN, ROSE HARLOW   A Southern Home in War Times.   Broadway,
New York, 1914. Uncut, Bell Wiley's copy. Broadfoot 46-272 1978 $16

WARREN, SAMUEL   Ten Thousand a-Year.   1841. First English ed.,
3 vols., contemp. half mor., gilt tops, backs faded, 8vo. Howes 194-1316 1978
£25

WARREN, SAMUEL   The Lily and the Bee. 1851. Ist. ed., half title,
orig. blue gilt, dec. cloth, v.g. Jarndyce 16-1162 1978 £18.50

WARREN, SAMUEL   Memoirs and Select Letters of Mrs. Anne Warren.
1827. First ed., sm. 8vo., full contemp. navy grained calf gilt. Howes 194-
1315 1978 £12.50

WARREN, SAMUEL   Ten Thousand a Year. Philadelphia, 1840-41.
6 vols., sm. 8vo., Ist ed., orig. bds. cloth backs slightly faded, little foxing,
fine copy, rare, genuine Ist issue. Quaritch 979-324 1978 $315

WARREN, SAMUEL   Ten Thousand A-Year. Edinburgh and London,
1841. Ist. English ed., engraved plt., half titles, 3 vols., 8vo, orig. plum cloth,
little shaken, nice, clean copy. Fenning 32-354 1978 £55

WARREN, SAMUEL   Ten Thousand A-Year. Edinburgh, 1841. 3 vols.,
octavo, 3/4 green mor. over cloth, gilt rules, gilt spine panels, raised bands, marbled endpapers, t.e.g., author's A.L.s. tipped in, Ist English ed. Bennett 7-123
1978 $225

WARREN, SAMUEL   Ten Thousand A Year. 1854. 2 vols., stitching
weak, orig. cloth, dull. Eaton 45-529 1978 £5

WARREN, THOMAS   History and Genealogy of Warren Family, In
Normandy, Great Britain, Ireland, France, Holland, Tuscany and the United States.
1902. Baldwins' 51-270 1978 $45

WARREN, WILLIAM R.   The Life and Labors of Archibald McLean. St.
Louis, (1923). Cloth. Hayman 72-775 1978 $8.50

WARREN County History and Directory... Washington, 1886. Orig. cloth, rebacked, very scarce. MacManus 239-1336 1978 $60

WARRICK, JOHN   The History of Old Cumnock. Paisley, 1899.
Map, plts., cr. 4to., orig. cloth. K Books 244-459 1978 £12

WARTHIN, ALDRED SCOTT   Old Age the Major Involution. New York, 1929.
8vo., photo. plts., orig. purple cloth, gilt lettering on spine, author's signature,
fine copy, uncut. Zeitlin 245-285 1978 $75

WARWICK, PHILIP   Memories of the Reign of King Charles I. 1813.
Portraits, calf, octavo, good. Upcroft 10-180 1978 £15

WARWICKSHIRE. The Land of Shakespeare. London, 1922. Plts. in color, 2nd
ed. Biblo BL781-639 1978 $10

WASHBURN, CHARLES G.   Who was the Author of the Delcaration of Independence? Worcester, 1929. New cloth. Broadfoot 50-330 1978 $14

WASHBURN, WILLIAM T.   Fair Harvard. New York, 1869. 8vo., Ist ed.
Morrill 239-419 1978 $7.50

WASHBURNE, E. B.   Historical Sketch of Charles S. Hempstead...To
Which is Appended a Memoir of Edward Hempstead,.... Galena, 1875. Portrait,
original printed wr., Ist ed. Ginsberg 14-607 1973 $75

WASHINGTON, BOOKER TALIAFERO   Up From Slavery, an Autobiography.
New York, 1901. 1st ed. MacManus 239-856 1978 $15

WASHINGTON, BOOKER TALIAFERO   Working With the Hands. New York,
1904. Orig. binding, clean. Hayman 71-762 1978 $20

WASHINGTON, GEORGE   Atlas to Marshall's Life of Washington. Philadelphia, (1832). Contemp. bds., printed label on front cover, cloth backstrip.
Wolfe 39-554 1978 $150

WASHINGTON, GEORGE   Authenticated Copy of the Last Will and Testament of George Washington, of Mt. Vernon, Embracing a Schedule of His Real
Estate and Notes Thereto by the Testator. Washington, 1868. Wrs. Hayman 73-
726 1978 $8.50

WASHINGTON, GEORGE   A Collection of the Speeches of the President
of the United States to Both Houses of Congress, at the Opening of Every Session,
with Their Answers. Boston, 1796. 12mo., contemp. calf, 1st ed. Morrill 241-
608 1978 $30

WASHINGTON, GEORGE   The Diaries of...1748-1799. Boston, (1925).
4 vols., nice set. MacManus 239-481 1978 $42.50

WASHINGTON, GEORGE   Diaries of...., 1748-1799. 1925. 3rd. impression. Baldwins' 51-186 1978 $42.50

WASHINGTON, GEORGE   Diaries, 1791 to 1799. Summerfield, 1921.
Broadfoot 50-100 1978 $25

WASHINGTON, GEORGE   Diary of...Sept.-Dec. 1785. Boston, 1902.
Orig. wrs., fine unopened copy, ltd. to 250 copies. MacManus 239-482 1978
$10

WASHINGTON, GEORGE   Epistles Domestic, Confidential, and Official,
from General Washington, Written About the Commencement of the American Con-
test... New York, 1776. 1st ed., later cloth, fine. MacManus 239-483 1978
$75

WASHINGTON, GEORGE   Washington's Farewell Address. Windsor, 1812.
Leather backed bds., sm. piece missing from fly-leaf. Hayman 71-759 1978
$12.50

WASHINGTON, GEORGE   Farewell Address of...to the People of the United
States...September 17, 1796. New York, 1852. Wrs. Hayman 72-777 1978
$7.50

WASHINGTON, GEORGE   General Orders of George Washington...Issued at
Newburgh on the Hudson, 1782-83. Newburgh, 1883. First ed., wrs. Biblo 247-
145 1978 $15

WASHINGTON, GEORGE   The Last Will and Testament. Boston, 1800. 1st
ed., 8vo., Ist of 4 1800 prtgs., modern black 1/2 mor., damaged orig. wrs. bound
in. Current 24-109 1978 $295

WASHINGTON, GEORGE   Letters from George Washington to Tobias Lear.
Rochester, 1905. Folio, bds., uncut, engrav. frontis port. of Washington by S.
Hollyer, no. 265 of 300 copies. Wolfe 39-555 1978 $150

WASHINGTON, GEORGE   Official Letters to the Honourable American
Congress, Written During the War Between the United Colonies and Great Britain.
Boston, 1795. 2 vols., 12mo., first ed., old calf, worn, text foxed. Biblo 247-
1978 $75

WASHINGTON, GEORGE   Official Letters to the Honorable American Congress, Written During the War Between the United Colonies and Great Britain.
London, 1795. 2 vols., nice set, cloth. MacManus 239-485 1978 $40

WASHINGTON, GEORGE   The Washington-Duche Letters. Brooklyn, 1890.
8vo., orig. wrs., ed. ltd. to 500 copies. Morrill 239-648 1978 $7.50

WASHINGTON, GEORGE   The Writings...Being the Correspondence, Addresses, Message, and Other Papers... Boston, 1837. Orig. 1/2 mor. Mac-
Manus 239-487 1978 $150

WASHINGTON Loan and Trust Company...Farm Mortgage Loans and Municipal
Bonds. Walla Walla, 1886. Litho. plates, orig. pr. wr., Ist ed. Ginsberg
14-1049 1978 $150

WASHINGTONS Reception by the Ladies of Trenton Together with the Chorus Sung
as He Passed Under the Triumphal Arch Raised on the Bridge Over The Assun pink
April 21st, 1789. New York, 1903. Wr., illus., fine. Nestler Rare 78-85 1978
$35

WASSERMAN, J.   Christian Wahnschasse. Berlin, 1919. 2 vols.,
linen-backed bds., Ist. ed. Eaton 45-530 1978 £8

WASSON, E. A.   Religion and Drink. 1914. Austin 79-821 1978
$17.50

WATELET, CLAUDE HENRI   L'Art de Peindre Poeme Avec des Reflexions sur
les differentes Parties de la Peinture. Paris, 1760. 4to., orig. bds. covered with
painted paper, soiled, corners worn, uncut, first ed. King 7-395 1978 £50

THE WATER-Power of Maine. Augusta, 1868. Map, 8vo., ex-lib., orig. cloth.
Morrill 241-691 1978 $12.50

WATERBURY, M.   Seven Years Among the Freedmen. Chicago,
1893. Illus., cracked hinges, Bell Wiley's copy. Broadfoot's 44-808 1978
$16.00

THE WATERFALL Wag - The Pretoria Prisoners' Paper. London, 1900. Illus.,
orig. wrappers, 8vo. K Books 239-523 1978 £16

WATERHOUSE, BENJAMIN   Cautions to Young Persons Concerning Health in a Public Lecture. Cambridge, 1822. Rittenhouse 49-816 1976 $75

WATERHOUSE, E.   Painting in Britain, 1530 to 1790. London, 1934. Lg. 8vo., cloth, plts. Van der Peet H-64-92 1978 Dfl 40

WATERHOUSE, FRANCIS A.   Gun Running in the Red Sea. London, c.1935. 8 plts., 8vo, orig. cloth. K Books 239-522 1978 £7

WATERLAND, D.   A Critical History of the Athanasian Creed. Cambridge, 1724. Contemp. name on title, cr. 4to., contemp. calf, worn, joints cracked. George's 635-1150 1978 £8

WATERLOO, STANLEY   A Son of the Ages. New York, 1914. Illus., 1st ed., front inner hinge split, otherwise good. Biblo BL781-987 1978 $10

WATERMAN, THOMAS TILESTON   Domestic Colonial Architecture of Tidewater Virginia. New York, 1932. 1st ed., folio, illus., orig. cloth, soiled and rubbed, good copy. MacManus 239-712 1978 $100

WATEROUS ENGINE WORKS CO.   Motor Driven Fire Apparatus Manufactured By.... St. Paul, (1914). Oblong 8vo, fully illus. Baldwins' 51-77 1978 $100

WATERS, C. M.   A Swift Survey of the Economic Development of England and the Colonies, 1874-1914. 1926. 8vo. George's 635-421 1978 £5

WATERS, HENRY F.   Genealogical Gleanings in England. Boston, 1901. 2 vols., illus., orig. cloth, fine. MacManus 239-922 1978 $45

WATERS, NICHOLAS B.   System of Surgery. Philadelphia, 1806. Third ed., orig. bds., firm, clean. Rittenhouse 49-817 1976 $35

WATKINS, G. T.   Bibliography of Printing in America. Boston, (1906). One of 500. Battery Park 1-496 1978 $15

WATKINS, HAROLD   The Art of Gerald Moira. New York, (c. 1922). 4to., plts. Biblo 247-371 1978 $27.50

WATKINS, THOMAS   Travels through Swisserland, Italy, Sicily, the Greek Islands, to Constantinople;.... London, 1792. 2 vols., 8vo, contemporary calf, contrasting morocco labels, 1st ed., very nice copy. Ximenes 47-329 1978 $125

WATNEY, V. J.   The Wallop Family and Their Ancestry. Oxford, 1928. 4 vols., plts., folio, orig. niger morocco, scarce, only 100 copies printed. Traylen 88-461 1978 £90

WATSON, AARON   The Savage Club. A Medley of History Anecdote and Reminiscence. London, 1907. Illus., orig. full parchment, 1st ed., covers a bit worn and soiled, very good, scarce. MacManus 238-443 1978 $85

WATSON, ALBERT DURRANT   Robert Norwood... Toronto, n.d. Hood 116-718 1978 $7.50

WATSON, DOUGLAS S.   California in the Fifties. San Francisco, 1936. Illus., original wine buckram, oblong folio, 1st ed., limited to 850 copies. Ginsberg 14-218 1978 $150

WATSON, E. H. A.   History of the Ontario Red Cross, 1914-1946. Toronto, n.d. Illus. Hood 117-161 1978 $15

WATSON, E. L. G.   Enigmas of Natural History. (c. 1948). Engrav. by Barbara Greg, roy. 8vo., covers faded. George's 635-178 1978 £5

WATSON, E. L. G.   More Enigmas of Natural History. (c. 1950). Engrav. by Barbara Greg, roy. 8vo. George's 635-179 1978 £5.25

WATSON, FREDERICK   Life of Sir Robert Jones. London, 1934. Fading on spine. Rittenhouse 49-819 1976 $15

WATSON, GOODWIN   Civilian Morale. 1942. Austin 80-361 1978 $12.50

WATSON, J. ROBERTSON   The Case for Tariff Reform. Glasgow, 1909. 8vo., orig. cloth. K Books 244-460 1978 £6

WATSON, JAMES E.   As I Knew Them. Indianapolis, (1936). First ed., illus. Biblo 247-139 1978 $17.50

WATSON, JOHN FANNING   Annals of Philadelphia, and Pennsylvania, in the Olden Time. Philadelphia, 1887. Inner hinges sprung, bindings worn, 3 vols., illus. Biblo 247-124 1978 $52.50

WATSON, JOHN FANNING   Annals of Philadelphia, and Pa., in the Olden Times... Philadelphia. 3 vols., 4to., illus. MacManus 239-1603 1978 $50

WATSON, JOHN SELBY   Biographies of John Wilkes & William Cobbett. 1870. 1st. ed., portraits, orig. green cloth, v.g. Jarndyce 16-1177 1978 £12.50

WATSON, JONN B.   Behaviorism. New York, 1924. 1925. Library marks. Rittenhouse 49-818 1976 $10

WATSON, MARK SKINNER   Chief of Staff: Prewar Plans and Preparations. 1950. Illus. Austin 80-362 1978 $27.50

WATSON, RALPH   A Brief Explanatory Statement of the Principle and Application of a Life and Ship Preserver Invented, or Contrived. 1827. 8vo., wrappers. F. Edwards 1013-220 1978 £10

WATSON, RICHARD   An Apology for Christianity in a Series of Letters Addressed to Edward Gibbon Esq. Dublin, 1777. 1st. Dublin ed., half title, orig. calf, excellently rebacked, red label, v.g. Jarndyce 16-233 1978 £26

WATSON, RICHARD   Chemical Essays. Cambridge, 1781-86 & London, 1787. 5 vols., 12mo., fldg. table, contemp. calf, gilt, orig. labels, rubbed, few hinges cracked, but fine set, contemp. bkplt., 1st ed., inscr'd by author. Norman 5-**25 1978 $450

WATSON, THOMAS   The Greek. 1869. Reprinted from orig. ed. of c. 1581, sm. 4to., orig. wrappers. Howes 194-1212b 1978 £7.50

WATSON, THOMAS   Kirkintilloch: Town and Parish. Glasgow, 1894. Plts., gilt cloth, 8vo., frontis., map. K Books 244-461 1978 £7

WATSON, THOMAS   Lectures on the Principles and Practice of Physic. Philadelphia, 1845. 2nd Amer. from the 2nd London ed., rev. with additions, lea., some wear. Hayman 73-728 1978 $12.50

WATSON, THOMAS E.   The Life and Times of Thomas Jefferson. New York, 1903. Cloth. Hayman 73-729 1978 $8.50

WATSON, THOMAS L.   The Building and Ornamental Stones of North Carolina. Raleigh, 1906. Plts., new cloth. Broadfoot 50-331 1978 $15

WATSON, W.   Orchids: Their Culture and Management, with descriptions of all the kinds in general cultivation. London, 1890. Plates, 8vo, orig. cloth. Book Chest 17-408 1978 $80

WATSON, WILLIAM 1858-1935   The Eloping Angels. A Caprice. London, 1893. Orig. vellum, 1st ed., 1 of 75 copies prtd. on vellum, slightly soiled, vellum buckling. MacManus 238-408 1978 $85

WATSON, WILLIAM 1834-1915   Papers on Technological Education. Boston, 1872. 8vo., ex-lib. Morrill 239-651 1978 $7.50

WATSON, WILLIAM 1858-1935   The Muse in Exile. New York, 1913. First Amer. ed. Biblo 251-667 1978 $10

WATT, G. D.   Report of Three Nights Public Discussion in Bolton, ... Liverpool, 1851. Disbound, 1st ed. Ginsberg 14-695 1978 $45

WATT, JAMES   Correspondence of the Late James Watt on His Discovery of the Theory of the Composition of Water. London, 1846. 8vo., frontis. portr., text illus., orig. cloth, gilt, g.e. worn but very good copy, 1st ed. Norman 5-295 1978 $75

WATT, JOHN JAMES   An Encyclopedia of Surgery, Medicine, Midwifery, Physiology, Pathology, Anatomy, Chemistry... London, 1806. Sm. 8vo., fine copy, later 1/2 calf. MacManus 239-506 1978 $45

WATTERS, J.J.   The Natural History of the Birds of Ireland Indigenous & Migratory. 1853. 1st ed., amateur 1/2 leather binding, scarce. Hyland 128-753 1978 £12.50

WATTERSON, HENRY   Oddities in Southern Life and Character. NY, 1882. Bell Wiley's copy. Broadfoot's 44-813 1978 $10.00

WATTS, ALARIC ALEXANDER   The Literary Souvenir and Cabinet of Modern Art. 1835. Engraved title-pg., engraved plts., 8vo, half red morocco, gilt, t.e.g., nice. Fenning 32-355 1978 £6.50

WATTS, ISAAC   The Improvement of the Mind... 1800. Orig. tree calf, leading hinge weak & spine rubbed, otherwise good. Jarndyce 16-234 1978 £8.50

WATTS, ISAAC   The Improvement of the Mind. Berwick, 1801. Portrait, sm. 8vo., contemp. calf, joints weak. Howes 194-515 1978 £10

WATTS, ISAAC   Logick. 1782. 8vo., contemp. calf, nice. Howes 194-516 1978 £26

WATTS, ISAAC   Prayers Composed for the use and imitation of Children...instructions to Youth in the Duty of Prayer. Gainsborough, 1813. 12mo., contemp. sheep. Howes 194-350 1978 £10

WATTS, ISAAC   Watts Divine and Moral Songs, for Children. Cambridge, 1803. 12mo, bottom half of rear flowered wrapper lacking, water-staining, handsomely patterned wrappers. Victoria 34-847 1978 $35

WATTS, JOHN S.   Armendaris Grant. Santa Fe, [1870]. Orig. pr. wr., lst ed. Ginsberg 14-783 1978 $150

WATTS, M. S.   George Frederic Watts. 1912. Plts., 3 vols., spines faded. George's 635-222 1978 £21

WATTS, WILLIAM   The Yahoo. 1842. 12mo., contemp. cloth. P. M. Hill 142-299 1978 £20

WATTS, WILLIAM COURTNEY   Chronicles of a Kentucky Settlement. New York, 1897. 8vo., lst ed. Morrill 239-461 1978 $10

WAUGH, EDWIN   The Chimney Corner. 1879. lst. ed., frontis vignette title, some slight foxing, orig. maroon cloth, v.g. Jarndyce 16-1163 1978 £10.50

WAUGH, EVELYN   The Loved One. Boston, 1948. Near mint in d.w. Desmarais B-647 1978 $12.50

WAUGH, EVELYN   A Bachelor Abroad. New York, 1930. First U.S. ed., frontis. drawing by author, maps, plts., very good. Bell Book 17-896 1978 £12.50

WAUGH, EVELYN   Black Mischief. 1932. Map, very good, first English ed. Bell Book 16-877 1978 £30

WAUGH, EVELYN   Brideshead Revisited. 1945. Spine sl. faded, very good, first English ed. Bell Book 17-897 1978 £6.50

WAUGH, EVELYN   Brideshead Revisited. Boston, 1945. One of 600 copies, demy 8vo., very good, first U.S. ed. Bell Book 17-898 1978 £24

WAUGH, EVELYN   Compassion. 1950. Very good, d.w., first English ed. Bell Book 17-899 1978 £6.50

WAUGH, EVELYN   Edmund Campion. 1935. Very good, first English ed. Bell Book 17-900 1978 £25

WAUGH, EVELYN   Edmund Campion. 1947. 2nd ed., plts., very good, d.w., first English ed. Bell Book 16-878 1978 £4.50

WAUGH, EVELYN   The First Time I Went to the North. 1935. Very good, cloth-backed bds., first English ed. Bell Book 17-901 1978 £6.50

WAUGH, EVELYN   Labels; a Mediterranean Journal. London, 1930. First Trade ed., orig. binding, spine and covers faded, nice, inscribed by author. Rota 211-747 1978 £95

WAUGH, EVELYN   The Loved One. An Anglo-American Tragedy. (London), (1948). Illus. by Stuart Boyle, orig. cloth, 3rd impression, but signed by author, very good. MacManus 238-758 1978 $45

WAUGH, EVELYN   Miss Runcible's Sunday Morning. Oxford, 1929. Cloth-backed bds., good, first English ed. Bell Book 17-902 1978 £10

WAUGH, EVELYN   Mr. Loveday's Little Outing. 1936. Frontis. by Thomas Derrick, good, first English ed. Bell Book 17-903 1978 £27.50

WAUGH, EVELYN   Ninety-two Days. 1934. Plts., map, covers somewhat dampstained, good, first English ed. Bell Book 16-879 1978 £16.50

WAUGH, EVELYN   P.R.B.; an essay on the Pre-Raphaelite Brother-hood 1847-1854. London, 1926. One of only 50 copies, bds. a trifle discoloured at edges, nice, two autograph pres. inscriptions from author, first ed. Rota 212-58 1978 £650

WAUGH, EVELYN   Put Out More Flags. 1942. Very good, worn d.w., first English ed. Bell Book 17-904 1978 £18.50

WAUGH, EVELYN   Put Out More Flags. 1948. Pres. copy inscribed by author, post 8vo., near fine, uniform ed. Bell Book 17-905 1978 £27.50

WAUGH, EVELYN   Scoop. 1938. Bookplt., near fine, worn d.w., first English ed. Bell Book 17-906 1978 £27.50

WAUGH, EVELYN   Scott-King's Modern Europe. 1947. Very good, d.w., frontis. by John Piper, first English ed. Bell Book 17-907 1978 £6.50

WAUGH, EVELYN   Scott-King's Modern Europe. Boston, 1949. First American ed. Biblo 247-636 1978 $9.50

WAUGH, EVELYN   Vile Bodies. London, 1930. Decor. red & black cloth, lst ed. Bradley 49-340 1978 $30

WAUGH, EVELYN   Vile Bodies. 1949. Uniform ed., reprinted, pres. copy inscribed by author, post 8vo., near fine. Bell Book 17-908 1978 £25

WAUGH, EVELYN   Waugh in Abyssinia. 1936. Spine faded, very good, first English ed. Bell Book 17-909 1978 £24

WAUGH, EVELYN   When the Going was Good. 1946. Coloured frontis., near fine, d.w., first English ed. Bell Book 16-882 1978 £12.50

WAUGH, EVELYN   Wine in Peace and War. (1947). Coloured decorations by Rex Whistler, bds., good, scarce, first English ed. Bell Book 17-910 1978 £30

WAUGH, LORENZO   Autobiography of .... Oakland, 1883. Illus., original cloth, lst ed. Ginsberg 14-219 1978 $25

WAUGH, WILLIAM TEMPLETON   James Wolfe, Man and Soldier. Montreal, 1928. 4to., one of an extra illus. lst ed., ltd. to 750 numbered copies, orig. binding. Wolfe 39-569 1978 $20

WAUTERS, A. J.   Stanley's Emin Pasha Expedition. London, 1890. Folding map, 33 plts., gilt cloth, 8vo. K Books 239-524 1978 £10

WAVELL, ARCHIBALD   Generals and Generalship. 1943. Austin 80-363 1978 $8.50

THE WAVERLEY Album. London, c. 1860. Cr. 8vo., half red mor. K Books 244-323 1978 £12

WAVRIN, JOHN DE   A Collection of the Chronicles and Ancient His-tories of Great Britain. 1864-91. 3 vols., roy. 8vo., orig. qtr. roan, rubbed. George's 635-791 1978 £18

WAY, RONALD L.   Old Fort Henry, the Citadel of Upper Canada. Illus. Hood 117-772 1978 $10

WAY, THOMAS R.   Memories of James McNeill Whistler, the Artist. Coloured plts., sq. 8vo. George's 635-223 1978 £7.50

WAYLAND, JOHN W.   Battle of New Market. New Market, 1926. Wrs., Bell Wiley's copy. Broadfoot 46-273 1978 $20

WAYLAND, JOHN W.   A History of Rockingham County, Virginia. Dayton, 1912. 1st ed., thick 8vo., illus., orig. cloth, fine. MacManus 239-1132 1978 $40

WEALE, PUTNAM   Why China Sees Red. London, 1926. Illus.,
cloth, light wear and fading. Dawson's 449-92 1978 $27.50

WEARE, GEORGE E.   Cabot's Discovery of North America. London,
1897. Frontis., 8vo., lst ed. Morrill 239-652 1978 $12.50

WEARE, GEORGE E.   Cabot's Discovery of North America. London,
1897. Illus. MacManus 239-507 1978 $22.50

WEATHERFORD, W. D.   The Negro from Africa to America. New York,
(1924). MacManus 239-857 1978 $20

WEATHERFORD, W. D.   Negro Life in the South. NY, 1915. Spine worn,
Bell Wiley's copy. Broadfoot's 44-814 1978 $15.00

WEATHERLY, F. E.   Told in the Twilight. New York, c.1883.
Chromolithographed plates, very good. Victoria 34-849 1978 $25

WEATHERLY, LIONEL   The Supernatural? Bristol, (1891). lst. ed.,
illus., half title, orig. brown cloth, little rubbed. Jarndyce 16-1164 1978 £5.50

WEATHERWAX, CLARA   Marching! Marching! 1935. Austin 82-1059
1978 $12.50

WEAVER, COURT   Frickinger J. M. Schwaben & Leipzig, 1740.
Oblong 4 to., woodcut textile patterns, new half leather, 2nd ed., rare.
Quaritch Summer, 1978-19 1978 $2,750

WEAVER, F. W.   Somerset Incumbents. 1889. 4to., half calf,
worn, partly cracked, author's copy. Allen 234-1494 1978 $25

WEAVER, LAWRENCE   Cottages. London, 1926. 483 illus., 8vo.
Traylen 88-423 1978 £5

WEAVER, LAWRENCE   English Leadwork: Its Art and History. 1909.
4to., frontis., illus., cloth, soiled. Quaritch 983-132 1978 $120

WEAVER, LAWRENCE   Memorials & Monuments, Old and New.
London, 1915. Illus., 8vo., orig. bds., buckram back, lst ed. Morrill 241-611
1978 $25

WEAVER, LAWRENCE   The Story of the Royal Scots. 1915. Coloured
frontis., plts., illus., 8vo., orig. cloth, spine faded. F. Edwards 1013-482 1978
£12

WEAVER, RAYMOND M.   Herman Melvill, Mariner and Mystic. New
York, (1921). lst. ed., backstrip faded. Baldwins' 51-182 1978 $15

WEAVER, WARREN A.   Lithographs of N. Currier and Currier and Ives.
New York, (1925). Illus. MacManus 239-654 1978 $25

WEBB, A.P.   A Bibliography of the Works of Thomas Hardy.
London, 1916. 8vo., orig. cloth, 1st ed. MacManus 238-939 1978 $25

WEBB, ALEXANDER S.   The Peninsula McClellan's Campaign of 1862.
New York, 1881. Bell Wiley's copy. Broadfoot 46-274 1978 $10

WEBB, ALEXANDER S.   The Peninsula McClellan's Campaign of 1862.
Slight wear, Bell Wiley's copy. Broadfoot 46-274a 1978 $8

WEBB, CHARLES HENRY   Parodies. Prose and Verse. New York, 1876.
lst ed. in l vol., illus., orig. cloth, edges worn. Greene 78-302 1978 $65

WEBB, E. A. H.   A History of the Services of the 17th Regiment.
1912. 8vo., orig. cloth, coloured plts., second ed. F. Edwards 1013-493 1978
£60

WEBB, E. A. H.   History of the 12th Regiment 1685-1913. 1914.
Thick imp. 8vo., publisher's half mor., edges foxed, coloured plts. F. Edwards
1013-489 1978 £50

WEBB, ELIZABETH   A Letter from... to Anthony Boehn, With His
Answer. Philadelphia, 1798. 3rd. ed., orig. pamphlet as issued. Baldwins' 51-
476 1978 $27.50

WEBB, GILBERT   Four Score Years in Jack County, 1860-1940.
Jacksboro, 1940. Wr., Illus. Jenkins 116-711 1978 $17.50

WEBB, MARY   The Chinese Lion. London, 1937. 12mo., orig.
cloth-backed bds., 1st ed., 1 of 350 copies, some light foxing, but fine, pub.
slipcase. MacManus 238-759 1978 $35

WEBB, MARY   Gone to Earth. London, 1917. First ed., orig.
binding, spine faded, very good, scarce. Rota 211-751 1978 £40

WEBB, SIDNEY   The Break-Up of the Poor Law. 1909. 8vo.
George's 635-431 1978 £5

WEBB, SIDNEY   The Constitution for the Socialist Commonwealth
of Great Britain. 1920. Orig. bds., worn, 8vo. George's 635-422 1978 £5

WEBB, SIDNEY   The Consumers Cooperative Society. 1921.
Orig. bds., 8vo. George's 635-423 1978 £5

WEBB, SIDNEY   English Local Government, English Poor Law
History, Pt. 1. The Old Poor Law. 1927. 8vo. George's 635-424 1978 £5

WEBB, SIDNEY   English Local Government, V. The Story of the
King's Highway. 1913. 8vo. George's 635-425 1978 £5

WEBB, SIDNEY   The History of Liquor Licensing in England Principally, 1700-1830. 1903. Cr. 8vo. George's 635-426 1978 £5

WEBB, SIDNEY   The History of Trade Unionism. 1912-13. 8vo.
George's 635-428 1978 £5.25

WEBB, SIDNEY   Industrial Democracy. 1902. New ed., 2 vols.
in 1, 8vo. George's 635-428 1978 £5.25

WEBB, SIDNEY   Problems of Modern Industry. 1898. 8vo.
George's 635-429 1978 £5

WEBB, SIDNEY   Soviet Communism, a New Civilisation. 1935.
Map, bds., 8vo. George's 635-430 1978 £5

WEBB, SIDNEY   Soviet Communism: A New Civilization? New
York, 1936. 2 vols., 1st Amer. ed. Biblo BL781-889 1978 $12.50

WEBB, THOMAS SMITH   El Monitor de Los Masones Libres. Philadelphia,
1822. 12mo., roan-backed bds., some staining. P. M. Hill 142-113 1978 £20

WEBB, W.   Buffalo Land: An Authentic Narrative of the
Adventures & Misadventures of a late scientific & sporting party upon the Great
Plains of the West. Cincinnati, Chicago, 1872. Profusely illus., faded spine,
8vo, orig. cloth. Book Chest 17-409 1978 $50

WEBB, WALTER FREEMAN   United States Mollusca. Rochester, (1942).
Illus., 8vo., lst ed., orig. cloth. Morrill 241-612 1978 $15

WEBB, WALTER PRESCOTT   Divided We Stand, the Crises of a Frontier-
less Democracy. New York, 1937. Bell Wiley's copy. Broadfoot 46-583 1978
$8

WEBB, WALTER PRESCOTT   The Great Plains. New York, (1931). Illus.,
first ed. Biblo 247-275 1978 $32.50

WEBB, WALTER PRESCOTT   The Great Plains. Boston, 1931. Illus., orig.
cloth, lst ed. Ginsberg 14-1051 1978 $35

WEBB, WALTER PRESCOTT   The Great Plains. Boston, 1931. Pres. copy from
author to Bell Wiley. Broadfoot's 44-978a 1978 $70

WEBB, WALTER PRESCOTT   The Great Plains. Boston, 1931. Bell Wiley's
copy. Broadfoot's 44-978b 1978 $50

WEBB, WALTER PRESCOTT   The Great Plains. Boston, 1936. Orig. binding,
clean, later ed. Hayman 71-765 1978 $7.50

WEBB, WALTER PRESCOTT   The Last Treaty of the Republic of Texas. Austin,
1922. Offprint. Jenkins 116-1438 1978 $25

WEBB, WALTER PRESCOTT   Notes on the Folk-Lore of Texas. Austin, 1915.
Offprint. Jenkins 116-1440 1978 $45

WEBB, WALTER PRESCOTT   The Texas Rangers A Century of Frontier
Defense. Boston, 1935. Pres copy from author, Bell Wiley's copy. Broadfoot's
44-979 1978 $40.00

WEBBER, C. H.   The Strange Case of Josephine Marie Bedard, a
Young Lady, Stout and Active, Who Has Eaten Nothing for Seven Years. Boston,
n.d. (ca. 1889). 12mo., orig. wrs., piece torn from back wr. Morrill 239-272
1978 $30

WEBBER, CHARLES W.   Old Hicks the Guide... New York, 1848. 1st ed., bind. worn, signatures sprung, text lightly foxed, scarce. Biblo BL781-304 1978 $42.50

WEBBER, F. R.   The Small Church. How to Build and Furnish It. Cleveland, 1937. Sm. 4to., illus., bind. torn, contents very good. Biblo BL781-551 1978 $12.50

WEBBER, THOMAS   Stockton. Stockton, 1815. 12mo, disbound, 1st ed. (?), two very scarce poems. Ximenes 47-330 1978 $45

WEBBER, VIVIAN A.   Journal of a Voyage to Coquimbo and Back. Swansea, 1859. 8vo, orig. cloth, spine faded, 2 line passage on pg. 73 cut out. Edwards 1012-682 1978 £25

WEBBER, WINSLOW L.   Books About Books. 1937. Battery Park 1-495 1978 $45

WEBER, ALFRED   Kulturgeschichte Als Kultursoziologie. Leiden, 1935. 4to., cloth. Salloch 348-279 1978 $35

WEBER, BROM   Hart Crane. New York, (1948). Illus., first ed. Biblo 247-816 1978 $15

WEBER, EDUARD FRIEDRICH   Disquisitio Anatomica Uteri et Ovariorum Puellae Septima a Conceptione die Defunctae. Halis, (1830). 8vo., limp bds., very scarce. Offenbacher 30-157 1978 $125

WEBER, JESSIE P.   An Outline for the Study of Illinois State History Prepared Under the Direction of the Board of Trustees of the Illinois State Historical Library. Springfield, 1905. Stapled, light stain on edge of 1st several leaves. Hayman 73-273 1973 $3.50

WEBER, JOSEPH   Ueber die Gemeine und Durch Auflosung aus Korpern Entwickelte Luft. Landshut, 1785. Copperplt., 8vo., contemp. half calf, 1st ed. Offenbacher 30-159 1978 $125

WEBER, M. J.   Explanation of the Anatomical Atlas of the Human Body in Natural Size. London, n.d. (ca. early 1800s). 8vo., contemp. calf, text only, atlas not present. Morrill 239-273 1978 $15

WEBER, W. E.   Die Elegischen Dichter der Hellenen, Nach Ihren Ueberresten. 1826. New buckram, rubber stamp. Allen 234-1042 1978 $10

WEBSTER, C. A.   The Church Plate of the Diocese of Cork, Cloyne & Ross. 1909. 1st ed., illus., 4to, very good. Hyland 128-754 1978 £12

WEBSTER, C. A.   The Diocese of Ross, Its Bishops Clergy & Parishes. 1935. 1st ed., map, illus., very good, octavo bound in cloth. Hyland 128-755 1978 £15

WEBSTER, CAROLINE LE ROY   "Mr. W. and I." New York, (1942). Illus., page torn. Biblo 248-224 1978 $15

WEBSTER, DANIEL   Private Correspondence. Boston, 1857. Portrs., 2 vols., 8vo., polished calf backs and corners, marbled bd. sides, nice, 1st ed., bkplts. of Levi Parsons. Morrill 241-613 1978 $30

WEBSTER, DANIEL   Mr. Webster's Speech, in the U. S. Senate, March 23, 1848, Upon the War with Mexico. Boston, 1848. Wrs. Hayman 72-778 1978 $12.50

WEBSTER, DANIEL   Speech on Mr. Clay's Resolutions. Washington, 1850. 1st ed. Jenkins 116-1448 1978 $50

WEBSTER, DANIEL   Works of... Boston, 1851-57. 8 vols., royal octavo, orig. cloth, spines faded, Subscriber's copy, signed. Baldwins' 51-187 1978 $125

WEBSTER, GEORGE P.   Rip Van Winkle. New York, (c.1900s). Colored illus., stiff pict. wrs., cover little used. Petrilla 13-151 1978 $10

WEBSTER, H. T.   The Timid Soul. New York, 1931. 4to., 1st ed. Biblo 251-188 1978 $15

WEBSTER, JOHN   The Dramatic Works. 1897. 4 vols., fcap. 8vo. orig. cloth. Howes 194-1317 1978 £12.50

WEBSTER, JOHN   The Duchess of Malfi. Sylvan Press, 1945. Very good, drawings, d.w., first English ed. Bell Book 17-933 1978 £6.50

WEBSTER, JOHN   Love's Graduate, a Comedy. Oxford, 1885. 1 of 150 copies, orig. vellum-backed bds., uncut, spine somewhat time-darkened. Americanist 102-39 1978 $60

WEBSTER, JOHN   Love's Graduate. Oxford, 1885. 4to., bds., parchment back, dust-stained, bkplt. of Robert Gathorne-Hardy, ltd. to 150 copies, pres. inscr. Quaritch 979-108 1978 $40

WEBSTER, JOHN   The White Devil. N.P., 1631. Sm. 4 to., good clean, polished calf, 2nd ed., 3 leaves as trimmed, 1 letter of imprint and 1 catchword cropped. Quaritch Summer, 1978-45 1978 $2,000

WEBSTER, JOHN   Complete Works. London, 1927. 4 vols., 8 vo, fine set in d.w. Traylen 88-356 1978 £30

WEBSTER, JOHN CLARENCE   Wolfiana. (N.P.), 1927. Stiff printed wrappers, illus. Wolfe 39-570 1978 $25

WEBSTER, JOHN W.   Trial of Professor...for the Murder of Dr. George Parkman in the Medical College, November 23, 1849... Boston, 1850. Illus., 8vo., orig. self-wrs., mod. 3/4 red mor., 1st ed., rear wr. bound in as frontis, fine. Howell 5-59 1978 $75

WEBSTER, NESTA H.   World Revolution. London, 1921. Paper. Austin 79-822 1978 $12.50

WEBSTER, NOAH   The Elementary Spelling Book. New York, (1848). Fine woodcuts, illus. ed., papered boards chipped, very good. Victoria 34-851 1978 $22.50

WEBSTER, NOAH   A Grammatical Institute of the English Language.... New York, 1804. Good, solid copy, worn contemporary linen, prepared oak. Victoria 34-850 1978 $15

WEBSTER, R. G.   The Trade of the World. London, 1880. 8vo. Traylen 88-88 1978 £10

WEBSTER, RICHARD   A History of the Presbyterian Church in America, From Its Early Ministers. Philadelphia, 1857. 1st ed., frontis. port., orig. cloth, fine. MacManus 239-508 1978 $30

WEBSTER, WILLIAM   The Consequences of Trade. 1740. First ed., cut close, sm. 8vo., disbound. George's 635-432 1978 £16

WEBSTER, WILLIAM HENRY BAYLEY   Narrative of a Voyage to the Southern Atlantic Ocean in the Years 1828, 29, 30 Performed in H. M. Sloop Chanticleer .... London, 1834. 1st ed., 2 vols., royal 8vo., frontis. maps, plts. a bit soiled, text fine, orig. bds., 19th Cent. rebacking. Current 24-200 1978 $185

WEBSTER, WILLIAM HENRY BAYLEY   Narrative of a Voyage to the Southern Atlantic Ocean, In the Years 1828, 29, 30, Performed in H.M. Sloop Chanticleer, Under the Command of the Late Captain Henry Foster.... 1834. 1st ed., 2 vols., 8vo., aquatint plts., folding map, soiling & spotting, modern half calf, gilt backs. Deighton 5-191 1978 £145

WEBSTER, WILLIAM HENRY BAYLEY   Narrative of a Voyage to the Southern Atlantic Ocean, 1828-30.... 1834. Maps, engraved plts., 2 vols., orig. bds., rebacked, uncut, slight foxing on plts., some browning in text, 8vo. Edwards 1012-41 1978 £150

WECHSLER, ISRAEL S.   Clinical Neurology. Philadelphia, 1928. First ed. Rittenhouse 49-821 1976 $12.50

WECKLER, J. E., JR.   Polynesians Explorers of the Pacific. 1943. Illus., paper. Austin 80-364 1978 $8.50

WECTER, DIXON   The Saga of American Society. New York, 1937. Illus. MacManus 239-509 1978 $15

WEDDELL, ELIZABETH WRIGHT   St. Paul's Church Richmond, Va., Its Historic Years and Memorials. 2 vols. Richmond, 1931. Boxed, Bell Wiley's copy. Broadfoot's 44-989 1978 $14.00

WEDEL, GEORG WOLFGANG   Introduction in Alchimiam. Jena, 1705. Sm. 4to., full antique calf, sm. expert paper repair on title, 1st ed., 1st issue. Norman 5-299 1978 $300

WEDEL, HASSO VON   Die Soldaten des Fuhrers im Felde. Munich, 1940. Coloured plts., 2 vols., imp. 8vo., orig. bds., photos. F. Edwards 1013-598 1978 £140

WEDGEWOOD, J.   The Imperial Russian Dinner Service... 1909. Roy, 4to., coloured frontis., plts., half vellum, spine spotted, ltd. to 310 copies. Quaritch 983-119 1978 $330

WEDMORE, FREDERICK   Etching in England. London, 1895. Illus., sq. demy 8vo, orig. cloth, little worn, good. Sexton 7-54 1978 £11

WEDMORE, FREDERICK   Fine Prints. Illus. and Bibliography. London, 1897. Covers worn. Biblo BL781-711 1978 $13.50

WEDMORE, FREDERICK   Whistler and Others. New York, 1906. Bind. worn. Biblo BL781-761 1978 $9

WEEDON, L.L.   Child Characters from Dickens. London, (c.1900). Colored plts., sm. piece torn from lower margin, orig. bind. Petrilla 13-152 1978 $10

WEEGE, FRITZ   Dionysischer Reigen. Leid und Bild in der Antike. Halle, 1926. 4to., illus. Biblo BL781-512 1978 $12

WEEGEE, PSEUD.
Please turn to
FELLIG, ARTHUR 1900

WEEKLEY, ERNEST   The Romance of Words. Edinburgh, 1913. 2nd ed., half prize calf, 8vo. K Books 244-324 1978 £6

WEEKS, LYMAN H.   Among the Azores. Boston, 1882. Map, illus., 12mo., 1st ed., orig. cloth. Morrill 241-614 1978 $7.50

WEEKS, STEPHEN B.   Southern Quakers and Slavery. Baltimore, 1896. Front endpaper missing, slight spine wear, Bell Wiley's copy. Broadfoot's 44-815 1978 $33.00

WEEKS, STEPHEN B.   Southern Quakers and Slavery. Baltimore, 1896. Fold. map, fine. MacManus 239-858 1978 $27.50

WEEKS, WILLIAM F.   Debates of the Texas Convention. Houston, 1846. Full morocco, gilt. Jenkins 116-1449 1978 $2,250

WEEMS, MASON LOCKE   God's Revenge Against Adultery... Philadelphia, 1828. Rare, 12mo., orig. roan backed bds., some foxing. Americanist 102-119 1978 $45

WEEMS, MASON LOCKE   The Life of Benjamin Franklin... Philadelphia, 1835. Illus., full contemp. calf, wormed, hinges cracking, else good, bookplt. MacManus 239-162 1978 $15

WEEMS, MASON LOCKE   The Life of George Washington. Philadelphia, 1810. 10th ed., illus., calf, front cover lacking, very good. Victoria 34-852 1978 $12.50

WEESE, ARTUR   L'Ancienne Suisse Villes. Edifices et Interieurs. Zurich, 1925. 4to., illus. Biblo BL781-552 1978 $32.50

WEESE, ARTUR   Die Bildnisse Albrecht Von Hallers... Bern, 1909. Tall 4to., illus., orig. paper bds., dust soiled, v.g. lg. paper copy, uncut and partially unopened, article by Weese laid in, rare first ed., ltd. to 300 copies. Zeitlin 245-111 1978 $125

WEGG, J.   The Decline of Antwerp under Philip of Spain. 1924. Plans, illus., 8vo. George's 635-792 1978 £5

WEIGHTMAN, RICHARD H.   To The Congress of the United States...Requesting the Passage of a Bill Declaring New Mexico one of the United States of America on Certain Conditions. Washington, 1851. Orig. pr. wr., 1st ed., inscribed fr. wr. Ginsberg 14-784 1978 $150

WEINBERGER, M.   George Grey Barnard Collection. 1941. Plt. Allen 234-1102 1978 $12.50

WEINBRENNER, JOHANN   Eine Kurze Ansicht, Der Bildung, Regierung Und Zucht, Der Gemeine Gottes. Harrisburg, 1830. 12mo, contemp. scuffed calf, spine worn, leaves soiled, front blanks gone, 8vo. Americanist 101-147 1978 $50

WEINMANN, J. G.   Tractatus de cuneo militari veterum. Reutlingae, 1770. Diagrams, fcap. 8vo., parchment stained. George's 635-869 1978 £6.50

WEINSTEIN, GREGORY   The Ardent Eighties and After. International Press, 1947. 3rd ed., illus. Austin 79-825 1978 $12.50

WEIR, F. G.   Scugog and Its Environs. Port Perry, 1927. Black cloth, marbled end papers. Hood 116-788 1978 $35

WEIR, WILLIAM   Sixty Years in Canada. Montreal, 1903. Hood 116-789 1978 $20

WEIS, FREDERICK L.   The Colonial Clergy and the Colonial Churches of New England. Lancaster, 1936. Illus., fine. MacManus 239-510 1978 $17.50

WEISE, ARTHUR J.   The Discoveries of America to...1525. New York, 1884. 1st ed., illus., maps, nice copy, orig. cloth, recased. MacManus 239-511 1978 $27.50

WEISE, ARTHUR J.   The Discoveries of America to the Year 1525. New York, 1884. Fldg. map, modern cloth, scarce, lacks 2 maps. Hayman 73-730 1978 $10

WEISE, CHRISTIAN   Curieuse Fragen Ueber Die Logica. Leipzig, 1696. Frontis., very thick 8vo., wallet-edged vellum. Salloch 348-280 1978 $450

WEISER, C. Z.   The Life of John Conrad Weiser, the German Pioneer, Patriot, and Patron of Two Races. Reading, 1876. 1st ed., orig. cloth, fine copy. MacManus 239-1713 1978 $45

WEISER, C. Z.   A Monograph of the New Goschenhoppen and Great Swamp Reformed Charge, 1731-1881. Reading, 1882. MacManus 239-1714 1978 $25

WEISMANN, AUGUST FRIEDRICH LEOPOLD   Vortrage Uber Descendenztheorie. Jena, 1902. 2 vols., 8vo., color plts., illus., orig. prtd. wrs., very good, uncut copy from the library of Louis Waldstein of London, 1st ed. Zeitlin 245-286 1978 $120

WEISS, FERI FELIX   The Sieve. Boston, 1921. Illus., ex-lib. Austin 79-826 1978 $12.50

WEISS, HARRY B.   Thomas Say. Illinois, 1931. 8vo, orig. cloth. Book Chest 17-411 1978 $40

WEITENKAMPF, F.   How to Appreciate Prints. London, 1921. Illus., 3rd. ed., 8vo, orig. cloth, good. Sexton 7-55 1978 £10

WEIZMANN, CHAIM   Trial and Error. 1949. 2 vols., 1st ed. in slightly frayed dust jacket. Austin 79-827 1978 $17.75

WELCH, DENTON   In Youth is Pleasure. 1944. 1st. ed., one corner bumped, slightly creased, otherwise v.g. in d.w. Jarndyce 16-1215 1978 £6.50

WELCH, DENTON   Maiden Voyage. New York, 1945. First U.S. ed., frontis. & decorations by author, very good, d.w. Bell Book 17-912 1978 £18.50

WELCH, DESHLER   Stephen Grover Cleveland, A Sketch of His Life. New York, 1884. Orig. binding, clean, lib. stamp on title, o/w very good. Hayman 71-652 1978 $10

WELCH, J.   Tenant-Right: Its Nature & Requirements; Together with a Plan... 1848. Disbound, reprint. Hyland 128-757 1978 £10

WELCH, MOSES C.   The Addressor Addressed. Norwich, 1796. 8vo., unbound, 1st ed. Morrill 241-615 1978 $10

WELCH, WILLIAM H.   The Interdependence of Medicine, with other Sciences of Nature. Baltimore, 1934. Rittenhouse 49-822 1976 $10

WELD, CHARLES RICHARD   A Vacation Tour in the United States and Canada. 1855. Folding map, half calf, 8vo. Edwards 1012-411 1978 £25

WELD, I.   Statistical Survey of the County of Roscommon. 1832. 1/2 leather, front board loose, map, text very good, reprint. Hyland 128-758 1978 £40

WELD, LEWIS   An Address Delivered in the Capitol, in Washington City, Feb. 16th, 1828, at an Exhibition of Three of the Pupils of the Pennsylvania Institution for the Education of the Deaf and Dumb. Washington, 1828. 8vo., unbound, 1st ed., pres. from Weld. Morrill 239-275 1978 $12.50

WELD, M.   No Union Being an Appeal to Irishmen. 1798. 3rd ed., plain wr. Hyland 128-759 1978 £7

WELDON, ANTHONY   The Court and Character of King James... London, 1651. 24mo., port., worn calf, spine label, front bd. detached, rear bd. lacking. Petrilla 13-153 1978 $45

WELEVELD, L. A. VAN   Handboek van den Nederlandschen Adel. N.P., 1848. 2 parts of text, 3 portfolios with plts., 5 vols. in all, 8vo., half cloth, loose engr. plts., lacking 5 plts., rare set. Van der Peet H-64-579 1978 Dfl 750

WELLAND COUNTY HISTORICAL SOCIETY, Papers and Records, Vol. II. Welland, 1926. Hood's 115-857 1978 $20

WELLCOME, HENRY S.   The Story of Metlakahtla. London, 1887. Illus. Hood 117-714 1978 $40

WELLER, C. H.   Athens & Its Monuments. 1913. Allen 234-1045 1978 $10

WELLER, JOHN B.   Remarks of Mr..., of Ohio, in Reply to Mr. Stewart, of Pennsylvania. House...Jan. 17 and 18, 1844. N.P., n.d. Disbound. Hayman 72-679 1978 $7.50

WELLES, A. M.   Reminiscent Ramblings. Denver 1905. Illus., orig. cloth, 1st ed. Ginsberg 14-1052 1978 $75

WELLES, GIDEON   Diary of Gideon Welles, Secretary of the Navy under Lincoln and Johnson. Boston, 1911. Illus., pres. copy to George Dewey, 3 vols. Broadfoot's 44-384 1978 $50

WELLES, GIDEON   Diary of Gideon Wells, Secretary of the Navy Under Lincoln and Johnson. Boston, (1911). 3 vols. MacManus 239-913 1978 $27.50

WELLES, GIDEON   The Diary of..., Sec. of the Navy Under Lincoln and Johnson. Boston, (1911). 3 vols., cloth, very good, d.j. Hayman 72-779 1978 $25

WELLES, LEMUEL A.   The History of the Regicides in New England. New York, (1927). 1st ed., ltd. to 500 copies, uncut, fine. MacManus 239-512 1978 $22.50

WELLESLEY, DOROTHY   A Broadcast Anthology of Modern Poetry. London, Hogarth Press, 1930. First ed., orig. binding, spine and bds. faded and marked, very good. Rota 211-8 1978 £6

WELLESLEY, VISCOUNT   The Irish Question Considered in Its Integrity. 1844. 1st ed., very good in original cloth, spine faded. Hyland 128-760 1978 £12.50

WELLINGTON, DUKE OF   Dispatches During His Various Campaigns in India ... 1837-38. 12 vols., orig. bds., rubbed. George's 635-870 1978 £55

WELLINGTON, BARRETT R.   The Mystery of Elizabeth Canning. New York, 1940. Illus. Biblo 251-305 1978 $17.50

WELLMAN, D. L.   Saskatchewan Fife Wheat. Detroit, 1886. Original printed wr., 1st ed. Ginsberg 14-576 1978 $85

WELLMONT, EMMA   Uncle Sam's Palace. Boston, 1853. Illus., 8vo., 1st ed. Morrill 239-622 1978 $8.50

WELLONS, JAMES WILLIS   A Historical Sketch of the Wellons Family. Richmond, 1910. Illus., pencil underlining. Broadfoot 50-333 1978 $17

WELLS, CAROLYN   The Lover's Baedeker and Guide to Arcady. New York, (1912). 1st ed., illus. Biblo 251-669 1978 $17.50

WELLS, CAROLYN   The Rubaiyat of Bridge. New York, 1909. 1st ed., illus. by May Wilson Preston. Biblo 251-670 1978 $17.50

WELLS, DAVID A.   Revenue. (Washington, 1869). Sewed as issued. Hayman 71-766 1978 $7.50

WELLS, GABRIEL   These Three. One of 750. Battery Park 1-497 1978 $35

WELLS, HERBERT GEORGE   Anticipations. 1902. T.e.g., very good, first English ed. Bell Book 17-914 1978 £12.50

WELLS, HERBERT GEORGE   Bealby. 1915. First ed., spine faded, orig. cloth, 8vo. Howes 194-1318 1978 £5

WELLS, HERBERT GEORGE   Christina Alberta's Father. New York, 1925. First U.S. ed., near fine, worn d.w. Bell Book 17-915 1978 £10

WELLS, HERBERT GEORGE   The Country of the Blind and Other Stories. London, (1913). 1st ed., color frontis., very good or better. Limestone 9-314 1978 $37.50

WELLS, HERBERT GEORGE   The Croquet Player. 1936. Fine, d.w., first English ed. Bell Book 16-883 1978 £8.50

WELLS, HERBERT GEORGE   The Croquet Player. London, 1936. Ownership inscription, very nice in lightly soiled & worn d.w. Desmarais B-649 1978 $7.50

WELLS, HERBERT GEORGE   The Dream. New York, 1924. 1st American ed., 1st printing, d.j., t.e.g., very good. Houle 10-360 1978 $25

WELLS, HERBERT GEORGE   An Experiment in Autobiography. London, 1934. 2 vols., 1st ed., illus., d.j., very good. Limestone 9-313 1978 $40

WELLS, HERBERT GEORGE   First & Last Things, a confession of faith and rule of life. 1908. Very good, first English ed. Bell Book 16-885 1978 £8.50

WELLS, HERBERT GEORGE   The First Men in the Moon. London, 1901. Illus., orig. cloth, 1st ed., slightly worn. MacManus 238-762 1978 $85

WELLS, HERBERT GEORGE   The First Men in the Moon. 1901. Plts., orig. cloth, covers & some pages soiled, else good, first English ed. Bell Book 16-886 1978 £20

WELLS, HERBERT GEORGE   First & Last Things: A Confession of Faith and Rule of Life. 1908. First ed., orig. cloth, 8vo. Howes 194-1319 1978 £5

WELLS, HERBERT GEORGE   The First Men in the Moon, The World Set Free, and Short Stories. London, n.d. Spine faded, very good or better. Limestone 9-315 1978 $8.50

WELLS, HERBERT GEORGE   The History of Mr. Polly. 1910. First ed., coloured frontispiece, orig. cloth, 8vo. Howes 194-1320 1978 £7.50

WELLS, HERBERT GEORGE   In the Days of the Comet. 1906. First ed., orig. cloth, 8vo. Howes 194-1321 1978 £8

WELLS, HERBERT GEORGE   The Island of Doctor Moreau. London, 1896. Orig. pict. cloth, frontis., 1st ed., covers a bit soiled. MacManus 238-761 1978 $100

WELLS, HERBERT GEORGE   Joan and Peter: The Story of an Education. 1918. First ed., orig. cloth, 8vo. Howes 194-1322 1978 £7.50

WELLS, HERBERT GEORGE   Kipps: the story of a simple soul. 1905. Orig. patterned cloth, very good, first English ed. Bell Book 17-916 1978 £22.50

WELLS, HERBERT GEORGE   Mankind in the Making. 1903. First ed., orig. cloth, 8vo. Howes 194-1323 1978 £6.50

WELLS, HERBERT GEORGE   Mind at the End of its Tether. 1945. Very good, slightly worn d.w., first English ed. Bell Book 17-917 1978 £10

WELLS, HERBERT GEORGE   A Modern Utopia. 1905. Plts., cloth gilt, first English ed., t.e.g., rear hinge weak, good. Bell Book 17-918 1978 £6

WELLS, HERBERT GEORGE   The Plattner Story and others. 1897. First ed., orig. cloth, 8vo., cover trifle dull. Howes 194-1324 1978 £7.50

WELLS, HERBERT GEORGE   The Sea Lady: a tissue of moonshine. 1902. Covers somewhat worn, good, first English ed. Bell Book 16-888 1978 £6

WELLS, HERBERT GEORGE   The Sea Lady: A Tissue of Moonshine. 1902. First ed., orig. cloth, 8vo. Howes 194-1325 1978 £7.50

WELLS, HERBERT GEORGE   The Shape of Things to Come: the ultimate re-volution. 1933. Very good, slightly worn d.w., first English ed. Bell Book 17-919 1978 £25

WELLS, HERBERT GEORGE   The Soul of a Bishop. New York, 1917. First U.S. ed., coloured frontis. by C. Allan Gilbert, fine, repaired d.w. Bell Book 17-921 1978 £22.50

WELLS, HERBERT GEORGE   The Stolen Bacillus, and Other Incidents. London, 1895. Orig. cloth, 1st ed., front inner hinge cracked, otherwise very good. MacManus 238-760 1978 $75

WELLS, HERBERT GEORGE   A Thesis on the Quality of Illusion in the Continuity of the Individual Life in the Higher Metazoa. London, (1942). First ed., wrappers, very nice. Rota 211-760 1978 £15

WELLS, HERBERT GEORGE   The Time Machine. Illus., some in color. Battery Park 1-76 1978 $22.50

WELLS, HERBERT GEORGE   The Treasure in the Forest. (New York, Press of the Wooly Whale, 1936). Decor. bds., very fine, 1 of 130 copies, prospectus laid in, color illus. Dawson's 447-36 1978 $50

WELLS, HERBERT GEORGE   The Undying Fire. (1919). First ed., orig. cloth, 8vo. Howes 194-1327 1978 £7.50

WELLS, HERBERT GEORGE   The War in the Air and Particularly how Mr. Bert Smallways fared while it lasted. 1908. Plts., first ed., orig. blue cloth, 8vo. Howes 194-1329 1978 £15

WELLS, HERBERT GEORGE   War in the Air. London, 1914. 3rd ed., very good or better. Limestone 9-316 1978 £10

WELLS, HERBERT GEORGE   War of the Worlds. New York, (c. 1944). 1st Armed Services ed., No. 745, oblong 16mo., pictorial wr., very good. Houle 10-361 1978 $20

WELLS, HERBERT GEORGE   The Way The World Is Going. 1928. Fine, d.w., first English ed. Bell Book 16-889 1978 £12.50

WELLS, HERBERT GEORGE   A Year of Prophesying. 1924. Spine little faded, some foxing, else very good, first English ed. Bell Book 16-890 1978 £5.50

WELLS, J. W.   An Alphabetical List of the Battles of the War of the Rebellion, with Dates. Washington, 1883. 8vo., orig. wrs. Morrill 239-276 1978 $30

WELLS, J. W.   An Alphabetical List of the Battles of the War of the Rebellion. Washington, 1883. Wrs., Bell Wiley's copy. Broadfoot's 44-385 1978 $15

WELLS, JAMES MONROE   The Chisholm Massacre. Washington, 1878. Pres. copy from Chisolm. Broadfoot's 44-910 1978 $17

WELLS, NATHANIEL ARMSTRONG   The Picturesque Antiquities of Spain... London, 1846. Sm. 4to, engraved frontispiece, engraved plts., woodcut illus., some staining, little loose in binding, orig. cloth, worn & stained. Deighton 5-228 1978 £70

WELLS, P.   Modern Cabinet Work, Furniture and Fitments. London, Batsford, 1909. 4to, orig. cloth, good, illus. Sexton 7-56 1978 £15

WELLS, ROLLA   Episodes of My Life. St. Louis, 1933. Illus., orig. boards with leather spine foxed, 1st ed. Ginsberg 14-1053 1978 $75

WELLS, SAMUEL   The Revenue and the Expenditure of the United Kingdom. London, 1834. 1st. ed., 8vo, half calf, leather label. Traylen 88-89 1978 £30

WELLS, SAMUEL R.   How to Read Character: Phrenology and Physiognomy. New York, 1870. Some markings on top cover. Rittenhouse 49-823 1976 $12.50

WELLS, THOMAS   Letters on Palestine. Boston, 1846. 8vo., 1st ed., orig. cloth. Morrill 241-617 1978 $17.50

WELLS, W. B.   The Irish Convention, The Sinn Fein. 1918. Signed pres. copy from Hone, very good, reprint, octavo bound in cloth. Hyland 128-764 1978 £12

WELLS, W. B.   Irish Indiscretions. Dublin, 1923. 1st ed., very good, octavo bound in cloth. Hyland 128-762 1978 £5

WELLS, WALTER   The Water-Power of Maine. Augusta, 1869. Illus., 8vo., ex-lib., orig. cloth. Morrill 241-692 1978 $17.50

WELLS, WILLIAM CHARLES   An Essay on Dew, and Several Appearances Connected with it. London, 1814. 8vo., modern half calf, gilt lettering, ex-lib. inscr. of the Royal Society of Edinburgh, good copy, 1st ed. Zeitlin 245-287 1978 $275

WELLS, WILLIAM CHARLES   An Essay on Dew and Several Appearances Connected With It. London, 1866. Slight wear top of spine. Rittenhouse 49-824 1976 $55

WELLS, WILLIAM V.   The Life and Public Services of Samuel Adams... Boston, 1865. 3 vols. MacManus 239-545 1978 $55

WELSER, MARCUS   Rerum Augustanar..Vindelicar..Libriocto. Venice, 1594. Folio, map, contemp. limp vellum, rare, 1st ed., some light spots, otherwise good. Gilhofer 74-51 1978 sFr 2,500

WELSEY, JOHN   Journal. 1840. Engraved portrait, 4 vols., post 8vo., worn. George's 635-1151 1978 £5.50

WELSFORD, H.   Mithridates Minor. 1848. 8vo. George's 635-1373 1978 £5

WELSH, HERBERT   Four Weeks Among Some of the Sioux Tribes of Dakota and Nebraska,... Philadelphia, 1882. Orig. pr. wr., 1st ed. Ginsberg 14-1054 1978 $85

WELSH, WILLIAM   Report and Supplementary Report of a Visit to Spotted Tail's Tribe of Brule Sioux Indians,.... Philadelphia, 1870. Orig. pr. wr., 1st ed. Ginsberg 14-1055 1978 $75

WELTER, G.   Eloge de la Danse. Paris, 1925. Sm. 8vo., orig. covers, colored illus., ltd. ed. Van der Peet H-64-225 1978 Dfl 30

WELTON, C.   Substance of a Lecture..Upon the Mutual Relation Between Landlord & Tenant. 1849. Disbound, very good, reprint. Hyland 128-766 1978 £10

WELTY, EUDORA   Delta Wedding. 1946. First ed. Austin 82-1061 1978 $12.50

WELTY, EUDORA   The Golden Apples. New York, 1949. Fine in lightly soiled d.w., chipped with several sm. tears. Desmarais B-552 1978 $20

WELTY, EUDORA   Short Stories. New York, 1949. First U.S. ed., 1 of 1500 copies, some fading of covers. Bell Book 16-893 1978 £8.50

WELWOOD, JAMES   Memoirs of the Most Material Transactions in England, for the last Hundred Years.... 1702. Fourth ed., newly bound in half dark mor. antique style, 8vo. Howes 194-517 1978 £18

WELWOOD, JAMES   Memoirs of the Most Material Transactions in England for the Last Hundred Years... London, 1710. Sm. 8vo, old sheep rebacked with calf. Traylen 88-357 1978 £10

WELZENBACH, W.   Bergfahrten unter Mitwirkung von E. Allwein.... 1935. Photographs, cr. 8vo., orig. linen. George's 635-1516 1978 £5

WENDELL, BARRETT   English Composition. 1910. Austin 82-1062 1978 $11

WENDELL, BARRETT   A History of Literature in America. 1904. Austin 82-1065 1978 $11

WENDELL, BARRETT   Liberty Union and Democracy. 1906. First ed. Austin 82-1063 1978 $12.50

WENDELL, BARRETT   The Mystery of Education and Other Academic Performances. 1909. First ed. Austin 82-1064 1978 $17.50

WENDINGEN 7-8. Amsterdam, 1921. 4to., orig. pict. bds., texts in Dutch, English & German. Goldschmidt 110-79 1978 $25

WENDLING, GEORGE R.   A Remarkable Tribute to the Jews. 1912 (1892).
Paper. Austin 79-829 1978 $10

WENIGER, L.   Von Hellenischer Art und Kunst. 1922. 4to.,
map, illus. Allen 234-1046 1978 $10

WENNER, GEORGE U.   The Lutherans of New York. Petersfield Press,
1918. Illus. Austin 79-830 1978 $12.50

WENSLEY, AMELIA   At Summer's End. Toronto, 1941. Card cover.
Hood 117-831 1978 $7.50

WENTWORTH, EDWARD NORRIS   America's Sheep Trails. Ames, 1948.
Pic. cloth, illus., 1st ed., spine browning, very good. Dykes 34-284 1978
$37.50

WENTWORTH, TRELAWNEY   The West India Sketch Book. 1834. 1st. ed.,
map, plts., 2 coloured, 2 tinted, illus. 2 vols., sm. 8vo, orig. cloth, rebacked,
plts. browned. Edwards 1012-746 1978 £125

WENTWORTH, WALTER   The Drifting Island or the Slave-Hunters of the
Congo. London, 1893. Illus. frontispiece & title, cr. 8vo, dec. cloth.   K Books
239-526 1978 £5

WENTZ, ABDEL R.   The Beginnings of the German Element in York
County Pennsylvania. Lancaster, 1916. Inscribed by author, scarce. MacManus
239-1716 1978 $22.50

WEPPNER, MARGARETHA   The North Star and the Southern Cross... London, 1876. 1st English ed., 2 vols., frontis., orig. cloth, very good set. Mac-
Manus 239-514 1978 $30

WEREKHA, P. N.   An Account of the Forests of Russia and Their
Products in Comparison with the Total Territorial Area and with the Population.
Toronto, 1896. Mended paper cover. Hood 117-968 1978 $7.50

WERENFELS, SAMUEL   Opuscula Theologica, Philosophica and Philo-
logica. Lausanne and Geneva, 1739. 2nd ed., 2 vols. in 1, port., thick 4to.,
contemp. vellum. Salloch 348-281 1978 $85

WERFEL, FRANZ   The Forty Days of Musa Dagh. 1934. 1st ed.
Austin 79-831 1978 $10

WERGE, JOHN   A Collection of Original Poems, Essays and Epistles. Stamford, 1753. 19th cent. qtr. calf, cloth sides, label missing, first ed.,
some gatherings water-stained. Howes 194-518 1978 £18

WERNER, ABRAHAM GOTTLOB   Von den ausserlichen Kennzeichen der Fos-
silien. Leipzig, 1774. Very rare 1st ed., folding tables, contemp. boards.
Gilhofer 75-115 1978 SFr 3,300

WERNER, J.   River Life on the Congo. London, 1889.
TD Carter bookplate, Lang namestamp, folding colored map, 8vo, orig. cloth.
Book Chest 17-413 1978 $75

WERNER, M. R.   Tammany Hall. New York, 1928. Illus., 1st
ed. Biblo 251-75 1978 $16.50

WERNER, M. R.   Tammany Hall. Garden City, 1928. Cloth, 1st
ed. Hayman 72-783 1978 $7.50

WERNER, MAX   The Great Offensive. 1942. Austin 80-367
1978 $7.50

WERNHAM, H.   The Genus Sabicea. 1914. 8vo, orig. cloth.
Book Chest 17-414 1978 $14

WERTENBAKER, CHARLES C.   Invasion. 1944. Photos by R. Capa. Austin
80-366 1978 $8.50

WERTENBAKER, THOMAS JEFFERSON   Father Knickerbocker's Rebels. New
York, 1948. First ed., fine, d.w. Biblo 248-205 1978 $20

WERTENBAKER, THOMAS JEFFERSON   Norfolk-Historic Southern Port. Durham,
1931. Bell Wiley's copy. Broadfoot's 44-990 1978 $16

WERTENBAKER, THOMAS JEFFERSON   The Old South. NY, 1942. Signed by
author, cover speckled, Bell Wiley's copy. Broadfoot's 44-820 1978 $9.00

WERTENBAKER, THOMAS JEFFERSON   The Planters of Colonial Virginia.
Princeton, 1922. Bell Wiley's copy. Broadfoot's 44-991 1978 $12

WERTENBAKER, THOMAS JEFFERSON   Virginia Under the Stuarts. 1607-1688.
Princeton, 1914. 1st ed. MacManus 239-1886 1978 $17.50

WERTH, ALEXANDER   Leningrad. 1944. Austin 80-368 1978 $8.50

WESCOTT, GLENWAY   Apartment in Athens. 1945. First ed., d.j.
Austin 82-1067 1978 $12.50

WESCOTT, GLENWAY   The Babe's Bed. 1930. 8vo., cloth, boxed, 1
of 375 copies prtd. on Pannekock paper, signed by Glenway Wescott. Battery
Park 1-162 1978 $200

WESCOTT, GLENWAY   Good-Bye Wisconsin. 1928. First ed., good.
Austin 82-1068 1978 $15

WESCOTT, GLENWAY   Good-Bye Wisconsin. 1928. Austin 82-1069
1978 $10

WESCOTT, GLENWAY   The Grandmothers. 1927. Austin 82-1070
1978 $10

WESCOTT, GLENWAY   The Grandmothers. 1950. First of this ed.
Austin 82-1071 1978 $12.50

WESCOTT, GLENWAY   The Pilgrim Hawk. New York, 1940. Near
mint in d.w. Desmarais B-655 1978 $12.50

WESLAGER, C. A.   Delaware's Forgotten River. Wilmington, 1947.
Illus. Baldwins' 51-239 1978 $10

WESLEY, JOHN   Primitive Physic. London, 1828. 32nd ed.,
12mo., orig. roan. K Books 244-325 1978 £12

WESLEYAN UNIVERSITY   The College Argus. Middletown, June 1868-
July 1869. 15 issues in 1, 4to., contemp. roan-backed bds. Morrill 241-90
1978 $10

WESSELITSKY, GABRIEL DE   Russia & Democracy: The German Canker in
Russia. (1915). 1st. ed., 8vo, wrapper, nice. Fenning 32-357 1978 £8

WEST, BENJAMIN   An Account of the Observation of Venus upon
the Sun, the Third Day of June, 1769, at Providence, in New England. Providence, 1769. Illus., 12mo., cloth backed bds., 1st ed. Argosy Special-92
1978 $200

WEST, CHARLES   Ulceration of the Os Uteri. Philadelphia, 1854.
Chipped on spine. Rittenhouse 49-826 1976 $12.50

WEST, G.   Observations on the History and Evidence of the
Resurrection of Jesus Christ. 1747. First ed., half title, contemp. calf, slightly
rubbed, joints cracked, 8vo. George's 635-1152 1978 £6.50

WEST, GOLDSMITH B.   The Golden Northwest;... Chicago, 1878.
Illus., orig. cloth, 1st ed. Ginsberg 14-1056 1978 $75

WEST, HERBERT FAULKNER   The Mind on the Wing. New York, 1947. 16mo,
black cloth, gilt lettering on spine, uncut, spine faded, near Fine, tight, 1st ed.
Desmarais 1-419 1978 $20

WEST, HERBERT FAULKNER   The Mind on the Wing. 1947. Good. Nestler
Rare 78-253 1978 $10

WEST, HERBERT FAULKNER   A Stephen Crane Collection. Hanover, 1948.
Orig. cloth, 1st ed., 1 of 350 copies, fine. MacManus 238-896 1978 $25

WEST, JANE   The Refusal. 1810. 3 vols. in one, 12mo., 19th
century half calf, gilt back, split at top of upper hinge, first ed. P. M. Hill 142-
198 1978 £65

WEST, JANE   A Tale of the Times. 1803. 3rd. ed., 3 vols.,
half titles in vols. 2 & 3, orig. half calf, marbled bds., v.g. Jarndyce 16-1165
1978 £32

WEST, JOHN   The Substance of a Journal During a Residence
at the Red River Colony, British North America... 1824. 1st. ed., plts., half
calf, spine gilt, 8vo. Edwards 1012-461 1978 £225

WEST, L.   The Natural Trout Fly and its Imitation. Liverpool, 1921. Coloured plts., illus., orig. buckram, 8vo. George's 635-1499 1978 £27.50

WEST, MATTHEW   Poems &c. On Several Occasion. Dublin, c. 1785. 1st. ed., 4to, recent bds., some light signs of use, very good. Fenning 32-358 1978 £24.50

WEST, MICHAEL   Clair de Lune and other Troubadour Romances. (c. 1930). Roy. 8vo., orig. mor., rubbed. George's 635-1524 1978 £7.50

WEST, MOSES   A Treatise Concerning Marriage. Wherein the Unlawfulness of Mixt-Marriages is Laid Open from the Scriptures of Truth... London, 1761. 3rd ed. Hayman 72-784 1978 $12.50

WEST, REBECCA   Black Lamb and Grey Falcon. 1941. 2 vol. ed., illus. Austin 79-832 1978 $27.50

WEST, REBECCA   Black Lamb and Grey Falcon. London, 1946. 2 vols., 8vo, orig. cloth, d.w., good. Sexton 7-128 1978 £6

WEST, REBECCA   Black Lamb and Grey Falcon. New York, 1948. Illus., one vol. ed. Biblo 247-759 1978 $16.50

WEST, REBECCA   D. H. Lawrence. London, 1930. First ed., orig. binding, nice. Rota 211-295 1978 £5

WEST, REBECCA   Henry James. 1916. 12mo., near fine, first English ed. Bell Book 16-897 1978 £10

WEST, REBECCA   The Modern Rake's Progress. 1934. Paintings by David Low, 4to. George's 635-126 1978 £7.50

WEST, RICHARD S.   The Second Admiral, A Life of David Dixon Porter 1813-1891. New York, 1937. Bell Wiley's copy. Broadfoot's 44-386 1978 $16

WEST AFRICA Missionary Records. London, c.1840. Sm. 8vo, engraved maps, contemporary half calf, marbled bds., morocco labels, gilt. Deighton 5-218 1978 £30

WEST Chester...Past and Present 1799-1899. Illus., map, orig. cloth, some wear. MacManus 239-1717 1978 $27.50

THE WEST Church Boston and Its Ministers... Boston, 1856. Orig. cloth. MacManus 239-299 1978 $10

WESTALL, WILLIAM   Great Britain Illustrated. 1830. Plts., 4to, contemp. qtr. green roan, rubbed, some foxing. Howes 194-1449 1978 £85

WESTALL, WILLIAM   Roy of Roy's Court. 1892. 1st. ed., 2 vols., half titles, orig. red cloth, good. Jarndyce 16-1166 1978 £38

WESTALL, WILLIAM   Views of Australian Scenery. 1814. 1st. ed., oblong 4to, 9 engraved views, orig. blue paper wrapper, embossed with diagonal ribs & floral design, spine defective, black paper label, gilt. Deighton 5-107 1978 £360

WESTBURY, HUGH   Acte, A Novel. 1890. 1st. ed., except for 1st. vol. which is 2nd. ed., 3 vols., 8vo, contemp. half calf, nice copy. Fenning 32-110 1978 £12

WESTCOTT, EDWARD NOYES   David Harum. 1900. Ltd. to 750 copies, good. Austin 82-1073 1978 $27.50

WESTCOTT, THOMPSON   The Historic Mansions of Philadelphia...with Some Notice of Their Owners and Occupants. Philadelphia, (1877). 1st. ed., illus., nice, orig. dec. cloth, a.e.g. MacManus 239-1615 1978 $45

WESTERFIELD, R. B.   Middlemen in English Business particularly between 1660-1760. New Haven, 1915. Roy. 8vo., orig. wrappers, front wrapper defective. George's 635-433 1978 £5

WESTERMAN, DIEDRICH   The African To-Day. London, 1934. Cr. 8vo, orig. cloth. K Books 239-527 1978 £6

WESTERMEIR, CLIFFORD P.   Man, Beast, Dust... (Denver, 1947). Dec. cloth, illus., 1st ed., #74 of ltd. ed. signed by author, almost mint, perfect d.w. Dykes 35-114 1978 $40

THE WESTERN Calendar: or, an Almanack for...1801. Washington, (1800). Hayman 73-10 1978 $100

WESTERN EDUCATION SOCIETY Third Annual Report of the Directors of the Western Education Society Presented at the Annual Meeting Held in the City of Cincinnati, November 9th, 1837. Cincinnati, 1837. Wrs., sm. piece lacking from back wr. Hayman 73-579 1978 $12.50

WESTERN LITERARY INSTITUTE AND COLLEGE OF PROFESSIONAL TEACHERS Transactions of the 8th Annual Meeting of... Cincinnati, 1839. Bds. Hayman 71-597 1978 $20

THE WESTERN Traveler's Pocket Directory. Schenectady, 1834. Orig. prtd. bds., cloth back, scarce, 24mo., minor breaks in inside hinges, very good. Butterfield 21-468 1978 $75

WESTERN Texas, The Australia of America:.... Cincinnati, 1860. Green printed wr., bound into half morocco. Jenkins 116-1451 1978 $1,850

THE WESTERNERS Brand Book. (Chicago), 1944. Vols. I through No. 6. Nestler Rare 78-72 1978 $25

WESTLAKE, H. F.   The Parish Gilds of Mediaeval England. 1919. Royal 8vo., plts., table. Upcroft 12-487 1978 £10

WESTMACOTT, CHARLES M.   Memoirs of the Life, Public and Private Adventures of Madame Vestris... 1839. 1st. ed., half morocco, marbled bds., good. Jarndyce 16-1168 1978 £20

WESTMACOTT, CHARLES M.   Points of Misery; or, Fables for Mankind. 1823. 1st. ed., illus. by Robert Cruikshank, uncut, half red morocco. Jarndyce 16-446 1978 £35

WESTMAN, E. G.   The Swedish Element in America. Chicago, 1931-1934. 4 vols., 4tos., illus. MacManus 239-453 1978 $75

WESTON, CHRISTINE   Indigo. New York, 1943. Orig. cloth, spine discoloured, signature of Bessie Sullivan on front paste-down. Eaton 45-533 1978 £5

WESTON, E. A.   A History of Brooklyn, Pa. Susquehanna County, Pa. Its Homes and Its People. Brooklyn, 1889. Very scarce, fine, old 1/2 calf. MacManus 239-1718 1978 $75

WESTON, RICHARD   Directions Left by a Gentleman to His Sonns.... London, 1670. Sm. 4to, old boards, calf spine. Traylen 88-90 1978 £105

WESTON, SILAS   Life in the Mountains; or, Four Months in the Mines of California. Providence, 1854. Original printed wr., 1st ed. Ginsberg 14-222 1978 $350

WESTON, THOMAS   History of the Town of Middleboro, Mass. Boston, 1906. 1st ed., illus., fold. map, orig. cloth, fine. MacManus 239-1038 1978 $25

WESTON, THOMAS   A Treatise of Arithmetic, in whole numbers and Fractions. London, 1734. 2nd ed., full contemporary calf with gilt borders and gilt spine, cover hinges lightly cracked, text is white and crisp. Victoria 34-855 1978 $30

WESTROPP, M. S. D.   Irish Glass: an Account of Glass-making in Ireland from the XVIth Century to the Present Day. (1920). 4to., plts., some dampstaining, cloth. Quaritch 983-120 1978 $100

WESTWARD March of Emigration in the United States, Considered in Its Bearing Upon the Near Future of Colorado and New Mexico. Lancaster, 1874. Half mor., 1st ed. Ginsberg 14-275 1978 $75

WESTWOOD, J. O.   The Butterflies of Great Britain. (1854). Engraved coloured title, coloured plts., roy. 8vo. George's 635-976 1978 £45

WESTWOOD, THOMAS   Bibliotheca Piscatoria. A Catalogue of Books on Angling, the Fisheries, and Fish-Culture... London, 1883. Orig. cloth, front inner hinge cracked, otherwise good. MacManus 238-854 1978 $45

WET, C. R. DE   Three Years War (October 1899 - June 1902). London, 1902. 8vo, orig. cloth, good. Sexton 7-119 1978 £5

WETHERELL, J. E.   Later Canadian Poems. Toronto, 1893. Neatly mended. Hood's 115-915 1978 $25

WETMORE, A.   Birds Collected in Cuba & Haiti. 1932. Plates, wr., 8vo. Book Chest 17-416 1978 $12

WETMORE, ALPHONSO   Gazetteer of the State of Missouri.... St. Louis, 1837. Illus., frontis., large folding map, orig. cloth, 1st ed. Ginsberg 14-1057 1978 $300

WETMORE, HELEN CODY   Last of the Great Scouts (Buffalo Bill). New York, (1918). Cloth, inscr. from author's daughter, nice copy in dust jacket. Hayman 73-750 1978 $10

WETTERGREN, E.   l'Art Decoratif Moderne en Suede. Malmo, 1925. 8vo., cloth, plts., some in color. Van der Peet H-64-226 1978 Dfl 65

WETTICH, H.   Die Maschine in der Karikatur. Berlin, 1916. 8vo., illus. cloth, illus. on plts. Van der Peet H-64-291 1978 Dfl 95

WEXELSTEIN, LEON   Building Up Greater Brooklyn. Brooklyn, (1925). 1st ed., illus., orig. cloth, very good. MacManus 239-361 1978 $17.50

WEY, F.   Rome. 1875. Wood-engravings, folio. George's 635-1525 1978 £7.50

WEYBURN, S. FLETCHER   Following the Connecticut Trail from Delaware River to Susquehanna Valley. Scranton, 1932. Illus., scarce. MacManus 239-516 1978 $15

WEYGANDT, CORNELIUS   The Blue Hills, Rounds and Discoveries in the Country Places of Penna. New York, 1936. Fine copy, inscribed by Weygandt. MacManus 239-1719 1978 $20

WEYGANDT, CORNELIUS   Down Jersey. Folks and Their Jobs... New York, 1940. 1st ed., illus., fine. MacManus 239-1340 1978 $30

WEYGANDT, CORNELIUS   Down Jersey: Folks & Their Jobs, Pine Barrens, Salt Marsh & Sea Islands. New York, 1940. 1st printing, large 8vo, illus., orig. binding. Americanist 101-149 1978 $27.50

WEYGANDT, CORNELIUS   The Dutch Country. Folks and Treasures in the Red Hills of Pennsylvania. New York, 1939. Illus., 1st ed., d.w. Biblo BL781-187 1978 $10

WEYGANDT, CORNELIUS   The Dutch Country. Folks and Treasures in the Red Hills of Penna. New York, 1939. Illus., inscribed. MacManus 239-1720 1978 $25

WEYGANDT, CORNELIUS   The Dutch Country Folks and Treasures in the Red Hills of Penna. New York, 1939. Illus. Baldwins' 51-493 1978 $20

WEYGANDT, CORNELIUS   The Heart of New Hampshire. New York, (1944). D.j. MacManus 239-329 1978 $15

WEYGANDT, CORNELIUS   New Hampshire Neighbors: Country Folks and Things in the White Hills. New York, (1937). Illus. MacManus 239-331 1978 $12.50

WEYGANDT, CORNELIUS   November Rowan. New York, 1941. 1st ed., illus., nice copy, d.j., inscribed by author. MacManus 239-517 1978 $15

WEYGANDT, CORNELIUS   A Passing America... New York, (1932). 1st ed., illus., colored frontis. MacManus 239-518 1978 $15

WEYGANDT, CORNELIUS   Philadelphia Folks. Ways and Institutions in and About the Quaker City. New York, 1938. Illus. MacManus 239-1721 1978 $15

WEYGANDT, CORNELIUS   Philadelphia Folks. New York, 1938. Illus. Baldwins' 51-494 1978 $12.50

WEYGANDT, CORNELIUS   The Plenty of Pennsylvania. Samples of Seven Cultures Persisting from Colonial Days. New York, 1942. Illus. MacManus 239-1722 1978 $15

WEYGANDT, CORNELIUS   The Red Hills. Philadelphia, 1929. Illus. Baldwins' 51-495 1978 $20

WEYGANDT, CORNELIUS   The Red Hills. A Record of Good Days Outdoors and In with Things Pennsylvania Dutch. Philadelphia, 1929. Inscribed. MacManus 239-1723 1978 $20

WEYGANDT, CORNELIUS   The Wissahickon Hills. Philadelphia, 1930. Illus., inscribed by author. MacManus 239-1724 1978 $17.50

WEYMAN, D.   Melodia Sacra; or the Psalms of David. Dublin, 1812. 4 parts in 1 vol., lacks t.p. to part 1, good, binding rough, reprint, octavo bound in cloth. Hyland 128-768 1978 £6

WEYMAN, STANLEY   From the Memoirs of a Minister of France. London, 1895. 1st ed., orig. cloth, spine sunned, very good or better. Limestone 9-318 1978 $25

WEYMOUTH, A. B.   A Memorial Sketch of Lieut. Edgar M. Newcomb, of the Nineteenth Mass. Vols. Malden, 1883. Illus., thin 8vo., 1st ed., orig. cloth. Morrill 241-618 1978 $20

THE WHALE, & The Perils of the Whale-Fishery. New Haven, c. 1830's. Chapbook, illus., good. Nestler Rare 78-196 1978 $25

WHALLEY, THOMAS SEDGWICK   Edwy and Edilda, A Tale, in Five Parts. London, 1794. 4to, 6 eng. plts., modern 1/4 calf, gilt spine. Eaton 45-534 1978 £30

WHARTON, ANNE HOLLINGSWORTH   Colonial Days & Dames. Philadelphia, 1895. Illus., ltd. to 508 copies, 2 pg. letter from author laid in. Baldwins' 51-496 1978 $22.50

WHARTON, ANNE HOLLINGSWORTH   English Ancestral Homes of Noted Americans. Philadelphia, 1915. 1st. ed., illus., inscribed & signed by author on front free-end paper. Baldwins' 51-498 1978 $15

WHARTON, ANNE HOLLINGSWORTH   Heirlooms in Miniature. Philadelphia, 1898. Backstrip dull. Nestler Rare 78-211 1978 $12

WHARTON, ANNE HOLLINGSWORTH   In Old Pennsylvania Towns. Philadelphia, 1920. 1st ed., illus., orig. pic. cloth, fine. MacManus 239-1725 1978 $15

WHARTON, ANNE HOLLINGSWORTH   In Old Pennsylvania Towns. Philadelphia, 1920. 1st. ed., 39 illus. Baldwins' 51-497 1978 $12.50

WHARTON, ANNE HOLLINGSWORTH   Through Colonial Doorways. Philadelphia, 1893. Ltd. to 442 copied, illus. Baldwins' 51-499 1978 $17.50

WHARTON, CLARENCE R.   Texas, Under Many Flags. Chicago, 1930. 4 vols., illus. Jenkins 116-1452 1978 $110

WHARTON, EDITH   The Custom of the Country. New York, 1913. First U.S. ed., very good. Bell Book 17-922 1978 $12.50

WHARTON, EDITH   The House of Mirth. New York, 1905. First U.S. ed., plts., very good. Bell Book 16-898 1978 £10

WHARTON, EDITH   Madame de Treymes. 1907. Spine faded, very good, first English ed. Bell Book 16-899 1978 £8.50

WHARTON, EDITH   The Marne: a tale of the war. 1918. Near fine, first English ed. Bell Book 16-900 1978 £6.50

WHARTON, FRANCIS   A Digest of the International Law of the United States... Washington, 1866. 3 vols., leather, little scuffed but solid set. Hayman 71-779 1978 $22.50

WHARTON, GRACE   The Wits and Beaux of Society. New York, 1861. 1st Amer. ed., illus., orig. cloth, two small binding damages, good. Greene 78-316 1978 $20

WHARTON, H.   Anglia sacra, sive collectio historiarum.... Londini, 1691. Vol. 2 (ex 2) only, half title, folio, contemp. calf, label defective. George's 635-1155 1978 £10.50

WHARTON, H. M.   War Songs & Poems of the Southern Confederacy, 1861-1865. Philadelphia, 1904. Excellent copy, Bell Wiley's copy. Broadfoot 46-275 1978 $40

WHARTON, H. M.   War Songs and Poems of the Southern Confederacy 1861-1865. Phila., 1904. Illus., pict. cover, front hinge cracked, several pgs & cover frayed and worn, Bell Wiley's copy. Broadfoot's 44-387 1978 $15.00

WHARTON, PHILIP, DUKE OF   The Life and Writings. 1732. 1st. ed., 2 vols., frontis portrait, vol. 2 lacks front endpaper, orig. calf, red & green labels, good. Jarndyce 16-235 1978 £65

WHARTON, THOMAS   "Bobbo" and Other Fancies. New York, 1897. Cloth, fine copy. Hayman 72-244 1978 $10

WHARTON, VERNON LANE   The Negro in Mississippi 1865-1890. Chapel Hill, 1947. Signed by author, minor cover blemishes, Bell Wiley's copy. Broadfoot's 44-911 1978 $16.00

WHATELY, RICHARD   Elements of Rhetoric. Oxford, 1830. 3rd. ed., 8vo, lib. stamp on verso of title, new buckram, paper label on spine. Eaton 45-535 1978 £8

WHEAT, CARL I.   The Shirley Letters from the California Mines, 1851-1852. New York, 1949. Illus., fine, d.w. Biblo 247-276 1978 $17.50

WHEATCROFT, R.   Siam and Cambodia; in Pen and pencil. London, 1928. Cloth, folding map, plts., 8vo. Van der Peet 127-265 1978 Dfl 65

WHEATLEY, DENNIS   Herewith the Clues! (1939). 4to., wraps, very good, solution seal opened, first English ed. Bell Book 16-240 1978 £35

WHEATLEY, DENNIS   Murder Off Miami. London, (1936). 1st ed., 4to., unpaginated, orig. wrs., tie binding, very fine throughout, rare. Current 24-63 1978 $115

WHEATLEY, DENNIS   Murder Off Miami. n.d. 4to., wraps, very good, plts., pres. copy inscribed by author, first English ed. Bell Book 17-229 1978 £75

WHEATLEY, DENNIS   Who Killed Robert Prentice? n.d. 4to., wraps, very good, plts., pres. copy inscribed by author. Bell Book 17-230 1978 £65

WHEATLEY, DENNIS   Who Killed Robert Prentice? n.d. 4to., very good, wraps, covers slightly frayed, first English ed. Bell Book 16-239 1978 £25

WHEATLEY, HENRY BENJAMIN   How to Catalogue a Library. Battery Park 1-267 1978 $35

WHEATLEY, HENRY BENJAMIN   How to Form a Library. Battery Park 1-268 1978 $35

WHEATLEY, HENRY BENJAMIN   How to Make an Index. Battery Park 1-271 1978 $35

WHEATLEY, HENRY BENJAMIN   Literary Blunders. Newly rebound. Battery Park 1-269 1978 $35

WHEATLEY, PHILLIS   Phillis Wheatley: Poems and Letters. New York, (1915). Tall 8vo., t.e.g., #6 of total ed. of 400, 1 of 9 copies on Japan vellum, engr. frontis, 3/4 blue mor. over marbled bds. & endpapers, rebacked, fine copy, scarce. Current Misc. 8-47 1978 $300

WHEATLEY, PHILLIS   Poems on Various Subjects, Religious and Moral by Phillis Wheatley, Negro Servant to Mr. John Wheatley, of Boston, in New England. London, 1773. 1st ed., 8vo., ads, bound in 1/2 brown mor. with marbled bds. & gilt lettering on spine, slightly foxed text, occas. pencil notations, very good copy. Current 24-64 1978 $1,000

WHEATON, HENRY   An Address, Pronounced at the Opening of the New-York Athenaeum, December 15, 1824. New York, 1824. Wr., loose, review copy. Butterfield 21-526 1978 $10

WHEATON, HENRY   Oration...Before the Different Republican Societies, at the Theatre, Anthony-St., New York, on...July 4, 1814. New York, 1814. Sewn, self-wr., uncut, margins frayed. Butterfield 21-236 1978 $12.50

WHEATON, J. M.   Report on the Birds of Ohio. (Columbus, 1879). Wrs., sm. piece torn from back wr. Hayman 73-585 1978 $7.50

WHEELER, A. C.   The Chronicles of Milwaukee: Being a Narrative History of the Town from Its Earliest Period to the Present. Milwaukee, 1861. Cloth, mod. wear to spine. Hayman 72-805 1978 $32.50

WHEELER, CANDACE   The Development of Embroidery in America. New York, 1921. 67 illus. Baldwins' 51-164 1978 $15

WHEELER, DANIEL   Extracts from the Letters and Journal of... London, 1839. 8vo., spine chipped & slightly torn with few pieces missing, fr. hinge repaired. Morrill 239-653 1978 $25

WHEELER, DANIEL   Extracts from the Letters and Journal of...While Engaged in a Religious Visit...Island of the Pacific Ocean.... Philadelphia, 1840. Orig. calf. MacManus 239-519 1978 $40

WHEELER, E. J.   Prohibition: The Principle, The Policy and The Party. New York, 1889. Orig. binding, clean. Hayman 71-780 1978 $8.50

WHEELER, G. A.   History of Brunswick, Topsham, and Harpswell, Maine. Boston, 1878. Illus. MacManus 239-984 1978 $45

WHEELER, G. D.   The Homes of Our Ancestors in Stoningham, Conn. Salem, 1903. Illus. MacManus 239-101 1978 $22.50

WHEELER, JOHN H.   Historical Sketches of North Carolina, From 1584 to 1851. Philadelphia, 1851. 1st ed., 2 vols. in 1, illus., cloth, nice copy. MacManus 239-1845 1978 $60

WHEELER, JOHN H.   Historical Sketches of North Carolina, from 1584 to 1851... Philadelphia, 1851. 1/2 leather, 2 vols. in 1 as issued, lightly rubbed, 1st. ed., very good set. Hayman 71-781 1978 $50

WHEELER, JOHN H.   Historical Sketches of North Carolina from 1584 to 1851. Philadelphia, 1851. Pres. from author, 3/4 leather, front bd. soiled. Broadfoot 50-334b 1978 $40

WHEELER, JOHN H.   Historical Sketches of North Carolina from 1584 to 1851. Philadelphia, 1851. 2 vols. in 1, new cloth. Broadfoot 50-334a 1978 $25

WHEELER, JOSEPH   A Revised System of Cavalry Tactics for the Use of the Cavalry and Mounted Infantry, C.S.A. Mobile, 1863. 1st & only ed., sm. thick 16mo., plts., bound in its orig. paper covered bds. simulating birchbark, light foxing throughout, very good, Joseph Wheeler's autograph, very rare. Current 24-111 1978 $550

WHEELER, JOSEPH TOWNE   The Maryland Press 1777-1790. Baltimore, 1938. 8vo., orig. cloth, 1st ed. MacManus 238-979 1978 $27.50

WHEELER, JOSEPH TOWNE   The Maryland Press 1777-1790. 1938. Illus., very good. Nestler Rare 78-52 1978 $20

WHEELER, JOSEPH TOWNE   The Maryland Press 1777-1790. Baltimore, 1938. Fine. Ballinger 11-99 1978 $45.00

WHEELER, JULIA M.   Ways of Pleasantness. Knowlton, 1945. Second printing, orig. binding. Wolfe 39-175 1978 $15

WHEELER, MONROE   Modern Painters and Sculptors as Illustrators. New York, (1936). Cover etching by Picasso, t.p. by Matisse, lower spine chip, fine. Victoria 34-856 1978 $15

WHEELER, OLIN D.   The Lewis and Clark Exposition Portland, Oregon June 1 to October 15, 1905... St. Paul, n.d. (1905). 5th ed., fold. plt., wrs. Hayman 72-791 1978 $7.50

WHEELER, OLIN D.   Wonderland 1903. St. Paul, 1903. Pic. wrs., maps, illus., 1st ed., fine. Dykes 35-169 1978 $10

WHEELER, OLIN D.   Wonderland 1904. St. Paul, 1904. Colored pic. wrs., maps, illus., frontis., 1st ed., back strip frayed else fine. Dykes 35-170 1978 $15

WHEELER, OLIN D.   Yellowstone National Park. St. Paul, 1901. Wrps. Hayman 71-782 1978 $7.50

WHEELER, OPAL   Sing for America. New York, (1944). 1st ed., color plates, fine, tattered d. j. Victoria 34-786 1978 $15

WHEELER, OPAL   Sing for Christmas. New York, 1943. Illus. in color, 4to., 1st ed., d.w. Biblo BL781-1035 1978 $9

WHEELER, OPAL   Sing Mother Goose. New York, 1945. 1st ed., quarto, illus. by Marjorie Torrey with color plates, very gine, d.j. Victoria 34-857 1978 $25

WHEELER, R.   Hard Knocks At Christianity. Salida, (1892). Wrps., some chipping. Hayman 71-783 1978 $8.50

WHEELER, R. A.   The Ports of Port Arthur, Sabine, Beaumont, and Orange, Texas. Washington, 1940. Color folding maps, photos. Jenkins 116-727 1978 $25

WHEELER, W. M.　　　　Social Life Among the Insects.　London, 1922. Illus., 8vo.　Traylen 88-639 1978 £12

WHEELER, WILLIAM REGINALD　The Road to Victory.　Yale University Press, 1946. 2 vols., plts.　Austin 80-369 1978 $27.50

WHEELER-BENNETT, JOHN W.　The Nemesis of Power.　1953. 8vo, orig. cloth, inner hinges weak, pres. copy to Winston Churchill, photo illus.　Sawyer 298-122 1978 £135

WHEELOCK, J. A.　　　　Minnesota: Its Progress and Capabilities, Being the Second Annual Report of the Commissioner of Statistics for 1860 and 1861.　St. Paul, 1862. Original printed wr., 1st ed.　Ginsberg 14-577 1978 $75

WHEELWRIGHT, JOHN T.　Rollo's Journey to Cambridge.　Boston, 1926. Illus. by Francis C. Attwood, tall 8vo., orig. colored pict. bds., d.w., very nice.　Morrill 239-420 1978 $10

WHEEN, A. W.　　　　Two Masters.　London, 1929. 32mo, orange paper covers, near Pristine copy, 1st ed.　Desmarais 1-111 1978 $15

WHELAN, EDWARD　　The Union of the British Provinces.　Charlottetown, 1865. Orig. printed bds.　Wolfe 39-558 1978 $85

WHELER, G.　　　　A Journey Into Greece...　1682. Folding map, plts., folio, contemp. calf, rebacked.　Edwards 1012-62 1978 £250

WHIBLEY, L.　　　　Companion to Greek Studies.　1906. 2nd ed. Allen 234-1050 1978 $10

WHIPPLE, HENRY B.　　The Apostolic Workman:....　Chicago, 1866. Orig. pr. wr., 1st ed.　Ginsberg 14-1058 1978 $125

WHISHAW, E. M.　　　　Atlantis in Andalucia.　London, n.d.　Rittenhouse 49-827 1976 $22.50

WHISHAW, JAMES　　A New Law Dictionary...　1829. 1st. ed., 8vo, orig. bds., old rebacking, retaining worn label, light spotting of title, very good. Fenning 32-360 1978 £14.50

WHISTLER, H.　　　　Popular Handbook of Indian Birds.　1928. 8vo., coloured plts., text illus. by H. Gronwold, roughly rebacked, letteringpiece upside down.　George's 635-1014 1978 £5

WHISTLER, JAMES ABBOT MC NEIL　Catalogue of Lithographs by J. McN. Whistler.　New York, 1907. 12mo., orig. wrs., dust-soiled.　Morrill 241-619 1978 $12.50

WHISTLER, JAMES ABBOTT MC NEILL　The Etchings of...　London, The Studio, 1922. First ed., 4to., plts.　Biblo 247-411 1978 $67.50

WHISTLER, JAMES ABBOTT MC NEILL　The Gentle Art of Making Enemies. 1890. Sq. 8vo., 1st ed., orig. decor. bds., yellow cloth spine, worn, uncut, pres. copy signed by Whistler.　Quaritch 979-327 1978 $180

WHISTLER, JAMES ABBOTT MC NEILL　The Portraits and Caricatures of... London, 1913. 1st ed., scarce, illus.　Biblo 247-444 1978 $27.50

WHISTLER, JAMES ABBOTT MC NEILL　Ten O'Clock.　Portland, 1917. One of 450 copies on Van Gelder handmade paper, 8vo., 2nd ed., gilt stamped tan bds., uncut, very good.　Houle 10-362 1978 $45

WHISTLER, JAMES ABBOTT MC NEILL　Whistler v. Ruskin: Art and Art Critics. London, n.d. (1878). 8vo., orig. brown prtd. wr., 1st ed., nice copy.　Ximenes 47-332 1978 $125

WHISTLER, LAURENCE　　The English Festivals.　1947. Plts., cloth, fine, worn d.w., first English ed.　Bell Book 16-905 1978 £8.50

WHISTLER, LAURENCE　　Four Walls.　London, 1932.　Fine in dumpstained & spotted d.w.　Desmarais B-660 1978 $7.50

WHISTLER, LAURENCE　　Four Walls.　1934. Very good, worn d.w., first English ed.　Bell Book 16-906 1978 £6.50

WHISTLER, LAURENCE　　Rex Whistler 1905-1944, His Life and His Drawings. London, 1948. Sq. 8vo., orig. cloth, d.w.　Sexton 7-57 1978 £6

WHISTLER, REX　　　　Designs for the Theatre.　Part 2.　London, 1947. Color plts., illus.　Biblo BL781-760 1978 $8.50

WHISTLER, REX　　　　Engravings By Rex Whistler for Jonathan Swift's Gulliver's Travels.　(London, 1970).　1 of only 100 numbered copies on Saunders handmade paper, folio, colored plts., enclosed in 3/4 mor. folding case, fine.　Houle 10-365 1978 $325

WHISTLER, REX　　　　The New Forget-Me-Not.　London, 1929. 1st ed., 8 vo., 3/4 Japan vellum over decorative bds., uncut, very good, color illus. by Rex Whistler, 1 of 350 numbered copies signed by Whistler. Houle 10-366 1978 $85

WHISTLER, REX　　　　The New Forget-Me-Not.　1929. 8vo., 1st ed., colour plts. & illus. by Rex Whistler, orig. half parchment, back faded, decor. bds. sides, ltd. to 360 signed copies, 1 of 30 with ornamented signature.　Quaritch 979-329 1978 $65

WHISTLER, REX　　　　The New Forget-Me-Not: a calendar.　1929. Coloured plts., cloth-backed bds., good.　Bell Book 16-907 1978 £6.50

WHISTLER, REX　　　　The New Forget-Me-Not.　1929.　Coloured plts., decorations by Rex Whistler.　George's 635-224 1978 £5

WHISTLER, REX　　　　The New Keepsake.　1931. 8vo., decor. by Rex Whistler.　George's 635-225 1978 £5

WHITACRE, AELRED　　St. Thomas Aquinas; being papers read at the celebrations of the sixth centenary of the canonization...Manchester, 1924. 1925. Recased, 8vo.　Upcroft 12-488 1978 £5.50

WHITAKER, MR.　　　　The Genuine History of the Britons Asserted Against Mr. MacPherson. 1773. 2nd ed., orig. boards, good.　Hyland 128-769 1978 £15

WHITAKER, ARTHUR PRESTON　The Mississippi Question 1795-1803, A Study in Trade, Politics, and Diplomacy.　New York, 1934. Autographed by author, Bell Wiley's copy.　Broadfoot's 44-912 1978 $15

WHITAKER, BESSIE LEWIS　The Provincial Council and Committees of Safety in North Carolina.　Chapel Hill, 1908. New cloth, marginal stains.　Broadfoot 50-335 1978 $10

WHITAKER, FESS　　　　History of Corporal Fess Whitaker: Life in the Kentucky Mountains, Mexico, and Texas.　Louisville, 1918. Cloth, 1st ed. Jenkins 116-1456 1978 $35

WHITAKER, WALTER C.　　History of the Protestant Episcopal Church in Alabama 1763-1891.　Birmingham, 1898. Cloth, nice.　MacManus 239-1796 1978 $22.50

WHITCOMB, C. D.　　　A Lake Tour to Picturesque Mackinac.　Historical and Descriptive...　Detroit, (1884). Flexible silk, illus.　Hayman 72-467 1978 $20

WHITCOMB, CAROLINE E.　History of the Second Massachusetts Battery of Light Artillery, 1861-1865.　Concord, (1912). Illus., 8vo., orig. cloth, 1st ed. Morrill 241-356 1978 $20

WHITCOMB, ROBERT　　Talk United States.　1935. First ed.　Austin 82-1077 1978 $15

WHITE, A. B.　　　　The Making of the English Constitution, 449-1485.　New York, 1908. Spine dull, 8vo.　Upcroft 12-489 1978 £5

WHITE, A. C.　　　　The Irish Free State.　(1923). 1st ed., good, octavo bound in cloth.　Hyland 128-770 1978 £7

WHITE, ANDREW DICKSON　Autobiography.　New Yor, 1905. 2 vols., ports., 1st ed.　Biblo 248-105 1978 $22.50

WHITE, ARNOLD　　　The Modern Jew.　1899.　Austin 79-836 1978 $27.50

WHITE, ARTHUR SILVA　　The Expansion of Egypt Under Anglo-Egyptian Condominium.　London, 1899. 4 folding coloured maps, 10 tables, 8vo., orig. cloth, rather foxed throughout.　K Books 239-528 1978 £7

WHITE, BISHOP ALMA　　Klansmen.　Zarephath, 1926. Portr., sm. 8vo., orig. wrs., 1st ed.　Morrill 241-620 1978 $22.50

WHITE, BOUCK　　　The Book of Daniel Drew.　New York, 1910. 8vo., 1st ed., orig. cloth.　Morrill 241-621 1978 $10

WHITE, CHARLES　　　"Power Belongeth Unto God".　Boston, 1854. Hayman 73-330 1978 $7.50

WHITE, DIANA　　　　The Descent of Ishtar.　Eragny Press, 1903.　Ltd. to 226 copies, pr. in red and black, woodcut frontis., sm. 8vo., orig. patterned bds., edges uncut.　George's 635-893 1978 £90

WHITE, E. B.　　　　Stuart Little.　New York, (1945). 1st ed., illus. by Garth Williams, fine copy, d.j. somewhat worn.　Victoria 34-858 1978 $45

WHITE, E. LUCAS   Andivius Hedulio. New York, (1921). First ed., rebound, bookplate, extra illus. laid in. Biblo 247-637 1978 $15

WHITE, E. LUCAS   Why Rome Fell. New York, 1927. Maps, first ed. Biblo 247-493 1978 $17.50

WHITE, E. V.   A Study of Rural Schools in Texas. Austin, 1914. Jenkins 116-1457 1978 $13.50

WHITE, ERIC WALTER   Stravinsky; a critical survey. London, 1947. First ed., orig. binding, nice. Rota 211-311 1978 £5

WHITE, FRANCIS BUCHANAN W.   The Flora of Perthshire. Edinburgh, 1898. Map, frontis., full green mor., handsome, 8vo. K Books 244-326 1978 £25

WHITE, GEORGE FRANCIS   Views in India Chiefly Among the Himalaya Mountains. 1838. 4to., contemp. half calf, plts., engrav. title. Howes 194-1416 1978 £48

WHITE, GEORGE FRANCIS   Views on India, Chiefly Among the Himalaya Mountains. (c.1840). Roy. 4to., frontis., plts., slightly foxed, orig. cloth gilt. Quaritch 983-379 1978 $105

WHITE, GEORGE S.   Memoir of Samuel Slater, Father of American Manufactures, Connected With a History of the Rise & Progress of Cotton Manufacture in England & America. Philadelphia, 1836. Illus., very good, rebacked copy. Nestler Rare 78-223 1978 $65

WHITE, GILBERT   The Natural History and Antiquities of Selborne, In the County of Southampton. London, 1789. 4to, contemporary full calf, spine repaired, engravings, index. Baldwins' 51-375 1978 $600

WHITE, GILBERT   The Natural History and Antiquities of Selborne, in the County of Southampton. London, 1875. Tall 8vo., gilt-decor. orig. green cloth. Salloch 345-193 1978 $50

WHITE, GILBERT   The Natural History of Selborne. c. 1930. Cr. 4to., orig. cloth, plts. Howes 194-1331 1978 £5

WHITE, GILBERT   The Writings of...of Selborne. London: The Nonesuch Press, 1938. 2 vols., illus., wood engravings by Eric Ravilious, fold. map, orig. cloth, 1 of 850 sets designed by Francis Meynell, lightly foxed throughout, otherwise fine. MacManus 238-842 1978 $200

WHITE, GLEESON   Book-Song. London, 1893. Orig. binding, clean. Hayman 71-785 1978 $10

WHITE, HENRY KIRKE   The Beauties of Henry Kirke White...Poetry & Prose. Hartford, 1831. Fronts., 12mo., orig. lea., very good. Americanist 103-107 1978 $30

WHITE, HENRY KIRKE   Clifton Grove, a Sketch in Verse, with Other Poems. 1803. Sm. 8vo., 1st ed., orig. bds., bkplt., very good copy, mor. slipcase. Quaritch 979-331 1978 $140

WHITE, HENRY KIRKE   The Remains of ... 1823. 10th. ed., 2 vols., fine frontis portrait & vignette title, orig. grey bds., paper labels, v.g. Jarndyce 16-1171 1978 £10.50

WHITE, JAMES C.   The Autonomic Nervous System. New York, 1935. Clean, fresh. Rittenhouse 49-828 1976 $15

WHITE, JAMES C.   The Autonomic Nervous System. New York, 1945. Second ed., ex-library. Rittenhouse 49-829 1976 $15

WHITE, JOHN   Arts Treasury:.... London, 1687/8. Original leather binding, binding poor, detached. Nestler Rare 78-190 1978 $245

WHITE, JOHN   An Essay on the Indigenous Grasses of Ireland. Dublin, 1808. Lea. & marbled bds., plts. in color, 1st ed., very good copy from the Allred Collection, rare. Dykes 34-129 1978 $75

WHITE, JOHN   An Essay on the Indigenous Grasses of Ireland. 1808. Plts., orig. boards, spine worn, very good, reprint. Hyland 128-771 1978 £32.50

WHITE, JOHN   An Essay on the Indigenous Grasses of Ireland. 1808. 1/4 leather, very good, reprint. Hyland 128-772 1978 £32.50

WHITE, JOSIAH   Josiah Whites Histofy Given by Himself. 1946. Only 100 copies, very good. Nestler Rare 78-53 1978 $35

WHITE, LEE A.   The Detroit News: Eighteen Hundred and Seventy-three – Nineteen Hundred and Seventeen – A Record of Progress. Detroit, (1918). Fold. plts., printed bds. with cloth spine. Hayman 72-468 1978 $7.50

WHITE, MELVILLE G. J.   Holmby House A Tale of Old Northamptonshire. 1860. 1st. ed., 2 vols., litho frontis, half red morocco, marbled bds., v.g. Jarndyce 16-1174 1978 £24

WHITE, MELVILLE G. J.   Un e John. 1874. 1st. ed., 3 vols., half purple calf, rebacked, v.g., except some slight foxing. Jarndyce 16-1175 1978 £22

WHITE, NEWMAN I.   Shelley. 1947. Orig. ed., scarce, 2 vols., lg. 8vo., orig. buckram, plts. Howes 194-1198 1978 £16

WHITE, OWEN P.   Just Me and Other Poems. El Paso, 1924. Deluxe ed., limited ed. to 275 numbered, signed copies, printed on Old Statford Paper, bound in gray-green double paper covers, hand-tied with gray ribbon, inscribed by author on preface page. Jenkins 116-631 1978 $600

WHITE, OWEN P.   Out of the Desert: The Historical Romance of El Paso. El Paso, 1924. 1st ed., scarce, signed by author, extrimities rubbed. Jenkins 116-1541 1978 $125

WHITE, OWEN P.   Texas: An Informal Biography. New York, 1945. 1st ed., d.j., autographed by author. Jenkins 116-1458 1978 $20

WHITE, OWEN P.   Them was the Days: From El Paso to Prohibition. New York, 1925. Illus. by Ross Santee. Jenkins 116-1459 1978 $25

WHITE, P.   History of Clare & The Dalcassion Clans of Tipperary, Limerick & Galway. 1893. 1st ed., very good, octavo bound in cloth. Hyland 128-773 1978 £40

WHITE, PATRICK   The Aunt's Story. 1948. Very good, d.w., first English ed. Bell Book 16-909 1978 £27.50

WHITE, RICHARD   Hemisphaerium Dissectum Opus Geometricus in Quo Obiter Tractatur de Maximis Inscriptibilibus, & Minimis Circumscribentibus. Romae, 1648. 4to., contemp. vellume, 1st ed., extremely rare, very good copy. Offenbacher 30-52 1978 $500

WHITE, ROBERT H.   Tennessee, Its Growth and Progress. Nashville, 1936. Pres. copy from author to Bell Wiley. Broadfoot's 44-964 1978 $10

WHITE, SAMUEL A.   Flaming Fur Lands. Toronto, 1948. Hood 117-546 1978 $10

WHITE, STEWARD EDWARD   African Camp Fires. London, 1914. 30 plts., binders cloth, 8vo. K Books 239-529 1978 £9

WHITE, STEWART EDWARD   Arizona Nights. New York, 1907. Cloth, illus. in color, 1st ed., very good copy, plastic d.w., slipcase. Dykes 34-71 1978 $40

WHITE, STEWART EDWARD   Camp and Trail. Toronto, 1907. Frontis. in color, illus. from photos. Hood 117-547 1978 $12.50

WHITE, STEWART EDWARD   The Claim Jumpers. New York, 1901. Orig. cloth, 1st ed., covers slightly soiled, but good. MacManus 238-583 1978 $35

WHITE, STEWART EDWARD   Daniel Boone, Wilderness Scout. New York, 1922. Illus. by Remington Schuyler, 1st ed., 1st issue, spine sunned, fine copy, scarce in this condition. Victoria 34-859 1978 $45

WHITE, STEWART EDWARD   Gold. 1914. Illus. Austin 82-1079 1978 $15

WHITE, STEWART EDWARD   The Mountains. 1904. Illus., first ed. Austin 82-1080 1978 $12.50

WHITE, STEWART EDWARD   The Mystery. 1907. Illus., first ed., ex-lib., Austin 82-1082 1978 $12.50

WHITE, STEWART EDWARD   The Riverman. New York, 1908. Illus. by N. C. Wyeth & C. F Underwood. Hood 117-543 1978 $12.50

WHITE, STEWART EDWARD   The Rules of the Game. 1910. Illus. in color. First ed. Austin 82-1081 1978 $15

WHITE, STEWART EDWARD   The Silent Places. Toronto, 1904. 1st ed.,
tinted illus. by P. F. Goodwin. Hood 117-549 1978 $12.50

WHITE, T. H.   The Elephant and the Kangaroo. 1948. Very
good, d.w., first English ed. Bell Book 16-911 1978 £7.50

WHITE, T. H.   Farewell Victoria. 1933. Spine somewhat
faded, good, d.w., first English ed. Bell Book 16-912 1978 £12.50

WHITE, T. H.   The Sword in the Stone. New York, 1939. First
U.S. ed., drawings by author, bookplt., very good, worn d.w. Bell Book 17-
926 1978 £15

WHITE, T. H.   The Sword in the Stone. New York, 1939. First
American ed. Biblo 247-639 1978 $9.50

WHITE, THOMAS   Our Great West. Montreal, 1873. Half mor.,
1st ed. Ginsberg 14-1059 1978 $125

WHITE, TRUMBULL   Our New Possessions...Four Books in One...
Book I. - The Philippine Islands. Book II. - Puerto Rico. Book III. - Cuba. Book
IV. - The Hawaiian Islands... Chicago, (1898). Illus., cloth. Hayman 72-793
1978 $10

WHITE, WALTER   Northumberland and The Border. 1859. 2nd.
ed., fine folding map, half title, lacks adverts., orig. cloth, little faded, o/w
fine. Jarndyce 16-1173 1978 £12.50

WHITE, WALTER   A Rising Wind. Garden City, 1945. 1st print.,
d.w., signed inscription by author. Americanist 102-17 1978 $25

WHITE, WILLIAM ALLEN   The Autobiography of... New York, 1946.
Illus., 1st ed. Biblo BL781-776 1978 $9

WHITE, WILLIAM ALLEN   Marital Adventures of Henry and Me. New
York, 1918. Illus. by Tony Sarg, 1st ed., 8 vo., orig. gilt stamped pictorial
red cloth, very good. Houle 10-287 1978 $15

WHITE, WILLIAM ALLEN   Selected Letters of... New York, (1947).
1st ed., d.w. Biblo 251-89 1978 $15

WHITE, WILLIAM N.   Gardening For The South. NY, 1858. Lacks f/l,
hinges cracked, cover badly worn, Bell Wiley's copy. Broadfoot's 44-821 1978
$12.00

WHITEHEAD, JOHN   The Judicial and Civil History of New Jersey.
Boston, 1897. 1st ed., 2 vols., 4to., illus., 3/4 mor., marbled bds., very good,
pres. copy from author. MacManus 239-1341 1978 $45

WHITEHEAD, JOHN   The Passaic Valley, New Jersey in Three Centuries... New York, 1901. 2 vols., illus., 4tos. MacManus 239-1342 1978
$40

WHITEHEAD, WILLIAM   Creusa, Queen of Athens. 1754. 1st. ed., fully
rebound in half calf, marbled bds., fine. Jarndyce 16-236 1978 £35

WHITEHEAD, WILLIAM A.   East Jersey Under the Proprietary Governments...
Newark, 1875. 2nd ed., rev'd. and enlarged, fold. maps. MacManus 239-
1343 1978 $40

WHITEHOUSE, EULA   Texas Flowers in Natural Colors. Austin,
1936. Illus., 1st ed. d.j., very good. Limestone 9-320 1978 $35

WHITEHOUSE, EULA   Texas Flowers in Natural Colours: Includes Many
Common Plants of the Southwest. N.P., 1936. Austin ed., gilt cloth, profusely
illus. in color. Jenkins 116-1460 1978 $27.50

WHITEHOUSE, J. H.   Nansen. London, 1930. 8vo., cloth, frontis.
portr. Van der Peet H-64-580 1978 Dfl 65

WHITEING, RICHARD   The Island, or An Adventure of a Person of
Quality. London, 1888. 1st ed., orig. cloth, good, owner's name on title page.
Greene 78-318 1978 $55

WHITELAW, W. M.   The Maritimes and Canada Before Confederation.
Toronto, 1934. Hood 116-233 1978 $65

WHITELEY, HENRY   Three Months in Jamaica, in 1832:.... London,
1833. 1st ed., thin 8vo., new quarter calf. Quaritch 978-160 1978 $150

WHITELOCKE, BULSTRODE   Memorials of English Affairs From the Beginning
of the Reign of Charles I to the Happy Restoration of Charles II. Oxford, 1853.
4 vols., orig. cloth, spine dull, octavo, good. Upcroft 10-184 1978 £35

WHITELOCKE, JAMES   Liber Famelicus. London, 1858. Sm. 4to., half
green mor., cover faded, inner hinge weak. K Books 244-327 1978 £10

WHITELOCKE, JOHN   The Trail at Large of .... 1808. Map, modern
half calf, 8vo, best ed. Edwards 1012-683 1978 £100

WHITELY, IKE   Rural Life in Texas. Atlanta, 1891. Original
yellow pictorial wr., rubbed. Jenkins 116-1461 1978 $275

WHITFIELD, THEODORE M.   Slavery Agitation in Virginia 1829-1832.
Baltimore, 1930. Bell Wiley's copy. Broadfoot's 44-992 1978 $14

WHITFORD, NOBLE E.   History of the Canal System of the State of New
York Together with Brief Histories of the Canals of the United States and Canada.
Albany, 1906. 2 vols., plts., charts, orig. cloth, near fine, very scarce. But-
terfield 21-99 1978 $150

WHITING, FREDERICK   The Modern Mastoid Operation. Philadelphia,
1905. Half leather, leather worn, library marks. Rittenhouse 49-833 1976
$22.50

WHITING, SYDNEY   Helionde; or, Adventures in the Sun. 1855.
2nd. ed., 8vo., orig. blue cloth, gilt, little worn, very good, sound copy.
Fenning 32-362 1978 £6.50

WHITINGHAM, D. S.   Primera parte de la tactica de la caballeria in-
geesa, traducida al Castellano. Algeciras, (c. 1760). Sm. 8vo., full straight
grained crimson mor., gilt. George's 635-872 1978 £7.50

WHITLESEY, CHARLES   Early History of Cleveland, Ohio... Cleveland,
1867. 1st ed., royal 8vo., illus., maps, orig. green cloth, ex-lib. with their plt.
interior fine, ex-lib. with their plt. & stamp, scarce. Current 24-96 1978 $115

WHITLOCK, B.   Monarchy Asserted to be the Best, most Ancient
and Legal From of Government:.... London, 1679. 12mo, early sheep, expertly
rehinged. Bennett 7-124 1978 $150

WHITMAN, ALFRED   British Mezzotinters, Valentine Green. 1902.
Plts., roy. 8vo. George's 635-176 1978 £15

WHITMAN, ALFRED   Whitman's Print-Collector's Handbook. 1912.
6th. ed., plts., 4to, cloth, nice. Fenning 32-363 1978 £10.50

WHITMAN, MALCOLM D.   Tennis. Derrydale Press, 1932. Illus., ltd. to
450 copies, inscribed by Whitman, binding badly worn, internally clean. Austin
82-1083 1978 $47.50

WHITMAN, WALT   An American Primer... Boston, 1904. Orig.
cloth, 1st ed., 2nd bind., 1 of 500 copies, nice. MacManus 238-589 1978 $30

WHITMAN, WALT   Calamus. A Series of Letters Written...1868-80
by...to a Young Friend, Richard Doyle. Boston, 1897. 12mo., orig. cloth, 1st
ed., fine. MacManus 238-585 1978 $75

WHITMAN, WALT   Complete Poetry & Selected Prose and Letters.
Nonesuch Press, 1938. Very good, first English ed. Bell Book 16-914 1978
£8.50

WHITMAN, WALT   Franklin Evans or the Inebriate. New York,
1929. Orig. cloth, paper label, ltd. to 700 copies, fine. MacManus 238-593
1978 $27.50

WHITMAN, WALT   Gems from.... Philadelphia, 1889. 12mo.,
orig. cloth, 1st ed., spine ends slightly worn, but nice. MacManus 238-586
1978 $37.50

WHITMAN, WALT   The Half-Breed and Other Stories. New York,
1927. Illus., woodcuts by Allen Lewis, orig. cloth-backed patterned bds., 1st
ed., 1 of 155 copies, covers slightly worn, but nice. MacManus 238-592 1978
$60

WHITMAN, WALT   I Hear the People Singing. New York, (1946).
1st ed, introduction by Langston Hughes, illus. by Alexander Dobkin, very fine,
d.j. Victoria 34-860 1978 $15

WHITMAN, WALT   Lafayette in Brooklyn... New York, 1905.
Illus., frontis. port., orig. grey bds., paper label, 1 of 250 copies signed by pub.,
very good. MacManus 238-591 1978 $50

WHITMAN, WALT   Leaves of Green. New York, 1867. 12mo.,
orig. mor.-backed cloth bds., 4th ed., spine worn, hinges cracked, but good.
MacManus 238-584 1978 $200

WHITMAN, WALT   Leaves of Grass. New York, Random House, 1930. Folio, mahogany board sides, red niger mor. back, woodcuts by Valenti Angelo, 1 of 400 copies, fine. Duschnes 220-130 1978 $750

WHITMAN, WALT   Leaves of Grass. New York, 1942. 4to., 2 vols., orig. cloth-backed bds., slipcase, fine, illus., photos by Edward Weston, signed and numbered by Weston. MacManus 238-594 1978 $375

WHITMAN, WALT   Song of the Redwood Tree. Eucalyptus Press, 1934. Sm. folio, no. 122 of 250 copies prtd. Battery Park 1-91 1978 $35

WHITMORE, GEORGE D.   Advanced Surveying and Mapping. Scranton, 1949. First ed., orig. binding. Wolfe 39-560 1978 $10

WHITMORE, WILLIAM H.   The Original Mother Goose's Melody,.... Boston, 1892. Sm.4to, profusely illus, in boards, with vellum spine, rubbed at tips, fine copy. Victoria 34-861 1978 $40

WHITNEY, MRS. A. D. T.   Sights & Insights. Patience Strong's Story of Over the Way. Boston, 1876. 1st ed., 2 vols., orig. cloth, internal damp staining, good. Greene 78-319 1978 $35

WHITNEY, ASA   Memorial of...Praying a Grant of Public Land to Enable Him to Construct a Railroad from Lake Michigan to the Pacific Ocean. Washington, 1846. Folding map, disbound, 1st ed. Ginsberg 14-869 1978 $45

WHITNEY, ASA   Whitney's Railroad to the Pacific.... Washington, 1850. Illus., folding map, half morocco. Ginsberg 14-870 1978 $75

WHITNEY, CASPAR   The Flowering Road. 1912. 8vo, orig. cloth. Book Chest 17-419 1978 $22.50

WHITNEY, EMMA ST. CLAIR   Michael Hillegas & His Descendants, By His Gt.-Granddaughter. Pottsville, 1891. 1st ed., portr., orig. binding, 8vo. Americanist 101-150 1978 $50

WHITNEY, J. P.   Le Colorado aux Etats-Unis D'Amerique. Paris, 1867. Original printed wr. bound in half morocco. Ginsberg 14-276 1978 $75

WHITNEY, JOSIAH DWIGHT   The Metallic Wealth of the United States,.... Philadelphia, 1854. Orig. cloth. Ginsberg 14-1061 1978 $37.50

WHITNEY, JOSIAH DWIGHT   The United States. Boston, 1889. Pres. by author. Biblo 247-167 1978 $27.50

WHITNEY, M.   Field Operations of Bureau of Soils. 1914. 13th report, plts, folio, orig. cloth. Book Chest 17-421 1978 $45

WHITNEY, THOMAS R.   A Defence of the American Policy, as Opposed to the Encroachments of Foreign Influence... New York, (1856). MacManus 239-30 1978 $35

WHITTEMORE, HENRY   The Past and the Present of Steam Navigation on Long Island Sound. (New York, 1893). Wr. Butterfield 21-423 1978 $15

WHITTIER, JOHN GREENLEAF   Among the Hills and Other Poems. Boston, 1869. Frontis., 1st ed., covers rubbed, bkplt. Biblo 251-671 1978 $17.50

WHITTIER, JOHN GREENLEAF   Home Ballads. Boston, 1860. Maroon cloth. Dawson's 447-279 1978 $25

WHITTIER, JOHN GREENLEAF   In War Time and Other Poems. Boston, 1864. Bell Wiley's copy. Broadfoot 46-276 1978 $12

WHITTIER, JOHN GREENLEAF   Literary Recreations and Miscellanies. Boston, 1854. 12mo., orig. cloth, 1st ed., extremities slightly worn, but very nice. MacManus 238-597 1978 $25

WHITTIER, JOHN GREENLEAF   Maud Muller. Boston, 1867. Orig. binding, clean, first sep. printing in book form. Hayman 71-788 1978 $15

WHITTIER, JOHN GREENLEAF   Old Portraits and Modern Sketches. Boston, 1830. 12mo., orig. cloth, 1st ed., front inner hinge cracked, else fine. Mac-Manus 238-596 1978 $25

WHITTIER, JOHN GREENLEAF   The Pennsylvania Pilgrim and Other Poems. Boston, 1872. 12mo., orig. full mor., a.e.g., 1st ed., spine very slightly worn, but near-fine, pub. elaborate gift bind. MacManus 238-599 1978 $35

WHITTIER, JOHN GREENLEAF   Poems. Written During the Progress of the Abolition Question in the United States, Between the Years 1830 and 1838. Boston, 1837. 12mo., orig. cloth, 1st ed., fine. MacManus 238-595 1978 $60

WHITTIER, JOHN GREENLEAF   A Sabbath Scene. Boston, 1854. Illus., orig. green-glazed paper wrs., 1st ed., very slightly soiled, fine. MacManus 238-598 1978 $35

WHITTLESEY, DERWENT   German Strategy of World Conquest. 1942. Austin 80-371 1978 $17.50

WHITTLESEY, FREDERICK   An Address...at Washington Square, Rochester, July Fourth...1842. Rochester, 1842. Sewn. Butterfield 21-237 1978 $35

WHITTLESEY, WALTER R.   Catalogue of the First Editions of Stephen C. Foster. 1915. Austin 82-383 1978 $27.50

WHITTMORE, THOMAS   The Early Days of Thomas Whittmore. Boston, 1859. Orig. binding, clean, some wear. Hayman 71-787 1978 $8.50

WHITTOCK, NATHANIEL   The Art of Drawing and Colouring from Nature, Flowers, Fruit, and Shells; to Which is Added, Correct Directions for Preparing the Most Brilliant Colours for Painting on Velvet with the Mode of Using Them... 1829. Oblong 4to., leaves, coloured plts., foxed, orig. bds., printed label, linen spine, inner joints neatly repaired. Quaritch 983-273 1978 $825

WHITTOCK, NATHANIEL   The Decorative Painters' and Glaziers' Guide... 1827. 4to., plain and coloured plts., some sl. foxing, contemp. half calf rebacked, rubbed, 1st ed. Quaritch 983-96 1978 $480

WHITTOCK, NATHANIEL   The Decorative Painters' & Glaziers' Guide... Methods of Imitating Oak, Mahogany, Maple, Rose, Cedar Coral...Designs for Decorating Apartments; also a complete Body of Information on the Art of Staining and Painting on Glass. London, 1828. Very fine litho. plts., many hand-colored, thick 4to., old 1/4 calf, joints repaired, early state. Argosy Special-93 1978 $350

WHITTOCK, NATHANIEL   The Oxford Drawing Book, or the Art of Drawing, and the Theory and Practice of Perspective, in a Series of Letters... (c. 1830). Oblong 4to., frontis., plts. with slight marginal soiling, a couple lightly spotted, orig. bds., calf. Quaritch 983-274 1978 $125

WHITTON, F. E.   Wolfe and North America. London, 1929. Maps, illus. Hood's 115-276 1978 $25

WHITTON, F. E.   Wolfe and North America. London, 1929. Orig. binding. Wolfe 39-571 1978 $25

WHO'S Who in Fremont:.... Denver, 1915. Orig. cloth, 1st ed. Ginsberg 14-726 1978 $40

THE WHOLE Art of Dying. London, 1705. 8vo., contemp. panelled calf, gilt, hinges weak, very good copy, 1st ed. in English, in two parts. Norman 5-86 1978 $500

WHY South Dakota Offers Better Opportunities and Possibilities to the Home Seeker and Home Builder than any other State... Pierre, [ca. 1898]. Illus., original pictorial wr., 1st ed. Ginsberg 14-326 1978 $65

WHYMPER, EDWARD   Travels Amongst the Great Andes of the Equator. New York, 1892. Maps, illus. Baldwins' 51-376 1978 $30

WHYMPER, EDWARD   Travels Amongst The Great Andes of the Equator. 1892. 2nd. ed., maps, woodcuts, 8vo, orig. cloth. Edwards 1012-684 1978 £35

WHYMPER, FREDERICK   Travel and Adventure in the Territory of Alaska, Formerly Russian America... New York, 1869. 1st ed., illus., orig. cloth, lib. marks, but good copy. MacManus 239-20 1978 $35

WHYMPER, FREDERICK   Travel and Adventure in the Territory of Alaska. New York, 1869. Map, illus. Baldwins' 51-377 1978 $30

WHYMPER, FREDERICK   Voyages et Aventures dans L'Alaska... Paris, 1871. Illus., very slight foxing of few pgs., map, pg.-edges gilt. Hood 116-104 1978 $110

WHYTE, ALEXANDER FREDERICK   Asia in the Twentieth Century. New York, 1926. 1st. ed., 8vo, orig. cloth, pres. copy to Winston Churchill. Sawyer 298-123 1978 £65

WHYTE, S.   The Shamrock: or Hibernian Cresses,..To Which Are Subjoined Thoughts on the Prevailing System of School Education..With Practical Proposals for a Reformation. 1772. Large Paper, full calf, much more substantial paper, some wear, text very good, reprint. Hyland 128-781 1978 £110

WHYTE, S.   The Shamrock: or Hibernian Cresses,..To Which are Subjoined Thoughts on the Prevailing System of School Education..With Practical Proposals for a Reformation. 1772. 1st ed., full calf, spine repaired. Hyland 128-780 1978 £80

WHYTE-MELVILLE, GEORGE JOHN   The Queen's Maries. A Romance of Holyrood. London, 1862. 2 vols., orig. cloth, 1st ed., spines a bit faded and soiled, but very good, bookplts. MacManus 238-409 1978 $50

WHYTE-MELVILLE, GEORGE JOHN   Sarchedon. A Legend of the Great Queen. London, 1871. 3 vols., orig. cloth, 1st ed., covers a bit warped on vol. 1, otherwise very nice, bookplts. MacManus 238-410 1978 $75

WHYTE-MELVILLE, GEORGE JOHN   Songs and Verses and The True Cross. London, c. 1900. Plts., full red mor., fine, 8vo. K Books 244-328 1978 £9

WICKENDEN, DAN   The Dry Season. 1950. First ed., backstrip faded. Austin 82-1084 1978 $12.50

WICKENDEN, DAN   The Running of the Deer. 1937. First ed., some cover soil, inscribed by author. Austin 82-1086 1978 $20

WICKENDEN, DAN   Tobias Brandywine. 1948. First ed., backstrip faded. Austin 82-1087 1978 $17.50

WICKENDEN, DAN   The Wayfarers. 1945. First ed., inscribed by author to his aunt. Austin 82-1088 1978 $27.50

WICKERSHAM, JAMES PYLE   A History of Education in Pennsylvania...from the Time the Swedes Settled on the Delaware. Lancaster, 1886. Illus., orig. cloth, fine. MacManus 239-1726 1978 $40

WICKERSHAM, JAMES PYLE   A History of Education in Penna, Private & Public, Elementary & Higher. Lancaster, 1886. 1st ed., tall 8vo, rebound in libr. buckram, portr. Americanist 101-151 1978 $30

WICKES, STEPHEN   History of the Oranges in Essex County, N.J. From 1666 to 1806. Newark, 1892. 1st ed., illus., maps, rebound. MacManus 239-1344 1978 $50

WICKHAM, HENRY A.   Rough Notes of a Journey through the Wilderness from Trinidad to Para, Brazil, by way of the Great Cataracts of the Orinoco, Atabapo, and Rio Negro. London, 1872. 1st ed., royal 8vo, frontis., plts., later blue cloth, blind stamp, else fine. Current 24-202 1978 $150

WICKHAM, HENRY L.   A Dissertation on the Passage of Hannibal Over the Alps. London, 1828. 2nd ed., plts., 8vo, ex-lib., orig. cloth, lacks map. Morrill 241-622 1978 $12.50

WICKLIFFE, ROBERT   Speech of...Delivered in the Senate of the Kentucky Legislature.... Lexington, 1839. Half mor., 1st ed. Ginsberg 14-1062 1978 $100

WICKSTEED, P. H.   Dante & Giovanni del Virgillo. 1902. 8vo., orig. cloth, spine faded. Howes 194-769 1978 £6.50

WICQUEFORT, JOACHIM   Lettres de M.J. De Wicquefort.... Amsterdam, 1696. 12mo., calf, spine gilt, good. King 7-322 1978 £25

WIDENER, JOSEPH   French Engravings of the Eighteenth Century in the Collection of ..., Lynnewood Hall. Riviere, 1923. 4 vols., folio, plts., some in colour, fine, red levant mor., gilt backs, gilt tops. Quaritch 983-275 1978 $1,200

WIED-NEUWIED, MAXIMILIAN ALEXANDER PHILLIP ZU   Abbildungen Zur Naturgeschichte Brasiliens. Weimar, 1822. Handcolored plts., bound together as a book, text in German & French, without orig. wrs., tall folio, 1/2 calf. Salloch 345-121 1978 $1,500

WIED-NEUWIED, MAXIMILIAN ALEXANDER PHILLIP ZU   Abbildungen Zur Naturgeschichte Brasiliens. Weimar, 1822-1831. Color plts., with German & French text, orig. printed wrs., extra tall folio, uncut. Salloch 345-120 1978 $2,500

WIED-NEUWIED, MAXIMILIAN ALEXANDER PHILLIP ZU   Beitraege Zur Naturgeschichte Von Brasilien. Weimar, 1825-1831. Vols. I-III of 4, bound in 4 vols., engr. plts., 8vo., contemp. bds. Salloch 345-122 1978 $200

WIEMAN, REGINA WESTCOTT   The Modern Family and the Church. 1937. Austin 79-838 1978 $12.50

DIE WIENER Werkstatte 1903-1928. Vienna, 1929. Sq. 8vo., orig. publisher's bds., on coated paper, illus. Goldschmidt 110-82 1978 $430

WIESE, KURT   Fish in the Air. New York, 1948. 1st ed., color plates, very good, torn d.j. Victoria 34-863 1978 $10

WIESE, LEOPOLD VON   Allgemeine Soziologie als Lehre von den Beziehungen und Beziehungsgebilden der Menschen. Munchen and Leipzig, 1924-1929. 2 vols., 8vo., fold. plt., orig. cloth, lib. stamps on titles., 1st ed. Gilhofer 74-21 1978 sFr 350

WIFFEN, J. H.   Memoirs and Miscellanies. 1880. Portraits, cr. 8vo. George's 635-1526 1978 £5.50

THE WIG and the Jimmy: or, a Leaf in the Political History of New York. New York, 1869. Portrs. Butterfield 21-550g 1978 $10

WIGGIN, KATE DOUGLAS   The Bird's Christmas Carol. Boston, (1902). Illus. in color, first illus. ed. Biblo 247-576 1978 $17.50

WIGGIN, KATE DOUGLAS   A Child's Journey With Dickens. Boston, 1912. 1st ed., 1/2 leather, pres. copy, inscribed to her husband. Ballinger 11-192 1978 $40.00

WIGGIN, KATE DOUGLAS   The Diary of a Goose Girl. Boston & New York, 1902. 1st ed., 1/2 leath., inscribed to her husband. Ballinger 11-193 1978 $45.00

WIGGIN, KATE DOUGLAS   New Chronicles of Rebecca. Boston, 1907. Illus., good. Nestler Rare 78-242 1978 $45

WIGGIN, KATE DOUGLAS   The Old Peabody Pew. A Christmas Romance of a Country Church... Boston, 1907. Cloth, illus., fine copy of 1st ed. Hayman 72-795 1978 $7.50

WIGGIN, KATE DOUGLAS   Penelope's Progress. Cambridge, 1899. Bound in Scottish silk plaid, inscribed on end-paper by author. Eaton 45-536 1978 £10

WIGGIN, KATE DOUGLAS   Rebecca of Sunnybrook Farm. Boston, 1903. 1st ed., 1st issue, very good. Victoria 34-864 1978 $25

WIGGIN, KATE DOUGLAS   Rebecca of Sunnybrook Farm. Boston, 1903. Orig. illus. cloth, 1st state, fine. MacManus 238-600 1978 $75

WIGGIN, KATE DOUGLAS   Rebecca of Sunnybrook Farm. Boston, 1903. Good copy, shaken. Desmarais B-662 1978 $25

WIGGIN, KATE DOUGLAS   The Romance of a Christmas Card. Boston, 1916. Good in damaged d.w. Desmarais B-663 1978 $7.50

WIGGIN, KATE DOUGLAS   A Summer in the Canyon. A California Story. Boston, 1890. Fine tight copy. Desmarais B-664 1978 $12.50

WIGGIN, KATE DOUGLAS   Susanna and Sue. 1909. Illus. by N. C. Wyeth, & Stephens, binding worn. Nestler Rare 78-235 1978 $15

WIGGINS, JOHN   Monster Misery of Ireland (Relation of Landlord & Tenant). 1844. 1st ed., cover shaky, good, octavo bound in cloth. Hyland 128-788 1978 £17

WIGGLESWORTH, MICHAEL   Meat Out of the Eater:.... Boston, 1717. 12mo, contemporary calf, "Fifth edition," occasional light stains, a fine and exceptionally well-preserved copy, rare. Ximenes 47-334 1978 $750

WIGHTMAN, JULIA B.   Haste to the Rescue; or, Work While It is Day. 1860. 8vo, frontis, recent bds., very good. Fenning 32-564 1978 £7.50

WIGHTMAN, WILLIAM M.   Life of William Capers. Nashville, 1902. Spine spotted, Bell Wiley's copy. Broadfoot's 44-822 1978 $8.00

WIJNAENDTS VAN RESANDT, W.   Het Geslacht van Van der Hoop uit Scherpenzeel te Arnhem. N.P., 1926. 4to., orig. covers, colored frontis., illus. Van der Peet H-64-584 1978 Dfl 100

WIKOFF, HENRY   Secession and Its Causes, in a Letter to Viscount Palmerston, K. G., Prime Minister of England. New York, 1861. 1st ed., 8vo., unbound. Morrill 241-623 1978 $12.50

WILBARGER, J.W.   Indian Depredations in Texas. Austin, 1889. Original decorated cloth, gilt, 1st ed., 1st issue. Jenkins 116-1584 1978 $225

WILBERFORCE, EDWARD   Brazil Viewed Through a Naval Glass... 1856. 1st. ed., sm. 8vo, wrapper, nice. Fenning 32-365 1978 £21

WILBERFORCE, ROBERT ISAAC   The Life of William Wilberforce. 1838. 5 vols., portraits, 8vo, orig. cloth, spines faded, facsimile specimens of Wilberforce's handwriting. Edwards 1012-272 1978 £55

WILBERFORCE, MRS. T.   Humbugs and Canterbury Folks. Providence, 1903. Illus., 8vo., 1st ed., orig. cloth. Morrill 241-624 1978 $15

WILBERFORCE, WILLIAM   A Letter on the Abolition of the Slave Trade... 1807. Contemp. calf, cover badly worn, 8vo. Edwards 1012-271 1978 £240

WILBOUR, CHARLES E.   Travels in Egypt. Dec. 1880 to May 1891. Letters. Brooklyn, 1936. Sm. 4to., illus., ltd. ed. Biblo BL781-515 1978 $34.50

WILBRAHAM, RICHARD   Travels In The Trans-Caucasian Provinces of Russia, and Along the Southern Shore of the Lakes of Van and Urumiah, In The Autumn and Winter of 1837. London, 1839. 1st. ed., 8vo, half-title, woodcut frontispiece, tinted lithograph plts., folding engraved map, orig. blind-stamped cloth, title in gilt on back, back faded, little loose in binding. Deighton 5-151 1978 £85

WILBRAHAM, RICHARD   Travels in the Trans-Caucasian Provinces of Russia, and Along the Southern Shore of the Lakes of Van and Urumiah, In the Autumn and Winter of 1837. 1839. 1st. & only ed., folding map, frontis, tinted litho. plts., 8vo, orig. cloth, joints strenthened & little shaken, very good. Fenning 32-366 1978 £56

WILBRAND, H.   Neurologie Des Auges ein Handbuch fur Nerven- und Augenarzie. Wiesbaden, 1901. Rittenhouse 49-835 1976 $20

WILBUR, MRS. C. E.   The Thread of Gold. Cincinnati, n.d. (1890's?). Cloth, little soiled. Hayman 72-796 1978 $7.50

WILBUR, EARL MORSE   A History of the First Unitarian Church of Portland, 1867-1892;.... Portland, 1893. Illus., full orig. mor., 1st ed. Ginsberg 14-856 1978 $25

WILBUR, HENRY W.   The Life and Labors of Elias Hicks. Philadelphia, 1922. 2nd ed., frontis. port., illus., orig. cloth, very good. MacManus 239-769 1978 $17.50

WILBUR, JAMES BENJAMIN   Ira Allen Founder of Vermont 1751-1814. Boston, 1928. Illus., very fine set. MacManus 239-719 1978 $42.50

WILBUR, MARGUERITE E.   Raveneau de Lussan Buccaneer of the Spanish Main and Early French Filibuster of the Pacific... Cleveland, 1930. 1st ed. in Eng., illus., fine. MacManus 239-1795 1978 $35

WILCOCKE, SAMUEL HULL   A Narrative of Occurrences in the Indian Countries of North America. London, 1817. Spine mended. Hood 117-925 1978 $200

WILCOX, ARTHUR RUSSELL   The Bar of Rye Township, Westchester County, New York. (New York, 1918). Illus., 8vo., orig. cloth, ltd. to 250 copies. Morrill 241-424 1978 $12.50

WILCOX, CADMUS M.   History of the Mexican War. Washington, 1892. Original cloth, maps, plates, 1st ed., scarce. Jenkins 116-935 1978 $125

WILCOX, FRANK   Ohio Indian Trails... Cleveland, 1933. Illus. by author, cloth, 1st ed., signed by author, damp spot on front cover otherwise very good. Hayman 72-589 1978 $65

WILCOX, MARRION   The Devil Is Dead & Scenes in General Dayton's Garden. London, 1889. 1st ed., orig. cloth, good. Greene 78-131 1978 $25

WILCZYNSKI, K.   An Artist's Diary in Pictures. The Hague-Oxford, 1949. Pen & Ink drwgs., lg. 8vo., oblong cloth, plts., ltd. & numbered ed. Van der Peet H-64-228 1978 Dfl 65

WILD, CHARLES   Select Examples of Architectural Grandeur in Belgium, Germany and France... London, 1837. Sm. folio, orig. leather backed cloth bds., slight foxing to plts. Sexton 7-58 1978 £20

WILD, J. J.   At Anchor... 1878. Coloured lithograph plts., illus., folio, orig. cloth gilt, spine repaired, sm. lib. stamp on title & few margins. Edwards 1012-42 1978 £150

WILD, JOSEPH   The Lost Ten Tribes. London, n.d. Cheap ed. Hood 116-322 1978 $7.50

WILD Flowers, Culled for Early Youth. New York, 1837. 1st ed., sm. 8vo, illus. and printed t.p.'s, very good. Victoria 34-865 1978 $12.50

WILD Flowers of Canada. Montreal, (1892-93). Oblong 4to., modern cloth, full colour illus., orig. colour-printed wrappers. Wolfe 39-562 1978 $100

WILD Flowers of Canada. Montreal, 1893. Colored plts., some wear on cover. Hood 117-644 1978 $65

WILD West Weekly: Young Wild West:... New York, 1902. Stapled, small tears in margins, pages unopened, small peices missing from covers. Totteridge 29-114 1978 $15

WILDE, OSCAR   After Berneval. 1922. 8vo., bds., vellum back, ltd. to only 75 copies on Japanese vellum signed by C. W. Beaumont and artist. Quaritch 979-21 1978 $100

WILDE, OSCAR   Art and Decoration. 1920. 12mo., very good, first English ed. Bell Book 16-1018 1978 £4.50

WILDE, OSCAR   The Ballad of Reading Gaol. 1898 (in fact 1904). Cloth-backed bds., some foxing, very good, pirated ed. Bell Book 16-917 1978 £10

WILDE, OSCAR   The Ballad Of Reading Gaol. 1899. Half title, uncut, orig. yellow bds., cream cloth spine, little rubbed, good. Jarndyce 16-1176 1978 £9.50

WILDE, OSCAR   Ballad of Reading Gaol. New York, (1903). 1 of only 29 numbered copies on Japan vellum, 8 vo., full gilt stamped limp vellum, silk ties, t.e.g., uncut, good-fine. Houle 10-368 1978 $95

WILDE, OSCAR   The Ballad of Reading Gaol. London, 1925. 1st Eng. ed., limited to 450 copies, scattered foxing, fine copy, split d.j. Victoria 34-529 1978 $45

WILDE, OSCAR   The Ballad of Reading Gaol. New York, 1928. 1st ed., tissue-guarded plates, very fine, colored d.j. Victoria 34-826 1978 $55

WILDE, OSCAR   The Ballad of Reading Gaol. New York, 1928. Limited to 200 copies, plates, internally very fine, uncut, spine partly dulled, light cover soiling, very scarce. Victoria 34-827 1978 $65

WILDE, OSCAR   A Critic in Pall Mall. 1919. 12mo., very good, first English ed. Bell Book 16-1019 1978 £4.50

WILDE, OSCAR   A Florentine Tragedy. Boston and London, 1908. First ed., orig. cloth, 8vo. Howes 194-1334 1978 £7.50

WILDE, OSCAR   For Love of the King. 1922. One of 1000 copies on handmade paper, buckram gilt, t.e.g., covers somewhat darkened, good, first English ed. Bell Book 17-927 1978 £10.50

WILDE, OSCAR   The Happy Prince & Other Stories. 1908. Spine chipped, good, octavo bound in cloth. Hyland 128-791 1978 £6

WILDE, OSCAR   The Harlot's House and Other Poems. New York, 1929. 1st ed., plates, pictorial cover vignette, very good, uncut copy. Victoria 34-828 1978 $40

WILDE, OSCAR   An Ideal Husband. London, 1899. Orig. cloth, 1st ed., covers soiled, worn. MacManus 238-412 1978 $75

WILDE, OSCAR   The Importance of Being Earnest. 1910. New ed., 1 of 1200 copies for pres., fscp. 8vo., cloth, fine. Bell Book 16-919 1978 £10

WILDE, OSCAR   Intentions. The Decay of Lying. Pen Pencil and Poison. The Critic as Artist. The Trust of Masks. London, 1891. Orig. cloth, 1st ed., cloth a little soiled, otherwise very good, half-mor. fold. box. MacManus 238-411 1978 $85

WILDE, OSCAR   Intentions. 1894. 2nd ed., cloth, good. Bell Book 16-920 1978 £8.50

WILDE, OSCAR   Oscariana. 1910. Vignettes, 12mo., stiff wraps, very good, worn slipcase, first English ed. Bell Book 16-921 1978 £8.50

WILDE, OSCAR   Poems. Boston, 1881. Buff cloth, gilt. Wolfe 39-561 1978 $60

WILDE, OSCAR   Poems. Boston, 1881. 1st Amer. ed., orig. bind. Petrilla 13-158 1978 $18.50

WILDE, OSCAR   De Profundis. London, 1905. 8vo, 1st ed., 1st issue, blue cloth, somewhat spotted and soiled, some foxing, t.e.g., fore and bottom edges uncut, Good. Desmarais 1-423 1978 $42.50

WILDE, OSCAR   De Profundis. London, (1908). 8vo, white buckram, issued with extra material, ltd. to 1000 copies, Fine, water stain on each cover, presentation copy inscribed by Sir Robert Ross, laid in is personal presentation slip from Ross, 1st ed. Desmarais 1-422 1978 $110

WILDE, OSCAR   The Portrait of Mr. W. H. (London), n.d. (c.1908). Sm. 4to, orig. printed wrappers, name on half title, no. 193 of 200 copies issued for private circulation. Traylen 88-358 1978 £15

WILDE, OSCAR   The Portrait of Mr. W. H. New York, 1921. 1 of 1000 numbered copies, very good. Bell Book 16-922 1978 £10.50

WILDE, OSCAR   Rose-Leaf and Apple-Leaf. London, 1904. 8vo, orig. wrappers, inscription on end paper, ltd. to 200 numbered copies. Traylen 88-359 1978 £10

WILDE, OSCAR   Salome. Boston, 1907. 12mo., drawings by Aubrey Beardsley, pirated ed. Biblo 247-345 1978 $17.50

WILDE, OSCAR   Salome; drame en un acte. Paris and London, 1893. Wrappers, very good, first ed. Rota 212-59 1978 £125

WILDE, OSCAR   Sixteen Letters from Oscar Wilde. 1930. One of 550 numbered copies, portrait, pink cloth gilt, t.e.g., nice, sl. worn slipcase, first English ed. Bell Book 17-928 1978 £22.50

WILDE, OSCAR   Wilde v Whistler. London, 1906. 1 of 400 copies, 1st ed., 8 vo., wr., good-fine. Houle 10-369 1978 $35

WILDE, W. R.   Catalogue of the Antiquities in the Museum of the R.I.A. 1857. 3 vols., part unopened, very good, octavo bound in cloth. Hyland 128-803 1978 $20

WILDEHAN, A.   "Life Pictures of Spener and His Times." Philipp Jacob Spener, a Historical Life Picture. Philadelphia, 1879. Cloth. Hayman 72-782 1978 $7.50

WILDEMAN, E.   Annales du Musee du Congo. Brussels, 1899-1902. Uncut, orig. printed folder, fine, plates, 8vo. Book Chest 17-422 1978 $45

WILDEMAN, E.   Etudes sur la Flore du Katanga.... Brussels, 1902-3. Full page plates, folio, orig. folders, ex-lib., complete. Book Chest 17-423 1978 $90

WILDER, DANIEL W.   The Annals of Kansas. Topeka, 1875. Tables, original cloth, 1st ed. Ginsberg 14-465 1978 $65

WILDER, DAVID   History of Leominster. Fitchburg, 1853. Rebound. MacManus 239-1032 1978 $22.50

WILDER, HARRIS H.   Laboratory Manual of Anthropometry. Philadelphia, 1920. Library marks. Rittenhouse 49-836 1976 $10

WILDER, LOUISE BEEBE   The Garden in Color. New York, 1937. 4to, orig. cloth. Book Chest 17-424 1978 $17.50

WILDER, LOUISE BEEBE   The Garden in Color. New York, 1937. Colored illus., 4to., d.w., 1st ed. Morrill 241-625 1978 $10

WILDER, LOUISE BEEBE   Pleasures and Problems of a Rock Garden. New York, 1937. 4to, orig. cloth. Book Chest 17-425 1978 $22

WILDER, THORNTON   The Bridge of San Luis Rey. New York, 1927. Illus. by Amy Drevenstedt, orig. cloth, 1st Amer. ed., signed inscription from author tipped in, bookplts. MacManus 238-764 1978 $75

WILDER, THORNTON   The Bridge of San Luis. London and New York, 1929. 8vo, cloth, d.j., woodcut illus. by Clare Leighton, 1st ed., fine. Duschnes 220-186 1978 $25

WILDER, THORNTON   The Bridge of San Luis Rey. 1929. First ed. Boni paper book ed. Austin 82-1090 1978 $10

WILDER, THORNTON   The Bridge of San Luis Rey. New York, 1929. 4to., illus. by Rockwell Kent, ltd. ed., signed by author & artist, binding slightly soiled. Biblo 251-672 1978 $42.50

WILDER, THORNTON   The Bridge of San Luis Rey. 1929. Hard cover ed. Austin 82-1089 1978 $12.50

WILDER, THORNTON   The Cabala. New York, 1926. Tan figured cloth, red buckram spine, 1st ed., 1st issue, covers soiled, scarce. Bradley 49-347 1978 $15

WILDER, THORNTON   The Cabala. New York, 1926. 8vo, 1st ed., decorated cloth boards, red cloth spine slightly faded, ownership signature on flyleaf, Fine. Desmarais 1-424 1978 $50

WILDER, THORNTON   The Cabala. New York, 1926. Orig. cloth-backed bds., 1st ed., fine. MacManus 238-763 1978 $85

WILDER, THORNTON   The Cabala. 1926. Very good, first English ed. Bell Book 17-930 1978 £10

WILDER, THORNTON   Heaven's My Destination. London, 1934. First English ed., frayed d.j. Austin 82-1092 1978 $20

WILDER, THORNTON   Heaven's My Destination. New York, 1935. Fine in damaged d.w. Desmarais B-668 1978 $7.50

WILDER, THORNTON   Heaven's My Destination. 1935. First ed. Austin 82-1091 1978 $12.50

WILDER, THORNTON   Heaven's My Destination. 1935. Dust jacket. Austin 82-1093 1978 $11

WILDER, THORNTON   The Woman of Andros. 1930. First ed., 162 pgs. Austin 82-1094 1978 $11

WILDER, THORNTON   The Woman of Andros. New York, 1930. 1st ed., covers faded, used copy. Biblo 251-674 1978 $8.50

WILDER, THORNTON   The Woman of Andros. 1930. Austin 82-1095 1978 $8.50

THE WILDERNESS Campaign. N.P., 1864. Wrs., Bell Wiley's copy. Broadfoot 46-277 1978 $8

WILDERSPIN, SAMUEL   The Infant System... London, 1834. Cr. 8vo, orig. bds., upper cover detached & backstrip missing, 1st. gathering loose, folding frontis. Sexton 7-210 1978 £25

WILDMAN, LIEUT.-COL.   Instructions for the Formations and Movements of Yeomanry Cavalry,.... Nottingham, 1831. 4to, full contemporary green morocco, gilt, spine gilt, a.e.g., 1st ed., presentation copy, inscribed on t.p., plates, most plates hand-colored, fine copy, rare. Ximenes 47-335 1978 $300

WILEY, BELL IRVIN   The Life of Johnny Reb. Indianapolis, 1943. Bell Wiley's copy. Broadfoot 46-279 1978 $30

WILEY, BELL IRVIN   Southern Reaction to Federal Invasion. N.P., 1950. Wrs., Bell Wiley's copy. Broadfoot 46-281 1978 $8

WILHELM, IGNATIUS FRANCISCUS XAVERIUS   Annus Politicus per Duodecim Discursus tum Critico-Politicos, tum Politico-Historicos Evolutus... Munich, 1731. Vol. I, frontis., plts., folio, calf gilt. Salloch 348-282 1978 $350

WILHELMINA Koninging. Amsterdam, 1898. Thick 4to., cloth, illus. Van der Peet H-64-581 1978 Dfl 60

WILKEN, F.   Institutions ad Fundamenta Linguae Persicae.
Leipsig, 1805. Binding worn. Biblo 247-928 1978 $17.50

WILKES, CHARLES   Narrative of the United States Exploring Expedition. During the Years 1838, 1839, 1840, 1841, 1842... Philadelphia, 1845. 1st trade ed., 5 vols., 8vo, illus., orig. cloth, fine set. MacManus 239-521 1978 $100

WILKES, CHARLES   Western America, Including California and Oregon, with Maps of those Regions and of "The Sacramento Valley". Philadelphia, 1849. Folding maps, orig. tan pr. wr. in half mor. slipcase, 1st ed. Ginsberg 14-1064 1978 $375

WILKES, JOHN   The North Briton. 1763. 1st. collected ed., 2 vols., orig. calf, slight local rubbing, otherwise v.g. Jarndyce 16-237 1978 £90

WILKES-Barre Record Almanac for 1886. Wilkes-Barre, 1886-1908. 1st issue, together 21 issues, 8vo., orig. wrs., ex-lib., some wrs. loose, torn. Morrill 239-580 1978 $17.50

WILKIE, FRANC B.   Personal Reminiscences of Thirty-Five Years of Journalism. Chicago, (1891). Cloth, little spotted. Hayman 73-753 1978 $15

WILKINS, ERNST HATCH   The Trees of the Genealogia Deorum of Boccaccio. Chicago, The Caxton Club, 1923. 4to., plts., bds., vellum spine, t.e.g., one of an ed. of 160 copies on paper made by hand. Battery Park 1-199 1978 $175

WILKINS, GEORGE   Body and Soul. London, 1823. 3rd. ed., 2 vols., 8vo, contemp. half calf. Traylen 88-360 1978 £10

WILKINS, GEORGE   The Two Rectors. London, 1825. Full blue mor., red label, gilt-tooled spine, marbled edges. Petrilla 13-159 1978 $27.50

WILKINS, GEORGE   The Two Rectors. 1825. 2nd. ed., uncut, orig. bds., paper label, slight rubbing, otherwise v.g. Jarndyce 16-1178 1978 £28

WILKINS, H. J.   Edward Colston (1636-1721); a Chronological Account of His Life and Work... 1920. Octavo, good. Upcroft 10-595 1978 £7.50

WILKINS, JOHN   An Essay Towards a Real Character, and a Philosophical Language. 1668. 1st. ed., folio, plts., lg. engravings, contemp. calf, rebacked & recornered. Hannas 54-200 1978 £150

WILKINS, JOHN   Mathematical Magick, or the Wonders that may be performed by Mechanichal Geometry. London, 1680. Fine copperplts., sm. 8vo., contemp. calf, early ed. Argosy Special-94 1978 $150

WILKINS, JOHN   Mathematical Magick... London, 1691. 4th ed., portr., woodcuts, engrs., sm. 8vo., 1/2 mor. Salloch 345-194 1978 $325

WILKINS, JOHN   Mercury. London, 1695. 2nd ed., engr. portr., sm. 8vo., calf, rebacked, foxed, worn. Salloch 345-195 1978 $150

WILKINS, JOHN D.D.   An Essay Towards a Real Character And a Philosophical Language. 1668. Folio, 1st. ed., folding tables, plt., 1/2 calf, joint & edges rubbed, bookplt. of Isaac King. Eaton 45-537 1978 £100

WILKINSON, MRS.   A Lady's Life and Travels in Zululand and the Transvaal During Cetewayo's Reign. London, 1882. Cr. 8vo, mounted photo frontispiece, slightly age-marked, new bds. K Books 239-532 1978 £40

WILKINSON, CAROLINE C.   Weeds and Wild Flowers: Their Uses, Legends and Literature. 1858. 1st. & only ed., coloured plts., illus., lg. 12mo, orig. cloth, edges gilt, 1 sm. section little spring, nice. Fenning 32-367 1978 £16

WILKINSON, E. S.   Shanghai Birds. Shanghai, 1929. Coloured plts., edges of last few pages stained, imp. 8vo., covers badly damp-stained. George's 635-1015 1978 £10

WILKINSON, J. B.   Annals of Binghamton... Binghamton, 1872. Illus. MacManus 239-1077 1978 $27.50

WILKINSON, J. B.   The Annals of Binghamton, and of the Country Connected with it. Binghamton, 1872. Enlarged & revised ed. Butterfield 21-78 1978 $20

WILKINSON, JAMES   Wilkinson, Soldier and Pioneer. New Orleans, 1935. Scarce. Jenkins 116-1469 1978 $22.50

WILKINSON, JOHN GARDNER   Dalmatia and Montenegro... London, 1848. First ed., 2 vols., tinted litho plts., woodcut plts., half polished calf, and marbled bds. Deighton 5-152 1978 #78

WILKINSON, JOHN GARDNER   Manners and Customs of the Ancient Egyptians... 1837. Plts., some colored, many woodcuts, 3 vols., 8vo., orig. cloth, headbands, slightly rubbed. Edwards 1012-234 1978 £20

WILKINSON, JOHN GARDNER   The Manners and Customs of the Ancient Egyptians. London, 1878. 3 vols., illus., 8vo., half calf, some fldg. & some colored plts., fine set. Sexton 7-99 1978 £60

WILKINSON, JOHN GARDNER   Modern Egypt and Thebes.... 1843. Illus., folding map, mounted on linen, 2 vols., 8vo., orig. cloth, nice. Fenning 32-368 1978 £26

WILKINSON, JOHN GARDNER   Topography of Thebes... 1835. Plts., half calf, 8vo., one plt. stained. Edwards 1012-233 1978 #20

WILKINSON, M.   The Dingbat of Arcady. New York, 1922. Hood's 115-277 1978 $7.50

WILKINSON, MORTON S.   Speech of Hon..., of Minnesota, on the Constitution as It is...in the Senate...March 2, 1861. Washington, 1861. Unbound. Hayman 72-797 1978 $7.50

WILKINSON, OSBORN   Heroes in Rhyme and Random Verses. London, 1900. 8vo, orig. cloth. K Books 239-531 1978 £10

WILKINSON, R. J.   A History of the Peninsular Malays... 1923. 3rd. ed., roy. 8vo., orig. roan-backed bds., paper label on upper cover, cover slightly worn. Edwards 1012-176 1978 £12

WILL, ALLEN SINCLAIR   Life of Cardinal Gibbons. 1922. 2 vols. Austin 79-840 1978 $37.50

WILLAN, FRANK   History of the Oxfordshire Regiment of Militia. Oxford, 1900. 8vo., coloured plts., orig. cloth, portrait frontis. F. Edwards 1013-570 1978 £18

WILLARD, EMMA   History of the United States of Republic of America... New York, 1828. Contemp. calf, worn and foxed. MacManus 239-522 1978 $10

WILLARD, MARGARET WHEELER   Letters on the American Revolution 1774-1776. Boston. 1st ed., ltd. to 1040 copies, cloth bds, untrimmed, nice. MacManus 239-633 1978 $35

WILLARD, SYLVESTER D.   Annals of the Medical Society of the County of Albany 1806-1851. Albany, 1864. Portrs., cloth backstrip scuffed, near fine, typed biography of Henry Hun, M. D. laid in, signed by Cuyler Reynolds. Butterfield 21-41 1978 $20

WILLCOCK, J.   The Life of Sir Henry Vane the Younger, Statesman and Mystic (1613-1662). 1913. Plts., octavo, good. Upcroft 10-600 1978 £6

WILLCOCK, J.   Sir Thomas Urquhart of Cromartie. 1899. Plts., octavo, good. Upcroft 10-598 1978 £6.50

WILLCOCK, J.   A Scots Earl in Covenanting Times... 1907. Plts., octavo, good. Upcroft 10-599 1978 £7.50

WILLCOCKS, A.   Pine Forests and Hacmatack Clearings; or, Travel, Life and Adventure in the British North American Provinces. London, 1853. Hood 116-658 1978 $200

WILLCOCKS, MARY   Caraboo. 1817. Portraits, half morocco, 8vo, slight foxing. Edwards 1012-177 1978 £50

WILLCOX, JAMES M.   A History of the Philadelphia Saving Fund Society, 1816-1916. Philadelphia, (1916). Illus., covers stained. Biblo BL781-101 1978 $10

WILLCOX, W. B.   Gloucestershire; A Study in Local Government 1590-1640. New Haven, 1940. Map, octavo, good. Upcroft 10-601 1978 £15

WILLCOX, WALTER T.   The Historical Records of the Fifth Lancers from their foundation...to the present day. 1908. Coloured frontis. & plts., sm. folio, orig. cloth. F. Edwards 1013-467 1978 £45

WILLERS, DIEDRICH   Centennial Historical Sketch of the Town of Fayette. Geneva, 1900. Butterfield 21-413 1978 $15

WILLERS, H. Die Roemischen Bronzeeimer von Hemmoor, nebst Einem Anhange ueber die Roem. 1901. 4to., plts., illus. Allen 234-1053 1978 $20

WILLET, W.N. Charles Vincent, or, the Two Clerks. New York, 1839. 2 vols., 12mo, early half calf, gilt, spines gilt, 1st ed., author's 1st and only novel, seminary library bookplates, fine and attractive copy. Ximenes 47-336 1978 $175

WILLEY, AUSTIN The History of the Anti-slavery Cause in State and Nation. Portland, 1886. Illus., fine. MacManus 239-859 1978 $32.50

WILLEY, BENJAMIN G. Incidents in White Mountain History. Boston, 1856. Illus. MacManus 239-520 1978 $30

WILLEY, GEORGE FRANKLYN Solitaire. Manchester, 1902. Illus., 8vo., pic. front cover, 1st ed. Morrill 241-395 1978 $15

WILLEY, MALCOLM MACDONALD The Country Newspaper... Chapel Hill, 1926. 1st ed., orig. cloth, bookplt., fine. MacManus 239-523 1978 $20

WILLEY, SAMUEL H. The Transition Period of California From a Province of Mexico in 1846 to a State of the American Union in 1850. San Francisco, 1901. Scarce. MacManus 239-1906 1978 $20

WILLIAM OF MALMESBURY Chronicle of the Kings of England. 1895. Cr. 8vo., orig. cloth, frontis. George's 635-560 1978 £6.50

WILLIAM, H. S. Historians' History of the World. 1908. 25 vols. in 73, orig. limp roan, some vols. rubbed. George's 635-682 1978 £18

WILLIAM, H. S. Historians' History of the World. 1908. Plts., text illus., 25 vols.; roy. 8vo., some covers faded and stained. George's 635-681 1978 £15

WILLIAM, H. S. Historians' History of the World. 1926. Maps, plates, 27 vols. in 15, 8vo. George's 635-683 1978 £10.50

WILLIAM and Eliza, or the Visit. New York, c.1823. Chapbook, woodcuts, pictorial orange wrappers, sewn, minor rubbing, very scarce. Victoria 34-867 1978 $75

WILLIAM Tell, and Other Stories. Worcester, c.1840. Wrappers, woodcuts, very good. Victoria 34-868 1978 $12.50

WILLIAMS, MRS. A Summary Method of Teaching Children to Read. 8vo., copperplts., orig. pink bds., fine, orig. state. Quaritch 979-94 1978 $190

WILLIAMS, A. BRYAN Game Trails in British Columbia... New York, 1926. 1st ed., illus., orig. cloth, bookplts., very good. MacManus 239-524 1978 $20

WILLIAMS, ALBERT A Pioneer Pastorate... San Francisco, 1882. Orig. cl., 1st ed., auto. pres. copy. Ginsberg 16-838 1978 $30.00

WILLIAMS, ALFRED An Address Delivered Before the Pioneer and Historical Society of Pickaway County. Circleville, 1873. Wrps., very scarce. Hayman 71-577 1978 $8.50

WILLIAMS, ALFRED An Address Delivered Before the Pioneer and Historical Society of Pickaway County. Circleville, 1873. Wrs., very scarce. Hayman 73-556 1978 $10

WILLIAMS, ALFRED B. Hampton and His Red Shirts: South Carolina's Deliverance in 1876. Charleston, 1935. Bell Wiley's copy. Broadfoot 46-282 1978 $30

WILLIAMS, ALFRED M. Sam Houston and the War of Independence in Texas. Boston, 1895. Folding map. Jenkins 116-689 1978 $45

WILLIAMS, B. Fire Marks and Insurance Office Fire Brigades. 1927. Illus., 8vo. George's 635-434 1978 £5

WILLIAMS, BEN AMES An End to Mirth. 1930. Ex-lib., unprocessed. Austin 82-1096 1978 $11

WILLIAMS, BEN AMES Pirates's Purchase. 1931. Ex-lib. Austin 82-1097 1978 $10

WILLIAMS, BENJAMIN SAMUEL The Orchid-Growers Manual. 1894. 7th ed., illus., lg. 8vo. George's 635-967 1978 £21

WILLIAMS, C. A Selection of Views in Egypt, Palestine, Rhodes, Italy, Minorca, and Gibraltar.... London, 1822. 1st ed., folio, coloured aquatint plts., one neatly repaired in margin, some soiling, red half morocco, neatly repaired, retaining orig. backstrip, gilt, corners neatly repaired, marbled bds., gilt. Deighton 5-193 1978 £525

WILLIAMS, C. E. Yuba and Sutter Counties, California: Their Resources, Advantages and Opportunities. San Francisco, 1887. Illus., map, original pr. pict. wr., 1st ed. Ginsberg 14-224 1978 $75

WILLIAMS, C. R. A Tour Through the Island of Jamaica... 1826. 1st. ed., litho. plts., 8vo, contemp. half calf, slight stain in corner of 1 plt. Edwards 1012-729 1978 £100

WILLIAMS, C. W. Observations on an Important Feature in the State of Ireland, & The Want of Employment of Its Population; With a Description of the Navigation of the River Shannon. 1831. 1st ed., t.p. repaired, very good, folding map, modern 1/4 leather, complimentary inscrip. from author has been trimmed in binding. Hyland 128-805 1978 £60

WILLIAMS, CHARLES All Hallows' Eve. 1945. Good, first English ed. Bell Book 17-931 1978 £5.50

WILLIAMS, CHARLES The Canterbury Festival. London, 1936. First ed., wrappers, internally fine. Rota 211-783 1978 £10

WILLIAMS, CHARLES The House of the Octopus. 1945. Very good, d.w., first English ed. Bell Book 16-925 1978 £8

WILLIAMS, CHARLES Rochester. 1935. Portrait, very good, d.w., first English ed. Bell Book 16-926 1978 £15

WILLIAMS, CHARLES Thomas Cranmer of Canterbury. 1936. Very good, slightly worn d.w., first English ed. Bell Book 17-932 1978 £14

WILLIAMS, CHARLES Three Plays. 1931. Cloth-backed pict. bds., good, first English ed. Bell Book 16-927 1978 £15

WILLIAMS, CHARLES R. The Life of Rutherford B. Hayes 19th President of the U.S. Boston, 1914. 2 vols., illus., orig. cloth, spotted, very scarce. MacManus 239-766 1978 $35

WILLIAMS, CHARLES W. The Combustion of Coal and the Prevention of Smoke Chemically and Practically Considered. 1854. 1st. complete ed., illus., 8vo, orig. cloth, gilt, very good. Fenning 32-369 1978 £24

WILLIAMS, CLARA ANDREWS Mammy's Li'l Chilluns. London, (1904). 1st English ed., color plates by author, colored pictorial boards, boards lightly worn, scarce, very good. Victoria 34-870 1978 $35

WILLIAMS, DOUGLAS Retreat from Dunkirk. 1941. Austin 80-373 1978 $8.50

WILLIAMS, EDWARD P. Extracts from Letters to A. B. T. from Edward P. Williams During His Service in the Civil War 1862-1864. New York, 1903. Ex libris, lacks spine, Bell Wiley's copy. Broadfoot's 44-481 1978 $20

WILLIAMS, EDWIN The New York Annual Register for the Year of Our Lord 1830. New York, (1830). 1st ed., illus., orig. calf-backed printed bds. MacManus 239-351 1978 $40

WILLIAMS, EDWIN The New York Annual Register for the Year 1831. New York, 1831. Frontis., orig. calf-backed pic. bds. MacManus 239-352 1978 $30

WILLIAMS, EDWIN The New York Annual Register for the Year of Our Lord 1832. New York, 1832. Orig. calf-backed pic. bds. MacManus 239-353 1978 $30

WILLIAMS, EDWIN The New-York Annual Register for...1833. New York, 1833. Plts., ads, library bkplt., spine number, very good. Butterfield 21-469 1978 $15

WILLIAMS, EDWIN The New-York Annual Register for...1835. Map by J. T. Hammond, lea. backstrip rubbed, orig. bds. Butterfield 21-470 1978 $35

WILLIAMS, EDWIN The New-York Annual Register for...1836. Plts., orig. bds., very good. Butterfield 21-471 1978 $25

WILLIAMS, EMMA INMAN   Historic Madison, The Story of Jackson and Madison County Tennessee. Jackson, 1946. Signed by author, cover speckled, Bell Wiley's copy. Broadfoot's 44-965 1978 $25

WILLIAMS, FLOS JEWELL   New Furrows. Ottawa, 1926. Hood 117-925 1973 $15

WILLIAMS, G. CROFT   A Social Interpretation of South Carolina. Columbia, 1946. Bell Wiley's copy. Broadfoot's 44-955 1978 $10.00

WILLIAMS, GAAR   Among The Folks In History. Winnetka, 1935. 1st ed., fine work by cartoonist, very good or better. Limestone 9-323 1978 $30

WILLIAMS, GARDNER F.   The Diamond Mines of South Africa. New York, 1902. Ed. de luxe ltd. to 100 copies, copiously illus., maps, plts., text-illus., lg. 4to, orig. gilt-cloth, g.t. K Books 239-533 1978 £200

WILLIAMS, GARDNER F.   The Diamond Mines of South Africa. New York, 1905. 2 vols., roy.8vo, maps some double-page & coloured, plts., illus., 3/4 green morocco, marbled sides & endpapers, gilt, head & foot of spines rubbed, corners worn, sl. dampstaining in margins, o/w very good copy. Deighton 5-27 1978 £165

WILLIAMS, GARDNER F.   The Diamond Mines of South Africa. New York, 1905. Author's ed., revised & enlarged, ltd. to 1000 copies, signed by author, 2 vols., copiously illus., maps, plts., text-illus., roy. 8vo, orig. morocco gilt, g.t., boxed, slightly rubbed. K Books 239-534 1978 £150

WILLIAMS, GATENBY   William Guggenheim. 1934. Austin 79-841 1978 $8.50

WILLIAMS, GEORGE ALFRED   The Boy's Book of Indians and the Wild West. New York, (1911). 1st ed., color plates, light rubbing, very good. Victoria 34-869 1978 $20

WILLIAMS, GEORGE F.   Bullett and Shell. New York, (1882). 8vo., illus., inner front hinge cracked, 1st ed. Morrill 241-627 1978 $10

WILLIAMS, GLUYAS   The Gluyas Williams Book. New York, 1929. 4to., 1st ed. Biblo 251-189 1978 $10

WILLIAMS, GRIFFITH   The True Church. 1629. First ed., contemp. calf, very good, folio. Howes 194-114 1978 £80

WILLIAMS, GURNEY   Stop or I'll Scream. New York, 1945. 4to., 1st ed. Biblo 251-190 1978 $9.50

WILLIAMS, HAROLD   Modern English Writers. London, 1890-1914. First ed., orig. binding, good, scarce, author's signed autograph pres. inscription. Rota 211-785 1978 £15

WILLIAMS, HELEN MARIA   A Narrative of the Events in France, from the Landing of Napoleon Bonaparte...1815, till the Restoration of Louis XVIII. 1815. 8vo., contemp. diced calf, nice. P. M. Hill 142-235 1978 £36

WILLIAMS, HELEN MARIA   A Tour in Switzerland... London, 1798. 1st. ed., 2 vols., 8vo, half calf, gilt backs. Deighton 5-153 1978 £45

WILLIAMS, HENRY HORACE   Modern Logic. Chapel Hill, 1927. Signed by author. Broadfoot 50-336 1978 $10

WILLIAMS, HUGH W.   Select Views in Greece with Classical Illustrations. 1829. 2 vols., cr. 4to., contemp. half mor., gilt edges, plts., orig. tissue guards in place. Howes 194-1417 1978 £75

WILLIAMS, J. B.   Memoirs of the Life, Character and Writings of Sir Matthew Hale, Lord Chief Justice of England. 1835. Portrait, orig. cloth, rebacked, octavo, good. Upcroft 10-603 1978 £10

WILLIAMS, J. F.   Old and New Columbia. Columbia, 1929. Bell Wiley's copy. Broadfoot's 44-952 1978 $15.00

WILLIAMS, JAMES   Narrative of..., an American Slave... New York and Boston, 1838. 16mo., frontis., stiff wrs., crude cloth backstrip, little staining throughout, else good., 2nd ed. Petrilla 13-161 1978 $35

WILLIAMS, JOHN 1664-1729   The Redeemed Captive Returning to Zion. Northampton, 1853. Hood 117-715 1978 $45

WILLIAMS, JOHN 1664-1729   The Redeemed Captive Returning to Zion. Springfield, 1908. Reprinted from sixth ed., frontis, uncut, orig. binding. Wolfe 39-563 1978 $15

WILLIAMS, JOHN   The Hamiltoniad... New York, 1865. Ltd. to 40 copies, uncut. MacManus 239-192 1978 $35

WILLIAMS, JOHN CAMP   An Oneida County Printer..William Williams, Printer, Publisher, Editor, With a Bibliography of the Press at Utica...N.Y. from 1803-1838. 1906. Illus., limited to 180 copies, very good. Nestler Rare 78-149 1978 $65

WILLIAMS, JOHN CAMP   William Williams...with a Bibliography of the Press of Utica...1803-1838. New York, 1906. Portr., illus. from wood engrs. by William Williams, plts., bound in blue bds., vellum back, orig. dust jacket, ltd. to 180 copies. Butterfield 21-320 1978 $85

WILLIAMS, JOHN S.   History of the Invasion and Capture of Washington, and of the Events that Preceded and Followed. New York, 1857. Map, 1st ed. MacManus 239-472 1978 $30

WILLIAMS, JONATHAN   Thermometrical Navigation Being a Series of Experiments and Observations... Philadelphia, 1799. 1st ed., 8vo., fldg. engr. map, pres. inscrip. in ink, very light browning, bound in polished, blind-stamped calf, scratched, orig. marbled wrs. bound in. Current 24-128 1978 $625

WILLIAMS, MICHAEL   The Catholic Church in Action. 1934. Ex-lib. Austin 79-842 1978 $12.50

WILLIAMS, MONIER   Sakoontala or the Lost Ring, an Indian Drama... from the Sanskrit of Kalidasa. New York, De Vinne Press, 1885. 4to., orig. Japan vellum illuminated wrs., 1 of 110 copies on Japan paper, very good. Americanist 103-108 1978 $60

WILLIAMS, MONTAGU   Round London, Down East & Up West. 1893. 2nd. ed., half title, orig. red cloth, v.g. Jarndyce 16-833 1978 £5.50

WILLIAMS, NATHAN BOONE   The Dust Bin. Washington, 1938. Ltd. ed. Biblo BL781-891 1978 $12

WILLIAMS, O. W.   Letter From O. W. Williams to His Son. Ft. Stockton, 1925. Jenkins 116-1472 1978 $8.50

WILLIAMS, OSCAR   Selected Poems. New York, 1947. 8vo, dark blue cloth, d.w. with small tears, very fine, 1st ed. Desmarais 1-425 1978 $7.50

WILLIAMS, PASCOE W.   The Helmer Family. St. Johnsville, 1931-32. Ex-lib. Butterfield 21-193 1978 $20

WILLIAMS, R. C.   Bibliography of the Seventeenth Century Novel in France. 8vo. Traylen 88-527 1978 £5

WILLIAMS, ROBERT FOLKESTONE   Mepistophles in England. New York, 1835. 1st Amer. ed., 2 vols., orig. cloth, paper labels, library markings, interior good. Greene 78-132 1978 $60

WILLIAMS, ROBERT FOLKESTONE   Shakespeare and His Friends; or "The Golden Age" of Merry England. London, 1838. 3 vols., 3/4 mor., t.e.g., 1st ed., fine. MacManus 238-413 1978 $75

WILLIAMS, ROBERT FOLKESTONE   The Youth of Shakespeare. London, 1839. 3 vols., orig. cloth-backed bds., 1st ed., ex-lib., very good. MacManus 238-414 1978 $125

WILLIAMS, ROGER   Letters of Roger Williams 1632-1682. Providence, 1874. Subscriber's ed., limited to 160 copies. Nestler Rare 78-3 1978 $55

WILLIAMS, S. W.   The Cistercian Abbey of Strata Florida; its history, and an account of the recent excavations made on its site. 1889. Plts., illus., ex-library copy, orig. cloth, 8vo. Upcroft 12-497 1978 £12

WILLIAMS, SAMUEL COLE   Lieutenant Henry Timberlakes' Memoirs 1856-1765. Marietta, 1948. Folding map, Bell Wiley's copy. Broadfoot's 44-823 1978 $15.00

WILLIAMS, TENNESSEE   Tennessee William's Letters To Donald Wyndham. Verona, 1976. 1 of 500 numbered copies on Favini paper, 1st ed., actetate jacket, slipcase, as new. Houle 10-371 1978 $125

WILLIAMS, W.   Constitutions of the Antient Fraternity of Free and Accepted Masons, Part the Second. 1815. 4to., full calf. George's 635-1440 1978 £12.50

WILLIAMS, WILLIAM CARLOS   The Complete Collected Poems. 1906-1938.
Norfolk, (1938). Orig. cloth, 1st ed., inscribed by author, good.   MacManus
238-767 1978 $250

WILLIAMS, WILLIAM CARLOS   The Complete Collected Poems of William Carlos
Williams 1906-1938. Norfolk, 1938. Very good.   Nestler Rare 78-86 1978
$35

WILLIAMS, WILLIAM CARLOS   The Great American Novel. Paris, 1923. Orig.
cloth-backed bds., 1st ed., ltd. to 300 no. copies, lacks label on spine, otherwise fine.   MacManus 238-766 1978 $200

WILLIAMS, WILLIAM CARLOS   Make Light of It. New York, 1950. First U.S.
ed., very good, worn d.w.   Bell Book 17-939 1978 £17.50

WILLIAMS, WILLIAM CARLOS   A Voyage to Pagany. 1928. First ed., covers
somewhat soiled.   Austin 82-1099 1978 $25

WILLIAMS-ELLIS, AMABEL   The Story of English Life. New York, (1936).
Illus.   Biblo 247-760 1978 $12.50

WILLIAMS-ELLIS, CLOUGH   The Tank Corps. (c. 1919). Portrait, plts.,
8vo., orig. cloth.   F. Edwards 1013-453 1978 £15

WILLIAMSON, CHARLES   Description of the Genesee Country. Albany,
1798. Plates, good.   Nestler Rare 78-150 1978 $65

WILLIAMSON, GEORGE   Memorials of the Lineage, Early Life, Education
and Development of the Genius of James Watt. Edinburgh, 1856. 4to., frontis.,
fldg. map, plts., facsimiles of letters, buckram, very good copy, 1st ed.   Norman
5-296 1978 $85

WILLIAMSON, GEORGE CHARLES   The Art of the Miniature Painter. London,
1926. Illus.   Baldwins' 51-165 1978 $17.50

WILLIAMSON, GEORGE CHARLES   The History of Portrait Miniatures. From
the time of Holbein, 1531 to that of Sir John Ross, 1860... 1904. 2 vols., folio,
plts., orig. buckram, ltd. to 520 copies.   Quaritch 983-276 1978 $480

WILLIAMSON, GEORGE CHARLES   Portrait Miniatures from the Time of Holbein, 1531 to that of Sir William Ross, 1860. London, 1897. 1st ed., illus., orig.
cloth, fine.   MacManus 239-714 1978 $25

WILLIAMSON, GEORGE CHARLES   Portrait Miniatures. 1910. Plts. in color,
imp. 8vo.   George's 635-69 1978 £7.50

WILLIAMSON, H. R.   George Villiers, First Duke of Buckingham.
1940. Plts., octavo, good.   Upcroft 10-606 1978 £6.50

WILLIAMSON, H. R.   John Hampden; a Life. 1933. Plts., octavo,
good.   Upcroft 10-605 1978 £7.50

WILLIAMSON, HAMILTON   Lion Cub. New York, (1931). 1st ed., plates in
color, fine, dj.   Victoria 34-367 1978 $15

WILLIAMSON, HENRY   The Beautiful Years. 1929. Fine, revised ed.,
slightly browned d.w.   Bell Book 17-941 1978 £16.50

WILLIAMSON, HENRY   The Clodhoppers. 1946. Coloured frontis.,
plts., very good, worn d.w., first English ed.   Bell Book 17-942 1978 £5.50

WILLIAMSON, HENRY   Dandelion Days. 1930. Revised ed., fine,
slightly browned d.w.   Bell Book 17-943 1978 £15

WILLIAMSON, HENRY   Norfolk Life. 1943. Very good, first English
ed.   Bell Book 17-948 1978 £8.50

WILLIAMSON, HENRY   The Old Stag, and other hunting stories. 1933.
First illus. ed., fine, d.w.   Bell Book 16-932 1978 £12.50

WILLIAMSON, HENRY   Salar the Salmon. London, 1934. Fine copy,
lightly dampstained, d.w. chipped with sm. tears.   Desmarais B-675 1978 £7.50

WILLIAMSON, HENRY   Salar the Salmon. 1935. Covers little rubbed,
good, first English ed.   Bell Book 17-946 1978 £8.50

WILLIAMSON, HENRY   Scribbling Lark. 1949. Fine, d.w., scarce,
first English ed.   Bell Book 17-947 1978 £17.50

WILLIAMSON, HENRY   The Sun in the Sands. London, 1945. Very
fine, bkplt., d.w. lightly darkened.   Desmarais B-676 1978 $7.50

WILLIAMSON, HENRY   Tales of a Devon Village. 1945. Very good,
worn d.w., first English ed.   Bell Book 16-936 1978 £4

WILLIAMSON, J. A.   Maritime Enterprise 1485-1558. Oxford, 1913.
Plts., octavo, good.   Upcroft 10-607 1978 £10

WILLIAMSON, J. B.   The History of the Temple London, From the
Institution of the Order of the Knights of the Temple to the Close of the Stuart
Period... 1925. 2nd. ed., plts., octavo, good.   Upcroft 10-608 1978 £6.50

WILLIAMSON, JOHN   A Treatise on Military Finance. 1795. 12mo.,
sheep rubbed.   George's 635-873 1978 £7.50

WILLIAMSON, JOHN P.   Dakota Odowan. New York, 1879. Orig.
cloth.   Ginsberg 14-1065 1978 $110

WILLIAMSON, S. T.   Trends in Collective Bargaining. New York,
1945.   Biblo BL781-892 1978 $9.50

WILLIAMSON, THOMAS   Oriental Field Sports.... London, 1808. 4to,
2 vols., 2 etched pictorial title-pgs., tinted plts., full dark blue diced morocco,
decorative blind & gilt borders, morocco labels, gilt, marbled endpapers, inside
leather hinges, a little rubbed, fine binding.   Deighton 5-192 1978 £215

WILLIAMSON, THOMAS   The Sword of the spirit to smite in pieces that
Antichristian Goliath, who daily defieth the Lords people of the host of Israel....
London, 1613. 8vo., half-page woodcuts, little stained and rumpled, contemp.
vellum, 1st and only ed.   Quaritch 978-161 1978 $1,200

WILLIS, JAMES F.   Bibliophily or Booklove. Boston, (1921). Bds.
Hayman 71-789 1978 $7.50

WILLIS, NATHANIEL PARKER   American Scenery, Or, Land, Lake, and River,
Illustrations of Translantic Nature. London, 1840. 2 vols., 4to, 2 coloured
engraved vignette title-pgs., coloured engraved map, coloured portrait, newly
rebound in half tan morocco, marbled bds., morocco labels, gilt, raised bands.
Deighton 5-61 1978 £650

WILLIS, NATHANIEL PARKER   Canadian Scenery Illustrated. London & New
York, c.1842. 2 vols., 4to, 2 coloured engraved vignette title-pgs., coloured
engraved map, coloured engraved plts. by W.H. Bartlett, newly rebound in red
morocco, gilt, new endpapers.   Deighton 5-60 1978 £700

WILLIS, NATHANIEL PARKER   Trenton Falls, Picturesque and Descriptive. New
York, 1851. Plts., 12mo., 1st ed.   Morrill 239-559 1978 $10

WILLIS, WILLIAM   Journals of the Rev. Thomas Smith, and the Rev.
Samuel Deane, Pastors of the First Church in Portland... Portland, 1849. 1st
ed., orig. cloth, minor chipping, frontis., illus., inscribed by author.   Mac -
Manus 239-273 1978 $42.50

WILLISON, GEORGE F.   Saints and Strangers. New York, (1945). First
ed., fine, d.w.   Biblo 247-36 1978 $12.50

WILLISON, J. S.   Sir Wilfrid Laurier and the Liberal Party, a Political History. Toronto, 1903. 2 vols., pgs. mostly unopened.   Hood 116-273
1978 $50

WILLISON, JOHN   Looking to Jesus. Boston, 1759. 12mo, bound
in old marbled paper but not original, fair copy.   Victoria 34-871 1978 $25

WILLKIE, WENDELL L.   An American Program. New York, 1944. First
ed., bound.   Biblo 247-140 1978 $8.50

WILLKIE, WENDELL L.   One World. New York, 1943. 1st ed., d.w.
Biblo 251-93 1978 $9.50

WILLKOMM, M.   Atlas d'histoire naturelle-vegetaux, texte ex-
plicatif d'apres M. Willkomm par J. Groenland. (c. 1870). Chromolithographs,
folio, orig. pict. bds., sewing loose.   George's 635-966 1978 £50

WILLMOTT, ELLEN   The Genus Rosa. London, 1914. Illus. in
black & white, coloured plts., 2 vols., thick folio, orig. half morocco, wrappers
bound in.   Traylen 88-640 1978 £350

WILLMOTT, ELLEN   Warley Garden in Spring and Summer. 1909.
Photo plts., folio, orig. cloth-backed printed bds., binding worn, but sound, very
good. Fenning 32-370 1978 £7.50

WILLMOTT, ROBERT ARIS   Summer Time in the Country. 1880. Illus.,
4to, orig. pale brown pictorial cloth, gilt, edges gilt, nice almost fine. Fenning
32-317 1978 £7.50

WILLOBY, HENRY   The Willoby his Avisa. 1886. From the ed. of
1635, sm. 4to., orig. wrappers. Howes 194-1212k 1978 £10

WILLOUGHBY DE BROKE, RICHARD GREVILLE VARNEY, BARON   The Sport
of Our Ancestors Being a Collection of Prose and Verse Setting Forth the Sport of
Fox-Hunting as They Knew It. London, 1921. Illus., plts., 4to., dec. cloth.
K Books 244-86 1978 £10

WILLS, W. A.   The Downfall of Lobengula. London, n.d.
Plts., text illus., roy. 8vo., pict. cloth. K Books 239-535 1978 £25

WILLS, W. G.   The Love that Kills. A Novel. London, 1867.
3 vols., orig. cloth, 1st ed., very good. MacManus 238-355 1978 $75

WILLSHIRE, W. H.   A Descriptive Catalogue of Early Prints in the
B.M. German and Flemish Schools. London, 1879-83. 2 vols., plts., roy. 8vo.,
orig. cloth. Forster 130-236 1978 £35

WILLSON, ARABELLA M.   Disaster, Struggle, Triumph. Albany, 1870.
Plts., lightly shaken. Butterfield 21-126 1978 $25

WILLSON, BECKLES   America's Ambassadors to France 1777-1927.
New York, 1928. Illus. MacManus 239-526 1978 $12.50

WILLSON, BECKLES   America's Ambassadors to England 1785-1929.
London, (1929). Illus. MacManus 239-527 1978 $12.50

WILLSON, BECKLES   John Slidell and the Confederates in Paris. New
York, 1932. Bell Wiley's copy. Broadfoot 46-284 1978 $20

WILLSON, BECKLES   The Life of Lord Strathcona and Mount Royal
1820-1914. London, 1915. Photos., fold. map. Hood 116-274 1978 $40

WILLSON, MARCIUS   Willson's Larger Speller... New York, (1864).
Pict. bds. Hayman 72-799 1978 $7.50

WILLSTACH, PAUL   Tidewater Maryland. Indianapolis, (1931).
Illus., 1st ed. MacManus 239-1891 1978 $10

WILLSTACH, PAUL   Tidewater Virginia. Indianapolis, (1929). 1st
ed., illus., fine. MacManus 239-1892 1978 $12.50

WILLSTATTER, RICHARD   Problems and Methods in Enzyme Research.
Ithaca, 1927. 8vo., old pebbled cloth, gilt, fine copy, 1st ed. Norman 5-302
1978 $30

WILLSTATTER, RICHARD   Untersuchungen Uber Chlorophyll. Berlin,
1913. 8vo., plts., text illus., contemp. cloth-backed bds., rubbed, very good
copy, stamp, 1st ed. Norman 5-300 1978 $85

WILLSTATTER, RICHARD   Untersuchungen Uber die Assimilation der Kohlen-
saure. Berlin, 1918. 8vo., illus., old pebbled cloth, slightly worn, but fine
copy, 1st ed. Norman 5-301 1978 $50

WILLYAMS, COOPER   A Voyage to the Mediterranean in His Majesty's
Ship the Swiftsure, one of the Squadron under the Command of Rear-Admiral Sir
Horatio Nelson.... London, 1802. Folio, half polished calf, plts., first ed.
King 7-397 1978 £125

WILLYAMS, JANE LOUISA   Chillon: A Tale of the Great Reformation in the
Sixteenth Century. Philadelphia, 1845. 1st Amer. ed., half-cloth & boards,
paper labels, scuffing, good copy, 2 vols. in 1. Greene 78-133 1978 $45

WILLYAMS, JANE LOUISA   Chillon: or, Protestants of the Sixteenth Century.
1845. 1st. ed., 2 vols., orig. half calf, marbled bds., good. Jarndyce 16-
1179 1978 £40

WILLYAMS, JANE LOUISA   Chillon; or, Protestants of the Sixteenth Century.
1845. 2 vols., sole ed.?, half-title, 8vo, orig. cloth, fine. Fenning 32-372
1978 £32

WILMER, RICHARD   The Recent Past from a Southern Standpoint...
New York, 1887. 1st ed. MacManus 239-1890 1978 $12.50

WILMOT, MRS. THOMAS MOORE   Ina, A Tragedy in Five Acts. 1815. Title
lightly spotted, modern 1/4 green morocco, gilt spine, marbled bds. Eaton 45-
539 1978 £30

WILMOTT, ROBERT A.   The Poets of the Nineteenth Century. 1857.
Sm. 4to, illus., full crimson morocco, gilt panelled, inner dentelles, a.e.g., very
slightly rubbed. Eaton 45-538 1978 £20

WILSON, MR.   Affairs of the Union Pacific Railroad Company.
Washington, 1873. Disbound, 1st ed. Ginsberg 14-992 1978 $45

WILSON, AMOS   The Pennsylvania Hermit. Harrisburg, 1840.
Orig. brown wrappers. Baldwins' 51-501 1978 $37.50

WILSON, ANDREW   The Abode of Snow... 1875. Folding map,
tinted litho frontis., half red morocco, 8vo. Edwards 1012-144 1978 £45

WILSON, ANDREW   Chapters on Evolution. London, 1886. 3rd ed.,
Illus., gilt cloth, 8vo. K Books 244-462 1978 £7

WILSON, ANGUS   The Wrong Set and other stories. London, 1949.
First ed., orig. binding, spine faded, nice. Rota 211-791 1978 £7.50

WILSON, ARTHUR HERMAN   A History of the Philadelphia Theatre 1835 to
1855. Philadelphia, 1935. 1st ed., orig. cloth, spine torn, but good, scarce.
MacManus 239-1621 1978 $40

WILSON, AUGUSTA J. EVANS   St. Elmo. New York, 1867. 1st ed., orig.
cloth, very good. Greene 78-340 1978 $70

WILSON, C.   Anglo-Dutch Commerce and Finance in the 18th
Century. Cambridge, 1941. Illus., 8vo. George's 635-435 1978 £6

WILSON, C. T.   James the Second and the Duke of Berwick.
1876. Octavo, good. Upcroft 10-610 1978 £8.50

WILSON, CARROL A.   13 Author Collections of the 19th Century. 1930.
2 vols., boxed, 1 of 375 numbered sets, very fine. Battery Park 1-345 1978 $75

WILSON, CAROL GREEN   Chinatown Quest. Stanford University Press,
1931. Illus. Austin 79-846 1978 $12.50

WILSON, CHARLES H.   Education for Negroes in Mississippi Since 1910.
Boston, 1947. Illus., Bell Wiley's copy. Broadfoot's 44-913 1978 $14.00

WILSON, CHARLES MORROW   Empire in Green and Gold...the American Ban-
ana Trade. New York, (1947). Illus. Biblo BL781-102 1978 $9

WILSON, CLIFFORD   Northern Treasury. Toronto, n.d. Illus.
Hood 117-112 1978 $15

WILSON, DAVID   Henrietta Robinson. New York & Auburn, 1855.
Frontis. portr., ads, orig. cloth, faded. Butterfield 21-368 1978 $15

WILSON, EDMUND   Classics and Commercials. 1950. Austin 82-1102
1978 $12.50

WILSON, EDMUND   Europe without Baedeker. 1947. First edition.
Austin 82-1105 1978 $15

WILSON, EDMUND   Europe without Baedeker: sketches among the
ruins of Italy, Greece & England. 1948. Very good, worn d.w., first English
ed. Bell Book 16-939 1978 £6.50

WILSON, EDMUND   Memoirs of Hecate County. n.d. Very good,
d.w., first English ed. Bell Book 16-1022 1978 £5.50

WILSON, EDMUND   Note-Books of Night. 1945. Very good, first
English ed. Bell Book 16-940 1978 £8.50

WILSON, EDMUND   To the Finland Station. 1940. First ed., very
good, d.j. Austin 82-1116 1978 $27.50

WILSON, EDWIN MOOD   The Congressional Career of Nathaniel Macon.
Chapel Hill, 1900. Wrs., spine frayed. Broadfoot 50-337 1978 $15

WILSON, ERASMUS   A System of Human Anatomy, General and Special. Philadelphia, 1850. Fourth Amer. ed. Rittenhouse 49-843 1976 $10

WILSON, ERNEST HENRY   America's Greatest Garden. Boston, 1925, 6.
8vo, orig. cloth. Book Chest 17-432 1978 $12.50

WILSON, ERNEST HENRY   Aristocrats of the Garden. Boston, 1926.
8vo, orig. cloth. Book Chest 17-430 1978 $16.50

WILSON, ERNEST HENRY   Aristocrats of the Trees. Boston, (1930). Pebbled
cloth binding, 4to, illus., fine ed. Book Chest 17-429 1978 $65

WILSON, ERNEST HENRY   If I Were to Make a Garden. Boston, 1931.
4to, orig. cloth. Book Chest 17-434 1978 $40

WILSON, ERNEST HENRY   The Lilies of Eastern Asia, A Monograph.
London, 1929. Plates, scarce, 8vo, orig. cloth. Book Chest 17-433 1978 $60

WILSON, ERNEST HENRY   More Aristocrats of the Garden. Boston, 1928.
8vo, orig. cloth. Book Chest 17-431 1978 $15

WILSON, FRANCIS   Recollections of a Player. New York, De-
Vinne Press, 1897. 1st ed., ltd. to 120 copies, unnumbered, 4to., orig. bds.,
uncut, boxed, illus., nice copy signed by Wilson. Americanist 103-109 1978
$35

WILSON, FRANCIS   Recollections of a Player. #2 of 120 copies,
signed by Wilson. Americanist 103-110 1978 $30

WILSON, G. H.   Views of South Africa. London, c. 1900.
Oblong 4to, photos, orig. cloth. K Books 239-538 1978 £10

WILSON, G. MURRAY   Fighting Tanks, An Account of the Royal Tank
Corps in action 1916-1919. 1929. Portrait frontis., plts., 8vo., orig. cloth.
F. Edwards 1013-455 1978 £15

WILSON, GEORGE   Electricity and the Electric Telegraphy....
1852. 1st. ed., illus., sm. 8vo, wrapper, nice. Fenning 32-373 1978 £8.50

WILSON, GEORGE   The Life of Henry Cavendish. London, 1851.
8vo., frontis. portr., orig. cloth, gilt, hinges repaired, dampstaining in portr.
margin, very good copy, 1st ed. Norman 5-51 1978 $75

WILSON, GEORGE   Memoir of Edward Forbes... 1861. 1st. ed.,
portrait, illus., 8vo, orig. cloth, nice. Fenning 32-374 1978 £16

WILSON, H. A.   The Pontifical of Magdalen College. 1910.
Plts., 8vo. Upcroft 12-498 1978 £20

WILSON, H. T.   Historical Sketch of Santa Fe, New Mexico.
Chicago, [188]. Illus., orig. pict. front wr., 1st ed. Ginsberg 14-785 1978
$250

WILSON, HARRIETTE 1789-1846   Memoirs. Stockdale, 1825. Contemp. half
calf, 4 vols., 12mo. Howes 194-1337 1978 £22

WILSON, HARRIETTE 1789-1846. Memoirs. 1924. Portraits, 2 vols., thick
8vo., printed on laid paper, orig. cloth. Howes 194-1338 1978 £7.50

WILSON, HARRY LEON   The Boss of Little Arcady. Boston, (1905). Illus., plts., spine rubbed, inner hinges cracked, minor cover spot, good, 1st ed.
Petrilla 13-163 1978 $8.50

WILSON, HARRY LEON   Lone Tree. New York, 1929. 1st. ed., cloth.
Eaton 45-540 1978 $5

WILSON, HARRY LEON   The Man from Home. New York, 1915. First
ed., illus. Biblo 247-651 1978 $15

WILSON, HARRY LEON   Merton of the Movies. Garden City, 1922.
1st ed., very good. Victoria 34-872 1978 $15

WILSON, HENRY   Leybourn's Dialling Improv'd. 1721. Plts., sm.
8vo., contemp. calf, joints weak. Howes 194-521 1978 £18

WILSON, HENRY   The Republican and Democratic Parties: What
They Have Done and They Propose to do. New York, (1868). Stitched. Hayman
71-645 1978 $7.50

WILSON, HENRY   Rise and Fall of the Slave Power in America.
Boston, 1872. 3 vols. Bell Wiley's copy. Broadfoot 46-586 1978 $35

WILSON, HERBERT WRIGLEY   With the Flag to Pretoria. London, 1900-02.
4 vols., nice set in orig. cloth, lg. 4to, illus. K Books 239-540 1978 £20

WILSON, HERBERT WRIGLEY   With the Flag to Pretoria. London, 1900-02.
4 vols., illus., 4to., orig. cloth. K Books 244-463 1978 £16

WILSON, HERBERT WRIGLEY   With the Flag to Pretoria. London, 1900-02.
4 vols., copiously illus., lg. 4to, half calf gilt. K Books 239-539 1978 £30

WILSON, ISAIAH W.   A Geography and History of the County of Digby,
N.S. Halifax, 1900. A.L.s. by author loosely inserted, orig. binding. Wolfe
39-396 1978 $125

WILSON, J. L.   Western Africa: Its History, Condition, and
Prospects. New York, 1856. 1st. ed., portrait, map, engravings, sm. 8vo, half
morocco. Edwards 1012-273 1978 £60

WILSON, JAMES   Biography of the Blind. Belfast, 1821. 12mo.,
orig. bds., soiled, uncut, first ed., scarce. P. M. Hill 142-42 1978 £28

WILSON, JAMES   The Description and Manner of Using Mr. Wilson's
Sett of Pocket-Microscopes. London, 1706. 8vo., unbound in case, plt., rare.
Gurney 75-114 1978 £185

WILSON, JAMES   First Missionary Voyage to the South Sea Islands.
(London), 1805. Full calf, front cover loose, plts. Wolfe 39-564 1978 $80

WILSON, JAMES   A Missionary Voyage to the Southern Pacific
Ocean,.... London, 1799. Quarto, folding maps, folding plates, full contemp.
calf, rebacked, bookplate, owner's inscription, 1st ed. Bennett 20-225 1978
$325

WILSON, JAMES   A Pamphlet Relating to the Claim of Senor Don
Jose Y Limantour to Four Leagues of Land in the County Adjoining and Near the
City of San Francisco, California. San Francisco, 1853. Half morocco, 1st ed.
Ginsberg 14-225 1978 $250

WILSON, JAMES GRANT   Colonel John Bayard (1738-1807) and the Bayard
Family of America. New York, 1885. Cloth & marbled bds., spine chipped at
top, orig. wrs. bound in, inscr'd on fr. wr., pres. by author, sm. blindstamp on
fr. wr. Hayman 73-755 1978 $10

WILSON, JAMES GRANT   Memoirs of an American Lady with Sketches of
Manners and Scenes in America.... New York, 1901. 2 vols., illus., orig.
parchment-backed bds., very good set, ltd. to 350 sets. MacManus 239-181
1978 $50

WILSON, JAMES H.   The Bon-Accord Repository of Local Instutiutions,
Municipal, Educational, Ecclesiastical and Commercial. Aberdeen, 1842.
1st. ed., lg. 12mo, orig. cloth, very good. Fenning 32-375 1978 £10.50

WILSON, JOB   An Inquiry Into the Nature and Treatment of the
Prevailing Epidemic Called Spotted Fever. Boston, 1815. In three parts, modern
bds., some browning. Rittenhouse 49-842 1976 $22.50

WILSON, JOHN   Lights & Shadows of Scottish Life.... Edinburgh, 1822. 1st. ed., half title, rebound in half calf, marbled bds., brown label,
good. Jarndyce 16-1180 1978 £14.50

WILSON, JOHN M.   The Rural Cyclopedia. Edinburgh, 1843. Roy.
8vo., half calf, hand-coloured plts., 4 vols. K Books 244-329 1978 £34

WILSON, JOSEPH S.   Railroad Lands in Western Oregon for Sale at Low Rates and on Liberal Terms. San Francisco, 1872. Cloth, 1st ed. Ginsberg 14-857 1978 $125

WILSON, JOSEPH T.   The Black Phalanx. Hartford, 1888. Illus., rebound, scarce. MacManus 239-860a 1978 $35

WILSON, JOSEPH T   The Black Phalanx: A History of the Negro Soldiers of the United States in the Wars of 1775-1812, 1861-1865. Hartford, 1891. New cloth, 56 illus., Bell Wiley's copy. Broadfoot's 44-400 1978 $45.00

WILSON, LOUIS R.   The Chronicles of the Sesquicentennial. Chapel Hill, 1947. Illus. Broadfoot 50-338 1978 $8

WILSON, MARCUS   American History: Comprising Historical Sketches of the Indian Tribes... New York, 1847. Maps, orig. cloth. MacManus 239-528 1978 $30

WILSON, MARGARET   The Crime of Punishment. New York, (1931). Biblo BL781-797 1978 $9

WILSON, MONA   The Life of William Blake. Nonesuch Press, 1927. Frontis, plts., sm. folio, orig. bds., parchment spine, ltd. ed. of 1480 copies. Traylen 88-116 1978 £35

WILSON, MONA   The Life of William Blake. London, Nonesuch Press, 1927. 1 of 1480 numbered copies, 4to., illus., plts., half jap. vellum over marbled bds., uncut, unopened, v.g. Houle 10-35 1978 $125

WILSON, PETER M.   Southern Exposure. Chapel Hill, 1927. Unsigned, cover stained. Broadfoot 50-339b 1978 $12

WILSON, PETER M.   Southern Exposure. Chapel Hill, 1927. Signed copy. Broadfoot 50-339a 1978 $25

WILSON, RUFUS ROCKWELL   Historic Long Island. New York, 1902. 1st ed., illus., lacks frontis., orig. pic. cloth. MacManus 239-258 1978 $7.50

WILSON, RUFUS ROCKWELL   Out of the West. New York, 1933. Pic. cloth, black end sheets, illus., 1st ed., corners creased, fine copy. Dykes 34-172 1978 $15

WILSON, RUFUS ROCKWELL   Washington, the Capital City and Its Part in the History of the Nation. Philadelphia, 1901. Illus., 2 vols. MacManus 239-126 1978 $8.50

WILSON, SARA   Fruits of Enterprize Exhibited in the Travels of Belzoni in Egypt and Nubia. Boston, New York, 1827. 1st Amer. printing, plates and engravings on each, light cover defects, very good. Victoria 34-873 1978 $35

WILSON, SARAH   South African Memories. London, 1909. 19 plts., bright ex-lib., 8vo, orig. cloth. K Books 239-541 1978 £7

WILSON, THOMAS   A Discourse upon Usury, by way of Dialogue and Orations.... 1925. 8vo. George's 635-436 1978 £7.50

WILSON, THOMAS   Sermons. Bath, 1785. 4 vols., engraved portrait, contemp. calf, slightly rubbed, 8vo. George's 635-1157 1978 £10.50

WILSON, V.   Guide to the Yukon Gold Fields... Seattle, 1895. 1st. ed., folding maps, illus., plts., orig. limp cloth, slight repair to spine. Edwards 1012-538 1978 £50

WILSON, W.   The Post Chaise Companion: or, Traveller's Directory Through Ireland. Dublin, 1795. 3rd. ed., engraved frontis, engraved title, engraved plts., maps, 8vo, old half calf, rubbed wanting label, but sound, very sm. portion neatly cut from extreme upper outer corner of titles, very good. Fenning 32-376 1978 £32.50

WILSON, W. H.   Japan's Fight for Freedom. (c. 1904-06). 4to., portraits, plts., illus., 3 vols., publisher's half mor. F. Edwards 1013-456 1978 £40

WILSON, WILLIAM BENDER   From the Hudson to the Ohio. 1902. 1st ed., illus., orig. cloth, very good copy, inscribed by author. MacManus 239-529 1978 $17.50

WILSON, WILLIAM JAMES ERASMUS   Plates Illustrative of Wilson on Diseases of the Skin. Philadelphia, 1868. 7th ed., 8vo., litho. plts., guardsheets, orig. purple cloth, gilt lettering, dampstains, good copy with former owner's ms. signature. Zeitlin 245-288 1978 $45

WILSTACH, PAUL   Correspondence of John Adams and Thomas Jefferson (1812...1826). Indianapolis, (1925). Cloth, pres. inscr. Hayman 73-757 1978 $12.50

WILSTACH, PAUL   Tidewater, Maryland. Indiana, (1931). Illus., no. 185 of 259 copies, autographed. Baldwins' 51-296 1978 $37.50

WILSTACH, PAUL   Tidewater, Maryland. Indiana, (1931). 1st. trade edition. Baldwins' 51-297 1978 $12.50

WILSTACH, PAUL   Tidewater Virginia. Indianapolis, (1929). Very fine in chipped dw. Bernard 5-277 1978 $10

WILSTACH, PAUL   Tidewater Virginia. 1929. Illus., maps, autographed, very good. Nestler Rare 78-256 1978 $25

WIMMER, G. A.   Neuestes Gemalde von Australien. Vienna, 1832. German text, heavy wrs., bit worn, labels on wrs. Dawson's 127-294 1978 $100

WIMPFELING, JACOB   DJrectorium concubinariorum saluberrimum quo quedam stupenda et ob tanti sceleris impunem tolerantiam.... Cologne, 1508. Sm. 4to., 1st ed., fine copy, modern half vellum. Schafer 19-43 1978 sFr. 1,200

WIMPFELING, JOSEPH   Avisamentum de concubinaris non absolvendis. Nurnberg, Nov. 12, 1507. Sm. 4to., woodcut, good copy, half vellum. Schafer 19-42 1978 sFr. 1,200

WIMPFFEN, FRANCIS A STANISLAUS   A Voyage to Saint Domingo, 1788-90... (1797). Folding map, outline coloured, browned, contemp. calf, 8vo. Edwards 1012-738 1978 £180

WINANS, WILLIAM H.   Reminiscences and Experiences in the Life of an Editor. Newark, 1875. Illus., 8vo., 1st ed., orig. cloth. Morrill 241-425 1978 $17.50

WINCHELL, ALEXANDER   The Doctrine of Evolution. New York, 1874. Sm. 8vo., 1st ed., orig. cloth. Morrill 241-628 1978 $12.50

WINCHELL, ALEXANDER   Geological Excursions or the Rudiments of Geology for Young Learners. Chicago, 1884. Illus., 8vo., 1st ed., orig. cloth. Morrill 241-629 1978 $7.50

WINDELBAND, W.   Geschichte der Abendlaendischen Philosophie im Altertum. 1923. Ex-lib. Allen 234-1059 1978 $12.50

WINDHAM, DONALD   The Dog Star. New York, 1950. First ed., d.w. Biblo 247-642 1978 $12.50

WINDOM, WILLIAM   The Northern Pacific Railway:..... Washington, 1869. Orig. wr. Ginsberg 14-791 1978 $22.50

WINDOM, WILLIAM   The Northern Pacific Railway; Its Effect Upon the Public Credit, the Public Revenues, and the Public Debt. Speech of Hon..., of Minnesota, Delivered in the House...January 5, 1869. Washington, 1869. Wrs. Hayman 72-800 1978 $15

WINDROW, JOHN EDWIN   John Berrien Lindsley, Educator, Physician, Social Philosopher. Chapel Hill, 1938. Bell Wiley's copy. Broadfoot's 44-826 1978 $10

WINDSHIP, CHARLES W.   An Introductory Discourse on the Phenomena of Vitality, or Laws of Mobility and Motion in Animal Bodies. Boston, 1818. 8vo., unbound, 1st ed. Morrill 239-277 1978 $15

THE WINE And Spirit Merchant. (1877). 1st. ed., illus., 8vo, orig. cloth, gilt, some signs of use, good sound copy. Fenning 32-377 1978 £14.50

WINFIELD, A. B.   Sermon at the Interment of the Bodies of John G. Van Nest, Mrs. Sarah Van Nest, G. W. Van Nest, their son, and Mrs. Phoebe Wykoff, who were Murdered March Twelfth Inst., by a Colored Man Named William Freeman. Auburn, 1848. Butterfield 21-110 1978 $8.50

WINFIELD, CHARLES H.   The Block-House by Bull's Ferry. New York, 1904. Illus., 1st ed., frontis. port., plts., orig. cloth, ltd. to 200 copies, fine. MacManus 239-634 1978 $22.50

WING, JOSEPH E.   In Foreign Fields. Chicago, 1913. Cloth, illus., 1st ed., fine, from the Allred Collection, slipcase. Dykes 34-285 1978 $50

WINGATE, F. R.   Ten Years' Captivity in the Mahdi's Camp 1882-1892. London, (1893). 13th. ed., revised & abridged, folding plan, illus., cr. 8 vo, orig. cloth, covers & fore-edge marked, working copy. K Books 239-542 1978 £8

WINGATE, RONALD   Wingate of the Sudan. 1955. 1st. ed., plts., maps, 8vo, orig. cloth, spine faded, pres. copy to Winston Churchill. Sawyer 298-126 1978 £250

WINGFIELD, J. H. D.   ...Official Register of the College of St. Augustine Benicia, California. [Oakland, 1889]. Plates, original printed wr. Ginsberg 14-226 1978 $30

WINGFIELD, MARSHALL   A History of Caroline County, Virginia. Richmond, 1924. Pres copy from author, Bell Wiley's copy. Broadfoot's 44-993 1978 $22.00

WINKLER, CLEMENS A.   Handbook of Technical Gas-Analysis.... 1885. 1st. English ed., illus., 8vo, orig. cloth, very good. Fenning 32-378 1978 £16

WINKLER, ERNEST WILLIAM   Journal of the Secession Convention of Texas, 1861. Austin, 1912. Very fine. Jenkins 116-1487 1978 $27.50

WINKLER, ERNEST WILLIAM   Manuscript Letters and Documents of Early Texans, 1821-1845. Austin, 1937. Lg. thick folio. Jenkins 116-1488 1978 $75

WINKLER, ERNEST WILLIAM   Platforms of Political Parties in Texas. Austin, 1916. Jenkins 116-1489 1978 $37.50

WINKLER, JOHN   John D. a Portrait in Oils. New York, 1929. 1928 dime glued to cover, good, wear on d. j. Nestler Rare 78-151 1978 $12

WINKWORTH, SUSANNA   The Life and Letters of George Bathold Niebuhr. 1852. 2nd. ed., 3 vols., half titles, orig. cloth, fine, Matthew Arnold's copy, signed by him. Jarndyce 16-905 1978 £40

WINN, DAVID WATSON   Ancestors and Descendants of John Quarles Winn and His Wife Mary Liscome Jarvis. Baltimore, 1932. 1st ed., illus., ports., orig. cloth, fine. MacManus 239-943 1978 $30

WINNER'S Perfect Guide for the Violin. Boston, (1861). Sewn, slight wear. Hayman 73-758 1978 $7.50

WINNIPEG COUNCIL OF SOCIAL AGENCIES   Report of Committee on Housing. Winnipeg, 1943. Card cover. Hood's 115-1004 1978 $7.50

WINSHIP, A. E.   The Louisiana Purchase As It Was and As It Is. Chicago, (1903). Illus., 12mo., orig. cloth. Morrill 241-630 1978 $7.50

WINSLOW, C. E. A.   The Late of Hermann M. Biggs. Philadelphia, 1929. Upper hinge loose. Rittenhouse 49-844 1976 $22.50

WINSLOW, EDWARD   Hypocrisie Unmasked a True Relation of the Proceedings of the Governor and Company of the Massachusetts Against Samuel Gorton of Rhode Island. Providence, 1916. Reprinted from London 1646 ed., orig. vellum-backed bds., ltd. to 100 copies. MacManus 239-530 1978 $30

WINSLOW, OLA ELIZABETH   Harper's Literary Museum. 1927. Illus., first ed. Austin 82-1118 1978 $27.50

WINSLOW, THYRA SAMTER   My Own Native Land. 1935. First ed., review copy. Austin 82-1119 1978 $17.50

WINSLOW, THYRA SAMTER   Show Business. 1926. Ex-lib. Austin 82-1120 1978 $10

WINSOR, JUSTIN   Cartier to Frontenac. Boston, 1900. Maps, gilt-topped. Hood 117-604 1978 $75

WINSTANLEY, GERRARD   Gerrard Winstanley; Selections From His Works. 1944. Octavo, good. Upcroft 10-187 1978 £5

WINSTED, the Gateway to the Berkshires. (Winsted, n.d. early 20th century). Wrs. Hayman 72-150 1978 $7.50

WINSTON, ROBERT WATSON   It's a Far Cry. 1937. First ed., frayed d.j., 381 pages. Austin 82-1121 1978 $15

WINSTON, ROBERT WATSON   It's A Far Cry. NY, 1937. Bell Wiley's copy. Broadfoot's 44-919 1978 $12.00

WINSTON, SANFORD   Illiteracy in the U. S. 1930. Austin 82-1122 1978 $17.50

WINTEMBERG, W. J.   Certain Eye Designs on Archaeological Artifacts from North America. 1923. Card cover, plts. Hood 116-447 1978 $10

WINTER, CHARLES E.   Grandon of Sierra. New York, (1907). Cloth, pres. copy. Hayman 72-245 1978 $8.50

WINTER, NEVIN O.   Texas, the Marvelous: The State of the Six Flags. New York, 1936. Centenary Ed., illus. Jenkins 116-1491 1978 $12.50

WINTER, RICHARD   A Sermon preached at New-Court, Carey-Street; on Thursday, November 29, 1759. Canada, 1759. 8vo, wr. Quaritch 978-26 1978 $90

WINTER. New York, 1815. Both wrappers illus., sewn, slightly rubbed, very good. Victoria 34-874 1978 $75

WINTER Haven, Florida, The Land of Sunshine. (Dayton, n.d., 1890's). Wrps. Hayman 71-249 1978 $8.50

WINTERBOTHAM, WILLIAM   An Historical, Geographical, Commerical and Philosophical View of the American United States and of the European Settlements in America and the West-Indies. London, 1795. Orig. full calf, 4 vols., very good condition, lacks general map of United States. Baldwins' 51-24 1978 $250

WINTERBOTTOM, THOMAS M.   An Account of the Native Africans in the Neighborhood of Sierra Leone. London, 1803. 2 vols., 8vo., lg. fldg. map, engr. plts., contemp. polished calf, rebacked & corners repaired, library stamp, lightly browned, very good copy, 1st ed., very rare. Zeitlin 245-289 1978 $850

WINTERICH, JOHN T.   Books and the Man. New York, 1929. 8vo., orig. cloth, illus. MacManus 238-1078 1978 $20

WINTERICH, JOHN T.   Early American Books and Printing. Boston and New York, 1935. 8vo., orig. cloth, boxed, 1st ed., lg. paper ed., ltd. to 300 copies signed by author, fine. MacManus 238-1079 1978 $45

WINTERICH, JOHN T.   A Primer of Book Collecting. New York, 1927. 12mo., orig. cloth, 1st ed. MacManus 238-1080 1978 $15

WINTERS, FRASTUS   Serving Uncle Sam in the 50th Ohio. East Walnut Hills, 1905. Wrs., Bell Wiley's copy. Broadfoot's 44-586 1978 $50

WINTERS, YVOR   Edwin Arlington Robinson. Norfolk, 1946. First U.S. ed., portrait, post 8vo., very good, worn d.w. Bell Book 17-773 1978 £6.50

THE WINTERS Art Lithographing Company's Popular Portfolios of the World's Columbian Exposition... Chicago, (1891). Wrs., color plts. Hayman 72-338 1978 $15

WINTHER, OSCAR OSBURN   With Sherman to the Sea, The Civil War Letters, Diaries, and Reminiscences of Theodore F. Upson. Baton Rouge, 1943. Bell Wiley's copy. Broadfoot's 44-482 1978 $22

WINTHROP, ROBERT C.   Oration on the 100th Anniversary of the Surrender of Lord Cornwallis...at Yorktown, Virginia. Boston, 1881. 8vo., orig. wrs., 1st ed., pres. copy. Morrill 239-640 1978 $7.50

WINTHROP, THEODORE   The Canoe and the Saddle. Boston, 1863. 5th ed. Hood 117-550 1978 $45

WIR. New York, 1939. Paper, illus. with photos, in German. Austin 79-275 1978 $37.50

WIRT, WILLIAM   Sketches of the Life and Character of Patrick Henry. Philadelphia, 1818. 3rd ed., frontis port., full contemp. calf, nice. MacManus 239-768 1978 $20

WIRTH, FREMONT P.   The Discovery and Exploration of the Minnesota Iron Lands. Cedar Rapids, 1937. 1st ed. Biblo BL781-307 1978 $12

WIRZ, HENRY   Trial of Henry Wirz, 2nd Sess, 40th Congress 1867-1868. Full leather, scuffed and worn, Bell Wiley's copy. Broadfoot's 44-404 1978 $25

WISCHNITZER, MARK   To Dwell in Safety. 1949. Illus. Austin 79-848 1978 $27.50

WISCONSIN. UNIVERSITY. BOARD OF REGENTS   Eleventh Annual Report of the...of the...for the Year Ending Sept. 30, 1858. Madison, 1858. Wrs., little worn, some stains. Hayman 72-802 1978 $8.50

WISCONSIN ACADEMY OF SCIENCES, ARTS AND LETTERS   Transactions of... 1875-76. Madison, 1876. Wrs. Hayman 71-793 1978 $8.50

WISDOM in Miniature. Worcester, 1796. 2nd Worcester ed., lacks f.p., leaves wormholed in margin, upper cover hanging by threads. Victoria 34-877 1978 $30

WISDOM in Miniature;.... Worcester, 1796. 2nd Worcester ed., calf, engraved f.p. by Amos Dolittle, many early inscriptions, f.p. lightly frayed, text browned, very good, solid copy with perfect binding. Victoria 34-876 1978 $85

WISE, BARTON H.   The Life of Henry A. Wise of Virginia 1806-1876. New York, 1899. 1st ed., port., partially unopened. MacManus 239-1893 1978 $27.50

WISE, BERNHARD R.   Industrial Freedom: A Study in Politics. 1892. 1st. ed., cr. 8vo, orig. cloth, gilt, few neat lib. stamps, very good. Fenning 32-379 1978 $8.50

WISE, DANIEL   Earnest Christianity Illustrated. Toronto, 1856. Covers scuffed, some staining. Hood 117-379 1978 $35

WISE, HENRY A.   Los Gringos: Or An Inside of Mexico and California... 1849. Sm. 8vo, rebacked, old spine laid down, cover faded, no half title, orig. cloth. Edwards 1012-412 1978 £30

WISE, HENRY A.   Los Gringos or an Inside View of Mexico and California... New York, 1849. 1st. ed., very good copy. Baldwins' 51-573 1978 $75

WISE, HERBERT C.   Colonial Architecture for Those About to Build... Philadelphia, 1924. 207 illus. Baldwins' 51-166 1978 $25

WISE, ISAAC M.   An Essay on the Temperance Question. Cincinnati, n.d. (ca. 1880). Austin 79-849 1978 $12.50

WISE, ISAAC M.   History of the Israelitish Nation. Albany, 1854. 1st ed. of only vol. published, slightly frayed backstrip, good copy, bkplt. of Moses Aaron Dropsie. Austin 79-850 1978 $75

WISE, JAMES WATERMAN   Liberalizing Liberal Judaism. 1924. Austin 79-851 1978 $8.50

WISE, JAMES WATERMAN   Mr. Smith Meet Mr. Cohen. 1940. Austin 79-852 1978 $8.50

WISE, STEPHEN S.   Are Jews Like That? 1929. Austin 79-853 1978 $10

WISE, STEPHEN S.   Challenging Years. 1949. Austin 79-854 1978 $11

WISE, THOMAS JAMES   A Bibliography of the writings in verse and prose of George Gordon Noel, Baron Byron. London, 1932-3. 2 vols., ltd. to 180 copies on antique paper, plts., cr. 4to, orig. buckram, t.e.g. Forster 130-311 1978 £35

WISE, THOMAS JAMES   A Bibliography of the Writings of Joseph Conrad. London, 1921. Sm. 4to, orig. bds., some rubbing, 2nd ed., rev'd and enlarged, ltd. to 170 copies. MacManus 238-893 1978 $80

WISE, THOMAS JAMES   A Bronte Library. London, 1929. Ltd. to 120 copies on antique paper, plts., cr. 4to, orig. buckram, t.e.g. Forster 130-251 1978 £65

WISE PUBLISHING CO.   Pictorial History of the Second World War. 1944-1949. 10 vols., red or black binding, unusual to find complete. Austin 80-378 1978 $125

WISEMAN, NICHOLAS PATRICK STEPHEN   Lectures on the Principal Doctrines & Practices of the Catholic Church. 1859. Revised & Corrected, 3rd ed., 2 vols. bound in 1, Bellew full leather binding. Hyland 128-814 1978 £9.50

WISSLER, CLARK   The American Indian. New York, 1922. Illus., maps. MacManus 239-1223 1978 $22.50

WISSLER, CLARK   Indians of the United States. New York, 1940. 1st. ed., illus., d.j., fine copy. Baldwins' 51-574 1978 $12.50

WISTAR, ISAAC JONES   Autobiography of Isaac Jones Wistar 1827-1905. Philadelphia, 1914. 2 vols., 1 of 250 prtd. copies, 4to, orig. bds. with red buckram backs, partially unopened, frontis., plts., fldg. map, interior near mint, tipped in slip. Current 24-112 1978 $245

WISTER, OWEN   The Virginian. New York, 1902. Decor. cloth, 1st ed., covers slightly dull, very good copy, slipcase. Dykes 34-42 1978 $75

WITH, K.   Bildwerke Ost-und Sudasiens aus der Sammlung Yi Yuan. Basel, 1924. 4to, cloth, plts., orig. covers. Van der Peet 127-268 1978 Dfl 65

WITH The Cape Mounted Rifles. London, 1877-81. Some marking & spotting, few inner margins strengthened, recent half blue calf, 8vo, scarce. K Books 239-543 1978 £25

WITH THE FIRST Canadian Contingent. Toronto and London, n.d. Photos. tipped in. Hood 116-153 1978 $25

WITHER, GEORGE   Britain's Remembrancer, 1628. 1880. Parts I-II complete, 2 vols., sm. 4to., orig. wrappers. Howes 194-1212f 1978 £16

WITHER, GEORGE   Exercises upon the First Psalme, both in Prose and Verse. 1882. From the ed. of 1620, sm. 4to., orig. wrappers. Howes 194-1212j 1978 £8.50

WITHER, GEORGE   Haleluiah. 1879. Parts I-III complete in 2 vols., sm. 4to., orig. wrappers. Howes 194-1212e 1978 £16

WITHER, GEORGE   The Hymnes and Songs of the Church. 1881. Reprinted from orig. ed. of 1623, sm. 4to., orig. wrappers. Howes 194-1212g 1978 £8.50

WITHER, GEORGE   Juvenilia. 1871. Parts II-III (of 3) only, 2 vols., sm. 4to., orig. wrappers. Howes 194-1212c 1978 £12.50

WITHER, GEORGE   A Love Song. (Concord: Will Bradley, 1903). 32mo., illus., frontis. by Bradley, orig. bds., paper label. MacManus 238-781 1978 $50

WITHER, GEORGE   Miscellaneous Works. 1872-78. Complete set, 6 vols., wrappers frayed, sm. 4to. Howes 194-1212d 1978 £48

WITHER, GEORGE   Parallelogrammaton. 1882. Reprinted from orig. ed. of 1662, sm. 4to., orig. wrappers. Howes 194-1212i 1978 £7.50

WITHER, GEORGE   Poetry. 1902. 2 vols., frontis, portraits, cloth, slightly frayed at head & foot of spines. Eaton 45-542 1978 £10

WITHER, GEORGE   The Psalms of David. 1881. Parts I-II complete, reprinted from ed. of 1632, sm. 4to., orig. wrappers. Howes 194-1212h 1978 £16

WITHERING, WILLIAM   An Account of the Foxglove, and Some of its Medical Uses. Birmingham, 1785. 8vo., fldg. color plts., orig. bds., paper backed, light browning, fine uncut copy laid in half red mor. slipcase, 1st ed. Zeitlin 245-290 1978 $3,750

WITHERS, ALEXANDER S.   Chronicles of Border Warfare, or a History of the Settlement by the Whites, of North-Western Virginia. Clarksburg, 1831. Lea., nice copy of 1st ed. Hayman 73-747 1978 $200

WITHROW, W. H.   Barbara Heck: A Tale of Early Methodism. Toronto, 1895. Hood 117-551 1978 $12.50

WITHROW, W. H.   A Popular History of the Dominion of Canada
From the Discovery of America to the Present Time... Toronto, 1885. Steel
portraits, maps, numerous wood engravings, leather binding, spine worn. Hood's
115-623 1978 £25

WITKOWSKI, GUSTAV J.   Anedotes & Curiosites Historique sur les Accouchements. Paris, 1892. Bds. Rittenhouse 49-846 1976 $40

WITKOWSKI, GUSTAVE J.   Les Accouchements a la Cour. Paris, 1889.
Bds. Rittenhouse 49-845 1976 $50

THE WITS Magazine and Attic Miscellany. London, n.d. (1818). 2 vols., 12mo,
contemporary half calf, cloth case, second vol. complete, 1st vol. gathered from
"oddments" and last portion laid-in. Ximenes 47-276 1978 $350

WLOSZCZEWSKI, STEFAN   History of Polish American Culture. 1946. Austin 79-857 1978 $20

WODEHOUSE, PELHAM GRENVILLE   Doctor Sally. 1932. Very good, repaired d.j., first English ed. Bell Book 16-943 1978 #15

WODEHOUSE, PELHAM GRENVILLE   Hot Water. Garden City, 1932. First
ed., pict. d.j., fine. Houle 10-372 1978 $55

WODHULL, MICHAEL   Poems. London, 1772. 8vo, contemporary
calf, gilt, spine gilt, contrasting morocco labels, 1st ed., armorial bookplate of
Thomas Carter of Edgcott, very nice copy. Ximenes 47-337 1978 $225

WODSON, H. M.   The Whirlpool. Toronto, 1917. Illus. by Lennox,
neatly mended. Hood 117-414 1978 $12.50

WOERMANN, K.   Geschichte de Junst Aller Zeiten und Volker.
Leipzig-Wien, 1915-1922. 6 vols., clothblund, richly illus. with plts. in color,
text illus. Van der Peet H-64-231 1978 Dfl 135

WOGLOM, WILLIAM H.   Discovers for Medicine. New Haven, 1949.
Rittenhouse 49-847 1976 $10

WOLCOTT, JOHN 1738-1819   The Agonies of Bonaparte. London, 1814.
8vo., first ed., disbound. Ximenes 47-246 1978 $30

WOLCOTT, JOHN 1738-1819   The Works of Peter Pindar, Esq. 1794-96.
4 vols., 8vo., orig. bds., uncut, printed paper labels, fine. Fenning 32-380
1978 £24

WOLF, CHRISTIAN   Jus Gentium Methodo Scientifica Pertractatum,
in quo Jus Gentium Naturale a eo.... Francofurti, 1764. 4to., marbled bds.,
calf spine, good. King 7-398 1978 £25

WOLF, EDWIN   Rosenbach. (1960). One of 250 numbered
copies signed by authors. Battery Park 1-482 1978 $150

WOLF, GEORGE A.   Blair County's First Hundred Years 1846-1946...
A Symposium... Hollidaysburg, 1945. 2nd ed., illus., orig. binding. Americanist 102-84 1978 $25

WOLF, LUCIEN   The Myth of the Jewish Menace in World Affairs.
1921. Austin 79-859 1978 $15

WOLF, SIMON   The American Jew as Patriot & Citizen. 1895.
Illus., ex-lib. Austin 79-860 1978 $17.50

WOLFE, DON M.   The Purple Testament. 1946. Austin 80-379
1978 $10

WOLFE, F.   How to Identify Oriental Rugs. (1931). 4to.,
plts., some coloured, cloth. Quaritch 983-77 1978 $85

WOLFE, HUMBERT   This Blind Rose. Poems. London, 1928. Very
good in soiled & chipped d.w. Desmarais B-682 1978 $10

WOLFE, HUMBERT   Cursory Rhymes. London, 1927. 8vo, orig.
cream boards, cream cloth spine, pr. paper label, t.e.g., 1st ed., one of 500
copies on Van Gelder paper, signed by author, illus. by Albert Rutherston, extra
label tipped in, fine copy, torn d.j. Ximenes 47-339 1978 $15

WOLFE, HUMBERT   Homage to Meleager. New York, 1930. 8vo,
original half blue morocco and cream buckram, t.e.g., 1st ed., one of 464
copies numbered and signed by author, nice copy. Ximenes 47-344 1978 $25

WOLFE, HUMBERT   Kensington, Gardens. London, 1924. 8vo,
original quarter green parchment and patterned boards, 1st ed., one of thirty
numbered copies printed on hand-made paper, presentation copy, inscribed by
author, fine copy. Ximenes 47-338 1978 $80

WOLFE, HUMBERT   Kensington Gardens. London, 1924. Fine in
damaged d.w. Desmarais B-680 1978 $10

WOLFE, HUMBERT   Others Abide. London, 1927. Fine in torn
d.w. Desmarais B-681 1978 $10

WOLFE, HUMBERT   Others Abide. London, 1927. 8vo, original
cream boards, cream cloth spine, printed paper label, t.e.g., 1st ed., one of 400
copies printed, hand-made paper and signed by author, extra label tipped in,
fine copy, torn d.j. Ximenes 47-340 1978 $15

WOLFE, HUMBERT   Others Abide. New York, 1928. 1st Amer.
ed. Biblo 251-678 1978 $12.50

WOLFE, HUMBERT   The Silver Cat and Other Poems. 1928. One
of 780 copies. Battery Park 1-24 1978 $45

WOLFE, HUMBERT   Troy. London, 1928. 8vo, original light blue
boards, 1st ed., one of 500 copies on large paper, numbered and signed by author,
drawings by Charles Ricketts. Ximenes 47-342 1978 $12.50

WOLFE, HUMBERT   The Uncelestial City. London, 1930. 8vo,
original light brown cloth, printed paper label, d.j., 1st ed., one of 400 copies,
numbered and signed by author, fine copy. Ximenes 47-345 1978 $27.50

WOLFE, HUMBERT   Veni Creator! (London, 1927). 12mo, original
stiff patterned boards, 1st ed., one of only thirty copies, author's signed statement
on flyleaf, fine copy. Ximenes 47-341 1978 $50

WOLFE, HUMBERT   A Winter Miscellany. 1930. First ed., ltd. to
225 signed copies, decor. by Frank Adams, cr. 8vo., orig. qtr. parchment.
George's 635-1339 1978 £5.25

WOLFE, JAMES   A Garland of New Songs. Newcastle Upon Tyne,
(c. 1800). Wolfe 39-566 1978 $35

WOLFE, THEODORE   Literary Haunts and Homes. Philadelphia, 1899.
Illus. Austin 82-1124 1978 $12.50

WOLFE, THOMAS   Autobiographical Sketch. In Portraits and Self-
Portraits. 1936. D.j., chipped. Broadfoot 50-401 1978 $25

WOLFE, THOMAS   Briefe and Die Mutter. 1949. 1st German ed.
Broadfoot 50-413 1978 $25

WOLFE, THOMAS   Englen Paa Torvet. 1941. Danish ed., 2 vols.,
paper. Broadfoot 50-422 1978 $16

WOLFE, THOMAS   The Face of a Nation. 1939. D.j. Broadfoot
50-404 1978 $25

WOLFE, THOMAS   From Death to Morning. New York, 1935. Cloth,
d.w. Dawson's 447-280 1978 $30

WOLFE, THOMAS   From Death to Morning. 1935. 1st ed., d.j.
Broadfoot 50-406 1978 $60

WOLFE, THOMAS   From Death to Morning. New York, 1935.
1st ed., 8 vo., d.j., very good, scarce. Houle 10-374 1978 $55

WOLFE, THOMAS   The Hills Beyond. New York, 1941. D.j.,
d.j. taped. Broadfoot 50-408 1978 $40

WOLFE, THOMAS   The Hills Beyond. 1943. D.j., taped. Broadfoot 50-409 1978 $12

WOLFE, THOMAS   Historien Om En Roman. 1948. Danish ed.,
paper. Broadfoot 50-440 1978 $16

WOLFE, THOMAS   Thomas Wolfe's Letters to His Mother, Julia Elizabeth Wolfe. New York, 1943. Portr. frontis., black cloth, 1st ed., fine in
chipped dust jacket. Bradley 49-359 1978 $15

WOLFE, THOMAS   Look Homeward, Angel. New York, 1929.
D.j., slipcase. Broadfoot 50-414 1978 $350

WOLFE, THOMAS　　　　Look Homeward, Angel.　New York, 1929(?)
Paper.　Broadfoot 50-415 1978 $16

WOLFE, THOMAS　　　　Look Homeward, Angel.　1934.　Broadfoot 50-416 1978 $10

WOLFE, THOMAS　　　　Look Homeward, Angel.　1947.　Illus. by Gorsline, d.j.　Broadfoot 50-417 1978 $35

WOLFE, THOMAS　　　　Mannerhouse.　1948.　1st ed., d.j.　Broadfoot 50-424 1978 $40

WOLFE, THOMAS　　　　A Note on Experts: Dexter Vespasian Joyner.
New York, 1939.　Lower margin of t.p. chipped and replaced.　Broadfoot 50-427 1978 $65

WOLFE, THOMAS　　　　Of Time and the River.　A Legend of Man's Hunger in His Youth.　New York, 1935.　Orig. cloth, 1st ed., somewhat soiled d.j.　MacManus 238-770 1978 $32.50

WOLFE, THOMAS　　　　Of Time and the River.　New York, 1935.　Black cloth, 1st ed., fine copy in jacket.　Bradley 49-357 1978 $60

WOLFE, THOMAS　　　　Of Time and the River.　New York, 1935.　Cloth, sm. bkplt.　Dawson's 447-281 1978 $25

WOLFE, THOMAS　　　　Of Time and the River.　New York, 1935.　D.j., inscribed by Julia Wolfe.　Broadfoot 50-430 1978 $60

WOLFE, THOMAS　　　　Of Time and the River.　New York, 1935.　D.j.
Broadfoot 50-429 1978 $50

WOLFE, THOMAS　　　　Of Time and the River.　1943.　Broadfoot 50-431 1978 $12

WOLFE, THOMAS　　　　Of Time and the River.　Worn dust jacket.　Bradley 49-358 1978 $30

WOLFE, THOMAS　　　　Spindelvaev Og Klippe.　1940.　Danish ed., 2 vols., paper.　Broadfoot 50-447 1978 $20

WOLFE, THOMAS　　　　A Stone, a Leaf, a Door.　New York, 1945.
Ex-lib.　Broadfoot 50-439 1978 $30

WOLFE, THOMAS　　　　The Web and the Rock.　1939.　First ed., with remnants of d.j.　Austin 82-1126 1978 $20

WOLFE, THOMAS　　　　The Web and the Rock.　New York, 1939.　Blue cloth, 1st ed., fine in dust jacket.　Bradley 49-360 1978 $50

WOLFE, THOMAS　　　　The Web and the Rock.　1939.　D.j.　Broadfoot 50-443 1978 $50

WOLFE, THOMAS　　　　The Web and the Rock.　1939.　No d.j.　Broadfoot 50-444 1978 $25

WOLFE, THOMAS　　　　The Web and the Rock.　London, 1947.　1st British ed.　Broadfoot 50-445 1978 $16

WOLFE, THOMAS　　　　The Web and the Rock.　England, 1947.　1st ed., d.j.　Broadfoot 50-446 1978 $12

WOLFE, THOMAS　　　　You Can't Go Home Again.　New York, 1940.
D.j.　Broadfoot 50-454 1978 $45

WOLFE, THOMAS　　　　You Can't Go Home Again.　New York, 1941.
D.j., frayed.　Broadfoot 50-455 1978 $30

WOLFE, THOMAS　　　　You Can't Go Home Again.　1942.　D.j.
Broadfoot 50-456 1978 $12

WOLFENDEN, HUGH H.　　　Unemployment Funds.　Toronto, 1934.　Orig. binding.　Wolfe 39-573 1978 $15

WOLFF, CASPAR FRIEDRICH　Theoria Generationis.　Halae ad Salam, (1759).　Fldg. copperplts., 4to., half calf, 1st ed., rare.　Offenbacher 30-160 1978 $1,200

WOLFF, EUGENE　　　The Anatomy of the Eye and the Orbit Including the Central Connections, Development, and Comparative Anatomy of the Visual Apparatus.　Philadelphia, 1933.　8vo., illus., blind-stamped green pebbled cloth, gilt lettering on spine, minor dampstains, very good copy, ms. signature of former owner.　Zeitlin 245-291 1978 $55

WOLFF, HENRY W.　　　People's Banks.　London, 1910.　3rd ed., revised & enlarged, ex-lib.　Bledsoe 134-3015 1979 $12.50

WOLFF, JOSEPH　　　Narrative of a Mission to Bokhara in the Years 1843-1845...　London, 1845.　2nd. ed., revised, 2 vols., 8vo, lithograph plts., orig. cloth, neatly rebacked.　Deighton 5-231 1978 £65

WOLFF, JULIUS　　　Das Gesetz Der Transformation Der Knochen.
Berlin, 1892.　Roy. 4to., litho. plts., orig. black stamped cloth, gilt lettering on upper cover & backstrip paste-on, worn, ex-lib. & library stamps, very good copy, 1st ed.　Zeitlin 245-319 1978 $385

WOLFF, MARITTA　　　Whistle Stop.　New York, (1941).　Signed by author, very good, dw.　Bernard 5-307 1978 $35

WOLFF, MARITTA M.　　　Whistle Stop.　1941.　First ed., d.j.　Austin 82-1128 1978 $12.50

WOLFGANG, CHAUNCEY E.　History of Columbiana, Ohio...　Columbiana, n.d. (1912).　Wrs., illus., very scarce.　Hayman 72-532 1978 $17.50

WOLFSON, HARRY AUSTRYN　Escaping Judaism.　Menorah Press, 1923.
Paper.　Austin 79-861 1978 $12.50

WOLLASTON, A. F. R.　　Pygmies and Papuans: The Stone Age To-Day in Dutch New Guinea.　1912.　Orig. cloth, 8vo, folding map, 6 coloured plts., other illus.　Edwards 1012-380 1978 £18

WOLLASTON, WILLIAM　　The Religion of Nature Delineated.　1725.　4to., contemp. mottled calf, gilt, bookplt., nice.　P. M. Hill 142-308 1978 £38

WOLLASTON, WILLIAM　　The Religion of Nature Delineated.　London, 1726.　Folio, 1/2 calf, label, new bind.　Salloch 348-285 1978 $125

WOLLCOTT, ALEXANDER　　While Rome Burns.　New York, 1934.　Orig. cloth, 1st ed., 1 of 500 no. copies signed by author, boxed, fine.　MacManus 238-769 1978 $27.50

WOLLENBERG, H. H.　　Fifty Years of German Film.　1948.　Plts., 4to., bds., very good, d.w., first English ed.　Bell Book 17-167 1978 £6.50

WOLLMAN, JOHN　　A Journal of the Life and Travels...in the Service of the Gospel.　(London, 1901).　1 of 250 numbered copies, thick 12mo., uncut, orig. stiff vellum, woodcut fronts by Reginald Savage, excellent copy.
Americanist 102-45 1978 $75

WOLLSTONECRAFT, MARY 1797-1851
Please turn to
SHELLEY, MARY WOLLSTONECRAFT GODWIN

WOLSELEY, GARNET JOSEPH　The Life of John Churchill Duke of Marlborough.
1894.　Port. frontis., plts., 2 vols., 8vo., orig. cloth.　F. Edwards 1013-359 1978 £20

WOLSEY, CARDINAL　　　The History of the Life & Times of ...　1742.
1st. ed., 4 vols., frontis, portraits, folding plt., orig. calf, gilt borders, lacking one label, otherwise v.g.　Jarndyce 16-238 1978 £18.50

WOLTMANN, A.　　　History of Painting.　1880.　2 vols., imp. 8vo., fold. plts., illus., orig. cloth.　Quaritch 983-277 1978 $25

WOMOCK, LAURENCE 1612-86　Arcana Dogmatum Anti-Remonstrantium.
1659.　Plt., thk. 12mo., contemp. calf, lettering-piece, very good, sole ed.
Howes 194-115 1978 £55

THE WONDERFUL Adventures of the Seven Champions of Christendom and the Giant with Golden Hairs.　New York, c.1840.　12mo, plates and illus. wrappers, very good.　Victoria 34-878 1978 $17.50

THE WONDERFUL History of an Enchanted Castle.　Albany, 1813.　36mo, woodcuts, wrappers, lower wrapper corner chipped, both wrappers rubbed so cuts and printing unclear, sewn.　Victoria 34-880 1978 $60

THE WONDERS of a Country Fair.　London, c.1870.　8vo, on linen, hand-colored plates, cover illus. chipped, very good.　Victoria 34-879 1978 $20

WONDERS of the Universe, or Curiosities of Nature and Art. Exeter, 1836. Plates, orig. mottled sheep, sev. signatures beginning to start, foxed, 8vo, orig. cloth. Book Chest 17-21 1978 $40

WOOD, CASEY A.   Benevnutus Grassus of Jerusalem. Stanford U. Press, 1929. Boxed. Rittenhouse 49-849 1976 $35

WOOD, CHARLES ERSKINE   Heavenly Discourse. 1928. Orig. ed., illus. Austin 82-1129 1978 $8.50

WOOD, CLEMENT   The Woman Who Was Pope. New York, 1931. 1st ed. Biblo 251-279 1978 $17.50

WOOD, E. M.   The Polytechnic and Its Founder Quinton Hogg. London, 1932. 8vo, orig. cloth, spine faded, illus., good. Sexton 7-214 1978 £5

WOOD, ELLEN (PRICE)   The Channings. Philadelphia, (1852). Amer. ed., 3 vols. in 1. Greene 78-134 1978 $25

WOOD, ELLEN (PRICE)   East Lynne. Leipzig, 1861. 3 vols., 12mo., copyright ed., orig. wrs. Morrill 241-632 1978 $20

WOOD, ELLEN (PRICE)   Verner's Pride. 1863. 1st. ed., 3 vols., orig. green cloth, gilt spines, slight rubbing to bds., loosening of vol. 3, otherwise v.g. Jarndyce 16-1181 1978 £48

WOOD, GEORGE B.   The Dispensatory of the United States of America. Philadelphia, 1877. Fourteenth ed., leather clean, fresh. Rittenhouse 49-850 1976 $20

WOOD, GEORGE B.   A Memoir of the Life and Character of the Late Joseph Parrish, M. D. Philadelphia, 1840. 8vo., orig. prtd. paper bds., foxed, very good copy, 1st ed. Zeitlin 245-183 1978 $25

WOOD, GEORGE B.   United States Dispensatory. Philadelphia, 1845. Some wear on leather, otherwise unusually clean & bright. Rittenhouse 49-851 1976 $25

WOOD, GORDON L.   The Pacific Basin. Oxford, 1930. Illus. Biblo BL781-894 1978 $9

WOOD, H. T.   Modern Methods of Illustrating Books. Battery Park 1-272 1978 $25

WOOD, HAROLD S.   Your Home and Mine. Toronto, 1932. Hood's 115-917 1978 $7.50

WOOD, MRS. HENRY
Please turn to
WOOD, ELLEN (PRICE)

WOOD, JOANNA E.   Judith Moore; Or Fashioning a Pipe. Toronto, 1898. Decorated cover, ex-lib. Hood's 115-464 1978 $10

WOOD, JOHN   The Suppressed History of the Administration of John Adams... Philadelphia, 1846. Frontis. port., orig. cloth, fine. MacManus 239-534 1978 $35

WOOD, JOHN GEORGE   The Boy's Modern Playmate. London, 1890. 600 orig. illus., 8vo, orig. pictorial cloth, binding worn. Sexton 7-215 1978 £5

WOOD, JOHN GEORGE   The Illustrated Natural History. New York, 1881. 7th ed., wood engrs., 8vo., orig. gilt-decor. green cloth. Salloch 345-196 1978 $45

WOOD, JOHN GEORGE   The Principal Rivers of Wales Illustrated. 1813. Coloured maps, 2 vols., lg. 4to., half dark green mor., lg. paper copy. Howes 194-1419 1978 £850

WOOD, L. S.   The Romance of the Cotton Industry in England. 1927. Maps, diagrams, illus., cr. 8vo. George's 635-437 1978 £5

WOOD, NICHOLAS   A Practical Treatise on Railroads. London, 1825. 8vo., engr. fldg. plts., orig. bds., uncut, rebacked, rear endpaper renewed, plts. little foxed, but fine copy, 1st ed. Norman 5-279a 1978 $275

WOOD, NICOLAS   A Practical Treatise on Rail-Roads and Interior Communication in General. London, 1832. 2nd ed., enlarged, thick 8vo., fldg. litho. plts., bound in modern cloth, sm. blind stamp. Current 24-237 1978 $90

WOOD, RICHARD D.   Biographical Sketch of .... Philadelphia, 1871. Private ed. ltd. to 100 copies, 3 vols. Baldwins' 51-271 1978 $50

WOOD, SAMUEL   The New-York Preceptor; or, Third Book. New York, (1823). 12mo, superbly printed and illus., woodcuts, both board covers illus., very fine. Victoria 34-881 1978 $55

WOOD, SAMUEL   The New York Reader, No. 3. New York, 1815. 1st ed., sm. 8vo, claf, foxed, upper spine chipped. Victoria 34-882 1978 $17.50

WOOD, T. MARTIN   George duMaurier: The Satirist of the Victorians. London, 1913. First ed., illus., very good or better. Limestone 9-93 1978 $35

WOOD, T. MARTIN   Whistler. London, (1908). Color plts., uncut, pictorial bds., very good or better. Limestone 9-319 1978 $15

WOOD, THEODORE   A Natural History for Young People. London, c. 1890. Coloured plts., illus., red calf gilt, 8vo. K Books 244-330 1978 £5

WOOD, THOMAS   An Inquiry Concerning the Primitive Inhabitants of Ireland. 1821. 1st ed., lacks map, modern 1/2 leather, good. Hyland 128-819 1978 £20

WOOD, WALTER   Fishing Boats & Barges. London, (1922). Woodcuts, 4to., d.w., 1st ed. Morrill 241-633 1978 $20

WOOD, WILLIAM   Flag and Fleet; How the British Navy Won the Freedom of the Seas. Toronto, 1919. Illus., inscribed and signed by author. Hood 116-154 1978 $20

WOOD, WILLIAM   Footnotes to Canadian Folk-Songs. 1896. Hood's 115-918 1978 $12.50

WOOD, WILLIAM MAXWELL   Wandering Sketches of People and Things in South America... Philadelphia, 1849. Orig. cloth, 1st ed. Ginsberg 14-1068 1978 $45

WOOD, WILLIAM MAXWELL   Wandering Sketches of People and Things in South America, Polynesia, California, and Other Places... Philadelphia, 1849. 1st ed., orig. cloth, extremities worn, otherwise good copy. MacManus 239-535 1978 $40

THE WOOD-lawn Cemetery, for the City of New York and Vicinity. New York, 1864. Lg. fldg. map, 8vo., orig. wrs., ex-lib., rebacked, wrs. chipped. Morrill 239-560 1978 $8.50

WOODBERRY, GEORGE EDWARD   America in Literature. 1903. First ed., covers rubbed. Austin 82-1130 1978 $12.50

WOODBERRY, GEORGE EDWARD   The Appreciation of Literature. 1907. First ed., lacks front fly, else good. Austin 82-1131 1978 $27.50

WOODBERRY, GEORGE EDWARD   Edgar Allan Poe. 1885. First ed. Austin 82-1132 1978 $12.50

WOODBERRY, GEORGE EDWARD   Great Writers. 1907. First ed. Austin 82-1133 1978 $12.50

WOODBERRY, GEORGE EDWARD   Heart of Man and Other Papers. 1920. First ed., d.j. Austin 82-1134 1978 $20

WOODBERRY, GEORGE EDWARD   Nathaniel Hawthorne. 1902. First ed. Austin 82-1135 1978 $12.50

WOODBERRY, GEORGE EDWARD   The Torch and Other Lectures and Addresses by George Edward Woodberry. 1920. First ed., frayed d.j. Austin 82-1136 1978 $27.50

WOODBERRY, GEORGE EDWARD   The Torch and Other Lectures and Addresses. 1920. First ed., d.j. Austin 82-1137 1978 $20

WOODBRIDGE, FREDERICK J. E.   Nature and Mind. Columbia University Press, 1937. Austin 82-1138 1978 $27.50

WOODBRIDGE, WILLIAM C.   Rudiments of Geography. Hartford, 1822. 2nd ed., 16mo, marbled boards, leather spine, scarce, very good. Victoria 34-602 1978 $40

WOODBURY, AUGUSTUS   Personal Narratives of Events in the War of the Rebellion. Providence, 1882. Wrs., Bell Wiley's copy. Broadfoot 46-287 1978 $12

WOODBURY, DAVID O.   What the Citizen Should Know About Submarine Warfare. 1942. Illus. Austin 80-381 1978 $8.50

WOODBURY, ELLEN C. D. Q.   Dorothy Quincy. Wife of John Hancock. Washington, 1905. 1st ed., frontis., orig. cloth. MacManus 239-764 1978 $10

WOODBURY, LEVI   On the Treaty for the Reannexation of Texas to the United States. Washington, 1844. Sewn. Jenkins 116-1500 1978 $30

WOODBURY, LEVI   Report from the Secretary of the Treasury, Transmitting a Report.... Washington, 1838. Maps, cloth with leather label, 1st ed. Ginsberg 14-517 1978 $35

WOODBURY, LEVI   Violation of the Revenue Laws: At The Mouth Of The Sabine River. Washington, 1838. Jenkins 116-1501 1978 $17.50

WOODCOCK, H. D.   Lilies - Their Culture & Management. London, (1935). Colored front., 8vo, orig. cloth. Book Chest 17-440 1978 $18

WOODVILLE, WILLIAM   Medical Botany: Containing Systematic and General Descriptions. London, 1832, 1810. 5 vols., 8vo., large paper, hand-coloured engrav. plts., orig. half roan, occasional spotting, third ed. Quaritch 977-82 1978 $1,500

WOODFALL, WILFRED   My Note-Book or, Sketches From the Gallery of St. Stephens. 1821. 1st. ed., half title, orig. grey bds., paper label, uncut, good. Jarndyce 16-1183 1978 £14.50

WOODFIN, MAUDE H.   Another Secret Diary of William Byrd of Westover 1739-1741. Richmond, 1942. Bell Wiley's copy. Broadfoot 46-588 1978 $9

WOODFORD, JACK   Here is My Body. New York, 1931. Pres. copy signed by author, with a.l.s. by author. Austin 82-1139 1978 $15

WOODFORDE, C.   The Norwich School of Glass-Painting in the Fifteenth Century. Oxford, 1950. Royal 8vo., plts. Upcroft 12-501 1978 £9.50

WOODHOUSE, JAMES   Poems on Sundry Occasions. London, 1764. 4to, later half calf (bit rubbed), 1st ed., paste-on errata slip on verso of t.p., very light waterstains, scarce. Ximenes 47-346 1978 $200

WOODLEY, THOMAS F.   Thaddeus Stevens. Harrisburg, 1934. 1st ed., illus., orig. cloth. MacManus 239-820 1978 $15

WOODLOCK, THOMAS F.   The Catholic Pattern. 1942. Austin 79-862 1978 $8.50

WOODMAN, HENRY   The History of Valley Forge. Oaks, 1922. Illus., map. MacManus 239-1727 1978 $17.50

WOODRUFF, CHARLES E.   Expansion of Races. New York, (1909). Biblo 247-300 1978 $16.50

WOODRUFF, GEORGE C.   History of Hillside, N.J. and Vicinity... Hillside, (1934). Illus., scarce. MacManus 239-1345 1978 $35

WOODS, DAVID W., JR.   John Witherspoon. New York, (1906). Port. MacManus 239-831 1978 $20

WOODS, GEORGE BRYANT   Essays, Sketches and Stories with Biographical Memoirs. 1872. Austin 82-1140 1978 $27.50

WOODS, H.   An Introductory Lecture on the Study of Zoology. Bath, (1825). Stiff wr., soiled, sm. 8vo. Book Chest 17-439 1978 $50

WOODS, H. F.   Historical Sketches of Brookline Mass. Boston, 1874. Fine, orig. cloth. MacManus 239-1016 1978 $30

WOODS, MARGARET L.   Sons of the Sword. London, 1901. First ed., orig. binding, fine. Rota 211-806 1978 £7.50

WOODS, R. A.   The Poor in Great Cities, their Problems and what is being done to solve them. 1896. Illus. by Hugh Thomson, O. H. Bacher, C. Broughton and others, covers stained, 8vo. George's 635-438 1978 £7.50

WOODS, RALPH   Pilgrim Places in North America. 1939. Austin 79-863 1978 $10

WOODS, WILLIAM   The Edge of Darkness. 1942. Austin 80-382 1978 $8.50

WOODWARD, ASHBEL   Life of General Nathaniel Lyon. Hartford, 1862. New cloth, Bell Wiley's copy. Broadfoot 46-289 1978 $20

WOODWARD, C. VANN   The Battle for Leyte Gulf. 1947. Austin 80-383 1978 $12.50

WOODWARD, CARL R.   Ploughs and Politics... New Brunswick, 1941. Illus., fine, d.j. MacManus 239-1346 1978 $35

WOODWARD, DAVID   The Narrative of Captain David Woodward and Four Seamen, Who Lost Their Ship While in a Boat at Sea, and Surrendered Themselves Up to the Malays in the Island of Celebes. London, 1805. Portr., maps, plts., 8vo., contemp. calf, rebacked, 2nd ed. Morrill 241-634 1978 $40

WOODWARD, E. M.   Bonaparte's Park, the Murats. Trenton, 1879. 1st ed., illus., fine, orig. cloth. MacManus 239-1347 1978 $35

WOODWARD, G. M.   An Essay on the Art of Ingeniously Tormenting. 1809. New ed., coloured engrav. plts., fcap. 8vo., new buckram. George's 635-1527 1978 £10.50

WOODWARD, JOSEPH JANVIER   Outlines of the Chief Camp Diseases of the United States Armies as Observed During the Present War. Philadelphia, 1863. 8vo., orig. black pebbled cloth, gilt lettering on spine, worn, lightly browned & foxed, former owner's two ms. signatures, 1st ed., scarce. Zeitlin 245-292 1978 $185

WOODWARD, M.   Leaves from Gerard's Herball arranged for Garden Lovers by Marcus Woodward. Boston & New York, 1931. Faded binding, 8vo., orig. cloth. Book Chest 17-441 1978 $15

WOODWARD, THOMAS S.   Woodward's Reminiscences of the Creek, or Muscogee Indians... (Tuscaloosa & Birmingham, 1939). Reprint, scarce, clean, orig. binding. Hayman 71-794 1978 $12.50

WOODWARD, WILLIAM E.   Bread and Circuses. 1925. First ed., signed by author. Austin 82-1141 1978 $20

WOODWARD, WILLIAM E.   Evelyn Prentice. 1933. First ed. Austin 82-1142 1978 $12.50

WOODWARD, WILLIAM E.   The Gift of Life. 1947. First ed., d.j. Austin 82-1143 1978 $12.50

WOODWORTH, F.   Stories about Birds with Pictures to Match. Boston, 1851. Ex-lib. with stamps, worn, gilt stamped binding, 12mo. Book Chest 17-442 1978 $35

WOODY, THOMAS   Early Quaker Education in Pennsylvania. New York, 1920. 1st ed. MacManus 239-1728 1978 $17.50

WOODY, THOMAS   Quaker Education in the Colony and State of New Jersey. Philadelphia, 1923. Map. MacManus 239-1348 1978 $25

WOOFTER, T. J. JR.   Black Yeomanry Life on St. Helena Island. NY, 1930. Illus., Bell Wiley's copy. Broadfoot's 44-957 1978 $20.00

WOOLF, LEONARD   The Hotel. Hogarth Press, 1939. Fine, d.w., first English ed. Bell Book 16-944 1978 £15

WOOLF, LEONARD   The Village in the Jungle. 1925. Very good, d.w., second ed. Bell Book 16-1023 1978 £12.50

WOOLF, VIRGINIA   Annees. Traduit de L'anglais par Germaine Dela-
main. Paris, 1938. Orig. wrs., 1st ed. in French, fine. MacManus 238-771
1978 $50

WOOLF, VIRGINIA   Between the Acts. London, 1941. Orig. cloth,
d.j. worn, 1st ed., bookplt., very good. MacManus 238-773 1978 $100

WOOLF, VIRGINIA   Between the Acts. Hogarth Press, 1941. Sm. 8vo.,
1st ed., orig. cloth, fine. Quaritch 979-333 1978 $50

WOOLF, VIRGINIA   The Captain's Death Bed and other essays. 1950.
Some fading of covers, very good, d.w., first English ed. Bell Book 17-953 1978
£17.50

WOOLF, VIRGINIA   The Common Reader. Hogarth Press, 1925. 8vo.,
1st ed., orig. decor. cloth, worn d.w., very neat inscr. Quaritch 979-366
1978 $80

WOOLF, VIRGINIA   A Haunted House and Other Short Stories. London, 1943. 1st. ed., thin 8vo, covers little stained & name on fly-leaf. Traylen
88-361 1978 £10

WOOLF, VIRGINIA   A Haunted House, and other short stories. Hogarth Press, 1943. Very good, worn d.w. Bell Book 16-945 1978 £12.50

WOOLF, VIRGINIA   Histoire de Ma Vie. Paris, 1856. Reprint, 10
vols., rebound, qtr. blue and green mor. with hand-blocked paper-covered bds.,
leather has become mottled, two autograph letters from author, first ed. Rota 212-
60 1978 £300

WOOLF, VIRGINIA   Jacob's Room. Hogarth Press, 1922. 8vo., 1st
ed., orig. yellow cloth, sm. orig. defect in upper cover, little light foxing,
1200 copies orig. prtd., from library of Bonamy Dobree with signature. Quaritch
979-334 1978 $90

WOOLF, VIRGINIA   Kew Gardens. Hogarth Press, 1927. Third ed.,
no. 285 of 500 copies, numbered in purple ink, 4to., decor. bds., backstrip
browned & split at joints, covers somewhat soiled, good. Bell Book 17-954 1978
£55

WOOLF, VIRGINIA   The Moment and Other Essays. London, 1947.
First ed., d.w. frayed, scarce. Biblo 247-644 1978 $42.50

WOOLF, VIRGINIA   The Moment, and other essays. Hogarth Press,
1947. Very good, d.w., first English ed. Bell Book 16-946 1978 £15

WOOLF, VIRGINIA   Orlando. London, Hogarth Press, 1928. Cloth,
bkplt., slight foxing, 1st English ed. Dawson's 447-282 1978 $25

WOOLF, VIRGINIA   Orlando. Leipzig, 1929. Good, wraps. Bell
Book 16-949 1978 £5.50

WOOLF, VIRGINIA   A Room of One's Own. 1929. First ed., cr.
8vo., fine, d.w., orig. cloth. Howes 194-1343 1978 £32

WOOLF, VIRGINIA   Street Haunting. San Francisco, The Grabhorn
Press, 1930. 8vo., 1st ed., decor. bds., green lea. back, back faded, slipcase,
bkplt., ltd. to 500 copies. Quaritch 979-335 1978 $300

WOOLF, VIRGINIA   Street Haunting. San Francisco, Westgate Press,
1930. Copy no. A-6 of 500 copies numbered and signed by author, qtr. mor.,
very good. Bell Book 16-950 1978 $90

WOOLF, VIRGINIA   Three Guineas. London, 1938. Orig. cloth,
d.j., faded and torn, 1st ed. MacManus 238-772 1978 $75

WOOLF, VIRGINIA   Three Guineas. 1938. First ed., plts., cr.
8vo., fine, d.w., orig. cloth. Howes 194-1344 1978 £18

WOOLF, VIRGINIA   Three Guineas. Hogarth Press, 1938. Plts.,
covers somewhat dull, good, first English ed. Bell Book 16-951 1978 £8.50

WOOLF, VIRGINIA   To the Lighthouse. Hogarth Press, 1927. First
ed., nice, orig. blue cloth, 8vo. Howes 194-1345 1978 £50

WOOLF, VIRGINIA   The Waves. Hogarth Press, 1931. Covers somewhat faded, good, first English ed. Bell Book 16-952 1978 £12.50

WOOLF, VIRGINIA   The Waves. Hogarth Press, 1931. Sm. 8vo.,
very good copy, slightly worn d.w., pres. copy inscr., 4940 copies, 2 A.L.s.
Quaritch 979-377 1978 $2,000

WOOLLCOTT, ALEXANDER   Long, Long Ago. New York, 1943. First ed.,
orig. binding, nice, d.w. Rota 211-808 1978 £5

WOOLLEY, C. LEONARD   Annual Volume 3. The Wilderness of Zin... 1915.
4to., maps, plts., illus., bds., buckram back, 1st ed. Quaritch 983-25 1978
$300

WOOLLEY, C. LEONARD   Ur Excavations. Vol. 2. British Museum, 1934.
Plts., illus., 2 vols., thick 4to, orig. wrappers. Traylen 88-32 1978 £50

WOOLLEY, EDWIN C.   The Reconstruction of Georgia. New York,
1901. Wrs., Bell Wiley's copy. Broadfoot 46-327 1978 $20

WOOLLRIGHT, H. H.   History of the Fifty-Seventh Regiment of Foot
1755-1881. 1893. Plts., coloured, maps, 8vo., orig. cloth. F. Edwards 1013-
522 1978 £60

WOOLMAN, JOHN   The Journal of...., 1720-72. Glasgow, 1882.
Cr. 8vo., orig. cloth. Edwards 1012-539 1978 £10

WOOLMAN, JOHN   Journal of John Woolman. Glasgow, 1883.
Ink inscr. on title page. Bell Wiley's copy. Broadfoot 46-589 1978 $15

WOOLMAN, JOHN   A Journal of the Life, Gospel Labours, and
Christian Experiences, of that Faithful Minister of Jesus Christ. Philadelphia,
1837. Full contemp. calf. MacManus 239-832 1978 $12.50

WOOLMAN, JOHN   A Journal of the Life, Gospel Labours and
Christian Experiences of... Philadelphia, 1869. Orig. binding, clean, slightly
wrinkled. Hayman 71-795 1978 $7.50

WOOLMAN, JOHN   Serious Considerations on Various Subjects of
Importance by.... London, 1773. 1st ed., orig. binding quite worn. Nestler
Rare 78-87 1978 $35

WOOLMAN, JOHN   Serious Considerations on Various Subjects of
Importance. 1773. 12mo., contemp. sheep, very fair, first ed. P. M. Hill 142-
236 1978 £75

WOOLNER, THOMAS   Pygmalion. 1881. Cloth gilt, good, first English
ed. Bell Book 16-731 1978 £8.50

WOOLNOTH, W.   A Graphical Description of the Metropolitan
Cathedral Church of Canterbury... London, 1816. Plts., rebound in half red
crushed morocco, slight foxing throughout. Sexton 7-109 1978 £45

WOOLSON, ABBA GOOLD   Woman in American Society. Boston, 1873.
1st ed., orig. cloth, fine. MacManus 239-533 1978 $22.50

WOOTEN, DUDLEY G.   A Comprehensive History of Texas, 1685 to 1897.
Dallas, 1899. Exceptionally fine, virtually mint, original gilt cloth. Jenkins
116-1503 1978 $350

WORCESTER, BENJAMIN   The Life and Mission of Emanuel Swedenborg.
Boston, 1883. 8vo., 1st ed., portr., orig. cloth. Morrill 241-635 1978 $15

WORCESTER, DEAN C.   The Philippine Islands and Their People. New
York & London, 1899. Lg. 8vo, folding maps, numerous plts., illus., orig. blue
cloth, gilt, spine soiled & chafed at head & foot, lib. labels removed, stamps on
some leaves, o/w very good. Deighton 5-230 1978 £45

WORDSWORTH, CHRISTOPHER   Discourses on Public Education. 1844. 1st.
collected ed., 8vo, orig. cloth, sm. lib. stamp on half-title, headbands chipped,
very good. Fenning 32-381 1978 £8.50

WORDSWORTH, CHRISTOPHER   Greece: Pictorial, Descriptive and Historical.
1853. New ed., plts., roy. 8vo., full dark mor. over thick bevelled bds., gilt
edges. Howes 194-1421 1978 £21

WORDSWORTH, JOHN   The National Church of Sweden. 1911. 8vo.
George's 635-1158 1978 £5

WORDSWORTH, WILLIAM   Peter Bell. A Lyrical Ballad. London, 1819.
Mod. cloth-backed bds., 1st ed., Shelley bookplt., fine. MacManus 238-415
1978 $125

WORDSWORTH, WILLIAM   Poems, In Two Volumes. 1807. 1st. ed., half-titles, 2 vols., lg. 12mo, contemp. half calf, old cloth rebacking, cancelled lib. stamps on end papers, sound & internally nice copy.   Fenning 32-382 1978 £125

WORDSWORTH, WILLIAM   The Poetical Works of William Wordsworth. London, 1832. "New" ed., 12mo, 4 vols., very good, orig. cloth.   Current Misc. 8-49 1978 $350

WORDSWORTH, WILLIAM   Poetical Works. 1845. New ed., roy. 8vo, frontis, portraits, title vignette eng. by W. Finden, marginal foxing, rebound in 1/4 buckram, marbled bds.   Eaton 45-543 1978 £8

WORDSWORTH, WILLIAM   The Prelude, or Growth of a Poet's Mind... 1851. 2nd. ed., half title, frontis, orig. black cloth, leading hinge repaired, otherwise v.g.   Jarndyce 16-1184 1978 £12.50

WORDSWORTH, WILLIAM   The Recluse. 1888. 1st. ed., half title, orig. green cloth, fine.   Jarndyce 16-1185 1978 £6.50

WORDSWORTH, WILLIAM   The Recluse. 1888. Orig. cloth, 1st. ed. of Part I.   Eaton 45-544 1978 £8

WORDSWORTH, WILLIAM   Yarrow Revisited and Other Poems. 1836. Second ed., contemp. tree calf, 8vo.   Howes 194-1347 1978 £14

WORK, HARRY L.   Waifs of the Press. Washington, 1898. Cloth, little soiled.   Hayman 72-806 1978 $10

WORKINGS of the "Machine." Grievances of the Republicans of Albany. Facts Which Should be Understood by the People. N.P., n.d. (1880?). Disbound.   Hayman 72-636 1978 $7.50

WORKMAN, G. C.   Messianic Prophecy Vindicated; or, an Explanation and Defence of the Ethical Theory. Toronto, 1899.   Hood 116-719 1978 $10

WORKMAN, JAMES   A Faithful Picture of the Political Situation of New Orleans... Boston, 1808. Half Morocco.   Ginsberg 14-518 1978 $350

WORLD JEWISH CONGRESS   Unity in Dispersion. 1948.   Austin 79-864 1978 $17.50

WORLD Missionary Conference, 1910, Reports of Commissions 1-8. 1910. 9 vols., cr. 8vo., spines faded.   George's 635-1159 1978 £10.50

WORLD of Adventure, a Collection of Stirring Scenes and Moving Accidents. 1889. Illus., 3 vols., half roan rubbed, 8vo.   George's 635-1528 1978 £5.25

WORLD'S COLUMBIAN EXPOSITION CHICAGO   Catalogue of the Russian Section. St. Petersburg, 1893. Lg. 8vo., orig. cloth-backed pict. bds.   Americanist 102-122 1978 $27.50

WORLD'S Fair Through a Camera... St. Louis, 1893. Pict. wrs., little soiled.   Hayman 72-339 1978 $12.50

THE WORLD'S Great Highway. New York, 1877. 8vo., orig. wrs., front cover soiled.   Morrill 241-637 1978 $10

WORMLEY, KATHERINE PRESCOTT   The Other Side of War, With the Army of the Potomac.... Boston, 1889. Ex libris, Bell Wiley's copy.   Broadfoot's 44-406 1978 $20.00

WORRELL, JOHN   A Diamond in the Rough. Indianapolis, 1906. Orig. binding, clean, quite scarce.   Hayman 71-798 1978 $35

WORRELL, JOHN   A Diamond in the Rough Embracing Anecdote,.... Indianapolis, 1906. Illus., orig. cloth, 1st ed.   Ginsberg 14-979 1978 $75

WORRINGER, WILHELM   Abstraktion und Einfuehlung. Ein Beitrag zur Stilpsychologie. Munich, 1911. 3rd ed.   Biblo BL781-762 1978 $9

WORRINGER, WILHELM   Aegyptische Kunst. Probleme Ihrer Wertung. Munich, 1927. Illus., some marginal pencil notes.   Biblo BL781-519 1978 $12.50

WORSLEY, F. A.   Under Sail in the Frozen North. 1927. 8vo, orig. cloth, illus.   Edwards 1012-613 1978 £18

WORSLEY, R.   The History of the Isle of Wight. 1781. 4to., coloured fold. map, plts., half calf.   Quaritch 983-380 1978 $300

WORSLEY, T. C.   Barbarians and Philistines; democracy and the public schools. London, (1940). First ed., orig. binding, nice.   Rota 211-809 1978 £7.50

WORTH, CLAUDE   Yacht Cruising. 1934. 4th ed., folding plts., text illus.   George's 635-874 1978 £8.50

WORTH, JONATHAN   The Correspondence of... Raleigh, 1909. 2 vols.   Broadfoot 50-83 1978 $16

WORTHINGTON, HUGH   A Sermon Delivered at Salters' Hall. 1805. 8vo., wrappers.   F. Edwards 1013-227 1978 £35

WORTHINGTON, JOHN 1618-71   Master of Jesus College. 1673. First ed., sm. 8vo., contemp. sheep, upper side nearly loose.   Howes 194-116 1978 £25

WORTHINGTON, W. H.   Portraits of the Sovereigns of England. 1824. Plts., contemp. calf, labels missing, 8vo.   Howes 194-1097 1978 £10

WORTHINGTON'S ANNUAL 1888. New York, 1888. Quarto, pictorial boards in color, almost mint copy.   Victoria 34-885 1978 $17.50

WORTLEY, EMMELINE CHARLOTTE ELIZABETH MANNERS STUART- Please turn to
STUART-WORTLEY, EMMELINE CHARLOTTE ELIZABETH MANNERS

WORTMAN, DENIS   Strangulatus Pro Republica. Fort Plain, 1881. Wr.   Butterfield 21-282 1978 $10

WOTTON, WILLIAM 1666-1727   Reflections upon Ancient and Modern Learning. 1694. First ed., contemp. calf, rebacked, fresh copy, 8vo.   Howes 194-117 1978 £55

WOTY, WILLIAM   The Poetical Works. London, 1770. 2 vols., 8vo, contemporary calf, gilt, spines gilt, (one hinge tender), 1st ed., good copy, scarce.   Ximenes 47-347 1978 $150

WOUK, HERMAN   Aurora Dawn. New York, 1947. First U.S. ed., covers faded & somewhat marked, good.   Bell Book 16-953 1978 £6.50

WOUK, HERMAN   Aurora Dawn. New York, 1947. Very good, dw.   Bernard 5-319 1978 $15

WRAGG, ARTHUR   Jesus Wept. n.d. (c. 1935). Imp. 8vo., very good, worn d.w., first English ed.   Bell Book 17-503 1978 £6.50

WREN, CHRISTOPHER   A Study of North Appalachian Indian Pottery. Wilkes-Barre, 1914. Illus., fine.   MacManus 239-1224 1978 $27.50

WREN, P. C.   Beau Sabreur. 1926. Advance copy of first ed., autographed photograph of author tipped in, spine faded, nice.   Bell Book 16-954 1978 £10.50

WREN, P. C.   Sowing Glory. London, 1931. First ed., orig. binding, nice, d.w.   Rota 211-810 1978 £7.50

WRIGHT, ALBERT H.   Our Georgia-Florida Frontier the Okefinokee Swamp Its History and Cartography. Ithaca, 1945. Vol. I, illus., maps.   MacManus 239-1894 1978 $25

WRIGHT, ANDREW   Court-Hand Restored. 1834. Copperplates, cr. 4to., half roan rubbed.   George's 635-798 1978 £8.50

WRIGHT, ANDREW   Court-Hand Restored. 1879. 9th ed., plts., 4to., orig. cloth, recased.   George's 635-799 1978 £12.50

WRIGHT, C. E.   The Cultivation of Saga in Anglo-Saxon England. 1939. 8vo.   Upcroft 12-503 1978 £9.50

WRIGHT, CHARLES THEODORE HAGBERG   Catalogue of the London Library. 1903. 4to., covers faded.   George's 635-1227 1978 £10.50

WRIGHT, E. M.   The Life of Joseph Wright. 1932. Illus., 2 vols., roy. 8vo.   George's 635-1267 1978 £12.50

WRIGHT, FRANCES   Introductory Address...at the Opening of the Hall of Science, New York, on Sunday, April 26, 1829. New York, 1829. Disbound. Butterfield 21-472 1978 $25

WRIGHT, G. FREDERICK   New Method of Estimating the Age of Niagara Falls. New York, 1899. Printed wrappers. Wolfe 39-393 1978 $7.50

WRIGHT, G. FREDERICK   Story of My Life and Work. Oberlin, 1916. Orig. binding, clean. Hayman 71-603 1978 $10

WRIGHT, G. FREDERICK   Story of My Life and Work. Oberlin, 1916. Cloth. Hayman 73-588 1978 $10

WRIGHT, GEORGE   Walking Amusements for Chearful Christians:.... London, 1775. Sm.8vo, contemporary calf, rebacked, 1st ed., engraved frontispiece, designed by Samuel Wale, large folding Bunyanesque map, unusual little book. Ximenes 47-348 1978 $90

WRIGHT, GEORGE NEWENHAM   The Shores and Islands of the Mediterranean. Fisher, (1840). 2 vols., 4to., plts., some marginal spotting, orig. cloth. Quaritch 983-381 1978 $210

WRIGHT, H. S.   The Great White North: The Story of Polar Explorations From the Earliest Times to the Discovery of the Pole. New York, 1910. Illus. Hood's 115-86 1978 $35

WRIGHT, J.   All Clear, Canada! Toronto, 1944. Illus. by Ruskin. Hood 17-163 1978 $12.50

WRIGHT, J. K.   The Geographical Lore of the Time of the Crusades. New York, 1925. Maps, 8vo. Upcroft 12-504 1978 £10

WRIGHT, J. M.   Account of Roger Earl Castlemaine's Embassy from James II...to Innocent XI, published formerly in the Italian Tongue. 1688. Plts., portrait, tall copy, good margins, folio, contemp. calf, rebacked, little used and stained. Thomas 37-36 1978 £150

WRIGHT, JAMES M.   The Free Negro in Maryland. New York, 1921. Orig. wrs. MacManus 239-861 1978 $27.50

WRIGHT, JOHN   The Fruit Grower's Guide. London, n.d. Orig. ed., 3 vols, coloured titles, coloured plts., illus., 4to., good, orig. cloth. K Books 244-331 1978 £55

WRIGHT, JOHN   Some Notable Altars in the Church of England and the American Episcopal Church. New York, 1908. Lg. 8vo., plts., covers torn, good. Biblo BL781-736 1978 $32.50

WRIGHT, L. A.   Documents Concerning English Voyages to the Spanish Main, 1569-1580. London, 1932. Illus., maps. Biblo BL781-48 1978 $12.50

WRIGHT, L. B.   The Secret Diary of William Byrd of Westover, 1709-1712. Richmond, 1941. 1st. ed., d.j., as new. Baldwins' 51-518 1978 $20

WRIGHT, M. O.   Flowers and Ferns in Their Haunts. New York, 1928, 1901. Plates, 8vo, orig. cloth. Book Chest 17-443 1978 $12

WRIGHT, MARCUS J.   General Scott. New York, 1894. Orig. binding, clean, pres. copy. Hayman 71-799 1978 $8.50

WRIGHT, NATHALIA   The Inner Room. Windham, 1933. 8vo., cloth, 1 of 250 numbered copies. Battery Park 1-165 1978 $50

WRIGHT, P.   Sermon Delivered at the Funeral of Noel Littage. Boonville, 1859. Uncut, wr. Butterfield 21-315 1978 $10

WRIGHT, R. E.   A Practical Digest of the Election Laws of Pennsylvania. Allentown, 1840. Lea. Hayman 73-609 1978 $10

WRIGHT, RICHARDSON   Forgotten Ladies...the American Family Album. Philadelphia, 1928. Illus., 1st ed. Biblo BL781-309 1978 $10

WRIGHT, RICHARDSON   Hawkers and Walkers in Early America. Philadelphia, 1927. 68 illus., 1st. ed., signed. Baldwins' 51-167 1978 $20

WRIGHT, RICHARDSON   Hawkers and Walkers in Early America. Philadelphia, 1927. Illus. MacManus 239-537 1978 $15

WRIGHT, RICHARDSON   The Practical Book of Outdoor Flowers. Philadelphia, (1924). Illus. in color, 8vo., orig. cloth. Morrill 241-638 1978 $9

WRIGHT, T.   Early Travels in Palestine. 1848. Cr. 8vo., orig. cloth, plan, foxed. George's 635-549 1978 £5.25

WRIGHT, THOMAS 1711-1786 Louthiana, or An Introduction to the Antiquities of Ireland. 1758. 2nd ed., 3 parts in 1 vol., fp, plates, 4to, leather, very good. Hyland 128-825 1978 £75

WRIGHT, THOMAS 1810-1877 Essays on Subjects Connected with the Literature, Popular Superstitions, and History of England in the Middle Ages. London, 1846. Two vols., large 12mo, original brown cloth, 1st ed., very fine copy. Ximenes 47-349 1978 $60

WRIGHT, THOMAS 1810-1877 Essays on Subjects Connected with the Literature, Popular Superstitions & History of England in the Middle Ages. 1846. 2 vols. Allen 234-1500 1978 $17.50

WRIGHT, THOMAS 1810-1877 The History and Topography of the County of Essex. 1831-35. 2 vols., 4to., plts., map, contemp. half green mor. gilt. Quaritch 983-382 1978 $380

WRIGHT, THOMAS 1810-1877 History of Caricature and Grotesque in Literature and Art. (c. 1865). Text illus., drawn and engraved by F. W. Fairholt, 8vo. George's 635-72 1978 £10.50

WRIGHT, THOMAS 1810-1877 The History of Ireland from the Earliest Period of the Irish Annals to the Present Time. (1855). 3 vols, 1/2 leather (rubbed), Tallis map, plts., good, reprint. Hyland 128-824 1978 £15

WRIGHT, THOMAS 1810-1877 The History of Ireland from the Earliest Period of the Irish Annals to the Present Time. (1855). 3 vols., 1/2 leather, Tallis map, plts., very good, reprint. Hyland 128-823 1978 £17.50

WRIGHT, THOMAS 1810-1877 Political Poems and Songs relating to English History, composed during the period from the Accession of Edw. III to that of Ric. III. 1859-61. 2 vols., roy. 8vo., orig. qtr. roan, corners rubbed. George's 635-742 1978 £35

WRIGHT, THOMAS 1859-1936 Blake for Babes. (London, 1924). Thin 8vo, gray cloth, gilt, black and white illus. by Blake, 1st ed., fine. Duschnes 220-29 1978 $50

WRIGHT, THOMAS 1859-1936 The Romance of the Lace Pillow. Bucks, 1919. Illus., 8vo., 1st ed., pres. Morrill 241-639 1978 $30

WRIGHT, THOMAS GODDARD   Literary Culture in Early New England, 1620-1730. New Haven, 1920. Baldwins' 51-408 1978 $10

WRIGHT, WILLARD HUNTINGTON   The Canary Murder Case. New York, 1927. First U.S. ed., v.g. Bell Book 17-269 1978 £18.50

WRIGHT, WILLARD HUNTINGTON   The Dragon Murder Case. 1934. Good, first Eng. ed. Bell Book 17-270 1978 £6.50

WRIGHT, WILLARD HUNTINGTON   The Greene Murder Case. New York, 1928. First ed. Biblo 251-456 1978 $20

WRIGHT, WILLARD HUNTINGTON   The Kennel Murder Case. 1933. Good, first Eng. ed. Bell Book 16-265 1978 £8.50

WRIGHT, WILLARD HUNTINGTON   Scarab Murder Case. New York, 1930. 1st ed., 8vo., d.j., v.g. Houle 10-348 1978 $35

WRIGHT, WILLIAM   A History of the Comstock Mines. Virginia City, 1889. Orig. pr. wr., fine. Ginsberg 14-747 1978 $50

WRIGHT, WILLIAM B.   The Quaternary Ice Age. Macmillan, 1937. 2nd. & best ed., plts., maps, illus., 8vo, orig. cloth, gilt, very good. Fenning 32-383 1978 £10.50

WRITERS and Writings of Texas. New York, 1913. 1st ed. Jenkins 116-1539 1978 $30

WRONG, GEORGE M.   The Chronicles of Canada. Toronto, 1914-1916.
32 vols., illus., red leather, gilt topped pgs., very good. Hood 116-937 1978
$200

WRONG, GEORGE M.   The Chronicles of Canada. Toronto, 1920. 32
vols., illus., blue cloth, fine. Hood 116-936 1978 $175

WROTH, LAWRENCE C.   The Early Cartography of the Pacific. New York,
1944. Ltd. to 100 copies, fine, illus. Biblo 247-457 1978 $85

WROTH, LAWRENCE C.   A History of Printing in Colonial Maryland. 1686-
1776. Baltimore, 1922. Lg. 8vo., illus., orig. cloth, 1st ed., fine. Mac-
Manus 238-980 1978 $50

WROTH, LAWRENCE C.   A History of the Printed Book, Being the Third
Number of the Dolphin. New York: Limited Editions Club, 1938. Illus., 4to.,
orig. cloth, 1st ed., ltd. to 1,800 copies, fine. MacManut 238-905 1978 $225

WUNDERLICH, CARL REINHOLD AUGUST   Das Verhalten Der Eigenwarme In
Krankheiten. Leipzig, 1868. 8vo., orig. half cloth, gilt on spine, browned,
very good copy from library of Ian Fleming, black cloth fldg. box, 1st ed.
Zeitlin 245-293 1978 $600

WUORINEN, JOHN H.   The Finns on the Delaware 1639-1655. New
York, 1938. Frontis., map, d.j., fine. MacManus 239-120 1978 $20

WURTZ, CHARLES ADOLPHE   Histoire des Doctrines Chimiques, Depuis Lavoisier Jusqu'a nos Jours. Paris, 1868. 8vo., orig. prtd. wrs., rebacked, foxed,
good copy, 1st ed. Norman 5-305 1978 $75

WURZBACH, E. F.   Life and Memoirs of Emil Frederick Wurzbach,
to Which is Appended Some Papers of John Meusebach. San Antonio, 1937.
Limited to 500 numbered copies. Jenkins 116-1508 1978 $8.50

WYATT, THOMAS   The Poetical Works. 1831. Sm. 8vo., portrait,
foxed, contemp. half calf. Howes 194-1350 1978 £8.50

WYATT, THOMAS   Poetical Works. London, 1854. Fcap. 8vo.,
half calf, spine sunned, extremities chafed. K Books 244-322 1978 £7

WYATT, THOMAS   Unfading Beauties... Hartford, 1838. 4to,
coloured litho. plts., orig. black morocco, tooled in gilt & blind, gilt edges.
Traylen 88-665 1978 £480

WYATT, W. CARL   Families of Joseph and Isaac Wyatt. N.P., 1950.
New cloth. Broadfoot 50-344 1978 $15

WYCLIF, JOHN   Latin Works. Vols. 1-13, 19, 21, 22, 24 and 25.
1883-1903. 18 vols., scarce, sm. lib. labels on spines, 8vo. George's 635-1160
1978 £75

WYETH, JOHN ALLAN   Life of General Nathan Bedford Forrest. New
York, 1899. With xerox of a forged Forrest letter purchased by Wiley, cover soiled,
int. uncut & fine, Bell Wiley's copy. Broadfoot's 44-702 1978 $50

WYETH, JOHN ALLAN   Life of General Nathan Bedford Forrest. New
York, 1899. Illus., 8vo., ex-lib., 1st ed. Morrill 241-640 1978 $30

WYETH, JOHN ALLAN   With Sabre and Scalpel. New York, 1914.
Illus., cover soiled, hinges cracked, spine wrinkled, Bell Wiley's copy. Broadfoot's 44-411 1978 $25

WYL, W.   Mormon Portraits;..... Salt Lake City, 1886.
Illus., orig. cloth, 1st ed. Ginsberg 14-696 1978 $50

WYLIE, ELINOR   Angels and Earthly Creatures. New York, 1929.
Portr. frontis., decor. bds., 1st Amer. trade ed., dust jacket. Bradley 49-363
1978 $15

WYLIE, ELINOR   Angels and Earthly Creatures. New York, 1929.
First ed., binding rubbed. Biblo 247-645 1978 $12.50

WYLIE, ELINOR   Collected Poems. New York, 1932. Orig.
cloth-backed bds., 1st ed., 1 of 210 no. copies, signed by editor, boxed, slightly
worn. MacManus 238-774 1978 $35

WYLIE, I. A. R.   Flight to England. 1943. Austin 80-384 1978
$7.50

WYLLARDE, DOLF   A Lonely Little Lady. n.d. 50 illus. by Ida
Lovering, orig. ribbed cloth, gilt upper cover & spine, a.e.g., shaken. Eaton
45-545 1978 £5

WYLLIE, W. L.   Marine Painting in Water-Colour. 1919. Sm.
oblong 4to., coloured plts., orig. cloth. F. Edwards 1013-228 1978 £20

WYLLY, H. C.   History of the Manchester Regiment. 1923-25.
Coloured plts., maps, 2 vols., roy. 8vo., green cloth. F. Edwards 1013-526
1978 £30

WYLLY, H. C.   The Loyal North Lancashire Regiment 1741-1919.
1933. Coloured plts., 2 vols., thick roy. 8vo., orig. cloth. F. Edwards 1013-
517 1978 £60

WYLLY, H. C.   Records of Services of the Officers of the 1st and
2nd Battalions.... (1931). Thick imp. 8vo., plts., orig. cloth, spine faded.
F. Edwards 1013-516 1978 £25

WYMAN, THOMAS B.   The Genealogies and Estates of Charlestown, in
the County of Middlesex. Boston, 1879. 2 vols., rebound. MacManus 239-
1020 1978 $65

WYNDHAM, HORACE   The Mayfair Calendar. New York, 1926. 2nd
ed., illus. Biblo 251-307 1978 $16.50

WYOMING   House Journal of the Eleventh Legislative Assembly of the Territory of Wyoming.... Laramie, 1890. Orig. pr. wrs., 1st ed.
Ginsberg 14-1078 1978 $75

WYOMING HISTORICAL AND GENEALOGICAL SOCIETY   Proceedings and
Collections of the... Wilkes-Barre, 1886, (1926, 1930, 1938). Vols. II-XIX,
XXI-XXII, illus., plts., ports., blue cloth, most vols. uncut or untrimmed, very
fine, 20 vols. MacManus 239-1730 1978 $150

WYRALL, EVERARD   The Gloucestershire Regiment in the War, 1914-
1918. 1931. Port. frontis., maps, 8vo., orig. cloth. F. Edwards 1013-502
1978 £12

WYRALL, EVERARD   The History of the Somerset Light Infantry, 1914-
1919. 1927. Port. frontis., plts., imp. 8vo., orig. cloth. F. Edwards 1013-491
1978 £15

WYSE, L. N. B.   Canal Interoceanique De Panama. Paris, 1891.
Folding plt., roy. 8vo, orig. printed wrapper. Edwards 1012-698 1978 £60

WYSS, JOHANN   The Swiss Family Robinson. London, (1950).
First ed., illus. by Mervyn Peake, orig. binding, very good. Rota 211-479 1978
£18

WYSS, JOHANN   The Swiss Family Robinson. n.d. Coloured plts.,
drawings by Mervyn Peake, rear hinge sprung, good, slightly worn d.w., first English ed. Bell Book 17-725 1978 £10

X Y Z

XENOPHON   Apomnenomeumaton Biblia D. Tou attou Sokratis
Apologia. Oxford, 1674. Old calf, one cover detached, other partly cracked,
port. Allen 234-1068 1978 $100

XENOPHON   De Cyri Institutione Libri Octo. Oxford, 1727.
Engrav. frontis., map, cr. 4to., contemp. calf, rebacked. Howes 194-522 1978
£35

XENOPHON   Cyropaedia, or, the Institution of Cyrus. Dublin, 1798. 2 vols. in 1, contemp. tree calf, 8vo. George's 635-520 1978
£7.50

XENOPHON   Xenophon's History of the Affairs of Greece.
London, 1770. 1st ed., quarto, folding, engraved frontispiece map, full contemp.
calf slightly worn, weak front hinges, former owner's bookplate and signature.
Bennett 20-196 1978 $175

YAGGY, L. W.   Museum of Antiquity. 1885. Engr. plts., half
calf, worn. Allen 234-1069 1978 $15

YALE, CYRUS   The Godly Pastor: Life of the Rev. Jeremiah
Hallock of Canton, Conn.... Boston, n.d. Orig. cl., new ed., rev. Ginsberg 16-872 1978 $7.50

YALE UNIVERSITY   Excavations at Dura-Europos. 1936. 4to., plt.,
corners of binding stained. Allen 234-1071 1978 $25

YAMADA, NAKABA   Ghenko: The Mongol Invasion of Japan. London,
1916. Illus., folding maps, cloth, good. Dawson's 449-204 1978 $35

YANKOFF, PETER D.   Peter Menikoff. 1928. Austin 79-867 1978
$12.50

YANKS, a Book of A. E. F. Verse. France, 1918. Wrs. Hayman 72-811 1978
$7.50

YARBOROUGH, MINNIE C.   The Reminiscences of William C. Preston.
Chapel Hill, 1933. Bell Wiley's copy. Broadfoot's 44-958 1978 $ 10.00

YARDLEY, JANE   A Superior Woman. Boston, 1885. 1st ed.
Biblo 251-679 1978 $17.50

YARRELL, WILLIAM   A History of British Fishes. 1836. First ed.,
engrav. in text, 2 vols., newly bound in qtr. calf, 8vo. Howes 194-1425 1978
£38

YARRELL, WILLIAM   A History of British Birds. London, 1843. 3
vols., 8vo, contemp. calf, vol. I rebacked & not quite uniform, 1st. ed. Traylen
88-641 1978 £20

YARRELL, WILLIAM   A History of British Birds. London, 1856. Wood
engrs., 3 vols., 3rd ed., 8vo., full dark green mor., gilt, gilt edges, fine set.
Salloch 345-198 1978 $110

YARRELL, WILLIAM   A History of British Birds. 1871-75. Fourth ed.,
wood engrav., 4 vols., half crimson mor. Howes 194-1424 1978 £55

YATES, DORNFORD   An Eye for a Tooth. 1943. Very good, worn
d.w., first English ed. Bell Book 17-956 1978 £5.50

YATES, DORNFORD   An Eye for a Tooth. 1943. D.w., very good,
first English ed. Bell Book 16-955 1978 £5.50

YATES, DORNFORD   The House that Berry Built. 1945. Very good,
slightly torn d.w., first English ed. Bell Book 17-957 1978 £5.50

YATES, EDMUND   His Recollections and Experiences. 1884. 1st.
ed., 2 vols., frontis & other portraits, engraved titles, half title, rebound in half
dark blue calf, marbeld bds., good. Jarndyce 16-1187 1978 £32

YATES, EDMUND   The Silent Witness. Boston, 1875. 1st Amer.
ed., binding rubbed, hinges split, good used copy. Biblo 251-680 1978 $15

YATES, HAYDIE   70 Miles from a Lemon. Boston, 1947. Illus.,
1st ed., d.w. Biblo BL781-306 1978 $9

YATES, J. B.   Statement of the Objections to the Passage of a
Bill Entitled "An Act to Regulate the Sale of Lottery Tickets"... Albany, 1827.
Disbound. Hayman 73-483 1978 $12.50

YAWGER, ROSE N.   The Indian and the Pioneer. Syracuse, 1893.
2 vols., plts., unopened, uncut, scarce. Butterfield 21-221 1978 $85

YBANEZ, C.   La Romanisation de la langue chinoise. Peking,
1920. Bound in marbled boards, half leather. Dawson's 449-99 1978 $50

YE Centennial. Boston, (1875). Wrps., slight wear, sm. stain of front wrapper.
Hayman 71-705 1978 $8.50

YEAR-BOOK and Almanac of Britich North America for 1867... Montreal, 1866.
Wrs. Hood 116-60 1978 $40

THE YEAR Book of Canadian Art, 1913, Compiled by the Arts and Letters Club of
Toronto. London, Toronto, 1913. Illus. Hood 117-227 1978 $30

YEAR Book of the Poetry Society of South Carolina, 1921. Charleston, 1921.
Very good, wrs., first English ed. Bell Book 16-021 1978 £4.50

YEARSLEY, ANN   The Royal Captives: A Fragment of Secret History.
Philadelphia, 1795. 1st Amer. ed., 2 vols., lacking 1st 2 text leaves, rubbed and
foxed. Victoria 34-889 1978 $10

YEAST: a Problem. London, 1851. Scarce 1st ed., later blue polished calf,
sm. rubbed spot on back cover, 8vo., very good. Americanist 103-48 1978 $75

YEATS, JOHN   Manuals of Commerce, Technical, Industrial and
Commercial. 1887. Maps, charts, tables, 4 vols., cr. 8vo. George's 635-439
1978 £12.50

YEATS, JOHN BUTLER   Early Memories. Dundrum, Cuala Press, 1923.
One of 500 copies, first ed., orig. binding, covers and end-papers severely foxed,
very good. Rota 211-813 1978 £42

YEATS, WILLIAM BUTLER   The Arrow. 1939. Wr., very good, reprint.
Hyland 128-887 1978 £5

YEATS, WILLIAM BUTLER   Autobiographies; Reveries over Childhood &
Youth and the Trembling of the Veil. 1926. 1st ed., illus., spine faded, very
good. Hyland 128-872 1978 £25

YEATS, WILLIAM BUTLER   Autobiographies. New York, 1927. Illus.,
1st Amer. ed. Biblo 251-681 1978 $17.50

YEATS, WILLIAM BUTLER   The Celtic Twilight. Men and Women, Dhouls
and Faeries. London, 1893. Illus., frontis. by J. B. Yeats, 12mo., orig.
olive-green ribbed cloth, 1st ed., variant bind., fine. MacManus 238-775 1978
$135

YEATS, WILLIAM BUTLER   Collected Poems. 1933. 1st ed., good, octavo
bound in cloth. Hyland 128-860 1978 £12

YEATS, WILLIAM BUTLER   Collected Works in Verse and Prose. Stratford-
on-Avon, Shakespeare Head Press, 1908. Portraits frontis., 8 vols., orig. brown
buckram, gilt tops, other edges untrimmed, 8vo. Howes 194-1351 1978 £175

YEATS, WILLIAM BUTLER   The Cutting of an Agate. 1919. First English
ed., cr. 8vo., orig. blue cloth, edges untrimmed. Howes 194-1352 1978 £32

YEATS, WILLIAM BUTLER   Deirdre. 1907. 1st ed., very good, octavo
bound in cloth. Hyland 128-859 1978 £25

YEATS, WILLIAM BUTLER   Essays. 1924. 1st ed., d.w., very good, octavo
bound in cloth. Hyland 128-870 1978 £25

YEATS, WILLIAM BUTLER   Essays. 1924. 1st ed., spine faded, very good,
octavo bound in cloth. Hyland 128-869 1978 £20

YEATS, WILLIAM BUTLER   Four Plays for Dancers. 1921. 1st ed., Dulac illus., good, octavo bound in cloth. Hyland 128-843 1978 £35

YEATS, WILLIAM BUTLER   A Full Moon in March. London, 1935. 8vo, green cloth, gilt lettering on spine, d.w. slightly browned but unchipped, near Mint, 1st ed. Desmarais 1-429 1978 $45

YEATS, WILLIAM BUTLER   The Green Helmet, An Heroic Farce. 1911. Seperated ed., wrs., very good. Hyland 128-873 1978 £11

YEATS, WILLIAM BUTLER   The Hour-Glass, Cathleen NI Houlihan, The Pot of Broth; Being Vol II of Plays for An Irish Theatre. 1904. 1st ed., very good, octavo bound in cloth. Hyland 128-857 1978 £30

YEATS, WILLIAM BUTLER   Ideas of Good and Evil. London, 1903. First ed., specially bound in full vellum, fine, inscribed by author. Rota 211-816 1978 £300

YEATS, WILLIAM BUTLER   Irish Fariy & Folk Tales. 1888. 1st ed., Scott Library issue, very good, octavo bound in cloth. Hyland 128-845 1978 £20

YEATS, WILLIAM BUTLER   Irish Fairy & Folk Tales. (1906). Scott Library issue, lacks fly, good, octavo bound in cloth. Hyland 128-846 1978 £11

YEATS, WILLIAM BUTLER   Irish Fariy & Folk Tales. n.d. Scott Library issue, octavo bound in cloth, reprint. Hyland 128-847 1978 £10

YEATS, WILLIAM BUTLER   John Sherman and Dhoya. London, 1891. Orig. cloth, nice, scarce, first ed., of an ed. of 2,000 copies only 356 were issued in cloth. Rota 212-61 1978 £150

YEATS, WILLIAM BUTLER   The King of the Great Clock Tower, Commentaries and Poems. Cuala Press, 1934. First ed., orig. bds., qtr. linen, 8vo. Howes 194-1353 1978 £65

YEATS, WILLIAM BUTLER   The Kings Threshold; and On Bailie's Strand. 1904. 1st ed., lacks spine label, very good. Hyland 128-858 1978 £30

YEATS, WILLIAM BUTLER   Last Poems & Plays. 1940. 1st ed., ex lib, rebound, very good working copy. Hyland 128-842 1978 £10

YEATS, WILLIAM BUTLER   Leda and the Swan. (Florence, n.d.). 12mo, 1st separate ed., orig. watercolour frontis., signed by Prokosch, decor. paper wrs., Prokosch bkplt., ltd. to 22 copies. Quaritch 979-269 1978 $435

YEATS, WILLIAM BUTLER   On Baile's Strand. Stratford-on-Avon, Shakespeare Head Press, 1907. First separate ed., sm. 8vo., orig. printed wrappers. Howes 194-1354 1978 £12

YEATS, WILLIAM BUTLER   On the Boiler. Dublin, Cuala Press, (1939). Lettered blue wrs., 1st ed., wr. edges chipped. Bradley 49-365 1978 £25

YEATS, WILLIAM BUTLER   A Packet for Ezra Pound. Dublin, Cuala Press, 1929. First ed., woodcut, orig. linen-backed bds., only 425 copies printed, 8vo. Howes 194-1355 1978 £40

YEATS, WILLIAM BUTLER   Per Amica Silentia Lunae. 1918. First ed., cr. 8vo., orig. cloth blocked in gilt. Howes 194-1356 1978 £25

YEATS, WILLIAM BUTLER   Per Amica Silentia Lunae. London, 1913. Fine copy in soiled & damaged d.w. Desmarais B-686 1978 $50

YEATS, WILLIAM BUTLER   Per Amica Silentia Lunae. 1918. 1st ed., light stain on top margin, good. Hyland 128-875 1978 £20

YEATS, WILLIAM BUTLER   Plays for an Irish Theatre. Shakespeare Head Press, 1911. Plts., linen-backed bds., very good, first English ed. Bell Book 16-957 1978 £55

YEATS, WILLIAM BUTLER   Plays for an Irish Theatre. 1913. 2nd imp., cover dull, text good, octavo bound in cloth. Hyland 128-871 1978 £8.50

YEATS, WILLIAM BUTLER   Plays in Prose & Verse. 1922. 1st ed., spine faded, very good, octavo bound in cloth. Hyland 128-849 1978 £20

YEATS, WILLIAM BUTLER   Plays in Prose & Verse. 1922. 1st ed., cover dull, text good, octavo bound in cloth. Hyland 128-851 1978 £15

YEATS, WILLIAM BUTLER   Plays in Prose & Verse. 1922. Reprint, very good, octavo bound in cloth. Hyland 128-850 1978 £10

YEATS, WILLIAM BUTLER   Poems of Blake. 1893. 1st ed., very good, octavo bound in cloth. Hyland 128-879 1978 £30

YEATS, WILLIAM BUTLER   Poems, 1899-1905. 1906. 1st ed., very good, octavo bound in cloth. Hyland 128-848 1978 £20

YEATS, WILLIAM BUTLER   Poems. 1908. Portrait, orig. cloth, very good, first English ed. Bell Book 16-958 1978 £22.50

YEATS, WILLIAM BUTLER   Poems. 1908. Very good, octavo bound in cloth, reprint. Hyland 128-852 1978 £15

YEATS, WILLIAM BUTLER   Poems. London, 1912. Sixth English ed., orig. binding, d.w. Rota 211-817 1978 £10

YEATS, WILLIAM BUTLER   Poems. 1913. Good, octavo bound in cloth, reprint. Hyland 128-853 1978 £5

YEATS, WILLIAM BUTLER   Poems of Blake. N.d. Very good, octavo bound in cloth. Hyland 128-880 1978 £10

YEATS, WILLIAM BUTLER   Responsibilities and Other Poems. New York, 1916. 8vo, 1st Amer. ed., issued in grey paper boards, buff linen spine, design by Sturge Moore in black on front cover, corners bumped and slightly worn, uncut, hinges started, near Fine, 1st ed. Desmarais 1-430 1978 $50

YEATS, WILLIAM BUTLER   Reveries over Childhood & Youth. 1916. 1st ed., Publisher's pres. copy, very good, octavo bound in cloth. Hyland 128-876 1978 £30

YEATS, WILLIAM BUTLER   Reveries over Childhood & Youth. 1916. 1st ed., colored f. p., illus., spine dull, good, octavo bound in cloth. Hyland 128-877 1978 £25

YEATS, WILLIAM BUTLER   Reveries over Childhood and Youth. 1916. Coloured frontis., portraits, cr. 8vo., orig. blue cloth, first English ed. Howes 194-1357 1978 £25

YEATS, WILLIAM BUTLER   Reveries over Childhood & Youth. 1916. Very good, coloured frontis. by Jack B. Yeats, first English ed. Bell Book 17-960 1978 £28.50

YEATS, WILLIAM BUTLER   The Secret Rose. 1897. 1st ed., J.B. Yeats illus., good, decor. cover, spine faded, generally good. Hyland 128-844 1978 £50

YEATS, WILLIAM BUTLER   The Secret Rose. London, 1897. 1st ed., orig. gilt stamped blue cloth, uncut, good, illus. by J. B. Yeats. Houle 10-389 1978 $40

YEATS, WILLIAM BUTLER   Selected Poems. London, 1929. First ed. of this selection, orig. binding, nice. Rota 211-819 1978 £15

YEATS, WILLIAM BUTLER   The Shadowy Waters. 1901. 2nd ed., lacks fly, very good, octavo bound in cloth. Hyland 128-868 1978 £12

YEATS, WILLIAM BUTLER   The Singing Head and the Lady. 1934. 12mo., 1st separate ed., decor. paper wrs., 1st copy off press, ltd. to 20 copies. Quaritch 979-270 1978 $485

YEATS, WILLIAM BUTLER   Stories from Carleton. (1889). Very good, octavo bound in cloth. Hyland 128-862 1978 £17.50

YEATS, WILLIAM BUTLER   Stories from Carleton. (1889). 1st ed., Scott Library issue, very good, octavo bound in cloth. Hyland 128-861 1978 £17.50

YEATS, WILLIAM BUTLER   Stories from Red Hanrahan & The Secret Rose. 1927. 1st ed., N. McGuinness illus., very good, octavo bound in cloth. Hyland 128-863 1978 £30

YEATS, WILLIAM BUTLER   Stories from Red Hanrahan & The Secret Rose.
1927. 1st ed., very good, N. McGuinness illus., octavo bound in cloth. Hyland
128-864 1978 £25

YEATS, WILLIAM BUTLER   Stories of Michael Robartes and his Friends.
Dublin, Cuala Press, 1931. Bds., cloth back, bkplt., 1 of 450 copies. Dawson's
447-283 1978 $85

YEATS, WILLIAM BUTLER   Three Things. London, (1929). Blue paper
cover, drawings by Gilbert Spencer, Mint, 1st ed. Desmarais 1-431 1978 $7.50

YEATS, WILLIAM BUTLER   Three Things. n.d. Coloured frontis., very
good, wraps, first English ed. Bell Book 16-960 1978 £5.50

YEATS, WILLIAM BUTLER   Trembling of the Veil. London, 1922.
1 of 1,000 signed by author, 1st ed., very good d.j., fine. Houle 10-378
1978 $195

YEATS, WILLIAM BUTLER   The Wanderings of Oisin and other poems. London, 1889. First ed., first issue, one of 500 copies, orig. binding, head of spine
defective and covers slightly marked, nice, rare. Rota 211-815 1978 £250

YEATS, WILLIAM BUTLER   Where There Is Nothing. 1903. 1st ed., boards
with cloth spine, very good. Hyland 128-854 1978 £30

YEATS, WILLIAM BUTLER   Where There is Nothing: Being Volume I of Plays
for an Irish Theatre. London, 1903. 8vo, boards, cloth back, paper label chipped,
uncut, 1st English ed, Fine. Desmarais 1-432 1978 $35

YEATS, WILLIAM BUTLER   Where There Is Nothing. 1903. Lacks spine
label, very good. Hyland 128-855 1978 £25

YEATS, WILLIAM BUTLER   Where There Is Nothing. 1903. Ex lib, good,
boards with cloth spine. Hyland 128-856 1978 £15

YEATS, WILLIAM BUTLER   The Wild Swans at Coole. London, 1919. First
Trade ed., orig. binding, nice, worn d.w. Rota 211-818 1978 £30

YEATS, WILLIAM BUTLER   The Winding Stair and Other Poems. London,
1933. Orig. blind-stamped cloth, 1st ed., very fine. MacManus 238-776 1978
$125

YELVERTON, BARRY   Speech of the Rt. Hon. Barry Lord Yelverton...
in the House of Lords of Ireland on 22nd Mar., 1800. Dublin, 1800. 1st ed.,
plain wrs. Hyland 128-832 1978 £10

YETTS, W. P.   The Cull Chinese Bronzes. 1939. Roy. 4to.,
plts., bds., buckram back, ed. ltd. to 350 signed copies. Quaritch 983-133
1978 $200

YEZIERSKA, ANZIA   Bread Givers. 1925. Austin 79-869 1978
$12.50

YOAKUM, CLARENCE S.   Army Mental Tests. New York, 1920. Sm. 8vo.,
fldg. plts., illus., black cloth, gilt lettered, pencil marks & notes, very good
copy from library of Dr. Herbert M. Evans, 1st ed. Zeitlin 245-294 1978 $45

YODER, ROBERT M.   There's No Front Like Home. 1944. Austin 80-
386 1978 $10

YONGE, CHARLOTTE MARY   The Armourer's Prentices. 1884. 1st. ed., 2
vols., half titles, orig. green cloth, blocked in black & gold. Eaton 45-548
1978 £15

YONGE, CHARLOTTE MARY   Heartsease or the Brother's Wife. 1855. 2 vols.,
3rd. ed., contemp. 1/2 leather, scuffed. Eaton 45-550 1978 £10

YONGE, CHARLOTTE MARY   Love and Life. An Old Story in Eighteenth Century Costume. London, 1880. 2 vols., orig. cloth, 1st ed., front inner hinge in
vol. I, extremities worn, otherwise good, inscriptions in both vols. MacManus
238-416 1978 $60

YONGE, WALTER   Diary of Walter Yonge. 1848. Octavo, good.
Upcroft 10-195 1978 £6.50

YORKE, JAMES   The Union of Honour. London, 1640. Engraved
title page, coloured coat of arms, headlines & other initials in red, folio, old
calf, repaired. Traylen 88-462 1978 £150

YORICK, PSEUD.
Please turn to
STERNE, LAURENCE

YOST, KARL   A Bibliography of the Works of Edna St. Vincent
Millay. New York, 1937. 8vo., orig. cloth, 1st ed. MacManus 238-987 1978
$35

YOUELL, GEORGE   Lower Class. An Autobiography. Seattle,
1938. Pic. fabricoid, frontis., 1st ed., very good. Dykes 35-295 1978 $15

YOUNG, ANDREW   Speak to the Earth. 1939. Very good, first
English ed. Bell Book 16-965 1978 £4.50

YOUNG, ANDREW W.   The Citizen's Manual of Government and Law...
Cleveland, 1853. Orig. binding, clean. Hayman 71-800 1978 $8.50

YOUNG, ANDREW W.   First Lessons in Civil Government; Including a Comprehensive View of the Government of the State of Ohio. Cleveland, 1946. Leather. Hayman 72-813 1978 $10

YOUNG, ANDREW W.   History of Chautauqua Co., N.Y... Buffalo,
1875. Illus., sm. thick 4to., nice, rebound, scarce. MacManus 239-1083
1978 $75

YOUNG, ARTHUR   A Six Months Tour Through the North of England.
London, 1771. 2nd. ed., engraved plts., 4 vols., 8vo, contemp. calf, rebacked,
new leather labels. Traylen 88-91 1978 £85

YOUNG, ARTHUR   A Tour in Ireland. London, 1780. Second ed.,
2 vols., plts., contemp. calf, new labels, 8vo. K Books 244-333 1978 £60

YOUNG, BRIGHAM   Governor's Message to the Legislative Assembly of
Utah Territory... Salt Lake City, 1852. Sewn as issued. Ginsberg 14-1014
1978 $175

YOUNG, C. C.   Under Twelve Flags. Waco, 1908. Cloth. Hayman 72-816 1978 $7.50

YOUNG, DONALD   Special Report on Immigration. 1872. 1st ed.
Austin 79-871 1978 $47.50

YOUNG, EDWARD   The Complaint. Glasgow, Foulis Press, 1776.
2 vols., 12mo., contemp. sheep. Howes 194-275 1978 £7.50

YOUNG, EDWARD   Night Thoughts on Life, Death & Immortality.
London, n.d. 8vo., engr. frontis., plts., full red calf, gilt decor. on spine &
bds., interior fine. Current Misc. 8-50 1978 $135

YOUNG, EDWARD HUDSON   Our Young Family in America. Durham, 1947.
Broadfoot 50-345 1978 $20

YOUNG, EGERTON RYERSON   By Canoe and Dog Train Among the Cree and
Salteaux Indians. New York, 1890. Illus. Hood's 115-780 1978 $15

YOUNG, FILSON   Christopher Columbus and the New World of his
Discovery. Philadelphia, 1906. Illus., maps & charts, 2 vols. Baldwins' 51-9
1978 $12.50

YOUNG, FRANCIS BRETT   The Christmas Box. (c. 1937). Illus. by Kay
Ambrose, roy. 8vo. George's 635-1529 1978 £5

YOUNG, FRANCIS BRETT   Jim Redlake. 1930. First ed., ltd. to 275 signed
copies, covers stained, 8vo. George's 635-1340 1978 £5.50

YOUNG, FRANCIS BRETT   Marching on Tango (With General Smuts in East
Africa). New York, (1917). Map, 10 plts., cr. 8vo., orig. cloth. K Books 239-
545 1978 £8

YOUNG, FRANCIS BRETT   Portrait of a Village. 1937. Engravings on wood
by Joan Hassall, 8vo. George's 635-180 1978 £5

YOUNG, FRANK C.   Echoes from Arcadia. Denver, 1903. Original
cloth, 1st ed., one of 200 numbered copies. Ginsberg 14-279 1978 $100

YOUNG, G. R.   The Ports of Port Arthur, Sabine, Beaumont, and
Orange, Texas. Washington, 1925. Photos and folding maps. Jenkins 116-728
1978 $35

YOUNG, GEORGE   Manitoba Memories, Leaves from My Life in the Prairie Province, 1868-1884. Toronto, 1897. Illus., ex-lib. Hood 116-903 1978 $17.50

YOUNG, HUGH   Hugh Young, a Surgeon's Autobiography. New York, 1940. Rittenhouse 49-854 1976 $10

YOUNG, J.   Demonology. Edinburgh, 1856. Fcap. 8vo., crudely rebacked. George's 635-1161 1978 £5.25

YOUNG, JESSE B.   What A Boy Saw In The Army. New York, (1894). Orig. binding, clean, orig. drawings by Fran Beard, lacks free endpaper in front, very good copy. Hayman 71-141 1978 $10

YOUNG, JOHN   The Diary of John Young. 1928. Plts., octavo, good. Upcroft 10-196 1978 £6

YOUNG, JOHN   The Origin of the Ocean Mail Streamers Between Liverpool and the St. Lawrence and the Advantages of the Northern Route. Montreal, 1877. Paper cover. Hood's 115-990 1978 $40

YOUNG, JOHN C.   An Address Delivered Before the Union Literary Society of Miami University, at Its Thirteenth Annual Celebration, August 8th, 1838. Oxford, 1838. Disbound. Hayman 73-590 1978 $12.50

YOUNG, JOSEPH   History of the Organization of the Seventies. Salt Lake City, 1878. Plates, orig. printed wr., 1st ed. Ginsberg 14-698 1978 $75

YOUNG, JOSEPH   A New Physical System of Astronomy...in which the Physical System of...Newton, is Examined, & Presumed to be Refuted... New York, 1800. 1st & only ed., pres. copy, "Walter Weed's" book, old full calf, little worn, illus., plts., 8vo., very good. Americanist 103-112 1978 $85

YOUNG, JOSEPH   Wartime Racketeers. 1945. Austin 80-387 1978 $10

YOUNG, MATHEW   An Analysis of the Principles of Natural Philosophy. Dublin, 1800. 8vo., folding plts., contemp. sprinkled calf, joint slightly cracked. Quaritch 977-137 1978 $65

YOUNG, MURDO   Antonia. 1818. Sm. 8vo., 1st ed., orig. bds., back defective & little worn. Quaritch 979-337 1978 $115

YOUNG, SAMUEL   Lecture on Civilization...Before the Young Men's Association of Saratoga Springs, March 8th, 1841. Saratoga Springs, 1841. Disbound. Butterfield 21-400 1978 $8

YOUNG, STARK   Addio, Madretta and Other Plays. Chicago, 1912. 1st ed., paper yellowed, binding, very good. Limestone 9-326 1978 $15

YOUNG, THOMAS   Elementary Illustrations of the Celestial Mechanics of Laplace. London, 1821. 8vo., orig. bds., uncut, spine worn, hinges repaired, but fine copy, 1st ed. Norman 5-*53 1978 $250

YOUNG, THOMAS   Narrative of a Residence on the Mosquito Shore, 1839-41... 1842. Plts., 1 slightly spotted, name on title, sm. 8vo., orig. cloth. Edwards 1012-699 1978 £35

YOUNG, WILLIAM E.   Shark! Shark! New York, 1933. Ltd. 425 signed copied, bound in full shark leather, illus. Baldwins' 51-558 1978 $50

YOUNG Days for Boys and Girls. Boston, (1889). Illus., pict. bds. in full color, little rubbed. Hayman 72-387 1978 $7.50

YOUNG Man's Book of Elegant Poetry. Philadelphia, 1835. 2 vols., 16mo., contemp. roan, 1st eds. Morrill 241-641 1978 $17.50

THE YOUNG Warrior Mower. Little Falls, 1870. Woodcut illus., pict. wr. Butterfield 21-440 1978 $20

YOUNGBLOOD, B.   An Economic Study of a Typical Ranching Area on the Edwards Plateau of Texas. College Station, 1922. Decor. wrs., illus., 1st ed., fine copy, laid in a 4-point slipcase, very scarce. Dykes 34-264 1978 $75

YOUNGBLOOD, B.   An Economic Study of a Typical Ranching Area on the Edwards Plateau of Texas. College Station, 1922. Dec. wrs., illus., 1st ed., fine, slipcase, very scarce. Dykes 35-278 1978 $75

YOUNGHUSBAND, FRANCIS   South Africa of Today. London, 1898. 12 plts., 8vo., orig. cloth, little shabby. K Books 239-546 1978 £8

YOUNGHUSBAND, FRANCIS   South Africa of Today. London, 1899. Plts., or. 8vo., slight foxing, orig. cloth, covers dull. K Books 239-547 1978 £6

YOUNGHUSBAND, GEORGE JOHN   The Philippines and Round About... 1899. Map, illus., orig. cloth, rebacked, 8vo. Edwards 1012-178 1978 £10

YOUNGMAN, W. E.   Gleanings From Western Prairies. Cambridge, 1882. Sm. 8vo., orig. cloth. Edwards 1012-540 1978 £25

YOUTH And Jobs in Canada. Toronto, 1945. Card Cover. Hood's 115-293 1978 $7.50

THE YOUTH'S Companion; or A Safe Guide to Eminence. Andover, 1820. Calf, light cover wear, very good. Victoria 34-890 1978 $25

YOUTHFUL Portraits. 1796. Sm. 8vo., 1st ed., engr. vignettes, orig. marbled bds., green vellum back, very good copy. Quaritch 979-345 1978 $250

YRIARTE, CHARLES   Livre de Souvenirs de Maso di Bartolommeo Dit Masaccio-Manuscrits Conserves a la Bibliotheque de Prato et a la Magliabecchiana de Florence. Paris, 1894. Lg. 4to., printed soft bds., illus. King 7-399 1978 £20

YVER, G.   Le Commerce et les marchands dans l'Italie meridionale au XIIIe et au XIVe siecle. 1903. Some pencil scoring, 8vo. George's 635-441 1978 £7.50

ZACCHIAE, LANFRANCI   De Salario seu Operariorum Mercede. Romae, 1679. Folio, full contemp. stiff vellum. Bennett 20-226 1978 $185

ZACHINYAEY, ALEXANDER   "Renovation of the School System". St. Petersburg, 1913. In Russian, 2nd ed., upper wrapper illus. in color by J. Bilibin. Victoria 34-708 1978 $30

ZADOKS, S.   Geschiedenis der Amsterdamsche Concessies. Amsterdam, 1899. 8vo., orig. covers, back cover gone. Van der Peet H-64-585 1978 Dfl 45

ZALLINGER ZUM THURN, FRANZ   Abhandlung von den Elektrischen Grundsatzen. (Innsbruck), 1779. 8vo., contemp. wrs., worn & foxed, but very good copy, 1st ed. Norman 5-307 1978 $275

ZALUZIANSKY, A.   Methodi Herbariae Libri Tres. Frankfurt, 1604. 4to., vellum with ties. Salloch 345-199 1978 $375

ZANGWILL, I.   The Bachelor's Club. 1891. Pres. copy, inscribed by author, illus., orig. pict. cloth, very good, first English ed., lower hinge sprung. Bell Book 16-966 1978 £10

ZANGWILL, ISRAEL   The Bachelor's Club. London, 1891. Orig. cloth, contemp. inscrip., notes and name on title page, good. Greene 78-137 1978 $50

ZANGWILL, ISRAEL   Children of the Ghetto. London, 1892. Orig. salmon-colored cloth, 1st ed., 3 vols., darkened, "grosvenor Gallery Library" labels, good sound copies. Greene 78-138 1978 $75

ZANGWILL, ISRAEL   Children of the Ghetto. 1926. Austin 79-873 1978 $10

ZANGWILL, ISRAEL   Les Enfants du Ghetto. Paris, 1925. 4to., orig. wr., uncut, ltd. issued in 565 copies, numbered copy on velin de Rives paper, illus. by Alice Halicka, excellent state of preservation. Goldschmidt 110-33 1978 $40

ZANGWILL, ISRAEL   The Master. 1895. Illus. Austin 79-877 1978 $8.50

ZANGWILL, ISRAEL   The Melting Pot. 1909. Austin 79-874 1978 $8.50

ZANGWILL, ISRAEL   Selected Works. 1938. 3 vols. in 1, orig. ed. Austin 79-876 1978 $21.25

ZANI, P.   Materiali per Servire alla Storia dell' Origine e de' Progressi dell' Incisione in Rame e in Legno... Parma, 1802. 8vo., plt., contemp. speckled calf. Quaritch 983-279 1978 $75

ZANOTTO, FRANCESCO   Pinacoteca della Imp. Reg. Accademia Veneta delle Belle Arti. Venezia, 1830. Lg. thick folio, half calf, marbled bds., very good. King 7-255 1978 £70

ZANUCK, DARRYL F.   Tunis Expedition. 1943. Illus. with photos. Austin 80-388 1978 $8.50

ZAPF, HERMANN   Feder und Stichel: Alphabete und Schriftblatter in zeitgemasser Darstellung, geschrieben von Hermann Zapf. Frankfurt am Main, (1949). Limp mor.-covered bds., mint in slightly soiled & worn mor.-backed fldg. case, lst ed., 1 of 80 numbered copies on Japan paper, inscr. & signed by Zapf. Dawson's 447-196 1978 $250

ZAPF, HERMANN   Feder und Stichel: Alphabete und Schriftblatter in zeitgemasser Darstellung, geschrieben von Hermann Zapf. Frankfurt am Main, (1950). Later prtg., bds. with lea. spine, 1 of 500 numbered copies prtd. on Fabriano paper. Dawson's 447-197 1978 $150

ZARA, LOUIS   Against This Rock. Creative Age Press, 1943. lst ed., signed by author. Austin 79-880 1978 $17.50

ZARA, LOUIS   Blessed is the Man. 1935. Austin 79-882 1978 $12.50

ZARA, LOUIS   This Land is Ours. Boston, 1940. Austin 82-1147 1978 $10

ZAVALA, LORENZO DE   Ensayo Historico De Las Revoluciones De Mexico. Mexico, 1845. 2 vols. in 1, illus., contemp. half morocco, signed by Gen. John A Quitman. Jenkins 116-1512 1978 $375

ZEARING Sketch of the Life of Major James Roberts Zearing, M. D. and Civil War Letters of Major James Roberts Zearing, M. C. 1861-1865. Springfield, 1922. New cloth, Bell Wiley's copy. Broadfoot 46-328 1978 $16

ZEBLEY, FRANK R.   The Churches of Delaware. Wilmington, 1947. Illus. MacManus 239-117 1978 $17.50

ZEEVELD, W. G.   Foundations of Tudor Policy. 1948. Plt. Allen 234-1503 1978 $8.50

ZEIDLER, SEBASTIAN CHRISTIAN   Somatotomia Anthropologica, seu Corporis Humani Fabrica Methodice divisa, & controversarum Quaestionum discussionibus illustrata. Pragae, 1686. Folio, copperplts., marbled bds. rebacked in calf with orig. backstrip & label preserved, signature, unusually well-preserved copy, lst ed., scarce. Zeitlin 245-295 1978 $1,250

ZEISBERGER, DAVID   David Zeisberger's History of the Northern American Indians. (1910). Orig. cloth, fine. MacManus 239-1225 1978 $37.50

ZEITLIN, JAKE   For Whispers and Chants. San Francisco, The Lantern Press. 8vo., bds., prtd. on Ingres paper, #103 of 450 numbered copies, illus. by Valenti Angelo, part of fr. cover darkened, signed pres. copy from Zeitlin to A. E. Newton. Battery Park 1-133 1978 $45

ZELOMEK, A. W.   This Peculiar War. 1940. Austin 80-389 1978 $10

ZENO, ANTONIO   In Concionem Periclis & Lepidi Ex libro primo historiarum,.... Venice, 1569. lst ed., quarto, full contemp. limp vellum, rare. Bennett 20-227 1978 $200

ZERVOS, C.   L'Art en Grece des Temps Prehistoriques au Debut du XVIIIe Siecle. Paris, 1933. 4to., lst ed., illus., bds. Quaritch 983-280 1978 $50

ZETTL, E.   An Anonymous Short English Metrical Chronicle. 1935. Cloth marked, 8vo. Upcroft 12-509 1978 £4

ZEUNER, GUSTAV ANTON   Grundzuge der Mechanischen Warmetheorie. Freiberg, 1860. 8vo., bds., orig. prtd. wrs. bound in, uncut, lst ed., very scarce. Offenbacher 30-161 1978 $150

ZIEBER, EUGENE   Heraldry In America. Philadelphia, 1909. 2nd. ed., 150 illus. Baldwins' 51-272 1978 $50

ZIEGISCHMID, A. J. F.   Die Alteste Chronik Der Hutterischen Bruder. 1943. Illus., plts., ltd. ed. of 1000 copies, in German. Austin 79-884 1978 $95

ZIEGLER, JESSE A.   Wave of the Gulf: Ziegler's Scrapbook of the Texas Gulf Coast Country. San Antonio, 1938. lst ed., illus., d.j., signed by author. Jenkins 116-1514 1978 $30

ZIMMER, H.   Die Romanischen Literaturen and Sprachen.... 1909. Roy. 8vo. George's 635-1387 1978 £5.25

ZIMMERMAN, E. A. W.   Taschenbuch de Reisen Oder Dartellung der Entdeckunger des 18 Jahrhunderts Achter Jahrgang fur das Jahr 1805. Leipzig, 1805. Illus., plates, maps, original 12mo boards, mended. Ginsberg 14-227 1978 $125

ZIMMERMANN, JOHANN GEORG   Solitude Considered, with Respect to Its Influence Upon the Mind and the Heart. New York, (1796). Engr. frontis., 12mo., contemp. calf, lacks fr. cover, lst New York ed. Morrill 239-279 1978 $15

ZIMMERMANN, JOHANN GEORG   Solitude considered with respect to its Influence upon the Mind and the Heart. 1797. Seventh ed., lg. 8vo., contemp. sprinkled calf, gilt, frontispiece. P. M. Hill 142-237 1978 £25

ZIMMERMANN, JOHANN GEORG   Solitude. New York, 1840. Engr. frontis., 12mo., orig. black lea., gilt stamping on spine, pict. embossed in blind on covers, bottom margin lightly dampstained, nice Amer. binding. Morrill 239-280 1978 $17.50

ZIMMERMAN, M.   Solitude. 1804. Engraved plts., 2 vols., new half calf, 8vo. George's 635-1530 1978 £12.50

ZINI, PIETRO FRANCESCO   De Philosophiae Laudibus Oratio. Venice, 1547. 12 leaves, 4to., wrs. Salloch 348-286 1978 $135

ZINK, HAROLD   Government in Wartime Europe and Japan. 1942. Rev. ed., ex-lib. Austin 80-390 1978 $12.50

ZOLA, EMILE   Nana. Philadelphia, 1880. lst (?) Amer. ed., orig. mustard cloth. Greene 78-139 1978 $75

ZOLLERS, GEORGE D.   Thrilling Incidents on Sea and Land. Mount Morris, 1892. Cloth. Hayman 73-780 1978 $12.50

ZOUCH, RICHARD   The Jurisdiction of the Admiralty of England Asserted, against Sir Edward Coke's Articuli Admiralitatis. 1663. First ed., sm. 8vo., contemp. calf, rebacked. F. Edwards 1013-229 1978 £110

ZSCHOKKE, FR.   Mediaeval Stained Glass of Zwitzerland. London, 1947. Lg. 4to., colored plts., orig. covers. Van der Peet H-64-234 1978 Dfl 55

ZUCKERMAN, NATHAN   The Wine of Violence. Association Press, 1947. Austin 79-886 1978 $12.50

ZUCKERMAN, S.   The Social Life of Monkeys & Apes. New York, 1932. lst Amer. ed., 8vo., orig. cloth. Book Chest 17-447 1978 $50

ZUGSMITH, LEANE   Never Enough. New York, (1932). First ed., author's signed pres, spine faded. Biblo 247-646 1978 $15

ZUIDERHOEK, D.   De Bouwkunst van het Kleine Landhuis. Amsterdam, 1947. Folio, 8vo., bds. portfolio. Van der Peet H-64-235 1978 Dfl 30

ZUM 29STEN AUGUST, 1783. N.P., n.d.(1783). Bound in later cloth-backed decor. boards, 8vo. Americanist 101-153 1978 $85

ZUNTZ, NATHAN   Hohenklima Und Bergwanderungen In Ihrer Wirkung Auf Den Menschen. Berlin, 1906. 4to., plts., illus., half lea., blue cloth, gilt lettering on cover, backstrip gone, rebacked with library tape, bkplts. of former owners, browned, lst ed. Zeitlin 245-296 1978 $125

ZWEIG, ARNOLD   The Case of Sergeant Grischa. 1928. Covers slightly dust-spotted, very good, d.w., first English ed. Bell Book 17-965 1978 £6

ZWEIG, STEFAN   Balzac. 1947. Plts., text illus., near fine, first English ed. Bell Book 16-037 1978 £5

ZWEIG, STEFAN   Drei Dichter Ihres Lebens. Casanova - Stendhal-Tolstoi. Leipzig, 1928. First ed. Biblo 247-870 1978 $17.50

ZWEIG, STEFAN   Die Heilung Durch Den Geist. Leipzig, 1931. 8vo., cloth, lst ed., dedicated to Einstein. Salloch 345-200 1978 $15

ZWEITER Bericht des Stadtischen Kaiser-Wilhelm-Museums in Krefeld, uber den Zeitraum Vom 1. April 1899 bis zum 31. Marz 1904. Krefeld, (1904). Lg. 8vo., orig. covers, frontis., plts., text illus. Van der Peet H-64-236 1978 Dfl 45

ZWORYKIN, VLADIMIR K.   Photocells and Their Application. New York, 1930. 8vo., illus., orig. cloth, gilt, fine copy, lst ed. Norman 5-308 1978 $75

Free Libraries—A Sketch at the
Public Library and Museum, Liverpool